BATTELLE RENCONTRES

BATTELLE RENCONTRES

1967 LECTURES IN MATHEMATICS AND PHYSICS

EDITED BY

Cecile M. DeWitt
University of North Carolina at Chapel Hill

AND

John A. Wheeler
Princeton University

W. A. BENJAMIN, INC.   *New York • Amsterdam •* 1968

BATTELLE RENCONTRES
1967 Lectures in Mathematics and Physics

W. A. BENJAMIN, INC. *New York, New York 10016*

List of Participants

RAOUL H. BOTT
 Department of Mathematics, Harvard University, Cambridge, Massachusetts 02138

JOHN B. BOYLING
 Department of Applied Mathematics and Theoretical Physics, Silver Street, Cambridge, England

BRANDON CARTER
 Department of Applied Mathematics and Theoretical Physics, Silver Street, Cambridge, England

YVONNE CHOQUET-BRUHAT
 Departement de Mathématiques, Université de Paris, 11 rue Pierre Curie, Paris 5, France

BRYCE S. DeWITT
 Department of Physics, University of North Carolina, Chapel Hill, North Carolina 27514

CECILE DeWITT
 Department of Physics, University of North Carolina, Chapel Hill, North Carolina 27514

BENO ECKMANN
 Höhere Mathematik, E.T.H., Zürich, Switzerland

LEON EHRENPREIS
 Courant Institute of Mathematical Sciences, New York University, New York, N. Y. 10012

PAUL FEDERBUSH
 Department of Mathematics, Massachusetts Institute of Technology, Cambridge, Massachusetts 02139

DIMITRI FOTIADI
 Centre de Physique Théorique, Ecole Polytechnique, Paris 5, France

MARCEL FROISSART
 Service de Physique Théorique, Saclay, 91 Gif-sur-Yvette, France

CHARLES J. FREIFELD
 Department of Mathematics, Harvard University, Cambridge, Massachusetts 02138

ROBERT P. GEROCH
Palmer Physical Laboratory, Princeton University, Princeton, New Jersey 08540

JACK GUNSON
Department of Mathematical Physics, University of Birmingham, England

STEPHEN W. HAWKING
Department of Applied Mathematics and Theoretical Physics, Silver Street, Cambridge, England

SIGURDUR HELGASON
Department of Mathematics, Massachusetts Institute of Technology, Cambridge, Massachusetts 02139

KLAUS HEPP
Theoretische Physik, E.T.H., Zürich, Switzerland

HEISUKE HIRONAKA
Department of Mathematics, Columbia University, New York, N. Y. 10027

JEAN LASCOUX
Centre de Physique Théorique, Ecole Polytechnique, Paris 5, France

HENRY LEUTWYLER
Institut de Physique Théorique, Université de Berne, Sidlerstrasse 5, Berne, Switzerland

ANDRÉ LICHNEROWICZ
Physique Mathématique, Collège de France, Paris 5, France

JOHN N. MATHER
Department of Mathematics, Princeton University, Princeton, New Jersey 08540

CHARLES W. MISNER
Department of Physics and Astronomy, University of Maryland, College Park, Maryland 20740

BERNARD C. MORIN
Department of Mathematics, University of Michigan, Ann Arbor, Michigan 48104

ROGER PENROSE
Department of Physics, Cornell University, Ithaca, New York 14850

FRÉDÉRIC PHAM
Theory Division, CERN, Geneva 23, Switzerland

TULLIO REGGE
International Centre for Theoretical Physics, Trieste, Italy

MICHAEL I. SHUB
Department of Mathematics, University of California at Berkeley 94720

STEPHEN SMALE
Department of Mathematics, University of California at Berkeley 94720

NORMAN E. STEENROD
Department of Mathematics, Princeton University, Princeton, New Jersey 08540

RENÉ THOM
Institut des Hautes Etudes Scientifiques, 91 Bures-sur-Yvette, France

JOHN A. WHEELER
Palmer Physical Laboratory, Princeton University, Princeton, New Jersey 08540
JAMES W. YORK, Jr.
Department of Physics, North Carolina State University, Raleigh, North Carolina 27607

Babel and Battelle

In 1947 John von Neumann wrote, "Mathematics falls into a great number of subdivisions, differing from one another widely in character, style, aims, and influence. It shows the very opposite of the extreme concentration of theoretical physics. A good theoretical physicist may today still have a working knowledge of more than half of his subject. I doubt that any mathematician now living has much of a relationship to more than a quarter." In the subsequent two decades, mathematics and physics have grown fantastically; and farther than ever from being Two Cultures, in the sense of Snow, they sometimes seem closer to being a hundred cultures, a modern version of the Tower of Babel. Those who work on molecular potential energy surfaces, on deutreron stripping reactions, on gravitational waves, or on parity nonconservation and the decay of elementary particles often seem to be as little aware of each other's aims and results as those who work on point set topology or on mathematical logic or on rings of operators. Why? It is not want of interest. It is want of opportunity. Hence the Battelle Rencontres in Mathematics and Physics!

Rare is the man in any area of mathematics or physics who does not feel that he is missing important developments, even ideas significant for his own life work. Who would not be happy to have better contact with the fields in mathematics and physics that are richest in new insights and outlooks! Keep up by reading all the literature? Impossible. No one can read or even scan the fifteen papers that appear every day in mathematics and the one hundred papers in physics. Would it help to wait for the day of "electronic information retrieval"? Hardly! To supply with more speed the same enormous bulk of printed matter, or even the abstracts to it, would seem the right answer to the wrong question. The right question? Did not Einstein state it in his biography when he spoke of his lifelong endeavor to capture the essence of a new idea in a key phrase or in a few sentences so that one can convey it to a colleague in all its vividness, free alike of equations and of jargon? The heart of our information system is not the memory of a computer but the mind of a colleague.

It is not new for colleagues from two distinct fields to meet together. Of a larger meeting one can say what Robert Oppenheimer said of tea, "It is where we explain to each other what we don't understand." Yet even a meeting of a week or more has its problems. Enough voices are there to be heard to give the whole enterprise too often a fragmented character. Colleagueship will not be hurried. There is no substitute for quietness and slow time and walks and talks.

Quietness and slow time, yes; but urgency too. Who does not know from his own experience what he has lost in time or stimulus or insight or pay-off from his work through not knowing at the time—as he did later—the work of his colleague in the other field? From discussions with colleagues both in mathematics and physics we know how widespread this feeling is. Sometimes it even reaches the stage of desperation. The words of Clemenceau about generals are revised to read, "Mathematics is too important to be left to the mathematicians" or "Physics is too important to be left to the physicists." From uttering words as strong as these it is but a small step to resolve to do something about exploring one's neighbor discipline. But how?

In the spring of 1966 Dr. Bertram D. Thomas, president of Battelle Memorial Institute, and Dr. Frederick J. Milford, director of Battelle Memorial Institute research in physics, approached us with the proposal that we invite a small number of mathematicians and a small number of physicists to meet together for some weeks on a topic or in an area where fruitful interactions could be expected. They promised to put at the disposal of the group the Battelle-Seattle Research Center. They promised funds for the enterprise. They promised to continue it in future summers if it worked out successfully. Feeling as we did we had no choice but to accept. This volume is the record of the first "Rencontres" as the meeting came to be called.

Directing Battelle is one activity; giving physics and mathematics a helping hand is another. What is the link? Gordon Battelle, when he died in Columbus, Ohio, September 21, 1923, the last of his family line, left his estate to found an institute. In writing his will, he sought for society "the social and economic benefits to be derived from scientific research and from the making of discoveries and inventions." The Battelle Memorial Institute, originally concerned, like Gordon Battelle himself, with mining and metallurgy, and a prime contributor during World War II to the metallurgy of uranium and with protective coatings for uranium, has today a far wider scope. From xerography its range of interests and contributions extend as far as drawing up plans for the Department of the Interior for the economic development of Alaska; and from a revolutionary technique for making reinforced concrete to holography. A scientific and charitable foundation, the Battelle Memorial Institute has grown over the years both in size and in science. Its first laboratory was in Columbus; subsequent laboratories in Frankfurt, Germany, Geneva, Switzerland, and Richland, Washington have brought the total staff to nearly 6500. With this increase in staff has gone an increase in the number of specialties represented from two or three as at the beginning to many score as of today. Dr. Thomas told us of the indebtedness that Battelle feels to all sectors of the community of learning as it goes on today in its task of applying science to meet the needs of society. He spoke in particular of Battelle's indebtedness to mathematics, the "queen of the sciences" and to physics, the foundation stone of all the physical sciences. Colleagues in these two disciplines had spoken to him and to Dr. Milford on more than one occasion of their regret that investigators in these two fields were not as close companions along the road as they had once been. If Battelle, closer than ever to the world of learning, were to enter into still more fraternal relations with the men who make up that world, were not then mathematics and physics the subjects with which to begin? Hence the Battelle initiative.

Discussions with Dr. Thomas, Dr. Milford, and colleagues active in mathematics and physics soon made it clear that for the best results it was essential to focus on an area of active current interest to both disciplines. These considerations led us, for the experiment of the first summer, to differential geometry and global topology on the mathematical side and to two areas of physics with strong ties to this realm of mathematics: Einstein's geometrical theory of gravitation; and the Feynman amplitudes or integrals which express the content of quantum mechanical perturbation theory, whether that theory is applied to gravitational interactions, or to electromagnetism, or to solid state physics.

Thirty-three workers in these fields met at the Battelle-Seattle Center, adjacent to the University of Washington campus, from 16 July to 31 August 1967. To provide a framework for discussion, four speakers were invited to give a series of lectures on topics of central interest to the participants. S. Helgason lectured on Lie groups and symmetric spaces, R. Penrose on differential geometry, spinors and space-time singularities, R. Bott on Morse theory and its applications to homotopy theory, and J. Lascoux on the topological analysis of Feynman amplitudes.

It was not intended that these lectures should contain new material—though here and there they do. The purpose was frankly pedagogical. The presentations were so clear that these lectures are included in the present volume in order to make them accessible to those working in neighbor fields as well as to specialists. In addition to these lectures there were informal accounts contributed by the participants at large. These were of two types: (1) expository lectures outlining the background, significance, and goals of the areas of research in which the speakers themselves are engaged —with technical details held to a mimimum—and (2) lectures on technical details, specifically requested by the participants to clarify otherwise obscure points. Many of these presentations were subsequently transformed to written form. They constitute the remainder of the present volume. In some cases the material of a lecture is already so well presented elsewhere that it seemed superfluous to include it here. Instead, only the pertinent reference is given.

A glance at the table of contents shows what an astonishing range of topics were discussed at the Rencontres: everything from Lie groups to the stability of differential systems, from homotopy theory to the quantization of the gravitational field, and from differential geometry to S-matrix theory. The fact that the majority of participants attended all the discussions shows the range of their interests and curiosity. May this book provide hours of delectable stimulus to the reader with an active mind and equally catholic tastes!

What can one conclude from the summer's experiment about the desirability and feasibility of widening the lines of communication between workers in mathematics and workers in physics? First, there is no universal answer valid for everyone. There are as many styles of investigation as there are people. On the ever-widening front line of research there is room for almost every type of personality. There are some brilliant workers in mathematical physics who disdain mathematics; and there are some distinguished mathematicians who have no interest in physics. Our surprise was only to find out how many workers in the one field want to learn more about the other, and conversely—as evidenced by spending seven weeks together. Second, mathematicians turned out rarely to be interested in having the results of physics translated into mathematical terms. When a new development came under discussion they wanted to get the key idea without the details. Third, physicists came to realize more clearly than ever the falsity of two old adages: "Just learn mathematics; then all your problems will be solved"; or "Just take your problem to a mathematician; then it will be solved!" What a physicist can gain from his mathematical colleagues is understanding of the general principles and some feel for the problems of active current interest. When he learns something, it will not be the answer to a particular problem; it will be a broad new insight. And most of all the physicist found that the new insight is converted into new power only by hard study and hard work. Fourth, communication demands time. One who has studied a language only at school and then finds himself in the appropriate country knows how two weeks go by before he begins to understand what is being said. Only then does the whole new world really begin to pour in upon him with all its richness. So it was in these Rencontres! The experiment was a success!

We cannot close without thanking speakers and participants for their manifold contributions. This book is the fruit of their labor. We also express our appreciation to the advisors who counseled us about the choice of topics and participants.   We are grateful to our colleagues at the University of Washington for their warm hospitality.   Most of all we are indebted to the officers and staff of Battelle who proposed the Rencontres in the first place, gave vital support at every step of the way, and through their helpfulness made the summer's work a pleasure.

Cecile M. DeWitt
John A. Wheeler

24 February 1968

Contents

* No manuscript has been submitted; only the title of the talk is given, with reference to material already published.

---

* No manuscript has been submitted; only the title of the talk is given, with reference to material already published.

---

* No manuscript has been submitted; only the title of the talk is given, with reference to material already published.

I

Lie Groups and Symmetric Spaces

SIGURDUR HELGASON

1

The purpose of these lectures is to give an account of the theory of those Lie groups which have played a particular role in geometry and in physics— the so-called semisimple Lie groups. Associated with these groups are the symmetric spaces, whose theory is a kind of an intersection of Riemannian geometry and Lie group theory.

The primary prerequisites for reading these notes are some familiarity with the elements of the theory of topological groups and differentiable manifolds. The emphasis is on noncompact semisimple Lie groups and the associated (noncompact) symmetric spaces. The function theory on these spaces is treated in a relatively detailed manner; however the holomorphic function theory is omitted altogether.

Although the definitions and theorems are usually stated in full generality, complete proofs are given only if they are either very short or particularly instructive. Verification for a special case is a frequent substitute for a proof. A study of special cases is in fact very important for understanding of Lie theory. With this in mind, Chapter 1 is devoted to the special group $G = SU(1, 1)$ and the associated symmetric space, the non-Euclidean disk. Chapters 2 and 3 deal with selected topics from the classical theory of Lie groups and symmetric spaces. The results in Chapter 4 are of more recent vintage but almost all of them have been published elsewhere. The only exceptions are the integral representation of the eigenfunctions of the Laplacian on the non-Euclidean disk (Theorem 5.1, Ch. 1) and the extension of Fatou's theorem to harmonic functions on symmetric spaces (Theorem 2.12, Ch. 4) proved by A. Korányi and the author.

I am indebted to members of the Summer Rencontre for helpful discussions during the writing of these notes, particularly B. Carter, Y. Choquet-Bruhat, and L. Ehrenpreis.

GENERAL NOTATION

We list here some standard notation which will be utilized throughout the lectures. The symbols R, C, and Z refer to the real numbers, the complex numbers, and the integers, respectively. The nonnegative reals are denoted by R^+ and the nonnegative integers by Z^+. The conjugate of a complex number c is denoted by $\bar{c}$. The empty set is denoted by $\emptyset$. If X is a set and $x \in X$ then the subset of X consisting of x alone is denoted by $\{x\}$.

If M is a manifold, the set of complex-valued indefinitely differentiable functions on M is denoted $C^\infty(M)$. The set of functions $f \in C^\infty(M)$ of compact support is denoted $C_c^\infty(M)$. If $p \in M$ the tangent space to M at p is denoted by M_p. Let M and N be manifolds and $\phi : M \to N$ a differentiable mapping. The differential of ϕ at a point $p \in M$, denoted $d\phi_p$, or just ϕ, is a mapping of M_p into $N_{\phi(p)}$ defined by $d\phi_p(X)(f) = X(f \circ \phi)$ if X is any vector in M_p and f any function in $C^\infty(N)$. If $t \to \gamma(t)$ is any curve in M with tangent vector X at the point p then $d\phi_p(X)$ is the tangent vector to the curve $t \to \phi(\gamma(t))$ at $\phi(p)$. The differentiable map $\phi : M \to N$ is called a diffeomorphism if it is a one-to-one map of M onto N and if the inverse map $\phi^{-1} : N \to M$ is differentiable.

CHAPTER 1: INTRODUCTION

1-1 Lie Groups

A *Lie group* is a group G which is also an analytic manifold such that the mapping $(g, h) \to gh^{-1}$ of the product manifold $G \times G \to G$ is analytic.

Roughly speaking, this means that, at least locally, a Lie group is parametrized by an n-tuple of real numbers such that the group operations are expressed by analytic functions in these parameters. This makes it possible to study these groups by analytical methods.

Lie group theory can be traced back to Sophus Lie's applications of group theory to geometric situations as well as to his desire to obtain a theory of differential equations which paralleled Galois' theory for algebraic equations. Since groups at that time were usually viewed as permutation groups, the geometric problems led naturally to the consideration of transformation groups with certain invariance properties. These invariance properties often give rise to a parametrization of the group, turning it into a Lie group.

Example

Let G denote the group of transformations of the plane $\mathbf{R}^2$ preserving distance as well as orientation. If $g \in G$ let $(x(g), y(g))$ denote the coordinates of $g \cdot 0$ (0 is the origin in $\mathbf{R}^2$) and $\theta(g)$ the angle from the x axis l to the line $g \cdot l$. The parametrization

$$g \to (x(g), y(g), \theta(g))$$

turns G into a Lie group.

1-2 Symmetric Spaces

Let M be a C^∞ manifold. A *Riemannian structure* on M is a positive definite inner product $\langle \, , \, \rangle$ on the tangent space M_p at an arbitrary point $p \in M$. It is assumed that if X, Y are C^∞ vector fields on M then the function $p \to \langle X_p, Y_p \rangle$ is a C^∞ function on M. A manifold with a Riemannian structure is called a *Riemannian manifold*.

Example

The following example is of basic importance and will accompany us throughout these lectures.

Let D be the open unit disk $|z| < 1$ in $\mathbf{R}^2$ with the usual manifold structure but given the following Riemannian structure: If u, v are tangent vectors at the point $z \in D$, put

$$\langle u, v \rangle = \frac{(u, v)}{[1 - |z|^2]^2} \tag{1}$$

$(\ ,\ )$ denoting the usual inner product on $\mathbf{R}^2$. Since

$$\frac{\langle u, v \rangle^2}{\langle u, u \rangle \langle v, v \rangle} = \frac{(u, v)^2}{(u, u)(v, v)}$$

the angle between u and v in the new Riemannian structure coincides with the Euclidean angle.

The length of a curve $\gamma(t)$ $(\alpha \leqslant t \leqslant \beta)$ on a Riemannian manifold is defined by

$$L(\gamma) = \int_\alpha^\beta \langle \gamma'(t), \gamma'(t) \rangle^{1/2}\, dt$$

and the distance between two points $p, q \in M$ is defined by

$$d(p, q) = \inf_\gamma L(\gamma)$$

the infimum taken over all curves joining p and q. In our case if $\gamma(t) = (x(t), y(t))$ and $s(\tau)$ is the arc-length of the segment $\gamma(t)$ $(0 \leqslant t \leqslant \tau)$, we get

$$\left(\frac{ds}{d\tau}\right)^2 = \frac{1}{\{1 - [\alpha\,(\tau)^2 + y(\tau)^2]\}^2}\left[\left(\frac{dx}{d\tau}\right)^2 + \left(\frac{dy}{d\tau}\right)^2\right]$$

In classical terminology this is written

$$ds^2 = \frac{dx^2 + dy^2}{[1 - (x^2 + y^2)]^2} \tag{2}$$

In particular, if $\gamma(\alpha) = 0$, $\gamma(\beta) = x$ (point on the x axis) and we denote by γ_0 the line segment from 0 to x, we get from

$$\frac{x'(\tau)^2}{[1 - x(\tau)^2]^2} \leqslant \frac{x'(\tau)^2 + y'(\tau)^2}{\{1 - [x(\tau)^2 + y(\tau)^2]\}^2}$$

the inequality

$$L(\gamma_0) \leqslant L(\gamma)$$

Thus

$$d(0, z) = \frac{1}{2} \log \frac{1 + |z|}{1 - |z|} \tag{3}$$

and the straight lines through the origin are geodesics.

Let us now determine the group $I(D)$ of all isometrics on D. If $a, b \in C$ then the transformation

$$g : z \to \frac{az + b}{\bar{b}z + \bar{a}} \qquad |a|^2 - |b|^2 = 1 \tag{4}$$

maps D onto itself. Let us verify that g preserves the Riemannian structure (1): Let $z(t)$ be a curve with $z(0) = z$, $z'(0) = u$. Then

$$g \cdot u = \left\{ \frac{d}{dt} g[z(t)] \right\}_{t=0} = \text{the vector } \frac{z'(0)}{(\bar{b}z + \bar{a})^2} \text{ at } g \cdot z$$

and the relation

$$\langle g \cdot u, g \cdot u \rangle = \langle u, u \rangle$$

follows immediately. Now if $h \in I(D)$ is arbitrary, there exists a g as in (4) such that gh^{-1} leaves the x axis pointwise fixed. But then gh^{-1} is either the identity or the conjugation $z \to \bar{z}$. Thus $I(D)$ is generated by the transformation (4) and the conjugation $c : z \to \bar{z}$. Denoting as usual

$$SU(1, 1) = \left\{ \begin{pmatrix} a & b \\ \bar{b} & \bar{a} \end{pmatrix} \middle| |a|^2 - |b|^2 = 1 \right\}$$

and by I the identity matrix, we have

$$I(D) = (SU(1, 1)/ \pm I) \cup c(SU(1, 1)/ \pm I)$$

In particular, $I(D)$ is a Lie group (a fact which was proved for all Riemann manifolds in Myers and Steenrod [55]).

Since the group of transformations (4) is transitive on D we deduce that the geodesics in D are the circular arcs perpendicular to the boundary $|z| = 1$. Since the expression for $d(0, z)$ can be written by means of the cross ratio

$$d(0, z) = \frac{1}{2} \log \left(\frac{0 - z/|z|}{0 + z/|z|} : \frac{z - z/|z|}{z + z/|z|} \right)$$

and since the cross ratio is invariant under fractional linear transformations we obtain

$$d(z_1, z_2) = \frac{1}{2} \log \left(\frac{z_1 - b_2}{z_1 - b_1} : \frac{z_2 - b_2}{z_2 - b_1} \right) \qquad z_1, z_2 \in D \tag{5}$$

(b_1, b_2 being shown in Fig. 1). But the space D with this distance d is of course the classical Poincaré model of non-Euclidean geometry.

Definition. A Riemannian manifold M is called *symmetric* (or *globally symmetric*) in the sense of É. Cartan if for each $p \in M$ there is an isometry s_p of M onto itself which reverses the geodesics through p (s_p is called the *geodesic symmetry* with respect to p).

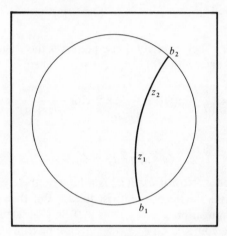

FIGURE 1

Since the symmetry $s_0 : z \to -z$ is of the form (4) it is an isometry of D. If $g \in I(D)$, then the isometry $g s_0 g^{-1}$ reverses the geodesics through $g \cdot 0$; $I(D)$ being transitive, D is therefore symmetric.

Let $\gamma(t)$ $(-\infty < t < \infty)$ be a geodesic in a symmetric space M, let $s_t = s_{\gamma(t)}$, and let τ_t denote the Levi–Civita parallel transport along γ from 0 to t. If L is a tangent vector to M at $\gamma(t)$, then since s_0 preserves parallelism and $s_0(\tau_{-t} L) = -\tau_{-t} L$ we see that $s_0(L) = -\tau_{-2t} L$. Consequently, the isometry $T_t = s_{t/2} s_0$ realizes the parallelism from 0 to t along γ. The isometries T_t actually form a one-parameter group—the group of *transvections* along the geodesic γ.

Let M be a Riemannian manifold, (U, ϕ) a local coordinate system and $\phi(q) = (x_1, \ldots, x_n)$ for $q \in U$. We put

$$g_{ij}(q) = \left\langle \left(\frac{\partial}{\partial x_i}\right)_q, \left(\frac{\partial}{\partial x_j}\right)_q \right\rangle,$$

$$g = \det(g_{ij}),$$

$$g^{ij} = (g_{ij})^{-1}$$

Then we can define a measure μ on U by

$$\mu(C) = \int_{\phi(C)} \sqrt{g} \, dx_1 \cdots dx_n \tag{6}$$

(where we have written $\sqrt{g}$ for $\sqrt{g} \circ \phi^{-1}$).   This definition is invariant under coordinate changes and defines a measure on M, the *Riemannian measure*. Somewhat imprecisely (M is not necessarily orientable) one refers to $\sqrt{g} \, dx_1 \ldots dx_n$ as the *volume element* on M.

We also recall the *Laplace–Beltrami operator* defined for $f \in C^{\infty}(U)$ by

$$\Delta : f \to \frac{1}{\sqrt{g}} \sum_k \frac{\partial}{\partial x_k} \left(\sum_i g^{ik} \sqrt{g} \, \frac{\partial}{\partial x_i} \right)(f) \tag{7}$$

Again, the expression on the right can be shown to be invariant under coordinate changes and so defines a differential operator on M.

In the case of D we find at once from (1),

$$g_{ij} = [1 - |z|^2]^{-2} \delta_{ij} \qquad (\delta_{ij} = \text{Kronecker delta})$$
$$g^{ij} = [1 - |z|^2]^2 \delta_{ij} \qquad g = (1 - |z|^2)^{-4}$$

The volume element is therefore given by

$$[1 - (x^2 + y^2)]^{-2} \, dx \, dy \tag{8}$$

and the Laplace–Beltrami operator is

$$\Delta = [1 - (x^2 + y^2)]^2 \left(\frac{\partial^2}{\partial x^2} + \frac{\partial^2}{\partial y^2} \right) \tag{9}$$

1-3 Non-Euclidean Fourier Analysis

We shall now define a Fourier transform on the non-Euclidean disk D. First we recall the Fourier inversion formula on $\mathbf{R}^n$.   For $f \in L^1(\mathbf{R}^n)$ put

$$\tilde{f}(u) = \int_{\mathbf{R}^n} f(x) e^{-i(x, u)} \, dx \tag{1}$$

$(\ ,\ )$ denoting the usual inner product on $\mathbf{R}^n$.   Then if $f \in C_c^{\infty}(\mathbf{R}^n)$,

$$f(x) = (2\pi)^{-n} \int_{\mathbf{R}^n} \tilde{f}(u) e^{i(x, u)} \, du \tag{2}$$

Let us introduce polar coordinates $u = \lambda w$, $\lambda \geqslant 0$, and w is a unit vector. Then (1) and (2) become

$$\tilde{f}(\lambda w) = \int_{\mathbf{R}^n} f(x) e^{-i\lambda(x, w)} \, dx \tag{3}$$

$$f(x) = (2\pi)^{-n} \int_{\mathbf{R}^+} \int_{S^{n-1}} \tilde{f}(\lambda w) e^{i\lambda(x, w)} \lambda^{n-1} \, d\lambda \, dw \tag{4}$$

where $R^+ = \{\lambda \in R \mid \lambda \geqslant 0\}$ and dw is the volume element on the unit sphere S^{n-1}.

Because the functions $e_u : x \to e^{i(x,\,u)}$ are characters of the group R^n, the Fourier transform (1) can be generalized to locally compact Abelian groups. Since D is not a group this viewpoint is not directly applicable here. However, the functions e_u have the following properties:

(i) e_u is an eigenfunction of the Laplace operator on R^n;

(ii) e_u is constant on each hyperplane perpendicular to u ("plane wave" with normal u).

These properties essentially characterize the exponentials and since they are geometric properties we shall see that they have analogs for the space D.

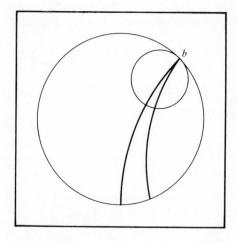

FIGURE 2

Parallel geodesics in D are by definition geodesics corresponding to the same point b on the boundary B of D. A *horocycle with normal b* is by definition an orthogonal trajectory to the family of all parallel geodesics corresponding to b. Thus a horocycle in D is the non-Euclidean analog of a hyperplane in R^n. Since the inner product (x, w) in (3) is the distance from the origin to the hyperplane with normal w passing through x we define $\langle z, b \rangle$ for $z \in D$, $b \in B$, as the non-Euclidean distance from 0 to the horocycle $\xi(z, b)$ with normal b, passing through z. (Here $\langle z, b \rangle$ is taken negative in case 0 falls inside the horocycle.)

For $\mu \in C$, $b \in B$ we consider the function

$$e_{\mu,\,b} : z \to e^{\mu\langle z,\,b \rangle} \qquad z \in D \tag{5}$$

These formal analogs of the exponential functions on R^n are also conceptual analogs for they satisfy the following non-Euclidean counterparts to (i) and (ii):

(i)′ $e_{\mu, b}$ is an eigenfunction of the Laplace–Beltrami operator on D (for example, use (9) in §1-2 and (11) below);

(ii)′ $e_{\mu, b}$ is constant on each horocycle with normal b.

Consequently, we define *Fourier analysis on D* to be decomposition of "arbitrary" functions into functions $e_{\mu, b}$ in (5).

Theorem 3.1. For $f \in C_c^\infty(D)$ set

$$\tilde{f}(\lambda, b) = \int_D f(z)e^{(-i\lambda + 1)\langle z, b\rangle}\, dz \qquad \lambda \in R,\, b \in B$$

where dz is the volume element on D. Then

$$f(z) = (2\pi)^{-2} \int_R \int_B \tilde{f}(\lambda, b)e^{(i\lambda + 1)\langle z, b\rangle}\lambda \tanh\left(\tfrac{1}{2}\pi\lambda\right) d\lambda\, db \qquad (6)$$

where db is the usual angular measure on B.

We shall now indicate how (6) follows from classical facts. Denote the measure $(2\pi)^{-2}\lambda \tanh\left(\tfrac{1}{2}\pi\lambda\right) d\lambda\, db$ by $d\mu(\lambda, b)$ and define the operators T and S by

$$(Tf)(\lambda, b) = \tilde{f}(\lambda, b) \qquad\qquad f \in C_c^\infty(X)$$

$$(SF)(z) = \int_{R \times B} F(\lambda, b)e^{(i\lambda + 1)\langle z, b\rangle}\, d\mu(\lambda, b)$$

the function F restricted such that the integral converges absolutely. Then

$$\int_D f(z)\overline{(SF)(z)}\, dz = \int_{R \times B} (Tf)(\lambda, b)\overline{F(\lambda, b)}\, d\mu(\lambda,b)$$

and by iteration

$$\int_D f(z)\overline{STg(z)}\, dz = \int_D (STf)(z)\overline{g(z)}\, dz \qquad f,\, g \in C_c^\infty(D) \qquad (7)$$

because Tf and Tg satisfy the growth restrictions placed on F.

Lemma 3.2. Let τ be an isometry of D and if g is a function on D, put $g^\tau(z) = g(\tau^{-1} \cdot z)$. Then

$$STf^\tau = (STf)^\tau \qquad \text{for } f \in C_c^\infty(D)$$

PROOF. Since τ preserves the volume element on D,

$$\tilde{f}^\tau(\lambda, b) = \int_D f(z)e^{(-i\lambda + 1)\langle \tau \cdot z, b\rangle}\, dz \qquad (8)$$

But the isometry τ extends in an obvious way to the boundary B (cf. (4) §1-2), and we have

$$\langle \tau \cdot z, \tau \cdot b \rangle = \langle z, b \rangle + \langle \tau \cdot 0, \tau \cdot b \rangle \tag{9}$$

This identity is easily seen by observing that the horocycles $\xi(\tau \cdot 0, \tau \cdot b)$ and $\xi(\tau \cdot z, \tau \cdot b)$ cut segments of equal length off the parallel geodesics $(0, \tau \cdot b)$ and $(\tau \cdot 0, \tau \cdot b)$. Thus

$$\langle \tau \cdot z, b \rangle = \langle z, \tau^{-1} \cdot b \rangle + \langle \tau \cdot 0, b \rangle$$

so (8) becomes

$$\tilde{f}^{\tau}(\lambda, b) = e^{(-i\lambda+1)\langle \tau \cdot 0, b \rangle} \tilde{f}(\lambda, \tau^{-1} \cdot b)$$

so

$$(STf^{\tau})(z) = \int_{R \times B} \tilde{f}(\lambda, \tau^{-1} \cdot b) e^{(-i\lambda+1)\langle \tau \cdot 0, b \rangle} e^{(i\lambda+1)\langle z, b \rangle} \, d\mu(\lambda, b)$$

Now we change variables; the Jacobian of the mapping $b \to \tau \cdot b$ satisfies

$$\left| \frac{d(\tau \cdot b)}{db} \right| = e^{2\langle \tau^{-1} \cdot 0, b \rangle} \qquad b \in B \tag{10}$$

In order to verify this observe that $\tau = \kappa_1 \sigma \kappa_2$, where κ_1, κ_2 are rotations around 0, and σ maps the x axis onto itself. We can thus assume τ of the form

$$\tau \cdot z = \frac{(\cosh t)z + \sinh t}{(\sinh t)z + \cosh t}$$

so if $b = e^{i\phi}$, the left-hand side of (10) equals $(\cosh 2t + \sinh 2t \cos \phi)^{-1}$. On the other hand, a simple computation using (3) §1-2 shows that if $z = |z| e^{i\theta}$, $b = e^{i\phi}$ then

$$e^{2\langle z, b \rangle} = \frac{1 - |z|^2}{1 - 2|z| \cos(\theta - \phi) + |z|^2} \tag{11}$$

so, in particular, (10) follows. Using also $\langle \tau^{-1} \cdot 0, b \rangle = -\langle \tau \cdot 0, \tau \cdot b \rangle$ [which follows from (9)], we obtain

$$(STf^{\tau})(z) = \int_{R \times B} \tilde{f}(\lambda, b) e^{(-i\lambda-1)\langle \tau \cdot 0, \tau \cdot b \rangle} e^{(i\lambda+1)\langle z, \tau \cdot b \rangle} \, d\mu(\lambda, b)$$

which again by (9) equals $(STf)(\tau^{-1} \cdot z)$, proving the lemma.

In order to prove Theorem 3.1, that $f = STf$, it suffices, by (7), to prove this for a sequence (f_n) where $f_n \to \delta_z$, the delta function at an arbitrary point $z \in D$. By Lemma 3.2 we can assume that z is the origin in D. But then the functions f_n could be taken to be radial functions. But if $f(z) = F(d(0, z))$, $F \in C_c^{\infty}(R)$ (F even), then $\tilde{f}(\lambda, b)$ is an even function $\tilde{F}(\lambda)$ of λ alone. If $r = d(0, z)$ then

$$z = |z| e^{i\theta} = (\tanh r) e^{i\theta}$$

In the coordinates (r, θ) the volume element (8) §1-2 becomes

$$dz = \tfrac{1}{2} \sinh 2r \; dr \; d\theta$$

If we now consider the Legendre function

$$P_\nu(\cosh r) = \frac{1}{2\pi} \int_0^{2\pi} (\cosh r + \sinh r \cos \theta)^\nu \, d\theta \qquad (\nu \in \mathbf{C})$$

the formulas in Theorem 3.1 become

$$\tilde{F}(\lambda) = \pi \int_0^\infty F(r) P_{-\frac{1}{2} + \frac{1}{2} i \lambda} \cosh (2r) \sinh (2r) \, dr \tag{12}$$

$$F(r) = \frac{1}{2\pi} \int_0^\infty \tilde{F}(\lambda) P_{-\frac{1}{2} - \frac{1}{2} i \lambda} \cosh (2r) \, \lambda \tanh (\tfrac{1}{2}\pi\lambda) \, d\lambda \tag{13}$$

After a harmless change of variables, (13) becomes simply the inversion formula for the Mehler transform (Erdélyi [17], Vol. I, p. 175, Fok [18] and Godement [22a]). Assuming this inversion formula, Theorem 3.1 is proved (*cf.* Helgason [35], [36]).

If we compare the formulas in Theorem 3.1 with (3) and (4) we note a factor $e^{2\langle z, b\rangle}$ which has no analog in the Euclidean case. But according to (11) this factor is just the classical Poisson kernel but expressed in non-Euclidean terms. Consequently, the classical Poisson integral formula for a harmonic function u on D with continuous boundary values $f(b)$ on B,

$$u(re^{i\theta}) = \frac{1}{2\pi} \int_0^{2\pi} \frac{1 - r^2}{1 - 2r \cos(\theta - \phi) + r^2} f(e^{i\phi}) \, d\phi$$

can be written

$$u(z) = \frac{1}{2\pi} \int_0^{2\pi} e^{2\langle z, b\rangle} f(b) \, db \tag{14}$$

According to our stated conventions this is a formula in Fourier analysis on D.

Note that the Euclidean harmonic functions coincide with the non-Euclidean harmonic functions according to (9) §1-2. Thus (14) is entirely non-Euclidean.

1-4 Interpretation by Representation Theory

Let X be a space with a measure μ and let G be a transformation group of X leaving the measure μ invariant. To each $g \in G$ we associate the operator $T(g) : f \to f^g$ on the space $L^2(X)$ of square-integrable functions on X. (As in Lemma 3.2, f^g denotes the function $x \to f(g^{-1} \cdot x)$ on X.) Then the mapping $g \to T(g)$ is a unitary representation of G on the Hilbert space $L^2(X)$. Now arises the natural problem of decomposing this unitary representation T

into irreducible representations T_λ acting on Hilbert spaces $\mathfrak{H}_\lambda$ such that for a suitable measure ν

$$L^2(X) = \int \mathfrak{H}_\lambda \, d\nu(\lambda) \qquad T = \int T_\lambda \, d\nu(\lambda) \qquad (1)$$

in the sense of direct integrals of Hilbert spaces (see, for example, Dixmier [15]). In §1-3 we have some examples of (1):

a. First let G denote the group of translations of R^n. Then for each $u \in R^n$ the space $\mathfrak{H}_u = Ce_u$ is invariant and irreducible under G; let T_u denote the representation of G on $\mathfrak{H}_u$ given by

$$[T_u(g)f](x) = f(g^{-1}x) \qquad \text{for } f \in \mathfrak{H}_u, g \in G, x \in R^n.$$

Then (2) in §1-3 (together with the Plancherel formula

$$\int |f(x)|^2 \, dx = (2\pi)^{-n} \int |\tilde{f}(u)|^2 \, du)$$

can be written

$$L^2(R^n) = \int \mathfrak{H}_u \, du^* \qquad T = \int T_u \, du^* \qquad (2)$$

where $du^* = (2\pi)^{-n} \, du$.

b. Next let G denote the group of all transformations of R^n preserving orientation and distance. For each $\lambda \in R^+$ consider the Hilbert space of functions on R^n given by

$$\mathfrak{H}_\lambda = \left\{ F_\lambda(x) = \int_{S^{n-1}} e^{i\lambda(x,\,\omega)} F(\omega) \, d\omega \mid F \in L^2(S^{n-1}) \right\} \qquad (3)$$

(defining $\|F_\lambda\|$ as the L^2 norm of F) and let T_λ denote the representation of G on $\mathfrak{H}_\lambda$ given by

$$(T_\lambda(g)F_\lambda)(x) = F_\lambda(g^{-1}x) \qquad F_\lambda \in \mathfrak{H}_\lambda, g \in G, x \in R^n$$

T_λ is in fact a unitary representation, because if $g = tk$ (t is the translation, k the rotation around 0), then

$$(T_\lambda(g)F_\lambda)(x) = \int_{S^{n-1}} e^{i\lambda(x,\,\omega)} e^{-i\lambda(g\cdot 0,\,\omega)} F(k^{-1}\omega) \, d\omega \qquad (4)$$

and T_λ is in fact irreducible (*cf.* Itô [42] and Mackey [51, §14]) and different λ in R^+ give inequivalent T_λ. Thus (4) in §1-3 together with the Plancherel formula

$$\int_R |f(x)|^2 \, dx = (2\pi)^{-n} \int_{R^+ \times S^{n-1}} |\tilde{f}(\lambda\omega)|^2 \lambda^{n-1} \, d\lambda \, d\omega$$

gives the direct integral decomposition

$$L^2(X) = \int_{\mathbf{R}^+} \mathfrak{H}_\lambda \, d\lambda^* \qquad T = \int_{\mathbf{R}^+} T_\lambda \, d\lambda^* \tag{5}$$

where $d\lambda^* = (2\pi)^{-n}\lambda^{n-1} \, d\lambda$.

c. Finally, we consider the case when G is the group $SU(1, 1)$ operating on D. For each $\lambda \in \mathbf{R}$ consider the Hilbert space

$$\mathfrak{H}_\lambda = \left\{ h_\lambda(z) = \int_B e^{(i\lambda + 1)\langle z, \, b \rangle} h(b) \, db \mid h \in L^2(B) \right\}$$

(defining $\|h_\lambda\|$ as the L^2 norm of h) and let T_λ denote the representation of G on $\mathfrak{H}_\lambda$ given by

$$[T_\lambda(g)h_\lambda](z) = h_\lambda(g^{-1}z)$$

Using formulas (9) and (10) in §1-3, we find

$$h_\lambda(g^{-1} \cdot z) = \int_B e^{(i\lambda + 1)\langle z, \, b \rangle} e^{(-i\lambda + 1)\langle g \cdot 0, \, b \rangle} h(g^{-1} \cdot b) \, db$$

[compare with (4)]; so using (10) again we see that T_λ is unitary; comparing with Bargmann [1], Thm. 1, p. 613, we see that T_λ is irreducible. Finally (6) in §1-3 and the Plancherel formula

$$\int_D |f(z)|^2 \, dz = \int_{\mathbf{R} \times B} |\tilde{f}(\lambda, b)|^2 \, d\mu(\lambda, b)$$

show that

$$L^2(D) = \int_{\mathbf{R}/\mathbf{Z}_2} \mathfrak{H}_\lambda \, d\mu(\lambda) \qquad T = \int_{\mathbf{R}/\mathbf{Z}_2} T_\lambda \, d\mu(\lambda) \tag{6}$$

where $d\mu(\lambda) = 2(2\pi)^{-2}\lambda \tanh\left(\tfrac{1}{2}\pi\lambda\right)$ and integration is taken over $\mathbf{R}/\mathbf{Z}_2$ since T_λ and T_μ can be shown equivalent if and only if $\lambda = -\mu$.

1-5 The Eigenfunctions of the Laplacian on the Non-Euclidean Disk

Let $P(z, b)$ denote the Poisson kernel

$$P(z, b) = \frac{1 - |z|^2}{1 - 2|z| \cos(\theta - \phi) + |z|^2}$$

$$z = |z| e^{i\theta} \qquad b = e^{i\phi}$$

If $\lambda \in \mathbf{C}$ is any complex number it is clear from (i)' and (11) in §1-3 that for for each $b \in B$ the power $P(z, b]^\lambda$ gives an eigenfunction of the non-Euclidean Laplacian Δ. A direct computation gives

$$\Delta_z(P(z, b)^\lambda) = 4\lambda(\lambda - 1)P(z, b)^\lambda$$

which shows that the eigenvalue is independent of b. Note that the eigenvalue is $\geqslant -1$ (and real) if and only if $\lambda \in R$. We shall now consider the problem of constructing the most general eigenfunctions of Δ.

Let $A(B)$ denote the set of analytic function *on the boundary* B, considered as an analytic manifold. The space $A(B)$ carries an atural topology (see, for example, Köthe [48]). The continuous linear functions $A(B) \to C$ are called *analytic functionals* on B; they constitute the dual space $A'(B)$ of $A(B)$. If $T \in A'(B)$, $f \in A(B)$ we write for $T(f)$ also $\int_B f(b) \, dT(b)$, since the elements of A are generalizations of measures. For the eigenfunctions of Δ we have the following result (unpublished):

Theorem 5.1. The functions

$$F(z) = \int_B P(z, b)^\lambda \, dT(b)$$

where $\lambda \in R$ and T is an analytic functional on B constitute precisely the eigenfunctions of Δ with eigenvalue $\geqslant -1$.

CHAPTER 2: LIE GROUPS AND LIE ALGEBRAS

2-1   The Lie Algebra of a Lie Group

Let M be a manifold, p a point in M, and M_p the tangent space to M at p; this is a vector space over R. In differential geometry one studies a manifold by means of its family of tangent spaces to which numerous objects are associated (vector fields, differential forms, arbitrary tensor fields).

If G is a Lie group, the tangent space G_g at an arbitrary point $g \in G$ is obtained from G_e (e is the identity element) by the left translation $L_g : x \to gx$ ($x \in G$), that is, $G_g = dL_g(G_e)$. This circumstance makes it possible to introduce an additional structure on G_e as follows:

Let $X, Y \in G_e$. Then we obtain vector fields $\tilde{X}$, $\tilde{Y}$ on G by left translations:

$$\tilde{X}_g = dL_g(X) \qquad \tilde{Y}_g = dL_g(Y) \qquad g \in G$$

The bracket $[\tilde{X}, \tilde{Y}] = \tilde{X}\tilde{Y} - \tilde{Y}\tilde{X}$ is another vector field on G which is invariant under left translations so there exists a unique vector $Z \in G_e$ such that

$$[\tilde{X}, \tilde{Y}]_e = \tilde{Z}$$

We write $[X, Y]$ instead of Z. The vector space G_e with the rule of composition $(X, Y) \to [X, Y]$ is called the *Lie algebra* of G and will be denoted by $\mathfrak{g}$.

The bracket [,] has the following properties:

(a) $[X, Y] = -[Y, X]$

(b) $[X, [Y, Z]] + [Y, [Z, X]] + [Z, [X, Y]] = 0$

A vector space $\mathfrak{a}$ with a bilinear map $(X, Y) \to [X, Y]$ of $\mathfrak{a} \times \mathfrak{a}$ into $\mathfrak{a}$ satisfying (a) and (b) above is called a *Lie algebra*. For Lie algebras one can in an obvious manner define *subalgebras*, *ideals*, *homomorphisms*, *isomorphisms*, and *automorphisms*.

If V is a vector space let $\mathfrak{gl}(V)$ denote the vector space of all linear transformations of V into V, with the bracket operation $[A, B] = AB - BA$. Then $\mathfrak{gl}(V)$ is a Lie algebra. A homomorphism of a Lie algebra $\mathfrak{a}$ into $\mathfrak{gl}(V)$ is called a *representation* of $\mathfrak{a}$ on V. In particular, if for a given $X \in \mathfrak{a}$, the mapping $Y \to [X, Y]$ is denoted ad X, the mapping ad $: X \to$ ad X is a representation of $\mathfrak{a}$ on $\mathfrak{a}$. The kernel of ad is called the *center* of $\mathfrak{a}$; $\mathfrak{a}$ is called *Abelian* if its center is $\mathfrak{a}$; that is, if $[X, Y] = 0$ for all $X, Y \in \mathfrak{a}$.

2-2 The Exponential Mapping

Let G be a Lie group with Lie algebra $\mathfrak{g}$. Let $X \in \mathfrak{g}$ and let $\tilde{X}$ be the left invariant vector field on G such that $\tilde{X}_e = X$. Let $\phi(t)$ $(t \in \mathbf{R})$ be the integral curve to $\tilde{X}$ passing through e, that is,

$$\dot{\phi}(t) = d\phi\left(\frac{d}{dt}\right) = \tilde{X}_{\phi(t)} \qquad \phi(0) = e \qquad (1)$$

For small t, $\phi(t)$ exists and is unique because (1) is a first-order system of ordinary differential equations. For the global statement one uses the group property to continue the solution. The mapping exp $: \mathfrak{g} \to G$ is now defined by

$$\exp X = \phi(1)$$

and is called the exponential mapping. It sets up a very far-reaching relationship between $\mathfrak{g}$ and G; some of the main results will be summarized below.

First we have

(i) $\quad \exp sX \exp tX = \exp (s + t)X \qquad (s, t \in \mathbf{R})$

that is, the curve $t \to \exp tX$ is a one-parameter subgroup of G. In fact, if $s \in \mathbf{R}$, then $L_{\exp sX}$ maps $\tilde{X}$ into itself so it maps the integral curve through e into the integral curve through exp sX. Thus, $L_{\exp sX}(\phi(t)) = \phi(s + t)$ which is (i).

By the definition of $\tilde{X}$,

$$\tilde{X}_g f = \left\{\frac{d}{dt} f(g \exp tX)\right\}_{t=0} \qquad f \in C^\infty(G), g \in G$$

Thus the value of the function $\tilde{X}f$ at $g \exp sX$ is

$$(\tilde{X}f)(g \exp sX) = \left\{\frac{d}{dt}f(g \exp sX \exp tX)\right\}_{t=0} = \frac{d}{ds}f(g \exp sX)$$

and by induction, if $n \in \mathbf{Z}^+$,

$$(\tilde{X}^nf)(g \exp sX) = \frac{d^n}{ds^n} f(g \exp sX) \tag{2}$$

(ii) If a function f is analytic in a neighborhood of a point $g \in G$, then

$$f(g \exp X) = \sum_0^\infty \frac{1}{n!} (\tilde{X}^nf)(g) \tag{3}$$

for all X in some neighborhood of 0 in $\mathfrak{g}$.

This relation follows by using (2) in Taylor's formula for the function $s \to f(g \exp sX)$.

(iii) The mapping $X \to \exp X$ is a diffeomorphism of an open neighborhood of 0 in $\mathfrak{g}$ onto an open neighborhood of e in G.

This is a direct consequence of the fact that the mapping $X \to \exp X$ has Jacobian $\neq 0$ at the origin $X = 0$.

(iv) If $X, Y \in \mathfrak{g}$ then

$$\exp tX \exp tY = \exp \{t(X + Y) + \tfrac{1}{2}t^2[X, Y] + 0(t^3)\} \tag{4}$$

where $0(t^3)$ denotes a vector such that $t^{-3}\, 0(t^3)$ is bounded near $t = 0$.

In fact, by (iii), we have for small t,

$$\exp tX \exp tY = \exp Z(t) \tag{5}$$

where $t \to Z(t)$ is a curve in $\mathfrak{g}$, analytic at $t = 0$ and

$$Z(t) = tZ_1 + t^2Z_2 + 0(t^3) \qquad (Z_1, Z_2 \in \mathfrak{g})$$

But by (2) and (3) we have for f analytic at e,

$$f(\exp tX \exp tY) = \sum_{m, n \geqslant 0} \frac{t^{m+n}}{m!\, n!} (\tilde{X}^m \tilde{Y}^nf)(e)$$

whereas

$$f(\exp Z(t)) = \sum_{m=0}^\infty \frac{1}{m!} [(t\tilde{Z}_1 + t^2\tilde{Z}_2 + 0(t^3))^mf](e)$$

Comparing coefficients we get $Z_1 = X + Y$, $\tfrac{1}{2}\tilde{Z}_1{}^2 + \tilde{Z}_2 = \tfrac{1}{2}\tilde{X}^2 + \tilde{X}\tilde{Y} + \tfrac{1}{2}\tilde{Y}^2$, whence $Z_2 = \tfrac{1}{2}[X, Y]$, proving (4).

From (4) we deduce that

$$\exp{(-tX)}\exp{(-tY)}\exp{tX}\exp{tY} = \exp{\{t^2[X, Y] + 0(t^3)\}}$$

which shows that $[X, Y]$ is the tangent vector at e to the curve

$$t \to \exp{(-\sqrt{t}\, X)}\exp{(-\sqrt{t}\, Y)}\exp{(\sqrt{t}\, X)}\exp{(\sqrt{t}\, Y)}$$

(v) Two Lie groups are locally isomorphic if and only if their Lie algebras are isomorphic.

The "only if" part is immediate from (4). On the other hand, it is possible to carry further the computation above and express $Z(t)$ in (5) completely in terms of t, X, Y and their repeated brackets. (The resulting formula is the so-called Campbell–Hausdorff formula, see for example, Jacobson [43].) The "if" part of (v) is an immediate consequence.

A Fundamental Example

Let $GL(n, R)$ denote the group of real $n \times n$ matrices of determinant $\neq 0$ and $\mathfrak{gl}(n, R)$ the Lie algebra of all real $n \times n$ matrices, the bracket being $[A, B] = AB - BA$. If $\sigma = (x_{ij}(\sigma))$ is a matrix in $GL(n, R)$ we consider the matrix elements $x_{ij}(\sigma)$ as coordinates of σ whereby $GL(n, R)$ is a manifold; if we express $x_{ij}(\sigma\tau^{-1})$ (σ, $\tau \in GL(n, R)$) in terms of $x_{kl}(\sigma)$, $x_{pq}(\tau)$ by ordinary matrix multiplication we see that $GL(n, R)$ is a Lie group. Let $\mathfrak{g}$ denote its Lie algebra and if $X \in \mathfrak{g}$ let $\tilde{X}$ denote the left invariant vector field on $GL(n, R)$ satisfying $\tilde{X}_e = X$. Let (X_{ij}) denote the matrix $(\tilde{X}_e x_{ij})$ and consider the mapping $\phi : X \to (X_{ij})$ of $\mathfrak{g}$ into $\mathfrak{gl}(n, R)$. The mapping ϕ is linear, one-to-one and onto. Furthermore if L_σ denotes the left translation $\tau \to \sigma\tau$ we have by the left invariance of $\tilde{X}$,

$$(\tilde{X}x_{ij})(\sigma) = X(x_{ij} \circ L_\sigma)$$

But

$$(x_{ij} \circ L_\sigma)(\tau) = x_{ij}(\sigma\tau) = \sum_k x_{ik}(\sigma)x_{kj}(\tau)$$

so

$$(\tilde{X}x_{ij})(\sigma) = \sum_k x_{ik}(\sigma)X_{kj} \tag{6}$$

It follows that

$$(\tilde{X}\tilde{Y} - \tilde{Y}\tilde{X})_e x_{ij} = \sum_k (X_{ik}Y_{kj} - Y_{ik}X_{kj}) = [\phi(X), \phi(Y)]_{ij}$$

so ϕ is a Lie algebra isomorphism. Thus the Lie algebra of $GL(n, R)$ is identified with $\mathfrak{gl}(n, \boldsymbol{R})$. In this statement one can replace the real field $\boldsymbol{R}$ by the field $\boldsymbol{C}$. In view of (2) and (6) we have

$$\frac{d}{dt}\, x_{ij}(\exp tX) = \sum_k x_{ik}(\exp tX)X_{kj}$$

so the matrix function $Y(t) = \exp tX$ satisfies

$$\frac{d}{dt}\, Y(t) = Y(t)X \quad Y(0) = I \tag{7}$$

But this equation is also satisfied by the matrix exponential function

$$e^{tX} = I + tX + \tfrac{1}{2}t^2X^2 + \cdots$$

so $\exp X = e^X$ for all $X \in \mathfrak{gl}(n, \boldsymbol{R})$. Thus the exponential mapping for Lie groups generalizes the exponential function for matrices.

Let G be any Lie group. A Lie group H is called a *Lie subgroup* of G if it is a subgroup of G and a submanifold of G. If this is the case the Lie algebra $\mathfrak{h}$ of H is a subalgebra of the Lie algebra $\mathfrak{g}$ of G, and the exponential maps for $\mathfrak{h}$ and $\mathfrak{g}$ coincide on $\mathfrak{h}$.

(vi) Let G be a Lie group with Lie algebra $\mathfrak{g}$. Let $\mathfrak{h} \subset \mathfrak{g}$ be a subalgebra. Then there exists exactly one connected Lie subgroup H of G with Lie algebra $\mathfrak{h}$.

This important fact is proved along the following lines: Consider the (abstract) subgroup H of G generated by the set $\exp \mathfrak{h}$. Using (iii), one introduces a topology in H (this is not necessarily the relative topology of G) as well as a coordinate system near the identity of H.   By left translations on H this gives a coordinate system in some neighborhood of an arbitrary point of H and one must finally prove that this manifold structure on H has the required properties. A connected Lie subgroup is usually called *analytic subgroup*.

(vii) Let G be a Lie group and H a subgroup of G which is closed as a subset of G.   Then there exists a unique manifold structure on H such that H is a topological Lie subgroup of G.

If $\mathfrak{h}$ and $\mathfrak{g}$ are the respective Lie algebras of H and G then

$$\mathfrak{h} = \{X \in \mathfrak{g} \,|\, \exp tX \in H \text{ for all } t \in \boldsymbol{R}\} \tag{8}$$

Example

Let us use (8) to find the Lie algebra of the group $\boldsymbol{S}\boldsymbol{U}(1, 1)$ considered in Chapter 1.   First note that $\boldsymbol{S}\boldsymbol{U}(1, 1)$ is the group of matrices of determinant

1 leaving invariant the Hermitian form $-z_1\bar{z}_1 + z_2\bar{z}_2$, that is, a matrix A belongs to $SU(1, 1)$ if and only if

$$^tAJ\bar{A} = J, \qquad \det A = 1$$

where ^tA is the transpose of A and

$$J = \begin{pmatrix} -1 & 0 \\ 0 & 1 \end{pmatrix}$$

Since $\mathfrak{gl}(2, C)$ is the Lie algebra of $GL(2, C)$ we see that X belongs to the Lie algebra $\mathfrak{su}(1, 1)$ of $SU(1, 1)$ if and only if

$$^t(\exp sX)J\,\overline{\exp sX} = J \qquad \det(\exp sX) = 1 \qquad (s \in R)$$

But $\exp(^tX) = {}^t(\exp X)$, so the first relation can be written

$$\exp s\bar{X} = J \exp(-s\,^tX)J^{-1}$$
$$= \exp s(-J\,^tXJ^{-1}) \qquad (s \in R)$$

Thus $X \in \mathfrak{su}(1, 1)$ if and only if $\bar{X} = -J\,^tXJ^{-1}$ and Trace $X = 0$. This is equivalent to

$$\mathfrak{su}(1, 1) = \left\{ X = \begin{pmatrix} i\alpha & \beta \\ \bar{\beta} & -i\alpha \end{pmatrix} \,\middle|\, \alpha \in R, \beta \in C \right\}$$

Property (v) shows that local properties of a Lie group are completely determined by the Lie algebra. This is of great consequence because all the machinery of linear algebra (theory of linear transformations of a vector space) can be applied to Lie algebras. In particular, let us see how the left invariant Haar measure on a Lie group can be written in Lie algebra terms.

Consider a Lie group G with Lie algebra $\mathfrak{g}$. If $X \in \mathfrak{g}$ the differential of the exponential map at X maps the tangent space $\mathfrak{g}_X$ onto the tangent space $G_{\exp X}$, which is $dL_{\exp X}(\mathfrak{g})$ (since $\mathfrak{g} = G_e$). We identify $\mathfrak{g}_X$ with $\mathfrak{g}$ via the ordinary parallelism of vectors. Thus if $Y \in \mathfrak{g}$ there exists a unique vector $Z \in \mathfrak{g}$ such that

$$d \exp{}_X(Y) = (dL_{\exp X})(Z)$$

Let us compute Z. By the definition of the differential of a map we have if f is differentiable at $\exp X$,

$$d \exp{}_X(Y)f = Y_X(f \circ \exp) \tag{9}$$

where Y_X is the vector Y viewed as a tangent vector to $\mathfrak{g}$ at X. But

$$Y_X(f \circ \exp) = \left\{ \frac{d}{dt} f(\exp(X + tY)) \right\}_{t=0} \tag{10}$$

Now take f to be analytic at e.   Then if X and t are sufficiently small,

$$f(\exp(X + tY)) = \sum_0^\infty \frac{1}{n!} [(\tilde{X} + t\tilde{Y})^n f](e)$$

so by (9) and (10),

$$d\exp{}_X(Y)f = \sum_0^\infty \frac{1}{(n+1)!} [(\tilde{X}^n\tilde{Y} + \tilde{X}^{n-1}\tilde{Y}\tilde{X} + \cdots + \tilde{Y}\tilde{X}^n)f](e)$$

Now consider the algebra generated by the left invariant vector fields on G and the operators

$$L(\tilde{X}) : A \to \tilde{X}A \qquad R(\tilde{X}) : A \to A\tilde{X} \qquad \theta(\tilde{X}) : A \to \tilde{X}A - A\tilde{X}$$

of this algebra.   Then $\theta(\tilde{X}) = L(\tilde{X}) - R(\tilde{X})$ and $L(\tilde{X})$ and $\theta(\tilde{X})$ commute so

$$R(\tilde{X})^m = (L(\tilde{X}) - \theta(\tilde{X}))^m = \sum_{p=0}^m (-1)^p \binom{m}{p} L(\tilde{X})^{m-p}\theta(\tilde{X})^p$$

and

$$\tilde{X}^n\tilde{Y} + \cdots + \tilde{Y}\tilde{X}^n = \sum_{p=0}^n \tilde{X}^p \sum_{k=0}^{n-p} (-1)^k \binom{n-p}{k} \tilde{X}^{n-p-k}\theta(\tilde{X})^k(\tilde{Y})$$

which by the elementary formula

$$\sum_{p=0}^{n-k} \binom{n-p}{k} = \binom{n+1}{k+1}$$

equals

$$\sum_{k=0}^n \binom{n+1}{k+1} \tilde{X}^{n-k}\theta(-\tilde{X})^k(\tilde{Y})$$

Hence,

$$d\exp{}_X(Y)f = \sum_{n=0}^\infty \left[\sum_{k=0}^n \left\{ \frac{\tilde{X}^{n-k}}{(n-k)!} \frac{\theta(-\tilde{X})^k}{(k+1)!} (\tilde{Y}) \right\}(f) \right](e) \qquad (11)$$

For sufficiently small X one can use the analyticity of f to interchange the two summations and use the formula

$$\sum_{n=0}^\infty \sum_{k=0}^n = \sum_{k=0}^\infty \sum_{n=k}^\infty$$

to equate the right-hand side with

$$\sum_{r=0}^\infty \left[\frac{\tilde{X}^r}{r!} \sum_{k=0}^\infty \frac{\theta(-\tilde{X})^k}{(k+1)!} (\tilde{Y})f \right](e) \qquad (12)$$

which by (3) equals

$$\sum_0^\infty \left[\frac{\theta(-\tilde{X})^k}{(k+1)!} (\tilde{Y})f \right](\exp X)$$

But $\theta(-\tilde{X})^k(\tilde{Y})$ is the left invariant vector field corresponding to the vector $\text{ad}(-X)^k(Y)$ in $\mathfrak{g}$ so we have proved

$$d \exp {}_X(Y) = dL_{\exp X}\left(\frac{1 - e^{-\text{ad }X}}{\text{ad }X}\right)(Y) \qquad (13)$$

at least if X is sufficiently small.   Because of the analyticity of both sides (13) holds actually for all $X \in \mathfrak{g}$.

Note that in the right-hand side of (13),

$$\frac{1 - e^{-\text{ad }X}}{\text{ad }X} = \int_0^1 e^{-t \text{ ad }X}\, dt$$

Now let $\exp : V_0 \rightarrow V_e$ be a diffeomorphism, V_0 and V_e being open sets in $\mathfrak{g}$ and G, respectively.   Let $f \in C_c^\infty(G)$ have support contained in V_e.   If dx denotes a left invariant Haar measure on G we have

$$\int_G f(x)\, dx = \int_{\mathfrak{g}} f(\exp X)J(X)\, dX$$

dX being a Euclidean volume element on $\mathfrak{g}$ and J the Jacobian of the exponential map.   In view of (13) we have

$$\int_G f(x)\, dx = c\int_{\mathfrak{g}} f(\exp X) \det \left(\frac{1 - e^{-\text{ad }X}}{\text{ad }X}\right) dX \qquad (14)$$

where c is a constant.   For a formulation of (13) for differential forms see [11] p. 21 and [12] p. 157.   For a generalization to Riemannian manifolds see [30].

(**ix**) Given a Lie algebra $\mathfrak{g}$ over $\boldsymbol{R}$ there exists a Lie group G with Lie algebra $\mathfrak{g}$.

The local result is called the third fundamental theorem of Lie; the global statement was later proved by É. Cartan.   One proof of (ix) uses Ado's theorem that there exists an isomorphism of $\mathfrak{g}$ into $\mathfrak{gl}(n, \boldsymbol{R})$.   Then the desired G can by (vi) be taken as a suitable subgroup of $\boldsymbol{GL}(n, \boldsymbol{R})$.   Another proof will be indicated later.

CHAPTER 3: STRUCTURE THEORY OF LIE GROUPS

3-1   Solvable and Semisimple Lie Algebras

Let $\mathfrak{g}$ be a Lie algebra and as before let ad X denote the linear transformation $Y \rightarrow [X, Y]$ of $\mathfrak{g}$.   Lie algebra theory is concerned with this family of linear transformations.

The vector space spanned by all elements $[X, Y]$ is an ideal in $\mathfrak{g}$, called the *derived algebra* of $\mathfrak{g}$ and denoted $\mathfrak{D}\mathfrak{g}$. The nth derived algebra $\mathfrak{D}^n\mathfrak{g}$ of $\mathfrak{g}$ is defined inductively by $\mathfrak{D}^0\mathfrak{g} = \mathfrak{g}$, $\mathfrak{D}^n\mathfrak{g} = \mathfrak{D}(\mathfrak{D}^{n-1}\mathfrak{g})$. A Lie algebra is called *solvable* if $\mathfrak{D}^n\mathfrak{g} = \{0\}$ for some $n \geqslant 0$. A Lie group is called solvable if its Lie algebra is solvable.

A Lie algebra is called *nilpotent* if for each $X \in \mathfrak{g}$, ad X is nilpotent. It can be proved that a Lie algebra is solvable if and only if its derived algebra is nilpotent. In particular we see that a nilpotent Lie algebra is solvable.

Example

Let $\mathfrak{t}(n)$ denote the Lie subalgebra of $\mathfrak{gl}(n, \mathbf{R})$ formed by the upper triangular matrices and let $\mathfrak{n}(n)$ denote the subalgebra of matrices in $\mathfrak{t}(n)$ with diagonal 0. Then $\mathfrak{t}(n)$ is solvable, $\mathfrak{n}(n)$ nilpotent and coincides with the derived algebra of $\mathfrak{t}(n)$.

Let $\mathfrak{g}$ be a Lie algebra. The *Killing form* of $\mathfrak{g}$ is defined as the bilinear form $B(X, Y) = \mathrm{Tr}\,(\mathrm{ad}\,X\,\mathrm{ad}\,Y)$ ($\mathrm{Tr} = $ trace); $\mathfrak{g}$ is called *semisimple* if B is nondegenerate and $\mathfrak{g}$ is called *simple* if in addition it has no ideals except 0 and $\mathfrak{g}$.

Example

Let $SL(n, \mathbf{R})$ denote the group of $n \times n$ real matrices of determinant 1. It is a closed subgroup of $GL(n, \mathbf{R})$, hence a Lie subgroup [*cf.* (vii) §2-2] and since the relation $\det(e^A) = e^{\mathrm{Tr}\,A}$ holds for any matrix A, we see from (8) §2-2 that the Lie algebra $\mathfrak{sl}(n, \mathbf{R})$ of the subgroup $SL(n, \mathbf{R})$ of $GL(n, \mathbf{R})$ is the subalgebra of $\mathfrak{gl}(n, \mathbf{R})$ consisting of all $n \times n$ matrices of trace 0. This statement holds also with $\mathbf{R}$ replaced with the complex field $\mathbf{C}$. Let us compute the Killing form of $\mathfrak{sl}(n, \mathbf{C})$. Let $\mathfrak{d}(n)$ denote the set of diagonal matrices in $\mathfrak{sl}(n, \mathbf{C})$. If $H \in \mathfrak{d}(n)$ each matrix E_{ij} with 1 at the ith row and the jth column, 0 elsewhere,

$$
E_{ij} = \begin{pmatrix} 0 & 0 & \cdots & 0 \\ 0 & 0 & \cdots & 0 \\ & & 1 & \\ 0 & 0 & \cdots & 0 \end{pmatrix}
$$

is an eigenvector for ad H and we find easily that

$$\mathrm{Tr}\,(\mathrm{ad}\,H\,\mathrm{ad}\,H) = 2n\,\mathrm{Tr}\,(HH) \tag{1}$$

The mapping $X \to gXg^{-1}$ ($g \in GL(n, \mathbf{C})$) is an automorphism of $\mathfrak{sl}(n, \mathbf{C})$ and any automorphism of a Lie algebra leaves the Killing form invariant. If $gXg^{-1} \in \mathfrak{d}(n)$ we have therefore

$$\mathrm{Tr}\,(\mathrm{ad}\,X\,\mathrm{ad}\,X) = \mathrm{Tr}\,(\mathrm{ad}\,(gXg^{-1})\,\mathrm{ad}\,(gXg^{-1})) = 2n\,\mathrm{Tr}\,(gXXg^{-1}) \tag{2}$$

so

$$\text{Tr} (\text{ad } X \text{ ad } X) = 2n \text{ Tr} (XX) \tag{3}$$

The matrices which are conjugate to a diagonal matrix in $\mathfrak{d}(n)$ form a dense subset of $\mathfrak{sl}(n, C)$ so (3) holds for all $X \in \mathfrak{sl}(n, C)$. Hence by "polarization"

$$B(X, Y) = 2n \text{ Tr} (XY) \qquad \text{for } X, Y \in \mathfrak{sl}(n, C) \tag{4}$$

It is a trivial matter to verify that B in (4) is nondegenerate so $\mathfrak{sl}(n, C)$ is semisimple.

A fundamental result in Lie algebra theory (the *Levi decomposition*) states that every Lie algebra $\mathfrak{g}$ is the direct vector space sum

$$\mathfrak{g} = \mathfrak{r} + \mathfrak{s} \tag{5}$$

where $\mathfrak{r}$ is the maximal solvable ideal in $\mathfrak{g}$ and $\mathfrak{s}$ is a semisimple subalgebra. To a large extent this result splits Lie group theory into two branches—one for solvable Lie groups, the other for semisimple Lie groups. The latter branch is further developed and has had more contact with physics and geometry and is therefore emphasized in these lectures. (Of course the two branches are related because semisimple Lie algebras always have solvable subalgebras.)

The Levi decomposition can for example be used as a basis of an alternative proof of (ix) §2-2. Let Aut ($\mathfrak{s}$) denote the group of all automorphisms of $\mathfrak{s}$. This is a closed subgroup of $GL(\mathfrak{s})$, hence a Lie subgroup, and by (8) §2-2 its Lie algebra is given by the set of endomorphisms A of $\mathfrak{s}$ for which $e^{tA} \in$ Aut ($\mathfrak{s}$) for all $t \in R$. But the relation

$$e^{tA}[X, Y] = [e^{tA}X, e^{tA}Y]$$

implies (by differentiation)

$$A[X, Y] = [AX, Y] + [X, AY] \tag{6}$$

and vice versa. A linear transformation A satisfying (6) for all $X, Y \in \mathfrak{s}$ is called a *derivation* of $\mathfrak{s}$ so we see that the Lie algebra of Aut ($\mathfrak{s}$) is the set of derivations of $\mathfrak{s}$. On the other hand, if $X \in \mathfrak{s}$, ad X is obviously a derivation of $\mathfrak{s}$. Using the semisimplicity, one can prove that all derivations of $\mathfrak{s}$ are of this form. Thus ad ($\mathfrak{s}$) is the Lie algebra of Aut ($\mathfrak{s}$); but the semisimplicity of $\mathfrak{s}$ shows that $X \to$ ad X is an isomorphism so we have verified that any semisimple Lie algebra is the Lie algebra of a Lie group. For solvable Lie algebras the statement can be proved by induction and by the Levi decomposition (5) the theorem can be proved in general by taking appropriate semidirect products.

For any Lie algebra $\mathfrak{g}$, let Int ($\mathfrak{g}$) denote the connected Lie subgroup of $GL(\mathfrak{g})$ with Lie algebra ad ($\mathfrak{g}$) $\subset \mathfrak{gl}(\mathfrak{g})$; Int ($\mathfrak{g}$) is called the *adjoint group of* $\mathfrak{g}$. If $\mathfrak{g}$ is semisimple then Int ($\mathfrak{g}$) is the identity component of Aut ($\mathfrak{g}$). If G is a

Lie group with Lie algebra $\mathfrak{g}$, and $g \in G$, the inner automorphism $x \to gxg^{-1}$ of G induces an automorphism of $\mathfrak{g}$, denoted Ad (g). If G is connected, $\mathrm{Ad}(G) = \mathrm{Int}(\mathfrak{g})$. In fact if X, $Y \in \mathfrak{g}$ we obtain by iterating (4) §2-2

$$\exp\left(\mathrm{Ad}\left(\exp tX\right)tY\right) = \exp tX \exp tY \exp\left(-tX\right) \tag{7}$$

$$= \exp\left(tY + t^2[X, Y] + 0(t^3)\right)$$

so

$$\mathrm{Ad}\left(\exp tX\right)Y = Y + t[X, Y] + 0(t^2) \tag{8}$$

On the other hand, the mapping $g \to \mathrm{Ad}\,(g)$ is a homomorphism of G into $\boldsymbol{GL}(\mathfrak{g})$. Hence $t \to \mathrm{Ad}\,(\exp tX)$ is a one-parameter subgroup of $\boldsymbol{GL}(\mathfrak{g})$, thus by the fundamental example in Ch. 2 of the form

$$\mathrm{Ad}\,(\exp tX) = e^{tA}$$

But then (8) shows $A = \mathrm{ad}\,X$ so

$$\mathrm{Ad}\,(\exp X) = e^{\mathrm{ad}\,X} \tag{9}$$

and the relation $\mathrm{Ad}\,(G) = \mathrm{Int}\,(\mathfrak{g})$ follows.

The homomorphism $g \to \mathrm{Ad}\,(g)$ is called the *adjoint representation* of G. For clarity it is sometimes written Ad_G.

3-2   Structure of Semisimple Lie Algebras

Let $\mathfrak{g}$ be a semisimple Lie algebra, B its Killing form. If $O(B)$ denotes the group of linear transformations of $\mathfrak{g}$ leaving B invariant, we have Aut $(\mathfrak{g}) \subset O(B)$; also

$$B(X, \mathrm{ad}\,Y(Z)) = -B(\mathrm{ad}\,Y(X), Z)$$

for X, Y, $Z \in \mathfrak{g}$, so each ad Y is skew-symmetric with respect to B.

Definition. A Lie algebra $\mathfrak{g}$ over $\boldsymbol{R}$ is called *compact* if its adjoint group Int $(\mathfrak{g})$ is compact.

Proposition 2.1

(i) Let $\mathfrak{g}$ be a semisimple Lie algebra over $\boldsymbol{R}$. Then $\mathfrak{g}$ is compact if and only if the Killing form of $\mathfrak{g}$ is negative definite.

(ii) Every compact Lie algebra is the direct sum $\mathfrak{g} = \mathfrak{z} + [\mathfrak{g}, \mathfrak{g}]$ where $\mathfrak{z}$ is the center of $\mathfrak{g}$ and the ideal $[\mathfrak{g}, \mathfrak{g}]$ is semisimple and compact.

PROOF OF (i). If the Killing form is negative definite $O(B)$ is compact and so are the groups Aut $(\mathfrak{g})$ and Int $(\mathfrak{g})$. On the other hand, if Int $(\mathfrak{g})$ is compact it leaves invariant a positive definite quadratic form Q on $\mathfrak{g}$. Let $X_1, \ldots, X_n$ be a basis of $\mathfrak{g}$ such that

$$Q(X) = \sum_{1}^{n} x_i^{2} \quad \text{if} \quad X = \sum_{1}^{n} x_i X_i$$

By means of this basis each $\sigma \in \text{Int}(\mathfrak{g})$ is given by an orthogonal matrix, so if $X \in \mathfrak{g}$ each ad X is skew-symmetric, that is, $^t(\text{ad } X) = -\text{ad } X$, where t denotes transpose. But then,

$$B(X, X) = \text{Tr}(\text{ad } X \text{ ad } X) = -\text{Tr}(\text{ad } X \, ^t(\text{ad } X))$$

$$= -\sum_{i,j} x_{ij}^2 \quad \text{if} \quad \text{ad } X = (x_{ij})$$

This proves (i); the second part is proved similarly.

Since the study of Lie algebras amounts to a study of the linear transformations ad $X (X \in \mathfrak{g})$, the first problem is, of course, diagonalization. Here one gets further by working with C as the base field, so we make the following definition.

Definition. Let $\mathfrak{g}$ be a semisimple Lie algebra over C. A *Cartan subalgebra* of $\mathfrak{g}$ is a subalgebra $\mathfrak{h}$ such that (1) $\mathfrak{h} \subset \mathfrak{g}$ is a maximal abelian subalgebra; and (2) for each $H \in \mathfrak{h}$, ad H is a semisimple endomorphism of $\mathfrak{g}$ (that is, it can be put into diagonal form by means of a suitable basis).

The idea behind this definition is: If $X_1, X_2 \in \mathfrak{g}$ are such that ad X_1 and ad X_2 have simultaneous diagonalization then $[\text{ad } X_1, \text{ad } X_2] = 0$ so $[X_1, X_2] = 0$; thus the set ad $(\mathfrak{h})$ is a maximal family of simultaneously diagonalizable endomorphisms of $\mathfrak{g}$. Although our objective is the study of semisimple Lie algebras $\mathfrak{a}$ over R the definition above is useful because the complexification $\mathfrak{g} = \mathfrak{a} + i\mathfrak{a}$ is also semisimple. If $\mathfrak{g}$ is any Lie algebra over C a *real form* of $\mathfrak{g}$ is a *real* linear subspace $\mathfrak{b}$ of $\mathfrak{g}$ (that is, $r \in R$, $X, Y \in \mathfrak{b} \Rightarrow rX$, $X + Y \in \mathfrak{b}$) which is closed under the bracket operation and satisfies $\mathfrak{g} = \mathfrak{b} + i\mathfrak{b}$ (direct sum). The mapping $X + iY \to X - iY (X, Y \in \mathfrak{b})$ is called the *conjugation* of $\mathfrak{g}$ with respect to $\mathfrak{b}$. A Lie algebra $\mathfrak{g}$ over C may have many real forms.

Examples

(i) $\mathfrak{sl}(n, R)$ is a real form of $\mathfrak{sl}(n, C)$. The diagonal matrices in $\mathfrak{sl}(n, C)$ form a Cartan subalgebra.

(ii) The Lie algebra $\mathfrak{su}(1, 1)$ is a real form of $\mathfrak{sl}(2, C)$. In fact, if

$$\begin{pmatrix} z_{11} & z_{12} \\ z_{21} & z_{22} \end{pmatrix} \in \mathfrak{sl}(2, C)$$

we can write (since $z_{22} = -z_{11}$)

$$\begin{pmatrix} z_{11} & z_{12} \\ z_{21} & z_{22} \end{pmatrix} = \begin{pmatrix} i\alpha_1 & \beta_1 \\ \bar{\beta}_1 & -i\alpha_1 \end{pmatrix} + i\begin{pmatrix} i\alpha_2 & \beta_2 \\ \bar{\beta}_2 & -i\alpha_2 \end{pmatrix}$$

for $\alpha_1, \alpha_2 \in R$, $\beta_1, \beta_2 \in C$.

(iii) The Lie algebra $\mathfrak{su}(2)$ of skew-Hermitian matrices of trace 0,

$$X = \begin{pmatrix} i\alpha & \beta \\ -\bar{\beta} & -i\alpha \end{pmatrix} \qquad \alpha \in R,\ \beta \in C$$

is obviously a real form of $\mathfrak{sl}(2, C)$. Since the Killing form of a real form is in general obtained by restriction we see from (4) §3-1 that

$$B(X, X) = 4\,\mathrm{Trace}\,(XX) = -8(\alpha^2 + |\beta|^2)$$

so $\mathfrak{su}(2)$ is a compact real form of $\mathfrak{sl}(2, C)$.

The following two results are of fundamental importance.

Theorem 2.2. Every semisimple Lie algebra $\mathfrak{g}$ over C contains a Cartan subalgebra $\mathfrak{h}$.

Theorem 2.3. Every semisimple Lie algebra $\mathfrak{g}$ over C has a real form $\mathfrak{u}$ which is compact.

Ordinarily Theorem 2.2 is proved first using theorems on solvable Lie algebras (Lie's theorem that a solvable Lie algebra of complex matrices has a common eigenvector). The simultaneous diagonalization of the endomorphisms ad $\mathfrak{h}$ leads to a detailed structure theory for $\mathfrak{g}$ by which the compact real form $\mathfrak{u}$ is constructed. The details are as follows:

Assume $\mathfrak{h}$ is a Cartan subalgebra of $\mathfrak{g}$. Given a linear form $\alpha \neq 0$ on $\mathfrak{h}$ let

$$\mathfrak{g}^\alpha = \{X \in \mathfrak{g} \mid \mathrm{ad}\,H(X) = \alpha(H)X \qquad \text{for all } H \in \mathfrak{h}\}$$

This linear form α is called a *root* if $\mathfrak{g}^\alpha \neq \{0\}$. Let Δ denote the set of all roots. Then

$$\mathfrak{g} = \mathfrak{h} + \sum_{\alpha \in \Delta} \mathfrak{g}^\alpha \qquad \text{(direct sum)} \tag{1}$$

and it can be proved that

$$\dim \mathfrak{g}^\alpha = 1 \qquad (\alpha \in \Delta) \tag{2}$$

Let $\mathfrak{h}^*$ denote the subset (real-linear subspace) of $\mathfrak{h}$, where all the roots have real values. Then for a suitable choice of vectors $X_\alpha \in \mathfrak{g}^\alpha$ the set

$$\mathfrak{u} = i\mathfrak{h}^* + \sum_{\alpha \in \Delta} R(X_\alpha - X_{-\alpha}) + \sum_{\alpha \in \Delta} R(i(X_\alpha + X_{-\alpha})) \tag{3}$$

is a compact real form of $\mathfrak{g}$.

Example

Consider again the Lie algebra $\mathfrak{g} = \mathfrak{sl}(n, C)$ and its Cartan subalgebra $\mathfrak{h}$ of diagonal matrices of trace 0. Let again E_{ij} denote the matrix

$$(\delta_{ai}\, \delta_{bj})_{1 \leqslant a,\, b \leqslant n}$$

and for each $H \in \mathfrak{h}$ let $e_i(H)$ denote the ith diagonal element in H. Then

$$[H, E_{ij}] = (e_i(H) - e_j(H))E_{ij}$$

for all $H \in \mathfrak{h}$ so the linear form $\alpha_{ij}(H) = e_i(H) - e_j(H)$ is a root for $i \neq j$ and by (1) this does give all the roots. The space $\mathfrak{h}^*$ consists of all real diagonal matrices of trace 0. Let us put $X_{\alpha_{ij}} = E_{ij}$ ($i \neq j$). Then it is easily seen that the space (3) is the set $\mathfrak{su}(n)$ of all skew-Hermitian $n \times n$ matrices, which is indeed a compact real form of $\mathfrak{sl}(n, C)$ (*cf.* example above).

It is tempting to try to prove Theorem 2.3 directly, because then Theorem 2.2 would be an immediate corollary. In fact, for each $X \in \mathfrak{u}$, ad X can be diagonalized, so if $\mathfrak{t} \subset \mathfrak{u}$ is any maximal Abelian subalgebra, the space $\mathfrak{h} = \mathfrak{t} + i\mathfrak{t}$ is a Cartan subalgebra of $\mathfrak{g}$.

A direct and elementary proof of Theorem 2.3 (without the use of Theorem 2.2) does not seem to be available. However, Cartan has proposed an idea for this purpose (*J. Math. Pures Appl.* **8** (1929), p. 23), which I shall describe here.

Since the Killing form of $\mathfrak{g}$ is nondegenerate, there exists a basis $e_1, \ldots, e_n$ of $\mathfrak{g}$ such that

$$B(Z, Z) = -\sum_1^n z_i^2 \qquad \text{if} \quad Z = \sum_1^n z_i e_i \tag{4}$$

Let the structural constants $c_{ijk} \in C$ be determined by

$$[e_i, e_j] = \sum_1^n c_{ijk} e_k$$

Then

$$B(Z, Z) = \operatorname{Tr}(\operatorname{ad} Z \operatorname{ad} Z) = \sum_{i,j}\left(\sum_{h,k} c_{ikh}\, c_{jhk}\right)z_i z_j$$

so by (4)

$$\sum_{h,k} c_{ikh}\, c_{jhk} = -\delta_{ij} \tag{5}$$

Also,

$$B([X_i, X_j], X_k) + B(X_j, [X_i, X_k]) = 0$$

so

$$c_{ijk} + c_{ikj} = 0$$

and by (5)

$$\sum_{i,h,k} c_{ihk}^2 = n$$

The space

$$\mathfrak{u} = \sum_1^n \boldsymbol{R} e_i$$

is a real form of $\mathfrak{g}$ if and only if all the c_{ijk} are real.

Consider now the set $\mathfrak{F}$ of all bases $(e_1, \ldots, e_n)$ of $\mathfrak{g}$ such that (4) holds. Consider the function f on $\mathfrak{F}$ given by

$$f(e_1, \ldots, e_n) = \sum_{i, j, k} |c_{ijk}|^2$$

Then we have seen that

$$\sum_{i, j, k} |c_{ijk}|^2 \geqslant \left| \sum_{i, j, k} c_{ijk}^2 \right| = \sum_{i, j, k} c_{ijk}^2 = n \tag{6}$$

and the equality sign holds if and only if all the c_{ijk} are real, that is, if and only if

$$\mathfrak{u} = \sum_1^n \boldsymbol{R} e_i$$

is a real form. In this case it is a compact real form in view of (4) and Prop. 2.1.

Thus Theorem 2.3 follows if one can prove: (I) The function f on $\mathfrak{F}$ has a minimum value; and (II) this minimum value is attained at a point $(e_1{}^0, \ldots, e_n{}^0) \in \mathfrak{F}$ for which the structural constants are real. Note that (II) is equivalent to (II'): The minimum of f is n.

3-3 Cartan Decompositions

We now go back to considering a semisimple Lie algebra $\mathfrak{g}$ over $\boldsymbol{R}$ and as usual we denote by B the Killing form of $\mathfrak{g}$. There are of course many possible ways to find a direct vector space decomposition $\mathfrak{g} = \mathfrak{g}^+ + \mathfrak{g}^-$ such that B is positive definite on $\mathfrak{g}^+$ and negative definite on $\mathfrak{g}^-$. However, we should like to find a decomposition which is directly related to the Lie algebra structure of $\mathfrak{g}$.

Definition. A *Cartan decomposition* of $\mathfrak{g}$ is a direct decomposition $\mathfrak{g} = \mathfrak{k} + \mathfrak{p}$ such that (i) $B < 0$ on $\mathfrak{k}$, $B > 0$ on $\mathfrak{p}$; and (ii) The mapping $\theta : T + X \to T - X$ $(T \in \mathfrak{k}, X \in \mathfrak{p})$ is an automorphism of $\mathfrak{g}$.

In this case θ is called a *Cartan involution* of $\mathfrak{g}$ and the positive definite bilinear form $(X, Y) \to -B(X, \theta Y)$ is denoted by B_θ. We shall now establish the existence of Cartan decompositions, using compact real forms for semisimple Lie algebras over $\boldsymbol{C}$.

Theorem 3.1. Suppose θ is a Cartan involution of a semisimple Lie algebra $\mathfrak{g}$ over $\mathbf{R}$ and σ an arbitrary involutive automorphism of $\mathfrak{g}$. There then exists an automorphism ϕ of $\mathfrak{g}$ such that the Cartan involution $\phi\theta\phi^{-1}$ commutes with σ.

PROOF. The product $N = \sigma\theta$ is an automorphism of $\mathfrak{g}$ and if $X, Y \in \mathfrak{g}$,

$$-B_\theta(NX, Y) = B(NX, \theta Y) = B(X, N^{-1}\theta Y) = B(X, \theta N Y)$$

so

$$B_\theta(NX, Y) = B_\theta(X, NY)$$

that is, N is symmetric with respect to the positive definite bilinear form B_θ. Let $X_1, \ldots, X_n$ be a basis of $\mathfrak{g}$ diagonalizing N. Then $P = N^2$ has a positive diagonal, say, with elements $\lambda_1, \ldots, \lambda_n$. Take P^t ($t \in \mathbf{R}$) with diagonal elements $\lambda_1^{\,t}, \ldots, \lambda_n^{\,t}$ and define the structural constants c_{ijk} by

$$[X_i, X_j] = \sum_{k=1}^{n} c_{ijk} X_k$$

Since P is an automorphism, we conclude

$$\lambda_i \lambda_j c_{ijk} = \lambda_k c_{ijk}$$

which implies

$$\lambda_i^{\,t} \lambda_j^{\,t} c_{ijk} = \lambda_k^{\,t} c_{ijk} \qquad (t \in \mathbf{R})$$

so P^t is an automorphism. Put $\theta_t = P^t \theta P^{-t}$. Since $\theta N \theta^{-1} = N^{-1}$, we have $\theta P \theta^{-1} = P^{-1}$, that is $\theta P = P^{-1}\theta$. In matrix terms (using still the basis $X_1, \ldots, X_n$) this means (since θ is symmetric with respect to B_θ)

$$\theta_{ij}\lambda_j = \lambda_i^{-1}\theta_{ij}$$

so

$$\theta_{ij}\lambda_j^{\,t} = \lambda_i^{-t}\theta_{ij}$$

that is, $\theta P^t \theta^{-1} = P^{-t}$. Hence,

$$\sigma\theta_t = \sigma P^t \theta P^{-t} = \sigma\theta P^{-2t} = N P^{-2t}$$

$$\theta_t \sigma = (\sigma\theta_t)^{-1} = P^{2t} N^{-1} = N^{-1} P^{2t}$$

so it suffices to put $\phi = P^{1/4}$ $(=\sqrt{\sigma\theta})$. (*cf.* [3], p. 100, [31], p. 156, [47], p. 884). The following result is given in Mostow [54].

Corollary 3.2. Let $\mathfrak{g}$ be a semisimple Lie algebra over $\mathbf{R}$, $\mathfrak{g}_c = \mathfrak{g} + i\mathfrak{g}$ its complexification, $\mathfrak{u}$ any compact real form of $\mathfrak{g}_c$, σ and τ the conjugations of $\mathfrak{g}_c$ with respect to $\mathfrak{g}$ and $\mathfrak{u}$, respectively. Then there exists an automorphism ϕ of $\mathfrak{g}_c$ such that $\phi \cdot \mathfrak{u}$ is invariant under σ.

PROOF. Let $\mathfrak{g}_c{}^R$ denote the Lie algebra $\mathfrak{g}_c$ considered as a Lie algebra over R, B^R the Killing form.   It is not hard to show that $B^R(X, Y) = 2\text{Re}\,(B_c(X, Y))$ if B_c is the Killing form of $\mathfrak{g}_c$.   Thus σ and τ are Cartan involutions of $\mathfrak{g}_c{}^R$ and the corollary follows (note that since $\sigma\tau$ is a (complex) automorphism of $\mathfrak{g}_c$, ϕ is one as well).

Corollary 3.3. Each semisimple Lie algebra $\mathfrak{g}$ over R has Cartan decompositions and any two such are conjugate under an automorphism of $\mathfrak{g}$.

PROOF. Let $\mathfrak{g}_c$ denote the complexification of $\mathfrak{g}$, σ the corresponding conjugation, and $\mathfrak{u}$ a compact real form of $\mathfrak{g}_c$ invariant under σ (Theorem 2.3 and Cor. 3.2).   Then put $\mathfrak{k} = \mathfrak{g} \cap \mathfrak{u}$, $\mathfrak{p} = \mathfrak{g} \cap i\mathfrak{u}$.   Then $B < 0$ on $\mathfrak{k}$, $B > 0$ on $\mathfrak{p}$, and since $\theta : T + X \to T - X$ $(T \in \mathfrak{k}, X \in \mathfrak{p})$ is an automorphism, $B\,(\mathfrak{k}, \mathfrak{p}) = 0$. It follows that $\mathfrak{g} = \mathfrak{k} + \mathfrak{p}$ is a Cartan decomposition.

Consider now two Cartan decompositions,

$$\mathfrak{g} = \mathfrak{k}_1 + \mathfrak{p}_1 \qquad \mathfrak{g} = \mathfrak{k}_2 + \mathfrak{p}_2$$

Then $\mathfrak{u}_1 = \mathfrak{k}_1 + i\mathfrak{p}_1$ and $\mathfrak{u}_2 = \mathfrak{k}_2 + i\mathfrak{p}_2$ are compact real forms of $\mathfrak{g}_c$.   Let τ_1 and τ_2 denote the corresponding conjugations.   By Cor. 3.2 there exists an automorphism ϕ of $\mathfrak{g}_c$ such that $\phi \cdot \mathfrak{u}_2$ is invariant under τ_1.   Thus $\phi \cdot \mathfrak{u}_2$ is equal to the direct sum of its intersections with $\mathfrak{u}_1$ and $i\mathfrak{u}_1$.   Now $B > 0$ on $i\mathfrak{u}_1$ and $B < 0$ on $\phi \cdot \mathfrak{u}_2$.   Hence $i\mathfrak{u}_1 \cap \phi \cdot \mathfrak{u}_2 = \{0\}$ so $\mathfrak{u}_1 = \phi \cdot \mathfrak{u}_2$. But τ_1 and τ_2 both leave $\mathfrak{g}$ invariant and ϕ can (according to the proof of Theorem 3.1) be taken as a power of $\tau_1\tau_2$ so it also leaves $\mathfrak{g}$ invariant.   Thus $\phi(\mathfrak{g} \cap \mathfrak{u}_2) = \mathfrak{g} \cap \mathfrak{u}_1$ so ϕ gives the desired automorphism of $\mathfrak{g}$.

Examples

Let $\mathfrak{g} = \mathfrak{sl}\,(n, R)$, the Lie algebra of the group $SL(n, R)$.   The group $SO(n)$ of orthogonal matrices is a closed subgroup, hence a Lie subgroup, and by (8) §2-2, its Lie algebra, denoted $\mathfrak{so}(n)$, consists of those matrices $X \in \mathfrak{sl}(n, R)$ for which $\exp tX \in SO(n)$ for all $t \in R$.   But

$$\exp tX \in SO(n) \Leftrightarrow \exp tX \exp t(^tX) = 1 \qquad \det\,(\exp tX) = 1$$

so

$$\mathfrak{so}(n) = \{X \in \mathfrak{sl}(n, R)\,|\, X + {}^tX = 0\}$$

the set of skew-symmetric $n \times n$ matrices (which are automatically of trace 0).

The mapping $\theta : X \to -{}^tX$ is an automorphism of $\mathfrak{sl}(n, R)$ and $\theta^2 = 1$. Since $B(X, X) = 2n \operatorname{Tr}(XX)$, $B(X, \theta X) < 0$ so θ is a Cartan involution and

$$\mathfrak{sl}(n, R) = \mathfrak{so}(n) + \mathfrak{p} \qquad\qquad (1)$$

where $\mathfrak{p}$ is the set of $n \times n$ symmetric matrices of trace 0, is the corresponding

Cartan decomposition. Now it is known that every positive definite matrix can be written uniquely e^X (X = symmetric) and every nonsingular matrix g can be written uniquely $g = op$ (o = orthogonal, p = positive definite). Thus we have a global analog of (1),

$$SL(n, R) = SO(n)P \tag{2}$$

where $P = \exp \mathfrak{p}$, the set of positive definite matrices of determinant 1.

We shall now state a generalization of (2).

Theorem 3.4. Let G be a connected semisimple Lie group with Lie algebra $\mathfrak{g}$. Let $\mathfrak{g} = \mathfrak{k} + \mathfrak{p}$ be a Cartan decomposition ($\mathfrak{k}$ the algebra), K the analytic subgroup of G with Lie algebra $\mathfrak{k}$. Then the mapping

$$(X, k) \to (\exp X)k$$

is a diffeomorphism of $\mathfrak{p} \times K$ onto G.

In Theorem 3.4, the center $\mathfrak{z}$ of $\mathfrak{g}$ is $\{0\}$, (immediate from the definition) so the center Z of G is discrete. One can prove $Z \subset K$ and that K is compact if and only if Z is finite. In this case K is a maximal compact subgroup of G, and every compact subgroup is conjugate to a subgroup of K.

Proposition 3.5. In terms of the notation of Theorem 3.4, the mapping

$$(\exp X)k \to \exp(-X)k \tag{3}$$

is an automorphism of G.

In fact let $\tilde{G}$ be the universal covering group of G. Since all simply connected Lie groups with the same Lie algebra are isomorphic (*cf.* (v) §2-2) the automorphism θ of $\mathfrak{g}$ induces an automorphism $\tilde{\theta}$ of $\tilde{G}$ such that $d\tilde{\theta}_e = \theta$. By the remarks above, the center $\tilde{Z}$ of $\tilde{G}$ is contained in the analytic subgroup $\tilde{K}$ of $\tilde{G}$ corresponding to $\mathfrak{k}$. But $G = \tilde{G}/N$, where $N \subset \tilde{Z}$ so $\tilde{\theta}$ induces an automorphism of G which is (3).

Consider now the set G/K of left cosets gK ($g \in G$). This set has a unique manifold structure such that the map $X \to (\exp X)K$ is a diffeomorphism of $\mathfrak{p}$ onto G/K. (More generally if K is a closed subgroup of a Lie group G, G/K is a manifold in a natural way.) The group G operates on G/K: each $g \in G$ gives rise to a diffeomorphism $\tau(g) : xK \to gxK$ of G/K. Since $Z \subset K$ we have $G/K = (G/Z)/(K/Z)$ and $G/Z = \text{Int}(\mathfrak{g})$ *so the space G/K is independent of the choice of the Lie group G with Lie algebra $\mathfrak{g}$.* In view of Cor. 3.3 the different possibilities for K are all conjugate so the space G/K is in a canonical way associated with $\mathfrak{g}$. Let o denote the point $\{K\}$ in G/K (the origin) and $(G/K)_o$ the tangent space. The mapping $\pi : g \to gK$ has a differential $d\pi$ mapping $\mathfrak{g}$ onto $(G/K)_o$ with a kernel which contains $\mathfrak{k}$. By reasons of dimensionality, we see therefore that the mapping

$$d\pi : \mathfrak{p} \to (G/K)_o \tag{4}$$

is an isomorphism and if $k \in K$ we have for $X \in \mathfrak{p}$, $t \in \mathbf{R}$

$$\pi(\exp \mathrm{Ad}\,(k)tX) = \pi(k \exp tX \; k^{-1}) = \tau(k)\pi(\exp tX)$$

so

$$d\pi\,(\mathrm{Ad}\,(k)X) = d\tau(k)\,d\pi(X). \tag{5}$$

Now the form B is > 0 on $\mathfrak{p}$ so by (4) and (5) we obtain a positive definite quadratic form Q_o on $(G/K)_o$ invariant under $d\tau(k)$ ($k \in K$). If $p \in G/K$ is arbitrary there exists a $g \in G$ such that $p = gK$ and $d\tau(g) : (G/K)_o \to (G/K)_p$ is an isomorphism giving rise to a quadratic form Q_p on $(G/K)_p$. If $g' \in G$ satisfies $g'K = gK$, $d\tau(g')$ gives the same quadratic form Q_p on $(G/K)_p$ because of the K-invariance of Q_o. Thus we have a Riemannian structure Q on G/K induced by B.

Proposition 3.6. The manifold G/K with the Riemannian structure induced by B is a symmetric space.

PROOF. Let θ denote the automorphism (3) and s_o the mapping $gK \to \theta(g)K$ of G/K onto itself. Then s_o is a diffeomorphism and $s_o^2 = I$, $(ds_o)_o = -I$. To see that s_o is an isometry let $p = gK$ ($g \in G$) and $X \in (G/K)_p$. Then the vector $X_o = d\tau(g^{-1})X$ belongs to $(G/K)_o$. But if $x \in G$ we have

$$s_o(gxK) = \theta(gx)K = \tau(\theta(g))(s_o(xK))$$

so $s_o \circ \tau(g) = \tau(\theta(g)) \circ s_o$ and therefore

$$Q(ds_o(X), ds_o(X)) = Q(ds_o \circ d\tau(g)(X_o), ds_o \circ d\tau(g)(X_o))$$

$$= Q(d\tau(\theta(g)) \circ ds_o(X_o), d\tau(\theta(g)) \circ ds_o(X_o))$$

$$= Q(X_o, Y_o) = Q(X, Y)$$

Thus s_o is an isometry and since $(ds_o)_o = -I$, it reverses the geodesics through o. The geodesic symmetry with respect to $p = gK$ is given by

$$s_p = \tau(g) \circ s_o \circ \tau(g^{-1})$$

which is an isometry, so the proposition follows.

Proposition 3.7. The geodesics through the origin in G/K are the curves $t \to \exp tX \cdot o \; (X \in \mathfrak{p})$.

Although the proof is not difficult we shall omit it. Instead let us take a second look at the example $G = SU(1, 1)$. The decomposition

$$\begin{pmatrix} i\alpha & \beta \\ \bar\beta & -i\alpha \end{pmatrix} = \begin{pmatrix} i\alpha & 0 \\ 0 & -i\alpha \end{pmatrix} + \begin{pmatrix} 0 & \beta \\ \bar\beta & 0 \end{pmatrix} \tag{6}$$

gives a Cartan decomposition of $\mathfrak{su}(1, 1)$. We have also if

$$X_\beta = \begin{pmatrix} 0 & \beta \\ \bar{\beta} & 0 \end{pmatrix}$$

$$\exp{(tX_\beta)} = \cosh{(t\,|\beta|)}I + \frac{1}{|\beta|}\sinh{(t\,|\beta|)}X_\beta$$

so

$$\exp{(tX_\beta)} \cdot o = (\tanh t\,|\beta|)\frac{\beta}{|\beta|}$$

verifying the proposition in this case.

3-4 Discussion of Symmetric Spaces

We shall now summarize some basic results in the general theory of symmetric spaces and indicate how the coset spaces G/K from the last section fit into this general theory.

Let M be a symmetric space as defined in Ch. 1. The group $I(M)$ of all isometries of M is transitive on M. (In fact, if $p, q \in M$ they can be joined by a broken geodesic and the product of the symmetries in the midpoints of these geodesics gives the desired isometry.) One can now parametrize the group $I(M)$ in a natural way turning it into a Lie group. The identity component $G = I_o(M)$ is still transitive on M. Fix a point $o \in M$ and let K be the group of elements in G which leaves o fixed. Then the mapping $gK \to g \cdot o$ is a diffeomorphism of G/K onto M. If s_o is the geodesic symmetry with respect to o the mapping $\sigma : g \to s_o\, gs_o$ is an involutive automorphism of G and $(K_\sigma)_o \subset K \subset K_\sigma$, where K_σ is the set of fixed points of σ and $(K_\sigma)_o$ its identity component. In order to verify these inclusions let $k \in K$. Then the maps k and $s_o ks_o$ are isometries leaving o fixed and inducing the same linear map of the tangent space M_o. Considering the geodesics starting at o we see that k and $s_o ks_o$ must coincide so $K \subset K_\sigma$. On the other hand, suppose X in the Lie algebra $\mathfrak{g}$ of G is fixed under the differential $(d\sigma)_e$. Then $s_o \exp tX\, s_o = \exp tX$ for all $t \in \boldsymbol{R}$, so applying both sides to the point o we see that $\exp tX \cdot o$ is fixed under s_o. But o is an isolated fixed point of s_o so $\exp tX \cdot o = o$ for all sufficiently small t. But then $X \in \mathfrak{k}$, the Lie algebra of K, whence $(K_\sigma)_o \subset K$. Note finally that the group $\mathrm{Ad}_G(K)$ is compact, being a continuous image of the compact group K.

Conversely, let G be a connected Lie group, K a closed subgroup, $\mathrm{Ad}_G(K)$ compact. Suppose there exists an involutive automorphism σ of G such that $(K_\sigma)_o \subset K \subset K_\sigma$. Then there exists a Riemannian structure on G/K invariant under G, and for every such Riemannian structure, G/K is a symmetric space.

Consider now M as above and $G = I_o(M)$; M is said to be of the *noncompact type* if G is noncompact, semisimple without a compact normal subgroup $\neq \{e\}$, and of the *compact type* if G is compact and semisimple.

Proposition 4.1. Let M be a symmetric space, which is simply connected. Then M is a product

$$M = M_o \times M_c \times M_n$$

where M_0 is a Euclidean space and M_c and M_n are symmetric spaces of the compact type and the noncompact type, respectively.

Proposition 4.2. A symmetric space of the compact type (noncompact type) has sectional curvature everywhere $\geqslant 0$ (respectively $\leqslant 0$).

There is a very interesting *duality* between the compact type and the noncompact type. Let $M = G/K$ be a symmetric space of the noncompact type where $G = I_o(M)$. Let $\mathfrak{g}$ and $\mathfrak{k}$ denote the Lie algebras of G and K, respectively. Let $\mathfrak{g} = \mathfrak{k} + \mathfrak{p}$ be the corresponding Cartan decomposition of $\mathfrak{g}$ and $\mathfrak{g}_c = \mathfrak{g} + i\mathfrak{g}$ the complexification of $\mathfrak{g}$. Since $[\mathfrak{p}, \mathfrak{p}] \subset \mathfrak{k}$, the subspace $\mathfrak{u} = \mathfrak{k} + i\mathfrak{p}$ of $\mathfrak{g}_c$ is actually a Lie algebra and another real form of $\mathfrak{g}_c$. Since the Killing form of $\mathfrak{g}_c$ is < 0 on $\mathfrak{k}$, and > 0 on $\mathfrak{p}$, it is < 0 on $\mathfrak{u}$, so $\mathfrak{u}$ is a compact real form. If U is a connected Lie group with Lie algebra $\mathfrak{u}$ and K' is the connected Lie subgroup with Lie algebra $\mathfrak{k}$, the space U/K' is a symmetric space of the compact type. This process can be reversed, that is, G/K can be constructed with U/K as a starting point.

Examples

(i) Consider the symmetric space G/K, where $G = SU(1, 1)$ and K the subgroup of matrices $\begin{pmatrix} t & 0 \\ 0 & t^{-1} \end{pmatrix}$, $|t| = 1$. In this case the Cartan decomposition (6) in §3-3 shows that $\mathfrak{u}$ is the set of all matrices of the form

$$\begin{pmatrix} i\alpha & 0 \\ 0 & -i\alpha \end{pmatrix} + \begin{pmatrix} 0 & i\beta \\ i\bar{\beta} & 0 \end{pmatrix}$$

so $\mathfrak{u} = \mathfrak{su}(2)$, the algebra of all 2×2 skew symmetric matrices of trace 0. For the space U/K' we can therefore take the space $SU(2)/K$. [$SU(n)$ denotes the special unitary group.] It is not hard to show that when the unit sphere S^2 is projected stereographically onto the complex plane the rotations of the sphere correspond to the transformations

$$z \to \frac{az + \bar{b}}{-bz + \bar{a}} \qquad |a|^2 + |b|^2 = 1$$

that is, to the members of $SU(2)$. In this manner $SU(2)$ acts transitively on

S^2 and the subgroup leaving the point $z = 0$ fixed is K.   Thus $U/K = S^2$ so the non-Euclidean disk D (Ch. 1) and the sphere S^2 correspond under the general duality indicated.   The formulas $\mathfrak{g} = \mathfrak{k} + \mathfrak{p}$ and $\mathfrak{u} = \mathfrak{k} + i\mathfrak{p}$ can be regarded as an explanation of the phenomenon that the triangle formulas in non-Euclidean trigonometry are obtained from the triangle formulas in spherical trigonometry by replacing the sides a, b, c by ia, ib, ic and using the relations $\sinh (ia) = i \sin a$, $\cosh (ia) = \cos a$.   Lobatschevsky did indeed speak of his non-Euclidean trigonometry as spherical trigonometry on a sphere of imaginary radius.

(ii) Let U be a connected, compact Lie group with Lie algebra $\mathfrak{u}$.   If Q is any positive definite quadratic form on $\mathfrak{u}$, we obtain by left translations such quadratic forms on each tangent space to U and therefore a Riemannian metric on U which is invariant under all left translations.   If Q is chosen invariant under Ad (U) then the Riemannian metric is invariant under right translations as well.   One can prove that the geodesics through e are the one-parameter subgroups and the symmetry $s_e : x \to x^{-1}$ is an isometry so U is a symmetric space.   If U^* denotes the diagonal in $U \times U$ one has a diffeomorphism $(u_1, u_2)U^* \to u_1 u_2^{-1}$ of $(U \times U)/U^*$ onto U.   The group involution $(u_1, u_2) \to (u_2, u_1)$ of $U \times U$ leaves U^* pointwise fixed and induces the symmetry s_e of U, via the diffeomorphism indicated.

If U is in addition semisimple, the symmetric space $(U \times U)/U^*$ has in the above sense a noncompact dual G/U', where U' has Lie algebra $\mathfrak{u}$ and the Lie algebra $\mathfrak{g}$ of G is a certain real form of the complexification of the product algebra $\mathfrak{u} \times \mathfrak{u}$.   One can prove that as $\mathfrak{u}$ runs through the compact semisimple Lie algebras, $\mathfrak{g}$ runs through the *complex* semisimple Lie algebras (regarded as Lie algebras over $\mathbf{R}$).

3-5   The Iwasawa Decomposition

Let $\mathfrak{g}$ be a semisimple Lie algebra, $\mathfrak{g} = \mathfrak{k} + \mathfrak{p}$ a Cartan decomposition. The operators ad X $(X \in \mathfrak{p})$ are all symmetric with respect to the positive definite form B_θ and each of them can therefore be diagonalized, and a commutative family can be simultaneously diagonalized.   Hence let $\mathfrak{a}$ denote a maximal Abelian subspace of $\mathfrak{p}$ and if α is a real-valued linear function on $\mathfrak{a}$ put

$$\mathfrak{g}_\alpha = \{X \in \mathfrak{g} \mid [H, X] = \alpha(H)X \text{ for all } H \in \mathfrak{a}\} \tag{1}$$

If $\mathfrak{g}_\alpha \neq \{0\}$, $\alpha \neq 0$, α is called a *restricted root*.   Clearly, if Σ denotes the set of restricted roots,

$$\mathfrak{g} = \sum_{\alpha \in \Sigma} \mathfrak{g}_\alpha + \mathfrak{g}_o \tag{2}$$

The dimension dim $(\mathfrak{g}_\alpha)$ is called the *multiplicity* of α.   Let $\mathfrak{a}'$ denote the set of elements in $\mathfrak{a}$, where all roots are $\neq 0$.   The connected components of $\mathfrak{a}'$

are intersections of half spaces; hence they are convex open sets. They are called *Weyl chambers*. Fix any Weyl chamber $\mathfrak{a}^+$ and call a restricted root *positive* if its values on $\mathfrak{a}^+$ are positive.

Let Σ^+ denote the set of positive restricted roots and put

$$\mathfrak{n} = \sum_{\alpha > 0} \mathfrak{g}_\alpha \qquad \rho = \frac{1}{2} \sum_{\alpha > 0} (\dim \mathfrak{g}_\alpha)\alpha \tag{3}$$

Then $\mathfrak{n}$ is a nilpotent Lie algebra. The following result is called the Iwasawa decomposition.

Theorem 5.1. $\mathfrak{g} = \mathfrak{k} + \mathfrak{a} + \mathfrak{n}$ (direct vector space sum). Let G be any connected Lie group with Lie algebra $\mathfrak{g}$, and let K, A, N denote the analytic subgroups corresponding to $\mathfrak{k}$, $\mathfrak{a}$, and $\mathfrak{n}$, respectively. Then the mapping

$$(k, a, n) \to kan$$

is a diffeomorphism of $K \times A \times N$ onto G.

Rather than give the proof we consider some examples. Consider the Cartan decomposition (1) §3-3,

$$\mathfrak{sl}(n, \mathbf{R}) = \mathfrak{so}(n) + \mathfrak{p} \tag{4}$$

The diagonal matrices of trace 0 form a maximal Abelian subspace $\mathfrak{a}$ of $\mathfrak{p}$ and as in §3-2 we find that the corresponding restricted roots are the linear forms $\alpha_{ij}(H) = e_i(H) - e_j(H)$ $(H \in \mathfrak{a})$, $e_i(H)$ being the ith diagonal element in H. Hence $\mathfrak{a}'$ consists of those H for which all $e_i(H)$ are different. The set

$$\{H \in \mathfrak{a} \mid e_1(H) > e_2(H) > \cdots > e_n(H)\} \tag{5}$$

is clearly a connected component of $\mathfrak{a}'$ and we take this as the Weyl chamber $\mathfrak{a}^+$. Then Σ^+ consists of the roots α_{ij} $(i < j)$ and $\mathfrak{n}$ is easily found to be the set of upper triangular matrices with 0 in the diagonal. An Iwasawa decomposition of the group $SL(n, \mathbf{R})$ is therefore $g = oan$, where $o \in SO(n)$, a is a diagonal matrix of determinant 1 and diagonal > 0, and n is an upper triangular matrix with all diagonal elements 1.

For another example consider the Cartan decomposition of $\mathfrak{su}(1, 1)$ given by

$$\begin{pmatrix} ix & y \\ \bar{y} & -ix \end{pmatrix} = \begin{pmatrix} ix & 0 \\ 0 & -ix \end{pmatrix} + \begin{pmatrix} 0 & y \\ \bar{y} & 0 \end{pmatrix}$$

where $x \in \mathbf{R}$, $y \in \mathbf{C}$. As the space $\mathfrak{a}$ we can take

$$\mathbf{R}\begin{pmatrix} 0 & 1 \\ 1 & 0 \end{pmatrix}$$

and since

$$\left[\begin{pmatrix} 0 & 1 \\ 1 & 0 \end{pmatrix}, \begin{pmatrix} ix & y \\ \bar{y} & -ix \end{pmatrix} \right] = \begin{pmatrix} \bar{y} - y & -2ix \\ 2ix & y - \bar{y} \end{pmatrix}$$

we see that the decomposition (2) equals

$$\mathfrak{g} = R\begin{pmatrix} i & -i \\ i & -i \end{pmatrix} + R\begin{pmatrix} i & i \\ -i & -i \end{pmatrix} + R\begin{pmatrix} 0 & 1 \\ 1 & 0 \end{pmatrix}$$

and the restricted roots are α and $-\alpha$, where

$$\alpha\begin{pmatrix} 0 & 1 \\ 1 & 0 \end{pmatrix} = 2$$

Thus $\mathfrak{a}'$ consists of the nonzero elements in $\mathfrak{a}$ and for $\mathfrak{a}^+$ we take for example

$$R^+\begin{pmatrix} 0 & 1 \\ 1 & 0 \end{pmatrix}$$

so

$$\mathfrak{n} = R\begin{pmatrix} i & -i \\ i & -i \end{pmatrix}$$

and $N = \exp \mathfrak{n}$ equals the group of matrices

$$\begin{pmatrix} 1 + in & -in \\ in & 1 - in \end{pmatrix} \in SU(1, 1)$$

The Iwasawa decomposition of a semisimple Lie algebra $\mathfrak{g}$ involves some free choices, namely, that of $\mathfrak{k}$, $\mathfrak{a}$, and $\mathfrak{a}^+$. We have seen that $\mathfrak{k}$ is unique up to conjugacy, and now we shall see that $\mathfrak{a}$ and $\mathfrak{a}^+$ are uniquely determined up to conjugacy by elements of K. We begin with a result which goes back to Weyl and Cartan with a proof given by Hunt [41].

Theorem 5.2. Let $\mathfrak{a}$ and $\mathfrak{a}'$ be two maximal Abelian subspaces of $\mathfrak{p}$. Then there exists an element $k \in K$ such that $\mathrm{Ad}_G(k)\, \mathfrak{a} = \mathfrak{a}'$. Also

$$\mathfrak{p} = \bigcup_{k \in K} \mathrm{Ad}_G(k)\, \mathfrak{a}$$

PROOF. Select $H \in \mathfrak{a}$ such that its centralizer in $\mathfrak{p}$ equals $\mathfrak{a}$. (It suffices to take H such that $\alpha(H) \neq 0$ for all restricted roots α.) Put $K^* = \mathrm{Ad}_G(K)$ and let $X \in \mathfrak{p}$ be arbitrary. The function

$$k^* \to B(H, k^* \cdot X) \qquad (k^* \in K^*)$$

has a minimum, say, for $k^* = k_0$. If $T \in \mathfrak{k}$ we have therefore

$$\left\{ \frac{d}{dt} B(H, \mathrm{Ad}\,(\exp tT)k_0 \cdot X) \right\}_{t=0} = 0$$

so

$$B(H, [T, k_o \cdot X]) = 0 \qquad T \in \mathfrak{k}$$

Thus

$$B(T, [H, k_o \cdot X]) = 0 \qquad \text{for all } T \in \mathfrak{k}$$

and since $[H, k_0 \cdot X] \in \mathfrak{k}$ we deduce $[H, k_0 \cdot X] = 0$ so by the choice of H, $k_0 \cdot X \in \mathfrak{a}$.

In particular, there exists a $k_1 \in K$ such that $H \in \text{Ad } (k_1)\mathfrak{a}'$. Thus each element in $\text{Ad } (k_1)\mathfrak{a}'$ commutes with H so $\text{Ad } (k_1)\mathfrak{a}' \subset \mathfrak{a}$. This proves the theorem.

3-6   The Weyl Group

Let $\mathfrak{g}$ be a semisimple Lie algebra, $\mathfrak{g} = \mathfrak{k} + \mathfrak{p}$ a Cartan decomposition, G any connected Lie group with Lie algebra $\mathfrak{g}$, K the analytic subgroup with Lie algebra $\mathfrak{k} \subset \mathfrak{g}$. Consider as before a maximal Abelian subspace $\mathfrak{a} \subset \mathfrak{p}$ and let M' and M denote, respectively, the *normalizer* and *centralizer* of $\mathfrak{a}$ in K; that is,

$$M' = \{k \in K \,|\, \text{Ad } (k)\mathfrak{a} \subset \mathfrak{a}\}$$

$$M = \{k \in K \,|\, \text{Ad } (k)H = H \text{ for all } H \in \mathfrak{a}\}$$

Clearly M is a normal subgroup of M' and the factor group M'/M can obviously be viewed as a group of linear transformations of $\mathfrak{a}$. It is called the *Weyl group* and denoted W.   In view of Theorem 5.2 it is (up to isomorphism) independent of the choice of $\mathfrak{a}$.

Now M and M' are Lie subgroups of K and their Lie algebras $\mathfrak{m}$ and $\mathfrak{m}'$ are given by (*cf.* (8) §2-2, (7) §3-1),

$$\mathfrak{m} = \{T \in \mathfrak{k} \,|\, [H, T] = 0 \text{ for all } H \in \mathfrak{a}\}$$

$$\mathfrak{m}' = \{T \in \mathfrak{k} \,|\, [H, T] \subset \mathfrak{a} \text{ for all } H \in \mathfrak{a}\}$$

Note, however, that if $T \in \mathfrak{m}'$ then for $H \in \mathfrak{a}$,

$$B([H, T], [H, T]) = -B([H, [H, T]], T) = 0$$

so $T \in \mathfrak{m}$, whence $\mathfrak{m} = \mathfrak{m}'$. Thus M'/M is a discrete group and being also compact, must be finite.

If λ is a complex-valued linear function on $\mathfrak{a}$ let H_λ denote the vector in $\mathfrak{a} + i\mathfrak{a}$ determined by $B(H, H_\lambda) = \lambda(H)$ for all $H \in \mathfrak{a}$. For $\alpha \in \Sigma$ let s_α denote the symmetry in the hyperplane $\alpha(H) = 0$:

$$s_\alpha(H) = H - 2 \frac{\alpha(H)}{\alpha(H_\alpha)} H_\alpha \qquad H \in \mathfrak{a}, \tag{1}$$

(Remember $\mathfrak{p}$ and hence $\mathfrak{a}$ have a Euclidean metric given by B.)

Theorem 6.1. $s_\alpha \in W$ for each $\alpha \in \Sigma$.

PROOF. Pick $Z_\alpha \in \mathfrak{g}$ such that $[H, Z_\alpha] = \alpha(H)Z_\alpha$. Decomposing $Z_\alpha = T_\alpha + X_\alpha$ ($T_\alpha \in \mathfrak{k}$, $X_\alpha \in \mathfrak{p}$) the relations $[\mathfrak{k}, \mathfrak{p}] \subset \mathfrak{p}$, $[\mathfrak{p}, \mathfrak{p}] \subset \mathfrak{k}$ imply that $(\operatorname{ad} H)^2 T_\alpha = T_\alpha$. Multiplying Z_α by a real factor if necessary we may assume $B(T_\alpha, T_\alpha) = -1$. Now if $\alpha(H) = 0$ we have $[H, T_\alpha] = 0$ so

$$\operatorname{Ad}(\exp tT_\alpha)H = e^{\operatorname{ad}(tT_\alpha)}(H) = H \qquad \text{if } \alpha(H) = 0$$

A simple computation shows that

$$e^{\operatorname{ad}(t_o T_\alpha)}H_\alpha = -H_\alpha$$

provided $t_o(\alpha(H_\alpha))^{1/2} = \pi$. Thus s_α coincides with the restriction of $\operatorname{Ad}(\exp t_o T_\alpha)$ to $\mathfrak{a}$.

If $s \in W$ and $\alpha \in \Sigma$ it is clear from the definitions that the linear function $\alpha^s : H \to \alpha(s^{-1}H)$ on $\mathfrak{a}$ is a restricted root. Consequently, s permutes the Weyl chambers. Now let C_1 and C_2 be two Weyl chambers and let $H_1 \in C_1$, $H_2 \in C_2$. If the segment $\overrightarrow{H_1 H_2}$ intersects a hyperplane $\alpha(H) = 0$ ($\alpha \in \Sigma$) then clearly the norm $|\ |$ in $\mathfrak{a}$ satisfies

$$|H_1 - H_2| > |H_1 - s_\alpha H_2| \tag{2}$$

As s runs through the finite group W the function $|H_1 - sH_2|$ takes a minimum, say for $s = s_0$. By (2) the segment from H_1 to $s_o H_2$ intersects no hyperplane $\alpha(H) = 0$ ($\alpha \in \Sigma$) so H_1 and $s_o H_2$ lie in the same Weyl chamber and thus $C_1 = s_o C_2$. This proves:

Corollary 6.2. Any two Weyl chambers in $\mathfrak{a}$ are conjugate under some element of $\operatorname{Ad}_G(K)$ which leaves $\mathfrak{a}$ invariant.

For orientation we state without proof a somewhat deeper result on the Weyl group.

Theorem 6.3. The Weyl group W is generated by the symmetries s_α ($\alpha \in \Sigma$) and it is simply transitive on the set of Weyl chambers in $\mathfrak{a}$.

3.7 Boundary and Polar Coordinates on the Symmetric Space G/K

For the non-Euclidean disk D we have a natural notion of boundary, namely, the unit circle $|z| = 1$. However, this boundary notion refers to the position of D in $\mathbf{R}^2$. In order to make this definition more intrinsic we can define the boundary of D as the set of all rays (half-lines) from the origin in D. This motivates the following definition of the boundary of the symmetric space G/K. First, we recall the isomorphism $d\pi : \mathfrak{p} \to (G/K)_o$ from §3-3, which permits us to think of $\mathfrak{p}$ as the tangent space to G/K at o. Then we understand by a *Weyl chamber in* $\mathfrak{p}$ a Weyl chamber in some maximal Abelian subspace pf $\mathfrak{p}$.   The *boundary* of G/K is now defined as the set of all Weyl chambers in $\mathfrak{p}$.   Now fix $\mathfrak{a} \subset \mathfrak{p}$ and $\mathfrak{a}^+$ a Weyl chamber in $\mathfrak{a}$.   Then according to Theorem 5.2 and Cor. 6.2, $\operatorname{Ad}(k)\mathfrak{a}^+$ $(k \in K)$ runs through the boundary and if $\operatorname{Ad}(k)\mathfrak{a}^+ = \mathfrak{a}^+$, then $k \in M'$ so $\operatorname{Ad}(k)$ on $\mathfrak{a}$ is a member of the Weyl group.   Using Theorem 6.3 we see that $k \in M$.   Thus the mapping

$$kM \to \operatorname{Ad}(k)\mathfrak{a}^+$$

identifies K/M with the boundary of G/K.   In view of the Iwasawa decomposition $G = KAN$ and the fact that M normalizes AN we have a diffeomorphism

$$kM \to kMAN$$

of K/M onto G/MAN.   In his paper [19], Furstenberg defines a boundary of G to be a compact coset space G/H of G such that for each probability measure μ on G/H there exists a sequence $(g_n) \subset G$ such that the transformed measures $g_n \cdot \mu$ converge weakly to the delta function on G/H.   It was proved by Furstenberg [19] and Moore [53] that a " maximal " boundary of this sort is given by G/MAN which, as we saw, coincides with the geometrically defined boundary above.   The relation $K/M = G/MAN$ shows in particular that G acts as a transformation group on the boundary; in an explicit manner

$$g(kM) = k(gk)M$$

if for $x \in G$, $k(x) \in K$ is given by $x \in k(x)AN$.

Now let $A^+ = \exp \mathfrak{a}^+$.   Then we have the following " polar coordinate representation " of the symmetric space G/K.

Theorem 7.1. The mapping $(kM, a) \to kaK$ is a diffeomorphism of $K/M \times A^+$ onto an open submanifold of G/K whose complement in G/K has lower dimension.

Without spelling out the proof in detail we remark that it is a fairly direct consequence of Theorems 3.4, 5.2, and 6.3.

CHAPTER 4: FUNCTIONS ON SYMMETRIC SPACES

4-1 Invariant Differential Operators

Let M be a manifold and D a differential operator on M, that is, a linear mapping of $C_c^\infty(M)$ into itself which in an arbitrary coordinate system is expressed by partial derivatives in the coordinates.   Let $\phi : M \to M$ be a diffeomorphism, and if f is a function on M put $f^\phi = f \circ \phi^{-1}$ and let D^ϕ denote the operator

$$D^\phi f = (Df^{\phi^{-1}})^\phi$$

Then D^ϕ is another differential operator, and we say D is *invariant under* ϕ if $D^\phi = D$.

Examples

Let us find all differential operators D on $\mathbf{R}^n$ which are invariant under all rigid motions. Since D is invariant under all translations it has constant coefficients so $D = P(\partial/\partial x_1, \ldots, \partial/\partial x_n)$, where P is a polynomial. But D is also invariant under all rotations around 0 so P is rotation-invariant, and since the rotations are transitive on each sphere $|x| = r$, we find P is constant on each such sphere so $P(x_1, \ldots, x_n)$ is a function of $x_1^2 + \cdots + x_n^2$, hence a polynomial in $x_1^2 + \cdots + x_n^2$.

Proposition 1.1. The differential operators on $\mathbf{R}^n$ which are invariant under all isometries are the operators $\Sigma a_n \Delta^n$ $(a_n \in \mathbf{C})$, where Δ is the Laplacian.

This result holds also if $\mathbf{R}^n$ is replaced by a symmetric space of rank 1 (and Δ by the Laplace–Beltrami operator) and also if we replace the isometries of $\mathbf{R}^n$ by the inhomogeneous Lorentz group, in which case the Laplacian is replaced (*cf.* [29], p. 271) by the operator

$$\frac{\partial^2}{\partial x_1^2} - \frac{\partial^2}{\partial x_2^2} - \cdots - \frac{\partial^2}{\partial x_n^2}$$

Now if M is a Riemannian manifold the Laplace–Beltrami operator Δ on M is invariant under all isometries of M. The examples above have a high degree of mobility, that is, a large group of isometries, so essentially only Δ is invariant. The following interesting generalization is essentially a combination of results of Harish–Chandra and Chevalley (see [31] p. 432). It expresses in a precise way how higher rank of the space, that is, lower degree of mobility, leads to more invariant operators.

Theorem 1.2. Let G/K be a symmetric space of rank *l*. Then the algebra of all G-invariant differential operators on G/K is a commutative algebra with *l* algebraically independent generators.

It will now be convenient to assume that G has finite center so K is compact. As pointed out in §3-3, this is no restriction on the symmetric space G/K. Let $L(g)$ and $R(g)$ denote left and right translations on G by the group element g and let $\mathbf{D}(G)$ denote the set of all differential operators on G invariant under all $L(g)$. If $X \in \mathfrak{g}$ the operator

$$\tilde{X} : F(g) \to \{(d/dt)F(g \exp tX)\}_{t=0}$$

belongs to $\mathbf{D}(G)$. Let $\mathbf{D}_K(G)$ denote the set of elements in $\mathbf{D}(G)$ which are invariant under all $R(k)$ $(k \in K)$. For $D \in \mathbf{D}(G)$ we put

$$D^\natural = \int_K D^{R(k)} \, dk \tag{1}$$

where dk denotes the normalized Haar measure on K. The integral makes sense since all the operators $D^{R(k)}$ $(k \in K)$ belong to a fixed finite-dimensional vector space, so $D^\natural$ is a differential operator on G. Clearly $D^\natural \in \boldsymbol{D}_K(G)$, and we have

$$(D^\natural F)(e) = (DF)(e) \tag{2}$$

for every $F \in C^\infty(G)$ which is bi-invariant under K (that is, $F(k_1 g k_2) = F(g)$, $g \in G$, $k_1, k_2 \in K$). In fact,

$$(D^\natural F)(e) = \int_K (D^{R(k)}F)(e)\, dk = \int_K ((DF^{R(k^{-1})})^{R(k)})(e)\, dk$$

$$= \int_K (DF)(k^{-1})\, dk = \int_K (DF)^{L(k)}(e)\, dk$$

$$= \int_K (DF)(e)\, dk = (DF)(e)$$

Let π denote the natural projection $g \to gK$ of G onto G/K; if f is a function on G/K we put $\tilde{f} = f \circ \pi$. Then the mapping $f \to \tilde{f}$ is an isomorphism of $C^\infty(G/K)$ onto the space $C_K^\infty(G)$ of functions $F \in C^\infty(G)$ satisfying $F(gk) \equiv F(g)$. Similarly, we would like to "lift" the operators in $\boldsymbol{D}(G/K)$ to the group G. If $D \in \boldsymbol{D}_K(G)$ let $\pi(D)$ denote the operator on $C^\infty(G/K)$ determined by $(\pi(D)f)^\sim = D\tilde{f}$ $(f \in C^\infty(G/K))$. It is easy to see (cf. [31], p. 390) that the map $D \to \pi(D)$ maps $\boldsymbol{D}_K(G)$ onto $\boldsymbol{D}(G/K)$.

As before let $\tau(g)$ denote the diffeomorphism $hK \to ghK$ of G/K onto itself. We shall often denote the symmetric space G/K by X.

4-2 Harmonic Functions on Symmetric Spaces

In view of Prop. 1.1 it is natural to make the following definition.

Definition. A function $u \in C^\infty(G/K)$ is called *harmonic* if $Du = 0$ for all $D \in \boldsymbol{D}(G/K)$ which annihilate the constants (that is, "without constant term").

Godement made this definition in [22] (even for nonsymmetric spaces G/K), where he proved also the mean value theorem below.

Theorem 2.1. A function $u \in C^\infty(G/K)$ is harmonic if and only if

$$\int_K u(gkh \cdot o)\, dk = u(g \cdot o) \qquad \text{for all } g, h \in G \tag{1}$$

This result is most easily interpreted if rank $(G/K) = 1$. Then the orbit $K \cdot (h \cdot o)$ is a sphere and $gK \cdot (h \cdot o)$ is a sphere with center $g \cdot o$. Thus the theorem states in this case that u is harmonic if and only if the mean value of u over an arbitrary sphere is equal to the value of u in the center (*cf.* Gauss' mean value theorem for harmonic functions in $\mathbf{R}^n$).

PROOF. Suppose first that u is harmonic and for a fixed $g \in G$ consider the function

$$F : h \to \int_K \tilde{u}(gkh) \, dk \qquad (h \in G)$$

Let D be an operator in $\mathbf{D}(G)$ annihilating the constants. Then using (2) in §4-1,

$$(DF)(e) = (D^\natural F)(e) = \left\{ (D^\natural)_h \left(\int_K \tilde{u}(gkh) \, dk \right) \right\}_{h=e}$$

which by the left invariance of $D^\natural$ equals

$$\int_K (D^\natural \tilde{u})(gk) \, dk = (D^\natural \tilde{u})(g)$$

(the last relation coming from the right invariance of $D^\natural \tilde{u}$ under K). However, $(D^\natural \tilde{u}) = (\pi(D^\natural)u)^\sim = 0$ since $\pi(D^\natural)$ annihilates the constants. Thus $(DF)(e) = 0$ for all $D \in \mathbf{D}(G)$ which annihilate the constants.

Since u satisfies the elliptic equation $\Delta u = 0$ and since Δ has analytic coefficients, it follows from a theorem of Bernstein (John [44], p. 142) that u is also analytic. Hence $\tilde{u}$ and F are also analytic so from Taylor's formula (§2-2) we can conclude that F is constant. But the relation $F(h) = F(e)$ is (1).

On the other hand, suppose (1) holds. Let $D \in \mathbf{D}(G/K)$ annihilate the constants. Writing (1) as

$$\int_K u^{\tau(k^{-1}g^{-1})}(x) \, dk = u(g \cdot o) \qquad g \in G, \, x \in X$$

we deduce by applying D to both sides (considered as functions of x),

$$\int_K (Du)(gk \cdot x) \, dk = 0$$

Taking $x = 0$ we conclude $Du \equiv 0$, so u is harmonic.

Now we intend to study bounded harmonic functions u on the symmetric space G/K and prove a Poisson integral representation formula due to Furstenberg [19]. Let Q_u denote the set of all functions $\psi \in L^\infty(G)$ (the space of bounded measurable functions on G) such that the sup norm $\|\psi\|_\infty = \sup_{h \in G} |\psi(h)|$ satisfies $\|\psi\|_\infty \leqslant \|u\|_\infty$ and such that

$$u(g \cdot o) = \int_K \psi(gkh) \, dk \qquad \text{for all } g, \, h \in G$$

According to Godement's theorem $\tilde{u} \in Q_u$, so Q_u is not empty. In addition it is a convex set and closed in the weak* topology of $L^\infty(G)$ (the weakest topology for which all the maps $\psi \to \int f(g)\psi(g)\,dg$ of $L^\infty(G)$ into C are continuous, f being an integrable function on G and dg being a Haar measure). Since the unit ball in $L^\infty(G)$ is compact in the weak* topology (see, for example, [50]) it follows that Q_u is compact. Now if $\psi \in Q_u$ we have $\psi^{R(g)} \in Q_u$ for all $g \in G$ so G acts as a transformation group of Q_u by right translations. We would like to find a fixed point under the sugbroup MAN, which then would give us a function on the boundary G/MAN.

Definition. A group has the *fixed point property* if whenever it acts continuously on a locally convex topological vector space by linear transformations leaving a compact convex set $Q \neq \varnothing$ invariant it has a fixed point in the set.

Lemma 2.2. Connected solvable Lie groups have the fixed point property (*cf.* [6], p. 115).

PROOF. Let V be a locally convex topological vector space and G any Abelian group of linear transformations of V. For each $g \in G$ let $g_n = (1/n)(I + g + \cdots + g^{n-1})$; let $\tilde{G}$ denote the set of all products $g_{n_1} \cdots g_{n_k}$ ($n_i \in \mathbf{Z}^+, g \in G$). All elements of $\tilde{G}$ commute. Let $Q \subset V$ be a nonempty compact convex subset of V. By convexity, $hQ \subset Q$ for $h \in \tilde{G}$. Let $h_1, \ldots, h_r \in \tilde{G}$. Then for each i, $1 \leqslant i \leqslant r$,

$$h_1 \ldots h_r Q = h_i h_1 \ldots h_{i-1} h_{i+1} \ldots h_r Q \subset h_i Q$$

whence

$$h_1 \ldots h_r Q \subset \bigcap_{i=1}^{r} h_i Q$$

so this intersection is $\neq \varnothing$. By compactness of Q (expressed by the finite intersection property), we have

$$\bigcap_{h \in \tilde{G}} hQ \neq \varnothing$$

Let x an element in this intersection and let $g \in G$. Then $x \in g_n Q$, so for a suitable element $y \in Q$,

$$x = \frac{1}{n}(y + gy + \cdots + g^{n-1}y)$$

so

$$gx - x = \frac{1}{n}(g^n y - y) \subset \frac{1}{n}(Q + (-Q))$$

for each n. Using again the compactness of Q we conclude $g \cdot x = x$.

Now assume G is a connected solvable Lie group of linear transformations of V. Let $\mathfrak{g}$ be its Lie algebra and let

$$\mathfrak{g} = \mathfrak{g}_0 \supset \mathfrak{g}_1 \supset \cdots \supset \mathfrak{g}_m = \{0\} \qquad \mathfrak{g}_{m-1} \neq \{0\}$$

be the sequence of derived algebras, $\mathfrak{g}_i = \mathfrak{D}^i \mathfrak{g}$. Let $G = G_0 \supset G_1 \supset \cdots \supset G_m = \{e\}$ be the corresponding series of analytic subgroups of G. Suppose now the lemma holds for all connected solvable Lie groups whose series (as defined above) has length $< m$. Let A denote the set of points in Q fixed under all $g \in G_1$. By the induction assumption, A is $\neq \varnothing$ and, of course, A is convex and compact. Let $\gamma \in G$. If $g \in G_1$ then $\gamma g \gamma^{-1} \in G_1$, so if $x \in A$, $\gamma g \gamma^{-1} x = x$ so $g \gamma^{-1} x = \gamma^{-1} x$. Thus $\gamma^{-1} x$ is fixed by all elements in G_1; being in Q, $\gamma^{-1} x$ belongs to A. Thus G maps A into itself. The closed subspace V_A of V generated by A is locally convex and since G_1 acts trivially on it, G acts on V_A as an Abelian group. By the first part of the proof there exists a $v \in A$ fixed under all $g \in G$. Q.E.D.

Lemma 2.3. *The group MAN has the fixed point property.*

PROOF. Let MAN act on a locally convex space V and let $Q \subset V$ be a compact convex subset $\neq \varnothing$ invariant under MAN. Since AN is solvable and connected there exists a point $q \in Q$ fixed under AN. If dm denotes the normalized Haar measure on the compact group M the integral

$$\int_M m \cdot q \, dm$$

(defined by means of approximating sums) represents, because of the compactness and convexity, a point q^* in Q. Since $m(AN)m^{-1} \subset AN$ we have for $s \in AN$

$$sq^* = \int_M sm \cdot q \, dm = \int_M m(m^{-1}sm)q \, dm = \int_M m \cdot q \, dm$$

so q^* is fixed under MAN.

We recall now that the boundary B of the symmetric space is given by the coset space representations $B = K/M$, $B = G/MAN$. The latter shows that G acts on B; this action will be denoted $(g, b) \to g(b)$ in order to distinguish it from the action $(g, x) \to g \cdot x$ of G on $X = G/K$, which we have already used. Let db denote the unique K-invariant measure on B satisfying

$$\int_B db = 1$$

Theorem 2.4. *If u is a bounded harmonic function on X then there exists a bounded measurable function $\hat{u}$ on B such that*

$$u(g \cdot o) = \int_B \hat{u}(g(b)) \, db \tag{2}$$

On the other hand, if $\hat{u}$ is a bounded measurable function on B then u as defined by (2) is a bounded harmonic function on X.

PROOF. As shown above (Lemma 2.3) the set Q_u has a fixed point under MAN, say u_1. Define $\hat{u}$ on G/MAN by $\hat{u}(gMAN) = u_1(g)$. Then by the definition of Q_u, we have

$$u(g \cdot o) = \int_K \hat{u}(gkhMAN)\, dk$$

Take $h = e$ and recall that $gkMAN$ is $g(b)$ if $b = kM$. Then (2) follows because if F is any continuous function on B,

$$\int_B F(b)\, db = \int_K F(kM)\, dk$$

On the other hand, if $\hat{u}$ is a function in $L^\infty(B)$, define u by (2). Then

$$u(gkh \cdot o) = \int_B \hat{u}(gkh(b))\, db \tag{3}$$

Now let $b = k'MAN$; then $gkh(b) = gkhk'MAN = gkk_1MAN$ if $hk' = k_1a_1n_1$ (Theorem 5.1, Ch. 3). Hence,

$$\int_K u(gkh \cdot o)\, dk = \int_K \left(\int_K \hat{u}(gkhk'MAN)\, dk' \right) dk$$

$$= \int_K \left(\int_K \hat{u}(gkhk'MAN)\, dk \right) dk' = \int_K \left(\int_K \hat{u}(gkk_1MAN)\, dk \right) dk'$$

$$= \int_K \left(\int_K \hat{u}(gkMAN)\, dk \right) dk' = \int_K \hat{u}(gkMAN)\, dk = u(g \cdot o).$$

By Theorem 2.1, u is harmonic, so the theorem is proved.

Now define the *Poisson kernel* $P(x, b)$ on the product space $X \times B$ by the Jacobian

$$P(g \cdot o, b) = \frac{d(g^{-1}(b))}{db} \tag{4}$$

As we saw in Ch. 1. (11) §1-3 this does indeed give the classical Poisson kernel in the case when G/K is the non-Euclidean disk. We shall give the general formula for (4) later. But at any rate formula (2) can be written

$$u(x) = \int_B P(x, b)\hat{u}(b)\, db \tag{5}$$

giving a Poisson integral representation of an arbitrary bounded harmonic function on X. Furstenberg showed in [19], p. 366, that in the weak topology of measures the values of $\hat{u}$ can be regarded as boundary values of u. We shall now see that this is also the case, when we approach the boundary in a more geometric fashion.

Let $\bar{n}$ denote the subalgebra of $\mathfrak{g}$ given by

$$\bar{n} = \sum_{\alpha < 0} \mathfrak{g}_\alpha$$

where the $\mathfrak{g}_\alpha$ are given by (2) §3-5. Let $\bar{N}$ denote the corresponding analytic subgroup of G. As an immediate consequence of the Bruhat lemma (see Harish–Chandra [26]) we have that the subset $\bar{N}MAN \subset G$ is an open subset whose complement has lower dimension. As a result the mapping $T : \bar{n} \rightarrow k(\bar{n})M$ maps $\bar{N}$ onto a subset of K/M whose complement has lower dimension [Here $k(\bar{n})$ is the K-component of $\bar{n}$ according to the decomposition $G = KAN$.] One can also prove that the mapping T is one-to-one.

Lemma 2.5. For a certain positive integrable function ψ on $\bar{N}$, we have

$$\int_{K/M} f(kM)\, dk_M = \int_{\bar{N}} f(k(\bar{n})M)\psi(\bar{n})\, d\bar{n} \qquad f \in C^\infty(K/M)$$

Here dk_M is the normalized K-invariant measure on K/M and $d\bar{n}$ is a Haar measure on $\bar{N}$.

PROOF. Let $dk_M \circ T$ denote the measure on $\bar{N}$ given by

$$(dk_M \circ T)(C) = \int_{T(C)} dk_M \qquad C \text{ compact in } \bar{N}$$

Let $\psi(\bar{n})$ denote the Radon–Nikodym derivative (see, for example, [24], p. 128). Then the lemma follows at once from the properties of T given above.

REMARK. This lemma is given in Harish–Chandra [27], p. 287, with an explicit formula for $\psi(\bar{n})$ which will be derived later (Proposition 2.10).

The mapping T is particularly useful for studying the action of A on the boundary. In fact, if $a \in A$, $\bar{n} \in \bar{N}$ we have

$$a(k(\bar{n})M) = ak(\bar{n})MAN = k(a\bar{n})MAN = k(a\bar{n}a^{-1})MAN$$

that is,

$$a(k(\bar{n})M) = k(\bar{n}^a)M \tag{6}$$

the superscript denoting conjugation.

Theorem 2.6. Let F be a continuous function on B and u its Poisson integral

$$u(x) = \int_B P(x, b)F(b)\, db \qquad x \in X$$

Then u has boundary values given by F, that is,

$$\lim_{t \to \infty} u(k \exp tH \cdot o) = F(kM) \tag{7}$$

for each $k \in K$ and each $H \in \mathfrak{a}^+$.

PROOF. We may assume $k = e$. We must prove that if $a_t = \exp tH$ then as $t \to \infty$

$$\int_{K/M} F(a_t(kM)) \, dk_M \to F(eM)$$

But by Lemma 2.5 and (6) the integral on the left equals

$$\int_N F(a_t(k(\bar{n})M))\psi(\bar{n}) \, d\bar{n} = \int_N F(k(\bar{n}^{a_t})M)\psi(\bar{n}) \, d\bar{n} \tag{8}$$

Now

$$\bar{n} = \exp\left(\sum_{\alpha<0} X_\alpha\right)$$

where $X_\alpha \in \mathfrak{g}_\alpha$ and by (7) and (9) in §3-1,

$$\bar{n}^{\exp H} = \exp H \exp\left(\sum_\alpha X_\alpha\right) \exp(-H) = \exp\left(\mathrm{Ad}\,(\exp H)\left(\sum_\alpha X_\alpha\right)\right)$$

$$= \exp\left(e^{\mathrm{ad}\,H}\left(\sum_\alpha X_\alpha\right)\right) = \exp\left(\sum_\alpha e^{\alpha(H)} X_\alpha\right)$$

But $\alpha(H) < 0$ whenever $\alpha < 0$ so we see that for each $\bar{n} \in N$, $\bar{n}^{\exp tH} \to e$. It follows (using the dominated convergence theorem) that the right-hand side of (8) has a limit

$$\int_N F(eM)\psi(\bar{n}) \, d\bar{n} = F(eM)$$

as $t \to \infty$. This proves the theorem.

The result above is not new (*cf.* Karpelevič [46], Theorem 18.3.2 and also Moore [53], p. 204). Next we prove that the boundary function $\hat{u}$ in Theorem 2.4 is unique.

Corollary 2.7. Let $F \in L^\infty(B)$ and

$$u(x) = \int_B P(x, b)F(b) \, db \qquad (x \in X)$$

Then if $u \equiv 0$, we have also $F \equiv 0$.

In fact, let $\phi \in L^1(G)$ be continuous and consider the function

$$F_1(b) = \int_G \phi(g)F(g(b)) \, dg \qquad b \in B$$

The function F_1 is continuous (as a convolution of a continuous integrable function with a bounded function) and its Poisson integral u_1 is given by

$$u_1(h \cdot o) = \int_B P(h \cdot o, b) F_1(b) \, db = \int_B F_1(h(b)) \, db$$

$$= \int_B \left(\int_G \phi(g) F(gh(b)) \, dg \right) db = \int_G \phi(g) u(gh \cdot o) \, dg$$

Now if $u \equiv 0$ we have $u_1 \equiv 0$ so by Theorem 2.6, $F_1 \equiv 0$. But since ϕ is arbitrary, we conclude $F \equiv 0$.

The Topology of $X \cup B$

It is possible to define a topology on the union $X \cup B$ such that the limit relation (7) is convergence in this topology. A vector $Y \in \mathfrak{p}$ is called regular if its centralizer Z_Y in $\mathfrak{p}$ is Abelian. A point $x = (\exp Y)K$ in X is called regular if Y is regular. Now a regular vector $Y \in \mathfrak{p}$ belongs to a unique Weyl chamber b_Y in the maximal Abelian subspace Z_Y. We say that a sequence of points $x_1, x_2, \ldots$ in X converges to a boundary point b if

(i) Each $x_n = (\exp Y_n)K$ (where $Y_n \in \mathfrak{p}$) is regular
(ii) The Weyl chambers b_{Y_n} converge to b (in the topology of B)
(iii) The distance from Y_n to the boundary of b_{Y_n} in Z_{Y_n} tends to ∞

It is not hard to verify that this convergence concept (together with the usual convergence definition on X itself) defines a topology on the union $X \cup B$.

We shall now prove some measure–theoretic results due to Harish–Chandra ([25], p. 239, [27], p. 294) and give an explicit formula for the Poisson kernel $P(x, b)$ as a consequence (*cf.* also Schiffmann [56]).

Lemma 2.8. Let dk, da, and dn be left invariant Haar measures on the groups K, A, and N, respectively. Then for a suitable normalization of the Haar measure dg of G, we have

$$\int_G f(g) \, dg = \int_{K \times A \times N} f(kan) e^{2\rho(\log a)} \, dk \, da \, dn$$

for all $f \in C_c^\infty(G)$. This ρ is defined in §3-5 and log denotes the inverse of the mapping $\exp : \mathfrak{a} \to A$.

PROOF. Since the mapping $(k, a, n) \to kan$ is a diffeomorphism of $K \times A \times N$ onto G (§3-5) there exists a function $D(k, a, n)$ on $K \times A \times N$ such that

$$\int_G f(g) \, dg = \int_{K \times A \times N} f(kan) D(k, a, n) \, dk \, da \, dn \qquad (9)$$

for all $f \in C_c^\infty(G)$. The groups G, K, A, N are all unimodular, that is, the left invariant Haar measures are all right invariant. Thus the left-hand side of (9) does not change if we replace $f(g)$ by $f(k_1 g n_1)$, $k_1 \in K$, $n_1 \in N$. It follows that $D(k_1^{-1}k, a, nn_1^{-1}) \equiv D(k, a, n)$ so $D(k, a, n)$ is a function $\delta(a)$ of a alone. Let $a_1 \in A$. Then

$$\int_G f(g)\, dg = \int_G f(ga_1)\, dg = \int_{KAN} f(kana_1)\delta(a)\, dk\, da\, dn$$

$$= \int_{KAN} f(kaa_1(a_1^{-1}na_1))\delta(a)\, dk\, da\, dn$$

$$= \int_{KAN} f(ka(a_1^{-1}na_1))\delta(aa_1^{-1})\, dk\, da\, dn$$

$$= \int_{KAN} f(kan)\delta(aa_1^{-1})J(a_1, n)\, dk\, da\, dn$$

where $J(a_1, b)$ denotes the Jacobian determinant of the mapping $n \to a_1 n a_1^{-1}$ of N onto N. The computation in the proof of Theorem 2.6 shows that

$$J(a_1, n) = e^{2\rho(\log a_1)}$$

Thus

$$\delta(a) = \delta(aa_1^{-1})e^{2\rho(\log a_1)}$$

and the lemma follows.

Given $g \in G$, let $k(g) \in K$, $H(g) \in \mathfrak{a}$, $n(g) \in N$ be determined by $g = k(g) \exp H(g) n(g)$.

Corollary 2.9. The Poisson kernel on $G/K \times K/M$ is given by

$$P(gK, kM) = e^{-2\rho(H(g^{-1}k))}$$

PROOF. The mapping $k \to k(gk)$ is a diffeomorphism of K onto itself. Now fix $h \in G$. Then for $f \in C_c^\infty(G)$,

$$\int f(kan)e^{2\rho(\log a)}\, dk\, da\, dn = \int f(g)\, dg = \int f(hg)\, dg \qquad (10)$$

Now if $g = kan$, then

$$hg = hkan = k(hk) \exp H(hk)n(hk)an = k(hk) \exp H(hk)a(a^{-1} n(hk)an)$$

which we write as $k_1 a_1 n_1$. Then our integral on the right-hand side of (10) equals

$$\int f(k_1 a_1 n_1)e^{2\rho(\log a)}\, dk\, da\, dn. \qquad (11)$$

But the map $a \to \exp H(hk)a$ preserves the measure da and the map $n \to (a^{-1}n(hk)a)n$ preserves the measure dn. The integral (11) therefore equals

$$\int f(k(hk)a_1 n)e^{2\rho(\log a_1)}e^{-2\rho(H(hk))}dk\, da_1\, dn$$

so comparing with the left-hand side of (10), we find

$$\int_K F(k)\, dk = \int_K F(k(hk))e^{-2\rho(H(hk))}\, dk \qquad (F \in C^\infty(K)) \tag{12}$$

In particular, let us use this for $F(k) = \phi(kM)$, ϕ being an arbitrary C^∞ function on the boundary. Since

$$\int_K F(k)\, dk = \int_{K/M} \phi(kM)\, dk_M$$

$$\int_K F(k(hk))e^{-2\rho(H(hk))}\, dk = \int_{K/M} \phi(k(hk)M)e^{-2\rho(H(hk))}\, dk_M$$

and since $k(hk)M = h(kM)$ the corollary follows from (12).

As another application let us compute the function $\bar{n} \to \psi(\bar{n})$ in Lemma 2.5.

Proposition 2.10. For a suitable Haar measure $d\bar{n}$ on $\bar{N}$ we have

$$\int_{K/M} f(k_M)\, dk_M = \int_{\bar{N}} f(k(\bar{n})M)e^{-2\rho(H(\bar{n}))}\, d\bar{n} \qquad \in C^\infty(K/M).$$

PROOF. Fix an element $\bar{n}_o \in \bar{N}$ and consider the function $f^{\bar{n}_o} : kM \to f(\bar{n}_0(kM))$ on K/M. Since $\bar{n}_0(k(\bar{n})M) = k(\bar{n}_0\bar{n})M$ we conclude from Lemma 2.5,

$$\int_{K/M} f(\bar{n}_o(kM))\, dk_M = \int_{\bar{N}} f(k(\bar{n}_o\bar{n})M)\psi(\bar{n})\, d\bar{n} = \int_{\bar{N}} f(k(\bar{n})M)\psi(\bar{n}_o^{-1}\bar{n})\, d\bar{n},$$

and from the definition of the Poisson kernel,

$$\int_{K/M} f(\bar{n}_o(kM))\, dk_M = \int_{K/M} f(kM)P(\bar{n}_o \cdot o, kM)\, dk_M$$

$$= \int_{\bar{N}} f(k(\bar{n})M)P(\bar{n}_o \cdot o, k(\bar{n})M)\psi(\bar{n})\, d\bar{n}$$

Comparing the formulas we conclude,

$$\psi(\bar{n}_o^{-1}\bar{n}) = P(\bar{n}_o \cdot o, k(\bar{n})M)\psi(\bar{n})$$

so putting $\bar{n} = e$ the proposition follows from Cor. 2.9.

To conclude this section we state two theorems without proof. Let Δ denote the Laplace–Beltrami operator on X.

Theorem 2.11. Let u be a bounded solution of the equation $\Delta u = 0$ on X. Then u is harmonic.

A probabilistic proof of this theorem is given in Furstenberg [19] (cf. also Berezin [2] and Karpelevič [46]).

Using this result, A. Korányi and the author ([38]) have proved the following theorem which generalizes the classical Fatou theorem for the unit disk.

Theorem 2.12. Let u be a bounded solution of the equation $\Delta u = 0$ on X. Then for almost all geodesics $t \to \gamma(t)$ in X starting at the origin o the limit

$$\lim_{t \to \infty} u(\gamma(t))$$

exists.

4-3   Spherical Functions on Symmetric Spaces

Let $X = G/K$ be a symmetric space of the noncompact type as in the last section.   A *spherical function* on G/K is by definition a K-invariant eigenfunction ϕ of all the operators $D \in D(G/K)$ satisfying $\phi(o) = 1$.   According to a theorem of Harish–Chandra the spherical functions are precisely the functions on G/K given by

$$\phi_\lambda(gK) = \int_K e^{(i\lambda - \rho)(H(gk))} \, dk \tag{1}$$

where λ is an arbitrary complex-valued linear function on $\mathfrak{a}$.

In the simplest case when X is the non-Euclidean disk D from Ch. 1 the spherical functions are the Legendre functions P_ν and their integral formula

$$P_\nu(\cosh r) = \frac{1}{2\pi} \int_0^{2\pi} (\cosh r + \sinh r \cos \theta)^\nu \, d\theta$$

is the simplest example of (1) (see, for example, [31], p. 406).

We shall now state Harish–Chandra's result ([27], p. 612, [28], p. 48) which describes how an arbitrary K-invariant function $f \in C_c^\infty(X)$ can be decomposed into spherical functions.   In view of Theorem 7.1, Ch. 3 such a function f is completely determined by the values $f(a \cdot o)$, $(a \in A^+)$ and we define the transform (spherical Fourier transform) $\tilde{f}(\lambda)$ by

$$\tilde{f}(\lambda) = \int_{A^+} f(a \cdot o)\overline{\phi_\lambda(a)}D(a) \, da \qquad (\lambda \in \mathfrak{a}^*) \tag{2}$$

Here $\mathfrak{a}^*$ is the dual of the vector space $\mathfrak{a}$ and the function $D(a)$ is the density for the volume element dx on X in polar coordinates (Theorem 7.1, Ch. 3). More precisely, if $x = ka \cdot o$ then $dx = D(a) \, dk_M \, da$.

The problem is now to invert formula (2). Motivated by the spectral theory of singular ordinary differential operators, Harish–Chandra expands the function $\phi_\lambda \,(\exp H)$ in a series of the form

$$\phi_\lambda(\exp H) = \sum_\mu \left(\sum_{s \in W} \gamma_\mu(s\lambda) e^{is\lambda(H)} \right) e^{-\mu(H)} \qquad (H \in \mathfrak{a}^+) \qquad (3)$$

Here μ runs through certain subset of $\mathfrak{a}^*$, the γ_μ are certain functions on $\mathfrak{a}^*$ and W denotes the Weyl group (which acts on $\mathfrak{a}^*$ by duality). The dominating term in this series has the form

$$e^{-\rho(H)} \sum_{s \in W} c(s\lambda) e^{is\lambda(H)} \qquad (4)$$

where $1/c(\lambda)$ is a certain analytic function on $\mathfrak{a}^*$. From (1) above and Prop. 2.10, Harish–Chandra derives the integral formula

$$c(\lambda) = \int_{\bar{N}} e^{(-i\lambda - \rho)(H(\bar{n}))} \, d\bar{n} \qquad (5)$$

whenever the integral converges absolutely.

Theorem 3.1. The inverse of the spherical Fourier transform $f \to \tilde{f}$ in (2) is given by

$$f(a \cdot o) = \int_{\mathfrak{a}^*} \tilde{f}(\lambda) \phi_\lambda(a) \, |c(\lambda)|^{-2} \, d\lambda \qquad (6)$$

where $d\lambda$ is a constant multiple of the Euclidean measure on $\mathfrak{a}^*$.

The simplest case of this theorem is the inversion formula for the Mehler transform stated in Ch. 1.

We shall now attempt to describe some of the main steps in the proof of this theorem. For a restricted root $\alpha > 0$ let $m_\alpha = \dim (\mathfrak{g}_\alpha)$, where $\mathfrak{g}_\alpha$ is as defined in §3.5. Let $(,)$ denote the inner product on $\mathfrak{a}^*$ induced by the Killing form B of $\mathfrak{g}$, restricted to $\mathfrak{a}$.

(i) The function $c(\lambda)$ is given by $c(\lambda) = I(i\lambda)/I(\rho)$, where

$$I(\nu) = \prod_{\alpha > 0} B\left(\frac{1}{2} m_\alpha, \frac{1}{4} m_{\alpha/2} + \frac{(\nu, \alpha)}{(\alpha, \alpha)}\right) \qquad (\nu \in \mathfrak{a}^*) \qquad (7)$$

and B denotes the Beta function,

$$B(x, y) = \frac{\Gamma(x)\Gamma(y)}{\Gamma(x + y)}$$

Let us first consider the case rank $(G/K) = 1$. Then $\phi_\lambda(a)$ is a function of one real variable and is characterized by a single second-order ordinary differential equation (which comes from ϕ_λ being an eigenfunction of Δ). One finds then that ϕ_λ is given by a hypergeometric function. If one now compares the series expansion for the hypergeometric function with the expansion (3), formula (7) follows. For the details see Harish–Chandra [27], p. 301.

Bhanu–Murthy [4, 5] extended (7) to several other special cases whereupon Gindikin and Karpelevič [21] proved (7) in general along the following lines. Let $\alpha > 0$ be a restricted root which is not a positive integral multiple of other restricted roots. Let $\mathfrak{g}^\alpha$ denote the subalgebra of $\mathfrak{g}$ generated by $\mathfrak{g}_\alpha$ and $\mathfrak{g}_{-\alpha}$. Then $\mathfrak{g}^\alpha$ is semisimple and has a Cartan decomposition

$$\mathfrak{g}^\alpha = \mathfrak{k}^\alpha + \mathfrak{p}^\alpha \qquad \mathfrak{k}^\alpha = \mathfrak{g}^\alpha \cap \mathfrak{k} \qquad \mathfrak{p}^\alpha = \mathfrak{g}^\alpha \cap \mathfrak{p} \tag{8}$$

Let G^α and K^α denote the analytic subgroups of G corresponding to $\mathfrak{g}^\alpha$ and $\mathfrak{k}^\alpha$, respectively. The symmetric space G^α/K^α (which can be identified with the orbit $G^\alpha \cdot o$ and is a totally geodesic submanifold of G/K) has rank one. In fact if $\mathfrak{a}^\alpha$ denotes the orthogonal complement in $\mathfrak{a}$ of the hyperplane $\alpha(H) = 0$ then $\mathfrak{a}^\alpha$ is maximal Abelian in $\mathfrak{p}^\alpha$. Now G^α has an Iwasawa decomposition $G^\alpha = K^\alpha A^\alpha N^\alpha$, and the c-function for G^α/K^α, denoted c^α, is given by an integral of the form (5) over the group $\bar{N}^\alpha$. Now Gindikin and Karpelevič prove that the product of these integrals (for the various α) is equal to the integral (5) over $\bar{N}$; more precisely,

$$c(\lambda) = \prod_\alpha c^\alpha(\lambda^\alpha) \tag{9}$$

where λ^α denotes the restriction of λ to $\mathfrak{a}^\alpha$ and α runs through the restricted roots specified above. Now (7) follows from the rank-one case.

Now let $\mathscr{S}(\mathfrak{a}^*)$ denote the set of rapidly decreasing functions on $\mathfrak{a}^*$ in the sense of Schwartz [57] and let $\mathscr{I}(\mathfrak{a}^*)$ denote the set of W-invariant functions in $\mathscr{S}(\mathfrak{a}^*)$. (Here W is the Weyl group.)

(ii) Let $\mu \in \mathfrak{a}^*$. Then the mapping

$$S_\mu : b \to \int_{A^+} \overline{\phi_\mu(a)} \left(\int_{\mathfrak{a}^*} b(\lambda) \phi_\lambda(a) \, |c(\lambda)|^{-2} \, d\lambda \right) D(a) \, da$$

$[b \in \mathscr{I}(\mathfrak{a}^*)]$ is a tempered distribution on $\mathfrak{a}^*$.

It is easy to see from (7) that the integral over λ is absolutely convergent. On the other hand to show that the integral with respect to a is absolutely convergent and makes S_μ a distribution requires very detailed study of the behavior of $\phi_\lambda(a)$ for large a (see Harish–Chandra [27], p. 588).

Eventually one wants to prove that for a suitable normalization of $d\lambda$, $S_\mu(b) = b(\mu)$. But first one proves

(iii) If p is a Weyl group invariant polynomial on $\mathfrak{a}^*$ then

$$pS_\mu = p(\mu)S_\mu$$

To see this select a differential operator $D \in D(G/K)$ such that $D\phi_\lambda = p(\lambda)\phi_\lambda$ (see [27], p. 591 or [31], p. 432). Then

$$pS_\mu(b) = S_\mu(pb) = \int_X \overline{\phi_\mu(x)} \left(\int_{\mathfrak{a}^*} p(\lambda)b(\lambda)\phi_\lambda(x) |c(\lambda)|^{-2} \, d\lambda \right) dx$$

Here we replace $p(\lambda)\phi_\lambda(x)$ by $(D\phi_\lambda)(x)$ and carry D over on $\overline{\phi}_\mu$ by replacing it with its adjoint; the result is $p(\mu)S_\mu(b)$ as desired.

As a fairly easy consequence of (iii) we obtain (*cf.* [27], p. 591).

(iv) There exists a function γ on $\mathfrak{a}^*$ such that

$$S_\mu(b) = \gamma(\mu)b(\mu) \qquad b \in \mathscr{I}(\mathfrak{a}^*).$$

Now we must prove that γ is a constant. Consider for f as in (2) the function F_f defined by

$$F_f(a) = e^{\rho(\log a)} \int_N f(\bar{n}a \cdot o) \, d\bar{n} \qquad a \in A$$

Then we have as a simple consequence of (1) and Lemma 2.8 that

$$\tilde{f}(\lambda) = \int_X f(x)\overline{\phi_\lambda(x)} \, dx = \int_A F_f(a)e^{-i\lambda(\log a)} \, da \tag{10}$$

If $b \in \mathscr{I}(\mathfrak{a}^*)$ consider the function

$$\phi_b(x) = \int_{\mathfrak{a}^*} b(\lambda)\phi_\lambda(x) |c(\lambda)|^{-2} \, d\lambda$$

The integral for F_{ϕ_b} can be shown to converge and by the inversion formula for the Fourier transform on A and $\mathfrak{a}^*$ we obtain

$$F_{\phi_b}(a) = e^{\rho(\log a)} \int_N \phi_b(\bar{n}a \cdot o) \, d\bar{n} = \int_{\mathfrak{a}^*} \tilde{\phi}_b(\lambda)e^{i\lambda(\log a)} \, d\lambda$$

$$= \int_{\mathfrak{a}^*} S_\lambda(b)e^{i\lambda(\log a)} \, d\lambda = \int_{\mathfrak{a}^*} \gamma(\lambda)b(\lambda)e^{i\lambda(\log a)} \, d\lambda$$

$$= \frac{1}{w} \int_{\mathfrak{a}^*} \gamma(\lambda)b(\lambda) \sum_{s \in W} e^{is\lambda(\log a)} \, d\lambda$$

where w denotes the order of W. The relation $\gamma \equiv w$ would therefore result from the following statement.

(v) The relation

$$|c(\lambda)|^{-2} e^{\rho(\log a)} \int_N \phi_\lambda(\bar{n}a \cdot o) \, d\bar{n} = \sum_{s \in W} e^{is\lambda(\log a)} \tag{11}$$

holds in the weak sense in λ, that is, it gives the right result when integrated against any $b \in \mathscr{I}(\mathfrak{a}^*)$.

This is carried out by means of a beautiful analysis in §15, p. 597, of Harish–Chandra [27]. Here we have to settle for a vague plausibility argument. Writing $\bar{n}a = k_1 a' k_2$ (k_1, $k_2 \in K$, $a' \in \overline{A^+}$) we have (*loc. cit.* p. 604)

$$\log a' \sim \log a + H(\bar{n})$$

as $a \to \infty$ in A^+. Since (4) is the dominating term in the expansion for ϕ_λ (exp H) let us replace $\phi_\lambda(\bar{n}a \cdot o) = \phi_\lambda(a' \cdot o)$ by

$$e^{-\rho(\log a + H(\bar{n}))} \sum_{s \in W} c(s\lambda) e^{is\lambda(\log a + H(\bar{n}))}$$

When this expression is integrated over $\bar{N}$ we obtain from (5) the expression

$$e^{-\rho(\log a)} \sum_{s \in W} c(s\lambda) c(-s\lambda) e^{is\lambda(\log a)}$$

which equals $e^{-\rho(\log a)} |c(\lambda)|^2 \sum_{s \in W} e^{is\lambda(\log a)}$ in accordance with (11).

In order to deduce Theorem 3.1 from the relation $S_\mu(b) = (\text{const})b(\mu)$ ($b \in \mathscr{I}(\mathfrak{a}^*)$) we still have to prove the following statement.

(vi) Each K-invariant function $f \in C_c^\infty(X)$ can be written in the form

$$f(x) = \int_{\mathfrak{a}^*} b(\lambda)\phi_\lambda(x) |c(\lambda)|^{-2} \, d\lambda \qquad b \in \mathscr{I}(\mathfrak{a}^*)$$

This was stated as a conjecture in Harish–Chandra [27], p. 612, and was finally proved by him in [28], p. 48. Since this proof involves so much work on the general Plancherel formula for G (in particular, the discrete series) it would not be feasible to describe it here. Instead let me outline a different effort [37] at proving (vi).

Let F be a W-invariant function in $C_c^\infty(A)$ and F^* its Fourier transform

$$F^*(\lambda) = \int_A F(a) e^{-i\lambda(\log a)} \, da$$

Writing the expansion (3) as

$$\phi_\lambda(\exp H) = \sum_\mu \psi_\mu(\lambda, H) \qquad (H \in \mathfrak{a}^+) \tag{12}$$

we assume that the term-by-term integration

$$\int_{\mathfrak{a}^*} F^*(\lambda)\phi_\lambda(\exp H) |c(\lambda)|^{-2} \, d\lambda = \sum_\mu \int_{\mathfrak{a}^*} F^*(\lambda)\psi_\mu(\lambda, H) |c(\lambda)|^{-2} \, d\lambda \tag{13}$$

is permissible. Then we have (*loc. cit.* p. 302).

(vii) For $H \in \mathfrak{a}$ let $|H| = B(H, H)^{1/2}$. Suppose $R > 0$ such that $F(\exp H) = 0$ for $|H| > R$. Then

$$\int_{\mathfrak{a}^*} F^*(\lambda)\psi_\mu(\lambda, H) |c(\lambda)|^{-2} \, d\lambda = 0 \qquad \text{for } |H| > R \tag{14}$$

This is proved by translating the integration into the complexification $\mathfrak{a}^* + i\mathfrak{a}^*$ by use of Cauchy's theorem. Because of the formula (7) the function $c(\lambda)^{-1}$ can be extended to a function on $\mathfrak{a}^* + i\mathfrak{a}^*$ with singularities, whose location can be determined. The functions $\psi_\mu(\lambda, H)$ are determined by certain recursion formulas which result from ϕ_λ being an eigenfunction of each $D \in D(G/K)$. It is therefore possible to describe the sets of singularities of the functions $\psi_\mu(\lambda, H)$ and the integration in $\mathfrak{a}^*$ can by Cauchy's theorem be translated away from these sets. This leads to estimates of the integral, which prove (14).

In order to prove (vi) let $f \in C_c^\infty(X)$ be K-invariant and let us use (14) on the function $F(a) = F_f(a)$, $(a \in A)$. We put

$$g(x) = \int_{\mathfrak{a}^*} F^*(\lambda)\phi_\lambda(x)\,|c(\lambda)|^{-2}\,d\lambda \qquad (15)$$

and by (13) and (14) we have $g \in C_c^\infty(X)$ and K-invariant. On the other hand, we have by (10) and the result $S_\mu(b) = b(\mu)$ (with $d\lambda$ suitably normalized),

$$\tilde{g}(\lambda) = F_g^*(\lambda) = F^*(\lambda) \qquad (16)$$

The Euclidean Fourier transform $F \to F^*$ is one-to-one so the last relation implies

$$F_g(a) = F(a) = F_f(a)$$

Thus, in view of (10), the function $h = f - g$ is a K-invariant function in $C_c^\infty(X)$ satisfying

$$\int_X h(x)\phi_\lambda(x)\,dx = 0$$

for all complex-valued linear forms λ on $\mathfrak{a}^*$. It is well-known (see, for example, [31], p. 409, 453) that this implies $h = 0$, so

$$f(x) = \int_{\mathfrak{a}^*} F^*(\lambda)\phi_\lambda(x)\,|c(\lambda)|^{-2}\,d\lambda$$

which gives (vi).

What is lacking in this proof of (vi) is a justification of the term-by-term integration (13). In the quoted paper this justification is given for the case rank $(G/K) = 1$; in this case the proof also gives a Paley–Wiener type of theorem for the transform $f \to \tilde{f}$, that is, an intrinsic characterization of the functions $\tilde{f}(\lambda)$ as f runs through the K-invariant functions in $C_c^\infty(X)$.

We conclude this section with a simple remark on the formulas

$$\tilde{f}(\lambda) = \int_{A^+} f(a \cdot o)\overline{\phi_\lambda(a)}D(a)\,da$$

$$f(a \cdot o) = \int_{\mathfrak{a}^*} \tilde{f}(\lambda)\phi_\lambda(a)\delta(\lambda)\,d\lambda \qquad \delta(\lambda) = |c(\lambda)|^{-2}$$

In analogy with the product formula (9)

$$\delta(\lambda) = \prod_\alpha \delta_\alpha(\lambda^\alpha) \tag{17}$$

one can prove (and this is an elementary result) that

$$D(\exp H) = \prod_\alpha D_\alpha(\exp H^\alpha) \tag{18}$$

where D_α is the D function for the space G^α/K^α, and H^α is the projection of H on $\mathfrak{a}^\alpha$. It seems conceivable that a fuller understanding of the reason for the product formulas (17) and (18) might lead to a reduction of Theorem 3.1 to the rank-one case.

4-4   Fourier Transform on Symmetric Spaces

As before let X denote the symmetric space G/K. Now we would like to define a Fourier transform for arbitrary functions $f \in C_c^\infty(X)$, not just for the K-invariant ones. We motivate this by means of the definition given in §1-3 for the non-Euclidean disk D. In this case the group G equals $SU(1, 1)$ and as calculated in §3-5 the group N consists of the group of matrices

$$\begin{pmatrix} 1 + in & -in \\ in & 1 - in \end{pmatrix} \quad n \in \mathbf{R}$$

The orbit $N \cdot O$ consists of the points $in/(in - 1)$, which clearly form a horocycle and it is a simple matter to verify that the horocycles in D are the orbits in D of all groups of the form gNg^{-1}.

Hence, we define for the general symmetric space $X = G/K$ a *horocycle* to be an orbit in X of a subgroup of G of the form gNg^{-1}, g being an arbitrary element in G.

Lemma 4.1. The group G permutes the horocycles transitively.

PROOF. The most general horocycle ξ is of the form $\xi = gNg^{-1}h \cdot o$, g and h being fixed elements in G. By the Iwasawa decomposition we can write $h^{-1}g = kan$ and deduce (since $aNa^{-1} \subset N$) that $gNg^{-1}h \cdot o = hkN \cdot o$. In other words, the element $hk \in G$ maps the horocycle $\xi_o = N \cdot o$ onto ξ, so the lemma is proved.

In particular, all the horocycles are submanifolds of X of the same dimension and since $N \cap K = \{e\}$ the mapping $n \to n \cdot o$ is a diffeomorphism of N onto ξ_o.

Lemma 4.2. Each horocycle ξ can be written

$$\xi = ka \cdot \xi_o \tag{1}$$

where $a \in A$ is unique and the coset $kM \in K/M$ is unique.

Although the proof of this lemma is not difficult we shall not stop to prove it here. For the case $X = D$ the lemma is quite obvious.

Definition. The Weyl chamber kM in (1) is called the *normal* to the horocycle ξ; the element $a \in A$ in (1) is called the *complex distance* from o to ξ.

Considering the example $X = D$ the term " normal " is quite reasonable; so is the term " complex distance " because the point $ka \cdot o$ is the unique point in ξ at minimum distance from o. (If $a = \exp H$, $H \in \mathfrak{a}$, the distance is $B(H, H)^{1/2}$, *cf.* [37], p. 306.)

We recall now that given the maximal Abelian subspace $\mathfrak{a} \subset \mathfrak{p}$, the group N is determined following a choice of a Weyl chamber $\mathfrak{n}^+ \subset \mathfrak{a}$.

Lemma 4.3. Let $\mathfrak{a}_1, \ldots, \mathfrak{a}_w$ denote the various Weyl chambers in $\mathfrak{a}$ and $N_1, \ldots, N_w$ the corresponding Iwasawa groups. Then the horocycles $N_1 \cdot o, \ldots, N_w \cdot o$ all have the same tangent space at the point o.

PROOF. The projection $\pi : G \to G/K$ given by $\pi(g) = g \cdot o$ maps N onto ξ_o and the differential $d\pi : \mathfrak{g} \to (G/K)_o$ maps $\mathfrak{n}$ onto $(\xi_o)_o$. But the map $d\pi : \mathfrak{p} \to (G/K)_o$ is an isomorphism so let $\mathfrak{q} \subset \mathfrak{p}$ be the subspace which $d\pi$ maps onto $(\xi_o)_o$. We shall prove that the manifolds $N \cdot o$ and $A \cdot o$ are orthogonal at o and since

$$(\xi_o)_o = d\pi(\mathfrak{q}) \qquad (A \cdot o)_o = d\pi(\mathfrak{a})$$

it suffices, because of the choice of metric on G/K (§3-3), to prove $B(\mathfrak{q}, \mathfrak{a}) = 0$, that is, $\mathfrak{q}$ and $\mathfrak{a}$ are orthogonal with respect to B. But if $H \in \mathfrak{a}$, $X \in \mathfrak{q}$ then there exists an $X_1 \in \mathfrak{n}$ such that $d\pi(X) = d\pi(X_1)$. Thus $X - X_1 \in \mathfrak{k}$ so since $B(\mathfrak{a}, \mathfrak{k}) = 0$ and $B(\mathfrak{a}, \mathfrak{n}) = 0$, we obtain

$$B(X, H) = B(X_1, H) = 0$$

Thus each of the tangent spaces $(N_i \cdot o)_o$ is perpendicular to the tangent space $(A \cdot o)_o$ and since $\dim N \cdot o + \dim A \cdot o = \dim G/K$, the lemma follows.

Lemma 4.4. Given $x \in X$, $b \in B$, there exists exactly one horocycle passing through x with normal b.

PROOF. Let $b = kM$. We must find a unique $a \in A$ such that x lies on the horocycle $\xi = ka \cdot \xi_o$. But $x \in \xi$ means $x = kan \cdot o$ for some $n \in N$ so $an \cdot o = k^{-1} \cdot x$. Thus, by the Iwasawa decomposition, a is uniquely determined by k and x.

We denote the horocycle determined by this lemma by $\xi(x, b)$ and write $\exp A(x, b)$ $(A(x, b) \in \mathfrak{a})$ for the complex distance from o to $\xi(x, b)$. We can now write down the analogs of the functions $e^{\mu \langle z, b \rangle}$ in §1-3.

For $b \in B$ and λ a complex-valued linear function on $\mathfrak{a}$, define the function $e_{\lambda, b}$ by

$$e_{\lambda,b} : x \to e^{\lambda(A(x, b))} \qquad x \in X$$

We state without proof two properties of $e_{\lambda, b}$, the second of which is trivial.

(i) $e_{\lambda, b}$ is an eigenfunction of each operator $D \in D(G/K)$

(ii) $e_{\lambda, b}$ is constant on each horocycle with normal b. A function on X with this property will be called a *plane wave with normal b*.

One can also prove that these two properties characterize the functions $e_{\lambda, b}$ (if certain singular eigenvalue systems are excluded). In accordance with the definition in §1-3 we define *Fourier analysis on the symmetric space X* to be a decomposition of "arbitrary" functions on X into functions of the form $e_{\lambda, b}$.

As before let dx denote the volume element on X and

$$\rho = \frac{1}{2} \sum_{\alpha > 0} \dim (\mathfrak{g}_\alpha)\alpha$$

Let $\mathfrak{a}^*$ denote the dual of $\mathfrak{a}$, that is, the set of real linear functions on $\mathfrak{a}$. Then the following theorem holds (*cf.* [35]).

Theorem 4.5. For $f \in C_c^\infty(X)$ define the Fourier transform $\tilde{f}$ on $\mathfrak{a}^* \times B$ by

$$(\lambda, b) = \int_X f(x)e^{(-i\lambda + \rho)(A(x, b))} \, dx \qquad \lambda \in \mathfrak{a}^*, b \in B$$

Then

$$(x) = \int_{\mathfrak{a}^*} \int_B \tilde{f}(\lambda, b)e^{(i\lambda + \rho)(A(x, b))} |c(\lambda)|^{-2} \, d\lambda \, db$$

if the Euclidean measure $d\lambda$ on $\mathfrak{a}^*$ is suitably normalized.

This theorem is proved by reducing it to Theorem 3.1 in a way which is similar to the reduction of Theorem 3.1, Ch. 1, to the inversion formula for the Mehler transform. That reduction made use of the geometric identity

$$\langle \tau \cdot z, \tau \cdot b \rangle = \langle z, b \rangle + \langle \tau \cdot o, \tau \cdot b \rangle \tag{2}$$

and the formula

$$\left| \frac{d(\tau \cdot b)}{db} \right| = e^{2\langle \tau^{-1} \cdot o, b \rangle} \tag{3}$$

valid for an arbitrary isometry τ of the non-Euclidean disk D.

The generalization of the formula (2) to the symmetric space X is

$$A(g \cdot x, g(b)) = A(x, b) + A(g \cdot o, g(b)) \tag{4}$$

for $g \in G$, $x \in X$ and $b \in B$. (Here the action of G on X and on B is denoted as in §2.) In order to prove (4) let $x = hK$, $b = kM$. Then

$$h \cdot o \in k \exp A(x, b)N \cdot o$$

so for some $n_1 \in N$, $k_1 \in K$

$$gh = gk \exp A(x, b)n_1 k_1$$

which by the Iwasawa decomposition can be written

$$gh = k(gk) \exp H(gk)n(gk) \exp A(x, b)n_1 k_1$$

Since $aNa^{-1} \subset N$ ($a \in A$), this relation implies

$$g \cdot x \in k(gk) \exp (H(gk) + A(x, b))N \cdot o$$

and since $k(gk)M = g(kM)$, we conclude

$$A(g \cdot x, g(b)) = H(gk) + A(x, b) \tag{5}$$

On the other hand, we have by the definition of $A(g \cdot o, kM)$ that for some $n_2 \in N$, $k_2 \in K$,

$$g = k \exp A(g \cdot o, kM)n_2 k_2$$

so

$$H(g^{-1}k) = -A(g \cdot o, kM) \tag{6}$$

Hence, (5) becomes

$$A(g \cdot x, g(b)) = -A(g^{-1} \cdot o, b) + A(x, b)$$

In particular, putting $x = o$, we get $A(g \cdot o, g(b)) = -A(g^{-1} \cdot o, b)$, so the desired formula (4) follows. The generalization of (3) to the space X is given by

$$\left| \frac{d(g(b))}{db} \right| = e^{2\rho(A(g^{-1} \cdot o, b))} \tag{7}$$

and this of course is a direct consequence of Cor. 2.9 and (6). Now the proof of Theorem 4.5 proceeds essentially as the proof of Theorem 3.1 in Ch. 1.

Finally we observe that the Poisson integral representation of bounded harmonic functions on X (*cf.* (5) in §2) can be written

$$u(x) = \int_B e^{2\rho(A(x, b))} \hat{u}(b) \, db$$

and is, therefore, according to our definition, to be regarded as a formula in Fourier analysis on X.

4-5 Interpretation by Representation Theory; Eigenfunctions of the Invariant Differential Operators

Since the group G leaves the volume element dx on X invariant we get a unitary representation T_X of G on $L^2(X)$ by associating to each $g \in G$ the operator $f \to f^{\tau(g)}$ on $L^2(X)$. (Here $f^{\tau(g)}$ denotes the function $x \to f(g^{-1} \cdot x)$.) We shall now indicate how Theorem 4.5 gives a decomposition of this representation into irreducible ones.

For $\lambda \in \mathfrak{a}^*$ let $\mathfrak{H}_\lambda$ denote the vector space

$$\mathfrak{H}_\lambda = \left\{ h_\lambda(x) = \int_B e^{(i\lambda + \rho)(A(x, b))} h(b) \, db \mid h \in L^2(B) \right\}$$

of functions on X. If λ is regular, that is, $s\lambda \neq \lambda$ for all $s \neq e$ in the Weyl group W, one can use an irreducibility criterion of Bruhat [7], p. 193, to prove that the function $h \in L^2(B)$ above is uniquely determined by h_λ. If we define a Hilbert space norm on $\mathfrak{H}_\lambda$ by

$$\|h_\lambda\| = \left\{ \int_B |h(b)|^2 \, db \right\}^{1/2}$$

then the mapping which assigns the operator $h_\lambda(x) \to h_\lambda(g^{-1} \cdot x)$ to each $g \in G$ is by (4) and (7) seen to be a unitary representation T_λ of G on $\mathfrak{H}_\lambda$. Using the irreducibility criterion cited, one can show this representation to be irreducible. Now with the notation of Theorem 4.5 there is a Plancherel formula, namely,

$$\int_X |f(x)|^2 \, dx = \int_{\mathfrak{a}^*} \int_B |\tilde{f}(\lambda, b)|^2 \, |c(\lambda)|^{-2} \, d\lambda \, db$$

In terms of direct integrals of representations (see, for example, Dixmier [15]), Theorem 4.5 can therefore be written:

$$L^2(X) = \int \mathfrak{H}_\lambda |c(\lambda)|^{-2} \, d\lambda \qquad T_X = \int T_\lambda |c(\lambda)|^{-2} \, d\lambda$$

λ running through $\mathfrak{a}^*$ (mod W).

The functions in $\mathfrak{H}_\lambda$ are eigenfunctions of each $D \in D(G/K)$. More generally, if T is an analytic functional on B and $\mu \in C$ the function

$$f(x) = \int_B e^{\mu(A(x, b))} \, dT(b)$$

is an eigenfunction of each $D \in D(G/K)$; it appears likely that for sufficiently general functionals T these functions constitute all the simultaneous eigenfunctions of the operators $D(G/K)$ (*cf.* Theorem 5.1, Ch. 1).

4-6 Invariant Differential Equations on Symmetric Spaces

We shall now discuss general existence theorems for invariant differential equations on the symmetric space G/K. In order to motivate the method followed we first describe a well-known geometric method for solving differential equations in R^n with constant coefficients (Courant–Lax [14], Gelfand–Shapiro [20], John [44]). The basis of the method is a formula of Radon–John which in an explicit manner describes a function on R^n by means of its integrals over the various hyperplanes in R^n.

For $f \in C_c^\infty(\mathbf{R}^n)$ let $\hat{f}(\omega, p)$ denote the integral of f over the hyperplane $(x, \omega) = p$ (here ω is a unit vector and $p \in \mathbf{R}$ and $(\ ,\ )$ the scalar product). The function $\hat{f}$ is called the *Radon transform* of f.

Theorem 6.1. For the Radon transform $f \to \hat{f}$ the following inversion formula holds:

$$(x) = c(\Delta_x)^{[(n-1)/2]}\left(\int_{S^{n-1}} \hat{f}(\omega, (x, \omega))\, d\omega \right) \tag{1}$$

for $f \in C_c^\infty(\mathbf{R}^n)$. Here Δ denotes the Laplacian, $d\omega$ is the surface element on the unit sphere S^{n-1}, and c is a constant.

For the proof see [44]. There the cases $n = $ odd and $n = $ even are presented in different forms; the unified version can be found in [34], p. 163.

Formula (1) states that when for $x \in \mathbf{R}^n$ we form the integral of f over each hyperplane through x, then take the average of these integrals, and finally apply the operator $\Delta^{(n-1)/2}$, we recover the function f. However, for the applications indicated, the important feature of (1) is an explicit decomposition of f into plane waves. (A plane wave is a function which is constant on each hyperplane with a given normal vector; this normal vector is then called the normal to the plane wave.) In fact, for any fixed $\omega \in S^{n-1}$ the function $f_\omega : x \to \hat{f}(\omega, (x, \omega))$ is a plane wave with normal ω.

We shall now apply formula (1) to differential equations. Let D be a differential operator on $\mathbf{R}^n$ with constant coefficients and consider a differential equation

$$Du = f \tag{2}$$

where $f \in C_c^\infty(\mathbf{R}^n)$ is a given function. We begin by considering the differential equation

$$Dv = f_\omega \tag{3}$$

where f_ω is as above and we look for a solution v which is a plane wave with normal ω. But a plane wave with normal ω is just a function of one variable; furthermore if v is a plane wave with normal ω then so is the function Dv. Our problem of finding v of the specified type satisfying (3) is therefore just an ordinary differential equation with constant coefficients. Pick a solution u_ω and assume that this choice can be made smoothly in ω. Then the function

$$u = c\, \Delta^{(n-1)/2} \int_{S^{n-1}} u_\omega\, d\omega \tag{4}$$

is a solution of the equation (1). In fact, since differential operators with constant coefficients commute we have (at least for n odd)

$$Du = c\, \Delta^{(n-1)/2} \int_{S^{n-1}} Du_\omega\, d\omega = c\Delta^{(n-1)/2} \int_{S^{n-1}} f_\omega\, d\omega = f$$

This proof actually works also for n even. The weakness of the method lies in the assumption that u_ω can be chosen so as to vary smoothly in ω. In fact the example $D = \partial^2/\partial x_1 \partial x_2$, $\omega = (1, 0)$ shows that u_ω may not exist for all ω.

For a symmetric space $X = G/K$ the inversion formula for the Fourier transform (Theorem 4.5) does give a decomposition of an arbitrary function $f \in C_c^\infty(X)$ into plane waves. In fact let as before

$$\tilde{f}(\lambda, b) = \int_X f(x) e^{(-i\lambda + \rho)(A(x, b))} \, dx \qquad \lambda \in \mathfrak{a}^*, b \in B$$

and put

$$f_b(x) = \int_{\mathfrak{a}^*} \tilde{f}(\lambda, b) e^{(i\lambda + \rho)(A(x, b))} \, |c(\lambda)|^{-2} \, d\lambda \tag{5}$$

Then $f_b(x)$ is a plane wave with normal b so the formula

$$f(x) = \int_B f_b(x) \, db \tag{6}$$

does indeed give a decomposition of f into plane waves. We shall now apply this formula to the problem of solving a differential equation

$$Du = f \tag{7}$$

where D is a given differential operator in $D(G/K)$ and $f \in C_c^\infty(X)$ is a given function. First we need a simple lemma concerning the action of invariant differential operators on plane waves (*cf.* [27], p. 247, or [45]).

Lemma 6.2. Let $D \in D(G/K)$. Then there exists a unique differential operator $\delta(D)$ on the submanifold $A \cdot o \subset X$ such that if bar denotes restriction to $A \cdot o$,

$$\overline{DF} = \delta(D)\overline{F}$$

for every $F \in C^\infty(X)$ which is N-invariant (that is, a plane wave with normal $\mathfrak{a}^+$). This differential operator $\delta(D)$ is invariant under A.

PROOF. Since the mapping $(n, a \cdot o) \to na \cdot o$ is a diffeomorphism of $N \times (A \cdot o)$ onto X the existence and uniqueness of $\delta(D)$ is obvious. Hence we just have to prove its invariance under A. Let $a \in A$ and, as before, if $F \in C^\infty(X)$ let $F^{\tau(a)}$ denote the function $x \to F(a^{-1} \cdot x)$ on X. If F is invariant under N then the function $F^{\tau(a)}$ is too; in fact,

$$F^{\tau(a)}(n \cdot x) = F(a^{-1}n \cdot x) = F(n_1 a^{-1} \cdot x)$$

for some $n_1 \in N$. Thus $F^{\tau(a)}(n \cdot x) = F^{\tau(a)}(x)$, and of course $\overline{F^{\tau(a)}} = (\overline{F})^{\tau(a)}$.

Thus,

$$(\delta(D)^{\tau(a)}\bar{F}) = (\delta(D)(\bar{F})^{\tau(a^{-1})})^{\tau(a)} = (\delta(D)\overline{F^{\tau(a^{-1})}})^{\tau(a)}$$

$$= ((\overline{DF^{\tau(a^{-1})}})^{\tau(a)} = ((DF^{\tau(a^{-1})})^{\tau(a)})^{-} = \overline{DF} = \delta(D)\bar{F}$$

This proves the lemma because each function in $C^{\infty}(A \cdot o)$ can be extended to an N-invariant function in $C^{\infty}(X)$.

In order to solve the differential equation (7) we begin by considering the differential equation

$$Dv = f_b \qquad (8)$$

for an arbitrary $b \in B$. We look for a solution $v = v^b$ which like the function f_b [*cf.* (5)] is a plane wave with normal b. For example, consider the case $b = \mathfrak{a}^{+}$. Then the function f_b is invariant under N and so is the required function v^b. According to Lemma 6.2, the differential equation $Dv^b = f_b$ on X amounts to the differential equation

$$\delta(D)\overline{v^b} = \overline{f_b} \qquad (9)$$

which is by the A-invariance of $\delta(D)$ a differential equation with constant coefficients on the Euclidean space $A \cdot o$. But by a result of Ehrenpreis [16] and Malgrange [52], a differential operator on $\boldsymbol{R}^n$ with constant coefficients maps the space $C^{\infty}(\boldsymbol{R}^n)$ onto itself. Hence a solution $v = v^b$ exists. Now we assume that v^b can be chosen so that it depends smoothly on b. Then we put

$$u(x) = \int_B v^b(x)\, db \qquad x \in X$$

and have

$$Du = \int_B Dv^b\, db = \int_B f_b\, db = f$$

This is not an existence proof for the differential equation (7) because of the smoothness assumption about v^b (see, however, Trèves [59], p. 131). Nevertheless, we have the following general theorem (Helgason [33], p. 577–578).

Theorem 6.3. Let $D \neq 0$ be an arbitrary G-invariant differential operator on the symmetric space G/K. For each $f \in C_c^{\infty}(G/K)$ the differential equation $Du = f$ has a solution $u \in C^{\infty}(G/K)$.

It suffices to find a distribution T on X satisfying the differential equation $DT = \delta$, where δ is the delta-distribution at the origin o. In fact, the desired solution is then $u = f \times T$, where $\times$ is the operation on distributions on X which is induced by the convolution product of distributions on G. Since D and δ are K-invariant we look for a K-invariant T. For this we use the transform $f \to F_f$ discussed in §3. As proved in Harish–Chandra [28],

p. 46, this transform is one-to-one on the space $I(X)$ of K-invariant, square-integrable functions on X which are rapidly decreasing on X in a certain technical sense, and the transform maps $I(X)$ into the space $I(A)$ of Weyl group invariant functions on A which are rapidly decreasing on A (considered as a Euclidean space). On the other hand, it is proved in Helgason [33] that the range of the mapping $f \to F_f$ ($f \in I(X)$) is precisely $I(A)$ and furthermore, $F_{Df} = \gamma(D)F_f$, where $\gamma(D)$ is a certain constant-coefficient differential operator on A. The isomorphism $f \to F_f$ of $I(X)$ onto $I(A)$ has a transpose, mapping the dual $I'(A)$ of $I(A)$ onto the dual $I'(X)$ of $I(X)$. Under this isomorphism the differential equation $DT = \delta$ on X is transformed into a differential equation for tempered distribution on A, and this last differential equation has constant coefficients since $\gamma(D)$ does. But by a theorem of Hörmander [40] and Lojasiewicz [49] any differential operator on R^n with constant coefficients maps the space of tempered distributions on R^n onto itself. This leads to the desired distribution T on X, proving the theorem.

4-7 The Wave Equation on Symmetric Spaces

We shall now discuss a different method for solving differential equations on the symmetric space X. It uses the Radon transform on X which we now define. Let Ξ denote the set of all horocycles in X. For $f \in C_c^\infty(X)$ we define the function $\hat{f}$ on Ξ by

$$(\xi) = \int_\xi f(x)\, d\sigma(x) \qquad (\xi \in \Xi) \tag{1}$$

where $d\sigma$ is the volume element on ξ. (The Riemannian structure on X induces in an obvious way a Riemannian structure on the submanifold ξ.) The function $\hat{f}$ is called the *Radon transform* of f.

If $x \in X$ the (compact) subgroup K_x of G which keeps x fixed permutes the horocycles through x transitively. For $x = o$ this is obvious from Lemma 4.2 and in general it follows by the homogeneity of X. The set of horocycles passing through x has a unique normalized measure, say v, invariant under K_x.

If ϕ is a function on Ξ the function $\check{\phi}$ on X is defined by

$$\check{\phi}(x) = \int_{x \in \xi} \phi(\xi)\, dv(\xi) \tag{2}$$

Theorem 7.1. Suppose all Cartan subgroups of G are conjugate. Then for a certain fixed differential operator $\square \in D(G/K)$

$$f = \square((\hat{f})^\vee) \qquad \in C_c^\infty(G/K) \tag{3}$$

This formula is analogous to the inversion formula of Radon–John (Theorem 6.1) for the case of an odd-dimensional Euclidean space. The even-dimensional Euclidean case corresponds here to the existence of non-conjugate Cartan subgroups and in this case (3) still holds in a slightly modified form (*cf.* [35], p. 759). We emphasize that the differential operator $\square$ can be written down quite explicitly.

By means of (3) one can write down a solution of the wave equation on X,

$$\frac{\partial^2 u}{\partial t^2} = \Delta u \tag{4}$$

with initial data

$$u(x, 0) = 0 \qquad \left\{ \frac{\partial}{\partial t} u(x, t) \right\}_{t=0} = f(x) \tag{5}$$

Here Δ denotes the Laplace–Beltrami operator on X and f is an arbitrary given function in $C_c^\infty(X)$.

In the notation of §1, let $\tilde{\square} \in D_K(G)$ be an operator satisfying $(\square f)^\sim = \tilde{\square} \tilde{f}$ for all $f \in C^\infty(G/K)$. Let $|\rho|$ denote the norm of the linear form ρ, and let dn be a Haar measure on N which corresponds to the volume element $d\sigma$ on $\xi_o = N \cdot o$ under the diffeomorphism $n \to n \cdot o$. Let Δ_A denote the Laplacian on the Euclidean space A.

Theorem 7.2. The solution to the wave equation (4) with initial data (5) is given by

$$u(g \cdot o, t) = \tilde{\square}_g \left(\int_K V_{k,g}(e, t) \, dk \right) \tag{6}$$

where $V_{k,g}$ is the solution to the equation for damped waves on $A \times \mathbf{R}$,

$$(\Delta_A - |\rho|^2) V_{k,g} = \frac{\partial^2}{\partial t^2} V_{k,g} \tag{7}$$

$$V_{k,g}(a, 0) \equiv 0, \qquad \left\{ \frac{\partial}{\partial t} V_{k,g}(a, t) \right\}_{t=0} = e^{\rho(\log a)} F_{k,g}(a)$$

where

$$F_{k,g}(a) = \int_N f(gkan \cdot o) \, dn$$

Although the verification of this theorem is not long (*cf.* [32], p. 688) we omit it here because it requires some further preparation. The function $V_{k,g}$ is given as a convolution of a certain Bessel function with $F_{k,g}$ so the solution (6) is explicitly given in terms of the initial data $f(x)$.

Huygens' Principle

Let M be an analytic pseudo-Riemannian manifold with Lorentzian signature, in short, a Lorentzian manifold. Since our considerations will be local we assume that M is convex, that is, any two points in M can be joined by a unique geodesic. The geodesics of zero length through a point $p \in M$ generate the light cone C_p in M with vertex p. A submanifold $S \subset M$ is called spacelike if each tangent vector to S is spacelike. Let Δ denote the (hyperbolic) Laplace–Beltrami operator on M, and suppose now that a Cauchy problem is posed for the wave equation $\Delta u = 0$ with initial data on a spacelike hypersurface $S \subset M$. Hadamard proved that the value $u(p)$ of the solution at a point $p \in M$ only depends on the initial data on the piece $S^* \subset S$ which lies inside the light cone C_p. Huygens' principle (in the strong sense) is said to hold for $\Delta u = 0$ if the value $u(p)$ only depends on the initial data in an arbitrary small neighborhood of the edge s of S^*, $s = C_p \cap S$. It is known that this is a property of the space M and does not depend on the particular choice of $S \subset M$. The wave equation

$$\frac{\partial^2 u}{\partial t^2} - \frac{\partial^2 u}{\partial x_1^2} - \cdots - \frac{\partial^2 u}{\partial x_{n-1}^2} = 0$$

for an odd-dimensional R^{n-1} satisfies Huygens' principle. A conjecture, attributed to Hadamard, was that these were essentially the only second-order hyperbolic equations satisfying Huygens' principle. A counter-example of the form $\Delta u + cu = 0$ ($n = 6$) was given by Stellmacher [58] in 1953, and in 1965, P. Günther [23] gave a whole series of counter-examples for the pure equation $\Delta u = 0$ ($n = 4$). These are based on Hadamard's criterion that Huygens' principle holds if and only if n is even and $\geqslant 4$ and the logarithmic part of the fundamental solution (in Hadamard's sense) vanishes.

If M is symmetric the evidence available seems to indicate that "Hadamard's conjecture" might hold for the pure equation $\Delta u = 0$. For M of constant curvature (a "de Sitter space" or an "anti de Sitter space") this is indeed so (cf. [29], p. 296; see also [13].) The answer is also affirmative if M has the form $M = M_o \times R$, where M_o has dimension 3 and constant curvature (Hölder [39]). Finally the answer is affirmative if $M = X \times R$, where X is a symmetric space whose group of isometries is a complex semisimple Lie group (Helgason [33], p. 582).

REFERENCES

1. V. Bargmann, Irreducible Representations of the Lorentz Group, *Ann. of Math.* **48** (1947), 568–640.

2. F. A. Berezin, An Analog of Liouville's Theorem for Symmetric Spaces of Negative Curvature, *Dokl. Akad. Nauk SSSR* **125** (1959), 1187–1189.

3. M. Berger, Les espaces symétriques non compacts, *Ann. Sci. Ecole Norm. Sup.* 74 (1957), 85–177.

4. Bhanu-Murthy, Plancherel's Measure for the Factor Space $SL(n, R)/SO(n)$, *Dokl. Akad. Nauk SSSR* 133 (1960), 503–506.

5. Bhanu-Murthy, The Asymtotic Behavior of Zonal Spherical Functions on the Siegel Upper Half-Plane, *Dokl. Akad. Nauk SSSR* 135 (1960), 1027–1030.

6. N. Bourbaki, Espaces vectoriels topologiques, I–II, Hermann, Paris, 1953.

7. F. Bruhat, Sur les représentations induites de groupes de Lie, *Bull. Soc. Math. France.* 84 (1956), 97–205.

8. É. Cartan, Sur une classe remarquable d'espace de Riemann, *Bull. Soc. Math. France.* 54 (1926), 214–264, 55 (1927), 114–134.

9. É. Cartan, Sur certaines formes riemanniennes remarquables des géométries a group fondamental simple, *Ann. Sci. École Norm. Sup.* 44 (1927), 345–467.

10. É. Cartan, Groupes simples clos et ouverts et géométrie riemannienne, *J. Math. Pures Appl.* 8 (1929), 1–33.

11. É. Cartan, La théorie des groupes finis et continus et l'Analysis situs, *Mém. Sci. Math. fasc.* XLII (1930).

12. C. Chevalley, *Theory of Lie Groups, Vol. I.* Princeton University Press, 1946.

13. Y. Choquet-Bruhat, Sur la théorie des propagateurs, *Ann. Mat. Pura Appl.* 4 (64) (1964), 191–228.

14. R. Courant and A. Lax, Remarks on Cauchy's Problem for hyperbolic Partial Differential Equations with Constant Coefficients in Several Independent Variables, *Comm. Pure Appl. Math.* 8 (1955), 497–502.

15. J. Dixmier, *Les algèbres d'operateurs dans l'espace hilbertien*, Gauthier-Villars, Paris 1957.

16. L. Ehrenpries, Solutions of some Problems of Division, *Am. J. Math.* 76 (1954), 883–903.

17. A. Erdélyi *et al. Higher Transcendental Functions* (Bateman Manuscript Project) McGraw-Hill, New York 1953.

18. V. A. Fok, On the Expansion of Arbitrary Functions in Integrals according to Legendre functions with arbitrary indices, *Dokl. Akad. Nauk SSSR* 49 (1943), 279–282.

19. H. Furstenberg, A Poisson Formula for Semisimple Lie Groups, *Ann. Math* 77 (1963), 335–386.

20. I. M. Gelfand and S. J. Shapiro, Homogeneous Functions and Their Applications, *Am. Math. Soc. Transl.* 8 (1958), 21–85.

21. S. G. Gindikin and F. I. Karpelevič, Plancherel Measure of Riemann Symmetric Spaces of Nonpositive Curvature, *Soviet Math.* 3 (1962), 962–965.

22. R. Godement, Une généralisation du théorème de la moyenne pour les fonctions harmoniques, *C. R. Acad. Sci. Paris* 234 (1952), 2137–2139.

22a. R. Godement, Séminaire Bourbaki (1957).

23. P. Günther, Ein Beispiel einer nicht trivialen huygensschen Differential-gleichung mit vier unabhängigen Variablen, *Arch. Rat. Mech. and Anal.* **18** (1965), 103–106.

24. P. R. Halmos, *Measure Theory*, Van Nostrand, Princeton, New Jersey, 1950.

25. Harish-Chandra, Representations of Semisimple Lie Groups I, *Trans. Am Math. Soc.* **75** (1953), 185–243.

26. Harish-Chandra, On a Lemma of F. Bruhat, *J. Math. Pures Appl.* **35**, (1956), 203–210.

27. Harish-Chandra, Spherical Functions on a Semisimple Lie Group I, II. *Am. J. Math.* **80** (1958), 241–310, 553–613.

28. Harish-Chandra, Discrete Series for Semisimple Lie Groups II, *Acta Math.* **116** (1966), 1–111.

29. S. Helgason, Differential Operators on Homogeneous Spaces, *Acta Math.* **102** (1959), 239–299.

30. S. Helgason, Some Remarks on the Exponential Mapping for an Affine Connection, *Math. Scand.* **9** (1961), 129–146.

31. S. Helgason, *Differential Geometry and Symmetry Spaces*, Academic Press, New York, 1962.

32. S. Helgason, Duality and Radon Transform for Symmetric Spaces, *Am. J. Math.* **85** (1963), 667–692.

33. S. Helgason, Fundamental Solutions of Invariant Differential Operators on Symmetric Spaces, *Am. J. Math.* **86** (1964), 565–601.

34. S. Helgason, The Radon Transform on Euclidean Spaces, Compact Two-Point Homogeneous Spaces and Grassmann Manifolds, *Acta Math.* **113** (1965), 153–180.

35. S. Helgason, Radon–Fourier Transforms on Symmetric Spaces and Related Group Representations, *Bull. Am. Math. Soc.* **71** (1965), 757–763.

36. S. Helgason, A Duality in Integral Geometry on Symmetric Spaces, *Proc. U.S.–Japan Seminar in Differential Geometry*, Kyoto, June 1965, Nippon Hyoronsha, Tokyo.

37. S. Helgason, An Analog of the Paley-Wiener Theorem for the Fourier Transform on Certain Symmetric Spaces, *Math. Ann.* **165** (1966), 297–308.

38. S. Helgason and A. Korányi, A Fatou-Type Theorem for Harmonic Functions on Symmetric Spaces, *Bull. Am. Math. Soc.* (1968) (to appear).

39. E. Hölder, Poissonsche Wellenformel in nichteuklidischen Räumen, *Ber. Verh. Sächs. Akad. Wis.* Leipzig **99** (1938).

40. L. Hörmander, On the Division of Distributions by Polynomials, *Ark. Mat.* **3** (1958), 555–568.

41. G. Hunt, A Theorem of Élie Cartan, *Proc. Am. Math. Soc.* **7** (1956), 307–308.

42. S. Itô, Unitary Representations of Some Linear Groups II, Nagoya Math. J. **5** (1953), 79–96.

43. N. Jacobson, *Lie Algebras*, Interscience, New York, 1962.

44. F. John, *Plane Waves and Spherical Means, Applied to Partial Differential Equations*, Interscience, New York, 1955.

45. F. I. Karpelevič, Orispherical Radial Parts of Laplace Operators on Symmetric Spaces, *Soviet Math.* 3 (1962), 528–531.

46. F. I. Karpelevič, Geometry of Geodesics and Eigenfunctions of the Laplace–Beltrami Operator on Symmetric Spaces, *Trudy Moscov. Mat. Obšč.* 14 (1965), 48–185.

47. S. Kobayashi and T. Nagano, On Filtered Lie Algebras and Geometric Structures, *J. Math. Mech.* 13 (1964), 875–908.

48. G. Köthe, Die Randverteilungen analytisher Funktionen, *Math. Zeitschr.* 57 (1952), 13–33.

49. S. Lojasiewicz, Sur le problème de division, *Studia Math.* 18 (1959), 87–136.

50. L. Loomis, *Abstract Harmonic Analysis*, Van Nostrand, Princeton, New Jersey, 1953.

51. G. W. Mackey, Induced Representations of Locally Compact Groups I, *Ann. Math.* 55 (1952), 101–139.

52. B. Malgrange, Existence et approximations des solutions des équations aux dérivées partielles et des équations de convolution, *Ann. Inst. Fourier Grenoble* 6 (1955–56), 271–354.

53. C. C. Moore, Compactifications of Symmetric Spaces, *Amer. J. Math.* 86 (1964), 201–218.

54. G. D. Mostow, A New Proof of É. Cartan's Theorem on the Topology of Semisimple Groups. *Bull. Am. Math. Soc.* 55 (1949), 969–980.

55. S. B. Myers and N. Steenrod, The Group of Isometries of a Riemannian Manifold, *Ann. of Math.* 40 (1939), 400–416.

56. G. Schiffmann, Frontières de Furstenberg et formules de Poisson sur un groupe de Lie semi-simple, *Séminaire Bourbaki* 16 (1963–64).

57. L. Schwartz, Théorie des distributions I, II, Hermann, Paris, 1950, 1951.

58. K. Stellmacher, Ein Beispiel einer huygensschen Differential-gleichung, *Gött. Nachr.* 1953 H.10.

59. F. Trèves, Équations aux dérivées partielles inhomogènes à coefficients constants dépendant de paramètres, *Ann. Inst. Fourier*, Grenoble 13 (1963), 123–138.

II

Special Functions and
Representations of Lie Groups

LEON EHRENPREIS

Most of the materials covered in this seminar will appear in *Fourier Analysis in Several Complex Variables* by L. Ehrenpreis (to be published).

III

Commutativité de l'algèbre des opérateurs différentiels invariants sur un espace symétrique

ANDRÉ LICHNEROWICZ

Si $V_n = G/H$ est un espace homogène de Lie, soit $\mathscr{D}(G/H)$ l'algèbre des opérateurs différentiels sur les scalaires invariants par G.   Le but de cette conférence est de montrer que si G/H est un *espace symétrique* (non nécessairement riemannien) *admettant un élément de volume invariant*, l'algèbre $\mathscr{D}(G/H)$ est commutative.   Ce résultat a été établi par Selberg [3] dans le cas des espaces riemanniens symétriques et par moi-même [2] sous l'hypothèse plus générale faite ici.

1   OPÉRATEURS DIFFÉRENTIELS SUR UNE VARIÉTÉ À CONNEXION LINÉAIRE

(a) Soit V_n une variété différentiable[1] munie d'une connexion linéaire W.   L'ensemble des fonctions f définies sur V_n à valeurs réelles et des classe C^∞ constitue une algèbre $C^\infty(V_n)$ sur le corps des réels.

---

[1] V_n est supposée paracompacte, de dimension k, de classe C^∞.   On pose $\partial\alpha = \partial/\partial x^\alpha$ $(\alpha = 1, \ldots, n)$.

Soit D un opérateur différentiel d'ordre N sur V_n. Sur un voisinage ouvert U rapporté à des coordonnées locales arbitraires, on peut écrire, en mettant en évidence dans D le polynôme de derivation d'ordre maximal

$$[Df](x) = \frac{1}{N!} t_{(N)}^{\alpha_1 \cdots \alpha_N} \partial_{\alpha_1} \cdots \partial_{\alpha_N} \hat{f}(x^\lambda) + Q_x(\partial_\alpha)\hat{f}(x^\lambda) \qquad (x \in U) \quad (1\text{-}1)$$

Dans (1-1), $\hat{f}$ désigne la fonction $f \in C^\infty(V_n)$ écrite dans le système de coordonnées locales envisagé, les $t_{(N)}$ sont supposés symétriques par rapport à leurs indices et le polynôme Q_x est de degré inférieur à N. En se plaçant dans l'intersection des domaines de deux systèmes de coordonnées locales, on voit que les $t_{(N)}^{\alpha_1 \cdots \alpha_N}$ constituent un système de composantes locales d'un *tenseur symétrique contravariant* d'ordre N de V_n que nous désignons par $t_{(N)}$.

Soit ∇ l'opérateur de dérivation covariante dans la connexion W. L'opérateur différentiel defini sur V_n par:

$$f \in C^\infty(V_n) \rightarrow [Df](x) - \frac{1}{N!} [t_{(N)}^{\alpha_1 \cdots \alpha_N} \nabla_{\alpha_1} \cdots \nabla_{\alpha_N} f](x) \qquad (x \in U)$$

est d'ordre inférieur à N. On en déduit par récurrence qu'il existe sur V_n des tenseurs symétriques contravariants $t_{(q)}$ $(q = 0, 1, \ldots, N)$ tels que:

$$[Df](x) = \sum_{q=0}^{N} \frac{1}{q!} [t_{(q)}^{\alpha_1 \cdots \alpha_q} \nabla_{\alpha_1} \cdots \nabla_{\alpha_q} f](x) \qquad (1\text{-}2)$$

Désignons par le symbole $(\,,)$ le produit intérieur divisé par $q!$ d'un q-tenseur contravariant par un q-tenseur covariant. Il existe ainsi des q-tenseurs symétriques contravariants $t_{(q)}$ tels que D soit défini par:

$$D: f \in C^\infty(V_n) \rightarrow Df = \sum_{q=0}^{N} (t_{(q)}, \nabla^q f) \in C^\infty(V_n) \qquad (1\text{-}3)$$

(b) Soit p une *transformation* (ou automorphisme) de la variété différentiable V_n. Nous désignons par p' l'application linéaire tangente; p' opère sur les tenseurs contravariants. A p correspond aussi une action notée p^* sur les tenseurs covariants; en particulier $p^*f(f \in C^\infty(V_n))$ n'est autre que la fonction composée $f \circ p$. Nous disons que p est une *transformation affine* de V_n si elle laisse invariante la connexion W.

Un opérateur D sur V_n est invariant par la transformation p si:

$$p^*D = Dp^*$$

Soit p une transformation affine de V_n. D'après (1-3):

$$p^*Df = \sum_{q=0}^{N} (p't_{(q)}, p^* \nabla^q f)$$

La connexion étant invariante par p, p^* commute avec la dérivation covariante et l'on a:

$$p^*Df = \sum_{q=0}^{N} (p't_{(q)}, \nabla^q p^*f) \qquad (1\text{-}5)$$

D'autre part

$$Dp^*f = \sum_{q=0}^{N} (t_{(q)}, \nabla^q p^*f) \qquad (1\text{-}6)$$

En considérant des fonctions f telles que, en x, $f(x) = 0$, $[\nabla^q f](x) = 0$ pour $q \leqslant N - 1$, puis $N - 2$, ..., on voit sur (1-5), (1-6) que pour que D soit invariant par p il faut et il suffit que $p't_{(q)} = t_{(q)}$ $(q = 0, 1, \ldots, N)$. Ainsi

Théorème. Etant donnée une variété différentiable V_n munie d'une connexion linéaire, pour qu'un opérateur différentiel D sur V_n

$$D: f \rightarrow Df = \sum_{q=0}^{N} (t_{(q)}, \nabla^q f)$$

soit invariant par une transformation affine p, il faut et il suffit que les tenseurs symétriques contravariants $t_{(q)}$ associés à D soient eux-mêmes invariants par p.

2   ESPACES HOMOGÈNES ET OPÉRATEURS ADJOINTS

(a) Soit G un groupe de Lie connexe, H un sous-groupe fermé de G. Nous désignons par G/H l'ensemble des classes à gauche gH de G et par p la projection canonique

$$p: G \rightarrow \frac{G}{H}$$

qui à tout $g \in G$ associe la classe à gauche $pq = gH$. Le groupe G opère transitivement sur G/H: si $\gamma \in G$ et $x = gH \in G/H$, l'image de x par γ, soit $K_\gamma(x)$, est donnée par la translation à gauche L_γ par γ, soit:

$$K_\gamma(x) = \gamma gH$$

ou

$$K_\gamma(pg) = p(L_\gamma g)$$

Ainsi K_γ se trouve défini par:

$$K_\gamma \circ p = p \circ L_\gamma \qquad (\gamma \in G) \qquad (2\text{-}1)$$

Si $x_0 = pe = H$, on peut écrire par abus de notation $x = gH = K_g(x_0)$ sous la forme $x = gx_0$.

On démontre que G/H admit une structure unique de *variété analytique réelle* telle que G opère analytiquement par (2-1) sur G/H, c'est-à-dire telle que l'application de $G \times G/H$ sur G/H définie par $\{\gamma,\ gH\} \to K_\gamma(gH)$ soit analytique, la projection p étant alors une application analytique. Nous appelons *espace homogène de Lie* la variété analytique réelle $V_n = G/H$ sur laquelle G opère transitivement et analytiquement; H est le groupe d'isotropie en x_0.

Un *opérateur différentiel* D sur $V_n = G/H$ est *invariant par* G si, pour tout $\gamma \in G$, il est invariant par la transformation K_γ, c'est-a-dire si:

$$K_\gamma{}^* D = D K_\gamma{}^* \tag{2-2}$$

Nous désignons par $\mathscr{D}(G/H)$ l'algèbre des opérateurs différentiels sur G/H invariants par G.

(b) Considérons un espace homogène de Lie $V_n = G/H$ *astreint seulement à admettre un élément de volume η invariant par* G. Si l'intersection des supports de $f_{(1)}, f_{(2)} \in C^\infty(V_n)$ est compacte, nous posons:

$$\langle f_{(1)}, f_{(2)} \rangle = \int_{V_n} f_{(1)}(x) f_{(2)}(x) \eta(x) \tag{2-3}$$

(2-3) est défini pour tout $f_{(1)} \in C^\infty(V_n)$ si $f_{(2)} \in C_c^\infty(V_n)$, algèbre des fonctions de $C^\infty(V_n)$ *à support compact*.

Nous appelons *opérateur adjoint* d'un opérateur différentiel D de V_n un opérateur différentiel $\tilde{D}$ tel que si $f_{(1)} \in C^\infty(V_n)$ et si $f_{(2)} \in C_c^\infty(V_n)$ on ait

$$\langle Df_{(1)}, f_{(2)} \rangle = \langle f_{(1)}, \tilde{D} f_{(2)} \rangle \tag{2-4}$$

Un tel opérateur existe et est uniquement déterminé par la condition (2-4). Soit D, D' deux opérateurs différentiels de V_n admettant les adjoints $\tilde{D}$ et $\tilde{D}'$. On a d'après (2-4):

$$\langle DD' f_{(1)}, f_{(2)} \rangle = \langle D' f_{(1)}, \tilde{D} f_{(2)} \rangle = \langle f_{(1)}, \tilde{D}' \tilde{D} f_{(2)} \rangle$$

Il en résulte que $D \cdot D'$ admet l'opérateur adjoint

$$(D \cdot D')^\sim = \tilde{D}' \tilde{D} \tag{2-5}$$

(c) Supposons $D \in \mathscr{D}(G/H)$. Il en est alors de même pour $\tilde{D}$. De l'invariance de η il résulte, en effet, qui si $\gamma \in G$

$$\langle K_{\gamma^{-1}}^* f_{(1)}, f_{(2)} \rangle = \langle f_{(1)}, K_\gamma{}^* f_{(2)} \rangle \tag{2-6}$$

A l'aide de (2-6), évaluons:

$$\langle K_{\gamma^{-1}}^* D f_{(1)}, f_{(2)} \rangle = \langle D f_{(1)}, K_\gamma{}^* f_{(2)} \rangle = \langle f_{(1)}, \tilde{D} K_\gamma{}^* f_{(2)} \rangle$$

D'autre part:

$$\langle D K_{\gamma^{-1}}^* f_{(1)}, f_{(2)} \rangle = \langle K_{\gamma^{-1}}^* f_{(1)}, \tilde{D} f_{(2)} \rangle = \langle f_{(1)}, K_\gamma{}^* \tilde{D} f_{(2)} \rangle$$

D étant invariant par G, les premiers membres des deux relations précédentes sont égaux. Il en résulte que, pour toute $f_{(1)} \in C^\infty(V_n)$:

$$\langle(\tilde{D}K_\gamma^* - K_\gamma^*\tilde{D})f_{(2)}, f_{(1)}\rangle = 0$$

Ainsi pour toute $f_{(2)} \in C_c^\infty(Vn)$:

$$\tilde{D}K_\gamma^* - K_\gamma^*\tilde{D})f_{(2)} = 0$$

ce qui entraine $\tilde{D}K_\gamma = K_\gamma \tilde{D}$.

Théorème. *Si G/H est un espace homogène admettant un élément de volume invariant, l'opérateur adjoint D d'un opérateur différentiel invariant D de G/H est lui-même invariant.*

3 NOTION D'ESPACE SYMÉTRIQUE

(a) Supposons qu'il existe sur un groupe de Lie connexe donné G, un *automorphisme involutif S de G*. S étant un automorphisme, quels que soient $g, g' \in G$

$$S(gg') = S(g)S(g') \tag{3-1}$$

S étant involutif

$$S^2 = Id \tag{3-2}$$

Soit H^S le sous-groupe des éléments de G fixes par S. C'est un sous-groupe fermé de G dont nous désignons par H_0^S la composante connexe de l'unité.

Définition. *Un espace homogène $V_n = G/H$ admet une structure d'espace symétrique s'il existe un automorphisme involutif S de G tel que:*

$$H_0^S \subset H \subset H^S$$

Si H_0 est la composante connexe de l'unité de H, on a $H_0 = H_0^S$. Nous pouvons supposer, sans nuire à la généralité, que G est *effectif* sur G/H. Les espaces riemanniens symétriques sont un cas particulier des espaces symétriques au sens précédent.

(b) L'automorphisme involutif S de G induit un automorphisme involutif $\mathbf{S}$ de l'algèbre de Lie $\mathbf{G}$ de G. De la relation

$$S(hgh^{-1}) = hS(g)h^{-1} \qquad (g \in G, h \in H) \tag{3-3}$$

on déduit:

$$\mathbf{S}\,\text{ad}(h) = \text{ad}(h)\mathbf{S} \qquad h \in H$$

Les valeurs propres de l'automorphisme involutif $\mathbf{S}$ de $\mathbf{G}$ ($\mathbf{S}^2 = Id$) sont nécessairement égales a ± 1. Considérons le sous-espace de $\mathbf{G}$ défini par

les vecteurs propres de S correspondant à la valeur propre 1. A tout élément
de ce sous-espace correspond un sous-groupe à un paramètre d'éléments de
G fixes par S. Inversement à tout sous-groupe à un paramètre de H_0
correspond un élément de **G** invariant par S. Ainsi le sous-espace envisagé
n'est autre que la sous-algèbre **H** de H_0 ou H. Soit M le sous-espace de **G**
défini par les vecteurs propres de S correspondant à la valeur propre -1;
M est supplémentaire de **H** dans **G**,

$$\mathbf{G} = \mathbf{H} \oplus M \tag{3-4}$$

et d'après (3-3)

$$\mathrm{ad}(H)M \subset M \tag{3-5}$$

Si $\lambda, \mu \in M$, on a:

$$S[\lambda, \mu] = [S\lambda, S\mu] = [\lambda, \mu]$$

et $[\lambda, \mu] \in \mathbf{H}$. Le sous-espace M vérifie donc:

$$[M, M] \subset \mathbf{H} \tag{3-6}$$

La décomposition (3-4) de **G** qui satisfait (3-5) définit sur G/H une structure
dite d'espace homogène réductif. On montre que, de par son invariance par
H, le sous-espace M permet de *définir sur l'espace symétrique $V_n = G/H$ une
connexion linéaire canonique W invariante par G* et que, d'après (3-6), cette
connexion est sans torsion. On montre de plus que *tout tenseur invariant par
G est à dérivée covariante nulle dans cette connexion.*

4   SYMÉTRIE PAR RAPPORT À UN POINT

A partir de S, on peut défini des transformations de l'espace symétrique
$V_n = G/H$; chacune de ces transformations laisse fixe un point de V_n.

(a) Si $x_0 = pe$, associons à tout élément g de G, le point

$$y = S(g)x_0 \in V_n \tag{4-1}$$

A l'élément gh, où $h \in H$, est associé le point:

$$S(gh)x_0 = S(g)S(h)x_0 = S(g)hx_0 = S(g)x_0 = y$$

Ainsi le point y défini par (4-1) ne dépend que de la classe à gauche gH de g,
c'est-à-dire du point $x = gx_0$ de V_n. Nous désignons par S_{x_0} la transformation $x \to y$ de V_n, transformation qui laisse fixe le point x_0 et qui vérifie
d'après sa définition:

$$S_{x_0} \circ p = p \circ S \tag{4-2}$$

On a manifestement:

$$S_{x_0}^2 \circ p = p$$

et S_{x_0} est un transformation involutive de $V_n (S_{x_0}^2 = \mathrm{Id})$; S_{x_0} est dite *la symétrie par rapport à* x_0.

Pour $\gamma \in G$, composons S_{x_0} avec K_γ. Pour $x = gx_0$, on a:

$$K_\gamma [S_{x_0}(x)] = K_\gamma [K_{S(g)}(x_0)] = K_{\gamma S(g)}(x_0) = K_{S[S(\gamma)g]}(x_0) = S_{x_0}[K_{S(\gamma)}(x)]$$

Ainsi, pour tout $\gamma \in G$,

$$K_\gamma \circ S_{x_0} = S_{x_0} \circ K_{S(\gamma)} \tag{4-3}$$

En particulier, pour $h \in H$

$$K_h \circ S_{x_0} = S_{x_0} \circ K_h \tag{4-4}$$

(b) Etant donné un élément g_1 de G, considérons la transformation de V_n définie par:

$$K_{g_1} \circ S_{x_0} \circ K_{g_1^{-1}}$$

Si à g_1, on substitue l'élément $g_1 h$ $(h \in H)$, on obtient:

$$K_{g_1} \circ K_h \circ S_{x_0} \circ K_{h^{-1}} \circ K_{g_1^{-1}} = K_{g_1} \circ S_{x_0} \circ K_{g_1^{-1}}$$

d'après (4-4). Ainsi à tout point $x_1 = g_1 x_0 \in V_n$ on peut associer la transformation S_{x_1}, ne dépendant que de x_1, définie par

$$S_{x_1} = K_{g_1} \circ S_{x_0} \circ K_{g_1^{-1}} = S_{x_0} \circ K_{S(g_1)g_1^{-1}} \tag{4-5}$$

D'après sa définition, S_{x_1} laisse fixe le point x_1 et est involutive; elle est dite *la symétrie par rapport à* x_1.

(c) De (4–2) on déduit

$$(S'_{x_0})_{x_0} \circ p' = p' \circ S$$

où $(S'_{x_0})_{x_0}$ est l'automorphisme de l'espace vectoriel tangent T_{x_0} en x_0 à V_n, défini par S_{x_0}. Si $\lambda \in M$

$$(S'_{x_0})_{x_0}(p'\lambda) = p'(S\lambda) = -p'\lambda$$

Ainsi à tout vecteur $p'\lambda$ de T_{x_0}, $(S'_{x_0})_{x_0}$ fait correspondre le vecteur opposé;

$$(S'_{x_0})_{x_0} = -\mathrm{Id} \tag{4-6}$$

On établit d'autre part que *la connexion canonique d'une espace symétrique est invariante pour* S'_{x_0}, *donc pour toute symétrie*. On retrouve ainsi aisément la construction du symétrique par rapport à x_0 d'un point d'un voisinage normal de centre x_0 au moyen des arcs géodésiques de la connexion canonique; il en résulte, en particulier, que S_{x_0} admet x_0 comme point fixe isolé.

Ces résultats, et en particulier (4-6), s'étendent immédiatement à la symétrie par rapport à un point arbitraire.

5   OPÉRATEURS ADJOINTS SUR UN ESPACE SYMÉTRIQUE

Nous considérons dans toute la suite *un espace symétrique* $V_n = G/H$ *admettant un élément de volume* η *invariant par* G.

(a) Le tenseur invariant η est à dérivée covariante nulle dans la connexion canonique W.   Dans un domaine U de coordonnées locales (x^α), on a :

$$\eta = \varphi_U \, dx^1 \wedge dx^2 \wedge \cdots \wedge dx^n = \varphi_U \, dx \qquad (\varphi_U > 0)$$

Désignons par $\Gamma^\alpha_{\beta\gamma}$ les coefficients sur U de la connexion canonique.   Il vient :

$$\nabla_\rho \eta_{\alpha_1 \cdots \alpha_n} = \left(\frac{\partial_\rho \varphi_U}{\varphi_U} - \Gamma^\sigma_{\sigma\rho} \right) \eta_{\alpha_1 \cdots \alpha_n} = 0$$

La connexion canonique W étant sans torsion, on obtient sur U :

$$\Gamma^\sigma_{\rho\sigma} = \Gamma^\sigma_{\sigma\rho} = \frac{\partial_\rho \varphi_U}{\varphi_U} \tag{5-1}$$

Désignons par δ l'opérateur de codérivation sur les tenseurs contravariants defini par :

$$\delta : T^{\alpha_1 \cdots \alpha_p} \to -\nabla_\rho \, T^{\rho \alpha_2 \cdots \alpha_p} \tag{5-2}$$

Si V est un champ de vecteurs à support relativement compact dans U,

$$\delta V = -\nabla_\rho V^\rho = -(\partial_\rho V^\rho + \Gamma^\rho_{\sigma\rho} V^\sigma) = -\frac{1}{\varphi_U} \partial_\rho (V^\rho \varphi_U)$$

et par suite :

$$\int_{V_n} \delta V \eta = -\int_{V_n} \partial_\rho (V^\rho \varphi_U) \, dx = 0$$

On en déduit par un procédé standard que, pour tout champ de vecteurs V à support compact dans V_n,

$$\int_{V_n} \delta V \eta = 0 \tag{5-3}$$

(b) Soit T un p-tenseur contravariant, W un $(p-1)$-tenseur covariant tels que l'intersection de leurs supports soit compacte.   Si V est le vecteur défini en coordonnées locales par :

$$V^\rho = \frac{1}{(p-1)!} \, T^{\rho \alpha_2 \cdots \alpha_p} W_{\alpha_2 \cdots \alpha_p}$$

on obtient par intégration par parties :

$$\int_{V_n} (T, \nabla W)\eta = -\frac{1}{p} \int_{V_n} \delta V \eta + \frac{1}{p} \int_{V_n} (\delta T, W)\eta$$

soit, d'après (5-3),

$$\int_{V_n} (T, \nabla W)\eta = \frac{1}{p} \int_{V_n} (\delta T, W)\eta \tag{5-4}$$

(c) Soit D un opérateur différentiel de $\mathscr{D}(G/H)$. Si $f_{(1)} \in C^\infty(V_n)$, on peut écrire:

$$Df_{(1)} = \sum_{q=0}^{N} (t_{(q)}, \nabla^q f_{(1)}) \tag{5-5}$$

où les *tenseurs symétriques contravariants* $t_{(q)}$ *sont invariants par* G (théorème du §1). Pour $f_{(2)} \in C_c^\infty(V_n)$ on a:

$$\langle Df_{(1)}, f_{(2)} \rangle = \sum_{q=0}^{N} \int_{V_n} (t_{(q)} f_{(2)}, \nabla^q f_{(1)})\eta$$

En appliquant q fois la relation (5-4) au terme d'indice q, il vient:

$$\langle Df_{(1)}, f_{(2)} \rangle = \sum_{q=0}^{N} \int_{V_n} \frac{1}{q!} (f_{(1)}, \delta^q(t_{(q)} f_{(2)}))\eta$$

Il en résulte que D admet l'opérateur adjoint défini par:

$$\tilde{D}f_{(2)} = \sum_{q=0}^{N} \frac{1}{q!} \delta^q(t_{(q)} f_{(2)}) \tag{5-6}$$

L'espace étant symétrique, les $t_{(q)}$ sont à dérivée covariante nulle dans W et d'après la définition de δ, on a simplement:

$$\tilde{D}f_{(2)} = \sum_{q=0}^{N} (-1)^q (t_{(q)}, \nabla^q f_{(2)}) \tag{5-6}$$

6 TRANSFORMÉ PAR SYMÉTRIE D'UN OPÉRATEUR DE $\mathscr{D}(G/H)$

(a) Si $D \in \mathscr{D}(G/H)$, considérons l'opérateur différentiel:

$$\hat{D} = S_{x_0}^* D S_{x_0}^*$$

Cet opérateur est invariant par G. De (4-3) il résulte en effet que pour $\gamma \in G$:

$$K_\gamma^* \hat{D} = K_\gamma^* S_{x_0}^* D S_{x_0}^* = S_{x_0}^* K_{S(\gamma)}^* D S_{x_0}^* = S_{x_0}^* D K_{S(\gamma)}^* S_{x_0}^* = S_{x_0}^* D S_{x_0}^* K_\gamma^*$$

C'est-à-dire:

$$K_\gamma^* \hat{D} = \hat{D} K_\gamma^*$$

(b) Supposons D défini par (5-5) et cherchons à évaluer $\hat{D}f$, où $f \in C^{\infty}(V_n)$. Il vient:

$$DS_{x_0}^* f = \sum_{q=0}^{N} (t_{(q)}, \nabla^q S_{x_0}^* f)$$

et

$$S_{x_0}^* DS_{x_0}^* f = \sum_{q=0}^{N} (S_{x_0}' t_{(q)}, S_{x_0}^* \nabla^q S_{x_0}^* f)$$

La connexion canonique étant invariante par symétrie, $S_{x_0}^*$ et ∇^q commutent et l'on a:

$$\hat{D}f = \sum_{q=0}^{N} (S_{x_0}' t_{(q)}, \nabla^q f)$$

Si S_x est la symétrie par rapport au point $x = \gamma x_0$, il résulte de (4-5):

$$S_{x_0} = S_x \circ K_{\gamma S(\gamma^{-1})}$$

et:

$$[S_{x_0}' t_{(q)}](x) = [S_x' K_{\gamma S(\gamma^{-1})}' t_{(q)}](x) = [S_x' t_{(q)}](x)$$

Au point x, $(S_x')_x = -\mathrm{Id}$ et nous obtenons:

$$S_{x_0}' t_{(q)} = (-1)^q t_{(q)}$$

Ainsi:

$$\hat{D}f = \sum_{q=0}^{N} (-1)^q (t_{(q)}, \nabla^q f)$$

et, d'après (5-7), les opérateurs $\tilde{D}$ et $\hat{D}$ coincident. On a donc établi:

$$\tilde{D} = S_{x_0}^* DS_{x_0}^* \qquad D = S_{x_0}^* \tilde{D} S_{x_0}^* \qquad\qquad (6\text{-}1)$$

7 THÉORÈME DE COMMUTATIVITÉ

La relation importante (6-1) entraîne *la commutativité de l'algèbre* $\mathscr{D}(G/H)$. En effet, soient $D^{(1)}$ et $D^{(2)}$ deux opérateurs de $\mathscr{D}(G/H)$, $\tilde{D}^{(1)}$ et $\tilde{D}^{(2)}$ leurs adjoints respectifs.

D'après (2-5):

$$(D^{(1)}D^{(2)})^{\sim} = \tilde{D}^{(2)}\tilde{D}^{(1)}$$

D'autre part, d'après (6-1):

$$(D^{(1)}D^{(2)})^{\sim} = S_{x_0}^* D^{(1)}D^{(2)}S_{x_0}^* = S_{x_0}^* D^{(1)}S_{x_0}^* S_{x_0}^* D^{(2)}S_{x_0}^* = \tilde{D}^{(1)}\tilde{D}^{(2)}$$

On en déduit:

$$\tilde{D}^{(2)}\tilde{D}^{(1)} = \tilde{D}^{(1)}\tilde{D}^{(2)}$$

soit

$$S_{x_0}^* D^{(2)}D^{(1)}S_{x_0}^* = S_{x_0}^* D^{(1)}D^{(2)}S_{x_0}^*$$

et par suite $D^{(1)}D^{(2)} = D^{(2)}D^{(1)}$.

Théorème. *Si G/H est un espace symétrique admettant un élément de volume invariant, l'algèbre $\mathscr{D}(G/H)$ des opérateurs différentiels invariants est commutative.*

Par passage à un revêtement, on en déduit qu'il y a encore commutativité pour $\mathscr{D}(G/H)$, si G/H est un espace homogène localement symétrique admettant une mesure positive invariante.

BIBLIOGRAPHIE

1. S. Helgason, *Differential geometry and symmetric spaces.* Academic Press, New York, 1962.

2. A. Lichnerowicz, *Géometrie des groups de transformations.* Dunod, Paris, 1958. Opérateurs différentiels invariants sur un espace symétrique. *Compt. Rend. Acad. Sci.* **257**, 1963, p. 3548.

3. A. Selberg, Harmonic analysis and discontinuous groups in symmetric Riemannian spaces. *Ind. Math. Soc.* **20**, 1956, pp. 47–87.

IV

Hyperbolic Partial Differential Equations on a Manifold

Y. CHOQUET-BRUHAT

1 DEFINITIONS

The term V_n will denote a paracompact, oriented manifold, which will be supposed for simplicity of class C^∞, although this assumption could be relaxed to some C^p. $C^k(V_n)$ and $C_o{}^k(V_n)$ will denote, respectively, the space of functions of class C^k on V_n and the space of these functions which have a compact support.

A linear partial differential operator on V_n is a linear map of $C^\infty(V_n)$ into $C^k(V_n)$,

$$u \to Lu$$

such that in every coordinate system (v, ϕ), v domain of the coordinate patch, ϕ homeomorphism of v onto the open set $\Omega \subset R_n$, $Lu \circ \phi^{-1}$ can be expressed by

$$Lu \circ \phi^{-1} = \sum_{p \le m} a_{p(x)_j^j}^{i_1 \cdots j_p} \frac{\partial^p}{\partial x^{i_1} \cdots \partial x^{i_r}} (u \circ \phi^{-1}) \tag{1.1}$$

where $a_p^{i_1 \cdots i_r} (x^\ell)$ are C^k functions on Ω.

A distribution u on V_n, $u \in \mathscr{D}'(V_n)$, is a continuous linear form on the space $C_0^\infty(V_n)$;

$$\langle u, \varphi \rangle \in R \qquad \forall \varphi \in C_0^\infty(V_n) \tag{1.2}$$

"continuous" meaning that for every compact $K \subset V_n$ and for a finite covering v_i, ϕ_i of K there exist positive constants $C(K)$ and $k(K)$ such that, for every $\varphi \in C_o(V_n)$ with support in K

$$\langle u, \varphi \rangle \le C(K) \sum_{q \le k(K)} \text{Sup} \, |D^q(\varphi \circ \phi_i^{-1})| \tag{1.3}$$

where D^q denotes the set of all partial derivatives of order q. If, for all compact K, there exist p such that $k(K) \le p$, the distribution u is said to be of order p. One identifies a locally summable function on V_n, $f \in L^1_{\text{loc}}(V_n)$, with a distribution f of order 0 in setting

$$\langle f, \varphi \rangle = \int_{V_n} f \varphi \eta \tag{1.4}$$

where $\int_{V_n}$ denotes the usual integral on V_n, η being an everywhere non-vanishing, C^∞, n-form on V_n, for instance, a Riemannian volume element: the set of distributions on V_n does not depend on the choice of η, though the identification of a particular function $f \in L^1_{\text{loc}}(V_n)$ with a distribution depends on this choice.

A differential operator L on distributions on V_n is defined by

$$\langle Lu, \varphi \rangle = \langle u, L^*\varphi \rangle \qquad u \in \mathscr{D}'(V_n) \qquad \varphi \in C_0^\infty(V_n) \tag{1.5}$$

where L is the adjoint operator of L, defined on $C_0^\infty(V_n)$ by a formula analogous to 1.5, where u and φ both belong to $C_0^\infty(V_n)$.

2 TENSOR-VALUED DISTRIBUTIONS ON A RIEMANNIAN MANIFOLD V_n (LICHNEROWICZ [2])

A p-covariant tensor distribution t on V_n is a continuous (in a sense analogous to 1.3) linear form on the space of C^∞ p-contravariant tensors φ on

V_n with compact support.[1] If t is an ordinary tensor, locally integrable, it is identified with a distribution by

$$\langle t, \varphi \rangle = \int_{V_n} (t, \varphi)_x \, \eta(x)$$

where $(t, \varphi)_x$ denotes the classical scalar product at the point $x \in V_n$, and $\eta(x)$ the Riemannian volume element at that point.

The covariant derivative of a tensor distribution with respect to the linear connection given by the metric (supposed to be C^∞) is defined by $\langle \nabla t, \varphi \rangle = \langle t, \delta \varphi \rangle$ where, written in local coordinates for simplicity,

$$(\delta \varphi)^{\alpha_1 \cdots \alpha_p} = -\nabla_\rho \, \varphi^{\rho \alpha_1 \cdots \alpha_p}$$

∇_ρ being the classical covariant derivative.

These definitions permit the easy writing of differential operators on V_n in the sense of §1, that is, on scalars, and also on tensors.

Example

Laplacians on V_n. The Laplace operator on scalars is

$$\Delta = -\nabla^\alpha \nabla_\alpha$$

It is defined on exterior forms (that is, on skew-symmetric tensors) by (de Rham)

$$\Delta = d\delta + \delta d$$

and has been extended to all tensors by Lichnerowicz [2]. Δ is a map of the space of C^∞ p-tensors of a given type into itself, expressed in local coordinates by

$$(\Delta T)_{\alpha_1 \cdots \alpha_p} = -\nabla^\rho \nabla_\rho \, T_{\alpha_1 \cdots \alpha_p} + \sum_k R_{\alpha_k \mu} \, T_{\alpha_1 \cdots \mu \cdots \alpha_p}$$

$$- \sum_{k \neq l} R_{\alpha_k \rho, \alpha_e \sigma} \, T_{\alpha_1 \cdots}{}^{\rho \cdots \sigma}{}_{\cdots \alpha_p}$$

where $R_{\alpha\beta, \lambda\mu}$, and $R_{\alpha\beta}$ are the curvature and Ricci tensor of V_n. The higher-order terms, in local coordinates, are the same for all equations; they are, if $g_{\alpha\beta}$ is the Riemannian metric,

$$-g^{\alpha\beta} \frac{\partial}{\partial x^\alpha} \frac{\partial}{\partial x^\beta}$$

The operators thus defined are invariant under isometries and are self-adjoint:

$$\langle \Delta u, \varphi \rangle = \langle u, \Delta \varphi \rangle \qquad \forall u, \varphi \in C_o^\infty(V_n)$$

and an analogous identity for tensors (cf. [2]).

---

[1] These tensor-distributions can be identified with de Rham's currents for *completely skew symmetric tensors*.

3 FUNDAMENTAL SOLUTIONS[2]

Definition. A fundamental solution for a partial differential operator L on V_n is a distribution $E(x, x')$ on $V_n \times V_n$ which satisfies

$$L_{x'} E(x, x') = \delta(x, x') \tag{3.1}$$

where $\delta(x, x') = \delta(x - x')$ is the Dirac kernel on $V_n \times V_n$; defined by $(\varphi, \psi \in C_0^\infty(V_n))$:

$$\langle \delta(x, x'), \varphi(x)\psi(x') \rangle = \int_{V_n} \varphi(x)\psi(x)\eta(x) \tag{3.2}$$

A fundamental solution is said to be regular if it is a regular kernel in the sense of Schwartz, that is, if the distribution $\theta(x)$ and $\theta'(x')$ on V_n defined, respectively, by

$$\langle \theta(x), \varphi(x) \rangle = \langle E(x, x'), \varphi(x)\psi(x') \rangle \tag{3.3}$$

$$\langle \theta(x'), \psi(x') \rangle = \langle E(x, x'), \varphi(x)\psi(x') \rangle \tag{3.4}$$

can be identified with locally summable functions on V_n, which will be denoted by

$$\theta(x) = \langle E(x, x'), \psi(x') \rangle \tag{3.5}$$

and

$$\theta'(x') = \langle E(x, x'), \varphi(x) \rangle \tag{3.6}$$

$E(x, x')$ will be called *regular of order p* if $\theta(x)$ and $\theta'(x')$ are both of class C^p.

Let us denote by $\mathscr{D}_0'^p$ the space of distributions on V_n of order p and compact support. From the definition, the following theorem [4] will easily follow:

Theorem. (1) A fundamental solution, regular of order p, gives a solution of the equation

$$Lu = v \qquad v \in \mathscr{D}_0'^p \tag{3.7}$$

by the following formula (convolution in the sense of Volterra)

$$u(x') = \int_{V_n} E(x, x')v(x) \tag{3.8}$$

(2) This solution is unique in $\mathscr{D}_0'^p$ if L^* has also a fundamental solution regular of order p.

---

[2] For simplicity, we will give the definitions for one operator on scalars, though it can be easily extended to operators on tensors, or systems of such operators: the fundamental solutions are, in that case, tensor-valued distributions on $V_n \times V_n$ (*cf.* Lichnerowicz [2]) or matrices of such distributions (*cf.* [5]).

PROOF. Equation (3.8) means that

$$\langle u(x'), \varphi(x') \rangle = \langle v(x), \theta(x) \rangle \qquad \varphi \in C_0(V_n) \tag{3.9}$$

where

$$\theta(x) = \langle E(x, x'), \varphi(x') \rangle \qquad \theta \in C^p(V_n) \tag{3.10}$$

By the properties of supports and differentiability $u(x')$ is well defined by (3.9). By definitions of §1, one has

$$\langle L_{x'} u(x'), \varphi(x') \rangle = \langle u(x'), L^*_{x'} \varphi(x') \rangle \tag{3.11}$$

and by (3.9),

$$\langle u(x'), L^*_{x'} \varphi(x') \rangle = \langle v(x), \theta^*(x) \rangle$$

with

$$\theta^*(x) = \langle E(x, x'), L^*_{x'} \varphi(x') \rangle = \langle L_{x'} E(x, x'), \varphi(x') \rangle$$

that is, by 3.1,

$$\theta^*(x) = \varphi(x)$$

Hence, $u(x')$ verifies, in the distribution sense,

$$Lu = v$$

(a) Let us denote by $E^*(x, x')$ the fundamental solution of L^*. A similar computation shows easily that, for every $u \in \mathscr{D}_0'^p(V_n)$:

$$\int E^*(x, x') L_{x'} u(x') = u(x) \tag{3.12}$$

from which uniqueness follows.

These two results will be extended to $u, v \in \mathscr{D}'^+(V_n)$ when L is hyperbolic.

4 HYPERBOLIC OPERATORS—LOCAL DEFINITIONS

Definition 1. The characteristic polynomial of the operator L, given by (1.1) in local coordinates, at a point $x \in V_n$, is

$$h(\xi) = \sum_{p=m} a^{i_1 \cdots i_m} \xi_{i_1} \cdots \xi_{i_m} \tag{4.1}$$

where ξ_i is a covariant vector at x. The cone in the cotangent plane T_x^* at x defined by

$$h(\xi) = 0$$

is called the characteristic cone. It does not depend on the choice of co-ordinates, because the higher-order terms of L transform into higher-order terms by a change of coordinates.

Definition 2. The operator L is called hyperbolic at the point x if there is a domain Γ_x (which is then a convex open cone) in T_x^* such that every line through $\lambda \in \Gamma_x$ (except λx) cuts the characteristic cone in m real distinct points.

EXAMPLE. The second-order differential operators with higher-order terms

$$g^{\alpha\beta} \frac{\partial}{\partial x^\alpha} \frac{\partial}{\partial x^\beta}$$

are hyperbolic at x if and only if the cone

$$g^{\alpha\beta} \xi_\alpha \xi_\beta = 0$$

is convex, that is, if the quadratic form is of signature $(1, n - 1)$.

5 TIMELIKE PATHS

Let us denote by C_x the closure of the dual of Γ_x; C_x is a convex closed cone in the tangent space at x.

If L is hyperbolic at every point of V_n, and has differentiable coefficients, there is defined on V_n a differentiable field of cones C_x in the tangent spaces. We will always suppose in the following that one can define globally on V_n (continuously) the two fields of half-cones C_x^+ and C_x^- which will be called, respectively, future and past cones (the manifold V_n will be said to be time-orientable with respect to the field C_x).

Definition 1. A differentiable, oriented path on V_n, $t \to \gamma(t)$, $a \leqslant t \leqslant b$, is called timelike if at each point its positive tangent is in C_x^+.

The set τ of timelike paths on V_n (called t-paths) is the closure in the compact-open topology of the set $\mathscr{C}$ of paths on V_n (Bott, this volume Ch. XVIII) of the set above defined of differentiable t-paths.

One can show that t-paths are rectifiables and have a tangent almost everywhere [3].

We will denote by $\mathscr{C}_x^+$ (resp. $\mathscr{C}_x^-$) the set of t-paths originating at x (resp. ending at x). $\mathscr{C}_x^+$ and $\mathscr{C}_x^-$ are closed sets in $\mathscr{C}$. We will denote by $\mathscr{E}_x^+$ (resp. $\mathscr{E}_x^-$), and call the future of x (resp. past of x), the image in V_n of $\mathscr{C}_x^+$ (resp. $\mathscr{C}_x^-$). The sets $\mathscr{E}_x^+$ and $\mathscr{E}_x^-$ are not necessarily closed sets in V_n.[3]

The space V_n being paracompact is metrizable: its topology can be induced by a positive Riemannian metric which can be chosen complete [6], p. 292. We will parametrize all rectifiable paths in V_n proportionally to

---

[3] For instance, take a point off Minkowski space (example given in [9]).

their arc length in such a metric [7]; they will then be defined by maps from the unit interval [0, 1] to V_n. The following definition turns the set of these paths into a metric space, whose topology is induced by the compact-open topology.

Definition 2. The distance between two paths γ_1, γ_2 is

$$d(\gamma_1, \gamma_2) = \operatorname*{Sup}_{t \in [0,1]} \| \gamma_1(t) - \gamma_2(t) \|$$

where $\| x - y \|$ denotes the Riemannian distance between the points x and y in V_n.

6 LOCAL PROPERTIES

Definition 1. The Jacobi equation of the operator L is the first-order partial differential equation on V_n:

$$h(\operatorname{grad} v) = 0 \qquad v \in C^\infty(V_n)$$

where grad v is the usual covariant vector defined by the differential of v and h the characteristic polynomial.

Definition 2. The Hamilton–Jacobi equations are a system of ordinary differential equations on $E^*(V_n)$ which are given, in a coordinate patch, by

$$\frac{dx^\alpha}{\partial h/\partial \xi^\alpha} = \frac{-d\xi_\lambda}{\partial h/\partial x^\lambda} = d\sigma \qquad h(x, \xi) = 0$$

The integral curves of these equations are the characteristic of the Jacobi equation; they are called the bicharacteristics of L.

Definition 3. It is classical to associate Lagrange equations of a variational problem to Hamilton equations: one shows that the bicharacteristics are a solution of

$$\frac{d}{d\sigma} \frac{(\partial g(x, v))}{\partial v^\lambda} - \frac{\partial}{\partial x^\lambda} g(x, v) = 0 \qquad v^\lambda = \frac{dx^\lambda}{ds} \qquad g(x, v) = 0$$

where $g(x, v)$ is obtained[4] by eliminating ξ between $h(x, \xi)$ and

$$v^\lambda = \frac{\partial h(x, \xi)}{\partial \xi^\lambda}$$

---

[4] *Cf.* J. Leray, par. 5.

so the bicharacteristics are the extremals of

$$\int g(x,\, dx)^{(m-1)/m}$$

verifying $g(x,\, dx) = 0$.

In the second-order case, we have

$$h(x,\, \xi) = g^{\alpha\beta}(x)\xi_\alpha\xi_\beta$$

$$g(x,\, v) = g_{\alpha\beta}(x)v^\alpha v^\beta$$

The bicharacteristics are the null geodesics corresponding to the Lorentzian metric.

Local Properties

1. For every point $y \in V_n$ there exists an open nieghborhood $\mathscr{B}_y$ (that is, of the path $[0,\, 1] \to y$), called canonical ball in $\mathscr{C}$, such that the image of $\mathscr{B}_y \cap \mathscr{C}_y^+$ (resp. $\mathscr{B}_y \cap \mathscr{C}_y^-$) is $B_y \cap C_y^+$ (resp. $B_y \cap C_y^-$), where B_y is an open neighborhood of y in V_n and C_y^+ (resp. C_y^-) a closed, convex half-cone, the boundary of which is generated by bicharacteristic t-paths. Moreover, a point z in B_y is interior to C_y^+ if and only if there is a t-path yz which is not a bicharacteristic. This local property has been known for a long time in the second-order case [it is sufficient to take normal coordinates at y to see it (Fig. 1)] and results from Leray [1] in the higher-order case.

2. It results from the property 1 that, for every $x \in V_n$, there exists a neighborhood $V(x)$ of x and points y and z such that

$$V(x) \subset \mathscr{E}_y^- \qquad V(x) \subset \mathscr{E}_z^+$$

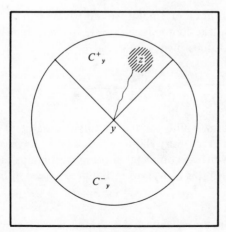

FIGURE 1

PROOF. Take zx (resp. xy), timelike and not bicharacteristic, and in a sufficiently small neighborhood of x; x will be interior to $B_z \cap C_z{}^+$, hence, there will exist $V(x) \subset B_z \cap C_z{}^+ \subset \mathscr{E}_z{}^+$.

3. There is a complete positive Riemannian metric on V_n, and canonical balls $\mathscr{B}_y$, such that the elliptic length of all t-paths in $\mathscr{B}_y$ is uniformly bounded, for each $y \in V_n$.

PROOF (in the second-order case). Denote by $g_{\alpha\beta}$ the hyperbolic metric tensor and v a strictly timelike vector field on V_n (such a field always exists on a hyperbolic manifold), such that

$$g_{\alpha\beta} v^\alpha v^\beta > k > 0$$

The metric on V_n

$$\overline{ds} = -g_{\alpha\beta}\, dx^\alpha\, dx^\beta + \frac{1}{k}(v_\alpha\, dx^\alpha)^2 \tag{6.1}$$

is an elliptic metric. The t-paths on $V_n, u \to x^\alpha(u)$ in local coordinates, $u_0 \leqslant u \leqslant u_1$, satisfy

$$g_{\alpha\beta} \frac{dx^\alpha}{du} \frac{dx^\beta}{du} \geqslant 0$$

Their elliptic length therefore satisfies

$$\bar{s} \leqslant \frac{1}{k} \int_{u_0}^{u_1} \left| v_\alpha \frac{dx^\alpha}{du} \right| du \tag{6.2}$$

In the neighborhood of a point we can always choose coordinates such that the vector v_α has the components $v_o = 1$, $v_i = o$ and, on a timelike arc [6]. $(dx^o/du) > 0$. We deduce then from (6.2)

$$\bar{s} \leqslant \frac{x^o(u_1) - x^o(u_0)}{k}$$

which gives a uniform bound for the lengths of t-paths in the metric (6.1).

It is known[5] that for every elliptic metric $\bar{g}$ on V_n there exists a conformal elliptic metric $\phi\bar{g}$ which is complete, ϕ being continuous and bounded in a neighborhood, the lengths of t-paths in the metric $\phi\bar{g}$ will be also uniformly bounded.

---

[5] If v^α, u^α are timelike $g_{\alpha\beta} v^\alpha u^\beta \geqslant 0$, if v^α is strictly timelike, $g_{\alpha\beta} v^\alpha u^\beta > 0$.

7 GLOBAL HYPERBOLICITY

The principal ideas in the next paragraphs are to be found in Leray [1]. The presentation is somewhat different, and I have made explicit some proofs which were implicit.

It is said that L is globally hyperbolic on V_n if (1) it is hyperbolic at every point, and (2) the set of timelike paths between two points $\mathscr{C}_x^+ \cap \mathscr{C}_y^-$ is compact, in the above defined topology, for all x and y.

Theorem 2. A necessary and sufficient condition for the global hyperbolicity is that, in a complete, positive, Riemannian metric on V_n,[6] all timelike paths joining x and y have a bounded length.

PROOF. a. To prove the sufficiency, we will use the Ascoli theorem, which we recall here:

Let $\mathscr{C}$ be the space of all continuous maps of X and Y (metric spaces). A subset F of $\mathscr{C}$ is compact if

1. F is closed in $\mathscr{C}$.
2. The closure of $F[t]$ is compact for every $t \in X$.
3. F is equicontinuous.

Here X is the closed interval $I = [0, 1]$ and Y is the manifold V_n with its positive Riemannian metric. The family $\mathscr{C}$ is the family of all continuous arcs, mappings $\gamma : I \to V_n$; F the family of these arcs parametrized proportionally to arc length in V_n, which are timelike and join two given points x and y. We suppose that these arcs have a length bounded by a positive number K. Let us show that they verify the conditions of the Ascoli theorem.

1. F is closed in $\mathscr{C}$, since $F = \mathscr{C}_x^+ \cap \mathscr{C}_y^-$, $\mathscr{C}_x^+$ and $\mathscr{C}_y^-$ being closed sets.

2. V_n being a complete Riemannian manifold, the closure of $F[t]$ will be compact if it is bounded, but it is so since for every arc $\gamma \in F$, and $t \in X$

$$\|\gamma(t) - x\| \leqslant K$$

3. The family $\gamma \in F$ is equicontinuous, since by the definition of the parametrization

$$\|\gamma(t_1) - \gamma(t_2)\| \leqslant k(\gamma)(t_2 - t_1)$$

where $k(\gamma)$ denotes the length of the arc γ, which verifies

$$k(\gamma) \leqslant K$$

---

[6] Such a metric always exists, *cf.* [7].

b. The necessary condition is the consequence of the following: all t-paths in a compact subset Γ of $\mathscr{C}$ have bounded length.

Such a subset Γ can be covered by a finite number of canonical balls $\mathscr{B}_y$, but in a canonical ball the proof results from the local property 3, §6.

Theorem 2 enables one to construct many examples of globally hyperbolic manifolds for the Laplacian operator.

Examples

1. $V_n = R^n$, hyperbolic metric

$$ds^2 = g_{\alpha\beta}\, dx^\alpha\, dx^\beta$$

such that all cones $C_x(g_{\alpha\beta} x^\alpha x^\beta \geqslant 0)$ translated at the origin are inside a given convex cone.

Put on V_n the Euclidean metric: It is complete, and the lengths of timelike paths between two points is bounded (it is easily shown in using the fact that there are globally defined spatial hypersurfaces).

2. $V_n = V_{n-1} \times R$
where V_{n-1} is a complete Riemannian manifold with metric (positive definite) $d\sigma^2$. Put on V_n the metric

$$ds^2 = (dx^o)^2 - d\sigma^2$$

The associated positive metric

$$\overline{ds}^2 = (dx^o)^2 + d\sigma^2$$

is complete, and the timelike paths of V_n satisfy

$$\left(\frac{dx^o}{du}\right)^2 \geqslant \left(\frac{d\sigma}{du}\right)^2 \qquad \frac{dx^o}{du} > 0$$

which gives

$$\left(\frac{\overline{ds}}{du}\right)^2 \leqslant 2\left(\frac{dx^o}{du}\right)^2$$

and for the length between the points x and y, of time coordinate x^o and y^o on a timelike arc length $(xy) \leqslant 2|y^o - x^o|$.

3. Let V_n be a C^∞ manifold with a hyperbolic metric, time-oriented. Let v be a strictly timelike vector field:

$$g_{\alpha\beta} v^\alpha v^\beta > k > 0 \qquad \text{on } V_n$$

V_n will be globally hyperbolic if the elliptic metric (6.1) is complete and if the integral

$$\int_x^y v_\alpha\, dx^\alpha$$

taken on any timelike path joining x and y is uniformly bounded, in particular [8] if there exists a continuous function on V_n such that $v_\alpha = \partial_\alpha f$ (the hypersurfaces $f = $ constant are then " global Cauchy surfaces ").

Remark. A globally hyperbolic manifold cannot have closed time lines. We will show in §11 that, moreover, it satisfies the " strong causality " assumption of Hawking–Penrose.

8 CONSEQUENCES OF GLOBAL HYPERBOLICITY

Lemma. For any two points x, y in V_n globally hyperbolic, there are neighborhoods $V(x)$, $W(y)$ such that the t-paths from $V(x)$ to $W(y)$, $\mathscr{C}^+_{V(x)} \cap \mathscr{C}^-_{W(y)}$ have a uniformly bounded elliptic length.

PROOF. If we choose y^* interior to $\mathscr{E}_y{}^+$, in a small neighborhood of y, such that y is interior to $\mathscr{E}_{y^*}^-$ (which is always possible by local property 1, §6), we can find a neighborhood $W(y)$ interior $\mathscr{E}_{y^*}^-$ (Fig. 2). We choose, by an

FIGURE 2

analogous method, $V(x)$ interior to $\mathscr{E}_{x^*}^+$. If $z \in V(x)$ and $u \in W(y)$ are joined by a t-path $\widehat{zu}$, this path is, by the construction included in a t-path $\widehat{x^*zuy^*}$, which proves that

$$\text{length } (\widehat{zu}) < \text{length } (\widehat{z^*zuy^*}) \leqslant K$$

We deduce from the lemma (Borel–Lebesgue) that the length of all t-paths joining two compact sets is bounded, which proves, again by the Ascoli theorem, the following:

Theorem. If P and Q are compact subsets of V_n, $\mathscr{C}_P{}^+ \cap \mathscr{C}_Q{}^-$ is compact.

Theorem. If V_n is globally hyperbolic, the image in V_n of $\mathscr{C}_P{}^+ \cap \mathscr{C}_Q{}^-$, which we denote by $\mathscr{E}_P{}^+ \cap \mathscr{E}_Q{}^-$, is compact.

PROOF. We will show that $\mathscr{E}_P{}^+ \cap \mathscr{E}_Q{}^-$ is closed and bounded in the metric of V_n. Since V_n is complete, such a set is compact.

1. $\mathscr{C}_P{}^+ \cap \mathscr{C}_Q{}^-$ being compact, all t-paths from P to Q are bounded in length by some fixed number N. The image $\mathscr{E}_P{}^+ \cap \mathscr{E}_Q{}^-$ in V_n is therefore contained in a bounded set.

2. Let $z_1 \cdots z_n \cdots$ be a sequence of points converging to z in V_n, that is,

$$\| z - z_n \| < \varepsilon \qquad \text{if } n > N \tag{8.1}$$

denote by $\gamma_i = \widehat{x_i z_i y_i}$ a sequence of t-paths in $\mathscr{C}_P{}^+ \cap \mathscr{C}_Q{}^-$; by the compactness of this set there is a subsequence, denoted γ_n, converging to a t-path $\gamma \in \mathscr{C}_P{}^+ \cap \mathscr{C}_Q{}^-$, that is,

$$\underset{0 \leqslant t \leqslant 1}{\mathrm{Sup}} |\gamma_n(t) - \gamma(t)| < \varepsilon, \qquad n > N$$

But z belongs to the t-path γ, since if z did not belong to γ (compact subset of V_n), we will have a number $\eta > 0$ such that

$$\underset{0 \leqslant t \leqslant 1}{\mathrm{Inf}} \| z - \gamma(t) \| > \eta \tag{8.2}$$

but for each z_n, there exists t_n such that

$$z_n = \gamma_n(t_n) \tag{8.3}$$

From (8.1) and (8.3) results

$$|z - \gamma(t_n)| < 2\varepsilon$$

which contradicts (8.3).

Corollary. $\mathscr{E}_P{}^+$ (resp. $\mathscr{E}_Q{}^-$) is a closed subset of V_n if P is compact.

PROOF. Apply the preceding theorem to $\mathscr{E}_P{}^+ \cap \mathscr{E}_{B(z)}^-$ where B is a compact containing the limit point of a sequence $z_1 \cdots z_n \cdots$ in $\mathscr{E}_P{}^+$.

Past and Future Compact Sets

Definition. A set $P \subset V_n$ is called past-compact if the set of paths $\mathscr{C}_P{}^+ \cap \mathscr{C}_x{}^-$ is compact for all $x \in V_n$. Analogous definition for future compact sets.

Theorem. A past (resp. future) compact set is closed. Every closed subset of a past compact set is past compact.

PROOF. Analogous to the preceding ones.

Theorem. The future $\mathscr{E}_P{}^+$ of a compact set is past-compact.

PROOF. We have already proved that $\mathscr{C}_P{}^+ \cap \mathscr{C}_x{}^-$ is compact if P is compact but, by the definition itself,

$$\mathscr{C}_P{}^+ \equiv \mathscr{C}_{\mathscr{E}_P{}^+}^+$$

Theorem. If Q is compact and P past-compact, $\mathscr{C}_P{}^+ \cap \mathscr{C}_Q{}^-$ is compact in $\mathscr{C}$ and $\mathscr{E}_P{}^+ \cap \mathscr{E}_Q{}^-$ is compact in V_n.

PROOF. Analogous to the one used in theorem 12. §7: take a small neighborhood $V(x)$ in Q, such that there exist x^* and $V(x) \subset \mathscr{E}_{x^*}^-$: all t-paths from P to $V(x)$ have an elliptic length bounded by the maximum of elliptic length of t-paths from x^* to P; then use the same arguments (Fig. 3).

FIGURE 3

9 BOUNDARIES

The boundary ∂U of a set U in V_n will be, as usual,

$$\partial U = \overline{U} \cap \overline{CU}$$

where $\overline{U}$ denotes the closure of U in V_n and CU the complementary set. The interior of U is

$$\overset{\circ}{U} = U - \partial U$$

The following important lemma, theorem, and corollary do not depend on the global hyperbolicity hypothesis.

Lemma. If xy is a t-path which is not a bicharacteristic, there exists a neighborhood $V(y)$ such that $V(y) \subset \mathscr{E}_x{}^+$.

PROOF. Let us take z on $\widehat{xy}$ such that $\widehat{zy}$ is in the canonical ball $\mathscr{B}_y$ of §6. Since $\widehat{zy}$ is not a bicharacteristic, there exists a neighborhood $V(y)$ such that $V(y) \subset \mathscr{E}_z{}^+$, but $\mathscr{E}_z{}^+ \subset \mathscr{E}_x{}^+$, since $z \in \mathscr{E}_z{}^+$, which proves that $V(y) \subset \mathscr{E}_x{}^+$.

Theorem. Let P be any subset of V_n, and $\widehat{xy}$ a t-path such that

$$x \in \mathscr{E}_P{}^+, \qquad y \in \partial \mathscr{E}_P{}^+$$

then $\widehat{xy}$ is a bicharacteristic and $x \in \partial \mathscr{E}_P{}^+$.

PROOF. (1) Since $y \in \partial \mathscr{E}_P{}^+$, there cannot be an open set $V(y)$ containing y such that $V(y) \subset \mathscr{E}_P{}^+$, hence, there cannot be such a set with $V(y) \subset \mathscr{E}_z{}^+$ with $z \in \widehat{xy}$, since $\mathscr{E}_z{}^+ \subset \mathscr{E}_P{}^+$. We deduce therefore from the lemma that zy is a bicharacteristic if $\widehat{zy} \in \mathscr{B}_y$.

(2) To show, then, that $\widehat{zy}$ belongs to $\partial \mathscr{E}_P{}^+$, take a point $z' \in \widehat{zy}$. If z' was interior to $\mathscr{E}_P{}^+$, we could find a neighborhood $V(z')$ interior also to $\mathscr{E}_P{}^+$, and in this neighbourhood (local property) a point z^* such that $\widehat{z^*z'}$ is strictly timelike. The path $\widehat{z^*z'y}$ would be a t-path in $\mathscr{E}_P{}^+ \cap B_y$ which would not be a bicharacteristic, which we have seen is impossible. Thus $z^* \in \partial \mathscr{E}_P{}^+$.

(3) The same argument, applied recurrently, shows that the whole path $\widehat{xy}$ is on $\partial \mathscr{E}_P{}^+$

10   SPATIAL BOUNDARIES (global hyperbolicity supposed)

Definition. The spatial boundary of a past-compact set P is the subset S of P such that

$$x \in S \Leftrightarrow \mathscr{E}_x{}^- \cap P = x$$

Theorem 1. If S is the spatial boundary of P,

$$\mathscr{C}_S{}^+ \equiv \mathscr{C}_P{}^+$$

Corollary. S is not empty.

PROOF. Let $\widehat{xy} \in \mathscr{C}_P{}^+$ and $\mathscr{E}_x{}^- \cap P \neq x$. There is then a point $x_1 \neq x$ with $x_1 \in \mathscr{E}_x{}^- \cap P$ and therefore a t-path $\widehat{x_1xy} \in \mathscr{C}_P{}^+$. If $x_1 \notin S$, the same argument gives a point x_2 such that $\widehat{x_2x_1xy} \in \mathscr{C}_P{}^+$ and so on; by the hypothesis $\mathscr{C}_P{}^+ \cap \mathscr{C}_y{}^-$ is compact; therefore, the strictly increasing sequence of paths $\widehat{x_nxy}$ has a limit point z, which is in P (closed) and therefore on S.

Theorem 2. Let us denote by $\mathscr{F}\mathscr{E}_P{}^+$ the part of $\partial\mathscr{E}_P{}^+$ which does not belong to S (spatial boundary of P). Then $\mathscr{F}\mathscr{E}_P{}^+$ is generated by bicharacteristics issued from S (but does not in general coincide with the set of all these bicharacteristics).

PROOF. $\mathscr{E}_P{}^+$ is a closed set, that is, $\partial\mathscr{E}_P{}^+ \subset \mathscr{E}_P{}^+$, which proves that any $y \in \partial\mathscr{E}_P{}^+$ is on a t-path $\widehat{xy}$, $x \in S$, since $\widehat{xy}$ is a bicharacteristic of $y \in \partial\mathscr{E}_P{}^+$.

Remark. One can prove that, in each point of $\mathscr{F}\mathscr{E}_P{}^+$ which is interior to a bicharacteristic, $\mathscr{F}\mathscr{E}_P{}^+$ admits a tangent hyperplane (the hyperplane ξ_α associated with the bicharacteristic vector).

Example

In Minkovski space, take two half-cones $\mathscr{E}_x{}^+$ and $\mathscr{E}_y{}^+$.   The boundary $\mathscr{F}(\mathscr{E}_x{}^+ \cup \mathscr{E}_y{}^+)$ is part of the union of the boundaries (Fig. 4).

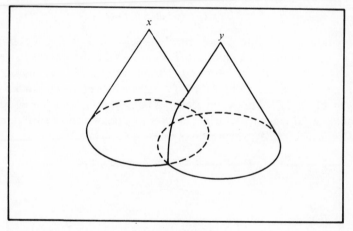

FIGURE 4

11   CONTINUITY PROPERTY OF $\mathscr{E}_P{}^+$

Definition. If A and B are compact subsets of V_n such that $A \subset B$, we call distance $d(A, B)$ the following number:

$$d(A, B) = \operatorname*{Sup}_{y \in B} \operatorname*{Inf}_{x \in A} \|x - y\|$$

It has the following properties:

(1) $d(A, B) = 0 \leftrightarrows A \equiv B$

(2) $A \subset B \subset C \rightarrow d(A, C) \geqslant \mathrm{d}(B, C)$

$\qquad\qquad\qquad\qquad d(A, C) \geqslant d(A, B)$

(3) $d(A, C) \leqslant d(A, B) + d(B, C)$

An ε-neighborhood of a set A is any set $B > A$ which verifies

$$d(A, B) < \varepsilon$$

Remark: If A is a closed ball of radius r, B is contained in a closed ball of radius $r + \varepsilon$.

A directed sequence of sets $B_1 \supset B_2 \supset \cdots \supset B_n \cdots$ is said to converge to a set B if for every ε there exists N such that

$$d(B, B_n) < \varepsilon \qquad \text{if } n > N$$

Theorem.[7] $\mathscr{E}_P{}^+ \cap Q$ (Q compact toward future) depends continuously on P in the following sense: If $P_1 \supset P_2 \cdots \supset P_n$ is a sequence of compact sets converging to P, then the sets $\mathscr{E}_{P_1}^+ \cap Q, \ldots, \mathscr{E}_{P_n}^+ \cap Q$ converge to the set: $\mathscr{E}_P{}^+ \cap Q$.

PROOF. The sequence $\mathscr{E}_{P_1}^+ \cap Q, \ldots,$ is a decreasing sequence of compact sets:

$$\mathscr{E}_{P_1}^+ \cap Q \supset \cdots \supset \mathscr{E}_{P_n}^+ \cap Q$$

therefore it tends to a limit H, contained in each set $\mathscr{E}_{P_n}^+ \cap Q$. To prove that $H = \mathscr{E}_P{}^+ \cap Q$, let us take a point $u \in H$. Since $u \in \mathscr{E}_{P_n}^+$ there exists $y_n \in P_n$ such that $\widehat{y_n u}$ is a t-path. By the compacity hypothesis (see §7, note that $P_n \subset P_1$), there is a subsequence, γ_k of this set of t-paths which converges to a t-path γ, ending in u (Fig. 5). Choose on each γ_k a point $z_k \in P_k$, and extract from the sequence z_k a subsequence which converges to a point z: necessarily $z \in P \cap \gamma$ since P_k converges to P, which proves that $u \in \mathscr{E}_z{}^+ \cap \mathscr{E}_P{}^+$.

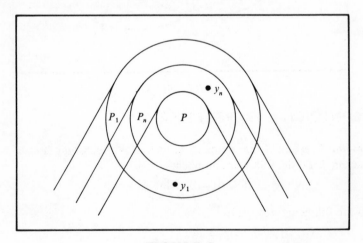

FIGURE 5

---

[7] Analogous results in changing past into future.

This theorem and the definition of the spatial boundary S will be useful in the construction of fundamental solutions through the following proposition, which results immediately from the theorem and the definition of S.

Proposition. If $x \in S$, where S is the spatial boundary of a set P compact toward the past, there exists a neighborhood $V(x)$ such that $\mathscr{E}^-_{V(x)} \cap \mathscr{E}_P{}^+$ is contained in a given ball of center x radius ρ (ρ arbitrarily).

PROOF. Take for Q and P of the preceding theorem (and changing past and future) the sets here denoted $\mathscr{E}_P{}^+$ and $\{x\}$, and for P_n a decreasing sequence of balls of center x, $V(x) \subset P_n$, $n > N$.

Remarks. (1) The preceding theorem shows that global hyperbolicity implies that the sets $\mathscr{E}^+_{V(x)} \cap \mathscr{E}^-_{V(x)}$ [where $V(x)$ is any neighborhood of $x \in V_n$] form a basis of neighborhoods for V_n.

(2) It also implies the "strong causality" of Penrose and Hawking since, if $\gamma = \widehat{y_1 y_2 y y_3 y_4}$ is a t-path in $\mathscr{E}_V{}^+ \cap \mathscr{E}_V{}^-$, all points of γ are also in $\mathscr{E}_V{}^+ \cap \mathscr{E}_V{}^-$, and, following Remark 1, an arbitrarily small neighborhood of x contains such a set (Fig. 6). Under the "strong casuality" hypothesis, Penrose and Hawking have proved results related to those of §9 and §10.

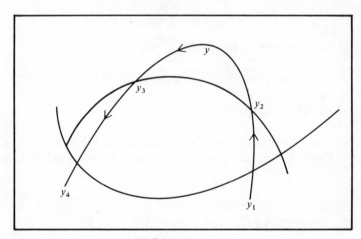

FIGURE 6

12 FUNDAMENTAL SOLUTIONS OF A GLOBALLY HYPERBOLIC DIFFERENTIAL OPERATOR ON V_n—CONSEQUENCES

We will in the next paragraphs sketch the proof of the following.

Theorem I. The hyperbolic partial differential operator (with C^∞ coefficient) L on V_n has one and only one fundamental solution on $V_n \times V_n$, $E^+(x, x')$

[resp. $E^-(x, x')$] which is a regular C^∞ kernel such that for each x the support of $E^+(x, x')$ [resp. $E^-(x, x')$] is in $\mathscr{E}_x^+$ (resp. $\mathscr{E}_x^-$).

The adjoint operator L^* which is also hyperbolic possesses then two fundamental solutions, $E^{*+}(x, x')$ and $E^{*-}(x, x')$ with the same properties.

Theorem II. The partial differential equation[8]

$$Lu = v \qquad v \in \mathscr{D}'^+ \tag{12.1}$$

has one and only one solution, $u \in \mathscr{D}'^+$.

PROOF [4]. (1) By an argument quite analogous to those of §3, one proves that one solution of (12.1) is

$$u(x') = \int_{V_n} E^+(x, x')v(x) \tag{12.2}$$

in using the fact that, here

$$\text{Supp } v \cap \text{Supp } \theta \text{ is compact} \tag{12.3}$$

since $v \in \mathscr{D}'^+$ and Supp θ is compact toward the future, because if

$$\theta(x) = \langle E^+(x, x'), \varphi(x') \rangle \tag{12.4}$$

$$\text{Supp } \theta \subset E^-(\text{Supp } \varphi) \tag{12.5}$$

2. An analogous argument shows that

$$u(x) = \int_{V_n} E^{*-}(x', x)L_x u(x) \qquad u(x) \in \mathscr{D}'^+ \tag{12.6}$$

from which follows uniqueness.

Corollary. (a) The uniqueness of the fundamental solution $E^+(x, x')$ [resp. $E^-(x, x')$] follows from the general uniqueness theorem since it verifies

$$L_x E^+(x, x') = \delta(x, x') \tag{12.7}$$

and belongs to $\mathscr{D}'^+$, for each x.

(b) In comparing 12.2 and 12.6, we get

$$E^+(x, x') = E^{*-}(x', x)$$

One also deduces easily from it the invariance by isometry of $E^\pm(x, x')$.

Remark: If v is a C^∞ function, so is u.

Propagator. The difference $E^+(x, x') - E^-(x, x')$ has been called by Lichnerowicz "propagator." It plays a fundamental role in the quantum

---

[8] $\mathscr{D}'^+$ is the space of distributions with support compact toward the past.

theory of fields on a curved space-time, as it has been developed independently by Lichnerowicz [2] and B. and C. DeWitt [11].

The propagator gives, by Volterra convolution, the general solution of the homogeneous equation (*cf.* [5a]).

13 CAUCHY PROBLEM

We look for a solution of

$$Lu = v \qquad v \in C^\infty(V_n)$$

such that, on a given Lipschitzian hypersurface S, compact toward the past, $u - w$ vanishes m times, w being a function given in a neighborhood of S, satisfying

$$Lw = v \qquad \text{on } S$$

The solution, in the sense of distributions, is given by

$$u(x') = \int_{V_n} E^+(x, x')(T(x) + v(x))$$

where $T(x)$ is the following distribution

$$LT(x) = \{Lw\} - [Lw]$$

$\{W\}$ being the distribution defined by the function equal to W on $\mathscr{E}_S{}^+$ and to zero outside: $T(x)$ is a distribution with support S.

One shows easily that, if S is spatial at each point the solution u is a solution of Cauchy problem in the usual sense. Results can be obtained when S has characteristic points, or is a characteristic manifold.

14 LOCAL EXISTENCE THEOREM FOR THE FUNDAMENTAL SOLUTION

The general existence theorem for the solution of the Cauchy problem, founded on a priori estimates, based on "energy" inequality and essentially due to Leray [1], proves the existence of a fundamental solution of hyperbolic linear systems of any order on a manifold. In the case of second-order equations, there are several methods of constructing explicitly these fundamental solution.[9] The result is as follows:

Theorem. If L is a hyperbolic operator on V_n (with C^∞ coefficient), every point $x \in V_n$ has an open neighborhood K such that L has a fundamental solution in $\mathscr{E}_K{}^- \cap \mathscr{E}_K{}^+$

---

[9] For an even number of dimensions a convenient one, which originates from Sobolev uses the fact that the wave operator in flat space has a fundamental solution which support on the characteristic cone (*cf.* [5]).

Global Existence Theorem for the Fundamental Solutions

1. Extension of a local fundamental solution by the properties of support:

Suppose we have constructed a fundamental solution in the open set $\mathscr{E}_Q^{\;-} \cap \mathscr{E}_P^{\;+}$ (P and Q compact subsets of V_n), $E^-(x, x')$ [analogous reasoning would hold for $E^+(x, x')$].

We define the extension of $E^-(x, x')$, which we will still denote by $E^-(x, x')$, distribution on $V_n \times V_n$ which will be a fundamental solution in $\tilde{D} \times \tilde{D}'$ with

$$D = \mathscr{E}_{\tilde{Q}}^{\;-} \cup C\mathscr{E}_P^{\;+} \qquad D' = \mathscr{E}_{\tilde{P}}^{\;+}$$

where $\tilde{D}$ means open set arbitrarily near D, with closure belonging to D

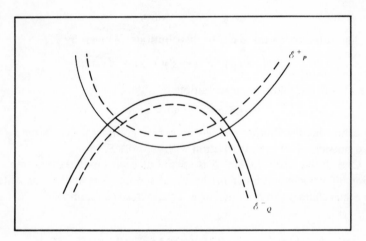

FIGURE 7

(Fig. 7). In setting, if $\varphi, \psi \in C_0^{\infty}(V_n)$

$$E^-(x, x'),\, \varphi(x)\psi(x') = \langle E^-(x, x'),\, \bar{\varphi}(x)\bar{\psi}(x')\rangle,$$

$$\bar{\varphi} = \varphi\theta,\, \bar{\psi} = \psi\phi$$

where ϕ denotes a given C^{∞} function such that

$$\phi = 1 \text{ on } \mathscr{E}_{\tilde{P}}^{\;-} \cap \mathscr{E}^{\;+},\, \phi = 0 \text{ on } \tilde{C}(\mathscr{E}_Q^{\;-} \cap \mathscr{E}_P^{\;+})$$

we have

$$L_{x'} E^-(x, x') = \delta(x, x') \text{ on } \tilde{D} \times \tilde{D}'$$

and $E^-(x, x')$ has, for every x, a future compact support (in $\tilde{\mathscr{E}}_x^{\;-}$).

2. Construction of a fundamental solution on an open set not contained in $D \times D'$:

Suppose that D is not identical to V_n. The set $CD = \mathscr{P}_1$ is a closed subset of $\mathscr{E}_P{}^+$. It is therefore past-compact and has a spatial boundary S. Take a point $x \in S$; there exist compact neighborhoods (with nonempty interiors) Q_1 of x such that the local fundamental solution exists in $\mathring{\mathscr{E}}_{Q_1} \cap \mathring{\mathscr{E}}_{P_1}^+$ (*cf.* §14), where $\mathscr{P} = C(C\mathscr{E}_P{}^+ \cup \mathring{\mathscr{E}}_Q{}^-)$, and $(\mathring{\mathscr{E}}_{Q_1}^- \cap \mathring{\mathscr{E}}_{P_1}^+)$ does not belong to D (since x was a point on its boundary) (Fig. 8).

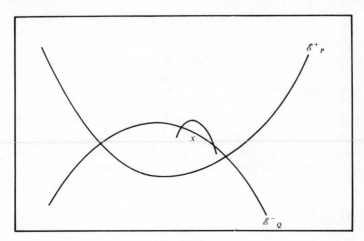

FIGURE 8

The extension construction 1 gives a distribution

$$E_1{}^-(x, x') \text{ on } V_n \times V_n$$

which is a fundamental solution in $\tilde{D} \times \tilde{D}_1'$.

$$D_1 = \mathring{\mathscr{E}}^-{}_1 \cap C\mathring{\mathscr{E}}_{P_1}^+ \qquad D_1' = \mathring{\mathscr{E}}_{P_1}^+$$

$$L_x E_1{}^-(x, x') = \delta(x, x') \text{ in } \tilde{D}_1 \times \tilde{D}_1'$$

Remark. We have $D_1 \neq D$, $\tilde{D}' - D_1' = \tilde{D}$

3. Piecing together of the two fundamental solutions:

We will construct a distribution $\widehat{E}^-(x, x')$ on $V_n \times V_n$, which will be a fundamental solution in $(\widehat{D \cup D_1}) \times \tilde{D}'$.

Define $\tilde{E}^-(x, x')$ by the Volterra convolution:

$$\tilde{E}^-(x, x') = \int_{V_n} E^-(x'', x')k(x'', x)$$

where we set on $V_n \times V_n$

$$k(k'', k) = \{\delta(k'', k) - L_{x''} E_1{}^-(x, x''')\}f$$

where f is a C^∞ function such that

$$f = 0 \text{ on } \tilde{C}(\tilde{D} \cup \tilde{D}_1)$$

$$f = 1 \text{ on } \tilde{D} \cup \tilde{D}_1$$

We note that by

$$\delta(x'', x) - L_x E_1^-(x, x'') = 0 \text{ on } \tilde{D}_1 \times \tilde{D}_1'$$

and get, since $\tilde{C}D_1'' \cup \tilde{D}_1 \subset \tilde{D}$

$$L_{x'} \tilde{E}^-(x, x') = k(x', x)$$

The distribution on $V_n \times V_n$

$$E_1^-(x, x') + \tilde{E}^-(x, x')$$

is a fundamental solution in $\widetilde{D \cup D} \times \tilde{D}'$ with future compact support for all x.

4. The preceding construction applied recurrently gives a fundamental solution in a strictly increasing sequence of sets, which enables one to prove the existence of a fundamental solution on $V_n \times \mathscr{E}_{P'}^+$, with the required property of support, when P is an arbitrary past-compact set.

REFERENCES

1. J. Leray, Hyperbolic Partial Differential Equations, Mimeographed notes, Princeton, 1952.

2. A. Lichnerowicz, *Propagateurs et commutateurs en relativité générale*, Publications I.H.E.S., No. 10, 1961.

3. A. Marchaud, *Compositio matematica*, Vol. 3, 1936, pp. 89–127.

4. Y. Bruhat, Equations ultrahyperboliques à coefficients variables, *Colloque Equations aux dériveés partielles*, C.N.R.S., 1956.

5. Y. Bruhat, In: *Gravitation, an introduction to current research*, edited by L. Witten; J. Wiley, 1962.

5a. Y. Bruhat, "Sur la théorie des propagateurs," *Annali di matematica* LXIV (1964), series IV, pp. 191–228.

6. S. Kobayashi and K. Nomizu, *Foundations of Differential Geometry*, Interscience.

7. R. Bott, in this volume, Chapter XVIII.

8. A. Lichnerowicz, Topics on Space-Times, in this volume, Chapter V.

9. R. Penrose, An Analysis of the Structure of Space-Time Mimeographed Notes, Princeton, 1966.

10. S. Hawking, "The Occurrence of Singularities in cosmology" I, II, III, *Proc. Roy, Soc. A.* **294**, 577 (1966); A295, 490 (1966).

11. B. DeWitt, "Quantum Theory" in *Relativity, Group and Topology*, Les Houches, 1964, edited by B. DeWitt and C. DeWitt, Gordon and Breach.

V

Topics on Space-Times

ANDRÉ LICHNEROWICZ

In this lecture, my primary purpose is to promote fruitful discussions between mathematicians and physicists who have an interest in relativity. I will give a survey of notions and questions rather than particular results—and my hope is that *you* will contribute something to the difficult construction of a good axiomatic approach to general relativity.

I SPACE-TIME AND ORIENTATIONS

1 Space-Time

(a) We consider here only *paracompact* differentiable manifolds. A manifold is called paracompact if any open covering of the manifold admits a refinement which is a locally finite open covering of the manifold.

A space-time is a connected (paracompact) differentiable manifold V_4 of dimension 4, with a *Lorentz* "*metric*." A Lorentz metric ds^2 is defined by a differentiable, symmetric, covariant 2-tensor g of signature $+ - - - -$. If T_x is the vector space tangent in x to V_4, the Lorentz metric defines, by the equation $ds^2 = 0$, a convex cone C_x in T_x. We have thus on V_4 a field of cones. A direction is timelike if $ds^2 > 0$, spacelike if $ds^2 < 0$. The affine space T_x admits a structure of Minkowski space.

For the moment, we assume that the differentiable structure of V_4 is (C^2, C^4 by pieces): in the intersection of the domains of two systems of local coordinates, the coordinates of a point x in the first system are functions of class (C^2, C^4 by pieces), with a nonvanishing Jacobian, of the coordinates of the same point x in the second system. We can assume now that the metric g is (C^1, C^3 by pieces): in admissible coordinates

$$ds^2 = g_{\alpha\beta} \, dx^\alpha \, dx^\beta \qquad (\alpha, \beta = 0, 1, 2, 3)$$

where the components $g_{\alpha\beta}$ are functions of class (C^1, C^3 by pieces).

(b) The main element for the physics is the principal fiber bundle $E(V_4)$ defined by the set of the orthonormalized frames $y = \{l_0, l_A\}(A = 1, 2, 3)$, with

$$l_\alpha l_\beta = \eta_{\alpha\beta} \qquad \eta_{\alpha\beta} = 0 \text{ for } \alpha \neq \beta \qquad \eta_{00} = 1 \qquad \eta_{AA} = -1$$

The structural group of $E(V_4)$ is the complete Lorentz group $L(4)$. With respect to the frames $y \varepsilon E(V_4)$, the metric can be written on an open neighborhood of V_4:

$$ds^2 = g_{\alpha\beta} \theta^\alpha \theta^\beta = (\theta^0)^2 - \sum_A (\theta^A)^2$$

where the θ^α are pfaffian forms and where $g_{\alpha\beta} = \eta_{\alpha\beta}$

2 Lorentz Group and Orientations

(a) It is well known that the Lorentz group has four connected components. If $A = (A_\alpha^{\lambda'}) \varepsilon L(4)$, we will study which component A belongs to. We call the *total signature* ρ_A of A a number equal to ± 1, according to the sign of $\det A$. The *time-signature* ρ_A of A is ± 1 according to the sign of $A_0^{0'}$. The *space-signature* of A, σ_A, is the product $\varepsilon_A \rho_A$. We obtain thus the four components:

$$L_0(4) : \varepsilon_A = 1 \qquad \rho_A = 1 \qquad L_1(4) : \varepsilon_A = -1 \qquad \rho_A = 1$$

$$L_2(4) : \varepsilon_A = -1 \qquad \rho_A = -1 \qquad L_3(4) : \varepsilon_A = 1 \qquad \rho_A = -1$$

(b) It is now necessary to study the number of connected components of $E(V_4)$. This question is strictly connected with the existence of the following geometrical objects:

An orientation—or *total orientation*—of V_4 is a pseudoscalar ε of square 1. If the manifold V_4 is *orientable*, that is, if such a geometrical object exists, it is defined by one component $\varepsilon_y = \pm 1$ such that, if $y = y'A(A\varepsilon L(4)$:

$$\varepsilon_y = \varepsilon_{y'}\varepsilon_A$$

It is clear that V_4 has at most two total orientations, ε and $-\varepsilon$.

We chose an orientation ε: Let us consider a covering of V_4 by neighborhoods provided with orthonormalized frames. The set of the local forms

$$\varepsilon\theta^0 \wedge \theta^1 \wedge \theta^2 \wedge \theta^3$$

defines onto V_4 a global 4-form, the volume element of V_4 for the considered orientation.

(c) A *time-orientation* ρ is defined onto V_4, with respect to the frames $y\varepsilon E(V_4)$, by one component $\rho_y = \pm 1$ such that if $y = y'A$, we have

$$\rho_y = \rho_{y'}\rho_A$$

V_4 has at most two time-orientations, ρ and $-\rho$.

We choose a time-orientation ρ. A vector $l_0(l_0{}^2 = 1)$ in x is oriented toward the future (resp. the past) if the component of ρ with respect to the orthonormalized frames (l_0, l_A) is 1 (resp. -1). The time-orientation ρ allows one to distinguish onto V_4, in a continuous way, the half-cones of C_x: future half-cone $C_x{}^+$ and past half-cone $C_x{}^-$. If a manifold is time-orientable, we have two fields of half-cones. The data ε and ρ define on V_4 a *spatial orientation* $\sigma = \varepsilon\rho$. These various orientations play a part in the definition of P and T.

3 Results Concerning the Existence of Lorentz Metrics and Time-Orientations

Now, I will recall the main results concerning the situation.

(a) *Every (paracompact) differentiable manifold admits a Riemannian metric.*

(b) If we consider the timelike eigen-direction of a Lorentz metric, with respect to a Riemannian metric, we define a direction field onto the manifold. Conversely, if a manifold admits a direction field, it is possible to construct a Lorentz metric such that these directions are timelike with respect to the metric. We obtain:

(i) *A differentiable manifold admits a Lorentz metric if and only if it admits a direction field and these directions can be choosen timelike.*

(ii) *Each space-time admits systems of time-lines. If the space-time is time-orientable, it admits systems of oriented time-lines.*

(c) *Every noncompact manifold admits oriented direction field and thus Lorentz metrics with time-orientations.*

(d) *A compact manifold admits Lorentz metrics if and only if the Euler–Poincaré characteristic χ is zero. If such is the case, there exists oriented direction fields and thus Lorentz metrics with time-orientations* [6].

(e) *But conversely it is known that a given orientable space-time V_4 can be non-time-orientable* [2].

We are thus led to ask some questions:

(1) Must a space-time be orientable, or time-orientable, or both? It appears perhaps that the existence of a time-orientation is physically necessary. *I assume this existence* in the following section.

(2) We have seen that every space-time admits global systems of time-lines. A *spacelike section* of V_4 is a regular spacelike hypersurface Σ such that every time-line of a global system of time-lines cuts Σ in one point and only one. But, in general, a space-time does not admit space-like sections. Is their existence physically necessary?

(3) For some theorems, the existence of a fibration of V_4 by a system of time-lines is a convenient assumption. However, in many cases, physicists and cosmologists assume, explicitly or implicitly, that V_4 is a product $V_3 \times R$. Is not this assumption generally too strong?

II DIFFERENTIABLE STRUCTURE AND FIELD EQUATIONS

4 Cauchy Problem for the Einstein Equations

(a) Exactly as in the Riemannian case, the Lorentz metric of V_4 defines a linear connection ω, without torsion, such that

$$\nabla g = 0$$

where ∇ is the operator of covariant derivation in this connection ω.

Let $R_{\alpha\beta}$ be the Ricci tensor of the Lorentz metric, $S_{\alpha\beta}$ the Einstein tensor of V_4 defined by

$$S_{\alpha\beta} = R_{\alpha\beta} - \tfrac{1}{2} g_{\alpha\beta} R \quad \text{with} \quad \nabla_\alpha S_\beta{}^\alpha = 0 \tag{4.1}$$

Equation (4.1) follows from the Bianchi identities for the curvature tensor. In general relativity, ds^2 satisfies the Einstein equations:

$$S_{\alpha\beta} = \chi T_{\alpha\beta} \tag{4.2}$$

where $T_{\alpha\beta}$ is the energy tensor corresponding to some energy distribution. In a domain which is empty, $T_{\alpha\beta} = 0$ and we have the so-called exterior system

$$S_{\alpha\beta} = 0 \qquad \text{or} \qquad R_{\alpha\beta} = 0$$

(b) In an open neighborhood Ω of V_4, let us consider a local space-like hypersurface Σ defined by the equation $\phi = 0$ (with ϕ of class C^2, C^4 by pieces). We adopt local coordinates such that $x^0 = \phi$ in Ω; then we have $g^{oo} > 0$.

We consider, for simplicity, the exterior Einstein system. Cauchy data onto Σ are the "potentials" $g_{\alpha\beta}$ and their first derivatives $\partial_0 g_{\alpha\beta}$. The Einstein system is equivalent to the set of the two systems:

$$R_{AB} \equiv \tfrac{1}{2}g^{oo}\partial_{oo}g_{AB} + \Phi_{AB} = 0 \qquad (A, B = 1, 2, 3) \tag{4.3}$$

$$S_0{}^\alpha \equiv \psi_0{}^\alpha = 0 \tag{4.4}$$

where, onto Σ, the Φ's and ψ's depend only on the Cauchy data and their first derivatives along Σ. According to (4.1), every solution of (4.3) satisfying (4.4) onto Σ, everywhere satisfies this system.

(c) g^{oo} being $\neq 0$, the system (4.3) gives the values on Σ of the second derivatives $\partial_{oo}g_{AB}$ and these derivatives are continuous across Σ. In the system (4.3), (4.4) the second derivatives $\partial_{oo}g_{\alpha o}$ are absent ("nonsignificative" derivatives).

We can analyze this phenomenon: it is possible to change in Ω the local coordinates, according to the formulas

$$x^{\alpha'} = x^\alpha + \frac{(x^0)^3}{6}\{\psi^\alpha(x^A) + \varepsilon^\alpha(x^\beta)\}$$

where $\varepsilon^\alpha \to 0$ when $x^0 \to 0$. The values of a point x of Σ and the values of the Cauchy data in x are invariant by this change. It is the same thing for the values of the "significative" derivatives $\partial_{oo}g_{AB}$. But it is possible, by the choice of the ψ^α, to give arbitrary values to the "nonsignificative" derivatives $\partial_{oo}g_{\alpha o}$. *Our differentiable structure is compatible with the choice of two different systems of ψ^α for both sides of Σ;* we can thus create or destroy discontinuities of the nonsignificative derivatives, discontinuities which are then physically meaningless. Thus, the assumed differentiable structure is strictly connected with the covariance of the field equations.

(d) It is possible to obtain discontinuities of the significative derivatives—or, equivalently, of the curvature tensor—if and only if $g^{oo} = 0$. We see that *the characteristics of the Einstein equations*—or, in another terminology, the gravitational waves—are the hypersurfaces tangent in each point x to the main cone C_x.

It is well known that we can determine precisely the differentiable structure of V_4 in a C^h-structure, where h is sufficiently large, and it is not absurd to consider Lorentz metrics which are (C^1, C^{h-1} by pieces). But it is necessary that we know that *this precision is physically meaningless.* The introduction of new changes of coordinates which are (C^2, C^4 by pieces) preserves all the physical properties (discontinuities of the curvature tensor for instance) of the space-time.

(e) If we consider gravitational shock waves, that is to say, cases where g is only (C^0, C^1 by pieces), Mrs. Choquet-Bruhat and Taub have proved that the situation is similar to the one which concerns ordinary waves: it is remarkable that the significative derivatives $\partial_o g_{AB}$ can be discontinuous only across the characteristics Σ, these discontinuities satisfying four convenient conditions of continuity.

III   COMPLETENESS AND GLOBAL HYPERBOLIC MANIFOLDS

5   The Mapping μ for the Arcs

(a) Let V_4 be a space-time; it admits the canonical connection ω.   If $\gamma : t \in [0, 1] \to x(t) \in V_4$ is a differentiable oriented arc issued from a point a of V_4, we will define a mapping μ of γ into the Minkowski space T_a tangent in a to V_4 (development).

Let us consider an arc $\Gamma : t \in [0, 1] \to y(t)$ of the fiber bundle $E(V_4)$ such that $p\Gamma = \gamma$.   We note $(\bar{x}, \bar{y})$ a frame of T_a, where $\bar{x}$ is the origin of the frame and where $\bar{y}$ is a base (ε_α) of T_a considered as a matrix.   We introduce the one-parameter sequence of frames of T_a satisfying the differential system

$$\frac{d\bar{x}}{dt} = \bar{y}\theta\left(\frac{dx}{dt}\right) \qquad d\bar{y} = \bar{y}\omega\left(\frac{dy}{dt}\right) \tag{5.1}$$

with the initial conditions $\bar{x}(0) = a$, $\bar{y}(0)$.   Here $\theta = (\theta^\alpha)$ and $\omega = (\omega_\beta{}^\alpha)$.

It is easy to see that the arc $\bar{y}$ of T_a defined by $t \in [0, 1] \to \bar{x}(t) \in T_a$ depends only on the given arc γ of V_4 and not on the arc Γ of the fiber bundle.

(b) By definition, the arc $\bar{y}$ is the image of the arc γ by the development μ. The arc γ is geodesic if and only if $\bar{y} = \mu(\gamma)$ is a line segment.

6   Completeness of a Space-Time

(a) An oriented $\mathscr{C}^1$ arc γ of a space-time is called *weakly timelike* if the positive half-tangent to γ at each point x is timelike or isotropic, but into or onto $\mathscr{C}_x{}^+$.   If we compose such arcs, we obtain weakly timelike piecewise $\mathscr{C}^1$ arcs ($pW\mathscr{C}_-{}^1$ arcs).

(b) A space-time V_4 is called *complete* if for all V_4 and for all oriented arc $\bar{y}$ of the Minkowski space tangent in a, there exists an arc γ issued from a, such that $\mu(\gamma) = \bar{y}$.   The space-time is called *t-complete* if the property is true only for the arcs $\bar{y}$ which are *weakly timelike*.

A space-time V_4 is called *geodesically complete* if for all $a \in V_4$ and for all oriented segment $\bar{y}$ of the Minkowski space tangent in a, there exists a geodesic arc γ issued from a, such that $\mu(\gamma) = \bar{y}$.   It is equivalent to say that each geodesic arc of V_4 can be extended to arbitrary values of the affine parameter. The space-time is called *geodesically t-complete* if the property is true only for the oriented segments $\bar{\gamma}$ which are timelike or isotropic.

We have trivially:

$$\begin{array}{ccc} \text{complete} & \longrightarrow & \text{geod. complete} \\ \downarrow & & \downarrow \\ \text{t-complete} & \longrightarrow & \text{geod. t-complete} \end{array}$$

I do not know nontrivial connections among these four notions.

7 Globally Hyperbolic Manifold

(a) We introduce now the *closure* $\mathscr{T}$ of the set of the weakly timelike $p.w.\mathscr{C}_{-}^{1}$ arcs, for the compact-open topology on the space of the continuous arcs of V_4. Each element γ of $\mathscr{T}$ is called now a *weakly timelike arc*. Such an arc is rectifiable for an arbitrary Riemannian metric of V_4.

If K is a set of V_4, let $A^+(K)$ be the set of the *weakly timelike arcs* starting at the points x of K in the future of x. *The future $E^+(K)$ is the set of the points of V_4 which correspond to the arcs of $A^+(K)$. We have similar definitions for $A^-(K)$ and for *the past $E^-(K)$ of K. The emission $E(K)$ of K is the union of the future $E^+(K)$ and of the past $E^-(K)$.

We denote $\partial E^+(K)$, $\partial E^-(K)$, $\partial E(K)$ the boundaries of $E^+(K)$, $E^-(K)$, $E^-(K)$. It follows from results of Leray and Mrs. Choquet-Bruhat that if $x \in \partial E^+(K)$ and $y \in E^+(K)$, each weakly timelike arc γ_0 joining x and y is a *null-geodesic arc* and that all the points of γ_0 are contained in $\partial E^+(K)$.

Then definitions and results are available for $K = \{z\}$; $\partial E(z) = \Gamma_z$ is, by definition, the *characteristic conoid* corresponding to $z \in V_4$. In the neighborhood of z, it is generated by null-geodesic arcs issued from z. But Γ_z is globally distinct from the set of the points of V_4 defined by the null-geodesics issued from z.

(b) According to Leray and Mrs. Choquet-Bruhat, a space-time V_4 is called *globally hyperbolic* if for all x, $y \in V_4$, *the set of arcs $A^+(x) \cap A^-(y)$ is compact in $\mathscr{T}$. If this condition is satisfied, the set of points of V_4 defined by $E^+(x) \cap E^-(y)$ is compact in V_4. This condition implies that a timelike arc cannot be closed. We assume now the global hyperbolicity.

A set K is called *compact toward the past* if, for all $x \in V_4$, the set $A^+(K) \cap A^-(x)$ is compact in $\mathscr{T}$; $E^+(K)$ and all closed subsets of $E^+(K)$ are then also compact toward the past. The set of points of V_4 defined by $E^+(K) \cap E^-(x)$ is compact in V_4.

Leray and Mrs. Choquet-Bruhat have proved the important following lemma: if K is *compact toward the past* and if K is *compact, $A^+(K) \cap A^-(K')$ is compact in $\mathscr{T}$.

(c) The interest of the assumption of global hyperbolicity is to ensure the existence of elementary solutions for the corresponding *linear hyperbolic differential operators*. If T is a p-tensor of V_4 we set

$$(\Delta T)_{\alpha_1 \cdots \alpha_p} = -\nabla^\rho \nabla_\rho T_{\alpha_1 \cdots \alpha_p}$$

Let C be a field of linear operators on the p-tensors and B a field of linear mappings on the $(p + 1)$-tensors into the p-tensors. Let us consider, for instance, the linear hyperbolic differential operator

$$LT = \Delta T + B^\rho \nabla_\rho T + CT$$

Under the assumption of global hyperbolicity, there exists for L two elementary kernels $E^{(p)+}(x, x')$, that is, two bi-p-tensor distributions satisfying

$$L_x^* E^{(p)\pm}(x, x') = \delta^{(p)}(x, x')$$

and which have, for each x', their supports, respectively, in $E^+(x')$ and $E^-(x')$; L^* is here the adjoint operator and $\delta^{(p)}$ the Dirac bi-p-tensor defined by

$$\langle \delta^{(p)}(x, x'), T(x') \rangle = T(x)$$

8 Homotopy

(a) If γ is a weakly timelike arc joining x and y, it defines a class of homotopy $C(x, y)$—a set of the weakly timelike arcs joining x and y and which are homotopic to γ; $C(x, y)$ is a closed subset of $A^+(x) \cap A^-(y)$. For given x and y, the set of the classes $C(x, y)$ is enumerable.

For a globally hyperbolic manifold, each class $C(x, y)$ is compact and, for given x, y, the number of the classes $C(x, y)$ is *finite*.

(b) It is perhaps interesting to study hyperbolic manifolds V_4 satisfying the following assumption: V_4 is called *weakly globally hyperbolic if each class $C(x, y)$ of homotopy defined by a weakly timelike arc is compact in $\mathscr{T}$.*

Let γ_0 be a strictly timelike geodesic arc sufficiently small joining x and y. It is easy to see that the length of γ_0 is always greater than or equal to the length of an arbitrary weakly timelike arc joining x and y. Otherwise, the length is an upper semicontinuous function on $\mathscr{T}$.

It follows that, if V_4 is *weakly globally hyperbolic*, each class of homotopy $C(x, y)$ contains *a geodesic arc which gives the maximum of the lengths of the arcs of the class.* In particular, two points of V_4 joined by a timelike arc can be joined by a timelike geodesic arc.

IV SPIN-STRUCTURE

9 Notion of Spin-Structure

(a) Let V_4 be a space-time admitting a total orientation ε and a time-orientation ρ. We denote $E_0(V_4)$ the principal fiber bundle on V_4 defined by the orthonormalized frames y such that $\varepsilon_y = 1$, $\rho_y = 1$. The structural group of $E_0(V_4)$ is the connected Lorentz group $L_0(V_4)$. If $y = \{l_\alpha\}$, $y' = \{l_\lambda'\}$ are two elements of $E_0(V_4)$, we have $l_\alpha = l_\lambda' A_\alpha^{\lambda'}$ or, in terms of matrices,

$$y = y'A$$

where $A \varepsilon L_0(4)$.

(b) Let $(\mathrm{Spin}_0(4), p)$ be the universal covering group of $L_0(4)$. The kernel N of $p : \mathrm{Spin}_0(4) \to L_0(4)$ is isomorphic to Z_2.

We say that V_4 admits a spin-structure if there exists on V_4 a principal fiber bundle $S_0(4)$, with $\mathrm{Spin}_0(4)$ as structural group, which is a 2-covering of $E_0(V_4)$, such that the restriction of the projection to the fibers of $S_0(V_4)$ is a 2-covering of the fibers of $E_0(V_4)$, the following diagram being commutative:

$$
\begin{array}{ccc}
\mathrm{Spin}_0(4) & \longrightarrow & S_0(V_4) \\
{\scriptstyle p} \downarrow & & \downarrow {\scriptstyle \bar{p}} \\
L_0(4) & \longrightarrow & E_0(V_4)
\end{array}
$$

We will say that $S_0(V_4)$ is deduced from $E_0(V_4)$ by extension of the structural group.

10 Existence of a Spin-Structure

(a) In the case of a Riemmannian manifold, we have a similar definition of the notion of spin-structure. Haefliger has proved that an orientable compact Riemannian manifold admits a spin-structure if and only if *the second Whitney characteristic class of the manifold is null.*

I will sketch a simple proof of the theorem of Haefliger in the present context. Let us consider the exact sequence of groups

$$0 \longrightarrow Z_2 \xrightarrow{\;i\;} \mathrm{Spin}_0(4) \xrightarrow{\;p\;} L_0(4) \longrightarrow 0$$

The sequence is exact, that is to say, the kernel of each mapping coincides with the image by the previous mapping: here the inclusion map i of Z_2 in $\mathrm{Spin}_0(4)$ is an isomorphism onto N; p admits the image N as kernel and $L_0(4)$ is the image of $\mathrm{Spin}_0(4)$ by p.

It is well known that such a sequence induces an exact sequence of sheafs of local cross sections. With usual notations, we have

$$0 \longrightarrow Z_2 \xrightarrow{\;i\;} \underline{\mathrm{Spin}_0(4)} \xrightarrow{\;p\;} \underline{L_0(4)} \longrightarrow 0$$

It follows the exact cohomology sequence

$$\cdots \longrightarrow H^1(V_4, \underline{\mathrm{Spin}_0(4)}) \xrightarrow{\;p^*\;} H^1(V_4, \underline{L_0(4)}) \xrightarrow{\;\delta^*\;} H^2(V_4, Z_2) \longrightarrow \cdots$$

where δ^* corresponds to the coboundary operator; $H^1(V_4, \underline{\mathrm{Spin}_0(4)})$ is isomorphic to the set of the equivalence classes of the principal fiber bundles on V_4, with $\text{Spin}_0(4)$ as the structural group. Likewise, $H^1(V_4, L_0(4))$ is isomorphic to the set of the equivalence classes of the principal fiber bundles on V_4, with $L_0(4)$ as structural group.

Let $E \in H^1(V_4, L_0(4))$ be the element corresponding to the given fiber bundle $E_0(V_4)$. There exists a corresponding spin-structure if and only if there exists an element $S \in H^1(V_4, \text{Spin}_0(4))$ such that

$$E = p^*S$$

The sequence being exact, we see that it is the case if and only if E belongs to the kernel of δ^*:

$$\delta^*E = 0$$

(b) In the case of an orientable compact Riemannian manifold V_n, we substitute $SO(n)$ to $L_0(4)$ and δ^*E defines the second Whitney class $C_2(V_4)$. We obtain thus the result of Haefliger.

In the case of a *compact space-time* with a total orientation and a time-orientation, δ^*E still defines a characteristic class which can be identified *with the second Whitney class.*

In the case of a *noncompact space-time the situation is the same*, except for the supports. More complicated results are obtained in the nonorientable cases (Bott).

REFERENCES

1. A. Avez, *Ann. Inst. Fourier* (1963) p. 105–190.

2. Y. Choquet-Bruhat, Séminaire de Physique mathématique, Collége de France Mimeogr. 1963.

3. Leray, Hyperbolic Differential Systems, Mimeogr. Notes, Institute of Advanced Study, Princeton.

4. A. Lichnerowicz, Propagateurs et commutateurs en relativité générale, Publ. Math. Inst. Hautes Etudes No. 10, Paris, 1961. Théories relativistes de la gravitation, Masson, Paris, 1954.

5. L. Markus, *Ann. Math* **62**, p. 411–417 (1955).

6. N. Steenrod, *Topology of fiber Bundles*, Princeton Univ. Press, 1951.

VI

Relativistic Fluids in Cosmology[1]

CHARLES W. MISNER

The present state of the universe seems to correspond to a pressureless dust of galaxies or galactic clusters which is a rather trivial fluid. However, there are reasons to think that in the past much more interesting fluids (and nonfluids) were significant.

The most crucial point of theory is the set of " singularity theorems " of Penrose and Hawking. The crucial observations are the Hubble expansion and the recent observations of the $3°K$ microwave radiation which apparently fills the universe.

Following up Penrose's brilliant insight (1965, *Phys. Rev. Letters* **14**, 57), Hawking has formulated and proven several theorems (1966, *Proc. Roy. Soc.* **A295**, 490, also 1967, *Proc. Roy. Soc.* in press) to the effect that all solutions of the Einstein equations which have a gross resemblance to the currently popular cosmological models have a singularity some finite time in the past. For example, one such theorem states that the following hypotheses are inconsistent: (a) M is a C^∞ pseudo-Riemannian 4-manifold of Lorentz signature, (b) M is timelike complete so all timelike geodesics can be continued to infinite proper length, (c) the Ricci tensor satisfies $R_{\mu\nu} u^\mu u^\nu \geq 0$ for all timelike vectors u^μ, (d) M contains a compact spacelike hypersurface Σ, (e) the normal n^μ to Σ satisfies $n^\mu_{;\mu} > 0$ everywhere on Σ. The Einstein

[1] No text of the lecture actually presented at the Battelle Rencontres, " Mathematical Problems in Chaotic Cosmology," was supplied. The following is the text of a talk given in Paris at the College de France on 19 June 1967 at " Colloque international du Centre National de la Recherche Scientifique, 'Fluides et Champ Gravitationnel en Relativité Générale,'" which covered some of the same ideas, and is reproduced here with the kind permission of the C.N.R.S.

Supported in part by NASA Grant NSG436 and the U.K. Science Research Council.

equations figure only in the weak hypothesis (c), while (d) and (e) provide the tie-in to some ideas of an expanding universe. The theorems of which this is a sample appear to me to be the most important development on the theoretical side of gravity physics since Einstein formulated general relativity. They are rigorous global theorems about solutions of the full nonlinear Einstein equations which state unexpected results of great physical interest. Although the theorem quoted above allows one to conclude that solutions of the Einstein equations for fluids satisfying $\varepsilon + 3p \geqslant 0$ determined by Cauchy data on an everywhere expanding closed initial hypersurface contain incomplete timelike geodesics, most of the theorems are not so specific about the nature of the singularity, and would allow for some failure of causality as an alternative to incompleteness. But even incompleteness does not imply infinite densities or infinite curvature as one knows from examples (Misner and Taub, *J.E.T.P.* 1968), so the nature of the singularity one must expect remains relatively unknown and is an important theoretical problem of current interest. Some rough categories for possible types of singularities are

(a) causality failure,
(b) isolated or "almost hidden" singularity,
(c) total singularity.

The presence of closed timelike curves might characterize the first type, and I would guess that this sort of singularity is very unstable and is easily converted by small perturbations into one involving infinite curvature. An example of the second type of singularity, where almost all geodesics are complete, has been given by Carter (1967, to be published). Because nothing is known about the nature of the typical singularity, and because it leads to interesting consequences, I will pursue the assumption that the typical singularity is "total" in that all the matter in the universe is processed by an initial singularity involving infinite density and infinite irregularity. This provides a starting point for a theory of "Chaotic Cosmology."

The main theoretical problems for Chaotic Cosmology are as follows:

(i) To formulate statistical methods of describing the initial data near the singularity.
(ii) To understand the nature of "horizons" in irregular expanding universes.
(iii) To "prove the cosmological principle."

The first point here is just another statement of the problem of understanding the nature of the singularity which the Einstein equations require, but a statement prejudiced toward an answer in language and content related to theories of turbulence. The second point emphasizes that it may take considerable time after the singularity before two different pieces of matter have time to influence each other through causal signals, so the evolution of disturbances on scales larger than the current horizon will be very different from that on smaller scales. The third point is a challenge to see whether enough well-founded physical processes can be invoked by the theory to allow the interactions (which take place within the horizon at any time) to modify the initially singular chaos in a way which will result in that homogeneity and isotropy of space at the present time which has been the starting assumption for Robertson–Walker cosmological models. At very high temperatures neutrinos are very effective in producing homogeneity and isotropy (Misner 1967, *Nature* **214**, 40), but on a very small scale involving only a fraction of a solar mass' worth of baryons. At lower temperatures when the horizons are larger, I expect shock waves to form from the large but smooth density and velocity gradients which would be noticed as the horizon expanded to allow one region to interact with a neighboring region which developed from different random initial conditions. Taub (*Phys. Rev.* **74** (1948) 328) has given an analytic description of the development of a large amplitude sound wave into a shock in special relativity, and it would be interesting to see the corresponding solution in general relativity as a modification of the $k = 0$ radiation-filled Robertson–Walker universe. These shocks could be effective in dissipating irregularities as long as the universe remained radiation-dominated and while photon mean-free paths remained too short to make simple viscosity very effective for dissipating large scale irregularities.

Nonfluids also play an important role in Chaotic Cosmology. Below about 10^{10} °K neutrinos are collisionless so no mechanism exists to ensure that their momentum distribution, and hence their pressure, is isotropic. If one assumes homogeneous collisionless radiation then its properties are relatively simple and similar to those of an elastic solid. Using this model, and a viscous fluid at higher temperatures, I have been able to show that arbitrary initial anisotropy in a *homogeneous* expanding universe will be reduced to a low level, below the stringent observational 0.2% limit in the case of the models considered (Misner, *Ap. J.*, Feb. 1968). This is an encouraging success for Chaotic Cosmology since I believe no other explanation for the isotropy of the blackbody radiation has been proposed. But it would be very important to be able to consider inhomogeneous collisionless radiation as well. This is a relatively simple, ideal medium, and since collisionless neutrinos probably account for from 45% to 65% of the mass density in the universe between 10^{10} °K and about 10^5 °K, considerable effort toward understanding its properties and behavior would be justified. Note also that because collisionless radiation can support transverse shear stresses, it interacts directly with gravitational radiation in a way which fluids cannot. It is possible, for instance, that gravitational waves propagating through collisionless radiation would travel at speeds less than light, just as do electromagnetic waves traveling through a plasma or other polarizable medium.

REFERENCES

1. C. W. Misner, "The Isotropy of the Universe," *Astrophys. J.*, Feb. 1968.

2. R. W. Michie, "On the Growth of Condensations in an Expanding Universe, "*Astrophys. J.*, 1968 (to be published).

3. S. W. Hawking, "The Occurrence of Singularities in Cosmology, III, " *Proc. Roy. Soc.*, **A300**, No. 1461, Aug. 1967.

4. C. W. Misner, *Nature* **214** (1967) 40–51.

5. C. W. Misner, *Phys. Rev. Lett.* **19** (1967) 533–5.

6. J. Silk, *Nature* **215** (1967) 1155–6.

7. E. R. Harrison, *Phys. Rev. Lett.* **18** (1967) 1011–3.

8. A. G. Doroshkevich, Ya. B. Zel'dovich, and I. D. Novikov, *ZhETF Pis'ma* (JETP Letters) **5** (1967) 119–121 (96–98).

VII

Structure of Space-Time*

R. PENROSE

1 INTRODUCTION

According to present-day theory, all the phenomena of physics take place within the framework of a certain differentiable manifold referred to as the *space-time continuum*. Our familiarity with this idea is such that it is now regarded as almost "obvious" that space and time should constitute such a structure. However, before discussing the nature of this structure, it is worth examining something of what lies behind this belief. Indeed, there is the definite possibility that some future theory may be found which describes nature more accurately than present theory, but for which the differentiable manifold picture of space-time would not be appropriate. We should not close our minds to such a possibility, but also we should keep in mind the extraordinary range over which the present-day view is such an excellent approximation.

---

* Section 10 (and also some small portions of other sections, notably 2 and 9) is based largely on the author's 1966 Adams Prize essay *An Analysis of the Structure of Space-Time*.

The very accurately "locally Euclidean" nature of space, and the continuity of time, would, indeed, seem to have supplied the prime motivation, in the first instance, for the rigorous development of the continuum concept. At the time of Zeno, no such rigorous concept of continuum existed, so that the idea of a limit, in space or time, seemed puzzling. It does not seem puzzling to us today, but perhaps we are wrong not to be puzzled! The standard resolution of Zeno's paradoxes refers more to the *mathematical* continuum concept than to the nature of space-time itself. The view of space-time as forming a continuum would imply that a continuous nature would persist, no matter how much a system is magnified. But it is not at all clear that continuous descriptions are really appropriate on a scale small enough that quantum phenomena become important. For example, at a scale of 10^{-13} cm (approximately the radius of an elementary particle), the mere attempt at localization of the position of a particle to that accuracy will, as a consequence of the uncertainty principle, imply the probable occurrence of a very large momentum, with the implication that *new* particles are created, some of which may be indistinguishable from the original particle. Thus the concept of "position" for the original particle becomes obscured [22]. More alarming, moreover, is the picture presented if we allow ourselves to discuss phenomena at a dimension of the order of 10^{-33} cm. At such a dimension, the quantum fluctuations in the curvature of space-time (if both present-day quantum theory and gravitation theory can be accurately extrapolated to this degree) would be large enough to produce alterations in topology. Thus, the view of space-time at this dimension would be some kind of chaotic linear superposition of different topologies [112]—a picture in no way resembling a smooth manifold.

Whether or not it is meaningful to talk about the nature of space-time at such dimensions is not at all clear. But it it if is *not* meaningful, then we *certainly* cannot refer to space-time as accurately constituting a smooth manifold. On the other hand, it may be argued that the smooth manifold picture is *adequate* for the discussion of all relevant physical processes. It is my personal view that this cannot *ultimately* be the case. I do not believe that a real understanding of the nature of elementary particles can ever be achieved without a simultaneous deeper understanding of the nature of space-time itself. But if we are concerned with a level of phenomena for which such an understanding is *not* necessary—and this will cover almost all of present-day physics—then the smooth manifold picture presents an (unreasonably!) excellent framework for the discussion of phenomena.

Let us now set aside the question of the submicroscopic structure of space-time and concentrate, instead, on its large-scale properties. In this case, we may imagine that the smooth manifold picture will be adequate and that its structure in the large can be obtained by piecing together smaller "locally Euclidean" patches, in the manner of the overlapping coordinate neighborhoods of differential geometry. Thus we might arrive at a topology for space-time, in the large, different from a Euclidean topology. Unfortunately, too little is known about the large-scale structure of the universe to enable us to make any statement with confidence concerning its global topology (apart, perhaps, from certain statements about its orientability). Thus, it *might* be that the topology of space-time on a large scale is not at all interesting.

Nevertheless, *irrespective* of this, it will be very worthwhile, here, to consider questions concerning topology of space-time manifolds in some generality. There are, in particular, two different but somewhat related special reasons for this. To appreciate, fully, the first of these, we must picture the universe in its four-dimensional entirety, rather than in terms of some three-dimensional spacelike section (the "present"). The one observational feature of the four-dimensional large-scale structure of the universe which *has* emerged with any semblance of certainty, is that at some "time" in the past (of the order of 10^{10} years ago) the material of the universe was apparently concentrated in a highly condensed and chaotic (hot) state. This follows from observed expansion of the universe and the equations of general relativity, if certain assumptions about the large-scale homogeneity of the universe are made. It also appears to follow more directly from the recent observation [25, 80a] of a general background of (electromagnetic) radiation permeating space. The present temperature of this radiation is about 3° absolute, which is what would be expected [33, 2] on the basis of a highly condensed general-relativistic "initial state." (The cooling down of the radiation to its present value would be an effect of the expansion of the universe.) Now, if we take completely seriously the smoothed-out cosmological models which are normally used in such calculations, we are actually presented with an initial *singular* state at which the curvature of space-time becomes infinite. In the neighborhood of the singularity, radii of curvature would become arbitrarily small—less than 10^{-13} cm; less, even, than 10^{-33} cm. Thus, we would expect the picture presented by our model to be inadequate at such levels, if only because of the reasons mentioned earlier for doubting the validity of the smooth manifold description of space-time at such dimensions.

But can we really trust our model in regions where the curvature even *remotely* approaches these values? We may expect that the deviations from homogeneity which are now present in the curvature of space-time (owing to irregularities in the matter density) could, if extrapolated backward to the early highly curved space-time regions, result in very great deviations from the smoothed-out picture. Indeed, is there reason to believe in the existence of a singularity at all? (We may take as a tentative definition of "singularity," a region at which curvatures have become so large, that the local physics becomes drastically altered—perhaps because of a breakdown in the smooth manifold picture of space-time.) Might it not be that when curvatures become only "moderately" large, the deviations from the *model* could be enormous, perhaps resulting even in a *topological* structure totally different from that of the model? It will be one of the main purposes of the later lectures in this series to give some precise results which strongly indicate (although, perhaps, they do not *quite* prove) the existence of singularities in space-time, in *generic* situations, on the basis of general relativity. In order to achieve these results it will be necessary to consider quite complicated possibilities of a somewhat topological nature—*even* if such complications are *not* actually realized in the universe!

This is the first of the two compelling reasons, alluded to above, for studying the subject of space-time topology. The second of these (leaving aside the question of relevance to the submicroscopic nature of space-time) concerns the question of gravitational collapse. The inherent *instability* of gravitation, as implied by general relativity, when too large concentrations of masses are present, is reflected in the existence of an initial singularity of the cosmological models. This instability becomes manifest again in the collapsing phase of those models for which the expansion does not continue idenfinitely and the universe returns to infinite curvature in a final singular state. But it is *not* necessary for the universe to be involved as a *whole*, for the effects of this instability to become manifest. In fact, even bodies which are not very much more massive than the sun may be expected to collapse catastrophically when they have exhausted their resources of internal energy. If the conditions are right, such a body will collapse past a "point of no return" at which (roughly speaking) the gravitational forces become so strong that even the *light* emitted by the body is dragged inward and no signal can escape to the outside world. Beyond this point the behavior of the body is much like the final phase of a collapsing universe (or, presumably, the time-reverse of the initial phase of an expanding one). Singularities in space-time would be expected to result, but (in the situation under consideration) these singularities would not be visible from the outside. Instead, there ensues something of the nature of a "hole" in space, into which objects can fall and out of which no object or signal can escape. Bearing in mind the mass range that might be likely to be involved, these "holes" could range in size from a few kilometers in diameter to a few times the dimension of the solar system. They would (apparently) be difficult—but not in principle impossible—to detect from outside. At the present time their probable existence is inferred theoretically rather than observationally, but in any case there are many intriguing questions of space-time topology involved in their study.

The nature of space-time is not quite what it "seems" to be—and in these respects it is not well understood at present. Undoubtedly, future theory will present us with many surprises and important new insights. But even the present theory of space-time (and by this I mean Einstein's 1916 theory of general relativity) contains surprises and insights which are only just beginning to be explored in any detail. There is surely a great wealth of results which may still be fairly readily obtained by use of the appropriate mathematical tools. I hope that by presenting a few of the results which have been so far obtained and by indicating some tools which have recently proved useful, I may be able to encourage experts in other fields to take a (possibly active) interest in this subject.

2 THE NATURE OF GENERAL RELATIVITY

The most important single lesson of relativity theory is, perhaps, that space and time are not concepts that can be considered independently of one another but must be combined together to give a *four*-dimensional picture of phenomena: the description in terms of *space-time*. Dynamics then becomes an aspect of geometry. It is somewhat instructive to see how this idea may be applied even in prerelativistic dynamical theories. Thus, we may compare the dynamics of Aristotle, Galileo, or Newton with special or general relativity, by expressing all five types of theory in space-time terms.

Let us consider five kinds of space-time, which I shall label as follows:

$$\text{ARISTOTELIAN SPACE-TIME} \qquad (2.1)$$
$$\text{GALILEAN SPACE-TIME} \qquad (2.2)$$
$$\text{NEWTONIAN SPACE-TIME} \qquad (2.3)$$
$$\text{MINKOWSKIAN SPACE-TIME} \qquad (2.4)$$
$$\text{EINSTEINIAN SPACE-TIME} \qquad (2.5)$$

In each case, the space-time will be a four-dimensional smooth manifold, but with some additional geometric structure which describes an important aspect of the dynamics. Any *point* of the space-time is really an "event," that is, something one pictures as a point in space, but with only an instantaneous existence. The history of a particle is a *curve*[1] in space-time, called the world line of the particle.

Aristotelian space-time is simply a product $E^3 \times E^1$, where E^n denotes the n-dimensional Euclidean space carrying the usual Euclidean metric and possessing the usual ($\frac{1}{2}n(n + 1)$-dimensional) group of motions. The metric of E^3 defines spatial separation and that of E^1 defines time-difference. Thus, in accordance with Aristotelian dynamics, it is meaningful to speak of an absolute spatial separation between two events, even when they possess a nonzero time difference. In particular, the state of rest of a particle is to be distinguished from all other motions, by the fact that the spatial separation

---

[1] Unless otherwise stated, a "curve" will not carry a parameter (cf. section 9).

vanishes between any two points on the particle's world line. The seven-parameter transitive group of motions of Aristotelian space-time is the direct product of the Euclidean group on E^3 with that on E^1.

Galilean and 'Newtonian space-times differ from Aristotelian space-time in that the spatial separation of two points is only well-defined if their time difference vanishes. On the other hand, the time difference is always well-defined. Thus, the structure is more accurately that of a *fiber bundle* over E^1 with fiber E^3, so that the "time" E^1 may be thought of as the *factor space* of the whole space by the fiber E^3. (The topology is, of course, still the same as in the Aristotelian case, but the bundle structure is different.[2]) The distinction between the Galilean and Newtonian space-times arises only after some further structure has been imposed. For this, we single out a special (six-parameter) family of curves in the space-time which we refer to as the "geodesics." (No extremal property of these curves is intended to be suggested here. We merely require that a unique such geodesic pass through each point of the space-time in each direction.) These geodesics (except for those lying in the E^3 fibers) will then be the world lines of particles in *inertial motion*. To obtain the geodesics for Galilean space-time, we merely postulate that they agree with the system of straight lines in some E^4, where the E^3 fibers are identified as a maximal system of parallel planes in E^4 and where the factor space E^1 is defined in the obvious way. The group of motions of the Galilean space-time which preserves this structure is the ten-parameter Galilei group.

The definition of the geodesics for Newtonian space-time is more complicated. The idea, here [20, 108, 109] is to treat Newtonian gravitational theory from the point of view presented by Einstein's general theory. Thus, we do *not* regard gravitation as a *true force*, but as an intertial or "fictional" force along with the acceleration, centrifugal, and Coriolis forces. This is possible[3] because of the Galilei–Einstein equivalence principle, which states the equality between inertial and passive gravitational mass. Then a particle moving under the action of gravity, but not influenced by any other force, is considered to be moving inertially and its world line is to be a

---

[2] I am grateful to A. Trautman for clarifying this point for me.

[3] In fact, the principle of equivalence really also tells us that it is *necessary* to take this view of Newtonian gravitation. A constant gravitational field (in the Newtonian sense), throughout the whole of space, would be totally unobservable, all bodies being accelerated equally. The intrinsic physics would be the same as if the field did not exist. The situation is somewhat similar to that of electric potential. If we add (for example) a constant potential over the whole universe, the intrinsic physics is totally unaltered. Thus we think of Newtonian gravitational "field" as being really a type of potential. We have to *differentiate* to get the true field, namely, the curvature. We might imagine fixing the potentials canonically by requiring that they go to zero at infinity, but it is difficult to see how one would apply this in the actual universe, there being no evidence that the density of gravitating bodies falls off toward infinity.

geodesic. Many different Newtonian space-times are possible, corresponding to the various inequivalent gravitational fields. Galilean space-time is a special case, corresponding to zero gravitational field—or, equivalently, for example, to a field of *constant* gravitational acceleration defined throughout space-time. For, as in general relativity proper, the physically meaningful aspect of a gravitational field is contained only in the "tidal force" which results from a *nonuniform* gravitational acceleration field. These tidal forces find expression in a "curvature" for Newtonian space-time which describes the extent to which the intrinsic geodesic structure differs from that of the Galilean space-time (Fig. 1). The "field equations" of Newtonian space-

FIGURE 1. The curvature of Newtonian space-time is directly measured by geodesic deviation, that is, by tidal forces.

time relate this curvature to the distribution of gravitating matter. These may be obtained by applying to limit $c \to \infty$ to the equations of general relativity (c being the velocity of light) but the details of this will not be entered into here.[4]

Minkowskian and Einsteinian space-times differ radically from the three previous cases in that *no* additive concept of time difference is defined

---

[4] For the details of this, see Trautman [108, 109]. Trautman also considers the more general case where the Newtonian spaces of constant time need not be Euclidean E^3's. This enables "Newtonian cosmology" to be considered.

between events. Instead, a pseudo-Riemannian[5] metric form ds^2, of hyperbolic normal signature (that is, $+$, $-$, $-$, $-$) is defined on the space-time. The time difference between two points A, B in the space-time *depends on the choice of world line connecting the points* and is given by the integral of ds along the world line:

$$\tau = \int_A^B ds \tag{2.6}$$

For an allowable (that is, "timelike" or "null") world line, we have $ds^2 \geqslant 0$ everywhere along the curve, whence τ is, in fact, a real number. The quantity τ defines the time interval (*proper time*) between A and B as measured by an (idealized) clock whose world line is the given curve. Since proper time is now a path-dependent concept, we can return to the definition of a "geodesic" as an *extremal* path. The system of (timelike) geodesics thus obtained, defines (according to the theory) the inertial motions of particles. Unlike in the Galilean and Newtonian cases just considered, the inertial motions are now *fixed* once the behavior of (idealized) clocks has been specified.

The relation between Minkowskian and Einsteinian space-times mirrors that between Galilean and Newtonian space-times. Thus, Minkowskian space-time has a unique description (for example, its geodesic structure is the same as that of E^4, the set of timelike geodesics corresponding to geodesics in E^4 making an angle of less than $45°$ with some fixed direction) and it does not describe gravitation. It has a ten-parameter transitive group of motions, namely, the Poincaré (that is inhomogeneous Lorentz) group. On the other hand, many Einsteinian space-times exist, corresponding to the various inequivalent gravitational fields. As with the Newtonian space-time, it is the *tidal* gravitational force which has physical significance, this being present when there is a gradient of the "gravitational acceleration field." This tidal force is described in terms of deviations of the intrinsic geodesic structure from that of Minkowskian space-time, that is to say, by the *curvature* of the Einsteinian space-time [*cf.* (7.8)]. Einstein's field equations then describe how this space-time curvature is to be related to the density of matter (that is of stress–energy–momentum).

Before adopting the Einsteinian point of view, it is reasonable to question whether space-time actually possesses a uniquely and accurately defined pseudo-Riemannian structure. This depends on the existence of accurate clocks in nature, on the fact that such clocks behave locally according to the laws of special relativity and on the fact that for two coincident

---

[5] The word "Riemannian" is generally reserved for the case of a positive-definite metric; thence the term "pseudo-Riemannian" for indefinite metrics. Sometimes the word "Lorentzian" is used for a pseudo-Riemannian manifold of signature $(+, -, \ldots, -)$.

clocks, the time rate they register is in a well-defined ratio which does not depend on their location in space-time nor on their histories. It seems that the existence of accurate clocks is deeply related to the quantum nature of matter. Ultimately this comes down to the fact that a natural frequency v is associated (via Planck's constant h) with any mass m. For, combining Einstein's mass–energy law $E = mc^2$ with Planck's formula $E = hv$ (and choosing units, as we shall, henceforth, so that the velocity of light $c = 1$) we have

$$v = mh^{-1} \tag{2.7}$$

Any fundamental particle therefore defines a scale of time via its own rest mass m. The time-scale may be thought of as a series of "ticks" along the world line of the particle,[6] these being (by definition) a separation v^{-1} apart. This gives us a definition of interval ds along the particle's world line and by allowing this world line to vary, we have ds for *any* timelike interval. Because of the very great local accuracy of special relativity, this then serves to define

FIGURE 2. The ds defined by a particle moving in different timelike directions at a point P is consistent with a pseudo-Riemannian structure. This is because of the local accuracy of special relativity.

---

[6] In practice, the Planck frequencies of elementary particles are extremely high and cannot be used directly as clocks. The corresponding Planck frequencies for compound systems are even higher! Essentially the frequencies used in atomic or nuclear clocks are obtained from *differences* of masses (that is, "beats").

a pseudo-Riemannian structure for space-time (see Fig. 2). Finally, it appears that the pseudo-Riemannian structure we obtain is independent of the choice of particle that we use to define it. This is because the masses of elementary particles seem to be in a definite fixed ratio to one another, which is independent of their location in space-time or their histories. (If this were found not to be the case, then we should only have a uniquely defined *conformal* geometry, that is, a metric up to a local factor.)

So far, I have made no mention of spacelike separations, even though one normally thinks of Riemannian geometry in terms of distances rather than times. This is because a distance measurement is really a more complicated process than a time measurement. Given any two nearby points P, Q with a spacelike separation, we cannot just put a " ruler " between them to measure their separation. A ruler is not really an appropriate object for measuring distances between events. In space-time, a ruler appears as a two-dimensional timelike strip. Unless we arrange that the points P, Q on the two edges of the strip are " simultaneous in the ruler's rest frame," we shall get the wrong answer for the interval PQ (Fig. 3). In fact, the rigidity of a ruler is also a complicated matter and depends ultimately on the intersections between the " clocks " defined by its constituent atoms. To measure

FIGURE 3. A ruler wrongly measuring a spacelike interval PQ. The events P, Q are not simultaneous in the rest-frame of the ruler.

spatial intervals, it is actually more direct to use a *clock*[7] and reflected light signals, such as in the manner indicated in Fig. 4.   The spacelike interval PQ is then equal to the timelike interval between emission and reception of the signals (assuming the signals are emitted in opposite directions relative to the clock, that is, that the whole figure lies in a timelike plane).

FIGURE 4. A clock correctly measuring the spacelike interval PQ by use of reflected light signals.   (The whole figure must lie in a plane.)

Let us, then, agree that space-time, via accurate clocks, possesses a uniquely defined natural pseudo-Riemannian metric (of signature $+$, $-$, $-$, $-$).   It is still reasonable to question whether the geodesics defined by this metric are likely to have anything to do with the inertial motions of particles.   When general relativity was first put forward, the identity of the inertial motions with the timelike geodesics was assumed as a *postulate* of the theory.   However, Einstein and Grommer [30] were later able to show,[8] that this property is actually a *consequence of Einstein's field equations* [*cf.* (7.1)] if certain reasonable assumptions are made about how a (test) particle is to be represented as a limitingly small distribution of energy–momentum.   The argument is a delicate one, but it depends ultimately on the existence of a covariant conservation law for the energy tensor [*cf.* (8.1)]. Beyond this, it does not depend critically on the exact form of Einstein's field equations.

It is also possible to run the argument the other way, that is, to regard inertial motions as primary and to try and construct the metric as a secondary concept.   According to an argument of Weyl [111] and of Marzke and Wheeler [56], if both the timelike geodesics (inertial particle world lines) and

---

[7] Synge [103] has particularly emphasized that the study of space-time geometry is essentially "chronometry."

[8] For an important later paper see [31]; for a more recent survey, see [36].

null geodesics (unscattered light rays) are known, then the metric of space-time can be constructed uniquely up to an overall factor.   This, in a sense, has some advantage over the definition in terms of clocks, since the primary concepts do not depend on parts of physics (that is, quantum theory) which may be felt to be foreign to general relativity.   My personal preference for regarding the clocks as more basic arises partly from the fact that one needs a number of apparently *ad hoc* assumptions on the geodesic structure of space-time in order that it be consistent with any metric at all, so it ceases to be clear that the structure of space-time is actually a pseudo-Riemannian one. In addition, it is my personal view that there *is* a deep connection between quantum theory and general relativity, so that it may actually be a mistake to attempt to build the subjects up separately.

For general relativity to be a subject of relevance to nature, it is necessary that the pseudo-Riemannian structure of space-time be not only accurately defined, but also *nontrivial* (that is, with somewhere nonvanishing curvature). The fact that the space-time metric *is* curved[9] is actually a consequence of very primitive considerations [96] concerning the nonexistence of a *perpetuum mobile*.   Consider a closed chain of buckets [9, p. 418] stretched between two pulleys, the axes of the two pulleys being fixed relative to the earth at different gravitational potentials (Fig. 5).   Each bucket contains an atom which is capable of two states, a ground state and an excited state.   The atoms on the left-hand side are all excited while those on the right are in the ground state.   Now, the excited atoms, possessing more energy than the ground-state atoms, are also more massive.   Therefore (by a very weak version of the principle of equivalence), they must also *weigh* more.   We assume that there is no friction in the system, whence the chain begins to rotate in a counterclockwise direction.   When each bucket reaches the bottom it is induced to give up its excess energy in the form of a photon which, by means of mirrors, is reflected back to the top atom.   Now *if* the photon could be reabsorbed to excite the top atom we would have a *perpetuum mobile* since the process could be repeated indefinitely and energy could, in

---

[9] The following argument will not show that space-time is *conformally* curved (that is, with a metric not expressible in the form $ds^2 = f(x, y, z, t) \{dt^2 - dx^2 - dy^2 - dz^2\}$). For this, the most direct argument is the bending of light by the sun.   Space-time curvature seems to be about the only way of "bending" light without the different frequencies being bent differently (chromatic dispersion).   In a conformally flat theory (for example, Nordström's [66] gravitational theory), there would be *no* resultant bending of light by gravitation (essentially because null geodesics are conformally invariant).   It may be taken that the existence of *some* achromatic bending is experimentally established.

The most obvious manifestation of space-time curvature is the existence of planetary orbits.   I do not choose to use this as the primary reason for believing in the curvature of space-time, because the connection of curved orbits with the behavior of clocks is not very direct, depending on the derivation of equations of motion from field equations on the metric (see above).

FIGURE 5. Bondi's endless chain of buckets.   The weight of the extra energy of
the excited atoms would cause the chain to rotate.

principle, be extracted from the continuing rotation of the chain.   Thus, we
must assume that the photon is *not* capable of being absorbed by the top
atom.   Presumably, if Newton had been presented with this situation, he
would have had a simple answer: The photon is " weakened " by the time it
reaches the top and possesses insufficient energy to excite the top atom.   But
because of quantum theory, we know that a photon cannot be *just* " weakened."
By Planck's formula, it must also be of a *lower frequency* when it reaches the
top than that required to raise the top atom to its excited state.   Thus, in a
well-defined sense, clocks must run more slowly at the bottom of the chain
than at the top.   Thus, the metric of space-time, as we have defined it, must
differ, in a gravitational field, from the ordinary flat space-time form.   (This
is a highly idealized piece of apparatus, but it is of interest to note that this
clock slowing effect has actually been directly observed on the earth, by
Pound and Rebka [85] by use of the Mössbauer effect.)   Note that the
principle of equivalence is only invoked in an exceedingly weak form, namely,

that energy just has *some* weight. (An extreme version of the experiment would be to employ π° mesons rather than atoms. These can decay entirely into photons, leaving the right-hand buckets empty. Thus, the argument will apply if π° mesons weigh anything at all!)

This argument is not, so far, quite sufficient to show that space-time is curved, however. The metric might still be flat but represented in an unusual way. From the spherical symmetry of the earth's field this is readily seen to be, in fact, impossible, since it would imply that the metric of the earth's field is related to a standard Minkowski space-time by transformations involving an acceleration outward from the center of the earth in all directions. The matter will not be pursued in further detail here, except that I feel it will be instructive just to examine the "uniform acceleration" transformation of Minkowski space-time explicitly. This illustrates quite clearly how a static situation *can* appear to involve a gravitational field, while the space-time is actually flat. This example also shares some features of the relation between the Schwarzschild and Kruskal representations of a true spherically symmetric gravitational field, as we shall see later ((10.1), (10.4); see also Bergmann [6a]).

Let x, y, z, t be standard Minkowskian coordinates, so that the metric takes the form

$$ds^2 = dt^2 - dx^2 - dy^2 - dz^2 \tag{2.8}$$

Introduce new coordinates X, Y, Z, T related to the original ones in the range $z > |t|$; $Z > 0$, by

$$x = X, \, y = Y, \, z = Z \cosh T, \, t = Z \sinh T \tag{2.9}$$

(see Fig. 6). The metric now becomes

$$ds^2 = Z^2 \, dT^2 - dX^2 - dY^2 - dZ^2 \tag{2.10}$$

The form (2.10) has the appearance of a static gravitational field with Z playing the role of a gravitational potential. The term $(Z \, dT)^2$ in (2.10) in place of the dt^2 seems to indicate that "time is running more slowly" near $Z = 0$. Any particle held "fixed" in the X, Y, Z, T system (that is with X, Y, Z constant) would experience a constant force in the direction of decreasing Z (since the particle's world line is "really" a constant acceleration "hyperbola" in the x, y, z, t system). A freely falling particle would appear, in the X, Y, Z, T system, to fall toward $Z = 0$ and then slow down and approach $Z = 0$ asymptotically (see broken curve in Fig. 6). There is an apparent "barrier" a $Z = 0$ which particles do not seem to be able to cross. That this is merely an effect of the inadequacy of the (X, Y, Z, T) coordinate patch becomes evident if we transform back to the form (2.8). It will be useful to bear this feature in mind when we come to consider the discussion of gravitational collapse given in Section 10.

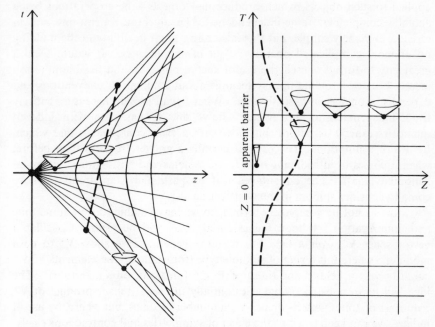

FIGURE 6. The uniform acceleration transformation. The apparent barrier at $Z = 0$ has no physical reality.

3 THE ABSTRACT INDEX NOTATION

When performing calculations in general relativity it is frequently necessary to operate with tensors of quite high valence.[10] Even such a basic quantity as the curvature tensor has valence four, and it possesses the familiar somewhat complicated symmetries. This makes it practically imperative that an index notation be employed for many calculations, so that the different connections between the quantities involved may be easily kept track of. It seems that there is a common feeling among mathematicians that such notations are to be avoided, presumably because of the connotation that their use entails explicit reference to a particular basis frame. However, when a physicist refers to "g_{ab}" or "$R^a{}_{bcd}$," I do not think that he usually means to be referring to a set of frame-dependent components but rather to a physical, frame-independent object which these components represent. But, the index notation allows a very convenient set of algebraic operations to be

---

[10] The term "valence" is used here in preference to "rank" because it is more descriptive and because the word "rank" has other connotations in the case of matrices.

applied to such objects, which produce new objects—these operations being actually completely frame-independent. The algebraic operations are, in essence, extremely simple, but they also allow great flexibility in the building up of more complicated operations out of simple ones. It would seem a great pity to forbid oneself the use of such a powerful and flexible notation merely because of some uneasy feelings about summation conventions and dependence on special basis frames. What I shall present here is an entirely frame-independent algebra which allows one to calculate with indexed quantities exactly as before (but now with a clear conscience!) and which, by use of a notational device, even permits a greater freedom than before, when it comes to introducing coordinate systems and basis frames (compare Schouten [96a]). The advantages will be particularly apparent when we come to consider spinors in the next section.

Let us not be completely formal, so we may be able to save some time and complication. I hope the essential ideas will be clear. Consider a vector space $\mathbf{V}^{\bullet}$ over a field $\mathbf{F}$—or, more generally, we allow $\mathbf{V}^{\bullet}$ to be a module,[11] where $\mathbf{F}$ is a ring of suitable type (for example, the elements of $\mathbf{V}^{\bullet}$ could be vector fields[12] and those of $\mathbf{F}$, C^{∞} functions, on a manifold). The idea will be to construct what is essentially the usual tensor product of $\mathbf{V}^{\bullet}$ a number of times with its dual[13] $\mathbf{V}_{\bullet}$ a number of times, but where, by use of indices, we can keep track of the effect of symmetries and contractions easily. This is done by simply mirroring the usual index notation (with summation conventions, etc.) but where now the indices a, b, c, ... are not to be thought of merely as generic symbols standing, say, for 0, 1, 2, ..., N, but as abstract labels. We shall require an infinite supply

$$a, b, c, \ldots, a_0, b_0, \ldots, a_1, b_1, \ldots, a_2, \ldots \qquad (3.1)$$

of abstract labels, so that expressions of arbitrary length can be built up. Let $\mathbf{L}$ denote the set of labels (3.1). For any element ξ of $\mathbf{V}^{\bullet}$ and any label $x \in \mathbf{L}$, we shall allow ourselves to write a symbol ξ^x. As ξ ranges over the elements of $\mathbf{V}^{\bullet}$, the associated object ξ^x ranges over a corresponding set $\mathbf{V}^x$. It should be emphasized here that ξ^x is an entity in its own right and not the set of components of ξ in some frame. Now, since we wish to mirror the usual tensor rules for indexed quantities, we are not permitted to write $\xi^a + \eta^b$, but $\xi^a + \eta^a$ and $\xi^b + \eta^b$ will be both allowable. (We must think of ξ^a and ξ^b as different objects.) For any $\lambda \in \mathbf{F}$, we shall also be permitted to write $\lambda \xi^a$. Thus, each of $\mathbf{V}^a$, $\mathbf{V}^b$, ..., $\mathbf{V}^{a_0}$, ... is a vector space or module canonically isomorphic with $\mathbf{V}^{\bullet}$.

---

[11] A module differs from a vector space in that the scalars form a ring with identity rather than a field. A ring differs from a field in that division by nonzero elements is not always possible.

[12] Here a "field" means a cross-section of the appropriate vector bundle over $\mathcal{M}$.

[13] The space of all linear mappings of the module $\mathbf{V}^{\bullet}$ into the ring $\mathbf{F}$.

It may be felt that it is unnatural to introduce an infinite number of isomorphic spaces, when actually we only have one space. But we may view the situation in a slightly different way. Each element of **L** is really just a kind of organizational marker which keeps a tag on a particular vector (etc) irrespective of where it may occur in an expression. Thus, ξ^x is just a *pair*, consisting of ξ together with the marker x. That is to say, it is an element of $\mathbf{V}^\bullet \times \mathbf{L}$. We then have $\mathbf{V}^a = \mathbf{V}^\bullet \times (a)$, $\mathbf{V}^b = \mathbf{V}^\bullet \times (b)$, etc. The vector space or module axioms will, of course, apply to each $\mathbf{V}^x$:

$$\xi^x + (\eta^x + \zeta^x) = (\xi^x + \eta^x) + \zeta^x$$

$$\lambda(\xi^x + \eta^x) = \lambda\xi^x + \lambda\eta^x$$

$$(\lambda + \mu)\xi^x = \lambda\xi^x + \mu\xi^x$$

$$\lambda(\mu\xi^x) = (\lambda\mu)\xi^x \tag{3.2}$$

$$1\xi^x = \xi^x$$

$$0\xi^x = 0\eta^x$$

Here $\lambda, \mu, 1, 0 \in \mathbf{F}$ with 1 and 0 being the multiplicative and additive identities, respectively. We also have $\xi^x + \eta^x = \eta^x + \xi^x$ (expanding $(1 + 1)(\xi^x + \eta^x)$) and $\xi^x + (-\xi^x) = 0$ (writing $-\xi^x$ for $(-1)\xi^x$ and 0 for $0\eta^x$).

The *dual* space $\mathbf{V}_\bullet$ will also have an infinite number of canonically isomorphic copies: $\mathbf{V}_a, \mathbf{V}_b, \ldots, \mathbf{V}_{a_0}, \ldots$. We may think of $\mathbf{V}_x$ as being the dual space of $\mathbf{V}^x$ for each $x \in \mathbf{L}$. The elements of $\mathbf{V}_x$ are linear mappings of $\mathbf{V}^x$ into $\mathbf{F}$. Thus, for $\theta_x \in \mathbf{V}_x$ we have

$$\theta_x(\xi^x + \eta^x) = \theta_x\xi^x + \theta_x\eta^x \tag{3.3}$$

$$\theta_x(\lambda\xi^x) = \lambda(\theta_x\xi^x) \tag{3.4}$$

where the effect of the mapping θ_x on ξ^x is written simply $\theta_x\xi^x$. We shall also allow this to be written in the reverse order: $\theta_x\xi^x = \xi^x\theta_x$. We require

$$\theta_a\xi^a = \theta_b\xi^b = \cdots = \theta_x\xi^x = \cdots \tag{3.5}$$

Now each of $\mathbf{V}_a, \mathbf{V}_b, \ldots$ will be vector space or module where $\lambda\theta_x$ and $\theta_x + \phi_x$ are defined by

$$(\lambda\theta_x)\xi^x = \lambda(\theta_x\xi^x) \qquad (\theta_x + \phi_x)\xi^x = \theta_x\xi^x + \phi_x\xi^x \tag{3.6}$$

The idea will be to use the elements of $\mathbf{F}, \mathbf{V}^a, \mathbf{V}^b, \ldots, \mathbf{V}_a, \mathbf{V}_b, \ldots$ to generate our algebra. To see what the rules of this algebra should be, we must recall what the rules are for the ordinary tensor index notation. We note, for instance, that products such as $\xi^a\eta^b$ will be permitted, whereas $\xi^a\eta^a$ will not. Furthermore, the allowable products must be *commutative*:

$$\xi^a\eta^b = \eta^b\xi^a \tag{3.7}$$

but in general $\xi^a \eta^b \neq \eta^a \xi^b$. The requirement (3.7) shows us that while *in essence* $\xi^a \eta^b$ is just the tensor product of elements $\xi^a \otimes \eta^b$, we cannot simply *identify* $\xi^a \eta^b$ with $\xi^a \otimes \eta^b$. For tensor products, according to the strict technical definition, are not commutative. Here we are allowed to define a commutative version of a tensor product, essentially for the reason that $\xi^a \eta^a$ is not defined. In a product $\xi^a \eta^b$, it is the *labels* a and b that tell us which factor is which, not the ordering of the factors. One method (suggested to me by S. Mac Lane) of precisely defining the type of product used here is to take the *symmetric algebra* [54a] on the direct sum $\mathbf{V}^a \oplus \mathbf{V}_a \oplus \mathbf{V}^b \oplus \mathbf{V}_b \oplus \ldots$ and then, for each pair of disjoint (finite) sets of elements of $\mathbf{L}$, say a, p, r and b, m, we select the corresponding subspace $\mathbf{V}_{bm}^{apr}$ spanned by the elements of the form

$$\xi^a \eta^p \zeta^h \theta_b \, \phi_m \tag{3.8}$$

The general element of $\mathbf{V}_{bm}^{abr}$ will be a linear combination of expressions like (3.8). The construction so made, ensures that each product (3.8) is fully commutative and also that the various distributive laws hold (for example, $\psi_m^{apr}(\theta_b + \chi_b) = \psi_m^{apr}\theta_b + \psi_m^{apr}\chi_b$ with $\psi_m^{apr} \in \mathbf{V}_m^{apr}$). There is no significance in the ordering of a, p, r in $\mathbf{V}_{bm}^{apr}$ or of b, m. Thus $\mathbf{V}_{bm}^{apr} = \mathbf{V}_{bm}^{par} = \mathbf{V}_{mb}^{arp}$, etc. However, the ordering of the indices for an element ρ_{bm}^{apr} *is* significant.

Every element $\rho_{bm}^{apr} \in \mathbf{V}_{bm}^{apr}$ is a linear combination of commutative products of the type (3.8):

$$\rho_{bm}^{apr} = \sum_{i=1}^{M} \lambda \overset{(i)}{\xi^a} \overset{(i)}{\eta^p} \overset{(i)}{\zeta^r} \overset{(i)}{\theta_b} \overset{(i)}{\phi_m} \tag{3.9}$$

but there will be many ways of expressing ρ_{bm}^{apr} as such. A convenient criterion for the equality of two expressions (3.9) for the modules that we are interested in is that for *every* choice $\alpha_a \in \mathbf{V}_a$, $\beta_p \in \mathbf{V}_p$, $\gamma_r \in \mathbf{V}_r$, $\sigma^b \in \mathbf{V}^b$, $\tau^m \in \mathbf{V}^m$, the scalar

$$\rho_{bm}^{apr}\alpha_a \beta_p \gamma_r \sigma^b \tau^m = \sum_{i=1}^{M} \lambda \, (\overset{(i)}{\xi^a}\alpha_a)(\overset{(i)}{\eta^p}\beta_p)(\overset{(i)}{\zeta^r}\gamma_r)(\overset{(i)}{\theta_b}\sigma^b)(\overset{(i)}{\phi_m}\tau^m) \tag{3.10}$$

should be the same for both expressions. From this all the algebraic properties will follow. (Note, that in general $\rho_{bm}^{arp} \neq \rho_{bm}^{par} \neq \rho_{mb}^{apr}$, etc.)

The entire tensor system $\{\mathbf{V}\}$ consists of all of the $\mathbf{V}_{u \ldots w}^{x \ldots z}$, including $\mathbf{V} = \mathbf{F}$:

$$\{\mathbf{V}\} = (\mathbf{V}, \mathbf{V}^a, \mathbf{V}^b, \ldots, \mathbf{V}_a, \mathbf{V}_b, \ldots, \mathbf{V}^{ab}, \ldots, \mathbf{V}_{u \ldots w}^{x \ldots z}, \ldots)$$

There are four basic operations on $\{\mathbf{V}\}$, namely

ADDITION: $\qquad \mathbf{V}_{u \ldots w}^{x \ldots z} \times \mathbf{V}_{u \ldots w}^{x \ldots z} \to \mathbf{V}_{u \ldots w}^{x \ldots z} \tag{3.11}$

MULTIPLICATION: $\quad \mathbf{V}_{p \ldots r}^{a \ldots d} \times \mathbf{V}_{u \ldots w}^{x \ldots z} \to \mathbf{V}_{p \ldots ru \ldots w}^{a \ldots dx \ldots z} \tag{3.12}$

INDEX SUBSTITUTION: $\;\; \mathbf{V}_{u \ldots w}^{x \ldots z} \to \mathbf{V}_{k \ldots m}^{f \ldots h} \tag{3.13}$

(a, b)-CONTRACTION: $\;\; \mathbf{V}_{bu \ldots w}^{ax \ldots z} \to \mathbf{V}_{u \ldots w}^{x \ldots z} \tag{3.14}$

In (3.11), (3.12), and (3.14), the differently denoted index letters appearing are all assumed to be different elements of **L**. In (3.13), the elements $x, \ldots,$ $z, u, \ldots, w$ of **L** are all distinct and so are $f, \ldots, h, k, \ldots, m$. Otherwise they are unrestricted except that $x, \ldots, z$ and $f, \ldots, h$ are equal in number and that $u, \ldots, w$ and $k, \ldots, m$ are equal in number. Addition and multiplication are defined the obvious way. Index substitution is induced simply by a permutation applied to **L**. (The validity of any equation is unaffected by a permutation of the elements of **L**.) To define contraction, we consider, for example, the (p, b)-contraction: $\mathbf{V}^{par}_{bm} \rightarrow \mathbf{V}^{ar}_{m}$ as applied to the element $\rho^{apr}_{bm} \in \mathbf{V}^{par}_{bm}$ given by (3.9). The result is

$$\rho^{axr}_{xm} = \sum_{i=1}^{M} \overset{(i)}{\lambda} (\overset{(i)}{\eta^x} \overset{(i)}{\theta_x}) \overset{(i)}{\xi^a} \overset{(i)}{\zeta^r} \overset{(i)}{\phi_m} \tag{3.15}$$

We have $\rho^{axr}_{xm} \in \mathbf{V}^{ar}_{m}$, so the x labels are "dummies" which do not contribute to the total valence type.

It may be verified algebraically that all the usual tensor rules[14] follow from the above constructions. Thus, addition gives an Abelian group structure to each $\mathbf{V}^{x \cdots z}_{u \cdots w}$. Multiplication is commutative and distributive over addition. Contraction appropriately commutes with addition, with multiplication, and with other contractions. The contraction of a zero element is again a zero element. (If we use equality between the scalars (3.10) as the definition of equality between formal expressions (3.9), then this last property follows from the property that any matrix over **F** whose square vanishes also has vanishing trace. This property holds in the cases which interest us here, but would not be true for certain rings of finite characteristic.)

So far, the question of a basis frame for $\mathbf{V}^{\bullet}$ has not even arisen. However, it is often convenient to work with basis frames and we shall need a notation to be able to distinguish basis indices from the abstract labels. I shall adopt the convention that *German* indices $\mathfrak{a}, \mathfrak{b}, \ldots, \mathfrak{a}_0, \ldots$ will denote the numbering of basis elements in the standard way, that is, each of $\mathfrak{a}, \mathfrak{b}, \ldots$ denotes one of the integers $0, 1, \ldots, N$ [for an $(N + 1)$-dimensional space]. The use of German indices will be to remind us of two things; first that a choice of a (possibly arbitrary) basis frame is involved in any expression containing such indices, with a consequent loss of covariance; and secondly that the Einstein *summation convention* is being used whenever repeated indices occur in a term in an expression. Now, let $\delta_0, \delta_1, \ldots, \delta_N \in \mathbf{V}^{\bullet}$ be a basis for $\mathbf{V}^{\bullet}$ (assuming finite-dimensionality) and let $\delta^0, \delta^1, \ldots, \delta^N \in \mathbf{V}_{\bullet}$ be the corresponding dual basis. For $x \in \mathbf{L}$ we have canonical images in $\mathbf{V}^x$ and $\mathbf{V}_x$:

$$\delta^x_0 \ldots, \delta^x_N \in \mathbf{V}^x, \qquad \delta^0_x, \ldots, \delta^N_x \in \mathbf{V}_x \tag{3.16}$$

---

[14] See any standard work on classical tensor calculus, for example, [100].

We may use the generic symbols $\delta_{\mathfrak{x}}^x \in \mathbf{V}^x$, $\delta_x^{\mathfrak{x}} \in \mathbf{V}_x$, so the basis orthogonality relation takes the form

$$\delta_{\mathfrak{y}}^x \delta_x^{\mathfrak{x}} = \delta_{\mathfrak{y}}^{\mathfrak{x}} \tag{3.17}$$

where $\delta_{\mathfrak{y}}^{\mathfrak{x}}$ is the ordinary Kronecker delta symbol. (No relation between x and $\mathfrak{x}$ is to be implied by the notation.) We can also define an element δ_y^x of $\mathbf{V}_y^x$ by

$$\delta_y^{\mathfrak{x}} \delta_{\mathfrak{x}}^x = \delta_y^x \tag{3.18}$$

The quantity δ_y^x satisfies the usual properties

$$\xi \cdots^y \cdots \delta_y^x = \xi \cdots^x \cdots \qquad \eta \cdots_x \cdots \delta_y^x = \eta \cdots_y \cdots \tag{3.19}$$

and is clearly actually independent of the choice of basis, by virtue of this. The *components*, with respect to the basis, of any element $\zeta_{u \cdots w}^{x \cdots z} \in \mathbf{V}_{u \cdots w}^{x \cdots z}$ are given by

$$\zeta_{u \cdots \mathfrak{w}}^{\mathfrak{x} \cdots \mathfrak{z}} = \zeta_{u \cdots w}^{x \cdots z} \delta_{\mathfrak{u}}^u \cdots \delta_{\mathfrak{w}}^w \delta_x^{\mathfrak{x}} \cdots \delta_z^{\mathfrak{z}} \tag{3.20}$$

Conversely, to express $\zeta_{u \cdots w}^{x \cdots z}$ in terms of its components, we simply write

$$\zeta_{u \cdots w}^{x \cdots z} = \zeta_{\mathfrak{u} \cdots \mathfrak{w}}^{\mathfrak{x} \cdots \mathfrak{z}} \delta_u^{\mathfrak{u}} \cdots \delta_w^{\mathfrak{w}} \delta_{\mathfrak{x}}^x \cdots \delta_{\mathfrak{z}}^z \tag{3.21}$$

One aspect of this notation which is an advantage in certain contexts is that we may convert some indices into component form and leave others as abstract labels:

$$\rho_{bm}^{apr} = \rho_{bm}^{ap\mathfrak{r}} \delta_{\mathfrak{p}}^{\mathfrak{p}} \delta_{\mathfrak{b}}^b \in \mathbf{V}_m^{ar} \tag{3.22}$$

Generally, all *algebraic* relations will be unaffected by whether or not an index is in German type. But when we consider covariant derivatives in the next section, we shall see that an important *formal* difference arises between the ways the two types of index are treated—in addition to the present merely conceptual difference.

An elementary, but important, property of the type of algebraic structure that we have built up here, is that we can sometimes embed one such structure in another by the device of *grouping together indices*. Thus, we may consider a new labeling set $\hat{\mathbf{L}}$, say, whose elements are (disjoint) subsets of elements of $\mathbf{L}$. For example, we could put $\alpha = abc$, $\beta = def$, $\gamma = ghi$, etc., where $\mathbf{L}$ is divided exhaustively into disjoint triplets, these triplets being the elements of $\hat{\mathbf{L}}$. It is clear that, in this case, the sets $\mathbf{V}^\alpha = \mathbf{V}^{abc}$, $\mathbf{V}^\beta = \mathbf{V}^{def}$, ..., $\mathbf{V}_\alpha = \mathbf{V}_{abc}$, ..., $\mathbf{V}_\gamma^{\alpha\beta} = \mathbf{V}_{ghi}^{abcdef}$, ... will satisfy just the same rules as before. More complicated groupings are also possible.

We may also consider systems where the labeling set contains elements of different "types." The only modifications of our scheme would then come in index substitution (where only labels of the *same* type may be substituted for one another) and in contraction, where only an upper and lower indices of the *same* type may be contracted together. When we consider spinors in the next section we shall see an example of this kind of system. We shall have labels of two different types (related to each other via an operation of complex conjugation).

4 SPACE-TIMES WITH SPINOR STRUCTURE

In order to discuss the structure of space-time in detail, we shall need a definition of a differentiable manifold. I shall use the definition as given by Chevalley, *cf.* Nomizu [65], which gives the differentiable structure of a manifold $\mathcal{M}$ entirely in terms of the C^∞ real-valued functions on $\mathcal{M}$. I have chosen to use this definition here, not because of any special intrinsic mathematical merit, but because I feel it reflects most nearly, the role that is played by coordinate systems in physics. Thus, a coordinate system in space-time is actually a set of four real-valued functions on the space-time such that, in some neighborhood, knowledge of the values of these functions will fix the point in a "smooth" manner.

Let us start with space-time $\mathcal{M}$ as a topological space. A set of subsets of $\mathcal{M}$, referred to as the *open* sets, is singled out subject to:

THE INTERSECTION OF ANY TWO OPEN SETS IS OPEN. (4.1)

THE UNION OF ANY SET OF OPEN SETS IS OPEN. (4.2)

THE HAUSDORFF CONDITION HOLDS (THAT IS, FOR ANY TWO POINTS
OF $\mathcal{M}$, TWO DISJOINT OPEN SETS EXIST EACH CONTAINING ONE
OF THE POINTS). (4.3)

$\mathcal{M}$ IS CONNECTED (THAT IS, NOT THE UNION OF TWO DISJOINT
NONEMPTY OPEN SETS). (4.4)

THERE IS A COUNTABLE NUMBER OF OPEN SETS, OF WHICH EVERY
OPEN SET ON $\mathcal{M}$ IS A UNION. (4.5)

The concept of an open set is a very nonphysical one, but it is essential to the mathematical idea of a manifold. To dispense with the open set concept we would have to change the theory. The question of defining open sets in terms of the more physical notion of *causality* will be touched upon in Section 11.

We now single out a certain set **T**, of real-valued functions on $\mathcal{M}$, which will turn out to be the C^∞ real functions on the space-time $\mathcal{M}$. We can characterize the differentiable structure of $\mathcal{M}$ by the following axioms on **T**:

IF $f_1, f_2, \ldots, f_n \in \mathbf{T}$ AND IF ϕ IS ANY REAL-VALUED C^∞-FUNCTION OF
n VARIABLES (IN THE ORDINARY SENSE), THEN $\phi(f_1, f_2, \ldots, f_n) \in \mathbf{T}$; (4.6)

IF f IS SUCH THAT, FOR EACH $P \in \mathcal{M}$ THERE EXISTS AN ELEMENT $f_{(P)} \in \mathbf{T}$, WHICH AGREES WITH f THROUGHOUT AN OPEN SET CONTAINING P, THEN $f \in \mathbf{T}$;   (4.7)

FOR EACH $P \in \mathcal{M}$, THERE IS AN OPEN SET $\mathcal{S}$ CONTAINING P AND FOUR ELEMENTS $x^0, x^1, x^2, x^3 \in \mathbf{T}$ SUCH THAT THE MAP WHICH CARRIES $Q \in \mathcal{S}$ INTO $(x^0(Q), x^1(Q), x^2(Q), x^3(Q))$ IS A HOMEOMORPHISIM ONTO AN OPEN SUBSET OF $\mathbf{R}^4$, AND SUCH THAT ANY $f \in \mathbf{T}$ AGREES, ON $\mathcal{S}$, WITH SOME C^∞-FUNCTION OF $x^0, \ldots, x^3$.   (4.8)

The property (4.8) expresses what is required of the functions $x^0, \ldots, x^3$ on $\mathcal{M}$ that they should be adequate as *local coordinates* about P.

We can define a C^∞ contravariant vector field ξ on $\mathcal{M}$ (that is, a C^∞ cross section of the tangent bundle of $\mathcal{M}$) as a *derivation* on the algebra $\mathbf{T}$ (over the constants) that is, a mapping $\xi : \mathbf{T} \to \mathbf{T}$ such that

$$\xi(f + g) = \xi(f) + \xi(g) \tag{4.9}$$

$$\xi(fg) = f\xi(g) + g\xi(f) \tag{4.10}$$

$$\xi(k) = 0 \text{ if } k \text{ is constant on } \mathcal{M} \tag{4.11}$$

The set $\mathbf{T}^{\bullet}$ of such ξ's is clearly a module over $\mathbf{T}$, with $(\xi + \eta)(f) = \xi(f) + \eta(f)$, $(\lambda\xi)(f) = \lambda\xi(f)$ ($\lambda \in \mathbf{T}$; $\xi, \eta \in \mathbf{T}^{\bullet}$). It can be shown that, in terms of local coordinates $x^0, \ldots, x^3$ in an open set $\mathcal{S} \in \mathcal{M}$, any $\xi \in \mathbf{T}^{\bullet}$ has the form

$$\xi \equiv \xi^a \frac{\partial}{\partial x^a} \tag{4.12}$$

throughout $\mathcal{S}$. Thus, we can think of ξ^a as the components of ξ in the coordinate system x^a on $\mathcal{S}$. (When we pass to another local coordinate patch, the components ξ^a transform in the overlap region in the familiar way.)

At this point we could introduce, via $\mathbf{V}^{\bullet} = \mathbf{T}^{\bullet}$, $\mathbf{F} = \mathbf{T}$, the system of tensors with labels, as in Section 3, and we should arrive at a coordinate-free "abstract index" version of the familiar tensor calculus. What I propose to do here is something slightly different. I wish to present a somewhat unusual development of space-time theory. The reason for this, touches on what is perhaps an essential difference between mathematics and physics. In mathematics, one is interested in formalisms of maximum generality, so that any results obtained will have the widest possible application. Sometimes these applications are very far removed from the original topic, and great conceptual unifications may be thereby achieved. In physics, the aim is somewhat different. We are given a very specific (?) structure which we do not adequately understand—namely, the universe. Certain aspects of this structure are mirrored very accurately (in a miraculous way!) by certain mathematical models. However, we know, for various reasons, that these models are not quite (?) right. Thus, we are always interested in altering the mathematical theory. Now a formalism for physics which contains even an arbitrary parameter (such as the *dimension* of differentiable manifold, for example) is in a sense *too* general. We search for a formalism which is *specific* rather than general. Sometimes, by reformulating an old theory in an unusual (though mathematically equivalent) way, previously unexpected possibilities for modifying the theory may appear as mathematically natural. An example of this would be Newtonian gravitational theory. In the normal version of the theory, one might, for example, envisage changing the exponent -2 in the inverse square law to some other power. (In fact, such alterations were tried, in order to explain the motion of Mercury, but this does not work!) On the other hand, if Newtonian theory had been reformulated as a *space-time theory* in the way indicated in Section 2, then a quite different alteration—namely, to some form of general relativity—would have appeared as mathematically natural.

What I propose to do here is introduce a formalism for the description of space-time which makes its *spinor* structure[15] emerge as more basic even than its pseudo-Riemannian structure. In fact, the particular dimensionality and signature $(+, -, -, -)$, will have to be built in at the outset. Thus, if a modification of the present-day differentiable manifold picture of space-time were to emerge, which depended *essentially* on the existence of such a spinor structure, then the dimension and signature of our space-time would be one of the consequences of the theory.

The formalism will be based on the isomorphism[16] between the group $SL(2, \mathbf{C})$ of unimodular (2×2) complex matrices, and the twofold (universal) covering of the connected component of the Lorentz group $O(1, 3)$. To express this isomorphism in its most direct form, consider the general (2×2) Hermitian matrix, which I shall write as

$$\begin{pmatrix} u^{00'} & u^{01'} \\ u^{10'} & u^{11'} \end{pmatrix} = \frac{1}{\sqrt{2}} \begin{pmatrix} u^0 + u^1 & u^2 + iu^3 \\ u^2 - iu^3 & u^0 - u^1 \end{pmatrix} \tag{4.13}$$

If the matrix (4.13) is multiplied on the left by a unimodular (2×2) complex matrix $(t^{\mathfrak{A}}{}_{\mathfrak{B}})$ and on the right by the conjugate transpose of this matrix, then both the Hermiticity and the value of the determinant of (4.13) will be preserved. Thus, we obtain a linear transformation of (u^0, u^1, u^2, u^3) which preserves both the reality of u^{α} and the form

$$g_{ab} u^a u^b = (u^0)^2 - (u^1)^2 - (u^2)^2 - (u^3)^2 \tag{4.14}$$

---

[15] I am using the phrase "spinor structure" rather than "spin structure," to emphasize that in addition to being a spin manifold, $\mathcal{M}$ must possess a structure defined by the *particular* type of spinor system used here.

[16] The $(2-1)$ isomorphism between $SU(2, 2)$ and the connected component of $O(2, 4)$ can also be used in the study of space-time structure (*cf.* [79, 80]).

where

$$(g_{ab}) = \text{diag}\,(1, -1, -1, -1) \tag{4.15}$$

This is therefore a Lorentz transformation on u^a:

$$u^a \to L^a{}_b u^b \tag{4.16}$$

which is continuous with the identity (since $t^{\mathfrak{A}}{}_{\mathfrak{B}}$ is continuous with $\delta^{\mathfrak{A}}_{\mathfrak{B}}$). Conversely, it follows (for a variety of reasons) that any such transformation (4.16) arises from precisely *two* unimodular matrices $(t^{\mathfrak{A}}{}_{\mathfrak{B}})$, namely, $(t^{\mathfrak{A}}{}_{\mathfrak{B}})$ and $(-t^{\mathfrak{A}}{}_{\mathfrak{B}})$. Thus, (4.16) is equivalent to

$$u^{\mathfrak{A}\mathfrak{A}'} \to t^{\mathfrak{A}}{}_{\mathfrak{B}}\,\bar{t}^{\mathfrak{A}'}{}_{\mathfrak{B}'}\,u^{\mathfrak{B}\mathfrak{B}'} \tag{4.17}$$

(The notation, here, is to regard $\mathfrak{A}$ and $\mathfrak{A}'$ as *distinct* letters, so, in particular, no summation is implied between them. Thus, (4.17) is *four* relations. When complex conjugates are taken, unprimed indices become primed and primed indices become unprimed. Thus, $\bar{t}^{0'}{}_{1'}$ is the complex conjugate of $t^0{}_1$, for example. Capital German indices run over the two values 0, 1 or $0', 1'$. Lower case German indices will run over 0, 1, 2, 3.)

The usual way to think of the components of a world vector in a pseudo-orthonormal frame is as a linearly ordered array (u^0, u^1, u^2, u^3). But alternatively, the matrix version (4.13) would be just as good, and the idea here will be to regard this matrix description as *more* basic. In this way, a world vector appears as *not* the most elementary " vectorial " quantity in space-time, since it is now a " divalent " object and we would expect that there might also be " univalent " (two-component) objects with some space-time meaning. In fact, this turns out to be the case. These " univalent " objects will be called *spin-vectors*. The idea, then, will be to take as our basic module (the " $\mathbf{V}^{\bullet}$ " of Section 2) not the set of world-vector fields $\mathbf{T}^{\bullet}$, but the C^∞ *spin-vector* fields[17] $\mathbf{S}^{\bullet}$ on $\mathcal{M}$. The fact that I have not yet defined a spin-vector in space-time terms will not matter. The procedure is more the other way around. The algebra generated by the spin-vectors will serve, instead, to define the structure of the space-time. Once we have this structure we shall then be able to go back and interpret the spin-vectors in more familiar terms. We shall, in fact, end up with a remarkably complete interpretation of a spin vector in " physical " terms (*cf.* Section 5).

Now what intrinsic structure should our module $\mathbf{S}^{\bullet}$ of spin-vector fields possess? At each point $P \in \mathcal{M}$, we require the fiber $\mathbf{S}^{\bullet}(P)$ above P to be a two-dimensional complex vector space (" spin space "). The symmetry of this space is to be given by the group $SL(2, \mathbf{C})$, so that the local Lorentz group symmetry of space-time will be reflected in spin space

---

[17] The system $\mathbf{S}^{\bullet}$ will turn out to be the C^∞ cross sections of the bundle of spin-vectors over $\mathcal{M}$, regarded as a module over the C^∞ complex valued functions on $\mathcal{M}$.

symmetry. If ω^0, ω^1 are the components of $\omega \in \mathbf{S}^*(P)$ in some basis frame, then an (active) symmetry transformation of $\mathbf{S}^*(P)$ will be given by

$$\omega^{\mathfrak{A}} \to t^{\mathfrak{A}}{}_{\mathfrak{B}} \omega^{\mathfrak{B}} \tag{4.18}$$

(keeping the basis frame fixed), the matrix $(t^{\mathfrak{A}}{}_{\mathfrak{B}})$ being complex and uni-modular. Comparing (4.18) with (4.17) and (4.16) [via (4.13)] we see that if we regard the world-vector space $\mathbf{T}^*(P)$ as being actually the tensor product of $\mathbf{S}^*(P)$ with its complex conjugate, then the allowable (active) symmetries of $\mathbf{T}^*(P)$ become just Lorentz transformations which do not involve space reflections or time reversals. Each element of the module $\mathbf{S}^*$ will be disjoint union over all $P \in \mathscr{M}$, of an element from each $\mathbf{S}^*(P)$. Some differentiable structure will be imposed as well. This will be defined axiomatically, shortly. An object built up of tensor products of $\mathbf{S}^*$, its dual $\mathbf{S}_*$ and the complex conjugates of these two spaces will be called a *spinor field* on $\mathscr{M}$. A world-vector field is thus seen to be a special case. Here, "tensor product" will be interpreted in the sense given in Section 3. The labeling system will be very useful in order to keep track of the various operations.

We shall need spinor labels of two types:

$$A, B, C, \ldots, A_0, \ldots, A_1, \ldots \tag{4.19}$$

$$A', B', C', \ldots, A_0', \ldots, A_1', \ldots \tag{4.20}$$

For each $\omega \in \mathbf{S}^*$, there will correspond elements $\omega^A \in \mathbf{S}^A$, $\omega^B \in \mathbf{S}^B$, ..., $\omega^X \in \mathbf{S}^X$, ... and also elements $\bar{\omega}^{A'} \in \mathbf{S}^{A'}$, $\bar{\omega}^{B'} \in \mathbf{S}^{B'}$, ..., $\bar{\omega}^{X'} \in \mathbf{S}^{X'}$, ... As before, we can, if desired, think of ω^X as being simply the *pair* (ω, X), etc. The ring $\mathbf{S}$ will be identified as the *complex* C^∞-functions on $\mathscr{M}$:

$$\mathbf{S} = \mathbf{T} \oplus i\mathbf{T} \tag{4.21}$$

The difference between the primed and unprimed labels arises because we shall require that, whereas each of the modules $\mathbf{S}^A$, $\mathbf{S}^B$, ... over $\mathbf{S}$ is canonic-ally isomorphic with $\mathbf{S}^*$, the modules $\mathbf{S}^{A'}$, $\mathbf{S}^{B'}$, ... over $\mathbf{S}$ are each canonically *anti-isomorphic* with $\mathbf{S}^*$. That is, if $\lambda, \mu \in \mathbf{S}$ and $\boldsymbol{\alpha}, \boldsymbol{\beta}, \boldsymbol{\gamma} \in \mathbf{S}^*$, with $\gamma = \lambda\boldsymbol{\alpha} + \mu\boldsymbol{\beta}$, then

$$\gamma^X = \lambda\alpha^X + \mu\beta^X \qquad \text{and} \qquad \bar{\gamma}^{X'} = \bar{\lambda}\bar{\alpha}^{X'} + \bar{\mu}\bar{\beta}^{X'} \tag{4.22}$$

We shall, in fact, regard each $\bar{\omega}^{X'}$ as being the *complex conjugate* of the corresponding ω^X and occasionally write

$$\overline{\omega^X} = \bar{\omega}^{X'}; \overline{\pi^{X'}} = \bar{\pi}^X \tag{4.23}$$

(We may think of the complex conjugation operation as effecting an inter-change of the list (4.19) with the list (4.20), when applied to the labels them-selves.) Our spinor system will then be built up just as in Section 3, but with the proviso that contractions and index substitutions can occur only between index labels of the *same* type (that is, only between primed or only

between unprimed labels).   Since index substitutions do not effect inter-
changes of primed index labels with unprimed ones, we shall regard the
relative ordering of primed and unprimed indices as irrelevant.   On the other
hand, it will be significant to maintain an ordering (in most cases) between
indices of the *same* type *even* when some are upper indices and others are
lower indices.   Thus, for example,

$$\rho^{AA'}{}_{B'B}{}^{Q} = \rho^{A'A}{}_{B}{}^{Q}{}_{B'} = \rho^{AA'Q}{}_{BB'} \neq \rho^{AA'Q}{}_{BB'} \tag{4.24}$$

Complex conjugation gives us a fifth operation on the spinor system $\{S\}$,
in addition to (3.11)–(3.14):

$$\text{complex conjugation}: S^{X\,\cdots\,ZW'\,\cdots\,Y'}_{P\,\cdots\,SQ'\,\cdots\,U'} \to S^{W\,\cdots\,YX'\,\cdots\,Z'}_{Q\,\cdots\,UP'\,\cdots\,S'} \tag{4.25}$$

defined on each element $\rho^{X\cdots ZW'\cdots Y'}_{P\,\cdots\,SQ'\cdots\,U'}$ [expanded as in (3.9)] in the
obvious way [*cf.* (4.23)].

So far, we have not incorporated into the spinor algebra, the fact that
the $(t^{\mathfrak{A}}{}_{\mathfrak{B}})$ matrices have to be unimodular.   This unimodular condition can
be written alternatively as

$$\varepsilon^{\mathfrak{A}\mathfrak{C}} = t^{\mathfrak{A}}{}_{\mathfrak{B}} t^{\mathfrak{C}}{}_{\mathfrak{D}} \varepsilon^{\mathfrak{B}\mathfrak{D}} \qquad \text{or} \qquad \varepsilon_{\mathfrak{B}\mathfrak{D}} = t^{\mathfrak{A}}{}_{\mathfrak{B}} t^{\mathfrak{C}}{}_{\mathfrak{D}} \varepsilon_{\mathfrak{A}\mathfrak{C}} \tag{4.26}$$

Here, the Levi–Civita symbols

$$(\varepsilon_{\mathfrak{A}\mathfrak{B}}) = (\varepsilon^{\mathfrak{A}\mathfrak{B}}) = \begin{pmatrix} 0 & 1 \\ -1 & 0 \end{pmatrix} \tag{4.27}$$

are being used.   Let us denote by ε_{AB} and ε^{AB} the elements of S_{AB} and S^{AB},
respectively, whose components in some basis are given by (4.27).   Then
(4.26) tells us that ε_{AB} and ε^{AB} are *invariant* under the active symmetry transformation of $S^{\bullet}(P)$ given by (4.18).   We shall regard ε_{AB}, ε^{AB} and their
complex conjugates $\varepsilon_{A'B'}$, $\varepsilon^{A'B'}$ as an essential part of the internal structure
of the spinor system.   (It would have been more logical to write $\bar{\varepsilon}_{A'B'}$ for
$\varepsilon_{A'B'}$ and $\bar{\varepsilon}^{A'B'}$ for $\varepsilon^{A'B'}$, but these bars are normally omitted.)   Any basis for
which the components $\varepsilon_{\mathfrak{A}\mathfrak{B}}$ have the form (4.27) will be called a normalized
basis or *spin frame*.

One effect of the presence of the ε's is that they establish a canonical
isomorphism between $S^{\bullet}$ and its dual $S_{\bullet}$.   This is achieved via the lowering
and raising of spinor index labels:

$$\xi^{\cdots\,A\,\cdots} \varepsilon_{AB} = \xi_{\cdots\,B\,\cdots} \qquad \varepsilon^{AB}\xi_{\cdots\,B\,\cdots} = \xi^{\cdots\,A\,\cdots} \tag{4.28}$$

$$\eta^{\cdots\,A'\,\cdots}\varepsilon_{A'B'} = \eta_{\cdots\,B'\,\cdots} \qquad \varepsilon^{A'B'}\eta_{\cdots\,B'\,\cdots} = \xi^{\cdots\,A'\,\cdots} \tag{4.29}$$

(In view of this, it may be felt that it is redundant to use *both* lower and upper
labels.   The reason for maintaining the distinction is essentially a matter
of "bookkeeping."   In fact, a notation *is* possible which does *not* maintain
this distinction, but it looks a little strange since spin vectors must then

anticommute! I have chosen to be conventional in this respect.) Note that

$$\zeta \cdots {}_X \cdots {}^X \cdots \cdots = -\zeta \cdots {}^X \cdots \cdots {}_X \cdots \qquad (4.30)$$

(and similarly for primed indices) because of the antisymmetry:

$$\varepsilon_{AB} = -\varepsilon_{BA} \qquad \varepsilon^{AB} = -\varepsilon^{BA} \qquad (4.31)$$

so we must be careful about orderings when we raise and lower indices. For this reason, and so as to avoid notational confusion at a later stage, the symbols δ_B^A and $\delta_{B'}^{A'}$, corresponding to (3.18) will *not* be used here. Instead, the equivalent symbols $\varepsilon_B{}^A$, $\varepsilon_{B'}{}^{A'}$ will be employed. We have

$$\varepsilon_{AB}\,\varepsilon^{CB} = \varepsilon_A{}^C = -\varepsilon^C{}_A \qquad \varepsilon_A{}^A = 2 \qquad (4.32)$$

$$\zeta \cdots {}_B \cdots = \zeta \cdots {}_A \cdots \varepsilon_B{}^A \qquad \zeta \cdots {}^B \cdots = \zeta \cdots {}^A \cdots \varepsilon_A{}^B \qquad (4.33)$$

so that $\varepsilon_B{}^A$ has the properties (3.19) required of a "δ_B." (Note that the raising and lowering operations are consistent.) With any choice of spin frame $\varepsilon_{\mathfrak{A}}{}^A$, $\varepsilon_A{}^{\mathfrak{A}}$ we have

$$\left(\varepsilon_{\mathfrak{A}}{}^{\mathfrak{B}} \right) = \begin{pmatrix} 1 & 0 \\ 0 & 1 \end{pmatrix} \qquad (4.34)$$

If a spinor is skew-symmetrical in three or more indices then it vanishes (from two-dimensionality). Hence,

$$\varepsilon_{AB}\,\varepsilon_{CD} + \varepsilon_{AC}\,\varepsilon_{DB} + \varepsilon_{AD}\,\varepsilon_{BC} = 0 \qquad (4.35)$$

One consequence of (4.35) is that if $\zeta \ldots {}_A \ldots {}_B \ldots$ is skew-symmetrical in A and B:

$$\zeta \ldots {}_A \ldots {}_B \ldots = -\zeta \ldots {}_B \ldots {}_A \ldots \qquad (4.36)$$

then

$$\zeta \ldots {}_A \ldots {}_B \ldots = \tfrac{1}{2}\varepsilon_{AB}\,\zeta \ldots {}_X \ldots {}^X \ldots \qquad (4.37)$$

This property is closely related to the representation theory of $SL(2, \mathbf{C})$, since it indicates that it is only spinors totally symmetrical in all unprimed indices and in all primed indices which cannot be reduced into simpler parts. The components of a spinor with r symmetric lower unprimed indices and with s symmetric lower primed indices are said to transform according to the $D(r/2, s/2)$ irreducible representation of the Lorentz group.

Let us now incorporate the world-tensors into our spinor scheme, introducing world-tensor labels (3.1) by identifying them as *pairs* of spinor labels as follows:

$$a = AA', b = BB', c = CC', \ldots, a_0 = A_0 A_0', \ldots \qquad (4.38)$$

This gives us the subsystem $(\mathbf{S}, \mathbf{S}^a, \mathbf{S}^b, \ldots, \mathbf{S}_a, \ldots, \mathbf{S}_{u \cdots w}^{x \cdots z}, \ldots)$ of *complex world tensors*, closed under the operations (3.11)–(3.14) and also under the complex conjugation operation (4.25), which here acts: $\mathbf{S}_{u \cdots w}^{x \cdots z} \to \mathbf{S}_{u \cdots w}^{x \cdots z}$.

The elements which are invariant under complex conjugation are the *real* world-tensors: $\bar{\alpha}_{u\,\cdots\,w}^{x\,\cdots\,z} = \alpha_{u\,\cdots\,w}^{x\,\cdots\,z}$. The real world-tensor fields from a subsystem $\{T\}$ of $\{S\}$:

$$\{T\} = (T, T^a, T^b, \ldots, T_a, \ldots, T_{u\,\cdots\,w}^{x\,\cdots\,z}, \ldots) \tag{4.39}$$

To see that this process is really what is involved in (4.13), let us consider a spin frame $\varepsilon_{\mathfrak{A}}{}^A$, $\varepsilon_A{}^{\mathfrak{A}}$ for $\mathbf{S}^{\bullet}$ and define (with $\varepsilon_{A'}{}^{\mathfrak{A}'} = \overline{\varepsilon_A{}^{\mathfrak{A}}}$)

$$\delta_a^0 = \frac{1}{\sqrt{2}}(\varepsilon_A{}^0 \varepsilon_{A'}{}^{0'} + \varepsilon_A{}^1 \varepsilon_{A'}{}^{1'})$$

$$\delta_a^1 = \frac{1}{\sqrt{2}}(\varepsilon_A{}^0 \varepsilon_{A'}{}^{0'} - \varepsilon_A{}^1 \varepsilon_{A'}{}^{1'})$$

$$\tag{4.40}$$

$$\delta_a^2 = \frac{1}{\sqrt{2}}(\varepsilon_A{}^1 \varepsilon_{A'}{}^{0'} + \varepsilon_A{}^0 \varepsilon_{A'}{}^{1'})$$

$$\delta_a^3 = \frac{i}{\sqrt{2}}(\varepsilon_A{}^1 \varepsilon_{A'}{}^{0'} - \varepsilon_A{}^0 \varepsilon_{A'}{}^{1'})$$

This is readily seen to give (4.13), where $u^a = u^{AA'}$ and

$$u^a = u^a \delta_a^a \qquad u^{\mathfrak{A}\mathfrak{A}'} = u^{AA'} \varepsilon_A{}^{\mathfrak{A}} \varepsilon_{A'}{}^{\mathfrak{A}'} \tag{4.41}$$

as is required by the convention (3.20). The definitions (4.40) give us a standard way of obtaining a world-vector basis from any spin frame. However, it is important that we not be tied down to this particular correspondence in all cases. Sometimes we shall prefer to obtain our world-vector basis as the one naturally obtained from a *coordinate system*. In other circumstances the *null-tetrad*

$$\delta_0^a = \varepsilon_0{}^A \varepsilon_{0'}{}^{A'} \qquad \delta_1^a = \varepsilon_1{}^A \varepsilon_1{}^{A'} \qquad \delta_2^a = \varepsilon_0{}^A \varepsilon_1{}^{A'} \qquad \delta_3^a = \varepsilon_1{}^A \varepsilon_0{}^{A'} \tag{4.42}$$

is a convenient basis to use. In each case, we can define the Infeld–van der Waerden translation symbols [46, 110]:

$$\sigma_a^{\mathfrak{A}\mathfrak{A}'} = \delta_a^a \varepsilon_A{}^{\mathfrak{A}} \varepsilon_{A'}{}^{\mathfrak{A}'} \qquad \sigma_{\mathfrak{A}\mathfrak{A}'}^a = \delta_a^a \varepsilon_{\mathfrak{A}}{}^A \varepsilon_{\mathfrak{A}'}{}^{A'} \tag{4.43}$$

(Recall that $a = AA'$, so a contraction is taking place between the *abstract* labels. On the other hand, no connection is to be implied between a, and $\mathfrak{A}, \mathfrak{A}'$, so no summation is involved. Each of (4.43) stands for 16 equations.) In fact, the Infeld–van der Waerden symbols are really just δ_a^b, but with the upper and lower indices expressed according to different kinds of bases. The relation between spinor components and world-tensor components is then exemplified by

$$\psi_a{}^b = \psi_{\mathfrak{A}\mathfrak{A}'}{}^{\mathfrak{B}\mathfrak{B}'} \sigma_a^{\mathfrak{A}\mathfrak{A}'} \sigma_{\mathfrak{B}\mathfrak{B}'}^b \qquad \psi_{\mathfrak{A}\mathfrak{A}'}{}^{\mathfrak{B}\mathfrak{B}'} = \psi_a{}^b \sigma_{\mathfrak{A}\mathfrak{A}'}^a \sigma_b^{\mathfrak{B}\mathfrak{B}'} \tag{4.44}$$

Now, consider twice the determinant of (4.13):

$$u^{\mathfrak{A}\mathfrak{A}'} u^{\mathfrak{B}\mathfrak{B}'} \varepsilon_{\mathfrak{A}\mathfrak{B}} \varepsilon_{\mathfrak{A}'\mathfrak{B}'} = u^a u^b g_{ab} \tag{4.45}$$

This becomes

$$u^a u^b (\varepsilon_{AB} \varepsilon_{A'B'} - g_{ab}) = 0 \tag{4.46}$$

on translation back to the abstract labels [*cf.* (3.21)], so [because of the symmetry of g_{ab} and of $\varepsilon_{AB} \varepsilon_{A'B'}$ under interchange of a, b and the fact that (4.46) holds for all u^a] we get

$$g_{ab} = \varepsilon_{AB} \varepsilon_{A'B'} \tag{4.47}$$

Equation (4.47) expresses the fundamental way in which the metric of space-time is defined by its spinor structure. Note, in particular, that the $(+, -, -, -)$ *signature is built into the formalism* by the identification (4.47), because with the choice of world-vector basis (4.40), we get (4.15). As a consequence of (4.47), (4.32), (4.31) we have

$$g^{ab} = \varepsilon^{AB} \varepsilon^{A'B'} \qquad \delta_a^b = \varepsilon_A{}^B \varepsilon_{A'}{}^{B'} \qquad g_{ab} = g_{ba} \qquad g_{ab} g^{bc} = \delta_a^c \tag{4.48}$$

so the spinor raising and lowering conventions yield

$$\zeta \overset{\cdots}{\underset{a}{\cdots}} \overset{\cdots}{\cdots} = \zeta \overset{\cdots}{\cdots}{}^b \overset{\cdots}{\cdots} g_{ab} \qquad \zeta \overset{\cdots}{\cdots}{}^b \overset{\cdots}{\cdots} = \zeta \overset{\cdots}{\underset{a}{\cdots}} \overset{\cdots}{\cdots} g^{ab} \tag{4.49}$$

Thus, the notation is consistent with the usual conventions.

So far, nothing has been said to relate the spinor structure to the manifold $\mathcal{M}$ as a whole. In order to connect the various $\mathbf{S}^{\bullet}(P)$'s to each other, it will be necessary to consider differentiation. Let us define axiomatically the various rules we shall need. We require an operation of *covariant differentiation*:

$$\nabla_{XY'} : \mathbf{S}_{F \cdots MH' \cdots K}^{P \cdots SR' \cdots T'} \to \mathbf{S}_{F \cdots MXH' \cdots K'Y'}^{P \cdots SR' \cdots T'} \tag{4.50}$$

satisfying

$$\nabla_{XY'} (\psi \overset{\cdots}{\cdots} + \chi \overset{\cdots}{\cdots}) = \nabla_{XY'} \psi \overset{\cdots}{\cdots} + \nabla_{XY'} \chi \overset{\cdots}{\cdots} \tag{4.51}$$

$$\nabla_{XY'} (\psi \overset{\cdots}{\cdots} \chi \overset{\cdots}{\cdots}) = \chi \overset{\cdots}{\cdots} \nabla_{XY'} \psi \overset{\cdots}{\cdots} + \psi \overset{\cdots}{\cdots} \nabla_{XY'} \chi \overset{\cdots}{\cdots} \tag{4.52}$$

$$\nabla_{XY'} \varepsilon_{AB} = 0$$

$$\nabla_{XY'} \varepsilon^{AB} = 0 \tag{4.53}$$

$$\psi \overset{\cdots}{\cdots} = \nabla_{XY'} \chi \overset{\cdots}{\cdots} \qquad \text{IMPLIES} \qquad \overline{\psi \overset{\cdots}{\cdots}} = \nabla_{YX'} \overline{\chi \overset{\cdots}{\cdots}} \tag{4.54}$$

$$\psi \overset{\cdots A \cdots}{\underset{\cdots B \cdots}{\cdots}} = \nabla_{XY'} \chi \overset{\cdots A \cdots}{\underset{\cdots B \cdots}{\cdots}} \qquad \text{IMPLIES} \qquad \psi \overset{\cdots A \cdots}{\underset{\cdots A \cdots}{\cdots}} = \nabla_{XY'} \chi \overset{\cdots A \cdots}{\underset{\cdots A \cdots}{\cdots}} \tag{4.55}$$

$\nabla_{XY'}$ COMMUTES WITH ANY INDEX SUBSTITUTION (NOT INVOLVING X OR Y') (4.56)

$$\nabla_x \nabla_z \phi = \nabla_z \nabla_x \phi \tag{4.57}$$

FOR ANY DERIVATION ξ ON $\mathbf{T}$, THERE EXISTS A UNIQUE ELEMENT $\xi^a \in \mathbf{T}^a$ SUCH THAT $\xi(\phi) = \xi^a \nabla_a \phi$, FOR EACH $\phi \in \mathbf{T}$ (4.58)

Actually, the axioms (4.51)–(4.58) are not quite independent of one another, but they express all the properties that we require. Note, that it is (4.58) which connects {**S**} with the tangent bundle of $\mathcal{M}$. The world-vectors become tangent vectors to $\mathcal{M}$. The operator $\nabla_{XY'}$ is uniquely defined by all these properties. (Clearly, for any other pair of labels M, N', say, we can also define $\nabla_{MN'}$ by index substitution.) Conversely, we may ask whether the existence of a system {**S**} satisfying all the requirements we have imposed implies any restriction on M as a differentiable manifold, or as a pseudo-Riemannian manifold with given $(+, -, -, -)$ metric (with which the g_{ab} of (4.47) is supposed to agree). The answer is that *locally* no such restriction is implied (that is an {**S**} exists for some open set containing any given $P \in \mathcal{M}$) whereas *globally* there *are* such restrictions. A similar remark applies to the uniqueness of {**S**}. These global restrictions on $\mathcal{M}$ will enter into the discussion in the next section.

5   THE INTERPRETATION OF A SPIN-VECTOR

In the previous section, spinors were introduced completely formally. Only the elements of {**T**} were given a direct interpretation in space-time terms. One might imagine that any geometrical interpretation of the remaining elements of {**S**} would necessarily be very indirect. However, this turns out not to be the case. Any spin-vector has, in fact, a very graphic space-time interpretation up to sign. Even the sign can be given a meaning in terms of physical constructions.

Let us try to interpret the spin-vector

$$\omega^A \in \mathbf{S}^A(P)$$

The most obvious world-tensor we can build from ω^A is the world-vector

$$u^a = \omega^A \overline{\omega}^{A'} \tag{5.1}$$

Now $u^a u_a = |\omega^A \omega_A|^2 = 0$ (since $\omega^A \omega_A = -\omega_A \omega^A = 0$), so u^a points along the null cone at P. In fact, *every* real null world-vector has either the form (5.1) or the form

$$v^a = -\omega^A \overline{\omega}^{A'} \tag{5.2}$$

and every complex world-vector, null in the sense $w^a w_a = 0$, has the form

$$w^a = \omega^A \pi^{A'} \tag{5.3}$$

These facts follow at once from the representation (4.13), since a (2×2) matrix of vanishing determinant has rank at most unity and is therefore the outer product of two vectors. Note that the existence of the spinor system {**S**} gives us an absolute distinction between the two null half-cones at P. We can *define* the *future-pointing* null vectors to be those for which (5.1) holds (with $\omega^A \neq 0$) and the *past-pointing* null vectors to be those for which (5.2) holds ($\omega^A \neq 0$). (This is consistent with (4.13) if positive u^0 corresponds to time increasing.) This gives us the first global restriction on $\mathcal{M}$, as a pseudo-Riemannian manifold, implied by the existence of $\{\mathbf{S}\}$: $\mathcal{M}$ must be *time-orientable*. That is to say, the division of the null half-cones of $\mathcal{M}$ into two classes, "future" and "past," can be made continuously over the whole manifold.

Equation (5.1) tells us, then, that a future-pointing real null world-vector is uniquely defined by any nonzero spin-vector. However, many spin-vectors will correspond to the same null world-vector since (5.1) is invariant under

$$\omega^A \to e^{i\theta}\omega^A \tag{5.4}$$

(θ real). To interpret the "phase" of ω^A we have to try something different. Let us "square" ω^A instead: $\omega^A\omega^B$. Then, to introduce as many primed indices as unprimed, we multiply by $\varepsilon^{A'B'}$. Finally, to get a real world-tensor we add the complex conjugate:

$$p^{ab} = \omega^A\omega^B\varepsilon^{A'B'} + \varepsilon^{AB}\overline{\omega}^{A'}\overline{\omega}^{B'} \tag{5.5}$$

Now p^{ab} is readily seen to be skew and simple:

$$p^{ab} = u^a k^b - k^a u^b \tag{5.6}$$

where

$$k^a = \omega^A\overline{\kappa}^{A'} + \kappa^A\overline{\omega}^{A'} \tag{5.7}$$

κ^A being any element of $\mathbf{S}^A(p)$ subject to $\omega_A\kappa^A = 1$, whence (by (4.37)) $\omega^A\kappa^B - \kappa^A\omega^B = \varepsilon^{AB}$. The vector k^a is a real, spacelike of length $\sqrt{2}$ and orthogonal to u^a:

$$\overline{k}^a = k^a \qquad k^a k_a = -2 \qquad k^a u_a = 0 \tag{5.8}$$

It is defined by p^{ab} up to the addition of a (real) multiple of u^a. The directions k^a therefore define a half-plane element at P (two-dimensional) which is tangent to the null cone along the null direction of u^a. Thus ω^A defines a kind of *null flag* [70, 73, 114] in the tangent space at P, whose flagpole is the future-pointing null vector u^a and whose flag plane is this null 2-plane through u^a (Fig. 7).

To get a better picture of the nature of this flag plane, let us take a section in the tangent space at P by a spacelike hyperplane not through P. This cuts the cone in a sphere S^2. The flagpole intersects S^2 in a *point* U and the flag plane gives us a *unit tangent vector* to S^2 at U (which we may identify with that choice of $2^{-1/2}k^a$ which lies parallel to our hyperplane). We can get a direct physical interpretation of this S^2 as the "celestial sphere"

FIGURE 7. The spin vector ω^A at P defines a null flag.   This may be pictured as
a tangent vector at a point U on the celestial sphere.

(or field of vision) of an observer at P.   (We can choose our spacelike
hyperplane orthogonal to the observer's world line at P.)   A photon arriving
at P has a world line (a null geodesic) which has a null tangent at P and is
therefore uniquely associated with a point U of S^2.   We may also describe
the *polarization* of the photon in terms of a flag plane, that is, as a tangent
vector at U to the celestial sphere.   Thus, a spin vector emerges as a natural
object for the description of a polarized photon.   This relation between
spinors and zero rest-mass particle fields (of various spins) will be discussed
in more detail in Section 8.

One final remark concerning the structure of the celestial sphere is
appropriate here.   The Riemannian metric induced on S^2 by the above
construction will depend on our choice of spacelike hyperplane, but the
conformal structure of S^2 is, on the other hand, well-defined.   One way of
seeing this is to refer to (4.18), which when applied to $\zeta = \omega^0/\omega^1$ yields the
fractional linear transformation $\zeta \to (t^0{}_0\zeta + t^0{}_1)/(t^1{}_0\zeta + t^1{}_1)$.   The complex
number ζ defines the point U, the complex ζ-plane being actually related
to S^2 by a stereographic projection [71].   Both these transformations are
conformal (and, in fact, send circles into circles).   Since (4.18) corresponds
to a Lorentz transformation, it follows that the celestial spheres of two
observers at P are related to each other by a conformal transformation [71,
106] (and a circular pattern seen by one observer will also appear as circular
to the other).   Another way of invariantly obtaining the conformal structure
of S^2 will emerge in a moment.

If we multiply ω^A by a nonzero complex number $\lambda = re^{i\theta}$ (r, θ real), then
u^a gets multiplied by r^2 and (taking $\kappa^A \to \lambda^{-1}\kappa^A$) k^a gets rotated through an
angle 2θ (in the plane spanned by k^a and $h^a = i\omega^A\bar{\kappa}^{A'} - i\kappa^A\bar{\omega}^{A'}$).   Thus, we
see that *under* $\omega^A \to \lambda\omega^A$, *the extent of the flagpole is multiplied by a factor* $\lambda\bar{\lambda}$
and the flag plane rotates through an angle 2 *arg* λ.   Note that this gives a
direct way of defining the conformal structure of our S^2 in terms of spinors.
If U is a point of S^2, then the angle between the two tangent vectors to S^2

at U given by ω^A and $e^{i\theta}\omega^A$, respectively, is simply 2θ. Having an invariant definition of angles on S^2 we therefore have an invariantly defined conformal structure for S^2. Note also that we have an invariantly defined *orientation* for S^2 and therefore also for $\mathscr{M}$. We can *define* the notion of *right-handed-ness* by simply specifying that "right-handed" is the sense in which the flag plane of $e^{i\theta}\omega^A$ rotates as θ increases. (This is consistent with the reference frame referred to in (4.13) being a right-hand one.) This gives us our second global restriction on $\mathscr{M}$ as a pseudo-Riemannian manifold: $\mathscr{M}$ must, in addition to being time-orientable, also be *space-orientable*. As a topological manifold, therefore, $\mathscr{M}$ is orientable.

The third and final global restriction on $\mathscr{M}$ as a pseudo-Riemannian (or topological) manifold, which is implied by the presence of $\{S\}$, arises in relation to another feature of the above representation of a spin-vector as a null flag. We note that both the u^a of (5.1) and the p^{ab} of (5.6) are invariant under

$$\omega^A \to -\omega^A \tag{5.9}$$

Explicitly, if we consider the flag plane given by $e^{i\theta}\omega^A$ as θ varies from 0 to π, we see that it executes one complete rotation through 2π and returns to its starting position, whereas ω^A becomes replaced by its negative. Only after a further complete rotation of the flag plane through 2π will the spin vector return to its original value. It is clear, moreover, that no additional local geometric structure added to the null flag, can distinguish ω^A from $-\omega^A$ (interpreting "local geometric structure" to refer to structure in the tangent space to $\mathscr{M}$ at P). For, a rotation of any such structure through 2π would return to its original configuration, whereas ω^A would undergo (5.9).

On the other hand, a *nonlocal* geometrical distinction between ω^A and $-\omega^A$ is possible. To obtain this, we consider a particular null flag at a particular point 0 of $\mathscr{M}$. Call this the *standard flag*. For simplicity, let us restrict our attention to a simply-connected region of $\mathscr{M}$ (or else work with the universal covering manifold of $\mathscr{M}$). The idea, then, is to identify a spin vector, not just with a null flag, but as an *equivalence class of flag paths*.[18] A flag path is a continuous sequence of null flags on $\mathscr{M}$ which start with the standard flag and end with some null flag at a point P of $\mathscr{M}$ (Fig. 8). Two flag paths are equivalent if they can be continuously distorted one into the other, keeping the end-points fixed, and the null flags at the end-points fixed. The existence of spin vectors now depends on the existence of *two* equivalence classes corresponding to each null flag at P. If we consider flag paths based on a *fixed* curve on $\mathscr{M}$ and ending at a fixed null flag, then it follows from the

---

[18] I have been deliberately somewhat vague as to whether the geometrical structure corresponding to the *zero* spin vector at P should be called a "null flag." However, in the case of a *flag path*, the "zero null flags" are to be definitely excluded.

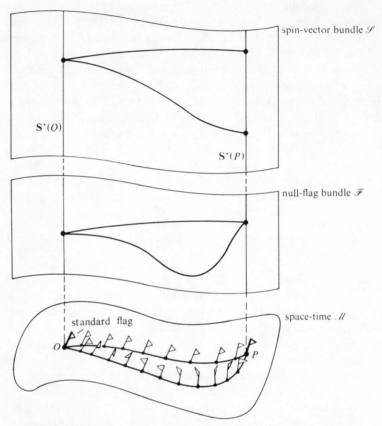

FIGURE 8. Flag paths in $\mathscr{M}$ and their images in $\mathscr{F}$ and $\mathscr{S}$.

topology of the Lorentz group that there are precisely two equivalence classes of flag paths associated with the curve, which are related to each other by a net relative rotation through 2π between 0 and P.   But if we allow the curve, on which the flag path is based, to vary over the manifold and then return to its original position, it may be that these equivalence classes become united inside a single equivalence class.   Then spin-vectors could not be defined on the manifold.   Another way of stating this property arises if we allow P to coincide with 0.   If the (closed) flag path consisting simply of a rotation through 2π of the standard flag about its flagpole can be continuously distorted, by moving the curve about the manifold, into the constant flag path (that is, no motion of the null flag at all), then a spinor structure does not exist.

The above construction clearly actually refers to the null-flag bundle $\mathscr{F}$ of $\mathscr{M}$ (an 8-dimensional space of all null flags at all points of $\mathscr{M}$).   A flag path corresponds to a curve in $\mathscr{F}$. If $\mathscr{M}$ is simply-connected, the above construction gives the spin-vector bundle $\mathscr{S}$ (space of all spin vectors at all points of $\mathscr{M}$) as the universal (twofold) covering space of $\mathscr{F}$—*provided* that $\mathscr{F}$ possesses a twofold covering. If $\mathscr{F}$ does not possess a twofold covering (that is, is simply-connected) then $\{\mathbf{S}\}$ does not exist for $\mathscr{M}$. When $\{\mathbf{S}\}$ does exist for $\mathscr{M}$, then we can interpret the elements of $\mathbf{S}^\bullet$ as the C^∞ cross sections of $\mathscr{S}$. When $\mathscr{M}$ itself is *not* simply-connected the situation becomes more complicated because flag paths belonging to nonhomotopic curves on $\mathscr{M}$ cannot be compared. The spinor structure $\{\mathbf{S}\}$ for $\mathscr{M}$, if it exists, becomes *nonunique*. But in any case, for the *existence* of a spinor structure we can refer to the universal covering manifold of $\mathscr{M}$ and the situation is the same as before.

The foregoing discussion has been given in terms of the bundle $\mathscr{F}$ of null-flags since this seems to be the most direct geometrical route to the space-time description of a spin-vector. It is more usual to use the bundle of all orthonormal frames on $\mathscr{M}$, however, and this is more appropriate for the general n-dimensional discussion. The two procedures are readily seen to be equivalent for a space-time manifold. Also, since $\mathscr{M}$ is orientable (that is vanishing of Steifel–Whitney class w_1), it is not difficult to adapt the above arguments to show that the remaining topological condition on $\mathscr{M}$ implied by the existence of $\{\mathbf{S}\}$ is that its *Steifel–Whitney class w_2* should vanish [38, 57]. This means that for every 2-surface in M, we can put a set of three linearly independent vectors at each point of the surface in a continuous way. (See [113a] and Chs. V and XVII by Lichnerowicz and Bott for discussions of this.) It is of interest that "plausible" space-time manifolds $\mathscr{M}$ do exist[19] which are space- and time-orientable and which contain no closed (or almost closed) timelike curves, but for which $w_2 \neq 0$. For such $\mathscr{M}$, the system $\{\mathbf{S}\}$ could not exist.

We may ask what are the physical grounds for believing in the existence of a spinor structure for space-time. How much physical reality can one indeed assign to an object which is not returned to its original state when a rotation through $360°$ is applied to it? The idea seems totally foreign to

---

[19] Take a complex projective plane $\mathscr{P}$ (a real 4-manifold) and choose a (positive definite) C^∞ Riemannian metric on $\mathscr{P}$. Let t be a real C^∞ function on $\mathscr{P}$ with only isolated critical points. Remove these points from the manifold and use the unit vector corresponding to the gradient of t to construct a C^∞ Lorentzian $(+, -, -, -)$ pseudo-Riemannian metric. The resulting "space-time" is time-orientable, space-orientable without closed (that is, $\cong S^2$) timelike curves [in fact, satisfying strong causality (11.1)], but possesses no spin structure ($w_2 \neq 0$). I am grateful to R. Bott and S. Smale for this example.

Added in proof: In a recent article (submitted to *J. Math. Phys.*), Geroch has shown that for a non-compact space-time, existence of a spinor structure is equivalent to global existence of a continuous field of orthonormal tetrads. He also shows that our assumption (4.5) is, in fact, redundant.

our experiences. Nevertheless, the wave functions of electrons, protons, neutrons, neutrinos, and many other particles do in fact behave in this way. But we might well argue that this is not conclusive, because a wave function is a somewhat nebulous concept. In any case, surely it is only the overall sign of the wave function which is altered upon rotation through 2π and is not the sign of a wave function supposed to be unobservable? In an interesting recent article, Aharonov and Susskind [1] argue that this view cannot be maintained. They show how it is possible, in principle, to construct an apparatus which, depending precisely on this spinor nature of the electron wave equation, exhibits such behavior under rotation on a *macroscopic* scale. The apparatus consists of two parts which, when fitted together, result in a detectable electric current flowing from one part to the other. The parts are then separated and one is rotated through 2π relative to the other. They are again fitted together in precisely the same relative orientation as before. A detectable current again flows from one part to the other, but now the direction of flow is reversed! Only by separating the parts and applying a further rotation, through 2π, of one part relative to the other, is the original direction of flow restored. Thus we have a situation in which the geometry of the apparatus, in the usual sense, does not define its behavior. In this case, by widening the concept of geometry to include spinorial quantities, we can again think of the geometrical configuration as determining the behavior.

The Aharonov–Susskind apparatus gives us a "physical" way of picturing a spin-vector. We may think of one part of the apparatus as being attached to our standard flag and allow the other part to be attached to another null flag which moves about the space-time. Then the apparatus keeps track of the parity of the number of complete relative rotations which take place, so in effect we have a spin-vector. If it could be convincingly argued that such pieces of apparatus could (in principle) retain their "memory" over large (say cosmological) distances and times, then we should have a fairly conclusive argument that w_2 for the universe really does vanish!

6 EXPLICIT CURVATURE FORMULAS

The notation of Section 3 yields, in an automatic way, all the familiar basic formulas involving the curvature, Christoffel symbols, and Ricci rotation coefficients, once certain basic definitions are given. This will be indicated here, in conjunction with a parallel description of the various spinor formulas, based on the notation of Section 4.

Consider a basis δ_a^a for $\mathbf{T}^a$ and a (possibly unrelated) basis $\varepsilon_{\mathfrak{A}}{}^A$ for $\mathbf{S}^A$. Let δ_a^a, $\varepsilon_A{}^{\mathfrak{A}}$ be the corresponding dual bases. Define

$$\Gamma^a_{bc} = \delta_a^a \nabla_c \delta_b^a = -\delta_b^a \nabla_c \delta_a^a \tag{6.1}$$

and

$$\gamma_{\mathfrak{ABCD}'} = \varepsilon_{A\mathfrak{B}} \nabla_{\mathfrak{CD}'} \varepsilon_{\mathfrak{A}}{}^A = \varepsilon_{\mathfrak{B}}{}^A \nabla_{\mathfrak{CD}'} \varepsilon_{\mathfrak{A}A} \tag{6.2}$$

[Here $\nabla_{\mathfrak{c}} \equiv \delta_{\mathfrak{c}}^c \nabla_c$ and $\nabla_{\mathfrak{CD}'} \equiv \varepsilon_{\mathfrak{C}}{}^C \varepsilon_{\mathfrak{D}'}{}^{D'} \nabla_{CD'}$, in accordance with (3.20). The equivalence of the two formulas in (6.1) and in (6.2) is an immediate consequence of the rules (4.51)–(4.56), (3.17), (4.30), (4.31).] The quantities $\Gamma^a{}_{bc}$ specialize either to *Ricci rotation coefficients* [in the case when the basis frame is chosen so that g_{ab} has a specific form, for example (4.15)] or to *Christoffel symbols* (when the basis is that naturally derived from a coordinate system). The quantities $\gamma_{\mathfrak{ABCD}'}$, are called *spin coefficients* [64]. As an example, let us derive the usual Christoffel symbol symmetry. Let $x^0, \ldots, x^3$ be a local coordinate system on $\mathcal{M}$. Then the associated coordinate basis is given by

$$\delta_a^{\mathfrak{a}} = \nabla_a x^{\mathfrak{a}} \tag{6.3}$$

with $\delta_{\mathfrak{a}}^a$ dual to this. Thus we have, in this case,

$$\Gamma^{\mathfrak{a}}{}_{\mathfrak{bc}} = -\delta_{\mathfrak{b}}^a \nabla_{\mathfrak{c}} \nabla_a x^{\mathfrak{a}} = -\delta_{\mathfrak{c}}^d \delta_{\mathfrak{b}}^a \nabla_d \nabla_a x^{\mathfrak{a}} \tag{6.4}$$

which is manifestly symmetric in $\mathfrak{cb}$ because of the vanishing torsion condition (4.57). Also the spin coefficient symmetry

$$\gamma_{\mathfrak{ABCD}'} = \gamma_{\mathfrak{BACD}'} \tag{6.5}$$

is immediate from (6.2).

The formulas (6.1) and (6.2), together with (3.20), (3.21) yield the usual formulas for covariant differentiation in terms of components. This is exemplified by

$$\delta_{\mathfrak{c}}^c \delta_{\mathfrak{b}}^b \delta_{\mathfrak{a}}^a (\nabla_c \zeta^{\mathfrak{a}}{}_b) = \delta_{\mathfrak{b}}^b \delta_{\mathfrak{a}}^a \nabla_c (\zeta^{\mathfrak{e}}{}_{\mathfrak{e}} \delta_{\mathfrak{b}}^a \delta_{\mathfrak{b}}^c)$$

$$= \nabla_{\mathfrak{c}} \zeta^{\mathfrak{a}}{}_{\mathfrak{b}} + \zeta^{\mathfrak{a}}{}_{\mathfrak{b}} \Gamma^{\mathfrak{a}}{}_{\mathfrak{Dc}} - \zeta^{\mathfrak{a}}{}_{\mathfrak{e}} \Gamma^{\mathfrak{e}}{}_{\mathfrak{bc}} \tag{6.6}$$

$$\varepsilon_{\mathfrak{C}}{}^C \varepsilon_{\mathfrak{D}'}{}^{D'} \varepsilon_{\mathfrak{A}}{}^A \varepsilon_{B'}{}^{\mathfrak{B}'} (\nabla_{CD'} \theta_A{}^{B'}) = \varepsilon_{\mathfrak{A}}{}^A \varepsilon_{B'}{}^{\mathfrak{B}'} \nabla_{\mathfrak{CD}'} (\theta_{\mathfrak{E}}{}^{\mathfrak{F}'} \varepsilon_A{}^{\mathfrak{E}} \varepsilon_{\mathfrak{F}'}{}^{B'})$$

$$= \nabla_{\mathfrak{CD}'} \theta_{\mathfrak{A}}{}^{\mathfrak{B}'} - \theta_{\mathfrak{E}}{}^{\mathfrak{B}'} \Gamma^{\mathfrak{E}}{}_{\mathfrak{ACD}'} + \theta_{\mathfrak{A}}{}^{\mathfrak{F}'} \overline{\Gamma}^{\mathfrak{B}'}{}_{\mathfrak{F}'\mathfrak{D}'\mathfrak{C}} \tag{6.7}$$

(Recall that when acting on quantities without abstract labels, $\nabla_{..}$ is just the ordinary gradient operator.)

Let us now define the *curvature tensor* and *curvature spinors*. Put

$$R^a{}_{bcd} = 2\delta_a^{\mathfrak{a}} \nabla_{[c} \nabla_{d]} \delta_b^{\mathfrak{a}} \tag{6.8}$$

and, defining

$$\square_{AB} \equiv \nabla_{Y'(A} \nabla_{B)}^{Y'} \qquad \square_{A'B'} \equiv \nabla_{Y(A'} \nabla_{B')}^Y \tag{6.9}$$

set

$$\Psi_{ABCD} = \varepsilon_{D\mathfrak{D}} \square_{(AB} \varepsilon_{C)}{}^{\mathfrak{D}} \tag{6.10}$$

$$\Phi_{CDA'B'} = \varepsilon_{D\mathfrak{D}} \square_{A'B'} \varepsilon_C{}^{\mathfrak{D}} \tag{6.11}$$

$$\Lambda = \tfrac{1}{6} \varepsilon_{A\mathfrak{D}} \square^{AB} \varepsilon_B{}^{\mathfrak{D}} \tag{6.12}$$

(Here the conventions are being employed that square brackets around indices denote antisymmetrization and round brackets around indices denote symmetrization, for example, $\alpha_{[ab]} = \frac{1}{2}(\alpha_{ab} - \alpha_{ba})$, $\beta_{[abc]} = \frac{1}{6}(\beta_{abc} + \beta_{bca} + \beta_{cab} - \beta_{acb} - \beta_{cba} - \beta_{bac})$, $\gamma_{(AB)} = \frac{1}{2}(\gamma_{AB} + \gamma_{BA})$, etc.) Since (6.8), (6.10)–(6.12) involve German indices on the right-hand sides we have to show that the expressions defined are, in fact, basis-independent. This follows because the operators $\nabla_{[c}\nabla_{d]}$, $\Box_{AB'}$ $\Box_{A'B'}$ all satisfy

$$\mathcal{D}(\xi\,\vdots\, + \eta\,\vdots\,) = \mathcal{D}\xi\,\vdots\, + \mathcal{D}\eta\,\vdots\,$$

$$\mathcal{D}(\xi\,\vdots\,\zeta\,\vdots\,) = \zeta\,\vdots\,\mathcal{D}\xi\,\vdots\, + \xi\,\vdots\,\mathcal{D}\zeta\,\vdots\, \tag{6.13}$$

$$\mathcal{D}\phi = 0$$

[cf. (6.16)], where $\mathcal{D}$ symbolically stands for any of these operators. To make a basis change in (6.8), (6.10)–(6.12) we make substitutions:

$$\delta_b^a \to T^a_{\ x}\,\delta_b^x \qquad \delta_{\mathfrak{a}}^a \to T^{(-1)\mathfrak{a}}_{\ \ \ \mathfrak{a}}\,\delta_{\mathfrak{z}}^a \tag{6.14}$$

$$\varepsilon_C^{\ \mathfrak{D}} \to t^{\mathfrak{D}}_{\ x}\,\varepsilon_C^{\ x} \qquad \varepsilon_{D\mathfrak{D}} \to t^{(-1)\mathfrak{z}}_{\ \ \ \mathfrak{D}}\,\varepsilon_{D\mathfrak{z}} \tag{6.15}$$

where (-1) denotes matrix inverse. By virtue of (6.13), the transforming matrix carries through the derivatives in each case and cancels with its inverse to leave the expression unchanged. (Note that abstract labels do not "transform"!)

The relation between these operators is given by

$$2\nabla_{[a}\nabla_{b]} \equiv \varepsilon_{A'B'}\,\Box_{AB} + \varepsilon_{AB}\,\Box_{A'B'} \tag{6.16}$$

so, for example, $\Box_{AB} \equiv \varepsilon^{A'B'}\,\nabla_{[a}\nabla_{b]}$. We can combine (6.10) and (6.12) in the form

$$\varepsilon_{D\mathfrak{D}}\,\Box_{AB}\,\varepsilon_C^{\ \mathfrak{D}} = \Psi_{ABCD} - 2\Lambda\varepsilon_{D(A}\varepsilon_{B)C} \tag{6.17}$$

Also, (6.17) combines with (6.11) to give (via (6.16))

$$2\varepsilon_{D\mathfrak{D}}\,\nabla_{[a}\nabla_{b]}\,\varepsilon_C^{\ \mathfrak{D}} = \Psi_{ABCD}\,\varepsilon_{A'B'} - 2\Lambda\varepsilon_{D(A}\varepsilon_{B)C}\,\varepsilon_{A'B'} + \Phi_{CDA'B'}\,\varepsilon_{AB} \tag{6.18}$$

In fact, Ψ_{ABCD}, Λ, and $\Phi_{ABC'D}$ are the parts [72, 115] of R_{abcd} irreducible under local $SL(2, \mathbf{C})$ (Lorentz) transformations:

$$R_{abcd} = \Psi_{ABCD}\,\varepsilon_{A'B'}\,\varepsilon_{C'D'} + \varepsilon_{AB}\,\varepsilon_{CD}\,\overline{\Psi}_{A'B'C'D'} + 2\Lambda\{\varepsilon_{AC}\,\varepsilon_{BD}\,\varepsilon_{A'B'}\,\varepsilon_{C'D'}$$

$$+ \varepsilon_{AB}\,\varepsilon_{CD}\,\varepsilon_{A'D'}\,\varepsilon_{B'C'}\} + \varepsilon_{AB}\,\Phi_{CDA'B'}\,\varepsilon_{C'D'} + \varepsilon_{CD}\,\Phi_{ABC'D'}\,\varepsilon_{A'B'} \tag{6.19}$$

Equation (6.19) follows by two applications of (6.18) [using (4.35)] to the definition (6.8). The symmetries

$$R_{abcd} = R_{cdab} = R_{[ab][cd]} \qquad R_{a[bcd]} = 0 \tag{6.20}$$

find expression in

$$\Psi_{ABCD} = \Psi_{(ABCD)} \qquad \Lambda = \overline{\Lambda} \qquad \Phi_{ABC'D'} = \Phi_{(AB)(C'D')} = \overline{\Phi}_{ABC'D'} \tag{6.21}$$

so that Ψ_{ABCD}, Λ, and $\Phi_{ABC'D'}$ belong, respectively, to a $D(2,0)$, a $D(0,0)$ and a $D(1,1)$ irreducible representation space for the local Lorentz group.

In tensor terms, the reduction of R_{abcd} into irreducible parts is somewhat more complicated. We can define the *Weyl* (conformal) tensor by

$$C_{abcd} = \Psi_{ABCD}\,\varepsilon_{A'B'}\,\varepsilon_{C'D'} + \varepsilon_{AB}\,\varepsilon_{CD}\,\overline{\Psi}_{A'B'C'D'} \tag{6.22}$$

Purely tensorially, this is given by

$$C^{ab}{}_{cd} = R^{ab}{}_{cd} - 2R^{[a}{}_{[c}\delta^{b]}_{d]} + \tfrac{1}{3}R\delta^{c}_{[a}\delta^{d}_{b]} \tag{6.23}$$

$$R_{ab} = R^{x}{}_{axb} \qquad R = R^{x}{}_{x} \tag{6.24}$$

Then, in addition to possessing all the Riemann tensor symmetries (6.20), C_{abcd} satisfies

$$C^{x}{}_{bxd} = 0 \tag{6.25}$$

The C_{abcd} is not yet irreducible (if we allow ourselves to consider complex tensors) and splits down further into its so-called self-dual and anti-self-dual parts: $C_{abcd} = C^{+}_{abcd} + C^{-}_{abcd}$, where $C^{+}_{abcd} = \Psi_{ABCD}\,\varepsilon_{A'B'}\,\varepsilon_{C'D'}$. ("Self-dual" means, here, $\tfrac{1}{2}C^{+}_{abxy}\,ie_{cd}{}^{xy} = C^{+}_{abcd}$, where $-e_{abcd}$ is the skew-symmetric Levi–Civita symbol in a right-handed orthonormal frame. In spinor terms $e_{abcd} = i\varepsilon_{AC}\varepsilon_{BD}\varepsilon_{A'D'}\varepsilon_{B'C'} - i\varepsilon_{AD}\varepsilon_{BC}\varepsilon_{A'C'}\varepsilon_{B'D'}$). The remaining irreducible parts of R_{abcd} are

$$R_{ab} - \tfrac{1}{4}Rg_{ab} = -2\Phi_{ABA'B'} \tag{6.26}$$

and

$$R = 24\Lambda \tag{6.27}$$

As a verification that the definition (6.8), of the Riemann tensor, actually agrees with the usual one, we can derive the *Ricci identities*. Consider, for example, $\xi^{a}{}_{b}$. Then,

$$2\nabla_{[a}\nabla_{b]}\xi^{c}{}_{d} = 2\nabla_{[a}\nabla_{b]}(\xi^{\mathfrak{d}}_{\mathfrak{c}}\delta^{\mathfrak{d}}_{d}\delta^{c}_{\mathfrak{e}})$$

$$= \xi^{c}{}_{x}R^{x}{}_{dab} - \xi^{x}{}_{d}R^{c}{}_{xab} \tag{6.28}$$

by (6.13) and the fact [which also follows from (6.13) applied to (6.8)] that $R^{a}{}_{bcd} = -2\delta^{a}_{b}\nabla_{[c}\nabla_{d]}\delta^{a}_{a}$. In an exactly similar way we obtain the corresponding spinor Ricci identities, taking as an example

$$\square_{A'B'}\theta_{C}{}^{D'} = \square_{A'B'}(\theta_{\mathfrak{c}}{}^{\mathfrak{D}'}\varepsilon_{\mathfrak{D}'}{}^{D'}\varepsilon_{C}{}^{\mathfrak{c}})$$

$$= \theta_{C}{}^{X'}(\overline{\Psi}^{D'}{}_{X'A'B'} - 2\Lambda\varepsilon_{X'(A'}\varepsilon_{B')}{}^{D'}) - \theta_{X}{}^{D'}\Phi^{X}{}_{CA'B'}. \tag{6.29}$$

We can also directly obtain the expression for the components R_{abcd} in terms of $\Gamma^{a}{}_{bc}$ by applying (6.1) to (6.8) [with (3.20)]. This includes both the familiar expression in terms of Christoffel symbols and the Ricci rotation coefficient curvature formula. Somewhat less familiar are the corresponding formulas which relate the spin coefficients to the components of the spinor curvature quantities. These will be given explicitly here, since we shall be interested in two particular cases later. Let us use (6.18) since this gives all the curvature quantities at once. The result is [64]:

$$\nabla_{\mathfrak{F}\mathfrak{E}'}\gamma_{\mathfrak{A}\mathfrak{C}\mathfrak{D}\mathfrak{B}'} - \nabla_{\mathfrak{D}\mathfrak{B}'}\gamma_{\mathfrak{A}\mathfrak{C}\mathfrak{F}\mathfrak{E}'} = \varepsilon^{\mathfrak{P}\mathfrak{Q}}\{\gamma_{\mathfrak{A}\mathfrak{P}\mathfrak{D}\mathfrak{B}'}\,\gamma_{\mathfrak{Q}\mathfrak{C}\mathfrak{F}\mathfrak{E}'} + \gamma_{\mathfrak{A}\mathfrak{C}\mathfrak{P}\mathfrak{B}'}\,\gamma_{\mathfrak{Q}\mathfrak{D}\mathfrak{F}\mathfrak{E}'} - \gamma_{\mathfrak{A}\mathfrak{P}\mathfrak{F}\mathfrak{E}'}\,\gamma_{\mathfrak{Q}\mathfrak{C}\mathfrak{D}\mathfrak{B}'}$$

$$- \gamma_{\mathfrak{A}\mathfrak{C}\mathfrak{P}\mathfrak{E}'}\,\gamma_{\mathfrak{Q}\mathfrak{F}\mathfrak{D}\mathfrak{B}'}\} + \varepsilon^{\mathfrak{R}'\mathfrak{E}'}\{\gamma_{\mathfrak{A}\mathfrak{C}\mathfrak{D}\mathfrak{R}'}\,\gamma_{\mathfrak{E}'\mathfrak{B}'\mathfrak{E}'\mathfrak{F}} - \gamma_{\mathfrak{A}\mathfrak{C}\mathfrak{F}\mathfrak{R}'}\,\gamma_{\mathfrak{E}'\mathfrak{E}'\mathfrak{B}'\mathfrak{D}}\}$$

$$+ \Psi_{\mathfrak{A}\mathfrak{C}\mathfrak{D}\mathfrak{F}}\,\varepsilon_{\mathfrak{E}'\mathfrak{B}'} + \Lambda\varepsilon_{\mathfrak{E}'\mathfrak{B}'}(\varepsilon_{\mathfrak{C}\mathfrak{D}}\,\varepsilon_{\mathfrak{A}\mathfrak{F}} + \varepsilon_{\mathfrak{A}\mathfrak{D}}\,\varepsilon_{\mathfrak{C}\mathfrak{F}}) + \Phi_{\mathfrak{A}\mathfrak{C}\mathfrak{B}'\mathfrak{E}'}\,\varepsilon_{\mathfrak{F}\mathfrak{D}} \qquad (6.30)$$

In this connection, we note also the commutator of two "intrinsic derivatives":

$$\{\nabla_{\mathfrak{A}\mathfrak{B}'}\nabla_{\mathfrak{C}\mathfrak{D}'} - \nabla_{\mathfrak{C}\mathfrak{D}'}\nabla_{\mathfrak{A}\mathfrak{B}'}\}\phi = \{\varepsilon^{\mathfrak{P}\mathfrak{Q}}(\gamma_{\mathfrak{P}\mathfrak{A}\mathfrak{C}\mathfrak{D}'}\,\nabla_{\mathfrak{Q}\mathfrak{B}'} - \gamma_{\mathfrak{P}\mathfrak{C}\mathfrak{A}\mathfrak{B}'}\,\nabla_{\mathfrak{Q}\mathfrak{D}'})$$

$$+ \varepsilon^{\mathfrak{R}'\mathfrak{E}'}(\gamma_{\mathfrak{R}'\mathfrak{B}'\mathfrak{D}'\mathfrak{C}}\,\nabla_{\mathfrak{A}\mathfrak{E}'} - \gamma_{\mathfrak{R}'\mathfrak{D}'\mathfrak{B}'\mathfrak{A}}\,\nabla_{\mathfrak{C}\mathfrak{E}'})\phi \qquad (6.31)$$

7 EINSTEIN'S EQUATIONS AND FOCUSING

The decomposition (6.19) of the Riemann tensor into its irreducible spinorial parts allows us to discuss the structure of space-time curvature, as is implied by Einstein's field equations, in some detail. Einstein's equations are

$$R_{ab} - \tfrac{1}{2}Rg_{ab} + \lambda g_{ab} = -2KT_{ab} \qquad (7.1)$$

where λ and K are real constants with $K > 0$ and where T_{ab} is the local stress–energy–momentum tensor (the "energy tensor") of matter. Here, the term "matter" refers to any field except gravitation itself. Thus, for example, free electromagnetic field counts as "matter" in this context. The question of the energy which must be assigned to gravitation *itself* is a more subtle one. This will be discussed a little more later. Gravitational energy cannot be adequately defined in a *local* way and emerges, instead, as some kind of non-local quantity. The local gravitational energy must apparently be thought of as zero, and this is consistent with (7.1). The cosmological term λ is generally put equal to zero, since there are no compelling theoretical or observational grounds for believing in its existence. In any case, λ would have to be extremely small, of the order of the reciprocal of the square of the radius of the universe.

As it stands, (7.1) implies no restriction on the curvature, since no restriction has yet been placed on T_{ab}. But we can study (7.1) in three different types of situation. In the first instance, we may be interested in *pure gravitation theory* for which $T_{ab} = 0$. Then (7.1) becomes a well-defined set of partial differential nonlinear equations on the g_{ab}, when expressed in terms of a coordinate system x^a. These equations are difficult to solve explicitly and only a very few solutions are known which have any direct relevance to physical situations. (Some of these will be given in later sections.) On the other hand, there are certain general statements which can be made about the nature (in particular the asymptotic nature, if suitable boundary conditions are imposed) of the solutions. Now, secondly, we may be interested in solutions of (7.1) for which the T_{ab}, though nonzero, is also subject to certain conditions ("equations of state") which are normally again partial differential equations, but which now refer to the field quantities which contribute to T_{ab}. (For example, in the case of the "Einstein–Maxwell" equations, T_{ab} is specified as being the energy tensor of a free electromagnetic field which is subject to Maxwell's source-free equations in covariant form.) Again the equations become virtually impossible to solve explicitly, in general, for realistic equations of state. Thirdly, we may be content to make general statements about solutions of (7.1) for which we merely impose *inequalities* on the T_{ab}. Such an inequality might state, for example, the positive definite nature of the local energy density, or some other such physically reasonable requirement. In many ways, this type of situation is the easiest to handle and the last two sections will be devoted mainly to the treatment of space-times under such conditions. Finally, it may be remarked that one way of attempting to treat (7.1) which strictly speaking is *not* valid, is to regard T_{ab} as some *given* source distribution for which we try to construct its gravitational field. This is a normal procedure in other branches of physics, but here, *until* we have our metric g_{ab} it is not even clear what is *meant* by a given source distribution.

If we now decompose R_{abcd} into its spinorial parts and use (6.26) and (6.27), we get

$$KT_{ab} = \Phi_{ABA'B'} + (3\Lambda - \tfrac{1}{2}\lambda)\varepsilon_{AB}\varepsilon_{A'B'} \qquad (7.2)$$

so Φ_{ab} represents the trace-free part of T_{ab} and Λ the trace:

$$\Phi_{ab} = K(T_{ab} - \tfrac{1}{4}T_x{}^x g_{ab}) \qquad \Lambda = \tfrac{1}{12}(KT_x{}^x + 2\lambda) \qquad (7.3)$$

The part of R_{abcd} which, locally, is left completely *undefined* by T_{ab} is the Weyl tensor C_{abcd}, or, equivalently, the spinor Ψ_{ABCD}. We may thus think of Ψ_{ABCD} as representing the *free gravitational part of the curvature*. In regions free of matter we can still have curvature. According to Einstein's equations, then, such curvature will be of a particular type, defined completely, in structure, by a totally symmetric spinor Ψ_{ABCD}. If $\lambda = 0$, then we shall have, in fact, $R_{abcd} = C_{abcd}$ [with C_{abcd} given by (6.22)]. Let us, therefore, examine the nature of Ψ_{ABCD}. Spinor methods are particularly well suited to this problem, the corresponding discussion of the Weyl tensor C_{abcd} being far less transparent.

Consider the form $\Psi_{\mathfrak{ABCD}}\zeta^{\mathfrak{A}}\zeta^{\mathfrak{B}}\zeta^{\mathfrak{C}}\zeta^{\mathfrak{D}}$, where for simplicity we choose $\zeta^0 = 1$, $\zeta^1 = z$. This is a quartic polynomial in z with complex coefficients and therefore factorizes into four linear factors:

$$\Psi_{\mathfrak{ABCD}}\zeta^{\mathfrak{A}}\zeta^{\mathfrak{B}}\zeta^{\mathfrak{C}}\zeta^{\mathfrak{D}} = (\alpha_{\mathfrak{A}}\zeta^{\mathfrak{A}})(\beta_{\mathfrak{B}}\zeta^{\mathfrak{B}})(\gamma_{\mathfrak{C}}\zeta^{\mathfrak{C}})(\delta_{\mathfrak{D}}\zeta^{\mathfrak{D}}) \qquad (7.4)$$

Equating coefficients [and eliminating the basis frame *cf.* (3.21)] we get

$$\Psi_{ABCD} = \alpha_{(A}\beta_B\gamma_C\delta_{D)} \tag{7.5}$$

The factorization is unique up to a complex multiplier for each of $\alpha_A, \ldots,$ δ_D. Thus, the null direction defined by each of $\alpha_A, \ldots, \delta_D$ is uniquely defined, so we see that Ψ_{ABCD} defines an unordered set of four (possibly coincident) directions along the null cone at each point P of M (at which $\Psi_{ABCD} \neq 0$) called the *gravitational principal null directions* [23, 72, 91] at P. The coincidence schemes for the principal null directions at P can be represented as follows:

$$
\begin{array}{c}
\{1111\} \searrow \{211\} \searrow \\
\{22\} \nearrow \searrow \{4\} \nearrow \{31\} \\
\{-\} \nearrow
\end{array} \tag{7.6}
$$

Petrov type: I   II   III

where the arrows point in the direction of increasing specialization. Here, $\{1111\}$ represents the general case when the null directions are distinct; $\{211\}$ is the case when there is one double null direction and two distinct simple ones; etc. The symbol $\{-\}$ denotes the case $\Psi_{ABCD} = 0$ at P. The "Petrov type," referring to the columns in (7.6), is a more direct classification [80b, 81] of C_{abcd} according to the dimension of the space spanned by eigenvectors of the matrix $(C^{ab}{}_{cd})$ (grouping a, b together and c, d together). The case $\{4\}$, when all the principal null directions coincide, is called the *null* case; $\{22\}$ is called *degenerate*; all cases but $\{1111\}$ are called *algebraically special*. In terms of C_{abcd}, we can write a necessary and sufficient condition [23, 93] on a null vector l^a for it to point in a principal null direction as

$$l_{[a}C_{b]cd[e}l_{f]}l^cl^d = 0 \tag{7.7}$$

The classification scheme (7.6) plays a significant part in the understanding of the geometric structure of gravitational fields. Perhaps the most directly physical role of the principal null directions emerges in the "peeling-off" property of Sachs [64, 76, 93–95]. This states that for an asymptotically flat space-time which is empty near infinity (definitions in Section 8), then along any null geodesic γ, the curvature tensor exhibits a certain characteristic asymptotic behavior. Let r be an affine parameter on γ. Then, in a well-defined sense, the curvature falls off along γ in such a way that to order r^{-1} it is null, with the quadruple principle null direction pointing along γ; to order r^{-2}, there is a triple principal null direction along γ; to order r^{-3}, a double one; to order r^{-4}, a simple one; and to order r^{-5} the curvature is unrelated to γ (Fig. 9). This is the generic situation and more special behavior is also possible. An outline of a proof of this result is given in Section 8.

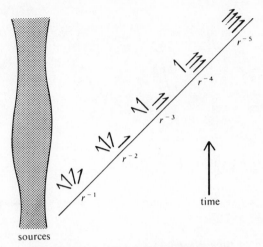

FIGURE 9. The peeling-off property.

The decomposition (6.19) was given purely algebraically. We may ask whether there is a more direct geometrical (or "physical") way of distinguishing the effect of the Weyl tensor from that of other parts of the curvature. Also, can one see physically what the meaning of the principal null directions is? The most direct physical manifestation of space-time curvature is to be found in the "tidal forces" due to the geodesic deviation effect on timelike geodesics [82, p. 266]. The relevant equation can be written

$$D^2 p^a - R^a{}_{bcd} t^b p^c t^d = 0 \tag{7.8}$$

where the t^a are tangents to a congruence of timelike geodesics, smoothly parametrized according to proper time s, say, so $t^a t_a = 1$. The vector p^a connects points of equal s value on two neighboring geodesics (Fig. 10). The operator D denotes covariant differentiation in the direction t^a, that is,

$$D \equiv t^a \nabla_a \tag{7.9}$$

The equation (7.8) is familiar to mathematicians as the *Jacobi equation*. [Actually (7.8) holds under more general conditions than those stated, namely, that the parameter s need only be affine on each geodesic.] If we choose p^a orthogonal to t^a (as we may) then $D^2 p^a$ measures the *relative acceleration* of neighboring intertial test particles. [A simple "intuitive derivation" of (7.8), when the two neighboring geodesics are initially parallel, is obtained by simply transporting the vector t^a around the loop $RQPSR$ of Fig. 10. The change in t^a gives us the change in the relative velocity of the neighboring particle.]

FIGURE 10. The relative acceleration of neighboring geodesics in the presence
of curvature.

As applied to timelike geodesics, (7.8) does not enable us to separate,
in any simple way, the effects due to the different irreducible parts of the
curvature tensor.   But if we use null geodesics, the effects due to the Weyl
tensor and due to the (trace-free) Ricci tensor become sharply distinguished
[83,102].   Since the case of null geodesics has some peculiar features which
are rather suitable to a spinor treatment, I shall give an independent spinor
derivation of the relevant equations, rather than trying to deduce them from
(7.8).   This will also give us an interpretation of some of the spin coefficients,
which will be useful later.

Choose a spin frame $\varepsilon_{\mathfrak{A}}{}^A$ and put

$$\varepsilon_0{}^A = o^A \qquad \varepsilon_1{}^A = \iota^A \tag{7.10}$$

From the normalization (4.27) we get

$$o_A \iota^A = 1 \tag{7.11}$$

Let us try to interpret the following spin coefficients [cf. (6.2)]:

$$\kappa = \gamma_{0000'} \qquad \rho = \gamma_{0010'} \qquad \sigma = \gamma_{0001'} \tag{7.12}$$

There are all of the form $o^A \nabla_{\mathfrak{C}\mathfrak{D}'} o_A$, where $\mathfrak{C}$, $\mathfrak{D}'$ are, respectively, $0, 0'$; $1, 0'$;
$01'$.   Thus, under

$$o^A \to \zeta o^A \qquad \iota^A \to \zeta^{-1} \iota^A \tag{7.13}$$

we have

$$\kappa \to \zeta^3 \bar{\zeta} \kappa \qquad \rho \to \zeta\bar{\zeta}\rho \qquad \sigma \to \zeta^3 \bar{\zeta}^{-1} \tag{7.14}$$

the derivative terms canceling because of $o^A o_A = 0$.   Now, consider the
meaning of the condition $\kappa = 0$:

$$o^A o^B \bar{o}^{C'} \nabla_{BC'} o_A = 0 \tag{7.15}$$

We can read this as something of the form $o^A \theta_A = 0$, from which we can infer $\theta_A = \chi o_A$, for some χ. Thus $\kappa = 0$ means

$$o^B \bar{o}^{C'} \nabla_{BC'} o_A = \chi o_A \tag{7.16}$$

Putting

$$l^a = o^A \bar{o}^{A'} \qquad m^a = o^A \bar{\iota}^{A'} \tag{7.17}$$

we rewrite (7.16) as $l^a \nabla_a o_A = \chi o_A$, which states that o_A is carried parallel to itself in the l^a-direction (that is, in the o^A-direction). That is to say, the condition $\kappa = 0$ is necessary and sufficient for the o^A-directions to be tangent to *null geodesics*. Thus, κ is a kind of measure of *curvature* of the o^A-curves. (It is complex, so it also indicates the *direction* of this curvature, in relation to the flag plane of o^A.)

Suppose now that $\kappa = 0$, so we have a congruence of null geodesic o^A-curves, and read (7.15) in two other ways, namely, as $o^B \phi_B = 0$ or as $\bar{o}^{C'} \psi_{C'} = 0$. Thus, similarly to the above, we have relations of the form

$$o^A \bar{o}^{C'} \nabla_{BC'} o_A = \rho o_B \tag{7.18}$$

$$o^A o^B \nabla_{BC'} o_A = \sigma \bar{o}_{C'} \tag{7.19}$$

for some ρ, σ. In fact, ρ and σ are the quantities given in (7.12) as follows at once by multiplying (7.18) by ι^B and (7.19) by $\bar{\iota}^{C'}$. The significance of (7.18) and (7.19) is that it shows that when $\kappa = 0$, the quantities ρ and σ are independent of ι^A. Also, since they are simply rescaled according to (7.14), as o^A undergoes (7.13), we expect to find a simple geometric meaning for ρ and σ, as a property of the congruence of null geodesics. To see that this is actually the case, consider a 2-plane element π at a point P of one of the geodesics γ. Choose π spacelike and orthogonal to the direction of γ. We can select ι^A also to have direction orthogonal to π, so π will be spanned by m^a and $\bar{m}^a$, with m^a as in (7.17). Now any (real) vector in π has the form

$$\bar{z} m^a + z \bar{m}^a \tag{7.20}$$

so we may regard π as being the Argand plane of $\sqrt{2} z$. In the neighborhood of γ, a two-dimensional set of the null geodesics "hit" π. These are the null geodesics which lie, to first order, in a null hyperplane through γ. There are also other null geodesics which are neighboring to γ, but we do not consider them. We shall examine how z varies as we follow one of the null geodesics which does hit π. [Note that the z, at P, for a particular null geodesic of the congruence, near γ, is actually independent of the choice of π at P. Altering π through P amounts merely to replacing m^a by $m^a + kl^a$ in (7.20), with k complex.] Put

$$D \equiv l^a \nabla_a \equiv \nabla_{00'} \tag{7.21}$$

For convenience, choose o^A, ι^A to be parallelly propagated along γ:

$$Do_A = 0 \qquad D\iota_A = 0 \qquad\qquad (7.22)$$

Then m^a, $\bar{m}^a$, and therefore also π, will be parallelly propagated along γ. Let ϕ be any function constant along the null geodesics:

$$D\phi = 0 \qquad\qquad (7.23)$$

We characterize the fact that we require a fixed value of z to label a definite geodesic of our system neighboring γ by

$$D\{(\bar{z}m^a + z\bar{m}^a)\nabla_a \phi\} \equiv 0 \qquad\qquad (7.24)$$

[see (7.20)]. This gives

$$D\bar{z}\nabla_{01'}\phi + Dz\nabla_{10'}\phi + \bar{z}(\nabla_{00'}\nabla_{01'} - \nabla_{01'}\nabla_{00'})\phi + z(\nabla_{00'}\nabla_{10'}$$
$$- \nabla_{10'}\nabla_{00'})\phi = 0 \quad (7.25)$$

that is, by (6.31) (or directly evaluating these particular commutators)

$$(D\bar{z} + \bar{\rho}\bar{z} + \bar{\sigma}z)\nabla_{01'}\phi + (Dz + \rho z + \sigma\bar{z})\nabla_{01'}\phi = 0 \qquad (7.26)$$

Thus

$$Dz = -\rho z - \sigma\bar{z} \qquad\qquad (7.27)$$

The interpretation of ρ and σ now becomes clear. The *real* part of ρ measures the *convergence* of the null geodesics and the *imaginary* part of ρ measures their *rotation* about γ. A nonvanishing σ indicates the presence of distortion or *shear* (Fig. 11). Thus, if $\sigma \neq 0$, a small circle will become elliptical as we follow the null geodesics. The axes of this ellipse are defined in relation to the flag plane of o^A by $\frac{1}{2}\arg\sigma$. If the null geodesics are the generators of null hypersurfaces then we can choose $l_a = \nabla_a u$, whence

$$o^A\bar{o}^{B'}(\nabla_a l_b - \nabla_b l_a) = 0$$

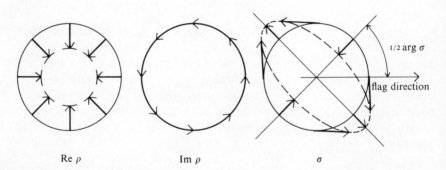

Re ρ Im ρ σ

FIGURE 11. The interpretation of ρ and σ in terms of their effect on an initially circular pattern in the null rays.

from which we get absence of rotation:

$$\rho = \bar{\rho} \tag{7.28}$$

Condition (7.28) is also sufficient for the null geodesics to generate null hypersurfaces. If (7.28) holds, then the ρ and σ pertain to the geometry of each null hypersurface individually and not to the relationship among the different null hypersurfaces.

Let us next consider the D-derivatives of ρ and σ. We can obtain these from (6.30) [using (7.22): $\gamma_{\text{ов}00'} = 0$], or else directly, using the definitions of ρ, σ, $\Phi_{ABC'D'}$, and Ψ_{ABCD}. Thus,

$$D\rho = \rho^2 + \sigma\bar{\sigma} + \Phi \tag{7.29}$$

$$D\sigma = \sigma(\rho + \bar{\rho}) + \Psi \tag{7.30}$$

where

$$\Psi = \Psi_{0000} \qquad \Phi = \Phi_{000'0'} \tag{7.31}$$

Equations (7.29) and (7.30) are the *Sachs equations* [93] for the "optical scalars" ρ, σ. Combining these with (7.27) we get

$$D^2 z = -\Phi z - \Psi\bar{z} \tag{7.32}$$

In fact, (7.32) can also be obtained directly from (7.8), if we put $t^a = l^a$ and $p^a = \bar{z}m^a + z\bar{m}^a$. In this connection, we note the formulas

$$\Psi = R_{abcd}\, l^a m^b l^c m^d \qquad \Phi = R_{abcd}\, l^a m^b l^c \bar{m}^d;$$
$$\rho = m^a \bar{m}^b \nabla_b l_a \qquad \sigma = m^a m^b \nabla_b l_a \tag{7.33}$$

We see from (7.29) that it is essentially Φ which governs the change in ρ and from (7.30) that it is essentially Ψ which governs the change in σ, but that in both cases there are additional nonlinear terms. To obtain the effects of Φ and Ψ in purest form, consider a particular situation in which Φ and Ψ are localized to a very small region on γ. [In fact idealized situations are also possible for which Φ and Ψ become Dirac delta functions. See the discussion of plane waves (9.23)–(9.26).] Suppose that we have a pulse of light which is initially a parallel beam. This is represented by the null geodesics constituting a small portion (neighboring γ) of a null hypersurface through γ, for which $\rho = \sigma = 0$. Then, by (7.29), we see that a patch of Φ curvature (with $\Psi = 0$) acts as a *lens without astigmatism* (since convergence ρ is introduced into the beam but the shear σ remains zero) while a patch of Ψ curvature (with $\Phi = 0$) acts as a *purely astigmatic lens*; that is, exactly as much positive convergence is introduced in one plane as negative convergence in the perpendicular plane (since ρ is initially zero for the emergent beam with σ nonzero). The interpretation of a patch of curvature in terms of lenses also holds good for a general incident beam, where ρ and σ needs not initially vanish. Also, the nonlinear terms in (7.29) and (7.30) correspond exactly to the way that the effects of separated lenses compose [78]. Thus, we may think of the effect on a beam of light, of the curvature of space-time, as being built up precisely from effects due to a series of lenses placed along the beam. The converging power is described locally by Φ and the astigmatism by Ψ. As γ varies, the components (7.31) generate *all* the information contained in Ψ_{ABCD} and $\Phi_{ABC'D'}$, because of the symmetries (6.21).

One important feature of this is that we always have *positive* focusing along any null geodesic γ, if we assume that the local energy density is positive definite. The energy density, measured by an observer whose world line has tangent vector t^a, is

$$T_{ab}\,t^a t^b \tag{7.34}$$

if we assume $t^a t_a = 1$. If we require (7.34) to be nonnegative, then we have $T_{ab} t^a t^b \geq 0$ for any timelike vector t^a (irrespective of the normalization condition on t^a). Thus, if we take the limit as t^a approaches a null vector l^a, we get [by (7.3)]

$$\Phi = KT_{ab}\,l^a l^b \geq 0 \tag{7.35}$$

(whether or not $\lambda = 0$, since $g_{ab} l^a l^b = 0$). In the absence of Ψ, this shows that the curvature Φ along the beam acts as a series of positive (converging) lenses. If Ψ is present, its effect is made felt in Eq. (7.29) via the $\sigma\bar{\sigma}$ term, which again acts positively. We can regard σ as being, roughly speaking, an *integral* of Ψ along γ. Thus, Ψ acts *nonlocally* to contribute to the focussing power along γ. An oscillating Ψ closely resembles the presence of Φ in its total effect. This is closely related to the question of gravitational energy. Although locally the gravitational field does not contribute to the energy density, a gravitational wave does carry a kind of nonlocal energy, the total energy carried by the wave being always *positive*. (A striking example of the effective positive energy of gravitational "ripples" is supplied by Wheeler's [112] theoretical construct: the gravitational "geon." This is a region of empty space which consists of ripples which remain bound for a long time. When viewed on a large enough scale, a geon appears as a "particle" with positive mass.)

Let us examine the positive focusing effect in a little more detail. If we choose a small triangle in the plane element π with vertices defined by $0, z_1, z_2$, then its area

$$a = \frac{i}{4}\,(z_1 \bar{z}_2 - z_2 \bar{z}_1) \tag{7.36}$$

satisfies [by (7.27)]

$$Da = -(\rho + \bar{\rho})a \tag{7.37}$$

With our beam chosen as a portion of a null hypersurface we have $\rho = \bar{\rho}$.
Thus,

$$D(a^{1/2}) = -\rho a^{1/2} \tag{7.38}$$

From (7.29),

$$D^2(a^{1/2}) = D(-\rho a^{1/2}) = -(\sigma\bar{\sigma} + \Phi)a^{1/2} \leqslant 0 \tag{7.39}$$

Thus, if $\rho > 0$ at some point of γ, (7.38) tells us that $a^{1/2}$ is decreasing. From
(7.39) it follows that $a^{1/2}$ decreases to zero[20] (see Fig. 12). Thus the beam
inevitably reaches a focal point Q. (This will in general be an astigmatic
focal point where the beam collapses locally to a line rather than a point.)
Note that, near Q, ρ *becomes unbounded* since by (7.38), $\rho = -1/2D$ (log a).

FIGURE 12. Once the local area of cross section of the null rays begins to
decrease, it inevitably decreases to zero.

This behavior is a limiting case of the *Raychaudhuri effect* [49, 86], which
applies to a hypersurface orthogonal timelike congruence of geodesics. Let
t^a be the tangent vectors to the geodesics of the congruence, parametrized
according to proper time s (so $t^a t_a = 1$; with t^a future-pointing) and orthogonal
to a spacelike hypersurface $s = 0$. Define the divergence of the geodesics by

$$\theta = \nabla_a t^a \tag{7.40}$$

From the Ricci identities we obtain Raychaudhuri's equation

$$D\theta = -\nabla_a t^b \nabla_b t^a + R_{ab} t^a t^b \tag{7.41}$$

with $D = t^a \nabla_a$ as in (7.9).

---

[20] There is one simple application of this property which does not seem to have been
noted before, namely, to the question of whether a spherically symmetrical body in asymptotically flat space-time can fail to have a center (see [9] p. 436). If we consider the light
rays (null goeodesics) converging inward from an instantaneous sphere situated symmetrically about the body at a reasonable distance from it, we see that the rays initially
converge, so that $\rho > 0$. They have to reach a (symmetrical) focal point (assuming (7.35)
holds) and this focal point defines the center. (Compare the discussion of trapped surfaces
given in Section 10.)

From the hypersurface orthogonality we get $\nabla_a t_b = \nabla_b t_a$, whence

$$\nabla_a t^b \nabla_b t^a = \nabla_a t_b \nabla^a t^b \geqslant \tfrac{1}{3}\theta^2 \qquad (7.42)$$

from Schwarz' inequality in the 3-space orthogonal to t^a [by the geodesic condition $t^a \nabla_a t_b = 0$ and $t^a \nabla_b t_a = \tfrac{1}{2}\nabla_b(t^a t_a) = 0$]. Thus,

$$D\theta \leqslant -\tfrac{1}{3}\theta^2 + R_{ab} t^a t^b \qquad (7.43)$$

Let V be a small 3-volume element orthogonal to t^a. Then

$$DV = \theta V \qquad (7.44)$$

by (7.40), so

$$D(V^{1/3}) = \tfrac{1}{3}\theta V^{1/3} \qquad (7.45)$$

and (7.43) gives

$$D^2(V^{1/3}) = \tfrac{1}{3}D(\theta V^{1/3}) \leqslant \tfrac{1}{3}V^{1/3}R_{ab} t^a t^b \leqslant 0 \qquad (7.46)$$

if we assume that the *energy condition*

$$T_{ab} t^a t^b \geqslant \frac{\lambda}{2K} + T^c{}_c \qquad (7.47)$$

holds [*cf.* (7.1)]. (If $\lambda = 0$, then (7.47) holds if in an "eigentetrad" of T_{ab}, the energy density is not less than *minus* each principal pressure, nor less than minus the sum of the principal pressures. This would be true of all normal matter.) At this point the argument proceeds just as before, with (7.45) replacing (7.38) and (7.46) replacing (7.39), showing that if $\theta < 0$ at some point on one of the geodesics, then a focal point ($V = 0$, $\theta \to -\infty$) is reached somewhere in the future on the geodesic. Similarly, if $\theta > 0$, then a focal point ($V = 0$, $\theta \to +\infty$) is reached in the past on the geodesic.

One final remark concerning (7.30) is appropriate here. We have, by (7.31),

$$\Psi = \Psi_{ABCD} o^A o^B o^C o^D \qquad (7.48)$$

so, comparing with (7.4) and (7.5) we see that Ψ vanishes when o^A points in a *principal null direction*. Thus, we can give a physical interpretation of the principal null directions as those null directions (at a point P) along which *no astigmatic focusing* takes place. From the fact that astigmatism is a directional quantity, we can actually see from topological considerations that there must be at least a net algebraic count of *four* null directions of vanishing astigmatism at P. We consider an S^2 representing the null directions at P, on which we put a small line element to represent the astigmatism for each null direction at P. The principal null directions emerge as four points where the line element vanishes, as indicated in Fig. 13. This type of argument applies to other spins (for example, to spin 1, namely, electromagnetism, when the analogous line element is *oriented*, so the Fig. 13 behavior cannot

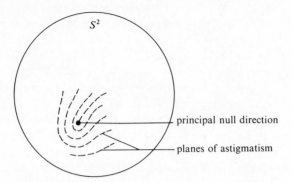

FIGURE 13. A principal null direction appears as a singularity in the field of directions of astigmatism, on the S^2 representing null directions at P.

occur and we get just two principal null directions). The argument can also be used in other situations, such as for the *asymptotic* fields for which S^2 would be at infinity rather than at P.

8 CONFORMAL INFINITY

The question of the meaning of gravitational energy has been briefly touched upon in the previous section. The utility of the concept of energy, in general, arises from the fact that it is *conserved*. In Einstein's theory there is a "local conservation law" for energy built in, namely,

$$\nabla_a T^{ab} = 0 \tag{8.1}$$

this being, by virtue of the field equations (7.1), a double contraction of the Bianchi identities:

$$\nabla_{[a} R_{bc]de} = 0 \tag{8.2}$$

However, (8.1) does *not* yield an *integral* conservation law of the usual type, that is, a law stating that an integral over the boundary of some compact 4-volume of the "flux" of some quantity across this boundary necessarily vanishes.

The prototype of such an integral conservation law is given by electric charge. If J^a denotes the charge current vector, then we have

$$\nabla_a J^a = 0 \tag{8.3}$$

Since J^a is a "vector" or, more appropriately, the "dual of a 3-form," the local conservation law (8.3) implies the existence of an integral conservation law of the above type, where the flux of charge across a surface element

dS_a is $J^a dS_a$. However, (8.1) is not of this form. We can get an *approximate* integral conservation law if we integrate over the boundary of some region whose dimension is very small compared with the radii of curvature involved in R_{abcd}. For this, we may introduce a basis frame δ_a^a which is approximately covariantly constant over the region, and read (8.1) as $\nabla_a T^{ab} \simeq 0$. This is now of the form (8.3), so an approximate energy-momentum integral conservation law arises with energy-momentum flux $T^{ab} dS_a$. We may regard the space-time curvature as giving a (nonlocal) *gravitational* contribution to the energy-momentum which has to be taken into account to get an exact integral conservation law. This can be formalized in various ways (by the use of "pseudotensors", etc.), but no method has yet emerged which, in general situations, assigns any kind of meaningful uniqueness to the gravitational energy-momentum flux, say, or to the total energy momentum in a region. I think we may regard the question of gravitational energy as one of the important unsolved problems in general relativity theory.

But have we any right to expect a solution to this problem at all? Might it not be that energy-momentum is simply not quite conserved in general relativity, or, put another way, that the energy-momentum concept is not (except locally) really an appropriate one for the subject. It may be that in general this is so. I do not know. However, it is (to my mind) a very remarkable fact that a meaningful (that is, "covariantly" or "geometrically" defined) energy-momentum concept really *does* exist for an interesting subclass of space-times, namely, those which are *asymptotically flat*.

The study of asymptotically flat space-times forms an important part of general relativity theory. This is not because it is believed that the universe is very likely to be asymptotically flat, but because in any situation in which general-relativistic effects are expected to be important—that is, with the notable exception of the study of the universe as a whole—the curvatures involved in the local process will exceed by many orders of magnitude the smoothed-out curvatures of the general background. (For example, even if we collapse an entire galaxy, the size of the resulting object of interest would be smaller than the radius of the background curvature of the universe by a factor of about 10^{11}. See the discussion in Section 10.) Thus, asymptotic flatness is an excellent approximation in a large number of situations. This is fortunate, because it is only with asymptotic flatness that general relativity begins to resemble much of the rest of physics. We can then discuss the question of advanced and retarded waves, gravitational or otherwise. We can discuss the energy carried by these waves, scattering problems, even perhaps quantization. I shall not go into any of this in any detail here. I merely describe a mathematically precise framework for the discussion of these questions and just indicate some of the applications.

In order to fix ideas, let us consider, in more physical terms, the question of whether gravitational waves emitted by an isolated system carry energy, and if they do, whether the energy they carry is necessarily positive. (The existence of gravitational waves emitted by a system of varying asymmetry, is inferred in the first instance, from the linear approximation to Einstein's theory.) To find out what energy we should assign to the waves, we envisage measuring the mass m_1 of the system before the waves are emitted and then measuring the mass m_2 of the system after the waves are emitted. If energy (that is, mass) conservation is to retain any meaning, we require that the total energy carried by the waves be just $m_1 - m_2$ (assuming incoming waves are not present, which might be absorbed by the system).

But how are we to measure the mass? One way might be to integrate some expression of mass density over a spacelike hypersurface $\mathscr{S}$. However, we would have to take into account the "nonlocal mass density" of the gravitational field itself and this complicates things. As an alternative, we might prefer to measure the mass by examining the field *only* in the neighborhood of *infinity* on $\mathscr{S}$, since the way in which the curvature falls off at large distances on $\mathscr{S}$ should fix the total mass. Instead of a 3-volume integral, we then use just a 2-surface integral at infinity. In fact, either method *can* be used to give a satisfactory definition. But in both cases, our spacelike hypersurface $\mathscr{S}$ has to extend to infinity and we have a difficulty when it comes to measuring the mass $m_1 - m_2$ carried by the waves. We would "normally" require that $\mathscr{S}$ should suitably tend to become a spacelike hyperplane as our space-time approaches flatness at infinity. This is not unreasonable for the hypersurface $\mathscr{S}_1$, which intercepts the source's world line before the emission of the radiation, to yield m_1 (Fig. 14). But in the case of such a hypersurface $\mathscr{S}_2$, which intercepts the source *after* the emission of the radiation, we do not get m_2 as our mass measurement, but simply m_1 again. This is because $\mathscr{S}_2$ intercepts all the waves, and *whatever* energy they carry has to be added in, giving $m_1 = m_2 + (m_1 - m_2)$.

We might try to carry out some complicated limiting process, allowing the hypersurface to move "upward" into the future while letting the size of the region of integration extend gradually out to infinity, the waves remaining outside the region. Let us apply this to the second of the above two suggestions for measuring the mass. Then we are led to considerations of 2-surface integrals at infinity, not in spacelike directions, but in *null directions*. This suggests the use of null (or, at least, asymptotically null) hypersurfaces $\mathscr{N}_1$, $\mathscr{N}_2$, in place of $\mathscr{S}_1$, $\mathscr{S}_2$. Here $\mathscr{N}_1$ lies entirely outside the cone of radiation, which in turn lies entirely outside $\mathscr{N}_2$. Then, a 2-surface integral at infinity on $\mathscr{N}_i$ might reasonably be used to measure $m_i (i = 1, 2)$, the difference $m_1 - m_2$ then giving the mass of the waves.

By achieving such a definition of mass and by showing that the difference $m_1 - m_2$ is positive in the presence of radiation, Bondi (with his co-workers) and subsequently, Sachs [8, 11, 95], made an important advance in

FIGURE 14. To measure mass loss through radiation, $\mathcal{N}_1$ and $\mathcal{N}_2$ are more appropriate than $\mathcal{S}_1$ and $\mathcal{S}_2$.

the understanding of gravitational energy. Their definition depended on the introduction of a specific type of coordinate system based on outgoing null hypersurfaces. The existence of a coordinate system of the required type was taken as the definition of the degree of asymptotic flatness required. I propose to give another definition for asymptotic flatness here, which is more evidently geometrical in character, but which is, in essentials, equivalent to the Bondi–Sachs definition. The idea involves the introduction of a *boundary* to space-time $\mathcal{M}$ whose points constitute future and past end-points to each null geodesic in $\mathcal{M}$. (We have just seen that the Bondi–Sachs mass is a 2-surface integral over "future end-points" to null geodesics, namely, the null geodesics which generate $\mathcal{N}_i$.) It turns out, somewhat miraculously, that Bondi–Sachs asymptotic flatness finds expression in the existence of a *smooth conformal structure* [74, 76] for the space-time with boundary. Having such a well-defined structure at infinity, we can then perform calculations by treating infinity as though it were a *local* structure and awkward asymptotic limits are thereby avoided.

Let us start by considering the nature of conformal infinity for Minkowski space-time $\mathcal{M}$. Choose null polar coordinates u, v, θ, φ related to the usual Minkowskian x^0, x^1, x^2, x^3 by

$$u = x^0 - r \qquad v = x^0 + r \tag{8.4}$$

with $r = [(x^1)^2 + (x^2)^2 + (x^3)^2]^{1/2}$ and

$$x^1 = r \cos\theta \cos\varphi \qquad x^2 = r \sin\theta \cos\varphi \qquad x^3 = r \sin\varphi. \tag{8.5}$$

Then

$$ds^2 = du\,dv - \tfrac{1}{4}(u - v)^2(d\theta^2 + \sin^2\theta\,d\varphi^2) \tag{8.6}$$

$(u \leqslant v)$. Let us choose new coordinates p, q with

$$v = \tan p \qquad u = \tan q \tag{8.7}$$

$(-\pi/2 \leqslant q \leqslant p \leqslant \pi/2$; see Fig. 15) so that points at infinity are assigned finite

FIGURE 15. The range of p and q. To construct $\mathcal{M}$, rotate about $p = q$, so each point $p > q$ describes an S^2 (but keep I^0 fixed!).

p, q coordinate values. The metric (8.6) ceases to be meaningful at such values ($p = \pi/2$ or $q = -\pi/2$) but if we pass to a *conformally related* metric

$$d\hat{s} = \Omega \, ds \qquad (8.8)$$

where we choose

$$\Omega = (1 + u^2)^{-1/2}(1 + v^2)^{-1/2} \qquad (8.9)$$

then (8.6) becomes

$$d\hat{s}^2 = dp \, dq - \tfrac{1}{4}\sin^2(p - q)(d\theta^2 + \sin^2\theta \, d\varphi^2) \qquad (8.10)$$

The metric (8.10) is perfectly regular at $p = \pi/2$ and at $q = -\pi/2$ (except that at $p = q$ or $p - q = \pi$, we have removable coordinate singularities). Thus, we have a well-defined conformal structure on a manifold ($-\pi/2 \leqslant q \leqslant p \leqslant \pi/2$) with *boundary*[21] ($q = -\pi/2$ or $p = \pi/2$) whose interior ($-\pi/2 < q \leqslant p < \pi/2$) is identical in conformal structure with Minkowski space-time. Note that $q = $ const. and $p = $ const. are null hypersurfaces (cones) and are therefore generated by null geodesics. This then applies, in particular, to the boundary hypersurfaces.

The metric (8.10) is, in fact, that of *Einstein's static universe* $\mathscr{E}$. If we allow $0 \leqslant p - q \leqslant \pi$, with $p + q$ unrestricted (and with the usual range for the spherical polar coordinates θ, φ), then (8.10) refers to a "cylinder" $\mathscr{E} \cong S^3 \times E^1$, it being a simple matter to rewrite (8.10) in the form $d\hat{s}^2 = dT^2 - d\Sigma^2$, with $d\Sigma^2$ standing for the usual metric on a 3-sphere. (The regions of coordinate singularity in (8.10) can now be covered by applying a rotation in S^3 to the coordinates p, q, θ, φ.) The portion of $\mathscr{E}$ which corresponds to $\mathscr{M}$ can be described geometrically as follows (see Fig. 16). Choose a point I^- on $\mathscr{E}$ (this will be $p = q = -\pi/2$). The null geodesics on $\mathscr{E}$ which have past end-point at I^- will generate the future null cone of I^-. These null geodesics will reach a first focal point which is diametrically opposite (with respect to S^3) to I^-. Call this point I^0 (this is to be $p = -q = \pi/2$).

The (open) null geodesic segments from I^- to I^0 sweep out a hypersurface region $\mathscr{I}^-$ (to be $-\pi/2 < p < \pi/2$, $q = -\pi/2$) which is bounded at the past by I^- and at the future by I^0. ($\mathscr{I}^-$ has topology $S^2 \times E^1$.) The

---

[21] Strictly speaking, we do not quite have a manifold with boundary here, because of "corners" on the boundary. These will be removed for the strict definition to be given shortly.

There is another version of compactified conformal Minkowski space-time in which the future boundary hypersurface is identified with the past. Then the whole structure becomes a compact conformal manifold without boundary ($\cong S^1 \times S^3$) (see [51, 92]; also [76, 79]).

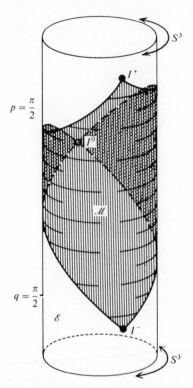

FIGURE 16. Conformal Minkowski space-time as a portion of the Einstein universe.

hypersurface $\mathscr{I}^-$ defines the past null cone at I^0. Continue these null geodesics into the future beyond I^0. They reach a second focal point I^+ (to be $p = q = \pi/2$), which is diametrically opposite to I^0 (with respect to S^3) and therefore lies directly "above" I^- in $\mathscr{E}$. The (open) null geodesic segments from I^0 to I^+ will sweep out a null hypersurface region $\mathscr{I}^+$ (to be $p = \pi/2$, $-\pi/2 < q < \pi/2$), again of topology $S^2 \times E^1$, and bounded by I^0 at the past and I^+ at the future. The part of $\mathscr{E}$ which may be identified with $\mathscr{M}$ (as regards conformal structure) is then just the set of points of $\mathscr{E}$ which lie "between" $\mathscr{I}^-$ and $\mathscr{I}^+$ (that is, the set of points which lie between I^- and I^+ on timelike curves from I^- to I^+). Thus $\mathscr{M}$ is an open subset of $\mathscr{E}$ and its boundary is $I^- \cup \mathscr{I}^- \cup I^0 \cup \mathscr{I}^+ \cup I^+$.

A useful way of picturing $\mathscr{M}$ is as the interior of two cones joined base to base (Fig. 17). Then the various parts of $\mathscr{M}$ are represented as portions of these bounding cones. We must bear in mind that this picture is not *conformally* accurate, however. The inaccuracy is greatest near I^0, as emerges particularly since I^0 appears as an equatorial region whereas it

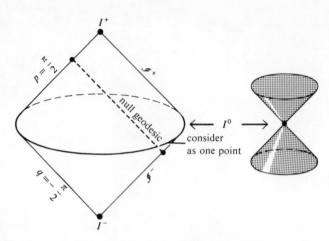

FIGURE 17. Any null geodesic in $\mathcal{M}$ attains two end-points in $\bar{\mathcal{M}}$, one on $\mathscr{I}^-$ and one on $\mathscr{I}^+$.

should be a point. (Of course, to be accurate, we should also have to think of the picture as four-dimensional.)

The interpretation of the points I^-, I^0, I^+ is as "past timelike infinity," "spacelike infinity," and "future timelike infinity." The hypersurfaces $\mathscr{I}^-$ and $\mathscr{I}^+$ are "past null infinity" and "future null infinity," respectively. The reason for labeling them as such becomes evident if we examine straight lines in $\mathcal{M}$ (straight according to the Minkowski metric ds). A timelike straight line becomes a curve from I^- to I^+; a spacelike straight line becomes a closed curve through I^0; a null straight line is a null geodesic originating at a point of $\mathscr{I}^-$ and terminating at a point of $\mathscr{I}^+$. In each case, the curve becomes "compactified" by the addition of the appropriate points at infinity.

The extension of $\mathcal{M}$ as a conformal manifold does not, of course, uniquely lead to the *entire* conformal Einstein universe. For, beyond the boundary $\dot{\mathcal{M}}$, we could bend the extended space as we wished. However, the closure $\bar{\mathcal{M}}$ of $\mathcal{M}$ in $\mathscr{E}$ is uniquely defined as a conformal manifold with boundary. For this to be quite precise, it is more logical to *delete* the points I^-, I^0, I^+ from the definition of $\bar{\mathcal{M}}$ and also from $\dot{\mathcal{M}} = \mathscr{I}$, since otherwise $\bar{\mathcal{M}}$ would not be a manifold with boundary at these three points. This will also fit in more accurately with the discussion of asymptotically flat space-times. (However, I shall not always be completely consistent in this respect, since it is useful to be able to talk about I^-, I^0, I^+.) There are various ways to see that this $\bar{\mathcal{M}}$ is conformally unique. Perhaps the most direct is to construct the points of $\mathscr{I}$ in terms of equivalence classes of null geodesics in $\mathcal{M}$ [an alternative way of defining the points of $\bar{\mathcal{M}}$ is in terms of event horizons and particle horizons (*cf.* Section 9). The nontrivial horizons can be used to define the points of $\mathscr{M}$]. The concept of a *null geodesic* is a *conformally invariant* one, so such a construction is appropriate here. We have to decide when two null geodesics in $\mathscr{M}$ are to be deemed as intersecting on $\dot{\mathscr{M}}$. A method given by Geroch [34, 35] (see Dr. Geroch's lecture, Chapter VIII) can be used here to treat quite general space-times. In the present case, where $\mathscr{M}$ is Minkowskian, two null geodesics meet at the same point of $\mathscr{I}^+$ if and only if they belong (according to the ds metric) to the same *null hyperplane* in $\mathscr{M}$. If they are merely parallel in $\mathscr{M}$, then they just meet the same generator of I^+. For this particular space-time $\mathscr{M}$, two null geodesics meeting on $\mathscr{I}^+$ must also meet on $\mathscr{I}^-$ and *vice versa*. However, this is a very special property of Minkowski space-time and will not hold for general $\mathscr{M}$.

Let us pass to a slightly more general space-time $\mathscr{M}$, namely, the Schwarzschild solution for the metric of the exterior field of a spherically symmetric massive body. I shall use the Eddington–Finkelstein [27, 32] form of the metric with one retarded null coordinate u:

$$ds^2 = du^2[1 - (2m/r)] + 2dr\, du - r^2(d\theta^2 - \sin^2\theta\, d\varphi^2) \tag{8.11}$$

($r > 0$). (This metric is discussed more completely in Section 10.) If we choose $d\hat{s} = \Omega\, ds$, with

$$\Omega = r^{-1} = l, \tag{8.12}$$

where l is to be a new coordinate which is finite for $r = \infty$, then we get

$$d\hat{s}^2 = du^2(l^2 - 2ml^3) - 2dl\, du - d\theta^2 - \sin^2\theta\, d\varphi^2 \tag{8.13}$$

($l \geqslant 0$). This is regular at $\mathscr{I}^+$, defined by $l = 0$, u finite. Here $\mathscr{I}^+$ is $S^2 \times E^1$ as before. To find $\mathscr{I}^-$, we re-express (8.11) in terms of an advanced null coordinate $v = u + 2r + 4m \log (r - 2m)$:

$$ds^2 = dv^2\left(1 - \frac{2m}{r}\right) - 2dr\, dv - r^2(d\theta^2 - \sin^2\theta\, d\varphi^2) \tag{8.14}$$

($r > 0$) and again use (8.12). This gives,

$$d\hat{s}^2 = dv^2(l^2 - 2ml^3) + 2dl\, dv - d\theta^2 - \sin^2\theta\, d\varphi^2 \tag{8.14a}$$

($l \geqslant 0$), which is regular at $\mathscr{I}^- \cong S^2 \times E^1$, defined by $l = 0$. The only real difference between this case and the previous Minkowskian one, as regards the structure of infinity, lies in the fact that we do *not* get *regular* points I^-, I^0, I^+ here. It is not surprising that I^- and I^+ turn out to be singular, since the source becomes concentrated at these points, at the two ends of its history. But I^0 is also a singular point, having infinite conformal curvature (although a C^0 conformal metric can be assigned at I^0). Thus we omit I^0 and $I^\pm$ from the definition of $\dot{\mathscr{M}}$ (and from $\mathscr{I} = \mathscr{I}^- \cup \mathscr{I}^+$).

The form of the Schwarzschild metric given in (8.11), (8.14) is a special case of

$$ds^2 = r^{-2}A dr^2 - 2B_i\, dx^i dr + r^2 C_{ij}\, dx^i\, dx^j \tag{8.15}$$

($i, j = 1, 2, 3$), where A, B_i, C_{ij} are functions of x^1, x^2, x^3, and r, such that if we put $x^0 = r^{-1}$, then these functions are to be sufficiently differentiable (say C^3) as functions of x^a ($a = 0, 1, 2, 3$) at and in the neighborhood of the hypersurface $\mathscr{I}$ defined by $x^0 = 0$.   If we assume that the relevant determinant in A, B_i, C_{ij} does not vanish, then clearly the metric $d\hat{s} = \Omega\, ds$, with $\Omega = r^{-1}$ is regular (C^3) on $\mathscr{I}$.   The metric (8.15) includes all metrics of the Bondi–Sachs type, so a regularity assumption for $\mathscr{I}$ seems a not unreasonable one to impose if we wish to study asymptotically flat space-times and allow the possibility of gravitational radiation.   In fact, with no field equations imposed to restrict R_{ab}, (8.15) is more general than the Bondi–Sachs metrics.   In particular, (8.15) includes the de Sitter space-time and also asymptotically de Sitter space-times.   These are cases which can arise if we have a cosmo-logical term present in Einstein's vacuum equations.

The choice of Ω for (8.15) which is required to make the metric ds regular at $\mathscr{I}$, has the important property that its gradient at $\mathscr{I}$ does not vanish ($\partial\Omega/\partial x^a = (1, 0, 0, 0)$ at $\mathscr{I}$) and thus defines the normal direction to $\mathscr{I}$ there. It is convenient to supplement an assumption of regularity at $\mathscr{I}$ with the condition that Ω has nonvanishing gradient at $\mathscr{I}$, but under certain circum-stances this condition can be deduced from the regularity assumption.

Let us be more precise as to the conditions to be satisfied.   We require that our space-time $\mathscr{M}$, with metric ds^2, be extendible to a conformal manifold with boundary $\bar{\mathscr{M}} \supset \mathscr{M}$ (int $\bar{\mathscr{M}} = \mathscr{M}$; $\dot{\mathscr{M}} = \bar{\mathscr{M}} - \mathscr{M}$) such that

THERE EXISTS A SMOOTH (SAY C^3, AT LEAST) REAL-VALUED FUNCTION $\Omega(\geqslant 0)$ ON $\bar{\mathscr{M}}$ AND A SMOOTH PSEUDO-RIEMANNIAN METRIC $d\hat{s}^2$ ON $\bar{\mathscr{M}}$ (CONSISTENT WITH ITS CONFORMAL STRUCTURE) SUCH THAT $ds^2 = \Omega^2\, d\hat{s}^2$ ON $\mathscr{M}$ $\hfill$ (8.16)

ON $\dot{\mathscr{M}}$, WE HAVE $\Omega = 0$, $\hat{\nabla}_a \Omega \neq 0$ $\hfill$ (8.17)

EVERY NULL GEODESIC IN $\mathscr{M}$ HAS TWO END-POINTS ON $\dot{\mathscr{M}}$ $\hfill$ (8.18)

If such an $\bar{\mathscr{M}}$ exists, we call $\mathscr{M}$ *asymptotically simple*.   Then $\bar{\mathscr{M}}$ is unique (as follows, for example, by Geroch's construction of $\dot{\mathscr{M}}$ in terms of null geodesics [34]).   We write $\dot{\mathscr{M}} = \mathscr{I}$, for the points at infinity for $\mathscr{M}$.

The condition (8.18) is to ensure that the whole of infinity for $\mathscr{M}$ has been included.   It is generally difficult to verify in practice, however, and is not even satisfied by some space-times that one might like to think of as being asymptotically *flat* but which contain bound null orbits (that is, null geodesics which do not escape to infinity such as are found at $r = 3m$ in the Schwarz-schild solution).   In order to cover this type of possibility, let us call a space-time $\mathscr{M}$ *weakly asymptotically simple* if an asymptotically simple $\mathscr{M}_0$ exists, such that for some open subset $\mathscr{K}$ of $\bar{\mathscr{M}}_0$, with $\dot{\mathscr{M}}_0 \subset \mathscr{K}$, the region $\mathscr{M}_0 \cap \mathscr{K}$ (with metric induced from $\mathscr{M}_0$) is isometric with a subset of $\mathscr{M}$. That is to say, a weakly asymptotically simple space-time possesses the conformal infinity $\mathscr{I} = \dot{\mathscr{M}}_0$ of an asymptotically simple space-time but it may possess other "infinities" as well.

To obtain the connection with Bondi–Sachs asymptotic flatness, let us suppose that $\mathscr{M}$ is weakly asymptotically simple with conformal infinity $\mathscr{I}$. Assuming Einstein's equations (7.1), it can be shown that, provided T_{ab} does not approach some nonzero multiple of g_{ab} near $\mathscr{I}$, then

$\mathscr{I}$ IS SPACELIKE, TIMELIKE, OR NULL, ACCORDING AS THE COS-
MOLOGICAL CONSTANT λ IS POSITIVE, NEGATIVE, OR ZERO. (8.19)

[Also, if $\lambda \neq 0$, then we do not need to assume the condition $\hat{\nabla}_a \Omega \neq 0$ of (8.17) but we can deduce it.] If $\mathscr{I}$ is spacelike or null, then $\mathscr{I}$ is the disjoint union of two null hypersurfaces $\mathscr{I}^-$, $\mathscr{I}^+$. The points of $\mathscr{I}^-$ are distinguished from the points of $\mathscr{I}^+$ by the fact that their future null cones, rather than their past null cones, lie in $\bar{\mathscr{M}}$. We are interested here in asymptotic flatness, rather than cosmology, so let us assume that $\mathscr{I}$ is *null*. Then it follows[22] (provided $\mathscr{M}_0$, in addition to being time- and space-orientable, is free of closed timelike curves—possibly an unnecessary assumption) that

$$\mathscr{I}^- \cong \mathscr{I}^+ \cong S^2 \times E^1 \qquad (8.20)$$

the E^1's being the null generators of $\mathscr{I}^{\pm}$. The result (8.20) shows that when $\mathscr{I}$ is null, it fairly closely resembles the infinity of Minkowski space-time.

To proceed further, we need stronger conditions on the way that T_{ab} behaves near $\mathscr{I}$. For simplicity of the discussion, let us assume, for the moment, that $T_{ab} = 0$ (and $\lambda = 0$) in the neighborhood of $\mathscr{I}$. Then more can be said. In fact,

$$\hat{\nabla}_{A(A'} \hat{\nabla}_{B')}{}^B \Omega = 0 \text{ AT } \mathscr{I} \qquad (8.21)$$

and as a consequence of (8.21) and (8.20), cf. [76],

$$\hat{\Psi}_{ABCD} = 0 \text{ AT } \mathscr{I} \qquad (8.22)$$

[We can also obtain $\hat{\nabla}\Omega \neq 0$ at $\mathscr{I}$, rather than assume it in (8.17).] On the basis of (8.22) it is possible to deduce the *peeling-off property* for principal null directions that was mentioned in Section 7. The arguments involved in this will be indicated next.

In spinor form, the Bianchi identities (8.2) become

$$\nabla^A_{P'} \Psi_{ABCD} = \nabla^{Q'}_B \Phi_{CDQ'P'} - 2\varepsilon_{B(C} \nabla_{D)P'} \Lambda \qquad (8.23)$$

Thus, with $T_{ab} = 0$, we get

$$\nabla^{AP'} \Psi_{ABCD} = 0 \qquad (8.24)$$

---

[22] An outline of an argument for obtaining this result is given in an appendix in [76]. It would seem that there must be a more satisfactory way of obtaining the result, however.

Equation (8.24) is of interest, because it is the curved-space version of the zero rest-mass free-field equation in the special case of spin $s = 2$. For general nonzero spins $s = \frac{1}{2}, 1, 1\frac{1}{2}, 2, \ldots$ we would have

$$\nabla^{AP'}\varphi_{AB \ldots L} = 0 \tag{8.25}$$

where

$$\varphi_{AB \ldots L} = \varphi_{(AB \ldots L)} \tag{8.26}$$

is a spinor with $2s$ indices. For $s = \frac{1}{2}$, Eq. (8.25) is the Weyl neutrino equation (zero-mass Dirac equation). For $s = 1$, (8.25) is the spinor version of Maxwell's free-space equations

$$\nabla_{[a} F_{bc]} = 0 \quad \nabla^a F_{ab} = 0 \tag{8.27}$$

with the Maxwell field tensor

$$F_{ab} = -F_{ba} = \varphi_{AB}\varepsilon_{A'B'} + \varepsilon_{AB}\bar{\varphi}_{A'B'} \tag{8.28}$$

In flat space-time, (8.25) is a very satisfactory equation, the solutions having the same number of "degrees of freedom" (namely two) for *any* value of s as they do in the two cases $s = \frac{1}{2}, 1$. However, in curved space-time we have the consistency condition [16, 84],

$$(2 - 2s)\Psi^{ABM}{}_{(C}\varphi_{D \ldots L)ABM} = \nabla^{(B}_{P'}\nabla^{A)P'}\varphi_{ABCD \ldots L}$$
$$= \nabla^B_{P'}\nabla^{AP'}\varphi_{ABCD \ldots L} = 0 \tag{8.29}$$

so that if $s \geqslant \frac{3}{2}$, (8.25) implies an interconnection between $\varphi_{AB \ldots L}$ and the conformal curvature spinor Ψ_{ABCD}. In the case $\varphi_{ABCD} = \Psi_{ABCD}$, (8.29) is, however, automatically satisfied because of symmetry considerations. We leave aside the general question of higher-spin field equations here and interpret (8.25) only in the cases $s = \frac{1}{2}$ (neutrinos) $s = 1$ (electromagnetism) and $s = 2$ (gravitation).

An important feature of (8.25) is that it is *conformally invariant* with

$$\hat{\varphi}_{AB \ldots L} = \Omega^{-1}\varphi_{AB \ldots L} \tag{8.30}$$

We require various conformal transformation formulas. From $d\hat{s} = \Omega\, ds$ we get

$$\hat{g}_{ab} = \Omega^2 g_{ab} \qquad \hat{g}^{ab} = \Omega^{-2} g^{ab} \tag{8.31}$$

so we can set[23]

---

[23] A somewhat different convention has been used here for treating spinors under conformal transformation than that used in [76], resulting in different transformation formulas. This difference is forced upon us by the attitude adopted in Section 3. In fact, the formulas obtained here are a little simpler than those of [76] and fractional powers of Ω are avoided.

$$\hat{\varepsilon}_{AB} = \Omega\varepsilon_{AB} \qquad \hat{\varepsilon}_{A'B'} = \Omega\varepsilon_{A'B'} \qquad \hat{\varepsilon}^{AB} = \Omega^{-1}\varepsilon^{AB} \qquad \hat{\varepsilon}^{A'B'} = \Omega^{-1}\varepsilon^{A'B'} \quad (8.32)$$

For a scalar χ, we have

$$\hat{\nabla}_a \chi = \nabla_a \chi \tag{8.33}$$

For indexed quantities we have, for example,

$$\hat{\nabla}_{AA'} \xi_B = \nabla_{AA'} \xi_B - \Upsilon_{BA'} \xi_A \qquad \hat{\nabla}_{AA'} \eta_{B'} = \nabla_{AA'} \eta_{B'} - \Upsilon_{AB'} \eta_{A'}$$

$$\hat{\nabla}_{AA'} \xi^B = \nabla_{AA'} \xi^B + \varepsilon_A{}^B \Upsilon_{CA'} \xi^C \qquad \hat{\nabla}_{AA'} \eta^{B'} = \nabla_{AA'} \eta^{B'} + \varepsilon_{A'}{}^{B'} \Upsilon_{AC'} \eta^{C'} \tag{8.34}$$

where

$$\Upsilon_{AA'} = \Omega^{-1} \nabla_{AA'} \Omega \tag{8.35}$$

To treat a quantity with more than one index we simply treat it as though it were a product, according to the Leibnitz rule. That is to say, we get one term in $\Upsilon_{XY'}$ for each index. To verify the correctness of (8.34) we need only show that the axioms (4.50)–(4.58) are satisfied.

From (8.34), we get that (8.30) substituted in (8.25) yields

$$\hat{\nabla}^{AP'} \hat{\varphi}_{AB\ldots L} = 0 \tag{8.36}$$

which is the required conformal invariance. However, when applying this to the gravitational field, we have to be careful. The Weyl tensor has the conformal invariance property $\hat{C}^a{}_{bcd} = C^a{}_{bcd}$, that is, $\hat{C}_{abcd} = \Omega^2 C_{abcd}$. Hence

$$\hat{\Psi}_{ABCD} = \Psi_{ABCD} \tag{8.37}$$

Thus, if according to the physical metric ds we set

$$\varphi_{ABCD} = \Psi_{ABCD} \tag{8.38}$$

then we have [by (8.30) and (8.37)]

$$\hat{\varphi}_{ABCD} = \Omega^{-1} \hat{\Psi}_{ABCD} \tag{8.39}$$

It is the field $\hat{\varphi}_{ABCD}$ which we identify with the gravitational field when we examine $\mathscr{M}$ according to its metric $d\hat{s}$.

The significance of this lies in the behavior of the field on $\mathscr{I}$ and the relation of this to the peeling-off property. Recall, from (8.22), that Ψ_{ABCD} *vanishes* on $\mathscr{I}$. From (8.39) and smoothness we obtain:

$$\hat{\varphi}_{ABCD} \text{ IS CONTINUOUS AT } \mathscr{I} \tag{8.40}$$

Since it costs us no more at this point, let us derive the peeling-off property for *general* spin s on the basis of the assumption that $\hat{\varphi}_{AB\ldots L}$ is continuous at $\mathscr{I}$.

We require a spin frame $o^A = \varepsilon_0{}^A$, $\iota^A = \varepsilon_1{}^A$. For the $d\hat{s}$ metric set

$$\hat{o}_A = o_A \qquad \hat{\iota}_A = \Omega\iota_A \qquad \hat{o}^A = \Omega^{-1} o^A \qquad \hat{\iota}^A = \iota^A \tag{8.41}$$

This is consistent with (8.32) and (4.27). The reason for the asymmetrical choice (8.41) is that we wish to arrange o_A to have its direction pointing along a null geodesic η, with o_A, ι_A parallelly propagated (according to ds) along η:

$$\nabla_{00'} o^A = 0 \qquad \nabla_{00'} \iota^A = 0 \tag{8.42}$$

Then (8.34) and (8.41) yield

$$\hat{\nabla}_{00'} \hat{o}^A = 0 \qquad \hat{\nabla}_{00'} \hat{\iota}^A = \Omega^{-1} \hat{o}^A \hat{\nabla}_{10'} \Omega \tag{8.43}$$

Thus o^A is parallelly propagated according to $d\hat{s}$ along η and attains a *well-defined value* at $Q^{\pm} = \eta \cap \mathscr{I}^{\pm}$. In fact $\hat{\iota}^A$ also has a well-defined limiting value at $Q^{\pm}$ and points along $\mathscr{I}^{\pm}$ at $Q^{\pm}$ (so $\hat{\nabla}_{10'} \Omega = 0$ at $\mathscr{I}$; cf. [76]). The affine parameter r on η (affine according to ds) defined by

$$\nabla_{00'} r = 1 \tag{8.44}$$

has the asymptotic behavior

$$r \sim \Omega^{-1} \tag{8.45}$$

Now, by hypothesis, the components $\hat{\varphi}_{\mathfrak{AB} \ldots \mathfrak{L}}$, according to the $\hat{o}^A$, $\hat{\iota}^A$ spin frame, are all continuous at $Q^{\pm}$. Substituting (8.30), (8.41), and (8.45) we interpret this in terms of the physical quantities as

$$\lim_{r \to \pm \infty} \{ r^{2s+1-i} \varphi_{(i)} \} \quad \text{EXISTS} \quad (i = 0, 1, \ldots, 2s) \tag{8.46}$$

where $\varphi_{(i)}$ stands for $\varphi_{00 \ldots 01 \ldots 1}$ with i "ones" and $2s - i$ "zeros." Equation (8.46) tells us that the r^{-k} part of $\varphi_{AB \ldots L}$ along η satisfies

$$\varphi_{AB \ldots DE \ldots L} o^A o^B \ldots o^D = 0 \tag{8.47}$$

($k = 1, 2, \ldots, 2s$) where k spinors o^A appear in (8.47). Condition (8.47) is just the condition for at least $2s - k + 1$ principal null direction of $\varphi_{A \ldots L}$ to coincide in the direction of η. This, then, is the peeling-off property.

For the case of gravitation, this peeling-off property is a characteristic feature of Bondi–Sachs asymptotic flatness. It is possible also, to relate more directly the precise type of coordinates used in the Bondi–Sachs approach to the conformal structure that arises in the present formalism. This has been done explicitly by Tamburino and Winicour [104]. In the present approach we may thus *define asymptotic flatness* for $\mathscr{M}$ just to be *weak asymptotic simplicity*, in the case when $\lambda = 0$ and $T_{ab} = 0$ near $\mathscr{I}$. If T_{ab} only approaches zero in some way toward infinity, we may need further conditions, such as (8.21), (8.22) in addition to weak asymptotic simplicity. In the case of the Einstein–Maxwell equations holding near $\mathscr{I}$, then (except for a possibility of some pathological exceptional cases) such extra conditions are not needed, and peeling-off can be deduced for both gravitation and electromagnetism.

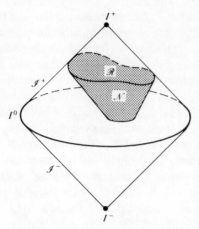

FIGURE 18. The Bondi–Sachs energy-momentum is an integral over $\mathscr{R} = \mathscr{N} \cap \mathscr{I}^+$.

Let us return, briefly, to the question of energy-momentum with which we started. If the outgoing null hypersurface $\mathscr{N}$ meets $\mathscr{I}^+$ in the 2-surface $\mathscr{R}$ (Fig. 18), then we can perform an integral over $\mathscr{R}$ to obtain the total energy-momentum intercepted by any hypersurface spanning $\mathscr{R}$. If we choose Ω so that the metric of $\mathscr{R}$ is that of a unit sphere, then we integrate

$$\hat{\sigma} N - \Psi_2 \tag{8.48}$$

over $\mathscr{R}$ to get the energy component (associated with this choice of Ω) and we integrate (8.48) with a suitable weighting factor to get the momentum components. Here

$$\Psi_2 = \hat{\varphi}_{0011} \tag{8.49}$$

on $\mathscr{R}$, so Ψ_2 comes from the r^{-3} part of the Weyl curvature in the peeling-off. The quantity $\hat{\sigma}$ is the shear $\hat{\Gamma}_{0001}$, of $\mathscr{N}$ at $\mathscr{R}$ (with $\hat{o}^A$ and $\hat{\imath}^A$ describing the null direction in $\mathscr{N}$ and $\mathscr{I}$, respectively). The quantity $\mathscr{N}$ is the Bondi–Sachs "news function" given here by

$$N = \hat{\Phi}_{110'0'} \tag{8.50}$$

Although this is a Ricci tensor component, it retains a certain conformal covariance by virtue of the above restriction on Ω. The whole energy-momentum turns out to have the correct transformation behavior for an "asymptotic 4-vector."

The Bondi–Sachs mass-loss formula finds expression in the fact that if we repeat the mass integral with a new null hypersurface lying to the future of the original one, the mass value so obtained is always less than or equal to the earlier mass value. The mass carried by the gravitational waves turns out to be the integral of $N\bar{N}$ over the part of $\mathscr{I}^+$ lying between the two null hypersurfaces. In fact $\bar{N}$ may be described as an integral, along the generators of $\mathscr{I}^+$ of $\Psi_4 = \hat{\phi}_{1111}$. [This follows from (8.50), in fact.] In the peeling-off, Ψ_4 is the r^{-1} part of the gravitational field and so may be thought of as the outgoing *radiation field.* "News function" is therefore essentially just the "time-integral of the outgoing gravitational radiation field." It turns out that the Bondi–Sachs mass loss formula is closely related to the positive focusing property (7.39) on a null line γ which lies just inside $\mathscr{I}^+$. Here N takes the place of σ in (7.39) and Ψ_4 takes the place of Ψ. (See [78].)

It may be remarked that the mass loss occurs *irrespective* of the presence of *incoming* radiation (that is, analog of Ψ_4 on $\mathscr{I}^-$). Such asymptotic flatness assumptions at $\mathscr{I}^+$ do *not* exclude incoming waves (as seems to have been believed at one time), although they forbid a too large concentration of incoming waves just inside $\mathscr{I}^+$. To see the mass *gain* due to incoming radiation, we should have to turn the above construction upside-down and perform our calculations on $\mathscr{I}^-$ instead.

As a final remark concerning energy in general relativity, we see that while the (future-measured) mass always decreases, there is no guarantee that the mass measurement never becomes negative! In the cases in which all sources finally are radiated away to $\mathscr{I}^+$ as zero-rest-mass fields, we can say from the Bondi–Sachs formula that the total mass *was* always positive.[24] But to my knowledge, it is an unsolved problem whether the total mass is positive in *general* situations where we just assume a suitable physically reasonable inequality on T_{ab}.

9 HORIZONS

When examining specific cosmological models, it is sometimes useful to represent infinity conformally, even though the space-time may not be (weakly) asymptotically simple. For example, in the usual Robertson–Walker "big bang" models, we can represent the initial infinite curvature singularity as a nonsingular hypersurface boundary in the past, but only if we allow $\Omega = \infty$ at this region. The nature of such boundary hypersurfaces is closely related to the question of four types of *horizon* which may occur in cosmology: the *event* horizon or *particle* horizon [88] and future or past *Cauchy* horizons [40, 42]. These will be defined precisely in a moment.

I shall first require some definitions. By a *curve* I mean *the image* of a (noncritical) C^1-map f of a real interval of nonzero length, where I shall

---

[24] Brill [14] obtained some partial results concerning positiveness of total mass of a system as measured on a spacelike hypersurface. A promising new approach to this problem has recently been given by Brill and Deser [14a].

demand that every point of $\mathcal{M}$ has a neighborhood $\mathcal{Q}$ for which $f^{-1}\bar{\mathcal{Q}}$ has no noncompact connected component. Thus *end-points* are required (at which the curve would have to be smooth, and therefore extendible) except where the curve continues indefinitely in one direction or the other. (Otherwise we could refer to an open-ended curve.) If the map f itself is required, this is a *parametrized* curve. A curve is timelike [resp. nonspacelike] if the tangent vectors of the map f are all timelike [resp. timelike or null]. A nonspacelike curve has a natural orientation, called a *future orientation*, which is induced by the time-orientation of $\mathcal{M}$.

If P and Q are two points of $\mathcal{M}$, then (see [50]) the notation $P \ll Q$ is used if there is a *timelike curve in $\mathcal{M}$ with past end-point P and future end-point Q*. The notation $P \prec Q$ is used if either $P = Q$ or there is a non-spacelike curve from P to Q. If $P \prec Q$ and $Q \ll R$ or if $P \ll Q$ and $Q \prec R$, then $P \ll R$. If $P \prec Q$ (with $P \neq Q$), then either $P \ll Q$ or there is a null geodesic from P to Q (or both). The chronological *future* and *past* of P, respectively, are

$$I_+(P) = \{X : P \ll X\} \qquad I_-(P) = \{X : X \ll P\} \qquad (9.1)$$

These are *open* sets, as is easily seen. On the other hand, the sets

$$J_+(P) = \{X : P \prec X\} \qquad J_-(P) = \{X : X \prec P\} \qquad (9.2)$$

are not necessarily closed. For example, let $\mathcal{M}$ be Minkowski space with a point removed and let P be on the null cone of the removed point. For another example, consider a plane wave, *cf.* (9.23)–(9.31). If $\mathcal{X}$ is any sub-set of $\mathcal{M}$, the chronological future and past of $\mathcal{X}$ are denoted, respectively, by

$$I_+[\mathcal{X}] = \bigcup_{P \in \mathcal{X}} I_+(P) \qquad I_-[\mathcal{X}] = \bigcup_{P \in \mathcal{X}} I_-(P) \qquad (9.3)$$

Again these are open sets. The *closures* of these sets are

$$\bar{I}_+[\mathcal{X}] = \{X : I_+(X) \subset I_+[\mathcal{X}]\} \qquad \bar{I}_-[\mathcal{X}] = \{X : I_-(X) \subset I_+[\mathcal{X}]\} \quad (9.4)$$

The proof of (9.4) is easy and will be omitted here. From (9.4), we obtain[25] the *boundaries* of $I_+[\mathcal{X}]$:

$$\dot{I}_+[\mathcal{X}] = \{X : I_+(X) \subset I_+[\mathcal{X}], \ X \notin I_+[\mathcal{X}]\}$$
$$\dot{I}_-[\mathcal{X}] = \{X : I_-(X) \subset I_-[\mathcal{X}], \ X \notin I_-[\mathcal{X}]\} \qquad (9.5)$$

A set of the form $\dot{I}_+[\mathcal{X}]$ will be called a *semispacelike boundary* or SSB. In fact, this is *time-symmetrical* since

$$\dot{I}_+[\mathcal{X}] = \dot{I}_-[\mathcal{L}] \qquad (9.6)$$

---

[25] The notation $\mathcal{A} \subset \mathcal{B}$ means just that $\mathcal{A}$ is a subset of $\mathcal{B}$, not necessarily a proper subset (so $\mathcal{A} \subset \mathcal{A}$).

where $\mathscr{L}$ is the complement in $\mathscr{M}$ of $\bar{I}_+[\mathscr{K}]$. Conversely, (9.6) still holds if it is $\mathscr{L}$ that is an arbitrary subset of $\mathscr{M}$ and $\mathscr{K}$ is, for example, the complement of $\bar{I}_-[\mathscr{L}]$. A *semispacelike set*, in general, is a subset of $\mathscr{M}$ no two points X, Y of which satisfy $X \ll Y$. Clearly an SSB is semispacelike. Although SSB's need not be smooth subsets of $\mathscr{M}$, they have certain nice properties. These will play an important part in the "singularity theorems" of Sections 10 and 11. For the moment, we simply note that:

ANY SSB IS A C^0 THREE-DIMENSIONAL SUBMANIFOLD OF $\mathscr{M}$

(WITHOUT BOUNDARY; AND IS A CLOSED SET)   (9.7)

To see that an SSB is locally homeomorphic to E^3, we examine a small normal coordinate neighborhood (x^a) of any point P of the SSB (with $\nabla_a x^0$ timelike and $\nabla_a x^i$ spacelike, $i \neq 0$) any curve $x^i = $ const. ($i \neq 0$) which is near enough to P intersects both $I_+(P)$ and $I_-(P)$. It therefore intersects the SSB at a point which must be unique. This gives a local homeomorphism onto an open set of the $\mathbf{R}^3$ of (x^1, x^2, x^3) (Fig. 19).

FIGURE 19. Any SSB is locally homeomorphic to E^3.

We are now in a position to define our four types of horizon. Let γ be any timelike curve in $\mathscr{M}$. Then (when nonvacuous)

EVENT HORIZON OF $\gamma = \dot{I}_-[\gamma]$

PARTICLE HORIZON OF $\gamma = \dot{I}_+[\gamma]$ (9.7a)

If γ has a future end-point F, then its event horizon is simply $\dot{I}_-(F)$; if γ has a past end-point P, then its particle horizon is $\dot{I}_+(P)$. These cases will be called *trivial*. An example of a space-time with *no* nontrivial event or particle horizons is the Einstein static universe mentioned in Section 8. However, Minkowski space-time *does* possess nontrivial event and particle

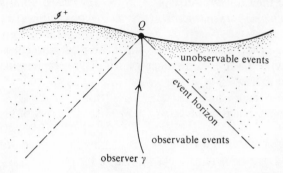

FIGURE 20. If $\mathscr{I}^{+}$ is spacelike, every timelike curve possesses an event horizon.

horizons, given, for example, when γ is a path of uniform acceleration. [See (2.8)–(2.10) and Fig. 6. If γ is $X = Y = 0$, $Z =$ const. > 0, then $z = t$ is an event horizon of γ and $z = -t$ is a particle horizon of γ.] On the other hand, no timelike *geodesic* in Minkowski space-time has an event or particle horizon. Physically, the event horizon of γ separates those events which are observable by an observer whose world line is γ from those events unobservable by him. Similarly, the particle horizon of γ separates those events from which a particle with world line γ can be observed (in principle), from those events from which the particle cannot be so observed.

Examples of space-times with nontrivial event or particle horizons for *geodesic* curves γ, are obtained if $\mathscr{M}$ possesses a *spacelike* conformal infinity $\mathscr{I}^{+}$ or $\mathscr{I}^{-}$. (We allow $\Omega \neq 0$ or $\Omega = \infty$ at $\mathscr{I}$.) If $\mathscr{I}^{+}$ is spacelike, then any timelike geodesic γ (indeed, *any* inextendible timelike curve in $\mathscr{M}$) through a point of $\mathscr{M}$ near enough to $\mathscr{I}^{+}$, will hit $\mathscr{I}^{+}$ at some point Q in $\bar{\mathscr{M}}$. We can define $\dot{I}_{-}(Q)$ (from the conformal structure of $\bar{\mathscr{M}}$) and this will be the required event horizon $\dot{I}_{-}[\gamma]$ (Fig. 20). Exactly similarly, if $\mathscr{I}^{-}$ is spacelike, we can find timelike geodesics γ with nontrivial particle horizons (Fig. 21).

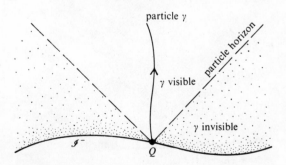

FIGURE 21. If $\mathscr{I}^{-}$ is spacelike, every timelike curve possesses a particle horizon.

To define the Cauchy horizons, let $\mathscr{S}$ be any closed semispacelike set. Define the *domains of dependence* $D_+(\mathscr{S})$, $D_-(\mathscr{S})$ as follows:

$D_+(\mathscr{S})$ IS THE COMPLEMENT OF THE UNION OF ALL TIMELIKE
CURVES WHICH ARE INEXTENDIBLE IN THE PAST AND WHICH DO
NOT INTERSECT $\mathscr{S}$ (9.8)

with $D_-(\mathscr{S})$ as just the time-reverse of (9.8). Another way of putting this is

$X \in D_+(\mathscr{S})$ IF AND ONLY IF EVERY TIMELIKE CURVE THROUGH X
CAN BE EXTENDED INTO THE PAST UNTIL IT MEETS $\mathscr{S}$ (9.9)

and similarly for $D_-(\mathscr{S})$. [We have $\mathscr{S} \subset D_+(\mathscr{S})$.] It is readily seen that the past-inextendible curves not meeting $\mathscr{S}$ sweep out an open subset of $\mathscr{M}$. Thus, by (9.8)

$D_+(\mathscr{S})$ AND $D_-(\mathscr{S})$ ARE CLOSED SETS   (9.10)

The *Cauchy horizons* (Fig. 22) are the "future boundary" of $D_+(\mathscr{S})$ and the "past boundary" of $D_-(\mathscr{S})$:

$$H_+(\mathscr{S}) = \{X: X \in D_+(\mathscr{S}), I_+(X) \cap D_+(\mathscr{S}) = \varnothing\}$$
$$H_-(\mathscr{S}) = \{X: X \in D_-(\mathscr{S}), I_-(X) \cap D_-(\mathscr{S}) = \varnothing\}$$
(9.11)

We have, easily,

$H_+(\mathscr{S})$ AND $H_-(\mathscr{S})$ ARE SEMISPACELIKE CLOSED SETS   (9.12)

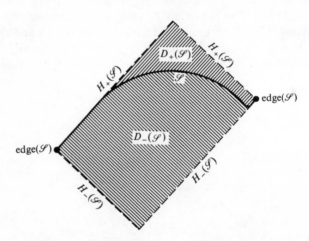

FIGURE 22. Domains of dependence and Cauchy horizons for a semispacelike set $\mathscr{S}$ (in a "trivial" case).

We can define the *edge* of a closed semispacelike set $\mathcal{S}$ as the set of points $P \in \mathcal{S}$ such that for any open set $\mathcal{Q}$ containing P, if $R \ll P \ll Q$ with R, $Q \in \mathcal{Q}$ then there is a timelike curve in $\mathcal{Q}$ from R to Q not meeting $\mathcal{S}$. We have

$$\text{edge } (\mathcal{S}) \subset H_+(\mathcal{S}) \cap H_-(\mathcal{S}) \tag{9.13}$$

The set edge $(\mathcal{S})$ is always closed. It consists of those points of $\mathcal{S}$ at which $\mathcal{S}$ is not locally homeomorphic to E^3. If edge $(\mathcal{S}) = \varnothing$, we can call $\mathcal{S}$ *edgeless*. If $\mathcal{S}$ is a smooth semispacelike set which is a *hypersurface* (without boundary) in $\mathcal{M}$ (so the tangent hyperplanes are everywhere spacelike or null), then $\overline{\mathcal{S}}$ is edgeless if and only if $\mathcal{S}$ is a *closed* subset of $\mathcal{M}$ (that is, $\mathcal{S}$ is properly embedded). As another example, any SSB is edgeless.

A Cauchy horizon (nonvacuous) will be called *nontrivial* if it is the $H_+(\mathcal{S})$ or $H_-(\mathcal{S})$ of some edgeless closed semispacelike set $\mathcal{S}$. Trivial Cauchy horizons are easily constructed (in space-times with no closed time-like curves) by just taking $\mathcal{S}$ to be a small closed portion of a spacelike hypersurface. The Einstein static universe contains no nontrivial Cauchy horizons. On the other hand, Minkowski space-time *does* contain nontrivial Cauchy horizons {for example, if $\mathcal{S}$ is $x^0 = x^1$, with usual Minkowskian coordinates, then $H_\pm(\mathcal{S}) = \mathcal{S}$; if $\mathcal{S}$ is $x^0 = -[1 + (x^1)^2 + (x^2)^2 + (x^3)^2]^{1/2}$, then $H_-(\mathcal{S}) = \varnothing$, but $H_+(\mathcal{S})$ is $x^0 = -[(x^1)^2 + (x^2)^2 + (x^3)^2]^{1/2}$}.

A *global Cauchy hypersurface* or GCH for $\mathcal{M}$ is a semispacelike set $\mathcal{S}$ (normally a smooth hypersurface) for which $H_+(\mathcal{S})$ and $H_-(\mathcal{S})$ are both empty. That is to say, $\mathcal{S}$ meets every inextendible timelike curve in $\mathcal{M}$. An equivalent condition on a semispacelike set $\mathcal{S}$ for it to be a GCH is that it should *intersect every inextendible null geodesic in $\mathcal{M}$ in a nonvacuous compact set*. This will follow from the later considerations concerning the structure of Cauchy horizons. It is not hard to see that the intersection of a null geodesic with an SSB must be *connected*. One property of a space-time $\mathcal{M}$, containing a GCH $\mathcal{S}$, which is easy to establish is that it is topologic-ally $\mathcal{S} \times E^1$, where the E^1's can be represented as timelike curves. It is less easy to establish, but still true,[26] that all the $\mathcal{S}$'s of the product can also be made to be GCH's for $\mathcal{M}$. It also turns out that the existence of a GCH is equivalent to Leray's " global hyperbolicity " condition.[27]

It is clear that the usual " constant time " sections of the Einstein static universe and of Minkowski space-time are GCH's. Among the examples of space-times which do *not* contain any GCH are all those which possess a *timelike* conformal infinity $\mathcal{I}$ (Fig. 23). Any point P near $\mathcal{I}$ lies on timelike curves to the future and past which reach $\mathcal{I}$ in a region near to P (from the point of view of $\overline{M}$). Thus, any candidate $\mathcal{S}$ for a GCH would have to

---

[26] One proof of this is given by Seifert [98].
[27] This will be shown elsewhere.

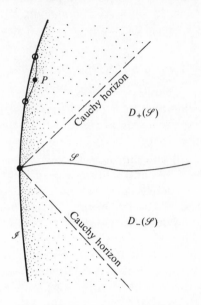

FIGURE 23. If $\mathscr{I}$ is timelike, every semispacelike set has a Cauchy horizon.

come near to P. Since this would apply to *all* points near $\mathscr{I}$, some of which have a definite timelike separation from each other, we see that this cannot be achieved with a semispacelike $\mathscr{S}$.

The de Sitter and anti-de Sitter space-times provide explicit examples where $\mathscr{I}$ is spacelike and timelike, respectively. To describe these models, we consider hyperspheres in five-dimensional pseudo-Euclidean space with two choices of signature. *De Sitter* space-time (Fig. 24) is given by

$$C^2 = -V^2 + W^2 + X^2 + Y^2 + Z^2 \tag{9.14}$$

where the metric is

$$ds^2 = dV^2 - dW^2 - dX^2 - dY^2 - dZ^2 \tag{9.15}$$

Anti-de Sitter space-time (Fig. 25) is the universal covering manifold of

$$C^2 = V^2 + W^2 - X^2 - Y^2 - Z^2 \tag{9.16}$$

with metric

$$ds^2 = dV^2 + dW^2 - dX^2 - dY^2 - dZ^2 \tag{9.17}$$

De Sitter space-time is topologically $S^3 \times E^1$ and possesses S^3 sections which are GCH's. But every timelike curve has both a particle horizon

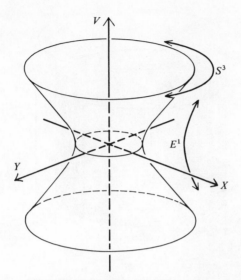

FIGURE 24. The de Sitter model.

and an event horizon. We can represent the space-time conformally on the Einstein static universe as the region between two parallel spacelike sections (Fig. 26). This evidently gives both $\mathscr{I}^+$ and $\mathscr{I}^-$ as *spacelike*. The steady-state model is just the "top-half" of the de Sitter model (see [97], for example), where we cut it at the intersection with, say, the hyperplane $V = W$ in (9.14) (Fig. 27). This cut leaves a *null* boundary in the past, so some timelike curves (for example, the substratum particles) do *not* possess particle horizons.

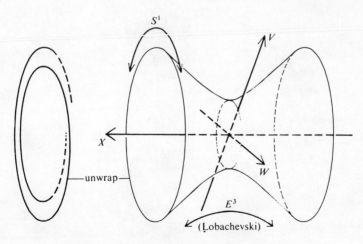

FIGURE 25. The anti-de Sitter model.

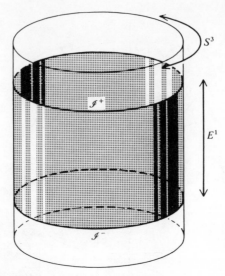

FIGURE 26. The de Sitter model as a conformal portion of the Einstein universe.
The Friedmann model with $\lambda = 0$, $k > 0$ is similarly represented.

The sections of (9.14) by $V - W = \text{const.} > 0$ give the (flat) hypersurfaces of constant time of the steady-state model.   Unlike the entire de Sitter and anti-de Sitter space-times, this model is not geodesically complete.

The hypersphere (9.16) has topology $S^1 \times E^3$ and is thus not simply-connected. It possesses closed timelike curves (S^1) which can be opened out by taking the universal covering manifold.   Then, when represented

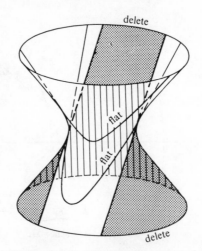

FIGURE 27. The steady-state model.

conformally on the Einstein static universe $S^3 \times E^1$ the "unwrapped" anti-de Sitter model becomes just a hemisphere of the S^3 times the E^1 (Fig. 28). The topology is thus just E^4, but its *conformal* structure is globally different from that of Minkowski space-time. We have a *timelike $\mathscr{I}$*, so every semispacelike $\mathscr{S}$ has a Cauchy horizon. On the other hand, no inextendible timelike geodesics possess particle or event horizons (although some inextendible timelike curves do. The existence of Cauchy horizons is connected with an interesting feature of the anti-de Sitter model. Let P be any point on the hypersphere (9.16) and let Q be diametrically opposite to P. Any plane through PQ cuts the hypersphere in a "great circle" which therefore must be a geodesic. One can see without great difficulty that, in fact, every timelike geodesic on the hypersphere, through P, must also pass through Q, but spacelike or null geodesics through P go to infinity and do not reach Q. We may pass to the "unwrapped" anti-de Sitter space (the universal covering space). For simplicity, choose versions of P and Q as near as possible, with $P \ll Q$ (Fig. 29). Choose R to be a point separated from Q by a spacelike geodesic. Then it is easy to convince oneself that there is *no geodesic connecting P to R* [17]. (We can get from P to R in two steps,

FIGURE 28. The anti-de Sitter model as a conformal portion of the Einstein universe.

FIGURE 29. The points P and R cannot be joined by a geodesic.

however, using a broken timelike geodesic.) The anti-de Sitter model is, in fact, geodesically complete, so the situation is here very different from the case of positive-definite metrics. The nonexistence of a geodesic from P to R is closely related to the fact that R lies beyond $H_+(\dot{I}_+(P))$, as we shall see in Section 11.

The models most often studied in cosmological contexts are the Friedmann models, with metric

$$ds^2 = dt^2 - R^2\,d\Sigma^2 \tag{9.18}$$

Here $d\Sigma^2$ stands for the metric of a unit 3-sphere ($k = 1$), or of a Euclidean 3-space ($k = 0$), or a unit hyperbolic (Lobachevski) 3-space ($k = -1$). The quantity $R = R(t)$ satisfies

$$\frac{4}{3}\pi\rho R^3 = M = \text{const.} > 0 \tag{9.19}$$

$$\dot{R}^2 = \frac{KM}{2\pi R} + \frac{1}{3}\lambda R^2 - k \tag{9.20}$$

which gives an energy-momentum tensor appropriate to "dust" (that is, a perfect fluid without pressure):

$$T_{ab} = \rho(t)t_a t_b \tag{9.21}$$

where

$$t_a = \nabla_a t \tag{9.22}$$

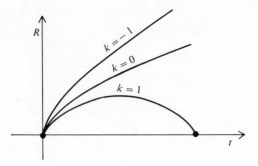

FIGURE 30. The different time-behaviors for the Friedmann models with $\lambda = 0$.

With $\lambda = 0$, the solutions of (9.20) are as indicated in Fig. 30. (The time-reverses of these are also solutions, but not consistent, if $k \leqslant 0$, with the observation that the universe is expanding.) Note that only in the case of a universe with positively curved (and therefore compact) space sections does the model collapse back to a singularity ($R = 0$). (By means of identifications, the cases $k \leqslant 0$ can also be given compact space sections, if desired, at the expense of a loss of global isotropy.)

We can represent the Friedmann models also as conformal subsets of the Einstein static universe. Let us take $\lambda = 0$. The case $k > 0$ resembles

FIGURE 31. The Friedmann models with $k \leqslant 0$, $\lambda = 0$ as conformal portions of the Einstein universe.

the situation for de Sitter space-time (Fig. 26) the difference being that $\Omega = \infty$ at $\mathscr{I}^{\pm}$ instead of $\Omega = 0$. The cases $k \leqslant 0$ are indicated in Fig. 31. In both cases $\mathscr{I}^-$ is spacelike with $\Omega = \infty$ and $\mathscr{I}^+$ is null with $\Omega = 0$. When $k = 0$ we get $\overline{\nabla}_a \Omega = 0$ at $\mathscr{I}^+$, and we have a point I^0. But $\overline{\nabla}_a \Omega \neq 0$ when $k < 0$ and I^0 is an S^2. All the Friedmann models possess GCH's, but they yield particle horizons for all timelike curves.

Let us finally consider two examples which do not possess GCH's, but which fail to do so in rather different ways. First, we consider the plane-fronted wave, which has metric [15, 28, 77]

$$ds^2 = 2\{du + H(v, x, y)\, dv\}\, dv - dx^2 - dy^2 \qquad (9.23)$$

the ranges of the real variables u, v, x, y being unrestricted. The nonvanishing curvature tensor components for (9.23) are defined by

$$\frac{\partial^2 H}{\partial x^2} \qquad \frac{\partial^2 H}{\partial x\, \partial y} \qquad \frac{\partial^2 H}{\partial y^2} \qquad (9.24)$$

The metric satisfies Einstein's vacuum equations with $\lambda = 0$ (and so represents a purely gravitational wave) if

$$\left(\frac{\partial^2}{\partial x^2} + \frac{\partial^2}{\partial y^2}\right) H = 0 \qquad (9.25)$$

but if (9.25) is not imposed then (9.23) covers the more general situation of a combined gravitational–electromagnetic–neutrino wave. All seven principal null directions then coincide. If H is quadratic in x, y, then we get the special case of a *plane wave*. Many plane waves are geodesically complete [28, p. 96].

If $H = 0$ over some range, we have a region of Minkowski space-time. We may, in fact, choose H to be zero over all but some finite range of v: $v_0 < v < v_1$. Then we have a "sandwich wave" [10]. An extreme case is the idealized situation in which the wave is allowed to become infinitesimal in duration (say v_0, $v_1 \to 0$) while still producing a nonzero resultant effect. This results in the function H becoming a delta function in v:

$$H(v, x, y) = \delta(v)h(x, y) \qquad (9.26)$$

With the substitution of (9.26) in (9.23), we get a metric which does not satisfy the conditions normally required for a space-time with a delta function in the *curvature*, as required in (9.24), since here the *metric* tensor components involve delta functions. It is possible to make a coordinate change so that the new metric tensor components are C^0 functions of the coordinates. But the present form is useful since it leads to a graphic "scissors and paste" construction of the manifold [80].

Divide Minkowski space-time, with metric

$$ds^2 = 2du\, dv - dx^2 - dy^2 \qquad (9.27)$$

into $\mathcal{M}^-(v < 0)$ and $\mathcal{M}^+(v > 0)$ by removing the null hyperplane $v = 0$. Reattach a boundary $v = 0$ to each half but identify the two halves so that each appears "warped" as viewed from the other (Fig. 32). This is achieved, on passing from $\mathcal{M}^-$ to $\mathcal{M}^+$, by

$$x \to x \qquad y \to y \qquad u \to u + h(x, y) \tag{9.28}$$

at the common boundary $v = 0$. The jump in coordinates given in (9.28) corresponds precisely to (9.26) substituted in (9.23).

FIGURE 32. A plane wave with a delta-function amplitude. The two half-spaces are flat, but joined with a warp.

For simplicity, let us consider the purely electromagnetic plane wave case. Then we can take

$$h(x, y) = a(x^2 + y^2) \tag{9.29}$$

where a = const. > 0. The null cone of the point $P \in \mathcal{M}^-$, with coordinates $u = x = y = 0$, $v = -a^{-1}$ has the equation

$$2u(v + a^{-1}) = x^2 + y^2 \tag{9.30}$$

At $v = 0$, this agrees with

$$2u(v - a^{-1}) = x^2 + y^2 \tag{9.31}$$

by virtue of (9.28) and (9.29). Equation (9.31) gives the null cone of the point $Q \in \mathcal{M}^+$ with coordinates $u = x = y = 0$, $v = a^{-1}$. This shows that the null cone of P is (in this example) exactly focused again, after passing through the wave, to the point Q. However, there is one exceptional null geodesic α, through P, namely $x = y = 0$, $v = -a^{-1}$, which never hits the wave at all. Correspondingly, the null geodesic β through Q, given by $x = y = 0$, $v = a^{-1}$ does not emerge on the other side. We have the situation that the *two* inextendible null geodesics α, β arise as the limiting configuration of a sequence of *single* null geodesics through both P and Q. (The space of null geodesics, in this example, is thus not Hausdorff.)

A spacelike GCH would have to intersect each null geodesic of the sequence just once. Thus it would have to meet the limit pair α, β in only *one* point. It could not meet both of α, β as would be required of a GCH. In terms of Fig. 32, any edgeless spacelike hypersurface through P gets trapped underneath the past null cone of Q and never reaches β. The nonexistence of a semispacelike GCH is also easily established. (This particular example can also be represented conformally as part of the Einstein static universe. In this case, the nonexistence of a GCH arises, not from a spacelike $\mathscr{I}$, but from the fact that $\mathscr{M}$ contains a null geodesic in the *interior* region of $\mathscr{M}$.) The more general conformally curved plane waves, such as the purely gravitational plane waves do not possess GCH's for essentially the same reason as the above case [77], but the situation becomes somewhat more complicated owing to the presence of astigmatism in the focusing.

As the final example of this section, we consider the Taub–NUT empty universe as described by Misner [59, 61, 63, 105] (see the lecture of Misner Ch.VI; Geroch Ch. VIII). Here, the entire space-time M is to be topologically $S^3 \times E^1$ (but conformally different from the Einstein universe). There is a particular spacelike section $\mathscr{S}$, of maximal proper volume, which has the metric of a 3-sphere (Fig. 33). The four-dimensional geometry at $\mathscr{S}$ does not possess the full rotational symmetry of S^3, however. The Weyl tensor is nonzero, the gravitational principal null directions coinciding in pairs $\{22\}$ [*cf*. (7.6)]. The orthogonal projection into $\mathscr{S}$ of these null directions gives us a nowhere vanishing line-element field on $\mathscr{S}$. (The two null directions project as diametrically opposite, at each point of $\mathscr{S}$.) These line elements are tangential to a congruence of great circles on S^3 which form a set of *Clifford parallels*. Thus, these circles form a Hopf fibering of S^3. The rotational symmetry that remains is a transitive four-parameter group.

Let us move our section parallelly upward, in Fig. 33, preserving this symmetry. We get similar spacelike sections but where the volume of the S^3 decreases. This volume finally decreases to zero [in accordance with the Raychaudhuri effect, *cf*. (7.40)–(7.47)], but instead of collapsing to a point we simply get $H_+(\mathscr{S})$, which is, here, a compact null hypersurface, generated by null geodesics which constitute a set of Clifford parallels on $H_+(\mathscr{S}) \cong S^3$. Beyond $H_+(\mathscr{S})$, the section becomes timelike[28] and therefore possesses closed timelike curves, in a gross violation of reasonable causality.

---

[28] These sections are compact Lorentzian 3-manifolds of a type considered by Avez [3]. Any closed timelike curve γ of this 3-manifold possess a curious property, namely, that whereas (clearly) it cannot be continuously deformed to a point while remaining timelike, there is (for each section) some integer n with the property that $n\gamma$ (that is, γ described with multiplicity n — for this, γ needs to be a proper parametrized curve) can be deformed remaining timelike into $(n+1)\gamma$. Hence, it can be so deformed into a curve of arbitrarily great length. This provides a counter-example to a result of Avez [4]. I am indebted to W. Kundt and H. J. Seifert for pointing this out to me.

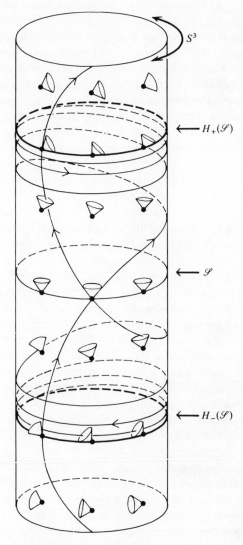

FIGURE 33. The Taub–NUT model.

The future-directed null and timelike geodesics emanating from points of $\mathscr{S}$ fall into two classes. There are those which enter the part of $\mathscr{M}$ beyond $H_+(\mathscr{S})$ (and so cross $H_+(\mathscr{S})$ at a definite point) and those which simply spiral round and round and approach $H_+(\mathscr{S})$ asymptotically. In fact, these latter curves have finite affine length into the future, so the model is not geodesically complete. Misner has shown that, curiously enough, an alternative extension can be fitted at $H_+(\mathscr{S})$ and beyond, other than the one shown in Fig. 33. The curves which previously crossed $H_+(\mathscr{S})$ now spiral round and round, while most of the geodesics which previuosly spiraled now cross the new $H_+(\mathscr{S})$ into the new extension. Both extensions are analytic, but can be added simultaneously only at the expense of giving up the requirement that $\mathscr{M}$ be a Hausdorff manifold [59, 61, Geroch lecture this volume, Ch. VIII]. The behavior at $H_-(\mathscr{S})$ is exactly similar to that at $H_+(\mathscr{S})$ (see Fig. 33). This model appears to be highly unstable, in the neighborhood of $H_\pm(\mathscr{S})$, against small perturbations in the initial conditions at $\mathscr{S}$. However, it is instructive in that it exhibits a kind of pathology that has to be taken into consideration when more general situations are studied.

10 GRAVITATIONAL COLLAPSE

A question of great interest in relativity theory and cosmology is that of the existence of singularities. The usual "big bang" models of relativistic cosmology are characterized by the presence of an initial state of infinite curvature and infinite density (*cf.* Fig. 30). At such an initial singularity the ordinary view of space-time as a smooth manifold would have to break down. Also, the existence of a particle horizon for each world line presents us with an essential problem. Different highly curved portions of the universe, which previously could not communicate with one another, must come together in such a way that they fit consistently. The only previous "causal" link between these portions was the initial singularity itself. We are presented with a problem of *principle* in addition to all the formidable, but essentially technical problems, concerned with the physics of early high-density states of these models. This is the question of *initial conditions* in an essentially singular situation. (See Prof. Misner's lecture, this volume, Ch. VI; also [60].)

It is a reasonable question to ask, however, whether the initial singularity of these models is not more a consequence of the mathematical idealizations involved, than of the actual physical situation that the model is supposed to describe. In particular, it is virtually essential to postulate a high degree of symmetry (for example, spatial homogeneity), for an exact model to be amenable to detailed mathematical treatment. And with such symmetry present, the picture is almost inescapable that all the matter in the universe should, at some time, have been compressed simultaneously into a single point, or at least into a line or into a two-dimensional surface [6, 43, 47a, 99]. Possible ways out of the dilemma that have been suggested include the adoption of a large enough cosmological constant, the presence of "unreasonable" matter (for example, negative energy densities—models with continual creation of matter throughout space would have to come under this heading), perhaps sufficient rotation, or a change in the laws of physics which could have been operative at very early stages of the universe. In addition, there are possible quantum effects of gravitation to be considered, although these might only be important at "ridiculously" high densities (for example, 10^{93} g/cc, or, at least, 10^{53} g/cc). But more significant in the first instance than any of these other considerations, is the role played by local irregularities of matter and curvature. In fact, near the singularity of the model, we really have no reason at all to expect that it should be realistic. The situation is perhaps clearer for the time-reversed process. If we imagine all the matter in the universe hurtling simultaneously to a single "central point" (or "line," etc.) then an infinite density at that point (or line, etc.) is hardly surprising. If, however, we perturb slightly the motion of the incoming matter, so that it is not exactly focused to one point (line, etc.) then we might expect that although the density could become very high, it would not become infinite. The possibility then may be considered of an effective "bounce" to the universe. Thus the presently observed expanding state of the universe might be regarded as the result of a previously contracting phase, the transition from contraction to expansion being achieved via a condensed but highly asymmetrical and complicated intermediate phase.

A picture of this kind has been suggested by many authors [54]. Also some detailed considerations by Lifshitz and Khalatnikov [53] had suggested that such avoidance of singularities by small perturbations of the motions might indeed be possible. However, recent work has ruled out most possibilities of this kind, as we shall see in Section 11. In the present section, I shall discuss the closely related phenomenon of the singularities encountered in gravitational collapse. The essential similarity between gravitational collapse and the time-reverse of the early stages of a "big bang" cosmology has been emphasized particularly by Wheeler [113]. Indeed, there are, perhaps, certain advantages in concentrating attention on the more local phenomenon of collapse, rather than on the global cosmological question. For we do not need to know the entire large-scale structure of the universe to study a local phenomenon (or do we?); if the local laws of physics are strongly affected by the structure of the universe as a whole ("Mach's principle"), then we might at least expect the local phenomenon to be the *less sensitive* to such changes in these laws; finally, unlike the universe as a whole, collapse is *not* something given to us just *once*, so we are freed to exploit the immense theoretical potentialities of the "gedanken experiment." My own personal feeling is that the deeper aspects of the cosmological problem will not be solved without a simultaneously deeper appreciation of what is involved in collapse.

But what is meant, precisely, by "gravitational collapse"? The idea comes originally from the classical study of large spherically symmetrical bodies. According to the work of Chandrasekhar [21, 39], a cold spherically symmetrical (nonrotating) body, which has reached the endpoint of thermonuclear activity, cannot hold itself apart against gravitational forces if its mass is much greater than that of the sun. Such a body would therefore collapse catastrophically and its collapse could only be halted if by some mechanism it were able to throw off sufficient mass to fall below Chandrasekhar's limit. In fact, certain detailed calculations (for references see [107]) have indicated that for initial masses between about 1.2 and 15 times that of the sun, the extreme intensity of the neutrino radiation from the collapsing core may be sufficient to blow off the outer regions of the star and leave a *neutron* star at the center. A cold neutron star (which is essentially an enormous atomic nucleus, bound together gravitationally rather than with nuclear forces) must actually be somewhat *less* massive than the sun (Oppenheimer–Volkoff limit [67]), though vastly smaller, with diameter of only about 10 kilometers. The gigantic explosion involved in such a process is thought to account for (at least) one type of supernova [107].

If no more matter falls into it, a neutron star could exist indefinitely. But what of larger initial masses? Stars with masses of the order of sixty times that of the sun are observed, for example. According to the above-mentioned calculations, the indications are that the core remains *too* massive to form a neutron star and therefore continues to collapse. Assuming that the *exact* spherical symmetry is maintained, the core would fall radially inward *through* its Schwarzschild radius $r = 2m$, to encounter a space-time singularity at the center $r = 0$. The remaining parts of the star which are not blown off would then follow the core in. An observer situated at large distances from the star would never see the collapse to within $r = 2m$, however. To him, the star's collapse would appear to slow down and approach $r = 2m$ asymptotically.

Before considering how physically realistic this picture is, let us examine the solution of Einstein's equations on which it is based, namely, the Schwarzschild solution. This defines the spherically symmetrical gravitational field outside the collapsing star. We have, with the usual Schwarzschild coordinates,

$$ds^2 = \left(1 - \frac{2m}{r}\right) dt^2 - \left(1 - \frac{2m}{r}\right)^{-1} dr^2 - r^2(d\theta^2 + \sin^2\theta\, d\varphi^2). \quad (10.1)$$

Let the star's boundary be given by $r = f(t)$. The metric (10.1) then only applies outside this boundary, that is, $r \geqslant f(t)$ (with the usual inequalities and identifications holding for θ and φ). The star's boundary must be time-like: $|f'(t)| < 1 - 2m/r$, from which it follows that this boundary never crosses $r = 2m$ in (10.1) (Fig. 34). One might be inclined to infer that the star therefore always remained outside $r = 2m$. But if we calculate the total proper time of a particle on the surface of the star, where we assume, for simplicity, that the star falls freely inward, we find that this proper time is *finite*. Thus, an observer who follows the star inward must, after this finite

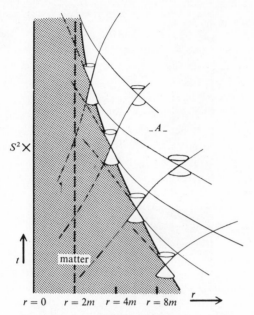

FIGURE 34. The Schwarzschild picture.

time has expired, either of necessity be destroyed (for example, because he encounters infinite tidal forces, or some other form of singularity), or else, find himself in a portion of the universe not covered by the coordinates of (10.1).

In fact, in this instance it is the latter possibility which holds. We can see this if we transform the coordinates in (10.1) by introducing an advanced time parameter $v = t + r + 2m \log (r - 2m)$. Then the metric takes the Eddington–Finkelstein [27, 32] form [compare (8.14)]:

$$ds^2 = \left(1 - \frac{2m}{r}\right) dv^2 - 2 \, dv \, dr - r^2(d\theta^2 + \sin^2 \theta \, d\varphi^2) \qquad (10.2)$$

When $r > 2m$, the forms (10.1) and (10.2) are precisely equivalent, but (10.2) has the advantage that the metric covers a larger region in a nonsingular way. The metric in the neighborhood of the (null) hypersurface $r = 2m$ is perfectly regular. It is only because the more familiar form (10.1) possesses a coordinate singularity at $r = 2m$, that this hypersurface is sometimes referred to as the "Schwarzschild singularity." The surface of the star crosses $r = 2m$ at a definite value of v (although, of course, the here unsuitable t parameter becomes infinite) and proceeds inward toward $r = 0$. But because of the positioning of the light cones (see Fig. 35), an outside observer cannot see any of the empty region $r \leqslant 2m$. More particularly,

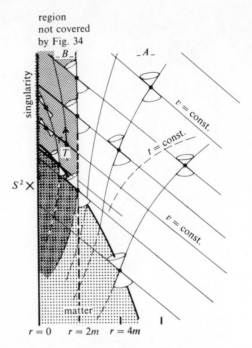

FIGURE 35. The Eddington–Finkelstein picture.

this is because, in the empty region, $r - 2m$ is a null hypersurface which lies "above" (that is, to the future of) the entire external region. An observer or signal can cross the hypersurface from the outside to the inside but not the other way around. The hypersurface $r = 2m$ is an *event horizon* of a more absolute character than most of those considered in Section 9. In fact, *all* geodesics which escape to infinity have this hypersurface as their event horizon.

If we trace the history of the star's surface inside the $r = 2m$ region, we see that it must, of necessity, encounter $r = 0$, for the surface must continue to move in a timelike direction and the null-cones are tipping over more and more toward the $r = 0$ axis. Again if we calculate the total proper time of a particle on the surface of the star (assuming free fall or otherwise), up until the point at which it encounters $r = 0$, we find that this is finite. But this time there is no hope of extending the solution further. If we evaluate the curvature scalars constructed from the Weyl tensor, we find that they tend to infinity as r approaches zero. Thus, our observer who successfully followed the star through $r = 2m$ must now be torn to pieces by the infinite tidal forces at the *true* singularity at $r = 0$.

This is the picture presented by Oppenheimer and Synder [68] when they considered the dynamics of a collapsing uniform dust cloud. In fact the space-time *interior* to such a dust cloud can also be described simply and explicitly and turns out to be nothing other than (a portion of) a Friedmann universe (see Section 9). This again emphasizes the close relationship between the situation of a final singularity in gravitational collapse and of a final (or initial) singularity for a relativistic cosmology.

If we wish to consider the entire history of a gravitationally bound Oppenheimer–Synder gas cloud and not just the final collapse phase, then even the metric form (10.2) does not cover a sufficient portion of the empty region. The behavior of such a dust cloud is time-symmetrical: Like the Friedmann universe with $k = 1$ ($\lambda = 0$), it starts from an initial singularity, expands to a maximum volume and then recontracts to a final singularity. Thus we may expect to join the matter-filled region to an empty, spherically symmetrical exterior region which is also time-symmetrical. We can, in fact, exhibit such a region if we use the U, V coordinates of Kruskal [50a], which are related to the Schwarzschild r, t (in the region $r > 2m$) by

$$\frac{V}{U} = -e^{t/2m} \qquad VU = e^{r/2m}\left(1 - \frac{r}{2m}\right) \tag{10.3}$$

The metric then takes the form

$$ds^2 = f^2\, dU\, dV - r^2(d\theta^2 + \sin^2\theta\, d\varphi^2) \tag{10.4}$$

where

$$f^2 = \left(\frac{32m^3}{r}\right)e^{-r/2m} \tag{10.5}$$

The matter region is joined to the Kruskal region along a timelike hypersurface. This hypersurface is described by a timelike geodesic in the Kruskal (U, V)-plane (Fig. 36). Thus, only the portion to the right of this geodesic in the diagram is to be considered in this model. The left-hand portion of Fig. 36 must be replaced by a spherically symmetric portion ($\cong D^3 \times E^1$) of the Friedmann universe (9.18) whose boundary is again a hypersurface ($\cong S^2 \times E^1$) generated by timelike geodesics. These two portions do, in fact, fit together adequately smoothly, *cf.* [107].

One drawback of the Kruskal form of the Schwarzschild metric is that (10.4) is not given "explicitly," depending on the solution, for r, of (10.3). The Eddington–Finkelstein form (10.2) is, however, much simpler, and it is interesting that the main features of the Kruskal extension can be obtained simply from (10.2). To achieve this, we note that (10.2) covers the two portions A, B of the Kruskal diagram (Fig. 36) (with $2mV^2 = e^{v/2m}$). By using a retarded parameter u [*cf.* (8.11)] in place of the advanced parameter v, we can likewise cover the portion A, D of Fig. 36 with another "coordinate patch," the overlap region being A. In an exactly similar way, we can cover the portion C, B or the portion C, D with a "coordinate patch" having the form of (10.2). The coordinate transformations in the overlap regions C and

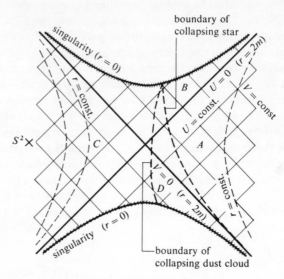

FIGURE 36. The Kruskal picture.

D can be obtained, if desired, by transforming back to the form (10.1) (with $0 < r < 2m$) as an intermediate stage. The one feature of the Kruskal extension which is not obtained by this method is the regular nature of the space-time at the 2-sphere $U = V = 0$. However, the method has a considerable heuristic value in that it applies at once to certain other more complicated extensions, notably those of the Kerr and Reissner–Nordström solutions [*cf.* (10.18), (10.20)] [12, 18, 37]. In this connection it is useful to have also the version (Fig. 37) of the Kruskal diagram in which conformal

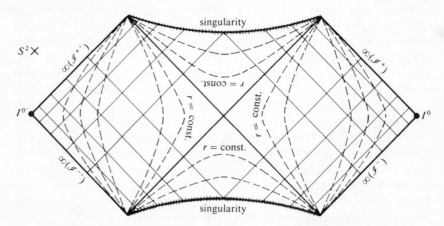

FIGURE 37. The Kruskal picture with conformal infinity represented.

infinity is represented (for example, use coordinates $p = \tan^{-1} \sinh^{-1} V$, $q = \tan^{-1} \sinh^{-1} U$).

Let us return, now, to the case of the collapsing star. Can the description that I have given be regarded as at all realistic? For example, even if we retain the exact spherical symmetry, can it be said that we really know enough about the properties of matter at the density (somewhat greater than that of an atomic neucleus, for the cases considered) at which the star is supposed to fall through its "Schwarzschild throat"? And might it not be that for some reason, a massive star inevitably ejects sufficient material, as it nears $r = 2m$, that its mass invariably falls below the Chandrasekhar or Oppenheimer–Volkoff limit, thus enabling a stable self-supporting state to become possible? It seems that for many years, the prevailing belief had been that a collapsing star would always be able to save itself by such means. This may have been partly because astronomers did not feel the need to consider self-supporting masses that were enormously greater than that of the sun. But with the discovery of the quasi-stellar objects (see, for example, [90]), renewed interest in the subject of gravitational collapse has been stimulated. For, considering the fantastic quantities of energy that these objects appear to be emitting, and their remarkably small size, it has been suggested that "individual" masses of the order, say, 10^6 or 10^8 times that of the sun may be involved. Now the Schwarzschild radius of a spherically symmetric body is proportional to its mass. Thus the characteristic density at which such a body crosses $r = 2m$ should be inversely proportional to the square of its mass. For an object of 10^6 or 10^8 solar masses, this density is not unreasonably high. Indeed, Fowler has emphasized that for an object of 10^{11} solar masses (such as a good-sized galaxy) this characteristic density is less than that of air! And there seems no reason at all to believe that such an object would necessarily eject virtually all its material before reaching $r = 2m$.

Then what about the role played by deviations from spherical symmetry? For example, can one even *define* the analog of $r = 2m$ for an asymmetrical body? And might it not be that the presence of *rotation* always prevents the final collapse? The question of rotation is a particularly pertinent one. For example, if differential rotation is present, then equilibrium states exist for objects of very much larger mass than Chandrasekhar's limit [69]. However, with viscosity present, only uniform rotation could represent a possible final state. Stability of such bodies is a crucial consideration [21a], and it appears that under suitable circumstances a rotating body can collapse. Now, fortunately, there is a known solution of Einstein's vacuum equations, namely that of Kerr [12, 48], which generalizes the Schwarzschild solution by the inclusion of *angular momentum*. The Kerr solution contains two arbitrary parameters m and a, where m defines the mass as in Schwarzschild's solution, and where ma defines the angular momentum. The solution [given explicitly in (10.18)] is still of a rather special character (for example, the quadrupole moment has to be given by $2ma^2$) but it seems likely that at least the main features of the geometry of the space-time surrounding a rotating collapsing body can be gleaned from a study of Kerr's solution. One of the most significant features of the solution, in fact, is that if $a > m$ there is no analog of the "Schwarzschild throat," that is, there is no event horizon for external observers, which would prevent signals from the interior regions being received outside. On the other hand, if $a < m$, there *is* such an event horizon and the solution qualitatively resembles the Schwarzschild solution in that it possesses a similar "throat" which can finally swallow up the material of the (super-) star. There are other features of the solution which qualitatively differ, however, from the case of the Schwarzschild solution. Some of these will be discussed shortly, but in the meantime, I shall concentrate on the question of the "throat" itself and give a definition which may be used as a criterion for its existence.

Let us return to the Schwarzschild solution. For convenience, consider the metric in the form (10.2) and examine Fig. 35. We wish to single out a property of the region B which characterizes it as "perculiar" in some sense. It should be emphasized, however, that there is nothing *locally* peculiar about the B-region. A small neighborhood of any point in the B-region is as good a solution of Einstein's vacuum equations as any other, and there is nothing at all "singular" about it. But it seems that in some way the whole B-region is "shrinking" in an apparently inevitable way to the space-time singularity at $r = 0$. To express this "shrinkage" we need to single out a partly *global* aspect of the B-region—but it must not be *too* global because we require a property that will not be destroyed by small perturbations in the metric at the "time" of collapse. Consider, then, a point T in the B-region of Fig. 35 which can lie just inside $r = 2m$ (but outside the matter region). Such a point describes a spacelike 2-sphere $\mathscr{T}$ in the whole space-time, of total surface area $4\pi r^2 (r < 2m)$. Now any system of material particles whose world-lines intersect $\mathscr{T}$ must have a subsequent motion which is bounded by the velocity of light. That is to say, if we consider the extreme situation of a flash of (idealized) light emitted at $\mathscr{T}$, there will be an "outgoing" flash and an "ingoing" flash, described by the two null geodesic segments in Fig. 35 with past endpoint $\mathscr{T}$. These two null geodesic segments describe null hypersurfaces through $\mathscr{T}$, which together constitute $\dot{I}_+[\mathscr{T}]$. Now the significant feature is that *both* parts of the boundary are "shrinking." Not only is the total surface area of the sphere described by a point moving up the "ingoing" null geodesic decreasing, but so also is the total surface area correspondingly decreasing for the "outgoing" flash. This, then, is the property of $\mathscr{T}$ which I shall use to characterize it as a *trapped surface* [75]. The presence of a trapped surface in a region will then be our indication that there may be something "peculiar" about the subsequent history of the region.

To be more precise:

A TRAPPED SURFACE $\mathscr{T}$ IS A SMOOTH COMPACT, SPACELIKE 2-SURFACE[29] WITH THE PROPERTY THAT THE NULL GEODESICS, WHICH MEET T ORTHOGONALLY LOCALLY CONVERGE IN FUTURE DIRECTIONS. (10.6)

The quantity ρ of Section 7 conveniently measures thic convergence. The null geodesics meeting a spacelike 2-surface orthogonally always generate a null hypersurface, so by (7.28) we have $\rho = \bar{\rho}$. Thus, the characteristic feature of a trapped surface is that

$$\rho > 0 \quad \text{AT} \quad \mathscr{T} \tag{10.7}$$

for both the null hypersurfaces through $\mathscr{T}$. As we move into the future up either of these null hypersurfaces, the surface area decreases, initially, at every point of $\mathscr{T}$.

The idea, here, is to establish a connection between the existence of a trapped surface in a space-time and the subsequent development either of a singularity in space-time [such as $r = 0$ in (10.2)] which may involve infinite curvature, or else of some other space-time behavior which would be very strange from the physical point of view. But before considering the rigorous mathematical result, let us ask the question whether it is reasonable to expect trapped surfaces to develop at all in our actual universe. For any *individual* case of a collapsing star or superstar, this is clearly a matter of the detailed astrophysics involved. The amount of rotation present, the mass loss via neutrinos, through gravitational radiation, the exact nature of the asymmetry present, the nature of the equations of state, magnetic fields, etc.; all these may be relevant. But the essential point I want to make here is that there can be no reason *of principle* against a trapped surface developing. To illustrate this, I shall consider the following "*gedanken experiment.*"

A technically advanced (but presumably exceedingly foolhardy) race of beings inhabit a galaxy (preferably elliptical) which contains about 10^{11} stars. By means of rockets, these beings contrive to alter the velocities of the stars, so that there remains practically no transverse component to the stars' motions. Furthermore, their radial motions are adjusted so that all the stars will fall toward the center so as to reach its vicinity at almost the same time. (The mass-energy expended in this operation would be small compared to the mass of the stars.) The region they have to aim for has roughly a radius 50 times that of the solar system. There is plenty of room in a volume of this size for all the stars, and they can arrive there before any serious problem of stellar collisions arises. (They can even steer to avoid

---

[29] It is convenient also to assume that $\mathscr{T}$ is a semispacelike set, but this is not strictly necessary for the proof of Theorem I.

collisions, if necessary!) But does this result in the development of a trapped surface? The fact that it does depends on the most primitive considerations of general relativity. We consider a flash of (idealized) light emitted at the center at about the time the stars enter the critical region. Because of the focusing effect on idealized light rays [7, 87] (that is, on null geodesics) by the gravitational field of each star (which is actually an *observed* effect of general relativity), a sufficient density of light rays which started off by diverging from the center will pass through (and near to) enough stars so that they start converging again. Under these circumstances it can be shown that a topological sphere which lies just inside the outermost boundary of the light rays will indeed be a trapped surface.

This example serves to illustrate, also, the fact that there is no reason why an observer should be "destroyed" as he enters the critical region. The curvature is still extremely small in the neighborhood of the trapped surface and the space-time there is perfectly regular.[30] Indeed, locally there is nothing peculiar about the trapped surface itself. Even in Minkowski space-time, many surfaces exist which are "locally trapped." That is to say, they satisfy the conditions of (10.6) *except* for the fact that they are not compact. To construct such a surface, we need only consider the intersection of the past null cones of two spatially separated points.

If, then, it is accepted that trapped surfaces can exist, what of the consequences? I shall show, in fact, that if we assume (provisionally) that the universe is *open* (that is, not spatially compact), then our present knowledge of the laws of physics is insufficient to enable us to calculate even *in principle* the future history of such a collapsing system.

To predict the future of a system, we would normally ask that adequate Cauchy data be specified on some spacelike hypersurface. We may take it that the relevant local laws of physics are such that effects can be propagated along timelike or null curves, but not along spacelike ones. Thus, if data are specified on some semispacelike closed set $\mathscr{S}$, then this can determine the situation only in $D_+(\mathscr{S})$ and $D_-(\mathscr{S})$. For regions exterior to these, we could have relevant information carried along nonspacelike curves which fails to "register" on $\mathscr{S}$. Now a collapse situation can be set up starting from perfectly reasonable data on a spacelike hypersurface $\mathscr{C}$, which (since we are trying to consider a local physical situation, rather than a cosmological one) we attempt to think of as *effectively* extending to infinity whether or not the universe is actually spatially noncompact. Thus, for *predictability*, we ask that a noncompact spacelike hypersurface $\mathscr{C}$ should exist which is a GCH for $\mathscr{M}$, or, more appropriately, for which $D_+(\mathscr{C}) = I_+[\mathscr{C}]$. The question of whether the cosmologial nature of space-time is *actually* relevant to a local collapse situation is not a trivial one, as we shall see later.

---

[30] In [26], slightly aspherical collapse is examined and it is verified that trapped surfaces evolve.

Theorem I. The following requirements on a space-time[31] $\mathscr{M}$ are mutually inconsistent:

(Ia) There exists a noncompact spacelike hypersurface $\mathscr{C}$ for which $D_+(\mathscr{C}) = I_+[\mathscr{C}]$

(Ib) There exists a trapped surface $\mathscr{T} \subset I_+[\mathscr{C}]$

(Ic) $R_{ab}l^al^b \leqslant 0$ for each null vector l^a

(Id) $\mathscr{M}$ is future-null complete

In (Id), "future-null complete" means that every null geodesic in $\mathscr{M}$ can be extended into the future to arbitrarily large values of a (given) affine parameter. We may think of this physically as the statement that "photons (or neutrinos or gravitons) cannot just disappear." This seems to be a very reasonable physical requirement on a space-time. In Section 11, we have to consider another type of completeness, namely, timelike geodesic completeness ("particles in inertial motion cannot just disappear"). Yet other types are possible, such as "bounded acceleration completeness" which states that all inextendible timelike curves of bounded curvature have infinite total length[32] (that is, "particles experiencing limited forces cannot just disappear"). These types of completeness are all *inequivalent* for suitably contrived examples [35, 52]. However, it probably does not make much physical difference which definition is used. It is possible that the definitions are only inequivalent in the presence of regions of arbitrarily large curvature. To establish the existence of such regions would really be nearer to the object of results such as Theorems I, II, III, in any case. Unfortunately no result which *directly* predicts the existence of such high-curvature regions, on the basis of "reasonable" and "generic" physical assumptions, has yet been established, although we may think of Theorem I, and particularly Theorems II and III, as strong indirect indications of this; *cf.* Geroch lecture Ch. VIII.

The condition $R_{ab}l^al^b \leqslant 0$ is simply (7.35), and is a consequence of Einstein's equations (7.1) (with or without the λ-term) and the positive definiteness of the energy density (7.34). (In an "eigentetrad" of T_{ab}, this positive definiteness means that $T_{00} \geqslant 0$, $T_{00} + T_{11} \geqslant 0$, $T_{00} + T_{22} \geqslant 0$, $T_{00} + T_{33} \geqslant 0$.) This is very desirable physically, especially since a violation of this inequality seems to lead to a serious problem in connection with quantum field theory, namely, an apparent catastrophic instability of the vacuum. But the issue is not completely clear-cut.

---

[31] Space-times considered here are always assumed to be time-orientable (*cf.* Section 5). However, all the results here (for example, Theorems I, II, III) will also apply in a suitable form without this assumption. For any non-time-orientable Lorentzian manifold, there always exists a double covering manifold which is time-orientable. (Consider the space of all null half-cones on the manifold. This gives the desired double covering, *cf.* [55].)

[32] The term "length" will often be used here to denote "proper time" for a timelike curve.

Before we proceed to the proof of Theorem I, it will be useful to establish some lemmas concerning the structure of a SSB. We recall [*cf.* (9.4)–(9.6)] that any SSB is a subset $\mathscr{S}$ of $\mathscr{M}$ of the form

$$\mathscr{S} = \dot{I}_+[\mathscr{K}] \text{ or, equivalently, } \mathscr{S} = \dot{I}_-[\mathscr{L}] \tag{10.8}$$

where $\mathscr{K}, \mathscr{L} \subset \mathscr{M}$. Let us divide $\mathscr{S}$ into four disjoint parts (some of which may be vacuous), $\mathscr{S}_N, \mathscr{S}_+, \mathscr{S}_-$, and $\mathscr{S}_0$, defined as follows. If $X \in \mathscr{S}$, then there *may* or *may not* exist points $Y, Z \in \mathscr{S}$, distinct from X, for which

$$I_+(X) \subset I_+(Y) \qquad I_-(X) \subset I_-(Z) \tag{10.9}$$

the different possibilities defining the subsets $\mathscr{S}_N$, $\mathscr{S}_+$, $\mathscr{S}_-$, $\mathscr{S}_0$ according to the scheme

$$
\begin{array}{c}
\qquad (\exists Z) \quad (\not\exists Z) \\
X \in \begin{array}{|c|c|} \hline \mathscr{S}_N & \mathscr{S}_+ \\ \hline \mathscr{S}_- & \mathscr{S}_0 \\ \hline \end{array} \begin{array}{l} (\exists Y) \\ (\not\exists Y) \end{array}
\end{array} \tag{10.10}
$$

The intuitive meanings of these subsets is that $\mathscr{S}_N$ represents the portion of $\mathscr{S}$ which is *null*, where $\mathscr{S}_+$ and $\mathscr{S}_-$ consist, respectively, of the future and past end-points of $\mathscr{S}_N$, and that $\mathscr{S}_0$ represents the spacelike portion of $\mathscr{S}$ (see Fig. 38). A more precise statement is contained in the following lemma,

FIGURE 38. The different portions of a semispacelike boundary. (Null directions are inclined at 45°.)

which also gives a somewhat more useful condition for a point to lie in $\mathscr{S}_N, \mathscr{S}_+$, or $\mathscr{S}_-$.

Lemma I. Let $X \in \mathscr{S}$, where $\mathscr{S}$ is an SSB given as in (10.8). Let $\mathscr{Q}$ be an open set containing X. Then

    (a) $I_+(X) \subset I_+[\mathscr{K} - \mathscr{Q}]$ implies $X \in \mathscr{S}_N \cup \mathscr{S}_+$
    (b) $I_-(X) \subset I_-[\mathscr{L} - \mathscr{Q}]$ implies $X \in \mathscr{S}_N \cup \mathscr{S}_-$

Furthermore, a null geodesic segment on $\mathscr{S}$

    (c) passes through X if $X \in \mathscr{S}_N$
    (d) has X as future end-point if $X \in \mathscr{S}_+$
    (e) has X as past end-point if $X \in \mathscr{S}_-$

To prove Lemma I, assume, first, that $I_+(X) \subset I_+[\mathcal{K} - \mathcal{Q}]$. Let $\mathcal{B}$ be a small normal coordinate ball with center X and boundary $\dot{\mathcal{B}}$, where $\bar{\mathcal{B}} \subset \mathcal{Q}$. Consider a sequence (X_n) of points, with $X_n \in I_+(X) \cap \mathcal{B}$ which converges to X. For each X_n, there exists $W_n \in \mathcal{K} - \mathcal{Q}$ with $W_n \ll X_n$. The timelike curve from W_n to X_n contains a connected portion in $\mathcal{B}$, with past end-point $Y_n \in \dot{\mathcal{B}}$ and future end-point X_n. Now $\dot{\mathcal{B}}$ is compact, so there is a point Y on $\dot{\mathcal{B}}$ such that a subsequence of (Y_n) converges to Y. The join of Y, X in the normal coordinate system is a geodesic k, through X. It is readily seen that k cannot be spacelike (for small $\mathcal{B}$). Also k cannot be timelike, since then we should have $Y \ll X$, so $W_n \ll Y_n \ll X$ for some n, violating $X \notin I_+[\mathcal{K}]$. Thus, k is a null geodesic. Hence $I_+(X) \subset I_+(Y)$. Now, $Y_n \in I_+[\mathcal{K}]$, so $Y \in \bar{I}_+[\mathcal{K}]$. Also $Y \notin I_+[\mathcal{K}]$, since $X \notin I_+[\mathcal{K}]$, so that $Y \in \mathcal{S}$. This establishes (a), (d) and half of (c). The proof of (d), (e) and the other half of (c) is exactly similar. (That the two geodesics thus obtained for (c) must coincide, follows since $\mathcal{S}$ is semispacelike.)

When *two* null geodesic segments on $\mathcal{S}$ have a point X in common, this can only happen at $X \in \mathcal{S}_+$ or $X \in \mathcal{S}_-$. This result also holds in the case of "infinitesimally neighboring" null geodesic segments on $\mathcal{S}$. The following result makes this more precise.

Lemma II. Let $\mathcal{S}$ be an SSB and k a null geodesic segment lying on $\mathcal{S}$, with a future [resp. past] end-point P. Suppose some open set $\mathcal{Q}$, containing $k - P$, meets $\mathcal{S}$ in a smooth null hypersurface $\mathcal{N}$ for which the convergence ρ is unbounded near P (choosing the tangent vector l^a to k smoothly at P). Then $P \in \mathcal{S}_+$ [resp. $\mathcal{S}_-$].

The proof of Lemma II that I give depends on another result (actually more detailed than is necessary):

Lemma III. Let k be a null geodesic segment in $\mathcal{M}$ and let $\mathcal{N}_1$, $\mathcal{N}_2$ be smooth null hypersurfaces through k for which $\mathcal{N}_1 \subset I_+[\mathcal{N}_2] \cup \mathcal{N}_2$. Then $\rho_2 - \rho_1 \geqslant |\sigma_2 - \sigma_1|$ on k (ρ_i, σ_i refer to $\mathcal{N}_i$, with the same l^a for each $\mathcal{N}_i$ at k; $i = 1, 2$).

To prove Lemma III, consider two smooth scalar functions $u_i (i = 1, 2)$ on $\mathcal{M}$, where $u_i = 0$ defines $\mathcal{N}_i$ (in some neighborhood of k), with u_i increasing toward the future with nonvanishing gradient on $\mathcal{N}_i$. We can scale the u_i's so that $\nabla_a u_1 = \nabla_a u_2 = l_a$ on k. In a small enough neighborhood of k we have $u_2 \geqslant u_1$. It follows that $X^a \nabla_a (u_2 - u_1) + \frac{1}{2} X^a X^b \nabla_a \nabla_b (u_2 - u_1) \geqslant 0$, on k, for each set of components (X^a) with $|X^a|$ small enough. Let $\nabla_a u_i = l_{(i)a}$, so $l_{(1)a} = l_{(2)a} = l_a$ on k. Choose m_a, on k, complex, null and orthogonal to l_a, with $m_a \bar{m}^a = -1$. Putting $X^a = \lambda m^a + \bar{\lambda} \bar{m}^a$, we get $\lambda^2 (\sigma_2 - \sigma_1) + 2 \lambda \bar{\lambda} (\rho_2 - \rho_1) + \bar{\lambda}^2 (\bar{\sigma}_2 - \bar{\sigma}_1) \geqslant 0$ [*cf.* (7.33)]. This must hold independently of λ, and $\rho_2 - \rho_1 \geqslant |\sigma_2 - \sigma_1|$ follows.

To prove Lemma II, suppose $P \in \mathscr{S}_N$ (with P a *future* end-point of k). Then, k can be extended into the future on $\mathscr{S}$ to a point $R \in \mathscr{S}$. The past null-cone $\dot{I}_-(R)$ is nonsingular in some open set $\mathscr{G}$ with $k - P \subset \mathscr{G} \subset \mathscr{Q}$ (for R near enough to P). Lemma III now applies with $\mathscr{N}_2 = \mathscr{G} \cap \dot{I}_-(R)$ and $\mathscr{N}_1 = \mathscr{G} \cap \mathscr{N}$. But if $\rho = \rho_1$ is unbounded near P (and positive, since Φ is not unbounded at P), then $\rho_2 - \rho_1$ must become negative near P, violating the inequality in Lemma III. Thus Lemma II is established.

One immediate consequence of Lemma I is that if $\mathscr{T}$ is any closed subset of $\mathscr{M}$ and

$$\mathscr{S} = \dot{I}_+[\mathscr{T}] \tag{10.11}$$

then,

$$\mathscr{S}_- \cup \mathscr{S}_0 \subset \mathscr{T} \tag{10.12}$$

This follows from part (a) since if $X \in \mathscr{S} - \mathscr{T}$, some neighborhood $\mathscr{Q}$ of X will not meet $\mathscr{T}$, so $\mathscr{K} - \mathscr{Q} = \mathscr{K}$, with $\mathscr{K} = \mathscr{T}$. From (10.12) and parts (c) and (d), it follows that each point of $\mathscr{S} - \mathscr{T}$ is the *future end-point of a null geodesic segment on $\mathscr{S}$.* As particular cases, this result applies to $\dot{I}_+(P)$ or to any particle horizon. We may also take the time-reverse of the result, so if $\mathscr{S} = \dot{I}_-[\mathscr{T}]$, then each point of $\mathscr{S} - \mathscr{T}$ is the past end-point of a null geodesic segment on $\mathscr{S}$. This applies, in particular, to $\dot{I}_-(P)$ or to any event horizon.

Another consequence of Lemma I concerns the structure of Cauchy horizons. The result is not needed for Theorem I, but will be required in the next section. There are two simple ways of obtaining any Cauchy horizon as a part of an SSB. Let $\mathscr{H}$ be closed and semispacelike. Then the set $\text{int} \{D_-(\mathscr{H}) \cup I_+[\mathscr{H}]\}$ is the union of the $I_+(P)$ with $P \in D_-[\mathscr{H}]$. The boundary of this set is an SSB which contains the Cauchy horizon $H_-(\mathscr{H})$ as part (that is, as the intersection with $D_-(\mathscr{H})$). This is the first way. The second way can be described as follows. Let $\mathscr{H}$ be closed and semispacelike, as before, and define [42]

$$W_-(\mathscr{H}) = I_-(\mathscr{H}) - D_-(\mathscr{H}) \tag{10.13}$$

(We can define $W_+(\mathscr{H})$ correspondingly.) Then $P \in W_-(\mathscr{H})$ if and only if P is both the past end-point of a future-inextendible timelike curve α *not* meeting $\mathscr{H}$, and also the past end-point of a timelike curve β with future end-point *on* $\mathscr{H}$ (Fig. 39). Clearly $W_-(\mathscr{H})$ is open. Also, if $Q \ll P$ and $P \in W_-(\mathscr{H})$, then $Q \in W_-(\mathscr{H})$, since $\mathscr{H}$ is semispacelike. Hence,

$$W_-(\mathscr{H}) = I_-[W_-(\mathscr{H})] \tag{10.14}$$

Thus $\dot{W}_-(\mathscr{H})$ is an SSB. It is readily verified that

$$H_-(\mathscr{H}) = \dot{W}_-(\mathscr{H}) \cap D_-(\mathscr{H}) \tag{10.15}$$

[use (9.5)], so again, our Cauchy horizon is obtained as a part of an SSB.

FIGURE 39. A semispacelike boundary containing the past Cauchy horizon of $\mathcal{H}$.

Now suppose $X \in \dot{W}_-(\mathcal{H})$, but $X \notin$ edge $(\mathcal{H})$ [*cf.* (9.13), etc.] Either an α-curve or a β-curve with past end-point X must exist (trivially—where we define a degenerate β-curve to exist whenever $X \in \mathcal{H}$) but not both, since $X \notin W_-(\mathcal{H})$. If it is the α-curve that fails to exist, then $X \in H_-(\mathcal{H})$; if it is the β-curve, then $X \in \dot{I}_-[\mathcal{H}] - \mathcal{H}$. Suppose $X \in H_-(\mathcal{H})$, so a β-curve (possibly degenerate) exists from X. Then we can choose a small open neighborhood $\mathcal{Q}$ of X so that every point of $\bar{\mathcal{Q}} \cap \dot{I}_-[\mathcal{H}]$ is the end-point of a β-curve (that is, $\dot{I}_-[\mathcal{H}] \cap \bar{\mathcal{Q}} = \mathcal{H} \cap \bar{\mathcal{Q}}$). For if $X \in \mathcal{H}$, then, since $X \notin$ edge $(\mathcal{H})$, there exist points A, B near X (with $A \ll X \ll B$) so that every timelike curve from A to B, in the neighborhood of X, meets $\mathcal{H}$. In this case we choose $\bar{\mathcal{Q}} \subset I_-(B) \cap I_+(A)$. If $X \notin \mathcal{H}$, then choose $\bar{\mathcal{Q}}$ within the past of the β-curve from X. Any point U of $\mathcal{Q} \cap I_-(X)$ is in $W_-(\mathcal{H})$, so U is the past end-point of an α-curve, which must meet $\mathcal{Q} \cap \dot{I}_-[\mathcal{H}]$ in V, say. Now V is the past end-point of a β-curve also, so $V \in \dot{\mathcal{Q}} \cap W_-(\mathcal{H}) \subset W_-(\mathcal{H}) - \mathcal{Q}$. Thus Lemma *i* condition (b) is satisfied, whence:

EVERY POINT OF $H_-(\mathcal{H})$ − edge $(\mathcal{H})$ IS THE PAST END-POINT
OF A NULL GEODESIC SEGMENT ON $H_-(\mathcal{H})$ $\qquad$ (10.16)

Of course, the same applies also to $\dot{I}_-[\mathcal{H}] - \mathcal{H}$. Note that if $H_-(\mathcal{H})$ does not meet edge $(\mathcal{H})$, then every point of $H_-(\mathcal{H})$ is the past end-point of a *future-inextendible* null geodesic on $H_-(\mathcal{H})$ (since extending the null geodesic into the future, we can never reach a future end-point on $H_-(\mathcal{H})$). This applies [*cf.* (9.13)] when $\mathcal{H}$ is an *edgeless semispacelike closed set*. The results will clearly also apply in the time-reversed versions.

Another consequence of (10.16) is that if $\mathcal{H}$ is a *semispacelike set which intersects every maximal null geodesic of $\mathcal{M}$ in a nonvacuous compact set, then $\mathcal{H}$ is a GCH for $\mathcal{M}$.* For, if $\mathcal{H}$ were not a GCH, it would possess a non-vacuous Cauchy horizon, a null geodesic generator of which would have to meet $\mathscr{H}$ in a compact set.   An end-point of this set would have to lie on edge $(\mathscr{H})$, by (10.16).   However edge $(\mathscr{H})$ must be vacuous.   To see this, consider $\dot{I}_-[\mathscr{H}]$.   Now $\mathscr{H} \subset \dot{I}_-[\mathscr{H}]$ since $\mathscr{H}$ is semispacelike.   Suppose $P \in \dot{I}_-[\mathscr{H}]$ but $P \notin \mathscr{H}$.   A null geodesic generator γ, of $\dot{I}_-[\mathscr{H}]$, passes through P and contains a separate compact portion of $\mathscr{H}$.   Let Q lie on γ between P and this portion.   Any null geodesic η through Q, distinct from γ can meet $\dot{I}_-[\mathscr{H}]$ only at Q.   Thus η could not meet $\mathscr{H}$, so P does *not* exist. We have $\mathscr{H} = \dot{I}_-[\mathscr{H}]$, so $\mathscr{H}$ is an SSB; $\mathscr{H}$ is therefore edgeless and the result is established.

As a converse, we note that if $\mathscr{H}$ is any semispacelike set and $P \in \text{int } D_-(\mathscr{H})$ then any future-inextendible null geodesic γ through P must meet $\mathscr{H}$.   This follows because a point $Q \in D_-(\mathscr{H})$ exists with $Q \ll P$, so if γ did not meet $\mathscr{H}$ we could follow just below γ with a future-inextendible *timelike* curve, contradicting $Q \in D_-(\mathscr{H})$.   Similarly, we have the time reverse of this result that any past-inextendible null geodesic through any point of int $D_+(\mathscr{H})$ must also meet $\mathscr{H}$.   This will be required in a moment.

PROOF OF THEOREM I.   Set $\mathscr{S} = \dot{I}_+[\mathscr{T}]$ as in (10.11).   Then if $P \in \mathscr{S} - \mathscr{T}$, there will be a null geodesic k, a segment of which lies on $\mathscr{S}$ and has P as a future end-point.   Extend the geodesic maximally into the past.   It hits $\mathscr{C}$ because $P \in \text{int } D_+(\mathscr{C})$.   Since $\mathscr{S}(\subset I_+[\mathscr{C}])$ is closed, there is a point $R \in \mathscr{S}$ which is a past end-point of $k \cap \mathscr{S}$.   This must lie on $\mathscr{S}_-$, so $R \in \mathscr{T}$. Furthermore k must meet the spacelike 2-surface $\mathscr{T}$ orthogonally at R, that is, lie on one of the two null hypersurfaces which intersect locally in $\mathscr{T}$, since these represent the local boundary of $I_+[\mathscr{T}]$.   Thus, $\mathscr{S}$ is generated by the null geodesic segments $\hat{k}$ which are orthogonal to $\mathscr{T}$ at a past end-point, and which may have a future end-point (where they encounter $\mathscr{S}_+$).   In fact, any such segment $\hat{k}$ *must* have a future end-point by Lemma II, because the trapped surface condition (10.7), together with the focusing property [*cf.* (7.39)] and null completeness (Id), imply that ρ becomes *unbounded at some first point* Q, on $\hat{k}$, or on the extension k of $\hat{k}$ into the future.   (In fact, the second possibility is the more usual one, corresponding to the occurrence of a *crossing region* of $\mathscr{S}$, which generally occurs before the *caustic* is reached, where $\rho = \infty$.)   Now Q varies continuously as k varies [*cf.* (7.29), (7.33), etc.] so the finite segments RQ of k generate a compact set.   Thus $\mathscr{S}$, being a closed subset of a compact set, is also compact.   So, we have (9.7) that:

$\mathscr{S}$ IS A SEMISPACELIKE COMPACT TOPOLOGICAL 3-MANIFOLD IN $\mathscr{M}$ (10.17)

Now, it is a well-known theorem (see, for example, [101, p. 201]) that any space-time admits a smooth timelike unit vector field.   We can use the integral curves of this vector field to achieve a one-to-one mapping of $\mathscr{S}$ into $\mathscr{C}$ (both sets are semispacelike) since, by (Ia), $\mathscr{S} \subset D_+(\mathscr{C})$.   This is impossible since the dimensionalities are the same but $\mathscr{S}$ is compact and $\mathscr{C}$ is noncompact. Thus (Ia), (Ib), (Ic), (Id) are mutually inconsistent and Theorem I is established.

In the face of Theorem I, we are led to ask which of the conditions is most likely to break down in the actual universe. The most immediate candidate is perhaps (Ia). There are two ways that (Ia) can fail to be satisfied. In the first instance, the universe might be "closed" (that is to say, spatially compact). Then we might envisage replacing ($\mathscr{C}$) by a *compact* spacelike hypersurface which is a GCH (or with $I_+[\mathscr{C}] = D_+(\mathscr{C})$). The proof of Theorem I would then break down at the final stage. Indeed, the result would no longer be true, because (for example) all the conditions would be satisfied by the de Sitter space (9.14), (9.15), with $\mathscr{C}$ as the section of (9.14) by $V = -2a < 0$ (a const.) and $\mathscr{T}$ as $V = -a$, $W = 0$. On the other hand, it seems hard to believe that the question of whether the universe, as a whole, is open or closed should seriously affect the discussion of a "local" collapsing system (which would be smaller by a factor of at least 10^{11}). Indeed, an examination of the proof of Theorem I shows that the argument can still be made to carry through in the case of a compact $\mathscr{C}$ *unless*, in a well-defined sense, the collapsing object eventually "swallows up" the entire universe! However, a closed universe (like the Friedmann model with $k = 1$) which eventually recontracts to a highly condensed state could, in principle, satisfy this condition. But the elimination of the singularity problem by this means seems to be ruled out by a theorem of Hawking [41], which states, in effect, that "almost all" space-times with a *compact* GCH must be incomplete if they satisfy the slightly stronger (but still "reasonable") condition on R_{ab} implied by (7.47).

The second way in which (Ia) might be violated is a more serious possibility. The "Laplacian" idea that the future of the universe should be completely determined by its behavior at one "time" predates both relativity and quantum theory. We have become accustomed to nondeterminism in the latter theory, so why should we still demand determinism in all cases for general relativity? The possibility that the universe should not possess a GCH is an intriguing one. There are a number of physically interesting space-times which do not possess GCH's. Two examples were considered in Section 9. Other examples which are more relevant to the question of collapse (although, possessing singularities) are the Kerr [48] and Reissner–Nordström (see, for example, [62]) space-times, as extended, respectively, by Boyer and Lindquist [12] (*cf.* also [18, 19]) and by Graves and Brill [37]. The Kerr metric is

$$ds^2 = dv^2 - \frac{2mr}{h}(dv + a \sin^2 \theta \, d\varphi)^2 - 2 \, dv \, dr + h d\theta^2$$

$$+ 2a \sin^2 \theta \, dr \, d\varphi + (r^2 + a^2) \sin^2 \theta \, d\varphi^2 \quad (10.18)$$

where m and a are constant (mass m, angular momentum ma) and where

$$h = r^2 + a^2 \cos^2 \theta \quad (10.19)$$

The Reissner–Nordström metric (with advanced time v and electric charge defined by e) is

$$ds^2 = \left(1 - \frac{2m}{r} + \frac{e^2}{r^2}\right) dv^2 - 2\, dv\, dr - r^2(d\theta^2 + \sin^2\theta\, d\varphi^2) \qquad (10.20)$$

The metric (10.18) with $m > |a|$ and the metric (10.20) with $m > |e|$ are somewhat similar in that they possess not only an event horizon for external geodesics (Schwarzschild "throat"), given, respectively, by

$$r_+ = m + (m^2 - a^2)^{1/2} \qquad r_+ = m + (m^2 - e^2)^{1/2} \qquad (10.21)$$

but also a second "horizon" at which the null cones tip back again:

$$r_- = m - (m^2 - a^2)^{1/2} \qquad r_- = m - (m^2 - e^2)^{1/2} \qquad (10.22)$$

Both metrics have true singularities at $r = 0$, but these differ somewhat in nature. In the case of the Kerr metric the singularity has a ring structure.

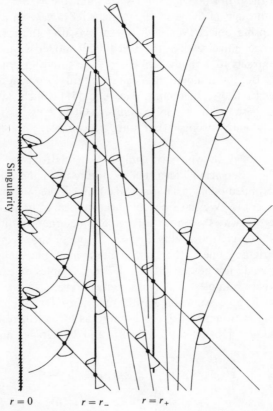

FIGURE 40. The Kerr picture (applicable also to the Reissner–Nordström metric).

By passing through the ring one enters a region with $r < 0$. (Then, as Carter [19] has shown, closed timelike curves are encountered near the ring.) Ignoring the nature of the metrics near (and through) the singularities, the situation is as in Fig. 40. By patchwork similar to that in the Schwarzschild case, but here more complicated, a " maximal " analytic extension is obtained (Fig. 41). The shaded portion in Fig. 41 represents the whole of Fig. 40. The entire Fig. 41 diagram can be pieced together (except for some exceptional central points) using overlapping patches isometric with the shaded region.

FIGURE 41. The Carter–Boyer–Lindquist picture (incorporating that of Graves–Brill).

(For this, one needs to be aware of a discrete symmetry of the metrics, which is not manifest in the forms (10.18), (10.20), cf. [12].)

Now, the significance of all this is that by following the star inward and then giving himself an acceleration outward after crossing $r = r_+$, an observer can find himself in a portion of the universe not causally determined by information on an apparently reasonable initial hypersurface $\mathscr{H}$. In fact, he crosses $H_+(\mathscr{H})$. The region he enters actually contains a singularity which he can "see." But of course, since he has crossed $H_+(\mathscr{H})$, we cannot guarantee that the space-time he enters is in fact the one that we have constructed for him. In effect, "another universe" has joined on to the universe he started from. The particular continuation we have chosen was obtained here by an *analytic* continuation rather than by the use of field equations. (But even analytic extensions do not ensure uniqueness globally. A striking example occurs with the Taub–NUT space-time described in Section 9, but also in flat space-time analytic extension does not imply uniqueness. The difficulty is that one does not know, in general, when to identify events reached in different ways.) Even if we can avoid the singularity in the "new universe" there is a problem of principle here, because, like in the early stages of a "big bang" cosmology, causally disconnected regions have to come together in such a way that they "fit." A striking example of this occurs with the Reissner–Nordström solution, since the "new universe" has to possess new charged particles of just the right total charge. (This follows even independently of the symmetry.)

There is a further difficulty confronting our observer who tries to cross $H_+(\mathscr{H})$. As he looks out at the universe that he is "leaving behind," he sees, in one final flash, as he crosses $H_+(\mathscr{H})$, the entire later history of the rest of his "old universe." It is here, in fact, that cosmological questions might be very relevant to him. If, for example, an unlimited amount of matter eventually falls into the star then presumably he will be confronted with an infinite density of matter along "$H_+(\mathscr{H})$." Even if only a finite amount of matter falls in, it may not be possible, in generic situations to avoid a curvature singularity in place of $H_+(\mathscr{H})$. This is at present an open question. But it may be, that the place to look for curvature singularities is in this region rather than (or as well as?) at the "center." In this connection, an example due to Bardeen [5] (cf. [23a, 66a]) of a collapsing charged dust cloud is of interest. Here *no* singularity occurs within $D_+(\mathscr{H})$, although a charge singularity has to be created in the "new universe" beyond $H_+(\mathscr{H})$ (see Fig. 41). Whether any reality can be attributed to this situation in which a "new universe" is created out of a collapse is an intriguing question. We might view (10.17) as an indication that a trapped surface results in a spatially compact universe "budding" off the original one. However, all this rests on the supposition that $H_+(\mathscr{H})$ can survive a generic perturbation on $\mathscr{H}$, without curvature singularities arising. We should also bear in mind that in any case it seems unlikely that curvature singularities can be avoided, in view of Theorem III of the next section.

11 SINGULARITIES IN COSMOLOGY

This section is devoted to two important theorems due to Hawking [40, 42]. The arguments will be given here partly in outline. For further details, the reader is referred to Hawking's original papers. The aim of the theorems is to show that on the basis of present physical understanding, there are (or were) very peculiar regions of space-time, probably involving enormous curvatures, at which we would have to expect a local physical behavior very different from that to which we have become accustomed. The interest of Theorem II will lie, perhaps, mainly in the fact that no causality assumptions whatever are made. It applies only to a spatially compact universe satisfying a condition (an inequality) which might possibly apply to the actual universe, but which would be virtually impossible to verify observationally. Theorem III, on the other hand, contains an analogous condition which, according to Hawking and Ellis [44], *is* likely to be satisfied on the basis even of present-day astronomical observations. In time-reversed form, Theorem III will also apply to suitable situations of gravitational collapse (such as a mildly perturbed Oppenheimer–Snyder collapsing dust cloud (see Section 10). A causality assumption is required for Theorem III, but of a much less severe kind than the global Cauchy hypersurface condition (Ia) of Theorem I. In effect, closed (that is, $\cong S^1$) timelike curves are to be excluded, but we shall require a slightly strengthened version of this.

Let $P \in M$, then the following conditions on $\mathcal{M}$ with respect to P are equivalent [42, 50]:

ARBITRARILY SMALL NEIGHBORHOODS OF P EXIST WHICH EACH
INTERSECT NO TIMELIKE CURVE IN A DISCONNECTED SET   (11.1)

that is, roughly speaking, timelike curves from the neighborhood of P cannot leave and then return to the neighborhood of P;

IF $P \prec Q$ AND EVERY POINT OF $I_-(Q)$ CHRONOLOGICALLY PRE-
CEDES EVERY POINT OF $I_+(P)$, THEN $P = Q$ (11.2)

(*cf.* Section 9); or

THE TIME-REVERSE OF (11.2)   (11.3)

If (11.1), (11.2), or (11.3) holds, then we say that *strong causality holds at P*. If the condition holds for *all* $P \in \mathcal{M}$, then we say *strong causality holds for* $\mathcal{M}$.

The equivalence of (11.1)–(11.3) is not hard to establish and will be omitted here.   An example, due to Hawking, for which the condition fails is indicated in Fig. 42.   (With Minkowski coordinates and metric, we omit $(x^0 > 1,$ $x^1 \leqslant -1)$, $(x^0 < -1,\ x^1 \geqslant 1)$, $(x^0 = -x^1 = 1)$ and $(x^0 = -x^1 = -1)$; then identify $(1,\ x^1,\ x^2,\ x^3)$ with $(-1,\ -x^1,\ x^2,\ -x^3)$, $x^1 < -1$; P is the origin.) If strong causality holds at P, we call a neighborhood $\mathscr{Q}$ of P *causally convex* if no timelike curve meets $\mathscr{Q}$ in a disconnected set [*cf*. (11.1)].

FIGURE 42. A future- and past-distinguishing space-time for which strong causality fails.

If strong causality fails at P, an arbitrarily small perturbation of the metric in the neighborhood of P could result in the actual presence of closed timelike curves, which for various reasons is highly undesirable physically. Thus, it appears to be a very reasonable supposition that strong causality should actually hold at every point of space-time.   Another condition, which is weaker than (11.1)–(11.3) but stronger than nonexistence of a closed timelike curve through P is *future distinguishability* [50] at P:

$$I_+(P) = I_+(Q) \text{ IMPLIES } P = Q \qquad\qquad (11.4)$$

This states that timelike curves through P into the future, cannot leave and then return arbitrarily close to P.   For the time-reverse of this, we say $\mathscr{M}$ is *past distinguishing at P* if and only if for all Q

$$I_-(P) = I_-(Q) \text{ IMPLIES } P = Q \qquad\qquad (11.5)$$

A hierarchy of causality conditions which are, on the other hand, stronger than (11.1), have been suggested by Carter.[33]   Again, violation of any of Carter's conditions could lead to closed timelike curves when $\mathcal{M}$ is perturbed slightly.

The condition that strong causality should hold at every point of $\mathcal{M}$ is an interesting one.   It is, in fact, equivalent to the statement that the "Alexandrov topology" $\mathcal{T}^{*}$ is Hausdorff [50], where the open sets of $\mathcal{T}^{*}$ have as a base, the sets $I_{+}(X) \cap I_{-}(Y)$.   This is again equivalent to the statement that $\mathcal{T}^{*}$ agrees with the ordinary manifold topology of $\mathcal{M}$.   We can refer to Fig. 42 for a situation under which the condition fails.   For this example, any open set in $\mathcal{T}^{*}$, containing P, meets any open set, in $\mathcal{T}^{*}$ containing Q, so the Hansdorff property fails.

Let us now state the theorems.

Theorem II. (Hawking)   The following requirements on a space-time $\mathcal{M}$ are mutually inconsistent:

- (IIa)   There exists a compact spacelike hypersurface (without boundary) $\mathcal{H}$.
- (IIb)   The divergence θ of the unit normals to $\mathcal{H}$ is positive at every point of $\mathcal{H}$.
- (IIc) $R_{ab} t^{a} t^{b} \leqslant 0$ for each timelike vector t^{a}.
- (IId) $\mathcal{M}$ is geodesically complete in past timelike directions.

We can think of (IIa) and (IIb) as stating that "the universe is (or was) spatially compact and expanding."   However, the "expansion" as implied by (IIb) has to take place at *every* point of $\mathcal{H}$.   Thus, in the presence of a collapsed object, we could not expect to be able to arrange (IIb) for an $\mathcal{H}$ "at the present time."   If the condition is satisfied, therefore, $\mathcal{H}$ would probably have to refer to an early phase of the expansion.

On the assumption of Einstein's equations (7.1), requirement (IIc) is the "energy condition" (7.47), which (assuming, preferably, that $\lambda = 0$) is very reasonable physically.

Theorem III. (Hawking)   The following requirements on a space-time $\mathcal{M}$ are mutually inconsistent:

- (IIIa)   Strong causality holds at every point of $\bar{I}_{-}(P)$, for some point $P \in M$.
- (IIIb)   The divergence of all the timelike and null geodesics through P changes sign somewhere to the past of P.

---

[33] One such condition would be violated if there were two points P, $R \in \mathcal{M}$, such that for any neighborhoods $\mathcal{P}$ of P and $\mathcal{R}$ of R, there would always be a timelike curve with past end-point in $\mathcal{P}$ and future end-point in $\mathcal{R}$, and another with future end-point in $\mathcal{P}$ and past end-point in $\mathcal{R}$.   This behavior can occur without strong causality failing, as can be seen by taking $\mathcal{M}$ as the twofold covering manifold of that of Fig. 42 (Carter).

(IIIc) $R_{ab} t^a t^b \leqslant 0$ for each timelike vector t^a.

(IIId) $\mathcal{M}$ is geodesically complete in past timelike and null directions.

Condition (IIIb) is a little awkwardly stated because the divergence in the case of the timelike geodesics is measured by the quantity θ of (7.40) while the divergence of the null geodesics is measured by ρ of (7.18), (7.33). The region at which ρ changes sign is not actually the limit of the region where θ changes sign.   Another way of stating (IIIb) would be to refer only to the timelike geodesics and state that the (relevant) change of sign takes place within a *compact region*.

I shall outline the proofs of Theorems II and III by indicating the main lemmas involved.   (These lemmas and their proofs are all essentially due to Hawking [40, 42], although the discussion given here deviates slightly from his.)

Lemma IV.   If a spacelike hypersurface $\mathcal{H}$ (without boundary) exists, which is a closed subset of $\mathcal{M}$ (that is, properly embedded), then a covering manifold $\mathcal{M}^*$ of $\mathcal{M}$ exists where the inverse image of $\mathcal{H}$ under the covering map consists of a set of discrete isometric copies of $\mathcal{H}$, each of which is semispacelike in $\mathcal{M}^*$.

The idea is to make $\mathcal{H}$, in (IIa), into a semispacelike set, by "unwrapping" $\mathcal{M}$, but not so much as might render the new $\mathcal{H}$ noncompact.   To achieve this, choose a point O in $\mathcal{M}$, then for each $P \in \mathcal{M}$ and for each equivalence class of curves from O to P whose intersection number with $\mathcal{H}$ is a given integer we assign a point of $\mathcal{M}^*$.   (This intersection number is homotopy invariant because $\mathcal{H}$ has no edges.)   One readily verifies that $\mathcal{M}^*$ has the properties required of it in the lemma.   [This construction effectively obtains $\mathcal{M}^*$ from the universal covering manifold of $\mathcal{M}$, by putting an equivalence relation on the elements of the fundamental group of $\mathcal{M}$, saying two such elements are equivalent if they give equal intersection numbers with $\mathcal{H}$ (see also, Geroch [34]).]

Without loss of generality, we now regard $\mathcal{M}^*$ as $\mathcal{M}$ in Theorem II, so we can *take $\mathcal{H}$ to be a semispacelike set*.   In order that we can treat Theorems II and III concurrently to a large extent, define, for Theorem III,

$$\mathcal{H} = \dot{I}_-(P) \tag{11.6}$$

(Strong causality at P implies that $\mathcal{H}$ is nonvacuous, resembling a null cone at P.)   Then, in both cases, we have $\mathcal{H} = \bar{\mathcal{H}}$ as an edgeless semispacelike set.

It will be useful to have in the back of one's mind a picture of some types of situation which might possibly arise.   For Theorem II, we envisage a situation like that of Fig. 43.   Neither $H_-(\mathcal{H})$ nor $\dot{I}_-[\mathcal{H}]$ can meet $\mathcal{H}$ since $\mathcal{H}$ is edgeless and a spacelike hypersurface.   Every point of $H_-(\mathcal{H})$ lies on a future-inextendible null geodesic on $H_-(\mathcal{H})$ which may go to infinity or (since causality assumptions are not made here) simply spiral round and round

FIGURE 43. The type of situation to keep in mind for Theorem II.

in some compact region [*cf.* Fig. 33]. For Theorem III, an awkward type of possible situation is illustrated in Fig. 44 for which $H_-(\mathcal{H})$ can intersect $\mathcal{H}$. (It is the presence of such a possibility which requires the causality assumption (IIIa) to be made.)

Lemma V. If $\mathcal{H} = \bar{\mathcal{H}}$ is edgeless and semispacelike, then int $D_-(\mathcal{H})$ consists of all points $X \in I_-[\mathcal{H}]$ for which the set $J_+(X) \cap \bar{I}_-[\mathcal{H}]$ is both compact and contains no points at which strong causality fails.

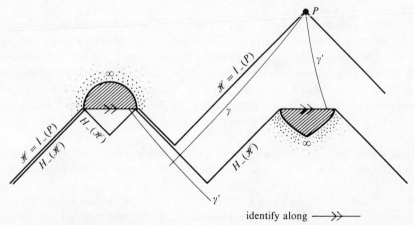

identify along ——≫——

FIGURE 44. An awkward possibility to bear in mind for Theorem III.

Write $\mathscr{X}$ for the set of such points X. [For $J_+(X)$, see (9.2).] Let $X \in \mathscr{X}$ and consider a future-inextendible timelike curve with X as past end-point. If this did not meet $\mathscr{H}$, it would, by the compactness of $\mathscr{Y} = J_+(X) \cap \bar{I}_-[\mathscr{H}]$, have to have an accumulation point in $\mathscr{Y}$. This is impossible since strong causality holds in $\mathscr{Y}$. Thus, $\mathscr{X} \subset D_-(\mathscr{H})$. Furthermore $X \notin H_-(\mathscr{H})$, since otherwise, by (10.16), a future-inextendible null geodesic with past end-point X would lie in $\mathscr{Y}$, $\mathscr{H}$ being edgeless. (Such a null geodesic could not be contained in a compact set unless strong causality failed in the set.) Hence $\mathscr{X} \subset$ int $D_-(\mathscr{H})$. For the converse, we recall, first, that if $Z \in$ int $D_-(\mathscr{H})$ then any future-inextendible *nonspacelike* curve through Z must meet $\mathscr{H}$. Now strong causality cannot fail at any point $Z \in$ int $D_-(\mathscr{H})$. (Otherwise, in the critical case, we could use the "Q" of (11.2) to get ZQ as a null geodesic along which strong causality fails and whose maximal extension would not meet $\mathscr{H}$.) Suppose, on the other hand, that $\mathscr{Z}_0 = J_+(Z_0) \cap \bar{I}_-[\mathscr{H}]$ fails to be compact for some $Z_0 \in$ int $D_-(\mathscr{H})$. Cover $\mathscr{Z}_0$ by a locally finite system of causally convex open sets $\mathscr{U}_i$ which are small enough to ensure that any point U in $\mathscr{U}_i$ is the center of a normal coordinate open ball $\mathscr{B}_U$ containing $\bar{\mathscr{U}}_i$. Let $Z_0 \in \mathscr{U}_{i_0}$. Since $\mathscr{Z}_0$ is noncompact it contains a sequence of points W_j with no accumulation point in $\mathscr{Z}_0$. A nonspacelike curve from Z_0 to W_j exists and meets $\dot{\mathscr{B}}_{Z_0}$ in V_j, say. Let V be an accumulation point of V_i. The nonspacelike geodesic segment $Z_0 V$ meets $\dot{\mathscr{U}}_{i_0}$ in a unique point $Z_1 \in \mathscr{U}_{i_1}$. Then $\mathscr{Z}_1 = J_+(Z_1) \cap \bar{I}_-[\mathscr{H}]$ contains a subsequence of the W_j without an accumulation point in $\mathscr{Z}_1$ and so also fails to be compact. Repeating the argument we obtain a sequence $Z_0 \prec Z_1 \prec Z_2 \prec \dots$ which lie on a nonspacelike curve γ. From the locally finite nature of the $\mathscr{U}_i$ system it follows that the Z_i have no accumulation point, so γ is a future-inextendible nonspacelike curve through Z_0 not meeting $\mathscr{H}$. Thus $Z_0 \notin$ int $D_-(\mathscr{H})$, showing that int $D_-(\mathscr{H}) \subset \mathscr{X}$. This completes the proof of Lemma V.

If $\mathscr{Q}$ and $\mathscr{R}$ are subsets of $\mathscr{M}$ or points of $\mathscr{M}$, define $d(\mathscr{Q}, \mathscr{R})$ to be the *least upper bound of the lengths of all timelike curves with past end-point* (*in*) $\mathscr{Q}$ *and future end-point* (*in*) $\mathscr{R}$. (Put $d(\mathscr{Q}, \mathscr{R}) = 0$ if there are no such curves.) In some cases we shall have $d(\mathscr{Q}, \mathscr{R}) = \infty$ (but for bounded subsets of Minkowski space-time, for example, it is always finite: a timelike straight line connecting two Minkowskian points has the *maximum* length among all timelike curves connecting the points).

Lemma VI. *If* $\mathscr{H} = \bar{\mathscr{H}}$ *is edgeless and semispacelike, then* $d(X, \mathscr{H})$ *is finite, and attained for some geodesic* γ *from* X *to* $\mathscr{H}$, *whenever* $X \in$ int $D_-(\mathscr{H})$.

By Lemma V, we know that $\mathscr{Y} = J_+(X) \cap \bar{I}_-(\mathscr{H})$ is compact, and can therefore be covered by a finite number of small open normal coordinate neighborhoods $\mathscr{B}_i$. Since strong causality holds in int $D_-(\mathscr{H})$, we can arrange the boundaries of the $\mathscr{B}_i$'s to be causally convex. Write d_i for the least upper bound of lengths of timelike curves in $\mathscr{B}_i$. Then from local arguments it follows d_i is finite, and attained (by a geodesic, in fact). If γ is a timelike curve from X to $\mathscr{H}$ then the length of γ cannot exceed $d = \Sigma d_i$. Hence $d(X, \mathscr{H})$ is finite. Furthermore, from the compactness, it will follow that the maximum of $d(X, Y)$ for $Y \in \mathscr{H}$, will be *attained*, say, for $Y = Y_0$.

To construct γ of maximal length from X to $\mathscr{H}$ [so that γ actually is of length $d(X, Y)$], choose a normal coordinate ball $\mathscr{B}$, with center Y_0, and choose $Z = Z_0$ to maximize $d(X, Z) + d(Z, Y_0)$, where $Z \in \mathscr{Y}$ varies over the compact boundary $\dot{\mathscr{B}}$ of $\mathscr{B}$. Define γ to be the geodesic with future end-point Y_0 which contains Z_0 and extends into the past to a length d. Repeat the above argument, applying it to Z_0 in place of Y_0 and maximize $d(X, V) + d(V, Z_0)$. We get V_0, which must lie on γ (since a timelike curve with a corner can always be increased in length by smoothing the corner). Continuing the process, we see that γ must terminate with past end-point at X, establishing Lemma VI.

Lemma VII. If $\mathscr{H}$ is a spacelike hypersurface and γ is a timelike geodesic segment from X to $\mathscr{H}$ which maximizes $d(X, \mathscr{H})$, then γ meets $\mathscr{H}$ orthogonally and contains no point (other than possibly X) which is conjugate to $\mathscr{H}$.

The argument is not essentially different from that for a manifold with a positive definite metric (see Milnor [58]). A point conjugate to $\mathscr{H}$ on γ is a focal point for the congruence Γ of null geodesics which meet $\mathscr{H}$ orthogonally [that is, a point at which the θ of (7.40) becomes infinite].

We can also apply Lemma VII in a limiting case, to the hypersurface $\mathscr{H}$ of (11.6) required for Theorem III. In this case, if γ is a timelike geodesic segment from X to $\mathscr{H}$ which maximizes $d(X, \mathscr{H})$, then γ, to be "orthogonal" to $\mathscr{H}$, would have to contain P. Every other point of $\mathscr{H}$ lies on a null geodesic on $\mathscr{H}$ which extends into the future to points more distant from X. In this case, then, we interpret Lemma VII as saying that γ passes through P and contains no point (other than possibly X) which is conjugate to P (that is, which is a focal point of the congruence Γ of timelike or null geodesics through P).

We are now in a position to apply these results to Theorems II and III. Let t^a denote the unit (future-pointing) tangent vector field to the timelike γ's of Γ (in each case). By (IIb) or (IIIb), we have $\theta > 0$ at some point in $\bar{I}_-[\mathscr{H}]$ on each $\gamma \in \Gamma$. Thus by (IIc) or (IIIc) and the Raychaudhuri effect [*cf.* (7.40)–(7.47); also (7.39)], we have a focal point $G(\theta = \infty; -\rho = \infty)$ somewhere on each $\gamma \in \Gamma$, to the past of $\mathscr{H}$. [This uses past-timelike completeness (IId), (IIId) and past-null completeness in (IIId).] If there is more than one such focal point, we choose the one nearest to $\mathscr{H}$ (and $\neq P$). Now

G will vary continuously with γ. By the compactness of $\mathscr{H}$ (Theorem II) or the fact (Theorem III) that the timelike and null directions at P constitute a compact system, we obtain the fact that the region $\mathscr{G}$ swept out by the sements of γ from G to $\mathscr{H}$ will be *compact*.

Now, by Lemmas VI and VII we have the result that $\operatorname{int} D_-(\mathscr{H}) \subset \mathscr{G}$, and thus $D_-(\mathscr{H}) \subset \mathscr{G} \cup \mathscr{H}$. In particular, $H_-(\mathscr{H}) \subset \mathscr{G} \cup \mathscr{H}$. In Theorem II, $\mathscr{H}$ is spacelike, so $H_-(\mathscr{H}) \cap \mathscr{H} = \varnothing$. The Cauchy horizon $H_-(\mathscr{H})$, being a closed subset of the compact set $\mathscr{G}$, is now *compact*. By (10.15) and (9.7), $H_-(\mathscr{H})$ is thus a compact C^0 manifold without boundary. By (IId), we can extend each γ into the past to length greater than $\max d(G, \mathscr{H})$. Then each γ meets $H_-(\mathscr{H})$ by Lemmas VI and VII. Put $F = \gamma \cap H_-(\mathscr{H})$ and define $p(F)$ to be the maximum of lengths of the segments of γ from F to $\mathscr{H}$. (Attained, for fixed F, because of the compactness of $\mathscr{H}$ and the Γ system.) It is not hard to see that $P(F)$ [with $F \in H_-(\mathscr{H})$] attains its *minimum* value. Let $F = F_0$ minimize $p(F)$. Now, a null geodesic η on $H_-(\mathscr{H})$ has F_0 as past end-point. Let F_1 be just to the future of F_0 on η. The length of the jointed curve from F_0 to $\mathscr{H}$, which consists of the small segment $F_0 F_1$ of η together with a maximal γ curve from F_1 to $\mathscr{H}$, cannot be less than $p(F_0)$. Such γ exists since $D_-(\mathscr{H}) \subset \mathscr{G}$. Smoothing the corner, and moving the curve just away from $H_-(\mathscr{H})$, we get a timelike curve ζ from F_0 to $\mathscr{H}$ of length k greater than $p(F_0)$. Taking B on ζ very close to F_0, so $d(B, \mathscr{H}) > p(F_0)$ and letting B approach F_0, we get a limiting position of the (relevant) γ through B (from the compactness of $\mathscr{H}$). This would give us $p(F_0) \geqslant k > p(F_0)$ which is the required contradiction establishing Theorem II.

In Theorem III, $\mathscr{H}$ is not spacelike, so $H_-(\mathscr{H})$ might intersect $\mathscr{H}$ (Fig. 44). Thus, we cannot assume that $H_-(\mathscr{H})$ is compact and the above argument will break down. Instead, we bring in the strong causality. Define a relation $\langle$ on $H_-(\mathscr{H})$ by

$$U \langle V \text{ IF AND ONLY IF } I_-(U) \subset I_-(V) \tag{11.7}$$

[that is, $U \in \bar{I}_-(V)$]. Then $\langle$ is an order relation on $H_-(\mathscr{H})$ (weaker than $\prec$). Put $\mathscr{A} = \mathscr{G} \cap H_-(\mathscr{H})$. Then $\mathscr{A}$ is compact $H_-(\mathscr{H})$ being closed and $\mathscr{G}$ compact. Set $\mathscr{K} = \mathscr{A} \cap \mathscr{G} \subset H_-(\mathscr{H}) - \operatorname{int} \mathscr{G} \subset \mathscr{H}$. Let $U \subset \mathscr{A}$. Then a future-inextendible null geodesic α on $H_-(\mathscr{H})$ has past end-point U. By compactness and strong causality, α must leave $\mathscr{A}$ at $U_0 \in \mathscr{K}$, say, and we shall have $U \langle U_0$. But in the neighborhood of $\alpha - \mathscr{A}$ are timelike curves leading to P [since $\alpha - \mathscr{A} \subset \mathscr{H} = \dot{I}_-(P)$]. These timelike curves must meet $H_-(\mathscr{H}) - \mathscr{H} \subset \mathscr{A}$ on their way to P. In the limit as such curves approach α, this intersection point has an accumulation point V on $\mathscr{A}$ and we readily verify $U_0 \langle V$ (with $U_0 \neq V$ because of strong causality). Similarly V gives rise to V_0 on $\mathscr{K}$ with $V \langle V_0$, and to W with $V_0 \langle W(V_0 \neq W)$, etc. The sequence of distinct points $U_0 \langle V_0 \langle W_0 \langle \ldots$ on $\mathscr{K}$ must have an accumulation point, by the compactness of $\mathcal{H}$. We would have to have a breakdown of strong causality at this point. This establishes Theorem III.

One of the significant features of Theorem III is that it is not necessary to make assumptions apart from strong causality as to the nature of the universe as a whole. The theorem refers only to the past null cone of P and its interior, these being regions in principle observable by an observer at P. In time-reversed form the theorem applies to sufficiently uniform collapse situations (although not quite of the generality of those treated in Theorem I) and requires no information of a global cosmological nature. (We choose P at the center and assume the collapse is similar to a late stage of the Oppenheimer–Snyder situation.) Also, since no Cauchy hypersurface condition is needed, one is led to believe that even if the Cauchy horizon of Fig. 41 still exists in generic situations, this would probably not enable us to avoid singularities elsewhere.

Of course, when applied to the past cone of P, we would not expect the divergence of the geodesics to change sign until a substantial portion of the entire universe has been encompassed. To estimate where this point should occur, one would need to know the density of material in the universe and knowledge of this is very uncertain at present. Also, much of the matter, for example, galaxies, is very irregularly distributed, so the total effect might be somewhat complicated. It ceases to be clear whether (IIIb) would be satisfied at all, by virtue merely of observed material objects. The idea of Hawking and Ellis [44], however, is to use the *radiation* density of the universe, whose present existence is in the form of a highly isotropic distribution with a spectrum apparently that of a blackbody at 3^0 absolute. They argue that this radiation density, owing to its uniformity, ought in *itself* to be sufficient ultimately to ensure that (IIIb) is satisfied, except in the unlikely possibility of there being a large amount of ionized gas present. If this gas is present, then *it* should be sufficient to produce the desired focusing instead.

The indications are, then, that if Einstein's equations hold, then (curvature?) singularities[34] are a real feature of our universe. (Actually, Einstein's equations are not very strongly used. For example, if we were to replace Einstein's theory by the Brans–Dicke [13] theory, then the conclusions of Theorems I, II, and III would be essentially unaffected.) More results are needed, however, if we are to get any feeling for the structure of these peculiar (presumably highly curved) regions of space-time. And really to ascertain the kind of physics that might be involved in such a region, we would need a much deeper understanding of the interrelation between matter, quantum theory, and space-time structure than we have at present.

---

[34] By a "singularity" I mean a peculiar region, in which the local physics would be drastically affected, possibly to the extent that the smooth manifold picture of space-time would no longer be adequate (*cf.* discussion in Section 1).

Under normal circumstances, general relativity can, for practical purposes, remain remarkably apart—almost aloof—from the rest of physics. At a space-time singularity, the very reverse must surely be the case!

REFERENCES

1. Y. Aharonov and L. Susskind, *Phys. Rev.* **158**, 1237 (1967).

2. R. A. Alpher and R. C. Herman, *Nature* **162**, 774 (1948).

3. A. Avez, *Compt. Rend.* **254**, 3984 (1962).

4. A. Avez, *Inst. Fourier* **105** (1963).

5. J. Bardeen, to be published.

6. C. Behr, *Zeit fur Astrophysik* **60**, 286 (1965).

6a. P. G. Bergmann, *Phys. Rev. Lett.* **12**, 139 (1964).

7. B. Bertotti, *Proc. Roy. Soc. (Lond.)* **A294**, 195 (1966).

8. H. Bondi, *Nature*, **186**, 535 (1960).

9. H. Bondi, in *Lectures on General Relativity: 1964 Brandeis Summer Institute in Theoretical Physics, Vol. I* (Prentice-Hall, Englewood Cliffs, 1965).

10. H. Bondi, F. A. E. Pirani, and I. Robinson, *Proc. Roy. Soc. (Lond.)* **A251**, 519 (1959).

11. H. Bondi, M. G. J. van der Burg, and A. W. K. Metzner, *Proc. Roy. Soc. (Lond.)* **A269**, 21 (1962).

12. R. H. Boyer and R. W. Lindquist, *J. Math. Phys.* **8**, 265 (1967).

13. C. Brans and R. H. Dicke, *Phys. Rev.* **124**, 925 (1961).

14. D. Brill, *Annals of Phys.* **7**, 466 (1959).

14a. D. Brill and S. Deser, *Phys. Rev. Lett.* **20**, 75 (1968).

15. H. W. Brinkmann, *Nat. Acad. Sci.* (U.S.) **9**, 1 (1923).

16. H. A. Buchdahl, *Nuovo Cim.* **10**, 96 (1958); **25**, 486 (1962).

17. E. Calabi and L. Markus, *Ann. Math.* **75**, 63 (1962).

18. B. Carter, *Phys. Rev.* **141**, 1242 (1966).

19. B. Carter, *Stationary Axi-symmetric Systems in General Relativity* (Ph.D. Dissertation, Cambridge University, 1967).

20. E. Cartan, *Ann. Ec. Norm. Sup.* **40**, 325 (1923); **41**, 1 (1924).

21. S. Chandrasekhar, *M. N.* **95**, 207 (1935).

21a. S. Chandrasekhar, *Proc. Nat. Acad. Sci.* **57**, (1967).

22. G. F. Chew, *Sci. Prog.* **51**, 529 (1963).

23. R. Debever, *Comptes Rend.* **249**, 1324, 1744 (1959).

23a. V. de la Cruz and W. Israel, *Nuovo Cim.* **51A**, 745, (1967).

24. R. H. Dicke, *Phys. Rev.* **125**, 2163 (1962).

25. R. H. Dicke, P. J. E. Peebles, P. G. Roll, and D. T. Wilkinson, *Ap. J.* **142**, 414 (1965).

26. A. G. Doroshkevich, Ya. B. Zel'dovich and I. D. Novikov, *Zhur. Eksp. Teor. Fiz.* **49**, 170 (1965); Engl. tr.: *Sov. Phys.—JETP.* **22**, 122 (1966).

27. A. S. Eddington, *Nature* **113**, 192 (1924).

28. J. Ehlers and W. Kundt, in *Gravitation* (ed. L. Witten; John Wiley and Sons, New York 1962).

29. A. Einstein, *Ann. Physik.* **94**, 769 (1916).

30. A. Einstein and J. Grommer, *S. B. Preuss. Akad. Wiss.* **2**, (1927).

31. A. Einstein, L. Infeld, and B. Hoffmann, *Ann. Math.* **39**, 65 (1938).

32. D. Finkelstein, *Phys. Rev.* **110**, 965 (1958).

33. G. Gamow, *Nature* **162**, 680 (1948).

34. R. P. Geroch, *J. Math. Phys* **8**, (1967).

35. R. P. Geroch, *Singularities in the Spacetime of General Relativity* (Ph.D. Dissertation, Princeton University, 1967).

36. J. N. Goldberg, in *Gravitation* (ed. L. Witten; John Wiley and Sons, New York, 1962).

37. J. C. Graves and D. R. Brill, *Phys. Rev.* **120**, 1507 (1960).

38. Haefliger; see *Topics on Space-Times* by A. Lichnerowicz, Ch. V, this volume.

39. B. K. Harrison, K. S. Thorne, M. Wakano, and J. A. Wheeler, *Gravitation Theory and Gravitational Collapse* (University of Chicago Press, Chicago, 1965).

40. S. W. Hawking, *Proc. Roy. Soc. (Lond.)* **A294**, 511 (1966).

41. S. W. Hawking, *Proc. Roy. Soc. (Lond.)* **A295**, 490 (1966).

42. S. W. Hawking, *Proc. Roy. Soc. (Lond.)* **A300**, 187 (1967).

43. S. W. Hawking and G. F. R. Ellis, *Physics Letters*, **17**, 246 (1965).

44. S. W. Hawking and G. F. R. Ellis, *Ap. J.* in press (1968).

45. S. Helgason, *Differential Geometry and Symmetric Spaces* (Academic Press, New York, 1962).

46. L. Infeld and B. L. van der Waerden, *S. B. Preuss Akad.* **9**, 380 (1933).

47. P. Jordan, J. Ehlers, and R. K. Sachs, *Akad. Wiss., Mainz* **1** (1961).

47a. R. Kantowski, and R. K. Sachs, *J. Math. Phys.* **7**, 443 (1966).

48. R. P. Kerr, *Phys. Rev. Lett.* **11**, 237 (1963).

49. A. Komar, *Phys. Rev.* **104**, 544 (1956).

50. E. Kronheimer and R. Penrose, *Proc. Camb. Phil. Soc.* **63**, 481 (1967).

50a. M. D. Kruskal, *Phys. Rev.* **119**, 1943 (1960).

51. N. H. Kuiper, *Ann. of Math.* **50**, 916 (1949).

52. W. Kundt, *Z. Phys.* **172**, 488 (1963).

53. E. M. Lifshitz and I. M. Khalatnikov, *Advan. in Phys.* **12**, 185 (1963).

54. R. W. Lindquist and J. A. Wheeler, *Revs. Mod. Phys.* **29**, 432 (1957).

54a. S. MacLane and G. Birkhoff, *Algebra* (Macmillan, New York, 1967).

55. L. Markus, *Ann. Math.* **62**, 411 (1955).

56. R. F. Marzke and J. A. Wheeler, in *Gravitation and Relativity* (ed. H. Y. Chiu and W. F. Hoffmann; Benjamin, New York, 1964).

234   R. PENROSE

57. J. W. Milnor, *Enseignement Math.* (2) **9**, 198 (1963).

58. J. Milnor, *Morse Theory* (Annals of Math. Studies, Princeton University Press, Princeton, 1963).

59. C. W. Misner, *J. Math. Phys.* **4**, 924 (1963).

60. C. W. Misner, *Ap. J.* in press (1968).

61. C. W. Misner and A. H. Taub, to be published.

62. C. Møller, *The Theory of Relativity* (Oxford Univ. Press, Oxford, 1952).

63. E. T. Newman, L. Tamburino, and T. Unti, *J. Math Phys.* **4**, 915 (1963).

64. E. T. Newman and R. Penrose, *J. Math. Phys.* **3**, 566 (1962); **4**, 998 (1963).

65. K. Nomizu, *Lie Groups and Differential Geometry* (Herald Printing Co. Ltd., Tokyo, 1956).

66. G. Nordström, *Ann. der Physik* **42**, 533 (1913).

66a. I. V. Novikov, *J E T P. Lett.* **3**, 142 (1966).

67. J. R. Oppenheimer and G. Volkoff, *Phys. Rev.* **55**, 374 (1939).

68. J. R. Oppenheimer and H. Snyder, *Phys. Rev.* **56**, 455 (1939).

69. J. P. Ostriker, P. Bodenheimer and D. Lynden-Bell, *Phys. Rev. Lett.* **17**, 816 (1966).

70. W. T. Payne, *Am. J. Phys.* **20**, 253 (1952).

71. R. Penrose, *Proc. Camb. Phil. Soc.* **55**, 137 (1959).

72. R. Penrose, *Ann. of Phys.* **10**, 171 (1960).

73. R. Penrose, in P. G. Bergmann's Aeronautical Research Lab. Tech. Documentary Rept. 63–56: *Quantization of Generally Covariant Fields* (Office of Aerospace Research, U.S. Air Force, 1963).

74. R. Penrose, in *Relativity, Groups, and Topology* (ed. C. M. DeWitt and B. S. DeWitt; Gordon and Breach, New York, 1964).

75. R. Penrose, *Phys. Rev. Letters* **14**, 57 (1965).

76. R. Penrose, *Proc. Roy. Soc.* (*Lond.*) **A284**, 159 (1965).

77. R. Penrose, *Rev. Mod. Phys.* **37**, 215 (1965).

78. R. Penrose, in *Perspectives in Geometry and Relativity* (Indiana University Press, Bloomington, 1966).

79. R. Penrose, *J. Math. Phys.* **8**, 345 (1967).

80. R. Penrose, *Intern. J. Theor. Phys.* **1**, (1968).

80a. A. A. Penzias and R. W. Wilson, *Ap. J.* **142**, 419 (1965).

80b. A. Z. Petrov, *Sci. Not., Kazan State University* **114**, 55 (1954).

81. F. A. E. Pirani, *Phys. Rev.*, **105**, 1089 (1957).

82. F. A. E. Pirani, in *Lectures on General Relativity: 1964 Brandeis Summer Institute in Theoretical Physics Vol. I* (Prentice-Hall, Englewood Cliffs, 1965).

83. F. A. E. Pirani and A. Schild, in *Perspectives in Geometry and Relativity* (Indiana University Press, Bloomington, 1966).

84. J. Plebanski, *Acta Phys. Polon.* **27**, 361 (1965).

85. R. V. Pound and G. A. Rebka, *Phys. Rev. Letters* **4**, 337 (1960).

86. A. K. Raychaudhuri, *Phys. Rev.* **98**, 1123 (1955).

87. S. Refsdal, *Mon. Not. R. Astr. Soc.* **128**, 295 (1964); **128**, 307 (1964).

88. W. Rindler, *Mon. Not. Roy. Astr. Soc.* **116**, 6 (1956).

89. I. Robinson, *J. Math. Phys.* **2**, 290 (1961).

90. I. Robinson, A. Schild, and E. L. Schucking, eds.: *Quasi-Stellar Sources and Gravitational Collapse* (University of Chicago Press, Chicago, 1965).

91. H. S. Ruse, *Proc. Lond. Math. Soc.* **50**, 75 (1948).

92. H. Rudberg, *The Compactification of a Lorentz Space* (Thesis, University of Uppsala, Uppsala, Sweden, 1958).

93. R. K. Sachs, *Proc. Roy. Soc. (Lond.)* **A264**, 309 (1961).

94. R. K. Sachs, in *Recent Developments in General Relativity* (PWN/Pergamon, Warsaw/New York, 1962).

95. R. K. Sachs, *Proc. Roy. Soc. (Lond)* **A270**, 103 (1962).

96. A. Schild, *Am. J. Phys.* **28**, 778 (1960).

96a. J. A. Schouten, *Ricci-Calculus* (Springer, Berlin, 1954).

97. E. Schrodinger, *Expanding Universes* (Cambridge Univ. Press, Cambridge, 1956).

98. H. J. Seifert, *Naturforsch.* **22a**, 1356 (1967).

99. L. C. Shepley, *Proc. Nat. Acad. Sci.* **52**, 1403 (1964).

100. B. Spain, *Tensor Calculus* (Oliver and Boyd, London, 1960).

101. N. Steenrod, *The Topology of Fibre Bundles* (Princeton Univ. Press, Princeton, 1951).

102. K. Stellmacher, *Math. Annalen* **123**, 34 (1951).

103. J. L. Synge, *Relativity: the General Theory* (North-Holland, Amsterdam, 1960).

104. L. A. Tamburino and J. Winicour, *Phys. Rev.* **150**, 1039 (1966).

105. A. H. Taub, *Ann. Math.* **53**, 472 (1951).

106. J. Terrel, *Phys. Rev.* **116**, 1041 (1959).

107. K. S. Thorne, Relativistic Stellar Structure and Dynamics in 1966, *Les Houches Lectures* (ed. C. M. DeWitt, Gordon and Breach, New York, 1967).

108. A. Trautman, in *Lectures on General Relativity: 1964 Brandeis Summer Institute in Theoretical Physics, Vol. I* (Prentice-Hall, Englewood Cliffs, 1965).

109. A. Trautman, in *Perspectives in Geometry and Relativity* (IndianaUniversity Press, Bloomington, 1966).

110. B. L. van der Waerden, *Nachr. Ges. Wiss. Göttingen* **100** (1929).

111. H. Weyl, *Nachr Göttingen.* **99** (1921).

112. J. A. Wheeler, *Geometrodynamics* (Academic Press, New York, 1962).

113. J. A. Wheeler, in *Relativity, Groups and Topology* (ed. C. M. DeWitt and B. S. DeWitt; Gordon and Breach, New York, 1964).

113a. H. Whitney, *Bull. Amer. Math. Soc.* **43**, 785 (1937).

114. E. T. Whittaker, *Proc. Roy. Soc. (Lond.)* **A158**, 38 (1937).

115. L. Witten, *Phys. Rev.* **113**, 357 (1959).

VIII

The Structure of Singularities[1]

ROBERT GEROCH

From recent work of Hawking and others [1] it is known that singularities occur in large classes of solutions of Einstein's equations. Our intuitive idea of what a singularity should be in general relativity comes from the comparatively well-understood infinities which arise in other classical field theories, for example, in electrodynamics and hydrodynamics. However, general relativity differs from these theories in an important respect: whereas in the other field theories one has a background (Minkowskian) metric to which the field can be referred, in general relativity the "background metric" is the very field whose singularities we wish to describe. Consequently, it is not immediately clear what properties a space-time [2] should have in order that it be considered "singular."

Consider electrodynamics. A solution of Maxwell's equations is said to have a singularity if the electromagnetic field cannot be defined at some points. (For example, in the static Coulomb solution the field cannot be defined at the spatial origin). However, it turns out to be quite difficult to construct an analogous definition for general relativity because one can always remove such undesirable points from the manifold. The resulting space-time would then appear to be nonsingular. To define a singularity in general relativity, we begin by assuming that all of the "real singularities" have been removed from the space-time manifold, that is, that the metric is defined and differentiable everywhere. The singularities are then expected to show up as geodesic incompleteness of the space-time [2]. That is, we define a space-time as singular if it is geodesically incomplete.[3]

The use of geodesic incompleteness as the defining characteristic of singularities leads, however, to a further problem. It is convenient (from experience with other theories) to think of singularities in terms of points,

---

[1] A more complete discussion of this work appears in *J. Math. Phys.*, February 1968.

[2] By a "space-time" we understand a 4-manifold carrying a C^∞ metric of Lorentz $(-, +, +, +)$ signature.

[3] One often restricts consideration to only the timelike or only the null geodesics.

that is, to ask questions such as: "Does the mass density become infinite in the vicinity of the singularity?" This very question presupposes that there are some "singular points" at which the singularity resides, and that we may ask questions about the neighborhoods of these points. But geodesic incompleteness does not at all provide us with the "singular points" or their "neighborhoods" that we should like to have in order to formulate physical questions. We shall outline an approach to bridging the gap between geodesic incompleteness on the one hand and the more physical notion of a singularity as a point on the other. We shall describe a construction by which, given any incomplete space-time, one may define the requisite singular points and describe their local properties.[4] Our problem is thus primarily one of formulating definitions and, where necessary, of choosing from among alternative definitions.

Were the metric positive-definite, we could consider the completion of the space-time as a metric space—that is, the "singular points" would be equivalence classes of Cauchy sequences. With our indefinite metric, this approach fails: instead, we consider equivalence classes of incomplete geodesics. Let M be the space-time, TM_P the tangent space at the point P, and TM the tangent bundle. Define:

$$H_+ \equiv \exp^{-1} M$$

$$H \equiv \bigcup_{\substack{P \in M \\ \xi \in TM_P}} \overline{(TM_{P,\,\xi} \cap H_+)}$$

$$H_0 \equiv H - H_+,$$

where exp is the exponential map, $TM_{P,\,\xi}$ is the one-dimensional subspace of TM_P spanned by the vector ξ, and a bar denotes closure in $TM_{P,\,\xi}$. Each point of H_0 generates an incomplete geodesic in M. In particular, $H_+ = TM$ if and only if M is geodesically complete.

Our plan is to form the singularity from equivalence classes of points of H_0. Each of H, H_+, and H_0 is a subset of TM, and therefore has a topology induced on it from TM. We define a new topology on H_0 as follows. Let O be any open subset of M. Define:

$S(O) \equiv \{\alpha \in H_0|$ there exists an open neighborhood

U of α in H such that $\exp(U \cap H_+) \subset 0\}$

where "open neighborhood" refers to the induced topology on H. The subsets $S(O)$ of H_0, where O ranges over all open sets in M, form a basis for a topology on H_0. If $\alpha, \beta \in H_0$, write $\alpha \approx \beta$ if every open neighborhood of α contains β and every open neighborhood of β contains α ("open neighborhood" in the topology we have just defined on H_0). The relation $\approx$ is an

---

[4] A similar construction has been described by S. W. Hawking (Essay Submitted for the Adams Prize, December, 1966).

equivalence relation.   Let ∂ denote the equivalence classes, and π the mapping $H_0 \to \partial$.   The set ∂ (with the quotient topology) is a T_o topological space which we call the *g-boundary*.   The points of ∂ are to represent the "singular points" of the space-time.

We next attach the *g*-boundary to the space-time M, thus allowing us to express the idea that a point of M is "close" to the singularity.   Set

$$\overline{M} \equiv M \cup \partial$$

the disjoint union.   We define a topology on $\overline{M}$ as follows: A subset $(O, U) \subset \overline{M}$, where $O \subset M$, $U \subset \partial$, is open in $\overline{M}$ if O is open in M, U is open in ∂, and $S(O) \supset U$. $\overline{M}$ will be called the *space-time with g-boundary*.

We may check with an example that our definitions of ∂ and of $\overline{M}$ are reasonable.   Let V be a geodesically complete space-time, and let S be a 3-submanifold of V which divides V into two disjoint parts, M and M'.   The incomplete geodesics of M are precisely those geodesics which, when viewed in V, have an endpoint on S.   We now ask for the *g*-boundary of M.   It is easy to show that two incomplete geodesics in M are in the same equivalence class if and only if they have the same endpoint on S.   Thus, in this case, the *g*-boundary of M is just the ordinary boundary, S, of M in V.   The space-time with *g*-boundary is homeomorphic to the union $M \cup S$.

In the above example, the boundary surface S has a differentiable and a metric structure.   It might be asked whether or not these two structures can be determined by examining only M.   More generally, even when a space-time M cannot be extended it may be possible under certain conditions to define a differentiable and metric structure on its *g*-boundary.   Such definitions can in fact be constructed.   We use the natural differentiable and metric structure of TM to induce these structures on $H_0 \subset TM$, and then (by means of the map $\pi : H_0 \to \partial$) onto ∂.[5]   In the example considered earlier (in which M has a regular boundary surface S) the differentiable and metric structure of the *g*-boundary of M is just the induced differentiable structure and metric on S.

We wish to apply these definitions to the singularities which arise in solutions of Einstein's equations.   The study of these singularities is made more difficult by the fact that it is not clear at the outset what questions one would like to have answered.   Perhaps one of the central issues is: "What modifications[6] of Einstein's equations—these directed toward alleviating the problem of singularities—are suggested by the nature of the singularities which do occur?"   Unfortunately, we have comparatively few exact solutions of

---

[5] The precise definitions are too cumbersome to be described here.   They may be found in the more complete discussion in *J. Math Phys.* (February 1968).

[6] Under the term "modifications," let us also include quantization.

Einstein's equations to investigate, and all of these possess some symmetry. To study the g-boundary of the general incomplete space-time (without imposing Einstein's equations) is not a very promising line of attack because of the possibility that only singularities with a particular structure arise in solutions of Einstein's equations [3]. Perhaps the most that we can hope for at present is to understand the singularity structure of those solutions which are available. In Table 1 we list the g-boundaries of a number of exact solutions.

TABLE 1

		The g-boundary	
The solution	Topology	Attached to space-time at	Coordinates on the g-boundary
Schwarzschild: $ds^2 = -(1 - 2m/r) \, dt^2 + (1 - 2m/r)^{-1} \, dr^2 + r^2(d\theta^2 + \sin^2\theta \, d\phi^2)$ $0 < r < 2m$	$S^2 \times R$	$r = 0$	t, θ, ϕ
Reissner–Nordstrom: $ds^2 = -(1 - 2m/r + e^2/r^2) \, dt^2 + (1 - 2m/r + e^2/r^2)^{-1} \, dr^2 + r^2(d\theta^2 + \sin^2\theta \, d\phi^2)$ $m > e$ $0 < r < m - (m^2 - e^2)^{1/2}$	$S^2 \times R$	$r = 0$	t, θ, ϕ
Friedmann: $ds^2 = -dt^2 + R^2(t)[d\chi^2 + \sin^2\chi(d\theta^2 + \sin^2\theta \, d\phi^2)]$ $R = a(1 - \cos\eta)$ $t = a(\eta - \sin\eta)$ $a = \text{const.}$	S^3	$t = 0$ and $t = 2\pi a$	χ, θ, ϕ
Kasner: $ds^2 = -dt^2 + t^{2p_1} \, dx^2 + t^{2p_2} \, dy^2 + t^{2p_3} \, dz^2$ $p_1 = -s/(1 + s + s^2)$ $p_2 = s(1 + s)/(1 + s + s^2)$ $p_3 = (1 + s)/(1 + s + s^2)$ $s = \text{const.} \; \varepsilon \, (0, 1)$	R^3	$t = 0$	x, y, z

There is one solution—Taub space [4]—which deserves special consideration. This is a geodesically incomplete, exact, source-free solution of Einstein's equations. The underlying manifold is $S^3 \times R$, with each S^3 spacelike. The spacelike sections may be chosen to be homogeneous, but not isotropic. (Each S^3 carries a preferred vector field which is a Hopf fibering.)

It is known [5] that there are two different extensions[7] of Taub space, these obtained by attaching a NUT space [6] through a null 3-sphere.

The g-boundary of Taub space consists of the disjoint union

$$\partial = A \cup B \cup C$$

where A and B are each an S^3 and C is an S^2. Both A and B are Hopf-fibered by C with Hopf maps $\phi_A : A \to C$, and $\phi_B : B \to C$. A basis for the open sets of ∂ is as follows: the ordinary open sets of A and of B, and also sets of the form $E \cup \phi_A^{-1}(E) \cup \phi_B^{-1}(E)$, where E is an ordinary open set of C. The g-boundary is not even a T_1 topological space. The two extensions of Taub space may now be described as follows: In the first extension, the surface A becomes a null 3-sphere (the null geodesics in A being the circles of the Hopf fibering) through which Taub space is extended into NUT space. In the second extension, the roles of A and B are reversed. Thus, the two extensions of Taub space are characterized in a simple way in terms of the g-boundary. (Note also that we have a proof that locally Taub space has no more than two extensions.[8])

If we ignore the sphere C and attach just A and B to Taub space we can then obtain a non-Hausdorff manifold with boundary. This suggests that we carry out both extensions of Taub space simultaneously. That is, we attach the 3-spheres A and B to Taub space by the g-boundary prescription, and then attach to each of A and B the appropriate (NUT space) extension. The result is a non-Hausdorff (but not otherwise pathological) space-time. Further, it appears that this extended space-time is physically reasonable. Each geodesic (other than the exceptional ones which strike the 2-sphere C) which was incomplete in the original Taub space now passes through either sphere A or sphere B, and then into one or the other NUT space. An observer on a geodesic which passes through sphere A, for example, never enters the NUT space beyond sphere B, and so need not be concerned about that part of the space-time. No observer (at least if he is on a geodesic) would ever know that his space-time is non-Hausdorff.[9]

Taub space is a nice example of the pathologies which can arise in incomplete space-times—and of the way these pathologies may be sorted out using the g-boundary.

---

[7] By an "extension" of a space-time M we mean a space-time M' containing M as a proper subset.

[8] More precisely, if T' is a space-time containing Taub space T as a subset, then $\bar{T} \subset T \cup A \cup B$, where $\bar{T}$ is the closure of T in T'. This appears to be the strongest uniqueness result one can reasonably expect.

[9] It appears likely that this non-Hausdorff behavior of the extensions of Taub space is not stable, that is, that a small change in the Cauchy data for Taub space results in a new space-time in which extensions through A and B are not possible (R. Penrose and S. W. Hawking, private communications). What is not so clear is whether the non-Hausdorff character of the g-boundary is stable.

Though we have given a prescription that succeeds in principle in defining the g-boundary of any space-time, in practice the construction may be quite difficult. In particular, one needs a considerable amount of information about the geodesics. In many of the known solutions of Einstein's equations, integrals for the geodesics can be obtained up to quadratures, and these suffice for the construction. But the known solutions are highly symmetric: one cannot expect such a simplification to be available in general. Since only the "asymptotic properties" of the geodesics are relevant, one might hope to find a method to carry out the g-boundary construction without any detailed properties of the geodesics. Unfortunately, this hope has not yet been realized. We have seen, however, that some properties of the metric must be used to define the g-boundary. Since the geodesics are among the simplest such properties, it is not clear where to look for a different, more easily applied, construction which is still applicable to the generic, unsymmetrical space-time.

REFERENCES

1. R. Penrose, *Phys. Rev. Lett.* **14**, 57 (1965); S. W. Hawking, *Phys. Rev. Lett.* **17**, 444 (1966), *Proc. Roy. Soc.* **294A**, 511 (1966), **295A**, 490 (1966), *Proc. Roy. Soc.* 1967 (to appear); R. Geroch, *Phys. Rev. Lett.* **14**, 445 (1966).

2. C. W. Misner, *J. Math. Phys.* **4**, 924 (1963); R. Geroch, *Ann. Phys.* (submitted for publication).

3. E. M. Lifshitz, I. M. Khalatnikov, *Adv. Phys.* **12**, 185 (1963).

4. A. H. Taub, *Ann. Math.* **53**, 472 (1951).

5. C. W. Misner, *J. Math. Phys.* **4**, 924 (1963).

6. E. T. Newman, L. Tamburino, T. Unti, *J. Math. Phys.* **4**, 915 (1963).

IX

Superspace and the Nature of Quantum Geometrodynamics

JOHN ARCHIBALD WHEELER

ALLOWABLE HISTORY SELECTED OUT OF ARENA OF DYNAMICS BY CONSTRUCTIVE INTERFERENCE

Particle dynamics takes place in the arena of spacetime. Geometro-dynamics takes place in the arena of superspace. One needs only to mount to this point of view to have the whole content of Einstein's theory spread out before his eyes, as in the outlook from a mountain peak, and as well quantum geometrodynamics as classical geometrodynamics. What is the nature of the landscape that we see from this height? What structures can we hope to build upon this landscape? And what kinds of mysteries are hidden in the mists beyond?

In looking at the terrain of dynamics, happily everyone by now is long accustomed to the Hamilton–Jacobi theory. It belongs entirely to the world of classical physics.   Yet it carries one in an instant into the world of the quantum of action.

When better has one ever seen the transition from quantum to classical than in the theory of a particle in motion? Call the potential $V = V(x)$. Call the energy of the particle E.   Then there is not the slightest hope of discussing the movement of the particle in space and time.   Complementarity forbids!   The wave function is spread out all over space.   That one sees in no way more easily than through the semiclassical approximation for the probability amplitude function,

$$\psi_E(x, t) = \begin{pmatrix} \text{SLOWLY VARYING} \\ \text{AMPLITUDE FUNCTION} \end{pmatrix} \exp\left(\frac{i}{\hbar}\right) S_E(x, t) \qquad (1)$$

It is of no help in localizing the probability distribution that the Hamilton–Jacobi function S has in many applications a value large in comparison with the quantum of angular momentum $\hbar = 1.02 \times 10^{-27}$ g-cm^2/sec.   It is of no help that this "dynamical phase"—to give S another name—obeys the simple Hamilton–Jacobi law of propagation,

$$\frac{\partial S}{\partial t} = H\left(\frac{\partial S}{\partial x}, x\right)$$

$$= \left(\frac{1}{2m}\right)\left(\frac{\partial S}{\partial x}\right)^2 + V(x) \qquad (2)$$

And finally, it is of no help that the solution of this equation for a particle of energy E is extraordinarily simple,

$$S(x, t) = -Et + \int^x \{2m[E - V(x)]\}^{1/2}\, dx + \delta_E \qquad (3)$$

The probability is still spread all over everywhere!   There is not the slightest trace of anything like a localized world line, $x = x(t)$!

How old the idea of building wave packets out of monofrequency waves—and how easy!   The probability amplitude is now a superposition of terms, qualitatively of the form

$$\psi(x, t) = \psi_E(x, t) + \psi_{E+\Delta E}(x, t) + \cdots \qquad (4)$$

Destructive interference takes place almost everywhere.   The wave packet is concentrated in the region of constructive interference.   There the phases of the various waves agree; thus

$$S_E(x, t) = S_{E+\Delta E}(x, t) \qquad (5)$$

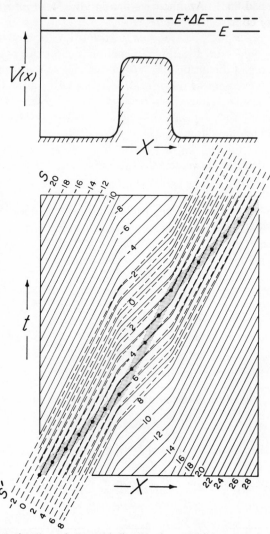

FIGURE 1. "Motion" and "world line" of a particle appear in quantum mechanics as the consequence of interference between wave trains that extend over all space. Above, potential energy as a function of distance for a model problem.

Below, smooth lines numbered -20, -18, ..., 28 are wave crests of probability amplitude function $\psi_E(x, t) \sim$ (slowly varying amplitude factor) $\exp (i/\hbar)S(x, t)$ for energy E. Dashed lines, same for energy $E + \Delta E$. Shaded area, region of constructive interference ("wave packet"). Black dots mark locus of classical world line ($S_{E+\Delta E} = S_E$).

At last a world line! And how easy to find the Newtonian motion from this condition of constructive interference:

$$0 = S_{E+\Delta E} - S_E$$
$$\Downarrow$$
$$0 = -t\,\Delta E + \int^x \Delta p_E(x)\,dx + (\delta_{E+\Delta E} - \delta_E)$$
$$\Downarrow$$
$$t = \int^x \frac{dx}{v_E(x)} + t_0 \qquad \text{(NEWTON)} \tag{6}$$

Here $v_E(x)$ denotes the velocity at the location x,

$$\frac{\Delta[2m(E-V)]^{1/2}}{\Delta E} = \frac{\Delta p_E}{\Delta E} \to \frac{\partial(\text{momentum})}{\partial E} = \frac{1}{v_E(x)} = \begin{pmatrix} \text{TIME TO COVER} \\ \text{A UNIT DISTANCE} \end{pmatrix} \tag{7}$$

and the quantity t_0 is an abbreviation for

$$\frac{\delta_{E+\Delta E} - \delta_E}{\Delta E} \to \frac{d\delta_E}{dE} \equiv t_0 \tag{8}$$

Marvelously, not one trace of the quantum of action appears in the final solution for the motion. Yet the quantum principle supplies the whole rationale and motivation for talking about "constructive interference." The quantum comes in only when one recognizes the finite spread of the wave packet (Fig. 1). Then the idea of a world line has to be renounced. A whole range of histories contribute to the propagation of the particle from start to finish. This is the way the real world of quantum physics operates!

Three Dimensions, Not Four

Similarly in geometrodynamics: Here the dynamic object is not spacetime. It is space. The geometrical configuration of space changes with time. But it is space, three-dimensional space, that does the changing. No surprise! In particle dynamics the dynamical object is not x *and* t, but only x. How to tell this to our friends in the world of mathematics? For so long they have heard us say that it was in default of the fourth dimension that Riemann could not have discovered general relativity. First there had to come special relativity and spacetime and the fourth dimension. Otherwise how could one have had any possibility to connect gravitation with the curvature of spacetime (Fig. 2)? This understood, how can physicists change their minds and "take back" one dimension? The answer is simple. A decade and more of work by Dirac, Bergmann, Schild, Pirani, Anderson, Higgs, Arnowitt, Deser, Misner, DeWitt, and others has taught us through many a hard knock that Einstein's geometrodynamics deals with the dynamics of geometry: of 3-geometry, not 4-geometry [1, 2].

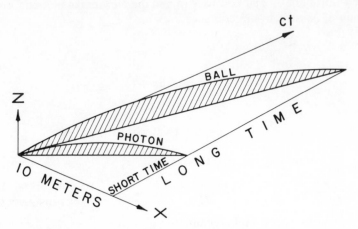

FIGURE 2. The track of the ball and the track of the photon through space $(x, z$ plane) have very different curvatures, but in space time $(x, z, ct$ space) the curvatures are comparable.

What is a 3-geometry? To simplify the question, rephrase it in an everyday context: What is a 2-geometry? Nothing illustrates a 2-geometry more clearly than an automobile fender. In whatever way coordinates are painted on its surface, in whatever way the points of that surface are named or renamed, the fender keeps the same 2-geometry. Similarly for a 3-geometry. In mathematical terms, a $^{(3)}\mathscr{G}$ is not a positive definite 3×3 metric; instead, it is an *equivalence class* of such metrics that are transformable, one into another, by diffeomorphisms.

Mere baggage is the right term not only for the points of the space, but also for the coordinates employed to label these points, and for the metric that tells the distance from each point to all its near neighbors. Behind all of that paraphernalia lies the real idea, the concept of 3-geometry, as solid and substantial as the 2-geometry of the fender. Down with "points"; up with "geometry"!

SUPERSPACE

One climbs up to the concept of geometry only to find a new height beyond—superspace [3]. Superspace is the manifold, a single point of which stands for an entire 3-geometry (Fig. 3). A 3-geometry stands at the halfway mark between point and superspace: risen though it is above the concept of point by abstractification, any one geometry of space counts as only a single point of superspace.

$$\psi(G) \sim A e^{iS(G)/\hbar} + A' e^{iS'(G)/\hbar} + ...$$

FIGURE 3. Superspace $\mathscr{S}$ is the manifold each of whose "points" $A, B, C, \ldots$ is an abbreviation for one 3-geometry. A submanifold H of $\mathscr{S}$ is the "classical history of the geometry of space" when space has been started off under some particular set of dynamical initial conditions. In other words, H consists of all those spacelike 3-geometries that can be obtained as spacelike sections through one particular 4-geometry (that satisfies Einstein's classical field equations). The 3-geometries of the classical history H may alternatively but equivalently be distinguished from other 3-geometries by the fact that they satisfy the classical "condition of constructive interference" $S(^{(3)}\mathscr{G}) = S'(^{(3)}\mathscr{G}) = S''(^{(3)}\mathscr{G}) = \cdots$ ("coincidence of wave crests" in lower magnified view of a region of superspace). In quantum theory the wave packet is not localized with unlimited sharpness. The probability amplitude ψ has significant values for 3-geometries at some small "distance" in superspace on each "side" of the classical history H; hence the "quantum fluctuations in the geometry of space" (depicted symbolically in more detail in Fig. 5).

Superspace is the arena for geometrodynamics, just as Lorentz–Minkowski space-time is the arena for particle dynamics (Table 1). The momentary configuration of the particle is an event, a single point in space-time. The momentary configuration of space is a 3-geometry, a single point in superspace.

TABLE 1   *Geometrodynamics Compared with Particle Dynamics*

Quality	Particle	Geometrodynamics
Dynamical entity	Particle	Space
Descriptors of momentary configuration	x, t (" event ")	$^{(3)}\mathscr{G}$ (" 3-geometry ")
History	$x = x(t)$	$^{(4)}\mathscr{G}$ (" 4-geometry ")
History is a stockpile of configurations?	Yes. Every point on world line gives a momentary configuration of particle	Yes. Every spacelike slice through $^{(4)}\mathscr{G}$ gives a momentary configuration of space
Dynamic arena	Spacetime (totality of all points x, t)	Superspace (totality of all $^{(3)}\mathscr{G}$'s)

Is superspace a proper manifold? Its construction is simple enough: call a 3-geometry a "point," and put all such points together. Or why limit attention to 3-geometries with positive definite metric? Build "extended superspace"; call every 3-geometry a "point" even if its signature is not $+ + +$, and put all these "points" together. Does the resulting mathematical object possess a reasonable topology? Is it a true manifold? No! In a proper manifold each point has a neighborhood homeomorphic to an open set in a Banach space, and two distinct points have disjoint neighborhoods. Not so here. In an important investigation Michael Stern has shown [4] that for each point of extended superspace there exists another point, distinct from it, which nevertheless cannot be isolated from it by open sets. The topology is not Hausdorf. Extended superspace is not a manifold. It can hardly be regarded as an acceptable arena for dynamics.

Superspace, in contrast, Stern has shown, does have Hausdorf topology and does constitute a manifold. According to these mathematical considerations, *superspace is the proper arena for geometrodynamics.*

Physical considerations point to the same conclusion. To insist that a 3-geometry shall have positive definite metric is to guarantee that no light ray can traverse this 3-geometry. No physical effect can propagate from one point of the $^{(3)}\mathscr{G}$ to another. A physical quantity local to the one point and a physical quantity local to the other have zero reciprocal coupling. They commute. Such quantities lend themselves to simultaneous specification over the entire 3-geometry. No simpler example exists of a "complete observation" in quantum geometrodynamics. Closely related is the initial value problem of classical geometrodynamics.

"Observation?" Does not observation imply an observer? If there is an observer, does he not respond to every event on his past light cone? And consequently does not that past light cone with its $+ + 0$ metric supply the appropriate geometry on which to specify physical conditions? No, and for two reasons. First, to know the state of the geometry on a past light cone, however completely, is still to be powerless to predict from Einstein's field equations the future of the geometry. Predict the 4-geometry within the past light cone? Yes [5]. Outside—to the future? No. Into the domain of the future, influences flow from afar without ever once impinging upon the light cone. "Demidynamics"—prediction into the past—one can do; full dynamics, no. The fault is in the choice of initial value hypersurface. The cone creates an unsymmetrical divide between past and future. How different from a spacelike initial value hypersurface! The initial value data on it allow a prediction of the complete geometrodynamical history, past and future.

Second, the original argument was mistaken that one should consider "a light cone converging upon an observer." The "observer" of dynamical theory is not and cannot be a single detector of events either in special relativity or in general relativity. Instead he "collects the printout" [6] from a multitude of detectors dotted densely about. Each of his detectors is sensitive only for an instant. These instants of sensitivity bear a spacelike relationship each to the other [7]. Collectively they define a spacelike hypersurface, a "simultaneity," a common moment of a rudimentary "time" variable that perhaps is not and certainly need not be specified any further. In its moment of sensitivity each detector responds to the appropriate influence: to particle proximity in particle physics, to local field strength in electrodynamics, and to local geometry in geometrodynamics. Whichever the dynamic entity, the measurements of it do not and cannot fully serve dynamic theory unless they span a spacelike hypersurface.

Distill this discussion! Where specify dynamically complete initial value data? On a spacelike 3-geometry, yes; on a null 3-geometry, no. What "points" belong to a topologically acceptable arena for geometrodynamics? Spacelike 3-geometries, yes; null 3-geometries, no. What a remarkable correspondence between dynamics and topology!

Wave Packet in Superspace and Its Propagation

So much for the dynamical entity, space; and so much for the arena in which the dynamics takes place, superspace; now for the dynamics itself. Not one trace of dynamics does one see when he examines the typical probability amplitude function, $\psi = \psi(^{(3)}\mathcal{G})$, for it is spread all over superspace. No surprise! Already in classical theory the Hamilton–Jacobi function, $S = S(^{(3)}\mathscr{G})$, is spread out over the manifold. Moreover, this "dynamical phase function" of classical geometrodynamics gives at once in the semiclassical approximation the actual phase of ψ, according to the formula

$$\psi(^{(3)}\mathscr{G}) = \begin{pmatrix} \text{SLOWLY VARYING} \\ \text{AMPLITUDE FUNCTION} \end{pmatrix} \exp\left(\frac{i}{\hbar}\right) S(^{(3)}\mathscr{G}) \qquad (9)$$

—indication enough that ψ and S are both unlocalized! Dynamics first clearly becomes recognizable when sufficiently many such spread-out probability amplitude functions are superposed to build up a localized wave packet [8, 9]:

$$\psi = c_1\psi_1 + c_2\psi_2 + \cdots \qquad (10)$$

Constructive interference occurs where the phases of the several individual waves agree [10]:

$$S_1(^{(3)}\mathscr{G}) = S_2(^{(3)}\mathscr{G}) = \cdots \qquad (11)$$

The $^{(3)}\mathscr{G}$'s compatible with these conditions of constructive interference constitute the classical geometrodynamical history of space (Fig. 3): Marvelously, every 3-geometry that satisfies the conditions of constructive interference (11) can be obtained as a spacelike slice through a certain 4-geometry. More marvelously, this $^{(4)}\mathscr{G}$ satisfies the ten field equations of Einstein. In other words, *in addition to the principle of constructive interference one needs only the single equation of Hamilton and Jacobi for the "dynamical phase" $S(^{(3)}\mathscr{G})$ to obtain all of classical geometrodynamics.* The proof of this important point has been announced by Gerlach [11].

The Hamilton–Jacobi equation itself was first given explicitly in the literature by Peres [12] on the foundation of earlier work by himself and others on the Hamiltonian formulation of geometrodynamics [13]:

$$g^{-1}(g_{ik}g_{jl} - \tfrac{1}{2}g_{ij}g_{kl})\left(\frac{\delta S}{\delta g_{ij}}\right)\left(\frac{\delta S}{\delta g_{kl}}\right) + {}^{(3)}R = 0 \qquad (12)$$

Here the g_{ij} are the coefficients in the metric on $^{(3)}\mathscr{G}$ and g is the determinant of these metric coefficients. The quantity $^{(3)}R$ is the local value of the scalar curvature invariant of the geometry intrinsic to $^{(3)}\mathscr{G}$. The Hamilton–Jacobi function depends only upon the 3-geometry, and not upon how that 3-geometry is expressed in terms of metric coefficients in a particular coordinate patch. However, S is treated in (12) as if it depended upon the metric coefficients individually, $S = S(g_{11}, g_{12}, \ldots, g_{33})$. With this understanding, $\delta S/\delta g_{ij}$ denotes the functional derivative of S with respect to alterations in the function $g_{ij}(x, y, z)$. The fact that coordinates in the end have nothing to do with the matter can be stressed by rewriting (12) symbolically in the form

$$\boxed{\left(\frac{\nabla S}{\delta^{(3)}\mathscr{G}}\right)^2 + {}^{(3)}R = 0}$$

(13)

This "Einstein–Hamilton–Jacobi equation" contains all of classical geometrodynamics in regions where no "real" sources of mass-energy are present. This one equation carries the entire content of Einstein's ten field equations. Consequently, this equation has been checked and is subject to further check, in the same sense and to the same degree that the predictions of Einstein's field equations have been verified, and are subject to further verification. In the simplest version of particle physics a world line has a simple meaning: It is a stockpile consisting of all those points (x, t) that satisfy the condition of constructive interference. There are ∞^1 of these points on the world line, if we use an obvious though loose way of counting. Dynamics marks out these points and gives preference to them over all the ∞^2 points in the arena of particle dynamics. In geometrodynamics a 4-geometry has a similar significance. It is a stockpile consisting of all those 3-geometries that satisfy the condition of constructive interference. There are ∞^{∞^3} of these 3-geometries, obtainable by making a spacelike slice through the 4-geometry in one or another way:

$$t = t(x, y, z)$$

(14)

thus,

(a) ∞^3 points (x, y, z)
(b) ∞^1 choices for t at each of these points

hence

(c) ∞^{∞^3} choices of 3-geometry altogether

(15)

Classical geometrodynamics marks out these ${}^{(3)}\mathscr{G}$'s and gives preference to them over the infinitely more numerous totality of ${}^{(3)}\mathscr{G}$'s to be found in the entire arena of geometrodynamics. That arena, superspace, contains ${}^{(3)}\mathscr{G}$'s to the number $(\infty^3)^{\infty^3}$, calculated most simply as follows:

(a) ∞^3 points; and, in a coordinate system that makes the metric diagonal,
(b) 3 diagonal components of the metric specifiable per space point;

and hence

(c) ∞^3 choices of the metric per space point;

and therefore

(d) $(\infty^3)^{\infty^3}$ choices of ${}^{(3)}\mathscr{G}$ altogether

(16)

From this totality of conceivable 3-geometries one has to pick out and exhibit all the dynamically allowed 3-geometries before he has told in all fullness how space evolves with time.   No new lesson!   One has long known that time in general relativity is a many-fingered entity.   The hypersurface drawn through spacetime to give one $^{(3)}\mathcal{G}$ can be pushed forward in time a little here or a little there or a little somewhere else to give one or another or another new $^{(3)}\mathcal{G}$.   "*Time*" conceived in these terms *means* nothing more or less than *the location of the $^{(3)}\mathcal{G}$ in the $^{(4)}\mathcal{G}$*.   In this sense "3-geometry is a carrier of information about time" [14].

"Spacetime," a Concept of Limited Validity

The child's toy can be removed from its box only to reveal another box and—that taken away—another box, and so on, until eventually there are dozens of boxes scattered over the floor.   Or conversely the boxes can be put back together, nested one inside the other, to reconstitute the original package. The packaging of $^{(3)}\mathcal{G}$'s into a $^{(4)}\mathcal{G}$ is much more sophisticated.   Nature provides no monotonic ordering of the $^{(3)}\mathcal{G}$'s.   Two of the dynamically allowed $^{(3)}\mathcal{G}$'s taken at random will often cross each other one or more times. When one shakes the $^{(4)}\mathcal{G}$ apart, he therefore gets enormously more $^{(3)}\mathcal{G}$'s "spread out over the floor" than he might otherwise have imagined.   Conversely, when one puts back together all of the $^{(3)}\mathcal{G}$'s allowed by the condition of constructive interference, he gets a structure with a rigidity that he might not otherwise have foreseen.   This rigidity arises from the infinitely rich interleaving and intercrossing of clear-cut well-defined $^{(3)}\mathcal{G}$'s one with another. In summary, (1) the $^{(3)}\mathcal{G}$'s allowed by (11) are the basic building blocks; (2) their interconnections give $^{(4)}\mathcal{G}$ its existence, its dimensionality [15], and its "magic structure"; and (3) in this structure every $^{(3)}\mathcal{G}$ has a rigidly fixed location of its own.

How different from the textbook concept of spacetime!   There the geometry of spacetime is conceived as constructed out of elementary objects, or points, known as "events."   Here, by contrast, the primary concept is 3-geometry, and the event is secondary: (1) The event lies at the "intersection" of such and such $^{(3)}\mathcal{G}$'s.   (2) Its timelike relation to some other $^{(3)}\mathcal{G}$ is determined by the structure of the $^{(4)}\mathcal{G}$, which in turn derives from the intercrossings of all the other $^{(3)}\mathcal{G}$'s.

Whether one starts with $^{(3)}\mathcal{G}$'s as primary and regards the "event" as a derived concept, or vice versa, might make little difference if one were to remain in the domain of classical geometrodynamics.   It makes all the difference when one turns to quantum geometrodynamics.

There is no such thing as a 4-geometry in quantum geometrodynamics, and for a simple reason.   No probability amplitude function $\psi(^{(3)}\mathcal{G})$ can propagate through superspace as an indefinitely sharp wave packet.   It spreads (Fig. 3). It has a finite probability amplitude in a domain of super-space of finite measure. This domain encompasses a set of $^{(3)}\mathcal{G}$'s far too numerous to accommodate in any one $^{(4)}\mathcal{G}$. One can express this situation in various terms. One can say that propagation takes place in superspace, not by following any one classical history of space, not by following any one $^{(4)}\mathcal{G}$, but by summation of contributions from an infinite variety of such histories. This extension of Feynman's concept of "sum over histories" has received special attention from Misner [16]. In whatever way one states the matter, however, the facts are clear. The $^{(3)}\mathcal{G}$'s that occur with significant probability amplitude do not fit and cannot be fitted into any single $^{(4)}\mathcal{G}$. That "magic structure" of classical geometrodynamics simply does not exist. Without that building plan to organize the $^{(3)}\mathcal{G}$'s of significance into a definite relation-ship, one to another, even the "time ordering of events" is a notion devoid of all meaning.

These considerations reveal that the concepts of spacetime and time itself are not primary but secondary ideas in the structure of physical theory. These concepts are valid in the classical approximation. However, they have neither meaning nor application under circumstances when quantum-geometrodynamical effects become important. Then one has to forgo that view of nature in which every event, past, present, or future, occupies its preordained position in a grand catalog called "spacetime." There is no spacetime, there is no time, there is no before, there is no after. The question what happens "next" is without meaning.

The Planck Length and Gravitational Collapse

Under everyday circumstances these unexpected consequences of the quantum principle never come into evidence. The characteristic dimension of quantum geometrodynamics is the Planck length [17], $(\hbar G/c^3)^{1/2} = 1.6 \times 10^{-33}$ cm. By comparison the normally relevant scale of any geometry of interest is stupendous. Negligible on the scale of the geometry is the quantum-mechanical spread of the wave packet in superspace. Con-sequently the dynamical evolution of the geometry can be treated in the context of classical geometrodynamics. Thus the geometries that occur with significant probability amplitude can be idealized to a good approxima-tion as if confined to a region in superspace of zero thickness. The $^{(3)}\mathcal{G}$'s of this limited set are sufficiently small in number to fit together into a single $^{(4)}\mathcal{G}$. They are sufficiently large in number to reproduce every conceivable spacelike slice of that $^{(4)}\mathcal{G}$. In this approximation it makes good sense to speak of "the classical geometrodynamical history of space."

If the dynamics of geometry thus normally lends itself to classical analysis, there are two contexts where it does not. One is the final stage of gravitational collapse. The other is analysis of the microscopic quantum-mechanical fluctuations in the geometry of space and their consequences for physics generally.

Of all the applications of quantum geometrodynamics, none would seem more immediate than gravitational collapse [18]. Here according to classical general relativity the dimensions of the collapsing system in a finite proper time are driven down to indefinitely small values. The phenomenon is not limited to the space occupied by matter. It occurs also in the space surrounding the matter. In a finite proper time the calculated curvature rises to infinity. At this point classical theory becomes incapable of further prediction. In actuality, classical considerations go wrong before this point. A prediction that is infinity is not a prediction. The wave packet in superspace does not and cannot follow the classical history when the geometry becomes smaller in scale than the quantum-mechanical spread of the wave packet. Not a new phenomenon! Throughout physics one sees examples of a wave impinging upon a region of interaction of dimensions small compared to a wavelength. The outcome is scattering or diffraction. One speaks of a probability for this, that, or the other outcome of the interaction. The photon or phonon or other entity entering from one direction emerges in another. The concept of a deterministic world line may serve adequately during the phase of approach to the zone of interaction, and during the phase of regression. It is completely out of place during the phase of scattering. So here. The concept of a deterministic history of geometry, a well-defined $^{(4)}\mathscr{G}$, makes sense in the early phase of gravitational collapse, but has absolutely no application in the decisive phase. There "space-time" is nonexistent, "events" and the "time ordering of events" are without meaning, and the question "what happens after the final phase of gravitational collapse" is a mistaken way of speaking.

The correct way of speaking deals with the propagation of the probability amplitude $\psi(^{(3)}\mathscr{G})$ in superspace. The semiclassical treatment of the propagation (Eqs. (9), (13)) is appropriate in most of the domain of superspace of interest for gravitational collapse. Not so in the decisive region. There, as in elementary problems of scattering, the mathematical analysis has to go straight back to the full and accurate wave equation for its foundation. What is the appropriate question to ask of the mathematics? One has learned how to formulate the right question, in the case of scattering, through long experience with the physics. However, if one had not had that physical experience, he would have learned out of the mathematical formalism itself to speak about incoming plane waves and outgoing spherical waves, and scattering amplitudes, and about all the other relevant concepts. Similarly in quantum geometrodynamics, where one has so much less experience. The mathematical formalism itself must serve as the final arbiter on how to pose the central question about gravitational collapse as well as how to answer it!

Quantum Fluctuations in Geometry of Space

"Quantum fluctuations in the geometry of space" is the other pressing field of application of quantum geometrodynamics. What a strange combination of words! Fluctuations are well known. The term "quantum fluctuations" carries a deeper meaning. It stands for a movement that can never be frozen out, however low the temperature. Such fluctuations are universal. In the hydrogen molecule both the separation of the two atoms and their relative momentum continually flucuate. Fixity of both would violate the uncertainty principle. In the frozen vaccuum of quantum electrodynamics the electric and magnetic fields both fluctuate. Were both of these dynamically conjugate field variables to vanish, the uncertainty principle would likewise fail. The same is true of quantum geometrodynamics. There the conjugate variables are the "intrinsic curvature" of three-dimensional space and the "extrinsic curvature," telling how this space is bent relative to the geometry of any 4-dimensional space-time that might envelop it. For both dynamic quantities to be stilled would equally contradict Heisenberg's uncertainty relation. Thus all space at the quantum scale of distances is the seat of the liveliest geometrodynamics, as it is also everywhere the scene of the most violent small-scale fluctuations in the electromagnetic field.

No prediction of quantum electrodynamics has been more impressively verified in the whole post-World War II era than these vacuum fluctuations in the electric field. Their perturbing influence on the motion of the electron (Fig. 4) accounts for the major component in the Lamb shift in the energy levels of the hydrogen atom [19].

In putting numbers to the fluctuations in geometry one is guided by the example of electromagnetism and, at a still earlier stage, by the example of the harmonic oscillator. For the oscillator the expression for the energy is

$$E = \left\langle \begin{pmatrix} \text{kinetic} \\ \text{energy} \end{pmatrix} + \begin{pmatrix} \text{potential} \\ \text{energy} \end{pmatrix} \right\rangle = \frac{p^2}{2m} + \tfrac{1}{2}m\omega^2 x^2$$

$$= \int \psi^*(x) \left[-\frac{\hbar^2}{2m}\frac{d^2}{dx^2} + \tfrac{1}{2}m\omega^2 x^2 \right] \psi(x)\, dx \tag{17}$$

For a probability amplitude function $\psi(x)$ of Gaussian form and range a,

$$\psi(x) = \pi^{-1/4} a^{-1/2} \exp\left(-\frac{x^2}{2a^2} \right) \tag{18}$$

the expectation value of the energy is

$$E = \frac{\hbar^2}{4ma^2} + \tfrac{1}{4}m\omega^2 a^2 \tag{19}$$

FIGURE 4. Symbolic representation of motion of electron in hydrogen atom
as affected by fluctuations in electric field in vacuum ("vacuum" or "ground state" or "zero-point" fluctuations). The
electric field associated with the fluctuation, $E_x(t) = \int E_x(\omega)e^{-i\omega t}\,d\omega$,
brings about in the most elementary approximation the displacement
$\Delta x = \int (e/m\omega^2)E_x(\omega)e^{-i\omega t}\,d\omega$. The average vanishes but the root
mean square $\langle(\Delta x)^2\rangle$ does not. In consequence the electron feels
an effective atomic potential altered from the expected value
$V(x, y, z)$ by the amount
$$\Delta V(x, y, z) = \tfrac{1}{2}\langle(\Delta x)^2\rangle\nabla^2 V(x, y, z)$$
The average of this perturbation over the unperturbed motion
accounts for the major part of the observed Lamb–Rutherford shift
$\Delta E = \langle \Delta V(x, y, z)\rangle$ in the energy level. Conversely, the observation of the expected shift makes the reality of the vacuum fluctuations
inescapably evident.

If quantum effects were absent, the first term would disappear. The minimum energy would be obtained by putting the oscillator at rest at the origin.
However, in the real world of quantum physics such a sharp localization in
position ($a = 0$) would make the effective wavelength zero and the momentum
and kinetic energy arbitrarily large (divergent first term in Eq. (19)). The

minimum energy, $E = \frac{1}{2}\hbar\omega$ ("half quantum" or "zero-point energy" or "fluctuation energy") is obtained for a range $a = (\hbar/m\omega)^{1/2}$ ("range of zero-point oscillations"). In other words, the oscillator in its ground state

$$\psi(x) = \left(\frac{m\omega}{\pi\hbar}\right)^{1/4} \exp\left[-\left(\frac{m\omega}{2\hbar}\right)x^2\right] \tag{20}$$

can be said to "resonate" between locations in space ranging over a region of extent $\sim(\hbar/m\omega)^{1/2}$.

The electromagnetic field can be treated as an infinite collection of independent "field oscillators," with amplitudes $\xi_1, \xi_2, \ldots$. When the Maxwell field is in its state of lowest energy, the probability amplitude for the first oscillator to have amplitude ξ_1, and simultaneously the second oscillator to have amplitude ξ_2, the third ξ_3, and so on, is the product of functions of the form (20), one for each oscillator. When the scale of amplitudes for each oscillator is suitably normalized, the resulting infinite product takes the form

$$\psi(\xi_1, \xi_2, \ldots) = N \exp\left[-(\xi_1^2 + \xi_2^2 + \cdots)\right] \tag{21}$$

This expression gives the probability amplitude ψ for a configuration $\mathbf{B}(x, y, z)$ of the magnetic field that is described by the Fourier coefficients $\xi_1, \xi_2, \ldots$. One can forgo any mention of these Fourier coefficients if he so desires, however, and rewrite (21) directly in terms of the magnetic field configuration itself [20]:

$$\psi(\mathbf{B}(x, y, z)) = \mathcal{N} \exp\left(-\iint \frac{\mathbf{B}(x_1) \cdot \mathbf{B}(x_2)}{16\pi^3 \hbar c r_{12}^2}\right) d^3x_1\, d^3x_2 \tag{22}$$

No longer does one speak of "the" magnetic field; he talks instead of the probability of this, that, or the other configuration of the magnetic field and this even under circumstances, as here, where the electromagnetic field is in its ground state.

It is reasonable enough under these circumstances that the configuration of greatest probability is $\bar{\mathbf{B}}(x, y, z) = 0$. Consider for comparison a configuration where the magnetic field is again everywhere zero except in a region of dimension L. There let the field, subject as always to the condition div $\mathbf{B} = 0$, be of the order of magnitude ΔB. The probability amplitude for this configuration will be reduced relative to the nil configuration by a factor exp $(-I)$. Here the quantity I in the exponent is of the order $(\Delta B)^2 L^4/\hbar c$. Configurations for which I is large compared to 1 occur with negligible probability. Configurations for which I is small compared to 1 occur with practically the same probability as the nil configuration. In this sense, one can say that the fluctuations in the magnetic field in a region of extension L are of the order of magnitude

$$\Delta B \sim \frac{(\hbar c)^{1/2}}{L^2} \tag{23}$$

In other words, the field "resonates" between one configuration and another with the range of configurations of significance given by (23). Moreover, the smaller is the region of space under consideration, the larger are the field magnitudes that occur with appreciable probability.

Still another familiar way of speaking about electromagnetic field fluctuations gives additional insight relevant to geometrodynamics. One considers a measuring device responsive in comparable measure to the magnetic field at all points in a region of dimension L. One asks for the effect on this device of electromagnetic disturbances of various wavelengths. A disturbance of wavelength short compared to L will cause forces to act one way in some parts of the detector and will give rise to nearly compensating forces in other parts of it. In contrast, a disturbance of a long wavelength λ produces forces everywhere in the same direction, but of a magnitude too low to have much effect. Thus the field, estimated from the equation

$$\begin{pmatrix} \text{ENERGY OF ELECTROMAGNETIC} \\ \text{WAVE OF WAVELENGTH } \lambda \text{ IN A} \\ \text{DOMAIN OF VOLUME } \lambda^3 \end{pmatrix} \sim \begin{pmatrix} \text{ENERGY OF ONE QUANTUM} \\ \text{OF WAVELENGTH } \lambda \end{pmatrix}$$

or

$$B^2 \lambda^3 \sim \frac{\hbar c}{\lambda}$$

or

$$B \sim \frac{(\hbar c)^{1/2}}{\lambda^2} \tag{24}$$

is very small if λ is large compared to the domain size L. The biggest effect is caused by a disturbance of wavelength λ comparable to L itself. This line of reasoning leads directly from (24) to the standard fluctuation formula (23).

Fluctuations Superposed on Classical Background

Nothing says that the electromagnetic field has to be in its ground state. It can be excited by a distant wireless antenna so that locally it is oscillating up and down at 10^6 cycles/sec in the range $B = \pm 3.3 \times 10^{-8}$ gauss, for example (accompanying electric fields 1 millivolt/meter). By comparison with this deterministic classical history of the local magnetic field,

$$B_z = 3.3 \times 10^{-8} \text{ gauss cos } 10^6 t \tag{25}$$

the quantum-mechanical fluctuation field of the same frequency (Eq. (24)) is quite negligible:

$$B \sim \frac{6 \times 10^{-9} (\text{erg cm})^{1/2}}{(3 \times 10^4 \text{cm})^2}$$

$$\sim 10^{-17} \text{ gauss} \tag{26}$$

Even the total effect of all the independent quantum fluctuations in the magnetic field is small as sensed by a detector of dimension $L \sim 1$ cm; thus, from Eq. (23),

$$\Delta B \sim \frac{6 \times 10^{-9}(\text{erg cm})^{1/2}}{(1 \text{ cm})^2}$$

$$\sim 6 \times 10^{-9} \text{ gauss} \tag{27}$$

However, when attention is fixed on the field in a still smaller domain, say $L \sim 0.1$ cm or less, then the quantum fluctuations in the magnetic field dominate over the deterministic classical field of (25):

$$\Delta B > 6 \times 10^{-7} \text{ gauss} \tag{28}$$

So much for the coexistence of classical fields and quantum fluctuations in electrodynamics!

Similar considerations apply in geometrodynamics [21]. Quantum fluctuations in the geometry are superposed on and coexist with the large-scale slowly varying curvature predicted by classical deterministic general relativity. Thus, in a region of dimension L, where in a local Lorentz frame the normal values of the metric coefficients will be $-1, 1, 1, 1$, there will occur fluctuations in these coefficients of the order

$$\Delta g \sim \frac{L^*}{L} \tag{29}$$

fluctuations in the first derivatives of the g_{ik}'s of the order

$$\Delta \Gamma \sim \frac{\Delta g}{L} \sim \frac{L^*}{L^2} \tag{30}$$

and fluctuations in the curvature of space of the order

$$\Delta R \sim \frac{\Delta g}{L^2} \sim \frac{L^*}{L^3} \tag{31}$$

Here

$$L^* = \left(\frac{\hbar G}{c^3}\right)^{1/2} = 1.6 \times 10^{-33} \text{ cm} \tag{32}$$

is the so-called [22] Planck length. It is appropriate to look at orders of magnitude. The curvature of space within and near the earth, according to classical Einstein theory, is of the order

$$R \sim \left(\frac{G}{c^2}\right)\rho \sim (0.7 \times 10^{-28} \text{ cm/g})(5 \text{ g/cm}^3)$$

$$\sim 4 \times 10^{-28} \text{ cm}^{-2} \tag{33}$$

This quantity has a very direct physical significance. It measures the "tide-producing component of the gravitational field" as sensed, for example, in a freely falling elevator or in a space ship in free orbit around the earth [23]. By comparison the quantum fluctuations in the curvature of space are only

$$\Delta R \sim 10^{-33} \text{ cm}^{-2} \tag{34}$$

even in a domain of observation as small as 1 cm in extent. Thus the quantum fluctuations in the geometry of space are completely negligible under everyday circumstances.

Even in atomic and nuclear physics the fluctuations in the metric,

$$\Delta g \sim \frac{10^{-33} \text{ cm}}{10^{-8} \text{ cm}} \sim 10^{-25}$$

and

$$\Delta g \sim \frac{10^{-33} \text{ cm}}{10^{-13} \text{ cm}} \sim 10^{-20} \tag{35}$$

are so small that it is completely in order to idealize the physics as taking place in a flat Lorentzian spacetime manifold.

The quantum fluctuations in the geometry are nevertheless inescapable, if we are to believe the quantum principle and Einstein's theory. They coexist with the geometrodynamical development predicted by classical general relativity. The fluctuations widen the narrow swathe cut through superspace by the classical history of the geometry. In other words, the geometry is not deterministic, even though it looks so at the everyday scale of observation. Instead, at a submicroscopic scale it "resonates" between one configuration and another and another. This terminology means no more and no less than the following: (1) Each configuration $^{(3)}\mathscr{G}$ has its own probability amplitude $\psi = \psi(^{(3)}\mathscr{G})$. (2) These probability amplitudes have comparable magnitudes for a whole range of 3-geometries included within the limits (29) on either side of the classical swathe through superspace. (3) This range of 3-geometries is far too variegated on the submicroscopic scale to fit into any one 4-geometry, or any one classical geometrodynamical history. (4) Only when one overlooks these small-scale fluctuations ($\sim 10^{-33}$ cm) and examines the larger-scale features of the 3-geometries do they appear to fit into a single space-time manifold, such as comports with the classical field equations.

Extrapolate Geometrodynamics to the Planck Scale of Distances?

Is it not preposterous to apply existing theory in a realm of dimensions smaller than nuclear sizes by twenty powers of ten? What a fantastic extrapolation! Yet it is the tradition of theoretical physics to adopt what might be called a "strong bargaining posture." It is not the custom to give up any long-established principle without pushing it to the limit and finding out where, if anywhere, it goes wrong. A direct contradiction between a prediction and an observation, or between two points of principle, is ordinarily necessary if one is to have any solid ground for change, or even any indication where to make a change! The physicist does not have the habit of giving up something unless he gets something better in return.

To pursue systematically the consequences of quantum geometrodynamics is recommended not merely by the absence of any contradiction and by the absence of any more comprehensive theory. It is also made attractive by an example out of the past. Who in the 1850's, measuring the attraction between electric charges and testing the Coulomb law at distances from meters to millimeters, could have predicted that it would be proved valid in 1911 to 10^{-12} cm, in 1933 to 10^{-13} cm, and in 1963 to 10^{-14} cm? The fantastic extrapolatory power of basic physical theory always seems a miracle [24]!

Electrodynamics contains no natural length. Neither do general relativity (G, c) or the quantum principle $(\hbar)$ individually. The union of geometrodynamics and the quantum does: $L^* = (\hbar G/c^3)^{1/2}$. The importance of what is essentially this length was stressed by Planck as early as 1899 [25]. He had taken up the study of blackbody radiation not least because it is universal: independent of the shape and size of the container, independent of the properties of its walls, and independent of the complexities of atomic, molecular, and solid state physics. In keeping with this search for the universal, he asked for standards of length, mass, and time that are independent of such special circumstances as the size of the planet we happen to inhabit, its period of rotation, and the density of the fluid that covers it. In excluding reference to special substances he found it natural also to exclude reference to special particles: both the electron, with its then known mass and charge, and all heavier entities—objects that even today pose unsolved structural problems. Excluding all else, he was left with the speed of light, the Newtonian constant of gravitation, and the constant newly discovered from the analysis of blackbody radiation as the quantities he was willing to accept as truly fundamental. Out of these three quantities there is but one way to construct a length. Planck's length, introduced to science before either special or general relativity, first acquired an understandable role in the context of quantum geometrodynamics as measure of the fluctuations in the geometry of space.

Accept seriously a length as small as 10^{-33} cm? Try to assess in any detail at all the physics that goes on at a scale of distances shorter by twenty powers of ten than the 10^{-13} cm of elementary particle physics? What could be more preposterous? Only three numbers are still more preposterous than 10^{20}: the factor of 10^{40} that distinguishes electric forces from gravitational forces; the 10^{40} from elementary particle dimensions to the estimated radius of the universe at the phase of maximum expansion; and the 10^{80} that furnishes an order of magnitude estimate as good as any that one knows for the number of particles in the universe. Eddington [26], Dirac [27], Jordan [28], Dicke [29], and Hayakawa [30] argue that it is unreasonable to think of such enormous numbers as having independent roles in physics. The correspondence between these numbers cannot be purely accidental, they stress [31]; there could hardly be a "regularity of the large numbers" if there were not a deep connection between cosmology, general relativity, and elementary particle physics. But where to begin in looking for this connection? Begin with asking why there are so and so many particles in the universe? Hardly. Physics can elucidate laws of motion, but it has proved powerless to explain initial conditions. Begin with asking why the universe has such and such dimensions? Again a matter of initial conditions, outside of the present scope of physics. Begin with trying to explain the charge structure of elementary particles, or the characteristic dimension of 10^{-13} cm? More hopeful, perhaps, but still beyond present power. No, of all the quantities coupled by the large numbers, one alone has a clear status within existing theory: the Planck length. Where else than here can one begin?

It could seem plausible to stop considering physics a little below 10^{-13} cm because accelerator budgets stop a little above $100 million a year. What good is it, one sometimes asks, to analyze what goes on if one has no way to observe it? Happily, experience has taught views less biased by mankind's temporary limitations. Wait until one had mastered the work hardening of metals before one took up the microscope and saw dislocations? Wait until one had explained dislocations before one started the study of atoms? Not so. The route to understanding did not go down the ladder, 1 cm $\rightarrow 10^{-4}$ cm $\rightarrow 10^{-8}$ cm, but up: 10^{-8} cm $\rightarrow 10^{-4}$ cm $\rightarrow 1$ cm. One had to understand something about atoms before he could explain dislocations, and something about dislocations before he could uncover the rationale of work hardening. Is it possible that one similarly must have some perspective on what happens at 10^{-33} cm before one can find the rationale of particles and 10^{-13} cm [32]? Right or wrong [33], quantum geometrodynamics alone has any suggestions to offer on this point. What then does it say?

Every new perspective offered by this long established theory radiates out from the central prediction: *geometry fluctuates violently at small distances.* This concept opens new views on the nature of electric charge, on the nature of the vacuum, and on the nature of particles.

ELECTRICITY AS LINES OF FORCE TRAPPED IN THE TOPOLOGY OF SPACE

To arrive at a new vision of electricity it is enough to question an old view of topology: "Space is Euclidean in character at small distances." The view is reasonable enough for everyday purposes. Equally reasonable is the conception of the surface of the ocean as endowed with Euclidean topology— reasonable to one flying miles above it. To one in a small boat the opposite impression is inescapable. He sees the breaking waves and the foam. He knows that the surface is multiply connected at the scale of millimeters and centimeters. If the ocean is violent, the geometry of space on the Planck scale of distances is even more violent. Nowhere is there any region of calm. Moreover, if the equations of hydrodynamics are nonlinear, so are the equations of geometrodynamics. What a contrast to the linearity of electro-dynamics! There the predicted fluctuations in potential

$$\Delta A \sim \frac{(\hbar c)^{1/2}}{L} \tag{36}$$

and in field

$$\Delta F \sim \frac{(\hbar c)^{1/2}}{L^2} \tag{37}$$

preserve always the same character, regardless of the smallness of the distances L to which one goes in his probing. There is no natural magnitude to mark off large fluctuations as different in nature from small ones. The contrary is the case for fluctuations in the metric, governed by the formula

$$\Delta g \sim \frac{L^*}{L} \tag{38}$$

Values of Δg comparable to unity and larger indicate changes in geometry so drastic that the word "curved space" is hardly adequate to describe them. "Changes in topology" seems a more reasonable description.

It is not so natural in mathematics as in physics to consider a transfor-mation that alters one topology to another. An oscillating drop of water undergoes fission. The topology changes. A point marks the place of separation of the two masses of liquid. That point lacks the full neighbor-hood of points that characterizes a normal point. Such a critical point is ruled out from any proper manifold by the very definition of the term "mani-fold" in mathematics. Before the division, the surface of the drop constituted a manifold. After the division, it is again a manifold, consisting of two dis-parate pieces. At the instant of division it is not a manifold. But little

attention does the drop pay to this distinction. It divides, despite all definitions. No more reason does one see in the definition of "manifold" against
space changing *its* topology.

No principle is at hand that would give one topology perpetual preference over all others. On the contrary, the field equations of relativity are
purely local in character. They make no statements at all about global
topology, as Einstein himself emphasized more than once. Moreover, the
whole character of physics speaks for the theme that "everything that can
happen will happen." An alpha particle penetrates through a region classically forbidden to it; the side group on a chain molecule undergoes "hindered
rotation"; and the umbrella structure of an ammonia molecule turns inside
out despite the apparent contradiction to the law of conservation of energy.
It is difficult to resist the conclusion that likewise the topology of space can
change and does change.

If these general considerations are relevant, and if fluctuations alter the
topology of space as well as its curvature [34], the consequences are decisive
for the nature of the physics that goes on at small distances, and even for the
nature of superspace itself. Superspace has to be broadened from the totality
of positive definite 3-geometries built on one topology to the totality of positive definite 3-geometries built on the totality of all topologies. It has new
implications to say that the probability amplitude $\psi(^{(3)}\mathscr{G})$ is appreciable for a
swathe of points in superspace, with a finite spread about the deterministic
history of classical geometrodynamics (Fig. 5): Geometry in the small fluctuates not only from one microscopic pattern of curvature to another, but much
more, from one microscopic topology to another. Moreover, those structures that are everywhere full of submicroscopic "handles" or "wormholes"
are overwhelmingly more numerous than 3-geometries of simpler topology.
In other words, space "resonates" between one foamlike structure and
another [35]. The space of quantum geometrodynamics can be compared to
a carpet of foam spread over a slowly undulating landscape. The undulations
symbolize deterministic classical geometrodynamics. The continual microscopic changes in the carpet of foam as new bubbles appear and old ones disappear symbolize the quantum fluctuations in the geometry. The fluctuations
change the microscopic connectivity of space itself. No longer is one
entitled to take it for granted that space is Euclidean in the small.

Nowhere in physics does the structure of geometry in the small play
a larger part than in electricity. Electric lines of force converge onto a region
of space and none come out of it. Something strange must go on in that
region. Either Maxwell's equations break down, or the region is filled with a
special substance, an electric jelly, a magic fluid beyond further explanation.
From the one picture or the other there has never been an escape. The reason
is simple. The region is tacitly assumed to have Euclidean topology. Give
up this assumption [36], but hold to Maxwell's field equations for empty

space.   Then the conclusion changes.   The region in question must contain the mouth of at least one " handle " or " wormhole " (Fig. 6).   Electric lines of force converge upon this mouth only to emerge from the other mouth, located somewhere else in space.   One comes in this way to a new picture of electricity: *A classical geometrodynamical electric charge is a set of lines of force trapped in the topology of space.*

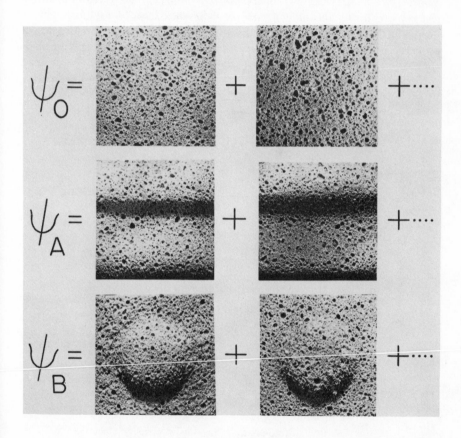

FIGURE 5. Symbolic representations of three alternative probability functions $\psi(^{(3)}\mathcal{G})$.   Above, ψ_0, normal fluctuations alone; middle, ψ_A, macroscopic classical gravitational wave plus superposed fluctuations; below, ψ_B, localized excitation plus superposed fluctuations.   The complex number ψ gives the probability amplitude for the occurrence of the 3-geometry $^{(3)}\mathcal{G}$.   Those 3-geometries that contribute most to the totalized probability are highly multiply connected at the scale of the Planck length ("foamlike structure of space in the small").

Someone can be imagined who first studies topology, next takes to heart Maxwell's equations for empty space, and then for the first time sees an electric charge. He takes it as experimental evidence that space must be multiply connected in the small (Table 2). Nothing prevents us from adopting the same point of view. On this view, *the occurrence of electric charges in nature is the single most impressive piece of evidence available today for the reality of the fluctuations that quantum theory predicts in the geometry of space, and suggests in the topology of space, at the Planck scale of distances.*

The "wormholes" predicted by quantum geometrodynamics are a property of all space, are submicroscopic, and they and the fluxes through

FIGURE 6. Classical geometrodynamical concept of charge as "electric lines of force trapped in the topology of space." The "wormhole" connects two regions in one otherwise nearly Eucildean space, not two different Euclidean spaces. The distance between the two mouths of the wormhole (1) via the nearly Euclidean space and (2) via the route through the wormhole are permitted by Einstein's field equations to be quite different, even in order of magnitude, contrary to what one might assume from the figure. There the geometry (one dimension suppressed!) is depicted for simplicity as if embedded in flat Euclidean 3-space. The third dimension (distance "off" of the geometry) is to be considered as unattainable as the stratosphere is unattainable to an ant crawling on the surface of the earth. An observer endowed with an instrument of inadequate resolving power sees one wormhole mouth as a positive charge, the other as a negative charge. To be contrasted with this classical picture of single indentifiable wormholes in the quantum-mechanical picture (Fig. 4) of a submicroscopic foamlike wormhole structure constantly fluctuating throughout all space.

them arise spontaneously, through quantum fluctuations. Nothing prevents one from considering also a single wormhole, of macroscopic dimensions, created *ab initio*, with a prescribed flux threading through it, and evolving deterministically in time in accordance with the classical field equations. However, this classical electric charge has not the slightest direct connection with the charges of the real world of quantum physics and requires no consideration here.

TABLE 2   *The Concepts of Electric Charge in Quantum and Classical Geometrodynamics, Compared and Contrasted*

Concept	Classical	Quantum
This type of electric charge interpretable as electric lines of force trapped in the topology of space?	Yes	Yes
Any "real" charge considered to be present?	No	No
Nature of topological trap?	Wormhole in 3-geometry	Wormhole in 3-geometry
Where are wormholes located?	Connecting opposite charges	Throughout all space
Dimension of wormhole	Enormous compared to 10^{-33} cm	Comparable to 10^{-33} cm
Status of wormhole?	Classical deterministic development with time; macroscopic size; this size determined by initial conditions; no observational evidence that any such macroscopic wormhole ever occurred, although by definition it is one of the solutions of Einstein's field equations	"Fluctuation"; consequence of fact geometry is not deterministic; that is, a consequence of the non-zero probability that exists for quite diverse 3-geometries; 3-geometries with wormholes almost everywhere (scale of 10^{-33} cm) are the most numerous ("foamlike 3-geometry"); wormholes do not have to be initiated; they occur naturally ("zero-point disturbance of the vacuum") and cannot be avoided

TABLE 2—(*Continued*)

Concept	Classical	Quantum
Wormhole pinches off?	Yes. Throat of radius a undergoes gravitational collapse in time of order a/c (10^{-10} sec for $a = 3$ cm)	Question strictly speaking is undefined; no meaning to deterministic small-scale geometrodynamics in context of quantum geometrodynamics; but in the loose way of speaking that is so useful in certain parts of quantum field theory one can say that "virtual wormholes" are continually being created and annihilated as "space resonates between one foam-like 3-geometry and another"
Charge as identified by flux through wormhole?	Does not change with time; a constant of the motion; not quantized	Flux through any one wormhole, like shape and dimensions of wormhole, subject to quantum-mechanical fluctuations; order of magnitude of this "fluctuation charge," $(\hbar c)^{1/2} \sim 12e$; not "constant" and not "quantized"
Relation of charge on an elementary particle to this kind of geometro-dynamical charge?	Not the slightest direct connection with classical geometrodynamical electric charge	Not the slightest direct connection with the charge on an elementary "fluctuation wormhole." Particle viewed as a quantum state of collective excitation of the entire geometrical continuum ("geometrodynamical exciton"). Charge associated with this exciton to be calculated when one understands how to do the calculation!

THE ENERGY OF THE VACUUM

If one insight out of fluctuations in geometry has to do with the nature of electricity, a second has to do with the energy of the vacuum. Already in quantum electrodynamics one has long known from both observation and theory that when one examines a region of the vacuum of dimension L (1) the fluctuation energy is found to be of the order hc/L, and (2) the effective density of energy of the fluctuation is found to be of the order hc/L^4. Not known out of electrodynamics is any natural lower limit for the L values that come into consideration. In quantum geometrodynamics formulas of the same type hold, but there is now a natural cutoff: the Planck length. It is unreasonable to apply linear theory when L is of the order of $L^* = (\hbar G/c^3)^{1/2} = 1.6 \times 10^{-33}$ or less. In other words, there is a certain sense in which one can say: (1) Elementary fluctuations measure in energy up to hc/L^*. The magnitude of this characteristic mass-energy is $\sim 10^{-5}$ g or $\sim 10^{28}$ eV; that is, about twenty powers of ten greater than the mass of an elementary particle and nine powers of ten greater than the energy of the most energetic cosmic ray that has ever been found. (2) These fluctuations take place throughout all space. (3) The density of the electromagnetic energy associated with these fluctuations [37] is of the characteristic order of magnitude $hc/L^4 = c^5/\hbar G^2 \sim 10^{95}$ g/cm^3, stupendous in comparison with the 10^{14} g/cm^3 of nuclear matter. (4) The effective density of the "gravitational" or geometrodynamical wave energy [38] associated with these fluctuations is of the same order of magnitude.

Every observation shows that the net density of energy in space is negligible by comparison with these huge figures. The enormous positive energy must be compensated in some way. How the compensation comes about was a major concern of Niels Bohr over the years. A new approach to the problem shows up when one considers the fluctuations at the Planck scale of distances. Two such fluctuations, each of mass-energy $\sim (\hbar c/G)^{1/2} \sim 10^{-5}$ g, interacting gravitationally at the distance L^*, have a coupling energy that is negative,

$$E_{\text{grav}} = -\frac{Gm_1 m_2}{r_{12}} \sim -\frac{G\left[\left(\frac{\hbar c}{G}\right)^{1/2}\right]^2}{L^*} \sim -\frac{hc}{L^*} \tag{39}$$

and of the order -10^{-5} g. This coupling between neighboring " fluctuons " thus has such a sign and such a magnitude as to be appropriate for compensating the energies of the individual fluctuons. It would seem surprising if this mechanism did not play a dominant part in bringing about compensation of vacuum energies.

Despite all the mysteries that enshroud the compensation process, one conclusion stands out clear: *Individually the components of the vacuum energy are enormous, and collectively they compensate.*

A PARTICLE AS A GEOMETRODYNAMICAL EXCITON

Quantum fluctuations in geometry offer not only a new picture of electricity and a new view of the violence of the vacuum, but also a third vista: the concept of a particle as a quantum state of excitation of the geometry of space.

A bit of nuclear matter with its density of $\sim 10^{14}$ g/cm^3 is completely unimportant compared to the calculated density of $\sim 10^{95}$ g/cm^3 of the fluctuation energy of the vacuum. A particle means less to the physics of the vacuum than a cloud (10^{-6} g/cm^3) means to the physics of the sky (10^{-3} g/cm^3). No single fact points more powerfully than this to the conclusion that a "particle" is not the right starting point for the description of nature.

From the standpoint of geometrodynamics the primordial entity is not one particle, nor an intercoupled family of particle fields, but the geometry of empty space itself. On this view a particle is not itself a 10^{-33}-cm fluctuation in the geometry; instead, it is a fantastically weak alteration in the pattern of these fluctuations, extending over a zone containing very many such 10^{-33} regions. In brief, a particle is a quantum state of excitation of the geometry; it is a *geometrodynamical exciton.* In mathematical terms, the vacuum is described by one probability amplitude $\psi_0 = \psi_0(^{(3)}\mathscr{G})$; and states where one or more particles are present are described by other functionals $\psi = \psi(^{(3)}\mathscr{G})$.

On this interpretation elementary particle physics ranks as a new and beautiful kind of chemistry. First came the chemistry of atoms and molecules, marvelous in its complexities and also in its regularities, all built on one single simple dynamical entity, the electron. Then came "nuclear chemistry," with nuclear shapes and energies and reaction rates all going back for their explanation to the dynamics of another elementary dynamical entity, the nucleon. Today we deal in effect with a chemistry of the elementary particles themselves. Wonderful advances in the subject classify the particles into families, tie their masses together into mathematical regularities, and systematize their rates of transformation—without, however, revealing the identity of the elementary dynamical entity beneath it all. That entity, on the present view, is geometry itself.

When in the first half of the nineteenth century Berzelius proposed that chemical forces are a manifestation of electrical forces [39], he excited investigations by many workers that eventually discredited his hypothesis. The homopolar bond: how could the observed affinity be reconciled with the known repulsion between like electric charges? Homopolar forces, ionic forces, van der Waals forces, valence forces: how could all this variety of magnitudes and particularities possibly be compatible with electrical forces, pure and simple? The tide against the electrical interpretation of chemical forces only turned with the discovery of the electron by J. J. Thomson in 1897. The dynamical entity once identified, the unraveling of the mystery eventually had to follow. Still it was not easy for the imagination to grasp what organizing power the quantum principle possesses. In encounters in the mid 1920's more than one physicist told his colleague from the laboratory across the way, " Your chemistry is now passé. All that jumble can now be explained in terms of electrons and quantum numbers." In more than one case the then justified reply came back, " What makes you think your circular and elliptic orbits have anything to do with chemistry? Have you ever heard of the valence angles of ammonia or the tetrahedral bonds of carbon? Don't ever forget that electrical forces are electrical forces and chemical forces are chemical forces." The Coulomb law had to be supplemented by the concept of probability amplitude before Heitler and London could explain valence forces. Today no one doubts that the Schroedinger equation accounts in principle for all of chemistry. Yet no surer way could be found to stop the advance of chemistry than to require everyone to calculate the wave function of his new compound before making it. Not the contemplation of 600-dimensional configuration space, but the analysis of the regularities between molecule and molecule, proves to be the fruitful way to make progress. It can hardly be otherwise when the energy of binding is the very small difference between the very much larger total energies of the associated and dissociated states.

In "elementary particle chemistry" the art of analyzing regularities is already highly advanced [40], thanks not least to applications of group theory even more far-reaching than the applications made in the chemistry of molecules. On the other hand, the possibility to derive particle masses from first principles would seem even more remote, from the standpoint of geometrodynamics, than the possibility to calculate the binding energy of a complex molecule from first principles. The energy with which one hopes to end up, 10^{-27} g to 10^{-24} g, is smaller by twenty powers of ten than the characteristic energy of the theory with which one starts. Still it would seem unwise to discount in advance the ingenuity of available methods to calculate reliably small effects against enormously larger backgrounds, as for example in the case of superconductivity [41] ($\sim 10^{-4}$ eV versus ~ 10 eV).

How can the geometrodynamical interpretation of particles (Table 3) be tested? Sooner to be expected than quantitative calculations are qualitative predictions and conceptual developments. Of such developments none gives more incentive than gravitational collapse [18] to believe in a tie between particles and geometry; and none gives more encouragement to believe in the relevance of the Planck length than the concept of charge as electric lines of force trapped in the topology of space.

TABLE 3   *Quantum–Geometrodynamical Interpretation of Particles and Forces*

Ultimate dynamical object	Not an electron or any other kind of particle, but geometry itself
Geometry of space	Not unique and classical, but everywhere resonating at the scale of the Planck length between configurations of varied submicroscopic curvature and varied topology
Topology of space	Those geometries that occur with appreciable probability amplitude are highly multiply connected throughout all space ("foamlike structure")
Particle	Not a foreign and physical entity moving about within the geometry of space, but a quantum state of excitation of that geometry itself; as unimportant for the physics of the vacuum as a cloud is unimportant for the physics of the sky. Not a localized ripple in the geometry, not a submicroscopic "wormhole" in the geometry of space at the Planck scale of distances, but an excitonlike change in the phase relations in the probability amplitude for a very large number of such wormholes
Charge	Not a place where Maxwell's equations fail, not a mysterious "foreign and physical" jelly introduced into geometry from outside, but "lines of electric force trapped in the topology of space" (Table 2 and Problem 2)
Spin	Not a dynamical object added to geometry but the nonclassical two-valuedness associated with geometry itself—because distinct probability amplitudes attach to a multiply connected 3-geometry endowed with alternative triad fields or "spin structure" (Problem 2)
Force	Strong forces, weak forces, and intermediate forces no more distinct in their character than van der Waals forces, ionic forces, and valence forces; not themselves primordial, but the residual effect of percentage-wise negligible changes in the enormous density of the energy of the zero-point fluctuations taking place in the geometry of space at small distances

Widening vistas open out for further investigation [42]. (1) What can one give in the way of simple principles to shortcircuit all the usual derivations of Einstein's field equations and pass in one leap from postulates to the Hamilton–Jacobi equation itself? (2) What deeper insights can one win into the structure of superspace? And (3) at what new point in geometrodynamics does one draw that old line between dynamic law and initial conditions that one sees throughout all of physics?

These issues are the foothills. The mountain looms above them: Is a particle a state of excitation of the geometry of space?

Einstein, above his work and writing, held a long-term vision: There is nothing in the world except curved empty space [43]. Geometry bent one way here describes gravitation. Rippled another way somewhere else it manifests all the qualities of an electromagnetic wave. Excited at still another place, the magic material that is space shows itself as a particle. There is nothing that is foreign and "physical" immersed in space. Everything that is, is constructed out of geometry. This is the dream. Is this dream coming to life?

Note: This article is the revised and extended version of reports made at the Académie Internationale de Philosophie des Sciences, Oberwolfach/ Freiburg im Breisgau, July, 1966; the International School of Nonlinear Mathematics and Physics, Munich, July, 1966; the Society of Engineering Science, Raleigh, North Carolina, October, 1966; the Colloque Internationale sur Fluides et Champ Gravitationel en Relativité Générale, Paris, June, 1967; and the Battelle Rencontres in Mathematics and Physics, Seattle, July, 1967. It appears in the proceedings of the second, third, and fifth organizations in English and in the proceedings of the fourth in French. Appreciation is expressed to the organizers of these conferences for their hospitality and to many colleagues for discussions and advice, among them especially Y. Choquet, Bryce DeWitt, Cecile DeWitt, L. Ehrenpreis, U. Gerlach, H. Leutwyler, C. W. Misner, and M. Stern.

PROBLEM 1. "DERIVATION" OF "EINSTEIN–HAMILTON–JACOBI EQUATION"

If one did not know the Einstein–Hamilton–Jacobi (EHJ) equation (Eq. (12) or (13)), how might one hope to derive it straight off from plausible first principles, without ever going through the formulation of the Einstein field equations themselves? To find one such direct derivation of the EHJ equation would not seem rash to hope for when one already knows five ways to derive the field equations in their traditional form: (1) Einstein's original derivation based upon the correspondence with Newtonian gravitational theory; (2) Weyl's derivation based upon enumeration of all covariant differential operations on the metric tensor that are linear in the second derivatives and that contain no higher derivatives; (3) Hilbert's derivation from a variational principle; (4) Cartan's capture [44] of the geometrical content of the field equations [45]; and (5) the derivation by Gupta, Thirring, and Feynman starting with the theory of a field of spin two and mass zero in flat space.

The central starting point in the proposed derivation would necessarily seem to be "imbeddability." On the basis of experience one can reasonably ask that the desired Hamilton–Jacobi equation, of course combined as always with the conditions of constructive interference, should pick out $^{(3)}\mathscr{G}$'s that will fit together into a $^{(4)}\mathscr{G}$.

In what way would one violate the "condition of imbeddability" if, for example, one left the differential operator unchanged in (13) but replaced the term $^{(3)}R$ by the square or by some other function of this curvature scalar? Without directly answering this question, one can say that the special form of the equation is governed in the most direct possible way by the four-dimensional character of space-time. When geometrodynamics is put into simplest terms, it comes out as the statement

$$(\text{CURVATURE}) = (\text{DENSITY OF MASS-ENERGY})$$

In the present considerations one looks apart from situations where there is any "real" mass-energy present. To write the equation as if there were such a term on the right is, however, a reminder that one is speaking about a tensorial quantity, dependent therefore not only upon one's choice of point, but also upon the choice of direction, or unit 4-vector, at that point. This circumstance illuminates the meaning of the curvature term on the left [44, 45]. It has to do with curvature of the 4-geometry in a tangent plane normal to the 4-vector in question. Good! But we are considering conditions, not merely at one point, but at a threefold infinity of points, that form a spacelike 3-geometry. This 3-geometry is not necessarily "free of extrinsic curvature" (vanishing "tensor K_{ij} of extrinsic curvature" or vanishing "second fundamental form") at the point under study. If it is, excellent! Then the desired curvature is given directly by the scalar curvature invariant $^{(3)}R$ of the geometry intrinsic to $^{(3)}\mathscr{G}$ at the point in question. However, any nonvanishing "extrinsic curvature of the 3-geometry relative to the enveloping 4-geometry" makes an additional contribution to the scalar curvature intrinsic to $^{(3)}\mathscr{G}$. One has to correct for this contribution before one secures a proper measure,

$$(\text{Tr } \mathbf{K})^2 - \text{Tr } \mathbf{K}^2 + {}^{(3)}R$$

of the curvature of the 4-geometry itself in the tangent plane in question (Gauss–Codazzi formula). Why this special bilinear expression in the tensor K_{ij} of extrinsic curvature and not some other one [46]? The rationale shows most directly when one considers the special case where the 4-geometry itself is flat. In this case the "correction terms" in the expression for the desired curvature must exactly compensate $^{(3)}R$. Let the 3-geometry be imbedded in the 4-geometry with "principal radii of curvature" at the point in question equal to ρ_1, ρ_2, and ρ_3. Then the scalar curvature invariant of the intrinsic geometry is $^{(3)}R = -2/\rho_2\rho_3 - 2/\rho_3\rho_1 - 2/\rho_1\rho_2$. The difference in sign here compared to the familiar $^{(3)}R = 6/a^2$ for a 3-sphere of radius a arises from the fact that the "radius of curvature" is being measured in a 4-geometry of signature $-+++$. The tensor of extrinsic curvature is

$$\mathbf{K} = \left\| \begin{array}{ccc} \dfrac{1}{\rho_1} & 0 & 0 \\[2ex] 0 & \dfrac{1}{\rho_2} & 0 \\[2ex] 0 & 0 & \dfrac{1}{\rho_3} \end{array} \right\|$$

It is desired to build up out of this tensor an expression that (1) is bilinear in the reciprocals of the ρ_i; (2) contains no terms in $1/\rho_1{}^2$, etc.; and (3) compensates $^{(3)}R$. These three requirements lead uniquely to the stated formula. The considerations outlined here by no means come close to providing a derivation of the Einstein–Hamilton–Jacobi equation, but they perhaps suggest some of the factors that may play a natural part in such a derivation.

Subscript on Relation of Hamilton–Jacobi Method to Conventional Analytic Solutions of Field Equations

To look toward the Hamilton–Jacobi equation as an illuminating way to found general relativity is not to look away from the field equations as a way to solve problems in general relativity. The Hamilton–Jacobi equation is divorced from the equations of motion no more in geometrodynamics than in particle mechanics. Even in the most elementary problem the connection between the two methods is inescapable. Yes, one can solve Lagrange's equation

$$m \frac{d^2 x}{dt^2} + \frac{\partial V}{\partial x} = 0$$

by direct numerical integration. Yes, one can translate the problem into Hamilton–Jacobi formalism, write down the equation

$$-\frac{\partial S}{\partial t} = \left(\frac{1}{2m} \right) \left(\frac{\partial S}{\partial x} \right)^2 + V(x, t)$$

and integrate *it* by the most elementary numerical methods (replacement of (x, t) continuum by lattice space, $t = m\tau$, $x = n\delta$, with m and n integers; replacement of partial differential equation by difference equation). However, the most penetrating method to integrate the partial differential equation has long been known to go straight back to the Lagrange equation itself for its start.   Not everywhere does one at first evaluate $S(x, t)$, but only along a classical world line or history H,

$$x = x_H(t)$$

$$\dot{x} = \frac{dx_H(t)}{dt}$$

thus

$$s(t) = S(x_H(t), t) = \int_{t_0}^{t} [\tfrac{1}{2}m\dot{x}_H{}^2 - V(x_H(t), t)]\, dt$$

or, in a more general problem, with Lagrange function L,

$$s(t) = S(x_H(t), t) = \int_{t_0}^{t} L(\dot{x}_H, x_H, t)\, dt$$

From a knowledge of S along the world line one goes to a knowledge of S in a narrow band on either side of the world line by using the relations

$$\begin{pmatrix} \text{RATE OF CHANGE} \\ \text{OF ACTION } S \\ \text{WITH POSITION } x \end{pmatrix} = (\text{MOMENTUM}) = \frac{\partial L}{\partial \dot{x}}\, (\text{GENERAL}) = m\dot{x}_H(t)\,(\text{HERE})$$

and

$$-\begin{pmatrix} \text{RATE OF CHANGE OF} \\ \text{ACTION } S \text{ WITH} \\ \text{TIME } t \end{pmatrix} = (\text{ENERGY}) = \dot{x}\frac{\partial L}{\partial \dot{x}} - L\,(\text{GENERAL})$$

$$= \tfrac{1}{2}m\dot{x}_H{}^2 + V(x_H(t), t)\,(\text{HERE})$$

Thus at the point

$$x = x_H(t^*) + \delta x$$

$$t = t^* + \delta t$$

a little way off the world line, the Hamilton–Jacobi function ("classical phase"; h times phase of quantum-mechanical wave function) is

$$S(x, t) = s(t^*) + \left(\frac{\partial S}{\partial x}\right)\delta x + \left(\frac{\partial S}{\partial t}\right)\delta t$$

An identical procedure gives $S_{\text{new}}(x, t)$, a new solution with infinitesimally different initial conditions, throughout a band extending on either side of an infinitesimally different world line, $S_{\text{new}}(x, t)$.   The "condition of constructive interference" between the new "wave" and the old "wave,"

$$S(x, t) = S_{\text{new}}(x, t)$$

gives back at once the original solution of the equation of motion—and all the history H that goes with that solution. So too in geometrodynamics!

One can use a known solution of the Einstein field equations to find the Hamilton–Jacobi function $S(^{(3)}\mathscr{G})$ throughout a certain narrow swathe through superspace. For this purpose one will find it easiest to start with one of the well-known analytic solutions of Einstein's field equations. Let the 4-geometry be written in the form

$$ds^2 = g_{\alpha\beta}\, dx^\alpha\, dx^\beta$$

where the metric coefficients $g_{\alpha\beta}$ are certain known functions of the four coordinates x^μ. The 4-geometry expressed in this way summarizes the dynamical history H of the 3-geometry of space. It also defines a submanifold—call it H—of the superspace $\mathscr{S}$. How now to determine the values taken on by the Hamilton–Jacobi function throughout the submanifold? First define the equivalent of the starting time t_0 in the one-particle problem. This equivalent is not a single number t_0, but in general a different number $t_0(x, y, z)$ for each point in 3-space; or better stated, it is a spacelike initial value hypersurface σ_0 slicing through the given $^{(4)}\mathscr{G}$. Next, give the equivalent of the point $x_H(t_0)$, t_0 along the classical history. It is the "momentary state of the geometry of space" on the hypersurface σ_0; that is, it is the 3-geometry $^{(3)}\mathscr{G}_0$ defined by the metric

$$ds^2(\sigma_0) = \left[g_{00}\left(\frac{\partial x^0}{\partial x^m}\right)\left(\frac{\partial x^0}{\partial x^n}\right) + 2g_{0m}\left(\frac{\partial x^0}{\partial x^n}\right) + g_{mn} \right] dx^m\, dx^n$$

Similarly with the equivalent of the running time t and the state $x_H(t)$ of the particle at this time. Thus, give a spacelike hypersurface σ by giving $t = t(x, y, z)$; and calculate the corresponding metric $ds^2(\sigma)$, which defines a 3-geometry $^{(3)}\mathscr{G}$ "on the classical history H." The value of the classical phase function S on this classical history is given by a fourfold integral. This integral is extended over the region of spacetime bounded by the two hypersurfaces. It has the form

$$s(\sigma) = \int_{\sigma_0}^{\sigma} \mathscr{L}(x^\alpha)\, d^4x$$

Here the Lagrange density $\mathscr{L}$ is given, for example, by Arnowitt, Deser, and Misner ([2]; see also GMD). Consider now a "point" $^{(3)}\mathscr{G}$ in superspace a little ways removed from some "point" $^{(3)}\mathscr{G}^*$ that lies on the classical history H. What is the value of S for this new 3-geometry? The difference between the two 3-geometries is expressed most conveniently for the present expository purpose in terms of the difference of the metric coefficients at corresponding points:

$$\delta g_{mn}(x, y, z) = g_{mn}(x, y, z; \sigma) - g_{mn}(x, y, z; \sigma^*)$$

This difference in 3-geometries has to be multiplied by the value of the conjugate geometrodynamical momentum $\pi^{mn}(x, y, x)$ at the point $^{(3)}\mathcal{G}*$ on the classical history H (details of definition and calculation of π^{mn} given, for example, in GMD) and integrated to give the change in the Hamilton–Jacobi function. Thus, throughout a thin swathe in superspace one can write

$$S(^{(3)}\mathcal{G}) = s(\sigma^*) + \int \pi^{mn}\delta g_{mn}\, d^3x$$

PROBLEM 2. STRUCTURE OF SUPERSPACE

Spacetime is the arena of particle dynamics. Superspace is the arena of geometrodynamics. How different our knowledge of these two arenas! In particle dynamics the structure of spacetime is taken to be given as from on high: an everywhere flat ideal Minkowski–Lorentz manifold. In geometrodynamics the structure of superspace is to be considered as defined entirely internally; that is to say, by the very form of the "Einstein–Schroedinger equation" itself. We write this equation symbolically as

$$-\frac{\nabla^2\psi}{(\delta^{(3)}\mathcal{G})^2} + {}^{(3)}R\psi = 0$$

To ask about the structure of this equation is therefore nothing more or less than to ask, what is the structure of superspace?

It is conceivable that a given geometry may be more appropriately identified with a whole class of points in superspace than with a single point, when that 3-geometry has less than maximal symmetry. In this way, Professor Stephen Smale kindly points out, one may keep from introducing "conical singularities" in superspace. To avoid such singularities would seem to be essential if superspace is to rise from a mere topological manifold to the status of a differentiable manifold.

Quantum theory once known, classical theory follows easily and uniquely, by way of the correspondence principle,

$$\psi \simeq \begin{pmatrix} \text{SLOWLY VARYING} \\ \text{AMPLITUDE FACTOR} \end{pmatrix} \exp\left(\frac{iS}{\hbar}\right)$$

However, classical theory alone being known, it is ordinarily difficult or impossible uniquely to determine the form of the quantum wave equation [47]. No system better illustrates this point than a particle moving in a prescribed external electromagnetic field. To know the Hamilton–Jacobi equation alone

$$g_{\alpha\beta}\left(\frac{\partial S}{\partial x^\alpha} + \frac{eA_\alpha}{c}\right)\left(\frac{\partial S}{\partial x^\beta} + \frac{eA_\beta}{c}\right) + m^2c^2 = 0$$

is to have no way to decide between the Schroedinger–Klein–Gordon equation, the Dirac equation, or one or another wave equation of higher spin; they all reduce to the same Hamilton–Jacobi equation in the appropriate semiclassical limit. Similarly in geometrodynamics. From the well-defined "Einstein–Hamilton–Jacobi" equation (12, 13)

$$\left(\frac{\nabla S}{\delta^{(3)}\mathcal{G}}\right)^2 + {}^{(3)}R = 0$$

no one knows a satisfying way to go to a unique "Einstein–Schroedinger" equation [48].

In the example of the particle most of the ambiguity about the form of the wave equation is resolved as soon as observation or other evidence reveals the spin [49]—or more directly—how many possible orientations there are for any spin degree of freedom over and above the three degrees of freedom that tell location in space. In other words, in addition to the Hamilton–Jacobi equation, one must know the "structure of configuration space" in order to end up with a well-defined wave equation. Hence our question here: What is the structure of superspace?

Unravel the structure of superspace? Hardly all in one jump, and hardly today! Instead a step by step penetration of the issues is more to be anticipated, if the history of electromagnetism or atomic structure or other branches of physics is any guide. At least three levels of analysis are to be perceived. First, one already knows the structure relevant to classical geometrodynamics: (a) Superspace has Hausdorf topology (Stern [4]). (b) Superspace is endowed with an indefinite metric, defined by the expression [50]

$$\left(\frac{1}{2g}\right)(g_{ik}g_{jl} + g_{il}g_{jk} - g_{ij}g_{kl})$$

that occurs in the Hamilton–Jacobi equation (Eq. (12)). Second, one searches for those features in the structure of superspace that come into play when space changes its topology. Third, one hopes in the longer term to uncover those deeper properties of superspace that give ordinary space its dimensionality, its metric structure, and its ability to propagate electromagnetic fields and neutrinos with the speed of light. It is appropriate to discuss the structure of superspace a little further at all three of these levels.

Level 1. Classical Geometrodynamics; Topology Does Not Change

In classical geometrodynamics space does not change its topology. Space may be "preparing" to change its topology, but it cannot actually make the change within the context of classical theory [51]. It can at most signal its "intention" to change topology by developing somewhere a curvature that increases without limit ("gravitational collapse" [18]). To go further with the analysis of the collapse phenomenon and treat changes in topology forces one to go outside the framework of classical theory. So long as one stays inside classical theory, he must restrict his attention in one dynamical problem to one topology. Which topologies are acceptable?

Of all topologies none is more familiar than that associated in Einstein's theory with the geometry in and around a dilute center of attraction such as the sun. Curved at small distances, the geometry becomes asymptotically flat at large distances. The topology, as distinguished from the geometry, is Euclidean: E_3 or $R \times R \times R$. In a broader context, however, Einstein thought of the space around one star as part of the space engulfing all stars [52], and of this total space as closed and endowed with the topology of the 3-sphere, S_3. No one has stated more strongly than he the arguments for considering space to be closed [53].

One acquires a new reason to consider space to be closed when he considers how hard it is to define "an open and asymptotically flat space" in the context of quantum geometrodynamics: Those $^{(3)}\mathcal{G}$'s that occur with overwhelming probability are everywhere endowed with all kinds of ripples and other geometrical structures at the scale of the Planck length. There is no direction that one can take and there is no distance that one can travel that will erase this structure. Under these circumstances it is difficult to attribute any well-defined meaning whatsoever to the term "asymptotically flat." On the other hand, one knows more than one example of a space that is open and *not* asymptotically flat, and that becomes wilder and wilder at great distances [54]. Not having any means to distinguish one open space from another as "good," one would seem justified at this stage in the development of the subject to exclude from attention all open spaces. This approach is the more attractive in that it appears possible [55] to distinguish between one type of closed 3-geometry and another by straightforward classificatory integers similar to the Betti numbers. In contrast, the concept of "asymptotically flat"—even in contexts where it is relevant—is much more complex to formulate [56].

Out of a manifold with the topology E_3 it is possible to cut out a block with the shape of a cube and obtain the topology of the 3-torus, $S_1 \times S_1 \times S_1$. On a manifold with this topology the initial value problem of classical geometrodynamics presents difficulties in certain cases, according to unpublished considerations of Brill and Avez. It is conceivable that these difficulties indicate that the topology $S_1 \times S_1 \times S_1$ is not acceptable. In that event one might almost say that this topology has inherited a "defective gene" from its parent topology E_3.

Another "black gene" that one can perhaps reasonably exclude is non-orientability. We assume in effect that "transport" of a right-handed glove shall never bring it back to its starting point left handed.

Compatible with these very tentative principles for selecting "acceptable topologies" are the 3-sphere (S_3); the 3-sphere with addition of one handle or "wormhole" ($S_2 \times S_1 = W_1$); and the 3-sphere with n wormholes (W_n). There may or may not be further acceptable topologies not included in this list [55].

Fixed Topology Excludes GMD Account of Particles and Fields

Taking the most familiar of these "acceptable topologies," S_3, as case example, one can discuss and treat quantitatively at the classical level a rich variety of physical processes, including gravitational radiation [38]; gravitational geons [20]; the planetary motion, collisions, and breakup of geons [20]; the Taub model of an expanding and recontracting universe [57]; and more complex model universes [38]. Even so, one is limited in the physics that he can include in any of these models. One has no place for particles. Nor can one treat classically the final stages of gravitational collapse. These limitations seem unrelated to each other. In classical theory they are unrelated. In that view, the geometry of space remains forever tied to a unique topology. Not so in the purely quantum-geometrodynamical model of physics. There (1) a particle is pictured in terms of space resonating from one topology to another [58]; and there (2) the final stages of gravitational collapse are viewed as a coupling of macroscopic motion and microscopic topology ("waterfall and foam"). In excluding from consideration all changes in topology, classical theory, on these views, also excludes any account of the rationale of particles. Particles have to be introduced as foreign and physical entities and space has to be viewed as arena, not as structural material. In this limited conceptual framework the particles and other fields are counted as having degrees of freedom over and above those of the geometry. The electromagnetic field, in particular, is viewed as an entity additional to geometry.

Attempts have been made to regard electromagnetism as an aspect of geometry. This enterprise limits itself to that classical framework of ideas where one looks apart from submicroscopic fluctuations in the geometry and the topology of space. One attempt has had some minor success. The second-order equations of Maxwell and the second-order equations of Einstein have been combined into one set of equations of the fourth order that make no reference to any but geometric magnitudes [59]. The Maxwell field is recognized by the "footprints" it leaves on the geometry of space. In a certain sense those "footprints" *are* the electromagnetic field; hence the name, "already unified theory" of gravitation and electromagnetism. Faithfully though this theory reproduces in other respects the dynamic content of the equations of Maxwell and Einstein, it turns out not to be adapted to treat the initial value problem. Geometrical measurements alone on an initial spacelike hypersurface do not always suffice completely to determine the future time evolution of the geometry [60]. In other words, one cannot uphold in "already unified field theory" a strict division of dynamics into "equations of motion" and "initial value data for these equations." Yet on that division one had learned to insist, not least by reason of hard-won lessons from the Hamilton–Jacobi theory and from quantum theory. Therefore the electromagnetic field, like a particle, can hardly be treated as anything but a foreign or "physical" entity immersed in space so long as one looks away from the microscopic geometry of space.

Formalism of Field When Treated as "Foreign and Physical"

In this nongeometric or "arena" approach to physics one considers the degrees of freedom of the "foreign and physical" entity as additional to those of the geometry. In the most elementary example, the case where only one such entity is contemplated, the pure source-free electromagnetic field, one writes the Hamilton–Jacobi function or the Schroedinger probability amplitude, as the case may be, in the form

$$S = S(g_{ik}(x, y, z), A_m(x, y, z))$$

or

$$\psi = \psi(g_{ik}, A_m)$$

Similarly when more fields are involved. Even at this level of analysis the geometrical approach has a contribution to make. The Hamilton–Jacobi function, ostensibly dependent upon the individual components of the metric and of the electromagnetic vector potential, actually has to be understood to depend only on the 3-geometry $^{(3)}\mathcal{G}$ and on the 2-form $\mathbf{B} = \mathbf{dA}$. Consequently it cannot change S to "push the rubber sheet on which the coordinates are painted" over space in such a way that the point P, which formerly had the coordinates x^i, now acquires the coordinates $x^i - \xi^i$. Similarly the point $P + dP$, which formerly had the coordinates $x^i + dx^i$, now acquires the coordinates

$$x^i + dx^i - \xi^i - \left(\frac{\partial \xi^i}{\partial x^j}\right) dx^j$$

The separation between the two points of course remains unchanged by this alteration in coordinates:

$$ds^2 = g_{ij}(x^s) \, dx^i \, dx^j$$
$$= g_{ij}^{\text{new}}(x^s - \xi^s)(dx^i - \xi^i_{,m} \, dx^m)(dx^j - \xi^j_{,n} \, dx^n)$$

To terms of the first order in the displacement ξ^s the alteration in the metric coefficients is

$$\delta g_{ij} = g_{ij}^{new} - g_{ij} = \left(\frac{\partial g_{ij}}{\partial x^s}\right)\xi^s + \xi_{i,j} + \xi_{j,i} = \xi_{i\,|\,j} + \xi_{j\,|\,i}$$

where the subscript $|\,j$ denotes covariant differentiation, in the space of the 3-geometry, with respect to the jth coordinate. In a similar way one finds the alteration in the electromagnetic vector potential,

$$\delta A_i = A_i^{new} - A_i = A_{i,s}\xi^s + A_j\xi^j_{,i}$$

These changes in the metric coefficients, taking place throughout all space, ostensibly produce a change in the Hamilton–Jacobi function determined by the functional derivatives of S; thus,

$$\delta S = \int\left[\left(\frac{\delta S}{\delta g_{ij}}\right)\delta g_{ij} + \left(\frac{\delta S}{\delta A_i}\right)\delta A_i\right]d^3x$$

However, the mere shift in coordinates cannot produce any real physical change. Consequently the quantity δS must vanish, independent of the choice of the coordinate displacements ξ^i. The consequences of this coordinate invariance are easily traced out. The functional derivatives that come into consideration have well-defined physical interpretations. Thus

$$\pi^{ij} = \frac{\delta S}{\delta g_{ij}}$$

is the geometrodynamical momentum [2, 3] conjugate to the geometrodynamical field coordinate g_{ij}. It is closely connected with the "extrinsic curvature" K^{ij} of the 3-geometry with respect to the yet-to-be constructed 4-manifold. The other derivative,

$$\mathfrak{E}^i = \frac{\delta S}{\delta A_i}$$

the electrodynamic momentum conjugate to the vector potential A_i, is nothing other than the electric field. This quantity satisfies the divergence condition [61]

$$\mathfrak{E}^i_{,i} = 0$$

The condition that S be invariant with respect to coordinate changes takes the form

$$0 = \delta S = \int[\pi^{ij}(\xi_{i\,|\,j} + \xi_{j\,|\,i}) + \mathfrak{E}^i(A_{i,j}\xi^j + A_j\xi^j_{,i})]\,d^3x$$

Integrating by parts, readjusting the positions of indices as appropriate, and making use of the divergence relation, one finds

$$0 = \int[-2\pi^{\,|s}_{js} + \mathfrak{E}^i(A_{i,j} - A_{j,i})]\xi^j\,d^3x$$

This must vanish for arbitrary choices of the field of coordinate displacements ξ^j. Consequently the quantity in square brackets must vanish. One finds in this way those three of Einstein's field equations that link the curvature of space with the Poynting density of flow of electromagnetic field energy [62]:

$$2\pi_{js}^{|s} = (\mathfrak{E} \times \mathbf{B})_j$$

How remarkable that one gets so much—including the Poynting vector itself—from the elementary condition that S should depend, not upon the components g_{ij} and A_i individually, but only upon the coordinate-independent geometrical quantities that are "dressed up" in these components [63]!

Express electrodynamics in geometric language, yes. See the footprints of the electromagnetic field on the geometry of space, yes. Conceive of classical geometrodynamical electric charge as lines of force trapped in the topology of space, yes. But explain geometrically the "necessity" for electromagnetism and other "physical" entities, no. Not within the context of classical geometrodynamics and its never-changing topology.

Level 2. Space Resonating between 3-Geometries of Varied Topology

A new world opens out for analysis in quantum geometrodynamics. The central new concept is space resonating between one foamlike structure and another. For this multiple connectedness of space at submicroscopic distances no single feature of nature speaks more powerfully than electric charge. Yet at least as impressive as charge is the prevalence of spin $\frac{1}{2}$ throughout the world of elementary particle physics. "It is impossible to accept any description of elementary particles that does not have a place for spin $\frac{1}{2}$." This quotation from the book *Geometrodynamics* [64] of 1962 goes on to say, "What then has any purely geometrical description to offer in explanation of spin $\frac{1}{2}$ in general? More particularly and more importantly, what possible place is there in quantum geometrodynamics for the neutrino—the only entity of half integral spin which is a pure field in its own right, in the sense that it has zero rest mass and moves with the speed of light? No clear or satisfactory answer is known to this question today. Unless and until an answer is forthcoming, *pure quantum geometrodynamics must be judged deficient as a basis for elementary particle physics.*" Happily the concept of spin manifold [65] has subsequently come to light, not least through the work of John Milnor. This concept suggests a new and interesting *interpretation of a spinor field* within the context of the resonating microtopology of quantum geometrodynamics, *as the nonclassical two-valuedness that attaches to the probability amplitude for otherwise identical 3-geometries endowed with alternative "spin structures."*

The Orientation Entanglement Relation or "Version"

Spin and topology: what is the connection? Take a cube (Fig. 7). To its upper northeast corner attach one end of a long elastic string. Run the other end to the upper northeast corner of the room and fasten it there. With seven other elastic strings attach the other corners of the cube to the corresponding corners of the room. Now select any axis running through the center of the cube and rotate the figure about that axis through 360°. The cube resumes its original configuration. Not so the strings. They are in a

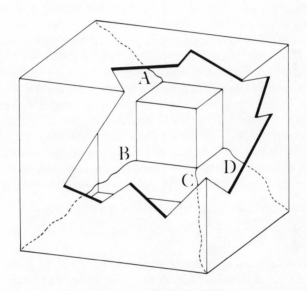

FIGURE 7. The elastic strings attached to the central cube keep account of its orientation entanglement relation with its surroundings.

tangle. Moreover, rejecting cuts, one has no way to untangle the strings. Consequently it needs more than orientation to tell the relation between the cube and its surroundings. The necessary bookkeeping is provided by a spinor,

$$s = \begin{pmatrix} \xi \\ \eta \end{pmatrix}$$

Under a rotation through the angle θ about an axis making angles α, β, γ with the x, y, and z axes this spinor is transformed to the new spinor $s' = \mathbf{q}s$. Here the quaternion or "versor" **q** has a value indicated in various ways in various well-known systems of nomenclature:

$$\mathbf{q} = \cos \tfrac{1}{2} \theta + \sin \tfrac{1}{2} \theta (\mathbf{i} \cos \alpha + \mathbf{j} \cos \beta + \mathbf{k} \cos \gamma)$$

$$\text{(with } \mathbf{ij} = -\mathbf{ji} = \mathbf{k}, \text{ etc.)}$$

$$= \cos \tfrac{1}{2} \theta - i \sin \tfrac{1}{2} \theta (\sigma_x \cos \alpha + \sigma_y \cos \beta + \sigma_z \cos \gamma)$$

$$\text{(with } i = (-1)^{1/2} \text{ and } \sigma_x \sigma_y = -\sigma_y \sigma_x = i\sigma_z, \text{ etc.)}$$

$$= \left\| \begin{array}{cc} (\cos \tfrac{1}{2} \theta + i \sin \tfrac{1}{2} \theta \cos \gamma) & \sin \tfrac{1}{2} \theta (\cos \beta - i \cos \alpha) \\ \sin \tfrac{1}{2} \theta (-\cos \beta - i \cos \alpha) & (\cos \tfrac{1}{2} \theta - i \sin \tfrac{1}{2} \theta \cos \gamma) \end{array} \right\|$$

The important point is the change of sign under a 360° rotation: $\mathbf{q}(360°) \cdot s = -s$. The 360° rotation alters what one may most appropriately call the "orientation entanglement relation" between the cube and its surroundings—or, more briefly, the "version" of the cube. The spinor keeps account of this orientation entanglement relation. Two successive rotations by 360° restore the cube to its original orientation entanglement relation with its surroundings. The strings at first appear to be tangled up with twice the twist they had before. Nevertheless, they can now be untangled completely, as one confirms by direct trial or by elementary reasoning [66, 67].

Arbitrarily pick out one way of placing the cube, call it the "standard orientation entanglement relation" between the cube and its surroundings, or the standard "version" of the cube, and associate with it the spinor $\begin{pmatrix} 0 \\ 1 \end{pmatrix}$. Proceed similarly at other points of space, taking care only that any changes in the standard version from point to point shall take place smoothly.

A special situation develops when an orientable 3-geometry [68] is endowed with a handle or wormhole. The cube can be transported in imagination from A to B "through the surrounding nearby space" or "through the wormhole." With one cube possessing a certain pattern of colored faces follow one route and with another identically colored cube follow the other route. It makes physical sense to ask if the two cubes have at B identical orientation entanglement relations to their surroundings [67]. If they do not, alter the definition of the standard orientation within the wormhole by a rotation. Let this rotation increase continuously from zero at the mouth of the handle near A to 360° at the mouth near B. At each point outside the wormhole a triad of axes a, b, c defines the direction of the axes of the cube when the cube is located at that point in its standard orientation. These triads are not affected by the alterations made inside the wormhole. They vary in direction as smoothly as ever from point to point. At the two mouths of the wormhole they join on as smoothly to the new field of triads inside as they did to the old field of triads. Now, however, one has at last achieved an everywhere continuous field of standard orientation entangle-ment relations. The associated spinor field is likewise continuous, having everywhere the standard value $\begin{pmatrix} 0 \\ 1 \end{pmatrix}$, whereas before it underwent somewhere a discontinuous change from this value to its negative. One can restate in mathematical language what has been accomplished. First, one has laid down a "spin structure" upon the manifold. This structure is defined by the field of triads, or by "the class of such fields that are equivalent under homotopy." Second, one has laid down a "spinor field" upon the manifold. This spinor field is defined with respect to the given "spin structure." Other spinor fields can of course be laid down, with components also varying con-tinuously from place to place.

Alternative Spin Structures in a Multiply Connected Space

Start again with another closed orientable 3-manifold endowed with the original topology and metric. One might hope to obtain an acceptable spin structure on this new manifold by taking over to it the identical field of triads that serves for the original manifold. It may be that this supposition is correct about the particular new manifold that one happens to have picked out. In this event identical colored cubes "taken from A to B by inequivalent routes" will preserve their orientation entanglement relation, one to the other. However, the supposition can equally well be incorrect. If so, the consequences are direct. The two cubes, carried by different routes from A to B, always in alignment with the canonical field of triads, will end up at B inequivalent to the extent of a 360° rotation. Moreover, this inequivalence in the orientation entanglement relation with the surroundings can be detected in principle by direct physical measurement [67]. In other words, the spin structure of the original manifold does not apply to the new manifold. To serve in the new manifold, the field of triads has to be modified to the extent of a 360° rotation within the wormhole or by an equivalent change. The dif-ference between the new manifold and the original manifold expresses itself in these terms: the two manifolds have the same topology and metric, but they have inequivalent spin structures. *The difference between the two manifolds is not only mathematical. It is physical.*

The Multisheeted Character of Superspace

One does not classify the closed orientable 3-manifold of physics com-pletely when he gives its topology, its differential structure, and its metric. He must tell in addition which spin structure it has. The spin structure, like the metric, lends itself in principle to observation. Consequently it is not enough for the purposes of quantum geometrodynamics to give the probability

amplitude for a "3-geometry" as the term 3-geometry was previously understood. One must introduce a new two-valued descriptor, w_k, for each ($k = 1$,
$2, \ldots, n$) of the n wormholes of the manifold, to distinguish the two inequivalent ways to lay down a spin structure in the interior of that wormhole. The
new, enlarged concept of a 3-geometry $^{(3)}\mathcal{G}$ adjoins these descriptors to the
continuous infinity of parameters which alone served previously to distinguish
one 3-geometry, $^{(3)}\mathcal{G}^{\text{old}}$, from another; thus,

$$^{(3)}\mathcal{G} = (^{(3)}\mathcal{G}^{\text{old}}; w_1, w_2, \ldots, w_n)$$

and

$$\psi(^{(3)}\mathcal{G}) = \psi(^{(3)}\mathcal{G}^{\text{old}}; w_1, w_2, \ldots, w_n)$$

In other words, *superspace acquires a multisheeted character* (Fig. 8) with 2^n
distinct sheets in that region of superspace where the 3-geometry is endowed
with n wormholes.

For the two values to be assigned to the descriptor w_n it is natural to pick
$+1$ and -1. However, there is nothing anomalous about the one spin
structure as compared to the other. No canonical way has ever been proposed to give preference to one as compared to the other. Therefore it is a
matter of arbitrary choice to which spin structure to assign the descriptor $+1$,
and to which, -1.

The words "spin structure" can mislead. They suggest that there is
something special about "laying down a spinor field" upon the manifold.
They conjure up visions of laying down upon the 3-geometry other kinds of
fields that transform according to groups other than the spinor group $SU(2)$;
for example, $SU(n)$ or $SL(n)$. However, the relevant point in the whole
analysis is not the field of spinors, but the field of triads and their orientation
entanglement relations. There is nothing in the concept of spin structure that
one could not have conveyed, with less chance of being misunderstood, by
using the phrase "triad structure." Moreover, there is not the slightest
indication that there is any other structure of a closed orientable 3-manifold
that remains to be brought to light. Consequently we take $^{(3)}\mathcal{G}$ in its new and
enlarged sense to be the full indicator of the configuration of space, and as
containing the full set of variables upon which ψ depends. In other words,
we take the new $^{(3)}\mathcal{G}$ to comprise a set of commuting observables, *complete* in
the sense of quantum mechanics, and therefore suitable for analysis of the
probability amplitude ψ.

We do not add a spinor field to geometry. Quite the contrary. We
take a spinor field away from geometry. A 3-geometry, augmented by a
spin structure (as might for example be indicated by the descriptor
$(w_1, w_2, \ldots, w_5) = (+1, +1, +1, -1, +1))$ is a possible habitation for a
spinor field—but we have thrown out the inhabitant [69].

Spin $\frac{1}{2}$, if it occurs naturally in the context of quantum geometrodynamics, can hardly occur in any other sense than that in which Pauli spoke of

FIGURE 8. The multisheeted character of superspace.

spin from the very beginning, as a "nonclassical two-valuedness." Moreover, a nonclassical two-valuedness is already inescapable in the formalism. There are separate probability amplitudes for a 3-geometry with descriptor $w_k = +1$ and for an otherwise identical 3-geometry with descriptor $w_k = -1$. Does this circumstance imply that quantum geometrodynamics supplies all the machinery one needs to describe fields of spin $\frac{1}{2}$ in general and the neutrino field in particular? That is the proposal. That is the only way that has ever turned up within the framework of Einstein's general relativity and Planck's quantum principle to account for spin. Is this the right path? It is difficult to name any question more decisive than this in one's assessment of "everything as geometry."

Electromagnetism as a Statistical Aspect of Geometry?
Other Questions

It would be tempting to stop with this major issue if it did not open the door to so many tributary questions. (1) When a new handle develops and the number of descriptors rises by one, what boundary condition in superspace connects the probability amplitude ψ for 3-geometries of the original topology with the probability amplitudes ψ_+ and ψ_- for the two spin structures of the new topology? (2) One may wish to describe for each newly developing wormhole something like "the fractional amplitude going from ψ into ψ_+." However, with the fantastic number of wormholes that typically come into consideration ($\sim 10^{99}/\mathrm{cm}^3$) any such individual bookkeeping would seem for many purposes to be out of the question. It is equally impractical to keep account of the orientation of each of the $\sim 10^{23}$ spins in a ferromagnet. It is much more appropriate to speak of the "density of magnetization" and of perturbations in that density carried by "magnons" [71]. What are the analogous quantities and concepts in geometrodynamics? What statistical approach is best suited to keep account of the many "matching ratios" ψ_+/ψ associated with all the nascent wormholes in the geometry? (3) One speaks of "magnetization," knowing well that the term "magnetization" has not the slightest real meaning at subatomic distances. Is the term "electromagnetic field" equally without submicroscopic physical significance? In other words, among the statistical parameters most appropriate for keeping account of the 10^{99} "matching ratios" per cubic centimeter, *is there one set of statistical parameters that one can identify with the electromagnetic field?*

The Example of Two-Geometries

No one can ask about the physics of changes in the topology of 3-space without at least a look at the mathematics of changes in the topology of 2-space. The superspace built on all 3-geometries is like no mathematical object so much as the superspace "built on all 2-geometries." No one did so much to bring this mathematical object to light as Riemann, the same Bernhard Riemann who taught that the curvature of space is a branch of physics, and who provided the mathematical machinery to describe not only curvature (the Riemann curvature tensor, $R_{\alpha\beta\gamma\delta}$) but also topology (the Betti numbers R_n).

In his 1857 paper Riemann noted that all algebraic 2-geometries endowed with the topology of a 2-sphere are equivalent to each other under conformal transformation (multiplication of all three metric coefficients by a common position-dependent factor λ). In other words the equivalence class of conformally equivalent 2-geometries of the given topology (S_2; or "genus $g = 0$") consists of a single object. It therefore constitutes a single "point" in what is not really a superspace itself, as we have been using that term, but a "reduced superspace": reduced in the sense that the "$(\infty^2)^\infty$" degrees of freedom in λ have here been "strained out" of superspace.

Two-geometries with the topology of the torus (T_2; or one wormhole W_1; or "genus $g = 1$"), Riemann showed, are not all equivalent to one another under conformal transformation. Instead, when conformally equivalent 2-geometries of the topology T_2 are identified, the family of objects that results is a complex continuum of dimension 1 (two real dimensions) [72]. Two-geometries endowed with a larger number of wormholes (topology W_g; genus $g \geqslant 2$), after extraction of the conformal degrees of freedom, reduce to a family of objects described by $3g - 3$ complex parameters ($6g - 6$ real parameters). "Reduced superspace," built on the totality of conformally equivalent closed orientable 2-geometries of all topologies, thus appears to consist of a series of disjoint spaces, the first of dimension 0, the second of dimension 1, the next of dimension 3, the next of dimension 6, and so on. However, great developments in the analysis have taken place since the days of Riemann through the efforts of many investigators [73]. Today, thanks not least to the works of Lipman Bers, one knows how to define one single infinite-dimensional reduced superspace in which all these apparently disparate parts fit smoothly together [74]. What a model for the mathematical treatment of the superspace of general relativity! Yet, at the risk of seeming overdemanding, one has to ask for more. The superspace of physics is not to have any "conformal factor strained out of it"; rather, it is if anything to be enlarged, so as to include all the descriptors w_k of the spin structure. How fit all the pieces of *this* superspace smoothly together? Challenging problem, at the very heart of quantum geometrodynamics!

Other Aspects of Superspace

Why all this emphasis on the structure of superspace? Why not simply spell out explicitly the form of the "Einstein–Schroedinger equation"? For the more elementary problem of a particle moving in flat 3-space it was straightforward for Schroedinger to derive his wave equation. Simple considerations of invariance with respect to translation and rotation show that ∇^2 is the only simple differential operator that can come into play. That clear, the principle of correspondence with classical physics gives all the rest. One can hope that equally compelling considerations will fix the detailed mathematical form of the expression that we write down so far only symbolically,

$$\frac{\nabla^2 \psi}{(\delta^{(3)}\mathcal{G})^2}$$

However, a precise formulation of such considerations would seem to be out of reach until one has a knowledge of the tranformations of superspace comparable to one's knowledge of the transformations of 3-space. Hence the emphasis on the structure of superspace.

A problem of such depth can hardly be examined from too many points of view. Six more aspects of superspace seem worthy of mention. One can summarize them under the names "metric," "residual causality,"

"initial value," "conjugate momentum," "collapse," and "pregeometry."
(1) There could hardly be a more helpful guide to the structure of superspace
than the metric that obtains in it,

$$\left(\frac{1}{2g}\right)(g_{ik}g_{jl} + g_{il}g_{jk} - g_{ij}g_{kl})$$

Reference is made to [2] for the most illuminating discussion of this metric
given to date. (2) This metric has a "light cone" associated with it. This
light cone makes propagation proceed anisotropically in superspace. This
anisotropy differs in character, however, from place to place according as
$^{(3)}R$ is positive or negative. This anisotropy imposes a kind of "residual
causality" upon superspace. Charles W. Misner has pointed out in a conversation that one cannot forget this residual causality when one says that the
customary ideas of "before" and "after" lose their meaning at the scale of
the Planck length. Perhaps one can say more: If the principle of causality
has been of service in analyzing the structure of flat spacetime, it can hardly
fail to help in studying the structure of superspace.

*Tangent Vectors on Superspace and the Classical Initial Value
Problem*

(3) In the classical mechanics of a particle one is accustomed to specifying freely x_0 and $(dx/dt)_0$. These initial conditions determine the whole
future history of the particle. What are the analogous freely disposable
initial value data of classical geometrodynamics? One is tempted to say:
conceive of a continuous one-parameter family of 3-geometries, specified for
example in one coordinate patch by the 6 metric coefficients $g_{ik}(x, y, z; \lambda)$; and
use this one-parameter family to define data analogous to x_0 and $(dx/dt)_0$ in
the one-particle problem; thus, $^{(3)}\mathscr{G}_0$ stands for the class of metrics equivalent
to $g_{ik}(x, y, z; 0)$; and $(d^{(3)}\mathscr{G}/d\lambda)_0$ is the "tangent vector in superspace"
defined by $[\partial g_{ik}(x, y, z, \lambda)/\partial \lambda]_{\lambda=0}$, modulo the group of coordinate transformations.

It is easy for a mere coordinate shift to mock up the appearance of a
change in geometry. Let the coordinates be shifted so that the point P, formerly characterized by the coordinates x^i, is now characterized by $x^i - \lambda\xi^i$,
with the vector field ξ^i a continuous function of position. The metric g_{ik}
is altered by this shift to

$$g_{ik} + \lambda(\xi_{i\,|\,k} + \xi_{k\,|\,i})$$

The derivative $(d^{(3)}\mathscr{G}/d\lambda)_0$ is $\xi_{i\,|\,k} + \xi_{k\,|\,i}$, modulo the group of coordinate
transformations. But this quantity, by reason of its very origin, is obviously
annullable by a coordinate transformation. Consequently there is in this

case no real change in the geometry. In other words, one cannot admit any otherwise reasonable-looking field of values for $(\partial g_{ik}/\partial \lambda)_0$ without running the risk of deception. One wants what has been called in [2] (GMD & IFS) a 3-geometry (of "acceptable" topology) and another "nearby" 3-geometry in order—one trusts (central hypothesis of the subject!)—to be able to determine the entire past and future of the space, and thereby a complete 4-geometry. But if one has been "deceived" in describing what is ostensibly a second and "nearby" 3-geometry, he may merely be repeating all over again the previously given 3-geometry. In that event he has only half the amount of initial value data needed to predict the dynamics. One can restate the situation in the following terms in the context of the 4-geometry (regarded temporarily as known!). A spacelike slice is made through the 4-geometry. That gives the one 3-geometry demanded as one of the essential ingredients of the initial value data. However, that one slice is not adequate to distinguish the given 4-geometry from any number of other, different 4-geometries that admit as slice the same 3-geometry. To complete the selection of the given 4-geometry from these alternative 4-geometries, erect vectors λn^{α} at each of the points of the 3-geometry, with n^{α} a continuous function of position. Their tips define a new hypersurface, the coordinates in which are connected continuously with the coordinates in the original hypersurface. Evaluate the metric coefficients $g_{ik}(x, y, z, \lambda)$ on this hypersurface. This hypersurface can be said to have been "pushed forward" with respect to the original hypersurface. But has it? Yes, if the normal component of λn^{α} nowhere vanishes. However, Hans Ohanian and Elliot Belasco have emphasized in unpublished remarks that it may happen that there are whole regions of the hypersurface where the normal component of λn^{α} vanishes. In that case one has not really pushed the hypersurface ahead at all in $^{(4)}\mathcal{G}$. In this event the second component of the initial value data, the derivatives $(\partial g_{ik}/\partial \lambda)_0$, will simply be inadequate for the purposes of the elliptic initial value equations [75]. This situation will be signaled by the fact that $(\partial g_{ik}/\partial \lambda)_0$ can be written in the form $\xi_{i\,|\,k} + \xi_{k\,|\,i}$. In other regions the 3-geometry *will* have been pushed forward in time. This situation will be signaled, except in special circumstances (time-symmetric initial value problem; change in g_{ik} proportional to λ^2 rather than λ; situation covered by appropriate care in the formulation), by the fact that $(\partial g_{ik}/\partial \lambda)_0$ (or $(\partial g_{ik}/\partial \lambda^2)_0$ in special cases like the time-symmetric initial value problem) is *not* representable in the form $\xi_{i\,|\,k} + \xi_{k\,|\,i}$.

It is natural to try to summarize the whole situation in the following form. *Give a point in superspace and give a "fully developed direction" at this point in superspace. Then (hypothesis!) this information is sufficient, together with Einstein's equations, uniquely to determine the entire 4-geometry.* Here the term "point in superspace" implies, as earlier, the demand that the 3-geometry in question have acceptable topology. The term "fully developed direction" implies that there is no point on the 3-geometry where the quantity

$(\partial g_{ik}/\partial \lambda)_0$ (or if it vanishes, the quantity $(\partial g_{ik}/\partial \lambda^2)_0$) can be expressed in the form $\xi_{i\,|\,k} + \xi_{k\,|\,i}$. In brief, does superspace provide a new approach to the classical initial value problem? And in turn, does that initial value problem throw new light on the concept of "direction" in superspace?

(4) Superspace is built on the concept of 3-geometry; but dynamically conjugate to 3-geometry is the geometrodynamical momentum, with components π_{ij}. Out of these objects, with all the varied topologies that *they* can have, one can build a "conjugate superspace." What are *its* properties?

(5) No crisis stands out more insistently in all of physics than gravitational collapse. No topic connects so immediately the world of the very large and the very small. What insights can one gain from the concept of superspace into the cause and consequences of gravitational collapse?

(6) How far can one go in analyzing the properties of superspace without getting into the problems of "pregeometry"?

Level 3. Pregeometry

Weyl remarks [76] "... a more detailed scrutiny of a surface might disclose that, what we had considered an elementary piece, in reality has tiny handles attached to it which change the connectivity character of the piece, and that a microscope of even greater magnification would reveal ever new topological complications of this type, *ad infinitum.*" Under such circumstances it would seem difficult to uphold the concept of dimensionality at the smallest distances. General arguments [77] emphasize the same point. Moreover, if electromagnetism and other fields have to do with the quantum-mechanical resonance of space between one topology and another, why should not the concept of metric itself be likewise a derived concept, going back for its foundation to topological or pretopological—and at any rate to pregeometric—ideas ("distance between A and B" being defined in the last analysis, for example, by "the ramification of the connections between A and B")? One cannot even mention these topics without recalling the universal sway of the quantum principle, and without stressing the "order of creation" as one thinks of it from physical evidence: Not first geometry and then the quantum principle, but first the quantum principle and then geometry!

It is enough to raise these issues, with all their depth, to see into what difficulties one can get with quantum geometrodynamics if one tries to think of it as an "ultimate" theory. However, physics has never depended for its progress on having an ultimate theory. There is no reason to think that the situation is different today. While one can raise ultimate issues of all kinds, there is no reason to believe that they all have to settled now! Nor that one *can* resolve them now! The subject presents an ever widening list of issues that have lively physical interest and lend themselves to well-known methods of analysis [78].

PROBLEM 3. INITIAL CONDITIONS

The classical initial value problem has already been discussed. What can one say about the corresponding problem in quantum geometrodynamics? In other words, how much information must one give about $\psi(^{(3)}\mathscr{G})$ on an appropriate submanifold of superspace in order to be able to predict this probability amplitude everywhere in superspace? And what is the character of this submanifold? In this connection one recalls that the "Einstein–Schroedinger wave equation" is of the second order. This second-order character raises a question of principle: In order to be able to calculate ψ everywhere, must one know on a hypersurface of superspace not only ψ but also its normal derivative? No, Leutwyler suggests in a most interesting paper [79]. He points out in the context of a simplified model that the natural features of superspace itself impose certain natural boundary conditions. They reduce the effective order of the equation from second to first.

Wider questions of principle are also posed by the very structure of quantum geometrodynamics. The arena of the dynamics is not space, but superspace. At first this development seems preposterous. How can one speak sensibly of any physical predictions when the outcome depends on what is taking place in unreachable regions of superspace? Nothing could seem more at variance with the spirit of science as dealing only with the knowable. However, a closer look shows that one has broken not at all with the traditional spirit of dynamics, but only with the details. In classical dynamics a clean distinction has always been maintained between (1) the equations of motion, which one can hope to know and understand, and (2) the origin of the initial conditions for those equations of motion—which is beyond one's power to investigate [80]. Quantum geometrodynamics maintains a similar cut between the knowable and the unknowable, but the cut comes in a new place [81]. Nothing seems to exclude the possibility ultimately to know (1) the detailed form of the Einstein–Schroedinger equation, and the concomitant structure of superspace; but as for (2) the source of the initial conditions on ψ, that would seem as far as ever beyond one's power ever to know. Happily, in neither classical dynamics nor quantum geometrodynamics does one have to know all initial conditions to make useful predictions! On the contrary, as Wigner has so often stressed [82], the role of physics is to predict the *correlations* between observations.

REFERENCES AND NOTES

1. L. Rosenfeld, *Annalen der Physik* **5**, 113 (1930) and *Z. Physik* **65**, 589 (1930) and *Annales de l'Institut Henri Poincaré* **2**, 25 (1932); P. G. Bergmann, *Phys. Rev.* **75**, 680 (1949); P. G. Bergmann and J. H. M. Brunings, *Rev. Mod. Phys.* **21**, 480 (1949); Bergmann, Penfield, Schiller, and Zatzkis, *Phys. Rev.* **78**, 329 (1950); P. A. M. Dirac,

Can. J. Math. **2**, 129 (1950); F. A. E. Pirani and A. Schild, *Phys. Rev.* **79**, 986 (1950); P. Bergmann, *Helv. Phys. Acta*, Suppl. IV, 79 (1956), *Nuovo Cimento* **3**, 1177 (1956) and *Rev. Mod. Phys.* **29**, 352 (1957); C. W. Misner, *Rev. Mod. Phys.* **29**, 497 (1957); B. S. Dewitt, *Rev. Mod. Phys.* **29**, 377 (1957); P. A. M. Dirac, *Proc. Roy. Soc.* (*London*) **A246**, 326 and 333 (1958) and *Phys. Rev.* **114**, 924 (1959); B. S. DeWitt, "The Quantization of Geometry", a chapter in *Gravitation: An Introduction to Current Research* (L. Witten, ed), Wiley, New York, 1962; J. Schwinger, *Phys. Rev.* **130**, 1253 (1963) and **132**, (1317) (1963);

R. P. Feynman, mimeographed letter to V. F. Weisskopf dated 4 January to 11 February 1961; *Acta Physica Polonica* **24**, 697 (1963); *Lectures on Gravitation* (notes mimeographed by F. B. Morinigo and W. G. Wagner, California Institute of Technology, 1963); report in *Proceedings of the 1962 Warsaw Conference on the Theory of Gravitation* (PWN-Editions Scientifiques de Pologne, Warszawa, 1964); S. N. Gupta, report in *Recent Developments in General Relativity*, Pergamon, New York, 1962; S. Mandelstam, *Proc. Roy. Soc.* (*London*) **A270**, 346 (1962) and *Annals of Physics* **19**, 25 (1962); J. L. Anderson in *Proceedings of the 1962 Eastern Theoretical Conference* (M. E. Rose, ed.), Gordon and Breach, New York, 1963, p. 387; I. B. Khriplovich, "Gravitation and Finite Renormalization in Quantum Electrodynamics" (mimeographed report, Siberian Section Academy of Science, U.S.S.R., Novosibirsk, 1965); H. Leutwyler, *Phys. Rev.* **134**, B1155 (1964); B. S. DeWitt, "Dynamical Theory of Groups and Fields," in *Relativity Groups and Topology* (C. DeWitt and B. DeWitt, eds.), Gordon and Breach, New York, 1964; S. Weinberg, *Phys. Rev.* **135**, B1049 (1964), **138**, B988 (1965), and **140**, B516 (1965); M. A. Markov, *Progr. Theor. Phys.*, *Yukawa Suppl.*, 1965, p. 85.

2. P. W. Higgs, *Phys. Rev. Letters* **1**, 373 (1958) and **3**, 66 (1959); R. Arnowitt, S. Deser, and C. W. Misner, a series of papers summarized in "The Dynamics of General Relativity" in *Gravitation: An Introduction to Current Research* (L. Witten, ed.), Wiley, New York, 1962; A. Peres, *Nuovo Cimento* **26**, 53 (1962); R. F. Baierlein, D. H. Sharp, and J. A. Wheeler, *Phys. Rev.* **126**, 1864 (1962); cf. also the Princeton A. B. Senior Thesis of D. H. Sharp, May 1960 (unpublished); J. A. Wheeler, *Geometrodynamics*, Academic Press, New York, 1962, cited hereafter as GMD, and "Geometrodynamics and the Issue of the Final State," cited hereafter as GMD & IFS, a chapter in *Relativity, Groups and Topology* (C. DeWitt and B. DeWitt, eds.), Gordon and Breach, New York, 1964; B. DeWitt, *Phys. Rev.* **160**, 1113 (1967), **162**, 1195 (1967) and **162**, 1239 (1967), together cited hereafter as QTG.

3. J. A. Wheeler, GMD & IFS; B. DeWitt, QTG.

4. Michael D. Stern, *Investigations of the Topology of Superspace*, Princeton A. B. Senior Thesis, May 1967 (unpublished) and *Proc. Natl. Acad. Sci. U.S.A.* (submitted for publication).

5. R. Penrose, *An Analysis of the Structure of Spacetime*, Adams Prize Essay (mimeographed for limited distribution, Princeton University, Princeton, New Jersey, December 1966), gives a beautiful procedure to prescribe on the past light cone exactly enough geometrical information to determine out of Einstein's field equations the complete 4-geometry everywhere within the past light cone. The treatment is given only in the analytic case (in which case the difference between "inside" and "outside" the light cone does not make itself felt) but from general

considerations one must expect in the nonanalytic case that the data in question determine the 4-geometry only *within* the past light cone. When the light cone points into the future instead of the past, similar considerations of course apply, obtained by the interchange of the words "past" and "future" in what is said in the text. Problems arise with such formulations of the initial value problem "on the light cone" when the propagation proceeds far in a space of variable curvature. Then the light cone develops more than one sheet. Compare the several claps of thunder often heard from a single localized explosion!

6. For a discussion of the "observer" as a "collector of printout" see for example E. F. Taylor and J. A. Wheeler, *Spacetime Physics*, W. H. Freeman, San Francisco, 1966.

7. For the idea of a general spacelike hypersurface as the manifold on which the magnitudes of quantum field theory are to be measured, see especially S. Tomonaga, *Progr. Theor. Phys.* **1**, 34 (1946) and J. Schwinger, *Phys. Rev.* **74**, 1449 (1948).

8. J. A. Wheeler, GMD & IFS.

9. B. DeWitt, QTG.

10. This way of writing the conditions for constructive interference is symbolic only. In actuality the Hamilton–Jacobi function S depends not only upon the $^{(3)}\mathcal{G}$, but upon an infinity of parameters that distinguish one solution of the Hamilton–Jacobi equation from another. Thus, in a problem with one degree of freedom we write $S = S_0(x, E) + \delta(E)$ and in a problem with n degrees of freedom $S = S_0(x_1, \ldots, x_n; \alpha_1, \ldots, \alpha_n) + \delta(\alpha_1, \ldots, \alpha_n)$. In geometrodynamics there are two degrees of freedom per space point, the magnitudes associated with which may be designated by α and β. Thus the infinitude of freely disposable parameters may be indicated by two freely disposable functions, $\alpha(u, v, w)$ and $\beta(u, v, w)$. The ∞^3 points are given by the ∞^3 possible choices of u, v, and w. The u, v, w manifold may be, but is not required to be, the same as the manifold x, y, z of points in the 3-geometry ("alternative choices of parametrization of Hamilton–Jacobi function"). In any case we write S as a functional of α and β; thus, $S = S_0(^{(3)}\mathcal{G}; \alpha(u, v, w), \beta(u, v, w)) + \delta(\alpha(u, v, w), \beta(u, v, w))$. Then the conditions of constructive interference become statements about functional derivatives; thus,

$$\frac{\delta S}{\delta \alpha} = 0$$

and

$$\frac{\delta S}{\delta \beta} = 0$$

This is an explicit form of the symbolic Eq. (11) of the text. Other ways of writing the equations of constructive interference also exist.

11. Ulrich Gerlach, *Bull. Am. Phys. Soc.* for the Washington meeting of April, 1966, paper DE7, p. 340.

12. A. Peres, *Nuovo Cimento* **26**, 53 (1962). Here the unit of length is $(16\pi)^{1/2}L^* = (16\pi\hbar G/c^3)^{1/2}$

13. See [1] and [2].

298   JOHN ARCHIBALD WHEELER

14. R. F. Baierlein, D. H. Sharp, and J. A. Wheeler, *Phys. Rev.* **126**, 1864 (1962).

15. The term "dimensionality" can be translated as the requirement of "imbeddability" of all the $^{(3)}\mathscr{G}$'s in a $^{(4)}\mathscr{G}$, a requirement that would seem the natural starting point for a derivation of the Einstein–Hamilton–Jacobi equation straight from first principles (see Problem 1).

16. C. W. Misner, *Rev. Mod. Phys.* **29**, 497 (1957); see also H. Leutwyler, *Phys. Rev.* **134**, B1155 (1964) and B. S. DeWitt, QTG.

17. M. Planck, *Sitzungsber. Preussische Akad. Wiss. Berlin, Math.-Phys. Klasse*, 1899, p. 440; J. A. Wheeler, GMD.

18. For a review of the subject of gravitational collapse, see for example B. K. Harrison, K. Thorne, M. Wakano, and J. A. Wheeler, *Gravitation Theory and Gravitational Collapse*, Univ. of Chicago Press, 1965; also A. G. Doroschkevich, Ya. B. Zel'dovich, and I. D. Novikov, *J. Exptl. Theor. Phys.* **49**, 170 (1965), English translation in *Soviet Physics JETP* **22**, 122 (1966) and Ya. B. Zel'dovich and I. D. Novikov, *Usp. Fiz. Nauk* **84**, 377 (1964) and **86**, 447 (1965), English translations in *Soviet Physics Usp.* **7**, 763 (1965) and **8**, 522 (1965).

19. For a presentation of the quantum electrodynamical calculation of the major part of the Lamb shift of hydrogen from this point of view, see T. A. Welton, *Phys. Rev.* **74**, 1157 (1948) and F. J. Dyson, *Advanced Quantum Mechanics*, Cornell Univ., Ithaca, 1954 (mimeographed), p. 54.

20. J. A. Wheeler, GMD.

21. J. A. Wheeler, GMD and GMD & IFS; B. S. DeWitt, QTG and "The Quantization of Geometry" in *Gravitation: An Introduction to Current Research* (L. Witten, ed.), Wiley, New York, 1962, p. 342 ff.

22. In GMD.

23. For an elementary discussion of the identity between the tide-producing component of the gravitational force and the Riemann curvature, see for example E. F. Taylor and J. A. Wheeler, *Spacetime Physics*, Freeman, San Francisco, 1966.

24. E. P. Wigner, "The Unreasonable Effectiveness of Mathematics in the Natural Sciences," in his book *Symmetries and Reflections*, Indiana Univ. Press, Bloomington, 1967; reprinted from *Comm. Pure App. Math.* **13**, No. 1 (February, 1960).

25. Reference 17.

26. A. S. Eddington, *Relativity Theory of Protons and Electrons*, Cambridge Univ. Press, 1936, and *Fundamental Theory*, Cambridge Univ. Press, 1946; also *Proc. Camb. Phil. Soc.* **27**, 15 (1931).

27. P. A. M. Dirac, *Nature* **139**, 323 (1937), *Proc. Roy. Soc. (London)* **A165**, 199 (1938).

28. P. Jordan, *Schwerkraft und Weltall*, Vieweg und Sohn, Braunschweig, 1955, and *Z. Physik* **157**, 112 (1959).

29. R. H. Dicke, *Science* **129**, 3349 (1959) and *The Theoretical Significance of Experimental Relativity*, Gordon and Breach, New York, 1964, p. 72.

30. S. Hayakawa, *Progr. Theor. Phys.* **33**, 538 (1965) and *Progr. Theor. Phys. Suppl.* p. 532 (1965).

31. It is permissible to take at full force the argument of Eddington, Dirac, Jordan, Dicke, and Hayakawa, that a physical correlation exists between 10^{20}, 10^{40} and 10^{80}, without accepting the suggestion sometimes made in the same context, that the physical constants may "change with time." There is increasing observational evidence against such changes, and no incontrovertible evidence for them has ever been found. Among the relevant observations one can cite as examples R. H. Dicke, *Nature* **183**, 170 (1959) and *Nature* **192**, 440 (1961); also R. H. Dicke and P. J. E. Peebles, *J. Geophys. Res.* **67**, 10 and 4063 (1962) and *Phys. Rev.* **128**, 5 and 2006 (1962), showing no detectable change with time in the relative rates of selected processes of radioactive decay. To search for changes with time in the reciprocal fine structure constant, $\alpha^{-1} = hc/e^2 = 137.03$, is simple in principle. One has only to compare the wavelength of the 21-cm line of hydrogen (red shifted because it was given out by a rapidly receding galaxy, far away and long ago) with the wavelength of a line in the optical spectrum (which has undergone the same red shift). The ratio R of the two wavelengths is α^{-1} multiplied by a known function of the atomic number of the source (an integer) and of the relevant quantum numbers (also integers):

$$R = \alpha^{-1} \text{ times function of integers}$$

The value of R for a source 1.4×10^9 light-years away (recession rate $\beta = v/c = 0.1$) should differ by several percent from the value of R for a laboratory source if any of the suggestions are correct that physical constants might change in proportion to the time (or some significant power of the time) measured from the start of the expansion of the universe. The writer is indebted to the kindness of Professor R. Minkowski of Berkeley for the following (July 28, 1967) summary of the observational situation: (1) Hopes have been dashed to observe the 21-cm line in the spectrum of galaxies anywhere near as far away as would correspond to a recession velocity of $\beta = 0.1$. (2) Observations have been made on 30 nearer objects by Dieter, Epstein, Lilley, and Roberts, *Astrophys. J.* **67**, 270 (1962) as supplemented by Roberts, *Astrophys. J.* **142**, 148 (1965). The red shift is the same for the 21-cm line and for the optical lines within the limits of error of the observations. It is difficult to evaluate the accuracy because individual motions amount to as much as 20–30% of the average recession velocity of $v = 1600$ km/sec ($\beta = 0.005$). It is probably safe to say that any change in α^{-1} must be less than a few percent to be compatible with the observations. However, a change anyway smaller than this limit would be expected on almost any of the varied theories of the change of α^{-1} with time, since the time lapse in this case is only one two-hundredth of the Hubble time. (3) Instead of comparing the wavelength of the 21-cm line with the wavelength of an optical transition, one can measure the fine structure separation of a related pair of lines in the optical spectrum itself. The fractional splitting $\Delta\lambda/\lambda$ should be independent of the red shift of the source if α^{-1} is constant. From the observations of R. Minkowski, *Astrophys. J.* **123**, 373 (1956), on Cygnus A ($v = 16830$ km/sec, $\beta = 0.056$: W. Baade and R. Minkowski, *Astrophys. J.* **119**, 206 (1954)), it is again probably safe to say that any change in the fine structure constant must be less than a few percent. Bahcall, Sargent, and Schmidt, *Ap. J. Lett*, **149**, 11 (1967) give $|\Delta\alpha/\alpha| < 0.05$ for $z = 2$.

32. The quark, so useful in doing bookkeeping on the beautiful regularities of elementary particle physics (summarized, for example, in M. Gell-Mann and Y. Ne'eman, *The Eightfold Way*, Benjamin, New York, 1964 and F. Dyson, *Symmetry Groups in Nuclear and Particle Physics*, Benjamin, New York, 1966) has sometimes been taken much more seriously, as if it were an actual "primordial building block" of matter. That view may or may not be correct. If it is, and if one still continues to take quantum geometrodynamics as the only available indicator of what goes on at very small distances, then it would still seem reasonable to expect that one must have some perspective on what happens at 10^{-33} cm before one can find the rationale of quarks and particles. That there is no such thing as a quark in the literal sense is, however, a point of view accepted by many investigators, and stressed especially by Heisenberg and Dürr: W. Heisenberg, *Introduction to the Unified Field Theory of Elementary Particles*, Wiley, New York, 1966 and H. P. Dürr, "On the non-linear spinor theory of elementary particles," *Acta Physica Austriaca*, Suppl. III, 1966. Dürr has made the same point even more vividly (kind personal communication of June, 1967) by considering in effect what one would conclude out of the first several dozen atomic energy levels of an atom such as, for example, carbon or iron if one had (1) good measurements of the energies and transition probabilities, and (2) today's aptitude for searching for symmetries, but (3) not the slightest idea of the actual internal machinery of an atom. He shows how groups of high symmetry will make their appearance. His discussion leads one to ask whether the innocent investigator will not conclude that the atom is made out of quarks!

33. The strongest statement easily available against taking general relativity seriously at small distances appears to be that made by Robert Oppenheimer in his article "On Albert Einstein" (*New York Review*, March 17, 1966, pp. 4, 5): "He also worked with a very ambitious program, to combine the understanding of electricity and gravitation in such a way as to explain what he regarded as the semblance—the illusion—of discreteness, of particles in nature. I think that it was clear then, and believe it to be obviously clear today, that the things that this theory worked with were too meager, left out too much that was known to physicists but had not been known much in Einstein's student days. Thus it looked like a hopelessly limited and historically rather accidentally conditioned approach."

34. For further discussion of the rationale of changes in topology see Problem 2.

35. GMD.

36. To take it as self-evident that space is Euclidean in character at small distances became impossible after Riemann. His Göttingen inaugural lecture of June 10, 1854 pointed out that space can be highly rippled at submicroscopic distances and yet look smooth to all ordinary means of observation: "Uber die Hypothesen welche der Geometrie zugrunde liegen" in his *Gesammelte Mathematische Werke* (H. Weber, ed.), 2nd ed., reprinted by Dover, New York, 1953, also in a translation in *Nature* **8**, 14 (1873), by W. K. Clifford. Clifford himself went further in his lecture before the Cambridge Philosophical Society February 21, 1870, "On the Space-Theory of Matter," reprinted in his *Mathematical Papers* (R. Tucker, ed.),

London, 1882, also in his *Lectures and Essays* (L. Stephen and F. Pollock, eds.), Vol. 1, London, 1879. He proposed to consider a particle as made up of nothing but curved empty space, differing from the surrounding space precisely in this localized curvature—and perhaps also in its connectivity or local topology. In *Was ist Materie* (Springer, Berlin, 1924, esp. pp. 57, 58) Hermann Weyl again pointed out that space may be multiply connected in the small, and consequently: "The argument that the charge of the electron must be spread over a finite region, because otherwise it would possess infinite inertial mass, has thus lost its force. One cannot at all say, here is charge, but only, this closed surface encloses charge." He went on to comment that the enormous value of the ratio of electric to gravitation forces "seems to indicate that the total number of electrons in the universe is important for the constitution of the individual electron." Albert Einstein and Nathan Rosen, *Phys. Rev.* **48**, 73 (1935), proposed the concept of two nearly Euclidean spaces, connected here and there by thin bridges or tubes, through which electric lines of force thread, to give the appearance of charges of variegated signs in the "upper" space and corresponding charges of the opposite sign in the "lower" space. J. A. Wheeler, *Phys. Rev.* **97**, 511 (1955), reprinted in GMD, proposed instead the concept of a tube or handle or "wormhole" reaching between two different localities in one and the same Euclidean space. It is an automatic consequence of this picture that the universe should contain equal amounts of positive and negative electricity. It is another consequence, proved by Misner in 1957 straight from Maxwell's equations for empty space, that the charge, or flux of lines through the wormhole, must stay constant with time. The proof, C. W. Misner and J. A. Wheeler, *Annals of Physics* **2**, 525 (1957), reprinted in GMD, holds no matter how tortuously the lines of force may be twisted, no matter how wanting in symmetry the geometry of the wormhole may be, and no matter how violently the field and the geometry may subsequently change with time. Misner also showed here the beautiful ties that exist between the Maxwell theory in a multiply connected empty space and the mathematics of differential forms and homology groups. In his analysis the field and the geometry were assumed to evolve deterministically in time, in accordance with the classical equations of electrodynamics and geometrodynamics. Reasons out of fluctuation theory to consider "wormholes" a property, not of particles, but of all space, were first given by J. A. Wheeler in *Annals of Physics* **2**, 604 (1957), expanded in GMD.

37. No one has pointed out a more direct tie between the energy of vacuum fluctuations and macroscopic physics than H. B. G. Casimir, *Proc. Nederland Akad. Wetenschappen, Amsterdam* **60**, 793 (1948), who predicted a force between two parallel metal plates. No attempt is made here to cite the extensive literature that verifies the existence and the predicted magnitude of this force. The same kind of fluctuations that are verified by this force at macroscopic distances are also checked at distances $\sim 10^{-12}$ cm by the Lamb shift, the most impressive single development in quantum electrodynamics in the post-World War II period (Fig. 4 and [19]).

38. D. R. Brill and J. B. Hartle, *Phys. Rev.* **135**, B271 (1964).

39. For a historical survey that treats chemistry and atomic physics as the two parts of a single development, see for example: W. G. Palmer, *A History of the Concept of Valency to 1930*, Cambridge Univ. Press, 1965, and especially J. J. Lagowski, *The Chemical Bond*, Houghton Mifflin, Boston, 1966.

40. On these regularities see for example the books cited in [32].

41. J. Bardeen, L. N. Cooper, and J. R. Schrieffer, *Phys. Rev.* **108**, 1175 (1957).

42. The three issues listed here are taken up in more detail in the Appendix.

43. A. Einstein, in P. A. Schilpp, ed., *Albert Einstein: Philosopher Scientist* (Library of Living Philosophers, Evanston, Illinois, 1949, p. 81) remarks: "If one had the field-equation of the total field, one would be compelled to demand that the particles themselves would *everywhere* be describable as singularity-free solutions of the completed field-equations. Only then would the general theory of relativity be a *complete* theory."

44. E. Cartan, *Leçons sur la géométrie des espaces de Riemann*, Gauthier-Villars, Paris, 2nd ed., 1959, Chapter 8.

45. J. A. Wheeler, Chapter 4 on Cartan's geometrical interpretation of Einstein's field equations in *Gravitation and Relativity* (H. Y. Chiu and W. F. Hoffmann, eds.), Benjamin, New York, 1964.

46. Arguments that the propagator appropriate for any particle of spin two and mass zero necessarily has a leading term of the form

$$k^{-2}(g^{\mu\alpha}g^{\nu\beta} + g^{\mu\beta}g^{\nu\alpha} - g^{\alpha\beta}g^{\mu\nu})$$

are given by S. Weinberg, *Phys. Rev.* **138**, B988 (1965); also in expanded form in his contribution to S. Deser and K. W. Ford, eds., Brandeis Summer Institute in Theoretical Physics, 1964, Vol. 2, *Lectures on Particle and Field Theory*, Prentice-Hall, Englewood Cliffs, New Jersey, 1965.

47. See for example W. Pauli in "Die allgemeinen Prinzipien der Wellenmechanik" in *Handbuch der Physik* (Geiger and Scheel, eds.), Springer, Berlin, 1933, Vol. 24, part 1; reprinted in revised form in the new *Handbuch der Physik* (S. Flügge, ed.), Springer, Berlin, 1958, Vol. 5, part 1.

48. See the discussion of the problem of factor ordering in B. DeWitt, QTG; also the references to earlier discussions of this issue cited by him there.

49. For a determination of the wave equation from (1) the principle of Lorentz covariance and (2) a selection of one or another set of spin quantum numbers see E. P. Wigner, *Ann. of Math.* **40**, 149 (1939) and V. Bargmann and E. P. Wigner, *Proc. Natl. Acad. Sci. U.S.A.* **34**, 211 (1946), both reprinted in the collection *Symmetry Groups in Nuclear and Particle Physics* (F. J. Dyson, ed., Benjamin, New York, 1966.

50. For an analysis of the metric of superspace see B. DeWitt, QTG [2], and other work cited by DeWitt; see also S. Weinberg [46], for the propagator in the linear theory of gravitation in the de Donder gauge, which mysteriously has the same form as the metric in superspace (but indices 0, 1, 2, 3 as compared to 1, 2, 3).

51. For the proof that the topology of space cannot change within the context of classical geometrodynamics, see R. P. Geroch, *J. Math. Phys.* **8**, 782 (1967).

52. For a model of a closed universe with the topology S_3 put together out of 720 identical pieces each endowed with the Schwarzschild geometry ("lattice universe") see R. W. Lindquist and J. A. Wheeler, *Rev. Mod. Phys.* **29**, 432 (1957) and further treatment in GMD & IFS, pp. 370–379.

53. A. Einstein, end of chapter dealing with Mach' principle in *The Meaning of Relativity*, Princeton Univ. Press, Princeton, New Jersey, 3rd ed., 1950.

54. See for example some of the solutions of Einstein's equations given by B. K. Harrison, *Phys. Rev.* **116**, 1285 (1959) and his fuller Princeton University Ph.D. thesis, *Exact Three-Variable Solutions of the Field Equations of General Relativity*, 1959 (unpublished).

55. Here it is assumed that the conjecture of H. Poincaré is correct, that every simply connected compact differentiable three-dimensional manifold is homeomorphic to the three-sphere. See C. D. Papakyriakopoulos, "The theory of differentiable manifolds since 1950," *Proc. Intern. Congr. Mathematicians, 1958* (Cambridge Univ. Press, 1960), pp. 433–440; also J. Milnor, *Topology from the Differentiable Viewpoint*, Univ. of Virginia Press, Charlottesville, 1965, and the bibliography cited by Milnor; also J. Derwent, "Handle decomposition of manifolds," *J. Math. Mech.* **15**, 329 (1966).

56. Particularly to be emphasized is the distinction between "asymptotically flat" as that concept is so often understood in the classical context of a 4-geometry, and the concept of flatness as it is applied to a 3-geometry in the context of Hamilton–Jacobi theory or quantum geometrodynamics. No example illustrates this distinction more clearly than the Schwarzschild geometry. There the rate of approach of the 4-geometry to flatness at infinity determines always a unique value for the mass of the center of attraction; but the analogous calculation for a spacelike 3-geometry slicing through the 4-geometry gives quite different values for the apparent mass, depending upon the choice of slice. Thus, in the 4-geometry

$$ds^2 = -(1 - 2m/r)dt^2 + (1 - 2m/r)^{-1} dr^2 + r^2(d\theta^2 + \sin^2 \theta \, d\phi^2)$$

take at large distances the spacelike slice

$$t = t_0 + (8\alpha r)^{1/2}$$

so that

$$dt = \left(\frac{2\alpha}{r}\right)^{1/2} dr$$

On this slice one finds a 3-geometry in which the coefficient of dr^2, also at large distances, is

$$1 + \frac{2(m - \alpha)}{r}$$

The dependence of the "effective mass" $(m - \alpha)$ upon the choice of slice, through the parameter α, suggests some of the many dangers that seem to lurk in the concept of "asymptotic flatness" as applied to *three*-geometries.

57. In the Taub universe the effective mass-energy arises entirely from excitation of that mode of gravitational radiation which has the longest wavelength capable of fitting into this universe. For the metric of this model see A. Taub, *Ann. of Math.* **53**, 472 (1959) and C. W. Misner, *J. Math. Phys.* **4**, 924 (1963).

58. To say that a particle is "pictured in terms of space resonating from one topology to another" means more precisely that it is "pictured as a geometrodynam-

ical exciton—a state of excitation in which space resonates from one topology and geometry to another according to a probability amplitude function slightly different from, and orthogonal to, the probability amplitude function $\psi(^{(3)}\mathscr{G})$ that describes the vacuum."

59. For a systematic development of "already unified field theory" see C. W. Misner and J. A. Wheeler, *Annals of Physics* 2, 525 (1957) (reprinted in GMD) where also reference is made to the earlier work of G. Y. Rainich.

60. In "already unified field theory" the electromagnetic field tensor is expressed, in accordance with Einstein's field equations, in terms of the "Maxwell square root" of the Ricci curvature tensor and its dual

$$F_{\mu\nu} = ("\, R^{1/2}\,")_{\mu\nu} \cos\alpha + *("\, R^{1/2}\,")_{\mu\nu} \sin\alpha$$

The change of the "complexion" α of the electromagnetic field from place to place is fully determined by Maxwell's equations in places where there is a field. However, consider a spacelike initial value hypersurface. On this hypersurface consider two regions, I, II, endowed with field and separated by a region III free of field. Within each region individually the relative complexion is well determined, which is all that matters momentarily for the electrodynamics. However, the complexion of region II relative to region I can never be found from purely geometrical measurements limited to this initial spacelike hypersurface. Moreover, this relative complexion is all important for the dynamic development of the electromagnetic field at those later points in space-time that can be reached by disturbances both from I and from II. In this sense the initial value problem of already unified field theory does not lend itself to purely geometrical formulation. For more on this topic see the chapter by L. Witten in the book of which he is also the editor, *Gravitation: An Introduction to Current Research*, Wiley, New York, 1962.

61. The divergence condition is well known to follow from the invariance of the Hamilton–Jacobi function with respect to the gauge transformation, $A_i^{\text{new}} = A_i + \partial\lambda/\partial x^i$; thus,

$$0 = \delta S = \int \left(\frac{\delta S}{\delta A_i}\right) \delta A_i\, d^3 x$$

$$= \int \left(\mathfrak{E}^i\, \frac{\partial\lambda}{\partial x^i}\right) d^3 x$$

$$= -\int \mathfrak{E}^i_{,i}\lambda\, d^3 x$$

The vanishing of this expression for arbitrary λ gives the desired relation. It should be emphasized that the quantity $\mathfrak{E}^i$ as employed here is not a contravariant vector, but $(g)^{1/2}$ times a contravariant vector ("vector density"). Were the contravariant vector itself employed, the divergence relation would have to be expressed in terms of covariant derivatives rather than ordinary derivatives, complicating the derivation in the text.

62. Here the symbol $(\mathfrak{E} \times B)_j$ stands for the covariant vector density $\mathfrak{E}^i B_{ij}$.

63. As Hermann Weyl emphasized long ago, *Math. Z.* **23**, 271 (1925), " In den geometrischen und physikalischen Anwendungen zeigte sich stets, dass eine Grössart nicht allein durch Angabe der Tensorstufe, sondern durch Symmetrie bedingungen charakterisiert ist." In other words, every physical quantity is represented by an irreducible tensorial quantity; that is to say, by what S. S. Chern terms "a geometrical object." Weyl conceived of these geometrical entities as local. However, it is a natural extension of his line of thought to speak of a *functional S* or ψ that depends *globally* upon a 3-geometry, and upon a 2-form imbedded in that 3-geometry.

64. GMD [2], p. 88.

65. John Milnor, "A survey of cobordism theory," *L'enseignement mathématique* **8**, 16 (1962); "Spin structures on manifolds," *ibid.* **9**, 198 (1963); "On the Stiefel–Whitney numbers of complex manifolds and of spin manifolds," *Topology* **3**, 223 (1965); "Remarks concerning spin manifolds" in S. S. Cairns, ed., *Differential and Combinatorial Topology*, Princeton Univ. Press, Princeton, New Jersey, 1965, p. 55; Andre Lichnerowicz, *Compt. Rend. Acad. Sci. Paris* **252**, 3742 (1961), **253**, 940 (1961), and **253**, 983 (1961), and summary of these results in the third part of the chapter by Lichnerowicz, "Propagateurs, Commutateurs et Anticommutateurs en Relativité Générale," in C. and B. DeWitt, eds., *Relativity, Groups and Topology*, Gordon and Breach, New York, 1964; D. W. Anderson, E. H. Brown, Jr., and F. P. Peterson, "Spin cobordism," *Bull. Am. Math. Soc.* **72**, 256 (1966); "*SU*-cobordism, *KO*-characteristic numbers and the Kervaire invariant," *Ann. of Math.* **83**, 54 (1966); W. C. Hsiang and B. J. Sanderson, "Twist-spinning spheres in spheres," *Illinois J. Math.* **9**, 651 (1965). Appreciation is expressed to John Milnor, Roger Penrose, and Robert Geroch for discussions clarifying the concept of spin structure.

66. Take a belt. Stretch it out flat and taut. Keeping the left-hand end A fixed in the left hand, twist the right-hand end B through 720°. Maintaining A and B all the time parallel to their present orientations, move B in a complete circle about A (releasing for an instant one's hold on B). The belt straightens out. Not so when there is only a 360° twist in it. The belt is relevant to the cube, the room, and the eight elastic strings. Before the cube is rotated at all, it can be pulled out through a window to some distance from the room. The eight elastic strings then take on the configuration of the belt. The distinction between 360° and 720° rotation for the belt applies equally to the "pseudo-belt" made up of the eight strings. Another way of seeing that a 720° rotation restores the orientation entanglement relation between the cube and its surroundings (picture of one cone rolling on another) is presented by R. Penrose and W. Rindler in a preprint of an appendix to a book that they have in preparation. Appreciation is expressed to Professor Penrose for the privilege of seeing this preprint.

67. The possibility has been suggested that one may eventually be able to detect what is here called the "orientation entanglement relation" between an object and its surroundings by measuring the contact potential between one metallic object (subject to rotation) and another (held fixed): Y. Aharonov and L. Susskind, *Phys. Rev.* **158**, 1237 (1967).

68. Cf. section on orientability, Problem 2, Level 1.

69. It is not new to abstractify geometry. Einstein's curved space-time was in the beginning nothing if it was not a home for geodesics. How else, one asked,

could he predict a planetary motion. Later Einstein, Grommer, Infeld, and Hoffman threw out the geodesics. The field equations themselves, they showed, predict the evolution of geometry with time, and hence the motion of concentrations of mass-energy.

70. For a history of the concept of spin, see W. Pauli's 1945 Nobel prize lecture, *Exclusion Principle and Quantum Mechanics*, Editions Grisson, Neuchatel, 1947, also the relevant discussion in M. Fierz and V. F. Weisskopf, *Theoretical Physics in the Twentieth Century: A Memorial Volume to Wolfgang Pauli*, Interscience, New York, 1960.

71. See for example C. Kittel, *Introduction to Solid-State Physics*, 3rd ed., Wiley, New York, 1966.

72. The torus can be converted into a single sheet by two cuts, and can then be conceived as laid out on the complex plane, with one corner at the origin. One adjacent corner can be identified arbitrarily with the number $1 + 0i$, by appropriate choice of scale ("conformal transformation"). The location of the other adjacent corner $\tau = \tau_1 + i\tau_2$ is then completely determined. Also completely determined is the concomitant 2-geometry, modulo the group of conformal transformations. The quantity τ can be identified with the complex parameter mentioned in the text.

73. For a survey, with many references to the literature, see H. E. Rauch, "A transcendental view of the space of algebraic Riemann surfaces," *Bull. Am. Math. Soc.* **71**, 1 (1965). Appreciation is expressed to Professor Leon Ehrenpreis for elucidation of the subject and for this and the following reference.

74. Lipman Bers, *On the Moduli of Riemann Surfaces*; lectures at the Forschunginstitut für Mathematik, Eidgenössische Technische Hochschule, Zürich, 1964. Notes by L. M. and R. J. Sibner (mimeographed).

75. For the initial value equations of classical geometrodynamics see G. Darmois, *Les équations de la gravitation einsteinienne*, Gauthier-Villars, Paris, 1927; K. Stellmacher, *Math. Ann.* **115**, 136 (1937); A. Lichnerowicz, *J. math. pure appl.* **23**, 37 (1944); *Helv. Phys. Acta Suppl.* **4**, 176 (1956); *Théories relativistes de la gravitation et de l'électromagnétisme*, Masson, Paris, 1955; Yvonne Fourés-Bruhat, *Acta Math.* **88**, 141 (1952); *J. Rational Mech. Anal.* **5**, 951 (1956); and the chapter by Y. Fourés (now Y. Choquet) in Louis Witten, ed., *Gravitation: An Introduction to Current Research*, Wiley, New York, 1962.

76. H. Weyl, *Philosophy of Mathematics and Natural Science* (original German in 1927; translation by O. Helmer), Princeton Univ. Press, Princeton, New Jersey, 1949, p. 91.

77. GMD & IFS, pp. 495–499.

78. An extensive list of problems open for further investigation is to be found in GMD & IFS.

79. H. Leutwyler in *Battelle Rencontres: 1967 Lectures in Mathematics and Physics*, this volume p. 309.

80. One is reminded in this connection of the statement of William James over a half a century ago, that "Actualities seem to float in a wider sea of possibilities

from out of which they were chosen; and *somewhere*, indeterminism says, such possibilities exist, and form a part of truth." Appreciation is expressed to Paul Van de Water for this quotation.

81. E. P. Wigner, *Symmetries and Reflections*, Indiana Univ. Press, Bloomington, Indiana, 1967; see J. M. Jauch, E. P. Wigner, and M. M. Yanase, *Nuovo Cimento* **48**, 144 (1967), also B. DeWitt, QTG; also H. Everett III, *Rev. Mod. Phys.* **29**, 454 (1957); J. A. Wheeler, *Rev. Mod. Phys.* **29**, 463 (1957) and GMD, p. 75.

X

The Topology of Wheeler's Superspace

BRYCE S. DEWITT

Most of the material covered in this seminar has appeared in *Physical Review* **160**, 1113 (1967).

XI

Boundary Conditions for
the State Functional
in Quantum Theory of Gravity

H. LEUTWYLER

There are various alternative formally equivalent formulations of the quantum theory of gravity, none of which has yet acquired anything like the status of rigorous existence.   For an excellent review of the literature on this subject the reader is referred to a forthcoming paper by B. S. DeWitt [1]. I shall in the following adopt the functional representation of the quantum theory of gravity; the physical interpretation of this formulation has been investigated most thoroughly by J. A. Wheeler [2].   In this framework the state of the gravitational field is described by a function ψ that maps the space of all possible 3-geometries into the complex numbers.   I refer the reader again to [1] for a detailed review of this formulation and simply quote the basic dynamical equation, the so-called Hamiltonian constraint:

$$\left\{ -\tfrac{1}{2}|g|^{-1}(g_{ik}\,g_{lm} - 2g_{il}\,g_{km})\,\frac{\delta^2}{\delta g_{ik}\,\delta g_{lm}} + l_0^{-4}R \right\}\psi = 0 \tag{1}$$

where we have chosen a suitable local coordinate system x^1, x^2, x^3 such that the 3-geometry is represented by the Riemannian metric $g_{ik}(\underline{x})$; i, $k = 1, 2, 3$.

309

The quantity $|g|$ denotes the determinant of the metric tensor and $R(\underline{x})$ is the curvature invariant belonging to $g_{ik}(\underline{x})$. The parameter l_0 is a fundamental physical constant with the dimension of a length

$$l_0 = (16\pi G \hbar c^{-3})^{1/2}$$

The numerical value of this constant is of the order of 10^{-33} cm.

Physical state functionals $\psi = \psi[g]$ are solutions of the functional differential equation (1) that are independent of the particular local coordinate system chosen to describe the geometry.

In the following I wish to make some very simple-minded heuristic remarks concerning the solutions of the dynamical equation (1).

1 SOME REMARKS ON FUNCTIONAL DIFFERENTIAL EQUATIONS

In order to get some feeling for the character of the dynamical equation (1) let me first give a definition of the notion of functional derivative[1] and then illustrate by means of a simple functional differential equation.

a. Definition of Functional Derivative

Let $f(x)$ be an element of some normed vector space V of functions over the real line, for example, $V = L_2$, and let ψ be a functional that maps V into $\mathbb{C}$. The functional ψ is then said to possess a functional derivative at $f \in V$ if the limit

$$\psi, g = \lim_{\varepsilon \to 0} \frac{1}{\varepsilon} \{\psi[f + \varepsilon g] - \psi[f]\}$$

exists for all $g \in V$ and moreover defines a linear functional on V. The functional derivative $\delta\psi/\delta f(x)$ is the distribution corresponding to this linear functional, symbolically,

$$\psi, g = \int dx \, \frac{\delta\psi}{\delta f(x)} g(x)$$

b. Example 1

As a very simple model for the dynamical equation (1) let us consider the following functional differential equation (FDE):

$$\frac{\delta^2\psi}{\delta f(x)\delta f(x)} + a^2\psi = 0 \tag{2}$$

---

[1] I am indebted to Prof. A. Lichnerowicz for an illuminating discussion of this point.

where a is a constant. To find the solutions of this FDE let us first solve the analogous problem in partial differential equations. Let us replace the function $f(x)$ by a countable number of arguments f_n which may be viewed as the values of $f(x)$ at a given set of lattice points x_n. The analog of (2) then reads

$$\frac{\partial^2 \psi}{\partial f_n^2} + a^2 \psi = 0$$

A complete set of solutions of this system is given by

$$\psi_\varepsilon = \exp ia \sum_n \varepsilon_n f_n$$

where $\varepsilon = \{\varepsilon_n\}$ is an arbitrary sequence of signs $\varepsilon_n = \pm 1$. This suggests an immediate analog in the case of the FDE (2). Let $\varepsilon(x)$ be some step function with values ± 1 such that the integral $\int dx\, \varepsilon(x) f(x)$ exists for all $f \in V$. Then the functional

$$\psi_\varepsilon = \exp ia \int dx\, \varepsilon(x) f(x) \tag{3}$$

possesses the functional derivatives

$$\frac{\delta \psi_\varepsilon}{\delta f(x)} = ia\varepsilon(x)\psi_\varepsilon$$

$$\frac{\delta^2 \psi_\varepsilon}{\delta f(x)\delta f(y)} = -a^2 \varepsilon(x)\varepsilon(y)\psi_\varepsilon$$

In particular $\delta^2 \psi / \delta f(x)\delta f(x)$ exists and satisfies the FDE (2). To every step function $\varepsilon(x)$ which is sufficiently well behaved to guarantee the existence of the integral in (3) there thus belongs a solution of the FDE (2).

c. Example 2

A more interesting example is provided by the FDE

$$\frac{\delta^2 \psi}{\delta f(x)\delta f(x)} - b^2 f(x)\psi = 0 \tag{4}$$

and we intend to show in the next section that this example has some bearing on the dynamical equation of the quantum theory of gravity. In this case the analogous system of partial differential equations reads

$$\frac{\partial^2 \psi}{\partial f_n^2} - b^2 f_n \psi = 0$$

To get a complete set of solutions we separate variables

$$\psi = \prod_n y_n(f_n)$$

The functions y_n satisfy an ordinary differential equation whose solutions are Airy functions with the asymptotic behavior

$$y^{\pm 1} = A f^{-1/4} \exp(\pm 2/3 b f^{3/2}) \qquad (f \to \infty)$$

A complete set of solutions may then be represented by means of products of the type

$$\psi_\varepsilon = \prod_n y^{\varepsilon_n}(f_n)$$

where $\varepsilon = \{\varepsilon_n\}$ is again a sequence of signs $\varepsilon_n = \pm 1$.

It does not seem to be a simple matter to construct the corresponding complete set of solutions of the FDE (4). For the present purpose we are only interested in a very particular solution that satisfies the boundary condition

$$\psi[\lambda f] \to 0 \qquad (\lambda \to \infty) \tag{5}$$

for all $f \in V$. The analogous solution of the system of partial differential equations is obviously characterized by the sequence $\varepsilon_n = -1$. A formal description of the solution defined by (5) may be obtained as follows: The boundary condition (5) guarantees at least formally that the functional $\psi[f]$ admits of a functional Fourier transform

$$\psi[f] = \int Dp \exp i \int dx\, p(x) f(x)\, \phi[p]$$

In Fourier space the FDE (4) reads

$$ib^2 \frac{\delta\phi}{\delta p(x)} + p(x)^2 \phi = 0$$

This first-order equation is easily solved with the result

$$\psi[f] = \int Dp \exp i \int dx \left\{ p(x) f(x) + \frac{1}{3b^2} p(x)^3 \right\} \tag{6}$$

This is of course only a formal solution since the existence of functional Fourier integrals of this type has not been established.

2   WEAK-FIELD MODEL

We now turn back to the dynamical equation of the quantum theory of gravity and consider the following simplified model. Let us restrict our attention to 3-geometries which admit of a global coordinate system such that the metric tensor $g_{ik}(x)$ is close to the Euclidean metric

$$g_{ik}(\underline{x}) = \delta_{ik} + h_{ik}(\underline{x}) \qquad |h_{ik}| \ll 1 \tag{7}$$

In first approximation the Ricci tensor of such a geometry takes the form

$$R_{ik}^{(1)} = -\tfrac{1}{2}(\partial_l{}^l h_{ik} + \partial_{ik} h_l{}^l - \partial_{li} h_k{}^l - \partial_{lk} h_i{}^l) \tag{8}$$

and the curvature invariant is given by

$$R^{(1)} = R_l^{l(1)} = (\partial^{ik} h_{ik} - \partial_i{}^i h_k{}^k)$$

In the same approximation the dynamical equation (1) now reads

$$\left\{ -\tfrac{1}{2}(\delta_{ik}\delta_{lm} - 2\delta_{il}\delta_{km}) \frac{\delta^2}{\delta h_{ik}\delta h_{lm}} + l_0^{-4} R^{(1)} \right\}\psi = 0 \tag{9}$$

We are interested in solutions of this equation that are independent of the choice of the coordinate system. To stay within the approximation (7) we restrict this requirement to small deformations of the coordinate frame

$$x^{i'} = x^i + f^i(\underline{x}) \qquad |\partial_i f^k| \ll 1$$

such that the transformation rule for the field $h_{ik}(\underline{x})$ reads

$$h'_{ik}(\underline{x}) = h_{ik}(\underline{x}) + \partial_i f_k(\underline{x}) + \partial_k f_i(\underline{x}) \tag{10}$$

The functional $\psi[h]$ is coordinate independent in this approximation if its values at $h'_{ik}(\underline{x})$ and at $h_{ik}(\underline{x})$ are the same. This invariance condition can be solved easily in the present approximation. It implies that $\psi[h]$ does depent on $h_{ik}(\underline{x})$ only through the gauge invariant "field strengths" $R_{ik}^{(1)}(\underline{x})$ defined in (8). The proof of this statement is elementary; it makes use of the condition that the geometry is asymptotically flat,[2] $h_{ik}(\underline{x}) \to 0(|\underline{x}| \to \infty)$. The gauge transformation rule (10) means that only three of the six components of $h_{ik}(\underline{x})$ are relevant. This makes it clear that the six gauge invariant field strengths $R_{ik}^{(1)}(\underline{x})$ cannot be independent. In fact the field strengths satisfy the three Bianchi identities

$$\partial^i \{ R_{ik}^{(1)} - \tfrac{1}{2}\delta_{ik} R^{(1)} \} = 0 \tag{11}$$

3 BOUNDARY CONDITION FOR WEAK-FIELD MODEL

We are now in a position to formulate the boundary condition[3] to be imposed on physically acceptable solutions of the dynamical equation (9). According to the statement made in the last section we can view the state

---

[2] The situation is quite different in the case of a closed topology, for example, for geometries that are close to a flat 3-torus. I am indebted to Prof. B. S. DeWitt for useful comments on this point. See also [1].

[3] For a discussion of the analogous problem in the framework of the 2 + 1 dimensional model for the quantum theory of gravity see [3].

vector ψ as a functional of the field strengths, $\psi[h] = \tilde{\psi}[R^{(1)}]$. To be physically acceptable this functional should associate zero amplitude with singularly curved geometries characterized by $R_{ik}^{(1)} \to \infty$. In our present approximation, infinite field strength corresponds to a geometry that oscillates infinitely fast around an almost flat space, and it seems to be reasonable to require that the amplitude for the occurrence of such geometries be zero. We therefore impose the boundary condition

$$\psi[h] \to 0 \qquad (R_{ik}^{(1)}(\underline{x}) \to \infty) \tag{12}$$

This boundary condition guarantees the existence of a formal Fourier transform of $\tilde{\psi}[R^{(1)}]$ with respect to $R_{ik}^{(1)}$.

$$\psi[h] = \int Dk \, \exp i \int dx \, k^{ik}(\underline{x}) R_{ik}^{(1)}(\underline{x}) \qquad \phi[k] \tag{13}$$

This representation is of course redundant since the field strengths are not independent; a large family of different functionals $\phi[k]$ leads to the same functional $\psi[R^{(1)}]$. To get rid of this redundancy we introduce the new variable of integration p^{ik} by

$$k^{ik} = p^{ik} - \tfrac{1}{2}\delta^{ik}p_l^{\ l}$$

The representation (13) then takes the form

$$\psi[h] = \int Dp \, \exp i \int dx \, p^{ik}(\underline{x}) \left\{ R_{ik}^{(1)}(\underline{x}) - \tfrac{1}{2}\delta_{ik} R^{(1)}(\underline{x}) \right\} \qquad \tilde{\phi}[p] \tag{14}$$

In this form the Bianchi identities are easily taken into account by decomposing the field $p^{ik}(\underline{x})$ into scalar, longitudinal, and transverse traceless parts

$$p^{ik}(\underline{x}) = p_s(\underline{x})\delta^{ik} + \partial^i p^k(\underline{x}) + \partial^k p^i(\underline{x}) + p_\perp^{ik}(\underline{x}) \tag{15}$$

where the transverse traceless part $p_\perp$ satisfies

$$\partial_i p_\perp^{ik} = p_{\perp i}^i = 0$$

By virtue of the Bianchi identities (11) the exponent in (14) is independent of the longitudinal part $p^i(\underline{x})$. We can thus carry out the integration over the longitudinal part and thereby eliminate the redundancy in the representation (14). The result reads

$$\psi[h] = \int Dp_s \, Dp_\perp \, \exp i \int dx \{ p_\perp^{ik} R_{ik}^{(1)} - \tfrac{1}{2} p_s R^{(1)} \} \qquad \phi[p_s, p_\perp] \tag{16}$$

This representation incorporates both the fact that ψ is independent of the coordinate frame and the boundary condition (12).

4 EXPLICIT SOLUTION OF THE WEAK-FIELD MODEL

The dynamical equation (9) of the weak-field model implies the following simple functional differential equation for the Fourier transform

$$-i\frac{\delta\phi}{\delta p_s(x)} + J(\underline{x})\phi = 0 \tag{17}$$

where J is a quadratic expression in the momenta p_s, $p_\perp$:

$$J = \frac{l_0^4}{8}\left[(\Delta p_s)^2 - \partial^{ik}p_s\partial_{ik}p_s - 2\partial_{ik}p_s\Delta p_\perp^{ik} - \Delta p_\perp^{ik}\Delta p_{\perp ik}\right]$$

The differential equation (17) fixes the dependence of the functional $\phi[p_s, p_\perp]$ on the variable p_s uniquely. Explicitly the solution reads

$$\phi[p_s, p_\perp] = \Phi[p_\perp]\exp - i\Omega[p_s, p_\perp] \tag{18}$$

$$\Omega[p_s, p_\perp] = \frac{l_0^4}{8}\int d\underline{x}\{(\partial^{ik}p_s + \Delta p_\perp^{ik})\partial_i p_s\partial_k p_s - p_s\Delta p_\perp^{ik}\Delta p_{\perp ik}\} \tag{19}$$

The quantity Φ is an arbitrary functional of the transverse traceless part $p_\perp$. To every such functional there corresponds a solution of the weak-field model

$$\psi[h] = \int Dp_s Dp_\perp \exp i \int d\underline{x}\{p_\perp^{ik}R_{ik}^{(1)} - \tfrac{1}{2}p_s R^{(1)}\}\exp - i\Omega[p_s, p_\perp]\Phi[p_\perp] \tag{20}$$

5 SUPERSPACE

It is instructive to reinterpret the solutions just obtained in the space of all 3-geometries, Wheeler's superspace [2]. In the weak-field model this is the space of all equivalence classes of fields $h_{ik}(\underline{x})$, two such fields being equivalent if they are related through a gauge transformation of the type (10). In terms of the decomposition

$$h_{ik} = h_s\delta_{ik} + \partial_i h_k + \partial_k h_i + h_{ik}^\perp \tag{21}$$

analogous to (15) a point in superspace corresponds to a given pair of fields $\{h_s(\underline{x}), h_{ik}^\perp(\underline{x})\}$. The fact that physical state functionals are independent of the coordinate frame implies that these functionals are independent of the longitudinal parts of h_{ik}, that is, they are functionals on superspace $\psi = \psi[h_s, h_\perp]$. The representation (20) of the physical state functionals then implies that the knowledge of $\psi[h_s, h_\perp]$ at one particular superhypersurface $h_s = h_s^0$ determines the functional completely:

$$\psi[h_s, h_\perp] = \int G(h_s, h_\perp | h_s^0, h_\perp^0)Dh_\perp^0\psi[h_s^0, h_\perp^0] \tag{22}$$

The kernel G is expressible in terms of formal Fourier integrals. This representation of the solutions manifests the impact of the boundary condition (12) most clearly. The original dynamical equation in superspace, Eq. (9), is second order in the derivatives and a solution of this equation is in general determined only if both the value of ψ and its normal derivative $\delta\psi/\delta h_s$ are given at the superhypersurface $h_s = h_s{}^0$. The boundary condition (12), however, reduces the manifold of solutions drastically, such that the value of the normal derivative cannot be specified independently, but is determined by the value of the functional itself.

6 STATIONARY PHASE APPROXIMATION

As a consistency check let us finally verify that the stationary phase approximation to the solution (20) satisfies the Hamilton–Jacobi equation. Assume that the functional Φ is of the form

$$\Phi[p_\perp] = \Phi_0[p_\perp] \exp i\phi[p_\perp]$$

where the real functional $\Phi_0[p_\perp]$ varies smoothly with $p_\perp$. The Fourier integral defining $\psi[h]$ may then be expected to pick up significant contributions only from a neighborhood of the point of stationary phase which occurs, say, at $\bar{p}_s, \bar{p}_\perp$. In the stationary phase approximation the functional $\psi[h]$ then takes the form[4]

$$\psi[h] = A \exp iS \tag{23}$$

where A is some slowly varying functional and S is the value of the phase of the integrand at the stationary point

$$S = \int d\underline{x}\{\bar{p}_\perp^{ik}R_{ik}^{(1)} - \tfrac{1}{2}\bar{p}_s R^{(1)}\} - \Omega[\bar{p}_s, \bar{p}_\perp] + \phi[\bar{p}_\perp]$$

and is a functional of the field $h_{ik}(\underline{x})$. We are interested in the functional derivative of S with respect to $h_{ik}(\underline{x})$. To compute this quantity we observe that a small change in the field $h_{ik}(\underline{x})$ slightly shifts the stationary values $\bar{p}_s, \bar{p}_\perp$. This does not produce a change in the value of S, however, since S is stationary with respect to variations of p_s and $p_\perp$. The variation of S induced by the given variation of the field $h_{ik}(\underline{x})$ is therefore given by

$$\delta S = \int d\underline{x}\{\bar{p}_\perp^{ik}\delta R_{ik}^{(1)} - \tfrac{1}{2}\bar{p}_s \delta R^{(1)}\}$$

and from this one reads off the value of the functional derivative

$$\frac{\delta S}{\delta h_{ik}(\underline{x})} = -\tfrac{1}{2}\{\Delta\bar{p}_\perp^{ik} + \partial^{ik}\bar{p}_s - \delta^{ik}\Delta\bar{p}_s\} \tag{24}$$

---

[4] The classical action is obtained from S by dividing through $\hbar = h/2\pi$, where h is Planck's constant.

Let us now determine the stationary point in the integration over the variable p_s. The condition reads

$$2\frac{\delta\Omega}{\delta p_s(\underline{x})} + R^{(1)}(\underline{x}) = 0 \tag{25}$$

The quantity $\delta\Omega/\delta p_s$ is a quadratic expression in the variables $\bar{p}_s$, $\bar{p}_\perp$ and it is straightforward to verify that it may be expressed in terms of the particular linear combination occurring in (24) with the result [6]

$$\tfrac{1}{2}l_0{}^4(\delta_{ik}\delta_{lm} - 2\delta_{il}\delta_{km})\frac{\delta S}{\delta h_{ik}}\frac{\delta S}{\delta h_{lm}} + R^{(1)} = 0 \tag{26}$$

This is indeed the Hamilton–Jacobi equation of the weak field model.

ACKNOWLEDGMENTS

It is a pleasure to acknowledge many stimulating remarks and critical comments by Professors B. DeWitt, A. Lichnerowicz, and J. A. Wheeler.

REFERENCES

1. B. S. DeWitt, Quantum Theory of Gravity, to be published in *Phys. Rev.*

2. J. A. Wheeler, *Relativity, Groups, and Topology*, 1963, *Les Houches Lectures* (Gordon and Breach, New York, 1964); see also "Superspace and the Nature of Quantum Geometrodynamics," in these Proceedings.

3. H. Leutwyler, *Nuovo Cim.* **42**, 159, (1966).

XII

The Everett–Wheeler
Interpretation of
Quantum Mechanics

BRYCE S. DeWITT

Every physical theory consists of two parts: (1) a mathematical formalism and (2) a metaphysical[1] framework which ascribes physical meaning to the theoretical symbols. In the case of the quantum theory part (2) plays an exceptionally large role because the theory, in spite of its enormous practical success, is so contrary to intuition and so strange, even after forty years, that the experts themselves do not all agree today what to make of it.

Most physicists more or less follow Bohr in maintaining that the formalism of quantum mechanics can make sense only if there exists a classical (and hence more familiar) realm in which the results of observations can be uniquely recorded and communicated. However, there is disagreement as to where the dividing line between "quantum" and "classical" is located and how the transition from one realm to the other should be described. Some, the *empiricists* or *pragmatists*, insist that it doesn't matter, that such questions arise only when one attempts to ascribe reality to the wave function, and that they automatically resolve themselves if one fully adopts the philosophy of Complementarity. Others, the *realists*, are more willing to face up to the literal consequences of the quantum formalism but try to compromise them at the classical level with the aid of statistical ensembles. A small minority of realists insists that the quantum theory is only a partial theory, the statistical aspects of which will someday follow from a more complete theory based on presently *hidden* variables.

---

[1] The word "metaphysics" is here to be understood as bearing the same relation to "physics" as "metamathematics" bears to "mathematics."

Ten years ago Everett and Wheeler [1, 2] proposed an entirely new interpretation of quantum mechanics, which accepts the literal consequences of the mathematical formalism without any compromises whatever. Because of the rather bizarre world view which this acceptance entails, the Everett–Wheeler proposal has thus far found little favor. It has, however, the merit of bringing clearly into the foreground most of the fundamental issues arising in quantum measurement theory, and therefore I can use as an excuse for describing it to you today the fact that it will be good for your general education!

I have also another excuse—a poor one perhaps, but one nevertheless worthy of consideration. Among the lectures to which we have listened in these Rencontres have been several by Penrose which called attention to the inadequacy of classical general relativity for dealing with the phenomenon of gravitational collapse. It has frequently been suggested that this inadequacy might be overcome by building a theory which takes quantum effects into account. Professor Wheeler has outlined to us some of the formal properties necessarily displayed by such a theory, and has given us many additional beautiful reasons for believing in it, having to do with the topology of space-time as a potential source of physical structure. According to this theory, space-time, in its role as a pseudo-Riemannian manifold, is not only the arena in which physical events take place but also, in the guise of the gravitational field, a dynamical Hamiltonian system subject to the laws of quantum mechanics. Since space-time serves as the common arena for both classical and quantum processes it is evident that one faces unusual difficulties in this theory in attempting to define Bohr's classical realm. The difficulties are particularly acute in a cosmology which assumes that space is compact. Wheeler has shown us that in this case the *state* of the world is very naturally represented as a *function over 3-geometries*. Although the structure of its domain manifold (that is, the *superspace* of 3-geometries) is as yet poorly understood there can be no doubt that this function is quite literally a *wave function for the universe*.

To anyone educated in the Copenhagen school such a function is meaningless, since it leaves no room for a classical realm. The external observer has no place to stand. In order to give meaning to a universal wave function one must find a radically new way of looking at quantum mechanics. This is what Everett and Wheeler have done.

Since the quantum theory of space-time is still under construction I cannot actually use it as a background for this talk. Fortunately I don't have to. The Everett–Wheeler metatheory applies equally well to ordinary nonrelativistic quantum mechanics, and this is the setting in which I shall discuss it. In fact, this is the setting in which Everett and Wheeler themselves discussed it and is the only setting in which it has thus far been applied. It could be extended in a fairly straightforward manner to quantum field theories satisfying the requirements of special relativity, provided one does not insist on too much rigor at points where the divergence difficulties of these theories enter.[2] However, apart from the possibility that the infinite number of degrees of freedom possessed by relativistic fields may expedite the randomization of phases which occurs during measurement processes, such an extension would not be expected to yield any unusual new insights. The famous investigations of Bohr and Rosenfeld [3] showed long ago that the measurements one can in principle perform on quantized fields are analogous in every respect to the measurements one can perform on non-relativistic systems. In both cases accuracy is limited only by the uncertainty principle.

Let us proceed then to the main topic. According to Everett and Wheeler the *real* world, or any isolated part of it we may wish for the moment to regard as "the world," is faithfully mirrored (in the nonrelativistic approximation) by the following collection of mathematical objects: (1) a Hilbert space, (2) a Hamiltonian operator, and (3) a Schrödinger equation for vectors in the Hilbert space. Nothing else is needed. In particular, the existence of Bohr's external classical world is denied.

As to why the good Lord chose to construct the world along these particular mathematical lines, Everett and Wheeler are silent. The economy of these lines, however, is remarkable. It turns out that only one additional postulate is necessary to give the mathematics physical meaning. This is the *postulate of complexity*: The Hamiltonian must be sufficiently complicated so that it may be regarded as describing at least two (but generally many more) distinct dynamical systems which, under certain conditions, but not always, can act as if they are isolated and independent. When these conditions hold it is convenient to decompose the Hilbert space into a corresponding Cartesian product.[3]

One may ask whether a postulate is not also needed which, in effect, says that the "states" of the world are represented by rays in the Hilbert space. We shall indeed use the word "state" in just this sense. However, a postulate is not needed for this purpose. In a carefully constructed syntax words like "state," "dynamical system," "isolated," "independent," which we are here using in an informal way for the sake of convenience and intelligibility, would be replaced by symbols subject, together with the

---

[2] It has been conjectured that some of these difficulties might be alleviated in a generally covariant theory, with the quantized gravitational field acting as a divergence regulator. But this is a question for the future to answer.

[3] In relativistic quantum field theories one encounters infinite Cartesian products, reflecting the infinitude of the numbers of degrees of freedom. This means that the relevant vector spaces are not strict Hilbert spaces but appropriate generalizations thereof. Because of the divergence difficulties of these theories the definition of "appropriate" has not yet been fully settled.

mathematical symbols of the formalism itself, to certain formal rules of manipulation but empty of any *a priori* meaning. These words acquire semantic content only after one has investigated the consequences of the genuine postulates, *viz.*, the statement of the mathematical content of the formalism and the postulate of complexity. It is, in fact, the *a posteriori* semantic content of the formalism that Everett and Wheeler wish to emphasize. Without drawing on any external metaphysics or mathematics other than the standard rules of logic they are able to prove the following metatheorem: *The mathematical formalism of the quantum theory is capable of yielding its own interpretation.*

The proof of this metatheorem is carried out in stages, with the world assuming an increasingly complex character at each stage. One begins by considering a "world" consisting of just two "dynamical systems." That is, one assumes the Hamiltonian to have a certain structure which, after the semantic content of the formalism has been established, will enable it to be recognized as capable of describing a pair of actual physical systems. One of these systems is conventionally called simply "the system," and the other is called "the apparatus." In discussing the "states" of these systems I find it convenient to employ the notation of Dirac.[4] Thus I will denote a member of an orthonormal set of basis vectors for the system by $|s\rangle$ and a member of an orthonormal set for the apparatus by $|A\rangle$. Here s is an eigenvalue of some system observable and A is an eigenvalue of some apparatus observable. (Additional labels which might, in a practical situation, be needed in order to specify the basis vectors uniquely are suppressed.) The Cartesian product structure of the Hilbert space of "the world" may be expressed by introducing for it the basis vectors

$$|s, A\rangle = |s\rangle|A\rangle \tag{1}$$

In order to keep the subsequent analysis as simple as possible I shall assume that the eigenvalue s ranges over a discrete set while the eigenvalue A ranges over a continuum. Orthonormality and completeness are then expressed by

$$\langle s, A \mid s', A' \rangle = \delta_{ss'} \delta(A - A') \tag{2}$$

$$\sum_s \int |s, A\rangle\langle s, A| \, dA = 1 \tag{3}$$

Suppose that the state of "the world" at some initial instant is represented by a vector of the form

$$|\Psi_0\rangle = |\psi\rangle|\Phi\rangle \tag{4}$$

where $|\psi\rangle$ is a vector in the system Hilbert space and $|\Phi\rangle$ is a vector in the apparatus Hilbert space. In such a state the system and apparatus are said

---

[4] Reference may be made to [4] for the formal definition (in terms of Hermitian operators) of the noun "observable" which is used in what follows.

to be *uncorrelated*. Let us assume that the role of the apparatus is to "learn" something about the system state. System and apparatus must then be coupled together during a certain period, so that the state of the world will not retain the form (4) as time passes. The final result of the coupling will be described by the action of a certain unitary operator U:

$$|\Psi_1\rangle = U|\Psi_0\rangle \tag{5}$$

Here it is convenient to work in the so-called *interaction picture* in which the state vector changes with time only during the coupling interval. The operator U is then the solution of a Schrödinger equation in which only that part of the Hamiltonian which refers to the coupling appears. Just one word of caution in regard to terminology is in order. In classical mechanics the word "state" usually refers to "position and velocity at a particular instant," but in the interaction picture of quantum mechanics it may refer to one of the vectors $|\Psi_0\rangle$ and $|\Psi_1\rangle$ which together describe (in a quantum sense) the entire space-time trajectory outside of the coupling interval. It should perhaps also be emphasized that the existence of a coupling interval need not imply a time dependence on the part of the Hamiltonian.[5] The coupling interval may be incorporated into the state vector $|\Psi_0\rangle$ instead. For example, let $|X, t\rangle$ represent the state in which the apparatus has the position X at the time t. Then if the function $\langle X, t | \Phi \rangle$ has the form of a wave packet, the coupling interval may be the period during which the wave packet is in a certain "region of interaction." Thus, in a scattering experiment, where the apparatus becomes a projectile, the system becomes a target, and U becomes the so-called *scattering operator* or *S-matrix*, the region of interaction is the neighborhood of the target.

If there were no coupling between system and apparatus the state vector of "the world" would remain permanently equal to $|\Psi_0\rangle$. It is therefore tempting to define the "measurement" which the apparatus performs on the system as the *difference* between $|\Psi_1\rangle$ and $|\Psi_0\rangle$. However, $|\Psi_1\rangle$ is the state vector of "the world" and not that of the apparatus. Moreover, system and apparatus have thus far been treated on an equal footing, so that we could with equal right speak of the "measurement" which the system performs on the apparatus. Evidently there must be some separation of function, so that a distinction may be made between the two. This is done by assuming that their mutual coupling is of such a form as to yield an operator U which has the following action on the basis vectors (1):

$$U|s, A\rangle = |s, A + gs\rangle = |s\rangle|A + gs\rangle \tag{6}$$

---

[5] If the Hamiltonian were time-dependent the law of energy conservation would not hold, and one would be disinclined to regard system and apparatus as forming a truly isolated and self-contained "world."

where g is a "coupling constant." If the initial state of the system were $|s\rangle$ and that of the apparatus were $|A\rangle$ then this coupling would be said to result in an "observation," by the apparatus, that the system observable has the value s. Moreover, this "observation" or "measurement" would be regarded as "stored" in the apparatus "memory" by virtue of the permanent shift, from $|A\rangle$ to $|A + gs\rangle$, in the apparatus state vector.

It would lead us too far from our main topic to describe the Hamiltonian structures and couplings which, to good approximation at least, are capable of yielding measurements of the form (6). Suffice it to say that such structures are not difficult to devise [5] and that, in principle, any system observable is capable of being measured by a suitable coupling. Whether such couplings can always (or even sometimes) be realized in the laboratory is irrelevant, being a question which concerns the practical limitations of the experimenter's art and not an issue of principle. There is, however, one limitation which must be mentioned because it has a somewhat more fundamental character than the rest. In most cases the measurement will not be a practical success unless the apparatus is "macroscopic," which means that the time integral, over the coupling period, of its mean energy in the initial state must be large compared to the time integral of the coupling energy, and hence large compared to Planck's unit of action. This is particularly true when the system itself contains only a few Planck units and is hence capable of being non-negligibly disturbed by the measurement process. Under these circumstances one frequently calls the system a "quantum system" and the apparatus a "classical system." It deserves emphasis, however, that this is only a manner of speaking. The apparatus is still in a "pure" state (that is, represented by a single ray in its Hilbert space), and no matter how complicated this state may be and how incomplete our knowledge of it, it does not represent a statistical ensemble.

In a measurement of the form (6) the value of the system observable appears to remain undisturbed by the coupling. While measurements of this type do exist (for example, the Stern–Gerlach experiment in first approximation), it is much more frequently the case that the observable suffers a change. Bohr and Rosenfeld [3] have nevertheless shown that if suitable compensation devices are introduced, which may be represented by certain second-order corrections to the coupling (see DeWitt, [5]), the apparatus is able to record what the value of the system observable would have been had there been no coupling. Given a knowledge of the explicit form of the coupling it is always possible to express this hypothetical value in terms of the actual dynamical variables. Hence the observable of which this value is an eigenvalue is not itself hypothetical, and no inconsistency will arise if we take it to be the observable to which the label s refers on the right-hand side of Eq. (6). We must remember, however, that its expression in terms of conventional dynamical variables may be very complicated, so that it would generally be very difficult to find a coupling which would, in effect, reconstruct it for us and allow us to measure it a second time. Moreover, there is another difficulty which affects both the apparatus and system observables equally. In the interaction picture it is incorrect to refer to "position" or "momentum" as observables. Rather one must speak of the "position at a given time" or the "momentum at a given time." Similarly, the quantities s and A, which label the system and apparatus basis vectors, must be understood as involving particular instants or intervals of time in their intrinsic definition. Unless the observables, of which these quantities are the eigenvalues, commute with the Hamiltonian, neither the state $|s\rangle$ nor the state $|A\rangle$ can be referred to as *stationary*, either before or after the coupling interval, in spite of the fact that the vectors themselves are time-independent. This means that even if the coupling leaves the system observable undisturbed it will not be easy to repeat the observation at a later time. Moreover, it will become increasingly difficult, as time passes, to "read out" the contents of the apparatus memory.

Bearing all these cautionary remarks in mind we now examine the outcome of the measurement process when the initial state of "the world" has the general form (4). Using (3), (5), and (6), we easily find

$$|\Psi_1\rangle = \sum_s c_s |s\rangle \,|\Phi[s]\rangle \tag{7}$$

$$c_s\langle = \langle s | \psi \rangle \tag{8}$$

$$|\Phi[s]\rangle = \int |A + gs\rangle \Phi(A)\,dA \tag{9}$$

$$\Phi(A) = \langle A | \Phi \rangle \tag{10}$$

It is convenient to adopt the normalizations

$$\langle \psi | \psi \rangle = 1 \qquad \langle \Phi | \Phi \rangle = 1 \tag{11}$$

which yield

$$\langle \Psi_0 | \Psi_0 \rangle = \langle \Psi_1 | \Psi_1 \rangle = 1 \tag{12}$$

and

$$\sum_s w_s = 1 \qquad w_s = |c_s|^2 \tag{13}$$

$$\int |\Phi(A)|^2 \,dA = 1 \tag{14}$$

The final state vector (7) does not represent the system observable as having any unique value. Rather it is a linear superposition of vectors $|s\rangle|\Phi[s]\rangle$, each of which represents the system observable as having assumed one of its possible values and the apparatus as having observed that value. Everett and Wheeler have coined the expression "relative state" to denote the state of the apparatus represented by the vector $|\Phi[s]\rangle$. Relative to each possible state $|s\rangle$ of the system there is a corresponding apparatus state $|\Phi[s]\rangle$. For each possibility the observation will be a good one, that is, capable of distinguishing between adjacent values of s, provided

$$\Delta A \ll g\Delta s \tag{15}$$

where Δs is the spacing between adjacent values and

$$\Delta A^2 = \int (A - \langle A \rangle)^2 |\Phi(A)|^2 \, dA \qquad \langle A \rangle = \int A |\Phi(A)|^2 \, dA \tag{16}$$

Under these conditions we have

$$\langle \Phi[s] \mid \Phi[s'] \rangle = \delta_{ss'} \tag{17}$$

That is, the wave function of the apparatus takes the form of a packet which is initially single but which subsequently breaks up, as a result of the coupling to the system, into a multitude of mutually orthogonal packets, one for each value of s. We note that the packet structure of $\Phi(A)$ suggests again the utility of choosing an apparatus which is macroscopic. With a macroscopic apparatus it is possible to reduce to tolerable limits the packet spreading which inevitably occurs when the states $|A\rangle$ are not stationary, so that some degree of practical permanence may be imparted to the apparatus memory.

We have now reached the point at which Everett and Wheeler part company with the rest of the physics community. According to the conventional interpretation of quantum mechanics the wave function "collapses" immediately after the measurement. Instead of consisting of a multitude of packets it reduces to a single packet, and the state vector $|\Psi_1\rangle$ reduces to a corresponding element $|s\rangle | \Phi[s]\rangle$ of the superposition (7). To *which* element of the superposition it reduces one cannot say. One instead assigns a *probability distribution* to the possible outcomes, with weights given by Eq. (13).

The collapse of the wave function and the assignment of statistical weights do not follow from the Schrödinger equation. They are consequences of an external *a priori* metaphysics which is allowed to intervene at this point and *suspend* the Schrödinger equation, or rather replace the boundary conditions on its solution by those of the collapsed wave function. The destruction of continuity and hence of the causal structure of quantum mechanics which this entails is repugnant to many physicists, not least to Everett and Wheeler. But in attempting to save the situation the latter differ from all others in the boldness of their solution. In brief, they throw the *a priori* metaphysics out the window and assert that the wave function *never* collapses.

In defense of this stand it may be argued that the conventional interpretation of quantum mechanics confuses two concepts which ought really to be kept distinct, namely, probability as it relates to quantum mechanics and probability as it is understood in statistical mechanics. Quantum mechanics is a theory which attempts to describe in mathematical language a world in which chance is not a measure of our ignorance but is *absolute*. It is inevitable that it should lead to states which, like (7), undergo multiple fission, corresponding to the many possible outcomes of a given measurement. Such behavior is built into the formalism. However, precisely because quantum mechanical chance is *not* a measure of our ignorance, we ought not to tamper with the wave function merely because we acquire new information as a result of a measurement.

The obstacle to taking such a lofty view of things, of course, is that it forces us to believe in the "reality" of all the simultaneous "worlds" represented in the superposition (7), in each of which the measurement has yielded a different outcome. Nevertheless, this is precisely what Everett and Wheeler would have us believe. According to them the "real universe" is faithfully represented by (one might even say "isomorphic to") a state vector similar to (7) but of vastly greater complexity. This universe is constantly splitting into a stupendous number of branches, all resulting from the measurementlike interactions between its myriads of components.

To those of us who immediately object that we do not feel ourselves split, Everett and Wheeler have a ready reply: To the extent that we can be regarded simply as automata, and hence on a par with ordinary measuring apparatuses, the laws of quantum mechanics do not allow us to feel the split. The demonstrability of this reply, which in fact constitutes one of the steps in the proof of the Everett–Wheeler metatheorem that we are still in the midst of, reveals at once both the strength and the weakness of the Everett–Wheeler philosophy. Although it is a beautifully self-consistent philosophy it can never receive operational support in the laboratory. There is no experiment which can reveal the existence of the "other worlds" in a superposition like (7).

To prove this we begin by noting that although the operator of which the apparatus variable A is an eigenvalue has been called an "observable," it has so far not actually been observed. What happens if we now introduce a second apparatus which not only looks at the memory bank of the first apparatus but also carries out an independent direct check on the value of the system observable? If the splitting of the wave function is to be unobservable the results had better agree.

For the system we again introduce the basis vectors $|s\rangle$, and for the apparatus we introduce basis vectors $|A_1\rangle$ and $|A_2, B_2\rangle$, respectively. The variable B_2 of the second apparatus is to be used to measure A_1. The total measurement will be carried out in two steps. In the first, both apparatuses observe the system variable s, by means of a unitary transition of the form:

$$U_1(|s\rangle |A_1\rangle |A_2, B_2\rangle) = |s\rangle |A_1 + g_2 s\rangle |A_2 + g_2 s, B_2\rangle \qquad (18)$$

In the second step apparatus 2 reads the memory contents of apparatus 1. The unitary transition which accomplishes this is

$$U_2(|s\rangle|A_1\rangle|A_2, B_2\rangle) = |s\rangle|A_1\rangle|A_2, B_2 + g_{12}A_1\rangle \quad (19)$$

Suppose now the initial state of "the world" has the form

$$|\Psi_0\rangle = |\psi\rangle|\Phi_1\rangle|\Phi_2\rangle \quad (20)$$

Then at the end of the first measurement it takes the form

$$|\Psi_1\rangle = U_1|\Psi_0 = \sum_s c_s|s\rangle|\Phi_1[s]\rangle|\Phi_2[s]\rangle \quad (21)$$

where

$$|\Phi_1[s]\rangle = \int|A_1 + g_1 s\rangle\Phi_1(A_1)\,dA_1 \qquad \Phi_1(A_1) = \langle A_1|\Phi_1\rangle, \quad (22)$$

$$|\Phi_2[s]\rangle = \int dA_2 \int dB_2\,|A_2 + g_2 s, B_2\rangle\Phi_2(A_2, B_2)$$

$$\Phi_2(A_2, B_2) = \langle A_2, B_2|\Phi_2\rangle \quad (23)$$

and where standard normalization has been assumed. At the end of the second measurement it becomes

$$|\Psi_2\rangle = U_2|\Psi_1\rangle = \sum_s \int c_s|s\rangle|A_1 + g_1 s\rangle\Phi_1(A_1)|\Phi_2[s, A_1 + g_1 s]\rangle\,dA_1 \quad (24)$$

where

$$|\Phi_2[s, A_1]\rangle = \int dA_2 \int dB_2\,|A_2 + g_2 s, B_2 + g_{12}A_1\rangle\Phi_2(A_2, B_2) \quad (25)$$

In order that the first measurement be good we must have

$$\Delta A_1 \ll g_1\Delta s \quad \text{and} \quad \Delta A_2 \ll g_2\Delta s \quad (26)$$

where ΔA_1 and ΔA_2 are defined in an obvious manner. If, in addition, we require

$$\Delta A_1 \ll \Delta B_2/g_{12} \quad \text{and} \quad \Delta B_2 \ll g_{12}g_1\Delta s \quad (27)$$

then we may, to good approximation, write

$$\int dA_1 \int dA_2 \int dB_2\,|\Phi_1(A_1)|^2\Phi_2^*(A_2, B_2)\Phi_2(A_2, B_2 + g_{12}(A_1 - \langle A_1\rangle))$$

$$\approx \int dA_2 \int dB_2\,|\Phi_2(A_2, B_2)|^2 = 1 \quad (28)$$

from which it follows that

$$\|\,|\Psi_2\rangle - \sum_s c_s|s\rangle|\Phi_1[s]\rangle|\Phi_2[s, \langle A_1\rangle + g_1 s]\rangle\| \approx 0 \quad (29)$$

and hence

$$|\Psi_2\rangle \approx \sum_s c_s|s\rangle|\Phi_1[s]\rangle|\Phi_2[s, \langle A_1\rangle + g_1 s]\rangle \quad (30)$$

The final state vector is again revealed as a linear superposition of vectors, each of which represents the system observable as having assumed one of its possible values. Although the value varies from one element of the superposition to another, not only do both apparatuses within a given element observe the value appropriate to that element, but also, by straightforward communication, they agree that the results of their observations are identical. In the above example apparatus 2 may be assumed to have "known in advance" that the "mean value" of A_1 was $\langle A_1 \rangle$ in the initial state of apparatus 1. When, after the second measurement, apparatus 2 "sees" that this mean value has shifted to $\langle A_1 \rangle + g_1 s$, it then "knows" that apparatus 1 has obtained the same value for the system observable, namely, s, as it did.

As another check on the unobservability of measurement-induced splittings of the wave function we may consider repeated measurements on ensembles of systems. Let $|s_1\rangle$, $|s_2\rangle$, ... be basis vectors for a sequence of systems, arbitrary in number, and let the basis vectors of an apparatus which observes these systems be denoted by $|A_1, A_2, \ldots\rangle$, where each variable A_i represents the state of one cell in the apparatus memory. Let $i_1, i_2, \ldots$ be a sequence of integers, not necessarily all distinct, and let us assume that the apparatus undergoes a sequence of couplings with the system ensemble, of which the nth consists of an observation of the i_nth system. Since the integers i_n are not necessarily all distinct it will be convenient to assume that the s_i are eigenvalues of observables which commute with the total Hamiltonian and that each measurement is of the easily repeatable nondisturbing type. The nth measurement will then have the following effect on the basis vectors:

$$U_n(|s_1\rangle\, |s_2\rangle \cdots |A_1, A_2, \ldots, A_n, \ldots\rangle) = |s_1\rangle\, |s_2\rangle \cdots$$
$$|A_1, A_2, \ldots, A_n + g_n s_{i_n}, \ldots\rangle \quad (31)$$

If the initial state of "the world" has the form

$$|\Psi_0\rangle = |\psi_1\rangle\, |\psi_2\rangle \cdots |\Phi\rangle \quad (32)$$

then, after an arbitrary number of measurements, it becomes

$$|\Psi\rangle = \cdots U_2\, U_1 |\Psi_0\rangle = \sum_{s_1, s_2, \ldots} c_{s_1}^1 c_{s_2}^2 \cdots |s_1\rangle\, |s_2\rangle \cdots |\Phi[s_{i_1}, s_{i_2}, \ldots]\rangle \quad (33)$$

where

$$c_{s_i}^i = \langle s_i | \psi_i \rangle \quad (34)$$

$$|\Phi[s_{i_1}, s_{i_2}, \ldots]\rangle = \int dA_1 \int dA_2 \cdots |A_1 + g_1 s_{i_1}, A_2 + g_2 s_{i_2} \cdots\rangle$$
$$\times\, \Phi(A_1, A_2, \ldots) \quad (35)$$

$$\Phi(A_1, A_2 \cdots) = \langle A_1, A_2 \cdots |\Phi\rangle \quad (36)$$

Once again the final state vector consists of a superposition of "branches." The important thing to note about this vector is that although within each branch the apparatus may have observed a given system any number of times, it always records the *same* value for the system observable, namely, the value appropriate to the branch in question and not that of some other branch. The splitting into branches is thus again unobserved.

It is not difficult to devise increasingly complicated situations, in which, for example, the apparatus can make decisions by switching on various couplings depending on the outcome of other observations. It should be clear by now, however, that no inconsistencies will ever arise which would permit a given apparatus to be aware of more than one "world" at a time.

We now turn to the final issue which must be settled; namely, the question of the coefficients c_s in the superpositions (7), (21), (30), etc.[6] Thus far no *a priori* interpretation has been given to these coefficients. In order to find an interpretation let us again use the formalism of the preceding example. Only now let us assume that all the systems in the ensemble are identical and in identical states. This means

$$\langle s | \psi_i \rangle = c_s \qquad \text{for all } i \tag{37}$$

Furthermore, let us assume that the apparatus observes each system exactly once, in sequence, which means $i_n = n$ for all n. After N measurements the state vector of "the world" then takes the form

$$|\Psi_N\rangle = \sum_{s_1, s_2, \ldots} c_{s_1} c_{s_2} \cdots |s_1\rangle |s_2\rangle \cdots |\Phi[s_1, s_2, \ldots, s_N]\rangle \tag{38}$$

It will be observed that although every system is initially in exactly the same state as every other, the apparatus does not generally record a sequence of identical values for the system observable, even within a single element of the superposition. Each "memory sequence" $s_1, s_2, \ldots, s_N$ yields a certain distribution of possible values for the system observable. This distribution is characterized by the so-called *relative frequency function*:

$$f(s; s_1 \ldots s_N) = \frac{1}{N} \sum_{n=1}^{N} \delta_{s s_n} \tag{39}$$

We shall need the following easily verified properties of this function:

$$\sum_{s_1 \ldots s_N} f(s; s_1 \ldots s_N) w_{s_1} \ldots w_{s_N} = w_s \tag{40}$$

$$\sum_{s_1 \ldots s_N} [f(s; s_1 \ldots s_N) - w_s]^2 w_{s_2} \ldots w_{s_N} = \frac{1}{N} w_s (1 - w_s) \tag{41}$$

where the w's are any numbers which, taken all together, add up to unity.

---

[6] The following discussion is essentially due to R. N. Graham.

Let us choose for the w's the numbers defined in Eq. (13), and let us introduce the function

$$\delta(s_1 \ldots s_N) = \sum_s [f(s; s_1 \ldots s_N) - w_s]^2 \qquad (42)$$

This function measures the degree to which the sequence $s_1 \cdots s_N$ deviates from a random sequence with weights w_s. Let ε be an arbitrarily small positive number. We shall call the sequence $s_1 \ldots s_N$ *random* if $\delta(s_1 \ldots s_N) < \varepsilon$ and *nonrandom* otherwise. Suppose we remove from the superposition (38) all those elements for which the apparatus memory sequence is nonrandom. Denote the result by $|\Psi_N{}^\varepsilon\rangle$ and define

$$|\chi_N{}^\varepsilon\rangle = |\Psi\rangle - |\Psi_N{}^\varepsilon\rangle = \sum_{\substack{s_1, s_2, \ldots \\ \delta(s_1 \ldots s_N) \geq \varepsilon}} c_{s_1} c_{s_2} \ldots |s_1\rangle |s_2\rangle \ldots |\Phi[s_1 \cdots s_N]\rangle \qquad (43)$$

Then if each measurement is good, so that

$$\langle \Phi[s_1 \ldots s_N] \,|\, \Phi[s_1' \ldots s_N']\rangle \prod_{n=1}^{N} \delta_{s_n s_n'} \qquad (44)$$

[cf. Eq. (17)], we have

$$\langle \chi_N{}^\varepsilon \,|\, \Psi_N{}^\varepsilon\rangle = 0 \qquad (45)$$

and also

$$\langle \chi_N{}^\varepsilon \,|\, \chi_N{}^\varepsilon\rangle = \sum_{\substack{s_1, s_2, \ldots \\ \delta(s_1 \ldots s_N) \geq \varepsilon}} w_{s_1} w_{s_2} \cdots = \sum_{\substack{s_1 \ldots s_N \\ \delta(s_1 .. s_N) \geq \varepsilon}} w_{s_1} \cdots w_{s_N}$$

$$\leq \frac{1}{\varepsilon} \sum_{s_1 \ldots s_N} \delta(s_1 \ldots s_N) w_{s_1} \ldots w_{s_N} = \frac{1}{N\varepsilon} \sum_s w_s(1 - w_s) < \frac{1}{N\varepsilon} \qquad (46)$$

in which use is made of (41) and (42). From this it follows that no matter how small we choose ε we can always find an N big enough so that the norm of $|\chi_N{}^\varepsilon\rangle$ becomes smaller than any positive number. This means that

$$\lim_{N \to \infty} (|\Psi_N\rangle - |\Psi_N{}^\varepsilon\rangle) = 0 \qquad \text{for all } \varepsilon > 0 \qquad (47)$$

The conventional probability interpretation of quantum mechanics thus emerges from the formalism itself. Nonrandom memory sequences in the superposition (38) are "of measure zero" in the Hilbert space, in the limit $N \to \infty$.[7] Each automaton (that is, apparatus *cum* memory sequence)

---

[7] The number of systems with which we work and the number of cells in the apparatus memory can, of course, never be infinite. However, all that we require is that the number of systems in the above derivation, although finite, be arbitrarily large. A given memory sequence will, if sufficiently long, approximate a random sequence with overwhelming probability.

It is worth noting that nowhere in these arguments does the imposition of a normalization condition on the initial state vectors play an essential role. If we had started with nonnormalized states we should simply have been forced to renormalize the weights w_s in order to relate them to the relative frequency function. Once the conventional probability interpretation is derived one then recognizes that the physical objects are the rays in Hilbert space and not the vectors themselves.

in the superposition sees the world obey the familiar statistical quantum laws. However, there exists no outside agency which can designate which branch of the superposition is to be regarded as the real world. All are equally real, and yet each is unaware of the others. These conclusions obviously admit of immediate extension to the world of cosmology. Its wave function is like a tree with an enormous number of branches. Each branch corresponds to a possible universe-as-we-actually-see-it. If I were facetious, I would now point out that human history has taken place along one of these branches, and hence human philosophy, and in particular the Everett–Wheeler interpretation of quantum mechanics, has, as it were, arisen from the formalism itself! This completes the proof of the Everett–Wheeler metatheorem.

There remains to be discussed only the question of the practical application of the formalism. How does it happen that I am able, without running into inconsistencies, to include as much or as little as I like of the real world of cosmology in my Hamiltonian? Why should I be so fortunate as to be able, in practice, to avoid dealing with the wave function of the universe? The answer to these questions is to be found in the statistical implications of sequences of measurements of the kind which led to the state vector (38). Consider one of the memory sequences in this state vector (that is, one of the elements of the superposition). This memory sequence defines an average value for the system observable, given by

$$\langle s \rangle_{s_1 \ldots s_N} = \sum_s sf(s; s_1 \ldots s_N) \tag{48}$$

If the sequence is random, as it is overwhelmingly likely to be, then this average will differ only by an amount of order ε from the average

$$\langle s \rangle = \sum_s s w_s \tag{49}$$

But the latter average may also be expressed in the form

$$\langle s \rangle = \langle \psi | \mathbf{s} | \psi \rangle \tag{50}$$

where $|\psi\rangle$ is the initial state vector of any one of the identical systems and **s** is the *operator* of which the s's are the eigenvalues. In this form the basis vectors $|s\rangle$ do not appear. It is evident therefore that had I chosen to introduce a different apparatus, designed to measure some observable **r** not equal to **s**, a sequence of repeated measurements would have yielded me in this case an average approximately equal to

$$\langle r \rangle = \langle \psi | \mathbf{r} | \psi \rangle \tag{51}$$

In terms of the basis vectors $|s\rangle$ this average is given by

$$\langle r \rangle = \sum_{s, s'} c_s^* \langle s | \mathbf{r} | s' \rangle c_{s'} \tag{52}$$

Now suppose, however, that I first measure **s** and *then* perform a statistical analysis on **r**. This could be accomplished by introducing a second apparatus which performs a sequence of observations on a set of identical two-component systems all in identical states given by the vector $|\Psi_1\rangle$ of Eq. (7). Each of the latter systems is composed of one of the original systems together with an apparatus which has just measured the observable **s**. In view of the packet orthogonality relations (17), I shall find for the average of **r** in this case

$$\langle r \rangle = \langle \Psi_1 | \mathbf{r} | \Psi_1 \rangle = \sum_s w_s \langle s | \mathbf{r} | s \rangle = \text{tr} \, (\rho_s \mathbf{r}) \tag{53}$$

where ρ_s is the density operator

$$\rho_s = \sum_s |s\rangle w_s \langle s| \tag{54}$$

The averages (52) and (53) are generally not equal. In (53) the measurement of *s*, which the first apparatus has performed, has destroyed the quantum interference effects which are still present in (52). This means that the elements of the superposition (7) may, insofar as the subsequent *quantum* behavior of the system is concerned, be treated as if they were members of a statistical ensemble. This is what allows us, *in practice*, to collapse the wave packet after a measurement has occurred. It is also what permits us to introduce, and study the quantum behavior of, systems having well-defined initial states, without at the same time introducing into the mathematical formalism the apparatuses which prepared the systems in those states.

It is, of course, possible in principle (although virtually impossible in practice) to restore the interference effects by bringing the apparatus packets back together again. But then the correlations between system and apparatus are destroyed, and no measurement results. If one attempts to maintain the correlations by sneaking in a second apparatus to "have a look" before the packets are brought back together, then the state vector of the second apparatus must be introduced, and the separation of *its* packets will destroy the interference effects. You cannot get around the laws of quantum mechanics.

REFERENCES

1. H. Everett, III, *Rev. Mod. Phys.* **29**, 454 (1957).

2. J. A. Wheeler, *Rev. Mod. Phys.* **29**, 463 (1957).

3. N. Bohr and L. Rosenfeld, det Kgl. Danske Vidensk. Selskab, *Mat.-fys. Med.* **12**, No. 8 (1933); *Phys. Rev.* **78**, 794 (1950).

4. P. A. M. Dirac, *The Principles of Quantum Mechanics*, Third Edition (Oxford University Press, 1947).

5. B. S. DeWitt, *Dynamical Theory of Groups and Fields*, Gordon and Breach, 1965), pp. 16–29.

XIII

Progress and Goals in
Renormalization Theory

KLAUS HEPP

For twenty years renormalization has been a magic cure for the "catastrophies" of relativistic quantum mechanics.   Since the pioneering work of Dyson, Feynman, Schwinger, and Tomonaga [1] we have learned to understand better the individual terms in the relevant perturbation expansions and finite relations among them [2].   Our expectations in the "better future" have been cast into frameworks as general quantum field theory [3, 4] and analytic S-matrix theory [5], and renormalized perturbation theory is very useful to illustrate some of their structure.   Yet only slowly, progress is being made in building up models for relativistic quantum systems, whose existence can be controlled in rigorous mathematical terms.

These notes are not addressed to physicists working in relativistic quantum mechanics: our exposition is not mathematical enough.   The material was informally presented to fill the image gap between mathematicians and physicists, to provide some background to Prof. Lascoux' lectures and because the author felt strongly that many consistent streaks of beauty in the present nontheory will eventually fit together.

FOCK SPACE AND RENORMALIZATION OF THE "GALI–LEE" MODEL

It is interesting to study quantum theories with an unbounded number of particles.   Fock space is the natural receptacle for such theories (until

333

one encounters Haag's theorem [3]). In nonrelativistic quantum mechanics we define

$$\mathcal{H}_0^B = \mathcal{H}_0^F = \mathbf{C} \qquad \mathcal{H}_1^B = \mathcal{H}_1^F = L^2(\mathbf{R}^3, d\underline{x}) \tag{1}$$

with $d\underline{x}$: Lebesgue measure, $\underline{x} \in \mathbf{R}^3$.

$$\mathcal{H}_n^B = \mathcal{H}_1^{\mathfrak{o}n} \qquad \mathcal{H}_n^F = \mathcal{H}_1^{an}$$

where $\mathfrak{o}n$, an stand for the symmetric and antisymmetric tensor product of n copies. The symmetric and antisymmetric algebras

$$S(\mathcal{H}_1) = \mathcal{H}^B = \bigoplus_{n=0}^{\infty} \mathcal{H}_n^B \qquad A(\mathcal{H}_1) = \mathcal{H}^F = \bigoplus_{n=0}^{\infty} \mathcal{H}_n^F \tag{2}$$

are called Fock spaces of one species of particles obeying Bose (symmetric) or Fermi (antisymmetric) statistics. Creation and annihilation operators are defined on any $\phi^B \in \mathcal{H}^B$, $\phi^B = \{\phi_n^B\}$, by

$$(a^B(\underline{p})\phi^B)_n(\underline{p}_1, \dots, \underline{p}_n) = (n+1)^{1/2}\phi_{n+1}^B(\underline{p}, \underline{p}_1, \dots, \underline{p}_n) \tag{3}$$

$$(a^B(\underline{p})^*\phi^B)_n(\underline{p}_1, \dots, \underline{p}_n) = (n)^{-1/2}\sum_{j=1}^{n} \delta(\underline{p} - \underline{p}_j)\phi_{n-1}^B(\underline{p}_1, \dots, \underline{p}_j, \dots, \underline{p}_n) \tag{4}$$

and similarly for Fermi operators $a^F(\underline{p})$, $a^F(\underline{p})^*$ with a factor $(-1)^j$ on the right-hand side of (4). Evidently $f \in L^2(\mathbf{R}^3) \rightsquigarrow a(f) = \int d\underline{p} f(\underline{p})a(\underline{p})$ and $a(f)^* = \int d\underline{p} f(\underline{p})a(\underline{p})^*$ define operator-valued tempered distributions. The $a^F(f)$, $a^F(f)^*$ are bounded operators in $\mathcal{H}^F$, as it is most easily seen from the commutation relations:

$$\begin{aligned} [a(\underline{p}), a(\underline{q})^*]_{\pm} &= \delta(\underline{p} - \underline{q}) \\ [a(\underline{p}), a(\underline{q})]_{\pm} &= [a(\underline{p})^*, a(\underline{q})^*]_{\pm} = 0 \end{aligned} \tag{5}$$

where $[A, B]_{\pm} = AB \pm BA$ and "+" applies to fermions, "−" to bosons. Let $\Omega_0 = \{\phi_0 = 1, \phi_n = 0, n > 1\}$. Then $a(\underline{p})\Omega_0 = 0$ for all $\underline{p}$. Ω_0 is cyclic with respect to the smeared-out polynomials in the creation operators. In $\mathcal{H}$ a projective unitary representation of the Galilei group G

$$g \in G: \underline{x} \rightsquigarrow R\underline{x} + \underline{v}t + \underline{a}, \qquad R \in SO(3), \quad \underline{v}, \underline{a} \in \mathbf{R}^3 \tag{6}$$

$$t \rightsquigarrow t + b$$

is trivially defined [6], the 1-parameter group of the time-translations being generated by the free Hamiltonian H_0:

$$(e^{iH_0 t}\phi)_n(\underline{p}_1, \dots, \underline{p}_n) = \exp\left(i \sum_{i=1}^{n} \frac{\underline{p}_i^2}{2m} t\right)\phi_n(\underline{p}_1, \dots, \underline{p}_n) \tag{7}$$

$$H_0 = \int d\underline{p} \frac{\underline{p}^2}{2m} a(\underline{p})^*a(\underline{p})$$

In this nonrelativistic framework quite interesting dynamical situations can be rigged up. The usual Schrödinger theory for identical particles with pair interaction leaves each $\mathscr{H}_n$ invariant: let $v(p) = v(-p)^* \in L^2(\mathbf{R}^3)$ and define

$$V = \frac{1}{2} \int \prod_{i=1}^{3} dp_i \, a\left(\frac{p_1}{2} + p_2\right)^* a\left(\frac{p_1}{2} - p_2\right)^* v(p_2 - p_3) a\left(\frac{p_1}{2} + p_3\right) a\left(\frac{p_1}{2} - p_3\right)$$

(8)

Then $V|\mathscr{H}_n$ gives the p-space representation of the sum of 2-body potentials. $H_0 + V$ is self-adjoint in $\mathscr{H}$ and can, for $v(p) = v(|p|)$, be imbedded as infinitesimal generator of time-translations into a projective unitary representation of the Galilei group.

A very interesting illustration of renormalization is the Lee model [7], which in its Galilei invariant version [6, 8] incorporates several nontrivial features:

    a. Pure Hilbert space theory (no "ghosts")
    b. Particle production and annihilation
    c. Point interaction
    d. Ten-parameter symmetry group

The Fock space is $\mathscr{H} = \mathscr{H}^F \otimes \mathscr{H}^B$, where $\mathscr{H}^B$ is the symmetric algebra over the 1-particle space of the θ-particle and $\mathscr{H}^F$ the antisymmetric algebra over the direct sum of 1-particle spaces of the N- and V-particles.

We have the following nontrivial (anti-) commutation relations:

$$[N(p), N(q)^*]_+ = [V(p), V(q)^*]_+ = [\theta(p), \theta(q)^*]_- = \delta(p - q) \qquad (9)$$

The free Hamiltonian H_0 is

$$H_0 = H_0(U_0) = \int dp \, \frac{p^2}{2m_1} N(p)^* N(p) + \int dp \, \frac{p^2}{2m_2} \theta(p)^* \theta(p)$$

$$+ \int dp \left(\frac{p^2}{2m_3} + U_0\right) V(p)^* V(p) \quad (10)$$

The elementary interaction is the tranisition $N + \theta \leftrightarrow V$. Let $\chi \in \mathscr{S}(\mathbf{R}^3)$ [9] be a spherically symmetric cutoff function with $0 \leqslant \chi \leqslant 1$ and define

$$H_1{}^\chi = \lambda_0 \int dp_1 \, dp_2 \, \chi(p_1 + p_2)[V(p_1 + p_2)^* N(p_1)\theta(p_2)$$

$$+ N(p_1)^*\theta(p_2)^* V(p_1 + p_2)] \quad (11)$$

The full Hamiltonian is $H^\chi = H_0 + H_1{}^\chi$. Then there are two parameters in the theory: the "bare" internal energy U_0 of the bare V-particle and the bare coupling constant λ_0 between the bare N-, θ-, and V-particles. The diminutive "bare" expresses the fact that in the free-particle basis of

Fock space the full Hamiltonian is no longer diagonal and that physical particles correspond to (generalized) eigenstates of H^χ. The cutoff χ is necessary to make $H_1{}^\chi$ densely defined: otherwise $H_1{}^\chi$ would be inapplicable to any state with a finite number of bare particles with at least one of the V-species.

There are important symmetries in the theory. Apparently the number operators $N_1 = N_V + N_N$, $N_2 = N_V + N_\theta$ commute with H_0 and $H_1{}^\chi$. Therefore the dynamics factorizes in subspaces $\mathscr{H}_{n_1 n_2}$ of eigenvalues n_1, n_2 of these operators:

$$\mathscr{H} = \bigoplus_{n_1, n_2 = 0}^{\infty} \mathscr{H}_{n_1 n_2} \tag{12}$$

$H_1{}^\chi$ restricted to any $\mathscr{H}_{n_1 n_2}$ is bounded and therefore H^χ is self-adjoint. If one requires [10]

$$m_3 = m_1 + m_2 \tag{13}$$

for the masses m_1, m_2, m_3, of the bare N-, θ-, and V-particles, then H^χ can be again imbedded into a projective unitary representation of the Galilei group.

Evidently, interaction occurs only in those subspaces $\mathscr{H}_{n_1 n_2}$ where $n_1 \cdot n_2 \neq 0$. Therefore the vacuum is an eigenstate of H^χ and bare and physical N- and θ-particles coincide. The first nontrivial sector has $n_1 = n_2 = 1$. It will turn out that the necessary reinterpretation of the theory in the limit of point interaction ($\chi \to 1$) can be entirely defined from the (1, 1)-sector, or in physical terms: the internal energy and charge renormalization in this sector carries consistently through into all $\mathscr{H}$.

Let $|N(\underline{p}_1)\theta(\underline{p}_2)\rangle = |N\theta(\underline{p}, \underline{q})\rangle = N(\underline{p}_1)^*\theta(\underline{p}_2)^*\Omega_0$ and $|V(\underline{p})\rangle = V(\underline{p})^*\Omega_0$ be the improper basis of $\mathscr{H}_{1,1}$. We have separated the center-of-mass movement: $\underline{p} = \underline{p}_1 + \underline{p}_2$, $\underline{q} = m_3^{-1}(m_2 \underline{p}_1 - m_1 \underline{p}_2)$. The eigenvalue problem for H^χ in $\mathscr{H}_{1,1}$ can be solved explicitly [7]: there exists a discrete eigenstate $|V(\underline{p})\rangle^\chi$, the physical V-particle,

$$H^\chi |V(\underline{p})\rangle^\chi = \left(\frac{p^2}{2m_3} + U_\chi\right) |V(\underline{p})\rangle^\chi \tag{14}$$

and a continuum of N- θ-scattering states

$$H^\chi |N\theta(\underline{p}, \underline{q})\rangle_\pm^\chi = \left(\frac{p^2}{2m_3} + \omega\right) |N\theta(\underline{p}, \underline{q})\rangle_\pm^\chi \tag{15}$$

of energy ω in the center of mass system ($\omega = q^2/2m$, $m_3 m = m_1 m_2$). The "$\pm$" stands for outgoing or incoming boundary conditions: for $f_1, f_2 \in \mathscr{S}(\mathbf{R}^3)$

$$|N(f_1)\theta(f_2)\rangle_\pm^\chi = \int d\underline{p}_1 \, d\underline{p}_2 f_1(\underline{p}_1) f_2(\underline{p}_2) |N(\underline{p}_1)\theta(\underline{p}_2)\rangle_\pm^\chi \tag{16}$$

is the wave packet of the interacting N- θ-system at time $t = 0$, which for $t \to \pm\infty$ can be described by a freely moving N- and θ-particle with wave packets f_1, f_2, or in the language of Hilbert space

$$\lim_{t \to \pm\infty} \|e^{iHt}|N(f_1)\theta(f_2)\rangle_{\pm}^{\chi} - e^{iH_0 t}|N(f_1)\theta(f_2)\rangle\| = 0 \tag{17}$$

The solutions of (14) and (15) are given by

$$|V(\underline{p})\rangle^{\chi} = Z_{\chi}^{1/2}|V(\underline{p})\rangle - \lambda_{\chi}\int\frac{\chi(\omega)\,dq}{\omega - U_{\chi}}|N\theta(\underline{p},\underline{q})\rangle, \tag{18}$$

$$|N\theta(\underline{p},\underline{q})\rangle_{\pm}^{\chi} = |N\theta(\underline{p},\underline{q})\rangle + \frac{\lambda_{\chi}\chi(\omega)}{h_{\chi}(\omega - U_{\chi} \pm io)}$$

$$\times \left\{Z_{\chi}^{1/2}|V(\underline{p})\rangle + \lambda_{\chi}\int\frac{\chi(\omega')\,dq'}{\omega - \omega' \pm io}|N\theta(\underline{p},\underline{q}')\rangle\right\} \tag{19}$$

where

$$Z_{\chi}^{1/2} \in \mathbf{R} \qquad \lambda_{\chi} = Z_{\chi}^{1/2} \cdot \lambda_0$$

and

$$Z_{\chi} = 1 - \lambda_{\chi}^2 \int\frac{dq\chi(\omega)^2}{(\omega - U_{\chi})^2} \tag{20}$$

$$U_{\chi} = U_0 - \lambda_0^2 \int\frac{dq\chi(\omega)^2}{(\omega - U_{\chi})} \tag{21}$$

$$h_{\chi}(y) = y\left(Z_{\chi} + \lambda_{\chi}^2 \int\frac{\chi(\omega)^2\,dq}{(\omega - U_{\chi})(\omega - U_{\chi} - y)}\right) \tag{22}$$

The requirement that this solution stay in Hilbert space is $0 < Z_{\chi} < 1$, which is possible in the finite range

$$|\lambda_{\chi}| < \lambda_c = \frac{1}{\pi}\left(\frac{-U}{2m^3}\right)^{1/4}$$

even in the limit $\chi \to 1$.

The observable parameters of the theory are λ_{χ} and U_{χ}: λ_{χ}^2 is determined by the limit $\omega \to 0$ of the $N - \theta$ scattering amplitude (as the fine-structure constant $\alpha = e^2/4\pi$ in quantum electrodynamics) and $U_{\chi} < 0$, the internal energy of the physical V-particle, is measurable by thresholds in the $N\theta\theta$-scattering. Therefore a reasonable limit of the theory for $\chi \to 1$ is expected, if one keeps the physical parameters fixed: $\lambda = \lambda_{\chi}$, $|\lambda| < \lambda_c$, and $U = U_{\chi} < 0$ and varies $\lambda_0 = \lambda_0(\lambda, U, \chi)$ and $U_0 = U_0(\lambda, U, \chi)$ accordingly. This is the basic idea of renormalization theory, which has been so extremely successful in quantum electrodynamics.

What happens for $\chi \to 1$? Nothing really in terms of the generalized eigenfunctions $|V(\underline{p})\rangle^\chi$ and $|N\theta(\underline{p}, \underline{q})\rangle^\chi_\pm$! They stay a complete system of improper vectors in $\mathcal{H}_{1,1}$, and if one defines

$$\exp(iH^1 t)|V(\underline{p})\rangle^1 = \exp i\left(\frac{\underline{p}^2}{2m_3} + U\right)t|V(\underline{p})\rangle^1$$

$$\exp(iH^1 t)|N\theta(\underline{p}, \underline{q})\rangle^1_\pm = \exp i\left(\frac{\underline{p}^2}{2m_3} + \omega\right)t|N\theta(\underline{p}, \underline{q})\rangle^1_\pm$$

(23)

then one obtains by Stone's theorem a self-adjoint renormalized Hamiltonian H^1. Formally we see from

$$H^\chi = H_0(U) + H_1{}^\chi + (U_0 - U)\int d\underline{p}\,V(\underline{p})^* V(\underline{p})$$

(24)

that H^1 is obtained by the subtraction of an infinite self-energy counterterm. In the limit $\chi \to 1$ the Haag–Ruelle asymptotic condition (17) remains valid, while $\exp(iH_0 t)|V\rangle$ only converges weakly toward $\exp(iH^1 t)|V\rangle^1 \cdot Z_1^{1/2}$.

The next interesting sector is the $N\theta\theta$-sector $\mathcal{H}_{1,2}$. Here the proposal is first to determine the scattering states

$$H^\chi |V(\underline{p}_1)\theta(\underline{p}_2)\rangle^\chi_\pm = \left(\frac{\underline{p}_1{}^2}{2m_3} + U + \frac{\underline{p}_2{}^2}{2m_2}\right)|V(\underline{p}_1)\theta(\underline{p}_2)\rangle^\chi_\pm$$

(25)

$$H^\chi |N(\underline{p}_1)\theta(\underline{p}_2)\theta(\underline{p}_3)\rangle^\chi_\pm = \left(\frac{\underline{p}_1{}^2}{2m_1} + \frac{\underline{p}_2{}^2}{2m_2} + \frac{\underline{p}_3{}^3}{2m_2}\right)|N(\underline{p}_1)\theta(\underline{p}_2)\theta(\underline{p}_3)\rangle^\chi_\pm$$

(26)

and then to prove completeness of these generalized eigenfunctions in $\mathcal{H}_{1,2}$ and continuity in χ. Finally one would define H^1 by its spectral projections.

Schrader [8] has "solved" the singular integral equation for this 3-body problem with recoil by estimates similar to those of Faddeev [11]. His results are positive for sufficiently small values of $|\lambda|$, proving the consistency of renormalization (24) in the first nontrivial sector. Although the coupled integral equations for the higher sectors become discouragingly complicated, our experience with the Schrödinger N-body problem [12] makes us believe that the renormalized Gali–Lee model is well-defined and asymptotically complete for fixed $U < 0$ and sufficiently small coupling constant $|\lambda| < \lambda_c = \lambda_c(n_1, n_2)$.

FUN AND FRUSTRATION WITH RELATIVISTIC HAMILTONIANS

It is tempting to pursue the same approach as in the Lee model and to explore relativistic Hamiltonians in Fock space. Although we shall encounter immediately formidable difficulties, it appears that in modern mathematical language, supported by powerful estimates, the classical difficulties of Hamiltonian quantum field theory can slowly be dissolved.

An interesting class of potentials in Fock space are polynomials in smeared-out creation and annihilation operators: $V = \sum\limits_{k,l} V_{k,l}$

$$V_{k,l} = \int \prod_{i=1}^{k+l} dp_i\, v_{k,l}(\underline{p}_1, \ldots, \underline{p}_{k+l}) a(\underline{p}_1)^* \cdots a(\underline{p}_k)^* a(\underline{p}_{k+1}) \cdots a(\underline{p}_{k+l}) \quad (27)$$

V is densely defined, if, for example, $v_{k,l} \in L^2(\mathbf{R}^{3(k+l)})$, and symmetric, if

$$v_{k,l}(\underline{p}_1, \ldots, \underline{p}_{k+l})^* = v_{l,k}(\underline{p}_{k+l}, \ldots, \underline{p}_1)$$

The first difficulty arises, if one wants V to commute with all space-translations $U_0(\underline{a}, \mathbf{1})$ in Fock space. $U_0(\underline{a}, \mathbf{1})VU_0(\underline{a}, \mathbf{1})^{-1} = V$ implies that $v_{k,l}$ depends on $\underline{p}_1 + \cdots - \underline{p}_{k+l}$ only via a δ-function. Then, however, every $V_{k,0} \neq 0$, $k \neq 0$, leads out of Fock space, since the δ-function in the wave functions of the images is not locally square integrable. Fock space translation invariance can hold only for potentials without "vacuum polarization," for which $V\Omega_0 = c\Omega_0$ holds, as in the Lee model. This observation can be refined to Haag's theorem [3].

A second difficulty occurs if $v_{k,l}$ is not sufficiently decreasing at infinity and $k > 1$. Such an "ultraviolet" (UV) divergence was the main obstacle in the Lee model in the limit of point interaction. Since all sets in $\mathbf{R}^4$ except for $\{0\}$ invariant under the homogeneous Lorentz group $L_+{}^\uparrow$ are unbounded, one is (in contradistinction to Galilei-invariant theories) quite naturally led to point interactions in relativistic theories. Sometimes it will be possible to cure the UV divergences by renormalization.

Relativistic quantum mechanics in Fock space can be built on a rich class of operator-valued distributions with a very attractive property— locality. In the simplest case of a neutral scalar particle of mass m, the 1-particle space $\mathscr{H}_1$ is $L^2(\mathbf{R}^3, m(\underline{p})^{-1}d\underline{p})$, where $m(\underline{p}) = (m^2 + \underline{p}^2)^{1/2}$, $m > 0$. We distinguish vectors in $\mathbf{R}^4$ (p, k, x) and their space $(\underline{p}, \underline{k}, \underline{x})$ and time (p^0, k^0, x^0) components. The Poincare group $iL_+{}^\uparrow$ operates on space-time by translation and (Lorentz-) rotation $:(a, \Lambda): x \in \mathbf{R}^4 \rightsquigarrow \Lambda x + a$, where $a \in \mathbf{R}^4$ and $\Lambda \in SL(4, \mathbf{R})$ leaves $(x, y) = x^0 y^0 - \underline{x} \cdot \underline{y}$ invariant as well as the direction of time. $\mathscr{H}_1$ carries a unitary irreducible representation $U_0(a, \Lambda)$ of $iL_+{}^\uparrow$:

$$(U_0(a, \Lambda)f)(\underline{p}) = \exp{(i(p, a))}f(\Lambda^{-1}p)|_{p^0 = m(\underline{p})} \quad (28)$$

Our Fock space is $\mathscr{H} = S(\mathscr{H}_1)$, with $\Omega_0 = \{1, 0, \ldots\}$ as vacuum state and $U_0(a, \Lambda)$ canonically extended to $\mathscr{H}_1$. Creation and annihilation operators are defined as in (3) and (4) with $(n + 1)^{1/2}$, $(n)^{-1/2}$ replaced by

$$\left(\frac{n+1}{2m(\underline{p})}\right)^{1/2}, \left(\frac{n}{2m(\underline{p})}\right)^{-1/2}$$

respectively.

The free field

$$A_0(x) = (2\pi)^{-3/2} \int_{p^0 = m(\underline{p})} \frac{d\underline{p}}{2m(\underline{p})} \{a(\underline{p})e^{-i(p,x)} + a(\underline{p})e^{i(p,x)}\} \qquad (29)$$

satisfies as operator-valued tempered distribution on a dense, invariant domain

$$(\Box + m^2)A_0(x) = 0$$
$$U_0(a, \Lambda)A_0(x)U_0(a, \Lambda)^{-1} = A_0(\Lambda x + a) \qquad (30)$$

where
$$\Box = \frac{\partial^2}{\partial x^{02}} - \Delta$$

In addition, A_0 is local, due to the choice of symmetric statistics [13], that is $[A_0(x), A_0(y)]_- = 0$ for spacelike $x - y$, $(x - y, x - y) < 0$. A_0 decomposes naturally into a creation (A_+) and annihilation part (A_-). Then Wick monomials of A_0 are defined by

$$: A_0(x_1) \cdots A_0(x_n) := \sum_{X \subset \{1,\ldots,n\}} \prod_{i \in X} A_+(x_i) \prod_{j \in CX} A_-(x_j) \qquad (31)$$

$: A_0(x)^n :$ is again a tempered operator-valued distribution and satisfies [14]:

$$U_0(a, \Lambda) : A_0(x)^n : U_0(a, \Lambda)^{-1} = : A_0(\Lambda x + a)^n : \qquad (32)$$
$$[: A_0(x)^m :, : A_0(y)^n :]_- = 0 \quad \text{for all } m, n \quad \text{and all } (x - y, x - y) < 0$$

We shall see soon why Wick polynomials of free fields and their generalizations [15, 16] are attractive building stones for relativistic Hamiltonians.

Our goal is to construct a model for an interacting relativistic quantum system. For a theory of one kind of massive neutral scalar particle the following general requirements are often introduced as "axioms" [17, 3, 18]:

(A): The Hilbert space of states $\mathcal{H}$ has to carry two basis systems of the structure of Fock spaces over $L^2(\mathbf{R}^3, m(p)^{-1} dp)$:

$$\mathcal{H} = \bigoplus_{n=0}^{\infty} \mathcal{H}_n^{\text{in}} = \bigoplus_{n=0}^{\infty} \mathcal{H}_n^{\text{out}}. \qquad (33)$$

$\mathcal{H}_n^{\text{in}}$ and $\mathcal{H}_n^{\text{out}}$ are the subspaces spanned by incoming and outgoing n-particle scattering states. The unitary representations of $iL_+^\uparrow$ connected with $\mathcal{H}^{\text{in}}$ and $\mathcal{H}^{\text{out}}$ are to coincide: $U_0^{\text{in}}(a, \Lambda) = U_0^{\text{out}}(a, \Lambda) \equiv U(a, \Lambda)$. There has to be particle production: $\mathcal{H}_2^{\text{in}} \neq \mathcal{H}_2^{\text{out}}$.

(B): A local relativistic quantum field $A(x)$ should "interpolate" between A_0^{in} and A_0^{out} by the Haag–Ruelle asymptotic condition [4]:

$$[A(x), A(y)]_- = 0 \quad \text{for} \quad (x - y, x - y) < 0$$
$$U(a, \Lambda)A(x)U(a, \Lambda)^{-1} = A(\Lambda x + a) \qquad (34)$$
$$P_1 A(x)\Omega \neq 0$$

where $\Omega \equiv \Omega_0^{in} = \Omega_0^{out}$ and P_1 is the projector on $\mathcal{H}_1^{in} = \mathcal{H}_1^{out}$. The relations (34) are to be valid as operator-valued generalized functions [18] on a dense invariant domain containing Ω.

The concentration on local fields (or local rings [19, 20] with a more general attitude) is as reactionary as our outline of the construction of relativistic models and perturbation expansions. It is the personal belief of the lecturer that the modest, but always reasonable, predictions based on (A) and (B) can be justified and extended to a qualitative understanding of relativistic dynamics, once we master the constructive approach to quantum field theory.

The simplest reasonable potential V for a relativistic Hamiltonian is the A^4 interaction in 2-dimensional space-time. Here only a space cutoff is necessary:

$$V(R) = \lambda \int d\underline{x} h_R(\underline{x}) : A_0(\underline{x})^4 : \tag{35}$$

Here $\lambda \in \mathbf{R}$ is the coupling constant and for $h_R \in \mathscr{S}(\mathbf{R}^1)$ we assume $h_R \geqslant 0$ and $h_R(\underline{x}) = 1$ for $|\underline{x}| \leqslant R$. $V(R)$ is a real, symmetric operator having a common dense domain with H_0, as one sees in p-space:

$$V(R) = \lambda \int \prod_{i=1}^{4} \frac{dp_i}{\sqrt{m(p_i)}} h_R(\sum p_i) \left\{ \prod_{i=1}^{4} a(\underline{p}_i)^* + 4 \prod_{i=1}^{3} a(\underline{p}_i)^* a(-\underline{p}_4) \right.$$

$$\left. + 6 \prod_{i=1}^{2} a(\underline{p}_i)^* \prod_{i=3}^{4} a(-\underline{p}_i) + 4 a(\underline{p}_1) \prod_{i=2}^{4} a(-\underline{p}_i) + \prod_{i=1}^{4} a(-\underline{p}_i) \right\} \tag{36}$$

Thus $H(R) = H_0 + V(R)$ has at least one self-adjoint extension. A proof of the essential self-adjointness of $H(R)$ on some standard domain would be desirable to support the following heuristic discussion [21].

One defines Heisenberg field operators

$$A_R(\underline{x})^n = \exp(iH(R)x^0) : A_0(\underline{x})^n : \exp(-iH(R)x^0) \tag{37}$$

If R is sufficiently large, one obtains a local solution of the superficially attractive field equation

$$(\square + m^2) A_R(x) = 4\lambda A_R(x)^3 \tag{38}$$

as one sees from the free-field commutation relations:

$$\frac{\partial^2}{\partial x^{02}} A_R(x) = -\exp(iH(R)x^0)[H(R), [H(R), A_0(\underline{x})]_-]_- \exp(-iH(R)x^0)$$

$$[A_0(\underline{x}), : A_0(\underline{y})^n :]_- = 0 \tag{39}$$

$$[[H_0, A_0(\underline{x})]_-, : A_0(\underline{y})^n :]_- = n : A_0(\underline{y})^{n-1} : \delta(\underline{x} - \underline{y}).$$

More important is the observation [22] that at least in perturbation theory

$A_R(x)^n$ is independent of R, for sufficiently large R, and local with respect to $A_R(y)^m$. The perturbation series in question can be obtained by iterating

$$U_R(t) = e^{iH_0 t} e^{-iH(R)t} = 1 - i \int_0^t ds\, V(R, s) U_R(s) \tag{40}$$

where $V(R, t) = \exp(iH_0 t) V(R) \exp(-iH_0 t)$. One obtains

$$e^{-iH(R)t} = e^{-iH_0 t} \sum_{n=0}^{\infty} (-i)^n \int_0^t dt_1 \int_0^{t_1} dt_2 \cdots \int_0^{t_{n-1}} dt_n\, V(R, t_1) \cdots V(R, t_n)$$

$$A_R(x) = U_R(x_0)^{-1} A_0(x) U_R(x_0) = A_0(x) + i \int_0^{x_0} dt [V(R, t), A_0(x)]_- + \cdots \tag{41}$$

The multiple commutators on the right-hand side, as

$$[V(R, t), A_0(x)]_- = i\lambda \int dy\, h_R(\underline{y})[: A_0(t, \underline{y})^4 :, A_0(x)]_- \tag{42}$$

depend only on $h_R(\underline{y})$ for $|y| \leqslant |x_0| + \delta$, $\delta > 0$, since all operators are local with respect to each other. These results and the manifest Lorentz covariance of the Gell-Mann–Low (GML) series [see (57)] motivate our interest in local combinations of creation and annihilation operators for relativistic Hamiltonians.

In this approach, the construction of a local quantum field theory has to proceed in several steps: First one constructs in Fock space using the $H(R)$ C^*-algebras [19] of local observables $\mathfrak{A}(O)$ for all bounded open regions $O \in \mathbf{R}^4$. The norm closure $\mathfrak{A}$ of $\bigcup_O \mathfrak{A}(O)$ would have the Euclidean group (space translations and rotations) and time translations as a continuous group of automorphisms, with the latter only locally unitarily implementable [22]. Having found a state ω on $\mathfrak{A}$ invariant under this automorphism group, one constructs a new representation π of $\mathfrak{A}$ in a Hilbert space with cyclic invariant vector state Ω by the Gelfand–Segal construction

$$(\Omega, \pi(A)\Omega) = \omega(A) \qquad A \in \mathfrak{A} \tag{43}$$

In this representation the space-time translations $(a, \mathbf{1})$ are unitarily implemented $(a, \mathbf{1}) \rightsquigarrow \exp i(P, a)$. If the spectrum of P lies in the forward light-cone and has isolated mass values, then Araki [20] has shown how to construct scattering states for any number of incoming or outgoing particles. To end our fiction, the S-matrix is expected to be nontrivial and the theory hopefully Lorentz invariant.

Before this program can be carried through, UV divergences have to be removed without destroying locality, unless the potential is a pure Wick polynomial of scalar fields in 2-dimensional space-time. The simplest UV divergences occur for the Yukawa coupling of a 2-component spinor field $\Psi = (\Psi^1, \Psi^2)$ with a scalar field A in two dimensions. The renormalization of this model has been masterfully carried out by Glimm [23].

Due to the particularities of 2-dimensional space-time ($L_+^\uparrow$ is Abelian), the 1-particle spaces for nucleons and antinucleons ($\mathcal{N}$, $\overline{\mathcal{N}}$) and mesons ($\mathcal{M}$) are

$$\mathcal{N} = \overline{\mathcal{N}} = L^2(\mathbf{R}^1, M(\underline{p})^{-1}\,d\underline{p}) \qquad \mathcal{M} = L^2(\mathbf{R}^1, m(\underline{p})^{-1}\,d\underline{p}) \tag{44}$$

where

$$M(\underline{p}) = (M^2 + \underline{p}^2)^{1/2} \qquad m(\underline{p}) = (m^2 + \underline{p}^2)^{1/2} \qquad M, m > 0$$

In the Fock space

$$\mathcal{H} = S(\mathcal{M}) \otimes A(\mathcal{N} \oplus \overline{\mathcal{N}})$$

the creation operators for mesons are $a(\underline{k})^*$ and for nucleons and antinucleons $b(\underline{k})^*$, $\overline{b}(\underline{k})^*$. The free meson field A_0 was defined in (29) and the free fermion field $\Psi_0 = (\Psi_0{}^1, \Psi_0{}^2)$ is

$$\Psi_0{}^1(x) = \frac{1}{\sqrt{2\pi}} \int d\underline{p} \left(\frac{M(\underline{p}) + \underline{p}}{2M(\underline{p})}\right)^{1/2} \{b(\underline{p})e^{-i(p,\,x)} + \overline{b}(\underline{p})^* e^{i(p,\,x)}\}_{p^0 = M(\underline{p})} \tag{45}$$

$$\Psi_0{}^2(x) = \frac{1}{\sqrt{2\pi}} \int d\underline{p} \left(\frac{M(\underline{p}) - \underline{p}}{2M(\underline{p})}\right)^{1/2} \{b(\underline{p})e^{-i(p,\,x)} - \overline{b}(\underline{p})^* e^{i(p,\,x)}\}_{p^0 = M(\underline{p})}$$

The choice of antisymmetric statistics for the fermions makes the $\Psi_0{}^i(x)$ local:

$$[\Psi_0{}^i(x), \Psi_0{}^j(y)]_+ = [\Psi_0{}^i(x)^*, \Psi_0{}^j(y)]_+ = 0 \tag{46}$$

for all $1 \leqslant i, j \leqslant 2$ and all $(x - y, x - y) < 0$. The free Hamiltonian is

$$H_0 = \int d\underline{p}\{m(\underline{p})a(\underline{p})^*a(\underline{p}) + M(\underline{p})b(\underline{p})^*b(\underline{p}) + M(\underline{p})\overline{b}(\underline{p})^*\overline{b}(\underline{p})\}. \tag{47}$$

One sees from (45) that the interaction density

$$V(x) = \lambda : \Psi_0{}^1(x)^*\Psi_0{}^2(x) + \Psi_0{}^2(x)^*\Psi_0{}^1(x) : A_0(x)$$

integrated over $\underline{x}$ with a space cutoff $h(\underline{x}) \in \mathscr{S}(\mathbf{R}^1)$, does not define an operator in $\mathcal{H}$.

$V(x)$ describes eight virtual processes: $\mathcal{M} + \mathcal{N} + \overline{\mathcal{N}} \leftrightarrow 0$, $\mathcal{N} + \overline{\mathcal{N}} \leftrightarrow \mathcal{M}$, $\mathcal{N} + \mathcal{M} \leftrightarrow \mathcal{N}$, $\overline{\mathcal{N}} + \mathcal{M} \leftrightarrow \overline{\mathcal{N}}$. In $\int d\underline{x}h(\underline{x})V(\underline{x})$ the processes $0 \to \mathcal{N} + \overline{\mathcal{N}} + \mathcal{M}$ and $\mathcal{N} \to \mathcal{N} + \overline{\mathcal{N}}$ are effected by the formal operators:

$$Q_{1,2} = \lambda \int \prod_{i=1}^{3} d\underline{p}_i\, b(\underline{p}_1)^*\overline{b}(\underline{p}_2)^*a(\underline{p}_3)^{(*)}q(\underline{p}_1, \underline{p}_2, \pm\underline{p}_3) \tag{48}$$

where

$$q(\underline{p}_1, \underline{p}_2, \underline{p}_3) = -\sqrt{2}\,\hat{h}(\textstyle\sum \underline{p}_i)(M(\underline{p}_1)M(\underline{p}_2)m(\underline{p}_3))^{-1/2}$$

$$\times (M(\underline{p}_1)M(\underline{p}_2) - \underline{p}_1\underline{p}_2 - M^2)^{1/2}\, \mathrm{sgn}\,(\underline{p}_1 - \underline{p}_2) \tag{49}$$

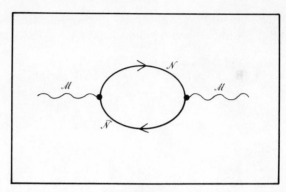

FIGURE 1

does not belong to $L^2(\mathbf{R}^3)$.   In perturbation theory, for example, in the GML series, no UV divergences would occur if Q_1 and Q_2 were better behaved. In fact, the theory is "overrenormalizable": in (57) only one Feynman graph and all its insertions into higher-order graphs are UV divergent.   One is led to make first $H_1 = H_0 + Q_1 + Q_2$ a bona fide operator in Fock space and then to deal with $V_2 = V - Q_1 - Q_2$.   An effective UV cutoff κ is the multiplication of $a(\underline{k})^{(*)}$, $b(\underline{k})^{(*)}$ and $\bar{b}(\underline{k})^{(*)}$ in V by the characteristic function of $\{|\underline{k}| \leqslant \kappa\}$.   Then $H_{1\kappa} = H_0 + Q_{1\kappa} + Q_{2\kappa}$ is densely defined in $\mathscr{H}$.

In the Lee model we were able to diagonalize H^χ in the (1, 1)-sector and to renormalize the theory by "calculating backward."   Instead of using the Friedrichs series [24] for finding an operator U, such that $HU = UH_0$, Glimm constructs from the first- and second-order terms in this series an approximate diagonalization T_κ of $H_{1\kappa}$:

$$(H_{1\kappa} + R_\kappa)T_\kappa = T_\kappa H_0 + F_\kappa \qquad (50)$$

Here the F_κ and T_κ are defined on a dense domain $\mathscr{D}$ common with H_0 for $\kappa \leqslant \infty$ and converge strongly on $\mathscr{D}$ for $\kappa \to \infty$. R_κ is the counter term to renormalize $H_{1\kappa}$, which on $T_\kappa \mathscr{D}$ has the simple form

$$R_\kappa = \delta m_\kappa^2 \int :A_\kappa(\underline{x})^2: h(\underline{x})^2 \, d\underline{x} + c_\kappa \mathbf{1} \qquad (51)$$

δm_κ^2 is a meson mass renormalization, which diverges as $\log \kappa$ for $\kappa \to \infty$, while c_κ copes with vacuum fluctuations, $c_\kappa \to \infty$ for $\kappa \to \infty$, which would cancel in the GML series.   The main result of Glimm is the following:

Theorem.   For all $\phi \in \mathscr{D}$, $\Psi_\kappa = T_\kappa \phi$, $\Psi = s\text{-}\lim\limits_{\kappa \to \infty} \Psi_\kappa = T\phi$

$$s\text{-}\lim_{\kappa \to \infty} (H_{1\kappa} + R_\kappa)\Psi_\kappa = H_{1,\,\mathrm{ren}}\Psi \qquad (52)$$

exists and defines $H_{1,\,\mathrm{ren}}$ as a symmetric operator with dense domain $\mathscr{D}_1 = T\mathscr{D}$.

The proof involves a long chain of nontrivial estimates. Next, the remainder is estimated as a bilinear form on $T_\kappa \, \mathcal{D} \times T_\kappa \, \mathcal{D}$, $\kappa \leqslant \infty$. The limit

$$\lim_{\kappa \to \infty} (\Psi_\kappa, (H_{1\kappa} + R_\kappa + V_{2\kappa})\Psi_\kappa) \qquad (53)$$

is shown to define a symmetric bilinear form on $\mathcal{D}_1 \times \mathcal{D}_1$. After an additional finite renormalization ($R_\kappa \to R_\kappa'$ with $\delta m_\kappa^{2\prime} - \delta m_\kappa^2$, $c_\kappa' - c_\kappa \in \mathbf{R}$, fixed), the final result is the following:

Theorem. There exists a positive self-adjoint operator H_{ren}, whose bilinear form extends $\lim_{\kappa \to \infty} (\Psi_\kappa, (H_{1\kappa} + R_\kappa' + V_{2\kappa})\Psi_\kappa)$.

Thus, both for the A^4 and Yukawa interaction, one has in two dimensions reasonable candidates for a local relativistic dynamics in the Heisenberg picture. However, very serious difficulties will be encountered in the renormalization of these Hamiltonians in a physical 4-dimensional theory.

THE INTRIGUING CONSISTENCY OF RENORMALIZED PERTURBATION THEORY

In this final section we shall outline how Feynman integrals appear in relativistic quantum mechanics and how gracefully renormalized perturbation theory survives the most violent manipulations.

Let us start with the Yukawa interaction in 4-dimensional space-time. Cutoffs are imposed as in Glimm's investigations, a space cutoff R and an UV cutoff κ at least for the fermion fields. Since the regularized Fermi fields are bounded operators, the only unboundedness of $V_\kappa(R)$ arises from the linear dependence on the smeared-out meson creators and annihilators. Their $\sqrt{N_M}$ growth (N_M: meson number operator) is infinitely small in the sense of T. Kato [25] with respect to H_0. Y. Kato [26] and O. E. Lanford [27] have proved the convergence of the perturbation series (41) for $\exp it[H_0 + V_\kappa(R)]$ for all $\lambda \in \mathbf{C}$, in the norm topology of $\mathcal{L}(D_\alpha, D_\beta)$, $\alpha > \beta > 0$. The D_α are a chain of Banach spaces dense in $\mathcal{H}$ ($D_\alpha \supset \mathcal{D}(\exp \beta N_M)$ for all $\beta < \alpha$). If the space cutoff is effected by considering the theory in a finite space volume with periodic boundary conditions, then $H_0 + V_\kappa(R)$ has a unique ground state $\Omega \in D_\alpha$ for sufficiently small $|\lambda|$, which is again in D_α given by a convergent perturbation expansion [25]

$$\Omega = \sum_{n=0}^{\infty} \lambda^n \Omega_n \qquad (54)$$

Physically, the most interesting quantities of quantum field theory are the vacuum expectation values (VEV) of the time-ordered products of field operators. For a scalar field satisfying (A) and (B), the time-ordered product $TA(x_1) \cdots A(x_n)$ is an operator-valued generalized function which for

$$x^0_{i,k} - x^0_{i,k+1} \geqslant \delta > 0 \qquad 1 \leqslant k \leqslant n-1 \qquad \{(i,1), \ldots, (i,n)\} = \{1, \ldots, n\}$$

coincides with $A(x_{i,1}) \cdots A(x_{i,n})$. The extension to $\mathscr{S}'(\mathbf{R}^{4n})$ can for the following theorem be fairly arbitrary. In perturbation theory this question is closely related to renormalization [see (68)]. Truncated time-ordered VEV are recursively defined by

$$\langle TA(x_1) \cdots A(x_n)\rangle^T = (\Omega, TA(x_1) \cdots A(x_n)\Omega)$$
$$- \sum_P \langle TA(x_{i,1}) \cdots A(x_{i,k})\rangle^T \cdots \langle TA(x_{j,1}) \cdots A(x_{j,m})\rangle^T \quad (55)$$

where $\sum\limits_P$ extends over all partitions of $\{1, \ldots, n\}$ into more than one set, and the recursion starts from $\langle TA(x)\rangle^T = (\Omega, A(x)\Omega)$. Let $\tilde{\tau}(p_1, \ldots, p_n)$ be the Fourier transform of (55). Then one has the following [17, 28].

Theorem. In a quantum field theory satisfying (A) and (B)

$$\langle p_1, \cdots p^{\text{out}}_m \mid p_{m+1}, \cdots p^{\text{in}}_n\rangle^T = c_{m,n} \prod_{i=1}^{n} ((p_i, p_i) - m^2)\tilde{\tau}(p_1, \ldots, -p_n)\bigg|_{p_i^0 = m(\underline{p}_i)} \quad (56)$$

$c_{m,n}$ is some constant, and the left-hand side is the nontrivial part of the scattering amplitude for the process

$$\underline{p}_{m+1} + \cdots + \underline{p}_n \to \underline{p}_1 + \cdots + \underline{p}_m$$

after having subtracted recursively as in (55) all contributions from independent scatterings of disjoint subsystems.

In the cutoff Yukawa theory, by combining (41) and (54), one obtains a convergent perturbation expansion for $\langle TO_1(x_1) \cdots O_n(x_n)\rangle^T$, $O_i = \Psi, \Psi^*$ or A, unfortunately, with a radius of convergence which depends very unfavorably on both cutoffs. However, this series is identical [27] with another, marvellous series, where for all finite partial sums:

(α) The volume cutoff can be trivially removed. This holds for every local interaction density $\lambda V(x)$. Hence one automatically reaches in perturbation theory the non-Fock representation of the canonical commutation relations which belong to the interaction $\lambda V(x)$ [30].

(β) The UV cutoff can be consistently removed within the ambiguities in the definition of time-ordered distributions.

The expansion in question is the Gell-Mann–Low series [29]:

$$\langle TO_1(x_1) \cdots O_m(x_m)\rangle^T$$
$$= \sum_{n=m}^{\infty} \frac{(-i\lambda)^{n-m}}{(n-m)!} \int \prod_{i=m+1}^{n} dx_i \langle TO_{01}(x_1) \cdots O_{0m}(x_m)V(x_{m+1}) \cdots V(x_n)\rangle^T_0 \quad (57)$$

On the left-hand side are VEVs of Heisenberg fields, truncated with respect to the physical vacuum Ω, and on the right-hand side the VEVs of the corresponding free fields truncated with respect to the Fock vacuum Ω_0. (α) can be proved by inspection for UV cutoff interactions $V_\varphi(x) = \int dy\,\varphi(x - y)V(y)$, $\varphi \in \mathscr{S}(\mathbf{R}^4)$, which are obviously translation-invariant. Concerning (β), one remarks that the VEV $\langle O_{1_0}(x_1) \cdots V(x_n)\rangle_o^T$ is a well-defined tempered distribution [14]. Furthermore, Wick's theorem [31] is certainly valid in the following typical case:

Theorem. Let $V(x) = :A_0(x)^4:$. Then for test functions in $\mathscr{S}(\mathbf{R}^{4n})$ with support in some $\{|x_i^0 - x_j^0| \geqslant \delta > 0, \ 1 \leqslant i < j \leqslant n\}$

$$\langle TA_0(x_1) \cdots A_0(x_m)V(x_{m+1}) \cdots V(x_n)\rangle_0^T = \begin{cases} 0 & m \equiv 1(2) \\ \sum \prod i\Delta_c(x_i - x_j) & m \equiv O(2) \end{cases}$$

$$(58)$$

Here $\sum$ extends over all partitions of

$$\{v_1, \ldots, v_m, v_{m+1}^1, \ldots, v_{m+1}^4, \ldots, v_n^1, \ldots, v_n^4\}$$

into sets of two elements, such that (1) v_i^r, v_i^s, $r \neq s$, never lie in the same set; (2) after the identification $v_i^r = v_i$, $1 \leqslant r \leqslant 4$, the n "vertices" $v_1, \ldots, v_n$ are connected by chains of sets $\{v_i, v_j\}$.

For every $\{v_i, v_j\}$ a "causal" distribution [32] or "Feynman propagator" contributes:

$$\Delta_c(x - y) = \langle TA_0(x)A_0(y)\rangle_0 = \lim_{\varepsilon \downarrow 0} \int \frac{dp \exp - i(p, x - y)}{(2\pi)^4((p, p) - m^2 + i\varepsilon)} \qquad (59)$$

To every $\prod i\Delta_c(x_i - x_j)$ corresponds a Feynman diagram [33]. The $v_1, \ldots, v_n$ are represented by n distinct points in a plane and every $i\Delta_c(x_i - x_j)$ by a line connecting v_i and v_j.

Example

If one takes (58) seriously as a tempered distribution, by Fourier transform, one would obtain for $\prod i\Delta_c(x_i - x_j)$ a Feynman integral of the type studied in Prof. Lascoux' lectures:

$$c \lim_{\varepsilon \downarrow 0} \int \prod_{i=1}^{K} dk_i \prod_{j=1}^{L} ((q_j, q_j) - m^2 + i\varepsilon)^{-1} \qquad (60)$$

Here $p_1, \ldots, p_n$ are the variables conjugate to $x_1, \ldots, x_n$, and the q_j for every line are linear combinations of the $p_1, \ldots, p_n$ and of K 4-vectors $k_1, \ldots, k_K$, if the graph has K independent cycles. The factor c contains $\delta(\sum p_i)$. For more general interactions $V(x)$, the propagators contribute

$$P_j(q_j)[(q_j, q_j) - m_j^2 + i\varepsilon]^{-1} \qquad (61)$$

with some polynomial P_j and the vertices v_i some constant "vertex part"

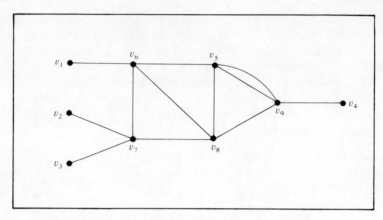

FIGURE 2

$\mathscr{X}_i$. In general a Feynman integral is not even conditionally convergent at infinity because of UV divergences. After a Laplace transform

$$P_j(q_j)((q_j, q_j) - m_j{}^2 + i\varepsilon)^{-1} = \frac{1}{i} P_j(q_j) \int_0^\infty d\alpha_j \exp i\alpha_j[(q_j, q_j) - m_j{}^2 + i\varepsilon]$$

(62)

the multiple Gaussian k-integrals can be carried out and lead to an α-integrand

$$I_\varepsilon(\alpha, p) = \delta\left(\sum_{i=1}^n p_i\right) R(\alpha, p) \exp i\left(\sum_{i,j=1}^n A_{ij}(\alpha)(p_i, p_j) - \sum_{j=1}^L \alpha_j(m_j{}^2 - i\varepsilon)\right)$$

(63)

For $r, \varepsilon > 0$ (63) is absolutely integrable in $D_r = \{\alpha_j \geqslant r, 1 \leqslant j \leqslant L\}$. The UV divergences appear as nonintegrable singularities on the boundary of D_0. If one studies for $\varphi \in \mathscr{S}(\mathbf{R}^4)$ and $\tilde{\varphi}$ its Fourier transform

$$\left\langle \prod i\Delta_c, \varphi \right\rangle = \lim_{\varepsilon \downarrow 0} \lim_{r \downarrow 0} \int_{D_r} \prod_{j=1}^L d\alpha_j \int \prod_{i=1}^n dp_i \, \tilde{\varphi}(p_1, \ldots, p_n) I_\varepsilon(\alpha, p)$$

(64)

then it can be shown [35] that (64) is well-defined and continuous for all $\varphi \in \mathscr{S}_N(\mathbf{R}^{4n})$ [the subspace with the induced topology of all $\varphi \in \mathscr{S}(\mathbf{R}^{4n})$, which vanish with all derivatives of order $\leqslant N$, whenever $x_i = x_j, i \neq j$]. Renormalization can be interpreted as an extension of this functional from $\mathscr{S}_N(\mathbf{R}^{4n})$ to $\mathscr{S}(\mathbf{R}^{4n})$, where the arbitrariness of the Hahn–Banach extension is strongly reduced by the requirements that (a) the axioms (A) and (B) of quantum field theory should be valid up every finite order in the perturbation expansion in λ; (b) the modifications of the Wick expansion of the GML series should be minimal.

A class of extensions of (64) satisfying (a) and (b) has been given by Bogoliubov and Parasiuk [34] for an arbitrary local interaction density $V(x)$.

Consider an arbitrary, fixed graph $G(\mathscr{V})$ with a set $\mathscr{V}$ of vertices $v_1, \ldots, v_n$ and a set $\mathscr{L}$ of lines $l_1, \ldots, l_L$ connecting them. We look for counter terms to make the Wick expression $I_\varepsilon(\alpha, p)$ absolutely integrable over D_0 which do not contribute in (64) for $\varphi \in \mathscr{S}_N(\mathbf{R}^{4n})$. The combinatorics of the counter terms will be controlled by the subgraphs $G(\mathscr{V}')$ of $G(\mathscr{V})$, which are defined by all lines from $\mathscr{L}$ connecting the vertices $v_1', \ldots, v_m' \in \mathscr{V}'$. For every $\mathscr{V}' \subset \mathscr{V}$ the "superficial divergence" $v(\mathscr{V}')$ is defined by

$$v(\mathscr{V}') = \sum{}' (r_j + 2) - 4(m' - 1) \tag{65}$$

where $\mathscr{V}'$ has m' elements, r_j is the degree of the polynomial P_j in (61), and $\sum'$ extends only over those lines which connect vertices from $\mathscr{V}'$.

In general, a counter term has to be introduced for any partition $\mathscr{V}_1, \ldots, \mathscr{V}_k$ of $\mathscr{V}$. When integrated over $D_r, r > 0$, the counter terms $\mathscr{F}^{r, \varepsilon}$. will have in x-space product structure:

$$\mathscr{F}^{r, \varepsilon}(\mathscr{V}_1, \ldots, \mathscr{V}_k) = \prod_{i=1}^{k} \mathscr{X}^{r, \varepsilon}(\mathscr{V}_i) \prod_{\text{conn}} i\Delta_j^{r, \varepsilon} \tag{66}$$

For every line which connects vertices in different $\mathscr{V}_1, \ldots, \mathscr{V}_k$, the contribution $\Delta_j^{r, \varepsilon}$, is the Fourier transform of (62) with the α-integration restricted to $[r, \infty)$. The "generalized vertex parts" $\mathscr{X}^{r, \varepsilon}(\mathscr{V}_i)$ are defined recursively: $\mathscr{X}^{r, \varepsilon}(\mathscr{V}') = \mathscr{X}_i$, if $\mathscr{V}'. = \{v_i\}$ for some $1 \leqslant i \leqslant n$. $\mathscr{X}^{r, \varepsilon}(\mathscr{V}') = 0$, if $G(\mathscr{V}')$ is one-particle reducible, that is, if $G(\mathscr{V}')$ is disconnected after deleting one of its lines. In all other cases

$$\mathscr{X}^{r, \varepsilon}(\mathscr{V}') = -M\left(\sum_{k(P) > 1} \mathscr{F}^{r, \varepsilon}(\mathscr{V}'_{P, 1}, \ldots, \mathscr{V}'_{P, k(P)}) \right). \tag{67}$$

The sum in (67) extends over all proper partitions $\mathscr{V}'_{P, 1}, \ldots, \mathscr{V}'_{P, k(P)}$ of $\mathscr{V}'$. The condition $k(P) > 1$ makes (67) into a recursion, starting with the original vertex parts $\mathscr{X}_i$, once the operation M is properly chosen. Let $\mathscr{V}' = \{v_a, \ldots, v_b\}$. By induction, every $\mathscr{F}^{r, \varepsilon}$, on the right-hand side of (67) is in p-space of the form: $\mathscr{F}^{r, \varepsilon}(p_a, \ldots, p_b) = \delta(p_a + \cdots + p_b)F^{r, \varepsilon}(p)$, where $F^{r, \varepsilon} \in \mathcal{O}_M$ [9] is holomorphic. Under M, every $F^{r, \varepsilon}$ is replaced by its Taylor series up to the order $v(\mathscr{V}')$, inclusively, in $(p_a, \ldots, p_b)$ around $(0, \ldots, 0)$. The Taylor coefficients depend on r, ε and diverge for $r \downarrow 0$. This definition of $\mathscr{X}^{r, \varepsilon}(\mathscr{V}')$ can be extended by a finite renormalization by adding to (67) a polynomial of degree $v(\mathscr{V}')$ with coefficients continuous in r and $\varepsilon \geqslant 0$. It is clear that none of the $\mathscr{F}^{r, \varepsilon}(\mathscr{V}_1, \ldots, \mathscr{V}_k)$, except for $\mathscr{F}^{r, \varepsilon}(\{v_1\}, \ldots, \{v_n\})$, contributes in (64) for N sufficiently large, since they are all in p-space polynomials in a subset of variables.

Theorem. Let $V(x)$ be an arbitrary local interaction and $G(\mathscr{V})$ a graph in the GML series. Define as regularized finite part

$$\mathscr{R}^{r, \varepsilon}(\mathscr{V}) = \sum_P \mathscr{F}^{r, \varepsilon}(\mathscr{V}_{P, 1}, \ldots, \mathscr{V}_{P, k(P)}) \tag{68}$$

with summation over all partitions P of $\mathscr{V}$. Then in p-space $\bigl($up to $\delta(\sum p_i)\bigr)$
$\lim_{r\downarrow 0} \mathscr{R}^{r,\,\varepsilon}(\mathscr{V})$ is holomorphic and tempered in $p_1, \ldots, p_n$, and $\lim_{\varepsilon\downarrow 0} \lim_{r\downarrow 0} \mathscr{R}^{r,\,\varepsilon}(\mathscr{V})$
exists in $\mathscr{S}'(\mathbf{R}^{4n})$.

The partial sums of the GML series are sums of Feynman integrals of
the type

$$\lim_{\varepsilon\downarrow 0} \int_C \frac{\prod d\alpha_j\, R(\alpha, p)}{\left(\sum\limits_{i,j=1}^{n} A_{ij}(p_i, p_j) - \sum\limits_{j=1}^{L} B_j\, m_j{}^2 + i\varepsilon\right)^K} \tag{69}$$

Here C is compact, $R(\alpha, p)$ is rational in α, a polynomial in p and locally integrable over C, $A_{ij}(\alpha)$ is rational and bounded in C and $B_j(\alpha)$ a polynomial with
$\sum B_j m_j \geqslant \min \{m_j\}$ in C. The partial sums of the GML series are holomorphic for real $p_1, \ldots, p_n$, except for multiple scattering singularities [36].

The proof is combinatorically involved [34, 35], but uses only elementary estimates. The requirements (A) and (B) of general quantum field
theory are satisfied [37, 38] up to distribution-theoretic technicalities.

The minimality of the Bogoliubov renormalization is best illustrated by
the following interesting result of Speer [39]: In the theory of generalized
functions [40] it is natural to study regularizations of the type

$$\Delta_j^{\varepsilon,\,\lambda}(q) = \Gamma(\lambda_j) e^{i\pi(\lambda_j - 1)/2} P_j(q)[(q, q) - m_j{}^2 + i\varepsilon]^{-\lambda_j}$$

$$= \frac{1}{i} P_j(q) \int_0^\infty d\alpha_j\, \alpha_j^{\lambda_j - 1} \exp i\alpha_j[(q, q) - m_j{}^2 + i\varepsilon] \tag{70}$$

For Re λ_j sufficiently large the convolutions in (60) with these regularized
propagators converge. Speer obtains a distribution-valued analytic function
$\mathscr{F}_{\mathscr{V}}(\lambda_1, \ldots, \lambda_L)$ which is meromorphic in $\mathbf{C}^L$ with poles only for $\sum\limits_{\mathscr{M}} \lambda_j = t$ ($\mathscr{M}$
any subset of $\mathscr{L}$, t any integer). Of interest is the behavior for $(\lambda_1, \ldots, \lambda_L) \to$
$(1, \ldots, 1)$, where the symmetrized constant term of an iterated Laurent
expansion can be computed by

$$\frac{1}{L!} \sum_P (2\pi i)^{-L} \int_{C_{P(1)}} d\lambda_1 \cdots \int_{C_{P(L)}} d\lambda_L \frac{\mathscr{F}_{\mathscr{V}}(\lambda_1, \ldots, \lambda_L)}{(\lambda_1 - 1) \cdots (\lambda_L - 1)} \tag{71}$$

using suitable contours C_i and summing over all permutations P of $(1, \ldots, L)$.

Theorem [39]. $\mathscr{R}(\mathscr{V})$ is, for some definite choice of the finite renormaliza-
tions, equal to the symmetrized constant term in the iterated Laurent expan-
sion of $\mathscr{F}_{\mathscr{V}}(\lambda_1, \ldots, \lambda_L)$ around $(1, \ldots, 1)$.

We finally come to an important distinction. In every order n of the
GML series the counter terms in $\mathscr{R}(\mathscr{V})$ arise formally from counter terms

to $V(x)$ which are Wick polynomials $W_n(x)$ in the free fields O_{0i} and their derivatives. A theory is called finitely renormalizable if the Wick powers in $W_n(x)$ stays the same for all orders n. Here the minimality of the renormalization is essential. In a finitely renormalizable theory, the time-ordered distributions in every order n are uniquely determined by a fixed, finite number of parameters. Typical in 4-dimensional space-time are the A^4 and the Yukawa interaction, where the parameters are the masses m_i of the physical particles and the normalization of the matrix elements of the field operators between vacuum and one-particle states and the physical coupling constants (see for example [35]). Exactly such parameters have defined in the Lee model the renormalized Hamiltonian!

For finitely renormalizable theories a number of different renormalization schemes have been devised:

1. The Dyson–Salam rules in p-space [41, 42]
2. The differentiation method [43, 44, 45, 46]
3. The definition of the currents for local field equations [47, 48, 38, 49]
4. The Bogoliubov scheme

Although the combinatorial structure of the subtractions is of extraordinary variety in these different approaches, there is good evidence that they all lead to the same renormalized GML series.

This "structural stability" of renormalized perturbation theory begs the question, whether there exist exact nontrivial solutions for some infinite system of equations, which couple the time-ordered distributions and which are suggested by perturbation theory. The advantage of this approach is the close connection to the scattering amplitudes and the absence of the vacuum problem, the difficulties come from the known divergence of the GML series for bosons [50] and the, at best, conditional convergence of p-space integrals in Minkowski space. Presently, this is a field of interesting possibilities with beautiful applications of nonclassical analysis [51, 52].

REFERENCES

1. J. Schwinger, *Quantum Electrodynamics*, Dover, New York, 1958.
2. J. Lascoux, this volume Chapter XIV.
3. R. F. Streater and A. S. Wightman, *PCT, Spin & Statistics and All That*, Benjamin, New York, 1964.
4. R. Jost, *The General Theory of Quantized Fields*, Am. Math. Soc. Providence, 1965.
5. R. J. Eden, P. Landshoff, D. I. Olive, and J. Polkinghorne, *Analytic S-Matrix Theory*, Cambridge, 1966.
6. J. M. Lévy-Leblond, *Comm. Math. Phys.* **4**, 157 (67).

7. T. D. Lee, *Phys. Rev.* **95**, 1329 (54).

8. R. Schrader, Thesis, Zürich, 1967.

9. L. Schwartz, *Theorie des distributions*, Hermann, Paris, 1957/59.

10. V. Bargmann, *Ann. Math.* **59**, 1 (54).

11. L. D. Faddeev, *Trudy Stehklov Math. Inst.* **69** (1963).

12. K. Hepp, to be published.

13. W. Pauli, *Rev. Mod. Phys.* **13**, 203 (41).

14. L. Gårding and A. S. Wightman, *Ark. Fysik* **28**, 129 (64).

15. H. Epstein, *Nuovo Cim.* **27**, 886 (63).

16. A. Jaffe, *Ann. Phys.* **32**, 127 (65).

17. H. Lehmann, K. Symanzik, and W. Zimmermann, *Nuovo Cim.* **1**, 205 (55); **6**, 319 (57).

18. A. Jaffe, *Phys. Rev.* **158**, 1454 (67).

19. R. Haag and D. Kastler, *J. Math. Phys.* **5**, 848 (64).

20. H. Araki, *Local Quantum Theory* (to be published, Benjamin, New York).

21. I. E. Segal, *Proc. N.A.S.* **57**, 1178 (67).

22. M. Guenin, *Comm. Math. Phys.* **3**, 120 (67).

23. J. Glimm, *Comm. Math. Phys.* **5**, 343 (67); **6**, 61 (67).

24. K. O. Friedrichs, *Perturbation of Spectra in Hilbert Space*, Am. Math. Soc., Providence, 1965.

25. T. Kato, *Perturbation Theory for Linear Operators*, Springer, Berlin, 1966.

26. Y. Kato, *Prog. Theor. Phys.* **26**, 99 (61).

27. O. E. Lanford, Thesis, Princeton, 1966.

28. K. Hepp, *Comm. Math. Phys.* **1**, 95 (65).

29. M. Gell-Mann and F. E. Low, *Phys. Rev.* **84**, 340 (51).

30. H. Araki, *J. Math. Phys.* **1**, 492 (60).

31. G. C. Wick, *Phys. Rev.* **80**, 268 (50).

32. E. C. G. Stueckelberg and D. Rivier, *Helv. Phys. Acta* **23**, 215 (50).

33. R. P. Feynman, *Phys. Rev.* **76**, 749, 769 (49).

34. N. N. Bogoliubov and O. S. Parasiuk, *Acta Math.* **97**, 227 (57).

35. K. Hepp, *Comm. Math. Phys.* **2**, 301 (66).

36. F. Pham, this volume Chapter XV.

37. N. N. Bogoliubov and D. V. Shirkov, *Introduction to the Theory of Quantized Fields*, Interscience, New York, 1959.

38. W. Zimmermann, *Comm. Math. Phys.* **6**, 161 (67).

39. E. R. Speer, Preprint, Princeton, 1967.

40. I. M. Gelfand and G. E. Shilov, *Generalized Functions, Vol. 1*, Academic Press, New York, 1964.

41. F. J. Dyson, *Phys. Rev.* **75**, 486, 1736 (49).

42. A. Salam, *Phys. Rev.* **82**, 217; **84**, 426 (51).

43. J. C. Ward, *Phys. Rev.* **78**, 182 (50).

44. R. L. Mills and C. N. Yang, *Suppl. Prog. Theor. Phys.* **37/38**, 507 (66).

45. T. T. Wu, *Phys. Rev.* **125**, 1436 (62).

46. J. P. Eckmann, *Diplomarbeit*, Zürich, 1967.

47. J. Valatin, *Proc. Roy. Soc.* A **222**, 93, 228; **225**, 535; **226**, 254 (54).

48. K. Wilson, Cornell report, unpublished.

49. R. Brandt, to be published.

50. C. Hurst, *Proc. Cambridge Phil. Soc.* **18**, 625 (52); W. Thirring, *Helv. Phys. Acta* **26**, 33 (53); A. Petermann, *Helv. Phys. Acta* **26**, 291 (53); A. Jaffe, *Comm. Math. Phys.* **1**, 127 (65).

51. K. Symanzik, *J. Math. Phys.* **7**, 510 (66) and in: *Mathematical Theory of Elementary Particles*, M.I.T., 1966.

52. J. G. Taylor, *J. Math. Phys.* **7** (66).

XIV

Perturbation Theory in Quantum Field Theory and Homology

JEAN LASCOUX

PART 1: NORMAL FORM OF AN INTEGRAL FROM PERTURBATION THEORY

Perturbation theory in classical analytical mechanics has achieved a high degree of perfection: one can even treat stability problems. . . .

354

But it has been fifty years since Poincaré and Birkhoff. The difficulty lies in the global change a trajectory experiences under a small perturbation, hence, in the "asymptotics."

Quantum field theory (if it exists and I shall assume that you are willing to accept that it exists in some sense) is two levels away from the world of classical mechanics.

This twofold difference unfolds as follows: First, there is the quantum mechanical wave aspect. Partial differential equations describe the phenomena by means of propagators or fundamental solutions. In some respects, the wave mechanics of the n-body problem and its asymptotics are even better understood now than the classical cases. On the other hand, the connection with classical mechanics is apparent if one looks at the "motion" of the singularities of the solution of partial differential equations. With the principal part of the differential operator, one can build a Hamiltonian for this motion.

The second difference is more drastic and dramatic: the production and annihilation of particles as the motion develops. Apparently, it is a radical negation of the concept of trajectory. Yet, some connection exists, as is well known in optics in the case of a reflecting layer with the three rays: "incident, refracted, and reflected." The singularities of the Feynman integrals shall lead us again to such a picture.

I shall refer to Hepp's lecture for a discussion of the basic features of quantum field theory—its vacuum and its operators. Our approach shall be most rough and primitive: we shall even have no need of Hilbert space! Further, we deal with only one kind of particle and no spin.

To a given order p in perturbation, the amplitude for n particles being created at $x_1 \ldots x_n$, propagating with p interactions, and ending up as m particles localized at $z_1 \ldots z_m$ is given by the following expression

$$G(z_1 \ldots z_m; x_1 \ldots x_n) = \sum A_G$$

$$A_G = \int d^4 y_1 \ldots d^4 y_p \prod D_F(x_i - y_j) \prod D_F(z_k - y_l) \prod D_F(y_i - y_l)$$

where the different factors of the product are built according to the following:

Rule 1. Draw a picture of the n initial points $x_1 \ldots x_n$ and of the m final points $z_1 \ldots z_m$, to be called "external vertices"; and of the points $y_1 \ldots y_p$: one for each integration variable, to be called "internal vertices."

At each internal vertex y_j, draw a fixed number of lines. We shall be definite: let us say three (3), in this case, and the picture looks as shown in Fig. 1. This is the basic "elementary interaction"; for an algebraic coupling with no derivatives, interaction in perturbation theory is nothing more than this rule of assigning to each internal vertex a "bouquet" of lines.

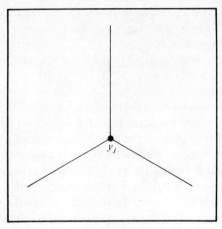

FIGURE 1

Now, using these lines, join the internal vertices among themselves and join them, too, to the external vertices but with the restriction that a unique line starts or ends up at an external vertex. The diagram so obtained is a Feynman graph. To attach a function to this definite Feynman graph, apply the following:

Rule 2. For each line of the graph introduce the factor $D_F(x_i - y_j) \dots$ between its end points. At this stage, it remains only to describe this Feynman propagator $D_F(x)$. In terms of creation and annihilation operators, the D_F function plays a miraculous role. It orders the noncommuting free-field operators according to the ordering in time of the points to which the operators refer:

$$(T A(x)A(y)) \quad \begin{array}{c} \text{if } x_0 > y_0 \\ \xrightarrow{\hspace{2cm}} A(x)A(y) \\ \text{if } x_0 < y_0 \\ \xrightarrow{\hspace{2cm}} A(y)A(x) \end{array}$$

and yet, because the fields are local, that is, they commute for spacelike distance $[A(x), A(y)] = 0$ for $(x - y)^2 > 0$ this chronological T-product is Lorentz invariant. $D_F(x - y)$ is simply the vacuum expectation value of this T-product. To place this in a proper perspective, I should discuss "General Field Theory," but I shall refer instead to Jost's basic book and simply write

$$D_F(x) = -\frac{1}{(2\pi)^4} \int \frac{e^{-ik \cdot x}}{k^2 - m^2 + i\varepsilon} d^4k$$

$$k \cdot x = k_0 x_0 - \underline{k} \cdot \underline{x}$$

where ε small positive number, and we consider the k_0 integral first. In the complex k_0 plane, one integrates along the real axis $(-\infty < k_0 < +\infty)$. I shall call this integration path h_F. On each side of h_F we have the two poles of $1/(k^2 - m^2 + i\varepsilon)$ that is,

$$k_0 = \pm\sqrt{\underline{k}^2 + m^2 - i\varepsilon} = \pm(\omega - i\eta)$$

where η is a small positive number. Hence, we see that if $x_0 > 0$ we can close h_F at "∞" by a large half-circle along which the integrand is exponentially small.

Then we have a "cycle" and can deform it in the standard "small circle around the pole" of Cauchy residue formula. Along the lower arc (in Fig. 2) $e^{-ik_0 x_0}$ is exponentially small if Im $k_0 < 0$ and $x_0 > 0$. Hence for

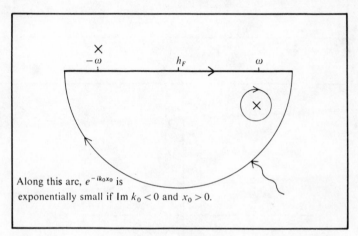

FIGURE 2

$x_0 > 0$, the particle propagates as a positive-frequency solution of the Klein–Gordon wave equation

$$\left(\frac{\partial^2}{\partial t^2} - \underline{\nabla}_x{}^2 - m^2\right)f^+ = 0$$

Note that if one compactifies the complex plane into the Riemann sphere, the picture is as shown in Fig. 3, where $S^2 =$ Riemann sphere of the k_0-complex plane.

The asymptotic behavior of $D_F(x)$ in x-space exhibits a remarkable behavior for large values of $|x|$; in the timelike direction, it decreases slowly as $\sim (1/|x^2|^{3/4})e^{imx_0}$; note the oscillating factor e^{imx_0}, and for spacelike direction, we have an exponential decrease $\sim (1|x^2|^{3/4})e^{-m\sqrt{|x^2|}}$. As this behavior is of fundamental value for the modern proofs of the existence of asymptotic states, we shall collect this information in Fig. 4.

FIGURE 3

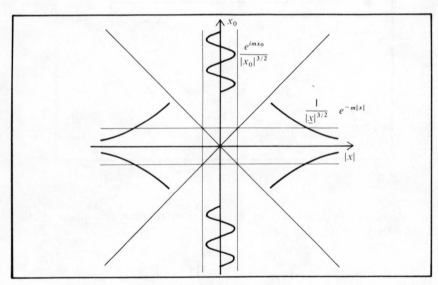

FIGURE 4

To describe the behavior of $D_F(x)$ in the neighborhood of the light cone, I shall borrow from Bogoliubov–Shirkov the following formula, which exhibits the type of singularities the Feynman function has in x-space

$$D_F(x) = \frac{1}{4\pi}\,\delta(x^2) + \frac{1}{4\pi^2 i}\frac{1}{x^2} - \frac{m^2}{16\pi}\,\theta(x^2) + \frac{im^2}{8\pi^2}\ln\left(\frac{m\,|x^2|^{1/2}}{2}\right)$$

$$+ \; O(\sqrt{|x^2|}\,\ln|x^2|)\ldots$$

where δ and θ are the usual distributions but here the support of the singularity is the algebraic lightcone

$$x^2 = x_0{}^2 - \underline{x}^2 = 0$$

which is itself singular at the origin (see Gelfand–Shilov *Theory of Distribution Vol. I*).

It is about the most complete table of singularities one can think of and we shall retreat rapidly to working exclusively in momentum space where the Fourier transform is so simple—

$$\frac{1}{k^2 - m^2 + i\varepsilon}$$

Hence, take the Fourier transform of $G(z_1 \ldots z_m, X_1 \ldots X_n)$ and substitute for each propagator

$$D_F(\mu_i - \mu_j) \qquad \text{where } \mu = x, y, \text{ or } z$$

the Fourier transform

$$\int_{h_F} \frac{e^{-ik_{ij}(\mu_i - \mu_j)}}{k_{ij}^2 - m^2} \, d^4 k_{ij}$$

The end result is

$$\tilde{G}(q_1 \cdots q_m ; p_1 \cdots p_n) = \frac{1}{\prod (p_i{}^2 - m^2 + i\varepsilon) \prod (q_j{}^2 - m^2 + i\varepsilon)}$$

$$\times \int_{h_F} \int \prod d^4 k_{ij} \frac{1}{\prod (k_{ij}^2 - m^2)} \prod \delta^{(4)} \left(\sum_i k_{ji}\varepsilon_{ji} + \sum_i p_i \varepsilon_{ji} + \sum_i q_i \varepsilon_{ji} \right)$$

where the variables p are Fourier conjugates of x, the q are Fourier conjugates of y and the ε_{ij} are the coefficients of the incidence matrix of the graph G. The k_{ij} are four-momenta associated with each internal line (y_i, y_j); h_F is the chain of integration obtained by applying Feynman's boundary conditions $(m^2 - i\varepsilon)$ in order to avoid the set of real points where the integrand becomes infinite. We already met this situation when we studied $D_F(x)$. We now prefer to express it as a displacement of the chain of integration h_F

instead of a displacement of the polar manifolds

The external vertices are suppressed from the picture: the external lines (x_i, y_j) or (y_k, z_l) are continued to ∞ and called ingoing and outgoing particles, respectively.

The explicit factor

$$\frac{1}{\prod (p_i^2 - m^2 + i\varepsilon) \prod (q_i^2 - m^2 + i\varepsilon)}$$

is a simple rational function of the external momenta (p, q). It really belongs to the "asymptotics" of perturbation theory. I shall refer to Hepp's description of the asymptotic states and on the pretext of its simple analytic structure, leave it out!

Hence, the final form of the integral attached to a graph G shall be

$$F_G(p) = \int_{h_F} \frac{d^4k_1 \wedge d^4k_2 \wedge \cdots \wedge d^4k_r}{\prod_{i=1}^{N} \left[\left(\sum_j \eta_{ij} k_j + \sum_j \eta_{ij} p_j \right)^2 - m^2 \right]}$$

where r is the rank of G, the number of independent cycles of the graph G, $(k_1 \ldots k_r)$ is a basic set of integration variables after we have taken into account all the conservation laws: $\delta^{(4)}(\because)$ at each vertex. Further, i is now a label for an internal line: $i = 1 \ldots N$ and

$$\sum_j \eta_{ij} k_j + \sum_j \eta_{ij} p_j$$

is simply the four-momentum associated with the line i and expressed in terms of the integration variables k and the external momenta p, where we have suppressed any distinction between the "outgoing" and "incoming" particles.

Assume further that *the integral is convergent.** Now, let us turn to an analysis of its mathematical structure.

1. The integrand is a rational differential form with respect to the variables k. Outside its polar locus, the form is closed since it is analytic and of maximal rank in C^{4r}.

2. The polar locus is the union of quadrics

$$\left(\sum_j \varepsilon_{ij} k_j + \sum_j \varepsilon_{ij} p_j \right)^2 - m^2 = 0$$

which we shall denote by S_i. These quadrics in C^{4r}, with signature $(+, -, -, -)$, depend algebraically on the external parameters p.

3. Compactify C^{4r} into the complex projective space P^{4r} by adjoining the hyperplane "at infinity" Π_∞. Denote by $\bar{S}_i$ the projective quadrics.

---

* Weinberg, *Phys. Rev.* **118**, 838 (1960).

Let Σ be the real algebraic set where the $\bar{S}_i$ intersect Π_∞. Then h_F is "almost" a cycle in $P^{4r} - \bigcup_{i=1}^{N} \bar{S}_i$, if we could move it away from the "bad" set Σ and close it again.

As a very rough first approximation the following mathematical idealization is of interest: *Normal form of an integral* (see Fotiadi, Froissart, Lascoux, Pham: Applications of an Isotopy Theorem *Topology, Vol. 4*, p. 159).

Consider an algebraic family $\mathscr{S}$ of hypersurfaces in $P^n \times T$, where T is an affine space; that is, introducing homogeneous coordinates $(x_0, x_1, \ldots, x_n)$ for P^n and coordinates $(t_1, t_2, \ldots, t_p)$ for T, the algebraic family $\mathscr{S}$ is globally given by the product

$$S_1(x, t) S_2(x, t) \ldots S_N(x, t) = 0$$

where the S_i are irreducible polynomials in x and t, homogeneous with respect to x.

Assume that the family $\mathscr{S}$ is such that for all t, $\mathrm{Cod}_{P^n} \mathscr{S}_t = 1$. Hence for any value of t, we have a nonempty union of algebraic hypersurfaces in P^n, where

$$\mathscr{S}_t = (P^n \times \{t\}) \cap \mathscr{S} = \bigcup_{i=1}^{N} S_i(t)$$

Assume that for a generic value of t, say, $t = t_0$, the hypersurfaces $S_i(t)$ are in general position in P^n, that is, their normals are linearly independent on their intersections:

$$d_x S_{i_1} \wedge d_x S_{i_2} \wedge \cdots \wedge d_x S_{i_r} \neq 0$$

on

$$S_{i_1} \cap S_{i_2} \cap \cdots \cap S_{i_r}$$

for $t = t_0$.

Assume that for $t = t_0$, we have a compact cycle in P^n which does not intersect the S_i

$$h_{t_0} \in H_n^c(P^n - \mathscr{S}_{t_0})$$

$$\mathscr{S}_{t_0} = \bigcup_{i=1}^{N} S_i(t_0)$$

where $H_n^c(P^n - \mathscr{S}t_0)$ is the n-dimensional compact homology group and h_{t_0} denotes both the compact cycle of integration and its homology class.

Then consider the analytic function defined by

$$F(t) = \int_{h_t} \frac{\omega}{\displaystyle\prod_{i=1}^{N} S_i(x, t)}$$

where $\omega/\Pi S_i(x, t)$ is an analytic differential form in the x variables closed outside its polar locus.   We shall call this "the normal form of the integral" and develop in the following the rather smooth mathematical treatment one can give to our idealized model.   But, we shall have to remember that a large part of the physical content of Feynman integrals was cut off with our neglect of the bad set Σ and of the *real* algebraic character of the integral (we have carried out a too easy complexification and disregarded the fact that our integral was first given as an integral over the *reals* of a differential form where the complex numbers enter only with *Feynman's prescription*: $m^2 - i\varepsilon$).

PART 2: ANALYTICAL CONTINUATION BY ISOTOPY

I shall refer to the pair $(X \times T, \mathscr{S})$ as "the family."   The "theorem" I want to talk about is obvious (I was told so) for the main application we made use of.   Yet, to understand it, we employ such heavy machinery that it is a pity the question should stay in such state.   The details of the machinery were all borrowed from what I shall call *Thom's main isotopy theorem*.   Then, the proper aim of my lecture should be to end by stating this theorem, and taken as a whole, it is only a biased introduction to this circle of questions.

Let me introduce a convention: Under the heading "Recall" I shall list notions, mainly topological, into the exact definition of which I do not wish to enter.

To begin:

Recall that a fiber space (E, T) is locally a product

$$
\begin{array}{ccc}
E & \longleftarrow & X \times U \\
\downarrow & & \downarrow{\scriptstyle p_2} \\
T & \longleftarrow & U
\end{array}
$$

with p_2 the projection on the second factor.   The local isomorphism will always be a homeomorphism, the only exception being a particular case of *mixed structure* that we need:

$$
\begin{array}{c}
E \xleftarrow{\ g\ } X \times T \\
\downarrow \;\; \swarrow{\scriptstyle p_2} \\
T
\end{array}
$$

where E, T, and X are C^∞-manifolds, $g(x, t)$ being differentiable with respect to t and satisfying the condition that for any vector field $\underline{Z}$, C^∞ on T, hence on $X \times T$, $g_* \underline{Z}$ exists and is a locally Lipschitzian vector field on E.

Definition. A vector field $\underline{V}$ on E is Lipschitzian if

$$\| V_y - V_{y'} \| \leqslant k \, \| y - y' \|$$

for $y, y' \in E$. In ordinary words $g(x, t)$ is differentiable with respect to t and a little more than continuous with respect to x, as could be expected from homeomorphisms generated by integrating along vector fields.

Recall:

is a fiber pair with base space T (see Spanier, p. 265, *Algebraic Topology*), if locally

is a commutative diagram. In ordinary parlance, there exists a common local trivialization of the two fiber spaces $\mathscr{S} \subset E$.

Then our main application shall be, referring to the conditions I gave in the definition of normal form, "there exists an algebraic set in T, called L (for Landau) such that $(E, \mathscr{S})_{T-L}$ is a fiber pair above $T - L$. Our main goal will be to describe the $(E, \mathscr{S})$ above L by further extraction from it of such fiber pairs: $(E, \mathscr{S})_{L-L_1}$, where L_1 is an algebraic set in L, $(E, \mathscr{S})_{L_1-L_2} \ldots$.

Recall. An isotopy map $(X, S_0) \overset{g}{\to} (X, \mathscr{S}_1)$ is a homeomorphism such that there exists a continuous family of homeomorphisms

$$G = \{g_t\}_{t \in I} : X \times I \to X$$

such that if we put $\mathscr{S} = $ trace of S_0 under G, then $(X \times I, \mathscr{S})_{p_2}$ defines a fiber pair with the restrictions $g = g_1$ and $Id_X = g_0$.

Why is this concept relevant to us? Let h be a cycle representative of a homology class $H_*^c (X - S_0)$. When we move the parameter continuously, we want to define, when it exists, a corresponding continuous motion of h; that is, we want to make sure that at the homology level

$$H_*^c(X - S_0) \overset{}{\underset{g^*}{\longrightarrow}} H_*^c(X - S_1)$$

h survives, that is, $g_* h \neq 0$. There are two ways to attack this:

1. Subdivide h into simplexes (small), move them, keeping them away from the boundary of $X - S_t$, then fix them again to obtain a cycle representing $g_* h$. This is the method of Nilsson and Leray second manner. It is also the physicist's way, before we start reading Leray and Thom.

2. Move the whole work, g being an isotopy, g_* is thus an isomorphism, hence taking care of all the cycles simultaneously. The "whole work"

denotes in an imprecise manner as many interesting topological invariants as you can put your hands on. For instance, it could include the singular complex $(S(X), S(S))$, the requirement that g_* or g^* be an isomorphism, the immersion $S \hookrightarrow X$ and its invariants.... We shall choose this second approach.

How to construct an isotopy? The answer is clear from Professor Bott's lecture—through vector fields. But we want to generate by integration along this vector field a group of homeomorphisms.

The maximal generality we shall require (although unnecessarily restricted according to Thom) is described as follows:

Lemma 1. (from Milnor's "Morse Theory") Let $\underline{F}$ be a vector field on a C^∞-manifold X. Assume Supp $\underline{F}$ compact and $\underline{F} \in$ Lip. Then $\underline{F}$ generates a one-parameter group of homeomorphism $\gamma(t)$.

It is a well-known lemma in ordinary differential equations

$$\frac{d\gamma(t, y)}{dt} = \underline{F}(\gamma(t, y))$$

Lip ensures the existence of a unique local solution and the Lip-dependence on the initial conditions.

Compact: You can do away with patching a finite number of neighborhoods without losing too much.

What requirements ought our Lip-vector fields to meet: the way I think best is to look at the simplest situation where $\mathscr{S}$ is irreducible. Hence, look at one manifold, S, embedded in the ambient space X.

Recall. *Tangent bundle of S:* It is the vector bundle of all vectors tangent to S, noted $T(S)$.

Normal bundle: Choose a Riemannian metric at least in the neighborhood of S. Take the normal vectors to S: $N(S)$ is again a vector bundle

$$N(S) + T(S) = T(X)$$

Tubular neighborhood of S: It is the union of the geodesic normal p-balls $\mathscr{T}(S)$ if S is of codimension p.

Repeat: How to move S? Take a global section of $N(S)$, and integrate the corresponding vector field. Note that global sections of $T(S)$ generate homeomorphisms of S into S. They are very interesting although they don't "move S" in X. If you can find better and better vector fields such as k-differentiable, C^∞, holomorphic, when it makes sense, then your notion shall be accordingly k-differentiable, C^∞, holomorphic.

Note now that the R-metric is unessential. The important concept we are after is transversality.

Recall. Two manifolds V, W are said to be transversal to each other if along $V \cap W$, $T(V) + T(W) = T(X)$ (or in general position if we deal with hypersurfaces: linear independence of the normals). Denote this transversality by $V \pitchfork W$. Returning to our family affair, let us make all these notions of tangent bundle and transversality *relative* to the map $\pi : X \times T \to T$. Denote the topological product space $X \times T$ by E.

Recall. In the tangent space $TE_{(x, t)}$ there are two kinds of vectors : the vectors tangent along the fiber X: vectors called *vertical* with their linear space denoted by $V_{(x, t)} \supset T(S_t)_x$, and the remaining vectors grouped into equivalence classes

$$X_1 \sim X_2 \text{ iff } \pi_* X_1 = \pi_* X_2$$

Call $H^x_{(x, t)}$ the corresponding vector space of equivalence classes. It is a good concept to define a motion compatible with the map π, that is, sending fiber into fiber.

Note that for $X \times T$, everything being manifold, we have trivially

$$0 \to V \to T \overset{\sigma}{\underset{\leftarrows}{}} H \leftrightarrow 0 \quad \text{(exact sequence)}$$

at each point, the sequence splits. If we want to, we can make the splitting σ global along the fiber $(X)_t$ because our family is trivial.

Similarly, one can define the horizontal vectors $H^{\mathscr{S}}_{(x, t)}$ of the tangent vector space $T\mathscr{S}_{(x, t)}$.

Recall. σ is a *connection* if one can choose in T a horizontal subspace continuously along the fiber. Let us return to a fiber of our family but now take the next stage of complication $\mathscr{S} = \mathscr{S}_1 \cup \mathscr{S}_2$ (but $\mathscr{S}_1 \pitchfork \mathscr{S}_2$) $S = S_1 \pitchfork S_2$ (but $S_1 \pitchfork S_2$). We can seek to factorize the simultaneous motion of the two manifolds into steps where only one manifold is displaced, the other being restricted to be invariant—To construct such a restricted motion, the "germ" is again in the almost infinitesimal tubular neighborhoods of S_1 and S_2. Choose the R-metric in such a way that S_1 is normal to S_2. To move S_1 into S_1' we look at the normal disk N_x at $x \in S_1$. Assume that S_1' meets the disk at a unique point x' (Fig. 5). The map $x \rightsquigarrow x^1$ is given by the implicit function theorem which can be applied by virtue of the transversality.

In the disk, the picture is as follows: We have an R-metric, hence geodesics. Let $\overline{(x, x')}$ be the unique geodesic joining x to x'. Extend the geodesic field along $\overline{(x, x')}$ into a continuous vector field which vanishes near the boundary of the disk (Fig. 6). Such a vector field is tangent to S_2 in a neighborhood of $S_1 \cap S_2$.

By integrating such a vector field, we obtain an homeomorphism of $\mathscr{T}(S_1)$ onto some $\mathscr{T}(S_1')$. We have still the fact that $S_1' \pitchfork S_2$. Repeat the same procedure to move S_2 into S_2'. Note that $S_1 \cap S_2 \to S_1' \cap S_2 \to$

FIGURE 5

$S_1' \cap S_2'$. The motion was therefore "in" the normal bundle of the inter-section, which is of complex dimension 2. Let X_1 be the first vector field ($\perp S_1$) and let X_2 be the second vector field ($\perp S_2$). The principal use of the tubular neighborhood of the intersection $S_1 \cap S_2$ is to show the place where some plumbing has to be done—look at the boundaries of the tubular neigh-borhoods and at their intersections. Note that $\partial \mathcal{T}(S_1) \pitchfork \partial \mathcal{T}(S_2)$.

Define. A plumbing function g (Thom prefers to refer to g as the carpeting function, so we shall use this name) as a C^∞ function on $X - (S_1 \cup S_2)$ posi-tive on $X - (S_1 \cup S_2)$ and such that g has a C^0 extension to $X - (S_1 \cup S_2)$ satisfying $g^{-1}(0) = S_1 \cup S_2$. Require also that, near the boundary of the

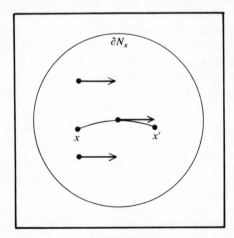

FIGURE 6

open manifold $X - (S_1 \cup S_2)$ (this open manifold is called a stratum), the differential of g does not vanish.

$$dg \neq 0$$

Define. μ_{S_1} the retraction of $\mathcal{T}(S_1)$ over $\mathcal{S}_1$ obtained by shrinking the geodesic normal disks of radius ε. We shall use it for Leray's definition of the cobord map, that is, to lift cycles from S_1 to the ambient open tubular neighborhood $\mathcal{T}(S_1) - S_1$.

Define. $K_{(S_1 - S_1 \cap S_2)}$ as the corresponding retraction obtained by letting the radius ε tend to 0 as we come close to the submanifold of S_1, $S_1 \cap S_2$. Now repeat the construction to define $K_{(S_2 - S_1 \cap S_2)}$.

Generalize: the corresponding structure when the $S_i(x, t)$ are transversal is easy to visualize. We have a set of open manifolds V_α, such that

$$\partial V_\alpha = \sum V_\beta$$

This allows us to define an incidence relation: $V_\alpha \succ V_\beta$ if V_β is in the boundary of V_α. On each V_α there exists a carpeting function g_α and a retraction k_α; the kind of differential $C - W$ complex so defined has for attaching map the k_{V_α} retractions which must satisfy a condition of compatibility:

$$k_{V_\gamma}|_{V_\alpha} = k_{V_\gamma}|_{V_\beta} \circ k_{V_\beta}|_{V_\alpha} \quad \text{if} \quad V_\gamma < V_\beta < V_\alpha$$

The following lemma is then relevant to the problem of constructing the composite of two maps if there is a further restriction to meet along the motions, such as leaving a closed subset invariant.

Lemma 2 (Chevalley). Let $\Sigma \subset X$ be a closed set, $\underline{X}_1$, $\underline{X}_2 \in \text{Lip}^c$ such that the corresponding groups of homeomorphisms γ_1, γ_2 leave Σ invariant. Consider $\underline{X} = \underline{X}_1 + \underline{X}_2$, then X generates a group of homeomorphisms γ such that $\gamma\Sigma \subset \Sigma$.

The usefulness of this lemma is that we can now localize our construction of vector fields and using partitions of unity patch the local vector fields in the intersection of the small neighborhoods where they are defined (Fig. 7).

HINT. Professor Helgason did the main algebraic job if you define

$$\gamma(t) = \lim_{n \to \infty} \left(\gamma_1\left(\frac{t}{n}\right) \circ \gamma_2\left(\frac{t}{n}\right) \right)^n$$

Use the algebraic identity

$$\alpha^n - \beta^n = \sum \alpha^r \alpha \, \beta^{n-r+1} - \alpha^r \beta \, \beta^{n-r+1}$$

Let $S_i(x, t) = 0$ be the global equation of the hypersurface S_i. Consider a neigborhood U of (x, t) such that

$$U \cap S_i \neq \phi \quad \text{for } i \in I \subset [1 \cdots n]$$

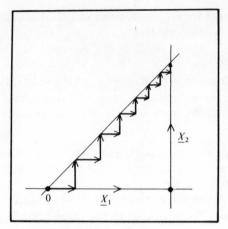

FIGURE 7

Then if $x = (x_1, \ldots, x_r)$ and $t = (t_1, \ldots, t_p)$ denote local coordinates, what we are looking for is a vector field with vertical components $\underline{X} = (X_1(x, t), \ldots, X_r(x, t))$ and horizontal components $\underline{T} = (T_1(t), \ldots, T_p(t))$, such that the vector field generates a group of homeomorphisms leaving $\mathscr{S}$ invariant and sending fiber into fiber. This is already taken care of by choosing $\underline{T}$ independent of x. As for $\mathscr{S}$ being left invariant, choose the vector field in U such that

$$dS_i = \sum \frac{\partial S_i}{\partial x_j} dx_j + \sum \frac{\partial S_i}{\partial t_k} dt_k = 0 \qquad i \in I$$

for

$$(dx, dt) = (X, T) \, d\tau$$

over the locus $(S_i = 0)$ $i \in I$ and such that similarly for the other partial intersections $(\cap S_i)_{i \in I_\alpha} \, dS_i = 0$ for $i \in I_\alpha$ over $(S_i = 0)_{i \in I_\alpha}$. Note that we are considering the natural decomposition of U into strata by the (S_i) and constructing a vector field tangent to these strata. Finally in the stratum $U - \bigcup_{i \in I} S_i$ there is no condition on the vector field except that the different choices should match as smoothly as possible since we want to solve the differential equations of motion

$$\frac{dx}{d\tau} = X(x, t) \qquad \frac{dt}{d\tau} = \underline{T}(t)$$

Assume that a neighborhood of each point along a fiber $(X \times t_0)$ exists such that we can find our Lip vector field leaving $\mathscr{S}$ invariant. This means that for $(x_0, t_0) \in X \times t_0$, there exists U such that $(X \times T|_U, \mathscr{S}|_U)$ is a fiber pair with map p_2, the projection over the second factor.

Lemma 3. If $X \times T \xrightarrow{\pi} T$ is proper then the two conditions are equivalent
1. $(X \times T, \mathscr{S})$ is a fiber pair.
2. For any (x, t), there exists a neighborhood U such that $(X \times T|_U, \mathscr{S}|_U)$ is a fiber pair.

The term π proper implies X compact, which implies in turn that one can cover a neighborhood in $X \times T$ of a fiber with a finite number of neighborhoods U_i, hence $\bigcap_i \pi(U_i)$ is a neighborhood of t_0 in T.

Then use partitions of unity and Lemma 2 to conclude the proof of Lemma 3.

"Little" Isotopy Theorem

If, for $t = t_0$, the hypersurfaces $\{S_i(t_0)\}_{i \in [1...n]}$ intersect transversally, then there exists an algebraic set L of codimension 1 such that

$$(X \times T|_{T-L}, \mathscr{S}|_{T-L})$$

is a fiber pair.

The linear system over $S_I = \bigcap_{i \in I} S_i$

$$\sum_{j=1}^{r} \frac{\partial S_i}{\partial x_j} X_j + \sum_{k=1}^{p} \frac{\partial S_i}{\partial t_k} T_k = 0$$

$$i \in I$$

has a continuous solution where one can choose $\underline{T}$ equal to a unit vector if

$$rk \left[\frac{\partial S_i}{\partial x_j} \right] = |I| \quad \text{over} \quad S_I$$

One can then solve by Cramer's rule the linear system with an "inhomogeneous" term:

$$\left[\frac{\partial S_i}{\partial x_j} \right] \underline{X} = - \left[\frac{\partial S_i}{\partial t_k} \right] \underline{T} \tag{A}$$

and this describes precisely the lifting of the vector field $\underline{T}$ from T into X that we are seeking for our special type of fiber pair. Note that these determinants call for an interpretation in terms of Grassman coordinates. We have the following features to determine $\underline{X}$ from our linear system of equations (Fig. 8):
1. An inhomogeneous term.
2. A different number of equations according the number of S_i which go through the neighborhood in X which we consider.
3. The equations depend on parameters $t \in T$. For $|I| = r$, we have r equations for the r unknowns ($X_i(x, t)$); we have no freedom of choice: move along the solution $x_i = x_i(t)$ given by the implicit function theorem.

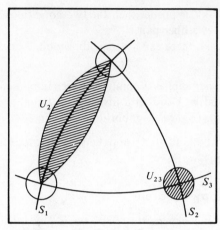

FIGURE 8

For the general case, it is easy to guess what arbitrariness we have to face: the kernel of $[\partial S_i/\partial x_j]$ is given by the vectors tangent to S_I; hence they generate homeomorphisms of S_I.

To end the proof of this "little" isotopy theorem, let us study the algebraic set $L \subset T$. To simplify, I take $X = P^{r-1}$. Let L_I denote the subset of T such that

$$rk\left[\frac{\partial S_i}{\partial x_j}\right]_{i \in I} < |I|$$

Consider the ideal (called a Jacobian extension)

$$H_I = \left(S_i(x, t)i \in I, \quad \det_\alpha\left[\frac{\partial S_i}{\partial x_j}\right] \right)$$

where $\det_\alpha[\partial S_i/\partial x_j]$ are the determinants of all minors with $|I|$ lines and $|I|$ rows that one can extract from $[\partial S_i/\partial x_j]$. Call the set of its zeros (the associated algebraic variety) $\tilde{L}_I$. Then elimination theory (or projection parallel to the fibers) tells us the following:

Lemma 4. Let $I = (1, \ldots, m)$; consider the system of polynomial equations, homogeneous with respect to X

$$\begin{cases} S_1(x, t) = 0 \ldots S_m(x, t) = 0 \\ \text{and } (n - m) \text{ independent equations} \\ \text{of the form } \dfrac{D(S_1 \ldots S_m)}{D(x_{i_1} \ldots x_{i_m})} = 0 \end{cases} \tag{B}$$

Then (B) has a nontrivial solution $(X) \neq 0$	$\xleftrightarrow{\text{iff}}$	The resultant $R_I(t) = 0$

For the proof, refer to VanderWaerden. For the subfamily

$$\mathcal{S}_I = \bigcap_{i \in I} \mathcal{S}_i$$

the subvariety of T associated with the principal ideal $(R_I(t))$ is of codimension 1 and can be interpreted as the "apparent branch" of the manifold $\mathcal{S}_I$ *and* the projection of its singularities on T. The apparent branch corresponds to the points where the tangent plane to $\mathcal{S}_I$ becomes too vertical, that is, (recall: V is the vertical tangent subspace to $X \times T$)

$$\dim V \cap T(\mathcal{S}_I) \geqslant \dim X - |I| + 1$$

Now there is a very important map in the sense of algebraic geometry to consider: from the obvious remark that if $t \in L_I$, we have $R_I(t) = 0$, then in Lemma 4 we can use the arrow from right to left and consider the corresponding solution $x = x_I(t)$. We shall call this algebraic map ε.

If one obtains a point, the singularity of S_I at $(x_I(t), t)$ is called *local*. But it can happen that $\varepsilon(t)$ is an algebraic set in $\mathcal{S}_I|_t$. In the simplest case, this means that the hypersurfaces in X, $\{S_i(t)\}_{i \in I}$, are *tangent along* some submanifold. If π_I is the projection map restricted to $\mathcal{S}_I$, then ε_I is a kind of algebraic section of π_I over L_I since $\pi_I \circ \varepsilon_I = Id_{L_I}$. One should think of these maps and ideals in a purely algebraic context (Hironaka). They could be used to describe what generalizations of the quadratic Picard–Lefschetz formula we should look for. But we shall digress for an immediate application. *The contracted Feynman diagrams as "symbols" of singularities.*

Consider the family of quadrics, corresponding to a diagram G, as algebraic hypersurfaces in C^{4r}.

Let $S_i = q_i^2 - m^2 = 0$ be one of them; then

$$\frac{\partial S_i}{\partial k_j} \approx q_i$$

is the normal to S_i for fixed external momenta. Recall that

$$q_i = \sum \varepsilon_{ij} k_j + \sum \varepsilon_{il} p_l$$

Hence, the lack of transversality for the hypersurfaces $(S_i)_{i \in I}$ implies a linear relation between the normal vectors (in C^{4r}),

$$\boxed{\sum_{i \in I} \alpha_i q_i = 0}$$

and at the same time the mass-shell equations

$$\boxed{q_i^2 - m^2 = 0 \qquad i \in I}$$

It is very convenient *not* to represent on the diagram G the hypersurfaces which do not participate in the singularity L_I by contracting the corresponding internal lines.

The graph G_I so obtained, with its generalized vertices resulting from contraction, is now thought to mean:

1. the lines of G_I are momenta on the mass-shell.

2. for any closed loop C of G_I, there exists a linear combination between 4-vectors in $\mathbb{C}^4$

$$\sum_{i \in C} \alpha_i q_i = 0$$

We shall attach a function to G_I, called the period around L_I, after we have discovered how the function $F_G(t)$ is ramified when one goes around L_I in the parameter variety T.

Example

Let us consider the simple case of the scattering of two particles, in the fourth order of perturbation. The Feynman diagram is shown in Fig. 9 and the corresponding amplitude is

$$F_G(p_1, p_2, p_3, p_4)$$

$$= \int_{h_F} \frac{d^4k}{(k^2 - m^2)[(k - p_2)^2 - m^2][(k + p_3)^2 - m^2][(k - p_1 - p_2)^2 - m^2]}$$

FIGURE 9

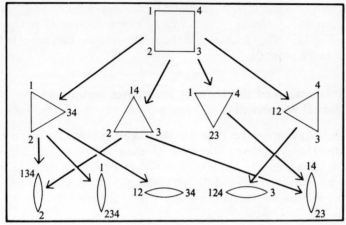

FIGURE 10

Singularity Symbol

The contraction procedure gives rise by iteration to the following hierarchy (only part of which is pictured in Fig. 10). This illustrates the different cases where we have to apply Lemma (4) to build the different components of the Landau set. Now, there exists a very pictorial way of describing the type of "algebraic relations" that elimination theory provides us with. Recall that $p_1 + p_2 + p_3 + p_4 = 0$. Hence the picture should be at most three-dimensional since even for the internal momenta q_i, there exists at least one linear relation among them; using the fact that we are interested in "algebraic relations," substitute the Euclidean metric for the Minkowskian

FIGURE 11

metric since one has only one quadratic form nondegenerate in C^4 over the complex numbers. Hence $\square$ corresponds to the packing of four spheres, shown in Fig. 11. They are centered at the four vertices, with equal radius m, and meet at the point 0!

Introduction of the Lorentz Invariants Instead of the External Momenta

This last picture makes clear that the singularities are Lorentz invariant. Recall the Hall–Wightman theorem. (I shall refer also to Ehrenpreis' separation of variables.) Let $s = (p_1 + p_2)^2$ and $t = (p_1 + p_4)^2$ (in Fig. 11, they are the two other edges of the tetrahedron). If you put $u = (p_1 + p_3)^2$, and if the external momenta are also on the mass-shell, that is, $p_i{}^2 = m^2$, where $i = 1, 2, 3, 4$, then

$$s + t + u = 4m^2$$

and, taking as parameters $\{s, t\} \in C^2 = T$, one can calculate the Landau set. It splits into several irreducible components, among which (see Fig. 12):

L_{1234} $st((s - 4m^2)(t - 4m^2) - 4m^4) = 0$

L_{123} $s(s - 3m^2) = 0$

L_{12} $s(s - 4m^2) = 0$

FIGURE 12

For two particles scattering, the experimental parameters are

$$s = (p_1 + p_2)^2 \qquad \text{(Total energy in channel I)}$$

and

$$t = (p_1 + p_4)^2 \qquad \text{(Momentum transfer in channel I)}$$

While channel I denotes one of the three famed physical regions represented on Fig. 13, it is also the region Φ_I, where the total "energy" $s = (p_1 + p_2)^2 = (p_3 + p_4)^2$ is larger than the rest mass squared of the two

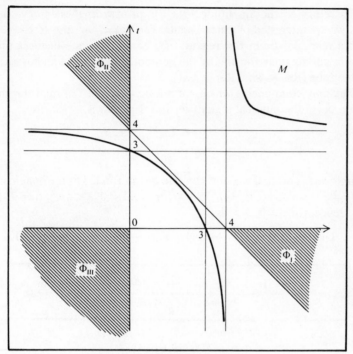

FIGURE 13

ingoing particles as well as of the two outgoing particles. For simplicity we have taken all the masses to be equal.

The forward scattering ($\cos \theta_s = 1$) is $t = 0$; backward scattering ($\cos \theta_s = -1$) is given by $t + s = 4m^2$, and the physical region corresponds to $s \geqslant 4m^2$ and $-1 \leqslant \cos \theta_s \leqslant 1$.

I have plotted all the Landau curves. Note that they are real algebraic, and that some components ($s = 0$, $t = 0$) occur with multiplicity. Note also that for the specialization to the equal masses case, the Landau curve II decomposes. In general (for arbitrary masses), we should expect the Landau curves to be singular, either from topological considerations, since they are apparent branches, or from the algebraic remark that the equations $R_I(t)$ are discriminants. One applies elimination theory to a set of functions which are partial derivatives of a unique function; therefore, the functions of this set are not " generic."

Example

Consider the following $X^3 + pX + q = 0$: the discriminant $4p^3 + 27q^2 = 0$ has a cusp.

To return to the amplitude $F_G(s, t)$, an easy analysis shows that the branch we are interested in is not singular for $\text{Re} s < 4m^2$ and $\text{Re} t < 4m^2$ and therefore real analytic in this region.   By continuity, one deduces that this branch is not singular for any of the components of the Landau set which enter the tube ($\text{Re} s < 4m^2$, $\text{Re} t < 4m^2$).

The only components which are relevant are the "normal thresholds" at which begin the physical regions Φ_I and Φ_{II}, that is,

$$s = 4m^2$$

$$t = 4m^2$$

The ramification around $s = 4m^2$ can also be interpreted as the imaginary part of the $F_G(s, t)$ s-plane (Fig. 14).   Since for t real < 0, $s < 4m^2$, then $F_G(s, t)$ is real.   Hence, for $t \leqslant 0$, $S > 4m^2$

$$\text{Disc } F_G(s, t) = F_G(s + i\varepsilon, t) - F_G(s - i\varepsilon, t) = 2i \text{ Im } F_G(s, t)$$

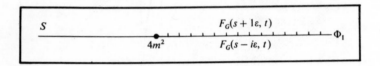

FIGURE 14

From a general principle, the unitarity of the scattering matrix, one can calculate this imaginary part.

Unitarity Relation

$$\underset{s>4m^2,\, t<0}{\text{Im}} F_G(s, t) = \int d^4k \, \frac{\delta_+(k^2 - m^2)\delta_+((p_1 + p_2 - k)^2 - m^2)}{((k + p_2)^2 - m^2 - i\varepsilon)((k + p_3)^2 - m^2 + i\varepsilon)}$$

Note that we have only two propagators left and with different prescriptions for the $i\varepsilon$.

The two δ_+-functions mean

$$k^2 = m^2 \qquad k_0 > 0$$
$$(p_1 + p_2 - k)^2 = m^2 \qquad p_{10} + p_{20} - k_0 > 0$$

Hence the integration domain is really now a two-dimensional sphere S^2 intersection of the two hyperboloids pictured in Fig. 15.   Applying Cauchy's theorem gives the following *dispersion relation* (keeping t real and less than 0)

$$F_G(s, t) = \frac{1}{2\pi i} \int_{s' > 4m^2} \frac{\text{Im } F_G(s', t) \, ds'}{s' - s}$$

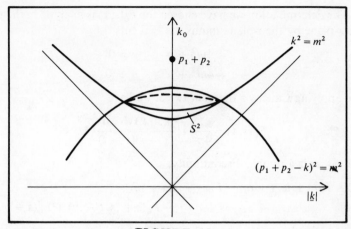

FIGURE 15

The remarkable feature of these two concepts of unitarity and dispersion relations is that they hold independently of perturbation theory and can be derived from basic principles in axiomatic field theory. A third concept stems from the remark that the function $F_G(s, t)$ being analytic except on the Landau set which is of complex codimension 1 can certainly be analytically continued from the region Φ_I, where this amplitude describes the scattering of two particles with total energy s to the region Φ_{II}. For the determination of $F_G(s, t)$ which we have chosen, this is very simple.

It is remarkable that the same function $F_G(s, t)$ describes by analytic continuation to Φ_{II} the physical process associated with this region precisely: the scattering of two particles with total energy t. Again, for $s < 0$, we have the dispersion relation

$$F_G(s, t) = \frac{1}{2\pi i} \int_{t' > 4m^2} \frac{\mathrm{Im}\, F_G(s, t')\, dt'}{t' - t}$$

with the unitary relation for Φ_{II} ($s < 0$, $t > 4m^2$)

$$2i\, \mathrm{Im}\, F_G(s, t) = F_G(s, t + i\varepsilon) - F_G(s, t - i\varepsilon)$$

$$= \int d^4k \frac{\delta_+((k + p_2)^2 - m^2)\delta_+((k + p_3)^2 - m^2)}{(k^2 - m^2 - i\varepsilon)((p_1 + p_2 - k)^2 - m_2 + i\varepsilon)}$$

Again, this property of "crossing" from Φ_1 to Φ_2 can be proved for the two-particle scattering from the axioms (Bros, Epstein, Glaser)! I shall end this digression by stating a property which is true for $F_G(s, t)$ but is not proved in perturbation theory nor in axiomatic field theory.

The determination we have chosen for $F_G(s, t)$ is analytic in the product of the s-plane by the t-plane minus the two cuts

$$s = 4m^2 + \rho \qquad \rho > 0$$
$$t = 4m^2 + \rho' \qquad \rho' > 0$$

Hence applying Cauchy's theorem twice, we have

$$F_G(s, t) = \frac{1}{4\pi^2} \iint \frac{\rho(s', t') \, ds' \, dt'}{(s' - s)(t' - t)} \quad (M)$$

where $\rho(s, t)$ is a double discontinuity,

$$\rho(s, t) \sim F_G(s + i\varepsilon, t + i\eta) - F_G(s - i\varepsilon, t + i\eta)$$
$$- F_G(s + i\varepsilon, t - i\eta) + F_G(s - i\varepsilon, t - i\varepsilon)$$

and Supp ρ is the region above the branch of the Landau curve called (M), since this double-integral representation is known as Mandelstam's representation.

Exercise. Does it make sense to write the following?

$$\rho(s, t) = \int d^4k \delta_+(k^2 - m^2)\delta_+((k + p_2)^2 - m^2)$$
$$\times \delta_+((k + p_3)^2 - m^2)\delta_+((p_1 + p_2 - k)^2 - m^2)$$

In the integral formula (M), one of the integrations is elementary, but the last one is then an elliptic integral.

We have thus finished the list of properties of this fourth-order example.

In the little isotopy theorem, we prove only that outside L, on the "big" residual space $T - L$, the mapping π was a fibering map for the fiber pair $(X \times T, \mathscr{S})_{T-L}$. It would be useful to know more: that is, can we break $L = UL_I$ into pieces U_α (open manifolds) such that on each of these pieces U_α, $\pi \mid_{U_\alpha}$ is the fibering map of the fiber pair $(X \times T, \mathscr{S} \mid_{U_\alpha})$? To find criteria in order that there exists an isotopy map between (X, S_t) and $(X, S_{t'})$ when S_t *and* $S_{t'}$ *have no more normal crossings in* X is very closely related to the question of *equivalence of singularities.*

Thom's isotopy theorem deals directly with the existence of such fiberings. To show the main steps, I shall have to recall a new series of notions.

Recall. If f is a proper map between two analytic spaces $X \xrightarrow{f} S$, let df be the tangent map; then, there exist two sequences of analytic subspaces (we shall call such a sequence a stratification)

$$X \supset X_1 \supset X_2 \supset \cdots \supset X_r$$
$$S \supset S_1 \supset S_2 \supset \cdots \supset S_r$$

such that

$$X_v = \{x \in X \mid rk\ df_x \leqslant m - v\}$$

where

$$m = \sup_{x \in X} rk\ df_x$$

$$S_v = f(X_v)$$

From this, one deduces that, on the set $X_v - X_{v+1}$, the rank of df is constant. (This property can also be formulated in the C^∞-case.)

Recall. $X_v - X_{v+1}$

$$\downarrow f|_{X_v - X_{v+1}} \qquad : \qquad f|_{X_v - X_{v+1}}$$

$$S_v - S_{v+1}$$

is a fibering map since it has constant rank over $S_v - S_{v+1}$.

Recall. A point is critical for a map if the map df is not surjective. It is clear that such a stratification (this "locally constant rank" stratification) should enter our picture if we want to go above the Landau surface L; for our family $(X \times T, \mathscr{S})$ and its projection map π, the formulation runs as follows: $X \times T \to T$ being trivial, only the stratification of the map $\pi \mid_{\mathscr{S}} : \mathscr{S} \to T$ is interesting. We have already introduced the subfamilies $\mathscr{S}_I$ of $\mathscr{S}$. The stratification of the $\mathscr{S}_I$ according to the rank of $\pi \mid \mathscr{S}_I$ shall be dealt with and illustrated by Pham in the next chapter.

I want to emphasize that, from the point of view of the isotopy theorem, what we want to establish is a common trivialization for all the manifolds which occur in the fiber. Therefore, when the hypersurfaces *have no more normal crossing*, we shall have to separate out *the singular locus of their intersection*. Hence the stratification of the fiber shall be augmented by the addition of new "critical strata."

The relevant notion here is the regular stratification of an analytic set. I shall follow Whitney.

Stratification of an Analytic Space V

Definition. Partition $S(V)$ of V into subsets M which are manifolds such that for all $M \in S(V)$, $\overline{M}$ is an analytic subspace such that

$$\overline{M} - M = \bigcup_{\substack{M' \in S(V) \\ M' \cap \overline{M} \neq \phi}} M'$$

Definition. A stratification is *regular* if the following holds:

(A) Let $p \in M_i \subset \overline{M}_j$. Each plane $T \in \tau(\overline{M}_j, p) = \{$SET OF LIMITS OF TANGENT PLANES AT M_j AT POINTS $q \in M_j$ AS $q \to p\}$ contains $T(M_i)_p$.

Now, to define a second set of limit tangent planes, let γ_{ij} be the holomorphic retraction defined by the plane transversal to M_i through $q \in M_j$; it cuts M_i at a point denoted $\gamma_{ij}(q)$. Let us denote by $\eta(q - \gamma_{ij}(q))$ the direction defined by the vector $q - \gamma_{ij}(q)$.

Consider $\tau(\overline{M}_j, M_i, p, \beta)$ equal to the closure of the set of tangent planes to M_j at points q as $q \to p$ in such a way that

$$\eta(q - \gamma_{ij}(q)) \to \beta$$

(B) Each plane $T \in \tau(\overline{M}_j, M_i, p, \beta)$ contains β, for all β.

Note that by taking *all directions* of approach to an analytic manifold M from the ambient analytic space V, we replace the normal bundle of M by a fiber space over M having as fiber a projective space instead of a vector space. Call it $\tilde{M}$. It is then possible to replace V by an analytic space $\tilde{V}$ such that

$$
\begin{array}{ccc}
\tilde{M} & \hookrightarrow & \tilde{V} \\
\downarrow & & \downarrow \pi \\
M & \hookrightarrow & V
\end{array}
$$

and π is an analytic isomorphism of $V - M$ with $\tilde{V} - \tilde{M}$.

This process of replacing M by the fiber space $\tilde{M}$ and fixing back to $\tilde{M}$ analytically $(V - M)$ to obtain an analytic space $\tilde{V}$ is known as blowing-up of V with the center the submanifold M ("permissible monoidal transformation" is the name used by Hironaka).

Exercise. Let M_i be in the boundary M_j : $M_i < M_j$. Blow up M_i into $\tilde{M}_i$ using the normal bundle of M_i. Transform M_j into V by means of the isomorphism $(\pi)^{-1}$. Take the closure of $\overset{-1}{\pi}(M_j)$ in $\tilde{M}_i$—to what properties do conditions (A) and (B) correspond?

A *regular* stratification exists for an analytic set (Whitney theorem). To dissect $(X \times T, \mathscr{S})_L$ into the union of fiber pairs, we should construct a refinement of the "constant rank" stratification such that: (1) The new stratification is regular; hence both $(X \times L, \mathscr{S}_L)$ and L are stratified and their strata satisfy (A) and (B). Above $T - L$, we already have a fibering map. (2) π is a proper stratified map, that is, it sends each stratum of $X \times T$ *onto* a stratum of T. (3) If the pair of strata $U > W$ is sent into the pair $U' > W'$, then we shall require a "vertical" property (A) (see Fig. 16): If $p \in V$ and $q \in U$,

$$\lim_{q \to p} V \cap T(U)_q \supset E \cap T(W)_p$$

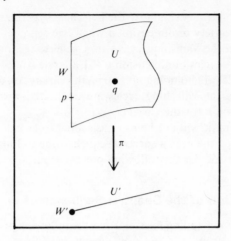

FIGURE 16

where V denotes again the tangent vector space vertical with respect to the map π.

Main Isotopy Theorem

(See Thom's lecture Theorem 1.) Let $\pi : (X \times T, \ \mathscr{S})_L \to L$ be a surjective stratified morphism. Let Y be a stratum of L and U a small open neighborhood in Y, then $\overset{-1}{\pi}U$ equipped with the induced stratification of $(X \times T, \mathscr{S})_L$ is isomorphic to a product of U by a stratified fiber (X, S).

Thom proves this theorem by changing (A, B) by his own construction of carpeting functions and tubular retractions which are better adapted to the construction of vector fields and of isotopies.   On the other hand, the proof of the existence of the stratification in the complex analytic case is more easily expressed in terms of (A, B).   Using this theorem, we can now think of the family $(X \times T, \mathscr{S})$ as a collection of fiber pairs above the strata into which the parameter variety T is decomposed by the stratification of the map π.

The main difficulty for the applications is that we have no efficient way of constructing the stratification for the family $(X \times T, \mathscr{S})$.   It would be very useful to have algebraic criteria to dissect the Landau set into strata having the differential properties expressed by (A) and (B).   One expects then that each stratum could be constructively defined by a " symbol," a refined version of the contracted diagram we have used to denote the different components of the Landau set.

If this stratification were done, we could then proceed to look for the relations between the fiber pairs above the different strata of the parameter variety.

The situation is very similar to the Lefschetz hyperplane section theorem for an algebraic variety of dimension n when one searches for the homology relations between the vanishing cycles in a generic section. On one hand, only the invariant cycles of dimension $n - 1$ are relevant for the variety since the vanishing cycles are homologous to 0 on the variety; on the other hand, the relations between the vanishing cycles are connected with the existence of cycles of dimension n for the variety.

Hence I think it will not be too misleading to give as an application of the Thom's isotopy theorem a spectral sequence due to Fary. I am grateful to Professor Steenrod for the following presentation.

Construction of the Spectral Sequence of Fary

Assume that a mapping $f: X \to Y$ has the following properties: there is a filtration $Y_0 \subset Y_1 \subset \cdots \subset Y_m = Y$ of Y by closed subsets, and for each k, if $X_k = f^{-1} Y_k$, then $f|_{X_k - X_{k-1}} X_k - X_{k-1} \to Y_k - Y_{k-1}$ is a fiber bundle (locally a product) with fiber F_k. To simplify the presentation, assume also that Y is a complex and that each Y_k is a subcomplex.

Let Y^p denote the p-dimensional skeleton of the complex on Y, and set $X^p = f^{-1} Y^p$. We have then two filtrations of X; we shall combine them into a single filtration and consider the associated spectral sequence. Let $X_k{}^p = X^p \cap X_k$, and define the rth term of the new filtration to be

$$_rX = \bigcup_{i=0}^{[r/2]} X_i^{r-2i}$$

A picture (Fig. 17) is useful in keeping track of the various sets. For example, the heavy stepped line denotes the upper boundary of $_7X$. The associated spectral sequence of this filtration of X is now well defined, and it will converge to the cohomology of X. The main point is to show that the E_2-term has the structure

$$E_2^{p,q} = \sum_{i=0}^{[p/2]} H^{p-2i}(Y_i, Y_{i-1}; H^{q+2i}(F_i))$$

and that the d_2-operator is a sum of two operators, one of which is that of the Leray–Serre spectral sequence of the fibration $(X_k - X_{k-1}) \to (Y_k - Y_{k-1})$. By definition,

$$E_1^{p,q} = H^{p+q}(_pX, {}_{p-1}X)$$

Since $_pX - {}_{p-1}X$ is the union

$$\bigcup_{i=0}^{[p/2]} (X^{p-2i} - X^{p-2i-1}) \bigcap (X_i - X_{i-1})$$

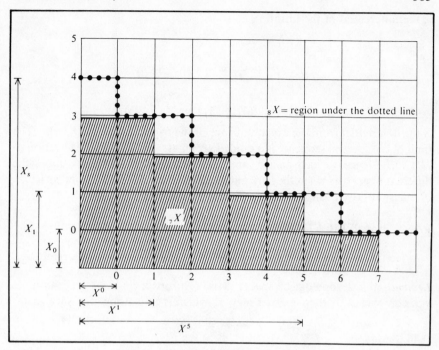

FIGURE 17

and these are disjoint open sets, the cohomology decomposes into a direct sum of terms, one for each set of the union. Since Y^{p-2i} is the $(p-2i)$ skeleton of Y, and $f \mid X_i - X_{i-1}$ is a fibration, we can identify the cohomology of the ith term with the cochain group $C^{p-2i}(Y_i, Y_{i-1}; H^{q+2i}(F_i))$.

Then,

$$E_1^{p,q} = \sum_{i=0}^{[p/2]} C^{p-2i}(Y_i, Y_{i-1}; H^{q+2i}(F_i))$$

One now computes d_1 and finds it to be the δ-operator for cochains of Y. In general, one expects d to have two components, one for each of the filtrations, but in our case the shift by two in the composite filtration makes the vertical component of d_1 be zero. However, the vertical component of d_2 will not be zero.

In fact the differential d_2 is the sum of two differentials d', d'', where

$$d'' : H^{p-2i}(Y_i, Y_{i-1}; H^{q+2i}(F_i))$$
$$\downarrow$$
$$H^{p+2-2i}(Y_i, Y_{i-1}; H^{q+2i-1}(F_i))$$

is the differential of the filtration

$$X_i - X_{i-1} \to Y_i - Y_{i-1}$$

and

$$d' : H^{p-2i}(Y_i, Y_{i-1} ; H^{q+2i}(F_i))$$

$$\downarrow$$

$$H^{p-2i+1}(Y_{i+1}, Y_i ; H^{q+2i}(F_{i+1}))$$

is the differential from the exact sequence of the triple (Y_{i+1}, Y_i, Y_{i-1}). The limit of the spectral sequence is a graded group associated with the filtration of $H^*(X)$. Hence, we have gained some information on the relations among the different fiber pairs when they are matched together to form the total space X. Needless to say, I know of no specific calculation.

PART 3: APPLICATIONS

Let us consider the following application of the isotopy theorem.

Lemma. X is a topological space; S is a subspace $i : S \hookrightarrow X$. Assume: $\forall\, K$ compact in X, there exists a map σ_K which is an isotopy of X such that

$$S \overset{\sigma k}{\hookrightarrow} X - K$$

then the map

$$i^* : H_c^q(X) \to H_c^q(S)$$

is the zero map. (Notation: we shall use from now on the mathematical symbols: $\exists$ = there exists and $\forall$ = for all, ...)

PROOF. Take h to be a representative of a compact cohomology class in $H_c^q(X)$. Then $\exists K$ such that Supp $h \subset K$. Let i_K be the inclusion map $\sigma_K S \hookrightarrow X - K$. One has $i_K^* h = 0$ from the commutative diagram.

$$
\begin{array}{ccc}
H_c^q(X) & \overset{i^*}{\longrightarrow} & H_c^q(S) \\
{\scriptstyle Id}\downarrow & & \downarrow{\scriptstyle \sigma_K^*} \\
H_c^q(X) & \overset{i_k^*}{\longrightarrow} & H_c^q(\sigma_K S)
\end{array}
$$

Note that a much weaker assumption than the existence of an isotopy is sufficient for the conclusion.

Corollaries

1. S_1, S_2 are closed subspaces of X

Assume : $\forall K$, $\exists \sigma_K^i$ such that

$$\sigma_K^i \begin{cases} S_i \hookrightarrow X - K \\ S_j \longrightarrow S_j \end{cases} \quad \text{for } i, j = 1, 2$$

Then

$$H_c^q(X - S_1 - S_2) = H_c^q(X - S_2) \oplus \delta H_c^{q-1}(S_1 - S_2)$$

PROOF. $S_1 - S_2$ is closed in $X - S_2$.

Hence we have the exact sequence:

$$\xrightarrow{\cdot i* = 0} H_c^{q-1}(S_1 - S_2) \xrightarrow{\delta} H_c^q(X - S_1 - S_2) \to H_c^q(X - S_2)$$

$$\to H_c^q(S_1 - S_2) \to \cdots$$

Now, *generalize*!

2. Let X be a complex manifold, $\dim_R X = 2n$. S_1, S_2 are two complex submanifolds of codimension 1; hence $\dim_R S_i = 2n - 2$.

Assume: (a) There exist isotopy maps $\sigma_K{}^i$, and (b) S_1 and S_2 are transversal $S_1 \pitchfork S_2$.

Write again the previous exact sequence for a closed set. One obtains

$$\begin{array}{ccccccc}
\longrightarrow & H_c^{q-1}(S_1 - S_2) & \xrightarrow{\delta} & H_c^q(X - S_1 - S_2) & \longrightarrow & H_c^q(X - S_2) & \xrightarrow{\;\;\circ\;\;} \\
& \downarrow s & & & & \downarrow s & \\
\longrightarrow & H_{p-1}^c(S_1 - S_2) & \xrightarrow{[\delta]} & H_p^c(X - S_1 - S_2) & \longrightarrow & H_p^c(X - S_2) & \longrightarrow
\end{array}$$

$$p + q = 2n$$

where the vertical isomorphisms are given by the usual Poincaré duality for manifolds. Hence the second line is exact. So,

$$H_p^c(X - S_1 - S_2) = H_p^c(X - S_2) \oplus [\delta] H_{p-1}^c(S_1 - S_2)$$

where $[\delta]$ is the map of the homology sequence.

3. Let $\{S_i\}_{i \in I}$ be algebraic manifolds in general position in P^n. Let $X = C^n \bigcap_{i \in J} S_i$, where $C^n = P^n - P_\infty^{n-1}$ is the affine space, and J is a subset of I. Then

$$H_*^c\left(X - \bigcup_{i \in I-J} S_i\right) = \bigoplus_{H \subset I-J} [\delta^H] H_{*-|H|}^c\left(X \bigcap_{i \in H} S_i\right)$$

Picard–Lefschetz Formula (a beginning!)

Consider the case of one hypersurface globally given in P^n by one equation $S(x, t) = 0$. We restrict severely the type of singularities.

Assume: (A) For $t = 0$, S has an isolated nondegenerate quadratic singularity, that is for $t = 0$, $S_x = 0$, but det (Hess S)$_x \neq 0$. (B) Localization in W, where we can assume W to be the open ball $\|X\| < 1$.

In $X - W$, we have an external isotopy which sends ∂W into ∂W since everything is transversal outside W.

For simplicity, we shall suppose that dim $T = 1$; hence we have a family $(X \times T, \mathscr{S})$ over the disk $|t| < 1$, the singular fiber of the family being the fiber above $t = 0$ only, and the singularity satisfying the restriction (A); for $t \neq 0$ in the disk we can apply the little isotopy theorem in W.

It is convenient (but not necessary: see the final formulas!) to introduce several types of "homologies." I hope it can make the picture clearer. If h is a cycle in $H*^c(X - S)$, it is natural to take its trace in the open ball W: we localize the cycle in a neighborhood of the singularity,

$$h \sim\!\!\!\wedge\!\!\!\wedge\!\!\!\wedge\!\!\!\sim \mathrm{tr}_W \, h$$

then $\mathrm{tr}_W \, h$ is a cycle with closed support in W, which avoids the manifold S.

Hence we can cook up the following homology group (usually defined by means of a family of supports): $H*^F(\underline{W} - S)$, where the superscript F and the underlined W mean that we are interested in cycles with closed supports in $W - S$ but the support has also to be a closed set in W!

Assumption (A) means that in W, there exists a local equation for S of the form $\Sigma x_i^2 = t$. By choosing such a simple form, we have further assumed that no extra complication was coming from the parametrization of the family of hypersurfaces over t, that is, $\partial S/\partial t \neq 0$.

Now let us look at W "under a microscope." Then we are simply considering a complex quadric S in C^n, and we can discover only one generator ξ for $H_n^F(C^n - S)$. (Hence, we choose an orientation.) Similarly, looking at the homology group $H_{n-1}^c(S \cap W)$, we find only one generator which we shall denote by e and which is explicitly described as follows:

$$e = \begin{cases} \sum x_i^2 = t \\ x_i/\sqrt{t} \text{ real} \end{cases} + \text{ choice of an orientation}$$

(a complex quadric is the tangent bundle of a real sphere, and can be retracted on this real part). But e is homologous to 0 in W. Hence there exists a chain (oriented) denoted $e(W, S)$ such that its boundary in S is the cycle e:

$$e(W, S) \xrightarrow{\ \partial\ } e$$

The basic "duality" we shall build in a very complicated manner is described by the formula

$$K.\, I(\varepsilon, e(W, S)) = +1$$

where $K.I$ is the old Kronecker index counting intersection with sign. (It is also the linking number of ε with e!)

We have finished setting up a trap for our Feynman cycle h_F. If $\mathrm{tr}_W \, h_F \sim n\varepsilon$, then h_F will change its homology class when we make a loop σ around $t = 0$ in the disk. If $\mathrm{tr}_W \, h_F$ is not homologous to a multiple of ε, then it is homologous to 0; hence it can be pushed away from the ball W which localizes the singularity, and therefore is left invariant by the automorphism induced by the loop σ on the homology group to which h_F belongs.

So let us go into some details of the *machinery* of this duality: Let $X = C^\infty$-paracompact manifold oriented, and $S =$ union of finite number of oriented, closed submanifolds which intersect transversally.

Let $\dim X = n = p + q$. The duality we are after can be expressed as a pairing

$$H_q^F(X - S) \otimes H_p^c(X, S) \to \mathbb{C}$$

Given a homology class α of dimension q, the usual Poincaré duality gives a cohomology class $\varphi\alpha$ of the same dimension q. For cohomology with support, this duality as formulated by Cartan, lands us in a cohomology group denoted by $H_F^p(X - S)$ (that is, cohomology with the same family of supports: closed sets in $X - S$ which are also closed in X). But this class $\varphi\alpha$ is a usual relative cohomology class. At the risk of sounding pedantic call G the isomorphism,

$$H_F^p(X - S) \xrightarrow[\sim]{G} H_F^p(X, S)$$

(G is for Godement Theorie des faisceaux or Grothendieck : *Local Cohomology*.)

Now, even a physicist can *integrate* a relative cohomology class $G \circ \varphi\alpha$ on a compact relative cycle β of dimension p. Hence we have a number, denoted by

$$\langle \alpha \,|\, \beta \rangle = \int_\beta G \circ \phi\alpha$$

Let us summarize these results in a diagram where S consists of a single submanifold of X:

$$\alpha \in H_q^F(X - S)$$
$$\downarrow S\ \varphi$$
$$\varphi\alpha \in H_F^p(X - S)$$
$$\downarrow S\ G$$
$$G\varphi\alpha \in H^p(X, S)$$

integration over $\beta \in H_p^c(X, S)$

$$\langle \alpha \,|\, \beta \rangle$$

We shall proceed now to construct the same duality for the case of two submanifolds $S = S_1 \cup S_2$ by using the exact sequence associated with a triple (X, S_1, S_2). This is the construction Leray develops in *Bull. Soc. Math. de France (III)* **87**, pp. 81–180, 1959.

Introducing exact triangles to represent the associated exact sequences, we have successively

$$H_q^F(\underline{X} - S_1 \cup S_2)$$

$$H_q^F(\underline{X} - S_2) \xrightarrow[\cap [S_1]]{} H_q^F(S_1 - S_2) \quad \delta$$

where the two interesting maps are:

1. The intersection by the submanifold S_1 which is a homology class, and gives a map lowering dimension by 2.
2. The cobord map [8] (Leray) for which we now have two definitions, the first one by applying the Poincaré duality to manifolds as we did in Corollary 2, the second the geometric definition we met in studying tubular neighborhoods.

The two following steps are classical,

$$H_F^p(\underline{X} - S_1 \cup S_2)$$
$$H_F^p(\underline{X} - S_2) \xrightarrow{i_*} H_F^p(\underline{S_1} - S_2)$$

$$H^p(X, S_1 \cup S_2)$$
$$H^p(X, S_2) \xrightarrow{i_*} H^*(S_1, S_2) \quad \partial$$

They are the usual exact sequence for a closed set.

The last stage is reached by

$$H_p^c(X, S_1 \cup S_2)$$
$$H_p^c(X, S_2) \longleftarrow H_p^c(S_1, S_2)$$
$$\downarrow S \text{ excision}$$
$$H_p^c(S_1 \cup S_2, S_2)$$

Note that this last triangle runs in the opposite direction. Duality reverses arrows.

We shall summarize the relevant parts in Fig. 18. The vertical lines are isomorphisms. We have the formula

$$\langle \delta\alpha \mid \beta \rangle = \langle \alpha \mid \partial\beta \rangle$$

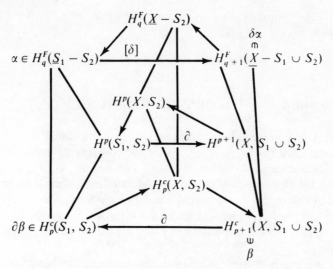

FIGURE 18

Its "true" origin is best seen by reverting to the simple case we treated at the beginning of this lecture: Let S again be the complex quadric in the ball W (See Fig. 19). We had

$$KI(\varepsilon, e(W, S)) = 1$$

If we define $\varepsilon = [\delta]\tilde{\varepsilon}$,

$$\tilde{\varepsilon} \in H_{n-1}^F(S \cap W)$$

then

$$KI(\tilde{\varepsilon}, e) = +1$$

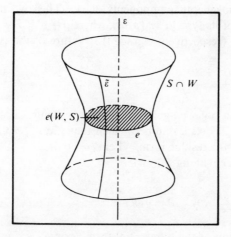

FIGURE 19

Hence, if the Feynman cycle h_F is trapped in the ball W, $\mathrm{tr}_W\, h_F$ is the lifting by the geometrical cobord map $[\delta]$ of a cycle $\widetilde{h_F}$ lying on S: $\mathrm{tr}_W\, h_F = \delta \tilde{h}_F$ and

$$KI(\mathrm{tr}_W\, h_F,\, e(W, S)) = K.\, I(\widetilde{h_F},\, e)$$

PART 4: LERAY—THEORY OF RESIDUES

Let X be a nonsingular complex analytic manifold $\dim X = l$. Introduce local coordinates $x = (x_1, x_2, \ldots, x_l)$ for the complex structure, but for the real C^∞-differentiable structure, we shall use $x = (x_1, \bar{x}_1, \ldots, x_l, \bar{x}_l)$. We shall note, for all complex manifolds of codimension 1, their local irreducible equation as follows: S, in the neighborhood of $y \in S$, is given by $s(x, y) = 0$.

Let $(S_i)\, i = 1 \ldots m$ be such that $ds_i \neq 0$ for $x = y$ and we shall say that $(S_1, \ldots, S_m)$ are in general position at $y \in S_I = \bigcap_{i \in I} S_i$ if the $(ds_i)_{i \in I}$ are linearly independent.

As we are interested in relative cohomology, the basic set up is as follows:

$$S = S_1 \cap S_2 \cap \cdots \cap S_m \quad \text{(intersection)}$$

This shall carry the residue class, and the cohomology relative to the *union* of submanifolds will be

$$S' = S_1' \cup S_2' \cup \cdots \cup S_m'$$

Recall. By a regular function, one means a function which is C^∞-differentiable over X.

A differential form $\varphi(x)$ is regular if it has regular coefficients. If $d\varphi = 0$, φ is closed.

Note that it is a differential form in $(dx, d\bar{x})$ and that we shall mainly consider the homogeneous components of φ. Then we shall speak of the degree of φ, and of its type $[d^0\varphi, (p, q)]$, where $p + q = d^0\varphi$. We shall make use of the graded (respectively bigraded) structure of the ring of differential forms.

Recall that $d = \partial + \bar{\partial}$

Definition. φ has a polar singularity of order p along S if $\varphi(x)$ is regular on $X - S$ and if there exists a number p such that $s(x, u)^p\, \varphi(x)$ is regular on X. Now, let us define the residue form. Let $d\varphi = 0$ on $X - S$, let φ have a polar singularity of order p along S. Then

Proposition. $\varphi = \dfrac{ds}{S} \wedge \psi + \theta \quad\quad (R)$

where the restriction of the differential form ψ on S, $\psi\,|_S$ is closed.

Definition. Res $[\varphi] = \psi_s$

NOTATION. $\mathrm{Res}[\varphi] = \dfrac{S\varphi}{dS}\Bigg|_s$; if $\varphi = \dfrac{\omega}{S}$, then $\mathrm{Res}[\varphi] = \dfrac{\omega}{dP}\Bigg|_s$

Let us postpone the proof. Basic for the formula (R), as its form suggests, is a division theorem for differential forms.

Local Division Theorem

Lemma. Let $\varphi(x)$ be a regular form on X, then

$$\boxed{dS(x, y) \wedge \varphi(x) = 0} \overset{\text{iff}}{\longleftrightarrow} \boxed{\begin{array}{l}\exists \text{ a form } \psi(x, y) \text{ regular} \\ \text{near } y \text{ such that} \\ \varphi(x) = dS(x, y) \wedge \psi(x, y)\end{array}}$$

Further, $\psi \mid_s$ is uniquely defined and if φ is holomorphic, one can choose $\varphi(x, y)$ holomorphic.

PROOF (Leray): Take $s = x_1$.

To get an idea of the difficult refinements this simple division admits, let us allow some singularity to S, say a nondegenerate quadratic point:

$$(S_x = 0 \qquad \det \mathrm{Hess}\, S \neq 0) \quad \text{for} \quad x = y$$

y is a "simple" singularity of S. Then (De Rham) "Let φ be holomorphic on X. Then there exists a form ψ holomorphic such that $\varphi = ds \wedge \psi$ if and only if $ds \wedge \varphi = 0$ when $d^0\varphi < l$ and, when $d^0\varphi = l$, that is,

$$\varphi = a(x)dx_1 \wedge \cdots \wedge dx_1,$$

then $a(y) = 0$."

To make this division, one has to introduce the ring A of holomorphic functions in a ball around y, small enough so that

$$\left(z_1(x) = \frac{\partial s}{\partial x_1}, z_2(x) = \frac{\partial s}{\partial x_2}, \ldots, z_l(x) = \frac{\partial s}{\partial x_l}\right)$$

are local coordinates. One recognizes the 1-jet of the function $s(x)$. The main property of (A) is now "$z_{k+1}(x)a(x) \in (I_k) = $ ideal generated by $(z_1, z_2, \ldots, z_k)$, then $a(x) \in (I_k)$."

We return now to the proof of the Proposition:

1. Existence: Note that $d(s\varphi) = ds \wedge \varphi$, since φ is closed. Applying the previous lemma, we have

$$ds \wedge \varphi = ds \wedge \theta \qquad \text{(first division)}$$

which we shall write

$$ds \wedge (s\varphi - s\theta) = 0$$

Note that $s\varphi - s\theta$ is regular; hence

$$s\varphi - s\theta = ds \wedge \psi \qquad \text{(second division)}$$

2. Uniqueness of $\psi \mid_S$: Consider the equation

$$\frac{ds}{s} \wedge \psi + \theta = 0$$

Hence $ds \wedge \theta = 0$. Thus (first division) we can divide : there exists ω such that $\theta = ds \wedge \omega$. Now $ds \wedge (\psi + s\omega) = 0$. Hence there exists $\bar{\omega}$ such that $\psi + s\omega = ds \wedge \bar{\omega}$ (second division) and $\bar{\omega}$ is regular. Hence $\psi \mid_S = 0$.

3. Let us change the local equation (associated vector bundle!)

$$s = us'$$

with u holomorphic; then

$$\varphi = \frac{ds'}{s'} \wedge \psi + \theta'$$

where $\theta' = \theta + d(\log U) \wedge \psi$.

4. $\psi \mid_S$ is closed on S. We have

$$-\frac{ds}{s} \wedge d\psi + d\theta = 0$$

Hence, by 2, $d\psi \mid_S = 0$.

For the case of quadratic nondegenerate singular points of S, one has that the residue form is still "holomorphic" at the singular point.

Let me quote without entering into details, a majorization of the residue form, very useful in applications:

$$\left| \frac{\omega}{ds} \right|_S \leqslant \frac{|\omega|_x}{|ds|_x}$$

at each point of S.

To put the residue form to work, let us go back to compact (relative) homology. The exact sequence of a triple (X, S, S') gives

$$
\begin{array}{ccc}
 & H^c_*(X, S') & \\
{}^p \nearrow & & \nwarrow {}^i \\
H^c_*(X, S \cup S') & \longrightarrow & H^c_*(S, S')
\end{array}
$$

with the three well-known homomorphisms. Again, let us introduce for $S = S_1$ ($m = 1$) the tubular neighborhood of S: V is a fiber space over S with

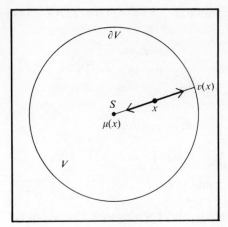

FIGURE 20

such small fiber that we have the picture shown in Fig. 20.

We have two obvious retractions $\begin{cases} \mu: \overline{V} \to S \\ v: X - S \to X - V \end{cases}$

and the corresponding maps at the homology level

$$v_* : H_*^c(X - S, S') \overset{\to}{\underset{\sim}{}} H_*(X - V, S')$$

are an isomorphism, since v is homotopic to the identity on $X - S$ and

$$\mu_* : H_*^c(S, S') \to H_{*+2}^c(X, (X - V) \cup S')$$

which is geometrically constructed as follows:

Over σ, simplex of S, construct the cell $\mu^{-1}(\sigma)$

$$\mu^{-1}(\sigma) = \{x \in \overline{V} \mid \mu(x) \in \sigma\}$$

The corresponding oriented cell is given by $\mu_* \sigma$. One makes certain that

$$(\mu_* \partial - \partial \mu_*)\sigma \subset X - V$$

and also sees that intersecting by S gives an inverse map for μ_*. Hence μ_* is a famous isomorphism.

Lemma. Let γ be a chain of X which is transversal to S. Let $\partial\gamma = \text{chain}_{X-S} + \text{chain}_{S'}$. Let $h(X - S, S')$ be the corresponding homology class $[\partial\gamma]$, and let $h(S, S') = [\gamma \cdot S]$. Then $\delta h(S, S') = h(X - S, S')$.

Denote by V_ε, μ_ε, δ_ε a fundamental system of such objects as considered above.

Let $\varphi(x)$ regular on $X - S$ be such that near each point $y \in S$, there exist regular forms $\psi(x, y)$, $\theta(x, y)$ such that

$$\varphi(x) = \frac{ds(x, y)}{s(x, y)} \wedge \psi(x, y) + \theta(x, y)$$

Then we have the following!

Lemma. $\psi \mid_S$ is independent of y and

$$\lim_{\varepsilon \to 0} \int_{\delta_\varepsilon \gamma} \varphi(x) = 2\pi i \int_\gamma \psi(x)$$

for any compact chain γ.

PROOF. Let σ be a simplex of S, take $s(x, y) = x_1$, then

$$\lim_{\varepsilon \to 0} \int_{\delta_\varepsilon \sigma} \varphi(x) = \int_{\delta_\varepsilon \sigma} \frac{dx_1}{x_1} \wedge \psi(\mu(x)) = \oint \frac{dx_1}{x_1} \cdot \int_\sigma \psi(x)$$

Hence we have the important *residue formula:*

$$\int_{\delta h(s, s')} \varphi(x) = 2\pi i \int_{h(s, s')} \text{Res } \varphi$$

And we have rebuilt in a most natural way the duality of

The triangles are exact.   Most interesting is to look at the exactitude of the right triangle, left corner.

First canonical problem: construct a form with given residue. Let V again be a tubular neighborhood of S.

Lemma. Let $\varphi \in \phi(S, S^1)$ equal the closed differential forms on S, which vanish on S'. There exists a differential form $\omega \in \Omega(X - S, S')$ and two differential forms $\psi(x, y)$, $\theta(x, y)$ such that

$$\omega \mid_{X-V} = 0 \quad (\text{or Supp } \omega \subset \overline{V})$$

$$\omega = \frac{ds}{s} \wedge \psi + \theta$$

with

$$\psi \mid_S = \varphi \qquad \psi \mid_{S'} = \theta \mid_{S'} = 0$$

and $d\psi = 0$ in a neighborhood of S.

PROOF. We have a map μ which is a retraction of $\overline{V}$ on S such that $\overline{V} \cap S'$ is sent into $S \cap S'$. $\varphi(\mu(X))$ is *closed* on $(\overline{V}, S')$. Let $\chi(x)$ a C^∞-function, 1 near S, 0 in $X - \overline{V}$. Let $\psi(x) = \chi(x)\varphi(\mu(x))$ on $\overline{V}$ and extended by 0 on $X - \overline{V}$. Then we have achieved $\psi|_S = \varphi$, $\psi|_{S'} = 0$, and $d\psi = 0$ near S.

Using a partition of unity $\pi(x, y)$ such that Supp $\pi(x, y)$ contains the set of points x where the local equation $s(x, y)$ is defined, we obtain

$$\omega(x) = \sum \pi(x, z) \frac{ds(x, z)}{s(x, z)} \wedge \psi(x)$$

and the remainder

$$\theta(x, y) = \sum \pi(x, z) \, d\left(\log \frac{s(x, z)}{s(x, y)} \right) \wedge \psi$$

Our first canonical problem is then solved by taking

Cohomology classes $\begin{cases} h^* (S, S') = \text{class of } \varphi \\ h^* (X, S') = \text{class of } d\omega \end{cases}$

We use this solution in the following lemma.

Lemma. If $h^*(X, S') = 0$, then $\varphi(x)$ is the residue of a form in $\Phi(X - S, S')$ with a polar singularity on S of order 1. There exists a form $\sigma \in \Omega(X, S')$ such that

$$d\omega = d\sigma$$

Hence

$$\omega - \sigma = \frac{ds}{s} \wedge \psi + \theta - \sigma$$

is a *closed* differential form. Thus we have constructed the map $\overline{\omega}^*$ of the figure.

We shall now look at the second canonical problem.

Lemma. If Res $h^*(X - S, S') = 0$, then $h^*(X - S, S')$ contains forms with nonzero residue (hence polar singularity of order 1).

Lemma. If $h^*(S, S') \in \text{Im Res}$, then any form $\varphi \in h^*(S, S')$ is residue form of some form in $\Phi(X - S, S')$.

Lemma. Let $\varphi \in \Phi(S, S')$

$$\varphi = \text{Res form of (something)} \in h^* (X - S, S')$$

$$\text{iff} \Big\uparrow$$

$$\phi \in \frac{1}{2\pi i} \text{Res } h^*(X - S, S')$$

Hence, *Theorem 1* of Leray, which is central if you think of the long path we followed:

Let φ be a closed form on $X - S$, 0 on S'. Then φ is homologous to $\bar{\varphi}$ in the ring of differential forms $\Omega(X - S, S)$: $\varphi \sim \bar{\varphi}$ where $\bar{\varphi}$ has polar singularities of *order 1*. The set of the forms $s\bar{\varphi}/ds \mid_S$ is *a cohomology class* of (S, S').

NOTE. This would be false if one has replaced the ring Ω of regular forms, by the ring of holomorphic forms.

For the case $m = 2$, if S_1, S_2 have global equations $S_1(x) = 0$, $S_2(x) = 0$, one has the division theorem suitably generalized!

Lemma. Let φ be a closed, form on $X - S_1 \cap S_2$ with polar singularity of order 1 on S_i, respectively, $i = 1, 2$: Assume $S_1(X, y)S_2(X, y)\varphi$ regular near $y \in S_1 \cap S_2$. Then

$$\varphi = \frac{dS_1}{S_1} \wedge \frac{dS_2}{S_2} \wedge \psi + \frac{dS_1}{S_1} \wedge \theta_1 + \frac{dS_2}{S_2} \wedge \theta_2 + \omega \cdots$$

where one deals with polar singularity of order 1 only. This leads to the iterated residue Res^m in the same way as the geometric construction of the iterated cobord δ^m. We shall not follow this very useful generalization— instead we use the following for the *Residue-form of a product* (if S has a global equation $S(x) = 0$).

Global Division Theorem

Lemma. If φ is closed, with polar singularity of order 1 then $\varphi = (ds/S) \wedge \psi + \theta$, where the differential forms *are defined globally*.

Then we can define the residue of a product.

Lemma. Let φ_1, φ_2 be two closed differential forms with polar singularity of order 1 on S, then $\varphi_1 \wedge \varphi_2$ has a polar singularity on S and we have the relation

$$\text{Res}\,[\varphi_1 \wedge \varphi_2] = \text{Res}\left[\varphi_1 \wedge \frac{dS}{S}\right] \wedge \text{Res}\,[\varphi_2] \pm \text{Res}\,[\varphi_1] \wedge \text{Res}\left[\varphi_2 \wedge \frac{dS}{S}\right]$$

PROOF. The proof of the foregoing is obvious if one uses the global division formula

$$\varphi_1 = \frac{dS}{S} \wedge \psi_1 + \theta_1$$

$$\varphi_2 = \frac{dS}{S} \wedge \psi_2 + \theta_2$$

Multiplying the two terms, one gets

$$\varphi_1 \wedge \varphi_2 = \frac{dS}{S} \wedge (\psi_1 \wedge \theta_2 + \theta_1 \wedge \psi_2) + \theta_1 \wedge \theta_2$$

Note that the polar singularity of $\varphi_1 \wedge \varphi_2$, which is of order 2, disappears (Theorem 1).

We shall now take up the case of a polar singularity of order $k > 1$. Consider $\varphi = \psi_1 \wedge ds/s^k$ a closed form, and then, successively

$$d\psi_1 = \frac{(-1)^h}{k-1} \psi_2 \wedge dS$$

$$\vdots$$

$$d\psi_j = \frac{(-1)^{h-j+1}}{k-j} \psi_{j+1} \wedge dS$$

$$\vdots$$

$$d\psi_{k-1} = \omega \wedge dS$$

Exercise. Prove that one can make these successive divisions.

Define $R(\varphi) = \omega \,|_S$. *Assume, from now on, the strong restriction that S is an algebraic nonsingular variety in P^n.* Consider the line bundle associated with $S \hookrightarrow P^n$, or, rather, to the global equation of S—$S(x) = 0$.

$$\left(\frac{L}{P^n} \right)$$

has a canonical section which is precisely this equation. $L \,|\, S$ is the normal bundle of S in P^n; but when patching local coordinates, it is natural to consider also the n-times twisted form of this normal bundle.

Using the standard covering of P_n by the $(n+1)$ affine open sets

$$U_i = \{x_i \neq 0\}$$

L^n is defined by the cocycle $(f_i/f_j)^n$, where $f_i = 0$, $f_j = 0$ are the equations defining S in U_i and U_j, respectively. We are introducing these notions because they are appropriate for expressing that the global meromorphic differential k-form ω has polar singularities of order n along some subvariety S, or vanishes with order p over some other subvariety S'. This is formulated as follows: ω is a global section of the sheaf of analytic k-forms with coefficients in $L^{-n} \otimes L'^p$, where L and L' are the line bundles associated with S and S'. Hence, it is a statement easy to write down in terms of local coordinates. Leray's theory of residues can be also written (without much profit) in terms of sheaves of differentiable, forms, that is, differential forms with differentiable coefficients or even weaker properties.

But we can also go in the opposite direction and ask for stronger properties of the coefficients. To require analytic or algebraic properties for these coefficients seems to lead us inescapably to sheaves and their cohomology. I shall simply state some results along these lines and give three references.

1. *Complex Manifolds*, Lectures by S. S. Chern (University of Chicago 1956).
2. *Integrals of the second kind on an algebraic variety*, Hodge and Atiyah, *Annals of Math.* **62**, p. 56, 1955.
3. *Some Results on Moduli and Periods of Integrals on Algebraic Manifolds I, II, III (Preprints)*, P. A. Griffiths (Berkeley University).

The first interesting property concerns the image of the residue map in the algebraic case. Differential forms now have the bigradation given by the complex structure $(d_X, d_{\bar{X}})$ and the cohomology groups are now direct sums of the cohomology groups obtained with the differential forms of a given type:

$$H^n(X) = H^{n,0}(X) + H^{n-1,1}(X) + \cdots + H^{0,n}(X)$$

One has then the following theorem.

Theorem. Let $A^{q+1}(S)$ be the closed rational $(q + 1)$—forms on X with poles of order $r + 1$ on S.
     Then the residue map sends

$$A_r^{q+1}(S) \xrightarrow{R} H^{q,0}(S) + H^{q-1,1}(S) + \cdots + H^{q-r,r}(S)$$

in such a way that $A_r^{q+1}(S)/A_{r-1}^{q+1}(S)$ maps into $H^{q-r,r}(S)$.

With this more algebraic setup, maybe we can now have a vague idea of the problem of defining residues on *a singular* variety S (that is, we shall be concerned with differential forms with polar singularity on S—S being singular). Consider first the simple case :

Let X be an algebraic *manifold* and S an irreducible algebraic subvariety with ordinary singularities, that is, locally S is given by $x_1 \ldots x_k = 0$. [$(x_1 \ldots x_n)$ = local coordinates on X]. Since S is irreducible, only the local problem looks like our initial family $(X \times T, \mathscr{S})$, where $\mathscr{S}$ was reducible. Then there exists a canonical model $\tilde{S}$ called the *normalization* of S which is a nonsingular algebraic manifold.

Thus, we are going a step further: the use of Hironaka's resolution of singularities reduces us to the case of algebraic hypersurfaces with normal crossings. Here to interpret our residue on an irreducible hypersurface with normal crossings, we are led to consider *coverings*. In fact, the normalized variety $\tilde{S}$ is a nice covering of S for which the k local sheets of S which meet transversally in a neighborhood of the "ordinary singularity $x_1 \ldots x_k = 0$" are separated. Let π be the covering map

$$
\begin{array}{c}
\tilde{S} \\
\big\downarrow{\scriptstyle\pi} \\
S \overset{i}{\hookrightarrow} X
\end{array}
$$

Recall that the embedding of S into X determines a line bundle over X, that we shall call L. Recall that X as an algebraic manifold carries a canonical bundle K_X. (See Professor's Bott lecture on the Jacobian bundle.)

Recall now that the local sections of an analytic vector bundle define an object called a sheaf, which—if it originates from a vector bundle—is locally free, hence coherent.

Recall that the map π being proper one can define for coherent sheaves the direct image by the map π:

$$
\begin{array}{c}
\tilde{S} \longrightarrow F \\
\big\downarrow{\scriptstyle\pi} \qquad \big\downarrow \\
S \longrightarrow \pi_* F
\end{array}
$$

Theorem. If F is a coherent sheaf on $\tilde{S}$, then, $\pi_* F$ is a coherent sheaf on S.

All these notions are forced upon us because, except for drastic restrictions on the map π, one cannot expect the direct image of a vector bundle, which is a nice geometric object, to be a vector bundle itself; or, in other words: Vector bundles can be pulled back but not torn down.

Yet, using only pull-back we have the geometrical picture that follows: Over X we have two line bundles L and K_X; construct the product $K_X \otimes L^{-1}$ of the two vector bundles K_x and L^{-1}. Then by pulling back, we can construct a vector bundle over S. We shall denote it by $\pi^{-1}(K_X \otimes L^{-1})$ [instead of the correct expression $(i \circ \pi)^{-1}$]:

$$
\begin{array}{c}
K_X \otimes L^{-1} \longrightarrow \pi^{-1}(K_X \otimes L^{-1}) \\
\big\downarrow \qquad\qquad\qquad \big\downarrow \\
X \overset{i}{\longleftarrow} S \overset{\pi}{\longleftarrow} \tilde{S}
\end{array}
$$

Look at the "sheaf" over $\tilde{S}$ of (local) sections of $\pi^{-1}(K_X \otimes L^{-1})$ which vanish on $\tilde{\Sigma}$, where Σ is the singular locus of S and $\pi^{-1}\Sigma = \tilde{\Sigma}$. Call this sheaf $\tilde{O}(K_X \otimes L^{-1})_\Delta$. It is a subsheaf of the sheaf of all local sections. Then we have the classical adjunct formula of the Italian geometers in a disguised form: The sheaf $\tilde{O}(K_X \otimes L^{-1})_\Delta$ is isomorphic to the sheaf of local sections of the canonical bundle of $\tilde{S} - \tilde{O}(K_X \otimes L^{-1})_\Lambda \simeq \tilde{O}(K_{\tilde{S}})$. The proof of all this high-brow construction is so easy that I most strongly recommend looking it up in Griffiths' work (III, p. 61).

The map giving the isomorphism is the residue map R followed by the lifting π^*. So let $S \hookrightarrow X$ be an embedding with ordinary singularities (Hironaka). Let S_k be the subvariety of S of points of order k through which k sheets of S intersect transversally. Then S_k is given locally by $\{x_1 = 0 \ldots x_k = 0\}$ if S is given locally as $S = (x_1 \ldots x_k = 0)$; so that $S - S_1$ is the nonsingular part of S, $S_1 - S_2$ is the nonsingular part of S, etc.

We are again led to consider a nice stratification of S. Let us call the strata Yv

$$Y_V = S_V - S_{V+1}$$

$$\begin{array}{c} \tilde{Y}_V \\ {\scriptstyle\pi}\downarrow \\ Y_V \end{array}$$

Let $\tilde{Y}_\nu = \pi^{-1} \tilde{Y}_\nu$ be the inverse image of Y_ν in S. Then $\tilde{Y}_\nu$ is an un-branched covering with ν sheets above Y_ν.

Griffiths' Proposition

Let N_ν be the normal bundle of Y_ν in X. Then taking germs of its local sections and denoting this sheaf $O(N_\nu)$, one has

$$O(N_\nu) = O(L) \otimes_{Q_{Y_\nu}} \pi_* O_{Y_\nu}$$

Now let us again define $A^q(k)$ as the closed q-forms on X with poles of order $k + 1$ along S.

We would like to apply to $A^q(k)$ a generalization of the residue map which holds for the case where S is singular. Some examples of this situation appear in our joint work with Regge, where we are dealing with algebraic differential forms with polar singularities on a linear family of hypersurfaces. Bertini's theorem asserts that the generic hypersurfaces has no singularity outside the basic locus of the family. But the physics of the problem, where we are dealing with a general diagram with more than *one* loop, oblige us to consider the case where the generic hypersurface is singular on this fixed locus.

It turns out that the residue map can still be defined on a linear subset of the differential forms $A^q(k)$. We shall denote this vector space by $A^q(k)_\Lambda$. For $k = 0$ the conditions to define the residue map R are linear: one requires that the differential forms vanish on the singular locus of S. For $k > 0$ they are still linear but more complicated to state. Griffiths sketches the definition only for the case of curves and surfaces. I shall refer to his paper and to Hodge and Atiyah.

The geometrical problem associated with these conditions is the relationship between the homological properties of S and of its desingularization $\tilde{S}$. Let f be the blowing down map from $\tilde{S}$ to S

$$\tilde{S}$$
$$\downarrow f$$
$$S \hookrightarrow X$$

Then the differential forms on S are mapped into the differential forms on $\tilde{S}$.

What is obtained by the operations of restriction and residue from the differential forms of X is the cohomology of $\tilde{S}$. We shall put on record this geometric interpretation of the residue map for the singular case.

Theorem. Let S be a hypersurface in X. Then there exists a residue map R such that

$$R : A^{q+1}(k)_\Delta \to \sum_{j \leqslant k} H^{q-j,j}(\tilde{S})$$

and further

$$\sum_{j \leqslant k} H^{q-j,j}(\tilde{S}) = \sum H^{q-j,j}(X) \oplus R(A^{q+1}(k)_\Delta)$$

What was achieved by the use of Hironaka's resolution of singularities and normalization was to bring us back to a situation quite similar to our starting simple case where the hypersurface S was not singular.

As in the following we shall have to deal with a linear family of hypersurfaces in P^n which has a fixed basis consisting of several linear subspaces of P^n, I want to record here a useful formula which shows how one can still calculate the relevant homology group after a "permissible" blowing up.

Theorem. (Denniston, *Annals of Mathematics* p. 10, 1956.) Let $\tilde{V}$ be the inverse image of a nonsingular algebraic variety V in P^n under the monoidal transformation having V as the center. Let $\tilde{P}^n$ be the transform of P^n. Then

$$H_r(\tilde{P}^n) = H_r(P) \oplus \sum_{q=1}^{m-n-1} H_{r-2q}(V)$$

$\tilde{V}$ is just a fiber space over V with projective fiber P^{n-m-1} ($m = \dim V$). Introducing Euler's characteristic (see Regge's talk), we have

$$\chi(\tilde{V}) = \chi^{(P^{n-m-1})}\chi(V)$$

PART 5: FEYNMAN INTEGRALS REVISITED—
THE α-REPRESENTATION

Let F be a holomorphic application of a complex analytic manifold X^* into X

$$F \doteq X^* \to X$$

Then we have an induced map on the differential forms F^* defined as follows: $(F^*\varphi)(x^*)$ is the form $\varphi(F(x^*))$. Let us restrict rather severely the map F. It can be quite generalized but, for simplicity, we follow Leray.

Let $F^{-1}(S)$ be the set of points that F maps onto S. We shall assume F, S, S' such that $F^{-1}(S)$, $F^{-1}(S')$ are also analytic manifolds, in general position again; we shall also require that the transforms of the local irreducible equations $S_i(F(X^*), F(y^*)) = 0$ still be local irreducible equations.

Then the main functorial property of this change of variables is the commutation of Res with F^*:

$$F^*\left(\frac{\omega}{dS}\bigg|_S\right) = \frac{F^*\omega}{dF^*S}\bigg|_{F^{-1}(S)}$$

It is a very interesting circle of equations which deserves a more complete investigation elsewhere. Trying to get rid of one particular integral representation in the hope of getting a "very good" one, we are led to consider all schemes of the form $X \xrightarrow{f} T$ and the relations (or maps) between them:

$$
\begin{array}{ccc}
X^* \times T & \xrightarrow{\quad F \quad} & X \times T \\
& \searrow \qquad \swarrow & \\
& T &
\end{array}
$$

If they define the *same germ* of analytic functions, we should expect that $\pi_1(T\text{-}L)$ operates "in a very similar manner" on their homology vector spaces or, rather, since $\pi_1(T\text{-}L)$ operates only through the "connection" which lifts vector fields from $T\text{-}L$ into vertical vector fields in X, that we have the same representation of $\pi_1(T\text{-}L)$. Indeed, something like a universal model M exists, but I shall refer to Griffiths' again (I, II, III) and his study of the map $\Phi: (T - L) \to M$, where Φ is obtained by studying all the periods of the basic differential forms over a basis of the homology cycles. I shall only make a remark: we are almost in a situation first considered by Grothendieck, and proved by Borel–Narashiman in the complex analytic case. I state only a simplified version.

Borel–Narashiman Theorem

Let Y be the complement in a *compact* analytic space $\overline{T}$ of an analytic set of codimension 1. Let M be a complex space which admits as *non-ramified covering a bounded, open set in some complex space C^m*.

Then, if two holomorphic maps

$$\Phi, \Phi' : Y \rightrightarrows M$$

take the same values in a point $t_0 \in Y$,

$$\Phi(t_0) = \Phi'(t_0) = m_0 \in M$$

and if they have the same action on $\pi_1(Y)$:

$$\Phi_* \pi_1(Y) = \Phi_*' \pi_1(Y)$$

then $\Phi \equiv \Phi'$.

To use (if possible) this theorem, the main problem here is what compactification of the parameter space T we have to choose?

My main purpose is to introduce you in a pedestrian way to a wider generalization.

There are at least two unsatisfactory features in our study of the k-integrals: first, Lorentz invariance was hidden although all "singularities" were obviously Lorentz invariant; second, the basic set $(k_1, \ldots, k_r)$ is arbitrary. One could perform a unimodular substitution $(k_1', \ldots, k_r') = A(k_1, \ldots, k_r)$ on the set of four-momenta

$$k_i' = \sum_j A_{ij} k_j$$

To get rid of these two defects, one performs a special form of Fourier transformation, to be called the Hankel transformation, which belongs properly to the subject of the lectures given by Professors Helgason and Ehrenpreis by its group theoretical flavor.

To begin simply, we write, following Feynman and Bogoliubov

$$\frac{1}{q^2 - m^2 + i\varepsilon} = \int_0^\infty d\alpha \, e^{i\alpha(q^2 - m^2 + i\varepsilon)}$$

So α is the Fourier conjugate variable to $(q^2 - m^2)$. Substitute for each internal line of the Feynman integral instead of

$$\frac{1}{q_i^2 - m^2 + i\varepsilon} \;\text{-\!\!\!\!\!\wedge\!\wedge\!\wedge\!\text{-}}\; \int_0^\infty d\alpha_i \, e^{i\alpha_i(q^2 - m^2 + i\varepsilon)}$$

So we have one α-parameter for each internal line. Now

$$F_G(t) = \int_{h_F} dk_1 \wedge dk_2 \wedge \ldots \wedge dk_r \int_0^\infty d\alpha_1 \wedge d\alpha_2 \wedge \ldots \wedge d\alpha_n \, e^{iQ(\alpha, \, p, \, k)}$$

where

$$Q(\alpha, p, k) = \sum_{i=1}^{n} \alpha_i \left(\sum_j \varepsilon_{ij} k_j + \sum_j \eta_{ij} p_j \right)^2 - \left(\sum_{i=1}^{n} \alpha_i \right)(m^2 - i\varepsilon)$$

is quadratic in the k-variables (and in the external momenta p_j).

Imagine that you refer this k-quadric to its axis, then to its center (Morse), and then perform the easy integration on the new k-variables. One obtains

$$F_G(t) = \int d\alpha \left(\int dk \, e^{iQ} \right)$$

Note the interchange of the order of integration. The end result is as follows:

Symanzik's Formula

$$F_G(t) = \int_0^\infty \int_0^\infty \frac{d\alpha_1 \wedge \dots \wedge d\alpha_n}{d_G(\alpha)^2} \, e^{i[D_G(t,\,\alpha)/d_G(\alpha) - \Sigma\, m_c^2 \alpha_i]}$$

where $D_G(t, \alpha)/d_G(\alpha)$ is a rational, homogeneous of degree 1 function of the parameter α, which is built as follows:

Rule. Let Γ be a cut separating G into two connected pieces $G_1{}^\Gamma$, $G_2{}^\Gamma$

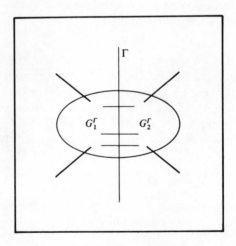

Let

$$z_\Gamma = \left(\sum_{G_1^\Gamma} p_k \right)^2 = \left(-\sum_{G_2^\Gamma} p_k \right)^2$$

where

$$\sum_{G_i} p_k \quad (i = 1, 2)$$

refers to the sum of all external momenta which end up in G_i. Then

$$D_G(t, \alpha) = \sum_\Gamma z_\Gamma \prod_{i \in \Gamma} \alpha_i \, d_{G_1 \Gamma}(\alpha) \, d_{G_2 \Gamma}(\alpha)$$

and

$$d_G(\alpha) = \sum_T \left(\prod_{i \in T^*} \alpha_i \right)$$

where T runs over all possible choices of a tree connecting all the vertices of G, and T^* is the complement of T

$$T + T^* = \text{All internal lines of } G$$

If T^* is empty, put $d_G = 1$. Note that $d^0 D_G$ is $r + 1$, $d^0 d_G$ is r, r being the number of independent cycles of G. The last touch is to introduce $\alpha_i = \lambda \bar{\alpha}_i$ and to get rid of the exponential by performing the integration over λ, but for purposes of " renormalization " it is often convenient not to do this last step (see Hepp).

What we shall proceed to " idealize mathematically," then, is an integral of the form

$$F_G(t) = \int_{T^n} d\alpha_1 \wedge \ldots \wedge d\alpha_{n-1} \frac{d_G(\alpha)^{n-2r-2}}{\left[D_G(t, \alpha) - \left(\sum_{i=1}^n m^2 \alpha_i \right) d_G(\alpha) \right]^{n-2r}}$$

Where T^n is the fundamental " affine " simplex $\alpha_i \geqslant 0$,

$$\sum_{i=1}^n \alpha_i = 1$$

This can be easily put in projective form and we end up with the following setup:

In the complex projective space P^{n-1}, let W be (with respect to the variables z) a linear family of hypersurfaces of degree $r + 1$ of the equation

$$\Delta_G(\alpha, z) = D_G(\alpha, z) - m^2 \left(\sum_{i=1}^n \alpha_i \right) d_G(\alpha)$$

Let h be a relative cycle in

$$H_{n-1} \left(P^{n-1} - W, \bigcup_{i=1}^n (\Pi_i - W) \right)$$

where Π_i is the complex hyperplane with equation $\alpha_i = 0$. Let η be the $(n-1)$-projective holomorphic form of P^{n-1}:

$$\eta = \sum_{i=1}^n (-1)^i \alpha_i \, d\alpha_1 \wedge d\alpha_2 \wedge \ldots \wedge d\alpha_i \wedge \ldots \wedge d\alpha_n$$

Assume W to be nonsingular and transversal to the n complex faces of the fundamental simplex T_C^n, that is, to the n-hyperplanes Π_i, at least for a generic value of t. In other words, $(W_{t_0}, \Pi_1, \ldots, \Pi_n)$ are in general position. Then our idealized model is

$$F_G(z) = \int_h \frac{d(\alpha)^{n-2r-2}}{\Delta(\alpha, z)^{n-2r}} \, \eta$$

Assume for simplicity $n - 2r - 2 \geq 0$. The integrand is trivally a closed rational $(n-1)$ form with polar singularity of order $(n-2r)$ on W. The restriction of this closed form to the Π_i vanishes for there is not "enough dimension" for the differential form, *holomorphic* on $P^{n-1} - W$ to survive.

Construct, as before, the new family $(P^{n-1} \times T, \mathscr{S})$, where $\mathscr{S}$ is the bunch formed by W_t (linear system) and the fixed hyperplanes Π_i $(i = 1 \ldots n)$. Now the same algebraic set as before L of codimension 1 is obtained as the locus of the points $t \in T$, where the little isotopy theorem does not apply, that is,

1. W_t is $\not\pitchfork$ to the Π_i, but is singular. In order that W_t be singular, t should be such that the system of n homogeneous equations of $d^0 \, \Gamma$ in the variables (α_i) has a nontrivial solution:

$$\boxed{\begin{aligned} \frac{\partial \Delta}{\partial \alpha_1}(\alpha, z) &= 0 \\[4pt] \frac{\partial \Delta}{\partial \alpha_2}(\alpha, z) &= 0 \\ &\vdots \\ \frac{\partial \Delta}{\partial \alpha_n}(\alpha, z) &= 0 \end{aligned}} \quad \xrightarrow{\text{Van der Waerden}} R_0(z) = 0$$

2. Let $\Pi_I = \bigcap_{i \in I} \Pi_i$, where I is a subset $I \subset [1 \ldots n]$; then W_t is tangent to Π_I, that is, $W_t \cap \Pi_I$ is singular. Again the system below has a nontrivial solution if :

$$\boxed{\begin{aligned} \frac{\partial \Delta}{\partial \alpha_i} &= 0 \quad i \notin I \\[4pt] \alpha_i &= 0 \quad i \in I \end{aligned}} \quad \xrightarrow{\text{Van der Waerden}} R_I(z) = 0$$

I shall not develop again the interesting interrelationship between elimination theory and the geometric singularity of the family $(P^{n-1} \times T, \mathscr{S})$.

The interesting new viewpoint we gained is that the tangential properties of W_t came neatly into focus. It would be quite natural, if I had time, to develop at this point Leray's second important memoir relevant to our problem. Instead, I shall write a long appendix, since I think this approach is best suited for physicists, and sketch here briefly the main ideas involved.

Differential Forms and Functions with Algebraic Singular Support (Nilsson)

Definition. Let A_n consist of all functions f such that there exists an algebraic manifold V_f in C^n with equation $p(X) = 0$ and such that

1. f is regular analytic in $C^n - V_f$ and in general multi-valued.
2. All the determinations of f in any point $x_0 \in C^n - V_f$ span a linear space over C *with finite dimension.*
3. There exists in $x_0 \in C^n - V_f$, a real number a, a polynomial $R(x)$ such that for every determination f_0 of f at x_0, there exists a constant C such that

$$|f_{0\gamma}(x)| \leqslant C \frac{(1 + |x|)^a}{|R(x)|}$$

for all paths γ of rank (n_1, n_2) and starting at $x^0 \cdot f_{0\gamma}$ is the analytic continuation of f_0 along γ.

The paths one uses are of a special nature. We shall call V_f the algebraic singular support of f and note

$$V_f = Ss[f]$$

We want to restrict the spiralling around V_f. Hence :

Definition of the Rank of a Path. Let $\gamma = x(t) = (x_1(t), \ldots, x_n(t))$ consist of a finite number of pieces where the components $(x_i(t))$ are *regular algebraic functions of t*—in fact, polynomials. If the number of pieces is smaller than n_1 and if n_2 is larger or equal to the degrees of the polynomials then γ is said to be of rank (n_1, n_2).

The local form of this notion—that is, f is of class A in an open neighborhood of a point—implies that analytic continuation of the function is of class A. Hence, for our germ f there exists *a globally defined algebraic variety*, V_f in C^n such that the analytic continuation is regular on $C^n - V_f$.

Let us now consider an algebraic manifold $V(t) \subset C^n$, where $t \in C^m$ and $V(t)$ is given by $(n - r)$ equations

$$s_1(x, t) = 0 \qquad s_2(x, t) = 0 \ldots s_{n-r}(x, t) = 0$$

Let $R(t)$ be the set of points $x \in V_t$, where the gradients $s_{1,x}$, $s_{2,x}, \ldots, s_{n-r,x}$ are linearly independent over C; $R(t)$ is an open algebraic manifold of dimension r. Introducing local coordinates, a holomorphic p-form on $R(t)$ can be written locally as

$$\omega_t(x) = \sum a_I(t, x) \, dx^I$$

where

$$dx^I = dx_{i_1} \wedge dx_{i_2} \wedge \ldots \wedge dx_{i_k}$$

$$I = [i_1 \leqslant i_2 \leqslant \cdots \leqslant i_k]$$

The definition of an ω_t belonging to class A_n is now straightforward. Require $a_I(t, x) \in A_n$. Denote by $SS[\omega]$ the union of the singular supports of the coefficients of the differential form.

Main Theorem. Let $\gamma(t)$ be a compact piecewise differentiable cycle on $R(t)$. Let ω_t be a closed holomorphic differential form on $R(t)$. Suppose (1) $\gamma(t)$ depends continuously on t, and (2) ω_t is of class A. Then

$$g(t) = \int_{\gamma(t)} \omega_t(x)$$

is of class A.

Application—Feynman integrals and their compositions such as defined by unitary relations belong to class A.

A cycle such as $\gamma(t)$ is termed regular. The proof is by induction from the one-dimensional case.

Lemma 1 (Nilsson-Leray). Let $f(x, y)$ be of class A with respect to $x \in C^n$ and $y \in C$. Let V_f be given by $s(x, t) = 0$. Let $\eta_1(x)$, $\eta_2(x)$ be algebraic functions on C^n such that

$$(x, \eta_1(x)) \notin V_f$$

$$(x, \eta_2(x)) \notin V_f$$

for some x and all determinations of the algebraic functions $\eta_i(x)$. Then

$$g(x) = \int_{\eta_1(x)}^{\eta_2(x)} f(x, y) \, dy$$

belongs to class $A/(x)$, where the path of integration $(\widehat{\eta_1(x), \eta_2(x)})$ does not meet V_f. We can further describe the algebraic singular support of g:

$$X - Vg = \left\{ \begin{array}{l} x \mid \text{the functions } y_\alpha(x), \text{ which are the roots of } S(x, y(x)) = 0 \\ \text{are regular and distinct and the } \eta_i(x) \text{ are regular and do not} \\ \text{meet } V_f, \text{ that is, } S(x, \eta_i(x)) \neq 0 \end{array} \right\}$$

Note that this lemma involves integration on a relative cycle $\partial(\eta_1(x), \eta_2(x)) = \eta_2(x) - \eta_1(x)$. The main lemma could be generalized to $\gamma(t)$ being also a relative cycle.

It is impossible to quote here all the references in the physical literature where Lemma 1 appears. I think that one can say that it was rightly understood from the beginning that it was basic.

Moving on, let us subdivide the cycle γ into small simplexes. Now, we note that : A simplex σ is given either by its vertices or by the Grassmann coordinates of its faces and support. We can define the motion of σ by two means, following either the vertices or the faces.

Then we are back to the basic problem we were faced with using the α-form of Feynman integrals. Simply, we now have to be prepared to move also the planes Π_i of our simplex, and to discuss also differential forms of any dimension. What Leray proceeds to do is to discuss our algebraic set of equations (A) using the *Cayley form of W_t* and the Grassmann coordinates of the simplex, then to glue back the simplices in a cycle γ, eliminating the parasitic singularities given by the planes of the subdivision. The notion he introduces to discuss the dual form of the system A is the notion of " appui " of a q-plane on the algebraic variety $W_{(t)}$ is fundamental, but I have no time left: see the appendix for more details.

We shall end up by making Lemma 1 more precise. Let us discuss the relevance question for the singular algebraic support V_g of the multivalued function g. We give the *Picard-Lefschetz formula* as an answer to the relevance problem.

Assume W_t in general position with the fundamental simplex. Then consider the exact triple

$$H_*(P^n - W_t, \bigcup_{i=1}^{n} (\pi_i - W_t)) \xrightarrow{\partial} H_*(\bigcup_{i=1}^{n} (\pi_i - W_t), \bigcup_{j \in A} (\pi_j - W_t))$$

$$H_*(P^n - W_t, \bigcup_{j \in A} (\pi_j - W_t))$$

A is a subset of $[1 \ldots n]$. Apply to this exact sequence the little isotopy theorem where it is assumed we are in a neighborhood of t_0 such that $R_A(t_0) = 0$. Assume the singularity to be localized in the face

$$\Pi_A = \bigcap_{j \in A} \Pi_j$$

Let σ be a loop around $R_A(t) = 0$. Then we can see that

$$H_*\left(\bigcup_{i=1}^{n} (\Pi_i - W_t), \bigcup_{j \in A} (\Pi_j - W_t) \right)$$

is invariant since it is isomorphic to

$$H_*(\bigcup_{i=1}^{n} (\pi_i - W_t), \bigcup_{j \in A} (\pi_1 - W_t)) \xrightarrow{\text{excision}} H_*(\bigcup_{i \notin A}, \bigcup_{i \notin A} \cap \bigcup_{i \in A})$$

$$H_*(\bigcup_{i \in A} \overline{(\pi_i - W_t)}) \leftarrow H_*(\bigcup_{i \notin A} (\pi_i - W_t) \cap \bigcup_{j \in A} (\pi_j - W_t))$$

This second triangle makes the invariance of

$$H_*\left(\bigcup_{i=1}^{n} (\Pi_i - W_t), \bigcup_{j \in A} (\Pi_j - W_t) \right)$$

more obvious; hence the critical module will be in the kernel of ∂, that is, the image of

$$H_*\left(P^n - W_t, \bigcup_{i \in A} (\Pi_i - W_t) \right)$$

It is easy to make this a little more precise for a simple quadratic non-degenerate singularity, localized in a ball B. The change of homology classes is given by $h \to h + \alpha(h)\delta e$, where δe is the image in

$$H_*\left(P^n - W, \bigcup_{i \in A} \Pi_i \right)$$

by the map δ of the vanishing cycle in

$$H_*\left(W_t, \bigcup_{i \in A} \Pi_i \right) .$$

The topological criteria for relevance is obtained by introducing as before

$$\varepsilon\left(B, W_t \bigcup_{i \in A} (\Pi_i - W_t) \right) \in H_n\left(B, W_t \bigcup_{i \in A} \Pi_i \right)$$

The vanishing cycle proper is

$$e \in H_{n-1}\left(W_t \bigcap B, \bigcup_{i \in A} \Pi_i \right)$$

and the trace of h in B, denoted as

$$h_B \in H_n{}^F\left(B - \bigcup_{i \in A} \Pi_i - W \right)$$

We have again by taking the relative boundary on W

$$\partial_W \varepsilon = e$$

Descending further on the face $\bigcap_{i \in A} \Pi_i$ we have easily

$$h_B^{|A|} = \partial_m \circ \partial_{m-1} \circ \cdots \circ \partial_1 h_B$$

$$e^{|A|} = \partial_m \circ \partial_{m-1} \circ \cdots \circ \partial_1 e$$

where we put finally $A = [1, \ldots, m]$ and $|A| = m$. The final formula is the topological expression of the number $\alpha(h)$ by a Kronecker index:

$$h \xrightarrow{\ \sigma*\ } h + \langle h^A, e^A \rangle \delta_W e$$

PART 6: WORK IN PROGRESS

In this last lecture, I want to review several points which are relevant to our problem:

1. Zeeman Theorem*

We have a spectral sequence for an arbitrary topological space X:

$$E: H^q(X, \mathscr{L}_p) \Rightarrow H_{p-q}(X)$$

$\mathscr{L}_p$ is the presheaf $U \rightsquigarrow \mathscr{L}_p(U) = H_p(X, X - U)$

Then to $H_s(X)$ is associated a filtration

$$F_s^0 = H_s(X) \supset F_s^1 \supset \cdots \supset F_s^q \supset F_s^{q+1} \supset \cdots$$

and for the dual spectral sequence $\hat{E}$

$$H^s(X) \supset \cdots \supset \hat{F}_{q+1}^s \supset \hat{F}_q^s \supset \cdots \supset \hat{F}_0^s$$

Then, if X is a polyhedron, we have:

Theorem 1.

$$H_{q+s} \cap H^q \subset F_s^q$$

For a cohomological class ξ, let

$$\operatorname{cod} \xi = \inf_{x \in \xi} (\dim \operatorname{supp} x)$$

Theorem 1'. If X is compact, then

$$\operatorname{cod} \xi > \text{filtration of } \xi$$

2. Lefschetz Theorems

Let W be a projective, nonsingular, irreducible, of dimension n, algebraic variety, V the corresponding affine variety $V = W - P_\infty$, W_0 a hyperplane section, and V_0 a similar quantity. Then:

Theorem 2.

$$H_{n-1}(W_0) = L + \operatorname{Inv} H_{n-1}(W_0)$$

where L is a module generated by the vanishing cycles (δ_i).

---

* *Proc. London Math. Soc.*, p. 155 (1963).

Theorem 2'.

$$0 \rightarrow \text{Inv } H_{n-1}(V_0) + L \rightarrow H_{n-1}(V_0) \rightarrow L' \rightarrow 0$$

where

$$L' = \ker (H_{n-2}(P) \rightarrow H_{n-2}(W_0))$$

where P is the axis of the pencil of hyperplane sections. Further, recently Moisheson has proved that the group of automorphisms corresponding to the Picard–Lefschetz formula for the vanishing cycles (δ_i) is transitive on L.

3. Manin's Theory

Consider the family of elliptic curves

$$C_t = \{y^2 = x(x-1)(x-t)\}$$

The Landau surfaces are $t = 0$, $t = 1$. Consider a period (integral of first kind).

$$F(t) = \int_h \frac{dx}{y} \qquad h \in H_1(C_t)$$

Let $\omega(x, t)$ be this algebraic differential of first kind. Then the differential operator

$$L_t = t(1-t)\frac{d^2}{dt^2} - (2t-1)\frac{d}{dt} + \frac{1}{4}$$

transforms ω into an *exact* form.

Hence, $F(t)$ is solution of the Gauss hypergeometric equation

$$L_t F = 0$$

In fact, Manin even considers the fundamental simplex defined by two sections of the family $(P_0(t), Q_0(t))$ and the integral

$$\int_{P_0(t)}^{Q_0(t)} \omega$$

Hence, it is interesting to make the differential operators with rational coefficients of the parameter variety T act on the cohomology of the fibers.

The vector fields of T on the complement of L act as an r-family $(r = \dim T)$ of integrable connections $(K(t) = \text{curvature} = 0$ for $t \in T - L)$. Speaking intuitively, one can say that the curvature is a distribution concentrated on L since, around L, the homology classes change according the Picard–Lefschetz formula.

There is evidence that the following is true: Let L_1 be the set of regular points of L. Then, if L_1 is locally given by an equation $R(t) = 0$, $\{R(t) = \varepsilon\}$ defines locally a tubular neighborhood of L_1 which can be shrunk to L_1 in such a way that on $L_1 \ni a$ $(r-1)$-family of integrable connections (note that the fibers above L_1 are singular). Hence, the distribution character of the curvature lies in the "transverse direction to L_1." Does it make sense to write $K(t) \sim \delta(R_1(t))$ or some transverse derivative of δ? (See Gelfand–Shilov Appendix Vol. 1 and 5 for the definition of δ-function for complex variables.)

4. Algebraic De Rham Theorem

We thought to apply differential operators to algebraic cohomology classes, rationally dependent on $t \in T$, when we came to learn that the following theorem was true (Grothendieck IHES, No. 29, p. 351): Let X be a nonsingular affine variety then

$$H^*(X, C) = \frac{\text{(Closed algebraic forms)}}{\text{(exact)}}$$

Let W be a hypersurface of P^n. Then, $H^* (P^n - W)$ can be calculated by classifying the algebraic closed differential forms with polar singularity of order k on W (and on W only).

Let $D = 0$ be the projective equation of W. For the n-differential forms, the needed algebraic division theorem is provided by the simple.

Lemma. Let η be the fundamental n-projective form.

Let $\omega = \eta H / D^k$ be a closed differential rational form on $P^n - W$, with H a homogeneous polynomial such that $d^0 H + n = k \cdot d^0 D$ then $\omega \sim \omega' = \eta H'/D^{k-1}$, iff $H \in (\partial D/\partial \alpha_i)$ ideal generated by the partial derivatives. We conjecture that if W is given by $Dd = 0$ (hence, is reducible), then

Lemma.

$$\omega = \frac{\eta H}{D^m d^n} \sim \omega' = \frac{\eta H'}{D^{m'} d^{n'}}$$

with $(m', n') < (m, n)$ iff

$$H \in \left(D \frac{\partial d}{\partial \alpha_i}, d \frac{\partial D}{\partial \alpha_i}, \frac{\partial d}{\partial \alpha_i} \frac{\partial D}{\partial \alpha_j} - \frac{\partial d}{\partial \alpha_j} \frac{\partial D}{\partial \alpha_i} \right)$$

Note that these ideals be considered as modules over the rational functions of T (in fact, polynomials in t suffice).

Recall.

$$F_G(t) = \int_{T^n} \eta \frac{d(\alpha)^{n-2r-2}}{D(\alpha, z)^{n-2r}}$$

if $2n - 2r - 2 \leqslant 0$, then the factor d in the denominator gives rise to divergence.   Noting that $F_G(t)$ is to be interpreted as a distribution in t

$$\langle F_G, \varphi \rangle = \iint\limits_{T(\alpha)^n \times T(z)} \frac{\eta\, \varphi(z)\, dz}{D(\alpha, z)^{n-2r} d(\alpha)^{-n+2r-2}}$$

we see that integrating by parts allows us to change the multiplicity $(n - 2r)$ of

$$D(\alpha, z) = \sum z_i A_i(\alpha) - m^2 \left(\sum_{i=1}^{n} \alpha_i \right) d(\alpha)$$

since

$$\frac{\partial}{\partial z_i} \frac{1}{D(\alpha, z)} = - \frac{A_i(\alpha)}{D(\alpha, z)^2}$$

Recall the role that the *finite dimension* of the linear space of all determinations was playing in the definition of the class A.   The differential equations which justify the name of "hyperfuchsian functions" for $F_G(t)$ are formed by applying differential operators with rational coefficients in t to the closed differential forms $\omega(x, t)$ in such a way that

$$\sum L_l(t)\omega(x, t) = d_x \eta(x, t)$$

or, differentiating through a single parameter $(\partial/\partial z, \partial^2/\partial z^2, \ldots)$ the cohomology class ω, we stop when the new cohomology classes $(\partial^i \omega/dz^i)$ are no longer linearly independent over the rational functions of T, that is,

$$\sum a_i(z) \frac{\partial^i \omega}{\partial z^i} = d_x \eta$$

Note that this justifies also the notion that the connection integrable over T-L, replaces the fundamental group $\Pi_1(T\text{-}L)$ which is ordinarily used to form the differential equations with uniform coefficients.   We checked that this procedure applied to our special situation (relative homology class for integration) (see Regge's lecture), and was leading again to the elimination theory and subsequent formation of discriminants we meet when dealing with the Landau set L.   We were led back to rediscover the way Macaulay came to write such resultants as "large determinants."

The most striking form one can give to this algebraic division theorem (to reduce the order of the polar singularity of the algebraic differential form) is the following formulation of a theorem of Macaulay.

Lemma (Griffiths–Mumford). Let $Q_1 \ldots Q_m$ be homogeneous polynomials in $(\alpha_1 \ldots \alpha_m)$ of degrees $(r_1 \ldots r_m)$, such that the radical of the ideal $(\dot{Q}_1, \ldots, Q_m)$

$$\sqrt{(Q_1, \ldots, Q_m)} = m = (\alpha_1, \alpha_2, \ldots, \alpha_m)$$

then

$$Qm^h \subset (Q_1, \ldots, Q_m) \quad\longleftrightarrow\quad \begin{array}{l} Q \in (Q_1, \ldots, Q_m) + m^{\rho - h} \\[2mm] \rho = \sum_{j=1}^{m} (r_j - 1) - 1 \end{array}$$

Note this gives a bound for dim $H^*(P^n - W)$ taking $Q_i = \partial D / \partial \alpha_i$.

Needless to say, the algebraic calculation agrees with the topological formula of Hirzebruch when W is nonsingular. For the general case, it seems that the K-theory for the algebraic coherent sheaves and the corresponding theory of intersection of algebraic cycles can be adapted to the differentiable case and hence could relate to Thom's stratification and isotopy theorem which we can vizualize more easily.

To end well, we shall begin to study an example: It is the triangle diagram (Fig. 21) which helped Kallen and Wightman to calculate the envelope

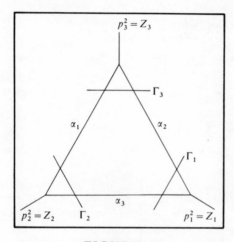

FIGURE 21

of holomorphy of the three-point function in axiomatic field theory. Let us work out some details:

$F(z_1, z_2, z_3)$

$$= \frac{1}{3} \int_{T^2} \frac{\alpha_1 \, d\alpha_2 \wedge d\alpha_3 - \alpha_2 \, d\alpha_1 \wedge d\alpha_3 + \alpha_3 \, d\alpha_1 \wedge d\alpha_2}{(z_1 \alpha_2 \alpha_3 + z_2 \alpha_1 \alpha_3 + z_3 \alpha_1 \alpha_2 - m^2 (\alpha_1 + \alpha_2 + \alpha_3)^2)(\alpha_1 + \alpha_2 + \alpha_3)}$$

where the domain of integration (Fig. 22) is

$$T^2 = \left\{ \begin{array}{ll} \alpha_1 \geqslant 0 & \alpha_1 \geqslant 0 \\ \alpha_1 + \alpha_2 \leqslant 1 \end{array} \right\}$$

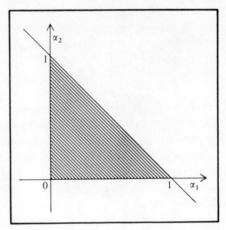

FIGURE 22

The Landau equations become

$$\left.\begin{array}{l} \dfrac{\partial D}{\partial \alpha_1}=0 \\[2mm] \dfrac{\partial D}{\partial \alpha_2}=0 \\[2mm] \dfrac{\partial D}{\partial \alpha_3}=0 \end{array}\right\} \Rightarrow \begin{vmatrix} -2m & z_3-2m^2 & z_2-2m^2 \\ z_3-2m^2 & -2m^2 & z_3-2m^2 \\ z_2-2m^2 & z_3-2m^2 & -2m^2 \end{vmatrix}=0$$

(symbol Δ. Denote this branch of the Landau set by Q)

$$\left.\begin{array}{l} \alpha_3=0 \\[2mm] \dfrac{\partial D}{\partial \alpha_1}=0 \\[2mm] \dfrac{\partial D}{\partial \alpha_2}=0 \end{array}\right\} \Rightarrow \begin{vmatrix} -2m^2 & z_3-2m^2 \\ z_3-2m^2 & -2m^2 \end{vmatrix}=(z_3-4m^2)z_3=0$$

symbol

and by permutation $\left\{\begin{array}{l} (z_1-4m^2)z_1=0 \\[4mm] (z_2-4m^2)z_2=0 \end{array}\right.$

from the factor $(\alpha_1+\alpha_2+\alpha_3)$ comes also the Landau surface

$$Z_1{}^2+z_2{}^2+z_3{}^2-2z_1z_2-2z_2z_3-2z_3z_1=0$$

which does not depend on the internal masses and expresses the vanishing of the gram determinant (but we shall not be concerned with this).

$$\begin{pmatrix} p_1{}^2 & p_1 \cdot p_2 \\ p_1 \cdot p_2 & p_2{}^2 \end{pmatrix} = 0$$

Fix $z_3 < 4m^2$ and study the multivalued analytic function $F_\Lambda(z_1, z_2)$ by first plotting the Landau curves (see Fig. 23): Then an easy majorization lemma on real quadratic forms gives $F_\Lambda(z_1, z_2)$ real analytic in the hatched region, since $D(\alpha, z)$ does not vanish for $\alpha \in T^2$ and Re z in this region.

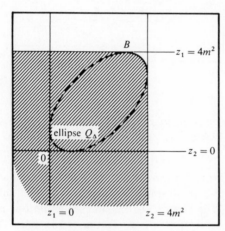

FIGURE 23

To each Landau curve is associated, in the α-integral "above," a vanishing cycle which describes topologically the relevance of the ramification for our function $F_\Lambda(z_1, z_2)$ and its "periods."

To have an example, let us study the absorptive part for $z_1 \sim 4m^2$, but starting from a real value (z_1, z_2) in the hatched region. It is easy to see that the Landau curve $z_1 = 4m^2$ is relevant and that the discontinuity of $F_2(z_1, z_2)$ is given by the integral

$$\int_{\delta e_1} \frac{d\alpha_1 \wedge d\alpha_2}{(z_1 \alpha_2 \alpha_3 + z_2 \alpha_1 \alpha_3 + z_3 \alpha_1 \alpha_2 - m^2(\alpha_1 + \alpha_2 + \alpha_3)^2)(\alpha_1 + \alpha_2 + \alpha_3)}$$

$$= \int_{e_1} \text{Res} \, [\;] \, d\alpha_2$$

where e_1 is the relative cycle of the next figure, and δe_1 the Leray cobord "normal to W (see Fig. 24)." Note then that the point of tangency between the Landau curves φ and $z_1 = 4m^2$ correspond to the "interference" of two singularities of different types

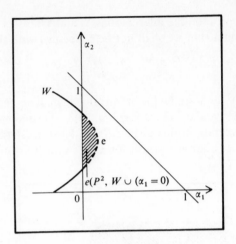

FIGURE 24

(1) $Z_1 = 4m^2 \to W$ tangent to $\alpha_1 = 0$

(2) $(z_1, z_2) \in Q \to W$ singular, that is, degenerating in two lines since W is a conic.

The local homotopy group near A, $\Pi_1(T\text{-}L)$, is easy to study.

Surround A by a small sphere S^3, and look at the intersection of S^3 with Q or $z_1 = 4m^2$. Using Hopf's fibering and the homotopy exact sequence of a fibering (see Professor Bott's lecture) one finds that $\Pi_1^{loc}(T\text{-}L)$ has two degenerators a, b, one for each Landau surface with the relation $(ab)^2 = (ba)^2$. Hence $\Pi_1^{loc}(T\text{-}L)$ is *not* Abelian

a: loop around Q_Δ

b: loop around the threshold $z_1 = 4m^2$

In the same manner, we have for B $(ac)^2 = (ca)^2$, where o is a loop around $z_2 = 4m^2$. Further $bc = cb$.

This obviously implies relations between the "periods" as you can see by applying the explicit description we have given of the actions on the homology groups corresponding to the generators a, b. Hence we are led once again to consider the representation of $\pi_1(T\text{-}L)$ in the vector space of the homology classes which is, in this case, a vector space V of easily computed dimension ($\dim_C V = 7$).

Consider the kernel of this representation : $\Pi_1(T\text{-}L) \overset{\rho}{\to} \text{End } V$. It is an invariant subgroup.

Hence, there exists a universal covering space for all determinations. But we deal with a particular form ω_F. It is a linear functional on V; hence has a kernel which is composed by the cycle σ on which

$$\int_\sigma \omega_F$$

vanishes. Hence the covering space associated to

$$F(z) = \int_{h_F} \omega_F$$

is in general non-Galoisian.

A last important question: Is the representation (ρ) irreducible? Physical reasoning (things are so nicely ordered in the world, hence in the physical region) leads us to suspect a hierarchy; hence, a filtration of nested vector spaces: the successive discontinuities seem to have fewer singularities than the initial integral.

Maybe we were misled; the global (relations between the periods in the generic fiber) is "local" and we need something like the filtration which occurs in the local study of the automorphisms induced by the fundamental group of the parameter variety of a general algebraic family.

For all this, I shall refer you to Griffiths' version of Grothendieck theorem (see Griffiths Part III, p. 217), or to Grothendieck himself.

The geometrical proof of Griffiths is by induction: One introduces "nice" pencils of hyperplane sections and construct the Picard–Lefschetz formula from the formula valid for the hyperplane section, by proving a relative Picard–Lefschetz. We shall leave the subject here with the remark that the study of the unitarity relations needs these generalizations of the Picard–Lefschetz formula (see also Pham, *Bull. Soc. Math. France*, **93**, 333, 1965).

REFERENCES

1. R. Thom, *Differential Analysis* (Bombay 1964), p. 191; and Battelle Seminar, Seattle, 1967.

2. Hironaka, "On the Equivalence of Singularities, I," in *Arithmetical Algebraic Geometry* (Purdue University, 1963), p. 153. "Resolution of Singularities of an Algebraic Variety," *Ann. Math.* **79**, 109–326 (1964).

3. O. Zariski, "Studies in Equi-Singularity, I, II," *Am. J. Math.*

4. J. Leray, "Complément à un théorème de J. Nilsson." (This last reference will appear soon in *Bull. Soc. Math. France*, hence will replace the intended appendix.)

XV

Landau Singularities
in the Physical Region

FREDERIC PHAM

Let me start by recalling (*cf.* Lascoux's lectures) that one calls "*Landau singularities*" the singularities of Feynman integrals considered as analytic functions of the "external" particle momenta in the corresponding Feynman graphs. It is not my aim to explain how Feynman integrals were introduced in physics, and why physicists have been interested in studying their singularities even though their faith in the integrals themselves was shaken; nor will I speak of the sophisticated motivations (the building of "dispersion relations") which led physicists to study singularities occurring for *complex* values of the momenta. Instead, I want to show that for *real* momenta, in the so-called "*physical region*," Landau singularities are rather simple geometrical objects which can be introduced directly by purely "kinematical" considerations and, therefore, should play an important role in *any* reasonable theory of elementary processes, whatever the "dynamical" content of such a theory may be. My talk will be divided into two parts: the first part will introduce the geometrical objects called "Landau singularities," and study their properties; the second part will deal with their physical meaning, and the way they fit in various theories of elementary processes.

1 THE KINEMATICS OF MULTIPLE SCATTERING PROCESSES

A "collision experiment" (also called "scattering experiment") consists of sending some particles toward each other and looking at what comes out, measuring as accurately as possible the momenta of the incoming and outgoing particles. Let us recall basic notions of relativistic kinematics: if $\mathbf{p}_i \in \mathbf{R}^3$ denotes the momentum of a particle i, of mass m_i, its energy p_i^0 is given by $p_i^0 = \sqrt{\mathbf{p}_i^2 + m_i^2}$; to have things expressed in a covariant way, one defines the four-momentum

$$p_i = (p_i^0, \mathbf{p}_i) \in \mathbf{R}^4$$

restricted to the "*mass shell*"

$$M_i = \{p_i \in \mathbf{R}^4 \mid p_i^2 = m_i^2, \, p_i^0 > 0\}$$

(where $p_i^2 \equiv (p_i^0)^2 - \mathbf{p}_i^2$ denotes the scalar product of p_i with itself in the Lorentz metric); in the sequel, we shall stick to this covariant description, and by "momentum" always mean the four-momentum. Every collision satisfies the law of *conservation of the momentum*, which says that the sum of the momenta of the incoming particles equals the sum of the momenta of the outgoing particles.

It is convenient to represent a collision process by a graph: for instance, Graph 1 (Fig. 1) represents a process where three particles 1, 2, 3 collide and give three particles 1', 2', 3'. What the detailed mechanism is of the collision,

Graph 1.
Elementary scattering graph.

FIGURE 1

and what kind of "catastrophy" occurs while the particles occupy the same region of space-time is not known, and the black box of Graph 1 symbolizes this ignorance. But imagine that by some finer experimental device one had been able to "resolve" the catastrophy of Graph 1 into a succession of finer catastrophies, as symbolized on Graph 2 (Fig. 2), for instance. For the time being we do not want to ask how this can be done, or whether it has a meaning or not; we simply want to ask whether this is kinematically permissible: for

Graph 2.
Multiple scattering graph.

FIGURE 2

which values of the "external" momenta $(p_1, p_2, p_3, p_{1'}, p_{2'}, p_{3'})$ can one find "internal" momenta $(p_4, p_5, p_{5'})$ such that the momentum conservation law will be satisfied at each vertex of Graph 2? Note that this question could be asked also in the more general case where Graph 1 is no longer an "elementary" scattering graph, but a multiple scattering graph from which Graph 2 would be deduced by "resolving" some vertex. To put the question in this general setting, denote by $\kappa\colon G_2 \longrightarrow\!\!\!\!\!\longrightarrow G_1$ the operation of "contracting" some lines of a graph G_2, thus getting a graph G_1; denote by $\mathscr{S}(G_i)$, $i = 1, 2$, the "*space of the graph*" defined as the product of the mass shells of all the particles of the graph, restricted by the momentum conservation law at each vertex; one has a canonical mapping

$$\mathscr{S}(\kappa)\colon \mathscr{S}(G_2) \to \mathscr{S}(G_1)$$

defined by "forgetting" the momenta of the contracted lines. Then the above question amounts to asking which points of $\mathscr{S}(G_1)$ belong to the image of this mapping.

Our notations for graphs will be the following: a *multiple scattering graph* is a connected oriented graph G, whose lines represent particles, and vertices collisions between particles; such a graph must have no directed loops, so that the set of vertices will be partially ordered: this corresponds to the *causal ordering* of the successive collisions. The set of vertices will be denoted by V, and the set of lines by I; $v(i)$ will be the *incidence number* of the vertex v with respect to the line i, equal to $+1$, -1, or 0. Z will denote the *group of cycles* of the graph, defined as the intersection of the kernels of all the homomorphisms

$$v_*\colon \mathbf{Z}(I) \to \mathbf{Z}$$

associated to the incidence functions

$$v\colon I \to \mathbf{Z}$$

of all the vertices of the graph ($\mathbf{Z}$ denotes the group of integers, and $\mathbf{Z}(I)$ the free Abelian group on the set I). If $z \in Z$, $z(i)$ will denote the contribution of the line i to the cycle z (a rational integer). Recall that a base of the free group Z can be constructed as follows: one chooses in G a maximal "*tree*" (subgraph without cycles); then for each line k outside this tree there is a unique cycle z_k such that $z_k(k) = 1$, and the z_k's form a base of Z. The space of the graph is defined by

$$\mathscr{S}(G) = \left\{ p^I \in \prod_{i \in I} M_i \,\middle|\, \sum_{i \in I} v(i)p_i = 0 \qquad \forall\, v \in V \right\}$$

It will sometimes be convenient to forget the mass shell conditions and consider the Euclidean space

$$\mathscr{E}(G) = \left\{ p^I \in (\mathbf{R}^4)^{|I|} \,\middle|\, \sum_{i \in I} v(i)p_i = 0 \qquad \forall\, v \in V \right\}$$

Then, introducing the polynomial map

$$s: \mathscr{E}(G) \to \mathbf{R}^{|I|}$$
$$p^I \mapsto (p_i^2)_{i \in I}$$

one sees that $\mathscr{S}(G)$ is a connected component of the algebraic variety $s^{-1}((m_i^2))$. If $(m_i^2)_{i \in I}$ is a regular value of the map s, this algebraic variety is a *manifold*. We thus get Proposition 1.

Proposition 1. For almost all values of the masses, the space $\mathscr{S}(G)$ is a manifold.

It is instructive to write explicitly the condition which makes the mapping s critical. Taking for coordinate basis on $\mathscr{E}(G)$ the system of momenta (p_k) associated to the complement of a maximal tree, one finds for the tangent map to s:

$$\frac{\partial s_i}{\partial p_k^{(\mu)}} = 2p_i \cdot \frac{\partial p_i}{\partial p_k^{(\mu)}} = 2p_i^{(\mu)} z_k(i) \qquad (\mu = 0, 1, 2, 3) \quad .$$

Therefore, the mapping s will be critical if and only if one can write a linear relation with not all vanishing coefficients:

$$\sum_{i \in I} \alpha_i \, p_i \, z_k(i) = 0 \qquad \forall \, k$$

that is,

$$\sum_{i \in I} \alpha_i \, p_i \, z(i) = 0 \qquad \forall \, z \in Z$$

EXAMPLE. In the case of Graph 1, the group of cycles can be generated by $1 - 2$, $2 - 3$, $1 + 1'$, $1' - 2'$, $2' - 3'$, so that the above relations read

$$\alpha_1 p_1 - \alpha_2 p_2 = 0$$
$$\alpha_2 p_2 - \alpha_3 p_3 = 0$$
$$\alpha_1 p_1 + \alpha_{1'} p_{1'} = 0$$
$$\alpha_{1'} p_{1'} - \alpha_{2'} p_{2'} = 0$$
$$\alpha_{2'} p_{2'} - \alpha_{3'} p_{3'} = 0$$

simply meaning that all the momenta of the particles are parallel to each other. This implies the following relation among the masses

$$m_1 + m_2 + m_3 = m_{1'} + m_{2'} + m_{3'}$$

Now we would like to study the mapping

$$\mathscr{S}(\kappa): \mathscr{S}(G_2) \to \mathscr{S}(G_1)$$

associated to a contraction

$$\kappa : G_2 \longrightarrow\!\!\!\!\!\!\!\rightarrow G_1$$

We shall denote by G the subgraph of G_2 formed by the lines which we want to contract, and by I, V, etc. the set of lines, vertices, etc. of this subgraph G. Let us first enounce the obvious

Proposition 2. The map $\mathscr{S}(\kappa)$ is proper (that is, the reciprocal set of any compact subset is compact). In fact, a closed subset of the mass shell is compact if and only if the *energy* p^0 is bounded. Thus, Proposition 2 simply means that the boundedness of the energies of the "external" lines (that is, the lines of G_1) implies the boundedness of the energies of the "internal" lines (lines of G), a result which easily follows from the conservation of energy at each vertex.

   If the masses are chosen noncritical, so that both $\mathscr{S}(G_2)$ and $\mathscr{S}(G_1)$ are *manifolds* (see Proposition 1), one can speak of the tangent mapping to $\mathscr{S}(\kappa)$, and look for the *critical points*, that is, the points where this tangent mapping is not surjective. Explicitly, a tangent vector to $\mathscr{S}(G_2)$ can be represented by a tangent vector X to $\mathscr{E}(G_2)$ subject to the restrictions $ds_j(X) = 0$, where $s_j = p_j{}^2$, $j \in I_2$. Let us compute Ker $d\mathscr{S}(\kappa)$, the kernel of the tangent mapping: it consists of the vectors X whose components along the "external" lines vanish; then the equations $ds_j(X) = 0$ are trivially satisfied for $j \in I_1$, and need only be written for $j \in I$, where they read

$$ds_i(X) = \sum_k \frac{\partial s_i}{\partial p_k} \cdot X_k = 2 \sum_k z_k(i) p_i \cdot X_k$$

where the four-vectors X_k denote the components of X along the lines k, complement in I of a maximal tree of G. Thus

$$\text{Ker } d\mathscr{S}(\kappa) = \left\{ X \left| \sum_k z_k(i) p_i \cdot X_k = 0 \qquad \forall \, i \in I \right. \right\}$$

As easily verified, saying that $d\mathscr{S}(\kappa)$ is not surjective is equivalent to saying that the above conditions for its kernel are not independent, that is, one has a relation

$$\sum_{i \in I} \alpha_i \, p_i \, z_k(i) = 0 \qquad \forall \, k$$

that is,

$$\sum_{i \in I} \alpha_i \, p_i \, z(i) = 0 \qquad \forall \, z \in Z$$

The not all vanishing parameters α_i are called the *Feynman parameters*, and the above equations are the *Landau equations*. Note that they are formally identical with the equations written in connection with Proposition 1, but the meaning of the letters I, Z is different, since they now refer to the *subgraph G* of the lines contracted under κ. We have thus proven the following:

Proposition 3. A point $p^{l_2} \in \mathscr{S}(G_2)$ is critical for $\mathscr{S}(\kappa)$ if and only if there exists a system of not-all vanishing Feynman parameters (α_i) satisfying the Landau equations. The possible systems of Feynman parameters form a vector space whose dimension is the corank (at the target) of the critical point.

We shall see in the second part that the Feynman parameters can be interpreted physically, up to a factor, as "time delays" between the creation and destruction of the corresponding particles. Thus the critical points where the Feynman parameters can be chosen *nonnegative* will play a privileged role. We shall call them *relevant critical points. If, moreover, the corank is* 1 (that is, the Feynman parameters are unique up to a proportionality factor), and if the Feynman parameters can be taken *all strictly positive*, we shall say that we have a *leading critical point.* The image in $\mathscr{S}(G_1)$ of a critical point will be called a *Landau point*, and it will be called a *relevant* resp. *leading Landau point* if it comes from a relevant resp. leading critical point.

Now comes the first nontrivial proposition.

Proposition 4. Near a leading critical point, the mapping $\mathscr{S}(\kappa)$ has the same local analytic type as the suspension of a Morse function of index zero, that is, one can choose local analytic coordinates $x_1, x_2, \ldots, x_m$ in $\mathscr{S}(G_2)$ and $y_1, y_2, \ldots, y_n$ in $\mathscr{S}(G_1)$ such that $\mathscr{S}(\kappa)$ reads:

$$y_1 = x_1$$
$$y_2 = x_2$$
$$\vdots$$
$$y_{n-1} = x_{n-1}$$
$$y_n = x_n{}^2 + x_{n+1}^2 + \cdots + x_m{}^2$$

COMMENTS. The last line above is the local model for a Morse function $y_n(x_n, x_{n+1}, \ldots, x_m)$ of index zero (*cf.* Bott's lectures). The "suspension" operation (in Thom's terminology) consists of increasing the dimension of the source and the target in a trivial way by adding the same set of variables. The resulting type of mapping is called S^1 in Thom's classification of singularities. Note its very simple features, which will be useful when we come to the physical interpretation: the Landau set is a *manifold of codimension* 1 (the manifold $y_n = 0$); every Landau point is the projection of *only one critical point* (at least in the neighborhood considered); finally, the image of $\mathscr{S}(\kappa)$ is *all on the same side of the Landau manifold* ($y_n \geqslant 0$), which can therefore be interpreted as the "*threshold of the multiple scattering process.*"

SKETCH OF THE PROOF. The Morse singularity of a function is characterized by the nondegeneracy of a quadratic form, the "Hessian" of the function, defined by the matrix of second partial derivatives. Similarly, in the case of a mapping having a critical point of corank 1, one can define *on the kernel of the tangent map* a quadratic form called the "transverse Hessian" (defined up to multiplication by a nonzero number), whose nondegeneracy will character- ize S^1-type singularities. The "S^1-type with zero transverse index" will be characterized by the positive-definiteness (or negative-definiteness) of the transverse Hessian. I have no time here to give a formal definition of the transverse Hessian, I simply indicate how it is calculated in the present situation: it is the quadratic form

$$H(X) = \sum_{i;\,k,\,\mu;\,k',\,\mu'} \alpha_i \frac{\partial^2 s_i}{\partial p_k^{(\mu)}\,\partial p_{k'}^{(\mu')}}\, X_k^{(\mu)} X_{k'}^{(\mu')}$$
$$= \sum_{i,\,k,\,k'} \alpha_i\, z_k(i) z_{k'}(i) X_k \cdot X_{k'}$$
$$= \sum_i \alpha_i\, Y_i^{\,2}$$

where we have put

$$Y_i = \sum_k z_k(i) X_k$$

Now the fact that $X \in \mathrm{Ker}\, d\mathscr{S}(\kappa)$ is expressed by the relations

$$p_i \cdot Y_i = 0 \qquad \forall\, i \in I$$

(See the proof of Proposition 3.) Since the p_i's are timelike vectors ($p_i^{\,2} > 0$), this implies that the Y_i must be *spacelike*. Therefore, for positive Feynman parameters, the transverse Hessian $H(X) = \sum_i \alpha_i Y_i^{\,2}$ is *negative-definite* (the Y_i cannot all vanish unless $X = 0$), and Proposition 4 is proved.

EXERCISE. Show that Proposition 4 still holds true when the Feynman parameters are allowed to vanish *on a tree* of G.

Proposition 4 gave only *local* information. But some *global* informa- tion can very easily be obtained in the following way. Let $p^c \in \mathscr{S}(G_2)$ be a relevant critical point of arbitrary corank, and choose a system (α_i) of non- negative Feynman parameters satisfying the Landau equations at p^c. On the Euclidean space $\mathscr{E}(G_2)$, consider the linear function

$$t(p) = \sum_{i \in I} \alpha_i (p_i - p_i^c) \cdot p_i^c$$

It vanishes at p^c, and is *nonnegative* on $\mathscr{S}(G_2)$: indeed, none of the terms $(p_i - p_i^c) \cdot p_i^c$ can be negative when both four-vectors p_i, p_i^c belong to the same mass-shell. Therefore $\{t(p) = 0\}$ is a *supporting hyperplane* for $\mathscr{S}(G_2)$ in $\mathscr{E}(G_2)$ (and even for $\mathscr{S}^*(G_2)$, the space deduced from $\mathscr{S}(G_2)$ by forgetting the mass shell conditions for the *external* lines—which play no role in the above reasoning). Now it immediately follows from the critical character of p^c—and it can also be checked directly on the Landau equations—that this hyperplane is the reciprocal image of a hyperplane in $\mathscr{E}(G_1)$, that is, the function $t(p)$ depends *only on the external momenta*. This function can therefore be considered as the equation of a hyperplane in $\mathscr{E}(G_1)$, "supporting" the projection of $\mathscr{S}^*(G_2)$. We thus get the "convexity" result:

Proposition 5. Through every relevant Landau point there passes a hyperplane which supports the projection of $\mathscr{S}^*(G_2)$. In particular, it will support the Landau set.

Further Problems

1. It would be interesting to investigate the possible topological structures of critical points of corank higher than one. In contradistinction with the corank 1 case, they do not seem to be generic.

2. "Hierarchy" of the singularities.

If some of the Feynman parameters vanish, one can contract the corresponding lines, thus getting another graph G_3 for which the given point will still be critical. One is thus led to study the singularities of a mapping given by the composition of two mappings:

The following example of a "composed singularity" is a simple version of a situation actually encountered in physics: let us consider the following composed mapping of the plane into the plane

$$\mathbf{R}^2 \xrightarrow{\ f\ } \mathbf{R}^2$$
$$h = g \circ f \searrow \quad \downarrow g$$
$$\mathbf{R}^2$$

$$\begin{cases} f: \begin{array}{l} x_1 \\ x_2 \end{array} \mapsto \begin{array}{l} y_1 = x_1 \\ y_2 = x_2{}^2 \end{array} \\[2ex] g: \begin{array}{l} y_1 \\ y_2 \end{array} \mapsto \begin{array}{l} z_1 = y_1 + y_2 \\ z_2 = y_1{}^2 \end{array} \\[2ex] h: \begin{array}{l} x_1 \\ x_2 \end{array} \mapsto \begin{array}{l} z_1 = x_1 + x_2{}^2 \\ z_2 = x_1{}^2 \end{array} \end{cases}$$

Intuitively, the mapping f can be thought of as "folding" the x-plane along the ($x_2 = 0$) axis and projecting it on the y-plane, with the fold projected on ($y_2 = 0$); then g "folds" the y-plane along another axis ($y_1 = 0$) and projects it on the z-plane, obliquely with respect to the image of the previous fold. Figure 3 shows the image of the composed map in the z-plane; the Landau set (set of critical values) consists of the ($z_2 = 0$, $z_1 \geqslant 0$) half-axis and a parabola tangent to it ($z_2 = z_1^2$). (This parabola is nothing but the image of the first fold.) This is the simplest example of what physicists call an "*effective intersection*" of Landau curves. For further study, see [5].

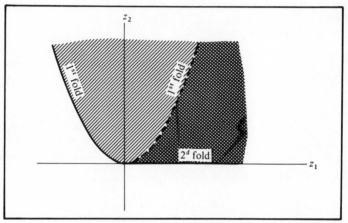

FIGURE 3. Image of a composed map. The hatched zone is covered two times, the cross hatched zone four times.

2 THE PHYSICAL MEANING OF LANDAU SINGULARITIES

The interest in physical region singularities was aroused recently by the following very simple remark of Coleman and Norton: Consider a multiple scattering process, for example, the one represented by Graph 2,[1] and imagine an ideal case where the various collisions would occur at *points* v, v', w of space-time; then the four-vectors $a_4 = \overline{vv'}$, $a_5 = \overline{vw}$, $a_{5'} = \overline{wv'}$ represent the space-time intervals traveled across by particles 4, 5, 5′, and must be proportional to the momenta of these particles:

$$a_i = \alpha_i p_i \qquad i = 4, 5, 5'$$

where the proportionality factors α_i can be interpreted as $\alpha_i = \tau_i/m_i$, where τ_i is the proper lifetime of particle i, measured in its rest frame. (Write

---

[1] For the clarity of exposition, all the reasoning of this second part are made on the specific example of Graph 2, although the generalization to an arbitrary graph would be quite straightforward.

$a_i = \tau_i p_i/m_i$, and note that p_i/m_i is the "four-velocity" of particle i.) With these notations, the Landau equations $\alpha_4\,p_4 = \alpha_5\,p_5 + \alpha_{5'}\,p_{5'}$ become $a_4 = a_5 + a_{5'}$, and can be interpreted as the obvious necessary and sufficient conditions for the space-time diagram (v, v', w) to exist. Furthermore, the *positivity of Feynman parameters* simply means that the τ_i are positive, that is, the particles cannot be destroyed before they are created.

Of course the above-considered ideal case goes against the laws of quantum mechanics, since we have been obliged to assign precise momenta *and* positions to the particles. But, anyway, we can hope to make sense out of it in the "*macroscopic*" limit, when the distances between the successive collisions are big with respect to the imprecisions on the positions. More precisely, let the wave functions φ_j of the incoming $(j = 1, 2, 3)$ and outgoing $(j = 1', 2', 3')$ particles be sufficiently sharply distributed, in the *momentum* representation, around some mean values $p_j{}^c$ defining a *leading Landau point* $(p_j{}^c)$ of Graph 2.

By Proposition 3, the datum of $(p_j{}^c)$ determines unambiguously (locally at least) a system of internal momenta $p_j{}^c$ $(i = 4, 5, 5')$ satisfying the Landau equations, with well-defined (up to a multiplicative factor) Feynman parameters; it therefore determines, *up to an arbitrary scale factor τ*, the space-time separations $a_i = \tau\alpha_i p_i{}^c$ at which we can hope to see the successive collisions occur, if they occur at all. Therefore, supposing the wave functions φ_j all overlap in some region of space-time, we can hope to make the multiple scattering more likely by performing different space-time translations on them, differing precisely by the above given separations a_i (for big enough τ); explicitly,

Particles 1 and 2 will undergo a translation a_v

Particles 1' and 2' will undergo a translation $a_{v'}$

Particles 3 and 3' will undergo a translation a_w

with $a_{v'} - a_v = a_4$, $a_w - a_v = a_5$, $a_{v'} - a_w = a_{5'}$. We then expect that asymptotically, for big space-time translations chosen in this particular way, the scattering amplitude of the process (Graph 1) will not decrease as quickly as it would for arbitrary space-time translations, and will behave like the product of the amplitudes associated to the vertices of Graph 2, integrated over all possible states of the intermediate particles.

Let us put this in equations. In the momentum representation, we are given a distribution $S(p_1, p_2, p_3; p_{1'}, p_{2'}, p_{3'})$—the integral kernel associated with the scattering operator S (by Schwartz's "nuclear theorem"). The scattering amplitude reads

$$\langle \varphi_{1'} \otimes \varphi_{2'} \otimes \varphi_{3'} | S | \varphi_1 \otimes \varphi_2 \otimes \varphi_3 \rangle$$

$$= \int \left(\prod_{\substack{j=1,2,3 \\ 1',2',3'}} \frac{d^3\mathbf{p}_j}{2p_j{}^0} \right) S(p_1, p_2, p_3; p_{1'}, p_{2'}, p_{3'})$$

$$\times \varphi_1(p_1)\varphi_2(p_2)\varphi_3(p_3)\overline{\varphi_{1'}(p_{1'})}\,\overline{\varphi_{2'}(p_{2'})}\,\overline{\varphi_{3'}(p_{3'})} \qquad (1)$$

and for the translated states it becomes

$$\langle \varphi_1^{a_{v'}} \otimes \varphi_2^{a_{v'}} \otimes \varphi_3^{a_w} | S | \varphi_1^{a_v} \otimes \varphi_2^{a_v} \otimes \varphi_3^{a_w} \rangle$$

$$= \int [\text{same integrand}]$$

$$\times \exp i[(p_1 + p_2)a_v + (p_3 - p_{3'}) \cdot a_w - (p_{1'} + p_{2'}) \cdot a_{v'}] \quad (1a)$$

where the notation φ^a is used for the state deduced from φ by the space-time translation a

$$\varphi^a(p) = \varphi(p) \times \exp ip \cdot a$$

We would like to get for this amplitude the following asymptotic behavior

$$(1\tau) \underset{\tau \to \infty}{\sim} \int \left(\prod_{\substack{h=1, 2, 3 \\ 1', 2', 3' \\ 4, 5, 5'}} \frac{d^3 \mathbf{p}_h}{2p_h^0} \right) S(p_1, p_2; p_4, p_5)$$

$$\times S(p_3, p_5; p_{3'}, p_{5'}) S(p_4, p_{5'}; p_{1'}, p_{2'})$$

$$\times \varphi_1(p_1)\varphi_2(p_2)\varphi_3(p_3)\overline{\varphi_{1'}(p_{1'})}\,\overline{\varphi_{2'}(p_{2'})}\,\overline{\varphi_{3'}(p_{3'})}$$

$$\times \exp i[p_4 \cdot a_4 + p_5 \cdot a_5 + p_{5'} \cdot a_{5'}] \quad (2)$$

which expresses the factorization of the processes v, w, v'; the phase factors $\exp i(p_i \cdot a_i)$ in the integrand represent the evolutions of the particles 4, 5, 5' between their birth and their death.

So how can we get from (1a) to (2)? An easy calculation shows that the phase factor in (1a) is precisely equal to the phase factor in (2) for any internal momenta $p_4, p_5, p_{5'}$ satisfying momentum conservation at each vertex. But note that

$$\sum_{i=4, 5, 5'} p_i \cdot a_i = \tau \sum_{i=4, 5, 5'} \alpha_i p_i \cdot p_i^c$$

is exactly—up to a constant phase which can be taken out of the integral—τ times the function

$$t(p) = \sum_i \alpha_i(p_i - p_i^c) \cdot p_i^c$$

considered in Proposition 5. Remember that this function depends actually only on the *external* momenta, and can be thought of as the linear approximation to the equation of the Landau manifold. Thus,

$$(1\tau) = \int \text{Integrand of (1)} \times \exp i\tau t(p)$$

an expression whose asymptotic behavior for $\tau \to \infty$ will clearly depend only on the singular behavior of the integrand of (1) near $t = 0$, that is, near the Landau manifold.

We shall not push the reasoning further, but stop at this conclusion: *The macroscopic "multiple scattering behavior" of a collision process is determined by the singular structure of the scattering operator on the corresponding Landau manifold.* For further details, the reader is referred to [5], where it is shown how a singular structure for the scattering operator can be postulated, which leads precisely to the "multiple scattering" behavior (2).

To conclude this talk, let me briefly sketch the various points of view currently adopted by physicists on "physical region Landau singularities." To begin with, the word "singularity" can be understood in two different ways: the *differentiable* sense and the *analytic* sense. On the other hand, one can distinguish essentially three kinds of physical approaches to the problem of singularities. The first is the study of *Feynman integrals*, which are generally considered to be good models as far as singularities are concerned; all the analyticity postulates required by [5] can be shown to hold true for Feynman integrals in the physical region, so we are happy. The second approach is the so-called "*S-matrix theory*," which tries to build a theory of the S-operator directly, without using field equations etc. Since the choice of the " S-matrix axioms" is more or less left to the discretion of the theorist, one could of course just postulate the analyticity properties formulated in [5]. However, S-matrix theorists do not like that because these properties are very redundant, both mathematically and physically: mathematically, because much can be deduced on the singular structure of a graph from the singular structure of other graphs, by reasoning from the "composition of singularities" (see the end of Part I); physically, because the *unitarity* of the S-operator imposes extraordinarily strong restrictions on its singular structure, so that it seems very difficult to imagine a unitary S-operator with analyticity properties different from the above mentioned. The third approach is "*general quantum field theory*" or "*axiomatic field theory*," surely the most satisfactory from a mathematical point of view. Although this theory is very difficult to handle, it has already given some encouraging indications concerning the asymptotic behavior.

The following table summarizes the present situation.

	Feynman integrals	S matrix theory	Field theory
Differentiable structure		IAGOLNITZER, WANDERS (Suitable hypotheses on the differentiable structure lead to the correct asymptotic behavior.)	HEPP: study of the double scattering process
Analytic structure	O.K. (cf. 5)	OLIVE, POLKINGHORNE, STAPP, ... (analyticity in connection with unitarity)	?

REFERENCES

1. S. Coleman and R. E. Norton, *Nuovo Cimento* **38**, 438, 1965.

2. R. J. Eden, P. V. Landshoff, D. I. Olive, and J. C. Polkinghorne, *The Analytic S Matrix* (Cambridge Univ. Press, 1966).

3. K. Hepp, *J. Math. Phys.* **6**, 1762, 1965.

4. D. Iagolnitzer, *J. Math. Phys.* **6**, 1576, 1965; and *Thèse*, Paris, 1967.

5. F. Pham, *Ann. Inst. Henri Poincaré*, **VI**, No. 2, p. 89, 1967; and *Symposia on Theoretical Physics*, *Vol. 7* (Plenum Press, New York), to be published.

6. G. Wanders, *Helv. Physica Acta* **38**, 192, 1965.

XVI

Algebraic Topology Methods in the Theory of Feynman Relativistic Amplitudes[1]

TULLIO REGGE

PART I

In this lecture I would like to introduce you to the spirit and to some of the technicalities of the work currently being carried out by Lascoux and myself on Feynman relativistic amplitudes (FRA).

FRA are analytic functions of a very special kind which have been defined in connection with relativistic field theory. It is not my job here to discuss at length their definition, as this has been done already by Lascoux and Hepp in previous lectures. The reason why these functions are interesting to so many people could be summarized as follows:

1. The scattering amplitude for any physical process can be in principle expressed, if field theory is right, as a power expansion in the coupling constants, each coefficient being a Feynman relativistic amplitude.

2. In general we cannot compute explicitly these amplitudes since they are given by rather complicated integrals. We are therefore happy to gather whatever information is available on them, including analytic properties, which may yield, hopefully, dispersion relations.

3. Even supposing that we know each amplitude, the following troubles may arise: the power expansion may not converge for some values of the parameters involved; the power expansion never converges and it should be interpreted as an asymptotic series; some of the coefficients are infinite.

---

[1] See also: *The Analytic S-Matrix*, R. J. Eden, P. V. Landshoff, D. I. Olive, and J. C. Polkinghorne, Cambridge University Press, 1966.

433

The last trouble is taken care of by the renormalization theory into which I shall not enter as Hepp has taken care of it in his very clear lecture. About the first, and related, second trouble, we have some partial information out of specific models.   There is a definite tendency to believe that we must be prepared for the worst and that the Feynman–Dyson expansion never converges.   However, these problems have never quite been solved and we possess surprisingly little information about each coefficient in the expansion.

The question more often asked is: What shall you do when you know in detail the analytic properties of each FRA? The answer is: I do not know. In fact, what will be done if we ever arrive at that point largely depends on what we shall find.   In general we would welcome theorems on classes of diagrams which have more chances of being applied to the scattering amplitude itself.   It might well be that after much work we find that we cannot make any sense out of all individual contributions and that the whole project has to be dropped.   But let us move close to the FRA.   One such FRA is given (Fig. 1) when we give the corresponding Feynman diagram, for example,

FIGURE 1

together with all the information regarding spins and masses of all the relevant particles. Usually we limit ourselves to spinless particles because of the simpler combinatorial rules.   In principle, however, we think that the arbitrary spin case is in no way more complicated and in fact once that combinatorics is worked over, it would be desirable to discuss all spins at the same time.

We shall sketch here briefly the relevant terminology and the Symanzik rules.   A Feynman diagram $\mathscr{D}$ is a closed connected one-dimensional simplicial complex; in detail:

(A). A set $\{P_j, j \dots q\}$ of 0-simplexes, called vertices of the diagram.

(B) A set $\mathscr{D} = \{L_i, i \dots z\}$ of 1-simplexes called lines of the diagram.

(C) A boundary operator ∂ which assigns to each oriented line L_h the difference $P_a - P_b$ of two points. We restrict ourselves to diagrams where no line is closed. We construct the incidence matrix $\mathscr{E}_{ij}$ defined by $\partial L_i = \sum \mathscr{E}_{ij} P_j$.

(D) We call external those points which belong to the boundary of one line only. A line having an external point on the boundary is called external. It is clear that no line has two external points on the boundary or else the diagram would not be connected. We avoid disconnected diagrams because they reduce trivially to the discussion of their connected components.

For the same reason we shall suppose that the diagram does not become disconnected upon removal of one line; this class of diagrams can also be reduced to simpler diagrams.

Similarly we shall suppose that every internal point is on the boundary of at least three lines.

From what we say it should be clear that these restrictions are here just labor-saving devices and that it is perfectly feasible to define amplitudes even if they are not satisfied.

We introduce the numbers:

p: number of internal vertices also called the perturbation order of the diagram.

n: number of internal lines of the diagram.

l: rank of the one-dimensional homology group of the diagram, shortly $H_1(\mathscr{D})$, sometimes vaguely referred to as the number of loops in the diagram.

As $-l + 1$ is the Euler characteristic of $\mathscr{D}$, we have $l = 1 + n - p$.

Next we consider a space $\mathbf{R}^m$ and the linear functions k:

$$C_1(\mathscr{D}) \xrightarrow{k} \mathbf{R}^m$$

from the group of cochains $C_1(\mathscr{D})$ to $\mathbf{R}^m$. Physically we think of the particular value $m = 4$, and $\mathbf{R}^4$ is the so-called momentum space; by introducing a pseudo-Euclidean metric of signature $1, 1, 1, -1$ we derive the standard interpretation of the theory according to special relativity. From the mathematical point of view there is nothing to be gained by this special choice at the moment and, therefore, we shall proceed in the general case. This is not to discount the fact that, if we want some physics at the end, we had better worry about the consequences of our choice. We further restrict our functions k by introducing the so-called conservation of momentum defined as:

$$k\left(\sum_{i \in \mathscr{D}} \mathscr{E}_{ij} L_i\right) = 0 \tag{1}$$

where $\mathscr{E}_{ij}$ is the incidence matrix. We introduce further a nondegenerate quadratic form in $\mathbf{R}^m$ which, by a suitable choice of basis in $\mathbf{R}^m$, can be written always as

$$(k)^2 = \sum_{\alpha=1}^{m} e_\alpha k_\alpha^2 \qquad e_\alpha = \pm 1$$

It is understood that whenever we specialize to Minkowski space this form reduces to the standard Lorentz metric form. Suppose now that we fix

$$k(L_i) = k_i \qquad i \text{ external}$$

It is clear that all functions k satisfying (1) and

$$k_i = 0 \tag{2}$$

form a linear space $\mathbf{R}^{lm}$. That the dimension of this space is just lm follows from the fact that k is determined by its values on the internal lines:

$$k(L_i) \qquad i \text{ internal}$$

subjected to the constraints:

$$k\left(\sum_{i \text{ int}} \mathscr{E}_{ij} L_i\right) = \sum_i \mathscr{E}_{ij} k(L_i) = 0$$

There are $m(p-1)$ constraints only since we have the identity

$$\sum_j \sum_i \mathscr{E}_{ij} k(L_i) = 0$$

which follows from

$$\sum_j \mathscr{E}_{ij} = 0$$

The functions k satisfying (1) and (2) form therefore a linear space $\mathbf{R}^{lm}$ of dimension $m(m - (p - 1)) = lm$. In this space we introduce the usual Euclidean measure $d\mu$. It is also evident that two functions with the same k and obeying (1) differ by an element of $\mathbf{R}^{lm}$. Let p be one such a function and let $\mathscr{D}$ have t external points and of course also t external lines. The t external values p_i are not all independent because of

$$\sum_{j \text{ int.}} \sum_i \mathscr{E}_{ij} p(L_i) = 0 \quad \text{and} \quad \sum_j \mathscr{E}_{ij} = 0 \tag{3}$$

if follows:

$$\sum_{j \text{ int.}} \sum_i \mathscr{E}_{ij} p(L_i) = -\sum_{j \text{ ext.}} \sum_i \mathscr{E}_{ij} p(L_i) = 0 \tag{4}$$

Equation (4) contains external lines only because they are the only ones which connect external points. This is well known as conservation of momentum. We define then

$$A(p_1 \cdots p_t, m_1 \cdots m_n) = \int_{k \in \mathbf{R}^{lm}} d\mu(k) \prod_{q \text{ int.}} \frac{1}{(k(L_q) + p(L_q))^2 - m_q^2 + i\varepsilon} \tag{5}$$

As the quadratic form $(k)^2$ is invariant under a $m(m-1)/2$ parameter orthogonal (or pseudo-orthogonal) group, the FRA will be a function of the invariants which can be constructed out of the p_i.

It is possible to exhibit this dependence more explicitly by going over an alternative representation of the same FRA according to a method originally devised by Feynman himself. I cannot report this method in this supposedly short lecture and, anyway, Lascoux has discussed it in some detail.

We introduce n complex variables $z = \{z_1 \ldots z_n\}$ one-to-one correspondence with the lines of $\mathscr{D}$. We use the same notation for a subset of $\mathscr{D}$ and the corresponding subset of variables. Consider all the subsets $\mathscr{E}$ of $\mathscr{D}$ consisting of l internal lines and such that by removing them $\overline{\mathscr{D}}$ becomes a tree; in the words of Lascoux $\mathscr{E}$ is a cotree. Consider the function:

$$d(z) = \sum_{\mathscr{E} \subset \mathscr{D}}^{\text{cotrees}} \prod_{i \in \mathscr{E}} z_i$$

As $\overline{\mathscr{D}}$ is of dimension 1, there are no 1-boundaries and all closed chains are cycles. We have the property:

A. Let $y \in H_1(\mathscr{D})$. Let y be of the form

$$y = \sum_{i \in \mathscr{Y}} e_i L_i \qquad e_i = \pm 1$$

Then $d(z) = 0$ on the set $z_1 = 0$, $i \in \mathscr{Y}$. In fact every monomial in the defining expansion of $d(\alpha)$ vanishes on the set $z_1 = 0$, $i \in \mathscr{Y}$. In the sequel we shall name $CP^{\mathscr{Y}'}$ the set $z_1 = 0$, $i \in \mathscr{Y}$, where $\mathscr{Y}' = \mathscr{D} - \mathscr{Y}$.

PROOF OF **A**. Suppose $\mathscr{E}$ exists such that $\prod_{i \in \mathscr{E}} z_i$ does not vanish on CP^Y. Then the cotree $\mathscr{E}$ has no line in common with Y else this common line would give a vanishing factor in $\prod_{i \in \mathscr{E}} z_i$ and the whole monomial would vanish. Therefore, by removing $\mathscr{E}$ the diagram $\mathscr{D}$, contrary to the definition of cotree, has still at least the cycle Y, this being absurd **A** must hold.

Similarly, we define the function $D(z, s)$ as follows. We name $\mathscr{C}$ cut if $\mathscr{C}$ is a subset of $\mathscr{D}$ made of $l+1$ internal lines and if by removing it $\mathscr{D}$ becomes disconnected into two trees. $\overline{\mathscr{D} - \mathscr{C}} = \overline{\mathscr{D}}_1 \cup \overline{\mathscr{D}}_2$. With each cut we associate the invariant

$$s(\mathscr{C}) = \left(\sum_{\substack{i \text{ ext.} \\ j \in \mathscr{D}_1}} p(L_i)\mathscr{E}_{ij} \right)^2 = \left(\sum_{\substack{i \text{ ext.} \\ j \in \mathscr{D}_2}} p(L_i)\mathscr{E}_{ij} \right)^2$$

By conservation of momentum $s(\mathscr{C})$ depends on the external p_i only. Similarly, we introduce the monomials $z(\mathscr{C}) = \prod_{i \in \mathscr{C}} z_i$. We define then

$$D(z, s) = \sum_{\mathscr{C} \subset \mathscr{D}} s(\mathscr{C})z(\mathscr{C}) - d(z) \sum_{i \text{ int.}} m_i^2 z_i$$

A few remarks before proceeding further: Different cuts may yield the same invariant $s(\mathscr{C})$. Secondly, all the $z(\mathscr{C})$ and hence $D(z, s)$ vanish on $CP^{\mathscr{A}'}$ like $d(z)$. Finally, and this is trivial but worth pointing out, we can choose the invariants and masses in such a way as to make $D(z, s)$ linear in all these variables. We suppose that this part of the job has been done already and that we have a complete list of all the relevant variables and related Symanzik polynomials:

$$D(z, s) = \sum_1^N s_i D_i(z) \qquad s = \{s_1 \cdots s_N\}$$

Because of the relative simplicity of this linear dependence we prefer to work out the analytic properties of the FRA starting directly from the alternative definition mentioned before, which can be written entirely in terms of $d(z)$ and $D(z, s)$ as follows:

$$A(s) = C \int \frac{dz_1 \cdots dz_n \, d(z)^{n-m(l+1)/2}}{D(z, s)^{n-ml/2}} \, \delta\!\left(\sum_1^n z_i - 1\right) \qquad (6)$$

Here we use directly the invariants s_i only. This choice is strictly a matter of personal taste and I do not intend to deny here the validity of other attempts based on Eq. (5).

We shall suppose that all the integrals in (6) converge since a discussion of divergent integrals according to renormalization theory is well outside our goal in this lecture.

In (6) we may consider the z_i as complex variables. We consider also CP^{n-1} the complex projective space of homogeneous coordinates z_i. In this space we introduce the linear system of algebraic varieties $D(z, s) = 0$. A generic element of the pencil will be written as W_s or simply W if no confusion arises. The linear variety defined by $z_i = 0$, where $i \in \mathscr{A} \subset \mathscr{D}$ will be written as $CP^{\mathscr{A}}$. A natural way of bringing in the complex projective space structure is provided by p. 298 of Gel'fand, Vol. I. This we shall see in detail in Part II.

In what follows we shall suppose m even so that $n - ml/2, n - m(l + 1)/2$ are always integer.

PART II

Consider the Grassman algebra of exterior forms in the differentials dz_i. We introduce some abbreviations. Let $\mathscr{D}$ denote as before the set of all lines in $\overline{\mathscr{D}}$. Let $\mathscr{A}, \mathscr{B}$ be generic subsets of $\mathscr{D}$. We write then

$$\omega_{\mathscr{A}} = dz_{i_1} \wedge dz_{i_2} \wedge \cdots \wedge dz_{i_q} \qquad \mathscr{A} = \{i_1 \cdots i_q\} \qquad |\mathscr{A}| = q$$

where $\wedge$ is the usual anticommuting product of the Grassmann algebra, and the i_t run from $i_1 \ldots i_q$ in increasing order.   Let

$$\mathscr{A}_k = \{i \in \mathscr{A}, i < k\}$$

$$\varepsilon_{k,\mathscr{A}} = \begin{cases} 0 & k \in \mathscr{A} \\ (-1)^{|\mathscr{A}_k|} & k \bar{\in} \mathscr{A} \end{cases}$$

We have then

$$dz_k \wedge \omega_\mathscr{A} = \omega_{\mathscr{A} \cup k}\, \varepsilon_{k,\mathscr{A}}$$

We also introduce the form

$$\eta_\mathscr{A} = \sum_{i \in \mathscr{A}} z_i\, \omega_{\mathscr{A}-i}\, \varepsilon_{i,\,\mathscr{A}-i}$$

Let d be the boundary operator.   By explicit computation we find

$$d\eta_\mathscr{A} = |\mathscr{A}|\,\omega_\mathscr{A}$$

We have also:

$$dz_i \wedge \eta_\mathscr{A} = z_i\,\omega_\mathscr{A} - \varepsilon_{i,\,\mathscr{A}}\,\eta_{\mathscr{A} \cup i}$$

In the sequel we shall restrict ourselves to forms with coefficients which are rational and homogeneous functions of the z singular on some fixed algebraic variety $W \subset CP^{n-1}$. If the coefficients are homogeneous of degree $-q$ and the form is given by

$$\alpha^q = \sum_{|\mathscr{A}|=q} R_\mathscr{A}\,\omega_\mathscr{A}$$

we say that the form α^q is affine.   It is easily checked that the boundary of an affine form is itself affine.   If furthermore α^q can be expressed in terms of the η as follows:

$$\alpha^q = \sum_{|\mathscr{B}|=q+1} T_\mathscr{B}\,\eta_\mathscr{B}$$

and α^q is affine we say that α^q is a projective form.   It is also true but much less obvious that the boundary of a projective form is also projective.   This is best seen by introducing the operator z:

$$\sum \mathscr{R}_\mathscr{A}\,\omega_\mathscr{A} \xrightarrow{z} \sum \mathscr{R}_\mathscr{A}\,\eta_\mathscr{A}$$

The operator z is of degree -1.   After some complicated but otherwise trivial manipulations one finds the identities:

$$z^2 = 0 \qquad zd + dz = 0$$

It should be pointed out that z maps affine forms into projective (and *a fortiori* affine) forms and that its kernel is the set of all projective forms.   The temptation to construct a cohomology theory out of z can be resisted by noting that the ensuing theory is trivial, all z-cycles are z-boundaries. Any projective form α^q can be written therefore as $\alpha^q = z\beta^{q+1}$, where β^{q+1} is affine. It follows that

$$d(z\beta^{q+1}) = -z\, d\beta^{q+1}$$

so that $d\alpha^q$ is itself projective, as expected. If α^q is closed by definition we have:

$$d\alpha^q = z\, d\beta^{q+1} = 0$$

Grothendieck has shown that the cohomology theory constructed out of these forms yields cohomology groups isomorphic to the usual de Rham cohomology theory in $CP^{n-1} - W^{n-2}$. Using the quoted Grothendieck result we shall simply write

$$C^q(CP^{n-1}, W^{n-2}), \quad Z^q(CP^{n-1} - W^{n-2}),$$
$$B^q(CP^{n-1} - W^{n-2}), \quad H^q(CP^{n-1} - W^{n-2})$$

respectively for the groups of projective (q-forms, q-closed forms, q-boundaries, q-cycles), respectively.

In what follows the forms are of the kind: $\omega^{n-1} = \eta R(z)$, where shortly

$$\eta = \eta_{\mathscr{D}}^{n-1}$$

will be the most interesting for us. They are closed since there is no form of higher dimension. They can obviously be written as:

$$\omega^{n-1} = \frac{\eta Q(z)}{D^P(z)} \qquad P \text{ integer}, \ Q \text{ of degree } (l+1)P - n$$

where $D(z, s)$ is the Symanzik polynomial introduced in Part I, if we select W to be the variety $D(z, s) = 0$. Consider now the integral:

$$\int_O \omega^{n-1}$$

where O is an open set on a sufficiently smooth hypersurface Σ in $C^n - 0$. The important fact is that the value of the integral depends only on the image of O in the map $C^n - 0 \to C^n - 0/(C - 0)$ which defines CP^{n-1}. In order to show it let O' be another such open set on another hypersurface Σ' having the same image in CP^{n-1}. We form a closed chain of integration by the combination $T = O - O' + \Delta$, where Δ is the set obtained by joining points on ∂O, $\partial O'$ having the same image in CP^{n-1} with a segment. The integral of the form on T is obviously zero since the form is closed; on the other hand, the integral of the form along Δ is also zero because such an integral vanishes on any subset of a cone in $C^n - 0$ as one can check easily. Therefore $\int_O \omega^{n-1} = \int_{O'} \omega^{n-1}$.

This final result really means that the integral of a projective form can be considered as an ordinary integral over the complex projective space. In the applications which we have in mind we shall integrate over the simplex $S^{\mathscr{D}}: z_i > 0,\ i \in \mathscr{D}$. Which hypersurface we select in C^n is then not critical. In order to carry out the integration, we choose then the plane $\Sigma: \sum_1^n z_i = 1$. It follows that on Σ:

$$dz_n = -\sum_1^{n-1} dz_i$$

and

$$\eta = \eta_{\mathscr{D}} = \bigwedge_1^{n-1} dz$$

Finally we have the identity

$$\int_{\mathscr{D}^{\mathscr{D}}} \frac{\eta Q(z)}{D^P(z,s)} = \int_{z_i > 0} \frac{dz_1 \cdots dz_{n-1}}{D^P(z,s)\Big|_{\sum_1^n z_i = 1}}\, Q(z)\Big|_{\sum_1^n z_i = 1}$$

$$= \int_{z_i > 0} \frac{dz_1 \cdots dz_n \delta(\sum_1^n z_i - 1) Q(z)}{D^P(z,s)}$$

and by selecting $Q(z) = d(z)^{n - ((l+1)/2)m}$ we may express the integral in (6) in the form:

$$A(s) = C \int_{S^{\mathscr{D}}} \frac{\eta}{D^{n - ml/2}}\, d(z)^{n - m(l+1)/2} \tag{7}$$

This we like because it brings directly into evidence the underlying complex projective structure in the integral. By looking at it we see two possible alternatives:

(A) The variety W is a general variety of degree $l + 1$ and is in general position with respect to the simplex S.

(B) The variety W has fixed singularities and/or contains some of the subsimplexes of S. This will be the general situation as we shall see.

In order to solve case (B) we need to discuss case (A) in advance. Diagrams with $l = 1$ belong in general to case (A) and diagrams with $l > 1$ do not. However, $l = 1$ also implies that the degree of D is 2 and this is too much of a simplification.

The best approach is to study the large class of fictitious FRA, that is, integrals of the form (6) which do not arise from (4) such that W is of general degree and in general position. These FRA can be investigated quite in detail. Once we know something about them we shall impose the specializations required by the physical applications.

Before we go into some detailed discussion of these integrals, let us see which results of significance to us are already known in the previous literature.

We may summarize them as follows:

(I) $A(s)$ is a multivalued analytic function of s.

(II) The singularities of $A(s)$ lie on an algebraic variety $\mathscr{L}$ (Landau variety) in the variables s. We suppose here that all the s are finite and not all of them zero. It is a trivial result that A is homogeneous in the s of degree $ml/2 - n$. It is therefore sometimes convenient to regard the s as homogeneous coordinates of a complex projective space CP^{n-1} and the Landau varieties as varieties L in this space or equivalently to $s_N = 1$.

(III) The FRA (fictitious and not) are generalized hypergeometric functions in the following sense. We select a point P (base point) not on L and a neighborhood O of P not intersecting L. Construct the fundamental group of the complement of L, that is, $\pi_1(CP^{N-1} - L)$ with base P. Define the value of A in O by means of the integral (7). To each element g of the fundamental group we may associate then a definite analytic continuation of A along a representative loop of g and this continuation will depend on the homotopy class g of the loop only. This continuation will be a new function gA also regular and defined in O. Then the property in question states that there exists a fixed finite set of elements of $\pi_1(CP^{N-1} - L)$: $g_1 \ldots g_K$ such that any gA is a linear combination with constant coefficients of the $g_1 A \ldots g_K A$.

Let $A_1 \ldots A_K$ be any linearly equivalent set to the $g_1 A \ldots g_K A$. We have then

$$gA_i = \sum_j^K \lambda_{ij}(g)A_j$$

where the λ_{ij} are constants. It is evident then that the map $g \to \lambda_{ij}(g)$ yields a representation of the fundamental group by means of K-dimensional matrices.

We may define our goal as the explicit construction of $\pi_1(CP - L)$ and of the corresponding representation. By explicit construction we mean a procedure by which a presentation of $\pi_1(CP - L)$ is given and such that to every loop with base point P an element of the fundamental group is explicitly assigned. In the known cases the fundamental group is extremely complicated and one succeeds in deriving partial results only. Very helpful in this direction is the remark that property III is equivalent to a set of differential equations which reduces to the ordinary differential equation for the hypergeometric functions case.

This equivalence has been pointed out to us by Parassiuk in Kiev and we think that it was known as far back as Schlaefli. The reasoning goes as follows. We keep all variables fixed but one, say s_1. We form the $K \times (K + 1)$ matrix:

$$\begin{vmatrix} A_1(s) & \cdots & A_K(s) \\ \dfrac{dA_1}{ds_1}(s) & \cdots & \dfrac{dA_K}{ds_1}(s) \\ A_1^{(K)}(s) & \cdots & A_K^{(K)}(s) \end{vmatrix}$$

Let $\Delta^p(s)$ be the determinant which one obtains by deleting the row of the pth derivatives in the matrix. Since the effect of g on the matrix is to replace each column with a linear combination of columns themselves according to

$$g A_i^{(n)}(s) = \sum_j \lambda_{ij}(s) A_1^{(n)}(s)$$

the effect on it is simply:

$$g \Delta^p(s) = (\det \lambda_{ij}) \Delta^p(s)$$

therefore $\Delta^p(s)/\Delta^0(s)$ remains unaffected and is a rational function of s.

Consider now the determinant:

$$\begin{vmatrix} A_1(s) & \cdots & A_K(s) & A(s) \\ \vdots & & \vdots & \vdots \\ A_1^{(K)}(s) & \cdots & A_K^{(K)}(s) & A^{(K)}(s) \end{vmatrix}$$

In this determinant the last column is a linear combination of the others, therefore it vanishes. By expanding it along the last column we find:

$$\sum_{p=0}^{K} A^{(p)}(s) \frac{\Delta^{(p)}(s)}{\Delta^{(0)}(s)} (-)^p = 0$$

This is the required differential equation of order K. It is a very easy matter to verify that the existence of the differential equation is equivalent to Property III. There are of course as many differential equations as variables. The knowledge of all these differential equations would imply practically the final goal. These differential equations are all ordinary equations in the sense that in each of them we may regard all variables but one as fixed parameters. All together their general integral does not depend on arbitrary functions as in the theory of partial differential equations but just on K constants as expected. We shall devote the rest of this lecture to showing how one can derive these equations in principle from (7). These equations are in fact just a slight generalization of the well-known Picard–Fuchs equations.

PART III

In this section I shall sketch the derivation of the differential equations from (7) in the case (A). For this purpose we consider all forms of the kind

$$\omega = \frac{\eta H(z)}{D^P} \tag{8}$$

since P can be chosen arbitrarily high, the set of these forms is an infinite-dimensional linear space. The factor space of these forms modulo the boundaries is, however, finite-dimensional. This means that for sufficiently high P

all forms are equivalent modulo a boundary to forms of smaller P. A reduction technique is therefore necessary if we want to evaluate the cohomology group with purely algebraic means.

The criterion is offered by the following identity:

$$\frac{\eta}{D^P}\left(\sum_{i=1}^{n} H_i(z)\frac{\partial D}{\partial z_i}\right) = \frac{1}{P-1}\frac{\eta}{D^{P-1}}\sum_{i=1}^{n}\frac{\partial H_i}{\partial z_i} + d\sum_{i=1}^{n}\eta_{\mathscr{D}-i}\frac{H_i}{D^{P-1}}(-1)^i \quad (9)$$

Therefore, if in (7),

$$H(z) = \sum_{i=1}^{n} H_i\frac{\partial D}{\partial z_i} \tag{10}$$

then the form can be reduced to one of lesser degree in the denominator modulo a boundary.

The difficult part is to prove that any form equivalent to a less singular one necessarily reduces through the proposed mechanism. This I do not intend to discuss here. In collaboration with Lascoux, I also conjectured a similar reduction criterion to be used when $D(z)$ is reducible. Suppose that $D = D_1 D_2$. Then the form

$$\eta = \frac{(z)}{D_1^{P_1} D_2^{P_2}}$$

is equivalent to another less singular form if

$$H(z) = D_1\sum_i H_1(z)\frac{\partial D_2}{\partial z_i} + D_2\sum K_i(z)\frac{\partial D_1}{\partial z_i} + \sum G_{ij}(z)\frac{\partial(D_1 D_2)}{\partial(z_i z_j)} \quad (11)$$

Again here as before the difficult point is not to check that the criterion is sufficient, but that it is necessary. This we have to assume or else there would be equivalent forms but such that equivalence could not be proved by use of these criteria and this would be an extremely disagreeable feature for computational purposes. We suppose now that the linear system $D(z, s)$ is given and that a basis for the cohomology groups has been selected.

Suppose now

$$s \in L$$

Let $\omega_\alpha^{\mathscr{D}, n-1}$ be a set of forms yielding such a basis. We may write, therefore,

$$\omega_\alpha^{\mathscr{D}, n-1} = \eta_{\mathscr{D}}\frac{Q_\alpha(z)}{D^P(z, s)} \qquad \alpha = 1 \cdots B^{\mathscr{D}, n-1} \tag{12}$$

For certain diagrams it can be verified that $H^{n-1}(CP^{n-1} - W)$ reduces to the identity. In this case every closed form is a boundary and we may transform the integral (7) into a surface integral. The study of (A) is then reduced to the discussion of similar but simpler integrals coming out of the surface terms. In what follows we shall suppose that there is a nontrivial set of forms according to (12). We may always select the first form to be the one given by the original FRA. The others will be chosen by some criterion of simplicity in the actual computation. It is in fact irrelevant in principle which forms we select. However, the actual writing of the differential equations may prove to be irksome following an unhappy choice. It would be interesting to see if it is possible to choose the other forms as those which correspond to processes with spin. In this case our discussion would unify the theory by including different values of spin at the same time. We suppose that the same classification of forms has been achieved for all dimensions. We define then

$$A_\alpha^{\mathcal{D}}(s) = \int_{S^{\mathcal{D}}} \omega_\alpha^{\mathcal{D},n-1} \qquad \alpha = 1 \cdots B^{\mathcal{D},n-1}$$

Of these the first integral is just the original FRA. We compute now:

$$\frac{\partial A_\alpha^{\mathcal{D}}(s)}{\partial s_k} = \int_{S^{\mathcal{D}}} \frac{\partial \omega_\alpha^{\mathcal{D},n-1}}{\partial s_k} = -P \int_{S^{\mathcal{D}}} \eta_{\mathcal{D}} \frac{Q_\alpha(z)(\partial D/\partial s_k)}{D^{P+1}(z,s)}$$

By hypothesis $D(z, s)$ is linear in s and therefore $\partial D/\partial s_k$ is independent of s. It follows that $\partial \omega/\partial s_k$ is again a form in $C^{n-1}(CP^{\mathcal{D}} - W)$ and that there exist constants (that is, independent of the z but still functions of s) $M_{\alpha\beta k}(s)^{\mathcal{D}}$ and a form τ_α^{n-2} such that

$$\frac{\partial \omega_\alpha^{\mathcal{D},n-1}}{\partial s_k} = \sum_\beta M_{\alpha\beta k}^{\mathcal{D}}(s)\omega_\beta^{\mathcal{D},n-1} + d\tau_\alpha^{n-2}$$

Clearly then

$$\frac{\partial A_\alpha^{\mathcal{D}}}{\partial s_k} = \sum_\beta M_{\alpha\beta k}^{\mathcal{D}}(s)A_\beta^{\mathcal{D}} + \int_{dS^{\mathcal{D}}} \tau_\alpha^{n-2}$$

The surface integral can be written as

$$\int_{dS^{\mathcal{D}}} \tau^{n-2} = \sum_i \int_{S^{\mathcal{D}-i}} \tau_\alpha^{\mathcal{D}-i,n-2} \varepsilon_{l,\mathcal{D}-i}$$

$\tau^{\mathcal{D}-i}$ is here the restriction of τ_α^{n-2} to $CP^{\mathcal{D}-i}$.

This surface integral can be expressed as a sum of terms, one for each subsimplex on the boundary of $S^{\mathcal{D}}$. Let $S^{\mathcal{A}} = CP^{\mathcal{A}} \cap S^{\mathcal{D}}$, $W^{\mathcal{A}} = CP^{\mathcal{A}} \cap W$. We also label forms and their integrals on $CP^{\mathcal{A}}$ with the label $\mathcal{A}$. We introduce now a corresponding basis of forms on $CP^{\mathcal{A}}$: $\omega_\alpha^{\mathcal{A},P}$, $\alpha = 1 \cdots B^{\mathcal{A},P}$. Let the corresponding integral be written as

$$A_\alpha^{\mathcal{A}}(s) = \int_{S^{\mathcal{A}}} \omega_\alpha^{\mathcal{A}|\mathcal{A}|-1} \qquad \alpha = 1 \cdots B^{|\mathcal{A}|-1}$$

By assumption we can always write

$$\tau_\alpha^{\mathcal{D}-i,n-2} = \sum_{\gamma=1}^{B^{\mathcal{D}-i,n-2}} M_{\alpha\gamma}^{\mathcal{D},\mathcal{D}-i}(s)\omega_\gamma^{\mathcal{D}-i,n-2} + d\sigma^{n-3}$$

The surface integral in turn can be expressed in terms of the corresponding $\omega_\alpha^{\mathscr{A}}$, $\mathscr{A} \subset \mathscr{D}$ and of other surface integrals of lesser dimension. The process is then repeated until we reach the lowest dimension where it trivially terminates. In this way we express $\partial A_\alpha(s)/\partial s_k$ in terms of all amplitudes $A^{\mathscr{A}}(s)$, where $\mathscr{A} \subset \mathscr{D}$:

$$\frac{\partial A_\alpha^{\mathscr{D}}(s)}{\partial s_k} = \sum_{\mathscr{A} \subset \mathscr{D}} \sum_{\gamma=1}^{B^{\mathscr{A},|\mathscr{A}|-1}} M_{\alpha\gamma}^{\mathscr{D}\mathscr{A}}(s) A_\gamma^{\mathscr{A}}(s)$$

By using the same procedure with A in place of $\mathscr{D}$ we can also compute all derivatives $\partial A^{\mathscr{A}}/\partial s_k$ in terms of the amplitudes $A^{\mathscr{B}}$, $\mathscr{B} \subset \mathscr{A}$. We may gather now all the components $A^{\mathscr{A}}$ in a single one-column matrix $\mathbf{N}$ and write all these equations in the form:

$$\frac{\partial \mathbf{N}}{\partial s_k} = M(s)\mathbf{N} \tag{13}$$

where M stands for a square matrix whose elements are functions of s. It turns out that these functions are rational functions of s and that their singularities are just the Landau varieties as expected. It we now eliminate all the amplitudes in (13) but $A_1^{\mathscr{D}}$ we arrive at an ordinary differential equation of order equal to the rank K of $\mathbf{N}$, which is the desired equation. In practice we do not want to do so because the system (12) is much handier to deal with and provides a lot of relationships among different amplitudes.

The order of the differential equation is, according to our investigation, just the number K of independent analytic continuations of A. This number may be very high and we may naïvely make it even higher if the number of components in the matrix $\mathbf{N}$ is not counted right. The reason for this is that we have no assurance, and in general it is false, that all the components of $\mathbf{N}$ are actually all independent. In order to count these independent components properly we recall the notation $B^{\mathscr{A},p}$ for the Betti numbers, that is, the rank of $H^p(CP^{\mathscr{A}} - W^{\mathscr{A}})$. It follows that in $\omega_\alpha^{\mathscr{A},p}$ the index α takes the values $1 \cdots B^{\mathscr{A},\beta}$. $\mathbf{N}$ has therefore in the naïve computation:

$$\sum_{\mathscr{A} \subset \mathscr{D}} B^{\mathscr{A},|\mathscr{A}|-1}$$

components. You may have noted that I also introduced in the lecture the forms $\omega^{\mathscr{A},p}$ belonging to the cohomology groups of smaller dimension $p < |\mathscr{A}| - 1$ and that so far in deriving our differential equation all these groups have remained unused because for every subsimplex $\mathscr{A}$ we used only the forms with the same and maximum dimension $|\mathscr{A}| - 1$.

Suppose now that we have a closed form $\omega^{\mathscr{D},p-2}$ corresponding to a nontrivial element of $H^{p-2}(CP^{\mathscr{D}} - W)$. Since $d\omega_\alpha^{\mathscr{D},p-2} = 0$ we have

$$\int_{dS^{\mathscr{D}}} \omega_\alpha^{\mathscr{D},p-2} = 0$$

By expressing the restrictions of $\omega^{\mathscr{Q},p-2}$ on the boundary simplexes in terms of the basis set of forms $\omega_\beta^{\mathscr{Q}-i,p-2}$ we obtain an identity among the relevant amplitudes $A_\beta^{\mathscr{Q}-i}$. This identity[2] could be trivially void of content if the restriction of $\omega_\alpha^{\mathscr{Q},p-2}$ to $dS^{\mathscr{Q}}$ would be an exact form, in which case we would get $0 = 0$.

This remark shows first of all that the final identity will depend on the cohomology class of the initial form only, and that therefore there are at most $B^{\mathscr{Q},n-2}$ identities. But it is also true that all these identities are actually independent and not void by virtue of the Lefschetz theorem. What we use here is actually an affine version of the Lefschetz result that

$$H^p(CP^{n-1} - U) = 0 \qquad p > n - 1 \tag{14}$$

whenever U is a complex variety of complex codimension 1. We may state the affine version as[3]

$$H^p(CP^{n-1} - U, V - V \cap U) = 0 \qquad p \neq n - 1 \tag{15}$$

provided the hypersurfaces U and V intersect transversally. It is not required that U and V be regular—indeed they could be reducible. In our case we take $U = W$ and $V = \bigcup_i CP^{\mathscr{Q}-i}$.

Before proceeding further, some justification of the affine theorem is not out of place. This is not directed toward the mathematicians in the audience—they have heard it already too often during the last weeks. Chances are, however, that this lecture will be read by people who were not present at the Rencontres.

We begin with the usual exact sequence:

$$H^{p-1}(V - V \cap U) \to H^p(CP^{n-1} - U, V - V \cap U) \to$$
$$\to H^p(CP^{n-1} - U) \xrightarrow{\mu} H^p(V - V \cap U) \to \tag{16}$$

The standard Lefschetz theorem states that:

$$H^{p-1}(V - V \cap U) = 0 \qquad H^p(CP^{n-1} - U) = 0 \quad \text{for} \quad p > n - 1.$$

Inserting these data into the sequence (16) we find

$$H^p(CP^{n-1} - U, V - V \cap U) = 0 \qquad p > n - 1 \tag{17}$$

We have reached the first half of (15) in a rather trivial fashion. We use now the fundamental duality theorem of Lefschetz (for cohomology) (see p. 142 of *Topology* by S. Lefschetz, Am. Math. Soc. Coll. Publ., Vol. XII, 1930).

---

[2] This identity has been first obtained for the triangle graph by Dr. B. Jakšić.

[3] R. Bott has just demolished by mail my unshakeable faith in the validity of (15) under the wildest hypothesis. Luckily enough the theorem is still true when we need it, that is, when U and V intersect nicely.

Fundamental Duality Theorem. Let K, L, L^1 be close complexes and $K \supset L \supset L^1$, let $K - L$ be a manifold. If $L^2 = L - L^1$ the duality theorem for absolute manifolds holds between the cohomology characters of $(K - L)L^2$ and that of $(K - L^2)/L^1$.

We take $K = CP$, $L = V \cup U$, $L^1 = U$. It follows that

$$\text{rank } H^p(CP^{n-1} - U, V - U \cap V) = \text{rank } H^{2n-p-2}((CP^{n-1} - V) \cap U, U)$$

If U and V intersect tranversally, we can thicken $U \cap V$ and use the excision theorem, and we get finally at

$$\text{rank } H^p(CP^{n-1} - U, V - U \cap V) = \text{rank } H^{2n-p-2}(CP^{n-1} - V, U - U \cap V)$$

$$(18)$$

This yields the second half of (15).

Thom and Steenrod have proposed other proofs of the same result and we plan to report them elsewhere. All these proofs assume that U and V intersect tranversally and in fact Bott has produced a counter example from a paper by Howards which also reports the affine Lefschetz theorem. In order to use (15) more efficiently we look again at (16) for $p \leqslant n - 1$, so that

$$0 \to H^p(CP^{n-1} - U) \overset{\rho}{\to} H^p(V - V \cap U) \overset{\delta}{\to} H^{p+1}(CP^{n-1} - U, V - V \cap U) \to$$

But the map ρ is just the restriction map, and by the exactness property ρ is an injection for $p = n - 2$ and an isomorphism for $p < n - 2$. It follows that exact forms only restrict into exact forms and this way we get always $B^{\mathscr{D},n-2}$ meaningful identities.

The same counting procedure could be repeated for each subsimplex $S^{\mathscr{A}} \subset S^{\mathscr{D}}$. Each element of the cohomology group $H^{|\mathscr{A}|-2}(CP^{\mathscr{A}} - W^{\mathscr{A}})$ brings in an identity on the amplitudes $A_{\alpha}^{\mathscr{A}-i}$. We expect therefore that the correct number of independent amplitudes will be:

$$\sum_{\mathscr{A} \subset \mathscr{D}} (B^{\mathscr{A},|\mathscr{A}|-1} - B^{\mathscr{A},|\mathscr{A}|-2})$$

This computation is again naïve, for the existence of a nontrivial element of $H^{\mathscr{D},n-3}$ shows that not all the identities generated by elements of $H^{\mathscr{A},n-3}$ are actually independent. A similar interpretation can be given for all elements of the lower dimensional cohomology groups $H^{\mathscr{A},p}$ and the net result is that the effective dimension of $\mathbf{N}$ is given by the alternating sum:

$$K = \sum_{\mathscr{A} \subset \mathscr{D}} \left(\sum_{p=1}^{|\mathscr{A}|} B^{\mathscr{A},|\mathscr{A}|-p}(-)^{p-1} \right)$$

By introducing the Euler characteristics:

$$\chi(CP^{\mathscr{A}} - W^{\mathscr{A}}) = \sum_{p=1}^{\mathscr{A}} B^{\mathscr{A},|\mathscr{A}|-p}(-)^{|\mathscr{A}|-p}$$

we see that K can be written as

$$K = \sum_{\mathscr{A}} (-)^{|\mathscr{A}|-1} \chi(P^{\mathscr{A}} - W^{\mathscr{A}})$$

By using now the Meyer–Vietoris sequence and the usual relative sequence one arrives at the compact form:

$$K = \chi\left(CP^{\mathscr{D}} - W, \bigcup_i (CP^{\mathscr{D}-i} - W^{\mathscr{D}-i})\right)(-1)^{n-1}$$

This number is also the rank of

$$H_{n-1}\left(CP^{\mathscr{D}} - W, \bigcup_i (CP^{\mathscr{D}-i} - W^{\mathscr{D}-i})\right)$$

Thus K is also the number of independent cycles of integration relative to the hyperplanes $CP^{\mathscr{D}-i}$. In fact had we started from the functions:

$$A_{\alpha}^{\mathscr{D}}(s, v) = \int_v \omega_{\alpha}^{\mathscr{D}} \qquad v \in H_{n-1}\left(CP^{\mathscr{D}} - W, \bigcup_i (CP^{\mathscr{D}-i} - W^{\mathscr{D}-i})\right)$$

we would have found the same set of differential equations for $A_{\alpha}^{\mathscr{D}}(s, v)$ and the corresponding matrix $\mathbf{N}(s, v)$. It follows that the general integral of (13) is given by:

$$\sum_{a=1}^{K} \lambda_a \mathbf{N}(s, v_a)$$

where the summation index a runs over all the elements of

$$v_a \in H_{n-1}\left(CP^{\mathscr{D}} - W, \bigcup_1 (CP^{\mathscr{D}-i} - W^{\mathscr{D}-i})\right)$$

In this way we have related the numerology of our differential equations to the corresponding numerology of homology theory. Of course my arguments here are at the best heuristic, but we hope to be able to formalize them sufficiently in detail as to make them rigorous.

The formula given so far for K can be used immediately in connection with the published Euler characteristics for algebraic varieties in general position. We just borrow them from Hirzebruch. We have first that:

$$\chi(CP^n) = n + 1 \quad \text{or} \quad \chi(CP^{\mathscr{A}}) = |\mathscr{A}|$$

For a general hypersurface $\mathscr{A}$ of degree $l + 1$ in $CP^{\mathscr{A}}$ we have:

$$\chi(W^{\mathscr{A}}) = \frac{1}{l+1} \left[|\mathscr{A}|(l+1) - 1 + (-l)^{|\mathscr{A}|} \right] \tag{19}$$

By replacing these values in (17) we find that:

$$K = (l + 1)^{n-1} \tag{20}$$

This result looks very neat and simple.   Unfortunately as we said it applies only to fictitious FRA as soon as $l > 1$.   The spinless box diagram is, however, included and for it we get $K = 8$.   In order to include higher order diagrams from real life we need to work even harder.   This we shall discuss in Part V.

The similar formula for the complete intersection $W_1^{\mathscr{A}} \cap W_2^{\mathscr{A}}$ of two general hypersurfaces of degree $l + 1$, $h + 1$, respectively, is

$$\chi(W_1^{\mathscr{A}} \cap W_2^{\mathscr{A}}) = |\mathscr{A}| - \frac{1}{h + 1} - \frac{1}{l + 1} + l^{|\mathscr{A}|}(-)^{|\mathscr{A}|} \frac{h + 1}{(l + 1)(h - l)}$$
$$+ h^{|\mathscr{A}|}(-)^{|\mathscr{A}|} \frac{l + 1}{(h + 1)(l - h)} \tag{21}$$

It follows that if $W = W_1 \cup W_2$ we have

$$K = \sum_{q=0}^{n-1} (l + 1)^{n-1-q}(h + 1)^q = \frac{(l + 1)^n - (h + 1)^n}{(l + 1) - (h + 1)} \tag{22}$$

For the triangle diagram $l = 1$, $h = 0$, $n = 3$, and $K = 7$.[4]

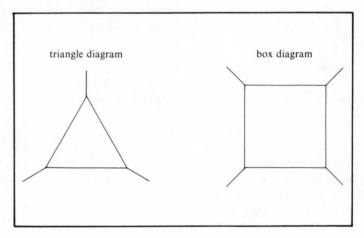

triangle diagram   box diagram

FIGURE 2

PART IV

FRA with $l > 1$ present difficulties and additional complications which increase with l.   These difficulties may be roughly classified into the following types:

---

[4] The complete analysis of the triangle diagram has been kindly communicated to me by Dr. B. Jakšić.

1. If $n - (l + 1)/2 \ m < 0$, W reduces into the two components $W_1 : D(z, s) = 0$ and $W_2 : d(z) = 0$. If W_1 and W_2 were regular and in general position and of degrees $l + 1$ and l, this case could be solved explicitly by the use of the Meyer–Vietoris sequence and K is given by (22).

2. W, or some of the components of W if (1) holds, is not regular. In this case the general treatment follows the lines sketched in the previous parts of the lecture. The main difficulty is that there are practically no available formulas for the Euler characteristics of nonregular hypersurfaces and in fact there is no classification of nonregular algebraic hypersurfaces with the exception of the lower dimensions and even there it is extremely complicated. This does not mean that in any specific case some ingenuity will not reach the final result.

3. The different components of W are not in general position with respect to each other. This may happen in concurrence with (2), and to make things worse there are simple diagrams like the envelope ($m = 4$), where the locus of singularities of one of the components of W lies entirely on the other (Fig. 3). Here for the moment I am stuck.

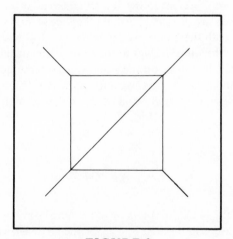

FIGURE 3

4. In addition to (1) to (3) W will contain the class of subsimplexes (hereafter named singular simplexes) of $S^{\mathscr{D}}$ obtained by putting $z_i = 0$, where $i \in \mathscr{Y}$ is the set of lines associated with a cycle of $\overline{\mathscr{D}}$ as described before in the definition of $d(z)$. In order to describe these sets more efficiently we label them with the complement of $\mathscr{Y}$ and we use end of the alphabet letters so that for instance $CP^{\mathscr{Z}}$ is the variety $z_i = 0 \ i \in \mathscr{Z}$, with $S^{\mathscr{Z}}$ the corresponding simplex, and it is understood that $S^{\mathscr{Z}}$ and $CP^{\mathscr{Z}}$ lie on W. If W is reducible then $S^{\mathscr{Z}}$, $CP^{\mathscr{Z}}$ lie on both components and therefore on their intersection. If

$l = 1$ all singular simplexes are disjoint for on their intersection all z_i would have to vanish. If $l > 1$ this is no longer true and we may consider a whole family of singular simplexes forming a partially ordered set under the inclusion relation. To this purpose we introduce a level function on the family of simplexes as follows. Let $S^{\mathscr{Y}}$ be a singular simplex and take the complex $\overline{\mathscr{D}\text{-}\mathscr{Y}}$, that is, the closure of $\mathscr{D}\text{-}\mathscr{Y}$. Define

$$\nu(S^{\mathscr{Y}}) = \text{rank } H_1(\overline{\mathscr{D}\text{-}\mathscr{Y}})$$

$\nu(S^{\mathscr{Y}})$ is essentially the number of loops on which the z_i vanish. Evidently $1 \leqslant \nu \leqslant l$ and also the smaller is ν, the larger the corresponding simplex. If $\nu = 1$ then the simplex is not contained in any other simplex and we call it maximal. Any singular simplex of level ν can be represented as the intersection of ν maximal simplexes. We see therefore that as soon as we reach $l > 1$, we encounter very complicated structures. It can be also verified that on a singular simplex of level ν both functions $d(z)$, $D(z, s)$ and their derivatives up to and including the order $\nu - 1$ vanish. Therefore on the levels $\nu > 1$ W is singular and if reducible both its components are singular.

It is reasonable therefore to try first to understand the case $l = 1$ where all singular simplexes are disjoint. Should there be several singular simplexes we can easily deal with them once we know how to deal with one simplex $S^{\mathscr{Y}}$ only; hence, we shall limit ourselves to this case. The usual approach, as we find it in the current literature on the subject, is to blow up along the linear variety $CP^{\mathscr{Y}}$ containing $S^{\mathscr{Y}}$. This amounts to the construction of a new pair of algebraic varieties $C\tilde{P}^{\mathscr{D}} \supset C\tilde{P}^{\mathscr{Y}}$ and of an analytical map f such that:

$$
\begin{array}{ccc}
C\tilde{P}^{\mathscr{D}} & \leftarrow & C\tilde{P}^{\mathscr{Y}} \\
{\scriptstyle f}\big\downarrow & & {\scriptstyle f}\big\downarrow \\
CP^{\mathscr{D}} & \leftarrow & CP^{\mathscr{Y}}
\end{array}
\tag{23}
$$

and such that $f \,|\, C\tilde{P}^{\mathscr{D}} - C\tilde{P}^{\mathscr{Y}}$ reduces to an isomorphism, and $C\tilde{P}^{\mathscr{Y}}$ is of codimension 1. We use also the notation $\tilde{V}$ for the strict blowing up of any set V defined as

$$\tilde{V} = \overline{f^{-1}(V - V \cap CP^{\mathscr{Y}})}$$

May I just remind those who are not familiar with these methods how the blow-up is actually achieved. Let $\mathscr{J}^{\mathscr{Y}}$ be the ideal of homogeneous polynomials vanishing on $CP^{\mathscr{Y}}$ and $\mathscr{J}_p^{\mathscr{Y}}$ the subset of $\mathscr{J}^{\mathscr{Y}}$ of polynomials of degree p. Select a basis of independent polynomials in $\mathscr{J}_p^{\mathscr{Y}}$: $P_i(z)$, i, $1 \cdots L$. Consider the complex projective space CP^{L-1} in the homogeneous coordinates $\zeta_1 \cdots \zeta_L$ and in it the algebraic variety of parametric representation:

$$\zeta_1 = P_i(z) \qquad i = 1 \cdots L$$

For sufficiently high p it can be shown that this variety is a model for $C\tilde{P}^{\mathscr{Y}}$ and that for larger values of p all models one obtains in this way are isomorphic. One could choose other ideals contained in $\mathscr{I}^{\mathscr{Y}}$ and one would achieve in this way different types of blow-ups. I think that at the end we shall consider all sorts of weird blow-ups in order to cope with the just a weird collection of singularities offered by the FRA. But for the moment it is enough to work out just the simplest case.

We come back to the motivations behind the blowing-up; they essentially reduce to the fact that on $C\tilde{P}^{\mathscr{Q}}$, $\tilde{S}^{\mathscr{Q}}$, and $\tilde{W}^{\mathscr{Q}}$ do not intersect. $\tilde{S}^{\mathscr{Q}}$ is no longer a simplex, however, and it will have a new " face " where $CP^{\mathscr{Y}}$ has been blown up into codimension 1. Since $C\tilde{P}^{\mathscr{Q}}$ is a manifold we may introduce local coordinates and carry out the integration of the FRA in these coordinates. By introducing these new coordinates the original differential form ω becomes a differential form $\tilde{\omega}$. There are then two possibilities:

(A) The form $\tilde{\omega}$ is singular on $\tilde{W}$ only. In this case we deal with a theory exactly similar to the one worked out so far, the domain of integration $\tilde{S}$ does not intersect the singularity, the integral converges and we may repeat our derivation of the differential equation with the enly difference that now we work in $C\tilde{P}^{\mathscr{Q}}$ which is not a complex projective space.

(B) $\tilde{\omega}$ is singular on the complete blow-up of W, that is, $f^{-1}|W|$ which is just $\tilde{W} \cup C\tilde{P}^{\mathscr{Y}}$. In this case a whole face of $\tilde{S}^{\mathscr{Q}}$ lies on a hypersurface $C\tilde{P}^{V}$ of singularities and the integral diverges. In fact there is no need to blow up in order to see that it diverges. If we look at the original form in $CP^{\mathscr{Q}}$ we see immediately that this corresponds to an integral where the power of the singularity in the denominator is too high for convergence. We see that convergence is translated by the blowing-up procedure into absence of singularities on $CP^{\mathscr{Y}}$. The nice thing about blowing up is that now we have again a proper homology group we can talk about (in case A); in fact,

$$ H_*\left(C\tilde{P}^{\mathscr{Q}} - \tilde{W}, \bigcup_i (C\tilde{P}^{\mathscr{Q}-i} - \tilde{W}^{\mathscr{Q}-i}) \cup (C\tilde{P}^{\mathscr{Q}} - C\tilde{P}^{\mathscr{Y}} \cap \tilde{W})\right) \qquad (24) $$

Here we can use compact chains of integration. Before, since the simplex $S^{\mathscr{Q}}$ was reaching W we could not use compact homology and all the relevant machinery. This is the reason why people working on FRA from the homological point of view are more or less forced to blow up. In this lecture, however, I have more emphasized the cohomology side and I think there is a nice way to have all the advantages of blow-up without the disadvantages: among these the need to use methods of algebraic geometry which are far removed from the daily life of the ordinary physicists. The idea here is contained in my previous remark that cohomology in $C\tilde{P}^{\mathscr{Q}} - \tilde{W}$ is essentially the convergent cohomology in $CP^{\mathscr{Q}} - W$. Convergent here means just the property of forms to converge when integrated over the subsimplexes of $S^{\mathscr{Q}}$ of the right dimension. In order to achieve convergence the power of the denominator in the form must not be too high. Lascoux and I have examined in detail the conditions of convergence of a form. The interesting part of it is that these conditions can be best described by means of the idea of filtration.

We may state it shortly as follows: To each group of forms $C^p(CP^{\mathscr{D}} - W)$ we associate a subgroup of convergent forms $C_1^p(CP^{\mathscr{D}} - W_i)$ with the property that

$$\partial C_1^p(CP^n - W) \subset C_1^{p+1}(CP^n - W)$$

The restriction of ∂ to the convergent forms has then all the properties of a boundary operator and we can construct a convergent cohomology out of it. From the previous discussion this cohomology will be isomorphic to $H^*(C\tilde{P}^p - \tilde{W})$. The groups C_1^p are commonly referred to as filtered groups. (In general one considers a sequence of nested subgroups $C \supset C_1^p \supset C_2^p \cdots C_n^p$ such that $\partial C_n^p \subset C_n^{p+1}$; this generalization will certainly be needed when several disjoint varieties are blown up.)

What Lascoux and I tried and up to a large extent succeeded in doing is to characterize the filtered cohomology without recourse to a specific and explicit blow-up procedure. At the same time we found an exact sequence, similar to Leray's sequence, which ties up together the ordinary, the filtered cohomology and the cohomology of $C\tilde{P}^{\mathscr{D}} - C\tilde{P}^{\mathscr{D}} \cap \tilde{W}$. This we do in the following way. We introduce a new set of variables, ξ_i, ρ:

$$z_i = \xi_i, i \in \mathscr{Y} \qquad z_i = \rho\xi_i', i \in \mathscr{Y} \qquad z_y = \{z_i, i \in \mathscr{Y}\} \text{ etc.}$$

where for convenience we label $\mathscr{Y}$ as $\{1 \cdots t\}$. By differentiating we find

$$dz_i = d\xi_i, i \leqslant t \qquad dz_i = \rho \, d\xi_i + \xi_i \, d\rho, i > t$$

We now replace dz_i with their expression in the right-hand side in the definitions of $\omega_{\mathscr{A}}$ and $\eta_{\mathscr{A}}$. We find

$$\omega_{\mathscr{A}} = \rho^{|\mathscr{A} \cap \mathscr{Y}'|}\left(\omega_{\mathscr{A}}{}^\xi + \frac{d\rho}{\rho} \wedge \omega_{\mathscr{A} \cap \mathscr{Y}}^\xi \wedge \eta_{\mathscr{A} \cap \mathscr{Y}'}^\xi (-1)^{|\mathscr{A} \cap \mathscr{Y}'|}\right) \tag{25}$$

$$\eta_{\mathscr{A}} = \rho^{|\mathscr{A} \cap \mathscr{Y}'|}\left(\eta_{\mathscr{A}}{}^\xi + \frac{d\rho}{\rho} \wedge \eta_{\mathscr{A} \cap \mathscr{Y}}^\xi \wedge \eta_{\mathscr{A} \cap \mathscr{Y}'}^\xi (-1)^{|\mathscr{A} \cap \mathscr{Y}'|}\right)$$

where

$$\omega_{\mathscr{A}}{}^\xi = \bigwedge_{i \in \mathscr{A}} d\xi_i \text{ etc.}$$

Similarly the projective form

$$\omega^{p-1} = \sum_{|\mathscr{A}| = p} R_A \eta_A$$

is replaced by the form

$$\omega^{p-1} = \sum_{\mathscr{A}} R_{\mathscr{A}}(\xi_{\mathscr{Y}}, \rho\xi_{\mathscr{Y}'})\rho^{|\mathscr{A} \cap \mathscr{Y}'|}\left(\eta_{\mathscr{A}}{}^\xi + \frac{d\rho}{\rho} \wedge \eta_{\mathscr{A} \cap \mathscr{Y}}^\xi \wedge \eta_{\mathscr{A} \cap \mathscr{Y}'}(-)^{|\mathscr{A} \cap \mathscr{Y}'|}\right)$$

The point $\rho = 0$ evidently corresponds to $z_i = 0$, $i \in \mathcal{Y}'$, that is, $CP^{\mathcal{Y}}$. In order to see more clearly what happens in the neighborhood of $CP^{\mathcal{Y}}$ we expand the coefficients of ω as

$$R_{\mathcal{A}}(\xi_{\mathcal{Y}}, \rho\xi_{\mathcal{Y}'}) = \sum_k R_{\mathcal{A}}^{(k)}(\xi_{\mathcal{Y}}, \xi_{\mathcal{Y}'})\rho^{k-|\mathcal{A} \cap \mathcal{Y}'|}$$

so that

$$\omega^{p-1} = \sum_k \rho^k \sum_{\mathcal{A}} R_{\mathcal{A}}^{(k)}(\xi_{\mathcal{Y}}, \xi_{\mathcal{Y}'})\eta_{\mathcal{A}}{}^{\xi} + \sum_k \rho^{k-1} d\rho \wedge \sum_{\mathcal{A}} R_{\mathcal{A}}^{(k)}\eta_{\mathcal{A} \cap \mathcal{Y}}^{\xi} \wedge \eta_{\mathcal{A} \cap \mathcal{Y}'}^{\xi}(-)^{|\mathcal{A} \cap \mathcal{Y}'|}$$

Our definition of filtered form is that all the terms with negative powers in the above expansion should vanish:

$$\sum_{\mathcal{A}} R_{\mathcal{A}}^{(k)}(\xi_{\mathcal{Y}}, \xi_{\mathcal{Y}'})\eta_{\mathcal{A}}^{\xi} = 0 \qquad k < 0$$

$$\sum_{\mathcal{A}} R^{(k)}\eta_{\mathcal{A} \cap \mathcal{Y}}^{\xi} \wedge \eta_{\mathcal{A} \cap \mathcal{Y}'}^{\xi}(-1)^{|\mathcal{A} \cap \mathcal{Y}'|} = 0 \qquad k \leqslant 0 \tag{26}$$

We can give here just a few words of explanation as to why these conditions are in fact a filtration. We introduce the auxiliary operators λ_k:

$$\lambda_k \omega = \sum_{\mathcal{A}} R_{\mathcal{A}}^{(k)}(z)\eta_{\mathcal{A}}$$

These operators are easily seen to commute with d and z. On affine forms we introduce also the partial z operators $z_{\mathcal{Y}} z_{\mathcal{Y}'}$, as

$$z_{\mathcal{Y}'} \sum_{\mathcal{A}} M_{\mathcal{A}}\omega_{\mathcal{A}} = \sum_{\mathcal{A}} M_{\mathcal{A}}\omega_{\mathcal{A} \cap \mathcal{Y}} \wedge \eta_{\mathcal{A} \cap \mathcal{Y}'}(-)^{|\mathcal{A} \cap \mathcal{Y}'|}$$

$$z_{\mathcal{Y}} \sum_{\mathcal{A}} M_{\mathcal{A}}\omega_{\mathcal{A}} = z_{\mathcal{Y}} \sum_{\mathcal{A}} M_{\mathcal{A}}\omega_{\mathcal{A} \cap \mathcal{Y}} \wedge \omega_{\mathcal{A} \cap \mathcal{Y}'} = \sum_{\mathcal{A}} M_{\mathcal{A}}\eta_{\mathcal{A} \cap \mathcal{Y}} \wedge \omega_{\mathcal{A} \cap \mathcal{Y}'} \tag{27}$$

We find after some algebra that

$$(z_{\mathcal{Y}'})^2 = (z_{\mathcal{Y}})^2 = 0$$

$$z_{\mathcal{Y}} z_{\mathcal{Y}'} + z_{\mathcal{Y}'} z_{\mathcal{Y}} = 0 \tag{28}$$

But in general it is not true that $dz_{\mathcal{Y}} + z_{\mathcal{Y}} d = 0$ unless we restrict ourselves to the image of λ_0. It follows that filtration conditions can be written as

$$\lambda_k \omega = 0 \quad k < 0 \quad \rightarrow \quad z_{\mathcal{Y}} \lambda_k \omega = 0 \quad k < 0$$

$$z_{\mathcal{Y}} \lambda_k \omega = -z_{\mathcal{Y}'} \lambda_k \omega = 0$$

We deduce immediately that

$$d\lambda_k \omega = \lambda_k d\omega = 0$$

$$dz_{\mathcal{Y}} \lambda_0 \omega = z_{\mathcal{Y}} d\lambda_0 \omega = z_{\mathcal{Y}} \lambda_0 d\omega = 0$$

It follows also that $d\omega$ is a filtered form.

In order to arrive at the Leray-type sequence we need some more definitions. We call *byprojective* the projective forms of the kind:

$$T = \sum_{|\mathscr{A}| = p} R_{\mathscr{A}}(z) \eta_{\mathscr{A} \cap \mathscr{Y}} \wedge \eta_{\mathscr{A} \cap \mathscr{Y}'}(-)^{|\mathscr{A} \cap \mathscr{Y}'|}$$

where R is separately homogeneous of degree $-|\mathscr{A} \cap \mathscr{Y}|$ and $-|\mathscr{A} \cap \mathscr{Y}'|$ in $z_{\mathscr{Y}}$ and $z_{\mathscr{Y}'}$, respectively. Clearly, $z_{\mathscr{Y}} \lambda_0 \omega$ is a biprojective form. The boundary of a biprojective form is again biprojective. We can repeat all the cohomology theory for biprojective forms just as we did for ordinary cohomology. We should think of biprojective forms as differential forms on the blowing up $C\tilde{P}^{\mathscr{Y}}$ of $CP^{\mathscr{Y}}$. It is well-known that $C\tilde{P}^{\mathscr{Y}}$ has the structure of a fiber space with base $CP^{\mathscr{Y}}$ and fiber $CP^{\mathscr{Y}'}$. We expect forms on $C\tilde{P}^{\mathscr{Y}}$ to be written locally as a direct product of forms on $CP^{\mathscr{Y}}$ and $CP^{\mathscr{Y}'}$ and this brings us to biprojective forms. The operator λ_0 gives us a map:

$$C^{p-1}(C\tilde{P}^{\mathscr{Y}} - C\tilde{P}^{\mathscr{Y}} \cap \tilde{W}) \leftarrow C^p(CP^{\mathscr{Q}} - W)$$

λ_0 maps boundaries into boundaries; therefore it generates a map between the corresponding cohomology groups:

$$H^p(CP^p - W) \xrightarrow{\lambda^*} H^{p-1}(C\tilde{P}^{\mathscr{Y}} - C\tilde{P}^{\mathscr{Y}} \cap \tilde{W})$$

We call λ_0 and λ_0^* the residue operators. We have also the injection

$$C^p(C\tilde{P}^{\mathscr{Q}} - \tilde{W}) \xrightarrow{i} C^p(C\tilde{P}^{\mathscr{Q}} - \tilde{W} \cup C\tilde{P}^{\mathscr{Y}}) \approx C^p(CP^{\mathscr{Q}} - W)$$

Also this map generates a map

$$H^p(C\tilde{P}^{\mathscr{Q}} - \tilde{W}) \xrightarrow{i^*} H^p(CP^{\mathscr{Q}} - W)$$

It is evident that $\lambda^* i^* = 0$ but it takes much more work to show that in fact the sequence:

$$H^p(C\tilde{P} - \tilde{W}) \xrightarrow{i^*} H^p(CP - W) \xrightarrow{\lambda^*} H^{p-1}(C\tilde{P}^{\mathscr{Y}} - C\tilde{P}^{\mathscr{Y}} \cap \tilde{W})$$

is exact at $H^p(CP - W)$. We skip the proof here.

Finally, suppose that we write the equation of W as $F(z_{\mathscr{Y}}, z_{\mathscr{Y}'}) = 0$ where $F = D(z, s)$ or $d(z)D(z)$. The leading term $F_0(z_{\mathscr{Y}}, z_{\mathscr{Y}'})$ in the expansion:

$$F(z_{\mathscr{Y}}, \rho z_{\mathscr{Y}'}) = \sum_{k}^{\infty} \rho^{k+m} F_k(z_{\mathscr{Y}}, z_{\mathscr{Y}'})$$

is the equation of $\tilde{W} \cap C\tilde{P}^{\mathscr{Y}}$. Suppose now that a closed biprojective form τ^{p-1} be given, singular on $\tilde{W} \cap C\tilde{Y}^{\mathscr{Y}}$:

$$\tau^{p-1} = \sum_{\mathscr{A} = p+1} \frac{P_{\mathscr{A}}(z_{\mathscr{Y}}, z_{\mathscr{Y}'})}{F_0(z_{\mathscr{Y}}, z_{\mathscr{Y}'})^{\mathscr{Q}}} \eta_{\mathscr{A} \cap \mathscr{Y}} \wedge \eta_{\mathscr{A} \cap \mathscr{Y}'}(-)^{|\mathscr{A} \cap \mathscr{Y}'|}$$

We call a projective form $\mu > 0$ an extension of τ if it satisfies the following conditions:

$$\lambda_k \mu^p = 0 \qquad k < 0$$

$$z_{\mathscr{Y}} \lambda_0 \mu^p = \tau \qquad \mu \text{ regular on } CP^{\mathscr{Q}} - W$$

Extensions of a given form τ can always be found and there actually are infinitely many of them; one example is

$$\mu^p = \sum_{\mathscr{A}} \frac{P_{\mathscr{A}}}{F(z)^{\mathscr{Q}}} \eta_{\mathscr{A}}$$

Once an extension μ of τ is found, we take its boundary. It can then be verified that $d\mu^p$ is a filtered form and that its filtered cohomology class depends only on the class of τ^{p-1}. It follows that we have a map

$$H^{p-1}(C\tilde{P}^{\mathscr{Y}} - C\tilde{P}^{\mathscr{Y}} \cap \tilde{W}) \overset{v^*}{\to} H^{p-1}(C\tilde{P}^{\mathscr{Q}} - \tilde{W})$$

It can be checked that the triangle of maps

$$H^*(C\tilde{P}^{\mathscr{Q}} - \tilde{W}) \overset{i}{\to} H^*(CP - W)$$
$$\begin{array}{cc} {}_{v^*}\searrow & \nearrow_{\lambda^*} \end{array} \qquad\qquad (29)$$
$$H^*(C\tilde{P}^{\mathscr{Y}} - C\tilde{P}^{\mathscr{Y}} \cap \tilde{W})$$

is everywhere exact. I like to see this sequence as a sort of affine Leray sequence. The usual Leray sequence reads

$$H^p_{?}(X) \to H^p(X - U)$$
$$\begin{array}{cc} {}_{p-1 \,\to\, p-2}\nwarrow & \nearrow \end{array} \qquad\qquad (30)$$
$$H^{p-1}(U)$$

where X, U are regular algebraic varieties.

Leray sequence is identical with ours provided one chooses $X = C\tilde{P}^{\mathscr{Q}} - \tilde{W}$, $U = C\tilde{P}^{\mathscr{Y}} - C\tilde{P}^{\mathscr{Y}} \cap \tilde{W}$. At the moment I do not know whether the Leray sequence automatically applies to noncompact manifolds; if so, then (29) is really nothing new. What is important anyway is the relation among the different Euler characteristics which one gets out of (29):

$$\chi(C\tilde{P}^{\mathscr{Q}} - \tilde{W}) = \chi(CP^{\mathscr{Q}} - W) + \chi(C\tilde{P}^{\mathscr{Y}} - C\tilde{P}^{\mathscr{Y}} \cap \tilde{W})$$

In the case $l = 1$ the group $H^*(C\tilde{P}^{\mathscr{Y}} - C\tilde{P}^{\mathscr{Y}} \cap \tilde{W})$ is easy to handle because the fiber becomes trivial. The reason for this is that it can be shown that in the neighborhood of the power expansion of d and D reads:

$$d(z) = \left(\sum_{i \in '\mathscr{Y}} z_i \right) d_{\mathscr{Y}}(z_{\mathscr{Y}}) + \cdots$$

$$D(z, s) = \sum_{i \in \mathscr{Y}} z_i \, D_{\mathscr{Y}}(z_{\mathscr{Y}})$$

where $d_{\mathcal{Y}}$ and $D_{\mathcal{Y}}$ are the same functions defined for a diagram where all the lines in $\mathcal{Y}'$ have been contracted and their boundary points identified. This is indeed just the diagram $D/\mathcal{Y}'$. Let $W^{\mathcal{Y}}$ be represented by $d^{\mathcal{Y}} D^{\mathcal{Y}} = 0$ or $D^{\mathcal{Y}}$ in $CP^{\mathcal{Y}}$ and let $CP_0{}^{\mathcal{Y}'}$ be the hyperplane

$$\sum_{i \in \mathcal{Y}'} z_i = 0$$

It follows that locally $\tilde{W} \cap C\tilde{P}^{\mathcal{Y}}$ is just the product of $CP^{\mathcal{Y}} - W^{\mathcal{Y}}$ and of $CP^{\mathcal{Y}'} - CP_0{}^{\mathcal{Y}'}$. But $CP^{\mathcal{Y}'} - CP_0{}^{\mathcal{Y}'}$ is just affine space and is retractable into a point. Therefore as far as cohomology is concerned we may replace everywhere $C\tilde{P}^{\mathcal{Y}} - C\tilde{P}^{\mathcal{Y}} \cap \tilde{W}$ with $CP^{\mathcal{Y}} - W^{\mathcal{Y}}$. The theory of $CP^{\mathcal{Y}} - W^{\mathcal{Y}}$ is just the theory of the contradicted diagram $D/\mathcal{Y}'$. It is striking that the same diagrams appear in renormalization theory as exemplified by the last monumental paper by Hepp[5] on the subject. I do not think that this coincidence is accidental. I am instead of the opinion that this way we shall ultimately reach a neater formulation of renormalization through algebraic topological methods. I have made no attempt so far to deal with the cases (7) but I feel that they will eventually be discussed with a generalization of the present methods.

I hope I have been able to summarize our present attempts and attitudes toward the whole subject of FRA in a way which should be understandable to both mathematicians and physicists in the spirit of these Rencontres. In spite of all these dedicated efforts by a lot of theoreticians, most of the diagrams have resisted any attempt to subjugate them by the sheer amount of the computations involved. I hope, however, that enough of them will be studied in detail as to give some hint as to what the general structure may be. Till that moment we cannot expect any reasonable application of the present techniques to real-life physics.

ACKNOWLEDGMENTS

This work has been performed mainly at the Institute for Advanced Study in Princeton and at the Istituto di Fisica dell'Universitá di Torino under E.O.A.R. Grant 66-29. I am particularly indebted here at the Rencontres to Drs. R. Bott, H. Hironaka, R. Thom, and N. Steenrod for many interesting discussions. I am also indebted to Dr. V. de Alfaro and M. B. Jakšić whose results in this field have been crucial in deriving many features of the present work.

---

[5] K. Hepp, *Comm. in Math. Physics*, **2**, 301 (1966).

XVII

The Use of Padé Approximations in Particle Physics

MARCEL FROISSART

For work on Padé approximants, see Preprint CERN TH794, July 5, 1967, "Unitary Padé Approximants in Strong Coupling Field Theory and Application to the Calculation of the p and f^o Meson Regge Trajectories" by D. Bessis and M. Pusterla.

XVIII

Topics in Topology and Differential Geometry

RAOUL BOTT AND JOHN MATHER*

In these lectures I had hoped to take my friends from physics on a few quite informal hikes into the topological countryside. Coming as I did after lectures on relativity and symmetrics, I fell back on an old love of mine and planned my first excursion around the Morse theory and the elementary homotopy properties of sphere and the classical groups. As it turned out, there was very little time left after this expedition. I mention this here in order to warn the physicist that I haven't in any way covered the field, and that many other excursions—for instance, into differential topology, cobordism, semi-simplicial theory, sheaf theory—might be of equal and possibly even greater interest to him.

The notes presented here are by and large the ones taken by John Mather during the lectures. He did, fortunately, cut out much of the hot air, and I hope all the wrong statements. Obviously the notes could have been polished quite a bit; however, even if we had wanted to, the ruthless timetable of our charming editor would have made that impossible.

Raoul Bott

---

* Lectures by Raoul Bott and notes by John Mather.

1 THE HOMOTOPY CATEGORY

We begin by defining a category. Its objects are finite-dimensional vector spaces over $\mathbf{R}$. Given two finite-dimensional vector spaces V and W, the notion of a linear map $\phi: V \to W$ is defined. We set Hom $(V, W) =$ the set of all linear maps from V to W.

The set of linear map satisfies two very trivial axioms.

1. For each V, there exists a unique mapping $1_V: V \to V$ called the identity.
2. Given ϕ, ψ as follows

$$U \xrightarrow{\phi} V \xrightarrow{\psi} W$$

we can form the composition $\psi \circ \phi: U \to W$.

This composition law is associative:

$$\phi \circ (\psi \circ \lambda) = (\phi \circ \psi) \circ \lambda$$

1 acts as a unit:

$$1_V \circ \phi = \phi$$

$$\phi \circ 1_U = \phi$$

In general a category $\mathbf{C}$ consists of: a class of *objects*, and for any objects A and B in $\mathbf{C}$, a set Hom (A, B) called the maps from A to B. Further, there is given for every triple of objects A, B, C in $\mathbf{C}$ a set mapping Hom (A, B) $\times$ Hom $(B, C) \to$ Hom (A, C) (abstract form of composition), and a singled-out element 1_A in Hom (A, A) such that composition is associative and 1_A acts as a unit.

Theorems in Linear Algebra

Classification Theorem. We say two spaces V and W are *isomorphic* if there exist mappings ϕ, ψ

$$V \underset{\psi}{\overset{\phi}{\rightleftarrows}} W$$

such that $\psi \circ \phi = 1$ and $\phi \circ \psi = 1$. In this case we call ψ and ϕ *isomorphisms*. We write $V \simeq W$.

Theorem. *Every* $V \simeq \underbrace{\mathbf{R}^1 \oplus \cdots \oplus \mathbf{R}^1}_{n} = \mathbf{R}^n$ *and* $\mathbf{R}^n \not\simeq \mathbf{R}^m$ *if* $n \neq m$.

Example. The category of finitely generated Abelian groups. Hom (A, B) = the group of homomorphisms from A to B.

Theorem. *Every finitely generated Abelian group is of the form*

$$A \simeq \underbrace{\mathbf{Z} \oplus \mathbf{Z} \oplus \cdots \oplus \mathbf{Z}}_{n} \oplus \mathbf{Z}_{p_1^{n_1}} \oplus \mathbf{Z}_{p_2^{n_2}} \oplus \cdots \oplus \mathbf{Z}_{p_r^{n_r}}$$

The Category Hot. This is the category in which homotopy theory operates. Objects are topological spaces.

Definition of Topological Space. It consists of the following data: A set X, and a family of subsets $\mathcal{O}$, called open sets, subject to three axioms.

    1. $\mathcal{O}$ is closed under union.
    2. $\mathcal{O}$ is closed under finite intersection.
    3. $\varnothing$ (the empty set) and X are in $\mathcal{O}$.

    Given

$$X \xrightarrow{f} Y$$

a set function, f is said to be a continuous map if $f^{-1}(U)$ is open when U is open in Y.

    We could now speak of Hom (X, Y) as the set of continuous maps from X to Y. Two isomorphic objects in this category are called *homeomorphic*. This is a very difficult category. Very little is known about the homeomorphism problem in general.

    There is a more sophisticated category, the homotopy category.

Definition. If there exists a continuous family $f_t \colon X \to Y$, $t \in I = [0, 1]$ then f_0 is called homotopic to f_1. More precisely, consider the following diagram.

$$X \underset{x \to (x, 0)}{\overset{x \to (x, 1)}{\rightrightarrows}} X \times I \xrightarrow{F} Y$$

if F is continuous, $f = F \circ l$ $(l(x) = \langle x, 0 \rangle)$, and $g = F \circ u$ $(u(x) = \langle x, 1 \rangle)$, then we say f is homotopic to g.

Mild Theorem. (1) *Homotopy is an equivalence relation. This means $f \sim f$, if $f \sim g$, then $g \sim f$; and if $f \sim g$ and $g \sim h$, then $f \sim h$ (where $\sim$ means "is homotopic to").*

$$(2) \quad f \sim f', g \sim g' \Rightarrow f \circ g \sim f' \circ g'$$

    The upshot is that we can make a new category whose maps are homotopy classes of maps (i.e., equivalence classes under the equivalence relation of "homotopic to"). Thus, we define

    Hot (1) Objects are topological spaces.
        (2) Hom (X, Y) are homotopy classes of maps.

In the homotopy category there is also a structure theorem that says that everything is the direct product of simple things; however, this is a twisted direct product.

Examples. Reasonable spaces.

Finite-Dimensional Simplicial Complexes (Polyhedra)

They look like, for example, Fig. 1.

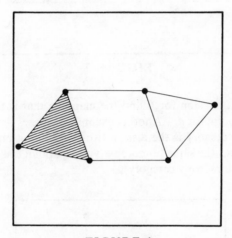

FIGURE 1

(1) Let $x_1, \ldots, x_n$ be points of R^m in general position. Then the *simplex* spanned by these, $\langle x_0, \ldots, x_n \rangle$, is the set

$$\{x = \sum \lambda_i x_i : \lambda_i > 0, \sum \lambda_i = 1\}.$$

The closure of this is a union of simplices, which are called the *faces* of the simplex.

The simplex τ spanned by any subset of the vertices of σ is called a face of σ.

A *polyhedron* $K \subset R^m$ is a finite union of simplices satisfying two conditions: (1) If σ is in K, then all the faces of σ are in K; (2) if σ and τ intersect, then they are the same. Consider the two complexes in Fig. 2. They are different in the topological category (i.e., nonhomeomorphic) but are isomorphic in the homotopy category; that is, there exist mappings

$$X \underset{g}{\overset{f}{\rightleftarrows}} Y \qquad f \circ g \sim 1 \qquad g \circ f \sim 1$$

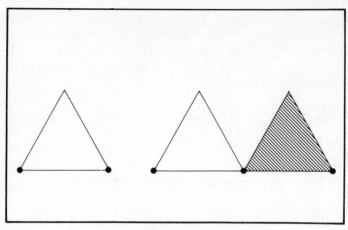

FIGURE 2

We may take the inclusion for f, and the mapping that is the identity on X
and maps σ^2 to a point for g.   Another example of spaces that are isomorphic
in the homotopy category is the disk in two-space and a point.   A tree like
the one in Fig. 3 has the same homotopy type as a point (i.e., it is isomorphic
to a point in the homotopy category).

FIGURE 3

Problem. Which of the complexes in Fig. 4 have the same homotopy type?
As one might expect, the circle is not homotopic to a point.

Why do we study the homotopy category? The homeomorphism
category seems bad enough, allowing all sorts of deformation. However,

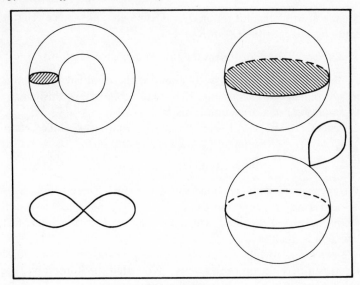

FIGURE 4

mathematicians discovered that the invariants used to distinguish homeo-morphism types mostly distinguished homotopy types also.

Building of Simplicial Complexes

Consider simplices of dim $\leqslant N$. Write $K' = K - \sigma^n$, where σ^n is an n-simplex. The idea is to take out σ^n, but remember how it was glued. That is, we are given σ_n and a map $f: \dot{\sigma}_n \to K'$ ($\dot{\sigma}_n$ denotes the boundary of σ_n) as in Fig. 5.

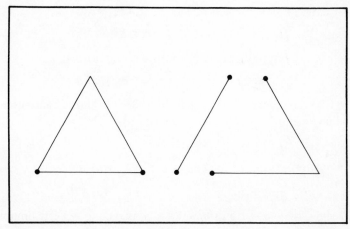

FIGURE 5

Define $\tilde{K} = K'$ disjoint union $\dot{\sigma}_n$. Define an equivalence relation in $\tilde{K}$ by identifying $x \in \dot{\sigma}_n$ with $f(x)$ in K'. Set

$$K = \tilde{K}/\sim \qquad \text{(where } \sim \text{ denotes the equivalence relation)}$$

In this case it is very easy to visualize the quotient space, since f is a homeomorphism onto a subset. However, we can make this construction without assuming f is a homeomorphism.

Given X, $e_n = \{|x| \leqslant 1 \text{ in } |R^n\}$ and a map $\alpha : \dot{e}_n \to X$. Here $\dot{e}_n = \{|x| \mid \sum y_1{}^2 = 1\}$. Then define $Y = X \bigcup_\alpha e_n$ as follows:

$$\tilde{Y} = X \text{ disjoint union } e_n$$

We say a point $x \in \dot{e}_n$ is equivalent with $\alpha(x)$. There results a quotient set $\tilde{Y}/\sim$ and a natural function $\pi : \tilde{Y} \to \tilde{Y}/\sim$. Define Y as the topological space with underlying set $\tilde{Y}/\sim$, where an open set $U \subset Y$ is one whose preimage $\pi^{-1}(U)$ is open in $\tilde{Y}$.

We are going to talk about the homotopy category whose objects are spaces that can be built up in this way. Note that the homotopy type of Y does not depend on α but only on its homotopy class.

Proposition 1. *If α is homotopic to α', then $X \bigcup_\alpha e^n$ has the same homotopy type as $X \bigcup_{\alpha'} e^n$.*

The proof presents purely technical difficulties. It would be a good exercise for the reader.

PROOF. Let $\alpha_t : \dot{e}_n \to X(t \in I = [0, 1])$ be a homotopy connecting α and α'. (Thus $(u, t) \to \alpha_t(u)$ is a continuous mapping of $\dot{e}_n \times I$ into X, $\alpha_0 = \alpha$, and $\alpha_1 = \alpha'$.) Let $r(x)$ denote the distance of $x \in R^n$ from the origin. Take $e_n = \{x : r(x) \leqslant 1\}$. Let γ denote the radial projection of $e_n - \{0\}$ on $\dot{e}_n$ (defined by $\gamma(x) = x/r$). Define $f : X \bigcup_\alpha e_n \to X \bigcup_{\alpha'} e_n$ by

$$f(x) = x \qquad\qquad\qquad\qquad x \in X$$

$$f(u) = \alpha_{2(1-r(u))}(\gamma(u)) \qquad u \in e_n, \; r(u) \geqslant \tfrac{1}{2}$$

$$f(u) = 2u \qquad\qquad\qquad\quad u \in e_n, \; r(u) \leqslant \tfrac{1}{2}$$

We leave it to the reader to verify that this indeed defines a continuous map. Define $g : X \bigcup_{\alpha'} e_n \to X \bigcup_\alpha e_n$ symmetrically. That is

$$g(x) = x \qquad\qquad\qquad\qquad x \in X$$

$$g(u) = \alpha_{2r(u)-1}(\gamma(u)) \qquad u \in e_n, \; r(u) \geqslant \tfrac{1}{2}$$

$$g(u) = 2u \qquad\qquad\qquad\quad u \in e_n, \; r(u) \leqslant \tfrac{1}{2}$$

One can show that $fg \sim 1$ and $gf \sim 1$ by constructing explicit homotopies. We construct a homotopy h connecting fg and 1, and leave the construction of the other homotopy to the reader. For $t \in I$, set

$$h_t(x) = x \qquad\qquad\qquad x \in X$$

$$h_t(u) = \alpha_{1 + 2(1 - t)(r(u - 1))}(\gamma(u)) \qquad u \in e_n, r(u) \geqslant \tfrac{1}{2}$$

$$= \alpha_{1 - (1 - t)(4r(u) - 1)}(\gamma(u)) \qquad u \in e_n, \tfrac{1}{4} \leqslant r(u) \leqslant \tfrac{1}{2}$$

$$= u + 3(1 - t)u \qquad\qquad u \in e_n, r(u) \leqslant \tfrac{1}{4}$$

We leave the verification that h is a continuous map of $(X \bigcup_{\alpha'} e_n) \times I$ into $X \bigcup_{\alpha'} e_n$ and that $h_0 = fg$, $h_1 = 1$ to the reader.

2   MORSE THEORY

Our program is to decompose an arbitrary differentiable manifold in the manner described above by means of Morse theory.

Definition of a C^∞ manifold. *A topological manifold is a topological space M that is Hausdorff and has a countable base for its topology, and that is locally Euclidean in the sense that every point has a neighborhood homeomorphic to Euclidean space.*

A C^∞ coordinate cover for M is a cover $\{U_\alpha\}$ of M, together with a homeomorphism $\phi_\alpha \colon U_\alpha \to V_\alpha$ of each U_α onto an open set V_α in R^n such that the maps

$$\phi_\beta \phi_\alpha^{-1} \colon \phi_\alpha(U_\alpha \cap U_\beta) \to V_\alpha \cap V_\beta$$

are of class C^∞ as maps of R^n into R^n.

Two coordinate covers $\{U_\alpha\}$ and $\{U_\alpha^1\}$ are equivalent if and only if $\{U_\alpha, U_\alpha^1\}$ is again a C^∞ coordinate cover.

A topological manifold M together with an equivalence class of C^∞ coordinate covers is a C^∞ structure on M.

If M is a C^∞ manifold and $f \colon M \to R$, then f is called C^∞ if $f \circ \phi_\alpha^{-1}$ is C^∞ for all U_α in some coordinate chart.

A level surface of f is a set $f^{-1}(a)$ for some $a \in R$.   In Morse theory, we consider $M_a = \{u \mid f(u) \leqslant a\}$.

Definition. A point $p \in M$ is *critical* for f if $(\partial f / \partial x_i) \mid_p = 0$ in some local coordinate system $(x_1, \ldots, x_n)$ at p.   The images under f of critical points are the *critical values* of f.

(A local coordinate system $(x_1, \ldots, x_n)$ at p is a set of functions $\xi_1 \circ \phi_\alpha, \ldots, \xi_n \circ \phi_\alpha$ where $\xi_1, \ldots, \xi_n$ are the standard coordinates for R^n and U_α and ϕ_α are as above.   These functions are defined, of course, in U_α.)

Example

Consider a torus in x, y, z space with its axis parallel to the y axis. This is illustrated in Fig. 6, where we imagine the y axis as being perpendicular to the page. Take f to be coordinate z. Then f has four critical points, at a, b, c, and d in the diagram. The critical values are all distinct.

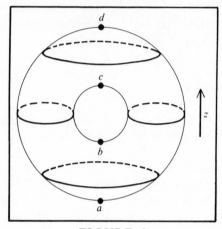

FIGURE 6

Theorem 1. *Let M be a compact C^∞ manifold. Let there be no critical values of f in the interval $[a, b]$. Then $M_a \simeq M_b$ (homotopy equivalence).*

PROOF. Construct a vector field X on M for which $Xf > 0$ except at critical points. For example, choose a Riemannian structure on M. The dual of df is a vector field $\nabla f = X$ with the required property. (This is the gradient of f. It is defined relative to the Riemannian structure.)

(We think of vector fields as differentiable operators on functions.)

Our definition of the gradient X of f is equivalent to

$$\langle X_p, Y_p \rangle = df_p(Y_p)$$

holding for all vector fields Y on M.

Define a vector field X' on $f^{-1}[a, b]$ by $X' = -X/Xf$. Then $X'f = -1$ on $f^{-1}[a, b]$. Extend X' to a C^∞ vector field on M. We denote the extended vector field by the same letter. Let g_t $(t \in R)$ denote the one-parameter group generated by X'. That is, assume g_t is a diffeomorphism of M into itself for each $t \in R$; that $g_0 = 1$; and that

$$\frac{\partial}{\partial t} g_t(x) = X'_{g_t(x)} \qquad x \in M, t \in R$$

(The existence of this one-parameter group follows from standard theorems in differential equations. From the conditions that we have imposed, it follows that $g_{t+s} = g_t g_s$, whence the terminology one-parameter *group*.) From

$$\frac{\partial}{\partial t} f(g_t(x)) = (X'f)(g_t(x)) = -1 \qquad \text{if} \qquad g_t(x) \in M^b - M^a$$

it follows that $f(g_t(x))$ becomes $\leq a$ for some $t \in b - a$. Then $f(g_t(x))$ stays $\leqslant a$ for larger t since X points into M_a along the boundary of M^a. Hence g_{b-a} maps M^b *into* M^a. Similarly, one shows that g_{a-b} maps M^a into M^b. Since $g_{a-b} = (g_{b-a})^{-1}$, this shows that g_{b-a} maps M^b diffeomorphically onto M^a. Then, of course, g_{b-a} is a homotopy equivalence.

Theorem 2. *Suppose that there is exactly one critical value in the interval $[a, b]$, say c, and exactly one critical point on the level c. Further assume that p is a nondegenerate critical point; that is, that the Hessian matrix $(\partial^2 f/\partial x_i \partial x_j)$ is nonsingular at p. Then $M_b \simeq M_a \bigcup e_k$, where k is the number of negative eigenvalues of the Hessian.*

Now consider the example of the torus in x, y, z space, as above. The critical points are nondegenerate and the number of negative eigenvalues at each of the critical points is 0 at a, 1 at b, 1 at c, 2 at d. Thus, by Theorem 2,

$$S^1 \times S^1 \simeq e_0 \bigcup_\alpha e_1 \bigcup_\alpha e_1 \bigcup_\beta e_2$$

This is the same as the decomposition that we described in the previous lecture.

Another example is complex projective space $\mathbf{CP}_n$. Let (Hz, z) be a Hermitian form in $n + 1$ variables. Set $f(z) = (Hz, z)/(z, z)$. Then f is a C^∞ function on $\mathbf{CP}^n$. The critical points are the eigendirections. If the eigenvalues are distinct, then all the critical points of f are nondegenerate and they have distinct eigenvalues, so Theorem 2 applies. Let $\lambda_1 < \lambda_2 < \cdots < \lambda_{n+1}$ be the eigenvalues. Then the number of negative eigenvalues in the *Hessian* are 0 for λ_1, 2 for λ_2, 4 for λ_3, ..., $2n$ for λ_n. Thus Theorem 2 shows $\mathbf{CP}^n \simeq pt \cdot \bigcup_\alpha e_2 \bigcup_\beta e_4 \bigcup \cdots \bigcup e_{2n}$. However, the theorem gives no information as to what the maps α, β, ... are.

PROOF OF THEOREM 2. We need the following

Morse Lemma. *If p is a nondegenerate critical point of f, then there exists a coordinate system $x_1, \ldots, x_n$ near p such that*

$$f = c - x_1{}^2 - x_2{}^2 - \cdots - x_k{}^2 + x_{k+1}^2 + \cdots + x_n{}^2$$

in the corresponding coordinate neighborhood. (*In any such coordinate system $x_1(p) = \cdots = x_n(p) = 0$.*)

The Morse lemma may be proved by the method used to diagonalize quadratic forms. (See Milnor, "Morse Theory" *Annals of Math. Studies* No. 51, p. 6, Princeton University Press, Princeton, N.J.)

To prove Theorem 2, we choose such a coordinate system near p.   We set

$$M^{c+\varepsilon} = \{q : f(q) \leqslant c + \varepsilon\}$$
$$M^{c-\varepsilon} = \{q : f(q) \leqslant c - \varepsilon\}$$
$$C = \{q : f(q) \leqslant c + \varepsilon \text{ and } x_1(p)^2 + \cdots + x_k(p)^2 \leq \delta\}$$

where δ is a small positive number, say $< \varepsilon^2$.   In Fig. 7 we have illustrated these sets in the special case that we described before. Figure 7a shows what

FIGURE 7a

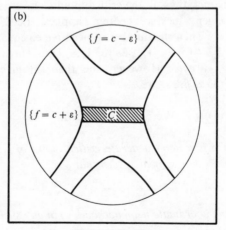

FIGURE 7b

these sets look like in the torus, and Fig. 7b shows their intersection with a suitable coordinate neighborhood (i.e., one given by the Morse lemma).

Set

$$B = \overline{M^{c+\varepsilon} - C}.$$

In our special case, the intersection of B with the coordinate neighborhood looks like Fig. 8. From the picture it appears that B can be contracted onto $M^{c-\varepsilon}$ by moving along the vector field ∇f. This is the case, provided we choose the Riemannian metric correctly, as we now show in complete generality.

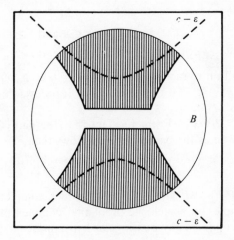

FIGURE 8

We choose the Riemannian metric so that inside the coordinate neighborhood it is $dx_1^2 + \cdots + dx_n^2$. We set $A = \overline{B - M^{c-\varepsilon}}$, and take $X = \nabla f$ and $X' = -X/Xf$. The latter is defined everywhere except at the critical points of f. In particular, it is defined in a neighborhood of A. For any $x \in A$, we let $t \to g(t, x)$ denote the maximal integral curve of X' through x, that is, the maximal curve satisfying $g(0, x) = x$ and

$$\frac{\partial g(t, x)}{\partial t} = X'_{g(t, x)}.$$

We claim that there exists $t_0(x)$ such that $g(t_0(x), x) \in M^{c-\varepsilon}$, and such that $g(t, x) \in A$ for $0 \leqslant t \leqslant t_0(x)$. This may be shown by eliminating the other possibilities. These are the following.

(a) $g(t, x)$ is defined only for $0 \leqslant t \leqslant t_1$ for suitable t_1, and $g(t, x) \in A$ for all such t. This is excluded by the fact that A is compact.

(b) $g(t, x)$ is defined for all positive t, and $g(t, x) \in A$. This is excluded by

$$\frac{\partial t(g(t, x))}{\partial t} = X'_{g(t, x)}f = -1 \qquad (*)$$

which implies $f(g(2\varepsilon, x)) = f(x) - 2\varepsilon \leqslant c - \varepsilon$, so that $g(2\varepsilon, x) \notin A$.

(c) $g(t, x)$ crosses the "upper" component of the boundary of A; that is, $(\dot{M}^{c+\varepsilon} - C) \cup (\dot{C} \cap A)$. This is excluded by the fact that X' points into A along this component of the boundary of A. We leave it to the reader to verify this.

Define $h_t \colon B \to M^{c-\varepsilon}$, for $t \geqslant 0$, as follows.

$$
\begin{aligned}
h_t(x) &= x   &&\text{if} && x \in M^{c-\varepsilon} \\
       &= g(t_0, x) &&\text{if} && x \in A \text{ and } t \geq t_0 \\
       &= g(t, x)   &&\text{if} && x \in A \text{ and } t \leq t_0
\end{aligned}
$$

Then h_t is a definition retraction of B into $M^{c-\varepsilon}$ (i.e., $h_0(x) = x$, $h_t(x) = x$ if $x \in M^{c-\varepsilon}$, and $h_t(x) \in M^{c-\varepsilon}$ if $t \geqslant 2\varepsilon$, by $(*)$). It follows that B has the same homotopy type as $M^{c-\varepsilon}$.

Now $M^{c+\varepsilon} = B \cup C$. From the fact that the pair $(C, C \cap B)$ has the same homotopy type as the pair $(e^k, \dot{e}^k)$ it follows that

$$M^{c+\varepsilon} \approx M^{c-\varepsilon} \bigcup_\alpha e_k \qquad \text{(homotopy equivalence)}$$

By Theorem 1, $M^{c+\varepsilon} \approx M^b$ and $M^{c-\varepsilon} \approx M^a$, which completes the proof.

As an example, we sketch the proof that complex projective n-space, $\mathbf{CP}_n$, can be built up from any nonsingular hypersurface X by attaching cells of dim $\geq n$. This result greatly simplifies the computation of the homology of such a hypersurface, for it implies that the inclusion induces isomorphisms $H_r(X) \approx H_r(\mathbf{CP}_n)$ and $H^r(\mathbf{CP}_n) \approx H^r(X)$ for $r < n - 1$. Then the homology $H_r(X)$ may be determined using Poincaré duality for all $r \neq n - 1$. In fact, we obtain $H_r(X) = \mathbf{Z}$ for all even $r \neq n - 1$ and $H_r(X) = 0$ for all odd $r \neq n - 1$.

We recall that $\mathbf{CP}_n$ is defined as the quotient of $\mathbf{C}^{n+1} - \{0\}$ by the equivalence relation $z \sim \lambda z$ for all $z \in \mathbf{C}^{n+1} - \{0\}, \lambda \in C - \{0\}$. We consider a polynomial p in variables $z_0, \ldots, z_n$ that is homogeneous of order k. The equation $p = 0$ defines a set X in $\mathbf{CP}_n$, since $p(z) = 0$ implies $p(\lambda z) = 0$. Such a set is called a hypersurface. It is called nonsingular if there is no common solution (in $\mathbf{CP}_n$) of the equations

$$p = \frac{\partial p}{\partial z_1} = \cdots = \frac{\partial p}{\partial z_n} = 0$$

Set

$$f(z) = \frac{|p(z)|^2}{\|z\|^k}$$

This is homogeneous of degree 0, so defines a function f on $\mathbf{CP}^n$. We claim that the Hessian of f at every critical point not on X has at least n negative eigenvalues. Assuming this, it is easy to see that $\mathbf{CP}^n$ can be built up from X by attaching cells of index $\geq n$. For it is a theorem that f can be approximated in the C^2 topology by a function g that has only nondegenerate critical points on $\mathbf{CP}^n - X$ and that equals f near X. (In the case of a compact domain, approximation in the C^2 topology means uniform approximation of the values and first two derivatives of the function.) If g is close enough to f in the C^2 topology, then the Hessian of g has at least n negative eigenvalues at every critical point not on X.

Thus, for $\varepsilon > 0$ small,

$$\mathbf{CP}^n \sim \mathbf{CP}^\varepsilon \bigcup_\alpha e^{(1)} \bigcup_\beta e^{(2)} \bigcup_\gamma \cdots e^{(r)}$$

where each $e^{(i)}$ is a cell of dimension $\geq n$ and $\mathbf{CP}^\varepsilon = \{z \in \mathbf{CP}^n : g(z) \leq \varepsilon\} = \{z \in \mathbf{CP}^n : f(z) \leq \varepsilon\}$. It is easily seen that $\mathbf{CP}^\varepsilon \sim X$. In fact, one can construct a deformation retraction of $\mathbf{CP}$ into X by following the gradients of f. Thus

$$\mathbf{CP}^n \sim X \bigcup_\alpha e^{(1)} \bigcup_\beta \cdots \bigcup e^{(r)}$$

The proof that the Hessian of f has at least n negative eigenvalues at every critical point not on X goes as follows. Let Λ^r denote the vector space of C^∞ complex-valued r forms on $\mathbf{CP}^n$. Then there is a canonical splitting

$$\Lambda^r = \Lambda^{r,0} \oplus \Lambda^{r-1,i} \oplus \cdots \oplus \Lambda^{0,r}$$

that can be described as follows: Let $w_1 = u_1 + iv_1, \ldots, w_n = u_n + iv_n$ be holomorphic local coordinates for $\mathbf{CP}^n$. Let $dw_j = du_j + i\,dv_j$ and $d\overline{w}_j = du_j - i\,dv_j$. Then $\Lambda^{r-k,k}$ consists of the r forms that may locally be expressed as sums of expressions of the form

$$u\,dw_{i(1)} \wedge \cdots \wedge dw_{i(r-k)} \wedge d\overline{w}_{j(1)} \wedge \cdots \wedge d\overline{w}_{j(k)}$$

where u is a C^∞ function.

It can be shown that for any $v \in \Lambda^{r-k,k}$, we have $dv \in \Lambda^{r-k+1,k} + \Lambda^{r-k,k+1}$. One denotes the $\Lambda^{r-k+1,k}$ component of dv by $d'v$ and the $\Lambda^{r-k,k+1}$ component of dv by $d''v$. If u is a C^∞ function, one has locally

$$d'u = \sum \frac{\partial u}{\partial z_i} \, dz_i$$

$$d''u = \sum \frac{\partial u}{\partial \overline{z}_i} \, d\overline{z}_i$$

where $\partial/\partial z_i = \frac{1}{2}(\partial/\partial x_i - i\,\partial/\partial y_i)$ and $\partial/\partial \overline{z}_i = \frac{1}{2}(\partial/\partial x_i + i\,\partial/\partial y_i)$. Also, from $d^2 = 0$, one obtains $(d') = (d'')^2 = 0$ and $d'd'' = -d''d'$.

Now one computes a formula for $d'd''f$ by computing $d'd'' \log f$ in two different ways.   Using the definition of f, we get

$$d'd'' \log f = d'd'' \log p + d'd'' \log \bar{p} - m \, d'd'' \log \|z\|^2$$

Since $\log p$ is holomorphic, $d'' \log p = 0$, so the first term vanishes.   Likewise $d' \log \bar{p} = 0$, so the second term is zero, by the anticommutativity of d' and d''.   Thus,

$$d'd'' \log f = -m \, d'd'' \log \|z\|^2$$

But,

$$d'd'' \log f = d'\left(\frac{d''f}{f}\right) = \frac{d'd''f}{f} - \frac{d'f \wedge d''f}{f^2}$$

so that

$$\frac{d'd''f}{f} = \frac{d'f \wedge d''f}{f^2} - m \, d'd'' \log \|z\|^2$$

At a critical point of f, this becomes

$$\frac{d'd''f}{f} = -m \, d'd'' \log \|z\|^2$$

From this formula, one can show that the Hessian of f has at least n negative eigenvalues at each critical point.   We leave this as a (difficult) exercise for the reader.

Next, we consider the application of Morse theory to the study of the space of loops on a manifold.   Let M be a compact manifold with a given smooth Reimannian structure.   Consider p and $q \in M$.   Let

$$\Omega M = \{\text{maps } u : I \to M\}$$

with the following properties.

(1) u is piecewise differentiable, $u(0) = p$, and $u(1) = q$.
(2) u is parametrized proportional to arc length.

We provide ΩM with a metric ρ defined as follows.

$$\rho(u, v) = \sup_{t \in I} \text{dist}(u(t), v(t)) + |Ju - Jv|$$

where Ju denotes the length of u.   Then the length function J is continuous. We set

$$\Omega^a M = \{u \in \Omega M : Ju \le a\}$$

Let $M^n = M \times M \times \cdots \times M$ (Cartesian product, n times).   Define $\phi^n : M^n \to R$ by

$$\phi^n(x_1, \ldots, x_n) = \sum_{i=1}^{n-1} d(x_i, x_{i+1})^2 + d(p, x_1)^2 + d(x_n, q)^2$$

where d denotes the distance function. This is a continuous function but, of course, it is not smooth. However, when the points are close there is a unique minimal geodesic joining them. This geodesic depends smoothly on the end points, so that in the region where the points are close, ϕ^n is smooth.

We will say a positive number a is *regular* if there is no geodesic from p to q of length a.

Set

$$b = \frac{a^2}{n+1} \qquad \text{and} \qquad M_b^n = \{x \in M^n : \phi^n(x) \le b\}$$

Theorem 3. *Suppose $a > 0$. Then, for all sufficiently large positive integers n, conditions (1)–(6) below hold.*

(1) *For any $x = \langle x_1, \ldots, x_n \rangle \in M_b^n$ there is a unique minimal geodesic joining x_i to x_{i+1} $(1 \le i \le n - 1)$, a unique minimal geodesic joining p to x_1, and a unique minimal geodesic joining x_n to q.*

Let $\beta(x)$ denote the curve (parametrized proportionally to arc length) obtained by first following the minimal geodesic from p to x_1, then (in succession) each of the minimal geodesics from x_i to x_{i+1}, and finally the minimal geodesic from x_n to q.

Define $\alpha : \Omega^a M \to M^n$ by the formula

$$\alpha(u) = \left\langle u\left(\frac{1}{n+1}\right), u\left(\frac{2}{n+1}\right), \ldots, u\left(\frac{n}{n+1}\right) \right\rangle$$

(2) *The mapping $\alpha : \Omega^a M \to M_b^n$ and $\beta : M_b^n \to \Omega^a M$ are inverse to one another in the category Hot, so we have a homotopy equivalence*

$$\Omega^a M \simeq M_b^n$$

(3) *ϕ^n is C^∞ on M_b^n.*

(4) *β maps the set of critical points of ϕ^n on M_b^n one-to-one onto the set of geodesics from p to q of length $\le a$.*

(5) *A critical point $x \in M_b^n$ is nondegenerate if and only if p and q are not conjugate on the geodesic $\beta(x)$.*

(6) *For a nondegenerate critical point $x \in M_b^n$, the index is precisely the number (counted with multiplicity) of conjugate points of p on the geodesic $\beta(x)$. (The notion of a conjugate point and its multiplicity will be defined below.)*

Example

Let M^n be the n sphere S^n with its usual Riemannian metric. (This is the restriction of the usual Riemannian metric on Euclidean $n + 1$ space, E^{n+1}, if S^n is considered as the unit sphere in E^{n+1}.) Let p be the north pole and q any point except the south pole. Then q is not conjugate to p. Arcs of great circles are geodesics, and a sufficiently small segment of any geodesic is an arc of a great circle, but, of course, a geodesic may wind several times around the great circle on which it lies. For each nonnegative integer k there is exactly one geodesic on S^n connecting p and q and passing through the poles k times. Each pole is a conjugate point of the north pole each time the geodesic passes through it, and its multiplicity (as a conjugate point) is $n - 1$.

A positive number a is regular if and only if $a \neq d(p, q) + \pi k$ for any nonnegative number k, since the geodesic connecting p and q that passes through the poles k times has length $d(p, q) + \pi k$. Thus if we take

$$d(p, q) + \pi k < a < d(p, q) + \pi(k + 1)$$

we obtain the following from Theorem 3.

   (a) $\Omega^a M \simeq M_b{}^n$ (n large)
   (b) There is one critical point of ϕ^n on $M_b{}^n$ for each geodesic from p to q of length $\leq a$, and these critical points are nondegenerate.
   (c) The critical point of ϕ^n corresponding to the geodesic of length $d(p, q) + \pi j$ (i.e., the geodesic passing through the poles j times) is of index $(n - 1)$.

Thus $M_b{}^n$ is a manifold with boundary, provided with a function ϕ^n with only nondegenerate critical points, of index 0, $(n - 1)$, $2(n - 1), \ldots$, $k(n - 1)$. The function ϕ^n takes its absolute maximum b on the boundary and is nondegenerate there. It follows from the Morse theory that

$$\Omega^a M \simeq M_b{}^n \simeq e_0 \underset{\alpha}{\bigcup} e_{n-1} \underset{\beta}{\bigcup} e_{2(n-1)} \underset{\gamma}{\bigcup} \cdots \bigcup e_{k(n-1)}$$

Since we may apply this with a arbitrarily large, we get

$$\Omega S^n \simeq S^{n-1} \underset{\beta}{\bigcup} e_{2(n-1)} \underset{\gamma}{\bigcup} \cdots \bigcup e_{k(n-1)} \bigcup \cdots$$

Now we begin the proof of Theorem 3. Since M is compact, there exists a $\delta > 0$ such that there is a unique minimal geodesic γ joining any two points x, y such that $d(x, y) > \delta$ and such that γ depends smoothly on x and y. In particular, $d(x, y)^2$ depends smoothly on x and y for $d(x, y) < \delta$. Choose n so that $a^2/(n + 1) < \delta$. Then

$$d(p, x_1), d(x_i, x_{i+1}), d(x_n, q) < \delta$$

so that conditions (1) and (3) hold.

In stating (2), we assumed that the image of α lies in $M_b{}^n$ and that the image of β lies in $\Omega^a M$. Let us verify this.

Let $u \in \Omega^a M$, so that $\alpha(u) = \langle x_1, \ldots, x_n \rangle$ where $x_i = u(i/(n + 1))$. Then each of the numbers

$$d(p, x_1), d(x_i, x_{i+1}), d(x_n, q)$$

is $\le a/(n + 1)$, since u is parametrized proportionally to arc length. Hence

$$\phi''(x) \le (n + 1) \left(\frac{a}{n + 1}\right)^2 = b$$

On the other hand, suppose $x \in M_b{}^n$. The Schwartz inequality, applied to the $(n + 1)$-tuples $\langle 1, \dots, 1 \rangle$ and $\langle d(p, x_1), d(x_1, x_2), \dots, d(x_n, q) \rangle$, yields

$$\begin{aligned} J(\beta(x)) &= d(p, x_1) + d(x_1, x_2) + \cdots + d(x_n, q) \\ &\le ((n + 1)(d(p, x_1)^2 + d(x_1, x^2 + \cdots + d(x_n, q)^2))^{1/2} \\ &= (n + 1)^{1/2}\alpha(x)^{1/2} \le a \end{aligned}$$

To show that α and β are inverse to one another in the category Hot, we will construct homotopies g_t connecting $\alpha\beta$ with 1 and h_t connecting $\beta\alpha$ with 1. First, we define g_t. Let $x \in M_b{}^n$ and set $u = \beta(x)$. We may choose numbers $s_1, s_2, \dots, s_n$ in a canonical way such that $u(s_i) = x_i$. Precisely, we let $s_1 = d(p, x_1)/J(u)$ and $s_i - s_{i-1} = d(x_{i-1}, x_i)/J(u)$. The fact that u is parametrized proportionally to arc length then guarantees that $u(s_i) = x_i$. We define $g_t(x) = \langle y_{1t}, \dots, y_{nt} \rangle$, where

$$y_{it} = u\left(ts_i + \frac{(1 - t)i}{n + 1}\right)$$

Clearly $g_0 = \alpha\beta$ and $g_1 = 1$. Continuity is easily verified. To see that $g_t(x) \in M_b{}^n$, we proceed as follows. Since u is parametrized by arc length

$$d(y_{it}, y_{i+1,t}) \le (Ju)\left(t(s_{i+1} - s_i) + \frac{1 - t}{n + 1}\right)$$

for $0 \le i \le n$, where we set $y_{0,t} = p$, $y_{n+1} = q$, $s_0 = 0$, and $s_{n+1} = 1$. The Schwartz inequality (in the form $(ta + (1 - t)b)^2 \le ta^2 + (1 - t)b^2)$ yields

$$\begin{aligned} \phi_n(g_t(x)) &= \sum_{i=0}^{n} d(y_{it}, y_{i+1,t})^2 \\ &\le t\sum_{i=0}^{n} (Ju)^2(s_{i+1} - s_i)^2 + (1 - t)\frac{(Ju)^2}{n + 1} \\ &= t\phi_n(x) + (1 - t)\frac{(Ju)^2}{n + 1} \end{aligned}$$

Since $\phi_n(x) \le b$ and $(Ju)^2/(n + 1) \le a^2/(n + 1) \le b$, this shows $\phi_n(g_t(x)) \le b$, as required.

Now, we define h_t. Let $u \in \Omega M$. On the interval $[i/(n + 1), (i + t)/(n + 1)]$ (where $0 \le i \le n$), $h_t(u)$ is the minimal geodesic connecting $u(i/(n + 1))$ and $u((i + t)/(n + 1))$, and parametrized by arc length. On the interval $[(i + t)/(n + 1), (i + 1)/(n + 1)]$, $h_t(u)$ is u. The required properties are easily checked.

Next, we prove (4).   For each $r > 0$ and each $x \in M$, we let $S_r(x)$ denote the set of points of distance r from x and $B_r(x)$ the set of points of distance $\leq r$ from x.   We need the following elementary fact from Riemannian geometry.   For $\delta > 0$ sufficiently small and all $x \in M$, $S_r(x)$ is a sphere differentiably embedded in M, and each geodesic emanating from x is perpendicular to $S_r(x)$ at the first point of intersection.   We suppose that the δ that we just chose satisfies this property.

Suppose $x = \langle x_1, \ldots, x_n \rangle \in M_b^n$.   First, we show that if $\beta(x)$ is not a geodesic, then x is not a critical point of ϕ^n; that is, β maps the set of critical points of ϕ_n on M_b^n into the set of geodesics.   Since $\beta(x)$ is parametrized proportionally to arc length and each segment of $\beta(x)$ is a geodesic, the only way for $\beta(x)$ to fail to be a geodesic is for the incoming tangent at some x_i to be different from the outgoing tangent, as in Fig. 9.   Assume that this is

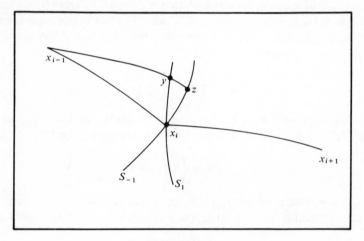

FIGURE 9

the case.   In Fig. 9, we let S_{-1} denote the sphere of radius $d(x_{i-1}, x_i)$ centered at x_{i-1} and S_1 the sphere of radius $d(x_i, x_{i+1})$ centered at x_{i+1}.   Then S_1 and S_{-1} have different tangent planes at x_i, since the tangent plane to S_1 (resp. S_{-1}) is orthogonal to the geodesic connecting x_i and x_{i+1} (resp. x_{i-1} and x_i).   Then we can find a curve $y(t)$ in S_1 such that $y(0) = x_i$ and $\partial y(t) \,|\, \partial t \notin S_{-1}$.   Set

$$x'(t) = \langle x_1, \ldots, x_{i-1}, y(t), x_{i+1}, \ldots, x_n \rangle$$

We claim that $\partial \phi_n(x'(t)) \,|\, \partial t < 0$, which shows that $x = x'(0)$ is not a critical point.   In fact, all terms in the sum defining $\phi_n(x'(t))$ are constant except the term $d(x_{i-1}, y(t))^2$.   Furthermore, if we let $z(t)$ denote the first intersection of the geodesic $\overline{x_{i-1}y}(t)$ with S_{-1}, then

$$d(x_{i-1}, y(t)) = d(x_{i-1}, z(t)) - d(z(t), y(t))$$

$$= d(x_{i-1}, x_i) \pm d(z(t), y(t))$$

Since $\partial y(t)/\partial t \notin S_{-1}$,

$$\frac{\partial (d(z(t), y(t)))}{\partial t} \neq 0.$$

From these two equations, $\partial \phi_n(x'(t))/\partial t \neq 0$ follows easily. This completes the proof that β maps the set of critical points of ϕ_n on $M_b{}^n$ into the set of geodesics.

To show that β maps the set of critical points of ϕ_n on $M_b{}^n$ onto the set of geodesics in $\Omega^a M$, it is enough to show that $\beta \alpha(\gamma) = \gamma$ and that $\alpha(\gamma)$ is a critical point for any geodesic of length $\leq a$. The first of these assertions is obvious. We prove the second by contradiction. If $\alpha(\gamma)$ is not a critical point, then there is a curve $t \to y_t \colon I \to M_b{}^n$ such that $y_0 = \alpha(\gamma)$ and $d\phi_n(y_t)/dt \neq 0$. But this is easily seen to imply $dJ(\beta(y_t))/dt \neq 0$. But this contradicts the assumption that $\gamma = \beta \alpha(\gamma) = \beta(y_0)$ is a geodesic.

Finally, to show that β is one-to-one on the set of critical points of ϕ^n on $M_b{}^n$, it is enough to show that $\alpha \beta(x) = x$ for any such x. In other words, we must show that if x is a critical point of ϕ^n on $M_b{}^n$, then $d(p, x_1) = d(x_1, x_2) = \cdots = d(x_n, q)$. Suppose otherwise. For example, suppose $d(x_{i-1}, x_i) > d(x_i, x_{i+1})$. Let $t \to x_i(t)$ denote the minimal geodesic from x_i to x_{i-1} (so that $x_i(0) = x_i$ and $x_i(1) = x_{i-1}$). Let $x(t) = x_1, \ldots, x_i(t), \ldots x_n$. It is easily seen that

$$\frac{d}{dt} \varphi^n(x(t))|_{t=0} \neq 0$$

which contradicts the hypothesis that $x = x(0)$ is a critical point of ϕ^n. The other cases are treated similarly.

This completes the proof of condition (4).

In order to say what conditions (5) and (6) mean, we must define the notion of conjugate point. We let the exponential mapping $\exp \colon TM_p \to M$ be defined as follows. For any $X \in TM_p$, let $\exp X = \gamma(1)$, where γ is the unique geodesic with $\gamma(0) = p$ and $\gamma'(0) = X$. (Here $\gamma'(0)$ denotes the velocity vector of γ at $t = 0$.) From the hypothesis that M is provided with a smooth Riemannian metric, it follows that γ is a smooth mapping. Let γ be a geodesic connecting p and q. Assume γ is parametrized so that $\gamma(0) = p$ and $\gamma(1) = q$. We say p and q are *conjugate along* γ if $\gamma'(0)$ is a critical point of the mapping $\exp$, that is, the rank of $d(\exp)$ at $\gamma'(0)$ is $< n$. We say p and q have *multiplicity k along* γ if the rank of $\exp$ at $\gamma'(0)$ is $n - k$. If p and q are conjugate along any geodesic, then q is a critical value of the mapping $\exp$, so by Sard's theorem, there exists $q \in M$ such that p and q are not conjugate. It is easily seen that the relation of being conjugate is symmetric in the following sense. If p and q are conjugate along γ, then q and p are conjugate along γ_1 where $\gamma_1(t) = \gamma(1 - t)$.

For example, consider the n sphere S^n. The conjugate points to the north pole are itself and the south pole, and these are conjugate along any geodesic (except the trivial geodesic connecting the north pole to itself) and have multiplicity $n - 1$. (In general, however, a point is not conjugate to itself.)

We will not prove (5) and (6). For details, see, for example, R. Bott, The Stable Homotopy of the Classical Groups (*Ann. of Math.* **70**, 1959), pp. 313–337.

3 HOMOTOPY GROUPS

Let X be a topological space with base point $*$. Let $*$ also denote a fixed "base" point in the k sphere S_k.

Definition. $\pi_k(X, *) = $ homotopy classes of maps of S_k into X that take $*$ in S^k to $*$ in X.

There is a group structure on $\pi_k(X, *)$ induced by a mapping $\pi: S^k \to S^k \vee S^k$. Here $S^k \vee S^k$ is formed by taking the disjoint union of S^k and S^k and identifying the two base points. A rough picture of the mapping π is given in Fig. 10, which is supposed to indicate how the outside sphere is stretched over the wedge of the two inner spheres. In words, this prescription of π could be given as follows. Consider S^k as the set of points

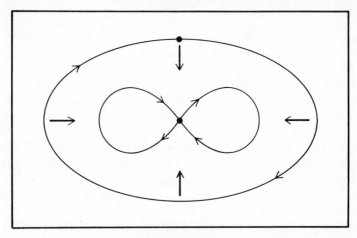

FIGURE 10

in E^{k+1} such that $x_1{}^2 + \cdots + x_{k+1}{}^2 = 1$. Map the western hemisphere $W = \{x_1 \leq 0\}$ into the first copy of S^k in $S^k \vee S^k$ by a mapping that takes $S^{k-1} = \{x_1 = 0\}$ into the base point and that takes $W - S^{k-1}$ homeomorphically in an orientation-preserving way onto $S^k - *$. Map the eastern hemisphere $E = \{x_1 \geq 0\}$ into the second copy similarly.

Now the group law is defined as follows. Let $[\alpha]$, $[\beta] \in \pi_k(X)$ be homotopy classes with representatives α, $\beta \colon (S^k, *) \to (X, *)$. (This notation means that α and β are mappings $S^k \to X$ that take $*$ to $*$.) Then $\alpha \vee \beta$ maps $S^k \vee S^k$ into X so $(\alpha \vee \beta) \circ \pi$ maps S^k into X. Also $(\alpha \vee \beta) \circ \pi(*) = *$. Thus $(\alpha \vee \beta) \circ \pi$ defines a member of $\pi_k(X)$, which we define to be $[\alpha][\beta]$. In symbols

$$[\alpha][\beta] = [(\alpha \vee \beta) \circ \pi]$$

To show that this is a real definition, one must show that this is independent of the choice of representative. Also, one must verify that this defines a group law. One would like to be able to give explicit formulas for the homotopies, etc., that are involved. Using the definition we have just given, this would be difficult. Therefore, we introduce another definition, which is technically easier to use, though perhaps not so geometrically appealing.

Let I^n be the cube $0 \leq x_i \leq 1$, in Euclidean n-space E^n. Consider maps $\mu \colon (I^n, \dot{I}^n) \to (X, *)$. (This means μ is a map of I^n into X, which maps the boundary $\dot{I}^n$ of I^n into $*$.) We let $\pi_k(X, *)$ denote homotopy classes of such maps. Since $I^n/\dot{I}^n$ (i.e., I^n with $\dot{I}^n$ identified to a point) is S^n, this may be identified with homotopy classes of maps $(S^n, *) \to (X, *)$.

We define the group multiplication as in Fig. 11. The precise prescription is as follows. Let $[\alpha]$ and $[\beta]$ be elements of $\pi_k(X)$ with representatives

$$\alpha, \beta \colon (I^n, \dot{I}^n) \to (X, *)$$

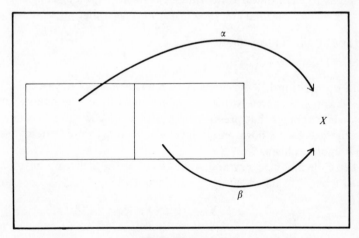

FIGURE 11

Now let $\gamma: (I^n, \dot{I}^n) \to (X, *)$ be given by

$$\gamma(x_1, x_2, \ldots, x_n) = \alpha(2x_1, x_2, \ldots, x_n) \qquad 0 \leq x_1 \leq \tfrac{1}{2}$$

$$= \beta(2x_1 - 1, x_2, \ldots, x_n) \qquad \tfrac{1}{2} \leq x_1 \leq 1$$

We define $[\alpha][\beta]$ as the homotopy class of γ.

Now it is a straightforward matter to check that $[\alpha][\beta]$ is independent of the choice of representatives α and β and that $\pi_k(X, *)$ is a group with this composition law.

Furthermore, $\pi_k(X, *)$ is an Abelian group if $k \geq 2$, that is, $[\alpha][\beta] = [\beta][\alpha]$.

If $f: (X, *) \to (Y, *)$ is a continuous mapping, then there is induced a mapping $f*: \pi_k(X) \to \pi_k(Y)$, defined by $f*([\alpha]) = [f \circ \alpha]$. This mapping is a group homomorphism. Further, $(g \circ f)* = g* \circ f*$ and $1* = 1$. In terms of categories, this means:

Proposition 1. π_k is a functor from the category of pointed spaces to the category of groups.

Definition. A *covariant functor* from category A to category B is a function that assigns to each object a in A an object $F(a)$ in B and assigns to every "map" $f: a \to a'$, a "map" $F(f): F(a) \to F(a')$ such that

    (1) $F(f \circ g) = F(f) \circ F(g)$
    (2) $F(1_a) = 1_{F(a)}$

A *contravariant functor* from a category A to a catogery B is a function that assigns to each object a in A an object $F(a)$ in B and assigns to every "map" $f: a \to a'$, a "map" $F(f): F(a') \to F(a)$ such that

    (1) $F(f \circ g) = F(g) \circ F(f)$
    (2) $F(1_a) = 1_{F(a)}$

In Proposition 1, "the category of pointed spaces" means the category whose objects are spaces with base points and whose "mappings" are the continuous mappings that preserve base points. "The category of groups" means the category whose objects are groups and whose "mappings" are group homomorphisms.

Let C be any category and A an object of C. Then we have functors F and G from A to the category of sets, defined by

$$F(X) = \operatorname{Hom}(X, A)$$

$$G(X) = \operatorname{Hom}(A, X)$$

The former is contravariant and the latter is covariant. A functor is said to be *representable* if it is of one of these two forms. For example, π_k is representable by definition.

Let $\Omega * X$ denote the set of mappings $(I, \dot{I}) \to (X, *)$. We consider the constant map as the base point of this space.

Proposition 2.

$$\pi_k(X) \overset{\lambda}{\simeq} \pi_{k-1}(\Omega * X),$$

where λ is defined by

$$\lambda(\mu)(x_1, \ldots, x_{k-1})(t) = \mu(t, x_1, \ldots, x_{k-1})$$

Thus for any mapping $\mu: (I^k, \dot{I}^{k-1}) \to X$, the map $\lambda\mu$ "reinterprets" μ as a map of $(I^{k-1}, \dot{I}^{k-1})$ into $\Omega * X$.

Proposition 3. *Assume p and q are in the same path component of X; that is, there exists a curve $v: I \to X$ joining p and q. Such a curve induces an isomorphism $v*: \pi_k(X, p) \to \pi_k(X, q)$. This isomorphism depends only on the homotopy class of the path v joining p and q.*

In particular, $\pi_1(X, *) = 0$ implies there is a canonical isomorphism $\pi_k(X, p) \simeq \pi_k(X, q)$.

We define $v*$ as follows. Let I^k denote the standard cube (given by $0 \le x_i \le 1$). Let C denote the cube $\frac{1}{4} \le x_i \le \frac{3}{4}$. Let $e: C \to I^k$ be the homeomorphism given by $e(x_1, \ldots, x_k) = 2x_1 - 1, \ldots, 2x_k - 1$. Let $[\alpha] \in \pi_k(X)$. Define $v*[\alpha] = [\beta]$, where $\beta: (I^k, \dot{I}^k) \to (X, *)$ is given by the prescription

(1) $\beta \,|\, C = \alpha \circ e$
(2) If $y \in \dot{I}^k$, then

$$\beta(ty + (1 - t)e^{-1}(y)) = v(t)$$

Since each point in I^k is in C or on a unique line segment joining a point $y \in \dot{I}^k$ with $e^{-1}y$, this defines $v*[\alpha]$.

As usual, one must check that this is independent of the choice of representative, and that the other assertions in the proposition hold, but we omit these details.

Remark. If $p = q$ and we are acting on π_1, then $v*: \pi_1(X, *) \to \pi_1(X, *)$ is given by $\alpha \to [v]\alpha[v]^{-1}$.

Definition. $\pi_0(X) =$ the set of arc components.
$\pi_0(X)$ is a pointed set (i.e., a set with a singled-out point).

Theorem 1. $\pi_k(S^n) = 0$, for $k < n$.

If the map of S^k into S^n representing a given homotopy class is fairly nice, say a polynomial mapping, then the image does not fill the sphere. Take a point p not in the image and contract the complement of p to a point. This defines a homotopy connecting the given map and a constant map. Unfortunately, there is a continuous map of S^k *onto* S^n, so we must first approximate the map by a nice map to make the argument work.

Consider $S^k \subseteq \mathbf{R}^{k+1}$, $S^n \subseteq \mathbf{R}^{n+1}$. Then $f: S^k \to S^n$ is given by continuous functions $x_1, \ldots, x_{n+1}$ defined on S^k. Approximate these functions to within ε by $p_1, \ldots, p_{n+1}$, which are polynomials in the y's (coordinates of $\mathbf{R}^{k+1}$). Dividing by norm $p = \sum |p_i|^2$, we get a map $P: S^k \to S^n$ given by rational functions. Furthermore, $P(y)$ is close to $f(y)$ for all $y \in S^n$, so there is a unique geodesic joining $P(y)$ to $f(y)$. This geodesic may be used to deform P into f, so we have that P is homotopic to f.

In particular, f is homotopic to a C^∞ map. The fact that $f[S^k] \neq S^n$ (always assuming $k < n$) is a consequence of the corollary of the following result. Thus Theorem 1 follows.

Theorem. Let $f: M \to N$ be a C^∞ map of C^∞ manifolds. Let Σ denote the set of $x \in M$ for which

$$\text{rank } df_x < \dim N$$

Then $f[\Sigma]$ has measure 0 in N.

This is usually referred to as *Sard's theorem*. For a proof, see Sternberg, *Lectures on Differential Geometry*, Prentice-Hall, Englewood Cliffs, N.J., 1964. In the case $\dim M \leq \dim N$, Sard's theorem is a quite easy consequence of the mean value theorem. However, in the general situation, the proof is difficult.

Corollary. If $\dim M < \dim N$, then $f[M]$ has measure 0 in N.

PROOF. In this case, $\Sigma = M$.

Proposition 4. Let $Y = X \cup_k e_n$. The inclusion $i: X \to Y$ induces an isomorphism $\pi_k(X) \to \pi_k(Y)$ for $k < n - 1$, and $\pi_{n-1}(X) \to \pi_{n-1}(Y)$ is onto.

The proof uses the same ideas as the proof of Theorem 1. For example, to show that $\pi_k(X) \to \pi_k(Y)$ is onto for $k < n$, we take a map of S^k into Y and approximate it by a map that is differentiable on the inverse image of e_n. Then by Sard's theorem the image of the map does not include all of e_n. Thus we may remove some point from e_n and push the remainder into X. This provides us with a homotopy of the given map to a map whose image lies in X. Thus $\pi_k(X) \to \pi_k(Y)$ is onto.

To show $\pi_k(X) \to \pi_k(Y)$ is an isomorphism, we must replace a homotopy connecting two mappings of S^k into X by a homotopy that stays in X. Thus we must replace a mapping $(S^k \times I, S^k \times \dot{I}) \to (Y, X)$ by a mapping of $S^k \times I$ into X that coincides with the original mapping on $S^k \times \dot{I}$. This can be done by the same argument, provided $k < n - 1$, because now we are mapping a $(k + 1)$-dimensional object into our target space.

Corollary (Freudenthal Suspension Theorem). $\pi_k(S^n) \simeq \pi_{k-1} (S^{n-1})$, *provided $k < 2(n - 1)$.*

(Here $\simeq$ means isomorphism of groups.)

PROOF. By Proposition 2, $\pi_k(S^n) \simeq \pi_{k-1}(\Omega_* S^n)$. By the Morse theory,

$$\Omega S^n \sim S^{n-1} \bigcup_{\alpha} e_{2(n-1)} \bigcup_{\beta} e_{3(n-1)} \cdots$$

It is not difficult to show that $\pi_l(\Omega_* S^{n-1}) \simeq \pi_l(\Omega S^{n-1})$, where $\Omega_* S^{n-1}$ denotes the loop space of Proposition 2 and ΩS^{n-1} denotes the loop space that we used in Morse theory. Thus Proposition 4 permits us to conclude the corollary.

Now let us compute $\pi_k(S^k)$. From the Freudenthal suspension theorem,

$$\pi_k(S^k) \simeq \pi_{k-1}(S^{k-1}) \qquad k \geqslant 3$$

Thus, it suffices to compute $\pi_2(S^2)$ and $\pi_1(S^1)$.

There are no conjugate points on S^1, so the Morse theory implies

$$\Omega S^1 \sim \text{pt.} \bigcup \text{pt.} \bigcup \cdots$$

Thus ΩS^1 has the homotopy type of a countable number of points. These points are in one-to-one correspondence with the geodesics from p to q.

In our Morse theoretical constructions, the only requirement on the points p and q was that they not be conjugate. Thus, in this case we could take $p = q$. Thus the geodesics are: the constant geodesic; the geodesics that wrap around the circle n times ($n > 0$) in the positive direction; and the geodesics that wrap around the circle n times ($n > 0$) in the negative direction. This sets up a one-to-one correspondence between the integers and $\pi_1(S^1)$. It is easy to check that this correspondence preserves products.

Now we want to compare $\pi_2(S^2)$ with $\pi_1(S^2)$. Note that

$$S^2 = S^1 \bigcup_{\alpha} e^2 \bigcup \cdots$$

We could show $\alpha \sim *$, which implies $\pi_2(S^2) \simeq \pi_1(S^1) = \mathbf{Z}$. However, we leave this as an exercise to the reader, and show $\pi_2(S^2) = \mathbf{Z}$ in another way.

The method that we use is based on the *Hopf fibering*, $\pi: S^3 \to S^2$. This map π is defined as follows. We have

$$S^3 = \{\langle z_1, z_2 \rangle \in \mathbf{C}^2 : |z_1|^2 + |z_2|^2 = 1\}$$

Also $S_2 = \mathbf{CP}_1$. That is, S_2 is the set of equivalence classes of elements in $\mathbf{C}^2 - \{0\}$, where $\langle z_1, z_2 \rangle \sim \langle \lambda z_1, \lambda z_2 \rangle$. Write the equivalence class of $\langle z_1, z_2 \rangle$ as $\{z_1, z_2\}$. Then we define π by $\pi(\langle z_1, z_2 \rangle) = \{z_1, z_2\}$. Clearly $\pi^{-1}(\text{pt.})$ is S^1. In fact, each point in S^2 has a neighborhood U such that there is a commutative diagram

$$
\begin{array}{ccc}
\pi^{-1}U & \xrightarrow{\ h\ } & U \times S^1 \\
\downarrow{\scriptstyle \pi} & & \downarrow{\scriptstyle \text{proj.}} \\
U & \xrightarrow{\ 1\ } & U'
\end{array}
$$

where h is a homeomorphism. Thus S^3 is *locally trivial* over S^2.

In n dimension, one can still construct a mapping $\pi: S^{2n-1} \to \mathbf{CP}_{n-1}$, taking $\langle z_1, \ldots, z_n \rangle \to \{z_1, \ldots, z_n\}$, where we consider S^{2n-1} as the unit sphere in $\mathbf{C}^n$ and $\mathbf{CP}_{n-1}$ as the quotient space $\mathbf{C}^n - \{0\}/\mathbf{C}^*$. Again, this mapping is locally trivial. However, it is not very useful in computing the homotopy groups of spheres, since $\mathbf{CP}_{n-1}$ is not a sphere, except when $n = 2$.

Since the Hopf mapping of S^3 onto S^2 is locally trivial and has fiber S^1, we should expect some relation between the homotopy of S^2, S^1, and S^3.

First, let us consider the example of a globally trivial mapping, that is, a product.

Proposition. $\pi_k(X \times Y) = \pi_k(X) \times \pi_k(Y)$.

PROOF. For any space Z, Hom $(Z, X \times Y) = $ Hom $(Z, X) \times $ Hom (Z, Y), where Hom denotes the set of continuous mappings. From this, the proposition is almost immediate.

From the fact that $\pi: S^3 \to S^2$ is locally trivial it follows that given a curve $u: I \to S^2$ and a point $p \in S^3$ above u (that is, in $\pi^{-1}(u(0))$), then there is a curve $v: I \to S^3$ covering u, that is, such that $\pi \circ v = u$, and starting at p, that is, such that $v(0) = p$.

Definition. Consider a map $\pi: E \to B$ and a space Z. Then π has the covering homotopy property, with respect to Z, if given a commutative diagram (as indicated by the solid arrows)

$$
\begin{array}{ccc}
Z \times \{0\} & \xrightarrow{\ f\ } & E \\
\downarrow & \nearrow{\scriptstyle F} & \downarrow \\
Z \times I & \xrightarrow{\ G\ } & B
\end{array}
$$

we can find a mapping F (as indicated by the broken arrow) that makes the complete diagram commutative.

This means: we suppose we are given mappings $f: Z = Z \times \{0\} \to E$ and $G: Z \times I \to B$ such that $\pi \circ f = G \,|\, Z \times \{0\}$ (i.e., such that G is a homotopy of $\pi \circ f$). Then we can find a map $F: Z \times I \to E$ such that $F \,|\, Z \times \{0\} = f$ and $\pi \circ F = G$. The first of these last two conditions is expressed by saying that F is a homotopy of f. The second is expressed by saying F covers G.

If this property holds for polyhedral Z, then we say π has the polyhedral covering homotopy property and call π a "fibering in the sense of Serre" and it is easily shown that if $\pi: E \to B$ is locally trivial, then π is a fibering in this sense.

Given such a fibering, let $F = \pi^{-1}(*)$ and let $*$ be a "base point" in F. Then we have an exact sequence of homotopy groups,

$$\to \pi_k(F, *) \overset{i_*}{\to} \pi_k(E, *) \overset{\partial}{\to} \pi_{k-1}(F, *) \overset{\pi_*}{\to} \pi_{k-1}(E) \to$$

(Here $i: F \to E$ denotes the inclusion.)   More precisely, we can define a homomorphism $\partial: \pi_k(B, *) \to \pi_{k-1}(F, *)$ that makes the resulting sequence exact.

A sequence

$$\cdots \to A \overset{u}{\to} B \overset{v}{\to} C \to \cdots$$

of group homomorphisms is said to be *exact at B* if kernel $v =$ image u, that is, $v(b) = 0$ if and only if there exists $a \in A$ such that $b = u(a)$.   It is *exact* if it is exact at every place where this definition makes sense.

The mapping $\partial: \pi_1(B, *) \to \pi_0(F, \tilde{*})$ is defined as follows.   Take a loop u in the base B, that is, a homotopy of $*$ that ends at $*$.   By the covering homotopy property, one can find a homotopy $\tilde{u}$ of $\tilde{*}$ in E covering this homotopy. Look at the end point of this homotopy.   Define $\partial([u])$ to be the arc component of the end point of $\tilde{u}$.

In general, ∂ is defined in a similar fashion.

Example.   Let $\pi: E \to B$ a proper submersion of differentiable manifolds. (A *proper* mapping f is a mapping such that $f^{-1}K$ is compact for compact K in the range.   A *submersion* is a C^1 mapping $f: E \to B$ such that at each $x \in E$, the differential $df_x: TE_x \to TB_{f(x)}$ is onto.)   Then π is locally trivial, and therefore has the covering homotopy property.

Proposition.   *If there exists a section s of* $\pi: E \to B$ *(that is, a map* $s: B \to E$ *such that* $\pi \circ s = 1$*), then* $\partial = 0$ *in the homotopy exact sequence.*

PROOF. $\pi \circ s = 1$ implies $\pi_* \circ s_* = 1$.   Hence π_* is onto.   By exactness of the homotopy sequence, $\partial = 0$.

Thus, we get an exact sequence

$$0 \to \pi_k(F, \tilde{*}) \to \pi_k(E, \tilde{*}) \to \pi_k(B, *) \to 0$$

This is an example of a *short* exact sequence. Any exact sequence

$$0 \to A \xrightarrow{\alpha} B \xrightarrow{\beta} C \to 0$$

having five terms and zeros on both ends is called a short exact sequence. Note that exactness at A means that α is injective (one-to-one) and exactness at C means β is surjective. For any groups A and C, there is a short exact sequence

$$0 \to A \to A \times C \to C \to 0$$

An example of a short exact sequence not of this form is

$$0 \to Z_2 \to Z_4 \to Z_2 \to 0$$

Proposition. *If $i: F \to E$ is homotopic to a constant map, then we get an exact sequence*

$$0 \to \pi_k(E) \to \pi_k(B) \to \pi_{k-1}(F) \to 0$$

PROOF. Since i is homotopic to a trivial map, $i_* = 0$.

Example. In the case of the Hopf fibration $\pi: S^3 \to S^2$, the inclusion $i: S^1 \to S^3$ is homotopic to a constant map. Thus we have a short exact sequence

$$0 \to \pi_2(S^3) \to \pi_2(S^2) \to \pi_1(S^1) \to 0$$

But $\pi_2(S^3) = 0$, so $\partial: \pi_2(S^2) \to \pi_1(S^1)$ is an isomorphism. We know $\pi_1(S^1) = \mathbf{Z}$, so we now know that $\pi_2(S^2) = \mathbf{Z}$. By the Freudenthal suspension theorem $\pi_k(S^k) = \mathbf{Z}, k \geq 1$.

Now that we know that $\pi_k(S^k) = \mathbf{Z}$, it is of interest to ask whether there is an effective way of telling which homotopy class a given mapping lies in. We now construct an isomorphism $\pi_k(S^k) \to \mathbf{Z}$ that provides a fairly effective way. We begin with a differentiable map $f: S^k \to S^k$. By Sard's theorem, the critical values constitute a set of measure 0. (The set of critical values is defined as $f[\Sigma]$, where Σ was the set occurring in the statement of Sard's theorem.) Choose a noncritical value $p \in S^n$. Then $f^{-1}(p)$ will be a finite set of points $q_1, \ldots, q_m$. Choose an orientation on the n sphere. Then it makes sense to say whether $df_q: TS_q^n \to TS_p^n$ preserves or reverses orientation, namely, we say df_q preserves orientation if it has determinant > 0 and that it reverses orientation if it has determinant < 0. Now we define

$$d(f) = \sum_{q \in f^{-1}(p)} \varepsilon(q),$$

where $\varepsilon(q) = +1$ if f preserves orientation and $\varepsilon(q) = -1$ if f reverses orientation.

Theorem. $d(f)$ *depends only on the homotopy class of* f, *and* d *induces an isomorphism* $\pi_k(S^k) \to \mathbf{Z}$.

The proof of this theorem depends on the Thom transversality lemma. Consider the following diagram of differentiable manifolds and mappings

$$N \xrightarrow{f} M$$
$$\cup$$
$$V$$

Definition. f is transversal to V if at every point $p \in V$ and every $q \in f^{-1}(p)$, the composition

$$TN_q \xrightarrow{df} TM_p \xrightarrow{\text{proj.}} \frac{TM_p}{TV_p}$$

is onto.

If $f: N \to M$ is transversal to V, then $f^{-1}V$ is a submanifold of N of dimension $= \dim N - \dim M + \dim V$. In other words, codim $f^{-1}V =$ codim V. (The codimension of a submanifold is the dimension of the ambient manifold minus the dimension of the submanifold.)

Thom Transversality Lemma. Suppose M is compact. If $f: M \to N$ is C^r, then there exists a map $g: M \to N$ transversal to V such that g together with its derivatives of order $\leq r$ approximates f together with its derivatives of order $\leq r$ arbitrarily closely.

Furthermore, one can show that if K is a closed subset of M and f is transversal to V on K, then one can choose g so that $g|K = f|K$.

Now we sketch the proof that $d(f)$ is independent of the homotopy class of f and of the choice of p. First suppose f' is homotopic to f and p is not a critical value of f'. Let F be a smooth homotopy connecting f and f'. (Thus F maps $S^n \times I$ into S^n; $F_0 = f$ and $F_1 = f'$.) By the Thom transversality theorem we can assume that F is transversal to p. Then $F^{-1}(p)$ is a one manifold whose boundary lies in $S^n \times \dot{I}$, as in Fig. 12. Then each point q in $f^{-1}(p)$ is connected by an arc in $F^{-1}(p)$ to either a point in $f^{-1}(p) \subseteq S^n \times \{0\}$ or a point in $f'^{-1}(p) \subseteq S^n \times \{1\}$. It is easily seen that if q and q' in $f^{-1}(p)$ are connected by an arc in $F^{-1}(p)$ then f preserves orientation at one of the two points and reverses it at the other. This is also true with f' in place of f. If $q \in f^{-1}(p)$ and $q' \in f^{-1}(p)$ are connected by an arc in $F^{-1}(p)$, then f preserves or reverses orientation at p according to whether f' preserves or reverses orientation at p'. From these facts, it follows that $d(f) = d(f')$ (where $d(f)$ and $d(f')$ are defined using the same p).

Next, consider a single map f and two points p and p', neither in the critical set of f. Let l be a smooth curve connecting p and p'. By changing f (but keeping it in the same homotopy class), we may suppose that f is

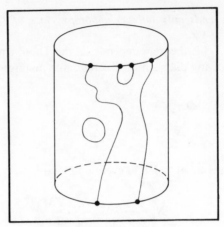

FIGURE 12

transversal to l.   Then $f^{-1}(l)$ is a one manifold whose boundary is $f^{-1}(p) \cup$
$f^{-1}(p')$.   Again, one has to check that a curve joining a point in $f^{-1}(p)$
with one in $f^{-1}(p')$ preserves orientation and that others reverse orientation.   Then the independence of $d(f)$ from the choice of p follows.

By the same methods, one can show that the map d is a homomorphism.
In fact, with a little more work, using the same ideas, one can show that the
map is an isomorphism.

Example. Brouwer Fixed Point Theorem.   Given a continuous map
$f: D^n \to D^n$, where $D^n = \{\langle x_1, \ldots, x_n \rangle : \sum x_i^2 \le 1\}$, there exists $x \in D_n$ such
that $f(x) = x$.

If $f(x) = x$, we say x is a *fixed point* of f.

PROOF. Suppose, to the contrary, there exists f with no fixed point.   Let $h(x)$
denote the place where the ray from $f(x)$ through x meets the boundary
S^{n-1} of D^n (Fig. 13).   Then $h: D^n \to S^{n-1}$ is continuous $h \circ i = 1$, where
$i: S^{n-1} \to D^n$ is the inclusion.   Hence the composition

$$\pi_{n-1}(S^{n-1}) \xrightarrow{i_*} \pi_{n-1}(D^n) \xrightarrow{h_*} \pi_{n-1}(S^{n-1})$$

is the identity; that is, $h_* \circ i_* = 1$.   But $\pi_{n-1}(S^{n-1}) = \mathbf{Z}$ and $\pi_{n-1}(D^n) = 0$, so
this is clearly impossible.   This contradiction proves the theorem.

Our next example is $\pi_k(U_n)$, where U_n denotes the unitary group.

Proposition. *If G is a Lie group and H is a closed subgroup, then the projection*
$G \to G/H$ is a fibering in the sense of Serre, with fiber H.

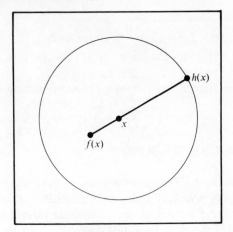

FIGURE 13

As an example, consider $U_{n-1} \subseteq U_n$ as all unitary $n \times n$ matrices of the form

$$
\begin{pmatrix}
1 & 0 & \cdots & 0 \\
0 & x_{11} & \cdots & x_{1,n-1} \\
\vdots & & \cdots & \\
0 & x_{n-1,1} & \cdots & x_{n,n}
\end{pmatrix}
$$

Then $U_n/U_{n-1} = S^{2n-1}$. Thus the mapping $\pi\colon U(n) \to S^{2n-1}$ is a fibering with fiber U_{n-1}. The homotopy exact sequence for this fibering is

$$\cdots \pi_{k+1}(S_{2n-1}) \to \pi_k(U_{n-1}) \to \pi_k(U_n) \to \pi_k(S_{2n-1}) \to \cdots$$

For $k + 1 < 2n - 1$, this implies $\pi_k(U_{n-1}) = \pi_k(U_n) = \pi_k(U_{n+1}) = \cdots$. Hence $\pi_k(U_n)$ is independent of n as $n \to \infty$. We call the common value of $\pi_k(U_n)$ for n large, $\pi_k(\mathbf{U})$. Similarly, $\pi_k(O_n)$ is independent of n for large n, so we may define $\pi_k(\mathbf{O}) = \pi_k(O_n)$, n large. Also $\pi_k(\mathrm{Sp}_n)$ is independent of n for n large, so we may define $\pi_k(\mathbf{Sp}) = \pi_k(\mathrm{Sp}_n)$, n large.

As an aside, we note that the exact sequence for a fibering can be used to calculate $\pi_k(S^1)$. We have a fibering $\exp\colon \mathbf{R} \to S^1$, which takes ϕ to $e^{i\phi}$. The fiber of this map is in one-to-one correspondence with the set Z of integers. Thus, we get an exact sequence

$$\pi_k(\mathbf{Z}, *) \to \pi_k(\mathbf{R}, *) \to \pi_k(S^1, *) \to \pi_{k-1}(\mathbf{Z}, *) \to \pi_{k-1}(\mathbf{R}, *) \to \pi_{k-1}(S^1, *)$$

Since $\mathbf{R}$ is contractible to a point, $\pi_k(\mathbf{R}, *) = 0$ for all k, and since $\mathbf{Z}$ is a discrete union of points $\pi_k(\mathbf{Z}, *) = 0$ for $k > 0$. Hence $\pi_k(S^1, *) = 0$ for $k > 1$.

Now consider the Hopf sequence

$$S^1 \to S^3 \xrightarrow{\pi} S^2$$

Then we get an exact sequence

$$\pi_3(S^1) \to \pi_3(S^3) \to \pi_3(S^2) \to \pi_2(S^1)$$

Since $\pi_3(S^1) = \pi_2(S^1) = 0$, the map $\pi_3(S^3) \to \pi_3(S^2)$ is an isomorphism. Hence $\pi_3(S^2) = \mathbf{Z}$.

Spheres other than S^1 have nonvanishing homotopy in infinitely many dimensions.

4 THE CLASSICAL GROUPS

Let G be a connected compact Lie group. Such a group has a Riemannian structure that is invariant under right and left translation. In fact, if we start with a positive definite symmetric bilinear form B on the Lie algebra $\mathfrak{g}$ of G, the bilinear form B' defined by

$$B'(X, Y) = \int_{g \in G} B(\operatorname{Ad} g \cdot X, \operatorname{Ad} g \cdot Y) \, d\mu(g)$$

(where μ is Haar measure) is a positive definite symmetric bilinear form that is invariant under the adjoint action. Then we get a right and left invariant form on the group by right translating this form around the group.

Let's study ΩG. To apply the Morse theory, we have to understand what the geodesics are and know what all the conjugate points are.

(1) Let T be a maximal torus in G and let p be a generic point of T (that is a point such that $\{p^n : n \in \mathbf{Z}\}$ is dense in T). Then all geodesics from e to p in G are given by geodesics on T.

(2) Let $\mathfrak{g} = \mathfrak{h} + \mathfrak{p}$ be the orthogonal decomposition of the Lie algebra of G into the Lie algebra of T and its orthogonal component.

Then for any $t \in T$, $\operatorname{Ad} t$ maps $\mathfrak{p}$ into itself. Let $\operatorname{Ad}^{\#}(t)$ denote the restriction of $\operatorname{Ad}(t)$ to $\mathfrak{p}$. What are the conjugate points on T? Let γ be a geodesic on T starting at e, that is, a one-parameter subgroup of T. Consider the function $s \to \operatorname{rank}(\operatorname{Ad}^{\#}(\gamma(s)) - 1)$ from the real numbers $\mathbf{R}$ into the non-negative integers. This function takes its maximum at all but a discrete set of points. It turns out that the conjugate points to e along γ are the points where this function drops below the maximum and the multiplicity is the amount that this function drops. In particular the multiplicity is always an even number, since $\operatorname{rank}(\operatorname{Ad}^{\#}(t) - 1)$ is always even.

Example. $SO(3)$

A maximal torus T is

$$\left\{ M(\theta) = \begin{pmatrix} \cos\theta & \sin\theta & 0 \\ -\sin\theta & \cos\theta & 0 \\ 0 & 0 & 1 \end{pmatrix} \right\}$$

The Lie algebra $\mathfrak{g}$ of $SO(3)$ is the set of skew 3×3 matrices. The Lie algebra $\mathfrak{h}$ in $\mathfrak{g}$ corresponding to this maximal torus is spanned (as an **R** vector space) by

$$\begin{pmatrix} 0 & 1 & 0 \\ -1 & 0 & 0 \\ 0 & 0 & 0 \end{pmatrix}$$

Its orthogonal complement p is spanned by

$$A_1 = \begin{pmatrix} 0 & 0 & 1 \\ 0 & 0 & 0 \\ -1 & 0 & 0 \end{pmatrix} \qquad A_2 = \begin{pmatrix} 0 & 0 & 0 \\ 0 & 0 & 1 \\ 0 & -1 & 0 \end{pmatrix}$$

Then

$$\text{Ad } M(\theta)(yA_1 + zA_2) = M(\theta)(yA_1 + zA_2)M(\theta)^{-1}$$

$$= y(\cos \theta \, A_1 + \sin \theta \, A_2) + z(-\sin \theta \, A_1 + \cos \theta \, A_2).$$

Thus $\text{Ad}^{\#} M(\theta) - 1$ has rank 2, except where θ is a multiple of 2π, where it has rank 0.

In Fig. 14 we unwrap T, and display the geodesics beginning at e and ending at an arbitrary point p that is not e. Each arrow in the figure represents a geodesic and the number written above it is the number of conjugate points it crosses, multiplicities counted. Thus, the Morse theory yields

$$\Omega SO(3) = e_0 \cup e_2 \cup e_4 \cup \cdots \oplus e_0 \cup e_2 \cup e_4 \cup \cdots$$

where $\oplus$ denotes disjoint union. In particular, we obtain

$$\pi_0\{\Omega SO(3)\} = \pi_1 SO(3) = Z_2$$

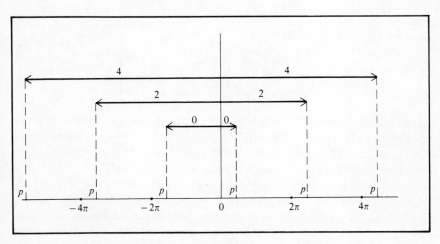

FIGURE 14

Using these techniques, one can show that for any semisimple Lie group

$$\Omega G = e_0 \cup \cdots \cup e_0 \cup e_2 \cup \cdots \cup e_2 \cup \cdots$$

As a consequence, we get that $\pi_1(G)$ is finite, $\pi_2(G) = 0$, and $\pi_3(G)$ is free.

Example. SU_2

Here a maximal torus is

$$\left\{ M(\theta) = \begin{pmatrix} e^{i\theta} & 0 \\ 0 & e^{-i\theta} \end{pmatrix} \right\}$$

A computation similar to that which we did for $SO(3)$ shows that $\mathrm{Ad}^{\#} M(\theta)^{-1}$ has rank 2, except at multiples of π, where it has rank 0.

We now mimic our diagram for SO_3. That is, we unwrap the maximal torus and represent the geodesics connecting e with an arbitrary point p that is neither e nor $-e$. Again, we write the number of conjugate points that each geodesic crosses above the arrow that represents the geodesic. We can read off the Morse theoretical decomposition of ΩSU_2 from the diagram. Namely,

$$\Omega SU_2 \approx e_0 \cup e_2 \cup e_4 \cup \cdots$$

Note that SU_2 is the twofold covering of SO_3 and ΩSO_3 is the disjoint union of ΩSU_2 with itself. As an exercise, the reader might verify that if X and Y are connected spaces and X is an n-fold covering of Y, then ΩY is (up to homotopy) the n-fold disjoint union of Y with itself.

Example. SU_3

In SU_3, the maximal torus is

$$\left\{ \begin{pmatrix} e^{i\theta_1} & 0 & 0 \\ 0 & e^{i\theta_2} & 0 \\ 0 & 0 & e^{i\theta_3} \end{pmatrix} : \theta_1 + \theta_2 + \theta_3 = 0 \right\}$$

Again we can unwrap the maximal torus. Since it is two-dimensional, we get a plane. The set of t for which $\mathrm{Ad}^{\#} t - 1$ has rank < 6 consists of three families of parallel straight lines equally spaced (Fig. 15). For t on any of these lines but not on an intersection point, the rank of $\mathrm{Ad}^{\#} t - 1$ is 4. On an intersection point the rank of $\mathrm{Ad}^{\#} t - 1$ is 0. Thus if p is a general point in T, we can determine the Morse theoretical decomposition of ΩSU_3 by marking all the points in the diagram corresponding to p, drawing a line segment from e to each of the points, and counting the number of times this line segment crosses one of the solid lines.

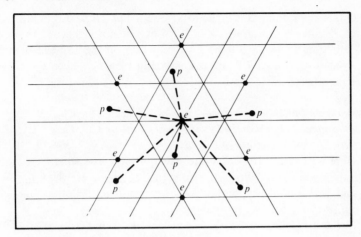

FIGURE 15

Remark. In a compact connected Lie group, all maximal tori are conjugate, so we get essentially the same picture no matter which maximal torus we pick.

Now our aim is to show how to use Morse theory to compute the stable homotopy groups. For this, we will need to generalize the notion of non-degenerate critical point.

Example. Consider a torus lying on the table with its height function. Precisely, what we want to consider is obtained by rotating the following around the z axis: a circle in the xz plane that does not intersect the z axis. This is a torus T. Let f denote the restriction of the z coordinate to T. The maxima of f constitute an S^1, and so do the minima. Thus the maxima and the minima are degenerate in the sense of our earlier definition. However, the circles of maxima and minima are nondegenerate in the sense of the following definition.

Definition. Let $V \subset M$ be a critical manifold for f on M (i.e., a submanifold such that $df = 0$ on it). Then V is nondegenerate if and only if Hf has the tangent space to V as its null space; that is, Hf is nonsingular in the normal directions to V.

Proposition 1. *The number of negative equivalues of Hf at $p \in V$ is independent of the point $p \in V$, if V is a connected nondegenerate critical manifold; we call this number the index $\lambda(V)$ of V as a critical manifold.*

Proposition 2. *If V is a nondegenerate critical manifold of f, then f can be jiggled in the vicinity of V so as not to affect other critical points of f, and in such a manner that f becomes nondegenerate near V, with points of index $\geq \lambda(V)$.*

One way of doing this is the following. Let TV be a tubular neighborhood of V with projection $\pi: TV \to V$. Let g be a nondegenerate (in the old sense) function on V. Let ψ be a C^∞ function on the ambient manifold M that vanishes outside of TV and is identically 1 on V. Then $f + \varepsilon\psi(g \circ \pi)$ is nondegenerate for some $\varepsilon \neq 0$.

Proposition 3. *Let G be a compact Lie group or, more generally, a compact symmetric space. Let p and q be arbitrary points on G. Then the critical sets in Ω_p^q are all nondegenerate manifolds.*

Here we use Ω_p^q to denote the space of piecewise differentiable curves from p to q, which we called ΩG in our section on Morse theory. What we have said here is very imprecise; what is meant is that critical sets in M_b^n have the property that we have stated.

For example, consider the n sphere. If p and q are not antipodes, then the critical sets are nondegenerate points. If p and q are antipodes, then the critical sets are nondegenerate manifolds, beginning with S^{n-1}.

The idea for computing the stable homotopy groups of the classical groups is to study nondegenerate critical manifolds in loop spaces.

Recall the definition of the stable homotopy groups.

$$\pi_k(\mathbf{U}) = \pi_k(U_n) \qquad n \text{ large}$$

$$\pi_k(\mathbf{O}) = \pi_k(O_n) \qquad n \text{ large}$$

$$\pi_k(\mathbf{Sp}) = \pi_k(\mathrm{Sp}_n) \qquad n \text{ large}$$

Let us also note some other relations. As a topological space, U_n decomposes as the product $SU_n \times S^1$. Thus the problems of computing $\pi_k(U_n)$ and $\pi_k(SU_n)$ are equivalent.

Spin (n) is the twofold covering of SO_n, so, the fibration

$$Z_2 \longrightarrow \text{Spin }(n)$$
$$\downarrow$$
$$SO_n$$

gives an isomorphism $\pi_k(\text{Spin }(n)) \approx \pi_k(SO_n)$ for $k \geq 2$. Recall that O_n, U_n, and Sp_n are the groups of linear transformations in $\mathbf{R}^n$, $\mathbf{C}^n$, and $\mathbf{H}^n$ preserving the inner product $(x, y) = \sum x_i \bar{y}_i$. One uses $\mathbf{H}$ to denote the quaternions. The symplectic group Sp_n can also be described as the set of unitary $2n \times 2n$ matrices such that

$$U^t J U = J$$

where the superscript t denotes transpose, and

$$J = \begin{pmatrix} 0 & 1_n \\ -1_n & 0 \end{pmatrix}$$

The fact that $\pi_k(\mathrm{Sp}_n)$ is constant for large n is a consequence of the existence of the fibration

$$\mathrm{Sp}_n \longrightarrow \mathrm{Sp}_{n+1}$$
$$\downarrow$$
$$S_{4n+1}$$

The existence of this fibration is a consequence of the fact that Sp_n is the group of linear transformations of $\mathbf{H}^n$ preserving the inner product $(x, y) = \sum x_i \bar{y}_i$.

Proposition. *Any connected Lie group is topologically the product of its maximal compact subgroup and a space homeomorphic to Euclidean space.*

For example,

$Gl(n, R) = O_n \times \{\text{positive definite symmetric matrices}\}$
$Gl(n, C) = U_n \times \{\text{positive definite Hermitian matrices}\}$
$Gl(n, H) = \mathrm{Sp}_n \times \{\ldots\}.$

Thus, as far as algebraic topology is concerned, it is enough to consider compact groups.

Theorem.

$$\pi_k(U) \simeq \pi_{k+2}(U)$$

$$\pi_k(O) \simeq \pi_{k+4}(\mathrm{Sp})$$

$$\pi_k(\mathrm{Sp}) \simeq \pi_{k+4}(O) \qquad k = 0, 1, \ldots$$

Now we begin a sketch of the proof. Consider the space $\Omega_I^{-I}SU_{2n}$ of piecewise smooth paths beginning at I and ending at $-I$. This accords with our philosophy of considering very degenerate loop spaces. Consider the arc μ

$$t \longrightarrow \begin{pmatrix} e^{\pi i t} I_n & 0 \\ 0 & e^{\pi i t} I_n \end{pmatrix}$$

in SU_{2n}.

A maximal torus for SU_n is the set of diagonal matrices.

The arc μ is the shortest geodesic between I and $-I$. Furthermore, the singular set of conjugate points on T is the union of the tori on which two entries are equal (e.g., the ith and jth entries).

Thus μ does not cross any of the singular tori. To compute the index of what we are attaching, we have to count the number of times the arc crosses the singular tori for $0 < t < 1$.

Observe that if x is anything in U_{2n}, then the curve

$$t \longrightarrow x u(t) x^{-1}$$

is another geodesic segment from I to $-I$ in SU_{2n}. Thus

$$x \rightarrow \{t \rightarrow xu(t)x^{-1}\}$$

is a map.

$$U_{2n} \rightarrow \{\text{geodesics going from } I \text{ to } -I\}.$$

Note that if x is of the form

$$\begin{pmatrix} x_1 & 0 \\ 0 & x_2 \end{pmatrix}$$

with $x_i \in U_n$, then $xu(t)x^{-1} = u(t)$. Hence, our map factors through

$$U_{2n}/U_n \times U_n$$

The resulting map

$$U_{2n}/U_n \times U_n \rightarrow \{\text{geodesics going from } I \text{ to } -I\}$$

is one-to-one and onto the set of shortest geodesics going from I to $-I$. This is a consequence of the "spectral theorem":

(1) Every element of G is in some maximal torus.

(2) All maximal tori are connected if G is a compact connected Lie group.

Now the modified Morse theory (where one considers nondegenerate critical manifolds rather than nondegenerate critical points) yields

$$\Omega SU_{2n} = U_{2n}/U_n \times U_n \cup \cdots$$

and the problem is to find the lowest-dimensional cell one needs to attach where we have written the three dots. (By "jiggling" the Morse function a bit, one can guarantee that one needs only attach *cells* to the first critical manifold $U_{2n}/U_n \times U_n$. That is, one can "jiggle" the function a bit to guarantee that all the critical points not on $U_{2n}/U_n \times U_n$ are nondegenerate.) The important point is that the size of the cells that have to be attached tends to ∞ as n goes to ∞. Thus, we obtain

$$\pi_k\{\Omega SU_{2n}\} \simeq \pi_k\{U_{2n}/U_n \times U_n\}$$

for k small relative to n, since homotopy in low dimensions is not affected by adding cells of high dimensions. This formula is equivalent to

(a) $$\pi_{k+1}\{SU_{2n}\} \simeq \pi_k\{U_{2n}/U_n \times U_n\}$$

Now we will show

(b) $$\pi_k(U_n) \simeq \pi_{k+1}\{U_{2n}/U_n \times U_n\}$$

and we will be done. We have a choice of two methods here. We can use the same techniques applied to symmetric spaces rather than to groups and get

$$\Omega(U_{2n}/U_n \times U_n) = U_n \cup e_{v(n)}$$

where $v(n)$ tends to ∞ with n. This is the method we have to use in the case of the orthogonal group; in fact, we have to apply it eight times. However, in this case there is an alternate method for step (b), which is much more elementary. Apply the exact sequence coming from the fibration

$$U_n \longrightarrow U_{2n}$$
$$\downarrow$$
$$U_{2n}/U_n$$

This sequence is

$$\pi_k(U_n) \xrightarrow{\approx} \pi_k(U_{2n}) \to \pi_k(U_{2n}/U_n) \to \pi_{k-1}(U_n) \xrightarrow{\approx} \pi_{k-1}(U_{2n}) \to \cdots$$

The precise form of our statement that $\pi_k(U_n)$ is stable for large n is that we have isomorphisms in the indicated places for k small relative to n. It follows from this exact sequence that $\pi_k(U_{2n}/U_n) = 0$ for k small relative to n. But now we have another fibering

$$U_n = \frac{U_n \times U_n}{U_n} \longrightarrow U_{2n}/U_n$$
$$\downarrow$$
$$U_{2n}/U_n \times U_n$$

In general, an inclusion $G \subset H \subset K$ of Lie groups gives rise to a fibration

$$H/K \longrightarrow G/K$$
$$\downarrow$$
$$G/H$$

It follows that we get an exact sequence

$$\cdots \to \pi_{k+1}(U_{2n}/U_n) \to \pi_{k+1}(U_{2n}/U_n \times U_n) \to \pi_k(U_n) \to \pi_k(U_{2n}/U_n) \to \cdots$$

Since $\pi_k(U_{2n}/U_n) = 0$ for low k, we get the isomorphism (b) for low k.

Combining (a) and (b), we get the periodicity for $\pi_k(\mathbf{U})$. It is not too difficult to compute $\pi_0(\mathbf{U})$ and $\pi_1(\mathbf{U})$. After this is done, we get $\pi_k(\mathbf{U})$ for all k by periodicity. Thus

Corollary

$$\pi_k(\mathbf{U}) = 0 \qquad k \text{ even}$$
$$= \mathbf{Z} \qquad k \text{ odd}$$

in the case of the orthogonal group, this game doesn't work, so we have to write down the formulas for the models.   We get

$$\Omega SO_{2n} \simeq SO_{2n}/U_n \cup \cdots$$
$$\Omega Sp_n \simeq Sp_n/U_n \cup \cdots$$
$$\Omega\{Sp_n/U_n\} \simeq U_n/O_n \cup \cdots$$
$$\Omega\{U_{2n}/O_{2n}\} \simeq O_{2n}/O_n \times O_n \cup \cdots$$
$$\Omega\{SO_{4n}/U_{2n}\} \simeq U_{2n}/Sp_n \cup \cdots$$
$$\Omega\{U_{4n}/Sp_{2n}\} \simeq Sp_{2n}/Sp_n \times Sp_n \cup \cdots$$

where the cells indicated by the dots have dimensions tending to ∞ as n tends to ∞.   The periodicity theorem follows from these relations, together with the elementary relations

$$\Omega\{Sp_{2n}/Sp_n \times Sp_n\} \simeq Sp_n$$
$$\Omega\{O_{2n}/O_n \times O_n\} \simeq O_n$$

(Recall that $\pi_k(\Omega X) = \pi_{k+1}(X)$, and attaching a high-dimensional cell does not affect homotopy in low dimensions.)

5   COHOMOLOGY

From the point of view of homotopy theory, cohomology arises from considering homotopy classes of maps of a space into a group.   The natural definition of group in the homotopy category is the following: A group is a pair (G, m), where G is a space with base point $*$ and $m: G \times G \to G$ is a map satisfying the following axioms.   (We will work entirely with base point-preserving maps.)

(1) The following diagram is commutative:

$$
\begin{array}{ccc}
G \times G \times G & \xrightarrow{\ m \times 1\ } & G \times G \\
{\scriptstyle 1 \times m}\downarrow & & \downarrow{\scriptstyle m} \\
G \times G & \xrightarrow{\ m\ } & G
\end{array}
$$

(2) There exists a map $\alpha: G \to G$ such that the composition

$$G \xrightarrow{\langle \alpha, 1 \rangle} G \times G \xrightarrow{\ m\ } G$$

is the constant map (in the homotopy category).

(3) The composition

$$G = * \times G \to G$$

is the identity (in the homotopy category).

Note that if we were working in the category of topological spaces and continuous mappings instead of the homotopy category, these axioms would be equivalent to the ordinary axioms for a topological group.

However, these are considerably weaker than the axioms for a topological group. For example, $\Omega * X$ is easily seen to be a group in the sense of homotopy as we have defined it, but there is no reason why it should be a topological group in general.

If (G, m) is a group in the sense of homotopy and X is a space, then the set $[X, G]$ of homotopy classes of mappings of X into G is an honest group. The product in $[X, G]$ is defined as follows: If $[f]$, $[g] \in [X, G]$ have representatives $f, g: X \to G$ then $[f][g] = [m \circ \langle f, g \rangle]$, where $\langle f, g \rangle: X \to G \times G$ is defined by $\langle f, g \rangle(x) = \langle f(x), g(x) \rangle$.

We will define the cohomology $H^n(X; \pi)$ as the set of homotopy classes $[X, K(\pi, n)]$ for a suitable group $K(\pi, n)$. This looks dual to our definition of homotopy: $\pi_n(X) = [S^n, X]$. Let's see what is dual to the exact sequence for a fibering.

A fibering was defined as a map $\pi: E \to B$ with the following property: Given a map $f: X \to E$ and a homotopy g_t of $\pi \circ f$, there exists a homotopy f_t of f that covers g_t.

This can be represented by the following diagram.

Now, if we reverse all the arrows, we get the condition for a map $i: K \to L$ to be a *co-fibering*.

The condition is this. Given any map $f: L \to X$ and any homotopy g_t of $f \mid K$, there exists a homotopy f_t of f such that $f_t \mid K = g_t$.

For reasonable spaces (e.g., simplicial complexes), this condition implies i is one-to-one.

Just as one can write down exact sequences in homotopy for fiberings, one can write down exact sequences in cohomology for co-fiberings. It is much easier to compute cohomology, since ordinary spaces are naturally built up by attaching cells and attaching a cell yields a co-fibration. That is, the inclusion $i: X \to X \cup_k e$ is always a co-fibration.

Let $i\colon X \to Y$ be an inclusion that is a co-fibering. Let G be a group and let $F(Z) = [Z, G]$ for any space Z. Then it is easily verified that the sequence

$$F(X) \leftarrow F(Y) \leftarrow F(Y/X)$$

is exact.

Let π be an arbitrary Abelian group. Let $K(\pi, n)$ be a complex such that

$$\pi_k(K(\pi, n)) = 0 \qquad k \neq n$$
$$= \pi \qquad k = n$$

These spaces are very nice objects to map into. Most spaces are tough to map into—we can not even classify maps of spheres into them.

For example, S^1 is $K(\mathbf{Z}, 1)$.

Another example is $\mathbf{CP}_\infty = \mathbf{CP}_1 \cup \mathbf{CP}_2 \cdots \cup \mathbf{CP}_n \cup \cdots$. There is a fibration

that gives rise to an exact sequence

$$\pi_k(S^1) \to \pi_k(S^{2n+1}) \to \pi_k(\mathbf{CP}_n) \to \pi_{k-1}(S^1) \to \cdots$$

It follows that for $k < 2n + 1$,

$$\pi_k(\mathbf{CP}_n) = 0 \qquad k \neq 2$$
$$= \mathbf{Z} \qquad k = 2$$

Thus, we obtain

$$\pi_k(\mathbf{CP}_\infty) = 0 \qquad k \neq 2$$
$$= \mathbf{Z} \qquad k = 2$$

In other words, $\mathbf{CP}_\infty$ is a $K(\mathbf{Z}, 2)$.

One can prove the existence of a $K(\pi, n)$ as follows: Write

$$\pi = (\mathbf{Z} \oplus \cdots \oplus \mathbf{Z})/R$$

Construct a bouquet of n spheres, one for each copy of $\mathbf{Z}$ appearing in the formula above. (A bouquet of spheres is constructed by taking a disjoint union of spheres and identifying their base points.)

Now kill everything in R by attaching $n + 1$ cells. Kill the $n + 1$ homotopy by attaching $n + 2$ cells, the $n + 2$ homotopy by attaching $n + 3$ cells, and so on. After attaching cells in infinitely many dimensions, one gets a $K(\pi, n)$.

Since $\pi_k(\Omega X) = \pi_{k+1}(X)$, one obtains: $\Omega K(\pi, n)$ is a $K(\pi, n - 1)$.

It can be shown that if G is a group in the homotopy category, then ΩG is an Abelian group in the homotopy category.

Now define the n cohomology group $H^n(X, \pi)$ of X with coefficients in π by

$$H^n(X, \pi) = [X, K(\pi, n)]$$

Cohomology has the following properties.

(1) $H^n(X, \pi)$ is a contravariant functor in X.

(2) Given a co-fibering

$$X \to Y \to (Y/X)$$

then there is an exact sequence

$$H^{n+1}(X) \leftarrow H^{n+1}(Y) \leftarrow H^{n+1}(Y/X) \xleftarrow{\text{coboundary}} H^n(X) \leftarrow H^n(Y) \leftarrow H^n(Y/X)$$

Why should this cohomology look like what we ordinarily think of as cohomology with cochains, coboundaries, and so forth? Let's try to compute $H^n(X)$, where X is a simplicial complex.

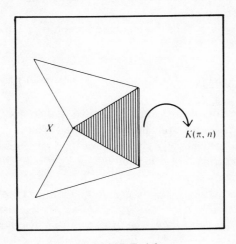

FIGURE 16

Given a map $f: X \to K(\pi, n)$ (Fig. 16), we can find a homotopic map f' such that all $n - 1$ simplices are mapped into base points. Define a function ϕ on n simplices.

$$\phi(\sigma_n) = \text{homotopy class of } f' \text{ restricted to } \sigma_n$$

Then one verifies that ϕ is a cocycle, that is, the sum of all $\phi(\sigma_n)$ as σ_n runs over all faces of an $n + 1$ simplex τ_{n+1} is 0. But this follows from the fact that f' restricted to the union of these faces is zero, since it extends over τ_{n+1}.

If we deform f in another way we get a different ϕ, call it ϕ'. Their difference is the coboundary of a lower-dimensional cochain

$$\phi - \phi' = \delta_n$$

Thus we get a map

$$[X, K(\pi, n)] \to \text{cocycles/coboundaries}$$

This map is an isomorphism.

One has certain rough duality features between cohomology and homotopy. For example, cohomology of a product is complicated (and of a fiber bundle even more so), while the homotopy of a product may be simply expressed in terms of the homotopy of the factors. On the other hand, the cohomology of a bouquet of spheres is very simple, while the homotopy is complicated.

This duality is best understood if one thinks of the $K(\pi, n)$'s as a set of basic building blocks for the category Hot dual to the cells that we are led to at the very start.

Indeed, let $\pi_0, \pi_1, \ldots$ be the sequence homotopy groups of a topological space X. Then the space

$$X' = K(\pi_0, 0) \times K(\pi_1, 1) \times \cdots \times K(\pi_n, n) \times \cdots$$

will have the same homotopy groups as X, and it of course would be marvelous if X and X' were of the same homotopy type. This is not true in general. What is true—and was already eluded to in the first lecture—is this.

One may construct a sequence of spaces $E_1, E_2, \ldots, E_n$, together with maps $f_n: X \to E_n$, such that

(1) *f_n induces isomorphisms in homotopy up to and including the dimension n;*

(2) *E_n is of the homotopy type of a fiber space over E_{n-1} with fiber a $K(\pi_n, n)$.*

Note that (1) can easily be shown to imply that f_n induces an isomorphism of the homotopy classes $[P, X]$ of maps of P into X with $[P, E_n]$ for all polyhedra of dim $\leq n - 1$. Thus—as far as can be observed with polyhedra (i.e., small spaces of dimension $\leq n - 1$)—X can be identified with E_n. On the other hand (2) implies that

$$E_n = E_{n-1} \underset{T}{\times} K(\pi_n, n)$$

so that by induction, E_n is a twisted product of the $K(\pi_i, i)$, $i \leq n$.

The construction of the $\{E_n\}$ and $\{f_n\}$ is in principle quite simple. We set E_n equal to X with all homotopy groups in dimension $>n$ killed. Thus one attaches cells inductively to kill all homotopy above n

$$E_n = X \cup e_{n+2} \cup \cdots$$

That this can be done follows from Proposition 4 of Section 3. We attach the cells systematically. That is, having constructed E_n we construct E_{n-1} by killing all the homotopy groups of E_n in dimension $\geq n$. Thus

$$E_{n-1} = E_n \cup e_{n+1} \cup \cdots$$

and in particular, E_{n-1} is a subset of E_n.

The first property again follows directly from Proposition 4 of Section 3. To see the second one, we must convert the inclusion map $E_{n-1} \to E_n$ into a fibering. This can always be done in the following manner.

Let A be a subspace of the space X and let $i: A \to X$ be the inclusion map. Let $\tilde{A}$ denote the space of maps $u: I \to X$ subject to the single boundary condition $u(0) \in A$, and define $\pi: \tilde{A} \to X$ by $\pi(u) = u(1)$.

It is then pretty obvious that (1) the inclusion of A into $\tilde{A}$ given by the point paths: $a \to u_a$, where $u_a(t) = a, t \in [0, 1]$, induces a homotopy equivalence of i with π; and (2) that π is a fiber space in the sense of Serre, with fiber over $x \in X$ the space of maps $u: I \to X$ subject to

$$u(0) \in A \qquad u(1) = x$$

Applying this construction to the inclusion

$$E_n \xrightarrow{i} E_{n-1}$$

and using the homotopy sequence for the resulting fibering

$$\tilde{E}_n \xrightarrow{\pi} E_{n-1}$$

we find that the fiber has vanishing homotopy except in the dimension n and there has homotopy $\pi_n(X)$. Hence it is a $K(\pi_n, n)$. Q.E.D.

The sequence of spaces $\{E_n\}$ just described is called a Postnikov system for X. As one by now has a deep understanding of how the cohomology of a fiber space is put together out of the cohomology of base and fiber (the spectral sequence), and knows explicitly the cohomology of all $K(\pi, n)$'s, one can use the Postnikov system to compute a certain amount of information about the homotopy of X, and this is the most powerful general method devised so far for the computation of homotopy groups.

6   VECTOR BUNDLES AND CHARACTERISTIC CLASSES

Recall that we talked vaguely about twisted products and things like that.   However, we went from the notion of twisted product to its consequence in homotopy (Serre fibration), since that was all that mattered before.   Now we go back to the more precise notion of bundles.

Definition.   Vector Bundles.   The intuitive notion is a family of vector spaces parametrized by a topological space X.   The prime example is the family of tangent spaces to a manifold.

A vector bundle consists of a space E, a map $\pi\colon E \to X$ such that

(1) $\pi^{-1}(x)$ is a vector space of dimension k over either **R** or **C**.

(2) There is a covering $\{U\}$ of X and k sections $\{s_u^{\,1}, s_u^{\,2}, \ldots, s_u^{\,k}\}$ over each $U \in \{U\}$ such that the map

$$\phi\colon U \times R^k \to \pi^{-1}(U)$$

defined by

$$\phi(x, r_1, \ldots, r_k) = \sum_{i=1}^{r} r_i\, s_u^{\,i}(x)$$

is a homeomorphism.

(By a section s over U we mean a continuous map $s\colon U \to \pi^{-1}U$ such that $\pi \circ s = 1$.)   Such a set of sections $s_u^{\,1}, s_u^{\,2}, \ldots, s_{uk}$ will be called a frame over U.

Note that if U and V are two different sets in the cover then two frames, one on U and one on V are related by a linear transformation on the overlap.

Note also that our map defines a commutative diagram:

$$
\begin{array}{ccc}
U \times R^k & \xrightarrow{\ \phi\ } & \pi^{-1}U \\
\Big\downarrow{\scriptstyle\text{proj.}} & & \Big\downarrow{\scriptstyle\pi} \\
U & \xrightarrow[\ 1\ ]{} & U
\end{array}
$$

Example 1

A trivial bundle

$$
\begin{array}{c}
X \times R^k = E \\
\Big\downarrow \\
X
\end{array}
$$

On this bundle, there is a "frame" of k linearly independent sections.

Example 2

A nontrivial bundle

For E, we take $I \times R/\sim$, where $\langle 0, x \rangle \sim \langle 1, -x \rangle$ for all $x \in R$. For B, we take $I/\sim$, where $0 \sim 1$. Thus B is an S^1. This is a bundle, since locally there is a frame. However, there is no global frame.

Example 3

Let V be a vector space. Let $G_k(V)$ denote the set of k-dimensional subspaces of V. There is a natural way of putting a topology on $G_k(V)$. We construct a vector bundle E as follows: We let E denote the set of all $\langle v, A \rangle$ with $A \in G_k(V)$ and $v \in A$. This is a subset of $V \times G_k(V)$, so we provide it with the induced topology. This is a vector bundle over $G_k(V)$, with the projection map $\langle v, A \rangle \to A$.

Example 4

$G_1(\mathbf{R}^2)$ consists of lines in the plane. The bundle in this case is isomorphic to that of Example 2.

Let E and F be vector bundles over X. Then E is isomorphic to F if and only if there is a diagram

$$
\begin{array}{ccc}
& \phi & \\
E & \rightleftarrows & F \\
& \psi & \\
\pi \downarrow & & \downarrow \pi' \\
X & \xrightarrow{\ 1\ } & X
\end{array}
$$

where ϕ and ψ map each fiber into itself and are linear on fibers, and $\phi \circ \psi = 1$, $\psi \circ \phi = 1$.

We write $E_x = \pi^{-1}(x)$, $F_x = \pi'^{-1}(X)$. Define a functor $X \rightsquigarrow \mathbf{F}_n(X)$, as follows. We let $\mathbf{F}_n(X)$ denote the set of isomorphism classes of n-dimensional vector bundles over X, with the trivial class singled out.

Given $f\colon Y \to X$ and a vector bundle $\pi\colon E \to X$, we define

$$f^{-1}E = \{\langle e, y \rangle : \pi(e) = f(y)\}$$

Now we make $\mathbf{F}_n$ into a contravariant functor by setting

$$\mathbf{F}_n(f)(E) = f^{-1}E$$

A basic question is, given a vector bundle by geometry, can you determine which isomorphism class it is in? For example, let M be a manifold and TM the tangent bundle. If TM is trivial, we say M is parallelizable.

Theorem 1. *Let X and Y be compact spaces. Let $f, g\colon X \to Y$ be mappings that are homotopic. Then $\mathbf{F}_n(f) = \mathbf{F}_n(g)$.*

(That is, $\mathbf{F}_n(X)$ is a homotopy invariant of X.)

Theorem 2. *F_n is representable, at least on finite simplicial complexes.*

This means there exists a space B_n and a natural equivalence

$$\mathbf{F}_n(X) \simeq [X, B_n]$$

where $[X, B_n]$ denotes the set of homotopy classes of maps of X into B_n. (However, B_n is not a finite complex.) This theorem "reduces" the classification problem of vector bundles to a homotopy problem. In general this homotopy problem is very difficult. However, in the case X is the sphere, we can apply our results on the homotopy groups of the classical spaces. First, some definitions.

Given a vector bundle

$$E \xrightarrow{\pi} X$$

then $E \times \mathbf{R}$ constitutes a vector bundle of one higher dimension over X, with $\pi'\colon E \times \mathbf{R} \to X$ defined by $\pi'(e) = \pi(e)$. This defines an operation $F_n(X) \to F_{n+1}(X)$. We call E and F *stably equivalent* if in some $\mathbf{F}_{n+k}(X)$ they become isomorphic.

Theorem 3. *The stable classes of vector bundles over X (X a finite complex) form an Abelian group $\tilde{K}(X)$.*

From the fact that the F_n are functors, it follows that $\tilde{K}$ is a functor. This is the basic functor in K theory.

Now we will sketch a proof of Theorem 1. Let $F: X \times I \to Y$ be a homotopy of X in Y and let $\pi: E \to Y$ be a bundle over Y. Set

$$F_t(x) = F(x, t)$$

for all $x \in X$ and $t \in I$. Theorem 1 states that the isomorphism class of $F_t^{-1}E$ is independent of t. It is enough to show that the two bundles over $X \times I$, namely, $F^{-1}E$ and $\pi^{-1}F_0^{-1}E$ are isomorphic, since

$$F_t^{-1}E = \iota_t^{-1}F^{-1}E$$

and

$$F_0^{-1}E = \iota_t^{-1}\pi^{-1}F_0^{-1}E$$

where $\iota_t: X \to X \times I$ is the inclusion defined by $\iota_t(x) = \langle x, t \rangle$.

We are given an isomorphism of $E_1 = F^{-1}(E)$ and $E_2 = \pi^{-1}F^{-1}E$ on the set $X \times 0$. We can construct a new vector bundle W, whose fiber is $W_x = \operatorname{Hom}(E_{1,x}, E_{2,x})$. The isomorphism between E_1 and E_2 on $X \times 0$ is a special sort of section over $X \times 0$. Now we use the following.

Proposition. *Given a section of a vector bundle over $X \times 0$, we can extend it to a section over $X \times I$.*

The method of proof is to patch local solutions of this problem with a partition of unity.

Now we extend our section over $X \times I$. The fact that our section gives rise to an isomorphism in each fiber over $X \times 0$ can be expressed as the non-vanishing of a certain determinant. Then there is an open neighborhood U of $X \times 0$ such that this determinant does not vanish on U; that is, the section gives rise to an isomorphism in each fiber over U. Since X is compact, $U \supseteq X \times [0, \varepsilon]$ for $\varepsilon > 0$ sufficiently small. Therefore

$$F^{-1}E \,|\, X \times [0, \varepsilon] \simeq \pi^{-1}F_0^{-1} \,|\, X \times [0, \varepsilon]$$

The same argument shows that for any $t \in I$,

$$F^{-1}E \,|\, X \times [t - \varepsilon, t + \varepsilon] \simeq \pi^{-1}F_t^{-1} \,|\, X \times [t - \varepsilon, t + \varepsilon]$$

Since I is connected, this yields the desired result.

Let's go back to

$$\mathbf{F}_n(X) \approx [X, B_n]$$

To any $E \in \mathbf{F}_n(X)$ we associate a map $f_E: X \to B_n$. Thus $f_E^*: H^*(B_n) \to H^*(X)$ is obtained. Anything in the image of f_A^* is called a characteristic class of E. Any characteristic class of a trivial bundle is 0, since the corresponding map is homotopic to a constant map. Thus the characteristic classes are obstructions to trivializing a bundle.

Let's see how to generalize the notion of vector bundle. First, let's observe that the notion of vector bundle can be reformulated in terms of the general linear group.

Let E be a vector bundle over X, and let $\{U\}$ be a covering, with frames $s_1^u, \ldots, s_n^u$ defined over a member U of the cover $\{U\}$.

Let $U, V \in \{U\}$. Then

$$s_i^u(x) = \sum_j g_{ij}(x) s_j^v(x)$$

for a suitable matrix $g_{ij}(x)$. Note that $g_{ij}(x)$ is defined for all $x \in U \cap V$ and that it is nonsingular. Thus we have defined a function

$$g = g^{u,v} : U \cap V \to Gl(n)$$

(We take the $i - j$th entry of $g(x)$ to be $g_{ik}(x)$.)

The following is easily verified.

Proposition. *On* $U \cap V \cap W$

($_*$) $$g_{uv}(x) g_{vw}(x) = g_{uw}(x)$$

We call this formula the *cocycle condition*.

Proposition. *Given the covering* $\{U\}$ *and the cocycle* $\{g^{uv}\}$, *we can reconstruct* E, *up to isomorphism*.

In fact, given any covering $\{U\}$ and any 1-cocycle (relative to this covering) with values in $Gl(n, \mathbf{R})$, we can construct a vector bundle E as follows. (By a cocycle, we mean a family g^{uv} satisfying $g^{uw} = g^{uv}g^{vw}$.)

(1) Form the disjoint union of all $U \times \mathbf{R}^n$, where U ranges over $\{U\}$.

(2) For any U, V in $\{U\}$ identify the subset $(U \cap V) \times \mathbf{R}^n$ of $U \times \mathbf{R}^n$ with the subset $(U \cap V) \times \mathbf{R}^n$ of $V \times \mathbf{R}^n$ by identifying (x, v) with $(x, (g^{uv})^{-1}v)$, for any $x \in U \cap V$ and any $v \in \mathbf{R}^n$.

This sets up a one-to-one correspondence between bundles with specified trivializations over the $\{U\}$ of our covering and cocycles with values in $Gl(n, \mathbf{R})$.

Remark. A 1-cochain is a function that is defined on the 1-skeleton of a simplex. The coboundary δc is a function on next-higher-dimensional simplices given by the formula $\delta c(123) = c(23) - c(13) + c(12)$. We call c a *cocycle* if $\delta c = 0$.

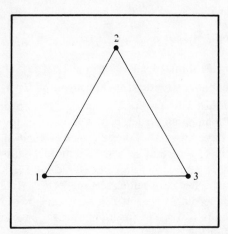

But our cocycle condition is the same formula written multiplicatively, except that our index set is an open cover of the space, rather than the vertices of a simplex. However, one can think of a simplicial complex in terms of open sets, by attaching to each vertex its open star. This is the set of all (open) simplices that have the given vertex in their boundaries.

One can thus define 1-cocycles with values in any group. However, to define higher cocycles, one needs an Abelian group.

Proposition. *Consider two sets of local frames $\{s_i{}^u\}$ and $\{\bar{s}_i{}^u\}$, associated to a cover $\{U\}$. Then we have matrix-valued functions*

$$\lambda_u : U \to Gl(n, \mathbf{R})$$

uniquely defined by $s_i{}^u = \lambda_u^{ij} \bar{s}_j{}^u$.

The new $\bar{g}^{uv}$ are related to g^{uv} by $\lambda^u \bar{g}^{uv} = g^{uv} \lambda^v$. Note that this is the non-Abelian analogue of being cohomologous.

In this way, one can construct an isomorphism between the set of isomorphism classes of vector bundles $\mathbf{F}_n(X)$ and the set $\check{H}^1(X, \underline{Gl(n, \mathbf{R})})$ consisting of equivalence classes of 1-cocycles with values in G. The $\check{H}$ means Čech cohomology, and we underline $Gl(n, \mathbf{R})$ to indicate that we are talking about sheaf cohomology.

We can replace $Gl(n)$ by any topological group G, and define $H^1(X, G)$, in the same way. An example of how this fact can be used is the following.

We have an exact sequence

$$0 \to \mathbf{Z}_2 \xrightarrow{i} \mathrm{Spin}(n) \to SO_n \to 0$$

of topological groups. From our experience in cohomology, we would expect to get an exact sequence of cohomology groups. This is the case. One gets an exact sequence

$$H^1(X, \mathbf{Z}_2) \overset{i^*}{\to} H^1(X, \underline{\mathrm{Spin}(n)}) \to H^1(X, \underline{SO_n}) \to H^2(X, \mathbf{Z}_2)$$

Geometrically, one can think of an element of $H^1(X, SO_n)$ as an oriented bundle with a Riemannian structure. An element of $H^1(X, \mathrm{Spin}\ (n))$ can be thought of as a bundle with a spin structure. Thus an oriented bundle E with an oriented Riemannian structure has a spin structure if and only if $\delta E = 0$. Thus, we have shown that the existence of a spin structure is equivalent to the vanishing of a certain second cohomology class. Note that the ambiguity in defining a spin structure is measured by $i^*H^1(X, \mathbf{Z}_2)$.

Let $\Gamma(E)$ be the set of continuous sections of E. (Examples of this are tensor fields on a manifold.) Now if E is constructed from the cocycle g^{uv}, then $\Gamma(E)$ corresponds to twisted functions on X. Precisely, a section s in $\Gamma(E)$ corresponds to a set of functions

$$f_j : U \to \mathbf{R}^n$$

such that on $U \cap V$,

$$f_u(x) = g^{uv}(x)f_v(x)$$

Example

On a manifold, let $\{U\}$ be a cover by coordinate neighborhoods with corresponding coordinate functions $x_u{}^1, \ldots, x_u{}^n$. Then on the overlap $U \cap V$ of two coordinate neighborhoods, we define

$$J^{uv}(x) = \left(\frac{\partial x_u{}^i}{\partial x_v{}^j} \right)$$

This defines the cotangent bundle. All tensor bundles on M are generated from $J^{uv}(x)$ by representations of $Gl(n, \mathbf{R})$. (A representation of $Gl(n, \mathbf{R})$ is a homomorphism $\rho : Gl(n, \mathbf{R}) \to Gl(m, \mathbf{R})$.) That is, any tensor bundle is given by the cocycle $\rho(J^{uv}(x))$ for suitable ρ, where $J^{uv}(x)$ is given by (*).

However, one can construct other bundles that have nothing to do with the Jacobian determinant.

Example

Bundles with group $Gl(1, \mathbf{R})$ are classified by $H^1(X, \mathbf{Z}_2)$ since $Gl(1, \mathbf{R}) \approx \mathbf{Z}_2 \times \mathbf{R}$ and

$$H^1(X, \mathbf{Z}_2 \times \mathbf{R}) = H^1(X, \mathbf{Z}_2)$$

In general, let G be a connected Lie group and let K be its maximal compact subgroup. Then $H^1(X, G) \approx H^1(X, K)$.

Now, let us try to construct m-dimensional vector bundles over S^n, that is, bundles with structure group $Gl(m, \mathbf{R})$. Let $U = S^n -$ south pole, $V = S^n -$ north pole. Then $U \cap V = S^{n-1} \times \mathbf{R}$. Note that U and V are contractible. According to Theorem 1 of this section, if U and V were compact, we could conclude that any vector bundle over U or over V is trivial. Actually, Theorem 1 is true in much more generality than we have stated it, and in fact it has an extension that includes this case. Thus the restriction of our bundle to either U or V is trivial. It follows that the bundle is determined up to isomorphism by the mapping $g^{uv}: S^{n-1} \times \mathbf{R} \to Gl(m, \mathbf{R})$. This construction leads to a one-to-one correspondence between $\pi_{n-1}(Gl(m, \mathbf{R}))$ and isomorphism classes of m-dimensional bundles on S^n. For details of the proof of this correspondence see N. Steenrod, *Topology of Fiber Bundles* (§18), Princeton University Press, Princeton, N.J., 1951.

Corollary. *Isomorphism classes of m-plane bundles over S^n are independent of m when m is large compared to n.*

As a matter of fact, we have already seen this result in more generality (Theorem 3), since the set of isomorphism classes of m-plane bundles over X, for m large, is essentially the same as what we called $\tilde{K}(X)$.

From the knowledge of the groups $\pi_k(0)$, we obtain Table 1 for $\tilde{K}(S^k)$

TABLE 1

k module 8	$\tilde{K}(S^k)$
1	$\mathbf{Z}_2$
2	$\mathbf{Z}_2$
3	0
4	$\mathbf{Z}$
5	0
6	0
7	0
8	$\mathbf{Z}$

Thus for m large, there are two isomorphism classes of real m-plane bundles on S^1, two on S^2, one on S^3, infinity on S^4, one on S^5, S^6, and S^7 and infinity on S^8.

We have shown

$$\mathbf{F}_n(S^k) \sim [S^{k-1}, Gl)n, \mathbf{R})]$$

Recall now that we already asserted that for an arbitrary finite complex X one has

$$\mathbf{F}_n(X) = [X, B_n]$$

for a suitable B_n.

The idea behind the construction of B_n is the following. We want to construct a bundle $\pi\colon E \to B_n$ such that for every bundle $\pi'\colon E' \to X_n$ there is a unique (up to homotopy) mapping $f\colon X \to B_n$ such that $E' \simeq f^{-1}E$. Start with $\pi'\colon E' \to X$, X compact. Let $\{U\}$ be a finite open cover of X, $\{s_u{}^i\}$ a family of local frames and let $\{\rho_u\}$ be a partition of unity subordinate to $\{U\}$. Then for each i and each U we set

$$\sigma_u{}^i(x) = \rho_u(x)s_u{}^i(x) \qquad x \in U$$
$$= 0 \qquad\qquad x \in X - U$$

Then $\sigma_u{}^i$ is a global section of E. These global sections generate a vector subspace of the space $\Gamma(E)$ of sections of E. Now, given $x \in X$, we let E_x be the fiber over x. Define

$$e\colon \Gamma(E) \to E_x$$

by $e(\sigma_u{}^i) = e_u{}^i(x)$ and linearity. Then e is a linear map of V onto E_x. Thus we get an exact sequence

$$*\qquad\qquad 0 \to K_x \to V \xrightarrow{e} E_x \to 0$$

Thus $x \to K_x$ is a mapping of X into $G_n(V)$, where $G_n(V)$ denotes the Grassmannian whose points are the subspaces of codimension n. Call this mapping f. Over the Grassmannian, there is a God-given bundle, called the quotient bundle Q, and

$$E = f^{-1}Q$$

The bundle Q is defined as follows. Let $A \in G_n(V)$. Then we have an exact sequence

$$0 \to A \to V \to V/A \to 0$$

The fiber of Q over a point A is V/A.

One finds $F_n(X) \simeq [X, G_n(V)]$ for some high-dimension V. One again proves a stability theorem: $[X, G_n(V)]$ is independent of V if the dimension of V is large enough. Out of this, one constructs B_n.

Now we know

$$\mathbf{F}_m(S^n) \approx \pi_n(Gl_m(V))$$
$$\wr\wr$$
$$\pi_{n-1}(Gl(m, \mathbf{R}))$$

Combining these, we get an isomorphism

$$\pi_{n-1}(Gl(m, \mathbf{R})) \approx \pi_n(G_m(V))$$

But this isomorphism also comes out of the exact sequence for the fibration

$$O(m) \to O(k + m)/O(k)$$
$$\downarrow$$
$$O(k + m)/O(k) \times O(m)$$

since $\pi_{n-1}(O(m)) = \pi_{n-1}(Gl(m, \mathbf{R}))$, $\pi_{n-1}(O(k + m)/O(k)) = 0$ for k large, and $O(k + m)/O(k) \times O(m)$ is homeomorphic to $G_m(V)$, if V is $(k + m)$-dimensional.

XIX

Continuous Solutions of Linear Equations—Some Exceptional Dimensions in Topology

BENO ECKMANN

This is a report on some elementary problems in real n-space $\mathbf{R}^n$ which admit solutions for a few exceptional values of n only. The results are stated in an elementary way, without reference to algebraic topology; the proofs, however, rely heavily on the technique of homology and general cohomology theory, and relate these results to a deep theorem in the topology of polyhedra.

516

1 VECTOR PRODUCTS AND CONTINUOUS SOLUTIONS

1.1 Vector Products

We first recall some properties of the usual "vector product" $a \times b$ of vectors a, b in $\mathbf{R}^3$:

(i)$_\circ$ $a \times b$ is bilinear in a and b.

(ii)$_\circ$ $a \times b$ is orthogonal to a and b, with respect to a positive-definite inner product $\langle \, , \, \rangle$ in $\mathbf{R}^3$.

(iii)$_\circ$ the length $|a \times b| = \langle a \times b, a \times b \rangle^{1/2}$ is given by $|a \times b|^2 = |a|^2 |b|^2 - \langle a, b \rangle^2$.

By a *continuous vector product of r vectors in* $\mathbf{R}^n$, $0 < r < n$, we understand a function $x(a_1, \ldots, a_r)$ of r variable vectors $a_1, \ldots, a_r \in \mathbf{R}^n$ with range $\mathbf{R}^n$ having properties analogous to those above, with (i)$_\circ$ replaced by continuity; i.e., a function satisfying

(i) x is continuous in $a_1, \ldots, a_r \in \mathbf{R}^n$.

(ii) $\langle x(a_1, \ldots, a_r), a_j \rangle = 0$ for $j = 1, \ldots, r$.

(iii) $|x(a_1, \ldots, a_r)|^2 = $ Determinant of $\langle a_i, a_j \rangle_{i, j = 1, \ldots, r}$.

$\langle \, , \, \rangle$ denotes again a positive-definite inner product in $\mathbf{R}^n$. The usual vector product $a \times b$ in $\mathbf{R}^3$ is an example for $n = 3$, $r = 2$. An example for n even, $r = 1$ can be given explicitly: Denote by $a^1, \ldots, a^n$ the components of the vector $a \in \mathbf{R}^n$ in a fixed orthonormal basis of $\mathbf{R}^n$, and let $x(a)$ be the vector with components $a^2, -a^1, a^4, -a^3, \ldots$. For arbitrary n and $r = n - 1$, a (multilinear) vector product is well known in linear algebra: consider the $n \times (n - 1)$ matrix of the components of the vectors $a_1, \ldots, a_{n-1} \in \mathbf{R}^n$, and take as components of $x(a_1, \ldots, a_{n-1})$ the $(n - 1) \times (n - 1)$ determinants of that matrix, in suitable order and with suitable signs.

There exist a further (bilinear) example for $n = 7$, $r = 2$; it is related to the Cayley number multiplication in $\mathbf{R}^8$ in the same manner the vector product $a \times b$ in $\mathbf{R}^3$ is related to the quaternion multiplication in $\mathbf{R}^4$. We recall that the quaternion multiplication in $\mathbf{R}^4$ can be described as follows: a vector $A \in \mathbf{R}^4 = \mathbf{R} \oplus \mathbf{R}^3$ is written uniquely as $A = \alpha + a$, $\alpha \in \mathbf{R}$, $a \in \mathbf{R}^3$; then the quaternion product $A \cdot B$, $A = \alpha + a$, $B = \beta + b$ is given by

$$A \cdot B = \alpha\beta - \langle a, b \rangle + \alpha b + \beta a + a \times b \tag{1}$$

It is immediately checked that this is indeed in agreement with the usual multiplication table of quaternions; the element $A = 1$ (that is, $\alpha = 1$, $a = 0$) is a two-sided unit. We note that the "norm product rule" valid for quaternions can be viewed as a consequence of (ii) and (iii): one extends the inner product of $\mathbf{R}^3$ to $\mathbf{R}^4$ by $\langle A, B \rangle = \alpha\beta + \langle a, b \rangle$; then the length of $A \cdot B$ is given by

$$
\begin{aligned}
|A \cdot B|^2 &= \alpha^2\beta^2 - 2\alpha\beta\langle a, b\rangle + \langle a, b\rangle^2 + \alpha^2|b|^2 + \beta^2|a|^2 + 2\alpha\beta\langle a, b\rangle \\
&\quad + |a \times b|^2 \\
&= \alpha^2\beta^2 + \alpha^2|b|^2 + \beta^2|a|^2 + \langle a, b\rangle + |a|^2|b|^2 - \langle a, b\rangle^2 \\
&= (\alpha^2 + |a|^2)(\beta^2 + |b|^2) = |A|^2|B|^2
\end{aligned}
$$

This equality

$$
|A \cdot B|^2 = |A|^2|B|^2
$$

is called the norm product rule.

One may, of course, define $a \times b$ in terms of the quaternion multiplication: we take, in (1), $\alpha = \beta = 0$ and obtain

$$
a \cdot b = -\langle a, b\rangle + a \times b \tag{2}
$$

Using this as a definition of $a \times b$, the associative law for quaternions yields $a \cdot (b \cdot b) = (a \cdot b) \cdot b$, where the left-hand side is in $\mathbf{R}^3$, since $b \cdot b = -|b|^2 \in \mathbf{R}$; the right-hand side is equal to $(-\langle a, b\rangle + a \times b) \cdot b = -\langle a \times b, b\rangle - \langle a, b\rangle b + (a \times b) \times b$, hence $\langle a \times b, b\rangle = 0$, and similarly $\langle a \times b, a\rangle = 0$. The above computation of $|A \cdot B|$ shows that then the norm product rule implies (iii): $|a \times b|^2 = |a|^2|b|^2 - \langle a, b\rangle^2$.

Now we turn to the Cayley multiplication in $\mathbf{R}^8 = \mathbf{R} \oplus \mathbf{R}^7$; it has all the properties which were just used for quaternions: $A = 1$ is a two-sided unit; the norm product rule holds; although the associative law is not valid for the Cayley numbers, its weaker form $(A \cdot B) \cdot B = A \cdot (B \cdot B)$ used above is valid. Thus $a \cdot b = -\langle a, b\rangle + a \times b$ defines $a \times b$ in $\mathbf{R}^7$ with all the required properties.

The Cayley numbers can further be used to define a (multilinear) vector product of 3 vectors in $\mathbf{R}^8$, cf. [7] or [6].

1.2   Nonexistence Theorems

In the case $r = 1$, the procedure given above to construct an example for n even obviously fails if n is odd, and it is clear that in this case a solution $x(a)$ which is linear in a cannot exist [for $\langle x(a), a\rangle = 0$ implies that $\langle x(a), b\rangle + \langle a, x(b)\rangle = 0$ for all $a, b \in \mathbf{R}^n$, and thus for n odd $x(a)$ has determinant 0, which contradicts (iii)]. But even if $x(a)$ is allowed to be continuous instead of linear, no such function can exist; for it would constitute on the unit sphere S^{n-1} given in $\mathbf{R}^n$ by $|a| = 1$ a continuous tangent unit vector field, and by a classical theorem of algebraic topology such a field does not exist on a sphere of even dimension. This is just the simplest case of the nonexistence theorem which is one of the objectives of this lecture (Theorem 1 below); it tells that except for the dimensions n and r which occur in the examples described in 1.1, vector products of r vectors in $\mathbf{R}^n$ cannot exist. Similar nonexistence theorems for related problems, allowing a few exceptional dimensions only, will be described in Section 2.

Theorem 1. Continuous vector products of r vectors in $\mathbf{R}^n$ exist only in the cases n even, $r = 1$; n arbitrary, $r = n - 1$; $n = 7$, $r = 2$; and $n = 8$, $r = 3$.

The proof of this theorem is discussed in 1.4 and in Section 3.

1.3 Continuous Solutions

An equivalent version of the existence problem of vector products can be given in terms of continuous solutions of linear equations. We consider a system of r linear equations:

$$\sum_{k=1}^{n} a_{ik} x_k = 0 \qquad i = 1, \ldots, r < n$$

in n unknowns $x_1, \ldots, x_n$ with real coefficients, and we ask for a solution $x_1, \ldots, x_n$ depending continuously on the coefficients a_{ik}, defined and nontrivial for all those real values of the $a_{11}, \ldots, a_{rn}$ for which the matrix has maximum rank r; that is, we ask for a system of continuous real functions $x_k = f_k(a_{11}, \ldots, a_{rn})$, defined and without common zeros for all admissible real values of the a_{ik} and satisfying the identities

$$\sum_{k=1}^{n} a_{ik} f_k(a_{11}, \ldots, a_{rn}) = 0 \qquad i = 1, \ldots, r$$

If such a solution exists, it can always be renormalized in such a way that

$$\sum_{k=1}^{n} x_k^2 = \mathrm{Det} \, \langle a_i, a_j \rangle_{i,j=1, \ldots, r}$$

where $\langle , \rangle$ is a positive-definite inner product in $\mathbf{R}^n$ and where a_i denotes the vector given in an orthonormal basis by the components $a_{i1}, \ldots, a_{in}, i = 1, \ldots, r$. If the functions $f_k(a_{11}, \ldots, a_{rn})$ are then extended to *all* real values of the a_{ik} by setting $f_k = 0$ if the rank of the matrix is $< r$, they remain continuous. The vector x with components $x_k = f_k(a_1, \ldots, a_r)$ is then a vector product of r vectors in $\mathbf{R}^n$.

Theorem 1'. A system of r real linear equations with r unknowns admits continuous solutions only for the values of n and r listed in Theorem 1.

In many applications solutions of linear systems should depend continuously upon the coefficients, or even in a more restricted way (differentiably, etc.). According to Theorem 1' this is possible—unless one is in the exceptional cases n, r—only if the domain of the coefficients a_{ik} is restricted in some way; or in different terms, if the solution is allowed to become trivial for some values of the coefficients. This statement can, of course, also be given a positive version: Let the pair of integers n, r with $0 < r < n$ be different from those in Theorem 1; if n continuous real functions $x_k = f_k(a_{11}, \ldots, a_{rn})$ defined for all real $n \times r$-matrices (a_{ik}) of rank r satisfy the identities

$$\sum_{k=1}^{n} a_{ik} f_k(a_{11}, \ldots, a_{rn}) = 0 \qquad i = 1, \ldots, r$$

then they must have a common zero.

1.4 Reduction

Lemma. If there exists a continuous vector product of r vectors in $\mathbf{R}^n$, then there also exists one of $r - 1$ vectors in $\mathbf{R}^{n-1}$.

PROOF. Let $x(a_1, \ldots, a_r)$ be the vector product in $\mathbf{R}^n$; consider $\mathbf{R}^{n-1}$ as a subspace of $\mathbf{R}^n$ and let $\mathbf{R}^1 = \mathbf{R}e$ be its orthogonal complement, with respect to $\langle , \rangle$. If we write $x(a_1, \ldots, a_r, e) = x' + x''$, $x' \in \mathbf{R}^{n-1}$, $x'' \in \mathbf{R}e$, one easily checks that x' as a function of $a_1, \ldots, a_{r-1}$ is a vector product in $\mathbf{R}^{n-1}$ (relative to the induced inner product).

To establish *nonexistence* (Theorem 1), it is therefore sufficient to do so for the lowest values of r.

The case $r = 1$ being settled, we have to consider $r = 2$. This case essentially reduces to the existence problem of continuous multiplications in $\mathbf{R}^{n+1}$: *If there exists a continuous vector product of two vectors in $\mathbf{R}^n$, then there exists in $\mathbf{R}^{n+1}$ a continuous multiplication $A \cdot B$ with two-sided unit and with norm product rule.*

Indeed, if $a \times b$ denotes the vector product in $\mathbf{R}^n$, and if $A \in \mathbf{R}^{n+1} = \mathbf{R} \oplus \mathbf{R}^n$ is written as $A = \alpha + a$, $\alpha \in \mathbf{R}$, $a \in \mathbf{R}^n$, then formula (1) above yields a continuous multiplication in $\mathbf{R}^{n+1}$ with $A = 1$ being the unit, and where the norm product rule follows from (ii) and (iii) exactly as shown above for the quaternions.

Multiplications in $\mathbf{R}^{n+1}$ of the required type are discussed in Section 2; the main result (Theorem A) states that they exist (if and) only if $n + 1 = 1, 2, 4$, or 8. Therefore a vector product of two vectors in $\mathbf{R}^n$ can only exist for $n = 3$ or 7; according to the reduction lemma a vector product of r vectors in $\mathbf{R}^n$ can only exist if $n - r = 1$ or $n - r = 5$. For $n = 7$, $r = 2$ and for $n = 8$, $r = 3$ (bilinear) vector products exist. To complete the proof of Theorem 1, one has therefore just to show that for $n = 9$, $r = 4$ no vector product can exist; this can be done by a simple cohomology ring argument (cf. [6]) in the Stiefel manifold $V_{9,5}$. The main burden of the proof, however, is transferred to the proof of Theorem A, sketched in Section 3.

2 CONTINUOUS MULTIPLICATIONS IN $\mathbf{R}^{n+1}$

The length $|A|$ of $A \in \mathbf{R}^{n+1}$ and the norm produced rule always refer to a positive-definite inner product in $\mathbf{R}^{n+1}$.

2.1 Adams' Theorem

Theorem A. A continuous multiplication in $\mathbf{R}^{n+1}$ with two-sided unit and with norm product rule exists only for $n + 1 = 1, 2, 4, 8$.

In the four exceptional cases multiplications of the required type do exist: the product of reals, of complex numbers, of quaternions, and of Cayley numbers have a unit and fulfill the norm product rule (for a suitable inner product). These multiplications are even bilinear; Hurwitz' classical theorem, the analog of Theorem A for the bilinear case, states that this can only occur in the dimensions $n + 1 = 1, 2, 4$, or 8. Thus Theorem A simply says that the possible dimensions remain the same if bilinearity is replaced by continuity.

Theorem A was first proved by Adams [1]. A very simple proof has been given by Adams–Atiyah [2] (*cf.* also [4] for a similar version which we use in Section 3 to give a sketch of the proof). The simplified proofs are based on the technique of *K*-theory and on some fundamental properties of the Chern character; for an introduction to these techniques see for example [4] and the reference given there.

As shown in 1.4, our Theorem 1 on continuous vector products (continuous solutions of linear equations) is essentially a corollary of Theorem A. The present section is devoted to further corollaries; they emphasize the great importance of Adams' theorem.

2.2 Division Algebras

$\mathbf{R}^{n+1}$ is turned into a division algebra, if a bilinear multiplication $A \cdot B$ is given which has no zero divisors. Note that the norm product rule is *not* required (but if it holds, there are, of course, no zero divisors). Without loss of generality, we can assume a bilinear multiplication to have a two-sided unit of length 1. If $A \cdot B$ is replaced by $A \cdot B \, |A| \, |B| / |A \cdot B|$ for $A, B \neq 0$, the new multiplication will satisfy the norm product rule. It will, however, have lost bilinearity, but remain continuous. Thus Theorem A implies

Theorem 2. $\mathbf{R}^{n+1}$ admits a division algebra structure (if and) only if $n + 1 = 1, 2, 4$ or 8.

2.3 Parallelizability of Spheres

The unit sphere $S^n \subset \mathbf{R}^{n+1}$ is said to be parallelizable, if there exist n tangent vector fields on S^n which are linearly independent at every point $X \in S^n$ ($X =$ unit vector $\in \mathbf{R}^{n+1}$). If this is the case, one can replace these fields by orthonormalized ones. The components of X and those of the n vector fields, with respect to an orthonormal basis of $\mathbf{R}^{n+1}$, taken as rows form an orthogonal $(n+1) \times (n+1)$ matrix $C = (c_{ik}(X))$, the elements $c_{ik}(X)$ being continous functions of X; we take the components of X as first row $c_{1k} = x_k$. Let y_k, $k = 1, \ldots, n$ be the components of $Y \in \mathbf{R}^{n+1}$ and define $Z \in \mathbf{R}^{n+1}$ by its components z_k,

$$z_k = \sum_{j=1}^{n} c_{jk}(X) y_j \qquad k = 1, \ldots, n$$

Writing $X \cdot Y$ for Z, this is a continuous multiplication in $\mathbf{R}^{n+1}$ (for $|X| = 1$, Y arbitrary) with $|X \cdot Y| = |Y|$. We extend it to all $X \in \mathbf{R}^{n+1}$ by $X \cdot Y = |X|((X/|X|) \cdot Y)$ for $X \neq 0$ and $0 \cdot Y = 0$. Then the norm product rule holds, and the vector $E = (1, 0, \ldots, 0)$ is a right unit. By a suitable choice of the basis one may assume $C(E)$ to be the unit matrix, that is, that E is also a left unit. Thus Theorem A implies

Theorem 3. S^n is parallelizable only for $n = 1$, 3, or 7.

Remarks. (a) In these three cases, the classical multiplications in $\mathbf{R}^2$, $\mathbf{R}^4$, and $\mathbf{R}^8$ actually yield a parallelization of S^n, by vector fields which are linear in X. (b) The multiplication $Z = X \cdot Y$ above is linear in Y and continuous in X. Thus Theorem A has not been used in its full generality. Other proofs of Theorem 3, not depending on Theorem A, have been given earlier (see, for example, [5]).

2.4 Almost-Complex Structures on Spheres

Let M be a complex-analytic manifold; its tangent bundle admits a complex vector bundle structure: Multiplication by $\sqrt{-1}$ of complex vector components in an admissible local complex coordinate system defines, at each point $p \in M$, a linear transformation $J(p)$ of the real tangent space M_p at p, with $J(p)^2 = -$identity, and $J(p)$ does not depend upon the complex coordinate system used. In fact the field $J(p)$ characterizes the complex-analytic structure given on M. If on a real differentiable manifold M such a field $J(p)$ of linear transformations with $J(p)^2 = -$identity is given, independently of any complex-analytic structure, M is called an almost-complex manifold (and $J(p)$ an almost-complex structure on M).

Theorem 4. S^n admits an almost-complex structure only for $n = 2$ or 6.

PROOF. If an almost-complex structure J is given on $S^{n-1} \subset \mathbf{R}^n$, a continuous vector product $a \times b$ can be defined in $\mathbf{R}^n$: for $a \in S^{n-1}$ and a unit tangent vector b at a (that is, for a and $b \in \mathbf{R}^n$ with $|a| = |b| = 1$, $\langle a, b \rangle = 0$), we consider the oriented tangent two-plane determined by b and $J(a)b$ and choose $a \times b$ to be the unit vector orthogonal to b in that plane and corresponding to the orientation; the product $a \times b$ is then easily extended to all a and $b \in \mathbf{R}^n$ so as to fulfill the properties of a vector product. Thus $n + 1$ must be $= 1$, 2, 4, or 8, that is, $n = 1$, 3, or 7, and hence the dimension of the sphere is 2 or 6. In these two dimensions, almost-complex structures actually exist.

2.5 Complex Vector Products

Theorem 5. A continuous vector product of two vectors in $\mathbf{C}^n$, with respect to a positive-definite Hermitian inner product in $\mathbf{C}^n$, only exists for $n = 3$.

The definition of the complex vector product is of course entirely analogous to the real case; the proof of Theorem 5 uses a construction similar to (1) to yield a continuous multiplication in $\mathbf{C}^{n+1}$ with two-sided unit and with norm product rule (with respect to the Hermitian length of vectors). This can be interpreted as a multiplication in $\mathbf{R}^{2n+2}$ with two-sided unit and norm product rule. Hence, $2n + 2 = 2$, 4, or 8, that is, $n = 3$.

3 PROOF OF THEOREM A AND GENERAL REMARKS

In this section we make free use, without reference, of concepts and results in algebraic topology of polyhedra (some of the material is covered in the course of R. Bott at these Rencontres); and further of K-theory and some of the fundamental properties of the Chern character of complex vector bundles. (For an introduction to these topics see, for example, [4] and references given there.)

In the proof of Theorem A the trivial case $n = 0$ will always be excluded.

3.1 Pseudoprojective Planes

If in $\mathbf{R}^{n+1}$ a continuous multiplication $A \cdot B$ with unit E and with norm product rule is given, we consider the map $f: S^n \times S^n \to S^n$ defined by $f(A, B) = A \cdot B$, $|A| = |B| = 1$ (that is, (A, B) is considered to be a point of $S^n \times S^n$). The map f restricted to $S^n \times E$ is the identity of S^n (that is, a map of degree 1), and so is f restricted to $E \times S^n$. By an elementary construction due to Hopf one obtains from f a map $F: S^{2n+1} \to S^{n+1}$ having "Hopf invariant one." F is used to attach to S^{n+1} a $(2n + 2)$-cell e^{2n+2} by mapping the boundary of e^{2n+2} to S^{n+1} by F (*cf.* Bott's course). The poly-hedron (finite CW-complex) $X = S^{n+1} \bigcup_F e^{2n+2}$ may be called the pseudo-projective plane over R^{n+1} relative to the given multiplication; for $n = 1$ and the **C**-multiplication in $\mathbf{R}^2$, X is the complex projective plane CP_2, and the above construction is a simple generalization of the usual procedure which leads from the affine plane $\mathbf{C}^2$ to CP_2.

The cohomology algebra with integer coefficients $H(X)$ of this poly-hedron X is easily computed from the explicit cell structure: it is the poly-nomial algebra $\mathbf{Z}[a]$ over the integers $\mathbf{Z}$ in a certain element $a \in H^{n+1}(X)$, modulo the ideal (a^3) generated by a^3,

$$H(X) = \mathbf{Z}[a]/(a^3) \qquad a \in H^{n+1}(X)$$

the generator a corresponds to the fundamental cohomology class of $S^{n+1} \subset X$. Theorem A is then an immediate consequence of the following purely cohomological theorem (which, in its turn, admits further interesting generalizations, see [2]).

Theorem A'. A finite polyhedron X with $H(X) = \mathbf{Z}[a]/(a^3)$, $a \in H^{n+1}(X)$, exists only for $n + 1 = 2, 4$, or 8.

From the anticommutativity of the graded algebra $H(X)$ it is clear that $n + 1$ must be even; we put $n + 1 = 2l$.

3.2 Properties of $K(X)$

We now consider the group $K(X)$ for an arbitrary finite polyhedron X; it is the Grothendieck group of complex vector bundles over X, or equiva-lently, the group of homotopy classes of maps of X into ΩU (the "loop space of the infinite unitary group," *cf.* Bott's lectures). We will use a few standard properties of the contravariant functor K, listed below.

The tensor product of complex vector bundles defines in $K(X)$ a com-mutative ring structure with unit. There exists a natural transformation ch, called the Chern character of complex vector bundles, of $K(X)$ into $H(X; \mathbf{Q})$, the cohomology algebra of X over the rationals $\mathbf{Q}$; it maps $K(X)$ into even-dimensional cohomology only:

$$\text{ch } z = a_0 + a_2 + \cdots + a_{2j} + \cdots \qquad a_{2j} \in H^{2j}(X; \mathbf{Q})$$

for $z \in K(X)$, and it is a ring homomorphism. Furthermore there exist natural transformations $\psi_k : K(X) \to K(X)$, the Adams operations, one for each $k = 1, 2, 3, \ldots$, which are ring homomorphisms and related to the Chern character by

$$\text{ch } \psi_k z = a_0 + k a_2 + \cdots + k^j a_{2j} + \cdots$$

where ch $z = a_0 + a_2 + \cdots + a_{2j} + \cdots$ as above with $a_{2j} \in H^{2j}(X; \mathbf{Q})$. The ψ_k are defined by means of exterior powers Λ_q of complex vector bundles; in particular, $\psi_2 z = z^2 - 2\Lambda_2 z$.

If the polyhedron X is without torsion, that is, if $H(X)$ over the integers has no torsion, ch $: K(X) \to H(X; \mathbf{Q}) = H(X) \otimes \mathbf{Q}$ has kernel 0. Moreover, in ch $z = a_0 + a_2 + \cdots + a_{2j} + \cdots$, the first nonvanishing term, say, a_{2i}, is *integral*, that is, it lies in the subgroup $H^{2i}(X) \subset H^{2i}(X; \mathbf{Q})$, where the integral cohomology is identified with its natural image in $H^{2i}(X; \mathbf{Q}) = H^{2i}(X) \otimes \mathbf{Q}$; any given element of $H^{2i}(X)$, $i = 0, 1, 2, \ldots$, appears in this way as the first nonvanishing component of ch z for some $z \in K(X)$ (these last statements constitute the Atiyah–Hirzebruch integrality theorem in its simplest version).

3.3 Proof of Theorem A′

In the case of Theorem A′ we consider a polyhedron X with $H(X) = \mathbf{Z}[a]/(a^3)$, $H(X; \mathbf{Q}) = \mathbf{Q}[a]/(a^3)$, $a \in H^{2l}(X)$, $2l = n + 1$. There exists an element $z \in K(X)$ with

$$\text{ch } z = a + \lambda a^2 \qquad \lambda \in \mathbf{Q}$$

For this z the properties listed in 3.2 yield the following relations:

$$\text{ch } z^2 = a^2$$
$$\text{ch } \psi_k z = k^l a + \lambda k^{2l} a^2$$
$$\text{ch } (\psi_k z - k^l z) = \lambda k^l (k^l - 1) a^2 = \lambda k^l (k^l - 1) \text{ ch } z^2$$

with $\lambda k^l (k^l - 1) \in \mathbf{Z}$. Since the kernel of ch is 0, $\psi_k z = k^l z + \lambda k^l (k^l - 1) z^2$. In particular, for $k = 2$, we have

$$\psi_2 z = 2^l z + \lambda 2^l (2^l - 1) z^2 = z^2 - 2\Lambda_2 z$$

therefore $\lambda 2^l (2^l - 1)$ is odd, and thus $\lambda \in \mathbf{Q}$ must be of the form

$$\lambda = \frac{\text{odd}}{\text{odd} \cdot 2^l}$$

For an arbitrary odd integer $k \geqslant 1$, $(\text{odd}/\text{odd} \cdot 2l) \cdot k^l (k^l - 1)$ is an integer, which means that 2^l divides $k^l - 1$.

Thus from the existence of a polyhedron X satisfying the assumption of Theorem A′, $n + 1 = 2l$, we conclude that 2^l *divides* $k^l - 1$ *for all odd integers* $k \geqslant 1$.

From this purely numerical result one easily draws very precise conclusions. First we note that for $l = 1$ the property holds, and we therefore assume $l > 1$. Taking $k = 2^{l-1} + 1$, the fact that 2^l divides $(2^{l-1} + 1)^l - 1 = 2^l \cdot \text{integer} + l2^{l-1}$ implies that l is even, $l = 2m$. Taking $k = 2^m + 1$, the fact that 2^{2m} divides $(2^m + 1)^{2m} - 1 = 2^{2m} \cdot \text{integer} + 2m2^m$ implies that 2^{2m} divides $m2^{m+1}$, that is, 2^{m-1} *divides m*. This is so for $m = 1$ and 2 only, whence $l = 2$ or 4. Together with $l = 1$, we thus have $n + 1 = 2l = 2, 4,$ or 8, which proves Theorem A′.

3.4 Remarks

We finally remark that Theorem A can be given the following interpretation: With regard to the existence of multiplications in $\mathbf{R}^{n+1}$ with unit and with norm product rule, the *dimensions which are exceptional* (in the sense that such a multiplication exists) *in the continuous case are also exceptional in the bilinear case* (the latter is solved by Hurwitz' classical theorem, that is, by elementary algebra). The proof reproduced above, although it is very simple, does not explain directly why this is so. The situation is similar in various other problems of that type; for example, in the vector product problem (continuous solutions of linear equations) from which we started; or in the problem of finding the maximum number of independent tangent vector fields on a sphere, also solved by Adams [8], and in the application thereof to linear families of nonsingular matrices [9]. It would be most interesting to find an *a priori* reason why the existence of "continuous solutions" in all these cases implies the existence of "linear solutions" (or, in any case, simple algebraic solutions). If such a reduction principle from the continuous to the algebraic case could be established, it might clarify the exceptional character of certain low dimensions n of the real n-spaces.

REFERENCES

1. J. F. Adams, *Ann. of Math.* **72** (1960), 20–104.
2. J. F. Adams and M. F. Atiyah, *Quart. J. Math.* **17** (1966), 31–38.
3. B. Eckmann, *Comm. Math. Helv.* **15** (1942/43), 318–339.
4. B. Eckmann, *Cours CIME* (cohomologie et classes caractéristiques) (1966).
5. M. Kervaire, *Proc. Nat. Acad. Sci. USA* (1958), 280–283.
6. G. W. Whitehead, *Comm. Math. Helv.* **37** (1962), 239–240.
7. P. Zvengrowski, *Comm. Math. Helv.* **40** (1965/66), 149–152.
8. J. F. Adams, *Ann. of Math.* **75** (1962), 603–632.
9. J. F. Adams, P. Lax, and R. S. Phillips, *Proc. A.M.S.*, **16** (1965), 318–322.

XX

Differentiable Dynamical Systems

STEPHEN SMALE

An article with the same title appears in the *Bulletin of the American Mathematical Society* **73**, 747 (1967).

XXI

Characterization of
Stable Mappings

JOHN N. MATHER

We let N and P be C^∞ manifolds without boundary. We suppose N and P are finite dimensional, have countable bases for their topologies, and are Hausdorff. We set $n = \dim N$, $p = \dim P$.

For each nonnegative integer k, we let $J^k(N, P)$ denote the bundle of k jets of mappings of N into P. This is a bundle over $N \times P$ and also over N and over P. For any C^k mapping $f: N \to P$, we let $j^k(f): N \to J^k(N, P)$ denote the k-jet extension of f. We let W_k denote the Whitney C^k topology on the set $C^\infty(N, P)$ of C^∞ mappings of N into P. This topology has for basis the family of sets $M(U)$, for U open in $J^k(N, P)$, where we set $M(U) = \{f \in C^\infty(N, P) : j^k(f)[N] \subset U\}$.

We let W denote the topology on $C^\infty(N, P)$ generated by $\bigcup_k W_k$.

Definition 1. $f \in C^\infty(N, P)$ is *stable* if there exists a neighborhood U of f in $C^\infty(N, P)$ (with respect to the topology W) such that for every $g \in U$ there exists $h \in \operatorname{Diff} N$ (the set of C^∞ diffeomorphisms of N into itself) and $h' \in \operatorname{Diff} P$ such that $g = h' \circ f \circ h$.

In this paper, we will state a theorem characterizing the stable proper mappings in terms of local data. We will outline part of the proof. Details will be given elsewhere.

For any manifold U and any $u \in U$ we let $C^\infty(U)_u$ denote the ring of germs at u of C^∞ functions on U. We let $\mathfrak{M}_u$ denote the maximal ideal in $C^\infty(U)_u$.

For each $z \in J^k(N, P)$, we set $Q(z) = C^\infty(N)_x/(f^*[\mathfrak{M}_y] \cdot C^\infty(N)_x + \mathfrak{M}_x^{k+1})$, where x is the source of z, y is the target of z, and f is any representative of z. [In other words $\langle x, y \rangle$ is the image of z under the bundle mapping of $J^k(N, P)$ on $N \times P$, and $z = j^k(f)(x)$.] $Q(z)$ is an $\mathbf{R}$ algebra. The term $\mathfrak{M}_x^{k+1}$ in the denominator guarantees that $Q(z)$ depends only on z, not on the choice of f.

We will say $z \in J^k(N, P)$ and $z' \in J^k(N', P')$ (where dim $N' = $ dim N, dim P' $= $ dim P) are *contact equivalent* if the **R** algebras $Q(z)$ and $Q(z')$ are isomorphic. By a *contact class* in $J^k(N, P)$, we mean an equivalence class under the relation of contact equivalence.

Lemma 1. If U is a contact class in $J^k(N, P)$, then U is a submanifold.

PROOF. For any $x \in N$ and any $y \in P$ we let $J^k_{x, y}$, denote the fiber of $J^k = J^k(N, P)$ over $\langle x, y \rangle$. We let $U_{x, y}$ denote the fiber of U over $\langle x, y \rangle$. It is enough to show that $U_{x, y}$ is a submanifold of $J^k_{x, y}$.

Let $K_{x, y}$ denote the group (under composition) of invertible C^∞ germs of mappings $H : (N \times P, x \times y) \longrightarrow (N \times P, x \times y)$ such that there exists a C^∞ germ of a mapping $h : (N, x) \longrightarrow (N, x)$ making Diag. 1 commutative.

$$(N, x) \xrightarrow{xy} (N \times P, x \times y) \xrightarrow{\text{proj.}} (N, x)$$

$$\downarrow h \qquad\qquad \downarrow H \qquad\qquad\qquad \downarrow h$$

$$(N, x) \xrightarrow{xy} (N \times P, x \times y) \xrightarrow{\text{proj.}} (N, x)$$

DIAGRAM 1

Let $K^k_{x, y}$ denote the quotient of $K_{x, y}$ by the subgroup of $K_{x, y}$ consisting of those H which have the same k-jet as the identity.

There is a natural action of $K^k_{x, y}$ on $J^k_{x, y}$ which may be described as follows: Let $\eta \in K^k_{x, y}$ and $z \in J^k_{x, y}$. Let $H : (N \times P, \ x \times y) \longrightarrow (N \times P, x \times y)$ be a representative of η and $f : (N, x) \longrightarrow (P, y)$ be a representative of z. Let $h : (N, x) \longrightarrow (N, x)$ be such that Diag. 1 commutes. Let $g : (N, x) \longrightarrow (P, y)$ be the unique germ of a mapping such that

$$\langle 1_N, g \rangle = H \circ \langle 1_N, f \rangle \circ h^{-1} : (N, x) \longrightarrow (N \times P, x \times y)$$

Then $\eta \cdot z$ is defined as the k-jet of g. It is easily seen that $\eta \cdot z$ is independent of the choices made and that this defines a left action of $K^k_{x, y}$ on $J^k_{x, y}$.

The space $J^k_{x, y}$ has, of course, a natural structure of a C^∞ manifold. Likewise $K^k_{x, y}$ has a natural structure of a Lie group. The action of $K^k_{x, y}$ on $J^k_{x, y}$ is C^∞. In fact, one may say more. We may regard $J^k_{x, y}$ (in a natural way) as the set of **R** rational points of a nonsingular variety defined over the field **Q** of rational numbers. Likewise, we may regard $K^k_{x, y}$ as the set of **R** rational points of an algebraic group defined over **Q**. The action of $K^k_{x, y}$ on $J^k_{x, y}$ is **Q** rational.

It follows that any orbit of the action of $K^k_{x, y}$ on $J^k_{x, y}$ is a C^∞ submanifold. It is easily seen that two points $z, z' \in J^k_{x, y}$ are in the same orbit if and only if they are contact equivalent. In particular, $U_{x, y}$ is an orbit of this action. This completes the proof.

An element $z \in J^k(N, P)$ will be said to be *submersive* if any representative f of z has the property that $Tf_x : TN_x \to TP_{f(x)}$ is onto, where x denotes the source of z. Clearly there are no submersive jets in $J^k(N, P)$ if dim $N < P$, and the submersive jets constitute a contact class if dim $N \geqslant$ dim P. This will be called the submersive contact class; all other contact classes will be said to be nonsubmersive.

Lemma 2. If U is a nonsubmersive contact class of $J^k(N, P)$ and $j^k(f)$ is transversal to U, then

$$|j^k(f)^{-1}U : j^k(f)^{-1}U \to P$$

is an immersion.

We will not give the proof here.

For any manifold U, we let TU denote the tangent bundle of U. For any C^∞ mapping $g : U \to V$, we let $Tg : TU \to TV$ denote the induced mapping. For any bundle E, we let $\Gamma(E)$ denote the set of C^∞ sections of E. We define $tf : \Gamma(TN) \to \Gamma(f^*TP)$ by $tf(\xi) = Tf \circ \xi$ and $\omega f : \Gamma(TP) \to \Gamma(f^*TP)$ by $\omega f(\eta) = \eta \circ f$. (Compare Diag. 2.)

$$
\begin{array}{ccc}
TN & \xrightarrow{\ Tf\ } & TP \\
\xi \Big\uparrow\Big\downarrow \text{proj} & & \text{proj} \Big\uparrow\Big\downarrow n \\
N & \xrightarrow[\ f\ ]{} & P
\end{array}
$$

DIAGRAM 2

Definition 2. f is *infinitesimally stable* if $tf + \omega f$ is onto.

Proposition A. Let $f : N \to P$ be a proper C^∞ mapping. Then (i), (ii), (iii) below are equivalent, if $k \geqslant$ dim P.

  (i) The following two conditions hold:

  (a) $j^k(f)$ is transversal to every contact class in $J^k(N, P)$.

  (b) If $U_1, \ldots, U_a$ are nonsubmersive contact classes of $J^k(N, P)$,

then the family of immersions

$$f|j^k(f)^{-1}U_i : j^k(f)^{-1}U_i \to P \qquad i = 1, \ldots, a$$

has only normal crossings.

  (ii) f is infinitesimally stable.

  (iii) f is stable.

In the above theorem "normal crossings" means the following: Given a family of C^∞ mappings $g_i : V_i \to Q$, $i = 1, \ldots, a$ of C^∞ manifolds, and points $x_1, \ldots, x_b$, where each x_i is contained in some $V_{j(i)}$, we say the

b-tuple $x = \langle x_1, \ldots, x_b \rangle$ is a *crossing* if $g_{j(1)}(x_1) = \cdots = g_{j(b)}(x_b)$. Let y denote this common value. We say x is a *normal* crossing if

$$\text{cod} \bigcap_{i=1}^{b} Tg_{j(i)}[T(V_{j(i)})_{x_i}]) = \sum_{i=1}^{b} \text{cod } Tg_{j(i)}[T(V_{j(i)})_{x_i}]$$

where cod means the codimension in TQ_y.

The proof goes (i) $\Rightarrow$ (ii) $\Rightarrow$ (iii) $\Rightarrow$ (i). We will now outline the proof that (i) $\Rightarrow$ (ii).

There is a natural identification

$$T(J_x^{\,k})_z = \frac{\Gamma(f^*TP)}{\mathfrak{M}_x^{k+1}\Gamma(f^*TP)} \tag{1}$$

for any $f \in C^\infty(N, P)$, and any $x \in N$, where $z = j^k(f)(x)$. $T(J_x^{\,k})_z$ denotes the tangent space to $J_x^{\,k}$ at z. We consider $\Gamma(f^*TP)$ as a $C^\infty(N)$ module in the obvious way. [$C^\infty(N)$ denotes the ring of C^∞ functions on N, with values in **R**.] We let $\mathfrak{M}_x$ denote the ideal in $C^\infty(N)$ consisting of those functions which vanish at x. Note that $\mathfrak{M}_x^{k+1}$ (which, by definition, is the set of all sums of products $f_1 \ldots f_{k+1}$, where each $f_i \in \mathfrak{M}_x$) is the set of $f \in C^\infty(N)$ which vanish at x together with their derivatives of order $\leqslant k$ (with respect to some coordinate system).

The identification (1) may be described as follows: Let

$$\bar{\xi} \in \Gamma(f^*TP)_x \mathfrak{M}_x^{k+1}\Gamma(f^*TP)$$

Let ζ be a member of $\Gamma(f^*TP)$ which projects onto $\bar{\zeta}$. Let f_t be a family of C^∞ mappings of N into P, depending differentiably on all variables, and defined for t in a small interval $(-\varepsilon, \varepsilon)$ about 0, such that $\partial f_t/\partial t|_{t=0} = \zeta$. For each $t \in (-\varepsilon, \varepsilon)$, let $z_t = j^k(f_t)(x)$. Then $\partial z_t/\partial t|_{t=0}$ is in $T(J_x^{\,k})_z$. We identify $\bar{\zeta}$ with $\partial z_t/\partial t|_{t=0}$. It is easily seen that this defines an identification of **R** vector spaces.

In terms of the identification (1), we obtain the following equalities: Trivially,

$$T(J_{x,y}^k)_z = \frac{\mathfrak{M}_x \Gamma(f^*TP)}{\mathfrak{M}_x^{k+1}\Gamma(f^*TP)} \tag{2}$$

where y is the target of z. Let U denote the contact class containing z. Let U_x, resp. $U_{x,y}$, denote the fiber of U over x, resp. x, y. Then

$$T(U_{x,y})_z = \frac{tf[\mathfrak{M}_x \Gamma(TN)] + (f^*[\mathfrak{M}_y] + \mathfrak{M}_x^{k+1})\Gamma(f^*TP)}{\mathfrak{M}_x^{k+1}\Gamma(f^*TP)} \tag{3}$$

and

$$T(U_x)_z = \frac{tf[\mathfrak{M}_x \Gamma(TN)] + \omega f[\Gamma(TP)] + (f^*[\mathfrak{M}_y] + \mathfrak{M}_x^{k+1})\Gamma(f^*TP)}{\mathfrak{M}_x^{k+1}\Gamma(f^*TP)} \tag{4}$$

Formula (3) is an easy consequence of the fact that $U_{x,y}$ is the orbit of z under the action of $K_{x,y}^k$. Then (4) follows from (3) by means of a computation using local coordinates.

Clearly the projection $T(U)_z \to TN_x$ is onto. Hence there is a subspace W of $T(U)_z$ such that the projection $W \to TN_x$ is an isomorphism. Then $T(J^k)_z = T(J_x)_z \oplus W$ so there is a unique linear mapping $\pi_W : T(J^k)_z \to T(J_x^k)_z$ such that $\pi_W | W = 0$ and $\pi_W | T(J_x^k)_z = $ identity. It is easily seen that for any subspace V of $T(J^k)_z$, $\pi_W [V + T(U)_z]$ is independent of the choice of W. The following formula is easily verified using local coordinates, and formula (4).

$$\pi_W [Tj^k(f)[TN_x] + T(U)_z]$$

$$= \frac{tf[\Gamma(TN)] + \omega f[\Gamma(TP)] + (f^*[\mathfrak{M}_y] + \mathfrak{M}_x^{k+1})\Gamma(f^*TP)}{\mathfrak{M}_x^{k+1}\Gamma(f^*TP)} \quad (5)$$

Since $j^k(f)$ is transversal to U at x if and only if $Tj^k(f)[TN_x] + T(U)_z = T(J^k)_z$ and since $W \subset T(U)_z$, it follows that $j^k(f)$ is transversal to U at x if and only if the left-hand side of (5) is $T(J_x^k)_z$. By the identification (1) this is true if and only if the right-hand side of (5) is $\Gamma(f^*TP)/\mathfrak{M}_x^{k+1}\Gamma(f^*TP)$. Thus we obtain the following:

Lemma 3. If condition (i-a) of Proposition A holds, then

$$tf[\Gamma(TN)] + \omega f[\Gamma(TP)] + (f^*[\mathfrak{M}_y] + \mathfrak{M}_x^{k+1})\Gamma(f^*TP) = \Gamma(f^*TP)$$

for any $x \in N$, where $Y = f(x)$.

For any subset S of N, let $\mathfrak{M}_S$ denote the ideal in $C^\infty(N)$ consisting of functions vanishing on S. Then Lemma 3 can be generalized as follows:

Lemma 3'. Suppose condition (i) of Proposition A holds. Then for any finite subset $S = \{x_1, \ldots, x_q\}$ of N, such that $f(x_1) = \cdots = f(x_q) = y$,

$$tf[\Gamma(TN)] + \omega f[\Gamma(TP)] + (f^*[\mathfrak{M}_y] + \mathfrak{M}_S^{k+1})\Gamma(f^*TP) = \Gamma(f^*TP) \quad (6)$$

The proof follows the same lines as the proof of Lemma 3; however, we will not give the details.

Using Lemma 3', Nakayama's lemma, and Malgrange's preparation theorem, we will now complete the proof that (i) $\Rightarrow$ (ii).

Let $\mathfrak{I}_S$ denote the ideal of $C^\infty(N)$ consisting of functions vanishing identically in a neighborhood of S. Then (6) (for $k \geq \dim P$) implies

$$tf[\Gamma(TN)] + \omega f[\Gamma(TP)] + (f^*[\mathfrak{M}_y] + \mathfrak{I}_S)\Gamma(f^*TP) = \Gamma(f^*TP) \quad (7)$$

(We have replaced $\mathfrak{M}_s^{k+1}$ by the smaller ideal $\mathfrak{I}_S$.) This is shown as follows:
Set

$$E_l = tf[\Gamma(TN)] + (f^*[\mathfrak{M}_y] + \mathfrak{M}_S^l)\Gamma(f^*TP)$$

Then E_{k+1} contains all of the terms of the left-hand side of (6), except $\omega f[\Gamma(TP)]$. Also E_{k+1} contains $\omega f(\mathfrak{M}_y \Gamma(TP))$, since this is contained in $f^*[\mathfrak{M}_y] \cdot \Gamma(f^*TP)$. Thus, it follows from (6) that the **R** codimension of E_{k+1} in $\Gamma(f^*TP)$ is at most $p = \dim P$. (By the **R** codimension of one **R** vector space E in another F, we mean the dimension of F/E, considered as an **R** vector space.) Since $E_0 \supset E_1 \supset \cdots \supset E_{k+1}$ and $k \geqslant p$, it follows that $E_j = E_{j+1}$ for some j, $0 \leqslant j \leqslant k$. It follows easily that

$$E_j = D + \mathfrak{M}_S E_j \tag{8}$$

where

$$D = tf[\Gamma(TN)] + f^*[\mathfrak{M}_y] \cdot \Gamma(f^*TP)$$

Now we apply Nakayama's lemma in the following form.

Nakayama's Lemma. Let R be a ring, $\mathfrak{I}_1$ and $\mathfrak{I}_2$ ideals in R, M a finitely generated module over R, and N a submodule of M. Suppose every maximal ideal which contains $\mathfrak{I}_2$ also contains $\mathfrak{I}_1$, and that

$$M = N + \mathfrak{I}_1 M$$

Then

$$M = N + \mathfrak{I}_2 M$$

This is well known in the case $\mathfrak{I}_2 = 0$, and is easily reduced to that case.

Applying Nakayama's lemma with $R = C^\infty(N)$, $\mathfrak{I}_1 = \mathfrak{M}_S$, $\mathfrak{I}_2 = \mathfrak{I}_S$, $M = E_j$, and $N = D$, we see that (8) implies

$$E_j = D + \mathfrak{I}_S E_j$$

Hence

$$D + \mathfrak{I}_S \Gamma(f^*TP) \supset \mathfrak{M}_S{}^j \Gamma(f^*TP)$$

Since $j \leqslant k$, this formula and (6) imply (7). Thus, we have established (7), assuming that condition (i) of the theorem holds.

Next, we use (7) to show

$$tf[\Gamma(TN)] + \omega f[\Gamma(TP)] + \mathfrak{I}_S \Gamma(f^*TP) = \Gamma(f^*TP) \tag{9}$$

The proof that (7) implies that (9) is based on Malgrange's preparation theorem and Nakayama's lemma.

As usual, we let $C^\infty(N)_S$ denote the ring of germs at S of C^∞ functions on N, and $f^* : C^\infty(P)_y \to C^\infty(N)_S$ the ring homomorphism given by $f^*(g) = g \circ f$.

Malgrange's Preparation Theorem [1]. If A is a finitely generated $C^\infty(N)_S$ module, and $A/f^*[\mathfrak{M}_y] \cdot A$ is finite dimensional as an **R** vector space, then

A is finitely generated as a $C^\infty(P)_y$ module, where the $C^\infty(P)_y$ module structure on A is induced by f^*.

This is a deep result and will not be proved here. Actually Malgrange stated the result only for the case when A is generated by a single element, and S was a single point, but the extension to the more general case is very easy.

Let

$$A = \frac{\Gamma(f^*TP)}{tf[\Gamma(TN)] + \mathfrak{J}_S\Gamma(f^*TP)}$$

Since $C^\infty(N)_S = C^\infty(N)/\mathfrak{J}_S$, A is a $C^\infty(N)_S$ module. Clearly it is finitely generated. Formula (7) implies $\bar{A} = A/f^*[\mathfrak{M}_y] \cdot A$ is finite dimensional as an **R** vector space. In fact, it implies that the canonical images of $\omega f(e_1), \ldots,$ $\omega f(e_q)$ in $\bar{A}$ span $\bar{A}$ as an **R** vector space for any set $e_1, \ldots, e_q$ of $C^\infty(P)$ generators of $\Gamma(TP)$. Thus A is finitely generated as a $C^\infty(P)_y$ module, by Malgrange's preparation theorem. Now we may apply Nakayama's lemma with $R = C^\infty(P)_y$, $\mathfrak{J}_1 = \mathfrak{M}_y$, $\mathfrak{J}_2 = 0$, $M = A$, and N the submodule generated by the canonical images of $\omega f(e_1), \ldots, \omega f(e_q)(e_1, \ldots, e_q$ as above). The conclusion $M = N$ means that the submodule of A generated by the canonical images of $\omega f(e_1), \ldots, \omega f(e_q)$ is all of A, which implies (9). Thus we have shown that condition (i) of Proposition A implies (9). (Note that we had to know A was finitely generated as a $C^\infty(P)_y$ module in order to be able to apply Nakayama's lemma.)

Now we conclude the proof that (i) implies (ii) by showing that (9) holding for all finite subsets S of N such that $f[S]$ is a single point implies f is infinitesimally stable.

For any $C^\infty(N)$ module E, let supp E denote the set of points $x \in N$ such that $\mathfrak{J}_x E \neq E$. Suppose E is finitely generated. Then $x \in$ supp E if and only if $\mathfrak{M}_x E \neq E$ (by Nakayama's lemma) and supp E is closed. If S is a finite set, then the number of points in supp $E \cap S$ is less than or equal to dim $_\mathbf{R} E/\mathfrak{M}_S E$.

Suppose $y \in P$ and S is a finite subset of N such that $f[S] = y$. Set

$$E = \frac{\Gamma(f^*TP)}{tf[\Gamma(TN)]} \qquad (10)$$

Let $\bar{p}$ be the projection of $\Gamma(f^*TP)$ on $\bar{E} = E/\mathfrak{M}_S E$. By (9), $\bar{p} \circ \omega f[\Gamma(TP)] = \bar{E}$. Clearly $\bar{p} \circ \omega f[\mathfrak{M}_y \cdot \Gamma(TP)] = 0$. Hence,

$$\dim{_\mathbf{R}}\bar{E} \leqslant \dim{_\mathbf{R}} \frac{\Gamma(TP)}{\mathfrak{M}_y \Gamma(TP)} = p$$

Hence supp $E \cap S$ contains no more than p points. Since we may take S to be an arbitrary finite subset of $f^{-1}(y)$, it follows that $f^{-1}(y) \cap$ supp E contains not more than p points.

To show $tf[\Gamma(TN)] + \omega f[\Gamma(TP)] = \Gamma(f^*TP)$, we consider an arbitrary $\zeta \in \Gamma(f^*TP)$. We let $e_1, \ldots, e_q$ be a basis for $\Gamma(f^*TP)$ over $C^\infty(N)$. For each $y \in P$, let $S_y = \operatorname{supp} E \cap f^{-1}(y)$, where E is given by (10). By the previous paragraph S_y is finite. Hence (9) holds for $S = S_y$, so there exist $\xi_y \in \Gamma(TN)$, $\eta_y \in \Gamma(TP)$, $g_{1,y}, \ldots, g_{q,y} \in \mathfrak{I}_S$ such that

$$tf(\xi_y) + \omega f(\eta_y) + \sum_{i=1}^{q} g_{i,y} e_i = \zeta \tag{11}$$

Let N_y be an open neighborhood of S in N such that $g_{1,y}|N_y = \cdots = g_{q,y}|N_y = 0$. A simple point set topological argument, using the assumption that f is proper, shows that there exists an open neighborhood P_y of y in P such that $f^{-1}[P_y] \cap \operatorname{supp} E \subset N_y$. Let $\{P_\alpha\}_{\alpha \in A}$ be a locally finite cover of P by open sets such that for each $\alpha \in A$ there exists $y = y(\alpha) \in P$ such that the closure $\bar{P}_\alpha$ of P_α is in $P_{y(\alpha)}$. Let $\{\rho_\alpha\}_{\alpha \in A}$ be a C^∞ partition of unity on P such that $\operatorname{supp} \rho_\alpha \subseteq P_\alpha$ for each $\alpha \in A$.

Set

$$\xi' = \Sigma_{\alpha \in A} f^*(\rho_\alpha) \xi_{y(\alpha)} \qquad \eta = \Sigma_{\alpha \in A} \rho_\alpha \eta_{y(\alpha)} \tag{12}$$

$$\zeta' = \zeta - tf(\xi') - \omega f(\eta)$$

By (11),

$$\zeta' = \sum_i \Sigma_{\alpha \in A} f^*(\rho_\alpha) g_{i,y(\alpha)} e_i$$

We claim ζ' vanishes identically in a neighborhood of $\operatorname{supp} E$. Clearly $f^*(\rho_\alpha)$ vanishes on $f^{-1}[P - \bar{P}_\alpha]$ and $g_{i,y(\alpha)}$ vanishes on $N_\alpha = N_{y(\alpha)}$. Hence ζ' vanishes on $\bigcap_{\alpha \in A} (N_\alpha \cup f^{-1}[P - \bar{P}_\alpha])$. This set contains $\operatorname{supp} E$ because $f^{-1}[P_\alpha] \cap \operatorname{supp} E \subset f^{-1}[P_{y(\alpha)}] \cap \operatorname{supp} E \subset N_\alpha$. It is open because each $N_\alpha \cup f^{-1}[P - \bar{P}_\alpha]$ is open and every point in N has a neighborhood contained in all but a finite number of the sets $f^{-1}[P - \bar{P}_\alpha]$. Thus ζ' vanishes on a neighborhood of $\operatorname{supp} E$.

It follows that for each $x \in N$, there exists $\xi_x'' \in \Gamma(TN)$ and $g_{x,1}'', \ldots, g_{x,q}'' \in \mathfrak{I}_x$ such that

$$\zeta' = tf(\xi_x'') + \sum_{i=1}^{q} g_{x,i}'' e_i \tag{13}$$

For each $x \in N$, let W_x be an open neighborhood of x in N such that $g_{x,1}'', \ldots, g_{x,q}''$ vanish on W_x. Let $\{W_\alpha\}_{\alpha \in A}$ be a locally finite cover of N such that for each $\alpha \in A$ there exists $x = x(\alpha) \in N$ such that $W_\alpha \subset W_{x(\alpha)}$. Let $\{\sigma_\alpha\}$ be a C^∞ partition of unity on N such that $\operatorname{supp} \sigma_\alpha \subseteq W_\alpha$. Set $\xi'' = \Sigma_\alpha \sigma_\alpha \xi_{x(\alpha)}''$. Then, $\sigma_\alpha g_{x(\alpha),i}'' = 0$, $1 \leqslant i \leqslant q$, so (13) yields

$$\zeta' = tf(\xi'')$$

Combining this with (12), we get

$$\zeta = tf(\xi) + \omega f(\eta)$$

where $\xi = \xi' + \xi''$.

This completes the outline of the proof that (i) implies (ii).

Now we will sketch the proof that (iii) implies (i). Let $N^{(q)}$ denote the set of q-tuples $\langle x_1, \ldots, x_q \rangle \in N^q$ such that $x_i \neq x_j$ if $i \neq j$. Let $_q J^k(N, P)$ denote the set of q-tuples $\langle z_1, \ldots, z_q \rangle$ of points in the q-fold Cartesian product $(J^k(N, P))^q$ such that $\langle x_1, \ldots, x_q \rangle \in N^{(q)}$, where x_i is the source of z_i. If $g : N \to P$ is any C^∞ mapping, we let $_q j^k(g) : N^{(q)} \to {_q}J^k(N, P)$ be defined by $_q j^k(f)\langle x_1, \ldots, x_q \rangle = \langle j^k(f)(x_1), \ldots, j^k(f)(x_q) \rangle$.

We next state two results, which together form a complement to Thom's transversality theorem. We say a subset of a topological space is *residual* if it contains a countable intersection of dense open subsets. We say a space is *Baire* if every residual set is dense.

Proposition 3. $C^\infty(N, P)$ is a Baire space with respect to the topology W.

The proof is not very difficult, but it is rather long, so we will omit it.

Proposition 4. If U is a submanifold of $_q J^k(N, P)$ then $\{g : {_q}j^k(g)$ meets U only transversally$\}$ is a residual subset of $C^\infty(N, P)$.

The proof of this is similar to the proof of Thom's transversality theorem. Like the proof of Thom's transversality theorem, it relies in an essential way on Sard's theorem. We omit it.

Assuming Propositions 3 and 4, the proof of (iii) $\Rightarrow$ (i) is easy. First we show (i-a). Let U be a contact class in $J^k(N, P)$. By Propositions 3 and 4, there exists a C^∞ mapping $g : N \to P$ arbitrarily close to f with respect to the topology W and such that $j^k(g)$ meets U only transversally. The assumption that f is stable implies that we may choose g such that $f = h' \circ g \circ h$, where h (resp. h') is a C^∞ diffeomorphism of N (resp. P) onto itself. There exists a unique diffeomorphism $h'_* h^*$ of $J^k(N, P)$ onto itself such that for any C^∞ mapping $u : N \to P$ and any $x \in N$, $h'_* h^*(j^k(u)(x)) = j^k(h' \circ u \circ h)(h^{-1}(x))$. Clearly $h'_* h^*$ maps U into itself. Thus, the fact that $j^k(g)$ meets U only transversally implies that $h'_* h^* \circ j^k(g) \circ h$ meets U only transversally. By definition of $h'^* h_*$,

$$h'_* h^* \circ j^k(g) \circ h = j^k(h' \circ g \circ h) = j^k(f)$$

Thus, $j^k(f)$ meets U only transversally. This shows (i-a).

Now consider nonsubmersive contact classes $U_1, \ldots, U_a$ in $J^k(N, P)$. Let $x = \langle x_1, \ldots, x_q \rangle$ be a crossing of the family of immersions

$$|j^k(f)^{-1}U_i : j^k(f)^{-1}U_i \to P \qquad i = 1, \ldots, a \tag{14}$$

that is, suppose that each x_i is in $j^k(f)^{-1}U_{j(i)}$ for suitable $j(i)$ and that $f(x_i) = \cdots = f(x_q)$. To prove (i-b) it is enough to show that x is a *normal* crossing.

Let Δ denote the diagonal in P^q, that is, $\{\langle y, \ldots, y \rangle : y \in P\}$. Let $\pi : {_q}J^k(N, P) \to P^q$ denote the canonical projection (which associates with

$z = \langle z_1, \ldots, z_q \rangle \in J^k(N, P)$ the point $y = \langle y_1, \ldots, y_q \rangle \in P^q$, where y_i denotes the target of z_i). Let $\tilde{\Delta} = \pi^{-1}\Delta$. Let $U = (U_{j(1)} \times \cdots \times U_{j(q)}) \cap \tilde{\Delta}$. The reasoning that was used to show that f being stable implies (i-a) also shows that f being stable implies that $_q j^k(f)$ meets U only transversally. On the other hand, the statement that x is a crossing of the family of immersions (14) is equivalent to $_q j^k(f)(x) \in U$, and the statement that x is a *normal* crossing of the family of immersions (14) is equivalent to the statement that $_q j^k(f)$ meets U transversally at x. Thus the fact that $_q j^k(f)$ meets U only transversally implies that x is a normal crossing. This completes the proof that (iii) implies (i).

We have outlined the proofs of (i) $\Rightarrow$ (ii) and (iii) $\Rightarrow$ (i). We have omitted outlining the proof of (ii) $\Rightarrow$ (iii), because it is very technical. The proof of (ii) $\Rightarrow$ (iii) will appear shortly [2].

REFERENCES

1. B. Malgrange, *Ideals of Differentiable Functions*, Oxford University Press, London, 1966.

2. J. Mather, *Stability of C^∞ Mappings*, I, II, to appear in the Annals of Math.

XXII

One-Parameter Subgroups Do Not Fill a Neighborhood of the Identity in an Infinite-Dimensional Lie (Pseudo-) Group

CHARLES FREIFELD

INTRODUCTION

In [1], S. Lie considered the question of whether a transformation sufficiently close to the identity in a Lie (pseudo-) group can be joined to the identity transformation by a one-parameter family of transformations. In this paper, we show that this *cannot* be done in the infinite case. By a Lie (pseudo-) group Lie meant a set of local, invertible, analytic transformations on some manifold which are the solutions of a set of partial differential equations. Lie assumed further that this set always contained the identity transformation, that it was closed under composition when composition was defined, and that the inverse of every transformation in it was still in it. For example, the set of local, complex-analytic, invertible transformations on C^n (the equations being the Cauchy–Riemann equations), the set of all invertible, local, analytic transformations of R^n, S^n (n-sphere) or C^n (the equations being the empty set of equations), are Lie (pseudo-) groups. For more examples, and a more precise treatment of the concept of Lie (pseudo-) group in general, see [6].

Throughout this note, we will use the term Lie (pseudo-) group for these objects, although the terms "infinite Lie group" or "infinite group of Lie and Cartan" are used in [2] and [6]. Also, Lie considered only analytic transformations, while we will consider both the C^∞ and analytic cases. Finally, it should be remarked that Lie proved that a neighborhood of the

538

identity *is* covered by one-parameter subgroups when the Lie group is finite-dimensional.

Note that since we always work formally, the result also holds when the locally defined T (below) is replaced by its germ at the origin.

PART I

In $\mathbf{C}$, let U and V be small open neighborhoods of the origin and let $T : U \to V$ be defined by

$$T(x) = \exp\left(\frac{2\pi i}{n}\right) x + \alpha x^{n+1}$$

where x is a complex number, α is a positive real number, and n a positive integer. Then we will prove the following.

Theorem. There exists an α (small) such that, for all n, T does not lie on a one-parameter subgroup of local, C^∞ transformations.

In [2], Sternberg showed that T does not lie on a one-parameter group of local transformations of $\mathbf{C}$ into itself, provided it is assumed that the transformations are complex-analytic and leave the origin fixed. (On page 454 of [2], the differential equation should read

$$a_p{}'(t) = \beta a_p(t) + a_p{}'(0) \exp(p\beta t)$$

and the solution should read

$$a_p(t) = \frac{c}{\beta(p-1)} [\exp(p\beta t) - \exp(\beta t)].)$$

But the set of transformations leaving the origin fixed is not a Lie (pseudo-) group because it is not the set of solutions of some system of partial differential equations, so that this is not, at least immediately, a proper counterexample to Lie's conjecture. The theorem above shows that it is. In our situation α will be chosen small and n large, so that "close to the identity" will mean that the local transformation and its derivatives are uniformly close to the identity in a small neighborhood of the origin.

CLAIM. A transformation S, leaving the origin fixed, that can be joined to the identity by a one-parameter group, must have an eigenvalue equal to one.

PROOF. In fact, if the one-parameter group does not leave the origin fixed, it defines a closed curve passing through the origin. This curve is clearly pointwise fixed by S and the tangent to this curve is the desired eigenvector of eigenvalue one.

Thus, in the analytic case, where we know T does not lie on a one-parameter group of transformations fixing the origin, we are done. We now consider the C^∞ case. Given a transformation, we can consider its formal Taylor series expansion at the origin. If T lies on a one-parameter group X_t, its formal Taylor series expansion must lie on the one-parameter group of formal Taylor series expansions of the X_t. We will show that this cannot happen by working formally.

Using $z, \bar{z}$ as C^∞ coordinates,

$$T = X_1(z, \bar{z}) = \exp\left(\frac{2\pi i}{n}\right)z + \alpha z^{n+1}$$

Let

$$X_t(z, \bar{z}) = a_1(t)z + a_2(t)\bar{z} + a_{1,1}(t)z^2 + a_{1,2}(t)z\bar{z} + a_{2,2}(t)\bar{z}^2 + \cdots$$

be the Taylor expansion of X_t. (By the preceding paragraph, we are allowed to assume that all X_t leave the origin fixed.) Assume n is some large integer.

First, we determine $a_1(t)$:

$$X_{1/2}(z, \bar{z}) \circ X_{1/2}(z, \bar{z}) = a_2(\tfrac{1}{2})(a_1(\tfrac{1}{2})z + a_2(\tfrac{1}{2})\bar{z} + \cdots$$
$$+ a_2(\tfrac{1}{2})(\overline{a_1(\tfrac{1}{2})}\bar{z} + \overline{a_2(\tfrac{1}{2})}z + \cdots) + \cdots$$

where the product is computed formally, of course. Equating terms, we have

$$\left.\begin{array}{l} \exp\left(\dfrac{2\pi i}{n}\right) = a_1(\tfrac{1}{2})a_1(\tfrac{1}{2}) + a_2(\tfrac{1}{2})\overline{a_2(\tfrac{1}{2})} \\[2mm] 0 = a_1(\tfrac{1}{2})a_2(\tfrac{1}{2}) + a_2(\tfrac{1}{2})\overline{a_1(\tfrac{1}{2})} \end{array}\right\}$$

Now $a_2(\tfrac{1}{2}) \neq 0$ implies $a_1(\tfrac{1}{2}) = -\overline{a_1(\tfrac{1}{2})}$, which implies that $a_1(\tfrac{1}{2})$ is pure imaginary. Therefore, $a_1(\tfrac{1}{2})^2$ is a real number. But $a_2(\tfrac{1}{2})\overline{a_2(\tfrac{1}{2})}$ is real also. This contradicts the first equation. Thus,

$$a_1(\tfrac{1}{2}) = \exp\left[\frac{1}{2}\left(\frac{2\pi i}{n} + 2\pi i h\right)\right]$$

and $a_2(\tfrac{1}{2}) = 0$. Repeating this reasoning for $X_{1/4} \circ X_{1/4}$, etc., all the equations remain in the above form because $a_2(\tfrac{1}{2}) = 0$. We have, finally, $a_1(t) = \exp(t\beta)$,

$$\beta = 2\pi i\left(\frac{1}{n} + k\right)$$

and $a_2(t) = 0$, for all t, by continuity. Now

$$X_{t+s}(z, \bar{z}) = X_s(X_t(z, \bar{z}))$$

so

$$X_t'(z, \bar{z}) = X_0'(X_t(z, \bar{z}))$$

by differentiating with respect to s at $s = 0$. Therefore,

$$a_1'(0)(a_1(t)z + a_2(t)\bar{z} + a_{1,1}(t)z^2 + a_{1,2}(t)z\bar{z} + a_{2,2}(t)\bar{z}^2 + \cdots)$$

$$a_2'(0)(\overline{a_1(t)}\bar{z} + \overline{a_2(t)}\bar{z} + \cdots) + a_{1,1}'(0)(a_1(t)z + \cdots)^2$$

$$+ a_{1,2}'(0)(a_1(t)z + a_2(t)\bar{z} + \cdots)(\overline{a_1(t)}\bar{z} + \overline{a_2(t)}z + \cdots)$$

$$+ a_{2,2}'(0)(\overline{a_1(t)}\bar{z} + \cdots)^2 + \cdots$$

$$= a_1'(t)z + a_2'(t)z^2 + a_{1,2}'(t)z\bar{z} + a_{2,2}'(t)\bar{z}^2 + \cdots$$

Thus,

$$a_{1,1}'(t) = \beta a_{1,1}(t) + a_{1,1}'(0) \exp(2\beta t)$$

which, by solving an ordinary differential equation, implies

$$\beta a_{1,1}(t) = K_{1,1}[\exp(2\beta t) - \exp(\beta t)]$$

which in turn implies $a_{1,1}(t) = 0$, since $a_{1,1}(0) = 0$ and $a_{1,1}(1) = 0$ by assumption. Thus, $K_{1,1} = 0$. Now

$$a_{1,2}'(t) = \beta a_{1,2}(t) + a_{1,2}'(0)$$

implies

$$a_{1,2}(t) = K_{1,2}\left[\exp(\beta t) - \frac{a_{1,2}'(0)}{\beta}\right]$$

so $a_{1,2}(t) = 0 \; [a_{1,2}(0) = a_{1,1}(1) = 0]$.

$$a_{2,2}'(t) = \beta a_{2,2}(t) + a_{2,2}'(0) \exp(-2\beta t)$$

implies

$$3\beta a_{2,2}(t) = K_{2,2}(\exp(\beta t) - \exp(-2\beta t))$$

so $a_{2,2}(t) = 0$. Thus, we can continue the procedure and obtain

$$a_{1,1,1}'(t) = \beta a_{1,1,1}(t) + a_{1,1,1}'(0) \exp(3\beta t)$$

The solution of this differential equation shows that $a_{1,1,1}(t) = 0$ for all t, in exactly the same way as before. Finally, we obtain, for our chosen large n, $a_{1,\dots,1}(t) = 0$ ($n + 1$ ones occurring), for all t, which is in contradiction with $a_{1,\dots,1}(1) = \alpha$. Q.E.D.

PART II

Since our considerations have been local, we may, in a suitable neighborhood of the origin, smooth the transformation T in a C^∞ way so that outside the neighborhood, T is just the linear map

$$T(x) = \exp\left(\frac{2\pi i}{n}\right)x$$

We would like to be able to make T close to the identity at all points, so we must be able to make the derivatives of $\alpha(x)x^n$ stay close to zero. To accomplish this, one takes a smoothing function which is constantly equal to α around the origin and which is constantly equal to zero outside a small interval around the origin. Such a function, for example, can be found in Steenrod [5]. It involves adding a constant to an exponential of the form

$$\alpha(x) = \alpha \exp\left(\frac{d - c}{(x - c)(x - d)}\right)$$

where (c, d) is a small interval. By taking α small (depending on n) and (c, d) small, the exponentials in the derivatives will control the derivatives of x^n, so that we can make

$$T(x) = \exp\left(\frac{2\pi i}{n}\right)x + \alpha(x)x^n$$

as close to the identity as we wish. Thus, for the group of global C^∞ diffeomorphisms of the complex line—or—since T can be extended to S^2 (it becomes a rotation at infinity)—for the group of diffeomorphisms of the two-sphere S^2, no neighborhood of the identity can be covered by one-parameter groups. Hence, Lie's conjecture fails for the group of diffeomorphisms of a compact manifold.

REMARK

The Lie (pseudo-) groups we have been considering are not Banach (local) Lie Groups in the sense of Maissen [3]. In that paper, it is shown that for a Banach (local) Lie group with a certain condition of uniformity on its multiplication, a sufficiently small neighborhood of the identity is covered by one-parameter groups. Our Lie (pseudo-) groups are not modeled on Banach spaces and the extra condition of uniformity, needed to obtain the existence of a local solution to an ordinary differential equation in a Banach space, is not satisfied because our topology depends on all the derivatives of the functions. For references on these infinite-dimensional groups, see Eells [4].

REFERENCES

1. Sophus Lie, Abhandlungen der Sachs. Gesellschaft der Wissenschaften, *Math.-Phys. Klasse* **21** (1895), pp. 43–46. Or, *Gesammelte Abhandlungen*, Sechster Band, pp. 395–399.

2. Shlomo Sternberg, Infinite Lie Groups and the Formal Aspects of Dynamical Systems, *J. Math. and Mech.* **10**, (1961), pp. 451–474.

3. Bernhard Maissen, Lie-Gruppen mit Banächraumen als Parameterräume, *Acta Math.* **108**, (1962), pp. 229–269.

4. James Eells, Jr., A Setting for Global Analysis, *Bull. Am. Math. Soc.* **72**, (1966), pp. 751–807.

5. Norman Steenrod, *Topology of Fibre Bundles*, Princeton Univ. Press, 1951, pp. 25–26.

6. I. Singer and S. Sternberg, The Infinite Groups of Lie and Cartan, I *Jour. d'Analyse Math.* **XV** (1965), pp. 1–114.

XXIII

A Dynamical Theory for Morphogenesis : Elementary Catastrophies on R^4

RENE THOM

(Explication du modèle différentiel local qui doit permettre l'interprétation des changements morphologiques observés en de nombreux phénomènes naturels.) Cette théorie sera exposée complètement dans un ouvrage intitulé "Stabilité structurelle et Morphogenèse" à paraitre chez W. A. Benjamin, Inc., New York.

XXIV

How to Turn a Sphere Inside Out

STEPHEN SMALE

"A Classification of Immersions of the Two-Sphere," *Transactions of the American Mathematical Society* **90**, 281–290 (1959).

XXV

Eversion of the 2-Sphere

BRYCE S. DeWITT

The purpose of this talk is to give a nonrigorous "popular" demonstration of Smale's theorem that the 2-sphere can be turned inside out via a differentiable homotopy of immersions in Euclidean 3-space.[1] The key to this demonstration is the sequence of diagrams shown in Fig. 1. If you can remember this sequence you can always reconstruct the demonstration.

The diagrams in the figure represent a sequence of parallel plane sections through a certain compact boundaryless 2-manifold which has been immersed in Euclidean 3-space. Part of my demonstration will consist of trying to convince you that this manifold is the 2-sphere.

The use of plane sections permits one to visualize immersions of 2-manifolds without resorting to perspective drawings or constructing actual 3-dimensional models.[2] It is true, of course, that a change in the orientation of the parallel planes may drastically alter the appearance of the sequence of sections of a given immersion, just as a real object may look quite different when viewed from different directions. In particular, the order in which *critical points* appear is subject to wide variation. The critical points in Fig. 1 are the dots in diagrams A, B, F, and H. At these points the intersecting plane is tangent to the immersion. The critical points in diagrams F and H are saddle points, while those in diagrams A and B are maxima (or

---

[1] An immersion may be loosely defined as a differentiable map from an n-manifold into $\mathbf{R}^{n+1}$ such that the derived *tangent* map from the n-manifold into the space of n-planes in $\mathbf{R}^{n+1}$ is everywhere defined and continuous.

[2] This is not meant to imply that drawings and models, when one has the time to make them, are not extremely helpful in yielding an overall visualization of immersions. A beautiful set of shaded drawings will be found in an article by A. Phillips in the *Scientific American* **214**, No. 5, 112 (1966). These drawings, which were studied in obtaining Fig. 1, are based on a sequence of deformations of the 2-sphere devised by A. Shapiro. Shapiro's sequence has suggested to Marcel Froissart and Bernard Morin another sequence, less complicated for purposes of 3-dimensional visualization, which they demonstrated during the Rencontres by constructing 3-dimensional models.

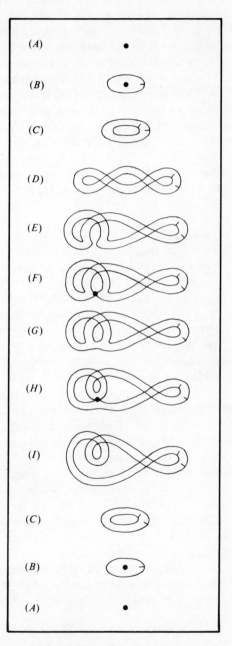

FIGURE 1. Key diagrams.

minima). It is important to take note of all the critical points which occur in a given sequence of sections. I shall always assume that the manifold has been rotated into a "general position" such that the critical points occur singly (that is, one by one, with no degeneracies) in the sequence.

Between any two successive occurrences of critical points the members of a given sequence of sections represent a differentiable homotopy of immersions of some compact boundaryless 1-manifold in the plane. A compact boundaryless 1-manifold is topologically the sum of a finite number of S^1's. It is therefore of preliminary interest to discuss the classification of immersions of S^1. I quote, without proof, the relevant theorem, due to Whitney:

THEOREM. Two immersions of S^1 in the plane can be connected by a differentiable homotopy of immersions if and only if they have the same winding number.

The "winding number" is defined as follows. Each immersion has an orientation determined by the parametrization $p(t) = (x(t), y(t))$ which defines it. Let $T(t)$ be the unit tangent vector at $p(t)$ in the direction of increasing t. Without loss of generality $p(t)$ and $T(t)$ may be taken to be periodic functions of period 1. Let Θ be the angle through which $T(t)$ turns as t runs from 0 to 1. Then $\Theta/2\pi$ is the winding number. The set of all possible winding numbers is the set of all positive and negative integers (including zero). You may easily convince yourselves of the plausibility of Whitney's theorem by drawing diagrams such as those of Fig. 2, in which various immersions have been grouped according to their winding numbers.

Each immersion of S^1 in the plane is two sided; that is, neighboring strips on either side of the curve which the point $p(t)$ traces out can be everywhere consistently distinguished.[3] One way of making the distinction graphically is to paint the strips in different colors. An easier way is to put "spikes" on one side of the curve thus: ———⊥———. I shall adopt the convention that the spikes are to be placed on the side which lies to the right when one moves along the curve in the direction of increasing t (as shown by the arrows) thus: ———←———⊥———. In the case of the circle, one of the sides may legitimately be called the "inside" and the other the "outside." It is a corollary of Whitney's theorem that the circle cannot be turned inside out by a differentiable homotopy of immersions.[4]

The concept of "sidedness" can be generalized to immersions of n-manifolds. An immersion is always two sided when the corresponding manifold is orientable and one sided when it is not. The two sidedness of

---

[3] The problem of overlap at intersections may be handled by ascribing a 4-sided character to the intersection points.

[4] Note the distinction which is made between the circle as an immersion and S^1 as a manifold.

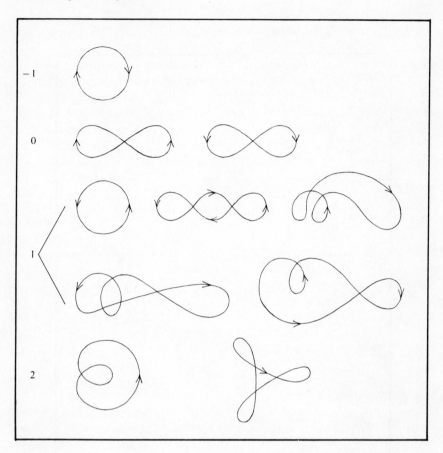

FIGURE 2. Winding numbers.

immersions of orientable 2-manifolds can be represented graphically by means of the sequences of plane sections already introduced. One may place spikes on the sectional curves, as in Fig. 1, or arrows, as in Fig. 3 (which depicts two distinct slicings of the torus). In each case the emplacement of the spikes or the arrows may be carried out in a "consistent" manner over the entire sequence. In the case of a nonorientable 2-manifold, such as the Klein bottle depicted in Fig. 4, no consistent emplacement of spikes or arrows can be found.

Each plane section of an immersion of an orientable 2-manifold can be assigned a unique set of winding numbers. If the section contains no critical point these numbers are integers, one for each immersion of S^1 which occurs in the section. If the section contains a critical point, *fractional* winding numbers are employed. For example, a critical point which corresponds to a

FIGURE 3. The torus.

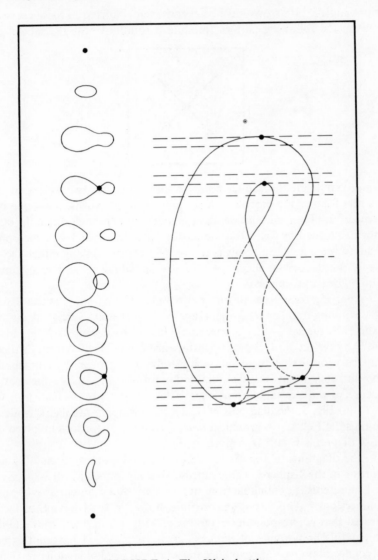

FIGURE 4. The Klein bottle.

maximum or a minimum will be assigned the number $\frac{1}{2}$ or the number $-\frac{1}{2}$ according as the circle whose imminent appearance or disappearance it signals has the winding number 1 or -1.   In the case of saddle points the assignment procedure is more complicated.   The immersion is first differentiably distorted so that the sectional curves running through the saddle point intersect at right angles.   If arrows have been consistently affixed to these curves they will form the following pattern (modulo a rotation) near the saddle point:

Starting out from the saddle point in either of the two emergent directions one follows the corresponding curve until it returns along one of the two re-entrant lines, and one divides the total angle through which the tangent vector has turned by 2π.   The same recipe is then applied with the opposite starting direction.   The result is a pair of fractions having either the form $\{m + \frac{3}{4},\ n + \frac{3}{4}\}$ or the form $\{m - \frac{3}{4},\ n - \frac{3}{4}\}$, where m and n are integers (positive, negative, or zero).

Applying these rules to Fig. 1, we find that diagram A is characterized by the winding-number set $\{-\frac{1}{2}\}$, diagram B by the set $\{-1, \frac{1}{2}\}$, diagrams C, D, and E by the set $\{-1, 1\}$, diagrams F and H by the set $\{-\frac{3}{4}, \frac{5}{4}\}$, and diagram G by the set $\{1\}$.   By a straightforward extension of Whitney's theorem it can be proved that these sets completely characterize the corresponding plane immersions up to differentiable homotopy.   Therefore there exists a sequence of differentiable homotopies which, *section by section*, transforms Fig. 1 into Fig. 5, the diagrams of which have winding-number sets identical with those of Fig. 1.   A graphical portrayal of the distortions involved in the case of diagrams F and H is given in Fig. 6.

The diagrams of Fig. 5 are recognizable as plane sections of a simple distortion of the 2-sphere.   This suggests that the immersion in 3-space which Fig. 1 represents is obtainable from the 2-sphere by a differentiable homotopy of immersions.   This is not yet obvious, however, for I have thus far only indicated that corrresponding diagrams of Figs. 1 and 5 are connectable by differentiable homotopies of immersions *in the plane*.   I have not extended this connectability to an overall connectability via immersions in 3-space. That is, I have established a "lateral" connection between Figs. 1 and 5, but I have yet to show that a "vertical" connection between the top and bottom of each figure (that is, canonical behavior in the neighborhood of each critical point and differentiable homotopies between successive occurrences of them) can be consistently maintained at every intermediate stage of the lateral connection.

That such a consistent overall connection can, in fact, be established is made intuitively clear by the following two-dimensional array of symbols:

A	A	A	A	A	A
B	B	B	B	B	B
C	C	C	C	C	C
D	D	D	D	C	$\bar{D}$
E	E	E	E	D	C
E	E	E	E	E	D
E	E	E	E	E	E
E	E	E	E	E	$F_1^{\,+}$
E	E	E	E	$F_1^{\,+}$	$F_2^{\,+}$
E	E	E	$F_1^{\,+}$	$F_2^{\,+}$	$F_3^{\,+}$
E	E	$F_1^{\,+}$	$F_2^{\,+}$	$F_3^{\,+}$	$F_4^{\,+}$
E	$F_1^{\,+}$	$F_2^{\,+}$	$F_3^{\,+}$	$F_4^{\,+}$	$\bar{E}$
F	F_1	F_2	F_3	F_4	$\bar{F}$
G	$F_1^{\,-}$	$F_2^{\,-}$	$F_3^{\,-}$	$F_4^{\,-}$	$\bar{G}$
G	G	$F_1^{\,-}$	$F_2^{\,-}$	$F_3^{\,-}$	$F_4^{\,-}$
G	G	G	$F_1^{\,-}$	$F_2^{\,-}$	$F_3^{\,-}$
G	G	G	G	$F_1^{\,-}$	$F_2^{\,-}$
G	G	G	G	G	$F_1^{\,-}$

G	G	G	G	G	G
G	G	G	G	G	$H_1^{\,+}$
G	G	G	G	$H_1^{\,+}$	$H_2^{\,+}$
G	G	G	$H_1^{\,+}$	$H_2^{\,+}$	$H_3^{\,+}$
G	G	$H_1^{\,+}$	$H_2^{\,+}$	$H_3^{\,+}$	$H_4^{\,+}$
G	$H_1^{\,+}$	$H_2^{\,+}$	$H_3^{\,+}$	$H_4^{\,+}$	$\bar{G}$
H	H_1	H_2	H_3	H_4	$\bar{F}$
I	$H_1^{\,-}$	$H_2^{\,-}$	$H_3^{\,-}$	$H_4^{\,-}$	$\bar{E}$
I	I	$H_1^{\,-}$	$H_2^{\,-}$	$H_3^{\,-}$	$H_4^{\,-}$
I	I	I	$H_1^{\,-}$	$H_2^{\,-}$	$H_3^{\,-}$
I	I	I	I	$H_1^{\,-}$	$H_2^{\,-}$
I	I	I	I	I	$H_1^{\,-}$
I	I	I	I	I	I
I	I	I	I	I	C
I	I	I	I	C	$\bar{D}$
C	C	C	C	C	C
B	B	B	B	B	B
A	A	A	A	A	A

With the exception of those symbols bearing a $+$ or $-$ sign each symbol stands for one of the diagrams pictured in Figs. 1, 5, and 6. The $+$ and $-$ signs are attached only to the symbols representing the intermediate diagrams of Fig. 6. Each of these diagrams depicts a plane section containing a saddle point. The attachment of a sign to its corresponding symbol indicates that the saddle is to be split, by moving the plane either upward ($+$) or downward ($-$).

The above array has the following properties: Its first column is a stretched-out version of Fig. 1, and its last column represents a differentiable distortion of the immersion depicted in Fig. 5.[5] Pick any diagram in the interior of the array. The diagrams immediately above and below it, and to either side of it, differ from it only by modest distortions (if at all) and are related to it in obvious differentiable ways. It becomes clear therefore that each column of the array represents an immersion of S^2, and that the immersion represented by Fig. 1 is indeed obtainable from the 2-sphere by a differentiable homotopy of immersions.

We have still not turned the sphere inside out. How do we accomplish this? The answer is to be found in a very special property possessed by the immersion depicted in Fig. 1. In this immersion the 2-sphere has been folded back on itself, through a maze of self-intersections, in such a way that

---

[5] One can easily trace the steps of the latter distortion by drawing further arrays of diagrams. It is difficult, however, to acquire a three-dimensional visualization of these steps, and this constitutes a pedagogical weakness of the present approach.

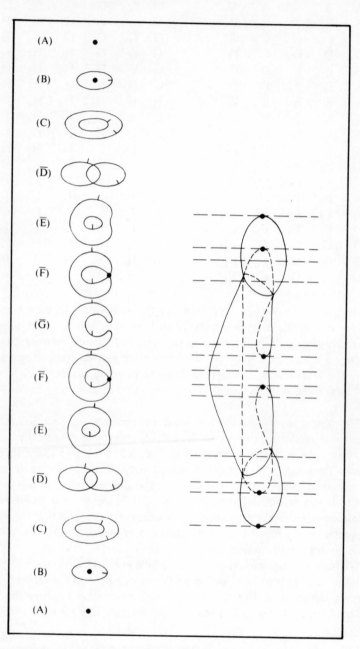

FIGURE 5. A distorted 2-sphere.

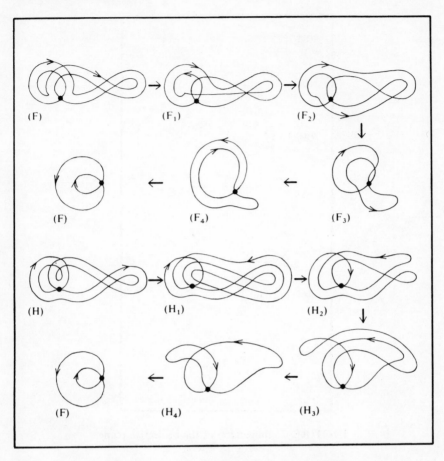

FIGURE 6. Distortions of diagrams F and H.

it *appears* to consist of a *pair* of self-intersecting surfaces which are separated everywhere by a more or less constant distance. It is a simple matter to cause the "two" surfaces to exchange places by a differentiable homotopy of immersions. The result of the interchange is then unfolded until it regains the form of a 2-sphere. The spikes which were originally on the outside of the 2-sphere (Fig. 5) are now to be found on the inside.[6]

It is evidently possible to cause the "two" surfaces of Fig. 1 to exchange places in such a way that they exactly coincide at some intermediate stage of the homotopy. At this moment of "crossover" they assume the configuration depicted in Fig. 7. Diagram A has become diagram U, diagrams B and

---

[6] It is amusing to note that although the spikes are initially on the outside, they are all hidden on the "inside" by the time the stage depicted in Fig. 1 is reached.

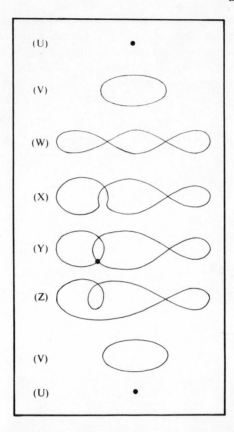

FIGURE 7. Immersion of the projective plane.

C have collapsed onto diagram V, diagrams D, E, and I have become diagrams W, X, and Z, respectively, and diagrams F, G, and H have collapsed onto diagram Y. The manifold whose immersion Fig. 7 represents is nonorientable and is, in fact, the projective plane P^2. The "crossover" configuration evidently yields a double covering of P^2 by S^2. It was the discovery that this double covering can be realized by a differentiable homotopy of immersions which led to the recognition that the 2-sphere can be everted.

By attaching tiny handles to the initial 2-sphere and carrying out the same steps as before it is not difficult to show that *any* compact orientable 2-manifold can be turned inside out via a differentiable homotopy of immersions in Euclidean 3-space. It is perhaps well to end with the remark that this result in no way contradicts the theorem which states that the *embedding*[7]

[7] An embedding is an injective map. An immersion with no self-intersections is an embedding.

of any compact orientable 2-manifold in Euclidean 3-space divides the latter into two disjoint regions, the *inside* and the *outside*, which are easily distinguished by their compactness and lack of compactness, respectively. When we evert such a manifold we do not simultaneously interchange these two regions. No homotopy can accomplish that.

ADVANCE PRAISE FOR
THE AMERICAN STORY

"Of all the American History survey texts I have read, this one is the best."

—Charles A. Pilant, Cumberland College

"This text balances the social, political, and economic aspects as well as any text I have read."

—Cherry L. Spruill, Indiana University–Purdue University at Indianapolis

"The writing throughout the text is clear and engaging. Indeed the prose and style are great strengths of the book."

—Kenneth E. Hendrickson, Sam Houston State University

"I do share the goal of a balanced presentation and think that the authors do a good job here. I particularly rely on the text for detailed descriptions of economic issues and cultural history."

—Juli A. Jones, St. Charles County Community College

"The writing is extremely clear and direct, easy to follow."

—William G. Morris, Midland College

"I like the strong, clear writing as well as its attractive appearance and integrated presentation."

—Bruce J. Dierenfield, Canisius College

"The scholarship of the text is both current and varied."

—H. Michael Tarver, McNeese State University

"The writing is the strength of this text. It is the clearest written text available with topic sentences virtually outlining the chapters for students."

—Dr. Peter Murray, Methodist College

ABOUT
THE AUTHORS

ROBERT A. DIVINE

Robert A. Divine, George W. Littlefield Professor Emeritus in American History at the University of Texas at Austin, received his Ph.D. from Yale University in 1954. A specialist in American diplomatic history, he taught from 1954 to 1996 at the University of Texas, where he was honored by both the Student Association and the Graduate School for teaching excellence. His extensive published work includes *The Illusion of Neutrality* (1962); *Second Chance: The Triumphs of Internationalism in America During World War II* (1967); and *Blowing on the Wind* (1978). His most recent work is *Perpetual War for Perpetual Peace* (2000), a comparative analysis of twentieth-century American wars. He is also the author of *Eisenhower and the Cold War* (1981) and editor of three volumes of essays on the presidency of Lyndon Johnson. His book, *The Sputnik Challenge* (1992), won the Eugene E. Emme Astronautical Literature Award for 1993. He has been a fellow at the Center for Advanced Study in the Behavioral Sciences and has given the Albert Shaw Lectures in Diplomatic History at Johns Hopkins University.

T. H. BREEN

T. H. Breen, William Smith Mason Professor of American History at Northwestern University, received his Ph.D. from Yale University in 1968. He has taught at Northwestern since 1970. Breen's major books include *The Character of the Good Ruler: A Study of Puritan Political Ideas in New England* (1974); *Puritans and Adventurers: Change and Persistence in Early America* (1980); *Tobacco Culture: The Mentality of the Great Tidewater Planters on the Eve of Revolution* (1985); and, with Stephen Innes of the University of Virginia, *"Myne Owne Ground": Race and Freedom on Virginia's Eastern Shore* (1980). His *Imagining the Past* (1989) won the 1990 Historic Preservation Book Award. In addition to receiving an award for outstanding teaching at Northwestern, Breen has been the recipient of research grants from the American Council of Learned Societies, the Guggenheim Foundation, the Institute for Advanced Study (Princeton), the National Humanities Center, and the Huntington Library. For his article "Narrative of Commercial Life: Consumption, Ideology, and Community on the Eve of the American Revolution," which appeared in the July 1993 issue of *William and Mary Quarterly*, Breen received an award for best article published in the quarterly in 1993, and the Douglass Adair Memorial

Prize for best article published in the quarterly during the 1988–1993 period. He has served as the Fowler Hamilton Fellow at Christ Church, Oxford University (1987–1988), the Pitt Professor of American History and Institutions, Cambridge University (1990–1991), and the Harmsworth Professor of American History at Oxford University (2000–2001).

GEORGE M. FREDRICKSON

George M. Fredrickson is Edgar E. Robinson Professor of United States History at Stanford University. He is the author or editor of several books, including *The Inner Civil War* (1965), *The Black Image in the White Mind* (1971), and *White Supremacy: A Comparative Study in American and South African History* (1981), which won both the Ralph Waldo Emerson Award from Phi Beta Kappa and the Merle Curti Award from the Organization of American Historians. His most recent books are *Black Liberation: A Comparative History of Black Ideologies in the United States and South Africa* (1995) and *The Comparative Imagination: Racism, Nationalism, and Social Movements* (1997). He received his A.B. and Ph.D. degrees from Harvard and has been the recipient of a Guggenheim Fellowship, two National Endowment for the Humanities Senior Fellowships, and a Fellowship from the Center for Advanced Studies in the Behavioral Sciences. Before coming to Stanford in 1984, he taught at Northwestern. He has also served as Fulbright lecturer in American History at Moscow University and as the Harmsworth Professor of American History at Oxford. He served as president of the Organization of American Historians in 1997–1998. In 2000 he delivered the University Lectures at Princeton University on the subject of racism in world history.

R. HAL WILLIAMS

R. Hal Williams is Professor of History at Southern Methodist University. He received his A.B. degree from Princeton University (1963) and his Ph.D. degree from Yale University (1968). His books include *The Democratic Party and California Politics, 1880–1896* (1973); *Years of Decision: American Politics in the 1890s* (1978); and *The Manhattan Project: A Documentary Introduction to the Atomic Age* (1990). A specialist in American political history, he taught at Yale University from 1968 to 1975 and came to SMU in 1975 as chair of the Department of History. From 1980 to 1988, he served as dean of Dedman College, the school of humanities and sciences, at SMU. In 1980, he was a visiting professor at University College, Oxford University. Williams has received grants from the American Philosophical Society and the National Endowment for the Humanities, and he has served on the Texas Committee for the Humanities. He is currently working on a biography of James G. Blaine, the late-nineteenth-century speaker of the House, secretary of state, and Republican presidential candidate.

Penguin Academics

THE AMERICAN STORY

ROBERT A. DIVINE
University of Texas

T. H. BREEN
Northwestern University

GEORGE M. FREDRICKSON
Stanford University

R. HAL WILLIAMS
Southern Methodist University

Longman

New York   San Francisco   Boston
London   Toronto   Sydney   Tokyo   Singapore   Madrid
Mexico City   Munich   Paris   Cape Town   Hong Kong   Montreal

Vice President and Publisher:	Priscilla McGeehon
Senior Acquisitions Editor:	Jay O'Callaghan
Development Manager:	Betty Slack
Executive Marketing Manager:	Sue Westmoreland
Production Manager:	Donna DeBenedictis
Project Coordination and Electronic Page Makeup:	Elm Street Publishing Services, Inc.
Senior Cover Designer/Manager:	Nancy Danahy
Cover Image:	*Library* (1934) by Bernard Zakheim. Coit Tower, San Francisco. Photo © Lito, 1996.
Art Studios:	Maps.com and Burmar Technical Corporation
Photo Researcher:	Photosearch, Inc.
Manufacturing Buyer:	Al Dorsey
Printer and Binder:	Quebecor World/Taunton
Cover Printer:	Phoenix Color Corp.

For permission to use copyrighted material, grateful acknowledgment is made to the copyright holders on pp. C1 – C5, which are hereby made part of this copyright page.

Library of Congress Cataloging-in-Publication Data

The American story / Robert A. Divine ... [et al.].
   p. cm. — (Penguin academics)
   Includes bibliographical reference and index.
   ISBN 0-321-09188-4—ISBN 0-321-09187-6 (P-copy)
   1. United States—History. I. Divine, Robert A. II. Series.

E178.A5545 2002
973—dc21

2001041710

Please visit our website at http://www.ablongman.com/divine

For more information about the Penguin Academics series, please contact us by mail at Longman Publishers, attn. Marketing Department, 1185 Avenue of the Americas, 25th Floor, New York, NY 10036, or by e-mail at www.ablongman.com/feedback

ISBN 0-321-09188-4 (Complete Edition)
ISBN 0-321-09196-5 (Volume One)
ISBN 0-321-09189-2 (Volume Two)

1 2 3 4 5 6 7 8 9 10—RNT—04 03 02 01

CONTENTS

CHAPTER 17 | THE WEST: EXPLOITING AN EMPIRE   537

CHAPTER 18 | THE INDUSTRIAL SOCIETY   569

CHAPTER 19 | TOWARD AN URBAN SOCIETY, 1877–1900   602

CHAPTER 20 | POLITICAL REALIGNMENTS IN THE 1890s   635

CHAPTER 21 | TOWARD EMPIRE   669

CHAPTER 22 | THE PROGRESSIVE ERA   699

CHAPTER 23 | FROM ROOSEVELT TO WILSON IN THE AGE OF PROGRESSIVISM   732

Maps, Figures, and Tables

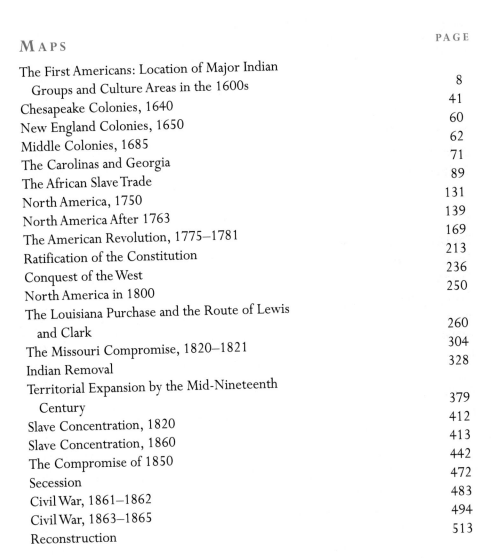

PREFACE

For many decades the traditional narratives that framed the story of the United States assumed a unified society in which men and women of various races and backgrounds shared a common culture. In recent years, however, a good many historians have come to believe that traditional narratives stressing the rise of democracy or the advance of free enterprise undervalue the complexity and diversity of the American story. This research makes it hard to sustain a perspective that presumes the inevitability of progress for all men and women and that allows one dominant group to speak for so many others who have struggled over the centuries to make themselves heard. Nevertheless, an awareness that the past is as much about controversy as agreement, as much concerned with diversity as with unity, does not preclude the possibility of a coherent narrative. To create such a narrative while still paying attention to the differences of race and class, ethnicity, and gender is the goal.

The authors of this volume accept the challenge, believing strongly that it is possible to craft a coherent story without silencing difference. We start with the conviction that to tell this story it is essential to listen closely to what people in the past have had to say about their own aspirations, frustrations, and passions. After all, they were the ones who had to figure out how to live with other Americans, many of them totally unsympathetic, even hostile to the demands of others who happened to march to different drummers. Readers of this book will encounter many of these individuals and discover how, in their own terms, they tried to make sense of everyday events connected to family and work, church and community.

We have done our best to avoid the tendency to lump individuals arbitrarily together in groups. It is true, for example, that many early colonists in America were called Puritans, and presumably in their private lives they reflected a bundle of religious values and beliefs known as Puritanism. But we must not conclude that an abstraction—in this case Puritanism—made history. To do so misses the complexity and diversity masked by the abstraction, for at the end of the day, what for the sake of convenience we term Puritanism was in fact a rich, spirited, often truculent conversation among men and women who disagreed to the point of violence on many details of the theology they allegedly shared. The same observation could be made about other movements in American history—unions or civil rights, political parties or antebellum reform, for example. A narrative that sacrifices the rough edges of dissent in the interest of getting on with the story may propel the reader smoothly through the centuries, but a subtler, more complex tale is more honest about how people in the past actually made events.

Even as we stress the significance of human agency, we resist transforming the long history of the peoples of the United States into a form of highbrow antiquarianism. The men and women who appear in this book lived for the most part in small communities. Even in the large cities that drew so many migrants after the Industrial Revolution, individuals defined their daily routines around family, friends, and neighborhoods. But it would be misleading to conclude that these people were effectively cut off from a larger world. However strong and vibrant their local cultures may have been, their social identities were also the product of the experience of accommodation and resistance to external forces, many of them beyond their own control. Industrialization changed the nature of life in the small communities. So too did nationalism, imperialism, global capitalism, and world war. In our accounts of such diverse events as the American Revolution, the Civil War, the New Deal, and the Cold War, we seek the drama of history in the efforts of ordinary people to make sense of the demands imposed upon them by economic and social change.

It was during these confrontations—moments of unexpected opportunity and frightening vulnerability—that ordinary Americans came to understand better those processes of justice and oppression, national security, and distribution of natural resources that we call politics. The outcome of international wars, the policies legislated by Congress, and the decisions handed down by the Supreme Court must be included in a proper narrative history of the peoples of the United States since these occurrences sparked fresh controversies. They were the stuff of expectations as well as disappointments. What one group interpreted as progress, another almost always viewed as a curtailment of rights. For some the conquest of the West, a process that went on for several centuries, opened the door to prosperity; for others it brought degradation and removal. The point is not to turn the history of the United States into a chronicle of broken dreams. Rather, we seek to reconstruct the tensions behind events, demonstrating as best we can why good history can never be written entirely from the perspective of the winners.

From the start of the project, we recognized the risk of treating minorities and women as a kind of afterthought, as if their contributions to the defining events of American history were postscripts, to be taken up only after the reader had learned of important battles and transforming elections. Our treatment of the American Revolution is one example of our balanced and integrated approach to telling the story of the past. Women were not spectators during the war for independence. They understood the language of rights and equality, and while they could not vote for representatives in the colonial assemblies, they made known in other ways their protests against British taxation. They formed the backbone of the boycotts that helped mobilize popular opinion during the prelude to armed confrontation. And they made it clear that they expected liberation from the legal and economic constraints that consigned them to second-class citizenship in the new republic. Their aspirations were woven into every aspect of the American Revolution, and although they were surely disappointed with the male response to their appeals, they deserve—and here receive—attention not as marginal participants in shaping events but as central figures in an on-going conversation about gender and power in a liberal society.

The story of how African Americans organized after World War II to demand that the nation live up to the promise of the Declaration of Independence offers yet another example of this book's integrated approach. Our account of the civil rights struggle ranges from the eloquent leadership of Martin Luther King, Jr., to the key roles played by unheralded blacks in the ranks at Selma and Birmingham. These brave men, women, and children suffered the blows of local sheriffs and the indignity of being swept off the streets by fire hoses, yet their travails ultimately persuaded white America to enact the landmark civil rights laws of the 1960s. The United States has yet to accord African Americans full equality, but the strides taken after World War II constitute a major step toward racial justice. Similarly, the stories of other grand events integrate the hopes and fears of other groups—Native Americans, new immigrants from Third World nations—into what philosopher Horace Kallen once described as "a multiplicity in a unity, an orchestration of mankind."

An overriding goal in our crafting of this narrative has been to produce a volume that would be enjoyable to read. Striving for this goal, we have sought to avoid the clumsy jargon that can be so irksome to the reader who—like us—believes that good history involves well-told stories. The structure and features of the book are intended to stimulate student interest and reinforce learning. Chapters begin with vignettes or incidents that introduce the specific chapter themes that drive the narrative and preview the topics to be discussed. Our interpretation of the central events of American history is based on the best scholarship of the past as well as the most recent historiography.

Although this book is a joint effort, each author took primary responsibility for a set of chapters. T. H. Breen contributed the first eight chapters, which deal with the long period from the first Indian migrations from Asia some 20,000 years ago to the War of 1812. George M. Fredrickson wrote Chapters 9 through

16, carrying the narrative through the Civil War and Reconstruction. R. Hal Williams was responsible for Chapters 17 through 24, focusing on the industrial transformation and urbanization of the late nineteenth century as well as on the events leading up to America's entry into World War I. Robert A. Divine wrote Chapters 25 through 33, bringing the story through the Great Depression, World War II, and the Cold War, and ending with the most recent national elections. Each author reviewed and revised the work of his colleagues and helped shape the story into its final form.

The Authors

1

NEW WORLD ENCOUNTERS

Ew world conquest sparked unexpected, often embarrassing contests over the alleged superiority of European culture. Not surprisingly, the colonizers insisted they brought the benefits of civilization to the primitive and savage peoples of North America. Native Americans never shared this perspective, voicing a strong preference for their own values and institutions. In early seventeenth-century Maryland the struggle over cultural superiority turned dramatically on how best to punish the crime of murder, an issue about which both Native Americans and Europeans had firm opinions.

The actual events that occurred at Captain William Claiborne's trading post in 1635 may never be known. Surviving records indicate that several young Native American males identified as Wicomesses apparently traveled to Claiborne's on business, but to their great annoyance, they found the proprietor entertaining Susquehannocks, their most hated enemies. The situation deteriorated rapidly after the Susquehannocks ridiculed the Wicomesses, "whereat some of Claiborne's people that saw it, did laugh." Unwilling to endure public humiliation, the Wicomesses later ambushed the Susquehannocks, killing five, and then returned to the trading post where they murdered three Englishmen.

Wicomess leaders realized immediately that something had to be done. They dispatched a trusted messenger to inform the governor of Maryland that they intended "to offer satisfaction for the harm . . . done to the English." The murder of the Susquehannocks was another matter, best addressed by the Native Americans themselves. The governor praised the Wicomesses for coming forward, announcing that "I expect that those men, who have done this outrage, should be delivered unto me, to do with them as I shall think fit." The Wicomess spokesman was dumbfounded. The governor surely did not understand basic Native American legal procedure. "It is the manner amongst us Indians, that if any such like accident happens," he explained, "we do redeem the life of a man that is so slain with a 100 Arms length of *Roanoke* (which is a sort of Beads that they make, and use for money)." The governor's demand for prisoners seemed doubly impertinent, "since you [English settlers] are here strangers, and coming into our Country, you should rather conform your selves to the Customs of our Country, than impose yours upon us." At this point the governor hastily ended the conversation, perhaps uncomfortably aware that if the legal tables had been turned and the murders committed in England, he would be the one loudly defending "the Customs of our Country."

Europeans sailing in the wake of Admiral Christopher Columbus constructed a narrative of dominance that survived long after the Wicomesses had been dispersed—a fate that befell them in the late seventeenth century. The story recounted first in Europe and then in the United States depicted heroic adventures, missionaries, and soldiers sharing Western civilization with the peoples of the New World and opening a vast virgin land to economic development. The familiar tale celebrated material progress, the inevitable spread of European values, and the taming of frontiers. It was a history crafted by the victors—usually by white leaders such as Maryland's governor—and by the children of the victors to explain how they had come to inherit the land.

This narrative of events no longer provides an adequate explanation for European conquest and settlement. It is not so much wrong as partisan, incomplete, even offensive. History recounted from the perspective of the victors inevitably silences the voices of the victims, the peoples who, in the victors' view, foolishly resisted economic and technological progress. Heroic tales of the advance of Western values only serve to deflect modern attention away from the rich cultural and racial diversity that characterized North American societies for a very long time. More disturbing, traditional tales of European conquest also obscure the sufferings of the millions of Native Americans who perished, as well as the huge numbers of Africans sold in the New World as slaves.

By placing these complex, often unsettling, experiences within an interpretive framework of *creative adaptations*—rather than of *exploration* or *settlement*—we go a long way toward recapturing the full human dimensions of conquest and resistance. While the New World often witnessed tragic violence and systematic betrayal, it allowed ordinary people of three different races and many different ethnic identities opportunities to shape their own lives as best they could. Neither the Native Americans nor the Africans were passive victims of European exploitation. Within their own families and communities they made choices, sometimes rebelling, sometimes accommodating, but always trying to make sense in terms of their own cultures of what was happening to them. Of course, that was precisely what the Wicomess messenger tried to tell the governor of Maryland.

NATIVE AMERICAN HISTORIES
BEFORE CONQUEST

As almost any Native American could have informed the first European adventurers, the peopling of America did not begin in 1492. In fact, although Spanish invaders such as Columbus proclaimed the discovery of a "New World," they really brought into contact three worlds—Europe, Africa, and America—that in the fifteenth century were already old. Indeed, the first migrants reached the North American continent some fifteen to twenty thousand years ago. The precise dating of this great human trek remains a hotly contested topic. Although some archaeologists maintain that settlement began as early as thirty thousand years ago, the scientific evidence in support of this thesis currently is not persuasive. However this debate eventually resolves itself, no one doubts that Native Americans have recorded a very long history in North America.

Twenty thousand years ago the earth's climate was considerably colder than it is today. Huge glaciers, often more than a mile thick, extended as far south as the present states of Illinois and Ohio and covered broad sections of western Canada. Much of the world's moisture was transformed into ice, and the oceans dropped hundreds of feet below their current level. The receding waters created a land bridge connecting Asia and North America, a region now submerged beneath the Bering Sea that modern archaeologists named Beringia.

Even at the height of the last Ice Age, much of the far North remained free of glaciers. Small bands of spear-throwing Paleo-Indians pursued giant mammals (megafauna)—woolly mammoths and mastodons, for example—across the vast tundra of Beringia. These hunters were the first human beings to set foot on a vast, uninhabited continent. Because these migrations took place over a long period of time and involved small, independent bands of highly nomadic people, the Paleo-Indians never developed a sense of common identity. Each group focused on its own immediate survival, adjusting to the opportunities presented by various microenvironments.

The material culture of the Paleo-Indians differed little from that of other Stone Age peoples found in Asia, Africa, and Europe. In terms of human health, however, something occurred on the Beringian tundra that forever altered the history of Native Americans. For complex reasons, the members of these small migrating groups stopped hosting a number of communicative diseases—smallpox and measles being the deadliest—and although Native Americans experienced illnesses such as tuberculosis, they no longer suffered the major epidemics that under normal conditions would have killed a large percentage of their population every year. The physical isolation of the various bands may have protected them from the spread of contagious disease. Another theory notes that epidemics have frequently been associated with prolonged contact with domestic animals such as cattle and pigs. Since the Paleo-Indians did not domesticate animals, not even horses, they may have avoided the microbes that caused virulent European and African diseases. Whatever the explanation for this curious epidemiological record, Native Americans lost inherited immunities that later might have protected them from many contagious germs. Thus when they first came into contact with Europeans and Africans, Native Americans had no defense against the great killers of the Early Modern world.

THE GREAT TRANSFORMATION: FOOD, CLIMATE, AND CULTURE

Some twelve thousand years ago global warming substantially reduced the glaciers, allowing nomadic hunters to pour into the heart of the North American continent. Within just a few thousand years, Native Americans had journeyed from Colorado to the southern tip of South America. Blessed with a seemingly inexhaustible supply of meat, the early migrants experienced rapid population growth. As archaeologists have discovered, however, the sudden expansion of human population coincided with the loss of scores of large mammals, many of them the spear-throwers' favorite sources of food. The animals that died out during this period included mammoths and mastodons; camels and, amazingly, horses were eradicated from the land. The peoples of the Great Plains did not obtain horses until the Spanish reintroduced them in the New World in 1547. Some archaeologists have suggested that the early Paleo-Indian hunters bear responsibility for the mass extinction of so many animals. It is more probable that climatic warming, which transformed well-watered regions into arid territories, put the large mammals under severe stress, and the early humans simply contributed to an ecological process over which they ultimately had little control.

The Indian peoples adjusted to the changing environmental conditions. As they dispersed across the North American continent, they developed new food sources, at first smaller mammals and fish, nuts and berries, and then about five thousand years ago, they discovered how to cultivate certain plants.

Knowledge of maize (corn), squash, and beans spread north from central Mexico. The peoples living in the Southwest acquired cultivation skills long before the bands living along the Atlantic Coast. The shift to basic crops—a transformation that is sometimes termed the Agricultural Revolution—profoundly altered Native American societies. The availability of a more reliable store of food helped liberate nomadic groups from the insecurities of hunting and gathering. It was during this period that Native Americans began to produce ceramics, a valuable technology for the storage of grain. The vegetable harvest made possible the establishment of permanent villages, that often were governed by clearly defined hierarchies of elders and kings, and as the food supply increased, the Native American population greatly expanded, especially around urban centers in the Southwest and in the Mississippi Valley. Although the evidence is patchy, scholars currently estimate that approximately four million Native Americans lived north of Mexico at the time of initial encounter with Europeans.

MYSTERIOUS DISAPPEARANCES

Several magnificent sites in North America provide powerful testimony to the cultural and social achievements of native peoples during the final two thousand years before European conquest. One of the more impressive is Chaco Canyon on the San Juan River in present-day New Mexico. The massive pueblo was the center of Anasazi culture, serving both political and religious functions, and it is estimated that its complex structures may have housed as many as fifteen thousand people. The Anasazis sustained their agriculture through a huge, technologically sophisticated network of irrigation canals that carried water long distances. They also constructed a transportation system connecting Chaco Canyon by road to more than seventy outlying villages. Some of the highways were almost a hundred miles long.

During this period equally impressive urban centers developed throughout the Ohio and Mississippi Valleys. In present-day southern Ohio, the Adena and Hopewell peoples—names assigned by archaeologists to distinguish differences in material culture—built large ceremonial mounds, where they buried the families of local elites. Approximately a thousand years after the birth of Christ, the groups gave way to the Mississippian culture, a loose collection of communities dispersed along the Mississippi River from Louisiana to Illinois that shared similar technologies and beliefs. Cahokia, a huge fortification and ceremonial site in Illinois that originally rose high above the river, represented the greatest achievement of the Mississippian peoples. Covering almost twenty acres, Cahokia once

The center of the Anasazi culture was Chaco Canyon, and Pueblo Bonita was the largest of Chaco's twelve towns. The pueblo rose five stories high on walls made of adobe and faced with sandstone slabs. More than 650 living quarters and storage rooms surrounded the central plaza. Roads extending some 400 miles linked Pueblo Bonita to outlying pueblos.

supported a population of almost twenty thousand, a city rivaling in size many encountered in late medieval Europe.

Recent research reveals that the various Native American peoples did not live in isolated communities. To be sure, over the millennia they developed many different cultural and social practices, reflecting the specific constraints of local ecologies. More than three hundred separate languages had evolved in North America before European conquest. But members of the groups traded goods over extremely long distances. Burial mounds found in the Ohio Valley, for example, have yielded obsidian from western Wyoming, shells from Florida, mica quarried in North Carolina and Tennessee, and copper found near Lake Superior.

Yet however advanced the Native American cultures of the southwest and Mississippi Valley may have been, both cultures disappeared rather mysteriously just before the arrival of the Europeans. No one knows what events brought down the great city of Cahokia or persuaded the Anasazis to abandon Chaco Canyon. Some scholars have suggested that climatic changes coupled with continuing population growth put too much pressure on food supplies; others insist that chronic warfare destabilized the social order. It has even been argued that diseases carried to the New World by the first European adventurers ravaged the cultures. About one point modern commentators are in full agreement: The breakdown of Mississippian culture caused smaller bands to disperse, construct new identities, and establish different political structures. They were the peoples who first encountered the Europeans along the Atlantic Coast and who seemed to the newcomers to have lived in the same places and followed the same patterns of behavior since the dawn of time.

AZTEC DOMINANCE

The stability resulting from the Agricultural Revolution allowed the Indians of Mexico and Central America to structure their societies in more complex ways. Like the Incas who lived in what is now known as Peru, the Mayan and Toltec peoples of Central Mexico built vast cities, formed government bureaucracies that dominated large tributary populations, and developed hieroglyphic writing as well as an accurate solar calendar.

Not long before Columbus began his first voyage across the Atlantic, the Aztecs, an aggressive, warlike people, swept through the Valley of Mexico, conquering the great cities that their enemies had constructed. Aztec warriors ruled by force, reducing defeated rivals to tributary status. In 1519, the Aztecs' main ceremonial center, Tenochtitlán, contained as many as 250,000 people as compared with only 50,000 in Seville, the port from which the early Spaniards had sailed. Elaborate human sacrifice associated with Huitzilopochtli, the Aztec sun god, horrified Europeans, who apparently did not find the savagery of their own civilization so objectionable. The Aztec ritual killings were connected to the agricultural cycle, and the Indians believed the blood of their victims possessed extraordinary fertility powers.

EASTERN WOODLAND CULTURES

In the northeast region along the Atlantic coast, the Indians did not practice intensive agriculture. These peoples, numbering less than a million at the time of conquest, generally supplemented farming with seasonal hunting and gathering. Most belonged to what ethnographers term the Eastern Woodland Cultures. Small bands formed villages during the warm summer months. The women cultivated maize and other crops while the men hunted and fished. During the

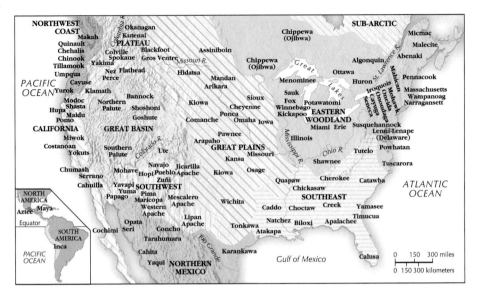

The First Americans: Location of Major Indian Groups and Culture Areas in the 1600s
Native Americans had complex social structures and religious systems and a well-developed agricultural technology when they came into initial contact with Europeans.

winter, difficulties associated with feeding so many people forced the communities to disperse. Each family lived off the land as best it could.

Seventeenth-century English settlers were most likely to have encountered the Algonquian-speaking peoples who occupied much of the territory along the Atlantic coast from North Carolina to Maine. Included in this large linguistic family were the Powhatans of Tidewater Virginia, the Narragansetts of Rhode Island, and the Abenakis of northern New England.

Despite common linguistic roots, however, the scattered Algonquian communities would have found communication extremely difficult. They had developed very different dialects. A sixteenth-century Narragansett, for example, would have found it hard to comprehend a Powhatan. The major groups of the Southeast, such as the Creeks, belonged to a separate language group (Muskogean); the Indians of the eastern Great Lakes region and upper St. Lawrence Valley generally spoke Iroquoian dialects.

Linguistic ties had little effect on Indian politics. Algonquian groups who lived in different regions, exploited different resources, and spoke different dialects did not develop strong ties of mutual identity, and when their own interests were involved, they were more than willing to ally themselves with Europeans or "foreign" Indians against other Algonquian speakers. Divisions among Indian groups would in time facilitate European conquest. Local Native American peoples greatly outnumbered the first settlers, and had the Europeans not forged alliances with the Indians, they could not so easily have gained a foothold on the continent.

However divided the Indians of eastern North America may have been, they shared many cultural values and assumptions. Most Native Americans, for example, defined their place in society through kinship. Such personal bonds determined the character of economic and political relations. As historian James Axtell explained, "The basic unit of social membership in all tribes was the exogamous clan, a lineal descent group determined through one parent." The farming bands living in areas eventually claimed by England were often matrilineal, which meant in effect that the women owned the planting fields and houses, maintained tribal customs, and had a role in tribal government. Among the native communities of Canada and the northern Great Lakes, patrilineal forms were much more common. In these groups, the men owned the hunting grounds that the family needed to survive.

Eastern Woodland communities organized diplomacy, trade, and war around reciprocal relationships that impressed Europeans as being extraordinarily egalitarian, even democratic. Chains of native authority were loosely structured. Native leaders were such renowned public speakers because persuasive rhetoric was often their only effective source of power. It required considerable oratorical skills for an Indian leader to persuade independent-minded warriors to support a certain policy.

Before the arrival of the white settlers, Indian wars were seldom very lethal. Young warriors attacked neighboring bands largely to exact revenge for a previous insult or the death of a relative, or to secure captives. Fatalities, when they did occur, sparked cycles of revenge. Some captives were tortured to death; others were adopted into the community as replacements for fallen relatives.

THE INDIANS DISCOVER A NEW WORLD

The arrival of large numbers of white men and women on the North American continent profoundly altered Native American cultures. Change did not occur at the same rates in all places. Indian villages located on the Atlantic coast came under severe pressure almost immediately; inland groups had more time to adjust. Wherever they lived, however, Indians discovered that conquest strained traditional ways of life, and as daily patterns of experience changed almost beyond recognition, native peoples had to devise new answers, new responses, and new ways to survive in physical and social environments that eroded tradition. Historian James Merrell reminded us the Indians found themselves living in a world that from their perspective was just as "new" as that which greeted the European invaders.

CREATIVE ADAPTATIONS

Native Americans were not passive victims of geopolitical forces beyond their control. So long as they remained healthy, they held their own in the early exchanges, and although they eagerly accepted certain trade goods, they generally resisted other aspects of European cultures. The earliest recorded contacts between Indians and explorers suggest curiosity and surprise rather than hostility. A Southeastern Indian who encountered Hernando de Soto in 1540 expressed awe (at least that is what a Spanish witness recorded): "The things that seldom happen bring astonishment. Think, then, what must be the effect on me and mine, the sight of you and your people, whom we have at no time seen . . . things so altogether new, as to strike awe and terror to our hearts."

What Indians desired most was peaceful trade. The earliest French explorers reported that natives waved from shore, urging the Europeans to exchange metal items for beaver skins. In fact, the Indians did not perceive themselves at a disadvantage in these dealings. They could readily see the technological advantage of guns over bows and arrows. Metal knives made daily tasks much easier. And to acquire such goods they gave up pelts, which to them seemed in abundant supply. "The English have no sense," one Indian informed a French priest. "They give us twenty knives like this for one Beaver skin." Another native announced that "the Beaver does everything perfectly well: it makes kettles, hatchets, swords, knives, bread . . . in short, it makes everything." The man who recorded these observations reminded French readers—in case they had missed the point—that the Indian was "making sport of us Europeans."

Trading sessions along the eastern frontier were really cultural seminars. The Europeans tried to make sense out of Indian customs, and although they may have called the natives "savages," they quickly discovered that the Indians drove hard bargains. They demanded gifts; they set the time and place of trade.

The Indians used the occasions to study the newcomers. They formed opinions about the Europeans, some flattering, some less so, but they never concluded from their observations that Indian culture was inferior to that of the colonizers. They regarded the beards worn by European men as particularly revolting. As an eighteenth-century Englishman said of the Iroquois, "They seem always to have Looked upon themselves as far Superior to the rest of Mankind and accordingly Call themselves *Ongwehoenwe,* i.e., Men Surpassing all other men."

For Europeans, communicating with the Indians was always an ordeal. The invaders reported having gained deep insight into Native American cultures through sign languages. How much accurate information explorers and traders took from these crude improvised exchanges is a matter of conjecture. In a letter written in 1493, Columbus expressed frustration: "I did not understand those people nor they me, except for what common sense dictated, although they were saddened and I much more so, because I wanted to have good information concerning everything."

In the absence of meaningful conversation, Europeans often concluded that the Indians held them in high regard, perhaps seeing the newcomers as gods. Such one-sided encounters involved a good deal of projection, a mental process of translating alien sounds and gestures into messages that Europeans wanted to hear. Sometimes the adventurers did not even try to communicate, assuming from superficial observation—as did the sixteenth-century explorer Giovanni da Verrazzano—"that they have no religion, and that they live in absolute freedom, and that everything they do proceeds from Ignorance."

Ethnocentric Europeans tried repeatedly to "civilize" the Indians. In practice that meant persuading natives to dress like the colonists, attend white schools, live in permanent structures, and, most important, accept Christianity. The Indians listened more or less patiently, but in the end, they usually rejected European values. One South Carolina trader explained that when Indians were asked to become more English, they said no, "for they thought it hard, that we should desire them to change their manners and customs, since they did not desire us to turn Indians."

To be sure, some Indians were strongly attracted to Christianity, but most paid it lip service or found it irrelevant to their needs. As one Huron told a French priest, "It would be useless for me to repent having sinned, seeing that I never have sinned." Another Huron announced that he did not fear punishment after death since "we cannot tell whether everything that appears faulty to Men, is so in the Eyes of God."

Among some Indian groups, gender figured significantly in a person's willingness to convert to Christianity. Native men who traded animal skins for European goods had more frequent contact with the whites, and they proved more receptive to the arguments of missionaries. But native women jealously guarded traditional culture, a system that often sanctioned polygamy—a husband having several wives—and gave women substantial authority over the distribution of food within the village. French Jesuits seemed especially eager to undermine the independence of Native American women. Among other demands, missionaries insisted on monogamous marriages, an institution based on Christian values but that made little sense in Indian societies where constant warfare killed off large numbers of young males and increasingly left native women without sufficient marriage partners.

The white settlers' educational system proved no more successful than their religion was in winning cultural converts. Young Indian scholars deserted stuffy classrooms at the first chance. In 1744, Virginia offered several Iroquois boys a free education at the College of William and Mary. The Iroquois leaders rejected the invitation because they found that boys who had gone to college "were absolutely good for nothing being neither acquainted with the true methods of killing deer, catching Beaver, or surprising an enemy."

Even matrimony seldom eroded the Indians' attachment to their own customs. When Native Americans and whites married—unions the English found less desirable than did the French or Spanish—the European partner usually elected to live among the Indians. Impatient settlers who regarded the Indians simply as an obstruction to progress sometimes developed more coercive methods, such as enslavement, to achieve cultural conversion. Again, from the white perspective, the results were disappointing. Indian slaves ran away or died. In either case, they did not become Europeans.

DEPENDENCY: TRADE AND DISEASE

Over time, cooperative encounters between the Native Americans and Europeans became less frequent. The Europeans found it almost impossible to understand the Indians' relation to the land and other natural resources. English planters cleared the forests and fenced the fields and, in the process, radically altered the ecological systems on which the Indians depended. The European system of land use inevitably reduced the supply of deer and other animals essential to traditional native cultures.

Dependency also came in more subtle forms. The Indians welcomed European commerce, but like so many consumers throughout recorded history, they discovered that the objects they most coveted inevitably brought them into debt. To pay for the trade goods, the Indians hunted more aggressively and even further reduced the population of fur-bearing mammals.

Commerce eroded Indian independence in other ways. After several disastrous wars—the Yamasee War in South Carolina (1715), for example—the natives learned that demonstrations of force usually resulted in the suspension of normal trade, on which the Indians had grown quite dependent for guns and ammunition, among other things. A hardened English businessman made the point quite bluntly. When asked if the Catawbas would harm his traders, he responded that "the danger would be . . . little from them, because they are too fond of our trade to lose it for the pleasure of shedding a little English blood."

It was disease, however, that ultimately destroyed the cultural integrity of many North American tribes. European adventurers exposed the Indians to bacteria and viruses against which they possessed no natural immunity. Smallpox, measles, and influenza decimated the Native American population. Other diseases such as alcoholism took a terrible toll.

After Native Americans were exposed to common Old World diseases, particularly smallpox, they died by the millions.

Within a generation of initial contact with Europeans, the Caribs, who gave the Caribbean its name, were virtually extinct. The Algonquian communities of New England experienced appalling rates of death. One Massachusetts colonist reported in 1630 that the Indian peoples of his region "above twelve years since were swept away by a great & grievous Plague . . . so that there are verie few left to inhabite the Country." Settlers possessed no knowledge of germ theory—it was not formulated until the mid-nineteenth century—and speculated that a Christian God had providentially cleared the wilderness of heathens.

Historical demographers now estimate that some tribes suffered a 90 to 95 percent population loss within the first century of European contact. The death of so many Indians decreased the supply of indigenous laborers, who were needed by the Europeans to work the mines and to grow staple crops such as sugar and tobacco. The decimation of native populations may have persuaded colonists throughout the New World to seek a substitute labor force in Africa. Indeed, the enslavement of blacks has been described as an effort by Europeans to "repopulate" the New World.

Indians who survived the epidemics often found that the fabric of traditional culture had come unraveled. The enormity of the death toll and the agony that accompanied it called traditional religious beliefs and practices into question. The survivors lost not only members of their families, but also elders who might have told them how properly to bury the dead and give spiritual comfort to the living.

Some native peoples, such as the Iroquois, who lived some distance from the coast and thus had more time to adjust to the challenge, withstood the crisis better than did those who immediately confronted the Europeans and Africans.

Refugee Indians from the hardest hit eastern communities were absorbed into healthier western groups. Nonetheless, the cultural and physical shock that the dwindling Native American population experienced is beyond the historian's power ever fully to comprehend.

WEST AFRICA: ANCIENT AND COMPLEX SOCIETIES

During the era of the European slave trade, roughly from the late fifteenth through the mid-nineteenth centuries, a number of enduring myths about sub-Saharan West Africa were propagated. Even today, commentators claim that the people who inhabited this region four hundred years ago were isolated from the rest of the world and had a simple, self-sufficient economy. Indeed, some scholars still depict the vast region stretching from the Senegal River south to modern Angola as a single cultural unit, as if at one time all the men and women living there must have shared a common set of African political, religious, and social values.

Sub-Saharan West Africa defies such easy generalizations. The first Portuguese who explored the African coast during the fifteenth century encountered a great variety of political and religious cultures. Many hundreds of years earlier, Africans living in this region had come into contact with Islam, the religion founded by the Prophet Muhammad during the seventh century. Islam spread slowly from Arabia into West Africa. Not until A.D. 1030 did a kingdom located in the Senegal Valley accept the Muslim religion. Many other West Africans, such as those in ancient Ghana, resisted Islam and continued to observe traditional religions.

As Muslim traders from North Africa and the Middle East brought a new religion to parts of West Africa, they expanded sophisticated trade networks that linked the villagers of Senegambia with urban centers in northwest Africa, Morocco, Tunisia, and Cyrenaica. Great camel caravans regularly crossed the Sahara carrying trade goods that were exchanged for gold and slaves. Sub-Saharan Africa's well-developed links with Islam surprised a French priest who in 1686 observed African pilgrims going "to visit Mecca to visit Mahomet's tomb, although they are eleven or twelve hundred leagues distance from it."

West Africans spoke many languages and organized themselves into diverse political systems. Several populous states, sometimes termed "empires," exercised loose control over large areas. Ancient African empires such as Ghana were vulnerable to external attack as well as internal rebellion, and the oral and written histories of this region record the rise and fall of several large kingdoms. When European traders first arrived, the list of major states would have included Mali, Benin, and Kongo. Many other Africans lived in what are known as stateless societies, really largely autonomous communities organized around lineage structures. In these respects, African and Native American cultures had much in common.

Whatever the form of government, men and women constructed their primary social identity within well-defined lineage groups, which consisted of persons claiming descent from a common ancestor. Disputes among members of lineage groups were generally settled by clan elders. The senior leaders allocated economic and human resources. They determined who received land and who might take a wife—critical decisions because within the villages of West Africa, women and children cultivated the fields. The communities were economically self-sufficient. Not only were they able to grow enough food to feed themselves, but they also produced trade goods, such as iron, kola, and gum.

The first Europeans to reach the West African coast by sail were the Portuguese. Strong winds and currents along the Atlantic coast moved southward, which meant a ship could sail with the wind from Portugal to West Africa without difficulty. The problem was returning. Advances in maritime technology allowed the Portuguese to overcome these difficulties. By constructing a new type of ship, one uniting European hull design with lateen (triangular) sails from the Middle East, Portuguese caravels were able to navigate successfully against African winds and currents. During the fifteenth century, Portuguese sailors discovered that by sailing far to the west, often as far as the Azores, they could, on their return trips to Europe, catch a reliable westerly wind. Columbus was evidently familiar with the technique. Before attempting to cross the Atlantic Ocean, he sailed to the Gold Coast, and on the way, he undoubtedly studied the wind patterns that would carry his famed caravels to the New World and back again.

The Portuguese journeyed to Africa in search of gold and slaves. Mali and Joloff officials were willing partners in this commerce but insisted that Europeans respect trade regulations established by Africans. They required the Europeans to pay tolls and other fees and restricted the foreign traders to conducting their business in small forts or castles located at the mouths of the major rivers. Local merchants acquired some slaves and gold in the interior and transported them to the coast, where they were exchanged for European manufactures. Transactions were calculated in terms of local African currencies: a slave would be offered to a European trader for so many bars of iron or ounces of gold.

European slave traders accepted these terms largely because they had no other choice. The African states fielded formidable armies, and outsiders soon

European traders built compounds along the African coast largely to expedite the slave trade. Each compound within these "slave factories" served a different European country. The first of the slave factories was Elmina, built by the Portuguese in the late fifteenth century. Africans captured inland were marched to the compound where they were held for months until a ship arrived to transport them across the Atlantic.

discovered they could not impose their will on the region simply by demonstrations of force. Moreover, local diseases proved so lethal for Europeans—six out of ten of whom would die within a single year's stay in Africa—that they were happy to avoid dangerous trips to the interior. The slaves were usually men and women taken captive during wars; others were victims of judicial practices designed specifically to supply the growing American market. By 1650, most West African slaves were destined for the New World rather than the Middle East.

Even before Europeans colonized the New World, the Portuguese were purchasing almost a thousand slaves a year on the West African coast. The slaves were frequently forced to work on the sugar plantations of Madeira (Portuguese) and the Canaries (Spanish), Atlantic islands on which Europeans experimented with forms of unfree labor that would later be more fully and more ruthlessly established in the American colonies. It is currently estimated that approximately 10.7 million Africans were taken to the New World as slaves. The figure for the eighteenth century alone is about 5.5 million, of which more than one-third came from West Central Africa. The Bight of Benin, the Bight of Biafra, and the Gold Coast supplied most of the others.

The peopling of the New World is usually seen as a story of European migrations. But in fact, during every year between 1650 and 1831, more Africans than Europeans came to the Americas. As historian Davis Eltis wrote, "In terms of immigration alone . . . America was an extension of Africa rather than Europe until late in the nineteenth century."

EUROPE ON THE EVE OF CONQUEST

In ancient times, the West possessed a mythical appeal to people living along the shores of the Mediterranean Sea. Classical writers speculated about the fate of Atlantis, a fabled Western civilization that was said to have sunk beneath the ocean. Fallen Greek heroes allegedly spent eternity in an uncharted western paradise. But because the ships of Greece and Rome were ill designed to sail the open ocean, the lands to the west remained the stuff of legend and fantasy. In the fifth century, an intrepid Irish monk, St. Brendan, reported finding enchanted islands far out in the Atlantic. He even claimed to have met a talking whale named Jasconius, who allowed the famished voyager to cook a meal on his back.

In the tenth century, Scandinavian seafarers known as Norsemen or Vikings actually established settlements in the New World, but almost a thousand years

Materials excavated at L'Anse aux Meadows, on the northernmost tip of Newfoundland, provide evidence of a Viking settlement in North America. Using the materials excavated at the site, archaeologists have reconstructed the typically Norse dwellings, which had turf walls and roofs and wooden doors and doorframes.

passed before they received credit for their accomplishment. In the year 984, a band of Vikings led by Eric the Red sailed west from Iceland to a large island in the North Atlantic. Eric, who possessed a fine sense of public relations, named the island Greenland, reasoning that others would more willingly colonize the icebound region "if the country had a good name." A few years later, Eric's son Leif founded a small settlement he named Vinland at a location in northern Newfoundland now called L'Anse aux Meadows. At the time, the Norse voyages went unnoticed by other Europeans. The hostility of Native Americans, poor lines of communication, climatic cooling, and political upheavals in Scandinavia made maintenance of these distant outposts impossible.

BUILDING NEW NATION-STATES

At the time of the Viking settlement, other Europeans were unprepared to sponsor transatlantic exploration. Nor would they be in a position to do so for several more centuries. Medieval kingdoms were loosely organized, and until the early fifteenth century, fierce provincial loyalties, widespread ignorance of classical learning, and dreadful plagues such as the Black Death discouraged people from thinking expansively about the world beyond their own immediate communities.

In the fifteenth century, however, these conditions began to change. Europe became more prosperous, political authority was more centralized, and the Renaissance fostered a more expansive outlook among literate people. A major element in the shift was the slow but steady growth of population after 1450. Historians are uncertain about the cause of the increase—after all, neither the quality of medicine nor sanitation improved much—but the result was a substantial rise in the price of land, since there were more mouths to feed. Landlords profited from these trends, and as their income expanded, they demanded more of the luxury items, such as spices, silks, and jewels, that came from distant Asian ports. Economic prosperity created powerful new incentives for exploration and trade.

This period also witnessed the centralization of political authority under a group of rulers whom historians refer to collectively as the New Monarchs. Before the mid-fifteenth century, feudal nobles dominated small districts throughout Europe. Conceding only nominal allegiance to larger territorial leaders, the local barons taxed the peasants and waged war pretty much as they pleased. They also dispensed what passed for justice. The New Monarchs challenged the nobles' autonomy. The changes that accompanied the challenges came slowly, and in many areas violently, but the results altered traditional political relationships between the nobility and the crown, and between the citizen and the state. The New Monarchs of Europe recruited armies and supported these expensive organizations with revenues from national taxes. They created effective national courts. While these monarchs were often despotic, they personified the emergent nation-states of Europe and brought a measure of peace to local communities weary of chronic feudal war.

The story was the same throughout most of western Europe. The Tudors of England, represented by Henry VII (r. 1485–1509), ended a long civil war known as the Wars of the Roses. Louis XI, the French monarch (r. 1461–1483), strengthened royal authority by reorganizing state finances. The political unification of Spain began in 1469 with the marriage of Ferdinand of Aragon and Isabella of Castile, setting off a nation-building process that involved driving both the Jews and Muslims out of Spain. These strong-willed monarchs forged nations out of groups of independent kingdoms. If political centralization had not occurred, the major European countries could not possibly have generated the financial and military resources necessary for worldwide exploration.

A final prerequisite to exploration was reliable technical knowledge. Ptolemy (second century A.D.) and other ancient geographers had mapped the known world and had even demonstrated that the world was round. During

Improved printing methods in the 1440s allowed navigators to share geographical findings more easily, sparking a new wave of exploration in the early 1500s.

the Middle Ages, however, Europeans lost effective contact with classical tradition. Within Arab societies, the old learning had survived, indeed flourished, and when Europeans eventually rediscovered the classical texts during the Renaissance, they drew heavily on the work of Arab scholars. This "new" learning generated great intellectual curiosity about the globe and about the world that existed beyond the Mediterranean.

The invention of printing from movable type by Johann Gutenberg in the 1440s greatly facilitated the spread of technical knowledge. Indeed, printing sparked a communications revolution whose impact on the lives of ordinary people was as far-reaching as that caused by telephones, television, and computers in modern times. Sea captains published their findings as quickly as they could engage a printer, and by the beginning of the sixteenth century, a small, though growing, number of educated readers throughout Europe were well informed about the exploration of the New World. The printing press invited Europeans to imagine exciting opportunities that they had hardly perceived when the Vikings sailed the North Atlantic.

MAKING SENSE OF A NEW WORLD

By 1500, centralization of political authority and advances in geographic knowledge brought Spain to the first rank as a world power. In the early fifteenth century, though, Spain consisted of several autonomous kingdoms. It lacked rich natural resources and possessed few good seaports. In fact, there was little about this land to suggest its people would take the lead in conquering and colonizing the New World.

By the end of the century, however, Spain suddenly came alive with creative energy. The union of Ferdinand and Isabella sparked a drive for political consolidation that, because of the monarchs' fervid Catholicism, took on the characteristics of a religious crusade. Spurred by the militant faith of their monarchs, the armies of Castile and Aragon waged holy war—known as the *Reconquista*—against the independent states in southern Spain that earlier had been captured by Muslims. In 1492, the Moorish (Islamic) kingdom of Granada fell, and, for the first time in centuries, the entire Iberian peninsula was united under Christian rulers. Spanish authorities showed no tolerance for people who rejected the Catholic faith.

During the Reconquista, thousands of Jews and Moors were driven from the country. Indeed, Columbus undoubtedly encountered such refugees as he was preparing for his famous voyage. From this volatile social and political environment came the *conquistadores,* men eager for personal glory and material gain, uncompromising in matters of religion, and unswerving in their loyalty to the crown. They were prepared to employ fire and sword in any cause sanctioned by God and king, and these adventurers carried European culture to the most populous regions of the New World.

CALCULATING RISKS AND REWARDS

If it had not been for Christopher Columbus (Cristoforo Colombo), of course, Spain might never have gained an American empire. Little is known about his early life. Born in Genoa in 1451 of humble parentage, Columbus soon devoured the classical learning that had so recently been rediscovered and made available in printed form. He mastered geography, and—perhaps while sailing the coast of West Africa—he became obsessed with the idea of voyaging west across the Atlantic Ocean to reach Cathay, as China was then known.

In 1484, Columbus presented his plan to the king of Portugal. However, while the Portuguese were just as interested as Columbus in reaching Cathay, they elected to voyage around the continent of Africa instead of following the route suggested by Columbus. They suspected that Columbus had substantially underestimated the circumference of the earth and that for all his enthusiasm, he would almost certainly starve before reaching Asia. The Portuguese decision eventually paid off quite handsomely. In 1498, one of their captains, Vasco da Gama, returned from the coast of India carrying a fortune in spices and other luxury goods.

Undaunted by rejection, Columbus petitioned Isabella and Ferdinand for financial backing. He boldly played on the rivalry between Spain and Portugal, talking of wealth and empire. Indeed, for a person with little success or apparent support, he was supremely confident.

Columbus's stubborn lobbying on behalf of the "Enterprise of the Indies" gradually wore down opposition in the Spanish court, and the two sovereigns provided him with a small fleet that contained two of the most famous caravels ever constructed, the *Niña* and the *Pinta,* as well as the square-rigged *nao Santa Maria.* The indomitable admiral set sail for Cathay in August 1492, the year of Spain's unification.

Educated Europeans of the fifteenth century knew the world was round. No one seriously believed that Columbus and his crew would tumble off the edge of the earth. The concern was with size, not shape. Columbus estimated the distance to the mainland of Asia to be about 3,000 nautical miles, a voyage his small ships would have no difficulty completing. The actual distance is 10,600 nautical miles, however, and had the New World not been in his way, he and his crew would have run out of food and water long before they reached China, as the Portuguese had predicted.

When the tiny Spanish fleet sighted an island in the Bahamas after only thirty-three days at sea, the admiral concluded he had reached Asia. Since his mathematical calculations had obviously been correct, he assumed he would soon encounter the Chinese. It never occurred to Columbus that he had stumbled upon a new world. He assured his men, his patrons, and perhaps himself that the islands were indeed part of the fabled "Indies." Or if not the Indies themselves, then they were surely an extension of the great Asian landmass. He searched for the splendid cities Marco Polo had described, but instead of meeting wealthy Chinese, Columbus encountered Native Americans, whom he appropriately, if mistakenly, called "Indians."

After his first voyage of discovery, Columbus returned to the New World three more times. But despite his considerable courage and ingenuity, he could never find the treasure his financial supporters in Spain angrily demanded. Columbus died in 1506 a frustrated but wealthy entrepreneur, unaware that he had reached a previously unknown continent separating Asia from Europe. The final disgrace came in December 1500 when an ambitious falsifier, Amerigo Vespucci, published a sensational account of his travels across the Atlantic that

Ships like this seventeenth-century freighter made the trip from Europe to America in six to ten weeks, depending upon the weather and winds. One of the most difficult tasks was keeping water fresh and food dry, and ships' passengers sometimes found themselves desperate for rations midway across the Atlantic. The transoceanic voyage was so full of such hardships that it acquired almost mythic meaning as a rite of passage for European settlers.

convinced German mapmakers he had proved America was distinct from Asia. Before the misconception could be corrected, the name *America* gained general acceptance throughout Europe.

Only two years after Columbus's first voyage, Spain and Portugal almost went to war over the anticipated treasure of Asia. Pope Alexander VI negotiated a settlement that pleased both kingdoms. Portugal wanted to exclude the Spanish from the west coast of Africa and, what was more important, from Columbus's new route to "India." Spain insisted on maintaining complete control over lands discovered by Columbus, which then still were regarded as extensions of China. The Treaty of Tordesillas (1494) divided the entire world along a line located 270 leagues west of the Azores. Any new lands discovered west of the line belonged to Spain. At the time, no European had ever seen Brazil, which turned out to be on Portugal's side of the line. (To this day, Brazilians speak Portuguese.) The treaty failed to discourage future English, Dutch, and French adventurers from trying their luck in the New World.

THE CONQUISTADORES

Spain's new discoveries unleashed a horde of conquistadores on the Caribbean. These independent adventurers carved out small settlements on Cuba, Hispaniola, Jamaica, and Puerto Rico in the 1490s and early 1500s. They were not interested in creating a permanent society in the New World. Rather, they came for instant wealth, preferably in gold, and were not squeamish about the means they used to obtain it. In less than two decades, the Indians who had inhabited the Caribbean islands had been exterminated, victims of exploitation and disease.

For a quarter century, the conquistadores concentrated their energies on the major islands that Columbus had discovered. Rumors of fabulous wealth in Mexico, however, aroused the interest of many Spaniards, including Hernán Cortés, a minor government functionary in Cuba. Like so many members of his class, he dreamed of glory, military adventure, and riches that would transform him from an ambitious court clerk into an honored *hidalgo.* On November 18, 1518, Cortés and a small army left Cuba to verify the stories of Mexico's treasure.

His adversary was the legendary Aztec emperor, Montezuma. The confrontation between the two powerful personalities is one of the more dramatic of early American history. A fear of competition from rival conquistadores coupled with a burning desire to conquer a vast new empire drove Cortés forward. Determined to push his men through any obstacle, he scuttled the ships that had carried them to Mexico in order to prevent them from retreating. Cortés led his band of six hundred followers across rugged mountains and on the way gathered allies from

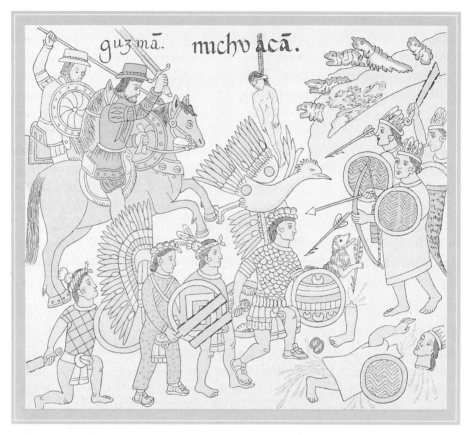

guzmā. michuācā.

At first contact with Cortés's army, the Aztecs, led by Montezuma, thought the Spaniards were demigods. The psychological advantage of their perceived omnipotence helped the Spanish score a decisive victory in Mexico. This Aztec drawing is believed to depict Cortés's conquest of the Aztecs.

among the Tlaxcalans, a tributary people eager to free themselves from Aztec domination.

In matters of war, Cortés possessed obvious technological superiority over the Aztecs. The sound of gunfire initially frightened the Indians. Moreover, Aztec troops had never seen horses, much less armored horses carrying sword-wielding Spaniards. But these elements would have counted for little had Cortés not also gained a psychological advantage over his opponents. At first, Montezuma thought that the Spaniards were gods, representatives of the fearful plumed serpent, Quetzalcoatl. Instead of resisting immediately, the emperor hesitated. When Montezuma's resolve hardened, it was too late. Cortés's victory in Mexico, coupled with other conquests in South America, transformed Spain, at least temporarily, into the wealthiest state in Europe.

FROM PLUNDER TO SETTLEMENT

Following the conquest of Mexico, renamed New Spain, the Spanish crown confronted a difficult problem. Ambitious conquistadores, interested chiefly in their own wealth and glory, had to be brought under royal authority, a task easier imagined than accomplished. Adventurers like Cortés were stubbornly independent, quick to take offense, and thousands of miles away from the seat of imperial government.

The crown found a partial solution in the *encomienda* system. The monarch rewarded the leaders of the conquest with Indian villages. The people who lived in the settlements provided the *encomenderos* with labor tribute in exchange for legal protection and religious guidance. The system, of course, cruelly exploited Indian laborers.

Spain's rulers attempted to maintain tight personal control over their American possessions. The volume of correspondence between the two conti-

Indian Slaves Working at a Spanish Sugar Plantation on the Island of Hispaniola *(1595) by Theodore de Bry. Contemporaries recognized that Spanish treatment of the Native Americans was brutal.*

nents, much of it concerning mundane matters, was staggering. All documents were duplicated several times by hand. Because the trip to Madrid took many months, a year often passed before receipt of an answer to a simple request. But somehow the cumbersome system worked. In Mexico, officials appointed in Spain established a rigid hierarchical order, directing the affairs of the country-side from urban centers.

The Spanish also brought Catholicism to the New World. The Dominicans and Franciscans, the two largest religious orders, established Indian missions throughout New Spain. Some friars tried to protect the Native Americans from the worst forms of exploitation. One courageous Dominican, Fra Bartolomé de las Casas, published an eloquent defense of Indian rights, *Historia de las Indias,* which among other things questioned the legitimacy of European conquest of the New World. Las Casas's work provoked heated debate in Spain, and while the crown had no intention of repudiating the vast American empire, it did initiate certain reforms designed to bring greater "love and moderation" to Spanish-Indian relations. It is impossible to ascertain how many converts the friars made. In 1531, however, a newly converted Christian reported a vision of the Virgin, a dark-skinned woman of obvious Indian ancestry, who became known throughout the region as the Virgin of Guadalupe. This figure—the result of a creative blending of Indian and European cultures—served as a powerful symbol of Mexican nationalism in the wars for independence fought against Spain almost three centuries later.

About 250,000 Spaniards migrated to the New World during the sixteenth century. Another 200,000 made the journey between 1600 and 1650. Most colonists were single males in their late twenties seeking economic opportunities. They generally came from the poorest agricultural regions of southern Spain—almost 40 percent migrating from Andalusia. Since so few Spanish women migrated, especially in the sixteenth century, the men often married Indians and blacks, unions which produced *mestizos* and *mulattoes.* The frequency of interracial marriage indicated that, among other things, the people of New Spain were more tolerant of racial differences than were the English who settled in North America. For the people of New Spain, social standing was affected as much, or more, by economic worth as it was by color. Persons born in the New World, even those of Spanish parentage (*criollos*), were regarded as socially inferior to natives of the mother country (*peninsulares*).

Spain claimed far more of the New World than it could possibly manage. Spain's rulers regarded the American colonies primarily as a source of precious metal, and between 1500 and 1650, an estimated 200 tons of gold and 16,000 tons of silver were shipped back to the Spanish treasury in Madrid. This great wealth, however, proved a mixed blessing. The sudden acquisition of so much money stimulated a horrendous inflation that hurt ordinary Spaniards. They were hurt further by long, debilitating European wars funded by American gold and silver. Moreover, instead of developing its own industry, Spain became dependent on the annual shipment of bullion from America, and in 1603, one insightful Spaniard declared, "The New World conquered by you, has conquered you in its turn." This somewhat weakened, although still formidable, empire would eventually extend its territorial claims north to California and the Southwest (see Chapter 4).

THE FRENCH CLAIM CANADA

French interest in the New World developed slowly. More than three decades after Columbus's discovery, King Francis I sponsored the unsuccessful efforts of Giovanni da Verrazzano to find a short water route to China, via a northwest passage around or through North America. In 1534, the king sent Jacques Cartier on a similar quest. The rocky, barren coast of Labrador depressed the

In the dead of winter, the streams of New France turned to ice. French voyageurs built sledges, placed their canoes and supplies on them, and proceeded down the frozen courses into the heart of the continent.

explorer. He grumbled, "I am rather inclined to believe that this is the land God gave to Cain."

Discovery of a large, promising waterway the following year raised Cartier's spirits. He reconnoitered the Gulf of Saint Lawrence, traveling up the magnificent river as far as modern Montreal. Despite his high expectations, however, Cartier got no closer to China, and discouraged by the harsh winters, he headed home in 1542. Not until sixty-five years later did Samuel de Champlain resettle this region for France. He founded Quebec in 1608.

As was the case with other colonial powers, the French declared they had migrated to the New World in search of wealth as well as in hopes of converting the Indians to Christianity. As it turned out, these economic and spiritual goals required full cooperation between the French and the Native Americans. In contrast to the English settlers, who established independent farms and who regarded the Indians at best as obstacles in the path of civilization, the French viewed the natives as necessary economic partners. Furs were Canada's most valuable export, and to obtain the pelts of beaver and other animals, the French were absolutely dependent on Indian hunters and trappers. French traders lived among the Indians, often taking native wives and studying local cultures.

Frenchmen known as *coureurs de bois* (forest runners), following Canada's great river networks, paddled deep into the heart of the continent in search of fresh sources of furs. Some intrepid traders penetrated beyond the Great Lakes into the Mississippi Valley. In 1673, Père Jacques Marquette journeyed down the Mississippi River, and nine years later, Sieur de La Salle traveled all the way to the Gulf of Mexico. In the early eighteenth century, the French established small settlements in Louisiana, the most important being New Orleans.

Catholic missionaries also depended on Indian cooperation. Canadian priests were drawn from two orders, the Jesuits and the Recollects, and although measuring their success in the New World is difficult, it seems they converted more Indians to Christianity than did their English Protestant counterparts to the south. Like the fur traders, the missionaries lived among the Indians and learned to speak their languages.

The French dream of a vast American empire suffered from serious flaws. The crown remained largely indifferent to Canadian affairs. Royal officials stationed in New France received limited and sporadic support from Paris. An even greater problem was the decision to settle what seemed to many rural peasants and urban artisans a cold, inhospitable land. Throughout the colonial period, Canada's European population remained small. A census of 1663 recorded a mere 3,035 French residents. By 1700, the figure had reached only 15,000. Moreover, because of the colony's geography, all exports and imports had to go through Quebec. It was relatively easy, therefore, for crown officials to control that traffic, usually by awarding fur-trading monopolies to court favorites. Such practices created political tensions and hindered economic growth.

THE ENGLISH ENTER THE COMPETITION

The first English visit to North America remains shrouded in mystery. Fishermen working out of Bristol and other western English ports may have landed in Nova Scotia and Newfoundland as early as the 1480s. John Cabot (Giovanni Caboto), a Venetian sea captain, completed the first recorded transatlantic voyage by an English vessel in 1497, while attempting to find a northwest passage to Asia.

Cabot died during a second attempt to find a direct route to Cathay in 1498. Although Sebastian Cabot continued his father's explorations in the Hudson Bay region in 1508–1509, England's interest in the New World waned. For the next three-quarters of a century, the English people were preoccupied with more pressing domestic and religious concerns. When curiosity about the New World revived, however, Cabot's voyages established England's belated claim to American territory.

BIRTH OF ENGLISH PROTESTANTISM

At the time of Cabot's death, England was not prepared to compete with Spain and Portugal for the riches of the Orient. Although Henry VII, the first Tudor monarch, brought peace to England after a bitter civil war, the country still contained too many "over-mighty subjects," powerful local magnates who maintained armed retainers and who often paid little attention to royal authority. Henry possessed no standing army; his small navy intimidated no one. To be sure, the Tudors gave nominal allegiance to the pope in Rome, but unlike the rulers of Spain, they were not crusaders for Catholicism.

A complex web of international diplomacy also worked against England's early entry into New World colonization. In 1509, to cement an alliance between Spain and England, the future Henry VIII married Catherine of Aragon. As a result of this marital arrangement, English merchants enjoyed limited rights to trade in Spain's American colonies, but any attempt by England at independent colonization would have threatened those rights and jeopardized the alliance.

By the end of the sixteenth century, however, conditions within England had changed dramatically, in part as a result of the Protestant Reformation. As they did, the English began to consider their former ally, Spain, to be the greatest threat to English aspirations. Tudor monarchs, especially Henry VIII (r. 1509–1547) and his daughter Elizabeth I (r. 1558–1603), developed a strong central administration, while England became more and more a Protestant society. The merger of English Protestantism and English nationalism affected all aspects

England's Tudor Monarchs

Henry VII
(d. 1509)
m.
Elizabeth of York

Arthur *(d.1502)* — **Henry VIII** *(r. 1509–1547)* — Margaret — Mary

m.

Catherine of Aragon — Anne Boleyn — Jane Seymour

Mary I *(r. 1553–1558)* — **Elizabeth I** *(r. 1558–1603)* — **Edward VI** *(r. 1547–1553)*

of public life. It helped propel England into a central role in European affairs and was crucial in creating a powerful sense of an English identity among all classes of people.

The catalyst for Protestant Reformation in England was the king's desire to rid himself of his wife, Catherine of Aragon, who happened to be the daughter of the former king of Spain. Their marriage had produced a daughter, Mary, but, as the years passed, no son. The need for a male heir obsessed Henry. He and his counselors assumed a female ruler could not maintain domestic peace and England would fall once again into civil war. The answer seemed to be remarriage. Henry petitioned Pope Clement VII for a divorce (technically, an annulment), but the Spanish had other ideas. Unwilling to tolerate the public humiliation of Catherine, they forced the pope to procrastinate. In 1527, time ran out. The passionate Henry fell in love with Anne Boleyn, who later bore him a daughter, Elizabeth. The king decided to divorce Catherine with or without papal consent.

The final break with Rome came swiftly. Between 1529 and 1536, the king, acting through Parliament, severed all ties with the pope, seized church lands, and dissolved many of the monasteries. In March 1534, the Act of Supremacy boldly announced, "The King's Majesty justly and rightfully is supreme head of the Church of England." Land formerly owned by the Catholic Church passed quickly into private hands, and within a short period, property holders throughout England had acquired a vested interest in Protestantism. Beyond breaking with the papacy, Henry showed little enthusiasm for theological change. Many Catholic ceremonies survived.

The split with Rome, however, opened the door to increasingly radical religious ideas. The year 1539 saw the publication of the first Bible in English. Before then the Scripture had been available only in Latin, the language of an educated elite. For the first time in English history, ordinary people could read the word of

God in the vernacular. It was a liberating experience that persuaded some men and women that Henry had not sufficiently reformed the English church.

With Henry's death in 1547, England entered a period of acute political and religious instability. Edward VI, Henry's young son by his third wife, Jane Seymour, came to the throne, but he was still a child and sickly besides. Militant Protestants took advantage of the political uncertainty, insisting the Church of England remove every trace of its Catholic origins. With the death of young Edward in 1553, these ambitious efforts came to a sudden halt. Henry's eldest daughter, Mary, next ascended the throne. Fiercely loyal to the Catholic faith of her mother, Catherine of Aragon, Mary I vowed to return England to the pope.

However misguided were the queen's plans, she possessed her father's iron will. Hundreds of Protestants were executed; others scurried off to the safety of Geneva and Frankfurt, where they absorbed the most radical Calvinist doctrines of the day. When Mary died in 1558 and was succeeded by Elizabeth, the "Marian exiles" flocked back to England, more eager than ever to rid the Tudor church of Catholicism.

MILITANT PROTESTANTISM

By the time Mary Tudor came to the throne, the vast popular movement known as the Reformation had swept across northern and central Europe, and as much as any of the later great political revolutions, it had begun to transform the character of the modern world. The Reformation started in Germany when, in 1517, a relatively obscure German monk, Martin Luther, publicly challenged the central tenets of Roman Catholicism. Within a few years, the religious unity of Europe was permanently shattered. The Reformation divided kingdoms, sparked bloody wars, and unleashed an extraordinary flood of religious publication.

Luther's message was straightforward, one ordinary people could easily comprehend. God spoke through the Bible, Luther maintained, not through the pope or priests. Scripture taught that women and men were saved by faith alone. Pilgrimages, fasts, alms, indulgences—none of the traditional ritual observances could assure salvation. The institutional structure of Catholicism was challenged as Luther's radical ideas spread rapidly across northern Germany and Scandinavia.

After Luther, other Protestant theologians—religious thinkers who would determine the course of religious reform in England, Scotland, and the early American colonies—mounted an even more strident attack on Catholicism. The most influential of these was John Calvin, a lawyer turned theologian, who lived most of his adult life in the Swiss city of Geneva. Calvin stressed God's omnipotence over human affairs. The Lord, he maintained, chose some persons for "election," the gift of salvation, while condemning others to eternal damnation. A man or woman could do nothing to alter this decision.

Common sense suggests that such a bleak doctrine—known as predestination—might lead to fatalism or hedonism. After all, why not enjoy the world's pleasures to the fullest if such actions have no effect on God's judgment? But many sixteenth-century Europeans did not share modern notions of what constitutes common sense. Indeed, Calvinists were constantly "up and doing," searching for signs that they had received God's gift of grace. The uncertainty of their eternal state proved a powerful psychological spur, for as long as people did not know whether they were scheduled for heaven or hell, they worked diligently to demonstrate that they possessed at least the seeds of grace. In Scotland, people of Calvinist persuasion founded the Presbyterian Church. And in seventeenth-century England and America, most of those who put Calvin's teachings into practice were called Puritans.

WOMAN IN POWER

Queen Elizabeth demonstrated that Henry and his advisers had been mistaken about the capabilities of female rulers. She was a woman of such talent that modern biographers find little to criticize in her decisions. She governed the English people from 1558 to 1603, an intellectually exciting period during which some of her subjects took the first halting steps toward colonizing the New World.

Elizabeth recognized her most urgent duty as queen was to end the religious turmoil that had divided the country for a generation. She had no desire to restore Catholicism. After all, the pope openly referred to her as a woman of illegitimate birth. Nor did she want to re-create the church exactly as it had been in the final years of her father's reign. Rather, Elizabeth established a unique institution, Catholic in much of its ceremony and government but clearly Protestant in doctrine. Under her so-called Elizabethan settlement, the queen assumed the title "Supreme Head of the Church."

The state of England's religion was not simply a domestic concern. One scholar aptly termed this period of European history "the Age of Religious Wars." Indeed, it is helpful to view Protestantism and Catholicism as warring ideologies, bundles of deeply held beliefs that divided countries and families much as communism and capitalism did during the late twentieth century. The confrontations between the two faiths affected Elizabeth's entire reign. Soon after she became queen, Pope Pius V excommunicated her, and in his papal bull *Regnans in Exelsis* (1570), he stripped Elizabeth of her "pretended title to the kingdom." Spain, the most fervently Catholic state in Europe, vowed to restore England to the "true" faith, and Catholic militants constantly plotted to overthrow the Tudor monarchy.

RELIGION, WAR, AND NATIONALISM

Slowly, but steadily, English Protestantism and English national identity merged. A loyal English subject in the late sixteenth century loved the queen, supported the Church of England, and hated Catholics, especially those who happened to live in Spain. Elizabeth herself came to symbolize this militant new chauvinism. Her subjects adored the Virgin Queen, and they applauded when her famed "Sea Dogs"—dashing figures such as Sir Francis Drake and Sir John Hawkins—seized Spanish treasure ships in American waters. The English sailors' raids were little more than piracy, but in this undeclared state of war, such instances of harassment passed for national victories.

In the mid-1580s, Philip II, who had united the empires of Spain and Portugal in 1580, decided that England's arrogantly Protestant queen could be tolerated no longer. He ordered the construction of a mighty fleet, hundreds of transport vessels designed to carry Spain's finest infantry across the English channel. When one of Philip's lieutenants viewed the Armada at Lisbon in May 1588, he described it as *la felicissima armada,* the invincible fleet. The king believed that with the support of England's oppressed Catholics, Spanish troops would sweep Elizabeth from power.

It was a grand scheme; it was an even grander failure. In 1588, a smaller, more maneuverable English navy dispersed Philip's Armada, and severe storms finished it off. Spanish hopes for Catholic England lay wrecked along the rocky coasts of Scotland and Ireland. English Protestants interpreted victory in providential terms: "God breathed and they were scattered."

AN UNPROMISING BEGINNING

By the 1570s, English interest in the New World revived. An increasing number of wealthy gentlemen were in an expansive mood, ready to challenge Spain and reap the profits of Asia and America. Yet the adventurers who directed Elizabethan expeditions were only dimly aware of Cabot's voyages, and their sole experience in settling distant outposts was in Ireland. Over the last three decades of the sixteenth century, English adventurers made almost every mistake one could possibly imagine. They did, however, acquire valuable information about winds and currents, supplies, and finance.

ROANOKE MYSTERY

In 1584, Sir Walter Ralegh dispatched two captains to the coast of present-day North Carolina to claim land granted to him by Elizabeth. The men returned with glowing reports, no doubt aimed in part at potential financial backers. "The

The manner of their fishing

John White, a late sixteenth-century artist, depicted several fishing techniques practiced by the Algonquian Indians of the present-day Carolinas. In the canoe, dip nets and multipronged spears are used. In the background, Indians stab at fish with long spears. At left, a weir traps fish by taking advantage of the river current's natural force.

soile," declared Captain Arthur Barlow, "is the most plentifull, sweete, fruitfull, and wholesome of all the world."

Ralegh diplomatically renamed this marvelous region Virginia, in honor of his patron, the Virgin Queen. Indeed, highly gendered vocabulary figured prominently in the European conquest of the New World. As historian Kathleen M. Brown explains, "Associations of the land with virgin innocence reinforced the notion that Virginia had been saved from the Spaniard's lust to be conquered by the chaste English." Elizabeth encouraged Ralegh in private conversation but rejected his persistent requests for money. With rumors of war in the air, she did not want to alienate Philip II unnecessarily by sponsoring a colony on land long ago claimed by Spain.

Ralegh finally raised the funds for his adventure, but his enterprise seemed ill-fated from the start. Despite careful planning, everything went wrong. The settlement was poorly situated. Located inside the Outer Banks—perhaps to avoid detection by the Spanish—the Roanoke colony proved extremely difficult to reach. Although the colonists coped well, a series of accidents transformed Ralegh's settlement into a ghost town. In the spring of 1586, Sir Francis Drake was returning from a Caribbean voyage and decided to visit Roanoke. Since an anticipated shipment of supplies was overdue, the colonists climbed aboard Drake's ships and went home.

In 1587, Ralegh launched a second colony. Once again, Ralegh's luck turned sour. The Spanish Armada severed communication between England and America. Every available English vessel was pressed into military service, and between 1587 and 1590, no ship visited the Roanoke colonists. When rescuers eventually reached the island, they found the village deserted. The fate of the "lost" colonists remains a mystery. The best guess is that they were absorbed by neighboring groups of natives.

DREAMS OF POSSESSION

Had it not been for Richard Hakluyt, the Younger, the dream of American colonization might have died in England. Hakluyt, a supremely industrious man, never saw America. Nevertheless, his vision of the New World powerfully shaped English public opinion. He interviewed captains and sailors upon their return from distant voyages and carefully collected their stories in a massive book titled *The Principall Navigations, Voyages, and Discoveries of the English Nation* (1589).

The work appeared to be a straightforward description of what these sailors had seen across the sea. That was its strength. In reality, Hakluyt edited each piece so it would drive home the book's central point: England needed American colonies. Indeed, they were essential to the nation's prosperity and independence. In Hakluyt's America, there were no losers. "The earth bringeth fourth all things in aboundance, as in the first creations without toil or labour," he wrote of Virginia. His blend of piety, patriotism, and self-interest proved immensely popular.

As a salesperson for the New World, Hakluyt was as misleading as he was successful. He failed to appreciate, or purposely ignored, the rich cultural diversity of the Native Americans and the varied backgrounds of the Europeans. He said not a word about the sufferings of Africans in America. Instead, he and many other polemicists for colonization led the ordinary English men and women who traveled to America to expect nothing less than a paradise on earth. This European perspective on development invited continuous human suffering and ecological disaster.

2

ENGLAND'S COLONIAL EXPERIMENTS
The Seventeenth Century

In the spring of 1644, John Winthrop, governor of Massachusetts Bay, learned that Native Americans had overrun the scattered tobacco plantations of Virginia, killing as many as five hundred colonists. Winthrop never thought much of the Chesapeake settlements. He regarded the people who had migrated to that part of America as grossly materialistic, and because Virginia had recently expelled several Puritan ministers, Winthrop decided the hostilities were God's way of punishing the tobacco planters for their worldliness. "It was observable," he related, "that this massacre came upon them soon after they had driven out the godly ministers we had sent to them." When Virginians appealed to Massachusetts for military supplies, they received a cool reception. "We were weakly provided ourselves," Winthrop explained, "and so could not afford them any help of that kind."

In 1675, the tables turned. Native Americans declared all-out war against the New Englanders, and soon reports of the destruction of Puritan communities were circulating in Virginia. "The Indians in New England have burned Considerable Villages," wrote one leading tobacco planter, "and have made them [the New Englanders] desert more than one hundred and fifty miles of those places they had formerly seated."

Sir William Berkeley, Virginia's royal governor, was not displeased by news of New England's adversity. He and his friends held the Puritans in contempt. Indeed, the New Englanders reminded them of the religious fanatics who had provoked civil war in England. The governor, sounding like a Puritan himself, described the warring Indians as the "Instruments" with which God intended "to destroy the King's Enemies." For good measure, Virginia outlawed the export of foodstuffs to their embattled northern neighbors.

Such extraordinary disunity—not to mention lack of compassion—comes as a surprise to anyone searching for the roots of American nationalism in this early period. English colonization in the seventeenth century did not spring from a desire to build a centralized empire in the New World similar to that of Spain or France. Instead, the English crown awarded colonial charters to a wide variety of merchants, religious idealists, and aristocratic adventurers who established separate and profoundly different colonies. Not only did New Englanders have little in common with the earliest Virginians and Carolinians, but they were often divided among themselves.

Migration itself helps to explain this striking division and diversity. At different times, different colonies appealed to different sorts of people. Men and women moved to the New World for various reasons, and as economic, political, and religious conditions changed on both sides of the Atlantic during the course of the seventeenth century, so too did patterns of English migration.

LEAVING HOME

English people in the early decades of the seventeenth century experienced what seemed to them an accelerating pace of social change. What was most evident was the rapid growth of population. Between 1580 and 1650, a period during which many men and women elected to journey to the New World, the population of England expanded from about 3.5 million to more than 5 million. Among other things, the expansion strained the nation's agrarian economy. Competition for food and land drove up prices, and people desperate for work took to the roads. Those migrants, many of them drawn into the orbit of London by tales of opportunity, frightened the traditional leaders of English society.

Even by modern standards, the English population of this period was quite mobile. To be sure, most men and women lived out their days rooted in the tiny country villages of their birth. A growing number of English people, however, were migrant laborers who took seasonal work. Many others relocated from the countryside to London, already a city of several hundred thousand inhabitants by the early seventeenth century.

Other, more exotic destinations also beckoned. A large number of English settlers migrated to Ireland, while lucrative employment and religious freedom attracted people to Holland. The Pilgrims, people who separated themselves from the established Church of England, initially hoped to make a new life in Leyden. The migrations within Europe serve as reminders that ordinary people had choices. A person who was upset about the state of the Church of England or who had lost a livelihood did not have to move to America. That some men and women consciously selected this much more dangerous and expensive journey set them apart from their contemporaries.

English colonists crossed the Atlantic for many reasons. Some wanted to institute a purer form of worship, more closely based on their interpretation of Scripture. Others dreamed of owning land and improving their social position. A few came to the New World to escape bad marriages, jail terms, or the dreary prospect of lifelong poverty. Since most seventeenth-century migrants, especially those who transferred to the Chesapeake colonies, left almost no records of their previous lives in England, it is futile to try to isolate a single cause or explanation for their decision to leave home.

In the absence of detailed personal information, historians usually have assumed that poverty, or the fear of soon falling into poverty, drove people across the Atlantic. No doubt economic considerations figured heavily in the final decision. But so too did religion, and it was not uncommon for the poor of early modern England to be among those demanding the most radical ecclesiastical reform.

Whatever their reasons for crossing the ocean, English migrants to America in this period left a nation wracked by recurrent, often violent political and religious controversy. During the 1620s, autocratic Stuart monarchs—James I (r. 1603–1625) and his son Charles I (r. 1625–1649)—who succeeded Queen Elizabeth on the English throne fought constantly with the elected members of Parliament. At stake were rival notions of constitutional and representative government.

Many royal policies—the granting of lucrative commercial monopolies to court favorites, for example—fu-

The Stuart Monarchs

James I
(r. 1603–1625)

Charles I
(r. 1625–
executed 1649)

Charles II
(r. 1660–
1685)

James II
(r. 1685–
deposed 1688)

William III
Prince of Orange
(r. 1688–1702)   m.   Mary II
(r. 1688–
1695)

Anne I
(r. 1702–
1714)

eled popular discontent, but the crown's hostility to far-reaching religi⌣⌣⌣ form sparked the most vocal protest. Throughout the kingdom, Puritans became adamant in their demand for radical purification of ritual.

Tensions grew so severe that in 1629, Charles attempted to rule the country without Parliament's assistance. The autocratic strategy backfired. When Charles finally was forced to recall Parliament in 1640 because he was running out of money, Parliament demanded major constitutional reforms. Militant Puritans, supported by many members of Parliament, insisted on restructuring the church—abolishing the office of bishop was high on their list. In this angry political atmosphere, Charles took up arms against the supporters of Parliament. The confrontation between Royalists and Parliamentarians set off a long and bloody civil war. In 1649, the victorious Parliamentarians beheaded Charles, and for almost a decade, Oliver Cromwell, a skilled general and committed Puritan, governed England, as Lord Protector.

In 1660, following Cromwell's death from natural causes, the Stuarts returned to the English throne. During a period known as the Restoration, neither Charles II (r. 1660–1685) nor James II (r. 1685–1688)—both sons of Charles I—was able to establish genuine political stability. When the authoritarian James lifted some of the restrictions governing Catholics, a Protestant nation rose up in what the English people called the Glorious Revolution (1688) and sent James into permanent exile.

The Glorious Revolution altered the course of English political history and, therefore, that of the American colonies as well. The monarchs who followed James II surrendered some of the prerogative powers that had destabilized English politics for almost a century. The crown was still a potent force in the political life of the nation, but never again would an English king or queen attempt to govern without Parliament.

Such political events, coupled with periodic economic recession and religious repression, determined, in large measure, the direction and flow of migration to America. During times of political turmoil, religious persecution, and economic insecurity, men and women thought more seriously about transferring to the New World than they did during periods of peace and prosperity. Obviously, people who moved to America at different times came from different social and political environments. A person who emigrated to Pennsylvania in the 1680s, for example, left an England unlike the one that a Virginian in 1607 or a Bay Colonist in 1630 might have known. Moreover, the young men and women who migrated to London in search of work and who then, in their frustration and poverty, decided to move to the Chesapeake carried a very different set of memories than those people who moved directly to New England from the small rural villages of their homeland.

Regardless of the exact timing of departure, English settlers brought with them ideas and assumptions that helped them make sense of their everyday experiences in an unfamiliar environment. Their values were tested and sometimes transformed in the New World, but they were seldom destroyed. Settlement involved a complex process of adjustment. The colonists developed different subcultures in America, and in each it is possible to trace the interaction between the settlers' values and the physical elements, such as the climate, crops, and soil, of their new surroundings. The Chesapeake, the New England colonies, the Middle Colonies, and the Southern Colonies formed distinct regional identities that have survived to the present day.

THE CHESAPEAKE: DREAMS OF WEALTH

After the Roanoke debacle in 1590, only a few aging visionaries such as Richard Hakluyt kept alive the dream of colonies in the New World. These advocates argued that the North American mainland contained resources of incalculable value. An innovative group, they insisted, might reap great profits and at the same time supply England with raw materials that it would otherwise be forced to purchase from European rivals: Holland, France, and Spain.

Moreover, any enterprise that annoyed Catholic Spain or revealed its weakness in America seemed a desirable end in itself to patriotic English Protestants. Anti-Catholicism and hatred of Spain became an integral part of English national identity during this period, and unless one appreciates just how deeply those sentiments ran in the popular mind, one cannot fully understand why ordinary people who had no direct financial stake in the New World so generously supported English efforts to colonize America. Soon after James I ascended to the throne, adventurers were given an opportunity to put their theories into practice in the colonies of Virginia and Maryland, an area known as the Chesapeake, or, somewhat later, as the Tobacco Coast.

ENTREPRENEURS IN VIRGINIA

During Elizabeth's reign, the major obstacle to successful colonization of the New World had been raising money. No single person, no matter how rich or well connected, could underwrite the vast expenses a New World settlement required. The solution to this financial problem was the "joint-stock company," a business organization in which scores of people could invest without fear of bankruptcy. A merchant or landowner could purchase a share of stock at a stated price, and at the end of several years the investor could anticipate recovering the initial amount plus a portion of whatever profits the company had made. Some

Chesapeake Colonies, 1640

The many deep rivers flowing into the Chesapeake Bay provided scattered English planters with a convenient transportation system, linking them directly to European markets.

projects were able to amass large amounts of capital, enough certainly to launch a new colony in Virginia.

On April 10, 1606, James issued the first Virginia charter. The document authorized the London Company to establish plantations in Virginia. The London Company was an ambitious business venture. Its leader, Sir Thomas Smith, was reputedly London's wealthiest merchant. Smith and his partners gained possession of the territory lying between present-day North Carolina and the Hudson River. These were generous but vague boundaries, to be sure, but the Virginia Company—as the London Company soon called itself—set out immediately to find the treasures Hakluyt had promised.

In December 1606, the *Susan Constant*, the *Godspeed*, and the *Discovery* sailed for America. The ships carried 104 men and boys who had been instructed to establish a fortified outpost some hundred miles up a large navigable river. The leaders of the colony selected—without consulting resident Native Americans—

NOVA BRITANNIA.

OFFERING MOST

Excellent fruites by Planting in
VIRGINIA.

Exciting all fuch as be well affected
to further the fame.

LONDON
Printed for SAMVEL MACHAM, and are to befold at
his Shop in Pauls Church-yard, at the
Signe of the Bul-head.
1609.

The title page of a 1609 brochure promoting the colony of Virginia. Irresponsible pamphlets such as these promised the settlers instant wealth.

what the Europeans considered a promising location more than thirty miles from the mouth of the James River. A marshy peninsula jutting out into the river became the site for one of America's most unsuccessful villages, Jamestown. Modern historians have criticized the choice, for the low-lying ground proved to be a disease-ridden death trap; even the drinking water was contaminated with salt. But the first Virginians were neither stupid nor suicidal. Jamestown seemed the ideal place to build a fort, since surprise attack by Spaniards or Native Americans rather than sickness appeared the more serious threat in the early months of settlement.

Almost immediately, dispirited colonists began quarreling. The adventurers were not prepared for the challenges that confronted them in America. Avarice exacerbated the problems. The adventurers had traveled to the New World in search of the sort of instant wealth they imagined the Spaniards to have found in

Mexico and Peru. Published tales of rubies and diamonds lying on the beach probably inflamed their expectations. Even when it must have been apparent that such expectations were unfounded, the first settlers often behaved in Virginia as if they fully expected to become rich. Instead of cooperating for the common good—guarding or farming, for example—individuals pursued personal interests. They searched for gold when they might have helped plant corn. No one was willing to take orders, and those who were supposed to govern the colony looked after their private welfare while disease, war, and starvation ravaged the settlement.

ORDER OUT OF ANARCHY

Virginia might have gone the way of Roanoke had it not been for Captain John Smith. Before coming to Jamestown, he had traveled throughout Europe and fought with the Hungarian army against the Turks—and, if Smith is to be believed, he was saved from certain death by various beautiful women. Because of his reputation for boasting, historians have discounted Smith's account of life in early Virginia. Recent scholarship, however, has affirmed the truthfulness of his curious story. In Virginia, Smith brought order out of anarchy. While members of the council in Jamestown debated petty politics, he traded with the local Indians for food, mapped the Chesapeake Bay, and may even have been rescued from execution by a young Indian girl, Pocahontas. In the fall of 1608, he seized control

Pocahontas bore no relation to the person caricatured in modern film. She married John Rolfe, a settler who pioneered the cultivation of tobacco as a cash crop. She converted to Christianity, taking the name Rebeka. This portrait, painted during a visit to London, shows her in court dress.

of the ruling council and instituted a tough military discipline. Under Smith, no one enjoyed special privilege. Individuals whom he forced to work came to hate him. But he managed to keep them alive, no small achievement in such a deadly environment.

Leaders of the Virginia Company in London recognized the need to reform the entire enterprise. After all, they had spent considerable sums and had received nothing in return. In 1609, the company directors obtained a new charter from the king, which completely reorganized the Virginia government. Moreover, in an effort to raise scarce capital, the original partners opened the "joint-stock" to the general public. For a little more than £12—approximately one year's wages for an unskilled English laborer—a person or group of persons could purchase a stake in Virginia. It was anticipated that in 1616 the profits from the colony would be distributed among the shareholders. The company exhorted patriotic English citizens to invest in the enterprise.

The burst of energy came to nothing. Bad luck and poor planning plagued the Virginia Company. A vessel carrying additional settlers and supplies went aground in Bermuda, and while this misadventure did little to help the people at Jamestown, it provided Shakespeare with the idea for *The Tempest*. Even the indomitable Captain Smith suffered a gunpowder accident and was forced to return to England.

Between 1609 and 1611, the remaining Virginia settlers lacked capable leadership, and perhaps as a result, they lacked food. The terrible winter of 1609–1610 was termed the "starving time." A few desperate colonists were driven to cannibalism, an ironic situation since early explorers had assumed that only Native Americans would eat human flesh. In England, Smith heard that one colonist had killed his wife, powdered [salted] her, and "had eaten part of her before it was known; for which he was executed." The captain, who possessed a droll sense of humor, ob-

In 1608, Powhatan, the father of Pocahontas, gave this shell-decorated ceremonial mantle to Captain Christopher Newport. Such gestures of friendship became less common, however, as coexistence became more and more difficult.

served, "Now, whether she was better roasted, broiled, or carbonadoed [sliced], I know not, but such a dish as powdered wife I never heard of."

The presence of so many Native Americans heightened the danger. The first colonists found themselves living—or attempting to live—in territory controlled by what was probably the most powerful Indian confederation east of the Mississippi River. Under the leadership of their *werowance*, Powhatan, these Indians had by 1608 created a loose association of some thirty tribes, and when Captain John Smith arrived to lead several hundred adventurers, the Powhatans (named for their king) numbered some 14,000 people, of whom 3,200 were warriors. These people hoped initially to enlist the Europeans as allies against native enemies. When it became clear that the two groups, holding such different notions about labor and property and about the exploitation of the natural environment, could not coexist in peace, the Powhatans tried to drive the invaders out of Virginia, once in 1622 and again in 1644. The failure of the second campaign ended in the complete destruction of the Powhatan empire.

In June 1610, the settlers who had survived despite starvation and conflicts with the Indians actually abandoned Virginia. Through a stroke of luck, however, they encountered their new governor Lord De La Warr just as they commenced their voyage down the James River. The governor and the deputy governors who succeeded him, Sir Thomas Gates and Sir Thomas Dale, ruled by martial law. Such methods saved the colony but could not make it flourish. In 1616, company shareholders received no profits. Their only reward was the right to a piece of unsurveyed land located three thousand miles from London.

"STINKING WEED"

The economic solution to Virginia's problems grew in the vacant lots of Jamestown. Only Indians bothered to cultivate tobacco until John Rolfe, a settler who achieved notoriety by marrying Pocahontas, realized this local weed might be a valuable export. Rolfe experimented with the crop, eventually growing in Virginia a milder variety that had been developed in the West Indies and was more appealing to European smokers.

Virginians suddenly possessed a means to make money. Tobacco proved relatively easy to grow, and settlers who had avoided work now threw themselves into its production with single-minded diligence. In 1617, one observer found that Jamestown's "streets and all other spare places [are] planted with tobacco . . . the Colony dispersed all about planting tobacco." Although King James I originally considered smoking immoral and unhealthy, he changed his mind when the duties he collected on tobacco imports began to mount.

The company sponsored another ambitious effort to transform Virginia into a profitable enterprise. In 1618, Sir Edwin Sandys (pronounced Sands) led a faction

Life is a Smoke!—If this be true,
Tobacco will thy Life renew;
Then fear not Death, nor killing Care,
Whil'st we have best Virginia here.

The praises of tobacco and Virginia on this English tobacco label express the change in King James's attitude toward the "stinking weed." Once the government saw that tobacco made a profit, it dropped its moral criticism of the American crop.

of stockholders that began to pump life into the dying organization by instituting a series of sweeping reforms and eventually ousting Sir Thomas Smith and his friends. Sandys wanted private investors to develop their own estates in Virginia. Before 1618, there had been little incentive to do so, but by relaxing Dale's martial law and promising an elective representative assembly called the House of Burgesses, Sandys thought he could make the colony more attractive to wealthy speculators. Even more important was his method for distributing land. Colonists who covered their own transportation cost to America were guaranteed a "headright," a 50-acre lot for which they paid only a small annual rent. Adventurers were granted additional headrights for each servant they brought to the colony. This procedure allowed prosperous planters to build up huge estates while they also acquired dependent laborers. This land system persisted long after the company's collapse. So too did the notion that the wealth of a few justified the exploitation of many others.

TIME OF RECKONING

Between 1619 and 1622, the company sent 3,570 individuals to the colony. People seldom moved to Virginia in families. Although the first women arrived in Jamestown in 1608, most emigrants were single males in their teens or early twenties who came to the New World as indentured servants. In exchange for transportation across the Atlantic, they agreed to serve a master for a stated number of years. The length of service depended in part on the age of the servant. The younger the servant, the longer he or she served. In return, the master promised to give the laborers proper care and, at the conclusion of their contracts, to provide them with tools and clothes according to "the custom of the country."

Whenever possible, planters in Virginia purchased able-bodied workers, in other words, persons (preferably male) capable of performing hard agricultural labor. This preference dramatically skewed the colony's sex ratio. In the early decades, men outnumbered women by as much as six to one. Such gender imbalance meant that even if a male servant lived to the end of his indenture—an unlikely prospect—he could not realistically expect to start a family of his own. Moreover, despite apparent legal safeguards, masters could treat dependent workers as they pleased; after all, these people were legally considered property. Servants were sold, traded, even gambled away in games of chance. It does not require much imagination to see that a society that tolerated such an exploitative labor system might later embrace slavery.

Most Virginians then did not live long enough to worry about marriage. Death was omnipresent. Indeed, extraordinarily high mortality was a major reason the Chesapeake colonies developed so differently from those of New England. On the eve of the 1618 reforms, Virginia's population stood at approximately 700. The company sent at least 3,000 more people, but by 1622 only 1,240 were still alive. "It Consequentilie followes," declared one angry shareholder, "that we had then lost 3,000 persons within those 3 yeares." The major killers were contagious diseases. And on Good Friday, March 22, 1622, the Powhatans slew 347 Europeans in a well-coordinated surprise attack.

No one knows for certain what effect such a horrendous mortality rate had on the men and women who survived. At the very least, it must have created a sense of impermanence, a desire to escape Virginia with a little money before sickness or violence ended the adventure.

SCANDAL AND REFORM

On both sides of the Atlantic, people asked why so many colonists died in a land so rich in potential. The burden of responsibility lay in large measure with the Virginia Company. Sandys and his supporters were in too great a hurry to make a profit. Settlers were shipped to America, but neither housing nor food awaited them in Jamestown. Weakened by the long sea voyage, they quickly succumbed to contagious disease.

Company officials in Virginia also bore a share of guilt. They were so eager to line their own pockets that they consistently failed to provide for the common good. Various governors and their councilors grabbed up the indentured servants and sent them to their own private plantations to cultivate tobacco, and, as the 1622 surprise attack demonstrated, officials ignored the colony's crumbling defenses. Jamestown took on all the most unattractive characteristics of a boomtown. There was no shared sense of purpose, no common ideology,

A reconstruction of an independent white planter's house from the late seventeenth-century Chesapeake. Even well-to-do colonists lived in structures that seemed by English standards quite primitive.

except perhaps unrestrained self-advancement, to keep the society from splintering into highly individualistic, competitive fragments.

The company's scandalous mismanagement embarrassed the king, and in 1624, he dissolved the bankrupt enterprise and transformed Virginia into a royal colony. The crown appointed a governor and a council. No provision was made, however, for continuing the local representative assembly, an institution the Stuarts heartily opposed. The House of Burgesses had first convened in 1619. While elections to the Burgesses were hardly democratic, the assembly did provide wealthy planters with a voice in government. Even without the king's authorization, the representatives gathered annually after 1629, and in 1639, Charles recognized the body's existence.

He had no choice. The colonists who served on the council or in the assembly were strong-willed, ambitious men. They had no intention of surrendering control over local affairs. In 1634, the assembly divided the colony into eight counties. In each one, a group of appointed justices of the peace—the wealthy planters of the area—convened as a court of law as well as a governing body. The "county court" was the most important institution of local government in Virginia, serving as a center for social, political, and commercial activities.

Changes in government had little impact on the character of daily life in Virginia. The planters continued to grow tobacco, ignoring advice to diversify, and as the Indians were killed, made into tributaries, or pushed north and south, Virginians took up large tracts of land along the colony's many navigable rivers. The focus of their lives was the isolated plantation, a small cluster of buildings housing the planter's family and dependent workers. These were modest wooden structures. Not until the eighteenth century did the Chesapeake gentry build the great Georgian mansions that still attract tourists. The dispersed pattern of settlement retarded the development of institutions such as schools and churches. Besides Jamestown there were no population centers, and as late as 1705, Robert Beverley, a leading planter, reported that Virginia did not have a single place "that may reasonably bear the Name of a Town."

MARYLAND: A TROUBLED REFUGE FOR CATHOLICS

By the end of the seventeenth century, Maryland society looked remarkably like that of its Chesapeake neighbor, Virginia. At the time of first settlement in 1634, however, no one would have predicted that Maryland, a colony wholly owned by a Catholic nobleman, would have survived, much less flourished.

The driving force behind the founding of Maryland was Sir George Calvert, later Lord Baltimore. Calvert, a talented and well-educated man, enjoyed the patronage of James I. He was awarded lucrative positions in the government, the most important being the king's secretary of state. In 1625, Calvert shocked almost everyone by publicly declaring his Catholicism; in this fiercely anti-Catholic society, persons who openly supported the Church of Rome were immediately stripped of civil office. Although forced to resign as secretary of state, Calvert retained the crown's favor.

Before resigning, Calvert sponsored a settlement on the coast of Newfoundland, but after visiting the place, the proprietor concluded that no English person, whatever his or her religion, would transfer to a place where the "ayre [is] so intolerably cold." He turned his attention to the Chesapeake, and on June 30, 1632, Charles I granted George Calvert's son, Cecilius, a charter for a colony to be located north of Virginia. The boundaries of the settlement, named Maryland in honor of Charles's queen, were so vaguely defined that they generated legal controversies not fully resolved until the mid-eighteenth century when Charles Mason and Jeremiah Dixon surveyed their famous line between Pennsylvania and Maryland.

Cecilius, the second Lord Baltimore, wanted to create a sanctuary for England's persecuted Catholics. He also intended to make money. Without Protestant settlers, it seemed unlikely Maryland would prosper, and Cecilius instructed his brother Leonard, the colony's governor, to do nothing that might frighten off hypersensitive Protestants. On March 25, 1634, the *Ark and Dove,* carrying about 150 settlers, landed safely, and within days, the governor purchased from the Yaocomico Indians a village that became St. Mary's City, the capital of Maryland.

The colony's charter was a throwback to an earlier feudal age. It transformed Baltimore into a "palatine lord," a proprietor with almost royal powers. Settlers swore an oath of allegiance not to the king of England but to Lord Baltimore. In England, such practices had long ago passed into obsolescence. As the proprietor, Lord Baltimore owned outright almost 6 million acres; he possessed absolute authority over anyone living in his domain.

On paper, at least, everyone in Maryland was assigned a place in an elaborate social hierarchy. Members of a colonial ruling class, persons who purchased 6000 acres from Baltimore, were called lords of the manor. These landed aristocrats were permitted to establish local courts of law. People holding less acreage enjoyed fewer privileges, particularly in government. Baltimore figured that land sales and rents would adequately finance the entire venture.

Baltimore's feudal system never took root in Chesapeake soil. People simply refused to play the social roles the lord proprietor had assigned. These tensions affected the operation of Maryland's government. Baltimore assumed that his brother, acting as his deputy in America, and a small appointed council of local aristocrats would pass necessary laws and carry out routine administration. When an elected assembly first convened in 1635, Baltimore allowed the delegates to discuss only those acts he had prepared. The members of the assembly bridled at such restrictions, insisting on exercising traditional parliamentary privileges. Neither side gained a clear victory in the assembly, and for almost twenty-five years, legislative squabbling contributed to the widespread political instability that almost destroyed Maryland.

The colony drew both Protestants and Catholics, and the two groups might have lived in harmony had civil war not broken out in England. When Cromwell and the Puritan faction executed Charles, transforming England briefly into a republic, it seemed Baltimore might lose his colony. To head off such an event and to placate Maryland's restless Protestants, in 1649, the proprietor drafted the famous "Act concerning Religion," which extended toleration to all individuals who accepted the divinity of Christ. At a time when European rulers regularly persecuted people for their religious beliefs, Baltimore championed liberty of conscience.

However laudable the act may have been, it did not heal religious divisions in Maryland, and when local Puritans seized the colony's government, they promptly repealed the act. For almost two decades, vigilantes roamed the countryside, and during the "Plundering Time" (1644–1646), one armed group temporarily drove Leonard Calvert out of Maryland. In 1655, civil war flared again.

In this troubled sanctuary, ordinary planters and their workers cultivated tobacco on plantations dispersed along riverfronts. Europeans sacrificed much by coming to the Chesapeake. For most of the century, their standard of living was primitive when compared with that of people of the same social class who had remained in England. Two-thirds of the planters, for example, lived in houses of only two rooms and of a type associated with the poorest classes in contemporary English society.

REINVENTING ENGLAND IN AMERICA

The Pilgrims enjoy almost mythic status in American history. These brave refugees crossed the cold Atlantic in search of religious liberty, signed a democratic compact aboard the *Mayflower,* landed at Plymouth Rock, and gave us our Thanksgiving Day. As with most legends, this one contains only a core of truth.

The Pilgrims were not crusaders who set out to change the world. Rather, they were humble English farmers. Their story began in the early 1600s in Scrooby Manor, a small community located approximately 150 miles north of London. Many people living in this area believed the Church of England retained too many traces of its Catholic origin. To support such a corrupt institution was like winking at the devil, and so, in the early years of the reign of James I, the Scrooby congregation formally left the established state church. Like others who followed this logic, they were called Separatists. Since English statute required citizens to attend Anglican services, the Scrooby Separatists moved to Holland in 1608–1609 rather than compromise.

The Netherlands provided the Separatists with a good home—too good. The members of the little church feared they were losing their distinct identity; their children were becoming Dutch. In 1617, therefore, a portion of the original Scrooby congregation vowed to sail to America. Included in this group was William Bradford, a wonderfully literate man who wrote *Of Plymouth Plantation,* one of the first and certainly most poignant accounts of an early American settlement.

Poverty presented the major obstacle to the Pilgrims' plans. They petitioned for a land patent from the Virginia Company of London. At the same time, they looked for someone willing to underwrite the staggering costs of colonization. The negotiations went well, or so it seemed. After stopping in England to take on supplies and laborers, the Pilgrims set off for America in 1620 aboard the *Mayflower,* armed with a patent to settle in Virginia and indebted to a group of English investors who were only marginally interested in religious reform.

Because of an error in navigation, the Pilgrims landed not in Virginia but in New England. The patent for which they had worked so diligently had no validity in the region. In fact, the crown had granted New England to another company. Without a patent, the colonists possessed no authorization to form a civil government. To preserve the struggling community from anarchy, 41 men agreed on November 11 to "covenant and combine our selves together into a civil body politick."

The Mayflower Compact could not ward off disease and hunger. During the first months in Plymouth, death claimed approximately half of the 102 people who had initially set out from England. Moreover, debts contracted in England severely burdened the new colony. To their credit, the Pilgrims honored their financial obligations, but it took almost twenty years to satisfy the English investors.

Almost anyone who has heard of the Plymouth Colony knows of Squanto, a Patuxt Indian who welcomed the first Pilgrims in excellent English. In 1614 unscrupulous adventurers kidnapped Squanto and sold him in Spain as a slave. Somehow this resourceful man escaped bondage, making his way to London, where a group of merchants who owned land in Newfoundland taught him to speak English. They apparently hoped that he would deliver moving public testimonials about the desirability of moving to the New World. In any case, Squanto returned to the Plymouth area just before the Pilgrims arrived. Squanto joined Massasoit, a local Native American leader, in teaching the Pilgrims much about hunting and agriculture, a debt that Bradford freely acknowledged. Although evidence for the so-called "First Thanksgiving" is extremely sketchy, it is certain that without Native American support the Europeans would have starved.

In time, the Pilgrims replicated the humble little farm communities they had once known in England. They formed Separatist congregations to their liking; the population slowly increased. In 1691, the colony was absorbed into its larger and more prosperous neighbor, Massachusetts Bay.

"THE GREAT MIGRATION"

In the early decades of the seventeenth century, an extraordinary spirit of religious reform burst forth in England, and before it had burned itself out, Puritanism had transformed the face of England and America. Modern historians have difficulty comprehending this powerful spiritual movement. Some consider the Puritans rather neurotic individuals who condemned liquor and sex, dressed in drab clothes, and minded their neighbors' business.

The crude caricature is based on a profound misunderstanding of the actual nature of this broad popular movement. The seventeenth-century Puritans were more like today's radical political reformers, men and women committed to far-reaching institutional change, than like naive do-gooders or narrow fundamentalists. To their enemies, of course, the Puritans were irritants, always pointing out civil and ecclesiastical imperfections and urging everyone to try to fulfill the commands of Scripture. A great many people, however, shared their vision, and not only did they found several American colonies, but they also sparked the English Civil War, an event that generated bold new thinking about republican government and popular sovereignty.

The Puritans were products of the Protestant Reformation. They accepted a Calvinist notion that an omnipotent God predestined some people to salvation and damned others throughout eternity (see Chapter 1). But instead of waiting passively for Judgment Day, the Puritans examined themselves for signs of grace, for hints that God had in fact placed them among his "elect." A member of this select group, they argued, would try to live according to Scripture, to battle sin and eradicate corruption.

For the Puritans, the logic of everyday life was clear. If the Church of England contained unscriptural elements—clerical vestments, for example—then they must be eliminated. If the pope in Rome was in league with the Antichrist, then Protestant kings had better not form alliances with Catholic states. If God condemned licentiousness and intoxication, then local officials should punish whores and drunks. There was nothing improper about an occasional beer or passionate physical love within marriage, but when sex and drink became ends in themselves, the Puritans thought England's ministers and magistrates should speak out. Persons of this temperament were more combative than the Pilgrims had been. They wanted to purify the Church of England from within, and before the 1630s at least, separatism held little appeal for them.

From the Puritan perspective, the early Stuarts, James I and Charles I, seemed unconcerned about the spiritual state of the nation. James tolerated corruption within his own court; he condoned gross public extravagance. His foreign policy appeased European Catholic powers. At one time, he even tried to marry his son to a Catholic princess. Neither king showed interest in purifying the Anglican Church. In fact, Charles assisted the rapid advance of William Laud, a bishop who represented everything the Puritans detested. Laud defended church ceremonies that they found obnoxious. He persecuted Puritan ministers, forcing them either to conform to his theology or lose their licenses to preach. As long as Parliament met, Puritan voters in the various boroughs and countries throughout England elected men sympathetic to their point of view. These outspoken representatives criticized royal policies and hounded Laud. Because of their defiance, Charles decided in 1629 to rule England without Parliament and four years later named Laud archbishop of Canterbury. The last doors of reform slammed shut. The corruption remained.

John Winthrop, the future governor of Massachusetts Bay, was caught up in these events. Little about his background suggested such an auspicious future. He

Voters in Massachusetts reelected John Winthrop governor many times, an indication of his success in translating Puritan values into practical policy.

owned a small manor in Suffolk. He dabbled in law. But the core of Winthrop's life was his faith in God, a faith so intense his contemporaries immediately identified him as a Puritan. The Lord, he concluded, was displeased with England. In May 1629, he wrote to his wife, "I am verily perswaded God will bringe some heavye Affliction upon this lande, and that speedylye." He was, however, confident that the Lord would "provide a shelter and a hidinge place for us."

Other Puritans, some wealthier and politically better connected than Winthrop, reached similar conclusions about England's future. They turned their attention to the possibility of establishing a colony in America, and on March 4, 1629, their Massachusetts Bay Company obtained a charter directly from the king. Charles and his advisers apparently thought the Massachusetts Bay Company was a commercial venture no different from the dozens of other joint-stock companies that had recently sprung into existence.

Winthrop and his associates knew better. On August 26, 1629, twelve of them met secretly and signed the Cambridge Agreement. They pledged to be "ready in our persons and with such of our severall familyes as are to go with us . . . to embark for the said plantation by the first of March next." There was one loophole. The charters of most joint-stock companies designated a specific place where business meetings were to be held. For reasons not entirely clear—a timely bribe is a good guess—the charter of the Massachusetts Bay Company did not contain this standard clause. It could hold meetings anywhere the stockholders, called "freemen," desired, even America, and if they were in America, the king and his archbishop could not easily interfere in their affairs.

"A CITY ON A HILL"

The Winthrop fleet departed England in March 1630. By the end of the first year, almost 2,000 people had arrived in Massachusetts Bay, and before the "Great Migration" concluded in the early 1640s, more than 16,000 men and women had arrived in the new Puritan colony.

A great deal is known about the background of these particular settlers. A large percentage of them originated in an area northeast of London called East Anglia, a region in which Puritan ideas had taken deep root. London, Kent, and the West Country also contributed to the stream of emigrants. In some instances, entire villages were reestablished across the Atlantic. Many Bay Colonists had worked as farmers in England, but a surprisingly large number came from industrial centers, such as Norwich, where cloth was manufactured for the export trade.

Whatever their backgrounds, they moved to Massachusetts as nuclear families, fathers, mothers, and their dependent children, a form of migration strikingly different from the one that peopled Virginia and Maryland. Moreover, because the settlers had already formed families in England, the colony's sex ratio was more balanced than that found in the Chesapeake colonies. Finally, and perhaps more significantly, once they had arrived in Massachusetts, these men and women survived. Indeed, their life expectancy compares favorably to that of modern Americans.

The first settlers possessed another source of strength and stability. They were bound together by a common sense of purpose. God, they insisted, had formed a special covenant with the people of Massachusetts Bay. On his part, the Lord expected them to live according to Scripture, to reform the church, in other words, to create an Old Testament "city on a hill" that would stand as a beacon of righteousness for the rest of the Christian world. If they fulfilled their side of the bargain, the settlers could anticipate peace and prosperity. No one, not even the lowliest servant, was excused from this divine covenant, for as Winthrop stated, "Wee must be knitt together in this worke as one man." Many people throughout the ages have espoused such communal rhetoric, but these particular men and women went about the business of forming a new colony as if they truly intended to transform a religious vision into social reality.

The colonists arrived in Massachusetts Bay without a precise plan for their church. Although the rituals and ceremonies enforced by Laud had no place in Massachusetts, the American Puritans refused to separate formally from the Church of England. In this matter, they thought the Pilgrims had made a serious

The only surviving Puritan meetinghouse is the Old Ship Meetinghouse in Hingham, Massachusetts. Its name derives from its interior design, which resembles the hull of a ship. The oldest wooden church in the United States, it could accommodate about seven hundred people, about the entire population of seventeenth-century Hingham, who would have sat on backless wooden benches in the unheated building, listening to the preacher address the congregation not from an altar but from an undecorated square speaking box.

mistake. After all, what was the point of reforming an institution if the reformers were no longer part of it?

The Bay Colonists gradually came to accept a highly innovative form of church government known as Congregationalism. Under the system, each village church was independent of outside interference. The American Puritans, of course, wanted nothing of bishops. The people (the "saints") were the church, and as a body, they pledged to uphold God's law. In the Salem Church, for example, the members covenanted "with the Lord and with one another and do bind ourselves in the presence of God to walk together in all his ways."

Simply because a person happened to live in a certain community did not mean he or she automatically belonged to the local church. The churches of Massachusetts were voluntary institutions, and in order to join one a man or woman had to provide testimony—a confession of faith—before neighbors who had already been admitted as full members. It was a demanding process. Whatever the personal strains, however, most men and women in early

Massachusetts aspired to full membership, which entitled them to the sacraments, and gave some of them responsibility for choosing ministers, disciplining backsliders, and determining difficult questions of theology. Although women and blacks could not vote for ministers, they did become members of the Congregational churches. Over the course of the seventeenth century, women made up an increasingly large share of the membership.

In creating a civil government, the Bay Colonists faced a particularly difficult challenge. Their charter allowed the investors in a joint-stock company to set up a business organization. When the settlers arrived in America, however, company leaders—men like Winthrop—moved quickly to transform the commercial structure into a colonial government. An early step in this direction took place on May 18, 1631, when the category of "freeman" was extended to all adult males who had become members of a Congregational church. This decision greatly expanded the franchise of Massachusetts Bay, and during the 1630s, at least 40 percent of the colony's adult males could vote in elections. This percentage was higher than anything the emigrants would have known in England. The freemen voted annually for a governor, a group of magistrates called the Court of Assistants, and after 1634, deputies who represented the interests of the individual towns. Even military officers were elected every year in Massachusetts Bay.

In New England, the town became the center of public life. In other regions of British America where the county was the focus of local government, people did not experience the same density of social and institutional interaction. In Massachusetts, groups of men and women voluntarily covenanted together to observe common goals. The community constructed a meetinghouse where religious services and town meetings were held. This powerful sense of shared purpose—something that later Americans have greatly admired—should not obscure the fact that the founders of New England towns also had a keen eye for personal profit. Seventeenth-century records reveal that speculators often made a good deal of money from selling "shares" in village lands. But acquisitiveness never got out of control, and entrepreneurial practices rarely disturbed the peace of the Puritan communities. Inhabitants generally received land sufficient to build a house to support a family. Although villagers escaped the kind of feudal dues collected in other parts of America, they were expected to contribute to the minister's salary, pay local and colony taxes, and serve in the militia.

DEFINING THE LIMITS OF DISSENT

The European settlers of Massachusetts Bay managed to live in peace—at least with each other. This was a remarkable achievement considering the chronic instability that plagued other colonies at this time. They believed in a rule of law, and in 1648 the colonial legislature, called the General Court, drew up the *Lawes*

Mr. Richard Mather.

This primitive woodcut depicts the Reverend Richard Mather, one of early New England's most influential Puritan ministers.

and Liberties, the first alphabetized code of law printed in English. This is a document of fundamental importance in American constitutional history. In clear prose, it explained to ordinary colonists their rights and responsibilities as citizens of the commonwealth. The code engendered public trust in government and discouraged magistrates from the arbitrary exercise of authority.

The Puritans never supported the concept of religious toleration. They transferred to the New World to preserve *their own* freedom of worship; about religious freedom of those deemed heretics, they expressed little concern. The most serious challenges to Puritan orthodoxy in Massachusetts Bay came from two brilliantly charismatic individuals. The first, Roger Williams, arrived in 1631 and immediately attracted a body of loyal followers.

William preached extreme separatism. The Bay Colonists, he exclaimed, were impure in the sight of the Lord so long as they remained even nominal members of the Church of England. Moreover, he questioned the validity of the colony's charter, since the king had not first purchased the land from the Indians, a view that threatened the integrity of the entire colonial experiment. Williams also insisted that the civil rulers of Massachusetts had no business punishing settlers for their religious beliefs. It was God's responsibility, not men's, to monitor people's consciences. The Bay magistrates were prepared neither to tolerate heresy nor to accede to Williams's other demands, and in 1636, after attempts to reach a compromise had failed, they banished him from the colony. Williams worked out the logic of his ideas in Providence, a village he founded in what would become Rhode Island.

The magistrates of Massachusetts Bay concluded that the second individual, Anne Hutchinson, posed an even graver threat to the peace. This intelligent woman followed John Cotton to the New World in 1634. Even contemporaries found her religious ideas, usually termed Antinomianism, somewhat confusing.

Hutchinson shared her ideas with other Bostonians, many of them women. Her outspoken views scandalized orthodox leaders of church and state. She suggested that all but two ministers in the colony were preaching a doctrine in the Congregational churches that was little better than that of Archbishop Laud. When authorities demanded she explain her unusual opinions, she suggested that she experienced divine inspiration independently of either the Bible or the clergy. In other words, Hutchinson's teachings could not be tested by Scripture, a position that seemed dangerously subjective. Indeed, Hutchinson's theology called the very foundation of Massachusetts Bay into question. Without clear, external standards, one person's truth was as valid as anyone else's, and from Winthrop's perspective, Hutchinson's teachings invited civil and religious anarchy. But her challenge to authority was not simply theological. As a woman, her aggressive speech sparked a deeply misogynist response from the colony's male leaders.

For two very tense days in 1637, the ministers and magistrates of Massachusetts Bay cross-examined Hutchinson; in this intense theological debate, she more than held her own. Hutchinson defied the ministers and magistrates to demonstrate exactly where she had gone wrong. Just when it appeared Hutchinson had outmaneuvered—indeed, thoroughly embarrassed—her opponents, she let down her guard, declaring forcefully that what she knew of God came "by an immediate revelation. . . . By the voice of his own spirit to my soul." Here was what her accusers had suspected all along but could not prove. She had confessed in open court that the Spirit can live without the Moral Law. This Antinomian statement fulfilled the worst fears of the Bay rulers, and they were relieved to exile Hutchinson and her followers to Rhode Island.

BREAKING AWAY

Massachusetts Bay spawned four new colonies, three of which survived to the American Revolution. New Hampshire became a separate colony in 1677. Its population grew very slowly, and for much of the colonial period, New Hampshire remained economically dependent on Massachusetts, its commercial neighbor to the south.

New England Colonies, 1650

The early settlers quickly carved up New England. New Haven briefly flourished as a separate colony before being taken over by Connecticut in 1662. Long Island later became part of New York; Plymouth was absorbed into Massachusetts; and New Hampshire became a separate colony.

Far more people were drawn to the fertile lands of the Connecticut River Valley. In 1636, settlers founded the villages of Hartford, Windsor, and Wethersfield. No one forced these men and women to leave Massachusetts, and in their new surroundings, they created a society that looked much like the one they had known in the Bay Colony. Through his writings, Thomas Hooker, Connecticut's most prominent minister, helped all New Englanders define Congregational church polity. Puritans on both sides of the Atlantic read Hooker's beautifully crafted works. In 1639, representatives from the Connecticut towns passed the Fundamental Orders, a blueprint for civil government, and in 1662, Charles II awarded the colony a charter of its own.

In 1638, another group, led by Theophilus Eaton and the Reverend John Davenport, settled New Haven and several adjoining towns along Long Island Sound. These emigrants, many of whom had come from London, lived briefly in Massachusetts Bay but then insisted on forming a Puritan commonwealth of their own, one that established a closer relationship between church and state than the Bay Colonists had allowed. The New Haven colony never prospered, and in 1662, it was absorbed into Connecticut.

Rhode Island experienced a wholly different history. From the beginning, it drew people of a highly independent turn of mind, and according to one Dutch visitor, Rhode Island was "the receptacle of all sorts of riff-raff people. . . . All the cranks of New-England retire thither." This description, of course, was an exaggeration. Roger Williams founded Providence in 1636; two years later, Anne Hutchinson took her followers to Portsmouth. Other groups settled around Narragansett Bay. Not surprisingly, these men and women appreciated the need for toleration. No one was persecuted in Rhode Island for his or her religious beliefs.

One might have thought the separate Rhode Island communities would cooperate for the common good. They did not. Villagers fought over land and schemed with outside speculators to divide the tiny colony into even smaller pieces. In 1644, Parliament issued a patent for the "Providence Plantations," and in 1663, the Rhode Islanders obtained a royal charter. These successes did not calm political turmoil. For most of the seventeenth century, colonywide government existed in name only. Despite their constant bickering, however, the settlers of Rhode Island built up a profitable commerce in agricultural goods.

DIVERSITY IN THE MIDDLE COLONIES

New York, New Jersey, Pennsylvania, and Delaware were settled for quite different reasons. William Penn, for example, envisioned a Quaker sanctuary; the Duke of York worried chiefly about his own income. Despite the founders' intentions, however, some common characteristics emerged. Each colony developed a strikingly heterogeneous population, men and women of different ethnic and religious backgrounds. This cultural diversity became a major influence on the economic, political, and ecclesiastical institutions of the Middle Colonies. The raucous, partisan public life of the Middle Colonies foreshadowed later American society.

ANGLO-DUTCH RIVALRY ON THE HUDSON

By the early decades of the seventeenth century, the Dutch had established themselves as Europe's most aggressive traders. Holland—a small, loosely federated nation—possessed the world's largest merchant fleet. Dutch rivalry with Spain, a fading though still formidable power, was in large measure responsible for the settlement of New Netherland. While searching for the elusive Northwest Passage in 1609, Henry Hudson, an English explorer employed by a Dutch company, sailed up the river that now bears his name. Further voyages led to the establishment of trading posts in New Netherland, although permanent settlement did not occur until 1624.

The directors of the Dutch West India Company sponsored two small outposts, Fort Orange (Albany) located well up the Hudson River and New Amsterdam (New York City) on Manhattan Island. The first Dutch settlers were

Middle Colonies, 1685

Until the Revolution, the Iroquois blocked European expansion into Western New York. The Jerseys and Pennsylvania initially attracted English and Irish Quakers, who were soon joined by thousands of Scots-Irish and Germans.

salaried employees, and their superiors in Holland expected them to spend most of their time gathering animal furs. They did not receive land for their troubles. Needless to say, this arrangement attracted relatively few Dutch immigrants.

The colony's population may have been small, only 270 in 1628, but it contained an extraordinary ethnic mix. One visitor to New Amsterdam in 1644 maintained he had heard "eighteen different languages" spoken in the city. Even if this report was exaggerated, there is no doubt the Dutch colony drew English, Finns, Germans, and Swedes. By the 1640s, a sizable community of free blacks (probably former slaves who had gained their freedom through self-purchase) had developed in New Amsterdam, adding African tongues to the cacophony of languages.

New Netherland lacked capable leadership. The company sent a number of director-generals to oversee judicial and political affairs. Without exception, these men were temperamentally unsuited to govern an American colony. They adopted autocratic procedures, lined their own pockets, and, in one case, blundered into a war that needlessly killed scores of Indians and settlers. The company made no provision for an elected assembly. As much as they were able, the scattered inhabitants living along the Hudson River ignored company directives. They felt no loyalty to the trading company that had treated them so shabbily.

In August 1664, the Dutch lost their tenuous hold on New Netherland. The English crown, eager to score an easy victory over a commercial rival, dispatched warships to New Amsterdam. The commander of this force, Colonel Richard Nicolls, ordered the colonists to surrender. The last director-general, a colorful character named Peter Stuyvesant (1647–1664), rushed wildly about the city urging the settlers to resist the English. No one obeyed. Even the Dutch remained deaf to Stuyvesant's appeals. They accepted the Articles of Capitulation, a generous agreement that allowed Dutch nationals to remain in the province and to retain their property.

Charles II had already granted his brother, James, the Duke of York, a charter for the newly captured territory and much else besides. The duke became absolute proprietor over Maine, Martha's Vineyard, Nantucket, Long Island, and the rest of New York all the way to Delaware Bay. The king perhaps wanted to encircle New England's potentially disloyal Puritan population, but whatever his aims may have been, he created a bureaucratic nightmare.

During the English Civil War, the duke had acquired a thorough aversion to representative government. The new proprietor had no intention of letting such a participatory system take root in New York. "I cannot *but* suspect," the duke announced, that an assembly "would be of dangerous consequence." In part to appease these outspoken critics, Governor Nicolls—one of the few competent administrators to serve in the Middle Colonies—drew up in March 1665 a legal code known as the Duke's Laws. It guaranteed religious toleration and created local governments.

There was no provision, however, for an elected assembly or, for that matter, for democratic town meetings. The legal code disappointed the Puritan migrants on Long Island, and when the duke's officers attempted to collect taxes, these people protested that they were "inslav'd under an Arbitrary Power."

The Dutch kept silent. For several decades they remained a large unassimilated ethnic group. They continued to speak their own language, worship in their own churches (Dutch Reformed Calvinist), and eye their English neighbors with suspicion. In fact, the colony seemed little different from what it had been under the Dutch West India Company: a loose collection of independent communities ruled by an ineffectual central government.

CONFUSION IN NEW JERSEY

Only three months after receiving a charter for New York, the Duke of York made a terrible mistake. As a gift to two courtiers who had served Charles during the English Civil War, the duke awarded the land lying between the Hudson and Delaware rivers to John, Lord Berkeley, and Sir George Carteret. This colony was named New Jersey in honor of Carteret's birthplace, the Isle of Jersey in the

English Channel. When Nicolls heard what the duke had done, he exploded. In his estimation, this fertile region contained the "most improveable" land in all New York, and to give it away so casually seemed the height of folly.

The duke's impulsive act bred confusion. Soon it was not clear who owned what in New Jersey. Before Nicolls had learned of James's decision, the governor had allowed migrants from New England to take up farms west of the Hudson River. He promised the settlers an opportunity to establish an elected assembly, a headright system, and liberty of conscience. In exchange for these privileges, Nicolls asked only that they pay a small annual rent to the duke. The new proprietors, Berkeley and Carteret, recruited colonists on similar terms. They assumed, of course, that they would receive the rent money.

The result was chaos. Some colonists insisted that Nicolls had authorized their assembly. Others, equally insistent, claimed that Berkeley and Carteret had done so. Both sides were wrong. Neither the proprietors nor Nicolls possessed any legal right whatsoever to set up a colonial government. James could transfer land to favorite courtiers, but no matter how many times the land changed hands, the government remained his personal responsibility. Knowledge of the law failed to quiet the controversy. Through it all, the duke showed not the slightest interest in the peace and welfare of the people of New Jersey.

Berkeley grew tired of the venture. It generated headaches rather than income, and in 1674, he sold his proprietary rights to a group of surprisingly quarrelsome Quakers. The sale necessitated the division of the colony into two separate governments known as East and West Jersey. Neither half prospered. Carteret and his heirs tried unsuccessfully to turn a profit in East Jersey. In 1677, the Quaker proprietors of West Jersey issued a remarkable democratic plan of government, the Laws, Concessions, and Agreements. But they fought among themselves with such intensity that not even William Penn could bring tranquility to their affairs. Penn wisely turned his attention to the unclaimed territory across the Delaware River. The West Jersey proprietors went bankrupt, and in 1702, the crown reunited the two Jerseys into a single royal colony.

QUAKERS IN AMERICA

The founding of Pennsylvania cannot be separated from the history of the Quaker movement. Believers in an extreme form of Antinomianism, the Quakers saw no need for a learned ministry, since one person's interpretation of Scripture was as valid as anyone else's. This radical religious sect, a product of the social upheaval in England during the Civil War, gained its name from the derogatory term that English authorities sometimes used to describe those who "tremble at the word of the Lord." The name persisted even though the Quakers preferred being called Professors of the Light or, more commonly, Friends.

QUAKER BELIEFS AND PRACTICE

By the time the Stuarts regained the throne in 1660, the Quakers had developed strong support throughout England. One person responsible for their remarkable success was George Fox (1624–1691), a shoemaker whose spiritual anxieties sparked a powerful new religious message that pushed beyond traditional reformed Protestantism. According to Fox, he experienced despair "so that I had nothing outwardly to help me . . . [but] then, I heard a voice which said, 'There is one, even Christ Jesus, that can speak to thy condition.'" Throughout his life, Fox and his growing number of followers gave testimony to the working of the Holy Spirit. Indeed, they informed ordinary men and women that if only they would look, they too would discover they possessed an "Inner Light." This was a wonderfully liberating invitation, especially for persons of lower-class origin.

Quakers practiced humility in their daily lives. They wore simple clothes and employed old-fashioned forms of address that set them apart from their neighbors. Friends refused to honor worldly position and accomplishment or to swear oaths in courts of law. They were also pacifists. According to Fox, all persons were equal in the sight of the Lord, a belief that generally annoyed people of rank and achievement.

Moreover, the Quakers never kept their thoughts to themselves. They preached conversion constantly, spreading the "Truth" throughout England, Ireland, and America. The Friends played important roles in the early history of New Jersey, Rhode Island, and North Carolina, as well as Pennsylvania. In some places, the "publishers of Truth" wore out their welcome. English authorities harassed the Quakers. Thousands, including Fox himself, were jailed, and in Massachusetts Bay between 1659 and 1661, Puritan magistrates ordered several Friends put to death. Such measures proved counterproductive, for persecution only inspired the martyred Quakers to redouble their efforts.

PENN'S "HOLY EXPERIMENT"

William Penn lived according to the Inner Light, a commitment that led eventually to the founding of Pennsylvania. Penn possessed a curiously complex personality. He was an athletic person who threw himself into intellectual pursuits. He was a bold visionary capable of making pragmatic decisions. He came from an aristocratic family and yet spent his entire adult life involved with a religious movement associated with the lower class.

Precisely when Penn's thoughts turned to America is not known. He was briefly involved with the West Jersey proprietorship. This venture may have suggested the possibility of an even larger enterprise. In any case, Penn negotiated in 1681 one of the more impressive land deals in the history of American real estate. Charles II awarded Penn a charter making him the sole proprietor of a vast area called Pennsylvania (literally, "Penn's woods"). The name embarrassed the modest Penn, but he knew better than to look the royal gift horse in the mouth.

Why the king bestowed such generosity on a leading Quaker who had recently been released from prison remains a mystery. The monarch may have regarded the colony as a means of ridding England of its troublesome Quaker population, or, quite simply, he may have liked Penn. In 1682, the new proprietor purchased from the Duke of York the so-called Three Lower Counties that eventually became Delaware. This astute move guaranteed that Pennsylvania would have access to the Atlantic and determined even before Philadelphia had been established that it would become a commercial center.

Penn lost no time in launching his "Holy Experiment." In 1682, he set forth his ideas in an unusual document known as the Frame of Government. The charter gave Penn the right to create any form of government he desired, and his imagination ran wild. His plan blended traditional notions about the privileges of a landed aristocracy with quite daring concepts of personal liberty. Penn guaranteed that settlers would enjoy among other things liberty of conscience, freedom from persecution, no taxation without representation, and due process of law.

In designing his government, Penn decided that both the rich and poor had to have a voice in political affairs; neither should be able to overrule the legitimate interests of the other class. The Frame of Government envisioned a governor appointed by the proprietor, a 72-member Provincial Council responsible for initiating legislation, and a 200-person Assembly that could accept or reject the bills presented to it. Penn apparently thought the Council would be filled by the colony's richest landholders, or in the words of the Frame, "persons of most note for their wisdom, virtue and ability." The governor and Council were charged with the routine administration of justice. Smaller landowners spoke through the Assembly. It was a clumsy structure, and in America the entire edifice crumbled under its own weight.

SETTLING PENNSYLVANIA

Penn promoted his colony aggressively throughout England, Ireland, and Germany. He had no choice. His only source of revenue was the sale of land and the collection of rents. Penn commissioned pamphlets in several languages extolling the quality of Pennsylvania's rich farmland. The response was overwhelming. People poured into Philadelphia and the surrounding area. In 1685 alone, eight thousand immigrants arrived. Most of the settlers were Irish, Welsh, and English Quakers. But Penn opened the door to men and women of all nations. He asserted that the people of Pennsylvania "are a collection of divers nations in Europe, as French, Dutch, Germans, Swedes, Danes, Finns, Scotch, Irish, and English."

The settlers were by no means all Quakers. The founder of Germantown, Francis Daniel Pastorius, called the vessel that brought him to the New World a "Noah's Ark" of religions, and within his own household, there were servants who subscribed "to the Roman [Catholic], to the Lutheran, to the Calvinistic, to the Anabaptist, and to the Anglican church, and only one Quaker." Ethnic and religious diversity were crucial in the development of Pennsylvania's public institutions, and its politics took on a quarrelsome quality absent in more homogeneous colonies such as Virginia and Massachusetts.

Penn himself emigrated to America in 1682. His stay, however, was unexpectedly short and unhappy. The Council and Assembly—reduced now to more manageable size—fought over the right to initiate legislation. Wealthy Quaker merchants, most of them residents of Philadelphia, dominated the Council. By

Penn's plan for Philadelphia shows the city laid out where the Scool Kill (Schuylkill) and Delaware rivers parallel each other. Four of the five public squares were intended to be parks while the fifth (at the center) was designated for public buildings. Today it is the site of Philadelphia's city hall.

contrast, the Assembly included men from rural settlements and the Three Lower Counties who showed no concern for the Holy Experiment.

Penn did not see his colony again until 1699. During his absence, much had changed. The settlement had prospered. Its agricultural products, especially its excellent wheat, were in demand throughout the Atlantic world. Despite this economic success, however, the population remained deeply divided. Even the Quakers had briefly split into hostile factions. Penn's handpicked governors had failed to win general support for the proprietor's policies, and one of them exclaimed in anger that each Quaker "prays for his neighbor on First Days and then preys on him the other six."

In 1701, legal challenges in England again forced Penn to depart for the mother country. Just before he sailed, Penn signed the Charter of Liberties, a new frame of government that established a unicameral or one-house legislature (the only one in colonial America) and gave the representatives the right to initiate bills. Penn also allowed the Assembly to conduct its business without proprietary interference. The charter provided for the political separation of the Three Lower Counties (Delaware) from Pennsylvania, something people living in the area had demanded for years. This hastily drafted document served as Pennsylvania's constitution until the American Revolution.

PLANTING THE CAROLINAS

In some ways, Carolina society looked much like the one that had developed in Virginia and Maryland. In both areas, white planters forced African slaves to produce staple crops for a world market. But such superficial similarities masked substantial regional differences. In fact, "the South"—certainly the fabled solid South of the early nineteenth century—did not exist during the colonial period. As a historian of colonial Carolina explained, "the southern colonies were never a cohesive section in the same way that New England was. The great diversity of population groups . . . discouraged southern sectionalism."

PROPRIETORS OF THE CAROLINAS

Carolina was a product of the Restoration of the Stuarts to the English throne. Court favorites who had followed the Stuarts into exile during the Civil War demanded tangible rewards for their loyalty. New York and New Jersey were obvious plums. So too was Carolina. Sir John Colleton, a successful English planter returned from Barbados, organized a group of eight powerful courtiers who styled themselves the True and Absolute Lords Proprietors of Carolina. On March 24, 1663, the king granted these proprietors a charter to the vast territory between Virginia and Florida and running west as far as the "South Seas."

The Carolina proprietors divided their grant into three distinct jurisdictions, anticipating no doubt that these areas would become the centers of settlement. The first region, called Albemarle, abutted Virginia. As the earlier ill-fated Roanoke colonists had discovered, the region lacked a good deepwater port. Nevertheless, it attracted a number of dissatisfied Virginians who drifted south in search of fresh land. Farther south, the mouth of the Cape Fear River seemed a second likely site for development. And third, within the present state of South Carolina, the Port Royal region contained a maze of fertile islands and meandering tidal streams.

Colleton and his associates waited for the money to roll in, but to their dismay, no one seemed particularly interested in moving to the Carolina frontier. A tiny settlement at Port Royal failed. One group of New Englanders briefly considered taking up land in the Cape Fear area, but these people were so disappointed by what they saw that they departed, leaving behind only a sign that "tended not only to the disparagement of the Land . . . but also to the great discouragement of all those that should hereafter come into these parts to settle." By this time, a majority of surviving proprietors had given up on Carolina.

THE BARBADIAN CONNECTION

Anthony Ashley Cooper, later Earl of Shaftesbury, was the exception. In 1669, he persuaded the remaining Carolinian proprietors to invest their own capital in the colony. Without such financial support, Ashley recognized, the project would surely fail. Once he received sufficient funds, this energetic organizer dispatched three hundred English colonists to Port Royal under the command of Joseph West. The fleet put in briefly at Barbados to pick up additional recruits, and in March 1670, after being punished by Atlantic gales that destroyed one ship, the expedition arrived at its destination. Only one hundred people were still alive. The unhappy settlers did not remain long at Port Royal, an unappealing, low-lying place badly exposed to Spanish attack. They moved northward, locating eventually along the more secure Ashley River. Later the colony's administrative center, Charles Town (it did not become Charleston until 1783) was established at the junction of the Ashley and Cooper rivers.

Ashley also wanted to bring order to the new society. With assistance from John Locke, the famous English philosopher (1632–1704), Ashley devised the Fundamental Constitutions of Carolina. The constitutions created a local aristocracy consisting of proprietors and lesser nobles called *landgraves* and *cassiques*, terms as inappropriate to the realities of the New World as was the idea of creating a hereditary landed elite. Persons who purchased vast tracts of land automatically received a title and the right to sit in the Council of Nobles, a body designed to administer justice, oversee civil affairs, and initiate legislation. A parliament in which smaller landowners had a voice could accept or reject bills drafted by the council. The very poor were excluded from political life altogether. Not surprisingly, the constitutions had little impact on the actual structure of government.

Before 1680, almost half the men and women who settled in the Port Royal area came from Barbados. This small Caribbean island, which produced an annual fortune in sugar, depended on slave labor. By the third quarter of the seventeenth century, Barbados had become overpopulated. Wealthy families could not provide their sons and daughters with sufficient land to maintain social status, and as the crisis intensified, Barbadians looked to Carolina for relief.

These migrants, many of whom were quite rich, traveled to Carolina as both individuals and family groups. Some even brought gangs of slaves with them to the American mainland. The Barbadians carved out plantations on the tributaries of the Cooper River and established themselves immediately as the colony's most powerful political faction.

Much of the planters' time was taken up with the search for a profitable crop. The early settlers experimented with a number of plants: tobacco, cotton, silk, and grapes. The most successful items turned out to be beef, skins, and naval stores (especially tar used to maintain ocean vessels). By the 1680s, some Carolinians had built up great herds of cattle—seven or eight hundred head in some cases. Traders who dealt with Indians brought back thousands of deerskins from the interior, and they often returned with Indian slaves as well. These commercial resources together with tar and turpentine enjoyed a good market. It was not until the 1690s that the planters came to appreciate fully the value of rice, but once they had done so, it quickly became the colony's main staple.

Proprietary Carolina was in a constant political uproar. Factions vied for special privilege. The Barbadian settlers, known locally as the Goose Creek Men, resisted the proprietors' policies at every turn. A large community of French Huguenots located in Craven County distrusted the Barbadians. The proprietors—an ineffectual group following the death of Shaftesbury—appointed a series of utterly incompetent governors who only made things worse. By the end of the century, the Commons House of Assembly had assumed the right to initiate legislation. In 1719, the colonists overthrew the last proprietary governor, and in 1729, the king created separate royal governments for North and South Carolina.

THE FOUNDING OF GEORGIA

The early history of Georgia was strikingly different from that of Britain's other mainland colonies. Its settlement was really an act of aggression against Spain, a country that had as good a claim to this area as did the English. During the eighteenth century, the two nations were often at war (see Chapter 4), and South

The Carolinas and Georgia

Caribbean sugar planters migrated to the Goose Creek area near Charles Town where, with knowledge supplied by African slaves, they eventually mastered rice cultivation. Poor harbors in North Carolina retarded the spread of European settlement in that region.

Carolinians worried that the Spaniards moving up from bases in Florida would occupy the disputed territory between Florida and the Carolina grant.

The colony owed its existence primarily to James Oglethorpe, a British general and member of Parliament who believed that he could thwart Spanish designs on the area south of Charles Town while at the same time providing a fresh start for London's worthy poor, saving them from debtors' prison. In 1732, the king granted Oglethorpe and a board of trustees a charter for a new colony to be located between the Savannah and Altamaha rivers and from "sea to sea." The trustees living in the mother country were given complete control over Georgia politics, a condition the settlers soon found intolerable.

During the first years of colonization, Georgia fared no better than had earlier utopian experiments. The poor people of England showed little desire to move to an inclement frontier, and the trustees, in their turn, provided little incentive for emigration. Slavery was prohibited. So too was rum.

Almost as soon as they arrived in Georgia, the settlers complained. The colonists demanded slaves, pointing out to the trustees that unless the new

ENGLAND'S PRINCIPAL MAINLAND COLONIES

NAME	ORIGINAL PURPOSE	DATE OF FOUNDING
Virginia	Commercial venture	1607
New Amsterdam (New York)	Commercial venture	1613 (made English colony, 1664)
Plymouth	Refuge for English Separatists	1620 (absorbed by Massachusetts, 1691)
New Hampshire	Commercial venture	1623
Massachusetts	Refuge for English Puritans	1628
Maryland	Refuge for English Catholics	1634
Connecticut	Expansion of Massachusetts	1635
Rhode Island	Refuge for dissenters from Massachusetts	1636
New Sweden (Delaware)	Commercial venture	1638 (included in Penn grant, 1681; given separate assembly, 1703)
North Carolina	Commercial venture	1663
South Carolina	Commercial venture	1663
New Jersey	Consolidation of new English territory, Quaker settlement	1664
Pennsylvania	Refuge for English Quakers	1681
Georgia	Discourage Spanish expansion; charity	1733

Sources: U.S. Bureau of the Census, *Historical Statistics of the United States: Colonial Times to 1970*, Washington, D.C., 1975; John J. McCusker and Russell R. Menard, *The Economy of British America, 1607–1789*, Chapel Hill, 1985.

planters possessed an unfree labor force, they could not compete economically with their South Carolina neighbors. The settlers also wanted a voice in local government. In 1738, 121 people living in Savannah petitioned for fundamental reforms in the colony's constitution.

PRINCIPAL FOUNDER	MAJOR EXPORT	ESTIMATED POPULATION CA. 1700
Captain John Smith	Tobacco	64,560
Peter Stuyvesant, Duke of York	Furs, grain	19,107
William Bradford	Grain	Included with Massachusetts
John Mason	Wood, naval stores	4,958
John Winthrop	Grain, wood	55,941
Lord Baltimore (George Calvert)	Tobacco	34,100
Thomas Hooker	Grain	25,970
Roger Williams	Grain	5,894
Peter Minuit, William Penn	Grain	2,470
Anthony Ashley Cooper	Wood, naval stores, tobacco	10,720
Anthony Ashley Cooper	Naval stores, rice, indigo	5,720
Sir George Carteret	Grain	14,010
William Penn	Grain	18,950
James Oglethorpe	Rice, wood, naval stores	5,200 (in 1750)

While the colonists grumbled about various restrictions, Oglethorpe tried and failed to capture the Spanish fortress at Saint Augustine (1740). This personal disappointment coupled with the growing popular unrest destroyed his interest in Georgia. The trustees were forced to compromise their principles. In 1750, they permitted the settlers to import slaves. Soon Georgians could drink rum. In 1751, the trustees returned Georgia to the king, undoubtedly relieved to be free of what had become a hard-drinking, slave-owning plantation society much like that in South Carolina. The king authorized an assembly in 1751, but even with these social and political changes, Georgia attracted very few new settlers.

RUGGED AND LABORIOUS BEGINNINGS

Over the course of the seventeenth century, women and men had followed leaders such as Baltimore, Smith, Winthrop, Bradford, Penn, and Berkeley to the New World in anticipation of creating a successful new society. Some people were religious visionaries; others were hardheaded businessmen. The results of their efforts, their struggles to survive in an often hostile environment, and their interactions with various Native American groups yielded a spectrum of settlements along the Atlantic coast.

The diversity of early English colonization must be emphasized precisely because it is so easy to overlook. Even though the colonists eventually banded together and fought for independence, persistent differences separated New Englanders from Virginians, Pennsylvanians from Carolinians. The interpretive challenge, of course, is to explain how European colonists managed over the course of the eighteenth century to develop the capacity to imagine themselves a nation.

3

PUTTING DOWN ROOTS
Families in an Atlantic Empire

The Witherspoon family moved from Great Britain to the South Carolina backcountry early in the eighteenth century. Although otherwise indistinguishable from the thousands of other ordinary families who put down roots in English America, the Witherspoons entered history through a candid account of pioneer life produced by their son, Robert, who was only a small child at the time of their arrival.

The Witherspoons' initial reaction to the New World—at least, that of the mother and children—was despondence. "My mother and us children were still in expectation that we were coming to an agreeable place," Robert confessed, "but when we arrived and saw nothing but a wilderness and instead of a fine timbered house, nothing but a very mean dirt house, our spirits quite sunk." For many years, the Witherspoons feared they would be killed by Indians, become lost in the woods, or be bitten by snakes.

The Witherspoons managed to survive the early difficult years on the Black River. To be sure, the Carolina backcountry did not look very much like the world they had left behind. The discrepancy, however, apparently did not greatly discourage Robert's father. He had a vision of what the Black River settlement might become. "My father," Robert recounted, "gave us all the comfort he [could] by telling us we would get all these trees cut down and in a short time [there] would be plenty of inhabitants, [and] that we could see from house to house."

Robert Witherspoon's story reminds us just how much the early history of colonial America was a history created by families, and not, as some commentators would have us believe, by individuals. Neither the peopling of the Atlantic frontier, the cutting down of the forests, nor the creation of new communities where one could see from "house to house" was a process that involved what we would today recognize as state policy. Men and women made significant decisions about the character of their lives within families. It was within this primary social unit that most colonists earned their livelihoods, educated their children, defined gender, sustained religious tradition, and nursed each other in sickness. In short, the family was the source of their societal and cultural identities.

Early colonial families did not exist in isolation but were part of larger societies. As we have already discovered, the character of the first English settlements in the New World varied substantially. During much of the seventeenth century, these initial differences grew stronger as each region acquired its own history and developed its own traditions. The various local societies in which families like the Witherspoons put down roots reflected several critical elements: supply of labor, abundance of land, unusual demographic patterns, and commercial ties with European markets. In the Chesapeake, for example, an economy based almost entirely on a single staple—tobacco—created an insatiable demand for indentured servants and black slaves. In Massachusetts Bay, the extraordinary longevity of the founders generated a level of social and political stability that Virginians and Marylanders did not attain until the very end of the seventeenth century.

By 1660, it seemed regional differences had undermined the idea of a unified English empire in America. During the reign of Charles II, however, a trend toward cultural convergence began. Although subcultures had evolved in strikingly different directions, countervailing forces such as common language and religion gradually pulled English American settlers together. Parliament took advantage of this trend and began to establish a uniform set of rules for the expanding American empire. The process was slow and uneven, often sparking violent colonial resistance. By the end of the seventeenth century, however, England had made significant progress toward transforming its New World provinces into an empire that produced needed raw materials and purchased manufactured goods.

SOURCES OF STABILITY: NEW ENGLAND COLONIES OF THE SEVENTEENTH CENTURY

Seventeenth-century New Englanders successfully replicated in America a traditional social order they had known in England. The transfer of a familiar way of life to the New World seemed less difficult for these Puritan migrants than it did for the many English men and women who settled in the Chesapeake colonies. Their contrasting experiences, fundamental to an understanding of the development of both cultures, can be explained, at least in part, by the development of Puritan families.

IMMIGRANT FAMILIES AND NEW SOCIAL ORDER

Early New Englanders believed God ordained the family for human benefit. It was essential to the maintenance of social order, since outside the family, men and women succumbed to carnal temptation. Such people had no one to sustain them or remind them of Scripture.

The godly family, at least in theory, was ruled by a patriarch, father to his children, husband to his wife, the source of authority and object of unquestioned obedience. The wife shared responsibility for the raising of children, but in decisions of importance, especially those related to property, she was expected to defer to her spouse.

The New Englanders' concern about the character of the godly family is not surprising. This institution played a central role in shaping their society. In contrast to those who migrated to the colonies of Virginia and Maryland, New Englanders crossed the Atlantic within nuclear families. That is, they moved within established units consisting of a father, mother, and their dependent children rather than as single youths and adults. People who migrated to America within families preserved local English customs more fully than did the youths who traveled to other parts of the continent as single men and women. The comforting presence of immediate family members reduced the shock of adjusting to a strange environment three thousand miles from home. Even in the 1630s, the ratio of men to women in New England was fairly well balanced, about three males for every two females. Persons who had not already married in England before coming to the New World could expect to form nuclear families of their own.

The great migration of the 1630s and 1640s brought approximately 20,000 persons to New England. After 1642, the English Civil War reduced the flood of people moving to Massachusetts Bay to a trickle. Nevertheless, by the end of the century, the population of New England had reached almost 120,000, an amazing increase considering the small number of original immigrants. Historians have been hard pressed to explain this striking rate of growth. Some have suggested that New Englanders married very young, thus giving couples extra years in which to produce large families. Other scholars have maintained that New England women must have been more fertile than their Old World counterparts.

Neither demographic theory adequately explains how so few migrants produced such a large population. Early New England marriage patterns, for example, did not differ substantially from those recorded in seventeenth-century England. The average age for men at first marriage was the mid-twenties. Wives were slightly younger than their husbands, the average age being about 22. There is no evidence that New Englanders favored child brides. Nor, for that matter, were Puritan families unusually large by European standards of the period.

The explanation for the region's extraordinary growth turned out to be survival rather than fertility. Put simply, people who, under normal conditions, would have died in contemporary Europe lived in New England. Indeed, the life expectancy of seventeenth-century settlers was not very different from our own. Males who survived infancy might have expected to see their seventieth birthday. Twenty percent of the men of the first generation reached the age of eighty. The figures for women were only slightly lower.

Longer life altered family relations. New England males lived not only to see their own children reach adulthood but also to witness the birth of grandchildren. In other words, this society produced real patriarchs. This may have been one of the first societies in recorded history in which a person could reasonably anticipate knowing his or her grandchildren, a demographic surprise that contributed to social stability. The traditions of particular families and communities literally remained alive in the memories of the colony's oldest citizens.

COMMONWEALTH OF FAMILIES

The life cycle of the seventeenth-century New England family began with marriage. Young men and women generally initiated courtships. If parents exercised a voice in such matters, it was to discourage union with a person of unsound moral character. Puritan ministers advised single people to choose godly partners, warning:

> *The Wretch that is alone to Mannon Wed,*
> *May chance to find a Satan in the bed.*

In this highly religious society, there was not much chance that young people would stray far from shared community values. The overwhelming majority of the region's population married, for in New England, the single life was not only morally suspect but also physically difficult.

A couple without land could not support an independent and growing family in these agrarian communities. While men generally brought farmland to the marriage, prospective brides were expected to provide a dowry worth approximately one-half what the bridegroom offered. Women often contributed money or household goods. During the seventeenth century, men and women generally lived in the communities of their parents and grandparents. New Englanders usually managed to fall in love with a neighbor, and most marriages took place between men and women living less than 13 miles apart.

The household was primarily a place of work—very demanding work. The primary goal, of course, was to clear enough land to feed the family. Additional cultivation allowed the farmer to produce a surplus that could then be sold or

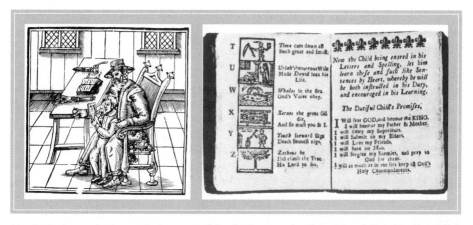

New England parents took seriously their responsibility for the spiritual welfare of their children. To seek the word of God, young people had to learn to read. The New-England Primer, *shown here, was their primary vehicle.*

bartered, and since agrarian families required items that could not be manufactured at home—metal tools, for example—they usually grew more than they consumed. Early American farmers were not economically self-sufficient.

Towns were collections of families, not individuals. Over time, these families intermarried, so the community became an elaborate kinship network. Social historians have discovered that in many New England towns, the original founders dominated local politics and economic affairs for several generations. Not surprisingly, newcomers who were not absorbed into the family system tended to move away from the village with greater frequency than did the sons and daughters of the established lineage groups.

Congregational churches were also built on a family foundation. During the earliest years of settlement, the churches accepted persons who could demonstrate they were among God's "elect." Members were drawn from a broad social spectrum. Once the excitement of establishing a new society had passed, however, New Englanders began to focus more attention on the spiritual welfare of their own families. This quite normal parental concern precipitated a major ecclesiastical crisis. The problem was the status of the children within a gathered church. Sons and daughters of full church members regularly received baptism, usually as infants, but as these people grew to adulthood, they often failed to provide testimony of their own "election." Moreover, they wanted their own children to be baptized. A church synod—a gathering of Congregational ministers—responded to this generational crisis by adopting the so-called Half-Way Covenant (1662). The compromise allowed the grandchildren of persons in full communion to be baptized even though their parents could not demonstrate conversion.

Colonists regarded education as primarily a family responsibility. Parents were supposed to instruct children in the principles of Christianity, and so it was necessary to teach boys and girls how to read. In 1642, the Massachusetts General Court reminded the Bay Colonists of their obligation to catechize their families. Five years later, the legislature ordered towns containing at least fifteen families to open an elementary school supported by local taxes. Villages of a hundred or more families had to maintain more advanced grammar schools, which taught a basic knowledge of Latin. At least eleven schools were operating in 1647, and despite their expense, new schools were established throughout the century.

This family-based education system worked. A large majority of the region's adult males could read and write, an accomplishment not achieved in the Chesapeake colonies for another century. The literacy rate for women was somewhat lower, but by the standards of the period, it was still impressive. A printing press operated in Cambridge as early as 1639.

After 1638, young men could attend Harvard College, the first institution of higher learning founded in England's mainland colonies. The school was originally intended to train ministers, and of the 465 students who graduated during the seventeenth century, more than half became Congregational divines. Harvard had a demanding curriculum. The boys read logic, rhetoric, divinity, and several ancient languages, including Hebrew. Yale College followed Harvard's lead, admitting its first students in 1702.

WOMEN'S LIVES IN PURITAN NEW ENGLAND

The role of women in the agrarian societies of New England is a controversial subject. Some scholars point out that common law as well as English custom treated women as inferior to men. Other historians, however, depict the colonial period as a "golden age" for women. According to this interpretation, wives worked alongside their husbands. They were not divorced from meaningful, productive labor. They certainly were not transformed into the frail, dependent beings much admired by middle-class males of the nineteenth century. Both views provide insights into the lives of early American women, but neither fully recaptures their community experiences.

To be sure, women worked on family farms. They did not, however, necessarily do the same jobs that men performed. Women usually handled separate tasks, including cooking, washing, clothes making, dairying, and gardening. Their production of food was absolutely essential to the survival of most households. Sometimes wives—and the overwhelming majority of adult seventeenth-century women were married—raised poultry, and by selling surplus birds they achieved some economic independence. In fact, during this period women were often described as "deputy husbands," a label that drew attention to their dependence on family patriarchs as well as to their roles as decision makers.

Women also joined churches in greater number than men. Within a few years of founding, many New England congregations contained two female members for every male, a process historians describe as the "feminization of colonial religion." Contemporaries offered different explanations for the gender shift. Cotton Mather, the leading Congregational minister of Massachusetts Bay, argued that God had created "far more *godly Women*" than men. Others thought that the life-threatening experience of childbirth gave women a deeper appreciation of religion. The Quakers gave women an even larger role in religious affairs, which may help to explain the popularity of this sect among ordinary women.

In political and legal matters, society sharply curtailed the rights of colonial women. According to English common law, a wife exercised no control over property. She could not, for example, sell land, although if her husband decided to dispose of their holdings, he was free to do so without her permission. Divorce was extremely difficult to obtain in any colony before the American Revolution. Indeed, a person married to a cruel or irresponsible spouse had little recourse but to run away or accept the unhappy situation.

Yet most women were neither prosperous entrepreneurs nor abject slaves. Surviving letters indicate that men and women generally accommodated themselves to the gender roles they thought God had ordained. One of early America's most creative poets, Anne Bradstreet, wrote movingly of the fulfillment she had found with her husband. In a piece titled "To my Dear and loving Husband," Bradstreet declared:

> *If ever two were one, then surely we.*
> *If ever man were lov'd by wife, then thee;*
> *If ever wife was happy in a man,*
> *Compare with me ye women if you can.*

Although Puritan couples worried that the affection they felt for a husband or a wife might turn their thoughts away from God's perfect love, they were willing to risk the danger.

RANK AND STATUS IN NEW ENGLAND SOCIETY

During the seventeenth century, the New England colonies attracted neither noblemen nor paupers. The absence of these social groups meant that the American social structure seemed incomplete by contemporary European standards. The settlers were not displeased that the poor remained in the Old World. The lack of very rich persons—and in this period great wealth frequently accompanied noble title—was quite another matter. According to the prevailing hierarchical view of the structure of society, well-placed individuals were natural rulers, people intended by God to exercise political authority over the rank and file. Migration forced the colonists, however, to choose their rulers from men of more modest status. Persons who would never have been "natural rulers" in England became provincial gentry in the various northern colonies.

The problem was that while most New Englanders accepted a hierarchical view of society, they disagreed over their assigned places. Both Massachusetts Bay and Connecticut passed sumptuary laws—statutes that limited the wearing of fine apparel to the wealthy and prominent—to curb the pretensions of those of lower status. Yet such restraints could not prevent some people from rising and others from falling within the social order.

Most northern colonists were yeomen (independent farmers) who worked their own land. While few became rich in America, even fewer fell hopelessly into debt. Their daily lives, especially for those who settled New England, centered on scattered little communities where they participated in village meetings, church-related matters, and militia training. Possession of land gave agrarian families a sense of independence from external authority. As one man bragged to those who had stayed behind in England, "Here are no hard landlords to rack us with high rents or extorting fines. . . . Here every man may be master of his own labour and land . . . and if he have nothing but his hands he may set up his trade, and by industry grow rich."

During the seventeenth century, this independence was balanced by an equally strong feeling of local identity. Not until the late eighteenth century, when many New Englanders left their familial villages in search of new land, did many northern yeomen place personal material ambition above traditional community bonds.

It was not unusual for northern colonists to work as servants at some point in their lives. This system of labor differed greatly from the pattern of servitude that developed in seventeenth-century Virginia and Maryland. New Englanders seldom recruited servants from the Old World. The forms of agriculture practiced in this region, mixed cereal and dairy farming, made employment of large gangs of dependent workers uneconomic. Rather, New England families placed their adolescent children in nearby homes. These young persons contracted for four or five years and seemed more like apprentices than servants. Servitude was not simply a means by which one group exploited another. It was a form of vocational training program in which the children of the rich as well as the poor participated.

By the end of the seventeenth century, the New England Puritans had developed a compelling story about their own history in the New World. The founders had been extraordinarily godly men and women, and in a heroic effort to establish a purer form of religion, pious families had passed "over the vast ocean into

Seventeenth-century Puritan carvers transformed the production of gravestones into a distinctive folk art form.

this vast and howling wilderness." Although the children and grandchildren of the first generation sometimes questioned their own ability to please the Lord, they recognized the mission to the New World had been a success: they were "as Prosperous as ever, there is Peace & Plenty, & the Country flourisheth."

THE PLANTERS' WORLD

Unlike New England's settlers, the men and women who emigrated to the Chesapeake region did not move in family units. They traveled to the New World as young unmarried servants, youths cut off from the security of traditional kin relations. Although these immigrants came from a cross section of English society, most had been poor to middling farmers. It is now estimated that 70 to 85 percent of the white colonists who went to Virginia and Maryland during the seventeenth century were not free; that is, they owed four or five years' labor in exchange for the cost of passage to America. If the servant was under age 15, he or she had to serve a full seven years. The overwhelming majority of these laborers were males between the ages of 18 and 22. In fact, before 1640, the ratio of males to females stood at 6 to 1. This figure dropped to about 2½ to 1 by the end of the century, but the sex ratio in the Chesapeake was never as favorable as it had been in early Massachusetts.

FAMILY LIFE IN A PERILOUS ENVIRONMENT

Most immigrants to the Chesapeake region died soon after arriving. It is difficult to ascertain the exact cause of death in most cases, but malaria and other diseases took a frightful toll. Recent studies also indicate that drinking water contaminated with salt killed many colonists living in low-lying areas. Throughout the entire seventeenth century, high mortality rates had a profound effect on this society. Life expectancy for Chesapeake males was about 43, some ten to twenty years less than for men born in New England. For women, life was even shorter. A full 25 percent of all children died in infancy; another 25 percent did not see their twentieth birthdays. The survivors were often weak or ill, unable to perform hard physical labor.

These demographic conditions retarded normal population increase. Young women who might have become wives and mothers could not do so until they had completed their terms of servitude. They thus lost several reproductive years, and in a society in which so many children died in infancy, late marriage greatly restricted family size. Moreover, because of the unbalanced sex ratio, many adult males simply could not find wives. Migration not only cut them off from their English families but also deprived them of an opportunity to form new ones. Without a constant flow of immigrants, the population of Virginia and Maryland would have actually declined.

High mortality compressed the family life cycle into a few short years. One partner in a marriage usually died within seven years. Only one in three Chesapeake marriages survived as long as a decade. Not only did children not meet grandparents—they often did not even know their own parents. Widows and widowers quickly remarried, bringing children by former unions into their new homes, and it was not uncommon for a child to grow up with persons to whom he or she bore no blood relation. The psychological effects of such experiences on Chesapeake settlers cannot be measured. People probably learned to cope with a high degree of personal insecurity. However they adjusted, it is clear family life in this region was vastly more impermanent than it was in the New England colonies during the same period.

Women were obviously in great demand in the early southern colonies. Some historians have argued that scarcity heightened the woman's bargaining power in the marriage market. If she was an immigrant, she did not have to worry about obtaining parental consent. She was on her own in the New World and free to select whomever she pleased.

Nevertheless, liberation from some traditional restraints on seventeenth-century women must not be exaggerated. As servants, women were vulnerable to sexual exploitation by their masters. Moreover, in this unhealthy environment, childbearing was extremely dangerous, and women in the Chesapeake usually died twenty years earlier than their New England counterparts.

RANK AND STATUS IN PLANTATION SOCIETY

Colonists who managed to survive grew tobacco—as much tobacco as they possibly could. This crop became the Chesapeake staple, and since it was relatively easy to cultivate, anyone with a few acres of cleared land could harvest leaves for export. Cultivation of tobacco did not, however, produce a society roughly equal in wealth and status. To the contrary, tobacco generated inequality. Some planters amassed large fortunes; others barely subsisted. Labor made the difference, for to succeed in this staple economy, one had to control the labor of other men and women. More workers in the fields meant larger harvests, and, of course, larger profits. Since free persons showed no interest in growing another man's tobacco, not even for wages, wealthy planters relied on white laborers who were not free, as well as on slaves. The social structure that developed in the seventeenth-century Chesapeake reflected a wild, often unscrupulous scramble to bring men and women of three races—black, white, and Indian—into various degrees of dependence.

Great planters dominated Chesapeake society. The group was small, only a trifling portion of the population of Virginia and Maryland. During the early decades of the seventeenth century, the composition of Chesapeake gentry was continually in flux. Some gentlemen died before they could establish a secure claim to high social status; others returned to England, thankful to have survived. Not until the 1650s did the family names of those who would become famous eighteenth-century gentry appear in the records. The first gentlemen were not—as genealogists sometimes discover to their dismay—dashing cavaliers who had fought in the English Civil War for King Charles I. Rather, such Chesapeake gentry as the Burwells, Byrds, Carters, and Masons consisted originally of the younger sons of English merchants and artisans.

These ambitious men arrived in America with capital. They invested immediately in laborers, and one way or another, they obtained huge tracts of the best tobacco-growing land. The members of this gentry were not technically aristocrats, for they did not possess titles that could be passed from generation to generation. They gave themselves military titles, sat as justices of the peace on the county courts, and directed local (Anglican) church affairs as members of the vestry. Over time, these gentry families intermarried so frequently that they created a vast network of cousins. During the eighteenth century, it was not uncommon to find a half dozen men with the same surname sitting simultaneously in the Virginia House of Burgesses.

Freemen formed the largest class in Chesapeake society. Their origins were strikingly different from those of the gentry, or for that matter, from those of New England's yeomen farmers. Chesapeake freemen traveled to the New World as indentured servants and, by sheer good fortune, managed to remain alive to the end of their contracts. If they had dreamed of becoming great planters, they were gravely disappointed. Most seventeenth-century freemen lived on the edge of poverty. Some freemen, of course, did better in America than they would have in contemporary England, but in both Virginia and Maryland, historians have found a sharp economic division separating the gentry from the rest of white society.

Below the freemen came indentured servants. Membership in this group was not demeaning; after all, servitude was a temporary status. But servitude in the Chesapeake colonies was not the benign institution it was in New England. Great planters purchased servants to grow tobacco. No one seemed overly concerned whether these laborers received decent food and clothes, much less whether they acquired trade skills. Young people, thousands of them, cut off from family ties, sick often to the point of death, unable to obtain normal sexual release, regarded their servitude as a form of slavery. Not surprisingly, the gentry worried that unhappy servants and impoverished freemen, what the planters called the "giddy multitude," would rebel at the slightest provocation, a fear that turned out to be fully justified.

The character of social mobility—and this observation applies only to whites—changed considerably during the seventeenth century. Until the 1680s, it was relatively easy for a newcomer who possessed capital to become a member of the planter elite. No one paid much attention to the reputation or social standing of one's English family.

Sometime after the 1680s, however—the precise date is impossible to establish—a dramatic demographic shift occurred. Although infant mortality remained high, life expectancy rates for those who survived childhood in the Chesapeake improved significantly, and for the first time in the history of Virginia and Maryland, important leadership positions went to men who had actually been born in America. This transition has been described by one political historian as the "emergence of a creole majority," in other words, as the creation of an indigenous ruling elite. The rise of this class helped give the tobacco colonies the kind of political and cultural stability that had eluded earlier generations of planter adventurers. Not surprisingly, it was during this period of demographic transition that creole leaders founded the College of William and Mary (1693) and authorized the construction of an impressive new capital called Williamsburg.

The key to success in this creole society was ownership of slaves. Those planters who held more blacks could grow more tobacco and thus could acquire fresh capital needed to purchase additional laborers. Over time, the rich not only became richer; they also formed a distinct ruling elite that newcomers found increasingly difficult to enter.

Opportunities for advancement also decreased for freemen in the region. Studies of mid-seventeenth-century Maryland reveal that some servants managed to become moderately prosperous farmers and small officeholders. But as the gentry consolidated its hold on political and economic institutions, ordinary people discovered it was much harder to rise in Chesapeake society. Those men and women with more ambitious dreams headed for Pennsylvania, North Carolina, or western Virginia.

Social institutions that figured importantly in the daily experience of New Englanders were either weak or nonexistent in the Chesapeake colonies. In part, the sluggish development resulted from the continuation of high infant mortality rates. There was little incentive to build elementary schools, for example, if half the children would die before reaching adulthood.

Tobacco influenced the spread of other institutions in the region. Planters were scattered along the rivers, often separated from their nearest neighbors by miles of poor roads. Since the major tobacco growers traded directly with English merchants, they had no need for towns. Whatever items they required were either made on the plantation or imported from Europe. Other than the centers of colonial government, Jamestown (and later Williamsburg) and St. Mary's City (and later Annapolis), there were no villages capable of sustaining a rich community life before the late eighteenth century. Seventeenth-century Virginia did not even possess a printing press.

RACE AND FREEDOM IN BRITISH AMERICA

Many people who landed in the colonies were Africans taken as slaves to cultivate rice, sugar, and tobacco. As the Native Americans were exterminated and the supply of white indentured servants dried up, European planters demanded even more African laborers.

ROOTS OF SLAVERY

Between the sixteenth and nineteenth centuries, slave traders carried almost eleven million blacks to the Americas. Most of these men and women were sold in Brazil or in the Caribbean. A relatively small number of Africans reached British North America, and of this group, the majority arrived after 1700. Because slaves performed hard physical labor, planters preferred purchasing young males. In many early slave communities, men outnumbered women by a ratio of two to one.

English colonists did not hesitate to enslave black people or, for that matter, Native Americans. While the institution of slavery had long before died out in the mother country, New World settlers quickly discovered how well this particular labor system operated in the Spanish and Portuguese colonies. The decision to bring African slaves to the colonies, therefore, was based primarily on economic considerations.

English masters, however, seldom justified the practice purely in terms of planter profits. Indeed, they adopted a quite different pattern of rhetoric. English writers associated blacks in Africa with heathen religion, barbarous behavior, sexual promiscuity—in fact, with evil itself. From such a racist perspective, the enslavement of Africans seemed unobjectionable. The planters maintained that if black slaves converted to Christianity, shedding their supposedly savage ways, they would benefit from their loss of freedom.

Africans first landed in Virginia in 1619. For the next fifty years, the status of the colony's black people remained unclear. English settlers classified some black laborers as slaves for life, as chattel to be bought and sold at the master's will. But other Africans became servants, presumably for stated periods of time, and it was even possible for a few blacks to purchase their freedom. Several seventeenth-century Africans became successful Virginia planters.

One reason Virginia lawmakers tolerated such confusion was that the black population remained very small. By 1660, fewer than fifteen hundred people of African origin lived in the entire colony (compared to a white population of approximately twenty-six thousand), and it hardly seemed necessary for the legislature to draw up an elaborate slave code to control so few men and women. If the planters could have obtained more black laborers, they certainly would have done so. The problem was supply. During this period, slave traders sold their cargoes on Barbados or the other sugar islands of the West Indies, where they fetched higher prices than Virginians could afford. In fact, before 1680, most blacks who reached England's colonies on the North American mainland came from Barbados or through New Netherland rather than directly from Africa.

By the end of the seventeenth century, the legal status of Virginia's black people was no longer in doubt. They were slaves for life, and so were their chil-

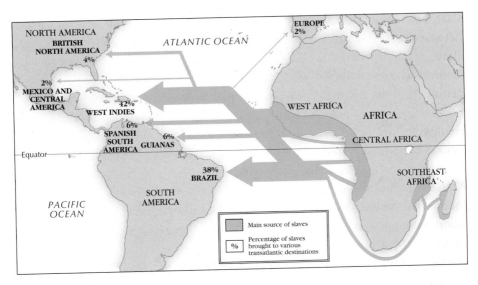

The African Slave Trade
Between 1619 and 1760, about a half million African captives were brought to the thirteen mainland English colonies, far fewer than were taken to other parts of the Americas.

dren after them. This transformation reflected changes in the supply of Africans to British North America. After 1672, the Royal African Company was chartered to meet the colonial planters' demands for black laborers. Between 1695 and 1709, more than eleven thousand Africans were sold in Virginia alone; many others went to Maryland and the Carolinas. Although American merchants—most of them based in Rhode Island—entered the trade during the eighteenth century, the British continued to supply the bulk of the slaves to the mainland market for the entire colonial period.

The expanding black population apparently frightened white colonists, for as the number of Africans increased, lawmakers drew up ever stricter slave codes. It was during this period that racism, always a latent element in New World societies, was fully revealed. By 1700, slavery was unequivocally based on the color of a person's skin. Blacks fell into this status simply because they were black. A vicious pattern of discrimination had been set in motion. Even conversion to Christianity did not free the African from bondage. The white planter could deal with his black property as he alone saw fit, and one revolting Virginia statute excused masters who killed slaves, on the grounds that no rational person would purposely "destroy his own estate." Black women constantly had to fear sexual violation by a master or his sons. Children born to a slave woman became slaves regardless of the father's race. Unlike the Spanish colonies, where persons of lighter color enjoyed greater privileges in society, the English colonies tolerated no mixing of the races. Mulattoes and pure Africans received the same treatment.

CONSTRUCTING AFRICAN AMERICAN IDENTITIES

The slave experience varied substantially from colony to colony. The daily life of a black person in South Carolina, for example, was quite different from that of an African American who happened to live in Pennsylvania or Massachusetts Bay. The size and density of the slave population determined in large measure how successfully blacks could maintain a separate cultural identity. In the lowlands of South Carolina during the eighteenth century, 60 percent of the population was black. The men and women were placed on large, isolated rice plantations, and their contact with whites was limited. In these areas blacks developed creole languages, which mixed the basic vocabulary of English with words borrowed from various African tongues. Slaves on the large rice plantations also were able to establish elaborate and enduring kinship networks that may have helped reduce the more dehumanizing aspects of bondage.

In the New England and Middle Colonies, and even in Virginia, African Americans made up a smaller percentage of the population: 40 percent in Virginia, 8 percent in Pennsylvania, and 3 percent in Massachusetts. In such environments, contact between blacks and whites was more frequent than in South Carolina and Georgia. These population patterns had a profound effect on northern and Chesapeake blacks, for while they escaped the physical drudgery of rice cultivation, they found the preservation of an independent African identity difficult. In northern cities, slaves working as domestics and living in the houses of their masters saw other blacks but had little opportunity to develop creole languages or reaffirm a common African past.

In eighteenth-century Virginia, native-born or creole blacks, people who had learned to cope with whites on a daily basis, looked with contempt on slaves who had just arrived from Africa. These "outlandish" Negroes, as they were called, were forced by blacks as well as whites to accept elements of English culture. It was especially important for newcomers to speak English.

Newly arrived men and women from Africa were far more likely to run away, assault their masters, and organize rebellion than were the creole slaves. The people described in colonial newspaper advertisements as "New Negroes" desperately tried to regain control over their lives. In 1770—just to cite one example—two young Africans, both recently sold in Virginia, "went off with several others, being persuaded that they could find their way back to their own Country."

Despite such wrenching experiences, black slaves creatively preserved elements of an African heritage. The process of establishing African American traditions involved an imaginative reshaping of African and European customs into something that was neither African nor European. It was African American. The slaves accepted Christianity, but they did so on their own terms—terms their

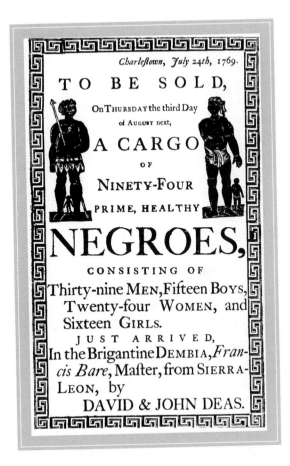

Charleſtown, *July 24th,* 1769.

TO BE SOLD,

On THURSDAY the third Day
of AUGUST next,

A CARGO

OF

NINETY-FOUR

PRIME, HEALTHY

NEGROES,

CONSISTING OF

Thirty-nine MEN, Fifteen BOYS,
Twenty-four WOMEN, and
Sixteen GIRLS.

JUST ARRIVED,
In the Brigantine DEMBIA, *Fran-
cis Bare,* Maſter, from SIERRA-
LEON, by
DAVID & JOHN DEAS.

*A typical public notice announces a
slave auction to be held at the Charles
Town wharf (1769).*

masters seldom fully understood. Blacks transformed Christianity into an expression of religious feeling in which an African element remained vibrant. In
music and folk art, they gave voice to a cultural identity that even the most de-
grading conditions could not eradicate.

A major turning point in the history of African American people occurred
during the early decades of the eighteenth century. At this time, blacks living in
England's mainland colonies began to reproduce successfully. The number of live
births exceeded deaths, and from that date, the expansion of the African
American population owed more to natural increase than to the importation of
new slaves. Even though thousands of new Africans arrived each year, the creole
population was always much larger than that of the immigrant blacks.

Although mainland blacks lived longer than the blacks of Jamaica or
Barbados, they were, after all, still slaves. They protested their debasement in
many ways, some in individual acts of violence, others in organized revolt. The
most serious slave rebellion of the colonial period was the Stono Uprising, which

Old Plantation, *a watercolor by an unknown artist (about 1800), shows that African customs survived plantation slavery. The man and women in the center dance (possibly to celebrate a wedding) to the music of drum and banjo. Instruments, turbans, and scarves reflect a distinctive African American culture in the New World.*

took place in September 1739. One hundred fifty South Carolina blacks rose up and, seizing guns and ammunition, murdered several white planters. "With Colours displayed, and two Drums beating," they marched toward Spanish Florida, where they had been promised freedom. The local militia soon overtook the rebellious slaves and killed most of them. Although the uprising was short-lived, such incidents helped persuade whites everywhere that their own blacks might secretly be planning bloody revolt. Fear bred paranoia. When a white servant woman in New York City announced in 1741 that blacks intended to burn the town, frightened authorities executed 34 suspected arsonists and dispatched 72 others, either to the West Indies or to Madeira, off the coast of Morocco. While the level of interracial violence in colonial society was quite low, everyone recognized that the blacks—in the words of one Virginia governor—longed "to Shake off the fetters of Slavery."

Even within the constraints of slavery, African Americans sometimes found opportunities that afforded a degree of personal freedom. Recent scholarship has discovered, for example, that during the eighteenth century a large number of black men became mariners. It is now estimated that by 1803, African Americans held at least 18 percent of all jobs open to American seamen, and although the number of positions may have been fewer before the Revolution, black colonial sailors—many of them slaves—sought work on sailing vessels to escape the drudgery of life on rice or tobacco plantations. These African American seamen connected black communities scattered throughout the Caribbean and along the mainland coast, bringing news about distant rebellions and spreading radical political ideologies to slaves who might otherwise not have known much about the transforming events of the eighteenth century.

COMMERCIAL BLUEPRINT FOR EMPIRE

Unlike the Spanish Empire which ruled its New World possessions from Madrid, the English Crown was slow to exercise direct authority over the American mainland colonies. The early Stuarts had other, more pressing matters with which to deal, and it was only after the Restoration of Charles II in 1660 that administrators in London began to develop a clear plan for empire. No one doubted that the colonists should be brought more tightly under the control of the mother country. The question before those who shaped imperial policies—a group of courtiers, merchants, and parliamentarians—was how to intervene most effectively in the affairs of men and women who lived so far away and who had learned to make decisions about local governance for themselves. The regulatory system that evolved during this period formed a framework for commercial empire that survived with only minor adjustment until 1776.

RESPONSE TO ECONOMIC COMPETITION

The famous eighteenth-century Scottish economist Adam Smith coined the term *mercantilist system* to describe Great Britain's commercial regulations, and ever since, his phrase has appeared in history books. An advocate of free trade, Smith argued that it made no sense for European states to exclude commercial competitors from their own colonial markets. More trade increased general prosperity. Smith's specific term, however, is misleading. It suggested that English policymakers during the reign of Charles II had developed a well-integrated set of ideas about the nature of international commerce and a carefully planned set of mercantilist government policies to implement them.

They did nothing of the sort. Administrators responded to particular problems, usually on an individual basis. National interest alone did not shape public policy. Instead, the needs of several powerful interest groups led to the rise of English commercial regulation.

Each group looked to colonial commerce to solve a different problem. For his part, the king wanted money. For their part, English merchants were eager to exclude Dutch rivals from lucrative American markets and needed government assistance to compete successfully with the Dutch, even in Virginia or Massachusetts Bay. From the perspective of the landed gentry who sat in Parliament, England needed a stronger navy, and that in turn meant expansion of the domestic shipbuilding industry. And almost everyone agreed England should establish a more favorable balance of trade, that is, increase exports, decrease imports, and grow richer at the expense of other European states. None of these ideas was particularly innovative, but taken together they provided a blueprint for England's first empire.

AN EMPIRE OF TRADE

Parliament passed a Navigation Act in 1660. The statute was the most important piece of imperial legislation drafted before the American Revolution. Colonists from New Hampshire to Georgia paid close attention to the details of this statute, which stated (1) that no ship could trade in the colonies unless it had been constructed in either England or America and carried a crew that was at least 75 percent English (for these purposes, colonists counted as Englishmen), and (2) that certain enumerated goods of great value that were not produced in England—tobacco, sugar, cotton, indigo, dyewoods, ginger—could be transported from the colonies *only* to an English or another colonial port. In 1704, Parliament added rice and molasses to the enumerated list; in 1705, rosins, tars, and turpentines needed for shipbuilding were included.

The act of 1660 was masterfully conceived. It encouraged the development of domestic shipbuilding and prohibited European rivals from obtaining enumerated goods anywhere except in England. Since the Americans had to pay import duties in England (for this purpose colonists did not count as Englishmen) on such items as sugar and tobacco, the legislation also provided the crown with another source of income.

In 1663, Parliament passed a second Navigation Act known as the Staple Act, which stated that, with a few noted exceptions, nothing could be imported into America unless it had first been transshipped through England, a process that greatly added to the price ultimately paid by colonial consumers.

The Navigation Acts attempted to eliminate the Dutch, against whom the English fought three wars in this period (1652–1654, 1664–1667, and 1672–1674), as the intermediaries of American commerce. Just as English merchants were celebrating their victory, however, an unanticipated rival appeared on the scene: New England merchant ships sailed out of Boston, Salem, and Newport to become formidable world competitors in maritime commerce.

During the 1660s, the colonists showed little enthusiasm for the new imperial regulators. Reaction to the Navigation Acts varied from region to region. Virginians bitterly protested them. The collection of English customs on tobacco

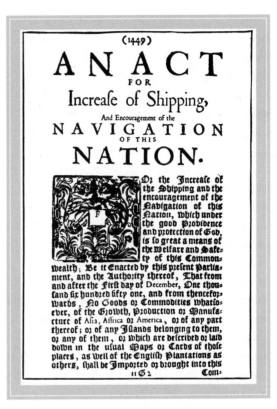

(1449)

A N A C T
FOR
Increase of Shipping,
And Encouragement of the
N A V I G A T I O N
OF THIS
NATION.

Or the Increafe of the Shipping and the encouragement of the Navigation of this Nation, which under the good Providence and protection of God, is so great a means of the Welfare and Safety of this Common-wealth; Be it Enacted by this prefent Parlia-ment, and the Authority thereof, That from and after the First Day of December, One thou-fand fix hundred fifty one, and from thenceforwards, No Goods or Commodities whatfo-ever, of the Growth, Production or Manufa-cture of Afia, Africa or America, or of any part thereof; or of any Iflands belonging to them, or any of them, or which are defcribed or laid down in the ufual Maps or Cards of thofe places, as well of the Englifh Plantations as others, fhall be Imported or brought into this
II G 2   Com-

In the 1650s and 1660s, Parliament enacted a series of measures known collectively as the Navigation Acts, designed to protect English shipping, enrich the treasury, and exploit colonial economies. Shown here is the title page of the Navigation Act of 1651.

greatly reduced the colonial planters' profits. Moreover, the exclusion of the Dutch from the trade meant that growers often had to sell their crops at artificially low prices. The Navigation Acts hit the small planters especially hard, for they were least able to absorb increased production costs. Even though the governor of Virginia lobbied on the planters' behalf, the crown turned a deaf ear. By 1670, import duties on tobacco accounted for almost £100,000, a sum the king could scarcely do without.

Some New England merchants found clever ways to circumvent the Navigation Acts. These crafty traders picked up cargoes of enumerated goods such as sugar or tobacco, sailed to another colonial port (thereby technically fulfilling the letter of the law), and then made directly for Holland or France. Along the way they paid no customs.

To plug the loophole, Parliament passed the Navigation Act of 1673. This statute established a plantation duty, a sum of money equal to normal English customs duties to be collected on enumerated products at the various colonial ports. New Englanders could now sail wherever they pleased within the empire, but they could not escape paying customs.

Despite these legal reforms, serious obstacles impeded the execution of imperial policy. The customs service did not have enough agents in American ports to enforce the Navigation Acts fully, and some men sent from the mother country did more harm than good. Edward Randolph, head of the imperial customs service in New England, was such a person. His behavior was so obnoxious, his reports about New Englanders so condescending, that he became the most hated man in late-seventeenth-century Massachusetts.

Parliament passed the last major piece of imperial legislation in 1696. Among other things, the statute tightened enforcement procedures, putting pressure specifically on the colonial governors to keep England's competitors out of American ports. The act of 1696 also expanded the American customs service and for the first time set up vice-admiralty courts in the colonies. This decision eventually rankled the colonists. Established to settle disputes that occurred at sea, vice-admiralty courts required neither juries nor oral cross-examination, both traditional elements of the common law. But they were effective and sometimes even popular for resolving maritime questions quickly enough to send the ships to sea again with little delay. The year 1696 witnessed one other significant change in the imperial system. William III created a body of policy advisers known as the Board of Trade. This group monitored colonial affairs closely and provided government officials with the best available advice on commercial and other problems. For several decades, at least, it energetically carried out its responsibilities.

The members of Parliament believed these reforms would belatedly compel the colonists to accept the Navigation Acts, and in large measure they were correct. By 1700, American goods transshipped through the mother country accounted for a quarter of all English exports, an indication the colonists found it profitable to obey the commercial regulations. In fact, during the eighteenth century, smuggling from Europe to America dried up almost completely.

COLONIAL GENTRY IN REVOLT, 1676–1691

The Navigation Acts created an illusion of unity. English administrators superimposed a system of commercial regulation on a number of different, often unstable American colonies and called it an empire. But these statutes did not remove long-standing differences. Within each society, men and women struggled to bring order out of disorder, to establish stable ruling elites, to diffuse ethnic and racial tensions, and to cope with population pressures that imperial planners only dimly understood. During the final decades of the seventeenth century, these efforts sometimes sparked revolt.

First, the Virginians rebelled, and then a few years later, political violence swept through Maryland, New York, and Massachusetts Bay, England's most populous mainland colonies. Historians once interpreted these events as rehearsals for the American Revolution, or even for Jacksonian democracy. They perceived the rebels as frontier democrats, rising in protest against an entrenched aristocracy.

Recent research suggests, however, that this view seriously misconstrued the character of these late-seventeenth-century rebellions. The uprisings certainly did not involve confrontations between ordinary people and their rulers. Indeed, the events were not in any modern sense of the word ideological. In each colony, the local gentry split into factions, usually the "outs" versus the "ins," and each side proclaimed its political legitimacy.

CIVIL WAR IN VIRGINIA: BACON'S REBELLION

After 1660, the Virginia economy steadily declined. Returns from tobacco had not been good for some time, and the Navigation Acts reduced profits even further. Into this unhappy environment came thousands of indentured servants, people drawn to Virginia, as the governor explained, "in hope of bettering their condition in a Growing Country."

The reality bore little relation to their dreams. A hurricane destroyed one entire tobacco crop, and in 1667, Dutch warships captured the tobacco fleet just as it was about to sail for England. Indentured servants complained about lack of food and clothing. No wonder that Virginia's governor, Sir William Berkeley, despaired of ever ruling "a People where six parts of seven at least are Poor, Endebted, Discontented and Armed."

Enter Nathaniel Bacon. This ambitious young man arrived in Virginia in 1674. He came from a respectable English family and set himself up immediately as a substantial planter. But he wanted more. Bacon envied the government patronage monopolized by Berkeley's cronies, a group known locally as the Green Spring faction. When Bacon attempted to obtain a license to engage in the fur trade, he was rebuffed. If Bacon had been willing to wait, he probably would have been accepted into the ruling clique, but as subsequent events would demonstrate, Bacon was not a man of patience.

Events beyond Bacon's control thrust him suddenly into the center of Virginia politics. In 1675, Indians reacting to white encroachment attacked several outlying plantations, killing a few colonists, and Virginians expected the governor to send an army to retaliate. Instead, early in 1676, Berkeley called for the construction of a line of defensive forts, a plan that seemed to the settlers both expensive and ineffective. Indeed, the strategy raised embarrassing questions.

Was Berkeley protecting his own fur monopoly? Was he planning to reward his friends with contracts to build useless forts?

While people speculated about such matters, Bacon stepped forward. He boldly offered to lead a volunteer army against the Indians at no cost to the hard-pressed Virginia taxpayers. All he demanded was an official commission from Berkeley giving him military command and the right to attack other Indians, not just the hostile Susquehannocks. The governor steadfastly refused. With some justification, Berkeley regarded his upstart rival as a fanatic on the subject of Indians. The governor saw no reason to exterminate peaceful tribes simply to avenge the death of a few white settlers.

What followed would have been comic had not so many people died. Bacon thundered against the governor's treachery; Berkeley labeled Bacon a traitor. Both men appealed to the populace for support. On several occasions, Bacon marched his followers to the frontier, but they either failed to find the enemy or, worse, massacred friendly Indians. At one point, Bacon burned Jamestown to the ground, forcing the governor to flee to the colony's Eastern Shore.

As the civil war dragged on, it became increasingly apparent that Bacon and his gentry supporters had only the vaguest notion of what they were trying to achieve. The members of the planter elite never seemed fully to appreciate that the rank-and-file soldiers, often black slaves and poor white servants, had serious, legitimate grievances against Berkeley's corrupt government and were demanding substantial reforms, not just a share in the governor's fur monopoly.

When Charles II learned of the fighting in Virginia, he dispatched a thousand regular soldiers to Jamestown. By the time they arrived, Berkeley had regained full control over the colony's government. In October 1676, Bacon died after a brief illness, and within a few months, his band of rebel followers had dispersed.

Berkeley, now an old and embittered man, was recalled to England in 1677. His successors, especially Lord Culpeper (1680–1683) and Lord Howard of Effingham (1683–1689), seemed interested primarily in enriching themselves at the expense of the Virginia planters. Their self-serving policies, coupled with the memory of near anarchy, helped heal divisions within the Virginia ruling class. For almost a century, in fact, the local gentry formed a united front against greedy royal appointees.

THE GLORIOUS REVOLUTION IN THE BAY COLONY

During John Winthrop's lifetime, Massachusetts settlers developed an inflated sense of their independence from the mother country. After 1660, however, it became difficult even to pretend that the Puritan colony was a separate state. Royal officials such as Edward Randolph demanded full compliance with the

Metacomet, the Wampanoag chief also known as King Philip, led Native Americans in a major war designed to remove the Europeans from New England.

Navigation Acts. A few Puritan ministers and magistrates regarded compromise with England as treason, a breaking of the Lord's covenant. Other spokesmen, recognizing the changing political realities within the empire, urged a more moderate course.

In 1675, in the midst of this ongoing political crisis, the Indians dealt the New Englanders a terrible setback. Metacomet, a Wampanoag chief the whites called King Philip, declared war against the colonists. The powerful Narragansetts, whose lands the settlers had long coveted, joined Metacomet, and in little more than a year of fighting, the Indians destroyed scores of frontier villages, killed hundreds of colonists, and disrupted the entire regional economy. More than one thousand Indians and New Englanders died in the conflict.

In 1684, the debate over the Bay Colony's relation to the mother country ended abruptly. The Court of Chancery, sitting in London and acting on a petition from the king, annulled the charter of the Massachusetts Bay Company. In one stroke of a pen, the patent that Winthrop had so lovingly carried to America in 1630, the foundation for a "city on a hill," was gone. The decision forced the most stubborn Puritans to recognize they were part of an empire run by people who did not share their particular religious vision.

James II decided to restructure the government of the entire region as the Dominion of New England. In various stages from 1686 to 1689, the Dominion incorporated Massachusetts, Connecticut, Rhode Island, Plymouth, New York, New Jersey, and New Hampshire under a single appointed royal governor. For this demanding position, James selected Sir Edmund Andros (pronounced Andrews), a military veteran of tyrannical temperament. Andros arrived in Boston in 1686, and within a matter of months he had alienated everyone: Puritans, moderates, and even Anglican merchants. Not only did Andros abolish elective assemblies, but he also enforced the Navigation Acts with such rigor that he brought about commercial depression.

Early in 1689, news of the Glorious Revolution reached Boston. The previous fall, the ruling class of England had deposed James II, an admitted Catholic, and placed his daughter Mary and her husband, William of Orange, on the throne as joint monarchs (see the chart of the Stuart monarchs on p. 38). As part of the settlement, William and Mary accepted a Bill of Rights, a document stipulating the constitutional rights of all Englishmen. Almost immediately, the Bay Colonists overthrew the hated Andros regime. The New England version of the Glorious Revolution (April 18, 1689) was so popular that no one came to the governor's defense.

However united as they may have been, the Bay Colonists could not take the crown's support for granted. William III could have declared the New Englanders rebels and summarily reinstated Andros. But thanks largely to the tireless efforts of Increase Mather, Cotton's father, who pleaded the colonists' case in London, William abandoned the Dominion of New England, and in 1691, Massachusetts received a new royal charter. The freemen no longer selected their governor. The choice now belonged to the king. Moreover, the franchise was determined on the basis of personal property rather than church membership, a change that brought Massachusetts into conformity with general English practice. On the local level, town government remained much as it had been in Winthrop's time.

CONTAGION OF WITCHCRAFT

The instability of the Massachusetts government following Andros's arrest—what Reverend Samuel Willard described as "the short Anarchy accompanying our late Revolution"—allowed what under normal political conditions would have been an isolated, though ugly, local incident to expand into a major colonial crisis. Excessively fearful men and women living in Salem Village, a small, un-prosperous farming community, nearly overwhelmed the new rulers of Massachusetts Bay. Accusations of witchcraft were not uncommon in seventeenth-century New England. Puritans believed that an individual might make a compact with the devil, but during the first decades of settlement, authorities executed only about fifteen alleged witches. Sometimes villagers simply left suspected witches alone. Never before had fears of witchcraft plunged an entire community into panic.

The terror in Salem Village began in late 1691, when several adolescent girls began to behave in strange ways. They cried out for no apparent reason; they twitched on the ground. When concerned neighbors asked what caused their suffering, the girls announced they were victims of witches, seemingly innocent persons who lived in the community. The arrest of several alleged witches did not relieve the girls' "fits," nor did prayer solve the problem. Additional accusations were made, and at least one person confessed, providing a frightening description of the devil as "a thing all over hairy, all the face hairy, and a long nose." In June 1692, a special court convened and began to send men and women to the gallows. By the end of the summer, the court had hanged nineteen people; another was pressed to death. Many more suspects were in jail awaiting trial.

Then suddenly, the storm was over. Led by Increase Mather, a group of prominent Congregational ministers belatedly urged leniency and restraint.

The publication of Cotton Mather's Memorable Providences, Relating to Witchcrafts and Possessions *(1689) contributed to the hysteria that resulted in the Salem witchcraft trials of the 1690s, but he did not take part in the trials. He is shown here surrounded by some of the forms a demon assumed in the "documented" case of an English family besieged by witches.*

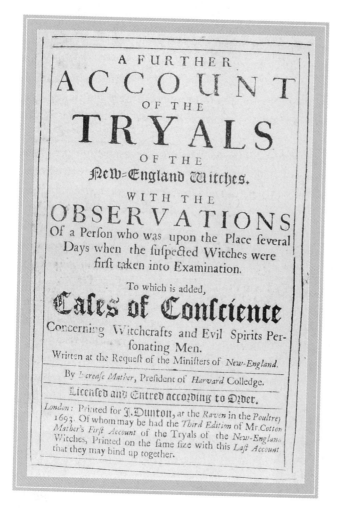

Title page of A Further Account of the Tryals of the New England Witches *(1693), Increase Mather's reflection on the incidents at Salem Village. Mather's* Cases of Conscience Concerning Witchcrafts and Evil Spirits *is credited with helping end the witchcraft executions in Salem.*

Especially troubling to the clergymen was the court's decision to accept "spectral evidence," that is, reports of dreams and visions in which the accused appeared as the devil's agent. Worried about convicting people on such dubious testimony, Mather declared, "It were better that ten suspected witches should escape, than that one innocent person should be condemned." The colonial government accepted the ministers' advice and convened a new court, which promptly acquitted, pardoned, or released the remaining suspects. After the Salem nightmare, witchcraft ceased to be a capital offense.

No one knows exactly what sparked the terror in Salem Village. The community had a history of religious discord, and during the 1680s, the people split into angry factions over the choice of a minister. Economic tensions played a part as well. Poorer, more traditional farmers accused members of prosperous, commercially oriented families of being witches. The underlying misogyny of the entire culture meant the victims were more often women than men. Terror of attack by Native Americans may also have played a part in this ugly affair. Indians in league with the French in Canada had recently raided nearby communities, killing people related to the families of the bewitched Salem girls, and significantly, during the trials some victims described the Devil as a "tawny man."

Whatever the ultimate social and psychological sources of this event may have been, jealousy and bitterness apparently festered to the point that adolescent girls who normally would have been disciplined were allowed to incite judicial murder.

THE GLORIOUS REVOLUTION IN NEW YORK

The Glorious Revolution in New York was more violent than it had been in Massachusetts Bay. Divisions within New York's ruling class ran deep and involved ethnic as well as religious differences. English newcomers and powerful Anglo-Dutch families who had recently risen to commercial prominence in New York City opposed the older Dutch elite.

Much like Nathaniel Bacon, Jacob Leisler was a man entangled in events beyond his control. Leisler, the son of a German minister, emigrated to New York in 1660 and through marriage aligned himself with the Dutch elite. While he achieved moderate prosperity as a merchant, Leisler resented the success of the Anglo-Dutch.

When news of the Glorious Revolution reached New York City in May 1689, Leisler raised a group of militiamen and seized the local fort in the name of William and Mary. He apparently expected an outpouring of popular support, but it was not forthcoming. His rivals waited, watching while Leisler desperately attempted to legitimize his actions. Through bluff and badgering, Leisler managed to hold the colony together, especially after French forces burned Schenectady (February 1690), but he never established a secure political base.

In March 1691, a new royal governor, Henry Sloughter, reached New York. He ordered Leisler to surrender his authority, but Leisler hesitated. The pause cost Leisler his life. Sloughter declared Leisler a rebel, and in a hasty trial, a court sentenced him and his chief lieutenant, Jacob Milbourne, to be hanged "by the Neck and being Alive their bodyes be Cutt downe to Earth and Their Bowells to be taken out and they being Alive, burnt before their faces. . . ." In 1695, Parliament officially pardoned Leisler, but he not being "Alive," the decision arrived a bit late.

COMMON EXPERIENCES, SEPARATE CULTURES

"It is no little Blessing of God," Cotton Mather announced proudly in 1700, "that we are part of the *English* nation." A half century earlier, John Winthrop would not have spoken these words, at least not with such enthusiasm. The two men were, of course, products of different political cultures. It was not so much that the character of Massachusetts society had changed. In fact, the Puritan families of 1700 were much like those of the founding generation. Rather, the difference was in England's attitude toward the colonies. Rulers living more than three thousand miles away now made political and economic demands that Mather's contemporaries could not ignore.

The creation of a new imperial system did not, however, erase profound sectional differences. By 1700, for example, the Chesapeake colonies were more, not less, committed to the cultivation of tobacco and slave labor. Although the separate regions were being pulled slowly into England's commercial orbit, they did not have much to do with each other. The elements that sparked a powerful sense of nationalism among colonists dispersed over a huge territory would not be evident for a very long time. It would be a mistake, therefore, to anticipate the coming of the American Revolution.

4

FRONTIERS OF EMPIRE
Eighteenth-Century America

William Byrd II (1674–1744) was a type of British American one would not have encountered during the earliest years of settlement. This successful Tidewater planter was a product of a new, more cosmopolitan environment, and as an adult, Byrd seemed as much at home in London as in his native Virginia. In 1728, at the height of his political influence in Williamsburg, the capital of colonial Virginia, Byrd accepted a commission to help survey a disputed boundary between North Carolina and Virginia. During his long journey into the distant backcountry, Byrd kept a detailed journal, a satiric, often bawdy chronicle of daily events that is now regarded as a classic of early American literature.

On his trip into the wilderness, Byrd met many different people. No sooner had he departed a familiar world of tobacco plantations than he came across a self-styled "Hermit," an Englishman who apparently preferred the freedom of the woods to the constraints of society. "He has no other Habitation but a green Bower or Harbour," Byrd reported, "with a Female Domestick as wild & as dirty as himself."

As the boundary commissioners pushed farther into the backcountry, they encountered highly independent men and women of European descent, small frontier families that Byrd regarded as living no better than savages. He attributed their uncivilized behavior to a diet of too much pork. "The Truth of it is, these People live so much upon Swine's flesh . . . [that it] makes them . . . extremely hoggish in their Temper, & many of them seem to Grunt rather than Speak in their ordinary conversation." The wilderness journey also brought

Byrd's party of surveyors into regular contact with Native Americans, whom he properly distinguished as Catawbas, Tuscaroras, Usherees, and Sapponis.

Byrd's journal invites us to view the rapidly developing eighteenth-century backcountry from a fresh perspective. It was not a vast empty territory awaiting the arrival of European settlers. Maps often sustain this erroneous impression, depicting cities and towns, farms and plantations clustered along the Atlantic coast; they suggest a "line of settlement" steadily pushing outward into a huge blank area with no mark of civilization. The people Byrd met on his journey into the backcountry would not have understood such maps. After all, the empty space on the maps was their home. They experienced the frontier as a populous multicultural zone stretching from the English and French settlements in the north all the way to the Spanish borderlands in the far southwest.

The point is not to discount the significance of the older Atlantic settlements. During the eighteenth century, Britain's thirteen mainland colonies underwent a profound transformation. The population in the colonies grew at unprecedented rates. German and Scots-Irish immigrants arrived in huge numbers. So too did African slaves.

Wherever they lived, colonial Americans of this period were less isolated from one another than colonists had been during most of the seventeenth century. Indeed, after 1690, men and women expanded their cultural horizons, becoming part of a larger Anglo-American empire. The change was striking. Colonists whose parents or grandparents had come to the New World to confront a "howling wilderness" now purchased imported European manufactures, read English journals, participated in imperial wars, and sought favors from a growing number of resident royal officials. No one—not even the inhabitants of the distant frontiers—could escape the influence of Britain. The cultural, economic, and political links connecting the colonists to the imperial center in London grew stronger with time.

This surprising development raises a difficult question. If the eighteenth-century colonists were so powerfully attracted to Great Britain, then why did they ever declare independence? The answer may well be that as the colonists became *more* British, they inevitably became *more* American as well. This was a development of major significance, for it helps to explain the appearance after midcentury of genuine nationalist sentiment. Political, commercial, and military links that brought the colonists into more frequent contact with Great Britain also made them more aware of other colonists. It was within an expanding, prosperous empire that they first began seriously to consider what it meant to be American.

EXPERIENCING DIVERSITY

The phenomenal growth of British America during the eighteenth century amazed Benjamin Franklin, one of the first persons to bring scientific rigor to the study of demography. The population of the English colonies doubled approximately every twenty-five years, and, according to calculations Franklin made in 1751, if the expansion continued at such an extraordinary rate for another century or so, "the greatest Number of Englishmen will be on this Side [of] the water." Not only was the total population increasing at a very rapid rate; it also was becoming more dispersed and heterogeneous. Each year witnessed the arrival of thousands of non-English Europeans, most of whom soon moved to the backcountry of Pennsylvania and the Southern Colonies.

Accurate population data from the colonial period are extremely difficult to find. The first national census did not occur until 1790. Still, various sources surviving from prerevolutionary times indicate that the total white population of

As white settlement spread westward from the coastal zones, the forests and swamps of the interior presented major challenges. In this engraving from the mid-eighteenth century, note the vast clearing of trees whose stumps would either be pulled up or cultivated around. The water traffic represented the colonists' and Indians' best means of travel and communication.

Britain's thirteen mainland colonies rose from about 250,000 in 1700 to 2,150,000 in 1770, an annual growth rate of 3 percent.

Few societies in recorded history have expanded so rapidly. Natural reproduction was responsible for most of the growth. More families bore children who in turn lived long enough to have children of their own. Because of this sudden expansion, the population of the late colonial period was strikingly young; approximately one-half of the populace at any given time was under age 16.

CONVICTS FOR AMERICA

Since the story of European migration tends to be upbeat—men and women engaged in a largely successful quest for a better material life—it often is forgotten that British courts compelled many people to come to America. Indeed, the African slaves were not the only large group of people coerced into moving to the New World. In 1718, Parliament passed the Transportation Act, allowing judges in England, Scotland, and Ireland to send convicted felons to the American colonies. Between 1718 and 1775, the courts shipped approximately fifty thousand convicts across the Atlantic. Some of these men and women may actually have been dangerous criminals, but the majority seem to have committed minor crimes against property. Although transported convicts—almost 75 percent of whom were young males—escaped the hangman, they found life difficult in the

Elizabeth Canning, convicted of perjury, stands at the bar to receive her sentence from the London court. For her crime, she was sentenced to one month's imprisonment and transport for seven years to the American colonies.

colonies. Eighty percent of them were sold in the Chesapeake colonies as indentured servants. At best they faced an uncertain future, and it is probably not surprising that few former convicts prospered in America. The Revolution forced the British courts to redirect the flow of convicts to another part of the world; an indirect result of American independence was the founding of Australia by transported felons.

ETHNIC CULTURES OF THE BACKCOUNTRY

The eighteenth century also witnessed fresh waves of voluntary European migration. Unlike those seventeenth-century English settlers who had moved to the New World in search of religious sanctuary or to obtain instant wealth (see Chapter 2), the newcomers generally transferred in the hope of obtaining their own land and setting up as independent farmers. These people often traveled to the backcountry, a region stretching approximately eight hundred miles from western Pennsylvania to Georgia. Although they planned to follow customs they had known in Europe, they found the challenge of surviving on the British frontier far more demanding than they had anticipated.

SCOTS-IRISH FLEE ENGLISH OPPRESSION

Non-English colonists poured into American ports throughout the eighteenth century, creating rich ethnic diversity in areas originally settled by Anglo-Saxons. The largest group of newcomers consisted of Scots-Irish. The experiences of these people in Great Britain influenced not only their decision to move to the New World but also their behavior once they arrived.

During the seventeenth century, English rulers thought they could thoroughly dominate Catholic Ireland by transporting thousands of lowland Scottish Presbyterians to the northern region of that war-torn country. The plan failed. English officials who were members of the Anglican Church discriminated against the Presbyterians. They passed laws that placed the Scots-Irish at a severe disadvantage when they traded in England; they taxed them at exorbitant rates.

After several poor harvests, many of the Scots-Irish elected to emigrate to America, hoping to find the freedom and prosperity that had been denied them in Ireland. Often entire Presbyterian congregations followed charismatic ministers to the New World, intent on replicating a distinctive, fiercely independent culture on the frontier. It is estimated that 150,000 Scots-Irish migrated to the colonies before the Revolution.

Most Scots-Irish immigrants landed initially in Philadelphia, but instead of remaining in that city, they carved out farms on Pennsylvania's western frontier. The colony's proprietors welcomed the influx of new settlers, for it seemed they would form an ideal barrier between the Indians and the older, coastal communities. The Penn family soon had second thoughts, however. The Scots-Irish squatted on whatever land looked best, and when colony officials pointed out that large tracts had already been reserved, the immigrants retorted that "it was against the laws of God and nature that so much land should be idle when so many Christians wanted it to labour on and to raise their bread."

GERMANS SEARCHING FOR A BETTER LIFE

A second large body of non-English settlers, more than 100,000 people, came from the upper Rhine Valley, the German Palatinate. Some of the migrants, especially those who relocated to America around the turn of the century, belonged to small pietistic Protestant sects whose religious views were somewhat similar to those of the Quakers. These Germans moved to the New World primarily in the hope of finding religious toleration. Under the guidance of Francis Daniel Pastorius (1651–1720), a group of Mennonites established in Pennsylvania a prosperous community known as Germantown.

By midcentury, however, the characteristics of the German migration had begun to change. Large numbers of Lutherans transferred to the Middle Colonies. Unlike members of the pietistic sects, these men and women were not in search of religious freedom. Rather, they traveled to the New World looking to better their material lives. The Lutheran Church in Germany initially tried to maintain control over the distant congregations, but even though the migrants themselves fiercely preserved many aspects of traditional German culture, they were eventually forced to accommodate to new social conditions. Henry Melchior Mühlenberg (1711–1787), a tireless leader, helped German Lutherans through a difficult cultural adjustment, and in 1748, Mühlenberg organized a meeting of local pastors and lay delegates that ordained ministers of their own choosing, an act of spiritual independence that has been called "the most important single event in American Lutheran history."

The German migrants—mistakenly called Pennsylvania Dutch because the English confused *deutsch* (meaning "German") with *Dutch* ("a person from Holland")—began reaching Philadelphia in large numbers after 1717, and by 1766, persons of German stock accounted for more than one-third of Pennsylvania's total population. Even their most vocal detractors admitted the Germans were the best farmers in the colony.

Ethnic differences in Pennsylvania bred disputes. The Scots-Irish as well as the Germans preferred to live with people of their own background, and they sometimes fought to keep members of the other nationality out of their neighborhoods. The English were suspicious of both groups. They could not compre-

This folk art painting from the cover of a clothes box depicts a well-dressed German farmer. The stock around the farmer's neck, his coat, and walking stick indicate that he enjoyed a middling to high status.

hend why the Germans insisted on speaking German in America. In 1753, for example, Franklin warned that "unless the stream of [German] importation could be turned from this to other colonies . . . they will soon outnumber us, . . . [and] all the advantages we have, will in my opinion, be not able to preserve our language, and even our government will become precarious."

Such prejudice may have persuaded members of both groups to search for new homes. After 1730, Germans and Scots-Irish pushed south from western Pennsylvania into the Shenandoah Valley, thousands of them settling in the backcountry of Virginia and the Carolinas. The Germans usually remained wherever they found unclaimed fertile land. By contrast, the Scots-Irish often moved two or three times, acquiring a reputation as a rootless people.

Wherever the newcomers settled, they often found themselves living beyond the effective authority of the various colonial governments. To be sure, backcountry residents petitioned for assistance during wars against the Indians, but most of the time they preferred to be left alone. These conditions heightened the importance of religious institutions within the small ethnic communities. Although the original stimulus for coming to America may have been a desire for economic independence and prosperity, backcountry families—especially the Scots-Irish—flocked to evangelical Protestant preachers, to Presbyterian and later Baptist and Methodist ministers who not only fulfilled the settlers' spiritual needs but also gave the scattered backcountry communities a pronounced moral character that survived long after the colonial period.

NATIVE AMERICANS DEFINE THE MIDDLE GROUND

After initial contact with the first European invaders, the Indians seem mysteriously to disappear from the central narrative of colonization, and it is not until the nineteenth century that they turn up again, this time to wage a last desperate battle against the encroachment of white society. This obviously inadequate account slights one of the richer chapters of Native American history. To be sure, during much of the seventeenth century, various Indian groups who contested the English settlers for control of coastal lands suffered terribly, sometimes from war, but more often from the spread of contagious diseases such as smallpox. The two races found it very difficult to live in close proximity. As one Indian informed the members of the Maryland assembly in 1666, "Your hogs & Cattle injure Us, You come too near Us to live & drive Us from place to place. We can fly no farther; let us know where to live & how to be secured for the future from the Hogs & Cattle."

Against such odds the Indians managed to survive. By the eighteenth century, the site of the most intense and creative contact between the races had shifted to the cis-Mississippian west, that is, to the huge territory between the Appalachian Mountains and the Mississippi River, where several hundred thousand Native Americans made their homes.

Many Indians had only recently migrated to the area. The Delawares, for example, retreated to far western Pennsylvania and the Ohio Valley to escape almost continuous confrontation with advancing European invaders. Other Indians drifted west in less happy circumstances. They were refugees, the remnants of Native American groups who had lost so many people that they could no longer sustain an independent cultural identity. These survivors joined with other Indians to establish new multiethnic communities. In this respect, the Native American villages may not have seemed all that different from the mixed European settlements of the backcountry.

Stronger groups of Indians such as the Creeks, Choctaws, Chickasaws, Cherokees, and Shawnees generally welcomed the refugees. Strangers were formally adopted to take the places of family members killed in battle or overcome by sickness, and it should be appreciated that many seemingly traditional Indian

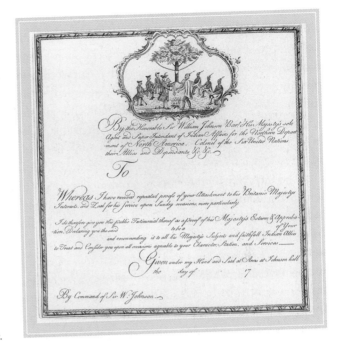

This certificate issued by William Johnson, superintendent of Indian affairs, signifies an alliance between the English settlers and the Native Americans in the "middle ground." Calumets (ceremonial pipes), wampum belts, and medals were other tokens used to mark alliances.

villages of the eighteenth century actually represented innovative responses to rapidly shifting external conditions.

The concept of a *middle ground*—a term that has recently entered the interpretive vocabulary—helps us more fully to comprehend how eighteenth-century Indians held their own in the backcountry beyond the Appalachian Mountains. The Native Americans never intended to isolate themselves completely from European contact. They relied on white traders, French as well as English, to provide essential metal goods and weapons. The goal of the Indian confederacies was rather to maintain a strong independent voice in these commercial exchanges, whenever possible playing the French off against the British, and so long as they had sufficient military strength—that is, large numbers of healthy armed warriors—they compelled everyone who came to negotiate in the "middle ground" to give them proper respect. It would be incorrect, therefore, to characterize their relations with the Europeans as a stark choice between resistance or accommodation, between total war or abject surrender. Native Americans took advantage of rivals when possible; they compromised when necessary. It is best to imagine the Indians' middle ground as an open, dynamic process of creative interaction.

However calculating the Indians may have been, European goods subtly eroded traditional structures of Native American authority. During the period of earliest encounter with white men, Indian leaders reinforced their own power by controlling the character and flow of commercial exchange. If a trader wanted a rich supply of animal skins, for example, he soon learned that he had better negotiate directly with a chief or tribal elder. But as the number of European traders operating within the "middle ground" expanded, ordinary Indians began to bargain on their own account, obtaining colorful and durable manufactured items without first consulting a Native American leader. Independent commercial dealings of this sort tended further to weaken the Indians' ability to resist organized white aggression.

The survival of the middle ground depended ultimately on factors over which the Native Americans had little control. Imperial competition between France and Great Britain enhanced the Indians' bargaining position, but after the British defeated the French in 1763, the Indians no longer received the same solicitous attention as they had in earlier times. Keeping old allies happy seemed to the British a needless expense. Moreover, contagious disease continued to take a fearful toll. In the southern backcountry between 1685 and 1790, the Indian population dropped an astounding 72 percent. By the time the United States took control of this region, the middle ground itself had become a casualty of history.

SPANISH BORDERLANDS
OF THE EIGHTEENTH CENTURY

In many traditional histories of North America, the Spanish make only a brief appearance, usually as fifteenth-century conquistadors. But as soon as they have conquered Mexico, they are dropped from the story as if they had no serious part to play in the ongoing development of the continent. This is, of course, a skewed perspective that masks the roots of ethnic diversity in the United States. The Spanish empire did not disappear. Indeed, it continued to shape the character of borderlands societies well into the eighteenth century. As anyone who visits the modern American Southwest quickly discovers, Spanish administrators and priests—not to mention ordinary settlers—left a lasting imprint on the cultural landscape of this country.

Until 1821, when Mexico declared independence from Madrid, Spanish authorities struggled to control a vast northern frontier. During the eighteenth century, the Spanish empire in North America included widely dispersed settlements such as San Francisco, San Diego, Santa Fe, San Antonio, and St. Augustine. In these borderland communities, European colonists mixed with peoples of other races and backgrounds, forming multicultural societies.

CONQUERING THE NORTHERN FRONTIER

Not until late in the sixteenth century did Spanish settlers, led by Juan de Oñate, establish European communities north of the Rio Grande. The Pueblos resisted the invasion of colonists, soldiers, and missionaries, and in a major rebellion in 1680 led by El Popé, the native peoples drove the whites completely out of New Mexico. "The heathen have conceived a mortal hatred for our holy faith and enmity for the Spanish nation," concluded one imperial bureaucrat. Not until 1692 were the Spanish able to reconquer this fiercely contested area. By then, Native American hostility coupled with the settlers' failure to find precious metal had cooled Spain's enthusiasm for the northern frontier.

Concern over French encroachment in the Southeast led Spain to colonize St. Augustine (Florida) in 1565. Although the enterprise never flourished, it claims attention as the first permanent European settlement established in what would become the United States, predating the founding of Jamestown and Plymouth by several decades. Pedro Menéndez de Avilés brought some fifteen hundred soldiers and settlers to St. Augustine, where they constructed an impressive fort, but the colony failed to attract additional Spanish migrants.

California never figured prominently in Spain's plans for the New World. Early explorers reported finding only impoverished Indians living along the

Baroque-style eighteenth-century Spanish mission at San Xavier del Bac in present-day Arizona. Spanish missions dotted the frontier of northern New Spain from Florida to California.

Pacific coast. Adventurers saw no natural resources worth mentioning, and since the area proved extremely difficult to reach from Mexico City—the overland trip could take months—California received little attention. Fear that the Russians might seize the entire region belatedly sparked Spanish activity, however, and after 1769, two indomitable servants of empire, Fra Junípero Serra and Don Gaspar de Portolá, organized permanent missions and *presidios* (forts) at San Diego, Monterey, San Francisco, and Santa Barbara.

PEOPLES OF THE SPANISH BORDERLANDS

In sharp contrast to the English frontier settlements of the eighteenth century, the Spanish outposts in North America grew very slowly. A few Catholic priests and imperial administrators traveled to the northern provinces, but the danger of Indian attack as well as a harsh physical environment discouraged ordinary colonists. The European migrants were overwhelmingly male, most of them soldiers in the pay of the empire. Although some colonists came directly from Spain, most had been born in other Spanish colonies such as Minorca, the Canaries, or New Spain, and because European women rarely appeared on the frontier, Spanish males formed relationships with Indian women, fathering large numbers of mestizos, children of mixed race.

The Spanish exploited Native American labor, reducing entire Indian villages to servitude. Many Indians moved to the Spanish towns, and although they lived in close proximity to the Europeans—something rare in British America—they were consigned to the lowest social class, objects of European contempt. However much their material conditions changed, the Indians of the Southwest resisted strenuous efforts to convert them to Catholicism. The Pueblos maintained their own religious forms—often at great personal risk—and they sometimes murdered priests who became too intrusive.

The Spanish empire never had the resources necessary to secure the northern frontier fully. The small military posts were intended primarily to discourage other European powers such as France, Great Britain, and Russia from taking possession of territory claimed by Spain. It would be misleading, however, to stress the fragility of Spanish colonization. The urban design and public architecture of many southwestern cities still reflect the vision of the early Spanish settlers, and to a large extent, the old borderlands remain Spanish speaking to this day.

BRITISH COLONIES IN AN ATLANTIC WORLD

The character of the older, more established British colonies changed almost as rapidly as that of the backcountry. The rapid growth of an urban cosmopolitan culture impressed eighteenth-century commentators, and even though most

Americans still lived on scattered farms, they had begun to participate aggressively in an exciting consumer marketplace that expanded their imaginative horizons.

PROVINCIAL CITIES

Considering the rate of population growth, it is surprising to discover how few eighteenth-century Americans lived in cities. Boston, Newport, New York, Philadelphia, and Charles Town—the five largest cities—contained only about 5 percent of the colonial population. In 1775, none had more than forty thousand persons. The explanation for the relatively slow development of colonial American cities lies in their highly specialized commercial character. Colonial port towns served as entrepôts, intermediary trade and shipping centers where bulk cargoes were broken up for inland distribution and where agricultural products were gathered for export. They did not support large-scale manufacturing. Indeed, the pool of free urban laborers was quite small, since the type of person who was forced to work for wages in Europe usually became a farmer in America.

Yet despite the limited urban population, cities profoundly influenced colonial culture. It was in the cities that Americans were exposed to and welcomed the latest English ideas. Wealthy colonists—merchants and lawyers—tried to emulate the culture of the mother country. They sponsored concerts and plays; they learned to dance. Women as well as men picked up the new fashions quickly, and even though most of them had never been outside the colony of their birth, they sometimes appeared to be the products of London's best families.

It was in the cities, also, that wealthy merchants transformed commercial profits into architectural splendor, for, in their desire to outdo one another, they built grand homes of enduring beauty. Most of these buildings are described as Georgian because they were constructed during the reign of Britain's early Hanoverian kings, who all happened to be named George. Actually these homes were provincial copies of grand country houses of Great Britain. They drew their inspiration from the great Italian Renaissance architect Andrea Palladio (1508–1580), who had incorporated classical themes into a rigidly symmetrical form. Their owners filled the houses with fine furniture. Each city patronized certain skilled craftsmen, but the artisans of Philadelphia were known for producing magnificent copies of the works of Thomas Chippendale, Great Britain's most famous furniture designer.

AMERICAN ENLIGHTENMENT

European historians often refer to the eighteenth century as an Age of Reason. During this period, a body of new, often radical, ideas swept through the salons and universities, altering the way that educated Europeans thought about God, nature, and society. This intellectual revolution, called the Enlightenment, involved the work of Europe's greatest minds, men such as Newton and Locke, Voltaire and Hume. The writings of these thinkers eventually reached the colonies, where they received a mixed reception. On the whole, the American Enlightenment was a rather tame affair compared to its French counterpart, for while the colonists welcomed experimental science, they defended the tenets of traditional Christianity.

Philosophers of the Enlightenment replaced the concept of original sin with a much more optimistic view of human nature. A benevolent God, having set the universe in motion, gave human beings the power of reason to enable them to comprehend the orderly workings of his creation. Everything, even human society, operated according to these mechanical rules. The responsibility of right-thinking men and women, therefore, was to make certain that institutions such as church and state conformed to self-evident natural laws. It was possible—or so some of the *philosophes* claimed—to achieve perfection in this world. In fact, human suffering had come about only because people had lost touch with the fundamental insights of reason.

For many Americans, the appeal of the Enlightenment was its search for useful knowledge, ideas, and inventions that would improve the quality of human life. What mattered was practical experimentation. A speech delivered in 1767 before the members of the American Society in Philadelphia reflected the new utilitarian spirit: "Knowledge is of little Use when confined to mere Speculation," the colonist explained, "But when speculative Truths are reduced to Practice, when Theories grounded upon Experiments . . . and the Arts of Living made more easy and comfortable . . . Knowledge then becomes really useful." The Enlightenment spawned scores of earnest scientific tinkerers, people who dutifully recorded changes in temperature, the appearance of strange plants and animals, and the details of astronomic phenomena.

BENJAMIN FRANKLIN

Benjamin Franklin (1706–1790) absorbed the new cosmopolitan culture. European thinkers regarded him as a genuine *philosophe,* a person of reason and science, a role that he self-consciously cultivated when he visited England and France in later life. Franklin had little formal education, but as a young man working in his brother's print shop, he managed to keep up with the latest intellectual currents. In his *Autobiography,* Franklin described the excitement of discovering a new British journal. "I met with an odd volume of *The Spectator,*" Franklin recounted; ". . . I had never before seen any of them. I bought it, read it over and over, and was much delighted with it. I thought the writing excellent, and wished if possible to imitate it."

Benjamin Franklin (left) exemplified the scientific curiosity and search for practical knowledge characteristic of enlightenment thinkers of the eighteenth century. Franklin's experiments on electricity became world famous and inspired many others to study the effects of the strange force. The ordinary citizens pictured at right, eager to try out a new phenomenon, are rubbing metal rods together to produce static electricity.

Franklin's opportunity came in August 1721 when he and his brother founded the *New England Courant*, a weekly newspaper that satirized Boston's leaders in the manner of the contemporary British press. Writing under the name Silence Dogood, young Franklin asked "Whether a Commonwealth suffers more by hypocritical Pretenders to Religion, or by the openly Profane?" Proper Bostonians were not prepared for a journal that one minister described as "full freighted with Nonesense." Franklin got the point; he left Massachusetts in 1723 in search of a less hostile intellectual environment.

After he had moved to Philadelphia, leaving behind an irritable brother as well as New England Puritanism, Franklin devoted himself to the pursuit of useful knowledge, ideas that would increase the happiness of his fellow Americans. Franklin never denied the existence of God. Rather, he pushed the Lord aside, making room for the free exercise of human reason. Franklin tinkered, experimented, and reformed. Almost everything he encountered in his daily life aroused his curiosity. His investigation of electricity brought him world fame, but Franklin was never satisfied with his work in this field until it yielded practical application. In 1756, he invented the lightning rod. He also designed a marvelously efficient stove that is still used today.

TRANSFORMING THE PROVINCIAL ECONOMY

The colonial economy kept pace with the stunning growth in population. Even with so many additional people to feed and clothe, the per capita income did not decline. Indeed, with the exception of poor urban dwellers, such as sailors whose employment varied with the season, white Americans did quite well. An abundance of land and the extensive growth of agriculture accounted for their economic success. New farmers were able not only to provide for their families' well-being but also to sell their crops in European and West Indian markets. Each year, more Americans produced more tobacco, wheat, or rice—to cite just the major export staples—and by this means, they maintained a high level of individual prosperity without developing an industrial base.

At midcentury, colonial exports flowed along well-established routes. More than half of American goods produced for export went to Great Britain. The Navigation Acts (see Chapter 3) were still in effect, and "enumerated" items such as tobacco had to be landed first at a British port. The Molasses Act of 1733—also called the Sugar Act—placed a heavy duty on molasses imported from foreign ports; the Hat and Felt Act of 1732 and the Iron Act of 1750 attempted to limit the production of colonial goods that competed with British exports.

These statutes might have created tensions between the colonists and the mother country had they been rigorously enforced. Crown officials, however, generally ignored the new laws. New England merchants imported molasses from French Caribbean islands without paying the full customs; ironmasters in the Middle Colonies continued to produce iron. Even without the Navigation Acts, however, a majority of colonial exports would have been sold on the English market. The emerging consumer society in Great Britain was beginning to create a new generation of buyers who possessed enough income to purchase American goods, especially sugar and tobacco. This rising demand was the major market force shaping the colonial economy.

Colonial merchants operating out of Boston, Newport, and Philadelphia also carried substantial tonnage to the West Indies. In 1768, this market accounted for 27 percent of all American exports. Colonial ships carrying food sailed for the Caribbean and returned immediately to the Middle Colonies or New England with cargoes of molasses, sugar, and rum. The West Indies helped preserve American credit in Europe. Without this source of income, colonists would not have been able to pay for the manufactured items they purchased in the mother country.

BIRTH OF A CONSUMER SOCIETY

The balance of trade was always a problem. After midcentury, it turned dramatically against the colonists. The reasons for this change were complex, but, in simplest terms, Americans began buying more English goods than their parents or grandparents had done. Between 1740 and 1770, English exports to the American colonies increased by an astounding 360 percent.

In part, this shift reflected a fundamental transformation in the British economy. Although the Industrial Revolution was still far in the future, the pace of the British economy picked up dramatically after 1690. Small factories produced certain goods more efficiently and more cheaply than the colonists could. The availability of these products altered the lives of most Americans, even those with modest incomes. Staffordshire china replaced crude earthenware; imported cloth replaced homespun. In this manner, British industrialization undercut American handicraft and folk art.

To help Americans purchase manufactured goods, British merchants offered generous credit. Colonists deferred settlement by agreeing to pay interest on their debts. The temptation to acquire English finery blinded many people to hard economic realities. They gambled on the future, hoping bumper farm crops would reduce their dependence on the large merchant houses of London and Glasgow. Some persons lived within their means, but the aggregate American debt continued to grow. Colonial leaders tried various expedients to remain solvent—issuing paper money, for example—and while these efforts delayed a crisis, the balance-of-payments problem remained a major structural weakness.

The eighteenth century also saw a substantial increase in intercoastal trade. Southern planters sent tobacco and rice to New England and the Middle Colonies, where these staples were exchanged for meat and wheat as well as goods imported from Great Britain. By 1760, approximately 30 percent of the colonists' total tonnage capacity was involved in this extensive "coastwise" commerce. In addition, backcountry farmers in western Pennsylvania and the Shenandoah Valley carried their grain to market along an old Iroquois trail that became known as the Great Wagon Road, a rough, hilly highway that by the time of the Revolution stretched 735 miles along the Blue Ridge Mountains to Camden, South Carolina. Most of their produce was carried in long, gracefully designed Conestoga wagons. These vehicles—sometimes called the "wagons of empire"—had been invented by German immigrants living in the Conestoga River Valley in Lancaster County, Pennsylvania.

The shifting patterns of trade had immense effects on the development of an American culture. First, the flood of British imports eroded local and regional identities. Commerce helped to "Anglicize" American culture by exposing colonial consumers to a common range of British manufactured goods. Deep sectional differences remained, of course, but Americans from New Hampshire to Georgia were increasingly drawn into a sophisticated economic network centered in London. Second, the expanding coastal and overland trade brought colonists of different backgrounds into more frequent contact. Ships that sailed between New England and South Carolina, and between Virginia and Pennsylvania, provided Americans with a means to exchange ideas and experiences on a more regular basis. Mid-eighteenth-century printers, for example, established several dozen new journals; these were weekly newspapers that carried information not only about the mother country and world commerce but also about events in other colonies.

RELIGIOUS REVIVALS IN PROVINCIAL SOCIETIES

A sudden, spontaneous series of Protestant revivals known as the Great Awakening had a profound impact on the lives of ordinary people; indeed, far greater than anything associated with the Enlightenment. This unprecedented evangelical outpouring altered the course of American history. And the new, highly personal appeal to a "new birth" in Christ caused men and women of all backgrounds to rethink basic assumptions about church and state, institutions and society.

THE GREAT AWAKENING

Only with hindsight does the Great Awakening seem a unified religious movement. Revivals occurred in different places at different times; the intensity of the events varied from region to region. The first signs of a spiritual awakening appeared in New England during the 1730s, but within a decade the revivals in this area had burned themselves out. It was not until the 1750s and 1760s that the Awakening made more than a superficial impact on the people of Virginia. The revivals were most important in Massachusetts, Connecticut, Rhode Island, Pennsylvania, New Jersey, and Virginia. Their effect on religion in New York, Delaware, and the Carolinas was marginal. No single religious denomination or sect monopolized the Awakening. In New England, revivals shattered Congregational churches, and in the South, especially in Virginia, they had an impact on Presbyterians, Methodists, and Baptists. Moreover, there was nothing peculiarly American about the Great Awakening. Mid-eighteenth-century Europe experienced a similar burst of religious emotionalism.

Whatever their origins, the seeds of revival were sown on fertile ground. In the early decades of the century, many Americans—but especially New Englanders—complained that organized religion had lost vitality. They looked back at Winthrop's generation with nostalgia, assuming that common people at that time must have possessed greater piety than did later, more worldly colonists. Congregational ministers seemed obsessed with dull, scholastic matters; they no longer touched the heart. And in the Southern Colonies, there were simply not enough ordained ministers to tend to the religious needs of the population.

The Great Awakening arrived unexpectedly in Northampton, a small farm community in western Massachusetts, sparked by Jonathan Edwards, the local Congregational minister. Edwards accepted the traditional teachings of Calvinism (see Chapter 1), reminding his parishioners that their eternal fate had been determined by an omnipotent God, there was nothing they could do to save themselves, and they were totally dependent on the Lord's will. He thought his fellow ministers had grown soft. They left men and women with the mistaken impression that sinners might somehow avoid eternal damnation simply by performing good works.

Why this uncompromising message set off several religious revivals during the mid-1730s is not known. Whatever the explanation for the popular response to Edwards's preaching, young people began flocking to the church. They experienced a searing conversion, a sense of "new birth" and utter dependence on God. "Surely," Edwards pronounced, "this is the Lord's doing, and it is marvelous in our eyes." The excitement spread, and evangelical ministers concluded that God must be preparing Americans, his chosen people, for the millennium. "What is now seen in America and especially in New England," Edwards explained, "may prove the dawn of that glorious day."

VOICE OF POPULAR RELIGION

Edwards did not possess the dynamic personality required to sustain the revival. That responsibility fell to George Whitefield, a young, inspiring preacher from England who toured the colonies from New Hampshire to Georgia. While Whitefield was not an original thinker, he was an extraordinarily effective public speaker. And like his friend Benjamin Franklin, he came to symbolize the powerful cultural forces that were transforming the Atlantic world. According to Edwards's wife, Sarah, it was wonderful to witness what a spell Whitefield "casts over an audience . . . I have seen upwards of a thousand people hang on his words with breathless silence, broken only by an occasional half-suppressed sob."

Whitefield's audiences came from all groups of American society: rich and poor, young and old, rural and urban. While Whitefield described himself as a Calvinist, he welcomed all Protestants. He spoke from any pulpit that was available. "Don't tell me you are a Baptist, an Independent, a Presbyterian, a dissenter," he thundered, "tell me you are a Christian, that is all I want."

Whitefield was a brilliant entrepreneur. Like Franklin, with whom he published many popular volumes, the itinerant minister possessed an almost intuitive

The fervor of the Great Awakening was intensified by the eloquence of itinerant preachers such as the Reverend George Whitefield, the most popular evangelical of the mid-eighteenth century.

sense of how this burgeoning consumer society could be turned to his own advantage, and he embraced the latest merchandising techniques. He appreciated, for example, the power of the press in selling the revival, and he regularly promoted his own work in advertisements placed in British and American newspapers. The crowds flocked to hear Whitefield, while his critics grumbled about the commercialization of religion. One anonymous writer in Massachusetts noted that there was "a very wholesome law of the province to discourage Pedlars in Trade" and it seemed high time "to enact something for the discouragement of Pedlars in Divinity also."

Other, American-born itinerant preachers followed Whitefield's example. The most famous was Gilbert Tennent, a Presbyterian of Scots-Irish background who had been educated in the Middle Colonies. His sermon "On the Danger of an Unconverted Ministry," printed in 1741, set off a storm of protest from established ministers who were understandably insulted. Lesser known revivalists traveled from town to town, colony to colony, challenging local clergymen who seemed hostile to evangelical religion. Men and women who thronged to hear the itinerants were called "New Lights," and during the 1740s and 1750s, many congregations split between defenders of the new emotional preaching and those who regarded the entire movement as dangerous nonsense.

While Tennent did not condone the excesses of the Great Awakening, his attacks on formal learning invited the crude anti-intellectualism of such fanatics as

James Davenport. This deranged revivalist traveled along the Connecticut coast in 1742 playing upon popular emotion. At night, under the light of smoky torches, he danced and stripped, shrieked and laughed. He also urged people to burn books written by authors who had not experienced the New Light as defined by Davenport. Like so many fanatics throughout history who have claimed a special knowledge of the "truth," Davenport later recanted and begged pardon for his disruptive behavior.

To concentrate on the bizarre activities of Davenport—as many critics of the Great Awakening have done—is to obscure the positive ways in which this vast revival changed American society. First, despite occasional anti-intellectual outbursts, the New Lights founded several important centers of higher learning. They wanted to train young men who would carry on the good works of Edwards, Whitefield, and Tennent. In 1746, New Light Presbyterians established the College of New Jersey, which later became Princeton University. Just before his death, Edwards was appointed its president. The evangelical minister Eleazar Wheelock launched Dartmouth (1769); other revivalists founded Brown (1764) and Rutgers (1766).

The Great Awakening also encouraged men and women who had been taught to remain silent before traditional figures of authority to speak up, to take an active role in their salvation. They could no longer rely on ministers or institutions. The individual alone stood before God. Knowing this, New Lights made religious choices that shattered the old harmony among Protestant sects, and in its place, they introduced a noisy, often bitterly fought competition. As one New Jersey Presbyterian explained, "There are so many particular *sects* and *Parties* among professed Christians . . . that we know not . . . in which of these different *paths,* to steer our course for *Heaven.*"

Expressive evangelicalism struck a particularly responsive chord among African Americans. Itinerant ministers frequently preached to large sympathetic audiences of slaves. Richard Allen (1760–1831), founder of the African Methodist Episcopal Church, reported he owed his freedom in part to a traveling Methodist minister who persuaded Allen's master of the sinfulness of slavery. Allen himself was converted, as were thousands of other black colonists. According to one historian, evangelical preaching "shared enough with traditional African styles and beliefs such as spirit possession and ecstatic expression . . . to allow for an interpenetration of African and Christian religious beliefs."

With religious contention came an awareness of a larger community, a union of fellow believers that extended beyond the boundaries of town and colony. In fact, evangelical religion was one of several forces at work during the mid-eighteenth century that brought scattered colonists into contact with one another for the first time. In this sense, the Great Awakening was a "national" event long before a nation actually existed.

People who had been touched by the Great Awakening shared an optimism about the future of America. With God's help, social and political progress was possible, and from this perspective, of course, the New Lights did not sound much different than the mildly rationalist American spokesmen of the Enlightenment. Both groups prepared the way for the development of a revolutionary mentality in colonial America.

CLASH OF POLITICAL CULTURES

The political history of this period illuminates a growing tension within the empire. Americans of all regions repeatedly stated their desire to replicate British political institutions. Parliament, they claimed, provided a model for the American assemblies. They revered the English constitution. However, the more the colonists studied British political theory and practice—in other words, the more they attempted to become British—the more aware they became of major differences. By trying to copy Great Britain, they unwittingly discovered something about being American.

THE ENGLISH CONSTITUTION

During the eighteenth century, political discussion began with the British constitution. It was the object of universal admiration. Unlike the U.S. Constitution of 1788, the British constitution was not a formal written document. It was something much more elusive. The English constitution found expression in a growing body of law, court decisions, and statutes, a sense of traditional political arrangements that people of all classes believed had evolved from the past, preserving life, liberty, and property. Eighteenth-century political commentators reluctantly admitted that the constitution had in fact changed. Historic confrontations between king and Parliament had generated new understandings about what the constitution did or did not allow. Nevertheless, almost everyone regarded change as dangerous and destabilizing, a threat to the political tradition that seemed to explain Britain's greatness.

In theory, the English constitution contained three distinct parts. The monarch was at the top, advised by handpicked court favorites. Next came the House of Lords, a body of 180 aristocrats who served with 26 Anglican bishops as the upper house of Parliament. And third was the House of Commons, composed of 558 members elected by various constituencies scattered throughout the realm.

Political theorists waxed eloquent on workings of the British constitution. Each of the three parts of government, it seemed, represented a separate socio-economic interest: king, nobility, and common people. Acting alone, each body would run to excess, even tyranny, but operating within a mixed system, they automatically checked each other's ambitions for the common good.

THE REALITY OF BRITISH POLITICS

The reality of daily political life in Great Britain, however, bore little relation to theory. The three elements of the constitution did not, in fact, represent distinct socioeconomic groups. Men elected to the House of Commons often came from the same social background as those who served in the House of Lords. All represented the interests of Britain's landed elite. Moreover, there was no attempt to maintain strict constitutional separation. The king, for example, organized parliamentary associations, loose groups of political followers who sat in the House of Commons and who openly supported the monarch's policies in exchange for patronage or pension.

The claim that the members of the House of Commons represented all the people of England also seemed far-fetched. As of 1715, no more than 20 percent of Britain's adult males had the right to vote. Property qualifications or other restrictions often greatly reduced the number of eligible voters. In addition, the size of the electoral districts varied throughout the kingdom. In some boroughs, representatives to Parliament were chosen by several thousand voters. In many districts, however, a handful of electors controlled the result. These tiny, or "rotten," boroughs were an embarrassment. Since these districts were so small, a wealthy lord or ambitious politician could easily bribe or otherwise "influence" the entire constituency, something done regularly throughout the century.

Before 1760, few people spoke out against these constitutional abuses. The main exception was a group of radical publicists whom historians have labeled the Commonwealthmen. These writers decried the corruption of political life, noting that a nation that compromised civic virtue, that failed to stand vigilant against fawning courtiers and would-be despots, deserved to lose its liberty and property. The most famous Commonwealthmen were John Trenchard and Thomas Gordon, who penned a series of essays titled *Cato's Letters* between 1720 and 1723. If England's rulers were corrupt, they warned, then the people could not expect the balanced constitution to save them from tyranny.

But however shrilly these writers protested, they won little support for political reforms. Most eighteenth-century Englishmen admitted there was more than a grain of truth in the commonwealth critique, but they were not willing to tamper with a system of government that had so recently survived a civil war and a Glorious Revolution. Americans, however, took Trenchard and Gordon to heart.

GOVERNING THE COLONIES:
THE AMERICAN EXPERIENCE

The colonists assumed—perhaps naively—that their own governments were modeled on the balanced constitution of Great Britain. They argued that within their political systems, the governor corresponded to the king and the governor's council to the House of Lords. The colonial assemblies were perceived as American reproductions of the House of Commons and were expected to preserve the interests of the people against those of the monarch and aristocracy. As the colonists discovered, however, general theories about a mixed constitution were even less relevant in America than they were in Britain.

By midcentury a majority of the mainland colonies had royal governors appointed by the crown. Many were career army officers who through luck, charm, or family connection had gained the ear of someone close to the king. These patronage posts did not generate income sufficient to interest the most powerful or talented personalities of the period, but they did draw middle-level bureaucrats who were ambitious, desperate, or both. It is perhaps not surprising that most governors decided simply not to "consider any Thing further than how to sit easy."

Whatever their demerits, royal governors in America possessed enormous powers. In fact, royal governors could do certain things in America that a king could not do in eighteenth-century Britain. Among these were the right to veto legislation and dismiss judges. The governors also served as military commanders in each province.

Political practice in America differed from the British model in another crucial respect. Royal governors were advised by a council, usually a body of about twelve wealthy colonists selected by the Board of Trade in London upon the recommendation of the governor. During the seventeenth century, the council had played an important role in colonial government, but its ability to exercise independent authority declined steadily over the course of the eighteenth century. Its members certainly did not represent a distinct aristocracy within American society.

If royal governors did not look like kings, nor American councils like the House of Lords, colonial assemblies bore little resemblance to the eighteenth-century House of Commons. The major difference was the size of the American franchise. In most colonies, adult white males who owned a small amount of land could vote in colonywide elections. One historian estimates that 95 percent of this group in Massachusetts were eligible to participate in elections. The number in Virginia was about 85 percent. These figures—much higher than those in contemporary England—have led some scholars to view the colonies as "middle-class democracies," societies run by moderately prosperous yeomen farmers who—in politics at least—exercised independent judgment. There were too many of them to bribe, no "rotten" boroughs, and when these people moved west, colonial assemblies usually created new electoral districts.

Colonial governments were not democracies in the modern sense of that term. Possessing the right to vote was one thing, exercising it quite another. Americans participated in elections when major issues were at stake—the formation of banks in mid-eighteenth-century Massachusetts, for example—but most of the time they were content to let members of the rural and urban gentry represent them in the assemblies. To be sure, unlike modern democracies, these colonial politics excluded women and nonwhites from voting. The point to remember, however, is that the power to expel legislative rascals was always present in America, and it was this political reality that kept autocratic gentlemen from straying too far from the will of the people.

COLONIAL ASSEMBLIES

Elected members of the colonial assemblies believed that they had a special obligation to preserve colonial liberties. They perceived any attack on the legislature as an assault on the rights of Americans. The elected representatives brooked no criticism, and several colonial printers landed in jail because they criticized actions taken by a lower house.

So aggressive were these bodies in seizing privileges, determining procedures, and controlling money bills that some historians have described the political development of eighteenth-century America as "the rise of the assemblies." No doubt this is exaggerated, but the long series of imperial wars against the French, demanding large public expenditures, transformed the small, amateurish assemblies of the seventeenth century into the more professional, vigilant legislatures of the eighteenth.

This political system seemed designed to generate controversy. There was simply no reason for the colonial legislators to cooperate with appointed royal governors. Alexander Spotswood, Virginia's governor from 1710 to 1722, for example, attempted to institute a bold new land program backed by the crown. He tried persuasion and gifts and, when these failed, chicanery. But the members of the House of Burgesses refused to support a plan that did not suit their own interests. Before leaving office, Spotswood gave up trying to carry out royal policy in America. Instead, he allied himself with the local Virginia gentry who controlled the House as well as the Council, and because they awarded their new friend with large tracts of land, he became a wealthy man.

A major source of shared political information was the weekly journal, a new and vigorous institution in American life. In New York and Massachusetts especially, weekly newspapers urged readers to preserve civic virtue, to exercise extreme vigilance against the spread of privileged power. In the first issue of the *Independent Reflector,* published in New York (November 30, 1752), the editor announced defiantly that no discouragement shall "deter me from vindicating the *civil and religious RIGHTS* of my Fellow-Creatures: From exposing the peculiar Deformity of publick *Vice,* and *Corruption;* and displaying the amiable Charms of Liberty, with the detestable Nature of *Slavery* and *Oppression.*" Through such journals, a pattern of political rhetoric that in Britain had gained only marginal respectability became after 1765 America's normal form of political discourse.

The rise of the assemblies shaped American culture in other, subtler ways. Over the course of the century, the language of the law became increasingly Anglicized. The Board of Trade, the Privy Council, and Parliament scrutinized court decisions and legislative actions from all thirteen mainland colonies. As a result, varying local legal practices that had been widespread during the seventeenth century became standardized. Indeed, according to one historian, the colonial legal system by 1750 "was substantially that of the mother country." Not surprisingly, many men who served in colonial assemblies were either lawyers or persons who had received legal training. When Americans from different regions met—as they frequently did in the years before the Revolution—they discovered that they shared a commitment to the preservation of the English common law.

As eighteenth-century political developments drew the colonists closer to the mother country, they also brought Americans a greater awareness of each other. As their horizons widened, they learned they operated within the same general imperial system, and the problems confronting the Massachusetts House of Representatives were not too different from those facing Virginia's House of Burgesses or South Carolina's Commons House. Like the revivalists and merchants—people who crossed old boundaries—colonial legislators laid the foundation for a larger cultural identity.

CENTURY OF IMPERIAL WAR

The scope and character of warfare in the colonies changed radically during the eighteenth century. The founders of England's mainland colonies had engaged in

North America, 1750

By 1750, the French had established a chain of settlements southward through the heart of the continent from Quebec to New Orleans. The English saw this development as a threat to their own seaboard colonies, which were expanding westward.

intense local conflicts with the Indians, such as King Philip's War (1675–1676) in New England. But after 1690, the colonists were increasingly involved in hostilities that originated on the other side of the Atlantic, in rivalries between Great Britain and France over political and commercial ambitions. The external threat to security forced people in different colonies to devise unprecedented measures of military and political cooperation.

On paper, at least, the British colonies enjoyed military superiority over the settlements of New France. Louis XIV (r. 1643–1715) possessed an impressive army of 100,000 well-armed troops, but he dispatched few of them to the New

World. He left the defense of Canada and the Mississippi Valley to the companies engaged in the fur trade. Meeting this challenge seemed almost impossible for the French outposts strung out along the St. Lawrence River and the Great Lakes. In 1754, New France contained only 75,000 inhabitants as compared to 1.2 million people living in Britain's mainland colonies.

For most of the century, the theoretical advantages enjoyed by the English colonists did them little good. While the British settlements possessed a larger and more prosperous population, they were divided into separate governments that sometimes seemed more suspicious of each other than of the French. When war came, French officers and Indian allies exploited these jealousies with considerable skill. Moreover, although the population of New France was comparatively small, it was concentrated along the St. Lawrence, so that while the French found it difficult to mount effective offensive operations against the English, they could easily mass the forces needed to defend Montreal and Quebec.

KING WILLIAM'S AND QUEEN ANNE'S WARS

Colonial involvement in imperial war began in 1689, when England's new king, William III, declared war on Louis XIV. Europeans called this struggle the War of the League of Augsburg, but to the Americans, it was simply King William's War. Canadians commanded by the Comte de Frontenac raided the northern frontiers of New York and New England, and while they made no territorial gains, they caused considerable suffering among the civilian populations of Massachusetts and New York.

The war ended with the Treaty of Ryswick (1697), but the colonists were drawn almost immediately into a new conflict. Queen Anne's War, known in Europe as the War of the Spanish Succession (1702–1713), was fought across a large geographic area. The bloody combat along the American frontier ended in 1713 when Great Britain and France signed the Treaty of Utrecht. European negotiators showed little interest in the military situation in the New World. Their major concern was preserving a balance of power among the European states. More than two decades of intense fighting had taken a heavy toll in North America, but neither French nor English colonists had much to show for their sacrifice.

Both sides viewed this great contest over control of the West in conspiratorial terms. From South Carolina to Massachusetts Bay, colonists believed the French planned to "encircle" the English settlements, to confine the English to a narrow strip of land along the Atlantic coast. The English noted that in 1682, La Salle had claimed for the king of France a territory—Louisiana—that included all the people and resources located on "streams and Rivers" flowing into the Mississippi

River. To make good on their claim, the French constructed forts on the Chicago and Illinois rivers. In 1717, they established a military post two hundred miles up the Alabama River, well within striking distance of the Carolina frontier, and in 1718, they settled New Orleans. One New Yorker declared in 1715 that "it is impossible that we and the French can both inhabit this Continent in peace but that one nation must at last give way to the other."

On their part, the French suspected their rivals intended to seize all of North America. Land speculators and frontier traders pushed aggressively into territory claimed by the French and owned by the Native Americans. In 1716, one Frenchman urged his government to hasten the development of Louisiana, since "it is not difficult to guess that their [the British] purpose is to drive us entirely out . . . of North America."

To their great sorrow and eventual destruction, the original inhabitants of the frontier, the Native Americans, were swept up in this undeclared war. The Indians maneuvered to hold their own in the "middle ground." The Iroquois favored the British; the Algonquian peoples generally supported the French. But regardless of the groups to which they belonged, Indian warriors—acting independently and for their own strategic reasons—found themselves enmeshed in imperial policies set by distant European kings.

Native Americans often depended on trade goods supplied by the British and sometimes adopted British dress. Here the Mohawk chief Theyanoguin, called King Hendrick by the British, wears a cloak he received from Queen Anne of England during a visit to London in 1710. During the Seven Years' War, Theyanoguin mobilized Mohawk support for the British.

KING GEORGE'S WAR AND ITS AFTERMATH

In 1743, the Americans were dragged once again into the imperial conflict. During King George's War (1743–1748), known in Europe as the War of the

Austrian Succession, New England colonists scored a magnificent victory over the French. Louisbourg, a gigantic fortress on Cape Breton Island, the easternmost promontory of Canada, guarded the approaches to the Gulf of St. Lawrence and Quebec.

The Americans, however, were in for a shock. When the war ended with the signing of the Treaty of Aix-la-Chapelle in 1748, the British government handed Louisbourg back to the French in exchange for concessions elsewhere. Such decisions exposed the deep and continuing ambivalence the colonists felt about participation in imperial wars. They were proud to support Great Britain, of course, but the Americans seldom fully understood why the wars were being fought, why certain tactics had been adopted, and why the British accepted treaty terms that so blatantly ignored colonial interests.

The French were not prepared to surrender an inch. But as they recognized, time was running against them. Not only were the English colonies growing more populous, but they also possessed a seemingly inexhaustible supply of manufactured goods to trade with the Indians. The French decided in the early 1750s, therefore, to seize the Ohio Valley before the Virginians could do so. They established forts throughout the region, the most formidable being Fort Duquesne, located at the strategic fork in the Ohio River and later renamed Pittsburgh.

Although France and England had not officially declared war, British officials advised the governor of Virginia to "repell force by force." The Virginians needed little encouragement. They were eager to make good their claim to the Ohio Valley, and in 1754, militia companies under the command of a promising young officer, George Washington, constructed Fort Necessity not far from Fort Duquesne. The plan failed. French and Indian troops overran the badly exposed outpost (July 3, 1754). Among other things, the humiliating setback revealed that a single colony could not defeat the French.

ALBANY CONGRESS AND BRADDOCK'S DEFEAT

Benjamin Franklin, for one, appreciated the need for intercolonial cooperation. When British officials invited representatives from the Northern Colonies to Albany (June 1754) to discuss relations with the Iroquois, Franklin used the occasion to present a bold blueprint for colonial union. His so-called Albany Plan envisioned the formation of a Grand Council, made up of elected delegates from the various colonies, to oversee matters of common defense, western expansion, and Indian affairs. A President General appointed by the king would preside. Franklin's most daring suggestion involved taxation. He insisted the council be authorized to collect taxes to cover military expenditures.

The first political cartoon to appear in an American newspaper was created by Benjamin Franklin in 1754 to emphasize the importance of the Albany Plan.

Initial reaction to the Albany Plan was enthusiastic. To take effect, however, it required the support of the separate colonial assemblies as well as Parliament. It received neither. The assemblies were jealous of their fiscal authority, and the English thought the scheme undermined the crown's power over American affairs.

In 1755, the Ohio Valley again became the scene of fierce fighting. Even though there was still no formal declaration of war, the British resolved to destroy Fort Duquesne, and to that end, they dispatched units of the regular army to America. In command was Major General Edward Braddock, an obese, humorless veteran who inspired neither fear nor respect.

On July 9, Braddock led a joint force of twenty-five hundred British redcoats and colonists to humiliating defeat. The French and Indians opened fire as Braddock's army waded across the Monongahela River, about eight miles from Fort Duquesne. Nearly 70 percent of Braddock's troops were killed or wounded in western Pennsylvania. The general himself died in battle. The French, who suffered only light casualties, remained in firm control of the Ohio Valley.

The entire affair profoundly angered Washington, who fumed, "We have been most scandalously beaten by a trifling body of men." The British thought their allies

A CENTURY OF CONFLICT: MAJOR WARS, 1689–1763

DATES	EUROPEAN NAME	AMERICAN NAME	MAJOR ALLIES
1689–1697	War of the League of Augsburg	King William's War	Britain, Holland, Spain, their colonies, and Native American allies against France, its colonies, and Native American allies
1702–1713	War of the Spanish Succession	Queen Anne's War	Britain, Holland, their colonies, and Native American allies against France, Spain, their colonies, and Native American allies
1743–1748	War of the Austrian Succession (War of Jenkin's Ear)	King George's War	Britain, its colonies and Native American allies, and Austria against France, Spain, their Native American allies, and Prussia
1756–1763	Seven Years' War	French and Indian War	Britain, its colonies, and Native American allies against France, its colonies, and Native American allies

the Iroquois might desert them after the embarrassing defeat. The Indians, however, took the news in stride, observing that "they were not at all surprised to hear it, as they [Braddock's redcoats] were men who had crossed the Great Water and were unacquainted with the arts of war among the Americans."

SEVEN YEARS' WAR

Britain's imperial war effort flirted with failure. No one in England or America seemed to possess the leadership necessary to drive the French from the Mississippi Valley. The cabinet of George II (r. 1727–1760) lacked the will to organize and finance a sustained military campaign in the New World, and colonial assemblies balked every time Britain asked them to raise men and money. On May 18, 1756, the British officially declared war on the French, a conflict called the French and Indian War in America and the Seven Years' War in Europe.

Had it not been for William Pitt, the most powerful minister in George's cabinet, the military stalemate might have continued. This supremely self-confident

ISSUES	MAJOR AMERICAN BATTLE	TREATY
Opposition to French bid for control of Europe	New England troops assault Quebec under Sir William Phips (1690)	Treaty of Ryswick (1697)
Austria and France hold rival claims to Spanish throne	Attack on Deerfield (1704)	Treaty of Utrecht (1713)
Struggle among Britain, Spain, and France for control of New World territory; among France, Prussia, and Austria for control of central Europe	New England forces capture Louisbourg under William Pepperrell (1745)	Treaty of Aix-la-Chapelle (1748)
Struggle among Britain, Spain, and France for worldwide control of colonial markets and raw materials	British and Continental forces capture Quebec under Major General James Wolfe (1759)	Peace of Paris (1763)

Englishman believed he was the only person capable of saving the British empire, an opinion he publicly expressed. When he became effective head of the ministry in December 1756, Pitt had an opportunity to demonstrate his talents.

In the past, warfare on the European continent had worked mainly to France's advantage. Pitt saw no point in continuing to concentrate on Europe, and in 1757 he advanced a bold new imperial policy, one based on commercial assumptions. In Pitt's judgment, the critical confrontation would take place in North America, where Britain and France were struggling to control colonial markets and raw materials. Indeed, according to Pitt, America was "where England and Europe are to be fought for." He was determined, therefore, to expel the French from the continent, however great the cost.

To effect this ambitious scheme, Pitt took personal command of the army and navy. He mapped strategy. He even promoted young promising officers over the heads of their superiors. He also recognized that the success of the war effort could not depend on the generosity of the colonial assemblies. Great Britain would have to foot most of the bill. Pitt's military expenditures, of course, created an enormous national debt that would soon haunt both Britain and its colonies, but at the time, no one foresaw the fiscal consequences of victory in America.

To direct the grand campaign, Pitt selected two relatively obscure officers, Jeffrey Amherst and James Wolfe. It was a masterful choice, one that a less self-assured man than Pitt would never have risked. Both officers were young, talented, and ambitious, and on July 26, 1758, forces under their direction captured Louisbourg, the same fortress the colonists had taken a decade earlier.

This victory cut the Canadians' main supply line with France. The small population of New France could no longer meet the military demands placed on it. As the situation became increasingly desperate, the French forts of the Ohio Valley and the Great Lakes began to fall. Duquesne was simply abandoned late in 1758 as French and Indian troops under the Marquis de Montcalm retreated toward Quebec and Montreal. During the summer of 1759, the French surrendered key forts at Ticonderoga, Crown Point, and Niagara.

The climax to a century of war came dramatically in September 1759. Wolfe, now a major general, assaulted Quebec with nine thousand men. But it was not simply force of arms that brought victory. Wolfe proceeded as if he were preparing to attack the city directly, but under cover of darkness, his troops scaled a cliff to dominate a less well defended position. At dawn on September 13, 1759, they took the French from the rear by surprise. The decisive action occurred on the Plains of Abraham, a bluff high above the St. Lawrence River. Both Wolfe and Montcalm were mortally wounded. When an aide informed Wolfe the French had been routed, he sighed, "Now, God be praised, I will die in peace." On September 8, 1760, Amherst accepted the final surrender of the French army at Montreal.

The Peace of Paris signed on February 10, 1763, almost fulfilled Pitt's grandiose dreams. Great Britain took possession of an empire that stretched around the globe. Only Guadeloupe and Martinique, the Caribbean sugar islands, were given back to the French. After a centurylong struggle, the French had been driven from the mainland of North America. Even Louisiana passed out of France's control into Spanish hands. The treaty gave Britain title to Canada, Florida, and all the land east of the Mississippi River. Moreover, with the stroke of a diplomat's pen, eighty thousand French-speaking Canadians, most of them Catholics, became the subjects of George III.

The Americans were overjoyed. It was a time of good feelings and national pride. Together, the English and their colonial allies had thwarted the "Gallic peril." Samuel Davies, a Presbyterian who had brought the Great Awakening to Virginia, announced confidently that the long-awaited victory would inaugurate "a new heaven and a new earth."

North America After 1763
The Peace of Paris (1763) redrew the map of North America. Great Britain received all the French holdings except a few islands in the Atlantic and some sugar-producing islands in the Caribbean.

PERCEPTIONS OF WAR

The Seven Years' War made a deep impression on American society. Even though Franklin's Albany Plan had failed, the military struggle had forced the colonists to cooperate on an unprecedented scale. It also drew them into closer contact with Britain. They became aware of being part of a great empire, military and commercial, but in the very process of waging war, they acquired a more intimate sense of an America that lay beyond the plantation and the village. Conflict had carried thousands of young men across colonial boundaries, exposing them to a vast territory full of opportunities for a booming population.

British officials later accused the Americans of ingratitude. England, they claimed, had sent troops and provided funds to liberate the colonists from the threat of French attack. The Americans, appreciative of the aid from England, cheered on the British but dragged their feet at every stage, refusing to pay the bills. These charges were later incorporated into a general argument justifying parliamentary taxation in America.

The British had a point. The colonists were, in fact, slow in providing the men and materials needed to fight the French. Nevertheless, they did make a significant contribution to the war effort, and it was perfectly reasonable for Americans to regard themselves at the very least as junior partners in the empire. After all, they had supplied almost twenty thousand soldiers and spent well over £2 million. In a single year, in fact, Massachusetts enlisted five thousand men out of an adult male population of about fifty thousand. After making such a sacrifice—indeed, after demonstrating their loyalty to the mother country—the colonists would surely have been disturbed to learn that General James Wolfe, the hero of Quebec, had stated, "The Americans are in general the dirtiest, the most contemptible, cowardly dogs that you can conceive. There is no depending upon them in action. They fall down in their own dirt and desert in battalions, officers and all."

Rule Britannia?

James Thomson, an Englishman, understood the hold of empire on the popular imagination of the eighteenth century. In 1740, he composed words that British patriots have proudly sung for more than two centuries:

> Rule Britannia, rule the waves,
> Britons never will be slaves.

Colonial Americans—at least, those of British background—joined the chorus. By midcentury they took their political and cultural cues from Great Britain. They fought its wars, purchased its consumer goods, flocked to hear its evangelical preachers, and read its many publications. Without question, the empire provided the colonists with a compelling source of identity.

Americans hailed Britannia. In 1763, they were the victors, the conquerors of the backcountry. In their moment of glory, the colonists assumed that Britain's rulers saw the Americans as "Brothers," as equal partners in the business of empire. Only slowly would they learn the British had a different perception. For them, "American" was a way of saying "not quite English."

→ ———— ←

5

THE AMERICAN REVOLUTION
From Gentry Protest to Popular Revolt, 1763–1783

During the American Revolution, a captured British officer spent some time at the plantation of Colonel Thomas Mann Randolph, a leader of Virginia's gentry. The Englishman described the arrival of three ordinary farmers who were members of the local militia. He characterized the militiamen as "peasants," for without asking their host's permission, the Americans drew chairs up to the fire, pulled off their muddy boots, and began spitting.

The British officer was appalled; after the farmers departed, he observed they had not shown Randolph proper deference. The colonel responded that such behavior had come to be expected, for "the spirit of independency" had been transformed into "equality." Indeed, every American who "bore arms" during the Revolution considered himself as good as his neighbors. "No doubt," Randolph remarked to the officer, "each of these men conceives himself, in every respect, my equal."

This chance encounter illuminates the character of the American Revolution. The initial stimulus for rebellion came from the gentry, from the rich and well-born, who resented Parliament's efforts to curtail their rights within the British empire. They voiced their unhappiness in carefully reasoned statements and in speeches before elected assemblies. Radical rhetoric made them uneasy.

But as these influential planters, wealthy merchants, and prominent clergymen discovered, the revolutionary movement generated a momentum that they could not control. As relations with Britain deteriorated, particularly after 1765, the traditional leaders of colonial society encouraged the ordinary folk to join the protest—as rioters, as petitioners, and finally, as soldiers. Newspapers, sermons, and pamphlets helped transform what had begun as a squabble among the gentry into a mass movement, and as Randolph learned, once the people had become involved in shaping the nation's destiny, they could never again be excluded.

A second, often overlooked, aspect of the American Revolution involved a massive military commitment. If common American soldiers had not been willing to stand up to seasoned British troops, to face the terror of the bayonet charge, independence would have remained a dream of intellectuals. Proportionate to the population, a greater percentage of Americans died in military service during the Revolution than in any war in American history, with the exception of the Civil War. The concept of liberty so magnificently expressed in revolutionary pamphlets was not, therefore, simply an abstraction, an exclusive concern of political theorists such as Thomas Jefferson and John Adams. It also motivated ordinary folk—mud-covered Virginia militiamen, for example—to take up weapons and risk death. Those who survived the ordeal were never quite the same, for the very experience of fighting, of assuming responsibility in battle and perhaps even of taking the lives of British officers, gave dramatic new meaning to the idea of social equality.

CONTESTED MEANINGS OF EMPIRE

Colonists who were alive during the 1760s did not anticipate the coming of national independence. It is only from a modern perspective that we see how the events of this period would lead to the formation of the United States. The colonists, of course, did not know what the future would bring. They would probably have characterized these years as "postwar," as a time of heightened economic and political expectation following the successful conclusion of the Seven Years' War (see Chapter 4).

For many Americans, the period generated optimism. The population continued to grow. Indeed, in 1776, approximately 2.5 million people, black and white, were living in Great Britain's thirteen mainland colonies. The striking ethnic and racial diversity of these men and women amazed European visitors who apparently rated homogeneity more highly than did the Americans. In 1775, for example, a traveler corrected the impression in London that the "colonists are the offspring of Englishmen." To be sure, many families traced their roots to Great Britain, but one also encountered "French, Dutch, Germans innumerable, Indians, Africans, and a multitude of felons." He then asked rhetorically, "Is it possible to tell which are the most turbulent amongst such a mixture of people?"

The American population on the eve of Independence was also extraordinarily young, a fact of great importance in understanding the development of effective political resistance. Nearly 60 percent of the American people were under age 21. At any given time, most people in this society were small children, and many of the young men who fought the British during the Revolution either had not been born or had been infants during the Stamp Act crisis. Any explanation for the coming of independence, therefore, must take into account the continuing political mobilization of so many young people.

Postwar Americans also experienced a high level of prosperity. To be sure, some major port cities went through a difficult period as colonists who had been employed during the fighting were thrown out of work. Sailors and ship workers, for example, were especially vulnerable to layoffs of this sort. In general, however, white Americans did very well. The quality of their material lives was not substantially lower than that of the English. In 1774, the per capita wealth of the Americans—this figure includes blacks as well as whites—was £37.4. On the eve of revolution, £37.4 would have purchased about 310 bushels of wheat, 1600 pounds of rice, 11 cows, or 6 horses. A typical white family of five—a father, mother, and three dependent children—not only would have been able to afford

Despite his insecurity over an inadequate education, George III was determined to take an active role in parliamentary affairs and colonial policy.

decent food, clothing, and housing but also would have had money left over with which to purchase consumer goods. Even the poorest colonists seem to have benefited from a rising standard of living, and they too wanted to preserve gains they had made.

Wealth, however, was not evenly distributed in this society. Regional variations were striking. The Southern Colonies enjoyed the highest levels of personal wealth in America, which can be explained in part by the ownership of slaves. More than 90 percent of America's unfree workers lived in the South, and they represented a huge capital investment. Even without including the slaves in these wealth estimates, the South did quite well. In terms of aggregate wealth, the Middle Colonies also scored impressively. In fact, only New England lagged noticeably behind, a reflection of its relative inability to produce large amounts of exports for a growing world market.

BREAKDOWN OF POLITICAL TRUST

Ultimate responsibility for preserving the empire fell to George III. When he became king of England in 1760, he was only 22 years of age. In public, contemporaries praised the new monarch. In private, however, they expressed grave reservations. The youth had led a sheltered, loveless life; his father, an irresponsible playboy, had died in 1751 before ascending the throne. Young George had not received a good education.

The new monarch was determined to play an aggressive role in government. This decision caused considerable dismay among England's political leaders. For decades, a powerful, though loosely associated, group of men who called themselves Whigs had set policy and controlled patronage. George II, his grandfather, had accepted this situation, and so long as the Whigs in Parliament did not meddle with his beloved army, the king had let them rule the nation.

In one stroke, George III destroyed this cozy relationship. He selected as his chief minister the Earl of Bute, a Scot whose chief qualification for office appeared to be his friendship with the young king. The Whigs who dominated Parliament were outraged. Bute had no ties with the members of the House of Commons; he owed them no favors. It seemed to the Whigs that with the appointment of Bute, George was trying to turn back the clock to the time before the Glorious Revolution, in other words, attempting to reestablish a personal Stuart monarchy free from traditional constitutional restraints.

By 1763 Bute, despairing of public life, left office. His departure, however, neither restored the Whigs to preeminence nor dampened the king's enthusiasm for domestic politics. Everyone agreed George had the right to select whomever he desired for cabinet posts, but until 1770, no one seemed able to please the monarch. Ministers came and went, often for no other reason than George's personal distaste. Because of this chronic instability, subministers (minor bureaucrats who directed routine colonial affairs) did not know what was expected of them. In the absence of clear long-range policy, some ministers made narrowly based decisions; others did nothing. Most devoted their energies to finding a political patron capable of satisfying the fickle king. Talent played little part in the scramble for office, and incompetent hacks were advanced as frequently as were men of vision. With such turbulence surrounding him, the king showed little interest in the American colonies.

The king, however, does not bear the sole responsibility for England's loss of empire. The members of Parliament who actually drafted the statutes that gradually drove a wedge between the colonies and Britain must share the blame, for they failed to provide innovative answers to the explosive constitutional issues of the day.

In part, the impasse resulted from sheer ignorance. Few Englishmen active in government had ever visited America. For those who attempted to follow colonial affairs, accurate information proved extremely difficult to obtain. Packet boats carrying passengers and mail sailed regularly between London and the various colonial ports, but the voyage across the Atlantic required at least four weeks. Furthermore, all correspondence was laboriously copied in longhand by overworked clerks serving in understaffed offices. One could not expect to receive from America an answer to a specific question in less than three months. As a result of the lag in communication between England and America, rumors sometimes passed for true accounts, and misunderstanding influenced the formulation of colonial policy.

But failure of communication alone was not to blame for the widening gap between the colonies and England. Even when complete information was available, the two sides were often unable to understand each other's positions. The central element in this Anglo-American debate was a concept known as parliamentary sovereignty. The English ruling classes viewed the role of Parliament from a historical perspective that most colonists never shared. They insisted that Parliament was the dominant element within the constitution. Indeed, this elective body protected rights and property from an arbitrary monarch. During the reign of the Stuarts, especially under Charles I (r. 1625–1649), the authority of Parliament had been challenged, and it was not until the Glorious Revolution of 1688 that the English crown formally recognized Parliament's supreme authority in matters such as taxation. Almost no one, including George III, would have dissented from a speech made in 1766 before the House of Commons, in which a representative declared, "The parliament hath, and must have, from the nature and essence of the constitution, has had, and ever will have a sovereign supreme power and jurisdiction over every part of the dominions of the state, *to make laws in all cases whatsoever.*"

Such a constitutional position did not leave much room for compromise. Most members of Parliament took a hard line on this issue. The notion of dividing or sharing sovereignty simply made no sense to the English ruling class. In fact, parliamentary leaders could never quite understand why the colonists were so difficult to persuade. In frustration, Lord Hillsborough, the British secretary of state, admonished the colonial agent for Connecticut, "It is essential to the constitution to preserve the supremacy of Parliament inviolate; and tell your friends in America . . . that it is as much their interest to support the constitution and preserve the supremacy of Parliament as it is ours."

NO TAXATION WITHOUT REPRESENTATION: THE AMERICAN PERSPECTIVE

Americans most emphatically did not see it in their "interest" to maintain the "supremacy of Parliament." The crisis in imperial relations forced the colonists first to define and then to defend principles deeply rooted in their own political culture. For more than a century, their ideas about the colonies' role within the British empire had remained a vague, untested bundle of assumptions about personal liberties, property rights, and representative institutions.

By 1763, however, certain fundamental American beliefs had become clear. From Massachusetts to Georgia, colonists aggressively defended the powers of the provincial assemblies. They drew on a rich legislative history of their own. Over the course of the century, the American assemblies had steadily expanded their authority over taxation and expenditure. Since no one in Britain bothered to clip their legislative wings, these provincial bodies assumed a major role in policymaking and routine administration. In other words, by midcentury the assemblies looked like American copies of Parliament. It seemed unreasonable, therefore, for the British suddenly to insist on the supremacy of Parliament.

The constitutional debate turned ultimately on the meaning of representation itself. In 1764, a British official informed the colonists that even though they had not elected members to Parliament—indeed, even though they had had no direct contact with the current members—they were nevertheless "virtually" represented by that august body. The members of Parliament, he declared, represented the political interests of everyone who lived in the British empire. It did not really matter whether everyone had cast a vote.

The colonists ridiculed this argument. The only representatives the Americans recognized as legitimate were those actually chosen by the people for whom they spoke. On this crucial point they would not compromise. As John

Adams insisted, a representative assembly should actually mirror its constituents: "It should think, feel, reason, and act like them." Since the members of Parliament could not possibly "think" like Americans, it followed logically they could not represent them. And if they were not genuine representatives, the members of Parliament—pretensions to sovereignty notwithstanding—had no business taxing the American people.

APPEAL TO POLITICAL VIRTUE

The political ideology that had the greatest popular appeal among the colonists contained a strong moral component, one that British rulers and American Loyalists (people who sided with the king and Parliament during the Revolution) never fully understood. The origins of this highly religious perspective on civil government are difficult to locate with precision, but certainly, the Great Awakening created a general awareness of an obligation to conduct public as well as private affairs according to Scripture (see Chapter 4).

Americans expressed their political beliefs in a language they had borrowed from English writers. The person most frequently cited was John Locke, the influential seventeenth-century philosopher whose *Two Treatises of Government* (first published in 1690) seemed, to colonial readers at least, a brilliant description of what was in fact American political practice. Locke claimed that all people possessed natural and inalienable rights. In order to preserve these God-given rights—the rights of life, liberty, and property, for example—free men (the status of women in Locke's work was less clear) formed contracts. These agreements were the foundation of human society as well as civil government, and they required the consent of the people who were actually governed. There could be no coercion. Locke justified rebellion against arbitrary forms of government that were by their very nature unreasonable. Americans delighted in Locke's ability to unite traditional religious values with a spirited defense of popular government, and even when they did not fully understand his technical writings, they seldom missed a chance to quote "the Great Mr. Locke."

Colonial Americans also enthusiastically subscribed to the so-called Commonwealthman tradition, a body of political assumptions generally identified with two eighteenth-century English publicists, John Trenchard and Thomas Gordon (see Chapter 4). The writings of such figures—most of whom spent their lives in political opposition—helped persuade the colonists that *power* was extremely dangerous, a force that would surely destroy liberty unless it was countered by *virtue*. Persons who shared this highly charged moral outlook regarded bad policy as not simply the result of human error. Rather, it was an indication of sin and corruption.

Insistence on public virtue—sacrifice of self-interest to the public good—became the dominant theme of revolutionary political writing. American pamphleteers seldom took a dispassionate, legalistic approach to their analysis of power and liberty. More commonly, they exposed plots hatched by corrupt courtiers, such as the Earl of Bute. None of them—or their readers—had any doubt that Americans were more virtuous than were the people of England.

During the 1760s, however, popular writers were not certain how long the colonists could hold out against arbitrary taxation, standing armies, Anglican bishops—in other words, against a host of external threats designed to crush American liberty. In 1774, for example, the people of Farmington, Connecticut, declared that "the present ministry, being instigated by the devil and led by their wicked and corrupt hearts, have a design to take away our liberties and properties, and to enslave us forever." Indeed, these Connecticut farmers described Britain's leaders as "pimps and parasites."

Colonial newspapers spread these ideas through a large dispersed population. A majority of adult white males—especially those in the Northern Colonies—were literate, and it is not surprising that the number of journals published in this country increased dramatically during the revolutionary period. For the first time in American history, persons living in various parts of the continent could closely follow events that occurred in distant American cities.

CHALLENGE AND RESISTANCE: ERODING THE BONDS OF EMPIRE

The Seven Years' War saddled Great Britain with a national debt so huge that more than half the annual national budget went to pay the interest on it. Almost everyone in government assumed that with the cessation of hostilities, the troops would be disbanded, thus saving a lot of money; George III had other plans. He insisted on keeping the largest peacetime army in British history on active duty, supposedly to protect Indians from predatory frontiersmen and to preserve order in the newly conquered territories of Florida and Quebec.

The growing financial burden weighed heavily on restive English taxpayers and sent government leaders scurrying in search of new sources of revenue. For their part, colonists doubted the value of this very expensive army. First, Britain did not leave enough troops in America to maintain peace on the frontier effectively. The weakness of the army was dramatically demonstrated during the spring of 1763. The native peoples of the backcountry—the Senecas, Ottawas, Miamis, Creeks, and Cherokees—had begun discussing how they might turn back the tide of white settlement. The powerful spiritual leader Neolin, known as the Delaware Prophet, and claiming vision from the "Master of Life," helped these Indians articulate their fear and anger. He urged them to restore their cultures to the "original state that they were in before the white people found out their country." If moral regeneration required violence, so be it. Neolin converted Pontiac, an Ottawa warrior, to the cause, and he, in turn, coordinated an uprising among the western Indians who had been French allies and who hated all British people—even those sent to protect them from land-grabbing colonists. In May, Pontiac attacked Detroit; other Indians harassed the Pennsylvania and Virginia frontiers. At the end of the year, after his followers began deserting, Pontiac sued for peace. During even this brief outbreak, the British army proved unable to defend exposed colonial settlements, and several thousand people lost their lives.

From the perspective of the Native Americans who inhabited the Ohio Valley this was a period of almost unmitigated disaster. In fact, more than any other group, the Indians suffered as a direct result of imperial reorganization. The defeat of the French made it impossible for native peoples to play off one imperial power against European rivals (see Chapter 4), and the victorious British made it clear that they regarded their former Indian allies as little more than a nuisance. Diplomatic gifts stopped; humiliating restrictions were placed on trade. But even worse, Pontiac's rising unloosed vicious racism along the colonial frontier, and American colonists often used any excuse to attack local Indians, peaceful or not. Late in 1763 a group of vigilantes known as the Paxton Boys murdered a score of Christian Indians, women and children, living near Lancaster, Pennsylvania. White neighbors treated the killers as heroes, and the atrocity ended only after the Paxton Boys threatened to march on Philadelphia in search of administrators who dared to criticize such cold-blooded crimes. One of the administrators, Benjamin Franklin, observed sadly, "It grieves me to hear that our Frontier People are yet greater Barbarians than the Indians, and continue to murder them in time of Peace."

Whatever happened to the Indians, the colonists fully intended to settle the fertile region west of the Appalachian Mountains. After the British government issued the Proclamation of 1763, which prohibited governors from granting land beyond the headwaters of rivers flowing into the Atlantic, disappointed Americans viewed the army as an obstruction to legitimate economic development, a domestic police force that cost too much money.

PAYING OFF THE NATIONAL DEBT

The task of reducing England's debt fell to George Grenville, the rigid, somewhat unimaginative chancellor of the exchequer who replaced Bute in 1763 as the king's first minister. After carefully reviewing the state of Britain's finances, Grenville concluded that the colonists would have to contribute to the maintenance of the army. The first bill he steered through Parliament was the Revenue Act of 1764, known as the Sugar Act.

This legislation placed a new burden on the Navigation Acts that had regulated the flow of colonial commerce for almost a century (see Chapter 3). Those acts had forced Americans to trade almost exclusively with Britain. The statutes were not, however, primarily intended as a means to raise money for the British government. The Sugar Act—and the acts that soon followed—redefined the relationship between America and Great Britain. Parliament now expected the colonies to generate revenue. The preamble of the Sugar Act proclaimed explicitly: "It is just and necessary that a revenue be raised . . . in America for defraying the expenses of defending, protecting, and securing the same." The purpose of the Sugar Act was to discourage smuggling, bribery, and other illegalities that prevented the Navigation Acts from being profitable. Parliament reduced the duty on molasses (set originally by the Molasses Act of 1733) from 6 to 3 pence per gallon. At so low a rate, Grenville reasoned, colonial merchants would have little incentive to bribe customs collectors. Much needed revenue would be diverted from the pockets of corrupt officials into the treasury so that it might be used to maintain the army.

Grenville had been too clever by half. The Americans immediately saw through his unconstitutional scheme. According to the members of the Rhode Island Assembly, the Sugar Act taxed the colonists in a manner "inconsistent with their rights and privileges as British subjects." James Otis, a fiery orator from Massachusetts, exclaimed the legislation deprived Americans of "the right of assessing their own taxes."

The act generated no violence. In fact, ordinary men and women were only marginally involved in the drafting of formal petitions. The protest was still confined to the members of the colonial assemblies, to the merchants, and to the well-to-do Americans who had personal interests in commerce.

MOBILIZING THE PEOPLE

Passage of the Stamp Act in 1765 transformed debate among gentlemen into a mass political movement. The imperial crisis might have been avoided. Colonial agents had presented Grenville with alternative schemes for raising money in America. But Grenville was a stubborn man, and he had little fear of parliamentary opposition. The majority of the House of Commons assumed that Parliament possessed the right to tax the colonists, and when the chancellor of the exchequer announced a plan to squeeze £60,000 annually out of the Americans by requiring them to purchase special seals or stamps to validate legal documents, the members responded with enthusiasm. The Stamp Act was scheduled to go into effect on November 1, 1765, and in anticipation of brisk sales, Grenville appointed stamp distributors for every colony.

Word of the Stamp Act reached America in May, sparking widespread protest. The most dramatic incident occurred in Virginia's House of Burgesses. Patrick Henry, young and eloquent, who contemporaries compared in fervor to evangelical preachers, introduced five resolutions protesting the Stamp Act on the floor of the assembly. He timed his move carefully. It was late in the session; many of the more conservative burgesses had already departed for their plantations. Even then, Henry's resolves declaring that Virginians had the right to tax themselves as they alone saw fit passed by narrow margins. The fifth resolution, stricken almost immediately from the legislative records, announced that any attempt to collect stamp revenues in America was "illegal, unconstitutional, and unjust, and has a manifest tendency to destroy British as well as American liberty." Henry was carried away by the force of his own rhetoric. He reminded his fellow Virginians that Caesar had had his Brutus, Charles I his Cromwell, and he hoped that "some good American would stand up for his country"—but an astonished speaker of the house cut Henry off in mid-sentence, accusing him of treason.

The Virginia Resolves might have remained a local matter had it not been for the colonial press. Newspapers throughout America printed Henry's resolutions, but, perhaps because editors did not really know what had happened in Williamsburg, they reported that all five resolutions had received the burgesses' full support. Several journals even carried two resolves that Henry had not dared to introduce. A result of this misunderstanding, of course, was that the Virginians appeared to have taken an extremely radical position on the issue of

The Stamp Act placed a tax on documents and printed matter—newspapers, marriage licenses, wills, deeds, even playing cards and dice. The stamps (like those shown here) varied in denomination. A tax stamp affixed to a legal document or bill of sale signified that the required tax had been paid.

the supremacy of Parliament, one that other Americans now trumpeted before their own assemblies.

Not to be outdone by Virginia, Massachusetts called a general meeting to protest Grenville's policy. Nine colonies sent representatives to the Stamp Act Congress that convened in New York City in October 1765. It was the first inter-colonial gathering held since the abortive Albany Congress of 1754; if nothing else, the new congress provided leaders from different regions with an opportunity to discuss common problems. The delegates drafted petitions to the king and Parliament that restated the colonists' belief "that no taxes should be imposed on them, but with their own consent, given personally, or by their representatives."

Resistance to the Stamp Act soon spread from the assemblies to the streets. By taxing deeds, marriage licenses, and playing cards, the Stamp Act touched the lives of ordinary women and men. Anonymous artisans and seamen, angered by Parliament's apparent insensitivity and fearful that the statute would increase unemployment and poverty, organized mass protests in the major colonial ports.

In Boston, the "Sons of Liberty" burned in effigy the local stamp distributor, Andrew Oliver, and when that action failed to bring about his resignation, they tore down one of his office buildings. Even after he resigned, the mob nearly demolished the elegant home of Oliver's close associate, Lieutenant Governor Thomas Hutchinson. The violence frightened colonial leaders, yet evidence suggests that they encouraged the lower classes to intimidate royal officials. Popular participation in these protests was an exciting experience for people who had traditionally deferred to their social betters. After 1765, it was impossible for either royal governors or patriot leaders to take the ordinary folk for granted.

By November 1, 1765, stamp distributors in almost every American port had publicly resigned, and without distributors, the hated revenue stamps could not be sold. The courts soon reopened; most newspapers were published. Daily life in the colonies was undisturbed with one exception: the Sons of Liberty persuaded—some said coerced—colonial merchants to boycott British goods until Parliament repealed the Stamp Act. The merchants showed little enthusiasm for such tactics, but the threat of tar and feathers stimulated cooperation.

The boycott movement was in itself a masterful political innovation. Never before had a resistance movement organized itself so centrally around the market decisions of ordinary consumers. The colonists depended on British imports—cloth, metal goods, and ceramics—and each year they imported more consumer goods than they could possibly afford. In this highly charged moral atmosphere, one in which ordinary people talked constantly of conspiracy and corruption, it is not surprising that Americans of different classes and backgrounds advocated a radical change in buying habits. Private acts suddenly became part of the public sphere. Personal excess threatened to contaminate the entire political commu-

Because the Stamp Act touched the lives of ordinary men and women, they were vocal and demonstrative in their protests against the measure. Here a crowd in New Hampshire stages a mock funeral of a hanged effigy of the stamp master.

nity. This logic explains the power of an appeal made in a Boston newspaper: "Save your money and you can save your country."

The boycotts mobilized colonial women. They were excluded from voting and civil office, but such legal discrimination did not mean that women were not part of the broader political culture. Since wives and mothers spent their days involved with household chores, they assumed special responsibility to reform consumption, to root out luxury, and to promote frugality. Indeed, in this realm they possessed real power; they monitored the ideological commitment of the entire family. Throughout the colonies, women altered styles of dress, made homespun cloth, and shunned imported items on which Parliament had placed a tax.

SAVING FACE

What most Americans did not yet know—after all, communication with Britain required months—was that in July, Grenville had fallen from power. This unexpected shift came about not because the king thought Grenville's policies inept, but rather because George did not like the man. His replacement as first lord of the treasury, Lord Rockingham, was young, inexperienced, and terrified of public speaking, a serious handicap to launching a brilliant parliamentary career. Rockingham wanted to repeal the Stamp Act, but because of the shakiness of his own political coalition, he could not announce such a decision until it enjoyed broad parliamentary support.

Grenville, now simply a member of Parliament, would tolerate no retreat on the issue of supremacy. He urged his colleagues in the House of Commons to be tough, to condemn "the outrageous tumults and insurrections which have been excited and carried on in North America." But William Pitt, the architect of victory in the Seven Years' War and a hero throughout America, eloquently defended the colonists' position, and after the Rockingham ministry gathered additional support from prominent figures such as Benjamin Franklin, who happened to be visiting England, Parliament felt strong enough to recommend repeal. On March 18, 1766, the House of Commons voted 275 to 167 to rescind the Stamp Act.

Lest its retreat on the Stamp Act be interpreted as weakness, the House of Commons passed the Declaratory Act (March 1766), a shrill defense of parliamentary supremacy over the Americans "in all cases whatsoever." The colonists' insistence on no taxation without representation failed to impress British rulers.

The Stamp Act crisis eroded the colonists' respect for imperial officeholders in America. Suddenly, these men—royal governors, customs collectors, military personnel—appeared alien, as if their interests were not those of the people over whom they exercised authority. One person who had been forced to resign the post of stamp distributor for South Carolina noted several years later, "The Stamp Act had introduc'd so much Party Rage, Faction, and Debate that the ancient Harmony, Generosity, and Urbanity for which these People were celebrated is destroyed, and at an End."

A FOOLISH BOAST: TEA AND SOVEREIGNTY

Rockingham's ministry soon gave way to a government headed once again by William Pitt, who was now the Earl of Chatham. The aging Pitt suffered horribly from gout, and during his long absences from London, Charles Townshend, his chancellor of the exchequer, made important policy decisions. Townshend was an impetuous man whose mouth often outran his mind. During a parliamentary debate in January 1767, he surprised everyone by blithely announcing that he knew a way to obtain revenue from the Americans.

His scheme turned out to be a grab bag of duties on American imports of paper, glass, paint, lead, and tea, which collectively were known as the Townshend Revenue Acts (June–July 1767). He hoped to generate sufficient funds to pay the salaries of royal governors and other imperial officers, thus freeing them from dependence on the colonial assemblies.

The chancellor recognized that without tough instruments of enforcement, his duties would not produce the promised revenues. Therefore, he created an American Board of Customs Commissioners, a body based in Boston and supported by reorganized vice-admiralty courts located in Boston, Philadelphia, and Charles Town. And for good measure, Townshend induced Parliament to order

The boycott movement drew many colonial women into popular politics. In this 1774 woodcut, a Daughter of Liberty stands ready to resist British oppression.

the governor of New York to veto all bills passed by that colony's assembly until it supplied resident British troops in accordance with the Quartering Act (May 1765). Many Americans regarded this as more taxation without representation, and in New York, at least, colonists refused to pay.

Colonists showed no more willingness to pay Townshend's duties than they had to buy Grenville's stamps. No congress was called; none was necessary. Recent events had taught people how to coordinate protest, and they moved to resist the unconstitutional revenue acts. In major ports, the Sons of Liberty organized boycotts of British goods. Men and women took oaths before neighbors promising not to purchase certain goods until Parliament repealed unconstitutional taxation.

On February 11, 1768, the Massachusetts House of Representatives drafted a circular letter, a provocative appeal that it sent directly to the other colonial assemblies. The letter requested suggestions on how best to thwart the Townshend Acts; not surprisingly, legislators in other parts of America, busy with local matters, simply ignored this general appeal. But not Lord Hillsborough, England's secretary for American affairs. This rather mild attempt to create a united colonial front struck him as gross treason, and he ordered the Massachusetts representatives to rescind their "seditious paper." After considering Hillsborough's demand, the legislators voted 92 to 17 to defy him.

Suddenly, the circular letter became a cause célèbre. The royal governor of Massachusetts hastily dissolved the House of Representatives. That decision compelled the other colonies to demonstrate their support for Massachusetts. Assembly after assembly now felt obligated to take up the circular letter, an action Hillsborough had specifically forbidden. Assemblies in other colonies were dissolved, creating a much broader crisis of representative government. Throughout America, the number 92 (the number of legislators who voted against Hillsborough) immediately became a symbol of patriotism. In fact, Parliament's challenge had brought about the very results it most wanted to avoid: a foundation for intercolonial communication and a strengthening of conviction among the colonists of the righteousness of their position.

CREATING PATRIOTIC MARTYRS

In October 1768, British rulers made another mistake. At the heart of the trouble was the army. In part to save money and in part to intimidate colonial troublemakers, the ministry transferred four thousand regular troops from Nova Scotia and Ireland to Boston. Most of the army had already been withdrawn from

Outrage over the Boston Massacre was fanned by propaganda, such as this engraving by Paul Revere, which showed British redcoats firing on ordinary citizens. In subsequent editions, the blood spurting from the dying Americans became more conspicuous.

the frontier to the seacoast to save revenue, thereby raising more acutely than ever the issue of why troops were in America at all. The armed strangers camped on the Boston Common, and when citizens passed the site, redcoats shouted obscenities. To make relations worse, redcoats—men who were ill treated and underpaid—competed in their spare time for jobs with local dockworkers and artisans.

When colonists questioned why the army had been sent to a peaceful city, pamphleteers responded that it was there to further a conspiracy originally conceived by Bute to oppress Americans, to take away their liberties, to collect illegal revenues. Grenville, Hillsborough, Townshend: they were all, supposedly, part of the plot. Colonists had no difficulty interpreting the violence that erupted in Boston on March 5, 1770. In the gathering dusk of that afternoon, young boys and street toughs threw rocks and snowballs at soldiers in a small, isolated patrol outside the offices of the hated customs commissioners in King Street. The details of this incident are obscure, but it appears that as the mob grew and became more threatening, the soldiers panicked. In the confusion, the troops fired, leaving five Americans dead.

Pamphleteers promptly labeled the incident a massacre. The victims were seen as martyrs and were memorialized in extravagant terms. Paul Revere's engraving of the massacre, appropriately splattered with blood, became an instant best-seller. Confronted with such intense reaction and with the possibility of massive armed resistance, crown officials wisely moved the army to an island in Boston Harbor.

At this critical moment, the king's new first minister restored a measure of tranquility. Lord North, congenial, well-meaning, but not very talented, became chancellor of the exchequer following Townshend's death in 1767. North was appointed the first minister in 1770, and for the next twelve years—indeed, throughout most of the American crisis—he managed to retain his office. His formula seems to have been an ability to get along with George III and to build an effective majority in Parliament.

North recommended to Parliament the repeal of the Townshend duties. Not only had these ill-conceived duties angered the colonists, but they also hurt English manufacturers. By taxing British exports such as glass and paint, Parliament had only encouraged the Americans to develop their own industries; thus, without much prodding, the House of Commons dropped all the Townshend duties—with the notable exception of tea. The tax on tea was retained not for revenue purposes, North insisted, but as a reminder that England's rulers still subscribed to the principles of the Declaratory Act. They would not compromise the supremacy of Parliament. In mid-1770, however, the matter of tea seemed trivial to most Americans. The colonists had drawn back from the precipice, a little frightened by the events of the past two years.

LAST DAYS OF THE OLD ORDER, 1770–1773

For a short while, American colonists and British officials put aside their recent animosities. Like England's rulers, some colonial gentry were beginning to pull back from protest, especially violent confrontation with established authority, in fear that the lower orders were becoming too assertive. It was probably in this period that Loyalist Americans emerged as an identifiable group. Colonial merchants returned to familiar patterns of trade, pleased no doubt to end the local boycotts that had depressed the American economy. British goods flooded into colonial ports; the level of American indebtedness soared to new highs.

Appearances were deceiving. The bonds of imperial loyalty remained fragile, and even as Lord North attempted to win the colonists' trust, crown officials in America created new strains. Customs commissioners whom Townshend had appointed to collect his duties remained in the colonies long after his Revenue Acts had been repealed. If they had been honest, unobtrusive administrators, perhaps no one would have taken notice of their behavior. But the customs commissioners regularly abused their powers of search and seizure and in the process lined their own pockets. In Massachusetts, Rhode Island, and South Carolina—to cite the most notorious cases—these officials drove local citizens to distraction by enforcing the Navigation Acts with such rigor that a small boat could not cross Narragansett Bay with a load of firewood without first obtaining a sheaf of legal documents. One slip, no matter how minor, could bring confiscation of ship and cargo.

The commissioners were not only corrupt; they were also shortsighted. If they had restricted their extortion to the common folk, they might have avoided becoming a major American grievance. But they could not control their greed. Some customs officers harassed the wealthiest, most powerful men around, men such as John Hancock of Boston and Henry Laurens of Charles Town. The commissioners' actions drove some members of the colonial ruling class into opposition to the king's government. When in the summer of 1772 a group of disguised Rhode Islanders burned a customs vessel, the *Gaspee,* Americans cheered. A special royal commission sent to arrest the culprits discovered that not a single Rhode Islander had the slightest idea how the ship could have come to such an end.

Samuel Adams (1722–1803) refused to accept the notion that the repeal of the Townshend duties had secured American liberty. During the early 1770s, while colonial leaders turned to other matters, Adams kept the cause alive with a drumfire of publicity. He reminded the people of Boston that the tax on tea remained in force. He organized public anniversaries commemorating the repeal of the Stamp Act and the Boston Massacre. Adams was a genuine revolutionary, an ideologue filled with a burning sense of indignation at the real and alleged wrongs suffered by his countrymen.

With each new attempt by Parliament to assert its supremacy over the colonists, more and more Bostonians listened to what Adams had to say. He observed ominously that the British intended to use the tea revenue to pay judicial salaries, thus freeing the judges from dependence on the assembly. When in November 1772 Adams suggested the formation of a committee of correspondence to communicate grievances to villagers throughout Massachusetts, he received broad support. Americans living in other colonies soon copied his idea. It was a brilliant stroke. Adams developed a structure of political cooperation completely independent of royal government.

THE FINAL PROVOCATION: THE BOSTON TEA PARTY

In May 1773, Parliament passed the Tea Act, legislation the Americans might have welcomed. After all, it lowered the price for their favorite beverage. Parliament wanted to save one of Britain's largest businesses, the East India Company, from possible bankruptcy. This commercial giant imported Asian tea into England, where it was resold to wholesalers. The tea was also subject to heavy duties. The

This broadside is an ode to the "glorious sons of freedom" who dumped East India Company tea into Boston Harbor in 1773.

Company tried to pass these charges on to the consumers, but American tea drinkers preferred the cheaper leaves that were smuggled in from Holland.

The Tea Act changed the rules. Parliament not only allowed the Company to sell directly to American retailers, thus cutting out intermediaries, but also eliminated the duties paid in England. If all had gone according to plan, the agents of the East India Company in America would have undersold their competitors, including the Dutch smugglers, and with the new profits would have saved the business.

Parliament's logic was flawed. First, since the tax on tea, collected in American ports, remained in effect, this new act seemed a devious scheme to win popular support for Parliament's right to tax the colonists without representation. Second, the act threatened to undercut powerful colonial merchants who did a good business trading in smuggled Dutch tea. Considering the American reaction, the British government might have been well advised to devise another plan to rescue the ailing company. In Philadelphia, and then at New York City, colonists turned back the tea ships before they could unload.

In Boston, however, the issue was not so easily resolved. Governor Hutchinson, a strong-willed man, would not permit the vessels to return to England. Local patriots would not let them unload. And so, crammed with the East India Company's tea, the ships sat in Boston Harbor waiting for the colonists to make up their minds. On the night of December 16, 1773, they did so in dramatic style. A group of men disguised as Mohawks boarded the ships and pitched 340 chests of tea worth £10,000 over the side. Whether Samuel Adams organized the famed Tea Party is not known.

When news of the Tea Party reached London in January 1774, the North ministry was stunned. The people of Boston had treated parliamentary supremacy with utter contempt, and British rulers saw no humor whatsoever in the destruction of private property by subjects of the Crown dressed as Indians. To quell such rebelliousness, Parliament passed a series of laws called the Coercive Acts. (In America, they were referred to as the Intolerable Acts.) The legislation (1) closed the port of Boston until the city fully compensated the East India Company for the lost tea; (2) restructured the Massachusetts government by transforming the upper house from an elective to an appointed body and restricting the number of legal town meetings to one a year; (3) allowed the royal governor to transfer British officials arrested for offenses committed in the line of duty to England, where there was little likelihood they would be convicted; and (4) authorized the army to quarter troops wherever they were needed, even if this required the compulsory requisition of uninhabited private buildings. George III enthusiastically supported this tough policy; he appointed General Thomas Gage to serve as the colony's new royal governor. Gage appar-

CHRONICLE OF COLONIAL–BRITISH TENSION

LEGISLATION	DATE	PROVISIONS	COLONIAL REACTION
Sugar Act	April 5, 1764	Revised duties on sugar, coffee, tea, wine, other imports; expanded jurisdiction of vice-admiralty courts	Several assemblies protest taxation for revenue
Stamp Act	March 22, 1765; repealed March 18, 1766	Printed documents (deeds, newspapers, marriage licenses, etc.) issued only on special stamped paper purchased from stamp distributors	Riots in cities; collectors forced to resign; Stamp Act Congress (October 1765)
Quartering Act	May 1765	Colonists must supply British troops with housing, other items (candles, firewood, etc.)	Protest in assemblies; New York Assembly punished for failure to comply, 1767
Declaratory Act	March 18, 1766	Parliament declares its sovereignty over the colonies "in all cases whatsoever"	Ignored in celebration over repeal of the Stamp Act
Townshend Revenue Acts	June 26, 29, July 2, 1767; all repealed—except duty on tea, March 1770	New duties on glass, lead, paper, paints, tea; customs collections tightened in America	Nonimportation of British goods; assemblies protest; newspapers attack British policy
Tea Act	May 10, 1773	Parliament gives East India Company right to sell tea directly to Americans; some duties on tea reduced	Protests against favoritism shown to monopolistic company; tea destroyed in Boston (December 16, 1773)
Coercive Acts (Intolerable Acts)	March–June 1774	Closes port of Boston; restructures Massachusetts government; restricts town meetings; troops quartered in Boston; British officials accused of crimes sent to England or Canada for trial	Boycott of British goods; First Continental Congress convenes (September 1774)
Prohibitory Act	December 22, 1775	Declares British intention to coerce Americans into submission; embargo on American goods; American ships seized	Drives Continental Congress closer to decision for independence

ently won the king's favor by announcing that in America, "Nothing can be done but by forcible means."

The sweeping denial of constitutional liberties confirmed the colonists' worst fears. To men like Samuel Adams, it seemed as if Britain really intended to enslave the American people. Colonial moderates found their position shaken by the vindictiveness of the Coercive Acts.

In the midst of the constitutional crisis, Parliament announced plans to establish a new civil government for the Canadian province of Quebec (Quebec Act, June 22, 1774). This territory had been ruled by military authority following the Seven Years' War. The Quebec Act not only failed to create an elective assembly— an institution the Americans regarded as essential for the protection of liberty— but also awarded French Roman Catholics a large voice in local political affairs. Moreover, since Quebec extended all the way south to the Ohio River and west to the Mississippi River, Americans concluded that Parliament wanted to deny the American settlers and traders in this fast-developing region their constitutional rights, a threat that affected all colonists, not just those of Massachusetts Bay.

The sticking point remained—as it had been in 1765—the sovereignty of Parliament. No one in Britain could think of a way around this constitutional impasse. In 1773, Benjamin Franklin had offered a suggestion. "The Parliament," he observed, "has no right to make any law whatever, binding on the colonies . . . the king, and not the king, lords, and commons collectively, is their sovereign." But so long as it still seemed possible to coerce the Americans into obedience, to punish these errant children, Britain's rulers had little incentive to accept such a humiliating compromise.

DECISION FOR INDEPENDENCE

During the summer of 1774, committees of correspondence analyzed the perilous situation in which the colonists found themselves. Something, of course, had to be done. But what? Would the Southern Colonies support resistance in New England? Would Pennsylvanians stand up to Parliament? Not surprisingly, the committees endorsed a call for a Continental Congress, a gathering of fifty-five elected delegates from twelve colonies (Georgia sent none but agreed to support the action taken). This momentous gathering convened in Philadelphia on September 5. It included some of America's most articulate, respected leaders; among them were John Adams, Samuel Adams, Patrick Henry, Richard Henry Lee, Christopher Gadsden, and George Washington.

Differences of opinion soon surfaced. Delegates from the Middle Colonies— Joseph Galloway of Pennsylvania, for example—wanted to proceed with caution, but Samuel Adams and other more radical members pushed the moderates toward confrontation. Boston's master politician engineered congressional com-mendation of the Suffolk Resolves, a bold statement drawn up in Suffolk County, Massachusetts, that encouraged forcible resistance of the Coercive Acts.

After this decision, the tone of the meeting was established. Moderate spokesmen introduced conciliatory measures, which received polite discussion but failed to win a majority vote. Just before returning to their homes (September 1774), the delegates created the "Association," an intercolonial agreement to halt all commerce with Britain until Parliament repealed the Intolerable Acts. This was a totally revolutionary decision. The Association autho-rized a vast network of local committees to enforce nonimportation. Violators were exposed, shamed, forced either to apologize publicly for their actions or to be shunned by all their patriot neighbors. In many of the communities, the com-mittees *were* the government, distinguishing, in the words of James Madison, "Friends from Foes."

Shots Heard Around the World

Before Congress reconvened, shots were fired at Lexington and Concord, two small farm villages in eastern Massachusetts. On the evening of April 18, 1775,

This 1775 engraving by Amos Doolittle, an eyewitness, shows the American attack on the British regulars as they marched from Concord back to Boston. The minutemen fired from cover, killing and wounding many red-coats who expected little armed resistance.

General Gage dispatched troops from Boston to seize rebel supplies. Paul Revere, a renowned silversmith and active patriot, warned the colonists that the redcoats were coming. The militia of Lexington, a collection of ill-trained farmers, boys as well as old men, decided to stand on the village green on the following morning, April 19, as the British soldiers passed on the road to Concord. No one planned to fight, but in a moment of confusion, someone (probably a colonist) fired; the redcoats discharged a volley, and eight Americans lay dead.

Word of the incident spread rapidly, and by the time the British force reached its destination, the countryside swarmed with "minutemen," special companies of Massachusetts militia prepared to respond instantly to military emergencies. The long march back to Boston turned into a rout. Lord Percy, a British officer who brought up reinforcements, remarked that "whoever looks upon them [the American soldiers] as an irregular mob, will find himself much mistaken." On June 17, colonial militiamen again held their own against seasoned troops at the battle of Bunker Hill (actually Breed's Hill). The British finally took the hill, but after this costly "victory" in which he suffered 40 percent casualties, Gage complained that the Americans had displayed "a conduct and spirit against us, they never showed against the French."

BEGINNING "THE WORLD OVER AGAIN"

Members of the Second Continental Congress gathered in Philadelphia in May 1775. They faced an awesome responsibility. British government in the mainland colonies had almost ceased to function, and with Americans fighting redcoats, the country desperately needed strong central leadership. Slowly, often reluctantly, Congress took control of the war. The delegates formed a Continental Army and appointed George Washington its commander, in part because he seemed to have greater military experience than anyone else available and in part because he looked like he should be commander in chief. The delegates were also eager to select someone who did not come from Massachusetts, a colony that seemed already to possess too much power in national councils. The members of Congress purchased military supplies and, to pay for them, issued paper money. But while they were assuming the powers of a sovereign government, the congressmen refused to declare independence. They debated and fretted, listened to the appeals of moderates who played on the colonists' remaining loyalty to Britain, and then did nothing.

Indecision drove men like John Adams nearly mad. Haste, however, would have been a terrible mistake. While Adams and Richard Henry Lee of Virginia were willing to sever ties with Britain, many Americans were not convinced that such a step was either desirable or necessary. If Congress had moved too quickly, it might have become vulnerable to charges of extremism, in which case the rebellion would have seemed—and indeed, might have been—more like an overthrow by a faction or clique than an expression of popular will.

The British government appeared intent on transforming colonial moderates into angry rebels. In December 1775, Parliament passed the Prohibitory Act, declaring war on American commerce. Until the colonists begged for pardon, they could not trade with the rest of the world. The British navy blockaded their ports and seized American ships on the high seas. Lord North also hired German mercenaries (the Russians drove too hard a bargain) to put down the rebellion. And in America, Virginia's royal governor Lord Dunmore further undermined the possibility of reconciliation by urging the colony's slaves to take up arms against their masters.

Thomas Paine (1737–1809) pushed the colonists even closer to independence. Nothing in this man's background suggested he would write the most important pamphlet in American history. In England, Paine had failed in a number of jobs, and exactly why he elected to move to America in 1774 is not clear. While still in England, Paine had the good fortune to meet Benjamin Franklin, who presented him with letters of introduction to the leading patriots of Pennsylvania. At the urging of his new American friends, Paine produced an essay that became an instant best-seller. In only three months, it sold more than 120,000 copies. Paine confirmed in forceful prose what the colonists had been thinking but had been unable to state in coherent form. "My motive and object in all my political works," he declared, ". . . have been to rescue man from tyranny and false systems of government, and enable him to be free."

Common Sense systematically stripped kingship of historical and theological justification. For centuries, the English had maintained the fiction that the monarch could do no wrong. When the government oppressed the people, the royal counselors received the blame. The crown was above suspicion. To this, Paine cried nonsense. Monarchs ruled by force. George III was simply a "royal brute," who by his arbitrary behavior had surrendered his claim to the colonists' obedience.

Paine's greatest contribution to the revolutionary cause was persuading common folk to sever their ties with Great Britain. It was not reasonable, he argued, to regard England as the mother country. "Europe, and not England," he explained, "is the parent country of America. This new world hath been the asylum for the persecuted lovers of civil and religious liberty from *every part* of Europe." No doubt that message made a deep impression on Pennsylvania's German population. The time had come for the colonists to form an independent republic. "We

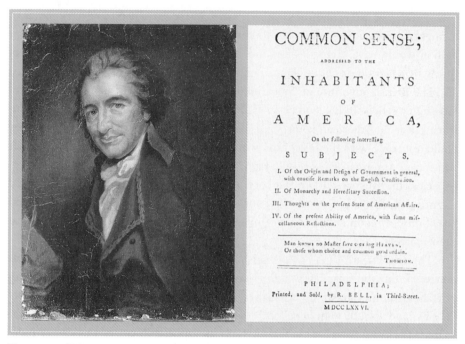

The message of Thomas Paine's pamphlet Common Sense *(title page shown) was easy to follow. His stark phrases calling for "The Free and Independent States of America" reverberated in people's hearts and minds.*

have it in our power," Paine wrote in one of his most moving statements, "to begin the world over again . . . the birthday of a new world is at hand."

On July 2, 1776, after a long and tedious debate, Congress finally voted for independence. The motion passed: twelve states for, none against (with New York abstaining). Thomas Jefferson, a young Virginia lawyer and planter who enjoyed a reputation as a graceful writer, drafted a formal declaration that was accepted with alterations two days later. Much of the Declaration of Independence consisted of a list of specific grievances against George III and his government. Like the skilled lawyer he was, Jefferson presented the evidence for independence. The document did not become famous for those passages. Long after the establishment of the new republic, the Declaration challenged Americans to make good on the principle that "all men are created equal." John Adams nicely expressed the patriots' fervor when he wrote on July 3, "Yesterday the greatest question was decided, which ever was debated in America, and a greater perhaps, never was or will be decided among men."

Many revolutionary leaders throughout the modern world—in Europe as in Asia—have echoed Adams's assessment. Of all the documents written during this period, including the Constitution, the Declaration remains the most powerful and radical invitation to Americans of all backgrounds to demand their equality and full rights as human beings.

FIGHTING FOR INDEPENDENCE

Only fools and visionaries expressed optimism about America's prospects of winning independence in 1776. The Americans had taken on a formidable military power. The population of Britain was perhaps four times that of its former colonies. England also possessed a strong manufacturing base, a well-trained regular army supplemented by thousands of hired German troops (Hessians), and a navy that dominated the world's oceans. Many British officers had battlefield experience. They already knew what the Americans would slowly learn: waging war requires discipline, money, and sacrifice.

The British government entered the conflict fully confident that it could beat the Americans. In 1776, Lord North and his colleagues regarded the war as a police action. They anticipated that a mere show of armed force would intimidate the upstart colonists. As soon as the rebels in Boston had been humbled, the British argued, people living in other colonies would desert the cause for independence.

As later events demonstrated, of course, Britain had become involved in an impossible military situation, in some ways analogous to that in which the United States would find itself in Vietnam some two hundred years later. Three separate elements neutralized advantages held by the larger power over its adversary. First, the British had to transport men and supplies across the Atlantic, a logistic challenge of unprecedented complexity. Unreliable lines of communication broke down under the strain of war.

Second, America was too vast to be conquered by conventional military methods. Redcoats might gain control over the major port cities, but as long as the Continental Army remained intact, the rebellion continued. As Washington explained, "the possession of our Towns, while we have an Army in the field, will avail them little . . . It is our Arms, not defenceless Towns, they have to subdue." Even if England had recruited enough soldiers to occupy the entire country, it would still have lost the war. As one Loyalist instructed the king, "if all America becomes a garrison, she is not worth your attention." Britain could only win by crushing the American will to resist.

And third, British strategists never appreciated the depth of the Americans' commitment to a political ideology. In the wars of eighteenth-century Europe, such beliefs had seldom mattered. European troops before the French Revolution served because they were paid or because the military was a vocation, but most certainly not because they hoped to advance a set of constitutional principles. Americans were different. To be sure, some young men were drawn to the military by bounty money or by the desire to escape unhappy families. A few were drafted. But taking such people into account, one still encounters among the American troops a remarkable commitment to republican ideals.

During the earliest months of rebellion, American soldiers—especially those of New England—suffered no lack of confidence. Indeed, they interpreted their courageous stands at Concord and Bunker Hill as evidence that brave yeomen farmers could lick British regulars on any battlefield. George Washington spent the first years of the war disabusing the colonists of this foolishness, for as he had learned during the French and Indian War, military success depended on endless drill, careful planning, and tough discipline—rigorous preparation that did not characterize the minutemen's methods.

Washington insisted on organizing a regular well-trained field army. Some advisers urged the commander in chief to wage a guerrilla war, one in which small partisan bands would sap Britain's will to rule Americans. But Washington rejected that course. He recognized that the Continental Army served not only as a fighting force but also as a symbol of the republican cause. Its very existence would sustain American hopes, and so long as the army survived, American agents could plausibly solicit foreign aid. This thinking shaped Washington's wartime strategy; he studiously avoided "general actions" in which the Continental Army might be destroyed. Critics complained about Washington's caution, but as they soon discovered, he understood better than they what independence required.

For the half million African American colonists, most of them slaves, the fight for independence took on special poignancy. After all, they wanted to achieve personal as well as political freedom, and many African Americans supported those who seemed most likely to deliver them from bondage. As one historian explained, "the black soldier was likely to join the side that made him the quickest and best offer in terms of those 'unalienable rights' of which Mr. Jefferson had spoken." It is estimated that some five thousand African Americans took up arms to fight against the British. The Continental Army included two all-black units, one from Massachusetts and the other from Rhode Island. In 1778, the legislature of Rhode Island voted to free any slave who volunteered to serve, since, according to the lawmakers, history taught that "the wisest, the freest, and bravest nations . . . liberated their slaves, and enlisted them as soldiers to fight in defence of their country." In the South, especially in Georgia and South Carolina, more than ten thousand African Americans supported the British, and after the patriots had won the war, these men and women left the United States, relocating to Nova Scotia, Florida, and Jamaica, with some eventually resettling in Africa.

The American Revolution, 1775–1781

The War for Independence ranged over a huge area. The major battles of the first years of the war, from the spontaneous rising at Concord in 1775 to Washington's well-coordinated attack on Trenton in December 1776, were fought in the northern colonies. In the middle theater of war, Burgoyne's attempt in 1777 to cut off New England from the rest of the colonies failed when his army was defeated at Saratoga. Action in the final years of the war, from the battles at Camden, Kings Mountain, Cowpens, and Guilford Courthouse to the final victory at Yorktown, occurred in the southern theater of war.

TESTING THE AMERICAN WILL

After the embarrassing defeats in Massachusetts, the king appointed General Sir William Howe to replace the ill-fated Gage. British rulers now understood that a simple police action would not be sufficient to crush the American rebellion. Parliament authorized sending more than fifty thousand troops to the mainland colonies, and after evacuating Boston—an untenable strategic position—the British forces stormed ashore at Staten Island in New York Harbor on July 3, 1776. From this more central location, Howe believed he could cut the New Englanders off from the rest of America. He enjoyed the powerful support of the British navy under the command of his brother, Admiral Lord Richard Howe.

When Washington learned the British were planning to occupy New York City, he transferred many of his inexperienced soldiers to Long Island, where they suffered a major defeat (August 27, 1776). In a series of engagements disastrous for the Americans, Howe drove the Continental Army across the Hudson River into New Jersey. Because of his failure to take full advantage of the situation, however, General Howe lost what seemed in retrospect an excellent opportunity to annihilate Washington's entire army. Nevertheless, the Americans were on the run, and in the fall of 1776, contemporaries predicted the rebels would soon capitulate.

"TIMES THAT TRY MEN'S SOULS"

Swift victories in New York and New Jersey persuaded General Howe that few Americans enthusiastically supported independence. He issued a general pardon, therefore, to anyone who would swear allegiance to George III. The results were encouraging. More than three thousand men and women who lived in areas occupied by the British army took the oath. Howe perceived that a lasting peace in America would require his troops to treat "our enemies as if they might one day become our friends." A member of Lord North's cabinet grumbled that this was "a sentimental manner of making war," a shortsighted view considering England's failure to pacify the Irish through fire and sword. In America, the pardon plan eventually failed not because Howe lacked toughness but because his soldiers and officers regarded loyal Americans as inferior provincials, an attitude that did little to promote good relations. In any case, as soon as the redcoats left a pardoned region, the rebel militia retaliated against those who had deserted the patriot cause.

In December 1776, Washington's bedraggled army retreated across the Delaware River into Pennsylvania. American prospects appeared bleaker than at any other time during the war. The Continental Army lacked basic supplies, and many men who had signed up for short-term enlistments prepared to go home.

"These are the times that try men's souls," Paine wrote in a pamphlet titled *American Crisis.* "The summer soldier and the sunshine patriot will, in this crisis, shrink from the service of their country, but he that stands it *now* deserves . . . love and thanks . . ." Before winter, Washington determined to attempt one last desperate stroke.

Howe played into Washington's hands. The British forces were dispersed in small garrisons across the state of New Jersey, and while the Americans could not possibly have defeated the combined British army, they did possess the capacity—with luck—to capture an exposed post. On the night of December 25, Continental soldiers slipped over the ice-filled Delaware River and at Trenton took nine hundred sleeping Hessian mercenaries by complete surprise.

Cheered by success, Washington returned a second time to Trenton, but on this occasion the Continental Army was not so fortunate. A large British force under Lord Cornwallis trapped the Americans. Instead of standing and fighting—really an impossible challenge—Washington secretly, by night, marched his little army around Cornwallis's left flank. On January 3, 1777, the Americans surprised a British garrison at Princeton. Washington then went into winter quarters. The British, fearful of losing more outposts, consolidated their troops, thus leaving much of the state in the hands of the patriot militia.

VICTORY IN A YEAR OF DEFEAT

In 1777, England's chief military strategist, Lord George Germain, still perceived the war in conventional European terms. A large field army would somehow maneuver Washington's Continental troops into a decisive battle in which the British would enjoy a clear advantage. Complete victory over the Americans certainly seemed within England's grasp. Unfortunately for the men who advocated this plan, the Continental forces proved extremely elusive, and while one British army vainly tried to corner Washington in Pennsylvania, another was forced to surrender in the forests of upstate New York.

In the summer of 1777, General John Burgoyne, a dashing though overbearing officer, descended from Canada with a force of more than seven thousand troops. They intended to clear the Hudson Valley of rebel resistance; join Howe's army, which was to come up to Albany; and thereby cut New England off from the other states. The campaign was a disaster. Military units, mostly from New England, cut the enemy force apart in the deep woods north of Albany. At the battle of Bennington (August 16), the New Hampshire militia under Brigadier General John Stark overwhelmed a thousand German mercenaries. After this setback, Burgoyne's forces struggled forward, desperately hoping that Howe would rush to their rescue, but when it became clear that their situation at Saratoga was hopeless, the haughty Burgoyne was forced to surrender fifty-eight hundred men to the American General Horatio Gates (October 17).

Soon after Burgoyne left Canada, General Howe unexpectedly decided to move his main army from New York City to Philadelphia. Exactly what he hoped to achieve was not clear, even to Britain's rulers, and of course, when Burgoyne called for assistance, Howe was sitting in the new nation's capital still trying to devise a way to destroy the Continental Army. Howe's campaign began in late July. The British forces sailed to the head of the Chesapeake Bay and then marched north to Philadelphia. Washington's troops obstructed the enemy's progress, first at Brandywine Creek (September 11) and then at Paoli (September 20), but the outnumbered Americans could not stop the British from entering Philadelphia.

Anxious lest these defeats discourage Congress and the American people, Washington attempted one last battle before the onset of winter. In an engagement at Germantown (October 4), the Americans launched a major counterattack on a fog-covered battlefield, but just at the moment when success seemed assured, they broke off the fight. "When every thing gave the most flattering hopes of victory," Washington complained, "the troops began suddenly to retreat." Bad luck, confusion, and incompetence contributed to the failure. A discouraged Continental Army dug in at Valley Forge, twenty miles outside of Philadelphia, where camp diseases took twenty-five hundred American lives. In their misery, few American soldiers realized their situation was not nearly as desperate as it had been in 1776.

THE FRENCH ALLIANCE

Even before the Americans declared their independence, agents of the government of Louis XVI began to explore ways to aid the colonists, not so much because the French monarchy favored the republican cause but because it hoped to embarrass the English. The French deeply resented the defeat they had sustained during the Seven Years' War. During the early months of the Revolution, the French covertly sent tons of essential military supplies to the Americans. The negotiations for these arms involved secret agents and fictitious trading companies, the type of clandestine operation more typical of modern times than of the eighteenth century. But when American representatives, Benjamin Franklin for one, pleaded for official recognition of American independence or for outright military alliance, the French advised patience. The international stakes were too great for the king openly to back a cause that had little chance of success.

The American victory at Saratoga convinced the French that the rebels had formidable forces and were serious in their resolve. Indeed, Lord North drew the same conclusion. In April 1778, he tried to avert a greatly expanded war by sending a peace commission to America. He instructed this group, headed by the Earl of Carlisle, to bargain with the Continental Congress "as if it were a legal body." If the colonists would agree to drop their demand for independence, they could turn the imperial calendar back to 1763. Parliament belatedly conceded the right of Americans to tax themselves, even to elect their own governors. It also promised to remove all British troops in times of peace. The proposal might have gained substantial support back in 1776. The war, however, had hardened American resolve; the Congress refused to deal with Carlisle.

In Paris, Franklin performed brilliantly. In meetings with French officials, he hinted that the Americans might accept a British peace initiative. If the French wanted the war to continue, if they really wanted to embarrass their old rival, then they had to do what the English refused: formally recognize the independence of the United States.

The stratagem paid off. On February 6, 1778, the French presented American representatives with two separate treaties. The first, called the Treaty of Amity and Commerce, established commercial relations between France and the United States. It tacitly accepted the existence of a new, independent republic. The Treaty of Alliance was even more generous, considering America's obvious military and economic weaknesses. In the event that France and England went to war (they did so on June 14, as everyone expected), the French agreed to reject "either Truce or Peace with Great Britain . . . until the independence of the United States shall have been formally or tacitly assured by the Treaty or Treaties that shall terminate the War." Even more amazing, France surrendered its claim to all territories formerly owned by Great Britain east of the Mississippi River. The Americans pledged they would not sign a separate peace with Britain without first informing their new ally. And in return, France made no claim to Canada, asking only for the right to take possession of certain British islands in the Caribbean. Never had Franklin worked his magic to greater effect.

French intervention instantly transformed British military strategy. What had been a colonial rebellion suddenly became a world conflict, a continuation of the great wars for empire of the late seventeenth century (see Chapter 4). Scarce military resources, especially newer fighting ships, had to be diverted from the American theater to guard the English Channel. In fact, there was talk in London of a possible French invasion.

THE FINAL CAMPAIGN

British General Henry Clinton replaced Howe, who resigned after the battle of Saratoga. Clinton was a strangely complex individual. As a subordinate officer, he had impressed his superiors as imaginative but easily provoked to anger. When he took command of the British army, his resolute self-confidence suddenly dissolved. Perhaps he feared failure. Whatever the explanation for his vacillation, Clinton's record in America was little better than Howe's or Gage's.

Military strategists calculated that Britain's last chance of winning the war lay in the Southern Colonies, a region largely untouched in the early years of fighting. Intelligence reports reaching London indicated that Georgia and South Carolina contained a sizable body of Loyalists, men who would take up arms for the crown if only they received support and encouragement from the regular army. The southern strategy devised by Germain and Clinton in 1779 turned the war into a bitter guerrilla conflict.

The southern campaign opened in the spring of 1780. Savannah had already fallen, and Clinton reckoned that if the British could take Charles Town, they would be able to control the entire South. A large fleet carrying nearly eight thousand redcoats reached South Carolina in February. Complacent Americans had allowed the city's fortifications to decay, and in a desperate, last-minute effort to preserve Charles Town, General Benjamin Lincoln's forces dug trenches and reinforced walls, but to no avail. On May 12, Lincoln surrendered an American army of almost six thousand men.

The defeat took Congress by surprise, and without making proper preparations, it dispatched a second army to South Carolina under Horatio Gates, the hero of Saratoga. He too failed. At Camden, General Cornwallis, Clinton's second in command, outmaneuvered the raw American recruits, capturing or killing 750 during the course of battle (August 16).

Even at this early stage of the southern campaign, the dangers of partisan warfare had become evident. Tory raiders showed little interest in serving as regular soldiers in Cornwallis's army. They preferred night riding, indiscriminate plundering or murdering of neighbors against whom they harbored ancient grudges. The British had unleashed a horde of banditti across South Carolina. Men who genuinely supported independence or who had merely fallen victim to Loyalist guerrillas bided their time. They retreated westward, waiting for their enemies to make a mistake. Their chance came on October 7 at King's Mountain, North Carolina. In the most vicious fighting of the Revolution, the backwoodsmen decimated a force of British regulars and Tory raiders who had strayed too far from base. One witness reported that when a British officer tried to surrender, he was summarily shot down by at least seven American soldiers.

Cornwallis, badly confused and poorly supplied, squandered his strength chasing American forces across the Carolinas. Whatever military strategy had compelled him to leave Charles Town had long since been abandoned. In early 1781, Congress sent General Nathanael Greene to the South with a new army. This young Rhode Islander was the most capable general on Washington's staff. Greene joined Daniel Morgan, leader of the famed Virginia Riflemen, and in a se-

French assistance on land and sea helped the Americans defeat the British in the American Revolution. In this French print of the battle at Yorktown, French ships block the entrance of Chesapeake Bay, preventing British vessels from resupplying their troops on land. Yorktown, which was unknown to the French artist who made this print, is depicted as a European walled city.

ries of tactically brilliant engagements, they sapped the strength of Cornwallis's army, first at Cowpens, South Carolina (January 17, 1781), and later at Guilford Courthouse, North Carolina (March 15). Clinton fumed in New York City. In his estimation, the inept Cornwallis had left "two valuable colonies behind him to be overrun and conquered by the very army which he boasts to have completely routed but a week or two before."

Cornwallis pushed north into Virginia, planning apparently to establish a base of operations on the coast. He selected Yorktown, a sleepy tobacco market located on a peninsula bounded by the York and James rivers. Washington watched these maneuvers closely. The canny Virginia planter knew this territory intimately, and he sensed that Cornwallis had made a serious blunder. When Washington learned the French fleet could gain temporary dominance in the Chesapeake Bay, he rushed south from New Jersey. With him marched thousands of well-trained French troops under the Comte de Rochambeau. All the pieces fell into place. The French admiral, the Comte de Grasse, cut Cornwallis off from the sea, while Washington and his lieutenants encircled the British on land. On October 19, 1781, Cornwallis surrendered his entire army of six thousand men. When Lord North heard of the defeat at Yorktown, he moaned, "Oh God! It is all over." The British still controlled New York City and Charles Town, but except for a few skirmishes, the fighting ended.

THE LOYALIST DILEMMA

The war lasted longer than anyone had predicted in 1776. While the nation won its independence, many Americans paid a terrible price. Indeed, a large number of men and women decided that however much they loved living in America, they could not accept the new government.

No one knows for certain how many Americans actually supported the crown during the Revolution. Some Loyalists undoubtedly kept silent and avoided making a public commitment that might have led to banishment or loss of property. But for many persons, neutrality proved impossible. Almost 100,000 men and women permanently left America. While a number of these exiles had served as imperial officeholders—Thomas Hutchinson, for example—in the main, they came from all ranks and backgrounds. A large number of humble farmers, more than 30,000, resettled in Canada. Others relocated to England, the West Indies, or Africa.

The political ideology of the Loyalists was not substantially different from that of their opponents. Like other Americans, they believed that men and women were entitled to life, liberty, and the pursuit of happiness. The Loyalists were also convinced that independence would destroy those values by promoting disorder. By turning their backs on Britain, a source of tradition and stability, the rebels seemed to have encouraged licentiousness, even anarchy in the streets. The Loyalists suspected that Patriot demands for freedom were self-serving, even hypocritical, for as Perserved Smith, a Loyalist from Ashfield, Massachusetts, observed, "Sons of liberty . . . did not deserve the name, for it was evident all they wanted was liberty from oppression that they might have liberty to oppress!"

The Loyalists were caught in a difficult squeeze. The British never quite trusted them. After all, they were Americans. During the early stages of the war, Loyalists organized militia companies and hoped to pacify large areas of the countryside with the support of the regular army. The British generals were unreliable partners, however, for no sooner had they called on loyal Americans to come forward than the redcoats marched away, leaving the Tories exposed to rebel retaliation. And in England, the exiles found themselves treated as second-class citizens.

Americans who actively supported independence saw these people as traitors who deserved their fate of constant, often violent, harassment. In many states—but especially in New York—revolutionary governments confiscated Loyalist property. Other friends of the king received beatings, or as the rebels called them, "grand Toory [sic] rides." A few were even executed. According to one patriot, "A Tory is a thing whose head is in England, and its body in America, and its neck ought to be stretched."

Long after the victorious Americans turned their attentions to the business of building a new republic, Loyalists remembered a receding colonial past, a comfortable, ordered world that had been lost forever at Yorktown. Although many Loyalists eventually returned to their homes, a sizable number could not do so. For them, the sense of loss remained a heavy emotional burden. Perhaps the most poignant testimony came from a young mother living in exile in Nova Scotia. "I climbed to the top of Chipman's Hill and watched the sails disappear in the distance," she recounted, "and such a feeling of loneliness came over me that though I had not shed a tear through all the war I sat down on the damp moss with my baby on my lap and cried bitterly."

WINNING THE PEACE

Congress appointed a skilled delegation to negotiate a peace treaty: Benjamin Franklin, John Adams, and John Jay. According to their official instructions, they were to insist only on the recognition of the independence of the United States. On other issues, Congress ordered its delegates to defer to the counsel of the French government.

But the political environment in Paris was much different from what the diplomats had been led to expect. The French had formed a military alliance with Spain, and French officials announced that they could not consider the details of an American settlement until after the Spanish had recaptured Gibraltar from the British. The prospects for a Spanish victory were not good, and in any case, it was well known that Spain coveted the lands lying between the Appalachian Mountains and the Mississippi River. Indeed, there were even rumors afloat in Paris that the great European powers might intrigue to deny the United States its independence.

While the three American delegates publicly paid their respects to French officials, they secretly entered into negotiations with an English agent. The peacemakers drove a remarkable bargain, a much better one than Congress could have expected. The preliminary agreement signed on September 3, 1783, not only guaranteed the independence of the United States; it also transferred all the territory east of the Mississippi River, except Spanish Florida, to the new republic. The treaty established generous boundaries on the north and south and gave the Americans important fishing rights in the North Atlantic. In exchange, Congress promised to help British merchants collect debts contracted before the Revolution and compensate Loyalists whose lands had been confiscated by the various state governments. Even though the Americans negotiated separately with the British, they did not sign a separate peace. The preliminary treaty did not become effective until France reached its own agreement with Great Britain. Thus did the Americans honor the French alliance. It is difficult to imagine how Franklin, Adams, and Jay could have negotiated a more favorable conclusion to the war. In the fall of 1783, the last redcoats sailed from New York City, ending 176 years of colonial rule.

POST-COLONIAL CHALLENGE

The American people had waged war against the most powerful nation in Europe and emerged victorious. The treaty marked the conclusion of a colonial rebellion, but it remained for the men and women who had resisted taxation without representation to work out the full implications of republicanism. What would be the shape of the new government? What powers would be delegated to the people, the states, the federal authorities? How far would the wealthy, well-born leaders of the rebellion be willing to extend political, social, and economic rights? No wonder Philadelphia physician Dr. Benjamin Rush explained, "There is nothing more common than to confound the terms of American Revolution with those of the late American war. The American war is over, but this is far from being the case with the American Revolution. On the contrary, nothing but the first act of the great drama is closed."

6

THE REPUBLICAN EXPERIMENT

A curious controversy shattered the harmony of Boston in 1785. The dispute broke out soon after a group of young adults, sons and daughters of the city's wealthiest families, announced the formation of a tea assembly or "Sans Souci Club." The members of this select group gathered once a week for the pleasure of good conversation, a game of cards, some dancing, and perhaps a glass of Madeira wine.

These meetings outraged other Bostonians, many of them old patriots. Samuel Adams, who dreamed of creating a "Christian Sparta," a virtuous society committed to republican values, sounded the alarm. "Say, my country," he thundered, "why do you suffer all the intemperances of Great Britain to be fostered in our bosom, in all their vile luxuriance?" The club's very existence threatened the "republican principles" for which Americans had so recently fought a revolution.

DEFINING A NEW POLITICAL CULTURE

Today, the term *republican* no longer possesses the evocative power it did for eighteenth-century Americans. For them, it defined an entire political culture. After all, they had done something that no other people had achieved for a very long time. They founded a national government without a monarch or aristocracy, in other words, a genuine republic. Making the new system work was a daunting task. Those Americans who read deeply in ancient and renaissance history knew that most republics had failed, often within a few years, only to be replaced by tyrants who cared not at all what ordinary people thought about the public good.

To preserve their republic from such a fate, victorious revolutionaries such as Adams recast fundamental political values. For them, republicanism represented more than a particular form of government. It was a way of life, a core ideology, an uncompromising commitment to liberty and a total rejection of aristocracy.

Adams and his contemporaries—some of whom probably visited the Sans Souci Club—certainly believed that creating a new nation-state involved more than simply winning independence from Great Britain. If American citizens substituted "luxury, prodigality, and profligacy" for "prudence, virtue, and economy," then their revolution surely would have been in vain. Maintaining popular virtue was crucial to success. An innocent tea party, therefore, set off alarm bells. Such "foolish gratifications" in Boston seemed to compromise republican goals. It is not surprising that in this situation Adams thundered, "Rome, Athens, and all the cities of renown, whence came your fall?"

White Americans were optimistic about their country's chances. This expansive outlook, encountered among so many ordinary men and women, owed much to the spread of Protestant evangelicalism. However skeptical Jefferson and Franklin may have been about revealed religion, the great mass of American people subscribed to an almost utopian belief that God had promised the new republic progress and prosperity. The signs were visible for everyone. "There is not upon the face of the earth a body of people more happy or rising into consequence with more rapid stride," one man announced in 1786, "than the Inhabitants of the United States of America. Population is increasing, new houses building, new lands clearing, new settlements forming, and new manufactures establishing with a rapidity beyond conception."

Such optimism did not translate easily into the creation of a strong central government. Modern Americans tend to take for granted the acceptance of the Constitution. Its merits seem self-evident largely because it has survived for two centuries. But in the early 1780s, no one could have predicted that the Constitution as we know it would have been written, much less ratified. It was equally possible that the Americans would have supported a weak confederation or perhaps allowed the various states and regions to go their separate ways.

In this uncertain political atmosphere, Americans divided sharply over the relative importance of *liberty* and *order*. The revolutionary experience had called into question the legitimacy of any form of special privilege. As one republican informed an aristocratic colleague in the South Carolina assembly, "the day is Arrived when *goodness,* and not *Wealth,* are the only *Criterions of greatness.*" Liberty was contagious, and Americans of all backgrounds began to make new demands on society and government. For them, the Revolution had suggested radical alternatives, and in many forums throughout the nation—especially in the elected state assemblies—they insisted on being heard.

In certain quarters, the celebration of liberty met with mixed response. Some Americans—often the very men who had resisted British tyranny—worried that the citizens of the new nation were caught up in a wild, destructive scramble for material wealth. Democratic excesses seemed to threaten order, to endanger the rights of property. Surely a republic could not long survive unless its citizens showed greater self-control. For people concerned about the loss of order, the state assemblies appeared to be the greatest source of instability. Popularly elected representatives lacked what men of property defined as real civic virtue, an ability to work for the common good rather than their private interests.

Working out the tensions between order and liberty, between property and equality, generated an outpouring of political genius. At other times in American history, persons of extraordinary talent have been drawn to theology, commerce, or science, but during the 1780s, the country's intellectual leaders—Thomas Jefferson, James Madison, Alexander Hamilton, and John Adams, among others—focused their creative energies on the problem of how republicans ought to govern themselves.

LIVING IN A REVOLUTIONARY SOCIETY

Revolution changed American society, often in ways no one had planned. National independence compelled people to reevaluate hierarchical social relations that they had taken for granted during the colonial period. The faltering first steps of independence raised fundamental questions about the meaning of equality in American society, some of which remain as pressing today as during the 1780s.

SOCIAL AND POLITICAL REFORM

Following the war, Americans aggressively denounced any traces of aristocratic pretense. As colonists, they had long resented the claims that certain Englishmen made to special privilege simply because of noble birth. Even so committed a republican as George Washington had to be reminded that artificial status was contrary to republican principles. In 1783, he and the officers who had served during the Revolution formed the Society of the Cincinnati, a hereditary organization in which membership passed from father to eldest son. The soldiers meant no harm; they simply wanted to maintain old friendships. But anxious republicans throughout America let out a howl of protest, and one South Carolina legislator, Aedanus Burke, warned that the Society intended to create "an hereditary peerage . . . [which would] undermine the Constitution and destroy civil liberty." After an embarrassed Washington called for appropriate reforms of the Society's

Questions of equality in the new republic extended to the rights of women. In this illustration, which appeared as the frontispiece in the 1792 issue of The Lady's Magazine and Repository of Entertaining Knowledge, *the "Genius of the Ladies Magazine" and the "Genius of Emulation" (holding in her hand a laurel crown) present to Liberty a petition for the rights of women.*

bylaws, the Cincinnati crisis receded. The fear of privilege remained, however, and wealthy Americans dropped honorific titles such as "esquire."

The appearance of equality was as important as its actual achievement. In fact, the distribution of wealth in postwar America was more uneven than it had been in the mid-eighteenth century. The sudden accumulation of large fortunes by new families made other Americans particularly sensitive to aristocratic display, for it seemed intolerable that a revolution waged against a monarchy should produce a class of persons legally, or even visibly, distinguished from their fellow citizens.

In an effort to root out the notion of a privileged class, states abolished laws of primogeniture and entail. In colonial times, these laws allowed a landholder either to pass his entire estate to his eldest son or to declare that his property could never be divided, sold, or given away. Jefferson claimed that the repeal of these practices would eradicate "antient [sic] and future aristocracy; a foundation [has been] laid for a government truly republican." However many planters actually suffered from entail or primogeniture, the symbolism of the law counted as much as real social practice. Republican legislators wanted to cleanse traces of the former feudal order from the statute books.

Republican ferment also encouraged many states to lower property requirements for voting. As one group of farmers declared, no man can be "free & independent" unless he possesses "a voice . . . in the choice of the most important Officers in the Legislature." Pennsylvania and Georgia allowed all white male taxpayers to participate in elections. Other states were less democratic, but with the exception of Massachusetts, they reduced property qualifications. The reforms, however, did not significantly expand the American electorate. Long before the Revolution, an overwhelming percentage of free white males had owned enough land to vote. In any case, during the 1780s, republican lawmakers were not prepared to experiment with universal manhood suffrage; John Adams observed that if the states pushed the reforms too far, "New claims will arise, women will demand a vote . . . and every man who has not a farthing, will demand an equal vote with any other."

The most important changes in voting patterns resulted from western migration. As Americans moved to the frontier, they received full political representation in their state legislatures, and because new districts tended to be poorer than established coastal settlements, their representatives seemed less cultured, less well trained than those sent by eastern voters. Moreover, western delegates who resented traveling so far to attend legislative meetings lobbied successfully to transfer state capitals to more convenient locations. During this period, Georgia moved the seat of its government from Savannah to Augusta, South Carolina from Charles Town to Columbia, North Carolina from New Bern to Raleigh, Virginia from Williamsburg to Richmond, New York from New York City to Albany, and New Hampshire from Portsmouth to Concord.

After gaining independence, Americans also reexamined the relation between church and state. Republican spokespersons such as Thomas Jefferson insisted that rulers had no right to interfere with the free expression of an individual's religious beliefs. As governor of Virginia, he strenuously advocated the disestablishment of the Anglican Church, an institution that had received tax monies and other benefits during the colonial period. Jefferson and his allies regarded such special privilege not only as a denial of religious freedom—after all, rival denominations did not receive tax money—but also as a vestige of aristocratic society.

In 1786, Virginia cut the last ties between church and state. Other southern states disestablished the Anglican Church, but in Massachusetts and New Hampshire, Congregational churches continued to enjoy special status. Moreover, while Americans championed toleration, they seldom favored theologies that radically challenged Christian values.

AFRICAN AMERICANS IN THE NEW REPUBLIC

Revolutionary fervor forced Americans to confront the most appalling contradiction to republican principles—slavery. The Quaker leader John Woolman (1720–1772) probably did more than any other white person of the era to remind people of the evils of this institution. A trip he took through the Southern Colonies as a young man forever impressed upon Woolman "the dark gloominess" of slavery. In a sermon, the outspoken humanitarian declared "that though we made slaves of the Negroes, and the Turks made Slaves of the Christians, I believed that Liberty was the natural Right of all Men equally."

During the revolutionary period, abolitionist sentiment spread. Both in private and in public, people began to criticize slavery in other than religious language. No doubt, the double standard of their own political rhetoric embarrassed many white Americans. They hotly demanded liberation from British enslavement at the same time that they held several hundred thousand blacks in bondage.

A 1798 sketch by Benjamin Henry Latrobe depicts life on a Chesapeake plantation. The white overseer relaxes with his pipe while two female slaves hoe tobacco fields.

By keeping the issue of slavery before the public through writing and petitioning, African Americans powerfully undermined arguments advanced in favor of human bondage. They demanded freedom, reminding white lawmakers that African American men and women had the same natural right to liberty as did other Americans. In 1779, for example, a group of African Americans asked the members of the Connecticut assembly "whether it is consistent with the present Claims, of the United States, to hold so many Thousands, of the Race of Adam, our Common Father, in perpetual Slavery."

This engraving of Phillis Wheatley appeared in her volume of verse, Poems on Various Subjects, Religious and Moral *(1773), the first book published by an African American.*

The scientific accomplishments of Benjamin Banneker (1731–1806), Maryland's African American astronomer and mathematician, and the international fame of Phillis Wheatley (1753–1784), Boston's celebrated "African muse," made it increasingly difficult for white Americans to maintain credibly that African Americans could not hold their own in a free society. Wheatley's poems went through many editions, and after reading her work, the French philosopher Voltaire rebuked a friend who had claimed "there never would be Negro poets." As Voltaire discovered, Wheatley "writes excellent verse in English." Banneker, like Wheatley, enjoyed a well-deserved reputation, in his case for contributions as a scientist. After receiving a copy of an almanac that Banneker had published in Philadelphia, Thomas Jefferson concluded "that nature has given to our black brethren, talents equal to those of the other colors of men."

In the northern states, where there was no economic justification for slavery, white laborers resented having to compete in the workplace against slaves. This economic situation, combined with the acknowledgment of the double standard represented by slavery, contributed to the establishment of antislavery societies. In 1775, Franklin helped organize a group in Philadelphia called the Society for the Relief of Free Negroes, Unlawfully Held. John Jay, Alexander Hamilton, and other prominent New Yorkers founded a Manumission Society in 1785. By 1792, antislavery societies were meeting from Virginia to Massachusetts, and in the northern states at least, these groups, working for the same ends as various Christian evangelicals, put slaveholders on the intellectual defensive for the first time in American history.

In several states north of Virginia, the abolition of slavery took a number of different forms. Even before achieving statehood, Vermont drafted a constitution (1777) that specifically prohibited slavery. In 1780, the Pennsylvania legislature passed a law effecting the gradual emancipation of slaves. Although the Massachusetts assembly refused to address the issue directly, the state courts took up the challenge and liberated the African Americans. By 1800, slavery was well on the road to extinction in the North.

These developments did not mean that white people accepted blacks as equals. In fact, in the very states that outlawed slavery, African Americans faced systematic discrimination. Free blacks were generally excluded from voting, juries, and militia duty—they were denied rights and responsibilities usually associated with full citizenship. They rarely enjoyed access to education, and in cities such as Philadelphia and New York, where African Americans went to look for work, they ended up living in segregated wards or neighborhoods. Even in the churches—institutions that had often spoken out against slavery—free African

Born to slaves, Richard Allen became a zealous evangelical minister. Allen organized the African Methodist Episcopal Church in 1814.

Americans were denied equal standing with white worshipers. Humiliations of this sort persuaded African Americans to form their own churches. In Philadelphia, Richard Allen, a former slave, founded the Bethel Church for Negro Methodists (1793) and later organized the African Methodist Episcopal Church (1814), an institution of great cultural as well as religious significance for nineteenth-century American blacks.

Even in the South, where African Americans made up a large percentage of the population, slavery disturbed thoughtful white republicans. Some planters simply freed their slaves, and by 1790, the number of free blacks living in Virginia was 12,766. By 1800, the figure had reached 30,750. Richard Randolph, one of Virginia's wealthier planters, explained that he freed his slaves "to make restitution, as far as I am able, to an unfortunate race of bond-men, over whom my ancestors have usurped and exercised the most lawless and monstrous tyranny." George Washington also manumitted his slaves. To be sure, most southern slaveholders, especially those living in South Carolina and Georgia, rejected this course of action. Perhaps more significant, however, is the fact that no southern leader during the era of republican experimentation defended slavery as a positive good. Such overtly racist rhetoric did not become part of the public discourse until the nineteenth century.

Despite promising starts in that direction, the southern states did not abolish slavery. The economic incentives to maintain a servile labor force, especially after the invention of the cotton gin in 1793 and the opening up of the Alabama and Mississippi frontier, overwhelmed the initial abolitionist impulse. An opportunity to translate the principles of the American Revolution into social practice had been lost, at least temporarily.

LIMITING WOMEN'S RIGHTS

The revolutionary experience accelerated changes in how ordinary people viewed the family. At the beginning of the eighteenth century, fathers claimed authority over other members of their families simply on the grounds that they were fathers. As patriarchs, they demanded obedience. If they behaved like brutal despots, so be it; fathers could treat wives and children however they pleased. The English philosopher John Locke (1632–1704) powerfully undermined arguments of this sort, and at the time of the American Revolution few seriously accepted the notion that fathers—be they tyrannical kings or heads of ordinary families—enjoyed unlimited powers over women and children. Indeed, people in England as well as America increasingly described the family in terms of love and companionship. Instead of duties, they spoke of affection. This transformation in the way men and women viewed relations of power within the family was most evident in the popular novels of the period. Americans devoured *Pamela* and

Clarissa, stories by the English writer Samuel Richardson about women who were the innocent victims of unreformed males, usually deceitful lovers and unforgiving fathers.

In this changing intellectual environment American women began making new demands not only on their husbands but also on republican institutions. Abigail Adams, one of the generation's most articulate women, instructed her husband, John, as he set off for the opening of the Continental Congress: "I desire you would Remember the Ladies, and be more generous and favourable to them than your ancestors. Do not put such unlimited power into the hands of the Husbands." John responded in a condescending manner. The "Ladies" would have to wait until the country achieved independence. In 1777, Lucy Knox took an even stronger line with her husband, General Henry Knox. When he was about to return home from the army, she warned him, "I hope you will not consider yourself as commander in chief in your own house—but be convinced . . . that there is such a thing as equal command."

If Knox accepted Lucy's argument, he did so because she was a good republican wife and mother. In fact, women justified their assertiveness largely on the basis of political ideology. If survival of republics really depended on the virtue of their citizens, they argued, then it was the special responsibility of women as mothers to nurture the right values in their children and as wives to instruct their husbands in proper behavior.

Ill-educated women could not possibly fulfill these high expectations. They required education that was at least comparable to what men received. Scores of female academies were established during this period to meet what many Americans, men as well as women, now regarded as a pressing social need. The schools may have received widespread encouragement precisely because they did not radically alter traditional gender roles. After all, the educated republican woman of the late eighteenth century did not pursue a career; she returned to the home, where she followed a familiar routine as wife and mother.

During this period, women petitioned for divorce on new grounds. One case is particularly instructive concerning changing attitudes toward women and the family. In 1784, John Backus, an undistinguished Massachusetts silversmith, was hauled before a local court and asked why he beat his wife. He responded that "it was Partly owing to his Education for his father treated his mother in the same manner." The difference between Backus's case and his father's was that Backus's wife refused to tolerate such abuse, and she sued successfully for divorce. Studies of divorce patterns in Connecticut and Pennsylvania show that after 1773, women divorced on about the same terms as men.

The war itself presented some women with fresh opportunities. In 1780, Ester DeBerdt Reed founded a large volunteer women's organization in

Westtown Boarding School in Pennsylvania was established by the Society of Friends to expand educational opportunities for women in the Middle Atlantic states. Instituted in 1794, the school opened in 1799.

Philadelphia—the first of its kind in the United States—that raised more than $300,000 for Washington's army. Other women ran family farms and businesses while their husbands fought the British. And in 1790, the New Jersey legislature explicitly allowed women who owned property to vote.

Despite these scattered gains, republican society still defined women's roles exclusively in terms of mother, wife, and homemaker. Other pursuits seemed unnatural, even threatening, and it is perhaps not surprising, therefore, that in 1807, New Jersey lawmakers—angry over a close election in which women voters may have determined the result—repealed female suffrage in the interests of "safety, quiet, and good order and dignity of the state."

POSTPONING FULL LIBERTY

The Revolution did not bring about a massive restructuring of American society, at least not in the short term. Nevertheless, republicans such as Samuel Adams and Thomas Jefferson raised issues of immense significance for the later history of the United States. They insisted that equality, however narrowly defined, was an essential element of republican government. Even though they failed to abolish slavery, institute universal manhood suffrage, or apply equality to women, they vigorously articulated a set of assumptions about people's rights and liberties that challenged future generations of Americans to make good on the promise of the Revolution.

THE STATES: THE LESSONS OF REPUBLICANISM

In May 1776, the Second Continental Congress invited the states to adopt constitutions. The old colonial charters filled with references to king and Parliament were no longer adequate, and within a few years, most states had taken action. Rhode Island and Connecticut already enjoyed republican government by virtue of their unique seventeenth-century charters that allowed the voters to select both governors and legislators. Eleven other states plus Vermont created new political structures, and their deliberations reveal how Americans reacting to different social pressures defined fundamental republican principles.

Several constitutions were boldly experimental, and some states later rewrote documents that had been drafted in the first flush of independence. Although these early constitutions were provisional, they provided the framers of the federal Constitution of 1787 with invaluable insights into the strengths and weaknesses of government based on the will of the people.

BLUEPRINTS FOR STATE GOVERNMENT

Despite disagreements over details, Americans who wrote the various state constitutions shared certain political assumptions. First, they insisted on preparing *written* documents. For many of them, of course, this seemed a natural step. As colonists, they had lived under royal charters, documents that described the workings of local government in detail.

However logical the decision to produce written documents may have seemed to the Americans, it represented a major break with English practice. Political philosophers in the mother country had long boasted of Britain's unwritten constitution, a collection of judicial reports and parliamentary statutes. But this highly vaunted system had not protected the colonists from oppression; hence, after declaring independence, Americans demanded that their state constitutions explicitly define the rights of the people as well as the power of their rulers.

NATURAL RIGHTS AND THE STATE CONSTITUTIONS

The authors of the state constitutions believed men and women possessed certain natural rights over which government exercised no control whatsoever. So that future rulers—potential tyrants—would know the exact limits of authority, these fundamental rights were carefully spelled out. Indeed, the people of Massachusetts rejected the proposed state constitution of 1778 largely because it lacked a full statement of their basic rights. They demanded a guarantee of "rights of conscience, and . . . security of persons and property, which every member in the State hath a right to expect from the supreme power."

Eight state constitutions contained specific declarations of rights. The length and character of these lists varied, but, in general, they affirmed three fundamental freedoms: religion, speech, and press. They protected citizens from unlawful searches and seizures; they upheld trial by jury.

In almost every state, delegates to constitutional conventions drastically reduced the power of the governor. The constitutions of Pennsylvania and Georgia abolished the governor's office. In four other states, terms such as *president* were substituted for *governor*. Even when those who designed the new state governments provided for a governor, they severely circumscribed his authority. He was allowed to make almost no political appointments, and while the state legislators closely monitored his activities, he possessed no veto over their decisions (Massachusetts being the lone exception).

Most early constitutions lodged nearly all effective power in the legislature. This decision made good sense to men who had served under powerful royal governors during the late colonial period. These ambitious crown appointees had used executive patronage to influence members of the colonial assemblies, and as the Americans drafted their new republican constitutions, they were determined to bring their governors under tight control.

The legislature dominated early state government. The constitutions of Pennsylvania and Georgia provided for a unicameral, or one-house, system, and since any male taxpayer could cast a ballot in these states, their legislatures became the nation's most democratic. Other states authorized the creation of two houses, but even as they did so, some of the more demanding republicans wondered why America needed a senate or upper house at all. What social and economic interests, they asked, did that body represent that could not be more fully and directly voiced in the lower house? After all, America had just freed itself of an aristocracy. The two-house form survived the Revolution largely because it was familiar and because some persons had already begun to suspect that certain checks on the popular will, however arbitrary they might have appeared, were necessary to preserve minority rights.

POWER TO THE PEOPLE

Massachusetts did not adopt a constitution until 1780, several years after the other states had done so. The experience of the people of Massachusetts is particularly significant because in their efforts to establish a workable system of republican government, they hit on a remarkable political innovation. After the rejection of two constitutions drafted by the state legislature, the responsibility fell to a specially elected convention of delegates whose sole purpose was the "formation of a new Constitution."

John Adams took a position of leadership at this convention and served as the chief architect of the governmental framework of Massachusetts. This framework included a house and senate, a popularly elected governor—who, unlike the chief executives of other states, possessed a veto over legislative bills—and property qualifications for officeholders as well as voters. The most striking aspect of the 1780 constitution, however, was the wording of its opening sentence: "We . . . the people of Massachusetts . . . agree upon, ordain, and establish." This powerful statement would be echoed in the federal Constitution. The Massachusetts experiment reminded Americans that ordinary officeholders could not be trusted to define fundamental rights. That important task required a convention of delegates who could legitimately claim to speak for the people.

In 1780, no one knew whether the state experiments would succeed. There was no question that a different type of person had begun to appear in public office, one who seemed, to the local gentry at least, a little poorer and less polished than they would have liked. When one Virginian surveyed the newly elected House of Burgesses in 1776, he discovered it was "composed of men not quite so well dressed, nor so politely educated, nor so highly born as some Assemblies I have formerly seen." This particular Virginian approved of such change, for he believed that "the People's men," however plain they might appear, possessed honesty and sincerity. They were, in fact, representative republicans, people who insisted they were anyone's equal in this burgeoning society.

Other Americans were less optimistic about the nation's immediate prospects. The health of a small republic depended entirely on the virtue of its people. If they or their elected officials succumbed to material temptation, if they failed to comprehend the moral dimensions of political power, or if personal liberty threatened the rights of property, then the state constitutions were no more than worthless pieces of paper.

STUMBLING TOWARD A NEW NATIONAL GOVERNMENT

When the Second Continental Congress convened in 1775, the delegates found themselves waging war in the name of a country that did not yet exist. As the military crisis deepened, Congress gradually—often reluctantly—assumed greater authority over national affairs, but everyone agreed such narrowly conceived measures were a poor substitute for a legally constituted government. The separate states could not possibly deal with the range of issues that now confronted the American people. Indeed, if independence meant anything in a world of sovereign nations, it implied the creation of a central authority capable of conducting war, borrowing money, regulating trade, and negotiating treaties.

ARTICLES OF CONFEDERATION

The challenge of creating a viable central government proved more difficult than anyone anticipated. Congress appointed a committee to draw up a plan for confederation. John Dickinson, the lawyer who had written an important revolutionary pamphlet titled *Letters from a Farmer in Pennsylvania,* headed the committee. Dickinson envisioned the creation of a strong central government, and the report his committee presented on July 12, 1776, shocked delegates who assumed that the constitution would authorize a loose confederation of states. Dickinson's plan placed the western territories, land claimed by the separate states, under congressional control. In addition, Dickinson's committee called for equal state representation in Congress.

Since some states, such as Virginia and Massachusetts, were more populous than others, the plan fueled tensions between large and small states. Also unsettling was Dickinson's recommendation that taxes be paid to Congress on the basis of a state's total population, black as well as white, a formula that angered Southerners who did not think slaves should be counted. Indeed, even before the British evacuated Boston, Dickinson's committee raised many difficult political questions that would divide Americans for several decades.

Not surprisingly, the draft of the plan—the Articles of Confederation—that Congress finally approved in November 1777 bore little resemblance to Dickinson's original plan. The Articles jealously guarded the sovereignty of the states. The delegates who drafted the framework shared a general republican conviction that power—especially power so far removed from the people—was inherently dangerous and that the only way to preserve liberty was to place as many constraints as possible on federal authority.

The result was a government that many people regarded as powerless. The Articles provided for a single legislative body consisting of representatives selected annually by the state legislatures. Each state possessed a single vote in Congress. It could send as many as seven delegates, as few as two, but if they divided evenly on a certain issue, the state lost its vote. There was no independent executive and no veto over legislative decisions. The Articles also denied Congress the power of taxation, a serious oversight in time of war. The national government could obtain funds only by asking the states for contributions, called requisitions, but if a state failed to cooperate—and many did—Congress limped along without financial support. Amendments to this constitution required assent by all thirteen states. The authors of the new system expected the weak national government to handle foreign relations, military matters, Indian affairs, and interstate disputes. They most emphatically did not award Congress ownership of the lands west of the Appalachian Mountains.

The new constitution sent to the states for ratification encountered apathy and hostility. Most Americans were far more interested in local affairs than in the actions of Congress. When a British army marched through a state, creating a need for immediate military aid, people spoke positively about central government, but as soon as the threat had passed, they sang a different tune. During this period, even the slightest encroachment on state sovereignty rankled republicans who feared centralization would inevitably promote corruption.

WESTERN LAND: KEY TO THE FIRST CONSTITUTION

The major bone of contention with the Articles, however, was the disposition of the vast, unsurveyed territory west of the Appalachians that everyone hoped the British would soon surrender. Some states, such as Virginia and Georgia, claimed land all the way from the Atlantic Ocean to the elusive "South Seas," in effect extending their boundaries to the Pacific coast by virtue of royal charters. State legislators—their appetites whetted by aggressive land speculators—anticipated generating large revenues through land sales. Connecticut, New York, Pennsylvania, and North Carolina also announced intentions to seize blocks of western land.

Other states were not blessed with vague or ambiguous royal charters. The boundaries of Maryland, Delaware, and New Jersey had been established many years earlier, and it seemed as if people living in these states would be permanently cut off from the anticipated bounty. In protest, these "landless" states stubbornly refused to ratify the Articles of Confederation. Marylanders were particularly vociferous. All the states had made sacrifices for the common good during the Revolution, they complained, and it appeared only fair that all states should profit from the fruits of victory, in this case, from the sale of western lands. Maryland's spokesmen feared that if Congress did not void Virginia's excessive claims to all of the Northwest Territory (the land west of Pennsylvania and north of the Ohio River) as well as to a large area south of the Ohio, beyond the Cumberland Gap, known as Kentucky, then Marylanders would desert their home state in search of cheap Virginia farms, leaving Maryland an underpopulated wasteland.

Virginians scoffed at the pleas for equity. They suspected that behind the Marylanders' statements of high purpose lay the greed of speculators. Private land companies had sprung up before the Revolution and purchased large tracts from the Indians in areas claimed by Virginia. Their agents petitioned Parliament to legitimize these questionable transactions. Their efforts failed. After the Declaration of Independence, however, the companies shifted the focus of their lobbying to Congress, particularly to the representatives of landless states like Maryland. By liberally distributing shares of stock, officials of the Indiana,

Illinois, and Wabash companies gained powerful supporters such as Benjamin Franklin, Robert Morris, and Thomas Johnson, governor of Maryland. These activities encouraged Delaware and New Jersey to modify their demands and join the Confederation, while Maryland held out for five years. The leaders of Virginia, though, remained firm. Why, they asked, should Virginia surrender its historic claims to western lands to enrich a handful of selfish speculators?

The states resolved the bitter controversy in 1781 as much by accident as by design. Virginia agreed to cede its holdings north of the Ohio River to the Confederation on condition that Congress nullify the land companies' earlier purchases from the Indians. A practical consideration had softened Virginia's resolve. Republicans such as Jefferson worried about expanding their state beyond the mountains; with poor transportation links, it seemed impossible to govern such a large territory effectively from Richmond. The western settlers might even come to regard Virginia as a colonial power. Marylanders prudently accepted the Articles (March 1, 1781). Other landed states followed Virginia's example. These transfers established an important principle, for after 1781, it was agreed that the West belonged not to the separate states but to the United States.

No one greeted ratification of the Articles with enthusiasm. When they thought about national politics at all, Americans concerned themselves primarily with winning independence. The new government gradually developed an administrative bureaucracy, and in 1781, it formally created the Departments of War, Foreign Affairs, and Finance. By far the most influential figure in the Confederation was Robert Morris (1734–1806), a freewheeling Philadelphia merchant who was appointed the first superintendent of finance. Although he was a brilliant manager, Morris's decisions as superintendent provoked controversy, indeed, deep suspicion. He hardly seemed a model republican. Morris mixed public funds under his control with personal accounts, and he never lost an opportunity to make a profit. While such practices were not illegal, his apparent improprieties undermined his own political agenda. He desperately wanted to strengthen the central government, but highly vocal critics resisted, labeling Morris a "pecuniary dictator."

NORTHWEST ORDINANCE:
THE CONFEDERATION'S MAJOR ACHIEVEMENT

Whatever the weaknesses of Congress may have been, it did score one impressive triumph. Congressional action brought order to western settlement, especially in the Northwest Territory, and incorporated frontier Americans into an expanding federal system. With thousands of men and women, most of them squatters, pouring across the Appalachian Mountains, Congress had to act quickly to avoid the past errors of royal and colonial authorities.

The initial attempt to deal with this explosive problem came in 1784. Jefferson, then serving as a member of Congress, drafted an ordinance that became the basis for later, more enduring legislation. Jefferson recommended carving ten new states out of the western lands located north of the Ohio River and recently ceded to the United States by Virginia. He specified that each new state establish a republican form of government. When the population of a territory equaled that of the smallest state already in the Confederation, the region could apply for full statehood. In the meantime, free white males could participate in local government.

The impoverished Congress was eager to sell off the western territory as quickly as possible. After all, the frontier represented a source of income that did not depend on the unreliable generosity of the states. A second ordinance, passed in 1785 and called the Land Ordinance, established an orderly process for laying out new townships and marketing public lands.

The 1785 scheme possessed geometric elegance. Surveyors marked off townships, each running directly from east to west. These units, 6 miles square, were subdivided into 36 separate sections of 640 acres (1 square mile) each. (Roads and property boundaries established according to this grid pattern survived long after the Confederation had passed into history.) The government planned to auction off its holdings at prices of not less than $1 an acre. Congress set the minimum purchase at 640 acres, and near-worthless paper money was not accepted as payment. Section 16 was set aside for public education; the federal government reserved four other sections for its own use.

Public response disappointed Congress. Surveying the lands took far longer than anticipated, and few persons possessed enough hard currency to make even the minimum purchase. Finally, a solution to the problem came from Manasseh Cutler, a New England minister turned land speculator and congressional lobbyist.

Cutler and his associates, representing the Ohio and Scioto companies, offered to purchase more than 6 million unsurveyed acres of land located in present-day southeastern Ohio by persuading Congress to accept, at full face value, government loan certificates that had been issued to soldiers during the Revolution. On the open market, the Ohio company could pick up the certificates for as little as 10 percent of their face value; thus, the company stood to make a fortune. Like so many other get-rich-quick schemes, however, this one failed to produce the anticipated millions. Unfortunately for Cutler and his friends, small homesteaders settled wherever they pleased, refusing to pay either government or speculators for the land.

Congress worried about the excess liberty on the frontier. In the 1780s, the West seemed to be filling up with people who by eastern standards were uncultured. Timothy Pickering, a New Englander, declared that "the emigrants to the

The widespread land speculation in the territory south of the Ohio River did not go unnoticed by European political cartoonists of the day. The French caption to the original cartoon explained, "Citizen Mignard signs today for some English companions who are selling imaginary lands in the United States. The better to ensnare dupes, they draw geological maps, converting rocky deserts into fertile plains, show roads cutting through impassable cliffs, and offer shares in lands that do not belong to them."

frontier lands are the least worthy subjects in the United States. They are little less savage than the Indians; and when possessed of the most fertile spots, for want of industry, live miserably." The Ordinance of 1784 placed the government of the territories in the hands of people who congressmen and speculators did not fully trust.

These various currents shaped the Ordinance of 1787, one of the final acts passed under the Confederation. The bill, also called the Northwest Ordinance, provided a new structure for government of the Northwest Territory. The plan authorized the creation of between three and five territories, each to be ruled by a governor, a secretary, and three judges appointed by Congress. When the population reached five thousand, voters who owned property could elect an assembly, but its decisions were subject to the governor's absolute veto. Once sixty thousand persons resided in a territory, they could write a constitution and petition for full statehood. While these procedures represented a retreat from Jefferson's original proposal, the Ordinance of 1787 contained several significant features. A bill of rights guaranteed the settlers the right to trial by jury, freedom of religion, and due process of law. In addition, the act outlawed slavery, a prohibition that freed the future states of Ohio, Indiana, Illinois, Michigan, and Wisconsin from the curse of human bondage.

By contrast, settlement south of the Ohio River received far less attention from Congress. Long before the end of the war, thousands of Americans streamed through the Cumberland Gap into a part of Virginia known as Kentucky. The most famous of these settlers was Daniel Boone. In 1775, the population of Kentucky was approximately one hundred; by 1784, it had jumped to thirty thousand. Speculators purchased large tracts from the Indians, planning to resell this acreage to settlers at handsome profits. One aggressive group of speculators in 1784 carved the State of Franklin out of a section of present-day Tennessee, then claimed by North Carolina. Rival speculators prevented formal recognition of Franklin's government. By 1790, the entire region south of the Ohio River had been transformed into a crazy quilt of claims and counterclaims that generated lawsuits for many years to come.

STRENGTHENING FEDERAL AUTHORITY

Despite its success in bringing order to the Northwest Territory, the Confederation increasingly came under heavy fire from critics who wanted a stronger central government. Complaints varied from region to region, from person to person, but most disappointment reflected frustration with the state of the economy.

THE NATIONALIST CRITIQUE

Even before England signed a treaty with America, its merchants flooded American ports with consumer items and offered easy credit. Families that had postponed purchases of imported goods—either because of British blockade or personal hardship—now rushed to buy European manufactures.

This renewal of trade with Great Britain on such a large scale strained the American economy. Gold and silver flowed back across the Atlantic, leaving the United States desperately short of hard currency. When large merchant houses called in their debts, ordinary American consumers often faced bankruptcy. "The disagreeable state of our commerce," observed James Wilson, an advocate of strong national government, has been the result "of extravagant and injudicious importation. . . . We seemed to have forgot that to pay was as necessary in trade as to purchase."

Critics of the Confederation pointed to the government's inability to regulate trade. Whenever a northern congressman suggested restricting British access to American markets, southern representatives, who feared any controls on the

"Not worth a Continental" became a common oath when inflation eroded the value of the Continental currency. Most currency issued by the states was equally worthless.

export of tobacco or rice, bellowed in protest. Southerners anticipated that navigation acts written by the Confederation would put planters under the yoke of northern shipping interests.

The country's chronic fiscal instability increased public anxiety. While the war was still in progress, Congress printed well over $200 million in paper money, but because of extraordinarily high inflation, the rate of exchange for Continental bills soon declined to a fraction of their face value. In 1781, Congress, facing insolvency, turned to the states for help. They were asked to retire the depreciated currency. The situation was spinning out of control. Several states—pressed to pay their own war-related debts—not only recirculated the Continental bills but also issued nearly worthless money of their own.

A heavy burden of state and national debt compounded the general sense of economic crisis. Revolutionary soldiers had yet to be paid. Women and men who had loaned money and goods to the government clamored for reimbursement. Foreign creditors demanded interest on funds advanced during the Revolution. These pressures grew, but Congress was unable to respond. The Articles specifically prohibited Congress from taxing the American people. It required little imagination to see that the Confederation would soon default on its legal obligations unless something was done quickly.

In response, an aggressive group of men known as the "nationalists"—persons such as Alexander Hamilton, James Madison, and Robert Morris—called for major constitutional reforms. They demanded an amendment allowing Congress to collect a 5 percent tax on imported goods sold in the states. Revenues generated by the proposed Impost of 1781 would be used by the Confederation to reduce the national debt. On this point the nationalists were adamant. They recognized that whoever paid the public debt would gain the public trust. If the states assumed the responsibility, then the country could easily fragment into separate republics. Twelve states accepted the Impost amendment, but Rhode Island—where local interests argued that the tax would make Congress "independent of their constituents"— refused to cooperate. One negative vote killed the taxing scheme.

State leaders did not trust the nationalists. The "localists" were apprehensive of fiscal plans advanced by Robert Morris. His profiteering as superintendent of finance appeared a threat to the moral fiber of the young republic. Richard Henry Lee and Samuel Adams, men of impeccable patriotic credentials, decried Morris's efforts to create a national bank. Such an institution would bring forth a flock of social parasites, the kind of people that Americans associated with corrupt monarchical government. One person declared that if an impost ever passed, Morris "will have all [the money] in his Pocket."

The nationalists regarded their opponents as economically naive. A country with the potential of the United States required a complex, centralized fiscal system. But for all their pretensions to realism, the nationalists of the early 1780s were politically inept. They underestimated the depth of republican and localist fears, and in their rush to strengthen the Articles, they overplayed their hand.

A group of extreme nationalists even appealed to the army for support. To this day, no one knows the full story of the Newburgh Conspiracy of 1783. Officers of the Continental Army stationed at Newburgh, New York, worried that Congress would disband them without funding their pensions, lobbied intensively for relief. In March, they scheduled general meetings to protest the weakness and duplicity of Congress. The officers' initial efforts were harmless enough, but frustrated nationalists such as Morris and Hamilton hoped that if the army exerted sufficient pressure on the government, perhaps even threatened a military takeover, then the localists might be compelled to amend the Articles.

The conspirators failed to take George Washington's integrity into account. No matter how much he wanted a strong central government, he would not tolerate insubordination by the military. Washington confronted the officers directly at Newburgh, intending to read a prepared statement. Fumbling with his glasses before his men, he commented, "Gentlemen, you must pardon me. I have grown gray in your service and now find myself growing blind." The unexpected vulnerability of this great soldier reduced the troops to tears, and in an instant, the mutiny was broken. Washington deserves credit for preserving civilian rule in this country.

In April 1783, a second impost failed to win unanimous ratification. Even a personal appeal by Washington could not save the amendment. With this defeat, nationalists gave up on the Confederation. Morris retired from government, and Madison returned to Virginia utterly depressed by what he had witnessed.

DIPLOMATIC HUMILIATION

In foreign affairs, Congress endured further embarrassment. It could not even enforce the provisions of its own peace treaty. American negotiators had promised Great Britain that its citizens could collect debts contracted before the Revolution. The states, however, dragged their heels, and several even passed laws obstructing the settlement of legitimate prewar claims. Congress was powerless to force compliance. The British responded to this apparent provocation by refusing to evacuate troops from posts located in the Northwest Territory.

Congress's postrevolutionary dealings with Spain were equally humiliating. That nation refused to accept the southern boundary of the United States established by the Treaty of Paris. Spain claimed sovereignty over much of the land located between Georgia and the Mississippi River. On July 21, 1784, it fueled the controversy by closing the lower Mississippi River to citizens of the United States.

This unexpected decision devastated western farmers. Free use of the Mississippi was essential to the economic development of the entire Ohio Valley. Because of the prohibitively high cost of transporting freight for long distances over land, western settlers—and southern planters eyeing future opportunities in this area—demanded a secure water link with the world's markets. Their spokesmen in Congress denounced anyone who claimed that navigation of the Mississippi was a negotiable issue.

In 1786, a Spanish official, Don Diego de Gardoqui, opened talks with John Jay, a New Yorker appointed by Congress to obtain rights to navigation of the Mississippi. Jay soon discovered that Gardoqui would not compromise. After making little progress, Jay seized the initiative. If Gardoqui would allow American merchants to trade directly with Spain, thus opening up an important new market to ships from New England and the middle states, then the United States might forgo navigation of the Mississippi for twenty-five years. When southern delegates heard of Jay's concessions, they were outraged. It appeared to them as if representatives of northern commerce were attempting to divide the

United States into separate confederations. Congress wisely terminated the negotiations with Spain.

By the mid-1780s, the Confederation could claim several notable achievements. Still, as anyone could see, the government was struggling. Congress met irregularly. Some states did not even bother to send delegates, and pressing issues often had to be postponed for lack of a quorum. The nation even lacked a permanent capital, and Congress drifted from Philadelphia to Princeton to Annapolis to New York City.

"HAVE WE FOUGHT FOR THIS?"

By 1785, the country seemed to have lost direction. The buoyant optimism that sustained revolutionary patriots had dissolved into pessimism and doubt. Many Americans, especially those who had provided leadership during the Revolution, agreed something had to be done. In 1786, Washington bitterly observed, "What astonishing changes a few years are capable of producing. Have we fought for this? Was it with these expectations that we launched into a sea of trouble, and have bravely struggled through the most threatening dangers?"

THE GENIUS OF JAMES MADISON

The conviction of people such as Washington that the nation was indeed in a state of crisis reflected tensions within republican thought. To be sure, they supported open elections and the right of individuals to advance their own economic well-being, but when these elements seemed to undermine social and political order, they expressed the fear that perhaps liberty had been carried too far. The situation had changed quite rapidly. As recently as the 1770s, men of republican persuasion had insisted that the greatest threat to the American people was concentration of power in the hands of unscrupulous rulers. With this principle in mind, they transformed state governors into mere figureheads and weakened the Confederation in the name of popular liberties.

By the mid-1780s, persons of property and standing saw the problem in a different light. Recent experience suggested to them that ordinary citizens did not in fact possess sufficient virtue to sustain a republic. The states had been plagued not by executive tyranny but by an excess of democracy, by a failure of the majority to preserve the property rights of the minority, by an unrestrained individualism that promoted anarchy rather than good order.

As Americans tried to interpret these experiences within a republican framework, they were checked by the most widely accepted political wisdom of the age. Baron de Montesquieu (1689–1755), a French political philosopher of immense international reputation and author of *The Spirit of the Laws* (1748), declared flatly that a republican government could not flourish in a large territory. The reasons were clear. If the people lost direct control over their representatives, they would fall prey to tyrants. Large distances allowed rulers to hide their corruption.

In the United States, Montesquieu's theories were received as self-evident truths. His writings seemed to demonstrate the importance of preserving the sovereignty of the states, for however much these small republics abused the rights of property and ignored minority interests, it was plainly unscientific to maintain that a republic consisting of thirteen states, several million people, and thousands of acres of territory could long survive.

James Madison challenged Montesquieu's argument, and in so doing, he helped Americans to think of republican government in radical new ways. This soft-spoken, rather unprepossessing Virginian was the most brilliant American political thinker of his generation.

Madison delved into the writings of a group of Scottish philosophers, the most prominent being David Hume (1711–1776), and discovered that Americans need not fear a greatly expanded republic. Madison perceived that it was in small states such as Rhode Island that legislative majorities tyrannized the propertied minority. In a large territory, Madison explained, "the Society becomes broken into a greater variety of interest, of pursuits, of passions, which check each other,

Among the framers of the Constitution, James Madison, not yet 40, was the most effective advocate of a strong central government.

whilst those who may feel a common sentiment have less opportunity of communication and contact."

Madison did not, however, advocate a modern "interest-group" model of political behavior. The contending parties were incapable of working for the common good. They were too mired in their own local, selfish concerns. Rather, Madison thought competing factions would neutralize each other, leaving the business of running the central government to the ablest, most virtuous persons the nation could produce. In other words, Madison's federal system was not a small state writ large; it was something entirely different, a government based on the will of the people and yet detached from their narrowly based demands. This thinking formed the foundation of Madison's most famous political essay, *The Federalist* No. 10.

CONSTITUTIONAL REFORM

A concerted movement to overhaul the Articles of Confederation began in 1786, when Madison and his friends persuaded the Virginia assembly to recommend a convention to explore the creation of a unified system of "commercial regulations." Congress supported the idea. In September, delegates from five states arrived in Annapolis, Maryland. The occasion provided strong nationalists with an opportunity to hatch an even bolder plan. The Annapolis delegates advised Congress to hold a second meeting in Philadelphia "to take into consideration the situation of the United States, to devise such further provisions as shall appear to them necessary to render the constitution of the Federal Government adequate to the exigencies of the Union." Whether states' rights advocates in Congress knew what was afoot is not clear. In any case, Congress authorized a grand convention to gather in May 1787.

Events played into Madison's hands. Soon after the Annapolis meeting, an uprising known as Shays's Rebellion, involving several thousand impoverished farmers, shattered the peace of western Massachusetts. They complained of high taxes, of high interest rates, and, most of all, of a state government insensitive to their problems. In 1786, Daniel Shays, a veteran of the battle of Bunker Hill, and his armed neighbors closed a county courthouse where creditors were suing to foreclose farm mortgages. At one point, the rural insurgents threatened to seize the federal arsenal located at Springfield. Congress did not have funds sufficient to support an army, and the arsenal might have fallen had not a group of wealthy Bostonians raised an army of four thousand troops to put down the insurrection.

For the Nationalists throughout the United States Shays's Rebellion symbolized the breakdown of law and order. "Great commotions are prevailing in Massachusetts," Madison wrote. "An appeal to the sword is exceedingly dreaded." The time had come for sensible people to speak up for a strong national govern-

This 1787 woodcut portrays Daniel Shays with one of his chief officers, Jacob Shattucks. Shays led farmers from western Massachusetts in revolt against a state government that seemed insensitive to rural needs. Their rebellion strengthened the demand for a strong new federal government.

ment. The unrest in Massachusetts persuaded persons who might otherwise have ignored the Philadelphia meeting to participate in drafting a new constitution.

THE PHILADELPHIA CONVENTION

In the spring of 1787, fifty-five men representing twelve states traveled to Philadelphia. Rhode Island refused to take part in the proceedings, a decision that Madison attributed to "wickedness and folly." The delegates were practical people—lawyers, merchants, and planters—many of whom had fought in the Revolution and served in the Congress of the Confederation. The majority were in their thirties or forties. The gathering included George Washington, James Madison, George Mason, Robert Morris, James Wilson, John Dickinson, Benjamin Franklin, and Alexander Hamilton, just to name the more prominent participants. Absent were John Adams and Thomas Jefferson, who were conducting diplomacy in Europe; Patrick Henry, a localist suspicious of strong central government, remained in Virginia, announcing he "smelled a rat."

As soon as the Constitutional Convention opened on May 25, the delegates made several procedural decisions of great importance. First, they voted "that nothing spoken in the House be printed, or communicated without leave." The rule was stringently enforced. Sentries guarded the doorways to keep out uninvited visitors, windows stayed shut in the sweltering heat to prevent sound from either entering or leaving the chamber, and members were forbidden to copy the daily journal without official permission. As Madison explained, the secrecy rule saved "both the convention and the community from a thousand erroneous and perhaps mischievous reports." It also has made it extremely difficult for modern lawyers and judges to determine exactly what the delegates had in mind when they wrote the Constitution.

In a second procedural move, the delegates decided to vote by state, but, in order to avoid the kinds of problems that had plagued the Confederation, they ruled that key proposals needed the support of only a majority instead of the nine states required under the Articles.

INVENTING A FEDERAL REPUBLIC

Even before all the delegates had arrived, Madison drew up a framework for a new federal system known as the Virginia Plan. He persuaded Edmund Randolph, Virginia's popular governor, to present this scheme to the convention on May 29. Randolph claimed that the Virginia Plan merely revised sections of the Articles, but everyone, including Madison, knew better. "My ideas," Madison confessed, "strike . . . deeply at the old Confederation." He was determined to restrain the state assemblies, and in the original Virginia Plan, Madison gave the federal government power to veto state laws.

The Virginia Plan envisioned a national legislature consisting of two houses, one elected *directly* by the people, the other chosen by the first house from nominations made by the state assemblies. Representation in both houses was proportional to the state's population. The Virginia Plan also provided for an executive elected by Congress. Since most delegates at the Philadelphia convention sympathized with the nationalist position, Madison's blueprint for a strong federal government initially received broad support, and the Virginia Plan was referred to further study and debate.

The Virginia Plan had been pushed through the convention so fast that opponents hardly had an opportunity to present their objections. On June 15, they spoke up. William Paterson, a New Jersey lawyer, advanced the so-called New Jersey Plan, a scheme that retained the unicameral legislature in which each state possessed one vote and that at the same time gave Congress extensive new powers to tax and regulate trade. Paterson argued that these revisions, while more modest than Madison's plan, would have greater appeal for the American people. The delegates listened politely and then soundly rejected the New Jersey Plan on

June 19. Indeed, only New Jersey, New York, and Delaware voted in favor of Paterson's scheme.

Rejection of this framework did not resolve the most controversial issue before the convention. Paterson and others feared that under the Virginia Plan small states would lose their separate identities. These delegates maintained that unless each state possessed an equal vote in Congress, the small states would find themselves at the mercy of their larger neighbors.

This argument outraged the delegates who favored a strong federal government. Paterson awarded too much power to the states. "For whom [are we] forming a Government?" Wilson cried. "Is it for men, or for the imaginary beings called States?" It seemed absurd to claim that the 68,000 people of Rhode Island should have the same voice in Congress as Virginia's 747,000 inhabitants.

COMPROMISE SAVES THE CONVENTION

Hard work and frustration, coupled with Philadelphia's sweltering summer heat, frayed nerves, prompting some members to predict that the meeting would accomplish nothing of significance. But despite the growing pessimism, the gathering did not break up. The delegates desperately wanted to produce a constitution, and they refused to give up until they had explored every avenue of reconciliation. Perhaps cooler heads agreed with Washington: "To please all is impossible, and to attempt it would be vain.

Mediation offered the only way to overcome what Roger Sherman, a Connecticut delegate, called "a full stop." On July 2, a "grand committee" of one person from each state was elected by the convention to resolve persistent differences between the large and small states. It recommended that the states be equally represented in the upper house of Congress, while representation was to be proportionate in the lower house. Only the lower house could initiate money bills. The committee also decided that one member of the lower house should be selected for every thirty thousand inhabitants of a state. Southern delegates insisted that this number include slaves. In the so-called three-fifths rule, the committee agreed that for the purpose of determining representation in the lower house, slaves would be counted, but not as much as free persons. For every five slaves, a congressional district received credit for three free voters, a deal that gave the South much greater power in the new government than it would have otherwise received. As with most compromise solutions, this one fully satisfied no one. It did, however, overcome a major impasse, and after the small states gained an assured voice in the upper house, the Senate, they cooperated enthusiastically in creating a strong central government.

REVOLUTION OR REFORM? THE ARTICLES OF CONFEDERATION AND THE CONSTITUTION COMPARED

POLITICAL CHALLENGE	ARTICLES OF CONFEDERATION	CONSTITUTION
Mode of ratification or amendment	Require confirmation by every state legislature	Requires confirmation by three-fourths of state conventions or legislatures
Number of houses in legislature	One	Two
Mode of representation	One to seven delegates represent each state; each state holds only one vote in Congress	Two senators represent each state in upper house; each senator holds one vote. One representative to lower house represents every 30,000 people (in 1788) in a state; each representative holds one vote
Mode of election and term of office	Delegates appointed annually by state legislatures	Senators chosen by state legislatures for six-year term (direct election after 1913); representatives chosen by vote of citizens for two-year term
Executive	No separate executive: delegates annually elect one of their number as president, who possesses no veto, no power to appoint officers or to conduct policy. Administrative functions of government theoretically carried out by Committee of States, practically by various single-headed departments	Separate executive branch: president elected by electoral college to four-year term; granted veto, power to conduct policy and to appoint ambassadors, judges, and officers of executive departments established by legislation
Judiciary	Most adjudication left to state and local courts; Congress is final court of appeal in disputes between states	Separate branch consisting of Supreme Court and inferior courts established by Congress to enforce federal law
Taxation	States alone can levy taxes; Congress funds the Common Treasury by making requisitions for state contributions	Federal government granted powers of taxation
Regulation of commerce	Congress regulates foreign commerce by treaty but holds no check on conflicting state regulations	Congress regulates foreign commerce by treaty; all state regulations must obtain congressional consent

COMPROMISING WITH SLAVERY

During the final days of August, a deeply disturbing issue came before the convention. It was a harbinger of the great sectional crisis of the nineteenth century. Northern representatives detested the slave trade and wanted it to end immediately. They despised the three-fifths ruling that awarded slaveholders extra power in government simply because they owned slaves. "It seemed now to be pretty well understood," Madison jotted in his private notes, "that the real difference of interest lay, not between the large and small but between the N. and Southn. States. The institution of slavery and its consequences formed a line of discrimination."

Whenever northern delegates—and on this point they were by no means united—pushed too aggressively, Southerners threatened to bolt the convention, thereby destroying any hope of establishing a strong national government. Curiously, even recalcitrant Southerners avoided using the word *slavery*. They seemed embarrassed to call the institution by its true name, and in the Constitution itself, slaves were described as "other persons," "such persons," "persons held to Service or Labour," in other words, as everything but slaves.

Largely ignoring northern attacks, the delegates reached an uneasy compromise on the continuation of the slave trade. Southerners feared that the new Congress would pass commercial regulations adversely affecting the planters—taxes on the export of rice and tobacco, for example. They demanded, therefore, that no trade laws be passed without a two-thirds majority of the federal legislature. They backed down on this point, however, in exchange for guarantees that Congress would not interfere with the slave trade until 1808 (see Chapter 8). The South even came away with a clause assuring the return of fugitive slaves. "We have obtained," Charles Cotesworth Pinckney told the planters of South Carolina, "a right to recover our slaves in whatever part of America they may take refuge, which is a right we had not before."

Although these deals disappointed many Northerners, they conceded that establishing a strong national government was of greater immediate importance than ending the slave trade. "Great as the evil is," Madison wrote, "a dismemberment of the union would be worse."

THE LAST DETAILS

On July 26, the convention formed a Committee of Detail to prepare a rough draft of the Constitution. After the committee completed its work—writing a document that still, after so many hours of debate, preserved the fundamental points of the Virginia Plan—the delegates reconsidered each article. The task required the better part of a month.

During these sessions, the members of the convention concluded that the president, as they now called the executive, should be selected by an electoral college, a body of prominent men in each state chosen by local voters. The number of "electoral" votes held by each state equaled its number of representatives and senators. This elitist device guaranteed that the president would not be indebted to the Congress for his office. Whoever received the second largest number of votes in the electoral college automatically became vice president. In the event that no person received a majority of the votes, the election would be decided by the lower house—the House of Representatives—with each state casting a single vote. Delegates also armed the chief executive with veto power over legislation as well as the right to nominate judges. Both privileges, of course, would have been unthinkable a decade earlier, but the state experiments revealed the importance of having an independent executive to maintain a balanced system of republican government.

As the meeting was concluding, some delegates expressed concern about a bill of rights. Such declarations had been included in most state constitutions, and Virginians such as George Mason insisted that the states and their citizens needed explicit protection from possible excesses by the federal government. While many delegates sympathized with Mason's appeal, they noted that the hour was late and, in any case, that the proposed Constitution provided sufficient security for individual rights. During the hard battles over ratification, the delegates to the convention may have regretted passing over the issue so lightly.

WE, THE PEOPLE

The delegates adopted an ingenious procedure for ratification. Instead of submitting the Constitution to the various state legislatures, all of which had a vested interest in maintaining the status quo and most of which had two houses, either of which could block approval, they called for the election of thirteen state conventions especially chosen to review the new federal government. The delegates may have picked up this idea from the Massachusetts experiment of 1780. Moreover, the Constitution would take effect after the assent of only nine states. There was no danger, therefore, that the proposed system would fail simply because a single state like Rhode Island withheld approval.

On September 17, thirty-nine men signed the Constitution. A few members of the convention, such as Mason, could not support the document. Others had already gone home. For more than three months, Madison had served as the convention's driving intellectual force. He now generously summarized the experience: "There never was an assembly of men, charged with a great and arduous trust, who were more pure in their motives, or more exclusively or anxiously devoted to the object committed to them."

WHOSE CONSTITUTION? STRUGGLE FOR RATIFICATION

Supporters of the Constitution recognized that ratification would not be easy. After all, the convention had been authorized only to revise the Articles. Instead, it produced a new plan that fundamentally altered relations between the states and the central government. The delegates dutifully dispatched copies of the Constitution to the Congress of Confederation, then meeting in New York City, and that powerless body referred the document to the separate states without any specific recommendation. The fight for ratification had begun.

FEDERALISTS AND ANTIFEDERALISTS

Proponents of the Constitution enjoyed great advantages over the opposition. In the contest for ratification, they took no chances. Their most astute move was the adoption of the label *Federalist.* The term cleverly suggested that they stood for a confederation of states rather than for the creation of a supreme national authority. Critics of the Constitution, who tended to be somewhat poorer, less urban, and less well educated than their opponents, cried foul, but there was little they could do. They were stuck with the name *Antifederalist,* a misleading term that made their cause seem far more obstructionist than it actually was.

The Federalists recruited the most prominent public figures of the day. In every state convention, speakers favoring the Constitution were more polished and more fully prepared than were their opponents. In New York, the campaign to win ratification sparked publication of *The Federalist,* a brilliant series of essays written by Madison, Hamilton, and Jay during the fall and winter of 1787 and 1788. The nation's newspapers threw themselves overwhelmingly behind the new government. In some states, the Federalists adopted tactics of questionable propriety in order to gain ratification. In Pennsylvania, for example, they achieved a legal quorum for a crucial vote by dragging several opposition delegates into the meeting from the streets. In New York, Hamilton intimidated upstate Antifederalists with threats that New York City would secede from the state unless the state ratified the Constitution.

In these battles, the Antifederalists articulated a political philosophy that had broad popular appeal. Like the extreme republicans who drafted the first state constitutions, the Antifederalists were deeply suspicious of political power. During the debates over ratification, they warned that public officials, however selected, would be constantly scheming to expand their authority. The preservation of individual liberty required constant vigilance. It seemed obvious that the larger the republic, the greater the opportunity for political corruption. Local voters could not possibly know what their representatives in a distant national capital were doing.

Antifederalists demanded direct, personal contact with their representatives. They argued that elected officials should reflect the character of their constituents as closely as possible. It seemed unlikely that in large congressional districts, the people would be able to preserve such close ties with their representatives. According to the Antifederalists, the Constitution favored persons wealthy enough to have forged a reputation that extended beyond a single community. Samuel Chase told the members of the Maryland ratifying convention that under the new system, "the distance between the people and their representatives will be so great that there is no probability of a farmer or planter being chosen . . . only the *gentry,* the *rich,* and the well-born will be elected."

Federalist speakers mocked their opponents' localist perspective. The Constitution deserved general support precisely because it ensured that future Americans would be represented by "natural aristocrats," individuals possessing greater insights, skills, and training than did the ordinary citizen. These talented leaders, the Federalists insisted, could discern the interests of the entire population.

It would be a mistake, however, to see the Antifederalists as "losers" or as persons who could not comprehend social and economic change. Although their rhetoric echoed an older moral view of political culture, they accepted more easily than did many Federalists a liberal marketplace in which ordinary citizens competed as equals with the rich and well-born. They believed the public good was best served by allowing individuals like themselves to pursue their own private interests. That is what they had been doing on the local level during the 1780s, and they resented the imposition of elite controls over their affairs.

The Constitution drew support from many different types of people. In general, Federalists lived in more commercialized areas than did their opponents. In the cities, artisans as well as merchants called for ratification, while those farmers who were only marginally involved in commercial agriculture frequently voted Antifederalist.

Despite passionate pleas from Patrick Henry and other Antifederalists, most state conventions quickly adopted the Constitution. Delaware acted first (December 7, 1787), and within eight months of the Philadelphia meeting, eight of the nine states required to launch the government had ratified the document. The contests in Virginia (June 1788) and New York (July 1788) generated bitter debate, but they too joined the union, leaving only North Carolina and Rhode Island outside the United States. Eventually (November 21, 1789, and May 29, 1790), even these states ratified the Constitution. Still, the vote had been very close. The Constitution was ratified in New York by a tally of 30 to 27, in Massachusetts by 187 to 168, and in Virginia by 89 to 79. A swing of a few votes in several key states could have defeated the new government.

While the state conventions sparked angry rhetoric, Americans soon closed ranks behind the Constitution. An Antifederalist who represented one Massachusetts village explained that "he had opposed the adoption of this Constitution; but that he had been overruled . . . by a majority of wise and un-

Ratification of the Constitution

Advocates of the new Constitution called themselves Federalists, and those who opposed its ratification were known as Antifederalists.

derstanding men [and that now] he should endeavor to sow the seeds of union and peace among the people he represented."

ADDING THE BILL OF RIGHTS

The first ten amendments to the Constitution are the major legacy of the Antifederalist argument. In almost every state convention, opponents of the Constitution pointed to the need for greater protection of individual liberties, rights that people presumably had possessed in a state of nature. "It is necessary," wrote one Antifederalist, "that the sober and industrious part of the community should be defended from the rapacity and violence of the vicious and idle. A bill of rights, therefore, ought to set forth the purposes for which the compact is made, and serves to secure the minority against the usurpation and tyranny of the majority." The list of fundamental rights varied from state to state, but most Antifederalists demanded specific guarantees for jury trial and freedom of religion. They wanted prohibitions against cruel and unusual punishments. There was also considerable, though not universal, support for freedom of speech and freedom of the press.

Madison and others regarded the proposals with little enthusiasm. In *The Federalist* No. 84, Hamilton bluntly reminded the American people that "the constitution is itself . . . a BILL OF RIGHTS." But after the adoption of the Constitution had been assured, Madison moderated his stand. If nothing else, passage of a bill of rights would appease able men such as George Mason and Edmund Randolph, who might otherwise remain alienated from the new federal system.

The crucial consideration was caution. A number of people throughout the nation advocated calling a second constitutional convention, one that would take Antifederalist criticism into account. Madison wanted to avoid such a meeting, and he feared that some members of the first Congress might use a bill of rights as an excuse to revise the entire Constitution or to promote a second convention.

Madison carefully reviewed these recommendations as well as the various declarations of rights that had appeared in the early state constitutions, and on June 8, 1789, he placed before the House of Representatives a set of amendments designed to protect individual rights from government interference. Madison told the members of Congress that the greatest dangers to popular liberties came from "the majority [operating] against the minority." A committee compressed and revised his original ideas into ten amendments that were ratified and became known collectively as the Bill of Rights. For many modern Americans these amendments are the most important section of the Constitution.

The Bill of Rights protected the freedoms of assembly, speech, religion, and the press; guaranteed speedy trial by an impartial jury; preserved the people's right to bear arms; and prohibited unreasonable searches. Other amendments dealt with legal procedure. Some opponents of the Constitution urged Congress to provide greater safeguards for states' rights, but Madison had no intention of backing away from a strong central government. Only the Tenth Amendment addressed the states' relation to the federal system. This crucial article, designed to calm Antifederalist fears, specified that those "powers not delegated to the United States by the Constitution, nor prohibited by it to the States, are reserved to the States respectively, or to the people."

On September 25, 1789, the Bill of Rights passed both houses of Congress, and by December 15, 1791, the amendments had been ratified by three-fourths of the states. Madison was justly proud of his achievement. He had effectively secured individual rights without undermining the Constitution. When he asked his friend Jefferson for his opinion of the Bill of Rights, Jefferson responded with typical republican candor: "I like [it] . . . as far as it goes; but I should have been for going further."

A NEW BEGINNING

By 1789, one phase of American political experimentation had come to an end. During these years, the people gradually, often haltingly, learned that in a republican society, they themselves were sovereign. They could no longer blame the failure of government on inept monarchs or greedy aristocrats. They bore a great responsibility. Americans had demanded a government of the people only to discover during the 1780s that in some situations, the people could not be trusted with power, majorities could tyrannize minorities, and the best of governments could abuse individual rights.

Although contemporaries had difficulty deciding just what had been accomplished, most Americans probably would have accepted Franklin's optimistic assessment. As he watched the delegates to the Philadelphia convention come forward to sign the Constitution, he noted that there was a sun carved on the back of George Washington's chair. "I have," the aged philosopher noted, ". . . often in the course of the session . . . looked at [the sun] behind the President without being able to tell whether it was rising or setting; but now at length I have the happiness to know that it is a rising and not a setting sun."

7

DEMOCRACY IN DISTRESS
The Violence of Party Politics, 1788–1800

While presiding over the first meeting of the U.S. Senate in 1789, Vice President John Adams called the senators' attention to a pressing procedural question: how would they address George Washington, the newly elected president? Adams insisted that Washington deserved an impressive title, a designation lending dignity and weight to his office. The vice president warned the senators that if they called Washington simply "president of the United States," the "common people of foreign countries [as well as] the sailors and soldiers [would] despise him to all eternity." Adams recommended "His Highness, the President of the United States, and Protector of their Liberties," but some senators favored "His Elective Majesty" or "His Excellency."

Adams's initiative caught many persons, including Washington, completely by surprise. They regarded the entire debate as ridiculous. James Madison, a member of the House of Representatives, announced that pretentious European titles were ill suited to the "genius of the people" and "the nature of our Government." Thomas Jefferson, who was then residing in Paris, could not comprehend what motivated the vice president, and in private correspondence, he repeated Benjamin Franklin's judgment that Adams "means well for his Country, is always an honest Man, often a wise one, but sometimes, and in some things, absolutely out of his senses." When the senators learned that their efforts embarrassed Washington, they dropped the topic. The leader of the new republic would be called president of the United States. One wag, however, dubbed the portly Adams "His Rotundity."

POWER OF PUBLIC OPINION

The comic-opera quality of the debate about how to address Washington should not obscure the participants' serious concern about the future of republican government. All of them, of course, wanted to secure the Revolution. The recently ratified Constitution transferred sovereignty from the states to the people, a bold and unprecedented decision that many Americans feared would generate chronic instability. Translating constitutional abstractions into practical legislation would have been difficult, even under the most favorable conditions. But these were especially trying times. Great Britain and France, rivals in a world war, put nearly unbearable pressures on the leaders of the new republic and, in the process, made foreign policy a bitterly divisive issue.

Although no one welcomed them, political parties gradually took shape during this period. Neither the Jeffersonians nor the Federalists—as the two major groups were called—doubted that the United States would one day become a great commercial power. They differed, however, on how best to manage the transition from an agrarian household economy to an international system of trade and industry. The Federalists encouraged rapid integration of the United States into a world economy, but however enthusiastic they were about capitalism, they did not trust the people or local government to do the job effectively. A modern economy, they insisted, required strong national institutions that would be directed by a social elite who understood the financial challenge and who would work in the best interests of the people.

Such claims frightened persons who came to identify themselves as Jeffersonians. Strong financial institutions, they thought, had corrupted the government of Great Britain from which they had just separated themselves. They searched for alternative ways to accommodate the needs of commerce and industry. Unlike the Federalists, the Jeffersonians put their faith in the people, defined for the most part politically as white yeoman farmers. The Jeffersonians insisted that ordinary entrepreneurs, if they could be freed from intrusive government regulations, could be trusted to resist greed and crass materialism and to sustain the virtue of the republic.

During the 1790s, former allies were surprised to discover themselves at odds over such basic political issues. One person—Hamilton, for example— would stake out a position. Another, such as Jefferson or Madison, would respond, perhaps speaking a little more extravagantly than a specific issue demanded, goaded by the rhetorical nature of public debate. The first in turn would rebut passionately the new position. By the middle of the decade, this dialectic had almost spun out of control, taking the young republic to the brink of political violence.

Leaders of every persuasion had to learn to live with "public opinion." The revolutionary gentry had invited the people to participate in government, but the gentlemen assumed that ordinary voters would automatically defer to their social betters. Instead, the Founders discovered they had created a rough-and-tumble political culture, a robust public sphere of cheap newspapers and street demonstrations. The newly empowered "public" followed the great debates of the period through articles they read in hundreds of highly partisan journals and magazines.

Just as television and the Internet have done, in our own times, print journalism opened politics to a large audience that previously might have been indifferent to the activities of elected officials. By the time John Adams left the presidency in 1800, he had learned this lesson well. The ordinary workers and farmers of the United States, feisty individuals who thought they were as good as anyone else and who were not afraid to let their political opinions be known, were not likely to let their president become an "Elective Majesty."

The front pages of Benjamin Franklin Bache's Aurora General Advertiser, *February 22, 1798, and William Cobbett's* Porcupine's Gazette, *February 27, 1798. The two fiercely partisan editors traded insults in print, referring to their rivals as "reptiles," "impudent dogs," "prostitute hireling wretches," and worse.*

PRINCIPLE AND PRAGMATISM: ESTABLISHING A NEW GOVERNMENT

In 1788, George Washington enjoyed great popularity throughout the nation. The people remembered him as the selfless leader of the Continental Army, and even before the states had ratified the Constitution, everyone assumed he would be chosen president of the United States. He received the unanimous support of the electoral college, an achievement that no subsequent president has duplicated. Adams, a respected Massachusetts lawyer who championed national independence in 1776, was selected vice present. As Washington left his beloved Virginia plantation, Mount Vernon, for New York City, he recognized that the people—now so vocal in his support—could be fickle. "I fear," he explained with mature insight, "if the issue of public measures should not correspond with their sanguine expectations, they will turn the extravagant . . . praise . . . into equally extravagant . . . censures."

Washington bore great responsibility. The political stability of the young republic depended in large measure on how he handled himself in office. In the eyes of his compatriots, he had been transformed into a living symbol of the new gov-

A view of the west front of George Washington's Virginia mansion, Mount Vernon, here depicted by an unknown artist in the 1790s. The house served as the headquarters for much of Washington's presidency and was the site of the first cabinet meetings of the new government of the United States.

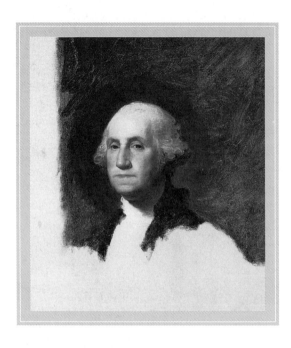

This unfinished portrait of George Washington was done by the portrait painter Gilbert Stuart in 1796. Because of the large demand for images of the first president, Stuart developed a brisk business copying his original painting. The image of Washington that appears on the U.S. dollar bill is based on this "Athenaeum" portrait.

ernment, and during his presidency (1789–1797), he carried himself with studied dignity and reserve—never ostentatious, he was the embodiment of classical republican values. Contemporaries persuaded themselves that although Washington put himself forward for elective office, he somehow stood above the hurly-burly of routine politics. A French diplomat who witnessed Washington's first inauguration in New York City reported in awe: "He has the soul, look, and figure of a hero united in him." But the adulation of Washington—however well meant—seriously affected the conduct of public affairs, for criticism of his administration was regarded as an attack on the president and, by extension, on the republic itself. During the earliest years of Washington's presidency, therefore, American public opinion discouraged partisan politics.

Washington created a strong, independent presidency. He had long advocated a strong federal government. Indeed, unlike some contemporaries, Washington rejected shrill states' rights claims, fearing that local political loyalties might compromise the integrity of the struggling republic, leaving it vulnerable to the predatory ambitions of European empires. While he discussed pressing issues with the members of his cabinet, he left no doubt that he alone made policy. Moreover, the first president resisted congressional efforts to restrict executive authority, especially in foreign affairs.

The first Congress quickly established executive departments. Some congressmen wanted to prohibit presidents from dismissing cabinet-level appointees without Senate approval, but James Madison—still a voice for a strong, independent executive—led a successful fight against this restriction on presidential authority. Madison recognized that the chief executive could not function unless he had personal confidence in the people with whom he worked. In 1789, Congress created the Departments of War, State, and the Treasury, and as secretaries, Washington nominated Henry Knox, Thomas Jefferson, and Alexander Hamilton, respectively. Edmund Randolph served as part-time attorney general, a position that ranked slightly lower in prestige than the head of a department. Since the secretary of the treasury oversaw the collection of customs and other future federal taxes, Hamilton could anticipate having several thousand jobs to dispense, an obvious source of political patronage.

To modern Americans accustomed to a huge federal bureaucracy, the size of Washington's government seems amazingly small. When Jefferson arrived in New York to take over the State Department, for example, he found two chief clerks, two assistants, and a part-time translator. With this tiny staff, he not only maintained contacts with the representatives of foreign governments, collected information about world affairs, and communicated with U.S. officials living overseas, but also organized the entire federal census! Jefferson immediately recognized that his new job would allow him little leisure for personal interests. The situation in other departments was similar. Overworked clerks scribbled madly just to keep up with the burden of correspondence.

Congress also provided for a federal court system. The Judiciary Act of 1789, the work primarily of Connecticut Congressman Oliver Ellsworth, created a

This Liverpool Ware jug records the results of the nation's first census in 1790. Symbols of prosperity surround the census figures, even though the results disappointed many people who hoped the final count would show a population of more than four million people. Perhaps the "Not Known" number of persons living northwest of Ohio would have brought the total to the expected figure.

Supreme Court staffed by a chief justice and five associate justices. In addition, the statute set up thirteen district courts authorized to review the decisions of the state courts. John Jay, a leading figure in New York politics, agreed to serve as chief justice, but since federal judges in the 1790s were expected to travel hundreds of miles over terrible roads to attend sessions of the inferior courts, few persons of outstanding talent and training joined Jay on the federal bench.

Remembering the financial insecurity of the old Confederation government, the newly elected congressmen passed the tariff of 1789, a tax of approximately 5 percent on imports. The new levy generated considerable revenue. Even before it went into effect, however, the act sparked controversy. Southern planters, who relied heavily on European imports and the northern shippers who could control the flow of imports into the South, claimed that the tariff discriminated against southern interests in favor of those of northern merchants.

CONFLICTING VISIONS: JEFFERSON AND HAMILTON

Washington's first cabinet included two extraordinary personalities, Alexander Hamilton and Thomas Jefferson. Both had served the country with distinction during the Revolution, were recognized by contemporaries as men of special genius as well as high ambition, and brought to public office a powerful vision of how the American people could achieve greatness. The story of their opposing views during the decade of the 1790s reveals how a common political ideology, republicanism (see Chapter 6), could be interpreted in such vastly different ways that decisions about government policy turned friends into adversaries. Indeed, the falling out of Hamilton and Jefferson reflected deep, potentially explosive political divisions within American society.

Hamilton was a brilliant, dynamic lawyer who had distinguished himself as Washington's aide-de-camp during the Revolution. Born in the West Indies, the child of an adulterous relationship, Hamilton employed charm, courage, and intellect to serve his inexhaustible ambition. He strove not for wealth but for reputation. Men and women who fell under his spell found him almost irresistible, but to enemies, Hamilton appeared a dark, calculating, even evil, genius. He advocated a strong central government and refused to be bound by the strict wording of the Constitution, a document Hamilton once called "a shilly shally thing." While he had fought for American independence, he admired British culture, and during the 1790s, he advocated closer commercial and diplomatic ties with the former mother country, with whom, he said, "we have a similarity of tastes, language, and general manners."

During the first years of Washington's administration, neither Hamilton (left) nor Jefferson (right) recognized the full extent of their differences. But as events forced the federal government to make decisions on economic and foreign affairs, the two secretaries increasingly came into open conflict.

Jefferson possessed a profoundly different temperament. This tall Virginian was more reflective and shone less brightly in society than Hamilton. Contemporaries sometimes interpreted his retiring manner as lack of ambition. They misread Jefferson. He thirsted not for power or wealth but for an opportunity to advance the democratic principles that he had stated so eloquently in the Declaration of Independence. When Jefferson became secretary of state in January 1790, he had just returned from Paris where he witnessed the first exhilarating moments of the French Revolution. These earthshaking events, he believed, marked the beginning of a worldwide republican assault on absolute monarchy and aristocratic privilege. His European experiences biased Jefferson in favor of France over Great Britain when the two nations clashed.

The differences dividing these two men could not long be contained. Washington's secretaries disagreed on precisely how the United States should fulfill its destiny. As head of the Treasury Department, Hamilton urged his fellow citizens to think in terms of bold commercial development, of farms and factories embedded within a complex financial network that would reduce the nation's reliance on foreign trade. Because Great Britain had already established an elaborate system of banking and credit, the secretary looked to that country for economic models that might be reproduced on this side of the Atlantic.

Hamilton also voiced concerns about the role of the people in shaping public policy. He assumed that in a republican society, the gravest threat to political stability was anarchy rather than monarchy. "The truth," he claimed, "unquestionably is, that the only path to a subversion of the republican system of the Country is, by flattering the prejudices of the people, and exciting their jealousies and apprehensions." The best hope for the survival of the republic, Hamilton believed, lay with the country's monied classes. If the wealthiest people could be persuaded their economic self-interest could be advanced—or at least made less insecure—by the central government, then they would work to strengthen it, and by so doing, bring a greater measure of prosperity to the common people. From Hamilton's perspective, there was no conflict between private greed and public good; one was the source of the other.

On almost every detail, Jefferson rejected Hamilton's analysis. The secretary of state assumed that the strength of the American economy lay not in its industrial potential but in its agricultural productivity. The "immensity of land" represented the country's major economic resource. Contrary to the claims of some critics, Jefferson did not advocate agrarian self-sufficiency or look back nostalgically to a golden age dominated by simple yeomen. He recognized the necessity of change, and while he thought that persons who worked the soil were more responsible citizens than were those who labored in factories for wages, he encouraged the nation's farmers to participate in an expanding international market.

Unlike Hamilton, Jefferson expressed faith in the ability of the American people to shape policy. Throughout this troubled decade, even when the very survival of constitutional government seemed in doubt, Jefferson maintained a boundless optimism in the judgment of the common folk. He instinctively trusted the people, feared that uncontrolled government power might destroy their liberties, and insisted public officials follow the letter of the Constitution, a frame of government he described as "the wisest ever presented to men." The greatest threat to the young republic, he argued, came from the corrupt activities of pseudoaristocrats, persons who placed the protection of "property" and "civil order" above the preservation of "liberty." To tie the nation's future to the selfish interests of a privileged class—bankers, manufacturers, and speculators— seemed cynical as well as dangerous. He despised speculators who encouraged "the rage of getting rich in a day," since such "gaming" activities inevitably promoted the kinds of public vice that threatened republican government. To mortgage the future of the common people by creating a large national debt struck Jefferson as particularly insane.

HAMILTON'S PLAN FOR PROSPERITY AND SECURITY

The unsettled state of the nation's finances presented the new government with a staggering challenge. In August 1789, the House of Representatives announced that "adequate provision for the support of public credit [is] a matter of high importance to the national honor and prosperity." However pressing the problem appeared, no one was prepared to advance a solution, and the House asked the secretary of the treasury to make suggestions.

Congress may have received more than it bargained for. Hamilton threw himself into the task. He read deeply in abstruse economic literature. He even developed a questionnaire designed to find out how the U.S. economy really worked and sent it to scores of commercial and political leaders throughout the country. But when Hamilton's three major reports—on public credit, on banking, and on manufacturers—were complete, they bore the unmistakable stamp of his own creative genius.

The secretary presented his *Report on the Public Credit* to Congress on January 14, 1790. His research revealed that the nation's outstanding debt stood at approximately $54 million. This sum represented various obligations that the U.S. government had incurred during the Revolutionary War. In addition to foreign loans, the figure included loan certificates the government had issued to its own citizens and soldiers. But that was not all. The states still owed creditors approximately $25 million. During the 1780s, Americans desperate for cash had been forced to sell government certificates to speculators at greatly discounted prices, and it was estimated that approximately $40 million of the nation's debt was owed to twenty thousand people, only 20 percent of whom were the original creditors.

FUNDING AND ASSUMPTION

Hamilton's *Report on the Public Credit* contained two major recommendations covering the areas of funding and assumption. First, under his plan, the United States promised to fund its foreign and domestic obligations at full face value. Current holders of loan certificates, whoever they were and no matter how they obtained them, could exchange the old certificates for new government bonds bearing a moderate rate of interest. Second, the secretary urged the federal government to assume responsibility for paying the remaining state debts.

Hamilton reasoned that his credit system would accomplish several desirable goals. It would significantly reduce the power of the individual states in shaping national economic policy, something Hamilton regarded as essential in maintaining a strong federal government. Moreover, the creation of a fully funded national debt signaled to investors throughout the world that the United States was now solvent, that its bonds represented a good risk. Hamilton argued that investment capital, which might otherwise flow to Europe, would remain in this country, providing a source of money for commercial and industrial investment. In short, Hamilton invited the country's wealthiest citizens to invest in the future of the United States.

To Hamilton's surprise, Madison—his friend and collaborator in writing *The Federalist*—attacked the funding scheme in the House of Representatives. The Virginia congressman agreed that the United States should honor its debts. He worried, however, about the citizens and soldiers who, because of personal financial hardship, had been compelled to sell their certificates at prices far below face value. Why should wealthy speculators now profit from their hardship? If the government treated the current holders of certificates less generously, Madison declared, then there might be sufficient funds to provide equitable treatment for the distressed patriots. Whatever the moral justification for Madison's plan may have been, it proved unworkable on the national level. Far too many records had been lost since the Revolution for the Treasury Department to be able to identify all the original holders. In February 1790, Congress soundly defeated Madison's proposal.

The assumption portion of Hamilton's plan unleashed even greater criticism. Some states had already paid their revolutionary debts, and Hamilton's program seemed designed to reward certain states—Massachusetts and South Carolina, for example—simply because they had failed to put their finances in order. In addition, the secretary's opponents in Congress became suspicious that assumption was merely a ploy to increase the power and wealth of Hamilton's immediate friends.

Some of those who protested, however, were simply looking after their own speculative schemes. These men had contracted to purchase huge tracts of vacant western lands from the state and federal governments. They anticipated that when settlers finally arrived in these areas, the price of land would skyrocket. In the meantime, the speculators had paid for the land with revolutionary certificates, often purchased on the open market at fifteen cents on the dollar. This meant that one could obtain 1000 acres for only $150. Hamilton's assumption proposal threatened to destroy these lucrative transactions by cutting off the supply of cut-rate securities. On April 12, a rebellious House led by Madison defeated assumption.

The victory was short-lived. Hamilton and congressional supporters resorted to legislative horse trading to revive his foundering program. In exchange for locating the new federal capital on the Potomac River, a move that would stimulate the depressed economy of northern Virginia, several key congressmen who shared Madison's political philosophy changed their votes on assumption. In August, Washington signed assumption and funding into law.

INTERPRETING THE CONSTITUTION: THE BANK CONTROVERSY

The persistent Hamilton submitted his second report to Congress in January 1791. He proposed that the U.S. government charter a national bank. This privately owned institution would be funded in part by the federal government. Indeed, since the bank would own millions of dollars of new U.S. bonds, its financial stability would be tied directly to the strength of the federal government and, of course, to the success of Hamilton's program. The secretary of the treasury argued that a growing financial community required a central bank to facilitate increasingly complex commercial transactions. The institution not only would serve as the main depository of the U.S. government but also would issue currency acceptable in payment of federal taxes. Because of that guarantee, the money would maintain its value while in circulation.

Madison and others in Congress immediately protested. While they were not oblivious to the many important services a national bank might provide for a growing country, they suspected that banks—especially those modeled on British institutions—might "perpetuate a large monied interest" in the United States. Moreover, the Constitution said nothing about chartering financial corporations, and they warned that if Hamilton and his supporters were allowed to stretch fundamental law on this occasion, popular liberties would be at the mercy of whoever happened to be in office. "To take a single step," Jefferson warned, "beyond the boundaries thus specifically drawn around the powers of Congress is to take possession of a boundless field of power, no longer susceptible to definition."

This intense controversy involving his closest advisers worried the president. Even though the bank bill passed Congress (February 8), Washington considered vetoing the legislation on constitutional grounds. Before doing so, however, he requested written opinions from the members of his cabinet. Jefferson's rambling, wholly predictable attack on the bank was not one of his more persuasive performances. By contrast, in only a few days, Hamilton prepared a masterful essay titled "Defense of the Constitutionality of the Bank." He assured the president that Article I, Section 8 of the Constitution—"The Congress shall have Power . . . To make all Laws which shall be necessary and proper for carrying into Execution the foregoing Powers"—justified issuing charters to national banks. The "foregoing Powers" on which Hamilton placed so much weight were taxation, regulation of commerce, and making war. He boldly articulated a doctrine of *implied powers*, an interpretation of the Constitution that neither Madison nor Jefferson had anticipated. Hamilton's "loose construction" carried the day, and on February 25, 1791, Washington signed the bank act into law.

The general public looked on Hamilton's actions with growing hostility. Many persons associated huge national debts and privileged banks with the decay of public virtue. Men of Jefferson's temperament believed that Great Britain—a country Hamilton held in high regard—had compromised the purity of its ancient constitution by allowing speculators to worm their way into positions of political power.

Hamilton seemed intent on reproducing this corrupt system in the United States. When news of his proposal to fund the national debt at full face value leaked out, for example, urban speculators rushed to rural areas, where they purchased loan certificates from unsuspecting citizens at bargain prices. When the greed of a former Treasury Department official led to several serious bankruptcies in 1792, ordinary citizens began to listen more closely to what Madison, Jefferson, and their associates were saying about growing corruption in high places.

SETBACK FOR HAMILTON

In his third major report, *Report on Manufactures*, submitted to Congress in December 1791, Hamilton revealed the final details of his grand design for the economic future of the United States. This lengthy document suggested ways by which the federal government might stimulate manufacturing. If the country wanted to free itself from dependence on European imports, Hamilton observed, then it had to develop its own industry, textile mills for example. Without direct government intervention, however, the process would take decades. Americans would continue to invest in agriculture. But, according to the secretary of the treasury, protective tariffs and special industrial bounties would greatly accelerate the growth of a balanced economy, and with proper planning, the United States would soon hold its own with England and France.

In Congress, the battle lines were drawn. Hamilton's opponents—a loose coalition of men who shared Madison's and Jefferson's misgivings about the secretary's program—ignored his economic arguments. Instead, they engaged him on moral and political grounds. Madison railed against the dangers of "consolidation," a process that threatened to concentrate all power in the federal government, leaving the states defenseless. Under the Confederation, of course, Madison had stood with the nationalists against the advocates of extreme states' rights. His disagreements with Hamilton over economic policy, coupled with the necessity of pleasing the voters of his Virginia congressional district every two years, transformed Madison into a spokesman for the states.

Jefferson attacked the *Report on Manufactures* from a different angle. He assumed—largely because he had been horrified by Europe's urban poverty—that cities breed vice. The government, Jefferson argued, should do nothing to promote their development. He believed that Hamilton's proposal guaranteed that American workers would leave the countryside and crowd into urban centers. "I think our government will remain virtuous for many centuries," Jefferson explained, "as long as they [the people] are chiefly agricultural. . . . When they get piled upon one another in large cities, as in Europe, they will become corrupt as in Europe." And southern congressmen saw tariffs and bounties as vehicles for enriching Hamilton's northern friends at the planters' expense. The recommendations in the *Report on Manufactures* were soundly defeated in the House of Representatives.

Washington detested political squabbling. The president, of course, could see that the members of his cabinet disagreed on many issues, but in 1792, he still believed that Hamilton and Jefferson—and the people who looked to them for advice—could be reconciled. In August, he personally begged them to rise above the "internal dissensions [that are] . . . harrowing and tearing at our vitals." The appeal came too late. By the conclusion of Washington's first term, neither secretary trusted the other's judgment. Their sparring had produced congressional factions, but as yet no real political parties with permanent organizations that engaged in campaigning had come into existence.

CHARGES OF TREASON: THE BATTLE OVER FOREIGN AFFAIRS

During Washington's second term (1793–1797), war in Europe dramatically thrust foreign affairs into the forefront of American life. The impact of this development on the conduct of domestic politics was devastating. Officials who had formerly disagreed on economic policy now began to identify their interests with either Britain or France, Europe's most powerful nations. Differences of political opinion, however trivial, were suddenly cited as evidence that one group or the other had entered into treasonous correspondence with external enemies eager to compromise the independence and prosperity of the United States.

Formal political organizations—the Federalists and Republicans—were born in this poisonous atmosphere. The clash between the groups developed over how best to preserve the new republic. The Republicans (Jeffersonians) advocated states' rights, strict interpretation of the Constitution, friendship with France, and vigilance against "the avaricious, monopolizing Spirit of Commerce and Commercial Men." The Federalists urged a strong national government, central economic planning, closer ties with Great Britain, and maintenance of public order, even if that meant calling out federal troops.

THE PERIL OF NEUTRALITY

Great Britain treated the United States with arrogance. Weakness justified such a policy. The young republic could not even compel its old adversary to comply with the Treaty of 1783, in which the British had agreed to vacate military posts in the Northwest Territory. In 1794, approximately a thousand British soldiers still occupied American land. Moreover, even though 75 percent of American imports came from Great Britain, that country refused to grant the United States full commercial reciprocity. Among other provocations, it barred American shipping from the lucrative West Indian trade.

France presented a very different challenge. In May 1789, Louis XVI, desperate for revenue, authorized a meeting of a representative assembly known as the Estates General. By so doing, the king unleashed explosive revolutionary forces that toppled the monarchy and cost him his life (January 1793). The men who seized power—and they came and went rapidly—were militant republicans, ideologues eager to liberate all Europe from feudal institutions. In the early years of the Revolution, France drew on the American experience, and Thomas Paine and the Marquis de Lafayette enjoyed great popularity. But the French found they could not stop the violence of revolution. Constitutional reform turned into bloody purges, and one radical group, the Jacobins, guillotined thousands of people who were suspected of monarchist sympathies during the so-called Reign of Terror (October 1793–July 1794). These horrific events left Americans confused. While those who shared Jefferson's views cheered the spread of republicanism, others who sided with Hamilton condemned French expansionism and political excess.

In the face of growing international tension, neutrality seemed the most prudent course for the United States. But that policy was easier for a weak country to proclaim than to defend. In February 1793, France declared war on Great Britain—what the leaders of revolutionary France called the "war of all peoples against all kings"—and these powerful European rivals immediately challenged the official American position on shipping: "free ships make free goods," meaning that belligerents should not interfere with the shipping of neutral carriers. To make matters worse, no one was certain whether the Franco-American treaties of 1778 (see Chapter 5) legally bound the United States to support its old ally against Great Britain.

Both Hamilton and Jefferson wanted to avoid war. The secretary of state, however, believed that nations desiring American goods should be forced to honor American neutrality and, therefore, that if Britain treated the United States

The execution of Louis XVI by French revolutionaries served to deepen the growing political division in America. Although Jeffersonian Republicans deplored the excesses of the Reign of Terror, they continued to support the French people. Federalists feared that the violence and lawlessness would spread to the United States.

as a colonial possession, if the Royal Navy stopped American ships on the high seas and forced seamen to serve the king—in other words, if it impressed American sailors—then the United States should award France special commercial advantages. Hamilton thought Jefferson's scheme insane. He pointed out that Britain possessed the largest navy in the world and was not likely to be coerced by American threats. The United States, he counseled, should appease the former mother country even if that meant swallowing national pride.

A newly appointed French minister to the United States, Edmond Genêt, precipitated the first major diplomatic crisis. This incompetent young man arrived in Charleston, South Carolina, in April 1793. He found considerable popular enthusiasm for the French Revolution, and, buoyed by this reception, he authorized privately owned American vessels to seize British ships in the name of France. Such actions violated U.S. neutrality and invited British retaliation. When U.S. government officials warned Genêt to desist, he threatened to take his appeal directly to the American people, who presumably loved France more than did members of Washington's administration.

This confrontation particularly embarrassed Jefferson, the most outspoken pro-French member of the cabinet. He described Genêt as "hot headed." Washington did not wait to discover whether the treaties of 1778 were still in force. Before he had formally received the impudent French minister, the president issued a Proclamation of Neutrality (April 22).

JAY'S TREATY SPARKS DOMESTIC UNREST

Great Britain failed to take advantage of Genêt's insolence. Instead, it pushed the United States to the brink of war. British forts in the Northwest Territory remained a constant source of tension. In June 1793, a new element was added. The London government blockaded French ports to neutral shipping, and in November, its navy captured several hundred American vessels trading in the French West Indies. The British had not even bothered to give the United States advance warning of a change in policy. Outraged members of Congress, especially those who identified with Jefferson and Madison, demanded retaliation, an embargo, a stoppage of debt payment, even war.

Before this rhetoric produced armed struggle, Washington made one final effort to preserve peace. In May 1794, he sent Chief Justice John Jay to London to negotiate a formidable list of grievances. Jay's main objectives were removal of the British forts on U.S. territory, payment for ships taken in the West Indies, improved commercial relations, and acceptance of the American definition of neutral rights.

Jefferson's supporters—by now openly called the Republican interest—anticipated a treaty favorable to the United States. After all, they explained, the war with France had not gone well for Great Britain, and the British people were surely desperate for American foodstuffs. Even before Jay departed, however, his mission stood little chance of success. Hamilton, anxious to placate the British, had already secretly informed British officials that the United States would compromise on most issues.

Not surprisingly, when Jay reached London, he encountered polite but firm resistance. The chief justice did persuade the British to abandon their frontier posts and to allow small American ships to trade in the British West Indies, but they rejected out of hand the U.S. position on neutral rights. The Royal Navy would continue to search American vessels on the high seas for contraband and to impress sailors suspected of being British citizens. Moreover, there would be no compensation for the ships seized in 1793 until the Americans paid British merchants for debts contracted before the Revolution. And to the particular annoyance of Southerners, not a word was said about the slaves the British army had carried off at the conclusion of the war. While Jay salvaged the peace, he appeared to have betrayed the national interest.

News of Jay's Treaty—perhaps more correctly called Hamilton's Treaty—produced an angry outcry in the nation's capital. Even Washington was apprehensive. He submitted the document to the Senate without recommending ratifica-

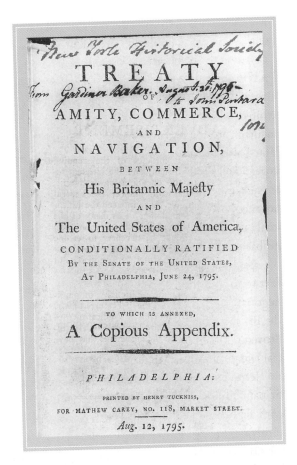

TREATY OF AMITY, COMMERCE, AND NAVIGATION, BETWEEN His Britannic Majesty AND The United States of America, CONDITIONALLY RATIFIED By the Senate of the United States, At Philadelphia, June 24, 1795. TO WHICH IS ANNEXED, A Copious Appendix. PHILADELPHIA: PRINTED BY HENRY TUCKNISS, FOR MATHEW CAREY, NO. 118, MARKET STREET. Aug. 12, 1795.

Printer Matthew Carey helped fire the protest over Jay's Treaty by printing the terms of the agreement and adding a series of partisan comments to the appendix.

tion, a sign that the president was not entirely happy with the results of Jay's mission. After an extremely bitter debate, the upper house, controlled by Federalists, accepted a revised version of the treaty (June 1795). The vote was 20 to 10, a bare two-thirds majority.

The details of the Jay agreement soon leaked to the press. This was an important moment in American political history. The popular journals sparked a firestorm of protest. Throughout the country, people who had generally been apathetic about national politics were swept up in a wave of protest. Urban mobs condemned Jay's alleged sellout; rural settlers burned him in effigy.

A storm broke in the House of Representatives. Republican congressmen, led by Madison, thought they could stop Jay's Treaty by refusing to appropriate funds for its implementation. As part of their plan, they demanded that Washington show the House state papers relating to Jay's mission. The partisan challenge raised complex issues of constitutional law. The House, for example, was claiming a voice in treaty ratification, a power explicitly reserved to the

Senate. Second, there was the question of executive secrecy in the interest of national security. Could the president withhold information from the public? According to Washington—as well as all subsequent presidents—the answer was yes. He took the occasion to lecture the rebellious representatives that "the nature of foreign negotiations requires caution; and their success must often depend on secrecy."

The president had a trump card to play. He raised the possibility that the House was really contemplating his impeachment. Such an action was, of course, unthinkable. Even criticizing Washington in public was politically dangerous, and as soon as he redefined the issue before Congress, petitions supporting the president flooded into the nation's capital. The Federalists won a stunning tactical victory over the opposition. Had a less popular man than Washington occupied the presidency, however, they would not have fared so well. The division between the two parties was beyond repair. The Republicans labeled the Federalists "the British party"; the Federalists believed that the Republicans were in league with the French.

By the time Jay's Treaty became law (June 14, 1795), the two giants of Washington's first cabinet had retired. Late in 1793, Jefferson returned to his Virginia plantation, Monticello, where, despite his separation from day-to-day political affairs, he remained the chief spokesman for the Republican party. His rival, Hamilton, left the Treasury in January 1795 to practice law in New York City. He maintained close ties with important Federalist officials.

PUSHING THE NATIVE AMERICANS ASIDE

Before Great Britain finally withdrew its troops from the Great Lakes and Northwest Territory, its military officers encouraged local Indian groups—the Shawnees, Chippewas, and Miamis—to attack settlers and traders from the United States. The Indians, who even without British encouragement fully appreciated that the newcomers intended to seize their land, won several impressive victories over federal troops in the area that would become western Ohio and Indiana. In 1790, General Josiah Harmar led his soldiers into an ambush. The following year, an army under General Arthur St. Clair suffered more than nine hundred casualties near the Wabash River. But the Indians were militarily more vulnerable than they realized, for when confronted with a major U.S. army under the command of General Anthony Wayne, they received no support from their former British allies. At the battle of Fallen Timbers (August 20, 1794), Wayne's forces crushed Indian resistance in the Northwest Territory, and the native peoples were compelled to sign the Treaty of Greenville, formally ceding to the U.S. government the land that became Ohio. In 1796, the last British soldiers departed for Canada.

Shrewd negotiations mixed with pure luck helped secure the nation's southwestern frontier. For complex reasons having to do with the state of European diplomacy, Spanish officials in 1795 encouraged the U.S. representative in Madrid to discuss the navigation of the Mississippi River. Before this initiative, the Spanish government not only had closed the river to American commerce but also had incited the Indians of the region to harass settlers from the United States (see Chapter 6). Relations between the two countries probably would have deteriorated further had the United States not signed Jay's Treaty. The Spanish assumed—quite erroneously—that Great Britain and the United States had formed an alliance to strip Spain of its North American possessions.

To avoid this imagined disaster, officials in Madrid offered the American envoy, Thomas Pinckney, extraordinary concessions: the opening of the Mississippi, the right to deposit goods in New Orleans without paying duties, a secure southern boundary on the 31st parallel (a line roughly parallel to the northern boundary of Florida and running west to the Mississippi), and a promise to stay out of Indian affairs. An amazed Pinckney signed the Treaty of San Lorenzo (also called Pinckney's Treaty) on October 27, 1795, and in March the Senate ratified the document without a single dissenting vote.

POPULAR POLITICAL CULTURE

More than any other event during Washington's administration, ratification of Jay's Treaty generated intense political strife. Even as members of Congress voted as Republicans or Federalists, they condemned the rising partisan spirit as a grave threat to the stability of the United States. Popular writers equated "party" with "faction" and "faction" with "conspiracy to overthrow legitimate authority." Party conflict also suggested that Americans had lost the sense of common purpose that had united them during the Revolution. Contemporaries did not appreciate the beneficial role that parties could play by presenting alternative solutions to foreign and domestic problems. Organized opposition smacked of disloyalty and therefore had to be eliminated by any means—fair or foul.

PARTISAN NEWSPAPERS AND POLITICAL CLUBS

Newspapers transformed the political culture of the United States. John Fenno established the *Gazette of the United States* (1789), a journal that supported Hamilton's political philosophy. The Republicans responded in October 1790 with Philip Freneau's influential *National Gazette*. While the format of the publications was similar to that of the colonial papers, their tone was quite different. These fiercely partisan journals presented rumor and opinion as fact. Jefferson, for example, was accused of cowardice; Hamilton, vilified as an adulterer. As

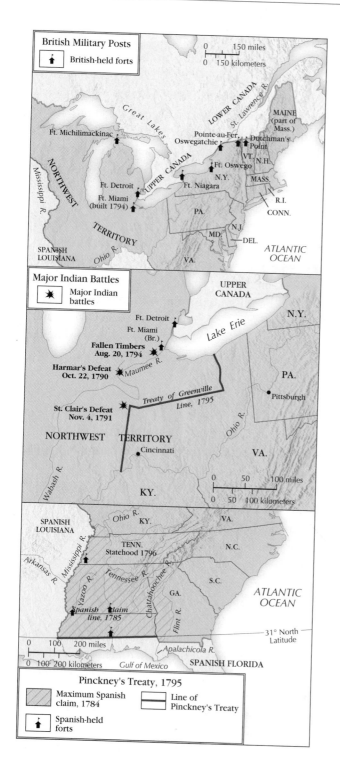

British Military Posts

⬆ British-held forts

0 ——— 150 miles
0 ——— 150 kilometers

Great Lakes

LOWER CANADA

St. Lawrence R.

MAINE (part of Mass.)

Ft. Michilimackinac

Pointe-au-Fer
Oswegatchie
Dutchman's Point

UPPER CANADA

Ft. Oswego

VT.
N.H.

NORTHWEST

Mississippi R.

Ft. Detroit
Ft. Niagara

N.Y.
MASS.

Ft. Miami (built 1794)

R.I.
CONN.

TERRITORY

PA.

N.J.
MD.
DEL.

SPANISH LOUISIANA

Ohio R.

VA.

ATLANTIC OCEAN

Major Indian Battles

✴ Major Indian battles

UPPER CANADA

N.Y.

Ft. Detroit

Ft. Miami (Br.)

Lake Erie

Fallen Timbers
Aug. 20, 1794

Harmar's Defeat
Oct. 22, 1790

Maumee R.

PA.

Pittsburgh

Treaty of Greenville Line, 1795

St. Clair's Defeat
Nov. 4, 1791

Ohio R.

NORTHWEST TERRITORY

Cincinnati

VA.

Wabash R.

0 ——— 50 ——— 100 miles
0 ——— 50 ——— 100 kilometers

KY.

SPANISH LOUISIANA

Ohio R.
KY.

VA.

Mississippi R.

TENN.
Statehood 1796

N.C.

Arkansas R.

Tennessee R.

Chattahoochee R.

S.C.

Yazoo R.

GA.

ATLANTIC OCEAN

Spanish claim line, 1785

Flint R.

31° North Latitude

0 ——— 100 ——— 200 miles
0 ——— 100 ——— 200 kilometers

Apalachicola R.

Gulf of Mexico

SPANISH FLORIDA

Pinckney's Treaty, 1795

▨ Maximum Spanish claim, 1784

▬ Line of Pinckney's Treaty

⬆ Spanish-held forts

Conquest of the West

Withdrawal of the British, defeat of Native Americans, and negotiations with Spain secured the nation's frontiers.

party competition became more bitter, editors showed less restraint. One Republican paper even suggested that George Washington had been a British agent during the Revolution.

Even poets and essayists entered the political fray. The better writers—and this was not a period of outstanding artistic achievement—often produced party propaganda. However much Freneau aspired to fame as a poet, he is remembered today chiefly as a champion of the Republican cause. Noah Webster, who later published *An American Dictionary of the English Language* (1828), spent the 1790s editing a strident Federalist journal, *American Minerva,* in New York City. And Joel Barlow, a Connecticut poet, celebrated the French Revolution in verse, thus identifying himself with the party of Jefferson. American writers sometimes complained that the culture of the young republic was too materialistic, too unappreciative of the subtler forms of art then popular in Europe. But poets who ignored patriotism and politics simply did not sell well in the United States.

This decade also witnessed the birth of political clubs. These "Democratic" or "Republican" associations, as they were called, first appeared in 1793 and were modeled on the political debating societies that sprang up in Paris during the early years of the French Revolution. Perhaps because of the French connection, Federalists assumed that the American clubs represented the interests of the Republican party. Their purpose seemed to be political indoctrination. A Democratic club in New York City asked each member to declare himself a "firm and steadfast friend of the EQUAL RIGHTS OF MAN." By 1794, at least twenty-four clubs were holding regular meetings.

WHISKEY REBELLION LINKED TO REPUBLICAN CONSPIRACY

Political tensions became explosive in 1794. The Federalists convinced themselves that the Republicans were actually prepared to employ violence against the U.S. government. Although the charge was without foundation, it took on plausibility in the context of growing party strife.

The crisis developed when a group of farmers living in western Pennsylvania protested a federal excise tax on distilled whiskey that Congress had originally passed in 1791. This tax struck them as particularly unfair, since the excise threatened to put them out of business.

Largely because the Republican governor of Pennsylvania refused to suppress the angry farmers, Washington and other leading Federalists assumed that the insurrection represented a direct political challenge. The president called out fifteen thousand militiamen, and, accompanied by Hamilton, who came out of retirement, he marched against the rebels. The expedition was an embarrassing fiasco. The distillers disappeared, and predictably enough, no one living in the Pittsburgh region seemed to know where the troublemakers had gone. As peace

Tarring and feathering federal officials was one way in which western Pennsylvanians protested the tax on whiskey in 1794. Washington's call for troops to put down the insurrection drew more volunteers than he had been able to raise during most of the Revolution.

returned to the frontier, Republicans gained much electoral support from voters the Federalists had alienated.

In the national political forum, however, the Whiskey Rebellion had just begun. Spokesmen for both parties offered sinister explanations for a seemingly innocuous affair. Washington blamed the Republican clubs for promoting civil unrest. He apparently believed that the opposition party had dispatched French agents to western Pennsylvania to undermine the authority of the federal government. In November 1794, Washington informed Congress that these "self-created societies"—in other words, the Republican political clubs—had inspired "a spirit inimical to all order."

The president's interpretation of this rural tax revolt was no less charitable than the conspiratorial explanation offered by the Republicans. Jefferson labeled the entire episode a Hamiltonian device to create an army for the purpose of intimidating Republicans. "An insurrection was announced and proclaimed and armed against," Jefferson noted, "but could never be found." The response of both parties reveals a pervasive fear of some secret evil design to destroy the republic. The clubs and newspapers—as yet unfamiliar tools for mobilizing public opinion—fanned these anxieties, convincing many government officials that the First Amendment should not be interpreted as protecting political dissent.

WASHINGTON'S FAREWELL

In September 1796, Washington published his famed Farewell Address, formally declaring his intention to retire from the presidency. In the address, which was printed in newspapers throughout the country, Washington warned against all political factions. Written in large part by Hamilton, who drew on a draft prepared several years earlier by Madison, the address served narrowly partisan ends. The product of growing political strife, it sought to advance the Federalist cause in the forthcoming election. By waiting until September to announce his retirement, Washington denied the Republicans valuable time to organize an effective campaign.

Washington also spoke to foreign policy matters in the address. He counseled the United States to avoid making permanent alliances with distant nations that had no interest in promoting American security. This statement guided foreign relations for many years and became the credo of later American isolationists, who argued that the United States should steer clear of foreign entanglements.

THE ADAMS PRESIDENCY

The election of 1796 took place in an atmosphere of mutual distrust. Jefferson, soon to be the vice president, informed a friend that "an Anglican and aristocratic party has sprung up, whose avowed object is to draw over us the substance, as they have already done the forms, of British government." On their part, the Federalists were convinced their Republican opponents wanted to hand the government over to French radicals. By modern standards, the structures of both political parties were primitive. Leaders of national stature, such as Madison and Hamilton, wrote letters encouraging local gentlemen around the country to support a certain candidate, but no one attempted to canvass the voters in advance of the election.

During the campaign, the Federalists sowed the seeds of their eventual destruction. Party stalwarts agreed that John Adams should stand against the Republican candidate, Thomas Jefferson. Hamilton, however, could not leave well enough alone. From New York City, he schemed to deprive Adams of the presidency, fearing that an independent-minded Adams would be difficult to manipulate. He was correct.

Hamilton exploited an awkward feature of the electoral college. In accordance with the Constitution, each elector cast two ballots, and the person who gained the most votes became president. The runner-up, regardless of party affiliation, served as vice president. Ordinarily the Federalist electors would have cast one vote for Adams and one for Thomas Pinckney, the hero of the negotiations with Spain and the party's choice for vice president. Everyone hoped, of course, there would be no tie. Hamilton secretly urged southern Federalists to support only Pinckney, even if that meant throwing away an elector's second vote. If everything had gone according to plan, Pinckney would have received

THE ELECTION OF 1796

CANDIDATE	PARTY	ELECTORAL VOTE
J. Adams	Federalist	71
Jefferson	Republican	68
T. Pinckney	Federalist	59
Burr	Republican	30

more votes than Adams, but when New Englanders loyal to Adams heard of Hamilton's maneuvering, they dropped Pinckney. When the votes were counted, Adams had 71, Jefferson 68, and Pinckney 59. Hamilton's treachery heightened tensions within the Federalist party.

Adams assumed the presidency under intolerable conditions. He found himself saddled with the members of Washington's old cabinet, a group of second-raters who regularly consulted with Hamilton behind Adams's back. The two most offensive were Timothy Pickering, secretary of state, and James McHenry, secretary of war. But to have dismissed them summarily would have called Washington's judgment into question, and Adams was not prepared to take that risk publicly.

Adams also had to work with a Republican vice president. Adams hoped that he and Jefferson could cooperate as they had during the Revolution—they had served together on the committee that drafted the Declaration of Independence—but partisan pressures soon overwhelmed the president's good intentions.

THE XYZ AFFAIR AND DOMESTIC POLITICS

Foreign affairs immediately occupied Adams's full attention. The French government regarded Jay's Treaty as an affront. By allowing Great Britain to define the conditions for neutrality, the United States had in effect sided with that nation against the interests of France.

Relations between the two countries had steadily deteriorated. The French refused to receive Charles Cotesworth Pinckney, the U.S. representative in Paris. Pierre Adet, the French minister in Philadelphia, openly tried to influence the 1796 election in favor of the Republicans. His meddling in domestic politics not only embarrassed Jefferson, it also offended the American people. In 1797, French privateers began seizing American ships. Since neither the United States nor France officially declared war, the hostilities came to be known as the Quasi-War.

The High Federalists—as members of Hamilton's wing of the party were called—counseled the president to prepare for all-out war, hoping that war would purge the United States of French influence. Adams was not persuaded to escalate the conflict. He dispatched a special commission in a final attempt to remove the sources of antagonism. This famous negotiating team consisted of Charles Pinckney, John Marshall, and Elbridge Gerry. They were instructed to obtain compensation for the ships seized by French privateers as well as release from the treaties of 1778. Federalists still worried that this old agreement might oblige the United States to defend French colonies in the Caribbean against British attack, something they were extremely reluctant to do. In exchange, the commission offered France the same commercial privileges granted to Great Britain in Jay's Treaty. While the diplomats negotiated for peace, Adams talked of strengthening American defenses, rhetoric that pleased the militant members of his own party.

The commission was shocked by the outrageous treatment it received in France. The commission reported that the French representative would not open negotiations without a bribe of $250,000. In addition, the French government expected a "loan" of millions of dollars. The Americans refused to play this insulting game. When they arrived home, Marshall offered a much-quoted toast: "Millions for defense, but not one cent for tribute."

Diplomatic humiliation set off a domestic political explosion. When Adams presented the commission's official correspondence before Congress—the names of the French agents were labeled X, Y, and Z—the Federalists burst out with a war cry. At last, they would be able to even old scores with the Republicans. In April 1798, a Federalist newspaper in New York City announced ominously that any American who refused to censure France "must have a soul black enough to be *fit for treasons, strategems,* and *spoils*." Rumors of conspiracy spread throughout the country. Personal friendships between Republicans and Federalists were shattered.

CRUSHING POLITICAL DISSENT

In the spring of 1798, High Federalists assumed that it was just a matter of time until Adams asked Congress for a formal declaration of war. In the meantime, they pushed for a general rearmament, new fighting ships, additional harbor fortifications, and most important, a greatly expanded U.S. Army. About the need for land forces, Adams remained understandably skeptical. He saw no likelihood of French invasion.

The army the High Federalists wanted was intended not to thwart French aggression but to stifle internal opposition. Indeed, militant Federalists used the XYZ Affair as the occasion to institute what Jefferson termed the "reign of witches." The threat to the Republicans was not simply a figment of the vice president's overwrought imagination. When Theodore Sedgwick, now a Federalist senator from Massachusetts, first learned of the commission's failure, he observed in words that capture the High Federalists' vindictiveness, "It will afford a glorious opportunity to destroy faction."

During the summer of 1798, a provisional army gradually came into existence. George Washington agreed to lead the troops, but he would do so only on condition that Adams appoint Hamilton as second in command. This demand placed the president in a terrible dilemma. Several revolutionary veterans—Henry Knox, for example—outranked Hamilton. Moreover, the former secretary of the treasury had consistently undermined Adams's authority, and to give Hamilton a position of real power in the government seemed awkward at best. When Washington insisted, however, Adams was forced to support Hamilton. The chief of the High Federalists threw himself into the task of recruiting and supplying the troops. No detail escaped his attention. He and Secretary of War McHenry made certain that in this political army, only loyal Federalists received commissions.

Hamilton should not have treated Adams with such open contempt. After all, the Massachusetts statesman was still the president, and without presidential cooperation, Hamilton could not fulfill his grand military ambitions. Yet whenever pressing questions concerning the army arose, Adams was nowhere to be found. He let commissions lie on his desk unsigned; he took overlong vacations to New England. He made it quite clear his first love was the navy. In May 1798, the president persuaded Congress to establish the Navy Department. Moreover, Adams further infuriated the High Federalists by refusing to ask Congress for a formal declaration of war. When they pressed him, Adams threatened to resign, making Jefferson president. As the weeks passed, the American people increasingly regarded the idle army as an expensive extravagance.

SILENCING POLITICAL OPPOSITION: THE ALIEN AND SEDITION ACTS

The Federalists did not rely solely on the army to crush political dissent. During the summer of 1798, the party's majority in Congress passed a group of bills known collectively as the Alien and Sedition Acts. This legislation authorized the use of federal courts and the powers of the presidency to silence the Republicans. The acts were born of fear and vindictiveness, and in their efforts to punish the followers of Jefferson, the Federalists created the nation's first major crisis over civil liberties.

Congress drew up three separate Alien Acts. The first, the Alien Enemies Law, vested the president with extraordinary wartime powers. On his own authority, he could detain or deport citizens of nations with which the United States was at war and who behaved in a suspicious manner. Since Adams refused to ask for a declaration of war, this legislation never went into effect. A second act, the Alien Law, empowered the president to expel any foreigner from the United States simply by executive decree. Congress limited the acts to two years, and Adams did not attempt to enforce them. The third act, the Naturalization Law, was the most flagrantly political of the group. The act established a fourteen-year probationary period before foreigners could apply for U.S. citizenship. Federalists recognized that recent immigrants, especially the Irish, tended to vote Republican. The Naturalization Law, therefore, was designed to keep "hordes of wild Irishmen" away from the polls for as long as possible.

The Sedition Law struck at the heart of free political exchange. It defined criticism of the U.S. government as criminal libel; citizens found guilty by a jury were subject to fines and imprisonment. Congress entrusted enforcement of the act to the federal courts. Republicans were justly worried that the Sedition Law undermined rights guaranteed by the First Amendment. When they protested, however, the High Federalists dismissed their complaints. The Constitution, they declared, did not condone "the most groundless and malignant lies, striking at the safety and existence of the nation."

Americans living in widely scattered regions of the country soon witnessed political repression firsthand. District courts staffed by Federalist appointees indicted seventeen people for criticizing the government. The most celebrated trial occurred in Vermont. A Republican congressman, Matthew Lyon, who was running for reelection, publicly accused the Adams administration of mishandling the Quasi-War. This was not the first time this Irish immigrant had angered the Federalists. On the floor of the House of Representatives, Lyon once spit in the eye of a Federalist congressman from Connecticut. Lyon was immediately labeled the "Spitting Lyon." A Federalist court convicted him of libel. Lyon had the last laugh. While he sat in jail, his constituents reelected him to Congress.

The federal courts had become political tools. While the fumbling efforts at enforcement of the Sedition Law did not silence opposition—indeed, they sparked even greater criticism—the actions of the administration persuaded Republicans that the survival of free government was at stake. "There is no event," Jefferson warned, ". . . however atrocious, which may not be expected."

KENTUCKY AND VIRGINIA RESOLUTIONS

By the fall of 1798, Jefferson and Madison were convinced that the Federalists wanted to create a police state. The Sedition Law threatened the free communication of ideas that Madison "deemed the only effectual guardian of every other right." Some extreme Republicans recommended secession from the Union; others advocated armed resistance. But Jefferson wisely counseled against such ex-

In the early years of the republic, political dissent sometimes escalated to physical violence. This fistfight took place on the floor of Congress, February 15, 1798. The combatants are Republican Matthew Lyon and Federalist Roger Griswold.

treme strategies. "This is not the kind of opposition the American people will permit," he reminded his desperate supporters. The last best hope for American freedom lay in the state legislatures.

As the crisis deepened, Jefferson and Madison drafted separate protests known as the Virginia and Kentucky Resolutions. In the Kentucky Resolutions (November 1798), Jefferson described the federal union as a compact. The states transferred certain explicit powers to the national government, but, in his opinion, they retained full authority over all matters not specifically mentioned in the Constitution. Jefferson rejected Hamilton's broad interpretation of the "general welfare" clause. "Every state," Jefferson argued, "has a natural right in cases not within the compact . . . to nullify of their own authority all assumptions of power by others within their limits." Carried to an extreme, this logic could have led to the breakup of the federal government, and in 1798, Kentucky legislators were not prepared to take such a radical stance. While they diluted Jefferson's prose, they fully accepted his belief that the Alien and Sedition Acts were unconstitutional and ought to be repealed.

When Madison drafted the Virginia Resolutions in December, he took a stand more temperate than Jefferson's. Madison urged the states to defend the rights of the American people, but he resisted the notion that a single state legislature could or should overthrow federal law.

The Virginia and Kentucky Resolutions were not intended as statements of abstract principles and most certainly not as a justification for southern secession. They were pure political party propaganda. Jefferson and Madison dramatically reminded American voters during a period of severe domestic tension that the Republicans offered a clear alternative to Federalist rule. No other state legislatures passed the Resolutions.

ADAMS'S FINEST HOUR

In February 1799, President Adams belatedly declared his independence from the Hamiltonian wing of the Federalist party. Throughout the confrontation with France, Adams had shown little enthusiasm for war. A French foreign minister now told American agents that the bribery episode had been an unfortunate misunderstanding. The High Federalists ridiculed this report. But Adams, still brooding over Hamilton's appointment to the army, decided to throw his own waning prestige behind peace. In February, he suddenly asked the Senate to confirm William Vans Murray as U.S. representative to France.

The move caught the High Federalists totally by surprise. They sputtered with outrage. "It is solely the President's act," Pickering cried, "and we were all thunderstruck when we heard of it." Adams was just warming to the task. In May, he fired Pickering and McHenry.

When the new negotiators—Oliver Ellsworth and William Davie joined Murray—finally arrived in France in November 1799, they discovered that yet another group had come to power there. This government, headed by Napoleon Bonaparte, cooperated in drawing up an agreement known as the Convention of Mortefontaine. The French refused to compensate the Americans for vessels taken during the Quasi-War, but they did declare the treaties of 1778 null and void. Moreover, the convention removed annoying French restrictions on U.S. commerce. Not only had Adams avoided war, but he had also created an atmosphere of mutual trust that paved the way for the purchase of the Louisiana Territory. In the short run, however, political courage cost Adams reelection.

THE PEACEFUL REVOLUTION: THE ELECTION OF 1800

On the eve of the election of 1800, the Federalists were fatally divided. Adams enjoyed wide popularity among the Federalist rank and file, especially in New England, but party leaders such as Hamilton vowed to punish the president for his betrayal of their militant policies. Hamilton even composed a scathing pam-

THE ELECTION OF 1800

CANDIDATE	PARTY	ELECTORAL VOTE
Jefferson	Republican	73
Burr	Republican	73
J. Adams	Federalist	65
C. Pinckney	Federalist	64

phlet titled *Letter Concerning the Public Conduct and Character of John Adams,* an essay that questioned Adams's ability to hold high office.

Once again the former secretary of the treasury attempted to rig the voting in the electoral college so that the party's vice presidential candidate, Charles Cotesworth Pinckney, would receive more ballots than Adams and America would be saved from "the fangs of Jefferson." As in 1796, the conspiracy backfired. The Republicans gained 73 votes while the Federalists trailed with 65.

To everyone's surprise, however, the election was not resolved in the electoral college. When the ballots were counted, Jefferson and his running mate, Aaron Burr, had tied. This accident—a Republican elector should have thrown away his second vote—sent the selection of the next president to the House of Representatives, a lame-duck body still controlled by members of the Federalist party.

As the House began its work on February 27, 1801, excitement ran high. Each state delegation cast a single vote, with nine votes needed for election. On the first ballot, Jefferson received the support of eight states, Burr six, and two states divided evenly. People predicted a quick victory for Jefferson, but after dozens of ballots, the House had still not selected a president.

The logjam finally broke when leading Federalists decided that Jefferson, whatever his faults, would make a more responsible president than would the shifty Burr. On the thirty-sixth ballot, Representative James A. Bayard of Delaware announced he no longer supported Burr, giving Jefferson the presidency, ten states to four.

The Twelfth Amendment, ratified in 1804, saved the American people from repeating this potentially dangerous turn of events. Henceforth, the electoral college cast separate ballots for president and vice president.

During the final days of his presidency, Adams appointed as many Federalists as possible to the federal bench. Jefferson protested the hasty manner in which these "midnight judges" were selected. One of them, John Marshall, became chief justice of the United States, a post he held with distinction for thirty-four years. But behind the last-minute flurry of activity lay bitterness and disappointment. Adams never forgave Hamilton. "No party," the Federalist president wrote, "that ever existed knew itself so little or so vainly overrated its own influence and popularity as ours." On the morning of Jefferson's inauguration, Adams slipped away from the capital—now located in Washington, D.C.—unnoticed and unappreciated.

In the address that Adams missed, Jefferson attempted to quiet partisan fears. "We are all republicans; we are all federalists," the new president declared. By this statement, he did not mean to suggest that party differences no longer mattered. Rather, whatever the politicians might say, the people shared a deep commitment to a federal union based on republican ideals set forth during the American Revolution. Indeed, the president interpreted the election of 1800 as a revolutionary episode, as the fulfillment of the principles of 1776.

The Federalists were thoroughly dispirited by the entire experience. In the end, it had not been Hamilton's foolish electoral schemes that destroyed the party's chances in 1800. Rather, the Federalists had lost touch with a majority of the American people. In office, Adams and Hamilton—whatever their own differences may have been—betrayed their doubts about popular sovereignty too often, and when it came time to marshal broad support, to mobilize public opinion in favor of the party of wealth and privilege, few responded. As Secretary of War Oliver Wolcott observed on hearing of Jefferson's victory, "Have our party shown that they possess the necessary skill and courage to deserve . . . to govern? What have they done? . . . They write private letters. To whom? To each other, but they do nothing to give a proper direction to the public mind."

DANGER OF POLITICAL EXTREMISM

From a broader historical perspective, the election of 1800 seems noteworthy for what did not occur. There were no riots in the streets, no attempted coup by military officers, no secession from the Union, nothing except the peaceful transfer of government from the leaders of one political party to those of the opposition. Americans had weathered the Alien and Sedition Acts, the meddling by predatory foreign powers in domestic affairs, the shrilly partisan rhetoric of hack journalists, and now, at the start of a new century, they were impressed with their own achievement. But as they well understood—indeed, as modern Americans must constantly relearn—extremism in the name of partisan political truth can easily unravel the delicate fabric of representative democracy and leave the republic at the mercy of those who would manipulate the public for private benefit.

8

JEFFERSONIAN ASCENDANCY
Theory and Practice of Government

British visitors often expressed contempt for Jeffersonian society. Wherever they traveled in the young republic, they met ill-mannered people inspired with a ruling passion for liberty and equality. Charles William Janson, an Englishman who lived in the United States for thirteen years, recounted an exchange that had occurred at the home of an American acquaintance. "On knocking at the door," he reported, "it was opened by a servant maid, whom I had never before seen." The woman's behavior astonished Janson. "The following is the dialogue, word for word, which took place on this occasion:—'Is your master at home?'—'I have no master.'—'Don't you live here?'—'I *stay* here.'—'And who are you then?'—'Why, I am Mr.———'s *help*. I'd have you know, *man,* that I am no *sarvant* [sic]; none but *negers* [sic] are *sarvants.*'"

Standing on his friend's doorstep, Janson encountered the authentic voice of Jeffersonian republicanism—self-confident, assertive, blatantly racist, and having no intention of being relegated to low social status. The maid who answered the door believed she was her employer's equal, perhaps not in wealth but surely in character. She may have even dreamed of someday owning a house staffed with "*help.*" American society fostered such ambition. In the early nineteenth century, thousands of settlers poured across the Appalachian Mountains or moved to cities in search of opportunity. Thomas Jefferson and individuals who stood for public office under the banner of the Republican party claimed to speak for these people.

The limits of the Jeffersonian vision were obvious even to contemporaries. The people who spoke most eloquently about equal opportunity often owned slaves. As early as the 1770s, the famed English essayist Samuel Johnson had chided Americans for their hypocrisy. "How is it," he asked the indignant rebels, "that we hear the loudest yelps for liberty from the drivers of Negroes?" Little had changed since the Revolution. African Americans, who represented one-fifth of the population of the United States, were excluded from the new opportunities opening up in the cities and the West. Indeed, the maid in the incident just described insisted—with no apparent sense of inconsistency—that her position was superior to that of blacks, who were brought involuntarily to lifelong servitude.

It is not surprising that leaders of the Federalist party accused the Republicans, especially those who lived in the South, of disingenuousness, and in 1804, one Massachusetts Federalist sarcastically defined "Jeffersonian" as "an Indian word, signifying '*a great tobacco planter, who had herds of black slaves.*'" The race issue was always just beneath the surface of political maneuvering. Indeed, the acquisition of the Louisiana Territory and the War of 1812 fanned fundamental disagreement about the spread of slavery to the western territories.

In other areas, the Jeffersonians did not fulfill even their own high expectations. As members of an opposition party during the presidency of John Adams, they insisted on a strict interpretation of the Constitution, peaceful foreign relations, and a reduction of the role of the federal government in the lives of the average citizens. But following the election of 1800, Jefferson and his supporters discovered that unanticipated pressures, foreign and domestic, forced them to moderate these goals. Before he retired from public office, Jefferson interpreted the Constitution in a way that permitted the government to purchase the Louisiana Territory when the opportunity arose; he regulated the national economy with a rigor that would have surprised Alexander Hamilton; and he led the country to the brink of war. Some Americans praised the president's pragmatism; others felt betrayed. For a man who played a leading role in the revolt against George III, it must have been shocking in 1807 to find himself labeled a "despot" in a popular New England newspaper. "Give ear no longer to the siren voice of democracy and Jeffersonian liberty," the editor shrieked. "It is a cursed delusion, adopted by traitors, and recommended by sycophants."

DEFINING IDENTITY IN A NEW REPUBLIC

During the early decades of the nineteenth century, the population of the United States experienced substantial growth. The 1810 census counted 7,240,000 Americans, a jump of almost 2 million in just ten years. Of this total, approximately 20 percent were black slaves, the majority of whom lived in the South.

The large population increase in the nation was the result primarily of natural re-production, since during Jefferson's presidency few immigrants moved to the New World. The largest single group in this society was children under the age of sixteen, boys and girls who were born after Washington's election and who de-fined their own futures at a time when the nation's boundaries were rapidly ex-panding. For white Americans, it was a time of heightened optimism, and many people possessing entrepreneurial skills or engineering capabilities aggressively made their way in a society that seemed to rate personal merit higher than family background.

Americans were also forming strong regional identifications. In commerce and politics, they perceived themselves as representatives of distinct subcul-tures—as Southerners, New Englanders, or Westerners. No doubt, the broaden-ing geographic horizons reflected improved transportation links that enabled people to travel more easily within the various sections. But the growing regional mentality was also the product of defensiveness. While local writers celebrated New England's cultural distinctiveness, for example, they were clearly uneasy about the region's rejection of the democratic values that were sweeping the rest of the nation. Moreover, during this period people living south of the Potomac

North America in 1800

In the 1790s, diplomatic agreements with Britain and Spain and defeat of the Native Americans at the bat-tle of Fallen Timbers opened the way to U.S. settlement of the land beyond the Appalachian Mountains.

River began describing themselves as Southerners, not as citizens of the Chesapeake or the Carolinas as they had done in colonial times.

This shifting focus of attention resulted not only from an awareness of shared economic interests but also from a sensitivity to outside attacks on slavery. Several times during the first fifteen years of the nineteenth century, conspirators actually advocated secession, and though the schemes failed, they revealed the powerful sectional loyalties that threatened national unity.

WESTWARD THE COURSE OF EMPIRE

The West dominated popular imagination. Before the end of the American Revolution, only Indian traders and a few hardy settlers had ventured across the Appalachians. After 1790, however, a flood of people rushed west to stake out farms. Many settlers followed the so-called northern route across Pennsylvania or New York into the old Northwest Territory. Pittsburgh and Cincinnati, both strategically located on the Ohio River, became important commercial ports. In 1803, Ohio joined the Union, and territorial governments were formed in Indiana (1800), Louisiana (1805), Michigan (1805), Illinois (1809), and Missouri (1812). Southerners poured into the new states of Kentucky (1792) and Tennessee (1796). Wherever they located, Westerners depended on water transportation. Because of the extraordinarily high cost of hauling goods overland, riverboats provided the only economical means of carrying agricultural products

By 1800, Cincinnati—one of the new western cities—had become a busy commercial center on the Ohio River with a post office, a Presbyterian church, and the Green Tree Hotel.

to distant markets. The Mississippi River was the crucial commercial link for the entire region, and Westerners did not feel secure so long as New Orleans, the southern gate to the Mississippi, remained under Spanish control.

Families that moved west attempted to transplant familiar eastern customs to the frontier. In some areas such as the Western Reserve, a narrow strip of land along Lake Erie in northern Ohio, the influence of New England remained strong. In general, however, a creative mixing of peoples of different backgrounds in a strange environment generated distinctive folkways. Westerners developed their own heroes, such as Mike Fink, the legendary keelboatman of the Mississippi River; Daniel Boone, the famed trapper and Indian fighter; and the eye-gouging "alligatormen" of Kentucky and Tennessee.

NATIVE AMERICAN RESISTANCE

At the beginning of the nineteenth century, a substantial number of Native Americans lived in the greater Ohio Valley; the land belonged to them. These Indians, many dependent on trade with the white people and ravaged by disease, lacked unity. Small groups of Native Americans, allegedly representing the interests of an entire tribe, sold off huge pieces of land, often for whiskey and trinkets.

Tenskwatawa, known as the Prophet, provided spiritual leadership for the union of the native peoples he and his brother Tecumseh organized to resist white encroachment on Native American lands.

Such fraudulent transactions disgusted the Shawnee leaders Tenskwatawa (known as the Prophet) and his brother Tecumseh. Tecumseh rejected classification as a Shawnee and may have been the first native leader to identify himself as "Indian." These men attempted to revitalize native cultures, and against overwhelming odds, they briefly persuaded Native Americans living in the Indiana Territory to avoid contact with whites, to resist alcohol, and, most important, to hold on to their land. White intruders saw Tecumseh as a threat to progress, and during the War of 1812, they shattered the Indians' dream of cultural renaissance. The populous Creek nation, located in the modern states of Alabama and Mississippi, also resisted the settlers' advance, but its warriors were crushed by Andrew Jackson's Tennessee militia at the battle of Horseshoe Bend (March 1814).

Jeffersonians disclaimed any intention to destroy the Indians. The president talked of creating a vast reservation beyond the Mississippi River, just as the British had talked before the Revolution of a sanctuary beyond the Appalachian Mountains. He sent federal agents to "civilize" the Indians, to transform them into yeoman farmers. But even the most enlightened white thinkers of the day did not believe the Indians possessed cultures worth preserving. In fact, in 1835, the Democratic national convention selected a vice presidential candidate whose major qualification for high office seemed to be that he had killed Tecumseh.

COMMERCIAL LIFE IN THE CITIES

Before 1820, the prosperity of the United States depended on its agriculture and trade. Jeffersonian America was by no stretch of the imagination an industrial economy. The overwhelming majority of the population—84 percent in 1810—was directly involved in agriculture. Southerners concentrated on the staple crops of tobacco, rice, and cotton, which they sold on the European market. In the North, people generally produced livestock and cereal crops. Regardless of location, however, the nation's farmers followed a backbreaking work routine that did not differ substantially from that of their parents and grandparents. Except for the cotton gin, important chemical and mechanical inventions did not appear in the fields for another generation. Probably the major innovation of this period was the agricultural fair, an idea first advanced in 1809 by a Massachusetts farmer, Elkanah Watson. In hopes of improving animal breeding, he offered prizes for the best livestock in the country.

The merchant marine represented an equally important element in America's economy. At the turn of the century, ships flying the Stars and Stripes transported a large share of the world's trade. Merchants in Boston, New York, and Philadelphia received handsome profits from such commerce. Their vessels provided essential links between European countries and their Caribbean colonies. France, for example, relied heavily on American transport for its sugar. These lucrative transactions, coupled with the export of domestic staples, especially cotton, generated impressive fortunes. Between 1793 and 1807, the year Jefferson imposed the embargo against Britain and France, American commerce enjoyed a more than 300 percent increase in the value of exports and in net earnings. Unfortunately, the boom did not last. The success of the "carrying trade" depended in large measure on friendly relations between the United States and the major European powers. When England and France began seizing American ships—as they both did after 1805—national prosperity suffered.

The cities of Jeffersonian America functioned chiefly as depots for international trade. Only about 7 percent of the nation's population lived in urban centers, and most of these people owed their livelihoods either directly or indirectly to the carrying trade. Recent studies revealed that several major port cities of the early republic—New York, Philadelphia, and Baltimore, for example—had some of the highest population densities ever recorded in this country's history. In 1800, more than 40,000 New Yorkers crowded into an area of only 1.5 square miles; in Philadelphia, some 46,000 people were packed into less than one square mile. As one historian explained, "The cities contains disproportionate numbers of young white males, free black men and women, and white widows. These people had below-average incomes and also an increasing propensity to live on their own rather than as dependents." As is common today, many city dwellers rented living space, and since the demand for housing exceeded the supply, the rents were high.

Within these densely crowded urban centers, artisans maintained the fleet; skilled workers produced new ships; laborers loaded cargoes. And as some merchant families became wealthy, they demanded luxury items such as fine furniture. This specialized market drew a small, but highly visible, group of master craftspeople, and their extraordinarily beautiful and intricate pieces—New England tall clocks, for example—were perhaps the highest artistic achievement of the period.

Despite these accomplishments, American cities exercised only a marginal influence on the nation's vast hinterland. Because of the high cost of land transportation, urban merchants seldom purchased goods for export—flour, for example—from a distance of more than 150 miles. The separation between rural and urban Americans was far more pronounced during Jefferson's presidency than it was after the development of canals and railroads a few decades later.

The booming carrying trade may actually have retarded the industrialization of the United States. The lure of large profits drew investment capital—a scarce resource in a developing society—into commerce. By contrast, manufacturing seemed too risky. To be sure, Samuel Slater, an English-born designer of textile machinery, established several cotton-spinning mills in New England, but until the 1820s these plants employed only a small number of workers. In fact, during this period far more cloth was produced in individual households than in factories. Another farsighted inventor, Robert Fulton, sailed the first American steamship up the Hudson River in 1807. In time, this marvelous innovation opened new markets for domestic manufacturers, especially in the West. At the end of the War of 1812, however, few people anticipated how greatly power generated by fossil fuel would transform the character of the American economy.

REPUBLICANS IN POWER

The District of Columbia seemed an appropriate capital for a Republican president. At the time of Jefferson's first inauguration, Washington was still an isolated rural village, a far cry from the crowded centers of Philadelphia and New York.

Although cotton was an important trade item in the early nineteenth century, technological advances in textile production were slow to take hold. Some spinning mills, such as the one pictured here, were built in New England, but most cloth was still manufactured in the home.

Jefferson fit comfortably into Washington society. He despised formal ceremony and sometimes shocked foreign dignitaries by meeting them in his slippers or a threadbare jacket.

The president was a poor public speaker. He wisely refused to deliver annual addresses before Congress. In personal conversation, however, Jefferson exuded considerable charm. His dinner parties were major intellectual as well as social events, and in this forum, the president regaled politicians with his knowledge of literature, philosophy, and science. According to Margaret Bayard Smith, the wife of a congressman, the president "has more ease than grace—all the winning softness of politeness, without the artificial polish of courts."

Notwithstanding his commitment to the life of the mind, Jefferson was a politician to the core. He ran for the presidency to achieve specific goals: the reduction of the size and cost of federal government, the repeal of obnoxious Federalist legislation such as the Alien Acts, and the maintenance of international peace. To accomplish his program, Jefferson realized he needed the full cooperation of congressional Republicans, some of whom were fiercely independent men. Over such figures Jefferson exercised political mastery. He established close ties with the leaders of both houses of Congress, and while he seldom announced his plans in public, he made certain his legislative lieutenants knew exactly what he desired. Contemporaries who described Jefferson as a weak president—and some Federalists did just that—did not read the scores of memoranda he sent to political friends or witness the informal meetings he held at the executive mansion with important Republicans. In two terms as president, Jefferson never had to veto a single act of Congress.

Jefferson carefully selected the members of his cabinet. During Washington's administration, he had witnessed—even provoked—severe infighting; as president, he nominated only those who enthusiastically supported his programs. James Madison, the leading figure at the Constitutional Convention, became secretary of state. For the Treasury, Jefferson chose Albert Gallatin, a Swiss-born financier who understood the complexities of the federal budget.

JEFFERSONIAN REFORMS

A top priority of the new government was reducing the national debt. Jefferson and Gallatin regarded a large federal deficit as dangerous to the health of republican institutions. In fact, both men associated debt with Alexander Hamilton's Federalist financial programs, measures they considered harmful to republicanism. Jefferson claimed that legislators elected by the current generation did not have the right to mortgage the future of unborn Americans.

Jefferson also wanted to diminish the activities of the federal government. He urged Congress to repeal all direct taxes, including the tax that had sparked the Whiskey Rebellion in 1794. Secretary Gallatin linked federal income to the carrying trade. He calculated that the entire cost of national government could be borne by customs receipts. As long as commerce flourished, revenues provided sufficient sums. When international war closed foreign markets, however, the flow of funds dried up.

To help pay the debt inherited from the Adams administration, Jefferson ordered substantial cuts in the national budget. The president closed several American embassies in Europe. He also slashed military spending. In his first term, Jefferson reduced the size of the U.S. Army by 50 percent. This decision left only three thousand soldiers to guard the entire frontier. In addition, he retired a majority of the navy's warships. When New Englanders claimed the cuts left the country defenseless, Jefferson countered with a glib argument. As ships of the U.S. Navy sailed the world's oceans, he claimed, they were liable to provoke hostilities, perhaps even war; hence, by reducing the size of the fleet, he promoted peace.

More than budgetary considerations prompted Jefferson's military reductions. He was deeply suspicious of standing armies. In the event of foreign attack, he reasoned, the militia would rise in defense of the republic. No doubt, his experiences during the Revolution influenced his thinking on military affairs, for in 1776, an aroused populace had taken up arms against the British. To ensure that the citizen soldiers would receive professional leadership in battle, Jefferson created the Army Corps of Engineers and the military academy at West Point in 1802.

Political patronage was a great burden to the new president. Loyal Republicans throughout the United States had worked hard for Jefferson's victory, and as soon as he took office, they stormed the executive mansion seeking federal employment. While the president controlled several hundred jobs, he refused to dismiss all the Federalists. To be sure, he acted quickly to remove the so-called midnight appointees, highly partisan selections that Adams had made after learning of Jefferson's election. But to transform federal hiring into an undisciplined spoils system, especially at the highest levels of the federal bureaucracy, seemed to Jefferson to be shortsighted. Moderate Federalists might be converted to the Republican party, and, in any case, there was a good chance they possessed the expertise needed to run the government. At the end of his first term, half of the people holding office were appointees of Washington and Adams.

Jefferson's political moderation helped hasten the demise of the Federalist party. This loose organization had nearly destroyed itself during the election of 1800, and following Adams's defeat, prominent Federalist spokesmen such as Fisher Ames and John Jay withdrew from national affairs. The mere prospect of flattering the common people was odious enough to drive these Federalists into political retirement.

After 1804, a group of younger Federalists belatedly attempted to pump life into the dying party. They experimented with popular election techniques. In some states, they tightened party organization, held nominating conventions, and campaigned energetically for office. These were essential reforms, but with the exception of a brief Federalist revival in the Northeast between 1807 and 1814, the results of these activities were disappointing. Even the younger Federalists thought it demeaning to appeal for votes. Diehards such as Timothy Pickering promoted wild secessionist schemes in New England, while the most promising moderates—John Quincy Adams, for example—joined the Republicans.

THE LOUISIANA PURCHASE

When Jefferson first took office, he was confident that Louisiana as well as Florida would eventually become part of the United States. After all, Spain owned the territory, and Jefferson assumed he could persuade the rulers of that nation to sell their colonies. If that peaceful strategy failed, the president was prepared to threaten forcible occupation.

In May 1801, however, prospects for the easy acquisition of Louisiana suddenly darkened. Jefferson learned that Spain had secretly transferred title to the entire region to France. To make matters worse, the French leader Napoleon seemed intent on reestablishing an empire in North America. Even as Jefferson sought additional information concerning the details of the transfer, Napoleon was dispatching a large army to put down a rebellion in France's sugar-rich Caribbean colony, Haiti. From that island stronghold in the West Indies, French troops could occupy New Orleans and close the Mississippi River to American trade.

A sense of crisis enveloped Washington. Some congressmen urged Jefferson to prepare for war against France. Tensions increased when the Spanish officials who still governed New Orleans announced the closing of that port to American commerce (October 1802). Jefferson and his advisers assumed that the Spanish had acted on orders from France, but despite this serious provocation, the president preferred negotiations to war. In January 1803, he asked James Monroe, a loyal Republican from Virginia, to join the American minister, Robert Livingston, in Paris. The president instructed the two men to explore the possibility of purchasing the city of New Orleans. Lest they underestimate the importance of their diplomatic mission, Jefferson reminded them, "There is on the globe one single

UNDER MY WINGS EVERY THING PROSPERS

President Jefferson recognized the strategic location of New Orleans and determined to buy it from the French. By 1803, when this view was painted, New Orleans was already a thriving port and an important outlet for exports produced by new communities in the Ohio and Mississippi Valleys.

spot, the possessor of which is our natural and habitual enemy. It is New Orleans." If Livingston and Monroe failed, Jefferson realized he would be forced to turn to Great Britain for military assistance. Dependence on that country seemed repellent, but he recognized that as soon as French troops moved into Louisiana, "we must marry ourselves to the British fleet and nation."

By the time Monroe joined Livingston in France, Napoleon had lost interest in establishing an American empire. The army he sent to Haiti succumbed to tropical diseases. The diplomats from the United States knew nothing of these developments. They were taken by complete surprise, therefore, when they learned that Talleyrand, the French minister for foreign relations, had offered to sell the entire Louisiana Territory in April 1803. For only $15 million, the Americans doubled the size of the United States. In fact, Livingston and Monroe were not certain how much land they had actually purchased. When they asked Talleyrand whether the deal included Florida, he responded ambiguously, "You have made a noble bargain for yourselves, and I suppose you will make the most of it." Even at that moment, Livingston realized that the transaction would alter the course of American history. "From this day," he wrote, "the United States take their place among the powers of first rank."

The Louisiana Purchase and the Route of Lewis and Clark

Not until Lewis and Clark had explored the Far West did citizens of the United States realize just how much territory Jefferson had acquired through the Louisiana Purchase.

Jefferson, of course, was immensely relieved. The nation had avoided war with France. Nevertheless, he worried that the purchase might be unconstitutional. The president pointed out that the Constitution did not specifically authorize the acquisition of vast new territories and the incorporation of thousands of foreign citizens. To escape this apparent legal dilemma, Jefferson proposed an amendment to the Constitution. Few persons, even his closest advisers, shared the president's scruples. Events in France soon forced Jefferson to adopt a more pragmatic course. When he heard that Napoleon had become impatient for his money, Jefferson rushed the papers to a Senate eager to ratify the agreement, and nothing more was said about the Constitution.

The Purchase raised other difficult problems. The area that eventually became the state of Louisiana (1812) contained many people of French and Spanish background who possessed no familiarity with representative institutions. Their laws had been autocratic, their local government corrupt. To allow such persons to elect a representative assembly struck the president as dangerous. He did not even know whether the population of Louisiana would remain loyal to the United States. Jefferson, therefore, recommended to Congress a transitional government consisting entirely of appointed officials. In March 1804, the Louisiana Government Bill narrowly passed the House of Representatives. Members of the president's own party attacked the plan. After all, it imposed taxes on the citizens of Louisiana without their consent. Most troubling perhaps was the fact that the legislation ran counter to Jefferson's well-known republican principles.

THE LEWIS AND CLARK EXPEDITION

In the midst of the Louisiana controversy, Jefferson dispatched a secret message to Congress requesting $2500 for the exploration of the Far West (January 1803). How closely this decision was connected to the Paris negotiations is not clear. Whatever the case may have been, the president asked his private secretary, Meriwether Lewis, to discover whether the Missouri River "may offer the most direct & practicable water communication across this continent for the purposes of commerce." The president also regarded the expedition as an opportunity to collect data about flora and fauna. He personally instructed Lewis in the latest techniques of scientific observation. While preparing for this adventure, Lewis's second in command, William Clark, assumed such a prominent role that the effort became known as the Lewis and Clark Expedition.

The exploring party set out from St. Louis in May 1804, and after crossing the snow-covered Rocky Mountains, with their food supply running dangerously low, the Americans reached the Pacific Ocean in November 1805. The group returned safely the following September. The results of the expedition not only fulfilled Jefferson's scientific expectations but also reaffirmed his faith in the future economic prosperity of the United States.

CONFLICT WITH THE BARBARY STATES

During this period, Jefferson dealt with another problem. For several decades, the North African states of Tangier, Algiers, Tripoli, and Tunis—the Barbary States—had preyed on commercial shipping. Most European nations paid the pirates tribute, hoping thereby to protect merchants trading in the Mediterranean. In 1801, Jefferson decided the extortion had become intolerable and dispatched a small fleet to the Barbary Coast, where, according to one commander, the Americans intended to negotiate "through the mouth of a cannon." Tripoli put up stiff resistance, however, and in one mismanaged engagement it captured the U.S. frigate *Philadelphia*. Ransoming the crew cost Jefferson's government another $60,000. An American land assault across the Libyan desert provided inspiration for the words of the "Marines' Hymn"—"to the shores of Tripoli"—but no smashing victory.

Despite a generally unimpressive American military record, a vigorous naval blockade brought hostilities to a conclusion. In 1805, the president signed a treaty formally ending the Barbary War. One diplomat crowed, "It must be mortifying to some of the neighboring European powers to see that the Barbary

THE ELECTION OF 1804

CANDIDATE	PARTY	ELECTORAL VOTE
Jefferson	Republican	162
C. Pinckney	Federalist	14

States have been taught their first lessons of humiliation from the Western World."

Jefferson concluded his first term on a wave of popularity. He had maintained the peace, reduced taxes, and expanded the boundaries of the United States. Not surprisingly, he overwhelmed Charles Cotesworth Pinckney, his Federalist opponent in the presidential election of 1804.

JEFFERSON'S CRITICS

At the moment of Jefferson's greatest electoral victory, a perceptive person might have seen signs of serious division within the Republican party and within the country. The president's heavy-handed attempts to reform the federal courts stirred deep animosities. Republicans had begun sniping at other Republicans, and one leading member of the party, Aaron Burr, became involved in a bizarre plot to separate the West from the rest of the nation. Congressional debates over the future of the slave trade revealed the existence of powerful sectional loyalties.

ATTACK ON THE JUDGES

Jefferson's controversy with the federal bench commenced the moment he became president. The Federalists, realizing they would soon lose control over the executive branch, had passed the Judiciary Act of 1801. This bill created several circuit courts and sixteen new judgeships. Through his "midnight" appointments, Adams had quickly filled these positions with stalwarts of the Federalist party. Such blatantly partisan behavior angered Jefferson. Even more infuriating was Adams's appointment of John Marshall as the new chief justice. This shrewd, largely self-educated Virginian of Federalist background, whose training in the law consisted of a series of lectures he attended at the College of William and Mary in 1780, held his own against the new president.

In January 1802, Jefferson's congressional allies called for repeal of the Judiciary Act. In public debate, they studiously avoided the obvious political issue. The new circuit courts, they claimed, were needlessly expensive. The judges did not hear enough cases to warrant continuance. The Federalists mounted an able defense. The Constitution, they observed, provided for the removal of federal judges only when they were found guilty of high crimes and misdemeanors.

By repealing the Judiciary Act, the legislative branch would in effect be dismissing judges without a trial, a clear violation of their constitutional rights. This argument made little impression on the Republican party. In March, the House, following the Senate, voted for repeal.

While Congress debated the Judiciary Act, another battle erupted. One of Adams's "midnight" appointees, William Marbury, complained that the new administration would not give him his commission for the office of justice of the peace for the District of Columbia. He sought redress before the Supreme Court, demanding that the federal justices compel James Madison, the secretary of state, to deliver the necessary papers. When they learned that Marshall had agreed to hear this case, the Republicans were furious. Apparently the chief justice wanted to provoke a confrontation with the executive branch.

Marshall was too clever to jeopardize the independence of the Supreme Court over such a relatively minor issue. In his celebrated *Marbury* v. *Madison* decision (February 1803), Marshall berated the secretary of state for withholding Marbury's commission. Nevertheless, he concluded that the Supreme Court did not possess jurisdiction over such matters. Poor Marbury was out of luck. The Republicans proclaimed victory. In fact, they were so pleased with the outcome that they failed to examine the logic of Marshall's decision. He had ruled that part of the earlier act of Congress, the one on which Marbury based his appeal, was unconstitutional. This was the first time the Supreme Court asserted its right to judge the constitutionality of congressional acts, and while contemporaries did not fully appreciate the significance of Marshall's doctrine, *Marbury* v. *Madison* later served as an important precedent for judicial review of federal statutes.

Neither Marbury's defeat nor repeal of the Judiciary Act placated extreme Republicans. They insisted that federal judges should be made more responsive to the will of the people. One solution, short of electing federal judges, was impeachment. This clumsy device provided the legislature with a way of removing particularly offensive individuals. By the spring of 1803, Jefferson found an appealing target. In a Baltimore newspaper, the president stumbled on the transcript of a speech allegedly delivered before a federal grand jury. The words seemed almost treasonous. The person responsible was Samuel Chase, a justice of the Supreme Court, who had frequently attacked Republican policies. Jefferson leapt at the chance to remove Chase from office. Indeed, the moment he learned of Chase's actions, the president wrote to a leading Republican congressman, asking, "Ought the seditious and official attack on the principles of our Constitution . . . go unpunished?" The congressman took the hint. In a matter of weeks, the Republican-controlled House of Representatives indicted Chase.

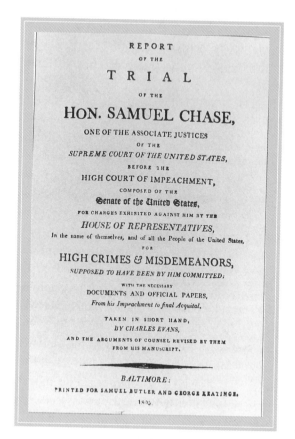

REPORT
OF THE

T R I A L

OF THE

HON. SAMUEL CHASE,

ONE OF THE ASSOCIATE JUSTICES
OF THE
SUPREME COURT OF THE UNITED STATES,
BEFORE THE
HIGH COURT OF IMPEACHMENT,
COMPOSED OF THE
Senate of the United States,
FOR CHARGES EXHIBITED AGAINST HIM BY THE
HOUSE OF REPRESENTATIVES,
In the name of themselves, and of all the People of the United States,
FOR

HIGH CRIMES & MISDEMEANORS,

SUPPOSED TO HAVE BEEN BY HIM COMMITTED;
WITH THE NECESSARY
DOCUMENTS AND OFFICIAL PAPERS,
From his Impeachment to final Acquital.

TAKEN IN SHORT HAND,
BY *CHARLES EVANS,*
AND THE ARGUMENTS OF COUNSEL REVISED BY THEM
FROM HIS MANUSCRIPT.

BALTIMORE:
PRINTED FOR SAMUEL BUTLER AND GEORGE KEATINGE,
1805.

Presiding officer Aaron Burr ordered extra seating installed in the Senate chamber to accommodate the spectators who attended Justice Chase's impeachment trial.

Even at this early stage of the impeachment, some members of Congress expressed uneasiness. The charges drawn up against the judge were purely political. There was no doubt that the judge's speech had been indiscreet. He had told the Baltimore jurors that "our late reformers"—in other words, the Republicans—threatened "peace and order, freedom and property." But while Chase lacked good judgment, his attack on the Jefferson administration hardly seemed criminal. Nathaniel Macon, a powerful Republican congressman from North Carolina, wondered aloud, "Is error of opinion to be dreaded where enquiry is free?" This was the sort of question that Jefferson himself had asked the Federalists following passage of the Alien and Sedition Acts. It was clear that if the Senate convicted Chase, every member of the Supreme Court, including Marshall, might also be dismissed.

Chase's trial before the U.S. Senate was one of the most dramatic events in American legal history. Aaron Burr, the vice president, organized the proceedings. For reasons known only to himself, Burr redecorated the Senate chamber so that it looked more like the British House of Lords than the meeting place of a republican legislature. In this luxurious setting, Chase and his lawyers conducted a masterful defense. By contrast, John Randolph, the congressman who served as chief prosecutor, behaved in an erratic manner, betraying repeatedly his ignorance of relevant points of law. While most Republican senators personally disliked the arrogant Chase, they refused to expand the constitutional definition of impeachable offenses to suit Randolph's argument, and on March 1, 1805, the Senate acquitted the justice of all charges.

POLITICS OF DESPERATION

The collapse of the Federalists on the national level encouraged dissension within the Republican party. Extremists in Congress insisted on monopolizing the president's ear, and when he listened to political moderates, they rebelled. The members of the most vociferous faction called themselves "the *good old* republicans"; the newspapers labeled them the "Tertium Quids," loosely translated as "nothings" or "no accounts." During Jefferson's second term, the Quids argued that the president's policies, foreign and domestic, sacrificed virtue for pragmatism. Their chief spokesmen were two members from Virginia, John Randolph and John Taylor of Caroline (the name of his plantation), both of whom were convinced that Jefferson had betrayed the republican purity of the Founders. They both despised commercial capitalism. Taylor urged Americans to return to a simple agrarian way of life. Randolph's attacks were particularly shrill. He saved his sharpest barbs for Gallatin and Madison, Republican moderates who failed to appreciate the congressman's self-righteous posturing.

The Yazoo controversy raised the Quids from political obscurity. This complex legal battle began in 1795 when a thoroughly corrupt Georgia assembly sold 35 million acres of western land, known as the Yazoo claims, to private companies at bargain prices. It soon became apparent that every member of the legislature had been bribed, and in 1796, state lawmakers rescinded the entire agreement. Unfortunately, some land had already changed hands. When Jefferson became president, a specially appointed federal commission attempted to clean up the mess. It recommended that Congress set aside 5 million acres for buyers who had unwittingly purchased land from the discredited companies.

Randolph immediately cried foul. Such a compromise, however well-meaning, condoned fraud. Republican virtue hung in the balance. For months, the Quids harangued Congress about the Yazoo business, but in the end, their impassioned oratory accomplished nothing. The Marshall Supreme Court upheld the rights of the original purchasers in *Fletcher v. Peck* (1810). The justices unanimously declared that legislative fraud did not impair private contracts and that the Georgia assembly of 1796 did not have authority to take away lands already sold to innocent buyers. This important case upheld the Supreme Court's authority to rule on the constitutionality of state laws.

MURDER AND CONSPIRACY:
THE CURIOUS CAREER OF AARON BURR

Vice President Aaron Burr created far more serious difficulties for the president. Burr's strange behavior during the election of 1800 raised suspicions that he had conspired to deprive Jefferson of the presidency. Whatever the truth may have been, the vice president entered the new administration under a cloud.

In the spring of 1804, Burr decided to run for the governorship of New York. Although he was a Republican, he entered into political negotiations with High Federalists who were plotting the secession of New England and New York from the Union. In a particularly scurrilous contest—and New York politics were always abusive—Alexander Hamilton described Burr as ". . . a dangerous man . . . who ought not to be trusted with the reins of government" and urged Federalists in the state to vote for another candidate.

Whether Hamilton's appeals influenced the voters is not clear. Burr, however, blamed Hamilton for his subsequent defeat and challenged him to a duel. Even though Hamilton condemned this form of violence—his own son had recently been killed in a duel—he accepted Burr's "invitation," describing the foolishness as a matter of personal honor. On July 11, 1804, at Weehawken, New

Frustrated in his attempt to win national political power, Aaron Burr initiated a series of maneuvers that led eventually to his downfall.

Jersey, the vice president shot and killed the former secretary of the treasury. Both New York and New Jersey indicted Burr for murder. His political career lay in shambles.

In his final weeks as vice president, Burr hatched a scheme so audacious that the people with whom he dealt could not decide whether he was a genius or a madman. On a trip down the Ohio River in April 1805, after his term as vice president was over, he hinted broadly that he was planning a private military adventure against a Spanish colony, perhaps Mexico. Burr also suggested that he envisioned separating the western states and territories from the Union. The region certainly seemed ripe for secession. The citizens of New Orleans acted as if they wanted no part of the United States. Burr covered his tracks well. No two contacts ever heard the same story. Wherever Burr traveled, he recruited adventurers; he mingled with the leading politicians of Kentucky, Ohio, and Tennessee. James Wilkinson, commander of the U.S. Army in the Mississippi Valley, accepted an important role in this vaguely defined conspiracy.

In the late summer of 1806, Burr put his ill-defined plan into action. A group of volunteers constructed riverboats on a small island in the Ohio River owned by Harman Blennerhassett, an Irish immigrant who, like so many contemporaries, found Burr's charm irresistible. By the time this armed band set out to join Wilkinson's forces, however, the general had experienced a change of heart. He frantically dispatched letters to Jefferson denouncing Burr. Wilkinson's betrayal destroyed any chance of success, and conspirators throughout the West rushed pell-mell to save their own skins. Facing certain defeat, Burr tried to escape to Spanish Florida. It was already too late. Federal authorities arrested Burr in February 1807 and took him to Richmond to stand trial for treason.

The trial judge was John Marshall, a strong Federalist not likely to do the Republican administration any favors. During the entire proceedings, Marshall insisted on a narrow constitutional definition of treason. He refused to hear testimony regarding Burr's supposed intentions. "Troops must be embodied," Marshall thundered, "men must be actually assembled." He demanded two witnesses to each overt act of treason.

Burr, of course, had been too clever to leave this sort of evidence. While Jefferson complained bitterly about the miscarriage of justice, the jurors declared on September 1, 1807, that the defendant was "not proved guilty by any evidence submitted to us." The public was outraged, and Burr prudently went into exile in Europe. The president threatened to introduce an amendment to the Constitution calling for the election of federal judges. Nothing came of his proposal. And Marshall, who behaved in an undeniably partisan manner, inadvertently helped protect the civil rights of all Americans. If the chief justice had allowed circumstantial evidence into the Richmond courtroom, if he had listened to rumor and hearsay, he would have made it much easier for later presidents to use trumped-up conspiracy charges to silence political opposition.

THE SLAVE TRADE

Slavery sparked angry debate at the Constitutional Convention of 1787 (see Chapter 6). If delegates from the northern states had refused to compromise on this issue, Southerners would not have supported the new government. The slave states demanded a great deal in return for cooperation. According to an agreement that determined the size of a state's congressional delegation, a slave counted as three-fifths of a free white male. This political formula meant that while blacks did not vote, they helped increase the number of southern representatives. The South in turn gave up very little, agreeing only that after 1808 Congress *might consider* banning the importation of slaves into the United States. Slaves even influenced the outcome of national elections. Had the three-fifths rule not been in effect in 1800, for example, Adams would surely have had the votes to defeat Jefferson in the electoral college.

In an annual message sent to Congress in December 1806, Jefferson urged the representatives to prepare legislation outlawing the slave trade. During the early months of 1807, congressmen debated various ways of ending the embarrassing commerce. It was clear that the issue cut across party lines. Northern representatives generally favored a strong bill; some even wanted to make smuggling slaves into the country a capital offense. But there was a serious problem.

Although the external slave trade was officially outlawed in 1808, the commerce in humans persisted. An estimated 250,000 African slaves were brought illicitly to the United States between 1808 and 1860. The internal slave trade continued as well. Folk artist Lewis Miller sketched this slave coffle marching from Virginia to new owners in Tennessee under the watchful eyes of mounted white overseers.

The northern congressmen could not figure out what to do with black people captured by the customs agents who would enforce the legislation. To sell these Africans would involve the federal government in slavery, which many Northerners found morally repugnant. Nor was there much sympathy for freeing them. Ignorant of the English language and subject to intense racism, these blacks seemed unlikely long to survive free in the American South.

Southern congressmen responded with threats and ridicule. They explained to their northern colleagues that no one in the South regarded slavery as evil. It appeared naive, therefore, to expect local planters to enforce a ban on the slave trade or to inform federal agents when they spotted a smuggler. The notion that these culprits deserved capital punishment seemed viciously inappropriate.

The bill that Jefferson finally signed in March 1807 pleased no one. The law prohibited the importation of slaves into the United States after the new year. Whenever customs officials captured a smuggler, the slaves were to be turned over to state authorities and disposed of according to local custom. Southerners did not cooperate, and for many years African slaves continued to pour into southern ports. Even more blacks would have been imported had Great Britain not outlawed the slave trade in 1807. As part of their ban of the slave trade, ships of the Royal Navy captured American slave smugglers off the coast of Africa, and when anyone complained, the British explained that they were merely enforcing the laws of the United States.

EMBARRASSMENTS OVERSEAS

During Jefferson's second term (1805–1809), the United States found itself in the midst of a world at war. A brief peace in Europe ended abruptly in 1803, and the two military giants of the age, France and Great Britain, fought for supremacy on land and sea. This was a kind of total war unknown in the eighteenth century. Napoleon's armies carried the ideology of the French Revolution across the Continent. The emperor—as Napoleon Bonaparte called himself after December 1804—transformed conquered nations into French satellites. Only Britain offered effective resistance. On October 21, 1805, Admiral Horatio Nelson destroyed the main French fleet at the battle of Trafalgar, demonstrating decisively the supremacy of the Royal Navy. But only a few weeks later (December 2, 1805), Napoleon crushed Britain's allies, Austria and Russia, at the battle of Austerlitz and confirmed his superiority on land.

During the early stages of the war, the United States profited from European adversity. As "neutral carriers," American ships transported goods to any port in the world where they could find buyers, and American merchants grew wealthy serving Britain and France. Since the Royal Navy did not allow direct trade between France and its colonies, American captains conducted "broken voyages." American vessels sailing out of French ports in the Caribbean would put in briefly in the United States, pay nominal customs, and then leave for France. For several years, the British did little to halt this obvious subterfuge.

Napoleon's successes on the battlefield, however, strained Britain's economic resources. In July 1805, a British admiralty court announced in the *Essex* decision that henceforth "broken voyages" were illegal. The Royal Navy began seizing American ships in record number. Moreover, as the war continued, the British stepped up the impressment of sailors on ships flying the U.S. flag. Estimates of the number of men impressed ranged as high as nine thousand.

Beginning in 1806, the British government issued a series of trade regulations known as the Orders in Council. These proclamations forbade neutral commerce with the Continent and threatened seizure of any ship that violated these orders. The declarations created what were in effect "paper blockades," for even the powerful British navy could not monitor the activities of every Continental port.

Napoleon responded to Britain's commercial regulations with his own paper blockade called the Continental System. In the Berlin Decree of November 1806 and the Milan Decree of December 1807, he announced the closing of all continental ports to British trade. Since French armies occupied most of the territory between Spain and Germany, the decrees obviously cut the British out of a large market. The French emperor also declared that neutral vessels carrying British goods were liable to seizure. The Americans were caught between two conflicting systems. The British ordered American ships to stop off to pay duties and secure clearances in England on the way to the Continent; Napoleon was determined to seize any vessel that obeyed the British.

This unhappy turn of international events baffled Jefferson. He had assumed that civilized countries would respect neutral rights; justice obliged them to do so. Appeals to reason, however, made little impression on states at war. In an attempt to avoid hostilities for which the United States was ill prepared, Jefferson ordered James Monroe and William Pinckney to negotiate a commercial treaty with Great Britain. The document they signed on December 31, 1806, said nothing about impressment, and an angry president refused to submit the treaty to the Senate for ratification.

The United States soon suffered an even greater humiliation. A ship of the Royal Navy, the *Leopard,* sailing off the coast of Virginia, commanded an American warship to submit to a search for deserters (June 22, 1807). When the captain of the *Chesapeake* refused to cooperate, the *Leopard* opened fire, killing three men and wounding eighteen. The attack violated the sovereignty of the United States and the American people demanded revenge.

Jefferson played for time. He recognized that the United States was unprepared for war against a powerful nation such as Great Britain. The president worried that an expensive conflict with Great Britain would quickly undo the fiscal reforms of his first term. As Gallatin explained, in the event of war, the United States "will be poorer, both as a nation and as a government, our debt and taxes will increase, and our progress in every respect be interrupted."

EMBARGO DIVIDES THE NATION

Jefferson responded to European predators with a policy called "peaceable coercion." If Britain and France refused to respect the rights of neutral carriers, then the United States would keep its ships at home. Not only would this action protect them from seizure, but it would also deprive the European powers of much needed American goods, especially food. The president predicted that a total embargo of

The Ograbme (embargo *spelled backward) snapping turtle, created by cartoonist Alexander Anderson, is shown here biting an American tobacco smuggler who is breaking the embargo.*

American commerce would soon force Britain and France to negotiate with the United States in good faith. "Our commerce is so valuable to them," he declared, "that they will be glad to purchase it when the only price we ask is to do us justice." Congress passed the Embargo Act by large majorities, and it became law on December 22, 1807.

"Peaceable coercion" turned into a Jeffersonian nightmare. The president apparently believed the American people would enthusiastically support the embargo. That was a naive assumption. Compliance required a series of enforcement acts that over fourteen months became increasingly harsh.

By the middle of 1808, Jefferson and Gallatin were involved in the regulation of the smallest details of American economic life. The federal government supervised the coastal trade, lest a ship sailing between two states slip away to Europe or the West Indies. Overland trade with Canada was proscribed. When violations still occurred, Congress gave customs collectors the right to seize a vessel merely on suspicion of wrongdoing. A final desperate act, passed in January 1809, prohibited the loading of any U.S. vessel, regardless of size, without authorization from a customs officer who was supported by the army, navy, and local militia. Jefferson's eagerness to pursue a reasonable foreign policy blinded him to the fact that he and a Republican Congress would have had to establish a police state to make it work.

Northerners hated the embargo. Persons living near Lake Champlain in upper New York State simply ignored the regulations. Determined to stop the smugglers, Jefferson urged the governor of New York to call out the militia. In a decision that Hamilton might have applauded, Jefferson dispatched federal troops—led by the conspiratorial General Wilkinson—to overawe the citizens of New York.

New Englanders regarded the embargo as lunacy. Merchants of the region were willing to take their chances on the high seas, but for reasons that few people understood, the president insisted that it was better to preserve ships from possible seizure than to make profits. Sailors and artisans were thrown out of work. The popular press maintained a constant howl of protest. One writer observed that embargo in reverse spelled "O grab me!"

By 1809, the bankruptcy of Jefferson's foreign policy was obvious. The embargo never damaged the British economy. In fact, British merchants rushed to take over the lucrative markets that the Americans had been forced to abandon. Napoleon liked the embargo, since it seemed to harm Great Britain more than it did France. Faced with growing popular opposition, the Republicans in Congress panicked. One newly elected representative declared that "peaceful coercion" was a "miserable and mischievous failure" and joined his colleagues in repealing the embargo a few days before James Madison's inauguration.

A NEW ADMINISTRATION GOES TO WAR

As president, James Madison suffered from several political handicaps. Although his intellectual abilities were great, he lacked the personal qualities necessary for effective leadership. In public gatherings, he impressed people as being "exceedingly modest."

During the election of 1808, Randolph and the Quids tried unsuccessfully to persuade James Monroe to challenge Madison's candidacy. Jefferson favored his old friend Madison. In the end, a caucus of Republican congressmen gave the official nod to Madison, the first time in American history that such a congressional group controlled a presidential nomination. The former secretary of state defeated his Federalist rival, Charles Cotesworth Pinckney, in the electoral college by a vote of 122 to 47, with New Yorker George Clinton receiving 6 ballots. The margin of victory was substantially lower than Jefferson's had been in 1804, a warning of political troubles ahead. The Federalists also made impressive gains in the House of Representatives, raising their delegation from 24 to 48.

THE ELECTION OF 1808

CANDIDATE	PARTY	ELECTORAL VOTE
Madison	Republican	122
C. Pinckney	Federalist	47

The new president confronted the same foreign policy problems that had occupied his predecessor. Neither Britain nor France showed the slightest interest in respecting American neutral rights. Threats against either nation rang hollow so long as the United States lacked military strength. Out of weakness, therefore, Madison was compelled to put the Non-Intercourse Act into effect. Congress passed this clumsy piece of legislation at the same time as it repealed the embargo (March 1, 1809). The new bill authorized the resumption of trade between the United States and all nations of the world *except* Britain and France. Either of these countries could restore full commercial relations simply by promising to observe the rights of neutral carriers.

The British immediately took advantage of this offer. Their minister to the United States, David M. Erskine, informed Madison that the British government had modified its position on a number of sensitive commercial issues. The president was so encouraged by these talks that he publicly announced that trade with Great Britain could resume in June 1809. Unfortunately, Erskine had not conferred with his superiors on the details of these negotiations. George Canning, the British foreign secretary, rejected the agreement out of hand, and while an embarrassed Madison fumed in Washington, the Royal Navy seized the American ships that had already put to sea.

Canning's apparent betrayal led the artless Madison straight into a French trap. In May 1810, Congress passed Macon's Bill Number Two, an act sponsored by Nathaniel Macon of North Carolina. In a complete reversal of strategy, this poorly drafted legislation reestablished trade with *both* England and France. It also contained a curious carrot-and-stick provision. As soon as either of these European states repealed restrictions upon neutral shipping, the U.S. government promised to halt all commerce with the other.

Napoleon spotted a rare opportunity. He informed the U.S. minister in Paris that France would no longer enforce the hated Berlin and Milan Decrees. Again, Madison acted impulsively. Without waiting for further information from Paris, he announced that unless Britain repealed the Orders in Council by November, the United States would cut off commercial relations. Only later did the president learn that Napoleon had no intention of living up to his side of the bargain; his agents continued to seize American ships. Madison, who had been humiliated by the Erskine experience, decided to ignore the French provocations, to pretend the emperor was behaving in an honest manner. The British could not explain why the United States tolerated such obvious deception. No one in London suspected that the president really had no other options.

Events unrelated to international commerce fueled anti-British sentiment in the newly conquered parts of the United States. Westerners believed—incorrectly, as it turned out—that British agents operating out of Canada had persuaded Tecumseh's warriors to resist the spread of American settlement. According to the rumors that ran through the region, the British dreamed of monopolizing the fur trade. In any case, General William Henry Harrison, governor of the Indiana Territory, marched an army to the edge of a large Shawnee village at the mouth of Tippecanoe Creek near the banks of the Wabash River. On the morning of November 7, 1811, the American troops routed the Indians at the battle of Tippecanoe. Harrison immediately became a national hero, and several decades later the American people rewarded "Tippecanoe" by electing him president. This incident forced Tecumseh—a brilliant leader who was trying to restore the confidence and revitalize tribal cultures of the Indians of the Indiana Territory—to seek British military assistance in battling the Americans, something he probably would not have done had Harrison left him alone.

FUMBLING TOWARD CONFLICT

In 1811, the anti-British mood of Congress intensified. A group of militant representatives, some of them elected to Congress for the first time in the election of 1810, announced they would no longer tolerate national humiliation. They called for action, for resistance to Great Britain, for any course that promised to win respect for the United States and security for its republican institutions. These aggressive nationalists, many of them elected in the South and West, have sometimes been labeled the War Hawks. The group included Henry Clay, an earthy Kentucky congressman who served as speaker of the House, and John C. Calhoun, a brilliant South Carolinian. These fiery orators spoke of honor and pride, as if foreign relations were a sort of duel between gentlemen.

Madison surrendered to the War Hawks. On June 1, 1812, he sent Congress a declaration of war against Great Britain. The timing of his action was peculiar. Over the preceding months, tensions between the two nations had relaxed. No new attacks had occurred. Indeed, at the very moment Madison called for war, the British government was suspending the Orders in Council, a conciliatory gesture that in all likelihood would have preserved the peace.

However confused Madison may have seemed, he did have a plan. The president's problem was to figure out how a militarily weak nation like the United States could bring effective pressure on Great Britain. Madison's answer was Canada. This colony supplied Britain's Caribbean possessions with much needed foodstuffs. The president reasoned, therefore, that by threatening to seize Canada, the Americans might compel the British to make concessions on maritime issues.

Congressional War Hawks, of course, may have had other goals in mind. Some expansionists were probably more concerned about conquering Canada

Patriotic symbols abound in this print by John Archibald Woodside, Jr. Miss Liberty, carrying a liberty cap on a pole, crowns an American sailor with a laurel wreath, signifying that American liberty is victorious. The sentiment expressed visually and emphatically, "We Owe Allegiance to No Crown," seems appropriate for the revolutionary era, but in fact this print dates much later, to the early nineteenth century, when the War of 1812 sparked nationalism.

THE ELECTION OF 1812

CANDIDATE	PARTY	ELECTORAL VOTE
Madison	Republican	128
Clinton	Republican* (antiwar faction)	89

*Clinton was nominated by a convention of antiwar Republicans and endorsed by the Federalists.

than they were about the impressment of American seamen. For others, the whole affair may have truly been a matter of national pride. Andrew Jackson wrote, "*For what are we going to fight? . . .* we are going to fight for the reestablishment of our national character, misunderstood and vilified at home and abroad." New Englanders in whose commercial interests the war would supposedly be waged ridiculed such chauvinism. The vote in Congress was close, 79 to 49 in the House, 19 to 13 in the Senate. With this doubtful mandate, the country marched to war against the most powerful maritime nation in Europe. Division over the war question was reflected in the election of 1812. A faction of antiwar Republicans nominated De Witt Clinton of New York, who was endorsed by the Federalists. Nevertheless Madison, the Republican, won narrowly, gaining 128 electoral votes to Clinton's 89.

THE STRANGE WAR OF 1812

The War Hawks insisted that even though the United States possessed only a small army and navy, it could easily sweep the British out of Canada. Such predictions flew in the face of political and military realities. Not only did the Republicans fail to appreciate how unprepared the country was for war, but they also refused to mobilize needed resources. The House rejected proposals for direct taxes and authorized naval appropriations only with the greatest reluctance. Indeed, even as they planned for battle, the Republican members of Congress did not seem to understand that a weak, highly decentralized government—the one that Jeffersonians championed—was incapable of waging an expensive war against the world's greatest sea power.

New Englanders refused to cooperate with the war effort, carrying on a lucrative, though illegal, commerce with the enemy. When the U.S. Treasury appealed for loans to finance the war, wealthy northern merchants failed to respond. The British government apparently believed the New England states might negotiate a separate peace, and during the first year of war, the Royal Navy did not bother to blockade the major northern ports.

American military operations focused initially on the western forts. The results were discouraging. On August 16, 1812, Major General William Hull surrendered an entire army to a smaller British force at Detroit. Michilimackinac was lost. Poorly coordinated marches against the enemy at Niagara and Montreal achieved nothing. On the sea, the United States did better. In August, Captain Isaac Hull's *Constitution* defeated the HMS *Guerrière* in a fierce battle.

The campaigns of 1813 revealed that conquering Canada would be more difficult than the War Hawks ever imagined. Both sides in this war recognized that whoever controlled the Great Lakes controlled the West. On Lake Erie, the Americans won the race for naval superiority. On September 10, 1813, Oliver Hazard Perry destroyed a British fleet at Put-in-Bay, and in a much quoted letter written immediately after the battle, Perry exclaimed, "We have met the enemy; and they are ours." On October 5, General Harrison overran an army of British troops and Indian warriors at the battle of Thames River. On the other fronts, however, the war went badly for the Americans. General Wilkinson suffered an embarrassing defeat near Montreal (battle of Chrysler's Farm, November 11), and the British navy held its own on Lake Ontario.

In 1814, the British took the offensive. Following their victory over Napoleon, British strategists planned to increase pressure on three separate American fronts: the Canadian frontier, Chesapeake coastal settlements, and New Orleans. Sir George Prevost, commander of the British forces in Canada, marched his army south into upper New York State. A hastily assembled American fleet led by Captain Thomas Macdonough turned back a British flotilla off Plattsburg on Lake Champlain (September 11, 1814). After news of Plattsburg reached London, the British government concluded that major land operations along the Canadian border were futile.

Throughout the year, British warships harassed the Chesapeake coast. To their surprise, the British found the region almost totally undefended, and on August 24, 1814, in retaliation for the Americans' destruction of the capital of Upper Canada (York, Ontario), a small force of British marines burned the American capital. Encouraged by their easy success, the British launched a full-scale attack on Baltimore (September 13–14). To everyone's surprise, the fort guarding the harbor held out against a heavy naval bombardment, and the British gave up the operation. The survival of Fort McHenry inspired Francis Scott Key to write "The Star-Spangled Banner."

The battle of New Orleans should never have occurred. The British landed a large assault force under General Edward Pakenham at precisely the same time as diplomats in Europe were preparing the final drafts of a peace treaty. The combatants, of course, knew nothing of these distant developments, and on January 8, 1815, Pakenham foolishly ordered a frontal attack against General Andrew Jackson's well-defended positions. In a short time, the entire British force had been destroyed. The victory not only transformed Jackson into a national folk hero, but it also provided the people of the United States with a much needed source of pride.

HARTFORD CONVENTION: THE DEMISE OF THE FEDERALISTS

In the fall of 1814, leading New England politicians, most of them moderate Federalists, gathered in Hartford to discuss relations between the people of their region and the federal government. The delegates protested the Madison administration's seeming insensitivity to the economic interests of the New England states. The embargo had soured New Englanders on Republican foreign policy, but the events of the War of 1812 added insult to injury. When British troops occupied the coastal villages of Maine, then part of Massachusetts, the president did nothing to drive out the enemy.

The men who met at Hartford on December 15 did not advocate secession from the Union. Although people living in other sections of the country cried treason, the convention delegates only recommended changes in the Constitution. They drafted a number of amendments that reflected the New Englanders' growing frustration. One proposal suggested that congressional representation be calculated on the basis of the number of white males living in a state. New England congressmen were tired of the three-fifths rule that gave southern slaveholders a disproportionately large voice in the House. The convention also wanted to limit each president to a single term in office, a reform that New Englanders hoped might end Virginia's monopoly of the executive

This scene of the battle of New Orleans, painted from sketches drawn during the engagement, shows the Americans standing their ground against the British frontal assault. The Americans suffered only light casualties in the battle, but more than two thousand British soldiers were killed or wounded.

mansion. And finally, the delegates insisted that a two-thirds majority was necessary before Congress could declare war, pass commercial regulations, or admit new states to the Union. The moderate Federalists of New England were confident these changes would protect their region from the tyranny of southern Republicans.

The Hartford Convention dispatched its resolutions to Washington, but soon after an official delegation reached the federal capital, the situation became extremely awkward. Everyone was celebrating the victory of New Orleans and the announcement of peace. Republican leaders in Congress accused the hapless New Englanders of disloyalty, and people throughout the country were persuaded that a group of wild secessionists had attempted to destroy the Union.

TREATY OF GHENT ENDS THE WAR

In August 1814, the United States dispatched a distinguished negotiating team to Ghent, a Belgian city where the Americans opened talks with British counterparts. During the early weeks of discussion, the British made impossible demands. They insisted on territorial concessions from the United States, the right to navigate the Mississippi River, and the creation of a large Indian buffer state in the Northwest Territory. The Americans listened to this presentation, more or less politely, and then rejected the entire package. In turn, they lectured their British counterparts about maritime rights and impressment.

Fatigue finally broke the diplomatic deadlock. The British government realized that no amount of military force could significantly alter the outcome of hostilities in the United States. Weary negotiators signed the Treaty of Ghent on Christmas Eve 1814. The document dealt with virtually none of the topics contained in Madison's original war message. Neither side surrendered territory; Great Britain refused even to discuss the topic of impressment. In fact, after more than two years of hostilities, the adversaries merely agreed to end the fighting, postponing the vexing issues of neutral rights. The Senate apparently concluded that stalemate was preferable to continued conflict and ratified the treaty 35 to 0.

Most Americans—except perhaps the diehard Federalists of New England—viewed the War of 1812 as an important success. Even though the country's military accomplishments had been unimpressive, the people of the United States had been swept up in a contagion of nationalism. The Hartford debacle served to discredit secessionist fantasies for several decades. Americans had waged a "second war of independence" and in the process transformed the Union into a symbol of national destiny. "The war," reflected Gallatin, had made Americans "feel and act more as a nation; and I hope that the permanency of the Union is thereby better secured."

REPUBLICAN LEGACY

During the 1820s, it became fashionable to visit retired presidents. These were not, of course, ordinary leaders. Jefferson, Adams, and Madison linked a generation of younger men and women to the heroic moments of the early republic. When they spoke about the Declaration of Independence or the Constitution of the United States, their opinions carried symbolic weight for a burgeoning society anxious about its political future.

A remarkable coincidence occurred on July 4, 1826, the fiftieth anniversary of the Declaration of Independence. On that day, Thomas Jefferson died at Monticello. His last words were, "Is it the Fourth?" On the same day, several hundred miles to the north, John Adams also passed his last day on earth. His mind was on his old friend and sometimes adversary, and during his final moments, Adams found comfort in the assurance that "Thomas Jefferson still survives."

James Madison lived on at his Virginia plantation, the last of the Founders. Throughout a long and productive career, he had fought for republican values. He championed a Jeffersonian vision of a prosperous nation in which virtuous, independent citizens pursued their own economic interests. He tolerated no aristocratic pretensions. Leaders of a Jeffersonian persuasion—and during his last years, that probably included John Adams—brought forth a democratic, egalitarian society. Although they sometimes worried that the obsessive grubbing for wealth might destroy public virtue, they were justly proud of the republic they had helped to create.

But many visitors who journeyed to Madison's home at Montpelier before he died in 1836 were worried about another legacy of the founding generation. Why, they asked the aging president, had the early leaders of this nation allowed slavery to endure? How did African Americans fit into the republican scheme? Try as they would, neither Madison nor the politicians who claimed the Jeffersonian mantle could provide satisfactory answers. In an open, egalitarian society, there seemed no place for slaves, and a few months before Madison died, a visitor reported sadly, "With regard to slavery, he owned himself almost to be in despair."

9

NATION BUILDING
AND NATIONALISM

The return of the Marquis de Lafayette to the United States in 1824 created a public sensation and an occasion for national stock-taking. For more than a year, the great French hero of the American Revolution toured the country that he had helped to bring into being, and he marveled at how much had changed since he had fought beside George Washington more than forty years before. Lafayette hailed "the immense improvements" and "admirable communications" that he had witnessed and declared himself deeply moved by "all the grandeur and prosperity of these happy United States, which . . . reflect on every part of the world the light of a far superior political civilization."

Americans had good reasons to make Lafayette's return the occasion for patriotic celebration and reaffirmation. Since the War of 1812, the nation had been free from serious foreign threats to its independence and way of life. It was growing rapidly in population, size, and wealth. Its republican form of government, which many had considered a risky experiment at the time of its origin, was apparently working well. James Monroe, the current president, had proclaimed in his first inaugural address that "the United States have flourished beyond example. Their citizens individually have been happy and the nation prosperous." Expansion "to the Great Lakes and beyond the sources of the great rivers which communicate through our whole interior" meant that "no country was ever happier with respect to its domain." As for the government, it was so near to perfection that "in respect to it we have no essential improvement to make."

Beneath the optimism and self-confidence, however, lay undercurrents of doubt and anxiety about the future. The visit of the aged Lafayette signified the passing of the Founders. Less than a year after his departure, Jefferson and Adams, except for Madison the last of the great Founders, died within hours of each other on the fiftieth anniversary of the Declaration of Independence. Most Americans saw the coincidence as a good omen for the nation. But, some asked, could their example of republican virtue and self-sacrifice be maintained in an increasingly prosperous and materialistic society? And what about the place of black slavery in a "perfect" democratic republic? Lafayette himself noted with disappointment that the United States had not yet extended freedom to southern slaves.

But the peace following the War of 1812 did open the way for a great surge of nation building. As new lands were acquired or opened up for settlement, hordes of pioneers often rushed in. Improvements in transportation soon gave many of them access to distant markets, and advances in the processing of raw materials led to the first stirrings of industrialization. Politicians looked for ways to encourage the process of growth and expansion, and an active judiciary handed down decisions that served to promote economic development and assert the priority of national over state and local interests. To guarantee the peace and security essential for internal progress, statesmen proclaimed a foreign policy designed to insulate America from external involvements. A new nation of great potential wealth and power was emerging.

EXPANSION AND MIGRATION

The peace concluded with Great Britain in 1815 allowed Americans to shift their attention from Europe and the Atlantic to the vast lands of North America. Although the British had withdrawn from the region north of the Ohio, they continued to lay claim to the Pacific Northwest. Spain still possessed Florida and much of the present-day American West. Between the Appalachians and the Mississippi, settlement had already begun in earnest, especially in the new states of Ohio, Kentucky, and Tennessee. In the lower Mississippi Valley, the former French colony of Louisiana had been admitted as a state in 1812, and a thriving settlement existed around Natchez in the Mississippi Territory. Elsewhere, however, the trans-Appalachian West was only sparsely settled by whites, and much good land remained in Indian hands. Diplomacy, military action (or at least the threat of it), and the westward movement of vast numbers of settlers were all needed before the continent would yield up its wealth.

EXTENDING THE BOUNDARIES

The first goal of postwar expansionists was to obtain Florida from Spain. In the eyes of the Spanish, their possession extended along the Gulf Coast to the Mississippi. Between 1810 and 1812, however, the United States had annexed the area between the Mississippi and the Perdido River in what became Alabama, claiming that it was part of the Louisiana Purchase. The remainder, known as East Florida, became a prime object of territorial ambition for President James Monroe and his energetic secretary of state, John Quincy Adams. Spanish claims east and west of the Mississippi stood in the way of Adam's grand design for continental expansion.

General Andrew Jackson provided Adams with an opportunity to acquire the Spanish claims. In 1816, U.S. troops crossed into East Florida in pursuit of hostile Seminole Indians. After taking command in late 1817, Jackson went beyond his official orders and occupied East Florida in April and May of 1818. Despite widespread condemnation of this aggressive action by government officials (except for Adams), no disciplinary action was taken, mainly because public opinion rallied behind the hero of New Orleans.

In November 1818, Adams informed the Spanish government that the United States had acted in self-defense and that further conflict would be avoided only if East Florida was ceded to the United States. The weakened Spanish government was in no position to resist American bullying. As part of the Adams-Onís Treaty, signed on February 22, 1819, Spain relinquished Florida to the United States. In return, the United States assumed $5 million of the financial claims of American citizens against Spain.

Adams used the confrontation over Florida to force Spain to cede its claim to the Pacific Coast north of California, thus opening a path for future American expansion. Taking advantage of Spain's desire to keep its title to Texas—a portion of which the United States had previously claimed as part of the Louisiana Purchase—Adams induced the Spanish minister Luis de Onís to agree to the creation of a new boundary between American and Spanish territory that ran north of Texas but extended all the way to the Pacific. Great Britain and Russia still had competing claims to the Pacific Northwest, but the United States was now in a better position to acquire frontage on a second ocean.

Interest in exploitation of the Far West continued to grow during the second and third decades of the nineteenth century. In 1811, a New York merchant John Jacob Astor founded the fur-trading post of Astoria at the mouth of the Columbia River in the Oregon Country. Astor's American Fur Company operated out of St. Louis in the 1820s and 1830s, with fur traders working their way up the Missouri to the northern Rockies and beyond. First they limited themselves to trading for furs with the Indians, but later businesses, such as the Rocky Mountain Fur Company founded in 1822, relied on trappers or "mountain men" who went after game on their own and sold the furs to agents of the company at an annual "rendezvous."

These colorful characters, who included such legendary figures as Jedediah Smith, Jim Bridger, Kit Carson, and Jim Beckwourth (one of the many African

Mountain men such as Jim Beckwourth and Native Americans met at a rendezvous to trade their furs to company agents in exchange for food, ammunition, and other goods. Feasting, drinking, gambling, and sharing exploits were also part of the annual event. Moccasins trimmed with trade beads, worn by both Native Americans and trappers, show how trade influenced both cultures. The painting Rendezvous (ca. 1837) is by Alfred Jacob Miller.

Americans who contributed to the opening of the West as fur traders, scouts, or settlers), accomplished prodigious feats of survival under harsh natural conditions. Following Indian trails, they explored many parts of the Rockies and the Great Basin. Although they actually depleted the animal resources on which the Indians depended, the mountain men were portrayed in American literature and popular mythology as exemplars of a romantic ideal of lonely self-reliance in harmony with unspoiled nature.

Reports of military expeditions provided better documented information about the Far West than did the tales of illiterate mountain men. The most notable of the postwar expeditions was mounted by Major Stephen S. Long in 1819–1820. Long surveyed parts of the Great Plains and Rocky Mountains, but his reports encouraged the misleading view that the Plains were a "great American desert" unfit for cultivation or settlement. The focus of attention between 1815 and the 1840s was the rich agricultural lands between the Appalachians and the Mississippi that were being opened up for settlement.

SETTLEMENT TO THE MISSISSIPPI

White Americans generally believed that complete occupation and exploitation of the trans-Appalachian interior required displacing the Indian communities inhabiting the region in 1815. In the Ohio Valley and the Northwest Territory, military defeat had already made Native Americans only a minor obstacle to the ambitions of white settlers and land speculators. British withdrawal from the Old Northwest in 1815 left their former Indian allies virtually defenseless before the white advance. Most of the tribes were eventually forced west of the Mississippi. The last stand of the Indians in this region occurred in 1831–1832, when a faction of the confederated Sac and Fox Indians under Chief Black Hawk refused to abandon their lands east of the Mississippi. Federal troops and Illinois state militia pursued Black Hawk's band and drove the Indians back to the river, where they were almost exterminated while attempting to cross to the western bank.

Uprooting once populous Indian communities of the Old Northwest was part of a national program for removing Indians of the eastern part of the country to an area beyond the Mississippi. Not everyone agreed with Thomas Jefferson's belief that Indians, unlike blacks, had the natural ability to adopt white ways and become useful citizens of the republic. People living on the frontier who coveted Indian land and risked violent retaliation for trying to take it were more likely to think of Native Americans as irredeemable savages, or even as vermin to be exterminated if necessary. Furthermore, Indians based property rights to land on use rather than absolute ownership; white settlers regarded this practice as an insuperable obstacle to economic development. As originally conceived by Thomas Jefferson, removal would have allowed those Indians who became "civilized" to remain behind on individually owned farms and qualify for American citizenship. This policy would reduce Indian holdings without appearing to violate American standards of justice. During the Monroe era, however, it became clear that white settlers wanted nothing less than the removal of all Indians, "civilized" or not. The issue was particularly pressing in the South, where state governments pressed for the total extinction of Indian land titles within their borders.

In the South, as in the Old Northwest, a series of treaties negotiated between 1815 and 1830 reduced tribal holdings and provided for the eventual removal of most Indians to the trans-Mississippi West. But some southern tribes held on tenaciously to their homelands. Many members of the so-called five civilized tribes—the Cherokees, Creeks, Seminoles, Choctaws, and Chickasaws—had become settled agriculturists. But pressure continued to mount to induce these civilized tribes to give up their substantial and relatively prosperous enclaves in Georgia, Florida, Alabama, and Mississippi. When deception, bribery, and threats by the federal government failed to induce land cessions fast enough to suit southern whites, state governments began to act on their own, proclaiming state jurisdiction over lands still allotted by federal treaty to Indians within the state's borders. The stage was thus set for the forced removal of the five civilized tribes to Oklahoma during the administration of Andrew Jackson.

While Indians were being driven beyond the Mississippi, settlers poured into the agricultural heartland of the United States. In 1810, only about one-seventh of the American population lived beyond the Appalachians; by 1840, more than one-third did. Eight new western states were added to the Union during this period. The government took care of Indian removal, but the settlers faced the difficult task of taking possession of the land and deriving a livelihood from it.

Much of the vast acreage opened up by the westward movement passed through the hands of land speculators before it reached farmers and planters. In the prosperous period following the War of 1812, and again during the boom of the early to mid-1830s, speculation in public lands proceeded at a massive and feverish rate. After a financial panic in 1819 brought ruin to many who had purchased tracts on credit, the minimum price was lowered from $2.00 to $1.25 an acre, but full payment was required in cash. Since few settlers could afford the necessary outlays, wealthy speculators continued to acquire most good land.

Eventually, most of the land did find its way into the hands of actual cultivators. In some areas, squatters arrived before the official survey and formed claims associations that policed land auctions to prevent "outsiders" from bidding up the price and buying their farms out from under them. Squatters also insisted that they had the right to purchase at the minimum price land they had already improved, a practice called "preemption." In 1841, Congress formally acknowledged the right to farm on public lands with the assurance of a *future* preemption right.

Settlers who arrived after speculators had secured title had to deal with land barons. Fortunately for the settlers, most speculators operated on credit and needed a quick return on their investment. They did this by selling land at a profit to settlers who had some capital, by renting out farms until tenants had earned enough to buy them, or by loaning money to squatters who would later pay for the land in installments. As a result, the family farm or owner-operated plantation became the characteristic unit of western agriculture.

Since the pioneer family was likely to be saddled with debt of one kind or another, farmers were often forced from the beginning to do more than simply raise enough food to subsist; they also had to produce something for market. Much of the earliest settlement occurred along rivers that provided a natural means of transportation for flatboats loaded with corn, wheat, cotton, or cured meat. Farmers from more remote areas drove livestock over primitive trails and roads to eastern markets. To turn bulky grain, especially corn, into a more easily transportable commodity, farmers in remote regions often distilled grain into whiskey. To meet the needs of farmers, local marketing centers quickly sprang up, usually at river junctions. In the Midwest especially, the rapid rise of towns and cities serving surrounding farming areas greatly accelerated regional development.

Most frontier people welcomed the opportunity to sell some of their crops in order to acquire the consumer goods they could not produce for themselves. Women especially benefited from the chance to buy some household necessities that they had previously made at home, such as soap, candles, and some articles of clothing. But many of them also valued self-sufficiency and tried to produce enough of the necessities of life to survive when cash crops failed or prices were low.

THE PEOPLE AND CULTURE OF THE FRONTIER

Most of the settlers who populated the West were farmers from the seaboard states. Rising land prices and declining fertility of the soil in the older regions often motivated their migration. Most moved in family units and tried to recreate their former ways of life as soon as possible. Women were often reluctant to migrate in the first place, and when they arrived in new areas, they strove valiantly to recapture the comfort and stability they had left behind.

New Englanders who moved westward brought with them their churches, schools, notions of community uplift, Puritan ideals of hard work and self-denial, and respect for law and government. Emigrating Southerners were more devoted to the defense of personal or family honor and independence. They therefore tended to be less committed to the development of public authority and institutions.

In general, pioneers sought out the kind of terrain and soil with which they were already familiar. People from eastern uplands favored western hill country. Piedmont and Tidewater farmers or planters usually made for the lower and flatter areas. Early settlers avoided the fertile prairies of the Midwest preferring instead river bottoms or wooded sections because they were more like home and could be farmed by tried-and-true methods. Rather than being the bold and deliberate innovators pictured in American mythology, typical agricultural pioneers were deeply averse to changing their habits.

Yet adjustments were necessary simply to survive under frontier conditions. Initially, at least, isolated homesteads required a high degree of self-sufficiency. Crops had to be planted, harvested, and readied for home consumption with

The log cabin and split-rail fence of this typical frontier farmstead were cut from trees on the land. Other nearby trees have been burned to clear the land for farming.

simple tools brought in wagons from the East—often little more than an axe, a plow, and a spinning wheel. Men usually cut down trees, built cabins, broke the soil, and put in crops. Women made clothes, manufactured soap and other household necessities, churned butter, preserved food for the winter, and worked in the fields at busy times in addition to cooking, keeping house, and caring for children.

But this picture of frontier self-reliance is not the whole story. Most settlers in fact found it extremely difficult to accomplish all the tasks using only family labor. A more common practice was the sharing of work by a number of pioneer families. Except in parts of the South, where frontier planters had taken slaves with them, the normal way to get heavy labor done in newly settled regions was through mutual aid. Assembling the neighbors to raise a house, burn the woods, roll logs, harvest wheat, husk corn, pull flax, or make quilts helped turn collective work into a festive social occasion. These communal events represented a creative response to the shortage of labor and at the same time provided a source for community solidarity. They probably tell us more about the "spirit of the frontier" than the conventional image of the pioneer as a lonely individualist.

Natty Bumppo, the legendary American frontiersman created by James Fenimore Cooper, from the frontispiece of Cooper's Last of the Mohicans.

Restlessness and geographic mobility also characterized many of these settlers. Improved land could be sold at a profit and the proceeds used to buy new acreage beyond the horizon where the soil was reportedly richer. The temptations of small-scale land speculation and the lure of new land farther west induced a large proportion of new settlers to pull up stakes and move on after only a few years. The wandering of young Abraham Lincoln's family from Kentucky to Indiana and finally to Illinois between 1816 and 1830 was fairly typical. Few early nineteenth-century American farmers developed the kind of attachment to the land that often characterized rural populations in other parts of the world.

Americans who remained in the East often imagined the West as an untamed American wilderness inhabited by Indians and solitary white "pathfinders" who turned their backs on civilization and learned to live in harmony with nature. James Fenimore Cooper, the first great American novelist, fostered this mythic view of the West in his series of novels featuring Natty Bumppo, or "Leatherstocking"—a character who became the prototype for the western hero of popular fiction. Natty Bumppo was a hunter and scout who preferred the freedom of living in the forest to the constraints of civilization. Through Natty Bumppo, Cooper engendered a main theme of American romanticism—the superiority of a solitary life in the wilderness to the kind of settled existence among the families, schools, and churches to which most real pioneers aspired.

TRANSPORTATION AND THE MARKET ECONOMY

It took more than the spread of settlements to bring prosperity to new areas and ensure that they would identify with older regions or with the country as a whole. Along the eastern seaboard, land transportation was so primitive that in 1813 it took seventy-five days for a horse-drawn wagon of goods to travel the thousand miles from Worcester, Massachusetts, to Charleston, South Carolina. Coastal shipping eased the problem somewhat and stimulated the growth of port cities. Traveling west over the mountains, however, meant months on the trail.

After the War of 1812, political leaders realized that national security, economic progress, and political unity would require a greatly improved transportation network. Accordingly, President Madison called for a federally supported program of "internal improvements" in 1815. Congressman John C. Calhoun described the program as a great nationalizing enterprise. In ensuing decades, Calhoun's vision of a transportation revolution was realized to a considerable extent, although the direct role of the federal government proved to be less important than anticipated.

A REVOLUTION IN TRANSPORTATION:
ROADS AND STEAMBOATS

The first great federal transportation project was the building between 1811 and 1818 of the National Road between Cumberland, Maryland, on the Potomac and Wheeling, Virginia, on the Ohio. This impressive gravel-surfaced toll road was subsequently extended to Vandalia, Illinois, in 1838. Another thoroughfare to the West completed during this period was the Lancaster Turnpike connecting Philadelphia and Pittsburgh. By about 1825, thousands of miles of turnpikes— privately owned toll roads chartered by the states—crisscrossed southern New England, upstate New York, much of Pennsylvania, and northern New Jersey.

Toll roads, however, failed to meet the demand for low-cost transportation over long distances. Transporters of bulky freight usually found that total expenses—toll plus the cost and maintenance of heavy wagons and great teams of horses—were too high to guarantee a satisfactory profit from haulage. Hence

Roads in the new republic often turned into thoroughfares of mud. If the driver managed to avoid getting the wheels mired in the mud, there was still the danger that the coach might break its wheels if it hit the stumps of felled trees that dotted the road.

traffic was less than anticipated, and the tolls collected failed to provide an adequate return to investors.

Even the National Road could not offer the low freight costs required for the long-distance hauling of wheat, flour, and the other bulky agricultural products of the Ohio Valley. For these commodities, water transportation of some sort was required.

The United States' natural system of river transportation was one of the most significant reasons for its rapid economic development. The Ohio-Mississippi system in particular provided ready access to the rich agricultural areas of the interior and a natural outlet for their products. By 1815, flatboats loaded with wheat, flour, salt pork, and cotton were floating toward New Orleans. Even after the coming of the steamboat, flatboats continued to carry a major share of the downriver trade.

The flatboat trade, however, was necessarily one-way. A farmer from Ohio or Illinois, or someone hired to do the job, could float down to New Orleans easily enough, but there was generally no way to get back except by walking overland through rough country. Until the problem of upriver navigation was solved, the Ohio-Mississippi could not carry the manufactured goods that farmers desired in exchange for their crops.

Fortunately, a solution was readily at hand: the use of steam power. In 1807, inventor Robert Fulton, backed by Robert R. Livingston—a New Yorker of great wealth and political prominence—demonstrated the full potential of the steam-

The Clermont on the Hudson *(ca. 1830–1835) by Charles Pensee. Although some called his* Clermont *"Fulton's Folly," Robert Fulton immediately turned a profit from his fleet of steamboats, which reduced the cost and increased the speed of river transport.*

boat by successfully propelling the *Clermont* 150 miles up the Hudson River. The first steamboat launched in the West was the *New Orleans*, which made the long trip from Pittsburgh to New Orleans in 1811–1812. Besides becoming a principal means of passenger travel on the inland waterways of the East, the river steamboat revolutionized western commerce. By 1820 sixty-nine steamboats with a total capacity of 13,890 tons were plying western waters.

Steam transport was a great boon for farmers and merchants. It reduced costs, increased the speed of moving goods and people, and allowed a two-way commerce on the Mississippi and Ohio. Eastern manufacturers and merchants now had a better way to reach interior markets.

The steamboat quickly captured the American imagination. Great paddle wheelers became luxurious floating hotels, the natural habitats of gamblers, confidence men, and mysterious women. Steamboats sometimes raced against each other, and their more skillful pilots became folk heroes. But the boats also had a lamentable safety record, frequently running aground, colliding, or blowing up. As a result of such accidents, the federal government began in 1838 to regulate steamboats and monitor their construction and operation. The legislation stands as virtually the only federal effort in the pre–Civil War period to regulate domestic transportation.

THE CANAL BOOM

A transportation system based solely on rivers and roads had one enormous gap—it did not provide an economical way to ship western farm produce directly east to the growing urban market of the seaboard states. The solution offered by the politicians and merchants of the Middle Atlantic and midwestern states was to build a system of canals to link seaboard cities directly to the Great Lakes, the Ohio, and ultimately the Mississippi.

The best natural location for a canal connecting a river flowing into the Atlantic with one of the Great Lakes was between Albany and Buffalo, a relatively flat stretch of 364 miles. When the New York legislature approved the bold project in 1817, no more than about 100 miles of canal existed in the entire United States, and the longest single canal extended only 26 miles. Credit for the project belongs mainly to New York's governor De Witt Clinton, who persuaded the New York state legislature to underwrite the project by issuing bonds. Begun in 1818, the completed canal opened in 1825, to great public acclaim.

At 364 miles long, 40 feet wide, and 4 feet deep, and containing 84 locks, the Erie Canal was the most spectacular engineering achievement of the young republic. Furthermore, it was a great economic success. It reduced the cost of moving goods from Buffalo to Albany to one-twelfth the previous rate, thus allowing both

Easterners and Westerners to buy each other's products at sharply lower costs. It also helped make New York City the commercial capital of the nation.

The great success of the Erie Canal inspired other states to extend public credit for canal building. Between 1826 and 1834, Pennsylvania constructed a canal covering the 395 miles between Philadelphia and Pittsburgh. But the Pennsylvania Main Line Canal did not do as well as the Erie, partly because of a bottleneck at the crest of the Alleghenies where an inclined-plane railroad had to haul canalboats over a high ridge. Ohio constructed a canal from the Ohio River to Cleveland on Lake Erie in 1833. Other states built shorter canals to connect navigable rivers with sea or lake ports. The Illinois and Michigan Canal, completed in 1848, linked Chicago and the Great Lakes with the Illinois River and the Mississippi.

The canal boom ended when it became apparent in the 1830s and 1840s that most of the waterways were unprofitable. State credit had been overextended, and the panic and depression of the late 1830s and early 1840s forced retrenchment. Moreover, by this time railroads were beginning to compete successfully for the same traffic, and a new phase in the transportation revolution was beginning.

But canals should not be written off as economic failures that contributed little to the improvement of transportation. Some of them continued to be important arteries up to the time of the Civil War and well beyond. Furthermore, the "failure" of many of the canals was due solely to their inability to yield an adequate return to investors. Had the canals been thought of as providing a service rather than yielding a profit their vital contribution to the nation's economic development would have been better appreciated.

EMERGENCE OF A MARKET ECONOMY

The desire to reduce the costs and increase the speed of shipping heavy freight over great distances laid the groundwork for a new economic system. With the advent of steamboats and canals, western farmers could inexpensively ship their crops to the east, while eastern manufacturers gained ready access to an interior market. Hence improved transport both increased farm income and stimulated commercial agriculture.

At the beginning of the nineteenth century, the typical farming household consumed most of what it produced and sold only a small surplus in nearby markets. Most manufactured articles were produced at home. Easier and cheaper access to distant markets caused a decisive change in this pattern. Between 1800 and 1840, agricultural output increased at an annual rate of approximately 3 percent, and a rapidly growing portion of this production consisted of commodities grown for sale rather than consumed at home. The rise in productivity was partly due to technological advances. Iron or steel plows proved better than wooden ones, the grain cradle displaced the scythe for harvesting, and better varieties or strains of crops, grasses, and livestock were introduced. But the availability of good land and the revolution in marketing were the most important spurs to profitable commercial farming. Transportation facilities made distant markets available and plugged farmers into a commercial network that provided credit and relieved them of the need to do their own selling.

The emerging exchange network encouraged movement away from diversified farming and toward regional concentration on staple crops. Wheat was the main cash crop of the North, and the center of its cultivation moved westward as soil depletion, pests, and plant diseases lowered yields in older regions. On the rocky hillsides of New England, sheep raising was displacing the mixed farming of an earlier era. But the prime examples of successful staple production in this era were in the South. Tobacco continued to be a major cash crop of the upper South, rice was important in coastal South Carolina, and sugar was a staple of southern Louisiana. Cotton, however, was the "king" crop in the lower South as a whole. In the course of becoming the nation's principal export commodity, it brought wealth and prosperity to a belt of states running from South Carolina to Louisiana.

A number of factors made the Deep South the world's greatest producer of cotton. First was the great demand generated by the rise of textile manufacturing in England and, to a lesser extent, in New England. Second was the effect of the cotton gin on processing. Invented by Eli Whitney in 1793, this simple device cut the labor costs involved in cleaning short-staple cotton, thus making it an easily marketable commodity. Third was the availability of good land in the Southwest. As yields fell in original areas of cultivation—mainly South Carolina and Georgia—the opening of the rich and fertile plantation areas or "black belts" of Alabama, Mississippi, and Louisiana shifted the Cotton Kingdom westward and resulted in a vast increase in total production. Between 1817 and 1840, the amount of cotton produced in the South tripled from 461,000 to 1,350,000 bales.

A fourth factor was the existence of slavery, which permitted operations on a scale impossible for the family labor system of the agricultural North. Finally, the cotton economy benefited from the South's natural transportation system—its great network of navigable rivers extending deep into the interior. The South had less need than other agricultural regions for artificial internal improvements such as canals and good roads. Planters could simply establish themselves on or near a river and ship their crops to market via natural waterways.

COMMERCE AND BANKING

As regions specialized in growing commercial crops, a new system of marketing emerged. During the early years of expansion, farmers did their marketing personally. With the growth of country towns, local merchants took charge of the crops near their sources, bartering clothing and other manufactured goods for produce. These intermediaries shipped the farmers' crops to larger local markets such as Pittsburgh, Cincinnati, and St. Louis. From there the commodities could be sent on to Philadelphia, New York, or New Orleans. Cotton growers in the South were more likely to deal directly with factors (agents) in the port cities from which their crop was exported. But even in the South, intermediaries trafficked goods in such inland towns as Macon, Atlanta, Montgomery, Shreveport, and Nashville.

Credit was a crucial element in the whole system. Farmers borrowed from local merchants, who received an advance of their own when they consigned crops to a commission house or factor. The commission agents relied on credit from merchants or manufacturers at the ultimate destination, which might be Liverpool or New York City. Even though the intermediaries all charged fees and interest, the net cost to the farmers was less than it had been when they had handled their own marketing.

Before the revolutions in transportation and marketing, small-scale local economies could survive to a considerable extent on barter. But long-distance transactions involving credit and deferred payment required money and lots of it. Under the Constitution, only the U.S. government is authorized to coin money and regulate its value. But in the early to mid-nineteenth century, the government printed no paper money and produced gold and silver coins in such small quantities that it failed to meet the expanding economy's need for a circulating currency.

Private or state banking institutions filled the void by issuing banknotes, promises to redeem their paper in *specie*—gold or silver—on the bearer's demand. The demand for money and credit during the economic boom after 1815 led to a vast increase in the number of state banks—from 88 to 208 within two years. The resulting flood of state banknotes caused this form of currency to depreciate well below its face value and threatened a runaway inflation. In an effort to stabilize the currency, Congress established a second Bank of the United States in 1816.

The Bank was expected to serve as a check on the state banks by forcing them to resume specie payments. But it did not perform this task well in its early years. In fact, its own free lending policies contributed to the overextension of credit that led to financial panic and depression in 1819. When the economy collapsed, many Americans questioned whether the new system of banking and credit was as desirable as it had seemed to be in times of prosperity. As a result, hostility to banks became a prominent feature of American politics.

EARLY INDUSTRIALISM

The growth of a market economy also created new opportunities for industrialists. In 1815, most manufacturing in the United States was carried on in households, in the workshops of skilled artisans, or in small mills. The factory form of production, in which supervised workers tended or operated machines under one roof, was rare and was found mainly in the textile mills of southern New England. Even in the textile industry, however, most spinning of thread, as well as the weaving, cutting, and sewing of cloth, was still done by women working at home.

As late as 1820, most clothing worn by Americans was made entirely by female family members. A growing proportion, however, was produced for market rather than direct home consumption. Under the "putting-out" system of manufacturing, merchant capitalists provided raw material to people in their own homes, picked up finished or semifinished products, paid the workers, and took charge of distribution. Simple shoes and hats, as well as clothing, were made under the putting-out system, which was centered in the Northeast.

Growth in one area of manufacturing often fostered growth in other types of industry. For example, the machinery used in textile mills was made from iron. Thus, growth in textile manufacturing helped stimulate the development of ironworks.

Artisans working in small shops in towns produced articles that required greater skill—such as high-quality shoes and boots, carriages or wagons, mill wheels, and barrels or kegs. But in the decades after 1815, shops expanded in size, masters tended to become entrepreneurs rather than working artisans, and journeymen often became wage earners rather than aspiring masters. At the same time, the growing market for low-priced goods led to a stress on speed, quantity, and standardization in the methods of production.

A fully developed factory system emerged first in textile manufacturing. The establishment of the first cotton mills utilizing the power loom as well as spinning machinery—thus making it possible to turn fiber into cloth in a single factory—resulted from the efforts of a trio of Boston merchants: Francis Cabot Lowell, Nathan Appleton, and Patrick Tracy Jackson. On a visit to England in 1810–1811, Lowell succeeded in memorizing the closely guarded industrial secret of how a power loom was constructed. Returning to Boston, he joined with Appleton and Jackson to acquire a water site at nearby Waltham and to obtain a corporate charter for textile manufacturing on a new and expanded scale.

Under the name of the Boston Manufacturing Company, the associates began their Waltham operation in 1813. Its phenomenal success led to the erection of a larger and even more profitable mill at Lowell, Massachusetts, in 1822 and another at Chicopee in 1823. Lowell became the great showplace for early American industrialization. Its large and seemingly contented workforce of unmarried young women residing in supervised dormitories, its unprecedented scale of operation, its successful mechanization of almost every stage of the production process—all captured the American middle-class imagination in the 1820s and 1830s. Other mills using similar methods sprang up throughout New England, and the region became the first important manufacturing area in the United States. But in the late 1830s and 1840s conditions in the mills changed for the worse as the owners began to require more work for lower pay, and some of the mill girls became militant labor activists.

The shift away from the putting-out system to factory production changed the course of capitalist activity in New England. Before the 1820s, New England merchants concentrated mainly on international trade. A major source of capital was the lucrative China trade carried on by fast, well-built New England vessels. When the success of Waltham and Lowell became clear, many merchants shifted their capital away from oceanic trade and into manufacturing. The political consequences of this change meant that politicians from New England no longer advocated a low tariff that favored importers over exporters. Instead they championed a high duty designed to protect manufacturers from foreign competition.

The young women who worked in the Lowell mills wrote and edited their own monthly magazine, the Lowell Offering, *from 1840 to 1845. The maga-zine's editors, Harriot F. Curtis and Harriet Farley, said that the cover repre-sented "The New England school-girl, of which our factories are made up, standing near a beehive, em-blem of industry and intelli-gence, and in the back-ground the Yankee schoolhouse, church, and factory."*

The development of other "infant industries" after the War of 1812 was less dramatic and would not come to fruition until the 1840s and 1850s. Technology imported from England to improve the rolling and refining of iron gradually en-couraged a domestic iron industry centered in Pennsylvania. The use of inter-changeable parts in the manufacture of small arms helped modernize the weapons industry while also contributing to the growth of new forms of mass production.

Although most manufacturing was centered in the Northeast, the West also experienced modest industrial progress. Increasing rapidly in number and size were facilities for processing farm products, such as gristmills, slaughterhouses, and tanneries. Distilleries in Kentucky and Ohio began during the 1820s to produce vast quantities of corn whiskey.

One should not assume, however, that America had already experienced an industrial revolution by 1840. Most of the nation's labor force was still employed in agriculture. Fewer than 10 percent of workers were directly involved in factory production. The revolution that did occur during these years was essentially one of distribution rather than production. The growth of a market economy of national scope—still based mainly on agriculture but involving a rapid flow of capital, commodities, and services from region to region—was the major economic development of this period. And it was one that had vast repercussions for all aspects of American life.

For those who benefited from it most directly, the market economy provided firm evidence of progress and improvement. But many of those who suffered from its periodic panics and depressions regretted the loss of the individual independence and security. These victims of boom and bust were receptive to politicians and reformers who attacked corporations and "the money power."

THE POLITICS OF NATION BUILDING
AFTER THE WAR OF 1812

Geographic expansion, economic growth, and the changes in American life that accompanied them were bound to generate political controversy. Farmers, merchants, manufacturers, and laborers were affected by the changes in different ways, as were Northerners, Southerners, and Westerners. Federal and state policies that were meant to encourage or control growth and expansion did not benefit all these groups or sections equally, and conflicts of interest inevitably arose.

But the temporary lack of a party system during the period following the War of 1812 meant that politicians did not have to offer voters a choice of programs and ideologies. A myth of national harmony prevailed, culminating in the "era of good feeling" during James Monroe's two terms as president. Behind this facade, individuals and groups fought for advantage, as always, but without the public accountability and need for broad popular approval that a party system would have required.

The absence of a party system did not completely immobilize the federal government. Congress legislated on some matters of national concern. The president took important initiatives in foreign policy. The third branch of government—the Supreme Court—made far-reaching decisions affecting the relationship between the federal government and the states. The common theme of the public policies that emerged between the War of 1812 and the age of Andrew

Jackson, which began in the late 1820s, was an awakening nationalism—a sense of American pride and purpose that reflected the expansionism and material progress of the period.

THE REPUBLICANS IN POWER

By the end of the War of 1812, the Federalist party was no longer a significant force in national politics, although Jefferson's party, now known simply as the Republicans, had adopted some of their rivals' programs and policies. Retreating from their original philosophy of states' rights and limited government, Republican party leaders now supported reestablishment of a national bank, a mildly protective tariff for industry, and a program of federally financed internal improvements.

Congressman Henry Clay of Kentucky advocated that the government take action to promote economic development. The keystone of what Clay called the "American System" was a high protective tariff to stimulate industrial growth and provide a "home market" for the farmers of the West, making the nation economically self-sufficient and free from dependence on Europe.

In 1816, Congress took the first step toward Clay's goal by enacting a tariff that raised import duties an average of 25 percent. Passed to protect American industry from British competition, the tariff had substantial support in all parts of the country. In 1816, manufacturing was not so much a powerful interest as a patriotic concern. Many Americans believed the preservation of the nation's political independence and victory in future wars required industrial independence.

Later the same year, Congress voted to establish the second Bank of the United States. The new national bank had a twenty-year charter, an authorized capital of $35 million, and the right to establish branches throughout the country as needed. Organized much like the first bank, it was a mixed public-private institution, with the federal government owning one-fifth of its stock and appointing five of its twenty-five directors. The Bank provided a depository for government funds, an outlet for marketing its securities, and a source of redeemable banknotes that could be used to pay taxes or purchase public lands. State banking interests and strict constructionists opposed the bank bill, but the majority of Congress found it a necessary and proper means for promoting financial stability and meeting the federal government's constitutional responsibility to raise money from taxation and loans.

Legislation dealing with internal improvements aroused stronger constitutional objections and sparked disagreements among sectional groups over who would benefit from specific projects. Except for the National Road, the federal

THE ELECTION OF 1816

CANDIDATE	PARTY	ELECTORAL VOTE
Monroe	Republican	183
King	Federalist	34

government undertook no major transportation projects during the Madison and Monroe administrations. Both presidents believed that a constitutional amendment was required before federal monies could legally be used for the building of roads and canals within individual states. Both of them vetoed internal improvement bills. Consequently, public aid for the building of roads and canals continued to come mainly from state and local governments.

MONROE AS PRESIDENT

As did Jefferson before him, President Madison chose his own successor in 1816. James Monroe thus became the third successive Virginian to occupy the White House. He served two full terms and was virtually uncontested in his election to each. Experienced, reliable, dignified, and high principled, Monroe was also stolid and unimaginative, lacking the intellectual depth and agility of his predecessors.

Monroe avoided controversy in his effort to maintain the national harmony that was the keynote of his presidency. His first inaugural address expressed the complacency and optimism of the time, and he followed it up with a goodwill tour of the country, the first made by a president since Washington. A local newspaper was so impressed with Monroe's warm reception in Federalist Boston that it announced that party strife was a thing of the past and that an "era of good feeling" had begun.

A principal aim of Monroe's administrations was to encourage the good feelings. He hoped to conciliate all the sectional or economic interests of the country and devote his main attention to the task of asserting American power and influence on the world stage.

The first challenge to Monroe's hopes for domestic peace and prosperity was the Panic of 1819, which brought an abrupt end to the postwar boom. After a period of rampant inflation, easy credit, and massive land speculation, the Bank of the United States called in loans and demanded the immediate redemption in specie of the state banknotes in its possession. This retrenchment brought a drastic downturn in the economy, as prices fell sharply, businesses failed, and land bought on credit was foreclosed.

Congress responded weakly to the resulting depression by passing in 1821 a relief act that eased the terms for paying debts owed on public land. Monroe himself had no program to relieve the economic crisis because he did not feel called on to exert that kind of leadership. The one-party system then prevailing left the president without the ability to work through an organized majority party in Congress; one-party rule had in fact degenerated into a chaotic "no-party" system. Unlike later presidents, Monroe could retain his popularity during a depression that began during his watch.

Monroe prized national harmony above economic prosperity. But during his first administration, a bitter controversy developed between the North and the South over the admission of Missouri to the Union. Once again Monroe remained outside the battle and suffered little damage to his own prestige. It was left entirely to Congress to deal with the nation's most serious domestic political crisis between the War of 1812 and the late 1840s.

THE MISSOURI COMPROMISE

In 1817, the Missouri territorial assembly applied for statehood. Because the petition made no provision for emancipation of the two to three thousand slaves already in the territory or for curbing further introduction of slaves, it was clear that Missouri expected to enter the Union as a slave state. Since Missouri was to be the first state, other than Louisiana, to be carved out of the Louisiana Purchase, resolution of the status of slavery there would have implications for the rest of the trans-Mississippi West.

When the question came before Congress in early 1819, sectional fears and anxieties bubbled to the surface. Many Northerners resented southern control of the presidency and the fact that the three-fifths clause of the Constitution, by which every five slaves were counted as three persons in figuring the state's population, gave the South's free population added weight in the House of Representatives and the electoral college. Southerners feared for the future of what they saw as a necessary balance of power between the sections. Up until 1819, strict equality had been maintained by alternately admitting slave and free states. But northern population was growing more rapidly than southern, and the North had built up a decisive majority in the House of Representatives. Hence the South saw its equal vote in the Senate as essential for preservation of the balance.

In February 1819, Congressman James Tallmadge of New York introduced an amendment to the statehood bill, banning further introduction of slaves into Missouri and requiring steps toward the gradual elimination of

THE ELECTION OF 1820

CANDIDATE	PARTY	ELECTORAL VOTE
Monroe	Republican	231
J. Q. Adams	No party designation	1

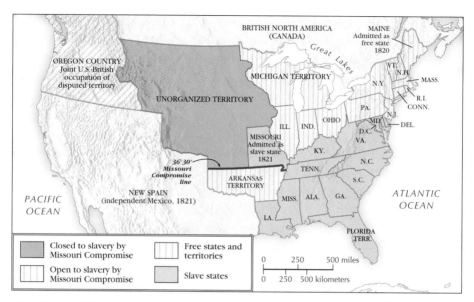

The Missouri Compromise, 1820–1821

The Missouri Compromise kept the balance of power in the Senate by admitting Missouri as a slave state and Maine as a free state. The agreement temporarily settled the argument over slavery in the territories.

slavery within the state. The House approved the Tallmadge amendment by a narrow margin, but the Senate voted it down. The issue remained unresolved until a new Congress convened in December 1819. In the great debate that ensued in the Senate, Federalist leader Rufus King of New York argued that Congress was within its rights to require restriction of slavery before Missouri could become a state. Southern senators protested that denying Missouri's freedom in this matter was an attack on the principle of equality among the states and showed that Northerners were conspiring to upset the balance of power between the sections. They were also concerned about the future of African American slavery and the white racial privilege that went with it.

A statehood petition from the people of Maine, who were seeking to be separated from Massachusetts, suggested a way out of the impasse. In February 1820, the Senate voted to couple the admission of Missouri as a slave state with the admission of Maine as a free state. A further amendment was also passed prohibiting slavery in the rest of the Louisiana Purchase north of the southern border of Missouri, or above the latitude of 36°30', and allowing it below that line. The Senate's compromise then went to the House. Through the adroit maneuvering of Henry Clay—who broke the proposal into three separate bills—it eventually won House approval. The measure authorizing Missouri to frame a constitution and apply for admission as a slave state passed by a razor-thin margin of 90 to 87, with most northern representatives remaining opposed.

A major sectional crisis had been resolved. But the Missouri affair had ominous overtones for the future of North-South relations. Thomas Jefferson described the controversy as "a fire bell in the night," threatening the peace of the Union. The congressional furor had shown that when the issue of slavery or its extension came directly before the people's representatives, regional loyalties took precedence over party or other considerations. An emotional rhetoric of morality and fundamental rights issued from both sides, and votes followed sectional lines much more closely than on any other issue. If the United States were to acquire any new territories in which the status of slavery had to be determined by Congress, renewed sectional strife would be inevitable.

POSTWAR NATIONALISM AND THE SUPREME COURT

While the Monroe administration was proclaiming national harmony and congressional leaders were struggling to reconcile sectional differences, the Supreme Court was making a more substantial and enduring contribution to the growth of nationalism and a strong federal government. Much of this achievement was due to the firm leadership and fine legal mind of the chief justice of the United States, John Marshall. A Virginian, a Federalist, and the devoted disciple and biographer of George Washington, Marshall served as chief justice from 1801 to 1835, and during that entire period he dominated the Court as no other chief justice has ever done.

As the author of most of the major opinions issued by the Supreme Court during its formative period, Marshall gave shape to the Constitution and clarified the crucial role of the Court in the American system of government. He placed the protection of individual liberty, especially the right to acquire property, above the attainment of political, social, or economic equality. Ultimately he was a nationalist, believing that the strength, security, and happiness of the American people depended mainly on economic growth and the creation of new wealth.

The role of the Supreme Court, in Marshall's view, was to interpret and enforce the Constitution in a way that encouraged economic development, especially against efforts of state legislatures to interfere with the constitutionally protected rights of individuals or combinations of individuals to acquire property through productive activity. Under Marshall's lead, the Supreme Court approved broad powers for the federal government so that the latter could fulfill its constitutional responsibility to promote the general welfare by encouraging economic growth and prosperity.

In a series of major decisions between 1819 and 1824, the Marshall Court enhanced judicial power and used the contract clause of the Constitution to limit the power of state legislatures. It also strengthened the federal government by

Chief Justice John Marshall affirmed the Supreme Court's authority to overrule state laws and congressional legislation that it held to be in conflict with the Constitution. The portrait is by Chester Harding, ca. 1829.

sanctioning a broad or loose construction of its constitutional powers and by clearly affirming its supremacy over the states.

In *Dartmouth College* v. *Woodward* (1819), the Court was asked to rule whether New Hampshire had the right to convert Dartmouth from a private college into a state university. Daniel Webster, arguing for the college, contended that Dartmouth's original charter of 1769 was a valid and irrevocable contract. The Court accepted his argument. Speaking for all the justices, Marshall made the far-reaching determination that any charter granted by a state to a private corporation was fully protected by the contract clause.

In practical terms, the Court's ruling in the Dartmouth case meant that the kinds of business enterprises then being incorporated by state governments—such as turnpike or canal companies and textile manufacturing firms—could hold on indefinitely to any privileges or favors that had been granted in their original charters. The decision therefore increased the power and independence of business corporations by weakening the ability of the states to regulate them or withdraw their privileges. The ruling helped foster the growth of the modern corporation as a profit-making enterprise with limited public responsibilities.

In March 1819, the Marshall Court handed down its most important decision. The case of *McCulloch* v. *Maryland* arose because the state of Maryland had levied a tax on the Baltimore branch of the Bank of the United States. The unanimous opinion of the Court, delivered by Marshall, was that the Maryland tax was unconstitutional. The two main issues were whether Congress had the right to establish a national bank and whether a state had the power to tax or regulate an agency or institution created by Congress.

In response to the first question, Marshall set forth his doctrine of "implied powers." Conceding that no specific authorization to charter a bank could be found in the Constitution, the chief justice argued that such a right could be deduced from more general powers and from an understanding of the "great objects" for which the federal government had been founded. Marshall thus struck a blow for loose construction of the Constitution.

In answer to the second question—the right of a state to tax or regulate a federal agency—Marshall held that the Bank was indeed such an agency and that giving a state the power to tax it would also give the state the power to destroy it. In an important assertion of the supremacy of the national government, Marshall argued that the American people "did not design to make their government dependent on the states." This opinion ran counter to the view of many Americans, particularly in the South, that the Constitution did not take away sovereignty from the states. The debate over federal-state relations was not resolved until the northern victory in the Civil War decisively affirmed the dominance of federal authority.

The *Gibbons* v. *Ogden* decision of 1824 bolstered the power of Congress to regulate interstate commerce. A steamboat monopoly granted by the state of New York was challenged by a competing ferry service operating between New York and New Jersey. The Court declared the New York grant unconstitutional because it amounted to state interference with Congress's exclusive right to regulate interstate commerce. The Court's ruling went a long way toward freeing private interests engaged in furthering the transportation revolution from state interference.

This case clearly showed the dual effect of Marshall's decision making. It broadened the power of the federal government at the expense of the states while at the same time encouraging the growth of a national market economy. The actions of the Supreme Court provide the clearest and most consistent example of the main nationalistic trends of the postwar period—the acknowledgment of the federal government's major role in promoting the growth of a powerful and prosperous America and the rise of a nationwide capitalist economy.

NATIONALISM IN FOREIGN POLICY: THE MONROE DOCTRINE

The new spirit of nationalism was also reflected in foreign affairs. The main diplomatic challenge facing Monroe after his reelection in 1820 was how to respond to the successful revolt of most of Spain's Latin American colonies after the Napoleonic wars. Henry Clay and many other Americans called for immediate recognition of the new republics, arguing that these neighbors to the south were simply following the example of the United States in its own struggle for independence.

Before 1822, the administration stuck to a policy of neutrality. Monroe and Secretary of State Adams feared that recognizing the revolutionary governments would antagonize Spain and impede negotiations to acquire Florida. But pressure for recognition continued to mount in Congress. After ratification of the Adams-Onís treaty in 1821, Monroe agreed to recognition and the establishment of diplomatic ties with the Latin American republics. Mexico and Colombia were recognized in 1822, Chile and Argentina in 1823, Brazil and the Federation of Central American States in 1824, and Peru in 1826.

Recognizing the republics put the United States on a possible collision course with the major European powers. Austria, Russia, and Prussia were committed to rolling back the tides of liberalism, self-government, and national self-determination that had arisen during the French Revolution and its Napoleonic aftermath. After Napoleon's first defeat in 1814, the monarchs of Europe had joined in a "Grand Alliance" to protect "legitimate" authoritarian governments from democratic challenges. Great Britain was originally a member of this concert of nations but withdrew when it found that its own interests conflicted with those of the other members. In 1822, the remaining alliance members, joined now by the restored French monarchy, gave France the green light to invade Spain and restore a Bourbon regime that might be disposed to reconquer the empire. Both Great Britain and the United States were alarmed by this prospect.

Particularly troubling to American policymakers was the role of Czar Alexander I of Russia in the maneuverings. Not only was the czar an outspoken and active opponent of Latin American independence, but he was attempting to extend Russian claims on the Pacific Coast of North America south to the 51st parallel—into the Oregon Country the United States wanted for itself.

The threat from the Grand Alliance compelled the United States to closer cooperation with Great Britain, for whom independent nations offered better and more open markets for British manufactured goods than the colonies of other nations. In 1823, British foreign secretary George Canning sought to involve the United States in a joint policy to prevent the Grand Alliance from intervening in Latin America.

In August, Canning broached the possibility of joint Anglo-American action against the Alliance to Richard Rush, U.S. minister to Great Britain, and Rush referred the suggestion to the president. Monroe welcomed the British initiative because he believed the United States should take an active role in transatlantic affairs by playing one European power against another. Secretary of State Adams, however, favored a different approach. Adams believed the national interest would best be served by avoiding all entanglements in European politics while at the same time discouraging European intervention in the Americas.

Political ambition also predisposed Adams against joint action with Great Britain; he hoped to be the next president and did not want to give his rivals the chance to label him as pro-British. He therefore advocated unilateral action by the United States rather than any joint declaration with the British.

In the end, Adams managed to swing Monroe around to his viewpoint. In his annual message to Congress on December 2, 1823, Monroe included a far-reaching statement on foreign policy that was actually written mainly by Adams. What came to be known as the Monroe Doctrine solemnly declared that the United States opposed any further colonization in the Americas or any effort by European nations to extend their political systems outside their own hemisphere. In return, the United States pledged not to involve itself in the internal affairs of Europe or to take part in European wars. The statement envisioned a North and South America composed entirely of independent republics—with the United States preeminent among them.

Although the Monroe Doctrine made little impression on the great powers of Europe at the time it was proclaimed, it signified the rise of a new sense of independence and self-confidence in American attitudes toward the Old World. The United States would now go its own way free of involvement in European conflicts and would energetically protect its own sphere of influence from European interference.

ADAMS AND THE END OF THE ERA OF GOOD FEELING

Monroe endorsed John Quincy Adams to succeed him as president. An intelligent and high-minded New Englander and the son of the second president, Adams seemed remarkably well qualified for the highest office in the land. More than anyone else, except perhaps Monroe himself, he seemed to stand for a nonpartisan nationalism that put the public good above special interests. Early in his career, Adams lost a seat in the Senate for supporting the foreign policies of Thomas Jefferson in defiance of the Federalist majority of his home state of Massachusetts. After becoming a National Republican, he served mainly in diplomatic posts, culminating in his tenure as secretary of state. In this office, he did more than negotiate treaties. Believing that the rising greatness of America should be reflected not only in economic development and territorial expansion but also in scientific and intellectual achievement, he single-handedly produced a monumental report prescribing a uniform system of weights and measures for the United States. For three years, he rose early every morning in order to put in several hours of research on the project before doing a full day's work conducting the nation's foreign policy. Uniformity of weights and measures, he argued, was essential to scientific and technological progress. Showing that his nationalism was not of a narrow and selfish kind, he called for an agreement with Great Britain and France to promote a single universal system.

Adams represented a type of leadership that could not survive the growth of the sectional and economic divisions foreshadowed by the Missouri controversy and the fallout from the Panic of 1819. Adams did become president, but only after a hotly contested election that led to the revival of partisan political conflict. As the nation's chief executive, he tried to gain support for government-sponsored scientific research and higher education, only to find the nation was in no mood for public expenditures that offered nothing immediate and tangible to most voters. As a highly educated "gentleman," he projected an image that was out of harmony with a rising spirit of democracy and veneration of "the common man."

The consensus on national goals and leadership that Monroe had represented could not sustain itself. The "era of good feeling" turned out to be a passing phase and something of an illusion. Although the pursuit of national greatness would continue, there would be sharp divisions over how it should be achieved. A general commitment to settlement of the West and the development of agriculture, commerce, and industry would endure despite serious differences over what role government should play in the process; but the idea that an elite of nonpartisan statesmen could define common purposes and harmonize competing elements—the concept of leadership that Monroe and Adams had advanced—would no longer be viable in the more contentious and democratic America of the Jacksonian era.

10

THE TRIUMPH OF
WHITE MEN'S DEMOCRACY

So many Americans were moving about in the 1820s and 1830s that new industries sprang up just to meet their needs. To service the rising tide of travelers, transients, and new arrivals, entrepreneurs erected large hotels in the center of major cities. There they provided lodging, food, and drink on an unprecedented scale. A prototype of the new hotel was the Boston Exchange Hotel with its eight stories and three hundred rooms. Opened in 1809, the Exchange burned down nine years later; and the depression that followed the financial panic of 1819 put a damper on hotel building. After the return of prosperity in 1825, the "first-class hotel" soon became a prominent feature of the American scene. By the 1830s, imposing hotels were springing up in commercial centers all over the country. The grandest of these was New York's Astor House, completed in 1836.

According to historian Doris Elizabeth King, "the new hotels were so obviously 'public' and 'democratic' in their character that foreigners were often to describe them as a true reflection of American society." Their very existence showed that many people, white males in particular, were on the move geographically and socially. Among the hotels' patrons were traveling salesmen, ambitious young men seeking to establish themselves in a new city, and restless pursuers of economic opportunities who were not yet ready to put down roots.

Hotel managers shocked European visitors by failing to enforce traditional social distinctions among their clientele. Under the "American plan," guests were required to pay for their meals and to eat at a common "table d'hôte" with anyone who happened to be there, including servants traveling with their employers. Ability to pay was the only requirement for admission (unless one happened to be an unescorted woman or dark-skinned), and every white male patron, regardless of social background and occupation, enjoyed the kind of personal service previously available only to a privileged class. Many patrons experienced such amenities as gaslight, indoor plumbing, and steam heat for the first time in their lives. Because a large proportion of the American population stayed in hotels at one time or another—a privilege that was, in Europe, reserved for the elite—foreigners inferred that there was widespread prosperity and a much greater "equality of condition" than existed in Europe.

The hotel culture also revealed some of the limitations of the new era of democratic ideals and aspirations. African Americans, Native Americans, and women were excluded or discriminated against, just as they were denied suffrage at a time when it was being extended to all white males. The genuinely poor—of whom there were more than met the eye of most European visitors—simply could not afford to patronize the hotels and were consigned to squalid rooming houses. If the social equality *within* the hotel reflected a decline in traditional status distinctions, the broad gulf between potential patrons and those who could not pay the rates signaled the growth of inequality based squarely on wealth rather than inherited status.

The hotel life also reflected the emergence of democratic politics. Professional politicians of a new breed, pursuing the votes of a mass electorate, spent much of their time in hotels as they traveled about. Those elected to Congress or a state legislature often stayed in hotels during the session, there conducting political deals and bargains.

When Andrew Jackson arrived in Washington to prepare for his administration in 1829, he took residence at the new National Hotel. The hotel was more than a public and "democratic" gathering place; it could also serve as a haven where the rising men of politics and business could find rest and privacy. In its lobbies, salons, and private rooms, the spirit of an age was expressing itself.

DEMOCRACY IN THEORY AND PRACTICE

During the 1820s and 1830s, the term *democracy* first became a generally accepted term to describe how American institutions were supposed to work. The Founders had defined democracy as direct rule by the people; most of them rejected this concept of a democratic approach to government because it was at odds with their conception of a well-balanced republic led by a "natural aristocracy." For champions of popular government in the Jacksonian period, however, the people were truly sovereign and could do no wrong. Conservatives were less certain of the wisdom of the common folk. But even they were coming to recognize that public opinion had to be won over before major policy decisions could be made.

Besides evoking a heightened sense of "popular sovereignty," the democratic impulse seemed to stimulate a process of social leveling. By the 1830s, the disappearance of inherited social ranks and clearly defined aristocracies or privileged groups struck European visitors such as Alexis de Tocqueville as the most radical feature of democracy in America. Historians have described this development as a decline of the spirit of "deference."

The decline of deference meant that "self-made men" of lowly origins could now rise more readily to positions of power and influence and that exclusiveness and aristocratic pretensions were likely to provoke popular hostility or scorn. But economic equality, in the sense of an equitable sharing of wealth, was not part of the mainstream agenda of the Jacksonian period. This was, after all, a competitive capitalist society. The watchword was equality of *opportunity,* not equality of *reward.* Life was a race, and so long as white males appeared to have an equal start, there could be no reason for complaint if some were winners and some were losers. Historians now generally agree that economic inequality—the gap between rich and poor Americans—was actually increasing during this period of political and social democratization.

DEMOCRACY AND SOCIETY

Although some types of inequality persisted or even grew during the age of democracy, they did so in the face of a growing belief that equality was the governing principle of American society. What this meant in practice was that no one could expect special privileges because of family connections. The plain folk, who in an earlier period would have deferred to their betters, were now likely to greet claims for special treatment with indifference or scorn. High-status Europeans who traveled in America were constantly affronted by democratic attitudes and manners.

With the exception of slaveholders, wealthy Americans could not depend on a distinctive social class for domestic service. Instead of keeping "servants," they hired "help"—household workers who refused to wear livery, agreed to work for only short periods of time, and sometimes insisted on eating at the same table as their employers. No true American was willing to be considered a member of a servant class, and those who engaged in domestic work regarded it as a temporary stopgap. Except as a euphemistic substitute for the word *slave,* the term *servant* virtually disappeared from the American vocabulary.

The decline of distinctive modes of dress for upper and lower classes conveyed the principle of equality in yet another way. The elaborate periwigs and knee breeches worn by eighteenth-century gentlemen gave way to short hair and pantaloons, a style that was adopted by men of all social classes. Serving girls on their day off wore the same kind of finery as the wives and daughters of the wealthy. Those with a good eye for detail might detect subtle differences in taste or in quality of materials, but the casual observer of crowds in a large city could easily conclude that all Americans belonged to a single social class.

Of course, Americans were not all of one social class. In fact, inequality based on control of productive resources was increasing during the Jacksonian period. The rise of industrialization was creating a permanent class of landless, low-paid, unorganized wage earners in urban areas. In rural areas, there was a significant division between successful commercial farmers and smallholders, or tenants who subsisted on marginal land, as well as enormous inequality of status between southern planters and their slaves. But most foreign observers overlooked the widening gap between the propertied middle class and the laboring population; their attention was riveted on the fact that all white males were equal before the law and at the polls, a situation that was genuinely radical by European standards.

Traditional forms of privilege and elitism were also under strong attack, as evidenced by changes in the organization and status of the learned professions. State legislatures abolished the licensing requirements for physicians, previously administered by local medical societies. As a result, practitioners of unorthodox modes of healing were permitted to compete freely with established medical doctors. The democratic tide also struck the legal profession. Local bar associations continued to set the qualifications for practicing attorneys, but in many places they lowered standards and admitted persons with little or no formal training and only the most rudimentary knowledge of the law.

For the clergy, "popular sovereignty" meant being increasingly under the thumb of the laity. The growing dependence of ministers on the support and approval of their congregations forced them to develop a more popular and emotional style of preaching. Ministers had ceased to command respect merely because of their office. To succeed in their calling, they had to please their public, in much the same way as a politician had to satisfy the electorate.

In this atmosphere of democratic leveling, the popular press came to play an increasingly important role as a source of information and opinion. Written and read by common folk, hundreds of newspapers and magazines ushered the mass of white Americans into the political arena. New political views—which in a previous generation might have been silenced by those in power—could now find an audience. Reformers of all kinds could easily publicize their causes, and the press became the venue for the great national debates on issues such as the government's role in banking and the status of slavery in new states and territories. As a profession, journalism was open to those who were literate and thought they had

Interior of an American Inn *(1813) by John Lewis Krimmel. In the early republic, people gathered in taverns to catch up on news—both the local news exchanged with their neighbors and the national news printed in newspapers and often read aloud to the patrons.*

something to say. The editors of newspapers with a large circulation were the most influential opinion makers of the age.

DEMOCRATIC CULTURE

The democratic spirit also found expression in the rise of new forms of literature and art directed at a mass audience. The intentions of individual artists and writers varied considerably. Some sought success by pandering to popular taste. Others tried to capture the spirit of the age by portraying the everyday life of ordinary Americans. A notable few hoped to use literature and art as a way of improving popular taste and instilling deeper moral and spiritual values. But all of them were aware that their audience was the broad citizenry of a democratic nation rather than a refined elite.

The romantic movement in literature, which came to the fore in the early nineteenth century in both Europe and America, valued strong feeling and mystical intuition over the calm rationality and appeal to common experience that had prevailed in the writing of the eighteenth century. Romanticism was not necessarily connected with democracy; in Europe, it sometimes went along with a reaffirmation of the right of a superior few to rule over the masses. In America, however, romanticism often appealed to the feelings and intuitions of ordinary people: the innate love of goodness, truth, and beauty that all people were thought to possess. Writers in search of popularity and economic success, however, often deserted the high plane of romantic art for crass sentimentalism—a willingness to pull out all emotional stops to thrill readers or bring tears to their eyes.

A rise in literacy and a revolution in the technology of printing created a mass market for popular literature. An increase in the number of potential readers and a decrease in publishing costs led to a flood of lurid and sentimental novels, some of which became the first American best-sellers. Gothic horror and the perils of virtuous heroines threatened by dastardly villains were among the ingredients that readers came to expect from popular fiction. By the 1840s and 1850s, writers such as George Lippard, Mrs. E. D. E. N. Southworth, and Augusta Jane Evans had perfected the formulas that led to commercial success. Lippard's *Quaker City* (1844) is a sensational tale of vice and corruption in Philadelphia. Southworth's *Hidden Hand* (1859) features an heiress who must go to extraordinary lengths to fend off villainous suitors. In one scene, which was extremely popular in the stage version, she disposes of the villain by springing a trap door conveniently located in her bedroom. Some women writers implicitly protested against their situation by portraying men as tyrannical, unreliable, or vicious and the women they abandoned or failed to support as resourceful individualists capable of making their own way in a man's world. But the standard happy endings sustained the convention that a woman's place was in the home, for a virtuous and protective man usually turned up and saved the heroine from independence.

In the theater, melodrama became the dominant genre. The standard fare involved the inevitable trio of beleaguered heroine, mustachioed villain, and a hero who asserted himself in the nick of time. Patriotic comedies extolling the common sense of the rustic Yankee who foiled the foppish European aristocrat were also popular and served to arouse the democratic sympathies of the audience. Men and women of all classes went to the theater, and those in the cheap seats often behaved raucously and even violently when they did not like what they saw. Unpopular actors or plays could even provoke serious riots. In an 1849 incident in New York, 134 people were killed in disorders stemming from hostility toward an English actor who was the rival of Edwin Forrest, the most popular American thespian of the time.

The spirit of "popular sovereignty" expressed itself less dramatically in the visual arts, but its influence was felt nonetheless. Beginning in the 1830s, painters turned from portraying great events and famous people to depicting

William Sidney Mount, Rustic Dance After a Sleigh Ride, *1830. Mount's portrayals of country people folk dancing, gambling, playing music, or horse trading were pieces that appealed strongly to contemporaries. Art historians have found much to praise in his use of architecture, particularly that of the common barn, to achieve striking compositional effects.*

scenes from everyday life. Democratic genre painters such as William Sidney Mount and George Caleb Bingham captured the lives of plain folk with great skill and understanding. Mount, who painted lively rural scenes, expressed the credo of the democratic artist: "Paint pictures that will take with the public—never paint for the few but the many."

Architecture and sculpture reflected the democratic spirit in a different way; they were viewed as civic art forms meant to glorify the achievements of the republic. In the 1820s and 1830s, the Greek style with its columned facades was favored for public buildings, banks, hotels, and private dwellings. Besides symbolizing an identification of the United States with the democracy of ancient Greece, it achieved monumental impressiveness at a fairly low cost. Even in newly settled frontier communities, it was relatively easy and inexpensive to put up a functional square building and then add a classical facade.

Sculpture was intended strictly for public admiration or inspiration, and its principal subjects were the heroes of the republic. The sculptors who accepted

The Clove, Catskills *(ca. 1827) by Thomas Cole. Cole was the leader of the Hudson River School of artists, a group of landscape painters who worked mainly in the area of the Hudson River and the Catskill Mountains. Although the artists were not a formally organized group, they did share a sense of wonder at the grandeur of the American landscape, and they devoted painstaking attention to the details of nature in their works.*

public commissions had to make sure their work met the expectations of politicians and taxpayers, who favored stately, idealized images. Horatio Greenough, the greatest sculptor of the pre–Civil War era, got into trouble when he unveiled a seated George Washington, dressed in classical garb and nude from the waist up. Much more acceptable was the equestrian figure of Andrew Jackson executed for the federal government by Clark Mills and unveiled in 1853. What most impressed the public was that Mills had succeeded in balancing the horse on two legs.

Serious exponents of a higher culture and a more refined sensibility sought to reach the new public in the hope of enlightening or uplifting it. The "Brahmin poets" of New England—Henry Wadsworth Longfellow, James Russell Lowell, and Oliver Wendell Holmes—offered lofty sentiments and moral messages to a receptive middle class; Ralph Waldo Emerson carried his philosophy of spiritual self-reliance to lyceums and lecture halls across the country; and great novelists such as Nathaniel Hawthorne and Herman Melville experimented with the popular romantic genres. But the ironic and pessimistic view of life that pervaded the work of these two authors clashed with the optimism of the age and they failed to gain a large readership. Later generations of American critics, however, regarded the works of Melville and Hawthorne as the centerpieces of the American literary "renaissance" of the mid-nineteenth century.

The modern ideal of art for art's sake was utterly alien to the instructional spirit of mid-nineteenth-century American culture. The responsibility of the artist in a democratic society, it was generally assumed, was to contribute to the general welfare by encouraging virtue and proper sentiments. The great landscape painters of the period—Thomas Cole, Asher Durand, and Frederic Edwin Church—believed their representations of untamed nature would elevate popular taste and convey moral truths. The most original of the antebellum poets, Walt Whitman, sought to be a direct mouthpiece for the rising democratic spirit, but his abandonment of traditional verse forms and his freedom in dealing with the sexual side of human nature left him relatively isolated and unappreciated during his most creative years.

THE DEMOCRATIC FERMENT

The supremacy of democracy was most obvious in the new politics of universal white manhood suffrage and mass political parties. By the 1820s, most states had removed the last remaining barriers to voting participation by all white males.

Accompanying this broadening of the electorate was a rise in the proportion of public officials who were elected rather than appointed. More and more judges, as well as legislative and executive officeholders, were chosen by "the people." A new style of politicking developed. Politicians had to get out and campaign, delivering dramatic speeches designed to appeal to voters' fears and concerns. Electoral politics began to assume a more festive quality.

Skillful and farsighted politicians—such as Martin Van Buren in New York—began in the 1820s to build stable statewide political organizations out of what had been loosely organized factions. Earlier politicians had regarded political parties as a threat to republican virtue and had embraced them only as a temporary expedient, but Van Buren regarded a permanent two-party system as essential to democratic government. In his opinion, parties were an effective check on the temptation to abuse power. The major breakthrough in American political thought during the 1820s and 1830s was the idea of a "loyal opposition," ready to capitalize politically on the mistakes or excesses of the "ins" without denying the right of the "ins" to act the same way when they became the "outs."

Changes in the method of nominating and electing a president fostered the growth of a two-party system on the national level. By 1828, presidential electors were chosen by popular vote rather than by state legislatures in all but two of the twenty-four states. The need to mobilize grassroots support behind particular candidates required national organization. Coalitions of state parties that could agree on a single standard-bearer gradually evolved into the great national parties of the Jacksonian era—the Democrats and the Whigs. When national nominating conventions made their appearance in 1831, candidate selection became a task for representative party assemblies, not congressional caucuses or ad hoc political alliances.

New political institutions and practices encouraged a great upsurge of popular interest and participation. In the presidential election of 1824, the proportion of adult white males voting was less than 27 percent. In 1840—the first election in which two fully organized national parties each nominated a single candidate and campaigned for their choices in every state in the Union—78 percent of eligible voters cast ballots.

Economic questions dominated the political controversies of the 1820s and 1830s. The Panic of 1819 and the subsequent depression heightened popular interest in government economic policy. Americans proposed a number of ways to keep the economy healthy. Small farmers favored a return to a simpler and more "honest" economy without banks, paper money, and the easy credit that encouraged speculation. Emerging entrepreneurs saw salvation in government aid and protection for venture capital and appealed to state governments for charters that granted special privileges to banks, transportation enterprises, and manufacturing corporations. Out of the economic distress of the early 1820s came a rapid growth of state-level political activity and organization that foreshadowed the rise of national parties, which would be organized around economic programs.

Party disputes involved more than the direct economic concerns of particular interest groups. They also reflected the republican ideology that feared conspiracy against American liberty and equality. Whenever any group appeared to be exerting decisive influence over public policy, people who did not identify with that group's aspirations were quick to charge its members with corruption and the unscrupulous pursuit of power.

The notion that the American experiment was a fragile one, constantly threatened by power-hungry conspirators, eventually took two principal forms. Jacksonians believed that "the money power" endangered the survival of republicanism; their opponents feared that populist politicians like Jackson himself—alleged "rabble-rousers"—would gull the electorate into ratifying high-handed and tyrannical actions contrary to the true interests of the nation.

An object of increasing concern for both sides was the role of the federal government. Almost everyone favored equality of opportunity, but there was serious disagreement over whether this goal could best be achieved by active government support of commerce and industry or by divorcing the government from the economy in the name of laissez-faire and free competition. National Republicans, and later the Whigs, favored an active role for the government; Jacksonians simply wanted to end "special privileges".

For one group of dissenters, democracy took on a more radical meaning. Leaders of workingmen's parties and trade unions condemned the growing gap between the rich and the poor resulting from early industrialization and the growth of a market economy. They argued that employers' dominance over workers was endangering the American tradition of "equal rights." To them, society was divided between "producers"—laborers, artisans, farmers, and small-business owners who ran their own enterprises—and nonproducing "parasites"—bankers, speculators, and merchant capitalists. Workingmen's parties aimed to give the producers greater control over the fruits of their labor.

These radicals advocated a number of reforms to achieve their goal of equal rights, including abolition of inheritance and a redistribution of property, extended and improved systems of public education, cooperative production, a ten-hour workday, abolition of imprisonment for debt, and a currency system based exclusively on hard money so workers could no longer be paid in depreciated banknotes.

Philadelphia was an especially active center of labor politics and trade union activity. In 1827, the city's skilled artisans formed the Mechanics Union of Trade Associations, the nation's first metropolitan labor movement, and shortly thereafter launched the Working Men's party to compete in local elections. In 1834, fifty craft associations incorporated into the General Trades' Union of the City and County of Philadelphia, and within a year the union took the leading role in the first general strike in American history. The strike was successful in getting the ten-hour day accepted in most Philadelphia industries, but the depression that began in 1837 destroyed the General Trades' Union and nullified most of its gains. Nevertheless, American labor had set a precedent for the use of mass action aimed at the achievement of better working conditions.

In the 1830s and 1840s, northern abolitionists and early proponents of women's rights also attempted to extend the meaning and scope of democracy. But Jacksonian America was too permeated with racism and male chauvinism to give much heed to claims that the equal rights prescribed by the Declaration of Independence should be extended to blacks and women. Most of those who advocated democratization explicitly limited its application to white males, and in some ways, the civil and political status of blacks and women actually deteriorated during "the age of the common *man*."

JACKSON AND THE POLITICS OF DEMOCRACY

The public figure who came to symbolize the triumph of democracy was Andrew Jackson, although he lost the presidential election of 1824. His victory four years later, his actions as president, and the great political party that formed around him refashioned national politics in a more democratic mold.

THE ELECTION OF 1824 AND J. Q. ADAMS'S ADMINISTRATION

As Monroe's second term ended, the ruling Republican party was in disarray and could not agree on who should succeed to the presidency. The party's congressional caucus chose William Crawford of Georgia, an old-line Jeffersonian. But a majority of congressmen disapproved of this outmoded method of nominating candidates and refused to attend the caucus. Monroe himself favored John Quincy Adams of Massachusetts. Supporters of Henry Clay and John C. Calhoun mounted campaigns for their favorites, and a group of local leaders in his home state of Tennessee tossed Jackson's hat into the ring.

Initially, Jackson was not given much of a chance. Although he was a famous military hero, not even his original supporters believed this would be sufficient to catapult him into the White House. But then Calhoun withdrew and chose instead to run for vice president. Crawford suffered a debilitating stroke that weakened his chances. These developments made Jackson the favorite in the South. He also found support among Northerners and Westerners who were disenchanted with the economic nationalism of Clay and Adams.

Jackson won a plurality of the electoral votes, but he lacked the required majority. The contest was thrown into the House of Representatives, where the leg-

THE ELECTION OF 1824

CANDIDATE	PARTY	POPULAR VOTE	ELECTORAL VOTE*
J. Q. Adams	No party designation	113,122	84
Jackson		151,271	99
Clay		47,531	37
Crawford		40,856	41

*No candidate received a majority of the electoral votes. Adams was elected by the House of Representatives.

islators were to choose from among the three top candidates. Adams emerged victorious over Jackson and Crawford when Clay, who had just missed making the final three, persuaded his supporters to vote for Adams. When Adams then appointed Clay as his secretary of state, Jacksonians charged that a "corrupt bargain" had deprived their favorite of the presidency. Even though the charge was unproven, Adams assumed office under a cloud of suspicion.

Adams had a difficult and frustrating presidency. The political winds were blowing against nationalistic programs, partly because the country was just recovering from a depression that many thought had been caused or exacerbated by federal banking and tariff policies. Adams refused to bow to public opinion and called for an expansion of federal activity. Congress, however, strongly opposed the administration's domestic program.

The new Congress elected in 1826 was clearly under the control of men hostile to the administration and favorable to the presidential aspirations of Andrew Jackson. The tariff issue was the main business on their agenda. Pressure for greater protection came not only from manufacturers but also from many farmers. The cotton-growing South—the only section where tariffs of all kinds were unpopular—was assumed to be safely in Jackson's camp regardless of his stand on the tariff. Therefore, promoters of Jackson's candidacy felt safe in supporting a high tariff to swing critical votes in Jackson's direction. Jackson himself had never categorically opposed protective tariffs so long as they were "judicious."

As it turned out, the resulting tariff law was anything but judicious. Congress had operated on a give-and-take principle, trying to provide something for everybody. The substantial across-the-board increase in duties that resulted, however, angered southern free traders and became known as the "tariff of abominations." The 1828 tariff was not, however, a complex Jacksonian plot that backfired; it was rather an early example of how special-interest groups can achieve their goals in democratic politics by trading votes in the legislative bargaining process known as logrolling.

JACKSON COMES TO POWER

The campaign of 1828 actually began with Adams's election in 1824. Rallying around the charge of a corrupt bargain between Adams and Clay, Jackson's supporters began to organize to get their candidate elected in 1828. So successful were their efforts that influential state or regional leaders who had supported other candidates in 1824 now rallied behind the Tennessean to create a formidable coalition.

The most significant of these were Vice President Calhoun, who now spoke for the militant states' rights sentiment of the South; Senator Martin Van Buren, who dominated New York politics through the political machine known as the

THE ELECTION OF 1828

CANDIDATE	PARTY	POPULAR VOTE	ELECTORAL VOTE
Jackson	Democratic	642,553	178
Adams	National Republican	500,897	83

Albany Regency; and two Kentucky editors, Francis P. Blair and Amos Kendall, who worked in the West to mobilize opposition to Henry Clay and his "American System," which advocated government encouragement of economic development through such measures as protective tariffs and federally funded internal improvements. These leaders and their many local followers laid the foundations for the first modern American political party—the Democrats. The fact that the Democratic party was founded to promote the cause of a particular presidential candidate revealed a central characteristic of the emerging two-party system. From this time on, according to historian Richard P. McCormick, national parties existed primarily "to engage in a contest for the presidency."

The election of 1828 saw the birth of a new era of mass democracy. Jackson's supporters made widespread use of such electioneering techniques as huge public rallies, torchlight parades, and lavish barbecues or picnics paid for by the candidate's supporters. Many historians believe that the massive turnout at such events during much of the rest of the nineteenth century revealed a deeper popular engagement with politics than at other times in American history. But it is also possible, as others have argued, that it merely showed that politicians had learned that providing entertainment and treats could lure people to the polls. Personalities and mudslinging dominated the campaign of 1828, which reached its low point when Adams' supporters accused Jackson's wife, Rachel, of bigamy and adultery because she had unwittingly married Jackson before being officially divorced from her first husband. The Democrats then countered with the utterly false charge that Adams's wife had been born out of wedlock!

What gave Jacksonians the edge was their success in portraying their candidate as an authentic man of the people, despite his substantial fortune in land and slaves. His backwoods upbringing, his record as a popular military hero and Indian fighter, and even his lack of education were touted as evidence that he was a true representative of the common people, especially the plain folk of the South and the West. Adams, according to Democratic propagandists, was the exact opposite—an overeducated aristocrat, more at home in the salon and the study than

An 1835 painting of Andrew Jackson in the heroic style by Thomas Sully. The painting shows Jackson as the common people saw him.

among plain people. Nature's nobleman was pitted against the aloof New England intellectual, and Adams never really had a chance.

Jackson won by a popular vote margin of 150,000 and by more than 2 to 1 in the electoral college. He had piled up massive majorities in the Deep South, but the voters elsewhere divided fairly evenly. Adams, in fact, won a majority of the electoral vote in the northern states. Furthermore, it was not clear what kind of mandate Jackson had won. Most of the politicians in his camp favored states' rights and limited government, but "Old Hickory," as Jackson was called, had never taken a clear public stand on such issues as banks, tariffs, and internal improvements. He did, however, stand for the removal of Indians from the Gulf states, and this was a key to his immense popularity in that region.

Jackson turned out to be one of the most forceful and domineering of American presidents. His most striking character traits were an indomitable will, an intolerance of opposition, and a prickly pride that would not permit him to forgive or forget an insult or supposed act of betrayal. His violent temper had led him to fight a number of duels, and as a soldier his critics charged him with using

Jackson's resigning cabinet members were, according to this cartoon, rats deserting a crumbling house.

excessive force. His experiences had made him tough and resourceful but had also deprived him of the flexibility normally associated with successful politicians. Yet he generally got what he wanted.

Jackson's presidency commenced with his open endorsement of rotation of officeholders or what his critics called "the spoils system." Although he did not actually depart radically from his predecessors in the extent to which he removed federal officeholders and replaced them with his supporters, he was the first president to defend this practice as a legitimate application of democratic doctrine.

Midway through his first administration, Jackson completely reorganized his cabinet, replacing almost all of his original appointees. At the root of this upheaval was a growing feud between Jackson and Vice President Calhoun, but the incident that brought it to a head was the Peggy Eaton affair. Peggy O'Neale Eaton, the daughter of a Washington tavern owner, married Secretary of War

John Eaton in 1829. Because of gossip about her moral character, the wives of other cabinet members refused to receive her socially. Jackson became her fervent champion, partly because he found the charges against her reminiscent of the slanders against his late wife, who had died in 1828. When he raised the issue of Mrs. Eaton's social status at a cabinet meeting, only Secretary of State Van Buren, a widower, supported his stand. This seemingly trivial incident led to the resignation of all but one of the cabinet members, and the president was able to begin again with a fresh slate. Although Van Buren resigned with the rest, his loyalty was rewarded by his appointment as minister to England and strong prospects of future favor.

INDIAN REMOVAL

The first major policy question facing the Jackson administration concerned the fate of Native Americans. Jackson had long favored removing eastern Indians to lands beyond the Mississippi. Jackson's support of removal was no different from the policy of previous administrations. The only real issues to be determined were how rapidly and thoroughly the process should be carried out and by what means. At the time of Jackson's election, the states of Georgia, Alabama, and Mississippi were clamoring for quick action. Since Adams seemed to have

Sequoyah's invention of the Cherokee alphabet enabled thousands of Cherokees to read and write primers and newspapers published in their own language.

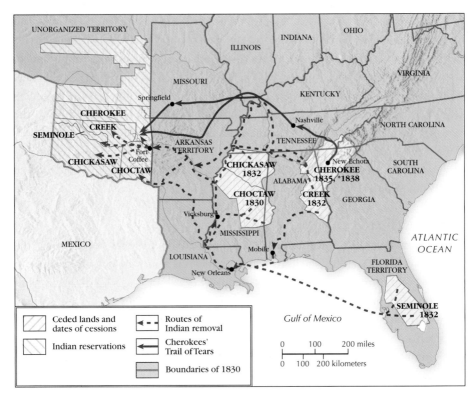

Indian Removal

Because so many Native Americans, uprooted from their lands in the East, died on the forced march to Oklahoma, the route they followed became known as the Trail of Tears.

*Treaty signed in 1835 by a minority faction was met with defiance from the majority, but removal was forced in 1838.

dragged his feet on the issue, voters in these states turned to Jackson, who promised to expel the Indians without delay.

The greatest obstacle to voluntary relocation was the Cherokee nation, which held lands in Georgia, Alabama, North Carolina, and Tennessee. The Cherokees refused to move. They had instituted a republican form of government for themselves, achieved literacy in their own language, and made considerable progress toward adopting a settled agrarian way of life similar to that of southern whites. The professed aim of the government's Indian policy was the "civilization" of the Indians, and the official reason given for removal was that this aim could not be accomplished in areas surrounded by white settlements, subject to demoralizing frontier influences. Missionaries and northeastern philanthropists argued that the Cherokees were a major exception and should be allowed to remain where they were.

The southern states disagreed. Georgia, Alabama, and Mississippi extended their state laws over the Cherokees, actions which defied provisions of the

Constitution that gave the federal government exclusive jurisdiction over Indian affairs and also violated specific treaties. As anticipated, Jackson quickly gave his endorsement to the state actions. His own attitude toward Indians was that they were children when they did the white man's bidding and savage beasts when they resisted. In his December 1829 message to Congress, he advocated a new and more coercive removal policy. He denied Cherokee autonomy, asserted the primacy of states' rights over Indian rights, and called for the speedy and thorough removal of all eastern Indians to designated areas beyond the Mississippi.

Early in 1830, the president's congressional supporters introduced a bill to implement this policy. The ensuing debate was vigorous and heated, but with strong support from the South and the western border states, the removal bill passed both the Senate and the House.

Jackson then moved quickly to conclude the necessary treaties, using the threat of unilateral state action to bludgeon the tribes into submission. In 1832, he condoned Georgia's defiance of a Supreme Court decision (*Worcester* v. *Georgia*) that denied the right of a state to extend its jurisdiction over tribal lands. By 1833, all the southeastern tribes except the Cherokees had agreed to evacuate their ancestral homes. A stubbornly resisting majority faction of the Cherokees held out until 1838 when military pressure forced them to march to Oklahoma. This trek—known as the Trail of Tears—was made under such harsh conditions that almost four thousand of approximately thirteen thousand marchers died on the way. The Cherokee removal exposed the prejudiced and greedy side of Jacksonian democracy.

THE NULLIFICATION CRISIS

During the 1820s, Southerners became increasingly fearful of federal encroachment on states' rights. Behind this concern, in South Carolina at least, was a strengthened commitment to the preservation of slavery and a resulting anxiety about possible uses of federal power to strike at the "peculiar institution." Hoping to keep the explosive slavery issue out of the political limelight, South Carolinians seized on another genuine grievance—the protective tariff—as the issue on which to take their stand in favor of a state veto power over federal actions they viewed as contrary to their interests. Tariffs that increased the prices that southern agriculturists paid for manufactured goods and threatened to undermine their foreign markets by inciting counterprotection hurt the economy of the staple-producing and exporting South.

Vice President John C. Calhoun emerged as the leader of the states' rights insurgency in South Carolina. After the passage of the tariff of abominations in 1828, the state legislature declared the new duties unconstitutional and endorsed a lengthy statement—written anonymously by Calhoun—that affirmed

Vice President John C. Calhoun emerged as a champion of states' rights during the nullification crisis.

the right of an individual state to nullify federal law. Calhoun supported Jackson in 1828 and expected Jackson to support his native region on questions involving the tariff and states' rights. He also entertained hopes of succeeding Jackson as president.

In the meantime, however, a bitter personal feud developed between Jackson and Calhoun. Jackson considered the vice president and his wife prime movers in the ostracism of Peggy Eaton. Furthermore, evidence came to light that Calhoun, as secretary of war in Monroe's cabinet in 1818, had privately advocated punishing Jackson for his incursion into Florida. As Calhoun lost favor with Jackson, it became clear that Van Buren rather than the vice president would be Jackson's designated successor. The personal breach between Jackson and Calhoun colored and intensified their confrontation over nullification and the tariff.

The two men differed on matters of principle as well. Although generally a defender of states' rights and strict construction of the Constitution, Jackson opposed the theory of nullification as a threat to the survival of the Union. In his view, federal power should be held in check, but this did not mean the states were truly sovereign. The differences between Jackson and Calhoun came into the open at the Jefferson Day dinner in 1830, when Jackson offered the toast "Our Union: It must be preserved," to which Calhoun responded, "The Union. Next to Liberty, the most dear. May we always remember that it can only be preserved by distributing equally the benefits and the burdens of the Union."

In 1830 and 1831, the movement against the tariff gained strength in South Carolina. In 1832, Congress passed a new tariff that lowered the rates slightly but retained the principle of protection. Supporters of nullification persuaded the South Carolina state legislature to call a special convention. When the convention met in November 1832, the members voted overwhelmingly to nullify the tariffs of 1828 and 1832 and to forbid the collection of customs duties within the state.

Jackson reacted with characteristic decisiveness. He alerted the secretary of war to prepare for possible military action, issued a proclamation denouncing nullification as a treasonous attack on the Union, and asked Congress to vote him the authority to use the army to enforce the tariff. At the same time, he sought to pacify the nullifiers somewhat by recommending a lower tariff. Congress responded by enacting the Force Bill—which gave the president the military powers he sought—and the compromise tariff of 1833. Faced with this combination of force and appeasement, South Carolina rescinded the nullification ordinance in March 1833. But to demonstrate that they had not conceded their constitutional position, the convention delegates concluded their deliberations by nullifying the Force Bill.

The nullification crisis revealed that South Carolinians would not tolerate any federal action that seemed contrary to their interests or raised doubts about the institution of slavery. The nullifiers' philosophy implied the right of secession as well as the right to declare laws of Congress null and void. As subsequent events would show, a fear of northern meddling with slavery was the main spur to the growth of a militant doctrine of state sovereignty in the South. At the time of the nullification crisis, the other slave states had not yet developed such strong anxieties about the future of the "peculiar institution." Jackson was himself a Southerner and a slaveholder. In general, he was a proslavery president; later he would use his executive power to stop antislavery literature from being carried by the U.S. mails.

Some farsighted southern loyalists, however, were alarmed by the Unionist doctrines that Jackson propounded in his proclamation against nullification. More strongly than any previous president, he had asserted that the federal government was supreme over the states and that the Union was indivisible. What was more, he had justified the use of force against states that denied federal authority.

THE BANK WAR AND THE SECOND PARTY SYSTEM

Jackson's most important and controversial use of executive power was his successful attack on the Bank of the United States. The "Bank war" revealed some of the deepest concerns of Jackson and his supporters and dramatically expressed their concept of democracy. It also aroused intense opposition to the president and his policies, an opposition that crystallized in a new national party—the

Whigs. The destruction of the Bank and the economic disruption that followed brought to the forefront the issue of the government's relationship to the nation's financial system. Differences on this question helped to sustain and strengthen the new two-party system.

MR. BIDDLE'S BANK

The Bank of the United States had long been embroiled in public controversy. Many, especially in the South and the West, blamed the Bank and its policies for the Panic of 1819 and the subsequent depression. But after Nicholas Biddle took over the Bank's presidency in 1823, the institution regained public confidence. Cultured, well-educated, and politically experienced, Biddle probably understood the mysteries of banking and currency better than any other American of his generation. But Biddle was also arrogant and vain, relied too much on his own judgment, and refused to admit his mistakes until it was too late to correct them. Still, actions he took in 1825 and again in 1828 to curb an overextension of credit by state banks helped avert a recurrence of the boom-and-bust cycle.

Old-line Jeffersonians had always opposed the Bank on the grounds that its establishment was unconstitutional and that it placed too much power in the hands of a small, privileged group. A chartered monopoly, the Bank was an essentially private corporation performing public services in return for exclusive economic rights. Because of its great influence, the Bank tended to be blamed for anything that went wrong with the economy. For those who had misgivings about the rise of the national market, the Bank epitomized the forces threatening the independence and prosperity of small producers. In an era of rising white men's democracy, an obvious and telling objection to the Bank was simply that it possessed great power and privilege without being under popular control.

THE BANK VETO AND THE ELECTION OF 1832

Jackson came into office with strong reservations about banking and paper money in general—in part as a result of his own brushes with bankruptcy. He also harbored suspicions that branches of the Bank of the United States had illicitly used their influence on behalf of his opponent in the presidential election. In his annual messages in 1829 and 1830, Jackson called on Congress to begin discussing ways to curb the Bank's power.

Biddle began to worry about the fate of the Bank's charter when it came up for renewal in 1836. At the same time, Jackson was listening to the advice of his "Kitchen Cabinet," especially Amos Kendall and Francis P. Blair, who thought an attack on the Bank would provide a good party issue for the election of 1832.

THE ELECTION OF 1832

CANDIDATE	PARTY	POPULAR VOTE	ELECTORAL VOTE
Jackson	Democratic	701,780	219
Clay	National Republican	484,205	49
Wirt	Anti-Masonic	100,715	7
Floyd	Independent Democratic	*	11

*Delegates chosen by South Carolina legislature.

Biddle then made a fateful blunder. Panicked by the presidential messages and the anti-Bank oratory of congressional Jacksonians like Senator Thomas Hart Benton of Missouri, he determined to seek recharter by Congress in 1832, four years ahead of schedule. Senator Henry Clay, leader of the antiadministration forces on Capitol Hill, encouraged this move because he was convinced that Jackson had chosen the unpopular side of the issue and would be embarrassed or even discredited by a congressional endorsement of the Bank.

The bill to recharter was introduced in the House and Senate in early 1832. Despite the opposition of Jackson and his administration, the bill to recharter passed Congress with ease.

The next move was Jackson's, and he made the most of the opportunity. He vetoed the bill and defended his action with ringing statements of principle. The Bank was unconstitutional, he claimed (notwithstanding the Supreme Court's ruling on the issue). He argued further that it violated the fundamental rights of the people in a democratic society: "In the full enjoyment of the gifts of Heaven and the fruits of superior industry, economy, and virtue, every man is equally entitled to protection by law; but when the laws undertake . . . to grant . . . exclusive privileges, the humble members of society—the farmers, mechanics, and laborers—who have neither the time nor the means of securing like favors to themselves, have a right to complain of the injustice of their government." Government, he added, should "confine itself to equal protection."

Jackson thus called on the common people to join him in fighting the "monster" corporation. His veto message was the first ever to use more than strictly constitutional arguments and to deal directly with social and economic issues. Congressional attempts to override the veto failed, and Jackson resolved to take the entire issue to the people in the upcoming presidential election.

The 1832 election, the first in which candidates were chosen by national nominating conventions, pitted Jackson against Henry Clay, standard-bearer of the National Republicans. The Democrats stood firmly behind Jackson in his opposition to rechartering the Bank. Jackson won a great personal triumph, garnering 219 electoral votes to 49 for Clay. His share of the popular vote was not quite as high as it had been in 1828, but it was substantial enough to be interpreted as a mandate for continuing the war against the Bank.

KILLING THE BANK

Not content with preventing the Bank from getting a new charter, Jackson now resolved to attack it directly by removing federal deposits from Biddle's vaults. Jackson told Van Buren, "The bank . . . is trying to kill me, but I will kill it." The Bank had indeed used all the political influence it could muster in an attempt to prevent Jackson's reelection, in an act of self-defense. Old Hickory regarded Biddle's actions during the presidential race as a personal attack. Although he presided over the first modern American political party, Jackson did not really share Van Buren's belief in the legitimacy of a competitive party system. In his view, his opponents were not merely wrong; they were evil and deserved to be destroyed. Furthermore, the election results convinced him that he was the only man who could save the people from the "monster bank."

In order to remove the deposits from the Bank, Jackson had to overcome strong resistance in his own cabinet. When one secretary of the treasury refused to support the policy, he was shifted to another cabinet post. When a second balked at carrying out removal, he was replaced by Roger B. Taney, a Jackson loyalist and dedicated opponent of the Bank. Beginning in late September 1833, Taney ceased depositing government money in the Bank of the United States and began to withdraw the funds already there. The problem of how to dispose of the funds was resolved by an ill-advised decision to place them in selected state banks. By the end of 1833, twenty-three state banks had been chosen as depositories. Opponents charged that the banks had been selected for political rather than fiscal reasons and dubbed them Jackson's "pet banks." Since Congress refused to approve administration proposals to regulate the credit policies of these banks, Jackson's effort to shift to a hard-money economy was quickly nullified by the use the state banks made of the new deposits. They extended credit more recklessly than before and increased the amount of paper money in circulation.

The Bank of the United States counterattacked by calling in outstanding loans and instituting a policy of credit contraction that helped bring on an economic recession. Biddle hoped to win support for recharter by demonstrating that weakening the Bank's position would be disastrous for the economy. The president's supporters accused Biddle of deliberately and unnecessarily causing economic distress out of personal resentment and a desire to maintain his unchecked powers and privileges. The Bank never regained its charter.

Strong opposition to Jackson's fiscal policies developed in Congress. Led by Henry Clay, the Senate approved a motion of censure against Jackson, charging him with exceeding his constitutional authority when he removed the deposits from the Bank. Jacksonians in the House were able to block such action, but the president was further humiliated when the Senate refused to confirm Taney as secretary of the treasury. Some congressmen who originally defended Jackson's veto now became disenchanted with the president because they thought he had gone too far in asserting the powers of his office.

THE EMERGENCE OF THE WHIGS

The coalition that passed the censure resolution in the Senate provided the nucleus for a new national party—the Whigs. The leadership of the new party and a majority of its support came from National Republicans and ex-Federalists. The Whigs also picked up critical support from southern proponents of states' rights who had been upset by Jackson's stand on nullification and then saw an unconstitutional abuse of power in his withdrawal of federal deposits from the Bank of the United States. The Whig label was chosen because of its associations with both English and American revolutionary opposition to royal power and prerogatives. The initial rallying cry for this diverse anti-Jackson coalition was "executive usurpation" by the tyrannical designs of "King Andrew" and his court.

The Whigs also gradually absorbed the Anti-Masonic party, a surprisingly strong political movement that had arisen in the northeastern states in the late 1820s and early 1830s. The Anti-Masons exploited traditional American fears of secret societies and conspiracies. They also appealed successfully to the moral concerns of the northern middle class under the sway of an emerging evangelical Protestantism. Anti-Masons detested Jacksonianism mainly because it stood for a toleration of diverse lifestyles. Democrats did not think government should be concerned about people who drank, gambled, or found better things to do than go to church on Sundays. Anti-Masonic opponents believed government should restrict such "sinful" behavior. This desire for moral and religious uniformity contributed an important cultural dimension to northern Whiggery.

As the election of 1836 approached, the government's fiscal policies also provoked a localized rebellion among the urban working-class elements of the Democratic coalition. In New York City, a dissident faction broke with the regular Democratic organization. These radicals—called Loco-Focos after the matches they used for illumination when their opponents turned off the

gaslights at a party meeting—favored a strict hard-money policy and condemned Jackson's transfer of federal deposits to the state banks as inflationary.
The Loco-Focos went beyond opposition to the Bank of the United States and
attacked state banks as well. Seeing no basis for cooperation with the Whigs,
they established the independent Equal Rights party and nominated a separate
state ticket for 1836.

Jackson himself had hard-money sentiments and regarded the "pet bank" solution as a stopgap measure rather than a final solution to the money problem.
Somewhat reluctantly, he surrendered to congressional pressure in early 1836
and signed legislation allocating surplus federal revenues to the deposit banks, increasing their numbers, and weakening federal controls over them. The result
was runaway inflation as state banks in the South and West responded to demands
from land-speculating interests by issuing a new flood of paper money. Reacting
somewhat belatedly to the speculative mania he had inadvertently helped to create, on July 11, 1836, Jackson issued his "specie circular," requiring that after
August 15 only gold and silver would be accepted in payment for public lands.
The action did curb inflation and land speculation but in such a sudden and drastic way that it helped precipitate the financial panic of 1837.

THE RISE AND FALL OF VAN BUREN

As his successor, Jackson chose Martin Van Buren, his loyal vice president during
his second term and the greatest master of practical politics in the Democratic
party. In accepting the nomination of the Democratic National Convention in
1835, Van Buren promised to "tread generally in the footsteps of General
Jackson."

The newly created Whig party, reflecting the diversity of its constituency, did
not try to decide on a single standard-bearer and instead supported three regional candidates—Daniel Webster in the East, William Henry Harrison of Ohio
(also the Anti-Masonic nominee) in the Old Northwest, and Hugh Lawson White
of Tennessee (a former Jackson supporter) in the South. Whigs hoped to deprive
Van Buren of enough electoral votes to throw the election into the House of
Representatives where one of the Whigs might stand a chance.

The stratagem proved unsuccessful. Van Buren carried fifteen of the twenty-
six states and won a clear majority in the electoral college. But the election foreshadowed future trouble for the Democrats, particularly in the South. There the
Whigs ran virtually even. The emergence of a two-party system in the previously
solid Deep South resulted from opposition to some of Jackson's policies and the
image of Van Buren as an unreliable Yankee politician. The division did not reflect
basic disagreement on the slavery issue. Both Southern Whigs and Democrats

An adroit politician and a loyal vice president to Jackson, Martin Van Buren was Jackson's choice and the Democratic party's nominee for president in 1836.

shared a commitment to protecting slavery, and each tried to persuade the electorate they could do the job better than the opposition.

As he took office, Van Buren was immediately faced with a catastrophic depression. The price of cotton fell by almost 50 percent, banks all over the nation suspended specie payments, and many businesses went bankrupt. The sale of public lands fell off so drastically that the federal surplus became a deficit.

The Panic of 1837, however, was not exclusively, or even primarily, the result of government policies. It was in fact international in scope and reflected some complex changes in the world economy that were beyond the control of American policymakers. But the Whigs were quick to blame the state of the economy on Jacksonian finance. Committed to a policy of laissez-faire on the federal level, Van Buren and his party could do little or nothing to relieve economic distress through subsidies or relief measures. But Van Buren could at least try to salvage the federal funds deposited in shaky state banks and devise a new system of public finance that would not contribute to future panics by fueling speculation and credit expansion.

THE ELECTION OF 1836

CANDIDATE	PARTY	POPULAR VOTE	ELECTORAL VOTE
Van Buren	Democratic	764,176	170
Harrison	Whig	550,816	73
White	Whig	146,107	26
Webster	Whig	41,201	14
Mangum	Independent Democratic	*	11

*Delegates chosen by South Carolina legislature.

Van Buren's solution was to establish a public depository for government funds with no connections whatsoever to commercial banking. His proposal for such an "independent subtreasury" aroused intense opposition from the congressional Whigs, who strongly favored the reestablishment of a national bank as the only way to restore economic stability. Whig resistance stalled the

A charismatic leader and a folksy man of the people — that was the image conveyed by the paraphernalia the Whig party created for the 1840 presidential campaign of William Henry Harrison, the hero of Tippecanoe.

Political candidates of the Jacksonian era traveled from town to town giving stump speeches. The political gatherings at which they spoke provided entertainment as well as an excellent source of political news. The sketch is by George Caleb Bingham, one of the most prolific of the democratic genre painters.

Independent Subtreasury Bill for three years, and it was not enacted into law until 1840.

The state of the economy undoubtedly hurt Van Buren's chances for reelection in 1840. The Whigs had the chance to offer alternative policies that promised to restore prosperity. The Whigs passed over the true leader of their party, Henry Clay, and nominated William Henry Harrison, a military hero of advanced age who was associated in the public mind with the battle of Tippecanoe and the winning of the West. To balance the ticket and increase its appeal in the South, they chose John Tyler of Virginia, a converted states' rights Democrat, to be Harrison's running mate.

Using the slogan "Tippecanoe and Tyler, too," the Whigs pulled out all stops in their bid for the White House. Matching the Democrats in grassroots organization and popular electioneering, the Whigs staged rallies and parades were organized in every locality, complete with posters, placards, campaign hats and emblems, special songs, and even movable log cabins filled with coonskin caps and barrels of cider for the faithful. Imitating the Jacksonian propaganda against Adams in 1828, they portrayed Van Buren as a luxury-loving aristocrat

THE ELECTION OF 1840

CANDIDATE	PARTY	POPULAR VOTE	ELECTORAL VOTE
Harrison	Whig	1,274,624	234
Van Buren	Democratic	1,127,781	60

and compared him with their own homespun candidate. Election day saw an enormous turnout—78 percent of those eligible to vote. Harrison carried 19 of the 26 states and won 234 electoral votes to 60 for Van Buren. Buoyed by the electorate's belief that their policies might revive the economy, the Whigs also won control of both houses of Congress.

Contrary to what most historians used to believe, personalities and hoopla did not decide the election of 1840. The economy was in dire straits, and the Whigs, unlike the Democrats, had a program that seemed to offer hope for a solution—the latest version of Henry Clay's American System. Whigs proposed to revive the Bank of the United States in order to restore fiscal stability, raise tariffs to protect manufacturers and manufacturing jobs, and distribute federal revenues to the states for internal improvements that would stimulate commerce and employment. Whig victories in the state and local elections of 1840, many of which preceded the presidential vote, strongly suggest that voters were responding to the party and its program, not merely to the man who headed the ticket and to the Whigs' newfound skill at entertaining the electorate.

HEYDAY OF THE SECOND PARTY SYSTEM

America's "second party system" came of age in the election of 1840. The rivalry of Democrats and Whigs made the two-party pattern a normal feature of electoral politics in the United States. During the 1840s, the two national parties competed on fairly equal terms for the support of the electorate. Allegiance to one party or the other became an important source of personal identity for many Americans and increased their interest and participation in politics.

In addition to drama and entertainment, the parties offered the voters a real choice of programs and ideologies. Whigs stood for a "positive liberal state"—in which government had the right and duty to subsidize or protect enterprises that could contribute to general prosperity and economic growth. Democrats normally advocated a "negative liberal state" in which government should keep its hands off the economy.

Conflict over economic issues helped determine each party's base of support. In the Whig camp were industrialists who wanted tariff protection, merchants who favored internal improvements as a stimulus to commerce, and farmers and planters who had adapted successfully to a market economy. Democrats appealed mainly to smaller farmers, workers, declining gentry, and emerging entrepreneurs who were excluded from the established commercial groups that stood to benefit most from Whig programs. To some extent, this division pitted richer, more privileged Americans against those who were poorer and less economically or socially secure. But it did not follow class lines in any simple or direct way. Many businessmen were Democrats, and large numbers of wage earners voted Whig. Merchants engaged in the import trade had no use for Whiggish high tariffs, whereas workers in industries clamoring for protection often concluded that their jobs depended on such duties.

Lifestyles and ethnic or religious identities also strongly affected party loyalties during this period. Some of the roots of party allegiance can be found in local divisions between old-stock Americans and immigrants over such matters as temperance, keeping the Sabbath, and reading the Protestant Bible in public schools. In the northern states, one way to tell the typical Whig from the typical Democrat was to see what each did on Sunday. A person who went to one of the evangelical Protestant churches was very likely to be a Whig. On the other hand, the person who attended a ritualized service—Catholic, Lutheran, or Episcopalian—or did not go to church at all was most probably a Democrat.

The Democrats were the favored party of immigrants, Catholics, freethinkers, backwoods farmers, and those of all classes who enjoyed traditional amusements condemned by the new breed of moral reformers. One thing all these groups had in common was a desire to be left alone, free of restrictions on their freedom to think and behave as they liked. The Whigs enjoyed particularly strong support among Protestants of old stock living in smaller cities, towns, and prosperous rural areas devoted to market farming. In general, the Whigs welcomed a market economy but wanted to restrain the individualism and disorder it created by enforcing cultural and moral values derived from the Puritan tradition.

Nevertheless, party conflict in Congress continued to center on national economic policy. Whigs stood firm for a loose construction of the Constitution and federal support for business and economic development. The Democrats persisted in their defense of strict construction, states' rights, and laissez-faire. Debates over tariffs, banking, and internal improvements remained vital and vigorous during the 1840s.

True believers in both parties saw a deep ideological or moral meaning in the clash over economic issues. Whigs and Democrats had conflicting views of the good society, and their policy positions reflected these differences. The Democrats were the party of white male equality and personal liberty. They perceived the American people as a collection of independent and self-sufficient white men. The role of government was to see to it that the individual was not interfered with—in his economic activity, in his personal habits, and in his religion (or lack of it). Democrats were ambivalent about the rise of the market economy because of the ways it threatened individual independence. The Whigs, on the other hand, were the party of orderly progress under the guidance of an enlightened elite. They believed that the propertied, the well-educated, and the pious were responsible for guiding the masses toward the common good. Believing sincerely that a market economy would benefit everyone in the long run, they had no qualms about the rise of a commercial and industrial capitalism.

TOCQUEVILLE'S WISDOM

The French traveler Alexis de Tocqueville, author of the most influential account ever written of the emergence of American democracy, visited the United States in 1831 and 1832. He had relatively little to say about national politics and the formation of political parties. For him, the essence of American democracy was local self-government, such as he observed in the town meetings of New England. The participation of ordinary citizens in the affairs of their communities impressed him greatly, and he praised Americans for not conceding their liberties to a centralized state.

Despite his generally favorable view of the American experiment, Tocqueville was acutely aware of the limitations of American democracy and of the dangers facing the republic. He believed the nullification crisis foreshadowed destruction of the Union and predicted the problem of slavery would lead eventually to civil war and racial conflict. He also noted the power of white supremacy, providing an unforgettable firsthand description of the sufferings of an Indian community in the course of forced migration to the West, as well as a graphic account of the way free blacks were segregated and driven from the polls in northern cities like Philadelphia. White Americans, he believed, were deeply prejudiced against people of color, and he doubted it was possible "for a whole people to rise . . . above itself." Tocqueville was equally sure that the kind of democracy men were practicing was not meant for women. Observing how women were strictly assigned to a separate domestic sphere, he concluded that

Americans had never supposed "that democratic principles should undermine the husband's authority and make it doubtful who is in charge of the family." His observations have value because of their clear-sighted insistence that the democracy and equality of the Jacksonian era were meant for only some of the people. The democratic idea could not be so limited; it would soon begin to burst the boundaries of white male supremacy.

11

THE PURSUIT OF PERFECTION

In the winter of 1830 to 1831, a wave of religious revivals swept the northern states. The most dramatic and successful took place in Rochester, New York. For six months, Presbyterian evangelist Charles G. Finney preached almost daily, emphasizing that every man or woman had the power to choose Christ and a godly life.

Finney broke with his church's traditional belief that it was God's inscrutable will that decided who would be saved when he preached that "sinners ought to be made to feel that they have something to do, and that something is to repent. That is something that no other being can do for them, neither God nor man, and something they can do and do now." He converted hundreds, and church membership doubled during his stay. The newly awakened Christians of Rochester were urged to convert relatives, neighbors, and employees. If enough people enlisted in the evangelical crusade, Finney proclaimed, the millennium would be achieved within months.

Finney's call for religious and moral renewal fell on fertile ground in Rochester. The bustling boomtown on the Erie Canal was suffering from severe growing pains and tensions arising from rapid economic development. Leading families were divided into quarreling factions, and workers were threatening to break free from the control their employers had previously exerted over their daily lives. Most of the early converts were from the middle class. Businessmen who had been heavy drinkers and irregular churchgoers now abstained from alcohol and went to church at least twice a week. They also pressured the employees in their workshops, mills, and stores to do likewise. More rigorous standards of proper behavior and religious conformity unified Rochester's elite and increased its ability to control the rest of the community. Evangelical Protestantism provided the middle class with a stronger sense of identity and purpose.

But the war on sin was not always so unifying. Finney concentrated on religious conversion and moral uplift of the individual, trusting that the purification of American society and politics would automatically follow. Other religious and moral reformers crusaded against social and political institutions that failed to measure up to the standards of Christian perfection. They attacked such collective "sins" as the liquor traffic, war, slavery, and even government. Religiously inspired reformism cut two ways. On the one hand, it imposed a new order and cultural unity to previously divided and troubled communities. But it also inspired a variety of more radical movements that threatened to undermine established institutions. One of these movements—abolitionism—challenged the central social and economic institution of the southern states and helped trigger political upheaval and civil war.

Although both evangelical reformers and Jacksonian politicians sought popular favor and assumed that individuals were free agents capable of self-direction and self-improvement, leaders of the two types of movements made different kinds of demands on ordinary people. Jacksonians idealized common folk pretty much as they found them and saw no danger to the community if individuals pursued their worldly interests. Evangelical reformers, by contrast, believed that the common people needed to be redeemed and uplifted. They did not trust a democracy of unbelievers and sinners. The republic would be safe, they insisted, only if a right-minded minority preached, taught, and agitated until the mass of ordinary citizens was reborn into a higher life.

THE RISE OF EVANGELICALISM

American Protestantism was in a state of constant ferment during the early nineteenth century. The separation of church and state, a process that began during the Revolution, was now complete. Government sponsorship and funding had ended, or would soon end, for the established churches of the colonial era. Dissenting groups, such as Baptists and Methodists, welcomed full religious freedom because it offered a better chance to win new converts. All pious Protestants, however, were concerned about the spread of "infidelity"—a term they applied to Catholics, freethinkers, Unitarians, Mormons, and anyone else who was not an evangelical Christian. But they faced opposition to their effort to make the nation officially Protestant. As deism—the belief in a God who expressed himself through natural laws accessible to human reason—declined in popularity in the early to mid-nineteenth century, Catholic immigration increased, and the spread of "Popery" became the main focus of evangelical concern. Both Catholics and Unitarians (who quietly carried forward the rationalistic traditions of the eighteenth century) resented and resisted the evangelicals' efforts to convert them to "the Christianity of the heart." Most of those who accepted Christ as their personal savior in revival meetings previously had been indifferent to religion rather than adhering to an alternative set of beliefs.

Revivalism proved to be a very effective means to extend religious values and build up church membership. The Great Awakening of the mid-eighteenth century had shown the wonders that evangelists could accomplish, and new revivalists repeated this success by greatly increasing the proportion of the population that belonged to Protestant churches. Spiritual renewals were often followed by mobilization of the faithful into associations to spread the gospel and reform American morals.

THE SECOND GREAT AWAKENING: THE FRONTIER PHASE

The Second Great Awakening began in earnest on the southern frontier around the turn of the century. In 1801, a crowd estimated at nearly fifty thousand gathered at Cane Ridge, Kentucky. According to a contemporary observer:

> *The noise was like the roar of Niagara. . . . I counted seven ministers all preaching at once. . . . At one time I saw at least five hundred swept down in a moment, as if a battery of a thousand guns had been opened upon them, and then followed immediately shrieks and shouts that rent the heavens.*

Highly emotional camp meetings, organized usually by Methodists or Baptists but sometimes by Presbyterians, became a regular feature of religious life in the South and the lower Midwest. On the frontier, the camp meeting met social as well as religious needs. In the sparsely settled southern backcountry, it was difficult to sustain local churches with regular ministers. To solve the problem, Methodists sent out circuit riders, while Baptists licensed uneducated farmers to preach to their neighbors. But for many people, the only way to get baptized or married or to have a communal religious experience was to attend a camp meeting.

Rowdies and scoffers also attended, drinking whiskey, carousing, and fornicating on the fringes of the small city of tents and wagons. Sometimes they were "struck down" by a mighty blast from the pulpit. Evangelists loved to tell stories of such conversions or near conversions. According to Methodist preacher Peter Cartwright, one scoffer was seized by the "jerks"—a set of involuntary bodily

Frontier camp meetings in the early 1800s were attended by large crowds (sometimes thousands at a time) who sang, prayed, wept, and begged for divine mercy as the spirit moved them. The meetings served as an emotional outlet for rural people whose lives lacked excitement and human contact.

movements often observed at camp meetings. Normally such an experience would lead to conversion, but this particular sinner refused to surrender to God. The result was that he kept jerking until his neck was broken.

Camp meetings obviously provided an emotional outlet for rural people whose everyday lives were often lonely and tedious. They could also promote a sense of community and social discipline. Conversion at a camp meeting could be a rite of passage, signifying that a young man or woman had outgrown wild or antisocial behavior and was now ready to become a respectable member of the community.

In the southern states, Baptists and Presbyterians eventually deemphasized camp meetings in favor of "protracted meetings" in local churches, which featured guest preachers holding forth day after day for up to two weeks. Southern evangelical churches, especially Baptist and Methodist, grew rapidly in membership and influence during the first half of the nineteenth century and became the focus of community life in rural areas. Although they encouraged temperance and discouraged dueling, they generally shied away from social reform. The conservatism of a slaveholding society discouraged radical efforts to change the world.

THE SECOND GREAT AWAKENING IN THE NORTH

Reformist tendencies were more evident in the revivalism that originated in New England and western New York. Northern evangelists were mostly Congregationalists and Presbyterians, strongly influenced by New England Puritan traditions. Their revivals, although less extravagantly emotional than the camp meetings of the South, found fertile soil in the small and medium-sized cities and towns of the North. Northern evangelism gave rise to societies devoted to the redemption of the human race in general and American society in particular.

The reform movement in New England began as an effort to defend Calvinism against the liberal views of religion fostered by the Enlightenment. The Reverend Timothy Dwight, who became president of Yale College in 1795, was alarmed by the younger generation's growing acceptance of the belief that the Deity was the benevolent master architect of a rational universe rather than an all-powerful, mysterious God. Dwight was particularly disturbed by those religious liberals who denied the doctrine of the Trinity and proclaimed themselves to be "Unitarians."

Horrified when Unitarians won control of the Harvard Divinity School, Dwight fought back by preaching to Yale undergraduates that they were "dead in sin" and succeeded in provoking a series of campus revivals. But the harshness and pessimism of orthodox Calvinist doctrine, with its stress on original sin and predestination, had limited appeal in a republic committed to human freedom and progress.

A younger generation of Congregational ministers reshaped New England Puritanism to increase its appeal to people who shared the prevailing optimism about human capabilities. The main theologian of early-nineteenth-century neo-Calvinism was Nathaniel Taylor, a disciple of Dwight. Taylor softened the doctrine of predestination by contending that every individual was a free agent who had the ability to overcome a natural inclination to sin.

The first great practitioner of the new evangelical Calvinism was Lyman Beecher, another of Dwight's pupils. In the period just before and after the War of 1812, Beecher helped promote a series of revivals in the Congregational churches of New England. Using his own homespun version of Taylor's doctrine of free agency, Beecher induced thousands to acknowledge their sinfulness and surrender to God.

During the late 1820s, Beecher was forced to confront the new and more radical form of revivalism being practiced in western New York by Charles G.

The Beecher family, shown here in a photograph by Mathew Brady, contributed four influential members to the reform movement. Lyman Beecher (seated center) was a successful preacher and a master strategist in the organized campaign against sin and "infidelity." His eldest daughter, Catharine (on his right), was a leader in the movement supporting higher education for women. Another daughter, Harriet (seated far right), wrote the novel Uncle Tom's Cabin. *Lyman's son, Henry Ward Beecher (standing far right), was an ardent anti-slavery advocate and later became one of the most celebrated preachers of the post–Civil War era. He also became involved in a notorious scandal and trial.*

Finney. Upstate New York was a seedbed for religious enthusiasms of various kinds. A majority of its population were transplanted New Englanders who had left behind their close-knit village communities and ancestral churches but not their Puritan consciences. Troubled by rapid economic changes and the social dislocations that went with them, they were ripe for a new faith and a fresh moral direction.

Although he worked within Congregational and Presbyterian churches (which were then cooperating under a plan of union established in 1804), Finney departed radically from Calvinist doctrines. Indifferent to theological issues, Finney appealed to emotion rather than to doctrine or reason. He wanted converts to feel the power of Christ and become new men and women. He eventually adopted the extreme view that redeemed Christians could be totally free of sin—as perfect as their Father in Heaven.

Beginning in 1823, Finney conducted a series of highly successful revivals in towns and cities of western New York. Even more controversial than his free-wheeling approach to theology were the means he used to win converts. Seeking instantaneous conversions, Finney held protracted meetings that lasted all night or several days in a row, placed an "anxious bench" in front of the congregation where those in the process of repentance could receive special attention, and encouraged women to pray publicly for the souls of male relatives.

The results could be dramatic. Sometimes listeners fell to the floor in fits of excitement. Although he appealed to emotion, Finney had a practical, almost manipulative, attitude toward the conversion process: it "is not a miracle or dependent on a miracle in any sense. . . . It is purely a philosophical result of the right use of constituted means."

Finney's new methods and the emotionalism that accompanied them disturbed Lyman Beecher and other eastern evangelicals. They were also upset because Finney violated long-standing Christian tradition by allowing women to pray aloud in church. Beecher and Finney met in an evangelical summit at New Lebanon, New York, in 1827, but failed to reach agreement on this and other issues. But it soon became clear that Finney was not merely stirring people to temporary peaks of excitement; he also was leaving strong and active churches behind him, and eastern opposition gradually weakened.

FROM REVIVALISM TO REFORM

Northern revivalists inspired a great movement for social reform. Converts were organized into voluntary associations that sought to stamp out sin and social evil and win the world for Christ. Most of the converts were middle-class citizens already active in the lives of their communities. They were seeking to adjust to the bustling world of the market revolution in ways that would not violate their traditional moral and social values. Their generally optimistic and forward-looking attitudes led to hopes that a wave of conversions would save the nation and the world.

In New England, Beecher and his evangelical associates were behind the establishment of a great network of missionary and benevolent societies. In 1810, Presbyterians and Congregationalists founded a Board of Commissioners for Foreign Missions and soon dispatched two missionaries to India. In 1816, the Reverend Samuel John Mills took the leading role in organizing the American Bible Society. By 1821, the society had distributed 140,000 Bibles, mostly in parts of the West where churches and clergymen were scarce.

Another major effort went into publication and distribution of religious tracts, mainly by the American Tract Society, founded in 1825. Special societies

THE MARCH of DEATH.

This March of Death is respectfully dedicated to the Temperance societies thro'out the United States
by their Obd.t Serv.t the Publisher.

Temperance propaganda, such as this broadside, warned that "demon rum" would lead the drinker down the direct path to poverty and wretchedness and would bring about the ruin of his entire family.

targeted groups beyond the reach of regular churches, such as seamen, Native Americans, and the urban poor. Middle-class women in New York, Philadelphia, Charleston, and Boston formed societies to spread the gospel in lower-class wards—where, as one of their missionaries put it, there was "a great mass of people beyond the restraints of religion."

Evangelicals founded moral reform societies as well as missions. Some of these aimed at curbing irreligious activity on the Sabbath; others sought to stamp out dueling, gambling, and prostitution. In New York in 1831, a zealous young clergyman published a sensational report claiming there were ten thousand prostitutes in the city laying their snares for innocent young men. As a result of this exposé, an asylum was established for the redemption of "abandoned women." When middle-class women became involved in this crusade, they shifted its focus to the men who patronized prostitutes, and they proposed that teams of observers record and publish the names of men seen entering brothels. The plan was abandoned because it offended those who thought the cause of virtue would be better served by suppressing public discussion and investigation of sexual vices.

Beecher was especially influential in the temperance crusade, the most successful of the reform movements. The temperance movement was directed at a real social evil. Since the Revolution, whiskey had become the most popular American beverage. Made from corn by individual farmers or, by the 1820s, in commercial distilleries, it was cheaper than milk or beer and safer than water (which was often contaminated). Hard liquor was frequently consumed with food as a table beverage, even at breakfast, and children sometimes imbibed along with adults. Per capita annual consumption of distilled beverages in the 1820s was almost triple what it is today, and alcoholism had reached epidemic proportions.

The temperance reformers viewed indulgence in alcohol as a threat to public morality. Drunkenness was seen as a loss of self-control and moral responsibility that spawned crime, vice, and disorder. Above all, it threatened the family. The main target of temperance propaganda was the husband and father who abused, neglected, or abandoned his wife and children because he was a slave to the bottle. Women played a vital role in the movement and were instrumental in making it a crusade for the protection of the home. The drinking habits of the poor or laboring classes also aroused great concern. Particularly in urban areas, the "respectable" and propertied elements lived in fear that lower-class mobs, crazed with drink, would attack private property.

Many evangelical reformers regarded intemperance as the greatest single obstacle to a republic of God-fearing, self-disciplined citizens. In 1826, a group of clergymen organized the American Temperance Society to encourage abstinence from "ardent spirits" or hard liquor (there was no agreement on the evils of beer and wine) and to educate people about the evils of "demon rum." Agents of the society organized revival meetings and called on those in attendance to sign a pledge promising abstinence from spirits.

The campaign was enormously effective. By 1834, there were five thousand local branches with more than a million members, a large proportion of them women. Although it may be doubted whether huge numbers of confirmed drunkards were cured, the movement did succeed in altering the drinking habits of middle-class American males. Per capita consumption of hard liquor declined more than 50 percent during the 1830s.

Cooperating missionary and reform societies—collectively known as "the benevolent empire"—were a major force in American culture by the early 1830s. A new ethic of self-control and self-discipline was being instilled in the middle class, equipping individuals to confront a new world of economic growth and social mobility without losing their cultural and moral bearings.

DOMESTICITY AND CHANGES IN THE AMERICAN FAMILY

The evangelical culture of the 1820s and 1830s influenced the family as an institution and inspired new conceptions of its role in American society. Many parents viewed children's rearing as essential preparation for self-disciplined Christian life and performed their nurturing duties with great seriousness and self-consciousness. Women—regarded as particularly susceptible to religious and moral influences—were increasingly confined to the domestic circle, but they assumed a greater importance within it.

MARRIAGE AND SEX ROLES

The white middle-class American family underwent major changes in the decades between the Revolution and the mid-nineteenth century. One was the triumph of marriage for love. Parents now exercised even less control over their children's selection of mates than they had in the colonial period. The desire to protect family property and maintain social status remained strong, but mutual affection was now considered absolutely essential to a proper union. Beginning in the late eighteenth century, romantic novels popularized the idea that marriage should be based exclusively on the promptings of the heart. It became easier for sons to marry while their fathers were still alive and for younger daughters to wed before their older sisters—trends that reflected a weakening of the traditional parental role.

Wives now began to behave more like the companions of their husbands and less like their servants or children. In the main, eighteenth-century correspondence between spouses had been formal and distant in tone. The husband often assumed a patriarchal role, even using such salutations as "my dear child" and rarely confessing that he missed his wife or craved her company.

By the early nineteenth century, first names, pet names, and terms of endearment such as "honey" or "darling" were increasingly used by both sexes, and absent husbands frequently confessed they felt lost without their mates. In their replies, wives assumed a more egalitarian tone and offered counsel on a wide range of subjects.

The change in middle- and upper-class marriage should not be exaggerated or romanticized. In law, and in cases of conflict between spouses, the husband remained the unchallenged head of the household. True independence or equality for women was impossible at a time when men held exclusive legal authority over a couple's property and children. Divorce was difficult for everyone, but the double standard made it easier for husbands than wives to dissolve a marriage on grounds of adultery.

The sentiment on this sampler, stitched in 1820 by Ruth Titus, typifies beliefs about woman's proper role, according to the Cult of True Womanhood.

Such power as women exerted within the home came from their ability to affect the decisions of men who had learned to respect their moral qualities and good sense. The evangelical movement encouraged this quiet expression of feminine influence. The revivals not only gave women a role in converting men but presented as the main object of worship a Christ with stereotypical feminine characteristics. A nurturing, loving, merciful savior, mediating between a stern father and his erring children, provided the model for woman's new role as spiritual head of the home. Membership in evangelical church–based associations inspired and prepared women for new roles as civilizers of men and guardians of domestic culture and morality. Female reform societies taught women the strict ethical code they were to instill in other family members; organized mothers' groups gave instruction in how to build character and encourage piety in children.

Historians have described the new conception of woman's role as the "Cult of True Womanhood" or the "ideology of domesticity." In the view of most men, a woman's place was in the home and on a pedestal. The ideal wife and mother was "an angel in the house," a model of piety and virtue who exerted a wholesome moral and religious influence over members of the coarser sex. A poem published in 1846 expressed well a masculine view of the true woman.

> *I would have her as pure as the snow on the mount—*
> *As true as the smile that to infancy's given—*
> *As pure as the wave of the crystalline fount,*
> *Yet as warm in the heart as the sunlight of heaven.*

The sociological reality behind the Cult of True Womanhood was an increasing division between the working lives of men and women. In the eighteenth century and earlier, most economic activity had been centered in and near the home, and husbands and wives often worked together in a common enterprise. By the early to mid-nineteenth century this way of life was declining, especially in the Northeast. In towns and cities, the rise of factories and countinghouses severed the home from the workplace. Men went forth every morning to their places of labor, leaving their wives at home to tend the house and the children. The cult of domesticity made a virtue of the fact that men were solely responsible for running the affairs of the world and building up the economy.

A new conception of sex roles justified and glorified this pattern. The "doctrine of two spheres"—as set forth in novels, advice literature, and the new women's magazines—sentimentalized the woman who kept a spotless house, nurtured her children, and offered her husband a refuge from the heartless world of commerce and industry. From a modern point of view, it is easy to condemn the cult of domesticity as a rationalization for male dominance; to a considerable extent, it was. But many women of the early to mid-nineteenth century do not seem to have felt oppressed or degraded by the new arrangement. The earlier pattern of cooperation had not implied sexual equality and the new norm of confinement to the home did not necessarily imply that women were inferior. By the standards of evangelical culture, women in the domestic sphere could be viewed as superior to men, since women were in a good position to cultivate the "feminine" virtues of love and self-sacrifice and thus act as official guardians of religious and moral values.

The domestic ideology had real meaning only for relatively affluent women. Working-class wives were not usually employed outside the home during this period, but they labored long and hard within the household. Besides cleaning, cooking, and taking care of large numbers of children, they often took in washing or piecework to supplement a meager family income. Their endless domestic drudgery made a sham of the notion that women had the time and energy for the "higher things of life." Life was especially hard for African American women. Most of those who were "free Negroes" rather than slaves did not have husbands who made enough to support them, and they were obliged to serve in white households or work long hours at home doing other people's washing and sewing.

In urban areas, unmarried working-class women often lived on their own and toiled as household servants, in the sweatshops of the garment industry, and in factories. Barely able to support themselves and at the mercy of male sexual predators, they were in no position to identify with the middle-class ideal of elevated, protected womanhood. For some of them, the relatively well-paid and gregarious life of the prostitute seemed to offer an attractive alternative to a life of loneliness and privation.

For middle-class women whose husbands or fathers earned a good income, freedom from industrial or farm labor offered some tangible benefits. They now had the leisure to read extensively the new literature directed primarily at housewives, to participate in female-dominated charitable activities, and to cultivate deep and lasting friendships with other women. The result was a distinctively feminine subculture emphasizing "sisterhood" or "sorority." This growing sense of solidarity with other women could transcend the barriers of social class. Beginning in the 1820s, middle- and upper-class urban women organized societies for the relief and rehabilitation of poor or "fallen" women. The aim of the organizations was not economic and political equality with men but the elevation of all women to true womanhood.

For some women, the domestic ideal even sanctioned efforts to extend their sphere until it conquered the masculine world outside the home. This domestic feminism was reflected in women's involvement in crusades to stamp out such masculine sins as intemperance, gambling, and sexual vice.

In the benevolent societies and reform movements of the Jacksonian era, especially those designated as women's organizations, women handled money, organized meetings and public appeals, made contracts, and sometimes even gave orders to male subordinates—activities they could not usually perform in their own households. The desire to extend the feminine sphere was the motivating force behind Catharine Beecher's campaign to make schoolteaching a woman's occupation. A prolific and influential writer on the theory and practice of domesticity, this unmarried daughter of Lyman Beecher saw the spinster-teacher as equivalent to a mother. By instilling in young males the virtues that only women could teach, the schoolmarm could help liberate America from corruption and materialism.

But Beecher and other domestic feminists continued to emphasize the role of married women who stayed home and did their part simply by being wives and mothers. Because husbands were away from home much of the time and tended to be preoccupied with business, women bore primary responsibility for the rearing of children. Since women were considered particularly well qualified to transmit piety and morality to future citizens of the republic, the cult of domesticity exalted motherhood and encouraged a new concern with childhood as the time of life when "character" was formed.

THE DISCOVERY OF CHILDHOOD

The nineteenth century has been called "the century of the child." More than before, childhood was seen as a distinct stage of life requiring the special and sustained attention of adults. The family now became "child-centered," viewing its main function as the care, nurture, and rearing of children. In earlier times, parents often sent children away from home for education or apprenticeship at a very early age. Among the well-to-do, children spent more time with servants or tutors than with their parents. By the early decades of the nineteenth century, however, children were staying at home longer and receiving much more attention from parents, especially mothers.

New customs and fashions heralded the "discovery" of childhood. Books aimed specifically at juveniles began to roll off the presses. Parents became more self-conscious about their responsibilities and sought help from a new literature providing expert advice on child rearing. One early-nineteenth-century mother wrote, "There is scarcely any subject concerning which I feel more anxiety than the proper education of my children. It is a difficult and delicate subject, the more I feel how much is to be learnt by myself."

The new concern for children resulted in more intimate relations between parents and children. The ideal family described in the advice manuals and sentimental literature was bound together by affection rather than authority. Firm discipline remained at the core of "family government," but there was a change in the preferred method of enforcing good behavior. Corporal punishment declined, partially displaced by shaming or withholding of affection. Disobedient middle-class children were now more likely to be confined to their rooms to reflect on their sins than to receive a good thrashing. The purpose of discipline was to induce repentance and change basic attitudes. The intended result was often described as "self-government"; to achieve it, parents used guilt, rather than fear, as their main source of leverage. A mother's sorrow or a father's stern and prolonged silence was deemed more effective in forming character than were blows or angry words.

Child-centered families also meant smaller families. If nineteenth-century families had remained as large as those of earlier times, it would have been impossible to lavish so much care and attention on individual offspring. The average number of children born to each woman during her fertile years dropped from 7.04 in 1800 to 5.42 in 1850. As a result, the average number of children per family declined about 25 percent.

The practice of various forms of birth control undoubtedly contributed to this demographic revolution. Ancestors of the modern condom and diaphragm were openly advertised and sold during the pre–Civil War period, but it is likely that most couples controlled family size by practicing the withdrawal method or limiting the frequency of intercourse. Abortion was also surprisingly common and was on the rise. One historian has estimated that by 1850 there was one abortion for every five or six live births.

Parents seemed to understand that having fewer children meant they could provide their offspring with a better start in life. Such attitudes were appropriate in a society that was beginning to shift from agriculture to commerce and industry. For rural households short of labor, large families were an economic asset. For urban couples who hoped to send their children into a competitive world that demanded special talents and training, they were a financial liability.

INSTITUTIONAL REFORM

The family could not carry the whole burden of socializing and reforming individuals. Children needed schooling as well as parental nurturing. Some adults, too, seemed to require special kinds of attention and treatment. Seeking to extend the advantages of "family government" beyond the domestic circle, reformers worked to establish or improve public institutions that were designed to shape individual character and instill a capacity for self-discipline.

THE EXTENSION OF EDUCATION

The period from 1820 to 1850 saw an enormous expansion of free public schools. The new resolve to put more children in school for longer periods reflected many of the same values that exalted the child-centered family. Up to a certain age, children could be effectively nurtured and educated in the home. But after that they needed formal training at a character-molding institution that would prepare them to make a living and bear the burdens of republican citizenship. Intellectual training at school was regarded as less important than moral indoctrination.

Sometimes more than just an extension of the family, the school served as a substitute for it. Alarmed at the masses of poor and immigrant children who allegedly failed to get proper nurturing at home, educational reformers believed schools should make up for this disadvantage. Otherwise, the republic would be in danger from masses of people "incapable of self-government."

Before the 1820s, schooling in the United States was a haphazard affair. The wealthy sent their children to private schools, and some of the poor sent their children to charity or "pauper" schools that were usually financed in part by local governments. Public education was most highly developed in the New England states, where towns were required by law to support elementary schools. It was weakest in the South, where almost all education was private.

Agitation for expanded public education began in the 1820s and early 1830s as a central demand of the workingmen's movements in eastern cities. These hard-pressed artisans viewed free schools open to all as a way of countering the growing gap between rich and poor. Initially, strong opposition came from more affluent taxpayers who did not see why they should pay for the education of other people's children. But middle-class reformers soon seized the initiative, shaped educational reform to the goal of social discipline, and provided the momentum needed for legislative success.

The most influential supporter of the common school movement was Horace Mann of Massachusetts. As a lawyer and member of the state legislature, Mann worked tirelessly to establish a state board of education and adequate tax support for local schools. In 1837, he persuaded the legislature to enact his proposals, and he subsequently resigned his seat to become the first secretary of the new board, an office he held with great distinction until 1848. He believed children were clay in the hands of teachers and school officials and could be molded to a state of perfection. Like advocates of child rearing through moral influence rather than physical force, he discouraged corporal punishment except as a last resort.

Against those who argued that school taxes violated property rights, Mann contended that private property was actually held in trust for the good of the community. Mann's conception of public education as a means of social discipline converted the middle and upper classes to the cause. By teaching middle-class morality and respect for order, the schools could turn potential rowdies and revolutionaries into law-abiding citizens. They could also encourage social mobility by opening doors for lower-class children who were determined to do better than their parents.

In practice, new or improved public schools often alienated working-class pupils and their families rather than reforming them. Compulsory attendance

THE ECLECTIC SERIES. 77

LESSON XXI.

1. IN'DO-LENT; *adj.* lazy; idle.
2. COM-MER'CIAL; *adj.* trading.
3. COM'IC-AL; *adj.* amusing.
3. DRONE; *n.* an idler.
4. NAV'I-GA-BLE; *adj.* in which boats can sail.

THE IDLE SCHOOL-BOY.

PRONOUNCE correctly. Do not say *indorlunt* for in-do-lent; *creepin* for creep-ing; *sylubble* for syl-*la*-ble; *colud* for col-ored; *scarlit* for scar-let; *ignerunt* for ig-no-rant.

1. I WILL tell you about the †laziest boy you ever heard of. He was indolent about every thing. When he played, the boys said he played as if the teacher told him to. When he went to school, he went creep-ing along like a snail. The boy had sense enough; but he was too lazy to learn any thing.

2. When he spelled a word, he †drawled out one syllable after another, as if he were afraid the †sylla-bles would quarrel, if he did not keep them a great way apart.

3. Once when he was †reciting, the teacher asked him, "What is said of †Hartford?" He answered, "Hartford is a †flourishing *comical* town." He meant that it was a "flourishing *commercial* town;" but he was such a drone, that he never knew what he was about.

4. When asked how far the River †Kennebec was navigable, he said, "it was navigable for *boots* as far as †Waterville." The boys all laughed, and the teacher could not help laughing, too. The idle boy †colored like scarlet.

5. "I say it is so in my book," said he. When one of the boys showed him the book, and pointed to the

The lessons and examples in McGuffey's Eclectic Readers upheld the basic virtues of thrift, honesty, and charity and taught that evil deeds never went unpunished.

laws in Massachusetts and other states deprived poor families of needed wage earners without guaranteeing new occupational opportunities for those with an elementary education. As the laboring class became increasingly immigrant and Catholic in the 1840s and 1850s, dissatisfaction arose over the evangelical Protestant tone of "moral instruction" in the schools. Quite consciously, Mann and his disciples were trying to impose a uniform culture on people who valued differing traditions.

In addition to the "three Rs" ("reading, 'riting, and 'rithmetic"), the public schools of the mid-nineteenth century taught the "Protestant ethic"—industry, punctuality, sobriety, and frugality. These were the virtues stressed in the famous *McGuffey's Eclectic Readers,* which first appeared in 1836. Millions of children learned to read by digesting McGuffey's parables about the terrible fate of those who gave in to sloth, drunkenness, or wastefulness. Such moral indoctrination helped produce generations of Americans with personalities and beliefs adapted to the needs of an industrializing society—people who could be depended on to adjust to the precise and regular routines of the factory or the office. But as an education for self-government—in the sense of learning to think for oneself—it left much to be desired.

Fortunately, however, education was not limited to the schools nor devoted solely to children. Every city and almost every town or village had a lyceum, debating society, or mechanics' institute where adults of all social classes could broaden their intellectual horizons. Lyceums featured discourses on such subjects as "self-reliance" or "the conduct of life," explanations and demonstrations of the latest scientific discoveries, and debates among members on controversial issues.

Young Abraham Lincoln, who had received less than two years of formal schooling as a child in backwoods Indiana, sharpened his intellect in the early 1830s as a member of the New Salem, Illinois, debating society. In 1838, after moving to Springfield, he set forth his political principles when he spoke at the local lyceum on "The Perpetuation of Our Political Institutions." More than the public schools, the lyceums and debating societies fostered independent thought and encouraged new ideas.

DISCOVERING THE ASYLUM

Some segments of the population were obviously beyond the reach of family government and character training provided in homes and schools. In the 1820s and 1830s, reformers became acutely aware of the danger to society posed by an apparently increasing number of criminals, lunatics, and paupers. Their answer was to establish special institutions to house those deemed incapable of self-discipline. Their goals were humanitarian; they believed reform and rehabilitation were possible in a carefully controlled environment.

In earlier times, the existence of paupers, lawbreakers, and insane persons had been taken for granted. Their presence was viewed as the consequence of divine judgment or original sin. For the most part, these people were dealt with in ways that did not isolate them from local communities. The insane were allowed to wander about if harmless and were confined at home if they were dangerous; the poor were supported by private charity or the dole provided by towns or counties; convicted criminals were whipped, held for limited periods in local jails, or—in the case of very serious offenses—executed.

By the early nineteenth century, these traditional methods had come to seem both inadequate and inhumane. Dealing with deviants in a neighborly way broke down as economic development and urbanization made communities less cohesive. At the same time, reformers were concluding that all defects of mind and character were correctable—the insane could be cured, criminals reformed, and paupers taught to pull themselves out of destitution. The result was what historian David Rothman termed "the discovery of the asylum"—the invention and establishment of special institutions for the confinement and reformation of deviants.

The 1820s and 1830s saw the emergence of state-supported prisons, insane asylums, and poorhouses. New York and Pennsylvania led the way in prison reform. Institutions at Auburn, New York, and Philadelphia attracted international attention as model penitentiaries, mainly because of their experiments in isolating inmates from one another. Solitary confinement was viewed as a humanitarian and therapeutic policy because it gave inmates a chance to reflect on their sins, free from the corrupting influence of other convicts. In theory, prisons and asylums substituted for the family. Custodians were meant to act as parents, providing moral advice and training.

In practice, the institutions were far different from the affectionate families idealized by the cult of domesticity. Most accommodated only a single sex or maintained a strict segregation of male and female inmates. Their most prominent feature was the imposition of a rigid daily routine. The early superintendents and wardens believed the enforcement of a rigorous set of rules and procedures would encourage self-discipline.

Prisons, asylums, and poorhouses did not achieve the aims of their founders. Public support was inadequate to meet the needs of a growing inmate population, and the personnel of the institutions often lacked the training needed to help the incarcerated. The results were overcrowding and the use of brutality to keep order. For the most part, prisons failed to reform hardened criminals, and the primitive psychotherapy known as "moral treatment" failed to cure most asylum patients. Poorhouses rapidly degenerated into sinkholes of despair. A combination of naive theories and poor performance doomed the institutions to a custodial rather than a reformatory role.

Conditions would have been even worse had it not been for Dorothea Dix. Between 1838 and the Civil War, this remarkable woman devoted her energies and skills to publicizing the inhumane treatment prevailing in prisons, almshouses, and insane asylums and to lobbying for corrective action. As a direct result of her activities, fifteen states opened new hospitals for the insane and others improved their supervision of penitentiaries, asylums, and poorhouses. Dix ranks as one of the most practical and effective of all the reformers of the pre–Civil War era.

Dorothea Dix (1802–1887). Her ef-forts on behalf of the mentally ill led to the building of more than thirty institu-tions in the United States and the re-form and restaffing—with well-trained personnel—of existing hospitals. She died in Trenton, New Jersey, in 1887, in a hospital that she had founded.

REFORM TURNS RADICAL

During the 1830s, internal dissension split the great reform movement spawned by the Second Great Awakening. Efforts to promote evangelical piety, improve personal and public morality, and shape character through familial or institutional discipline continued and even flourished. But bolder spirits went beyond such goals and set their sights on the total liberation and perfection of the individual.

DIVISIONS IN THE BENEVOLENT EMPIRE

Early-nineteenth-century reformers were, for the most part, committed to changing existing attitudes and practices gradually and in ways that would not in-vite conflict or disrupt society. But by the mid-1830s, a new mood of impatience and perfectionism surfaced within the benevolent societies. In 1836, for exam-ple, the Temperance Society split over two issues—whether the abstinence pledge should be extended to include beer and wine and whether pressure should be applied to producers and sellers of alcoholic beverages as well as to consumers. Radicals insisted on a total commitment to "cold water" and were prepared to clash head-on with an important economic interest. Moderates held back from such goals and tactics because they wanted to avoid hostility from prominent citizens who drank wine or had money invested in the liquor industry.

A similar rift occurred in the American Peace Society, an antiwar organization founded in 1828 by clergymen seeking to promote Christian concern for world peace. Most of the founders admitted the propriety of "defensive wars," but some members of the society denounced all use of force as a violation of the Sermon on the Mount. These dissidents withdrew from the organization in 1838 and formed the New England Non-Resistance Society to promote an absolute pacifism, which denied the right of self-defense to nations or individuals and repudiated all forms of government coercion.

The new perfectionism realized its most dramatic and important success within the antislavery movement. Before the 1830s, most people who expressed religious and moral concern over slavery were affiliated with the American Colonization Society, a benevolent organization founded in 1817. Most colonizationists admitted that slavery was an evil, but they also viewed it as a deeply rooted social and economic institution that could be eliminated only very gradually and with the cooperation of slaveholders. Reflecting the power of racial prejudice, they proposed to provide transportation to Africa for free blacks who chose to go, or were emancipated for the purpose, as a way of relieving southern fears that a race war would erupt if slaves were simply released from bondage and allowed to remain in America. In 1821, the society established the colony of Liberia in West Africa, and during the next decade a few thousand African Americans were settled there.

In the inaugural issue of his antislavery weekly, the Liberator, *William Lloyd Garrison announced that he was launching a militant battle against the evil and sin of slavery. The stirring words that appeared in that first issue are repeated on the* Liberator's *banner.*

Colonization proved to be grossly inadequate as a step toward the elimination of slavery. Many of the blacks transported to Africa were already free, and those liberated by masters influenced by the movement represented only a tiny percentage of the southern slave population. Northern blacks denounced the enterprise because it denied the prospect of racial equality in America. Black opposition to colonizationism helped persuade William Lloyd Garrison and other white abolitionists to repudiate the Colonization Society and support immediate emancipation without emigration.

Garrison launched a new and more radical antislavery movement in 1831 in Boston, when he began to publish a journal called the *Liberator.* Most of the early subscribers to Garrison's *Liberator* were free blacks, and radical abolitionists depended heavily on black support from then on. Black orators, especially escaped slaves such as Frederick Douglass, were featured at antislavery meetings, and some African Americans became officers of antislavery societies.

Besides calling for immediate and unconditional emancipation, Garrison denounced colonization as a slaveholder's plot to remove troublesome free blacks and as an ignoble surrender to un-Christian prejudices. His rhetoric was as severe as his proposals were radical. As he wrote in the first issue of the *Liberator,* "I will be as harsh as truth and as uncompromising as justice. . . . I am in earnest—I will not equivocate—I will not excuse—I will not retreat a single inch—And I WILL BE HEARD!" Heard he was. In 1833, Garrison and other abolitionists founded the American Anti-Slavery Society. The colonization movement was placed on the defensive, and during the 1830s, many of its most active northern supporters became abolitionists.

THE ABOLITIONIST ENTERPRISE

The abolitionist movement, like the temperance crusade, was a direct outgrowth of the Second Great Awakening. Many leading abolitionists were already committed to a life of Christian activism before they dedicated themselves to freeing the slaves. Several were ministers or divinity students seeking a mission in life that would fulfill spiritual and professional ambitions.

The career of Theodore Dwight Weld exemplified the connection between revivalism and abolitionism. After dropping out of divinity school, Weld migrated to western New York where he fell under the influence of Charles G. Finney. After a conversion experience in 1826, Weld became an itinerant lecturer for various reform causes. By the early 1830s, he focused his attention on the moral issues raised by the institution of slavery. After a brief flirtation with the colonization movement, Weld was converted to abolitionism in 1832, recognizing that colonizationists did not really accept blacks as equals or "brothers-in-Christ." In 1834, he instigated what amounted to a series of abolitionist revivals at Lane Theological Seminary in Cincinnati. When the trustees of the seminary attempted to suppress further discussion of the case for immediate emancipation, Weld led a mass walkout of most students. The "Lane rebels" subsequently founded Oberlin College as a center for abolitionist activity.

In 1835 and 1836, Weld toured Ohio and western New York preaching abolitionism. He also supervised and trained other agents and orators as part of a campaign to convert the entire region to immediate emancipation. The tried-and-true methods of the revival—fervent preaching, protracted meetings, and the call for individuals to come forth and announce their redemption—were put at the service of the antislavery movement. Weld and his associates left behind them tens of thousands of new abolitionists and hundreds of local antislavery societies. As a result of their efforts, northern Ohio and western New York became hotbeds of abolitionist sentiment.

Antislavery orators and organizers tended to have their greatest successes in the small- to medium-sized towns of the upper North. The typical convert came from an upwardly mobile family engaged in small business, the skilled trades, or market farming. In larger towns and cities, or when they ventured close to the Mason-Dixon line, abolitionists were more likely to encounter fierce and effective opposition. In 1835, Garrison was mobbed in the streets of Boston and almost lynched.

Abolitionists who thought of taking their message to the fringes of the South had reason to pause, given the fate of the antislavery editor Elijah Lovejoy. In 1837, while attempting to defend himself and his printing press from a mob in Alton, Illinois, just across the Mississippi River from slaveholding Missouri, Lovejoy was shot and killed.

Racism was a major cause of antiabolitionist violence in the North. Rumors that abolitionists advocated or practiced interracial marriage could easily incite an urban crowd. If it could not find white abolitionists, the mob was likely to turn on local blacks. Working-class whites tended to fear that economic and social competition with blacks would increase if abolitionists succeeded in freeing slaves and making them citizens. But a striking feature of many of the mobs was that they were dominated by "gentlemen of property and standing." Solid citizens resorted to violence, it would appear, because abolitionism threatened their conservative notions of social order and hierarchy.

By the end of the 1830s, the abolitionist movement was under great stress. Besides the burden of external repression, there was dissension within the movement. Becoming an abolitionist required an exacting conscience and an unwillingness to compromise on matters of principle. These character traits also made it difficult for abolitionists to work together and maintain a united front. Relations between black and white abolitionists were, for the most part, tense and uneasy. Blacks protested that they did not have a fair share of leadership positions or influence over policy. Not even abolitionists were entirely free of the prejudices rife in the larger white society, and blacks resented the paternalism and condescension that they detected.

During the late 1830s, Garrison, the most visible proponent of the cause, began to adopt positions that some other abolitionists found extreme and divisive. Embracing the "no-government" philosophy, he urged abolitionists to abstain from voting or otherwise participating in a corrupt political system. He also attacked the clergy and the churches for refusing to take a strong antislavery stand and encouraged his followers to "come out" of the established denominations rather than continuing to work within them.

These positions alienated those members of the Anti-Slavery Society who continued to hope that organized religion and the existing political system could be influenced or even taken over by abolitionists. But it was Garrison's stand on women's rights that led to an open break at the national convention of the American Anti-Slavery Society in 1840. Following their leader's principle that women should be equal partners in the crusade, a Garrison-led majority elected a woman abolitionist to the society's executive committee. A minority then withdrew to form a competing organization—the American and Foreign Anti-Slavery Society.

The schism weakened Garrison's influence within the abolitionist movement. When he later repudiated the U.S. Constitution as a proslavery document and called for northern secession from the Union, few antislavery people in the Middle Atlantic or midwestern states went along. Outside New England, most abolitionists worked within the churches and the political system and avoided controversial side issues such as women's rights and nonresistant pacifism. The Liberty party, organized in 1840, was their first attempt to enter the electoral arena under their own banner; it signaled a new effort to turn antislavery sentiment into political power.

Historians have debated the question of whether the abolitionist movement of the 1830s and early 1840s was a success or a failure. It obviously failed to convert a majority of Americans to its position that slavery was a sinful institution that should be abolished immediately. In the South, abolitionism caused a strong counteraction and helped inspire a more militant and uncompromising defense of slavery. The belief that peaceful agitation, or what abolitionists called "moral suasion," would convert slaveholders and their northern sympathizers to abolition was obviously unrealistic.

A leader in the abolitionist movement was Frederick Douglass, who escaped from slavery in 1838 and became one of the most effective voices in the crusade against slavery.

But in another sense the crusade was successful. It brought the slavery issue to the forefront of public consciousness and convinced a substantial and growing segment of the northern population that the South's peculiar institution was morally wrong and potentially dangerous to the American way of life. The South helped the antislavery cause in the North by responding hysterically and repressively to abolitionist agitation. In 1836, Southerners in Congress forced adoption of a "gag rule" requiring that abolitionist petitions be tabled without being read; at about the same time, the post office refused to carry antislavery literature into the slave states. Prominent Northerners who had not been moved to action by abolitionist depictions of slave suffering became more responsive to the movement when it appeared their own civil liberties might be threatened. The politicians who later mobilized the North against the expansion of slavery into the territories drew strength from the antislavery and antisouthern sentiments that abolitionists had already called forth.

FROM ABOLITIONISM TO WOMEN'S RIGHTS

Abolitionism also served as a catalyst for the women's rights movement. From the beginning, women were active participants in the abolitionist crusade. More than half of the thousands of antislavery petitions sent to Washington had women's signatures on them.

Some antislavery women defied conventional ideas of their proper sphere by becoming public speakers and demanding an equal role in the leadership of antislavery societies. The most famous of these were the Grimké sisters, Sarah and Angelina, who attracted enormous attention because they were the rebellious daughters of a South Carolina slaveholder. When some male abolitionists objected to their speaking in public to mixed audiences of men and women, Garrison came to their defense and helped forge a link between blacks' and women's struggles for equality.

The battle to participate equally in the antislavery crusade made a number of women abolitionists acutely aware of male dominance and oppression. For them, the same principles that justified the liberation of the slaves also applied to the emancipation of women from all restrictions on their rights as citizens. In 1840, Garrison's American followers withdrew from the first World's Anti-Slavery Convention in London because the sponsors refused to seat the women in their delegation. Among the women thus excluded were Lucretia Mott and Elizabeth Cady Stanton.

Wounded by men's reluctance to extend the cause of emancipation to include women, Stanton and Mott organized a new and independent movement for

Elizabeth Cady Stanton, a leader of the women's rights movement, reared seven children. In addition to her pioneering work, especially for women's suffrage, she also lectured frequently on family life and child care.

women's rights. The high point of their campaign was the famous convention at Seneca Falls, New York, in 1848. The Declaration of Sentiments issued by this first national gathering of feminists charged that "the history of mankind is a history of repeated injuries and usurpations on the part of man toward woman, having in direct object the establishment of an absolute tyranny over her." It went on to demand that all women be given the right to vote and that married women be freed from unjust laws giving husbands control of their property, persons, and children. Rejecting the cult of domesticity with its doctrine of separate spheres, these women and their male supporters launched the modern movement for gender equality.

RADICAL IDEAS AND EXPERIMENTS

Hopes for individual or social perfection were not limited to reformers inspired by evangelicalism. Between the 1820s and 1850s, a great variety of schemes for human redemption came from those who had rejected orthodox Protestantism. Some were secular humanists carrying on the freethinking tradition of the Enlightenment, but most were seekers of new paths to spiritual or religious fulfillment. These philosophical and religious radicals attacked established institutions, prescribed new modes of living, and founded utopian communities to put their ideas into practice.

A radical movement of foreign origin that gained a toehold in Jacksonian America was utopian socialism. In 1825–1826, the British manufacturer and reformer Robert Owen visited the United States and founded a community based on common and equal ownership of property at New Harmony, Indiana. About the same time, Owen's associate Frances Wright gathered a group of slaves at Nashoba, Tennessee, and set them to work earning their freedom in an atmosphere of "rational cooperation." The rapid demise of both of these model communities suggested that utopian socialism did not easily take root in American soil.

But the impulse survived. In the 1840s, a number of Americans, including the prominent editor Horace Greeley, became interested in the ideas of the French utopian theorist Charles Fourier. Fourier called for cooperative communities in which everyone did a fair share of the work and tasks were allotted to make use of the natural abilities and instincts of the members. Between 1842 and 1852, about thirty Fourierist "phalanxes" were established in the northeastern and midwestern states, and approximately a hundred thousand people lived for a time in these communities or otherwise supported the movement. Like the Owenite communities, the Fourierist phalanxes were short-lived, surviving for an average of only two years. The common complaint of the founders was that

Americans were too individualistic to cooperate in the ways that Fourier's theories required.

Two of the most successful and long-lived manifestations of pre–Civil War utopianism were the Shakers and the Oneida community. The Shakers—officially known as the Millennial Church or the United Society of Believers—began as a religious movement in England. In 1774, a Shaker leader, Mother Ann Lee, brought their radical beliefs to the United States. Lee believed herself to be the feminine incarnation of Christ and advocated a new theology based squarely on the principle of sexual equality. The Shakers, named for their expressions of religious fervor through vigorous dancelike movements, believed in communal ownership and strict celibacy. They lived simply and minimized their contact with the outside world because they expected Christ's Second Coming to occur momentarily. The Oneida community was established in 1848 at Oneida, New York, and was inspired by an unorthodox brand of Christian perfectionism. Its founder, John Humphrey Noyes, believed the Second Coming of Christ had already occurred; hence human beings were no longer obliged to follow the moral rules that their previously fallen state had required. At Oneida, traditional marriage was outlawed, and a carefully regulated form of "free love" was put into practice.

It was a literary and philosophical movement known as transcendentalism that inspired the era's most memorable experiments in thinking and living on a higher plane. The main idea was that the individual could transcend material reality and ordinary understanding, attaining through a higher form of reason—or intuition—a oneness with the universe as a whole and with the spiritual forces that lay behind it. Transcendentalism was the major American version of the romantic and idealist thought that emerged in the early nineteenth century. Throughout the Western world, romanticism was challenging the rationalism and materialism of the Enlightenment. Most American transcendentalists were Unitarians or ex-Unitarians who were dissatisfied with the sober rationalism of their denomination and sought a more intense kind of spiritual experience. Unable to embrace evangelical Christianity because of intellectual resistance to its doctrines, they sought inspiration from a philosophical and literary idealism of German origin.

Their prophet was Ralph Waldo Emerson, a brilliant essayist and lecturer who preached that each individual could commune directly with a benign spiritual force that animated nature and the universe, which he called the "oversoul." A radical individualist committed to "self-culture" and "the sufficiency of the private man," Emerson avoided all involvement in organized movements or associations because he believed they limited the freedom of the individual to develop inner resources and find a personal path to spiritual illumination. In the vicinity

Ritualized dances were part of the Shakers' spiritual preparation for the Second Coming. The dancers in this nineteenth-century etching exemplify the mixed heritage of the Shaker community.

of Emerson's home in Concord, Massachusetts, a group of like-minded seekers of truth and spiritual fulfillment gathered during the 1830s and 1840s. Among them for a time was Margaret Fuller, the leading woman intellectual of the age. In *Woman in the Nineteenth Century* (1845), she made a strong claim for the spiritual and artistic equality of women.

One group of transcendentalists, led by the Reverend George Ripley, rejected Emerson's radical individualism and founded a cooperative community at Brook Farm, near Roxbury, Massachusetts, in 1841. For the next four years, group members worked the land in common, conducted an excellent school on the principle that spontaneity rather than discipline was the key to education, and allowed ample time for conversation, meditation, communion with nature, and artistic activity of all kinds. In 1845, Brook Farm was reconstituted as a Fourierist phalanx, but some of the original spirit persisted until its dissolution in 1849.

Another experiment in transcendental living adhered more closely to the individualistic spirit of the movement. Between 1845 and 1847, Henry David Thoreau, a young disciple of Emerson, lived by himself in the woods along the shore of Walden Pond and carefully recorded his thoughts and impressions. In a

Henry David Thoreau explained that he went to live in solitude in the woods because he wanted to "front only the essential facts of life." The sketch at right appeared on the title page of the first edition of Walden *(1854), the remarkable record of his experiment in living.*

sense, he pushed the ideal of self-culture to its logical outcome—a utopia of one. The result was *Walden* (published in 1854), one of the greatest achievements in American literature.

FADS AND FASHIONS

Not only venturesome intellectuals experimented with new beliefs and lifestyles. Between the 1830s and 1850s, a number of fads, fashions, and medical cure-alls appeared on the scene, indicating that a large segment of the middle class was obsessed with the pursuit of personal health, happiness, and moral perfection. Dietary reformers such as Sylvester Graham convinced many people to give up meat, coffee, tea, and pastries in favor of fruit, vegetables, and whole wheat bread. Some women, especially feminists, began to wear loose-fitting pantalettes, or "bloomers," popularized by Amelia Bloomer. The clothes were more convenient and less restricting than the elaborate structure of corsets, petticoats, and hoopskirts then in fashion. A concern with understanding and improving personal character and abilities was reflected in the craze for phrenology, a popular pseudoscience that studied the shape of the skull to determine natural aptitudes and inclinations. In the 1850s, another craze swept through the United States—spiritualism. Spiritualists convinced an extraordinary number of people that it was possible to communicate with spirits and ghosts. Séances were held in parlors around the country as Americans sought advice and guidance from the world beyond. Spiritualism was one more manifestation of the American quest for the perfection of human beings.

COUNTERPOINT ON REFORM

One great American writer observed at close quarters the perfectionist ferment of the age but held himself aloof, suggesting in his novels and tales that pursuit of the ideal led to a distorted view of human nature and possibilities. Nathaniel Hawthorne lived in Concord, Massachusetts, knew Emerson and Margaret Fuller, and even spent time at Brook Farm. But his sense of human frailty made him skeptical about the claims of transcendentalism and utopianism. He satirized transcendentalism as unworldly and overoptimistic in his allegorical tale "The Celestial Railroad" and gently lampooned the denizens of Brook Farm in his novel *The Blithedale Romance* (1852). His view of the dangers of pursuing perfection too avidly came out in his tale of a father who kills his beautiful daughter by trying to remove her one blemish, a birthmark. His greatest novels, *The Scarlet Letter* (1850) and *The House of the Seven Gables* (1851), imaginatively probed New England's Puritan past and the shadows it cast on the present. By dwelling on original sin as a psychological reality, Hawthorne told his contemporaries that their efforts to escape from guilt and evil were futile. One simply had to accept the world as an imperfect place. Although he did not engage in polemics against humanitarian reformers and cosmic optimists, Hawthorne wrote parables and allegories that implicitly questioned the fundamental assumptions of pre–Civil War reform.

One does not have to agree with Hawthorne's view of the human condition to acknowledge that the dreams of perfectionist reformers promised more than they could possibly deliver. Revivals could not make all men like Christ; temperance could not solve all social problems; abolitionist agitation could not bring a peaceful end to slavery; and transcendentalism could not fully emancipate people from the limitations and frustrations of daily life. The consequences of perfectionist efforts were often far different from what their proponents expected. Yet, if the reform impulse was long on inspirational rhetoric but somewhat short on durable, practical achievements, it did at least disturb the complacent and opportunistic surface of American life and open the way to necessary changes. Nothing could possibly change for the better unless people were willing to dream of improvement.

12

An Age of Expansionism

I n the 1840s and early 1850s, politicians, journalists, writers, and entrepreneurs frequently proclaimed themselves champions of "Young America." One of the first to use the phrase was Ralph Waldo Emerson, who told an audience of merchants and manufacturers in 1844 that the nation was entering a new era of commercial development, technological progress, and territorial expansion. Emerson suggested that a progressive new generation—the "Young Americans"—would lead this surge of physical development. More than a slogan and less than an organized movement, Young America stood for a positive attitude toward the market economy and industrial growth, a more aggressive and belligerent foreign policy, and a celebration of America's unique strengths and virtues.

Although the Young America ideal attracted support across party lines, it came to be identified mainly with young Democrats who sought to purge their party of its traditional fear of the expansion of commerce and industry. Unlike old-line Jeffersonians and Jacksonians, Young Americans had no qualms about the market economy and the speculative, materialistic spirit it called forth.

Young Americans favored enlarging the national market by acquiring new territory. They called for annexation of Texas, assertion of an American claim to all of Oregon, and the appropriation of vast new territories from Mexico. They also celebrated the technological advances that would knit this new empire together, especially the telegraph and the railroad.

Walt Whitman in the "carpenter portrait" that appeared in the first edition of his great work, Leaves of Grass, *in 1855. The poet's rough clothes and slouch hat signify his identification with the common people.*

Young America was a cultural and intellectual as well as an economic and political movement. In 1845, a Washington journal hailed the election of forty-nine-year-old James K. Polk, the youngest man yet to become president. During the Polk administration, Young American writers and critics—mostly based in New York City—called for a new and distinctive national literature, free of subservience to European themes or models and expressive of the democratic spirit. Their organ was the *Literary World,* founded in 1847, and its ideals influenced two of the greatest writers the nation has produced: Walt Whitman and Herman Melville.

In his free verse poetry, Whitman captured much of the exuberance, optimism, and expansionism of Young America.

> *From this hour I ordain myself loos'd of limits and imaginary lines,*
> *Going where I list, my own master total and absolute,*
> *. . . . .*
> *I inhale great draughts of space,*
> *The east and the west are mine, and the north and the south are mine.*
> *I am larger, better than I thought.*

In *Moby-Dick,* Herman Melville produced a novel sufficiently original in form and conception to more than fulfill the demand of Young Americans for "a New Literature to fit the New Man in the New Age." But Melville was too deep a thinker not to see the perils that underlay the soaring ambition and aggressiveness of the new age. The whaling captain Ahab, who brings destruction on himself and his ship by his relentless pursuit of the white whale, symbolized—among other things—the dangers facing a nation that was overreaching itself by indulging its pride and exalted sense of destiny with too little concern for moral and practical consequences.

New York native Herman Melville, shown here in an 1870 portrait by Joseph Oriel Eaton, shaped the knowledge he gained as a merchant sailor into Moby-Dick, *a cautionary saga about the dark side of human ambition.*

MOVEMENT TO THE FAR WEST

In the 1830s and 1840s, the westward movement of population penetrated the Far West all the way to the Pacific. Pioneers pursued fertile land and economic opportunity beyond the existing boundaries of the United States and thus helped set the stage for the annexations and international crises of the 1840s. Some went for material gain, others went for adventure, and a significant minority sought freedom from religious persecution. Whatever their reasons, they brought American attitudes into regions that were already occupied or claimed by Mexico or Great Britain.

BORDERLANDS OF THE 1830S

U.S. expansionists directed their ambitions to the north, west, and southwest. For a time, it seemed that both Canada and Mexico might be frontiers for expansionism. Conflicts over the border between the United States and British North America led periodically to calls for diplomatic or military action to wrest the northern half of the continent from the British; similar conflicts in Mexican territory led ultimately to the United States' capture and acquisition of much of northern Mexico.

A long-standing dispute over the boundary between Maine and the Canadian province of New Brunswick was finally resolved in 1842, when Secretary of State Daniel Webster concluded an agreement with the British government, represented by Lord Ashburton. The Webster-Ashburton Treaty gave over half of the disputed territory to the United States and established a definite northeastern boundary with Canada.

On the other side of the continent, the United States and Britain both laid claim to Oregon, a vast area that lay between the Rockies and the Pacific from the 42nd parallel (the northern boundary of California) to the latitude of 54°40' (the southern boundary of Alaska). Although in 1818, the two nations agreed to joint occupation, each side managed to strengthen its claim. The United States acquired Spain's rights to the Pacific Northwest in the Adams-Onís Treaty, and Britain gained effective control of the northern portion of the Oregon Country through the activities of the Hudson's Bay Company. Neither side, however, wished to surrender access to the Columbia River basin and the adjacent territory extending north to the 49th parallel (which later became the northern border of the state of Washington).

The Oregon Country was scarcely populated before 1840. The same could not be said of the Mexican borderlands that lay directly west of Jacksonian America. Spanish settlements in present-day New Mexico date from the late sixteenth century. By 1820, about forty thousand people of Spanish descent populated this province, engaging mainly in sheep raising and mining. In 1821, Spain granted independence to Mexico, which then embraced areas that currently make up the states of Texas, New Mexico, Arizona, California, Nevada, Utah, and much of Colorado. The Republic of Mexico instituted a free-trade policy that stimulated commercial prosperity but also whetted expansionist appetites on the Anglo side of the border.

California was the other major northward extension of Mexico. In the 1820s and 1830s, this land of huge estates and enormous cattle herds was far less populous than New Mexico—only about four thousand Mexicans of Spanish origin lived in California in 1827. The region's other inhabitants were the thirty thousand Indians, many of whom were forced to work on vast land tracts owned by Spanish missions. At the beginning of the 1830s, a chain of twenty-one mission stations, stretching from San Diego to north of San Francisco, controlled most of the province's land and wealth. The Indian population had experienced a catastrophic decline during the sixty years of Spanish rule. The stresses and strains of forced labor and exposure to European diseases had taken an enormous toll.

In 1833, the Mexican Congress's "secularization act" emancipated the Indians from church control and opened the mission lands to settlement. The government awarded immense tracts of the mission land to Mexican citizens and left the

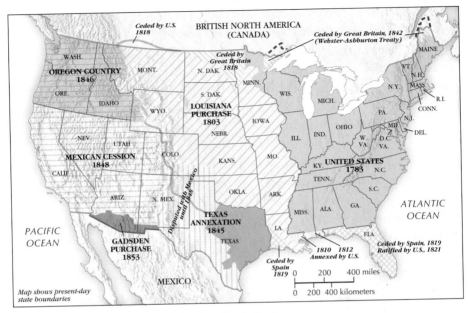

Territorial Expansion by the Mid-Nineteenth Century
Fervent nationalists identified the growth of America through territorial expansion as the divinely ordained "Manifest Destiny" of a chosen people.

Indians landless. A new class of large landowners, or *rancheros,* replaced the *padres* as masters of the province's indigenous population. The rancheros subjected the Indians to a new and even harsher form of servitude. During the fifteen years they held sway, the rancheros created an American legend through their lavish hospitality, extravagant dress, superb horsemanship, and taste for violent and dangerous sports. Their flamboyant lifestyle and devotion to the pursuit of pleasure captured the fancy and aroused the secret envy of many American visitors and traders.

The Americans who saw California in the 1830s were mostly merchants and sailors involved in the oceanic trade between Boston and California ports. By the mid-1830s, several Yankee merchants had taken up permanent residence in towns such as Monterey and San Diego in order to conduct the California end of the business. The reports they sent back about the Golden West sparked interest in eastern business circles.

THE TEXAS REVOLUTION

At the same time as some Americans were trading with California, others were taking possession of Texas. In the early 1820s, Mexican officials encouraged settlers from the United States to settle in Texas. Newly independent Mexico granted Stephen F. Austin, son of a onetime Spanish citizen, a huge piece of land in hopes he would help attract and settle new colonists from the United States. Some fifteen other Anglo-American *empresarios* received land grants in the 1820s. In 1823, three hundred families from the United States were settled on the Austin grant, and within a year, the colony's population had swelled to 2021. The offer of fertile and inexpensive land attracted many American immigrants.

Friction soon developed between the Mexican government and the Anglo-American colonists over the status of slavery and the authority of the Catholic Church. Under the terms of settlement, all people living in Texas had to become Mexican citizens and adopt the Roman Catholic faith. Settlers either converted to Catholicism only superficially or ignored the requirement entirely. Slavery presented another problem, for in 1829 Mexico freed all slaves under its jurisdiction. Slaveholders in Texas were given a special exemption that allowed them to emancipate their slaves and then sign them to lifelong contracts as indentured servants, but many refused to limit their ownership rights in any way.

A Mexican government commission reported in 1829 that Americans were the great majority of the Texas population and were flagrantly violating Mexican law—refusing to emancipate their slaves, evading import duties on goods from the United States, and failing to convert to Catholicism. The following year, the Mexican Congress prohibited further American immigration and importation of slaves to Texas.

Enforcement of the new law was feeble, and the flow of settlers, slaves, and smuggled goods continued virtually unabated. A long-standing complaint of the Texans was the failure of the Mexican constitution to grant them local self-government. Under the Mexican federal system, Texas was joined to the state of Coahuila, and Texan representatives were outnumbered three to one in the state legislature. In 1832, the colonists rioted in protest against the arrest of several Anglo-Americans by a Mexican commander.

Austin went to Mexico City in 1833 to present the Texans' grievances and seek concessions from the central government. He succeeded in having the ban against American immigration lifted, but failed to win agreement to the separation of Texas from Coahuila. As he was about to return to Texas, Austin was arrested and imprisoned for writing a letter recommending that Texans set up a state government without Mexico City's consent.

In 1835, some Texans revolted against Mexico's central government. The insurrectionists claimed they were fighting for freedom from oppression. Actually, Mexican rule had not been harsh; the worst that can be said was that it was inefficient, inconsistent, and sometimes corrupt. Furthermore, the Texans' devotion to "liberty" did not prevent them from defending slavery against Mexico's attempt to abolish it. Texans had done pretty much what they pleased, despite laws to the contrary and angry rumblings from south of the Rio Grande.

A threat to the Texans' status as "tolerated guests" occurred in 1834 when General Antonio López de Santa Anna made himself dictator of Mexico and abolished the federal system of government. News of these developments reached Texas late in the year, accompanied by rumors of the impending disfranchisement and even expulsion of American immigrants. The rebels, already aroused by earlier restrictive policies, were influenced by the rumors and prepared to resist Santa Anna's effort to enforce tariff regulations by military force.

When he learned that Texans were resisting customs collections, Santa Anna sent reinforcements. The settlers first engaged Mexican troops at Gonzales in October and forced the retreat of a cavalry detachment. Shortly thereafter, Austin laid siege to San Antonio with a force of five hundred men and after six weeks forced its surrender, thereby capturing most of the Mexican troops then in Texas.

THE REPUBLIC OF TEXAS

While this early fighting was going on, delegates from the American communities in Texas convened and after some hesitation voted overwhelmingly to declare their independence on March 2, 1836. A constitution, based closely on that of the United States, was adopted for the new Republic of Texas, and a temporary government was installed to carry on the military struggle. Although the ensuing conflict was largely one of Americans against Mexicans, some Texas Mexicans, or *Tejanos,* joined the fray on the side of the Anglo rebels. They too wanted to be free of Santa Anna's heavy-handed rule.

Within days after Texas declared itself a republic, rebels and Mexican troops in San Antonio fought the famous battle of the Alamo. Myths about that battle have magnified the Anglo rebels' valor at the Mexicans' expense. The folklore is based on fact—only 187 rebels fought off a far larger number of Mexican soldiers for more than a week before eventually capitulating—but it is not true that all rebels, including the folk hero Davy Crockett, fought to the death. Crockett and seven other survivors were captured and then executed. Moreover, the rebels fought from inside a strong fortress with superior weapons against march-weary Mexican conscripts. Nevertheless, a tale that combined actual and mythical bravery inspired the rallying cry "Remember the Alamo."

The revolt ended with an exchange of slaughters. A few days after the Alamo battle, another Texas detachment was surrounded and captured in an open plain near the San Antonio River and was marched to the town of Goliad, where most of its 350 members were executed. The next month, on April 21, 1836, the main Texas army, under General Sam Houston, assaulted Santa Anna's troops at an encampment near the San Jacinto River. The final count showed that 630 Mexicans and only a handful of Texans had been killed. Santa Anna was captured and marched to Velasco, the meeting place of the Texas government, where he was

One of the most colorful leaders of the struggle for Texas independence, Sam Houston lived for a time with the Cherokees and later served as a congressman and governor of Texas.

forced to sign treaties recognizing the independence of Texas and its claim to territory all the way to the Rio Grande.

Sam Houston, the hero of San Jacinto, became the first president of Texas. His platform sought annexation to the United States, but Andrew Jackson and others believed that domestic politics and fear of a war with Mexico made immediate annexation impossible. Congress and the Jackson administration did, however, formally recognize Texas sovereignty.

In its ten-year existence as the Lone Star Republic, Texas drew settlers from the United States at an accelerating rate. The Panic of 1837 impelled many debt-ridden and land-hungry farmers to take advantage of the free grants of 1280 acres that Texas offered to immigrating heads of white families. In the decade after independence, the population of Texas soared from 30,000 to 142,000. Most of the newcomers assumed, as did the old settlers, that they would soon be annexed and restored to American citizenship.

TRAILS OF TRADE AND SETTLEMENT

After New Mexico opened its trade to American merchants, a thriving commerce developed along the trail that ran from Missouri to Santa Fe. To protect themselves from the hostile Indians whose territory they had to cross, the traders traveled in large caravans, one or two of which would arrive in Santa Fe every summer. The federal government assisted them by providing troops when necessary and by appropriating money to purchase rights of passage from various tribes. Even so, the trip across the Cimarron desert and the southern Rockies was often difficult and hazardous. But profits from the exchange of textiles and other manufactured goods for furs, mules, and precious metals were substantial enough to make the risk worth taking.

Deteriorating relations between the United States and Mexico following the Texas revolution had a devastating effect on the Santa Fe trade. Much of the ill feeling was caused by further Anglo-American aggressions. After several clashes with the Texans, the Mexican government moved to curtail the Santa Fe trade. In April 1842, it passed a new tariff banning the importation of many of the goods sold by American merchants and prohibiting the export of gold and silver. Further restrictions in 1843 denied American traders full access to the Santa Fe market.

The famous Oregon Trail was the great overland route that brought the wagon trains of American migrants to the West Coast during the 1840s. Extending for two thousand miles, across the northern Great Plains and the mountains beyond, it crossed the Rockies at South Pass and then forked; the main northern route led to the Willamette Valley of Oregon, but alternative trails were opened during the decade for overlanders heading for California. The journey from Missouri to the West Coast took about six months; most parties departed in May, hoping to arrive in November before the great snows hit the last mountain barriers.

After small groups had made their way to both Oregon and California in 1841 and 1842, a mass migration—mostly to Oregon—began in 1843. Within two years, five thousand Americans, living in the Willamette Valley south of the Columbia River, were demanding the extension of full American sovereignty over the Oregon Country.

THE MORMON TREK

An important and distinctive group of pioneers followed the Oregon Trail as far as South Pass and then veered southwestward to establish a thriving colony in the region of the Great Salt Lake. These were Mormons, members of the largest religious denomination founded on American soil—the Church of Jesus Christ of Latter-day Saints.

The background of the Mormon trek was a history of persecution in the eastern states. Joseph Smith of Palmyra, New York, the founder of Mormonism, revealed in 1830 that he had received a series of revelations that called upon him

Carl Christian Anton Christensen, Handcart, *ca. 1840. Instead of buying wagons and oxen, some groups of Mormon colonists made their trek to Deseret on foot, hauling their possessions in handcarts and working together as families to move their heavy loads.*

to establish Christ's pure church on earth. As the prophet of this faith, he published the *Book of Mormon,* a new scripture that he claimed to have discovered and translated with the aid of an angel. It was the record of a community of pious Jews who left the Holy Land six centuries before the birth of Christ and sailed to the American continent. After his crucifixion and resurrection, Christ appeared to this community and proclaimed the Gospel. Four hundred years later, a fratricidal war annihilated the believing Christians but not all of the descendents of the original Jewish migrants. Mormons held that the survivors had contributed to the ancestry of the American Indians. Smith and those he converted to his new faith were committed to restoring the pure religion that had once thrived on American soil by founding a western Zion where they could practice their faith unmolested and carry out their special mission to convert the Native Americans.

In the 1830s, the Mormons established communities in Ohio and Missouri, but the former went bankrupt in the Panic of 1837 and the latter was the target of angry mobs and vigilante violence. In 1839, Smith led his followers back across the Mississippi to Illinois, where they found a temporary haven in the town of Nauvoo. But Smith soon reported new revelations that engendered dissension among his followers and hostility from neighboring "gentiles." Most controversial was his authorization of polygamy, or plural marriage. In 1844, Smith was killed by a mob while being held in jail in Carthage, Illinois, on a charge stemming from his quarrels with dissident Mormons who objected to his new policies.

Smith's death convinced Mormon leaders that they needed to move beyond the borders of the United States to establish their Zion in the wilderness. In late 1845, Smith's successor, Brigham Young, sent a party of fifteen hundred men to assess the chances of a colony in the vicinity of the Great Salt Lake (then part of Mexico). Twelve thousand Mormons took to the trail in 1846. Young himself arrived in Utah in 1847 and sent back word to the thousands encamped along the trail that he had found the promised land.

The Mormon community that Young established in Utah is one of the great success stories of western settlement. In contrast to the rugged individualism and disorder that often characterized mining camps and other new communities, "the state of Deseret" (the name the Mormons originally applied to Utah) was a model of discipline and cooperation. Because of its communitarian form of social organization, its centralized government, and the religious dedication of its inhabitants, this frontier society was able to expand settlement in a planned and efficient way and develop a system of irrigation that "made the desert bloom."

Utah's main problem was the determination of its political status. After Utah came under American sovereignty in 1848, the state of Deseret fought to maintain its autonomy and its custom of polygamy against the efforts of the federal government to extend American law and set up the usual type of territorial administration. In 1857, President Buchanan dispatched a military force to Utah, and the Mormons prepared to repel this "invasion." But after a heavy snow prevented the army from crossing the Rockies, Buchanan proposed a general pardon for Mormons who had violated federal law but agreed to cooperate with U.S. authorities in the future. The Mormons accepted, and in return, Brigham Young called off his plan to resist the army by force and accepted the nominal authority of an appointed territorial governor.

MANIFEST DESTINY AND THE MEXICAN-AMERICAN WAR

The rush of settlers beyond the nation's borders in the 1830s and 1840s inspired politicians and propagandists to call for annexation of those areas occupied by migrants. Some went further and proclaimed it was the "manifest destiny" of the United States to expand until it had absorbed all of North America, including Canada and Mexico. Such ambitions—and the policies they inspired—led to a major diplomatic confrontation with Great Britain and a war with Mexico.

TYLER AND TEXAS

President John Tyler initiated the politics of Manifest Destiny. He was vice president when William Henry Harrison died in office in 1841 after serving scarcely a month. Tyler was a states' rights, proslavery Virginian who had been picked as Harrison's running mate to broaden the appeal of the Whig ticket. Profoundly out of sympathy with the mainstream of his own party, he soon broke with the Whigs in Congress, who had united behind the latest version of Henry Clay's "American System." Although he lacked a base in either of the major parties, Tyler hoped to be elected president in his own right in 1844. To accomplish this difficult feat, he needed a new issue around which he could build a following that would cut across established party lines.

In 1843, Tyler decided upon the annexation of Texas as his issue. He anticipated that incorporation of the Lone Star Republic would be a popular move, especially in the slaveholding South. With Southern support, Tyler expected to have a good chance in the election of 1844.

To achieve his objective, Tyler enlisted the support of John C. Calhoun, the leading political defender of slavery and state sovereignty. Calhoun saw the annexation issue as a way of uniting the South. Success or failure in this effort would constitute a decisive test of whether the North was willing to give the southern states a fair share of national power and adequate assurances for the future of their way of life. If antislavery sentiment succeeded in blocking the acquisition of Texas, the Southerners would at least know where they stood and could begin to "calculate the value of the union."

To prepare the public for annexation, the Tyler administration launched a propaganda campaign in the summer of 1843. Rumors were circulated that the British were preparing to guarantee Texas independence and make a loan to the financially troubled republic in return for the abolition of slavery. Although the reports were groundless, they were believed and used to give urgency to the annexation cause.

Calhoun successfully negotiated an annexation treaty that was brought before the Senate in 1844. Denouncing the British for attempting to subvert the South's essential system of labor and racial control, Calhoun argued that the South's security and well-being—and by extension that of the nation—required the immediate incorporation of Texas into the Union.

The strategy of linking annexation explicitly to the interests of the South and slavery backfired. Northern antislavery Whigs charged that the whole scheme was a proslavery plot meant to advance the interest of one section of the nation against the other. Consequently, the Senate rejected the treaty by a decisive vote of 35 to 16 in June 1844. Tyler then attempted to bring Texas into the Union through a joint resolution of both houses of Congress admitting it as a state, but Congress adjourned before the issue came to a vote. The whole question hung fire in anticipation of the election of 1844.

THE TRIUMPH OF POLK AND ANNEXATION

Tyler's initiative made the future of Texas the central issue in the 1844 campaign. But the president was unable to capitalize on the issue because his stand was not in line with the views of either party. He tried to run as an independent, but his failure to gain significant support eventually forced him to withdraw from the race.

If the Democratic party convention had been held in 1843—as it was originally scheduled—former President Martin Van Buren would have won the nomination. But postponement of the Democratic conclave until May 1844 weakened his chances. Forced to take a stand on the annexation question, Van Buren persisted in the view he had held as president—that incorporation of Texas would risk war with Mexico, arouse sectional strife, and destroy the unity of the Democratic party. In an effort to keep the issue out of the campaign, Van Buren struck a gentleman's agreement with Henry Clay, the overwhelming favorite for the Whig nomination, that both of them would publicly oppose immediate annexation.

Van Buren's letter opposing annexation appeared shortly before the Democratic convention, and it cost him the nomination. Angry southern delegates, who secured a rule requiring approval by a two-thirds vote, blocked Van Buren's nomination. After several ballots, a dark horse candidate—James K. Polk of Tennessee—emerged triumphant. Polk, a protégé of Andrew Jackson, had been speaker of the House of Representatives and governor of Tennessee.

An avowed expansionist, Polk ran on a platform calling for the simultaneous annexation of Texas and assertion of American claims to all of Oregon. He identified

THE LIBERTY PARTY SWINGS AN ELECTION

CANDIDATE	PARTY	ACTUAL VOTE IN NEW YORK	NATIONAL ELECTORAL VOTE	IF LIBERTY VOTERS HAD VOTED WHIG	PROJECTED ELECTORAL VOTE
Polk	Democratic	237,588	170	237,588	134
Clay	Whig	232,482	105	248,294	141
Birney	Liberty	15,812	0	—	—

THE ELECTION OF 1844

CANDIDATE	PARTY	POPULAR VOTE	ELECTORAL VOTE
Polk	Democratic	1,338,464	170
Clay	Whig	1,300,097	105
Birney	Liberty	62,300	—

himself and his party with the popular cause of turning the United States into a continental nation, an aspiration that attracted support from all parts of the country. His was a much more astute political strategy than the overtly prosouthern expansionism advocated by Tyler and Calhoun. The Whig nominee, Henry Clay, was basically antiexpansionist, but his sense of the growing popularity of Texas annexation among southern Whigs caused him to waffle on the issue during the campaign. This vacillation cost Clay the support of a small but crucial group of northern antislavery Whigs, who defected to the abolitionist Liberty party.

Polk won the fall election by a relatively narrow popular margin. His triumph in the electoral college was secured by victories in New York and Michigan, where the Liberty party candidate, James G. Birney, had taken away enough votes from Clay to affect the outcome. Although the close election was hardly a clear mandate for expansionism, the Democrats claimed that the people had backed an aggressive campaign to extend the borders of the United States.

After the election, Congress reconvened to consider the annexation of Texas. The mood had changed as a result of Polk's victory, and some leading senators from both parties who had initially opposed Tyler's scheme for annexation by joint resolution of Congress now changed their position. As a result, annexation was approved a few days before Polk took office.

THE DOCTRINE OF MANIFEST DESTINY

The expansionist mood that accompanied Polk's election and the annexation of Texas was given a name and a rationale in the summer of 1845. John L. O'Sullivan, a proponent of the Young America movement and editor of the influential *United States Magazine and Democratic Review,* charged that foreign governments were conspiring to block the annexation of Texas in an effort to thwart "the fulfillment of our manifest destiny to overspread the continent allotted by providence for the free development of our yearly multiplying millions."

Besides coining the phrase Manifest Destiny, O'Sullivan pointed to the three main ideas that lay behind it. One was that God was on the side of American expansionism. This notion arose from the long tradition that identified the growth of America with the divinely ordained success of a chosen people. A second idea, implied in the phrase *free development,* was that the spread of American rule meant the extension of democratic institutions and local self-government if areas claimed by autocratic foreign governments were annexed to the United States. O'Sullivan's third premise was that population growth required the outlet that territorial acquisitions would provide.

In its most extreme form, the doctrine of Manifest Destiny meant that the United States would someday occupy the entire North American continent, that nothing less would appease its land-hungry population. "Make way, I say, for the young American Buffalo," bellowed a Democratic orator in 1844, "—he has not yet got land enough. . . . I tell you we will give him Oregon for his summer shade, and the region of Texas as his winter pasture. (Applause) Like all of his race, he wants salt, too. Well, he shall have the use of two oceans—the mighty Pacific and the turbulent Atlantic. . . . He shall not stop his career until he slakes his thirst in the frozen ocean. (Cheers)"

POLK AND THE OREGON QUESTION

In 1845 and 1846, the United States came closer to armed conflict with Great Britain than at any time since the War of 1812. The willingness of some Americans to go to war over Oregon was expressed in the rallying cry "Fifty-four forty or fight." This slogan was actually coined by Whigs seeking to ridicule Democratic expansionists, but Democrats later took it over as a vivid expression of their demand for what is now British Columbia. Polk fed this expansionist fever by laying claim in his inaugural address to all of the Oregon Country. Privately, however, he was willing to accept the 49th parallel as a dividing line. What made the situation so tense was that Polk was dedicated to an aggressive diplomacy of bluff and bluster.

In July 1845, Polk authorized Secretary of State James Buchanan to reply to the latest British request for terms by offering a boundary along the 49th parallel. The offer did not meet the British demand for all of Vancouver Island and free navigation of the Columbia River, and the British ambassador rejected the proposal out of hand. This rebuff infuriated Polk, who saw his offer as a generous and conciliatory retreat from his public position. Refusing a British request to submit the dispute to international arbitration, Polk called on Congress to terminate the agreement for joint occupation of the Pacific Northwest. Congress complied in April 1846.

Since abrogation of the joint agreement implied that the United States would attempt to extend its jurisdiction north to 54°40', the British government decided to take the diplomatic initiative in an effort to avert war, while at the same time dispatching warships to the Western Hemisphere in case conciliation failed. Their new proposal accepted the 49th parallel as the border, gave Britain all of Vancouver Island, and provided for British navigation rights on the Columbia River. The Senate recommended the treaty be accepted with the single change that British rights to navigate the Columbia be made temporary. It was ratified in that form on June 15.

Polk was prompted to settle the Oregon question because he now had a war with Mexico on his hands. His reckless and aggressive diplomacy had brought the nation within an eyelash of being involved in two wars at the same time. American policymakers got what they wanted from the Oregon treaty, namely Puget Sound and the strait that led into it south of Vancouver Island. Acquisition of this splendid natural harbor gave the United States its first deepwater port on the Pacific. By agreeing to compromise on the Oregon issue, however, Polk alienated expansionist advocates in the Old Northwest who had supported his call for "all of Oregon."

For many Northerners, the promise of new acquisitions in the Pacific Northwest was the only thing that made annexation of Texas palatable. They hoped new free states could be created to counterbalance the admission of slaveholding Texas to the Union. As this prospect receded, the charge of antislavery advocates that Texas annexation was a southern plot became more believable; to Northerners, Polk began to look more and more like a president concerned mainly with furthering the interests of his native region.

WAR WITH MEXICO

While the United States was avoiding a war with Great Britain, it was getting into one with Mexico. Although they had recognized Texas independence in 1845, the Mexicans rejected the Lone Star Republic's dubious claim to the unsettled territory between the Nueces River and the Rio Grande. When the United States annexed Texas and assumed its claim to the disputed area, Mexico broke off diplomatic relations and prepared for armed conflict.

Polk responded by placing troops in Louisiana on the alert and by dispatching John Slidell as an emissary to Mexico City in the hope he could resolve the boundary dispute and also persuade the Mexicans to sell New Mexico and California to the United States. But the Mexican government refused to receive Slidell. Then in January 1846, Polk ordered General Zachary Taylor, commander of American forces in the Southwest, to advance well beyond the Nueces and proceed toward the Rio Grande, thus invading territory claimed by both sides.

This 1846 cartoon titled "This Is the House That Polk Built" shows President Polk sitting forlornly in a house of cards, which represents the delicately balanced issues facing him.

By April, Taylor had taken up a position near Matamoros on the Rio Grande. On April 24, sixteen hundred Mexican soldiers crossed the river and the following day attacked a small American detachment, killing eleven and capturing the rest. After learning of the incident, Taylor sent word to the president: "Hostilities," he reported, "may now be considered as commenced."

The news was neither unexpected nor unwelcome. Polk in fact was already preparing his war message to Congress when he learned of the fighting on the Rio Grande. A short and decisive war, he had concluded, would force the cession of California and New Mexico to the United States. When Congress declared war on May 13, American agents and an "exploring expedition" under John C. Frémont were already in California stirring up dissension against Mexican rule, and ships of the U.S. Navy lay waiting expectantly off the shore. Two days later, Polk ordered a force under Colonel Stephen Kearny to march to Santa Fe and take possession of New Mexico.

The war lasted much longer than expected because the Mexicans refused to make peace despite a succession of military defeats. In the first major campaign of the conflict, Taylor took Matamoros and overcame fierce resistance to capture Monterrey, a major city of northern Mexico.

Taylor's controversial decision to allow the Mexican garrison to go free and his unwillingness or inability to advance farther into Mexico angered Polk and led him to adopt a new strategy for winning the war and a new commander to implement it. General Winfield Scott was ordered to prepare an amphibious attack on Veracruz with the aim of placing an American army within striking distance of Mexico City itself. Taylor was left to hold his position in northern Mexico, where at Buena Vista in February 1847 he defeated a sizable Mexican army sent northward to dislodge him. Taylor was hailed as a national hero and a possible candidate for president.

Meanwhile, the Kearny expedition captured Santa Fe, proclaimed the annexation of New Mexico by the United States, and set off for California. There they found that American settlers, in cooperation with John C. Frémont's exploring expedition, had revolted against Mexican authorities and declared their independence as the Bear Flag Republic. With the addition of Kearny's troops, a relatively small number of Americans were able to take possession of California against scattered and disorganized Mexican opposition, a process that was completed by the beginning of 1847.

The decisive Veracruz campaign was slow to develop, but in March 1847, the main American army under General Scott finally laid siege to the crucial port city. Veracruz fell after eighteen days, and then Scott began his advance on Mexico City. In the most important single battle of the war, Scott met forces under General Santa Anna at Cerro Gordo on April 17 and 18. A daring flanking maneuver that required soldiers to scramble up the mountainsides enabled Scott to win the decisive victory that opened the road to Mexico City. By August, American troops were drawn up in front of the Mexican capital. After a temporary armistice, a brief respite that the Mexicans used to regroup and improve their defenses, Scott ordered the massive assault that captured the city on September 14.

SETTLEMENT OF THE MEXICAN-AMERICAN WAR

Accompanying Scott's army was a diplomat, Nicholas P. Trist, who was authorized to negotiate a peace treaty whenever the Mexicans decided they had had enough. Despite a sequence of American victories, however, no Mexican leader was willing to invite the wrath of an intensely proud and patriotic citizenry by agreeing to the kind of terms that Polk wanted to impose. Even after the United States had achieved an overwhelming military victory, Trist found it difficult to exact an acceptable treaty from the Mexican government. In November, Polk ordered Trist to return to Washington.

Trist ignored Polk's instructions and continued to negotiate. On February 2, 1848, he signed a treaty that gained all the concessions he had been commissioned to obtain. The Treaty of Guadalupe Hidalgo ceded New Mexico and California to the United States for $15 million, established the Rio Grande as the border between Texas and Mexico, and promised that the U.S. government would assume the substantial claims of American citizens against Mexico. The treaty also provided that the Mexican residents of the new territories would become U.S. citizens. The Senate ratified the treaty on March 10.

As a result of the Mexican-American War, the United States gained 500,000 square miles of territory, enlarging the size of the nation by about 20 percent and adding to its domain the present states of California, Utah, New Mexico, Nevada, and Arizona and parts of Colorado and Wyoming. Soon those interested in a southern route for a transcontinental railroad pressed for even more territory along the southern border of the cession. That pressure led in 1853 to the Gadsden Purchase, through which the United States acquired the southernmost parts of present-day Arizona and New Mexico. But one intriguing question remains. Why, given the expansionist spirit of the age, did the campaign to acquire *all* of Mexico fail?

According to historian Frederick Merk, a major factor was the peculiar combination of racism and anticolonialism that dominated American opinion. It was one thing to acquire thinly populated areas that could be settled by "Anglo-Saxon" pioneers. It was something else again to incorporate a large population that was mainly of mixed Spanish and Indian origin. These "mongrels," charged racist opponents of the "All Mexico" movement, could never be fit citizens of a self-governing republic. They would have to be ruled in the way the British governed India, and the possession of colonial dependencies was contrary to American ideals and traditions.

Merk's thesis sheds light on why the general public had little appetite for swallowing all of Mexico, but those actually making policy had more mundane and practical reasons for being satisfied with the treaty of Guadalupe Hidalgo. What they had really wanted all along, historian Norman Graebner contended, were the great California harbors of San Francisco and San Diego. From these ports, Americans could trade directly with the Orient and dominate the commerce of the Pacific. Once acquisition of California had been assured, policymakers had little incentive to press for more Mexican territory.

The war with Mexico divided the American public and provoked political dissension. A majority of the Whig party opposed the war in principle, arguing that the United States had no valid claims to the area south of the Nueces. Whig congressmen voted for military appropriations while the conflict was going on, but they constantly criticized the president for starting it. More ominous was the charge of some Northerners from both parties that the real purpose of the war was to spread the institution of slavery and increase the political power of the southern states. While battles were being fought in Mexico, Congress was debating the Wilmot Proviso, a proposal to prohibit slavery in any territories that might be acquired from Mexico. A bitter sectional quarrel over the status of slavery in new areas was a major legacy of the Mexican-American War.

The domestic controversies aroused by the war and the propaganda of Manifest Destiny put a damper on additional efforts to extend the nation's boundaries. Concerns about slavery and race impeded acquisition of new territory in Latin America and the Caribbean. Resolution of the Oregon dispute clearly indicated that the United States was not willing to go to war with a powerful adversary to obtain large chunks of British North America, and the old ambition of incorporating Canada faded. After 1848, Americans concentrated on populating and developing the vast territory already acquired.

INTERNAL EXPANSIONISM

Young American expansionists saw a clear link between acquisition of new territory and other forms of material growth and development. In 1844, Samuel F. B. Morse perfected and demonstrated his electric telegraph, a device that made it possible to communicate rapidly over the expanse of a continental nation. Simultaneously, the railroad was becoming increasingly important as a means of moving people and goods over the same great distances. Improvements in manufacturing and agricultural methods led to an upsurge in the volume and range of internal trade, and the beginnings of mass immigration were providing human resources for the exploitation of new areas and economic opportunities.

The discovery of gold in newly acquired California in 1848 attracted a flood of emigrants from the East and several foreign nations. The gold they unearthed spurred the national economy, and the rapid growth of population centers on the Pacific Coast inspired projects for transcontinental telegraph lines and railroad tracks.

The spirit of Manifest Destiny and the thirst for acquiring new territory waned after the Mexican-American War. The expansionist impulse was channeled instead into internal development. Although the nation ceased to grow in size, the technological advances and population increase of the 1840s continued during the 1850s. The result was an acceleration of economic growth, a substantial increase in industrialization and urbanization, and the emergence of a new American working class.

THE TRIUMPH OF THE RAILROAD

More than anything else, the rise of the railroad transformed the American economy during the 1840s and 1850s. The technology came from England, where steam locomotives were first used to haul cars along tracks at the beginning of the century. In 1830 and 1831, two American railroads began commercial operation. After these pioneer lines had shown that steam locomotion was practical and profitable, several other railroads were built and began to carry passengers and freight during the 1830s.

Canals, however, proved to be strong competitors, especially for the freight business. By 1840, railroads had 2,818 miles of track—a figure almost equal to the combined length of all canals—but the latter still carried a much larger volume of goods. Passengers might prefer the speed of trains, which reached astonishing velocities of 20 to 30 miles an hour, but the lower unit cost of transporting freight on the canalboats prevented most shippers from changing their habits.

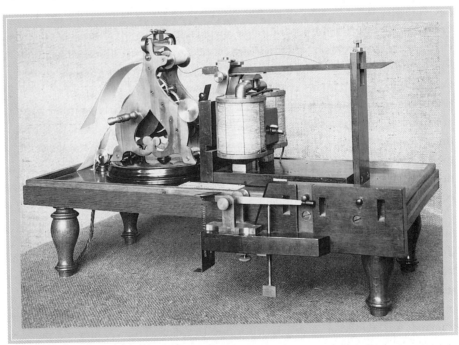

Morse's original model for the telegraph, patented in 1837, could send signals only about 40 feet. But multiple charges of batteries and series of relays boosted the strength of the electrical signals and led to more effective machines. By the early 1850s, over 23,000 miles of telegraph wires were in operation.

Furthermore, states such as New York and Pennsylvania had invested heavily in canals and resisted chartering a competitive form of transportation. Most of the early railroads reached out from port cities, such as Boston and Baltimore, that did not have good canal routes to the interior.

During the 1840s, rails extended beyond the northeastern and Middle Atlantic states, and mileage increased more than threefold, reaching a total of more than 9,000 miles by 1850. In the following decade, about 20,000 miles of additional track were laid. By 1860, all the states east of the Mississippi had rail service. Throughout the 1840s and 1850s, railroads cut deeply into the freight business of the canals and drove many of them out of business. The cost of hauling goods by rail decreased dramatically because of improved track construction and the introduction of powerful locomotives that could haul more cars.

The development of railroads had an enormous effect on the economy as a whole. Although the burgeoning demand for iron rails was initially met mainly by importation from England, it eventually spurred development of the domestic iron industry. Since railroads required an enormous outlay of capital, their promoters pioneered new methods for financing business enterprise. At a time when most manufacturing and mercantile concerns were still owned by families or partnerships, the railroad companies sold stock to the general public and helped to set the pattern for the separation of ownership and control that characterizes the modern corporation. They also developed new types of securities, such as "preferred stock" (with no voting rights but the assurance of a fixed rate of return) and long-term bonds at a set rate of interest.

Private capital did not fully meet the desires of the early railroad barons. State and local governments, convinced that railroads were the key to their future prosperity, loaned the railroads money, bought their stock, and guaranteed their bonds. Despite the dominant philosophy of laissez-faire, the federal government became involved by surveying the routes of projected lines and providing land grants. In all, forty companies received such aid before 1860, setting a precedent for the massive land grants of the post–Civil War era.

THE INDUSTRIAL REVOLUTION TAKES OFF

While railroads were initiating a revolution in transportation, American industry was entering a new phase of rapid and sustained growth. The factory mode of production, which had originated before 1840 in the cotton mills of New England, was extended to a variety of other products. The weaving and processing of wool, instead of being carried on in different locations, was concentrated in single production units beginning in the 1830s, and by 1860 some of the largest textile mills in the country were producing wool cloth. In the coal and iron regions of eastern Pennsylvania, iron was being forged and rolled in factories by 1850. Among the other industries that adopted the factory system during this period were those producing firearms, clocks, and sewing machines.

The essential features of the emerging mode of production were the gathering of a supervised workforce in a single place, the payment of cash wages to workers, the use of interchangeable parts, and manufacture by "continuous process." Within a factory setting, standardized parts, manufactured separately and in bulk, could be efficiently and rapidly assembled into a final product by an ordered sequence of continuously repeated operations. Mass production, which involved the division of labor into a series of relatively simple and repetitive tasks, contrasted sharply with the traditional craft mode of production, in which a single worker produced the entire product out of raw materials.

The bulk of American manufacturing of the 1840s and 1850s, however, was still carried on by traditional methods. Small workshops continued to predominate in most industries. But mass production was clearly the wave of the future.

New technology often played an important role in the transition to mass production. Just as power looms and spinning machinery had made textile mills possible, the development of new and more reliable machines or industrial techniques revolutionized other industries. Elias Howe's invention of the sewing machine in 1846 laid the basis for the ready-to-wear clothing industry and also contributed to the mechanization of shoemaking. During the 1840s, iron manufacturers adopted

A revolution in farming followed the introduction of new farm implements such as Cyrus McCormick's reaper, which could do ten times the work of a single person. The lithograph, by an anonymous artist, is titled The Testing of the First Reaping Machine near Steele's Tavern, Virginia, 1831.

THE AGE OF PRACTICAL INVENTION

YEAR*	INVENTOR	CONTRIBUTION	IMPORTANCE/DESCRIPTION
1787	John Fitch	Steamboat	First successful American steamboat
1793	Eli Whitney	Cotton gin	Simplified process of separating fiber from seeds; helped make cotton a profitable staple of southern agriculture
1798	Eli Whitney	Jig for guiding tools	Facilitated manufacture of interchangeable parts
1802	Oliver Evans	Steam engine	First American steam engine; led to manufacture of high-pressure engines used throughout eastern United States
1813	Richard B. Chenaworth	Cast-iron plow	First iron plow to be made in three separate pieces, thus making possible replacement of parts
1830	Peter Cooper	Railroad locomotive	First steam locomotive built in America
1831	Cyrus McCormick	Reaper	Mechanized harvesting; early model could cut six acres of grain a day
1836	Samuel Colt	Revolver	First successful repeating pistol
1837	John Deere	Steel plow	Steel surface kept soil from sticking; farming thus made easier on rich prairies of Midwest
1839	Charles Goodyear	Vulcanization of rubber	Made rubber much more useful by preventing it from sticking and melting in hot weather
1842	Crawford W. Long	First administered ether in surgery	Reduced pain and risk of shock in surgery during operations
1844	Samuel F. B. Morse	Telegraph	Made long-distance communication almost instantaneous
1846	Elias Howe	Sewing machine	First practical machine for automatic sewing
1846	Norbert Rillieux	Vacuum evaporator	Improved method of removing water from sugar cane; revolutionized sugar industry and was later applied to many other products
1847	Richard M. Hoe	Rotary printing press	Printed an entire sheet in one motion; vastly speeded up printing process
1851	William Kelly	"Air-boiling process"	Improved method of converting iron into steel (usually known as Bessemer process because English inventor Bessemer had more advantageous patent and financial arrangements)
1853	Elisha G. Otis	Passenger elevator	Improved movement in buildings; when later electrified, stimulated development of skyscrapers
1859	Edwin L. Drake	First American oil well	Initiated oil industry in the United States
1859	George M. Pullman	Pullman car	First sleeping car suitable for long-distance travel

*Dates refer to patent or first successful use.

Source: From *Freedom and Crisis: An American History,* Third Edition, by Allen Weinstein and Frank Otto Gatell. Copyright © 1974, 1978, 1981 by Random House, Inc. Reprinted by permission of Random House, Inc.

the British practice of using coal rather than charcoal for smelting and thus produced a metal better suited to industrial needs. Charles Goodyear's discovery in 1839 of the process for the vulcanization of rubber made a new range of manufactured items available to the American consumer, most notably the overshoe.

Perhaps the greatest triumph of American technology during the mid-nineteenth century was the development of the world's most sophisticated and reliable machine tools. Such advances as the invention of the extraordinarily accurate measuring device known as the vernier caliper in 1851 and the first production of turret lathes in 1854 were signs of a special American aptitude for the kind of precision toolmaking that was essential to efficient industrialization.

Progress in industrial technology and organization did not mean the United States had become an industrial society by 1860. Factory workers remained a small fraction of the workforce, and agriculture retained first place both as a source of livelihood for individuals and as a contributor to the gross national product. But farming itself, at least in the North, was undergoing a technological revolution of its own. John Deere's steel plow, invented in 1837, enabled midwestern farmers to cultivate the tough prairie soils that had resisted cast-iron implements. The mechanical reaper, patented by Cyrus McCormick in 1834, offered an enormous saving in the labor required for harvesting grain. Other new farm implements that came into widespread use before 1860 included seed drills, cultivators, and threshing machines.

A dynamic interaction between advances in transportation, industry, and agriculture gave great strength and resiliency to the economy of the northern states during the 1850s. Railroads offered western farmers better access to eastern markets. After Chicago and New York were linked by rail in 1853, the flow of most midwestern farm commodities shifted from the north-south direction based on riverborne traffic, which had still predominated in the 1830s and 1840s, to an east-west pattern.

The mechanization of agriculture did more than lead to more efficient and profitable commercial farming; it also provided an additional impetus to industrialization, and its laborsaving features released workers for other economic activities. The growth of industry and the modernization of agriculture can thus be seen as mutually reinforcing aspects of a single process of economic growth.

MASS IMMIGRATION BEGINS

The original incentive to mechanize northern industry and agriculture came in part from a shortage of cheap labor. Compared with that of industrializing nations of Europe, the economy of the United States in the early nineteenth century was labor-scarce. Since it was difficult to attract able-bodied men to work for low wages in factories or on farms, women and children were used extensively in

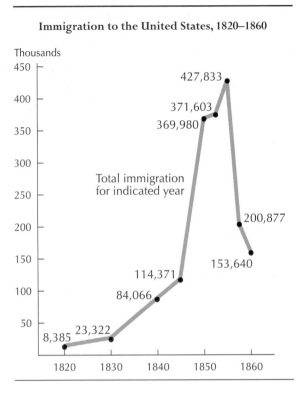

Immigration to the United States, 1820–1860

Thousands

427,833

371,603

369,980

Total immigration
for indicated year

200,877

114,371

153,640

84,066

8,385   23,322

1820   1830   1840   1850   1860

the early textile mills, and commercial farmers had to rely heavily on the labor of their family members. Labor-saving machinery eased but did not solve the labor shortage problem. Factories required increasing numbers of operatives, and railroad builders needed construction gangs. The growth of industrial work opportunities helped attract a multitude of European immigrants during the two decades before the Civil War.

Between 1820 and 1840, an estimated 700,000 immigrants arrived in the United States, mainly from the British Isles and German-speaking areas of continental Europe. During the 1840s, this substantial flow suddenly became a flood. No fewer than 4.2 million people crossed the Atlantic between 1840 and 1860, about 3 million of them coming in the single decade between 1845 and 1855. The largest single source of the new mass immigration was Ireland, but Germany was not far behind. Smaller contingents came from Switzerland, Norway, Sweden, and the Netherlands.

The massive transatlantic movement had many causes; some people were "pushed" out of their homes while others were "pulled" toward America. The great push factor that caused 1.5 million Irish to forsake the Emerald Isle between 1845

(a) Baron Biesele, upon his arrival in America (in German): "Hey, fellow countryman, where can we find a German tavern?" Countryman (in German): "Damme. Do you think I'm a no-good like you? I am an American."

(b) Baron Biesele, first week after arrival (in German): "Well, Marianel, how do you like it in America?" Marianel (in German): "Oh, Baron, the language, the language. I'll never learn it in all my life."

(c) Baron Biesele, two weeks after arrival (in German): "Can you tell us—Hey, beautiful Marianel, isn't that you?" Marianel (in English): "You are mistaken. I don't talk Dutch."

In this series of lithographs from an 1847 Cincinnati newspaper, two fellow Germans rebuff popular cartoon character Baron Biesele for not becoming an American.

and 1854 was the great potato blight, which brought famine to a population that subsisted on this single crop. Escape to America was made possible by the low fares then prevailing on sailing ships bound from England to North America. Ships involved in the timber trade carried their bulky cargoes from Boston or Halifax to Liverpool; as an alternative to returning to America partly in ballast, they packed Irish immigrants into their holds. The squalor and misery in these steerage accommodations were almost beyond belief.

The location of the ports involved in the lumber trade—Boston, Halifax, Saint John's, and Saint Andrews—meant that the Irish usually arrived in Canada or the northeastern states. Immobilized by poverty and a lack of the skills required for pioneering in the West, most of them remained in the Northeast. By the 1850s, they constituted a substantial portion of the total population of Boston, New York, Philadelphia, and many smaller cities of the New England and Middle Atlantic states. Forced to subsist on low-paid menial labor and crowded into festering urban slums, they were looked down on by most native-born Americans. Their devotion to Catholicism aroused Protestant resentment and mob violence.

The million or so Germans who also came in the late 1840s and early 1850s were somewhat more fortunate. Most of them were also peasants, but they had fled hard times rather than outright catastrophe. Those whose mortgages were foreclosed or who could no longer make regular payments to their landlords frequently opted for emigration to America. Unlike the Irish, they often escaped with a small amount of capital with which to make a fresh start in the New World.

Many German immigrants were artisans and sought to ply their trades in cities such as New York, St. Louis, Cincinnati, and Milwaukee—all of which became centers of German-American population. But a large portion of those with peasant backgrounds went back to the land. The possession of diversified agricultural skills and small amounts of capital enabled many Germans to become successful midwestern farmers. In general, they encountered less prejudice and discrimination than the Irish. For Germans who were Protestant, religious affinity with their American neighbors made for relative tolerance. But even Germans who were Catholic normally escaped the virulent scorn heaped on the Irish, perhaps because they were not so poverty stricken and did not carry the added burden of being members of an ethnic group Anglo-Americans had learned to despise from their English ancestors and cousins.

What attracted most of the Irish, German, and other European immigrants to America was the promise of economic opportunity. A minority, like some of the German revolutionaries of 1848, chose the United States because they admired its democratic political system. But most immigrants were more inter-

Hundreds of Irish immigrants crowded into the disease-ridden slums and shanties of places such as Boston's Burgess Alley. The illustration of the deplorable living quarters of the city's immigrants is from the Report of the Committee on Internal Health on the Asiatic Cholera, issued in 1849.

ested in the chance to make a decent living than in voting or running for office. Peak periods of immigration—1845 to 1854 is a prime example—coincided very closely with times of domestic prosperity and high demand for labor. During depressed periods immigration dropped off significantly.

The arrival of large numbers of immigrants exacerbated the already serious problems of America's rapidly growing cities. The old "walking city" in which rich and poor lived in close proximity near the center of town was changing to a more segregated environment. The advent of railroads and horse-drawn streetcars enabled the affluent to move to the first American suburbs, while areas nearer commercial and industrial centers became the congested abode of newcomers from Europe. Emerging slums, such as the notorious Five Points district in New York City, were characterized by overcrowding, poverty, disease, and crime. Recognizing that these conditions created potential dangers for the entire urban population, middle-class reformers worked for the professionalization of police forces, introduction of sanitary water and sewage disposal systems, and the upgrading of housing standards.

They made some progress in these endeavors in the period before the Civil War, but the lot of the urban poor, mainly immigrants, was not dramatically improved. For the most of them, life remained unsafe, unhealthy, and unpleasant.

Despite the increasing segregation of the city into ethnic neighborhoods, the urban experience also produced a unifying effect on its mixed population.

Individuals of all classes, occupations, and ethnicities met on the crowded streets and in the public squares of cities such as Boston and New York. Often, the entire population—or at least wide cross sections—came together in colorful parades, public celebrations, and political contests. Antebellum cities showed the dark side of urbanization in their crowded slums and growing poverty, but they also became cauldrons of democracy in which different elements of nineteenth-century America met face-to-face to create a wider definition of what it meant to be an American.

THE NEW WORKING CLASS

A majority of immigrants ended up as wage workers in factories, mines, and construction camps or as casual day laborers doing the many unskilled tasks required for urban and commercial growth. By providing a vast pool of cheap labor, they fueled and accelerated the Industrial Revolution.

In established industries and older mill towns of the Northeast, immigrants gradually displaced the native-born workers who had predominated in the 1830s and 1840s. In the New England textile mills especially, immigrant male laborers increasingly replaced the native female workforce. Irish males, employers found, were willing to perform tasks that native-born men had generally regarded as women's work.

This trend reveals much about the changing character of the American working class. In the 1830s, most male workers were artisans, and factory work was still largely the province of women and children. In the 1840s, the proportion of men engaged in factory work increased, although the workforce in the textile industry remained predominantly female. During that decade, work conditions in many mills deteriorated. Workdays as long as twelve to fourteen hours continued, while managers became more impersonal and concerned with cost cutting. During the depression that followed the Panic of 1837, bosses attempted to reduce expenses and increase productivity by cutting wages, increasing the speed of machinery, and "stretching out"—giving each worker more machinery to operate.

The result was a new upsurge of labor militancy involving female as well as male factory workers. Mill girls in Lowell, for example, formed a union of their own—the Female Labor Reform Association—and agitated for shorter working hours. On a broader front, workers' organizations petitioned state legislatures to pass laws limiting the workday to ten hours. Some such laws were actually passed, but they turned out to be ineffective because employers could still require a prospective worker to sign a special contract agreeing to longer hours.

The employment of immigrants in increasing numbers between the mid-1840s and the late 1850s made it more difficult to organize industrial workers.

Impoverished fugitives from the Irish potato famine tended to have lower economic expectations and more conservative social attitudes than did native-born workers. Consequently, the Irish immigrants were initially willing to work for less and were not so prone to protest bad working conditions.

But the new working class of former rural folk did not make the transition to industrial wage labor easily or without protesting in subtle and indirect ways. Tardiness, absenteeism, drunkenness, loafing on the job, and other forms of resistance to factory discipline reflected deep hostility to the unaccustomed and seemingly unnatural routines of industrial production. The adjustment to new styles and rhythms of work was painful and took time.

By 1860, industrial expansion and immigration had created a working class of men and women who seemed destined for a life of low-paid wage labor. This reality stood in contrast to America's self-image as a land of opportunity and upward mobility. This ideal still had some validity in rapidly developing regions of the western states, but it was mostly myth when applied to the increasingly foreign-born industrial workers of the Northeast.

Both internal and external expansion had come at a heavy cost. Tensions associated with class and ethnic rivalries were only one part of the price of rapid economic development. The acquisition of new territories became politically divisive and would soon lead to a catastrophic sectional controversy. In the late 1840s and early 1850s Democratic Senator Stephen A. Douglas of Illinois (called the Little Giant because of his small stature and large public presence) sought political power for himself and his party by combining an expansionist foreign policy with the encouragement of economic development within the territories already acquired. Recognizing that the slavery question was the main obstacle to his program, he sought to neutralize it through compromise and evasion. His failure to win the presidency or even the Democratic nomination before 1860 showed that the dream of a patriotic consensus supporting headlong expansion and economic development could not withstand the tensions and divisions that expansionist policies created or brought to light.

13

MASTERS AND SLAVES

On August 22, 1831, the worst nightmare of southern slaveholders became reality. A group of slaves in Southampton County, Virginia, rose in open and bloody rebellion. Their leader was Nat Turner, a preacher and prophet who believed God had given him a sign that the time was ripe to strike for freedom; a vision of black and white angels wrestling in the sky had convinced him that divine wrath was about to be visited upon the white oppressor.

Beginning with a few followers and rallying others as he went along, Turner led his band from plantation to plantation and oversaw the killing of nearly sixty whites. The rebellion was short-lived; after only forty-eight hours, white forces dispersed the rampaging slaves. The rebels were then rounded up and executed, along with dozens of other slaves who were vaguely suspected of complicity. Nat Turner was the last to be captured, and he went to the gallows unrepentant, convinced he had acted in accordance with God's will.

White Southerners were determined to prevent another such uprising. Their anxiety and resolve were strengthened by the fact that a more militant northern abolitionism began to emerge in 1831. Nat Turner and William Lloyd Garrison were viewed as two prongs of a revolutionary attack on the southern way of life. Although no evidence came to light that Turner was directly influenced by abolitionist propaganda, many whites believed that he must have been or that future rebels might be. Consequently, they launched a massive campaign to quarantine the slaves from possible exposure to antislavery ideas and attitudes.

A series of new laws severely restricted the rights of slaves to move about, assemble without white supervision, or learn to read and write. Other laws and the threat of mob action prevented white dissenters from publicly criticizing or even questioning the institution of slavery. The South rapidly became a closed society with a closed mind. Proslavery agitators sought to create a mood of crisis and danger requiring absolute unity and single-mindedness among the white population. This embattled attitude lay behind the growth of a more militant sectionalism and inspired threats to secede from the Union unless the South's peculiar institution could be made safe from northern or abolitionist attack.

The campaign for repression apparently achieved its original aim. Between 1831 and the Civil War, there were no further uprisings resulting in the mass killing of whites. But resistance to slavery did not end; rather it took less dangerous forms than open revolt. The response to Turner's rebellion provided slaves with a more realistic sense of the odds against direct confrontation with white power. As a result, they sought and perfected other methods of asserting their humanity and maintaining their self-esteem. The heroic effort to endure slavery without surrendering to it gave rise to an African American culture of lasting value.

SLAVERY AND THE SOUTHERN ECONOMY

Slavery would not have lasted as long as it did—and Southerners would not have reacted so strongly to real or imagined threats to its survival—if an influential class of whites had not had a vital and growing economic interest in this form of human exploitation. Since the early colonial period, forced labor had been considered essential to the South's plantation economy. In the period between the 1790s and the Civil War, plantation agriculture expanded enormously, and so did dependence on slave labor.

By the time of the Civil War, 90 percent of the South's four million slaves worked on plantations and farms. In the seven cotton-producing states of the lower South—South Carolina, Georgia, Alabama, Mississippi, Louisiana, Arkansas, and Texas—slaves constituted close to half of the total population and were responsible for producing 90 percent of the cotton and almost all of the rice and sugar. In the upper South—North Carolina, Virginia, Maryland, Delaware, Kentucky, Tennessee, and Missouri—whites outnumbered slaves by more than three to one and were less dependent on their labor. To understand southern thought and behavior, it is necessary to bear in mind these major differences between the Cotton Kingdom with its entrenched one-crop plantation system and

This artist's depiction of Nat Turner with some of his confederates captures the fears of many whites of the dire consequences that might result when slaves met outside the supervision of their masters.

the upper South, which was actually moving away from this pattern during the pre–Civil War period.

ECONOMIC ADJUSTMENT IN THE UPPER SOUTH

Tobacco, the original plantation crop of the colonial period, continued to be the principal slave-cultivated commodity of the upper South during the pre–Civil War era. But markets were often depressed, and profitable tobacco cultivation was hard to sustain for very long in one place because the crop rapidly depleted the soil. As a result, there were continual shifts in the areas of greatest production and much experimentation with new crops and methods of farming. The heart of tobacco cultivation moved westward; by 1860, Kentucky had emerged as a major producer.

During the lengthy depression of the tobacco market that lasted from the 1820s to the 1850s, agricultural experimentation was widespread in Virginia and Maryland. Increased use of fertilizer, systematic rotation of tobacco with other crops, and the growth of diversified farming based on a mix of wheat, corn, and livestock helped revive agriculture. Such changes increased the need for capital but reduced the demand for labor. Improvements were financed in part by selling surplus slaves from the upper South to the lower South, where staple crop production was more profitable. The interstate slave trade, which sent an estimated six to seven hundred thousand slaves in a southwesterly direction between 1815 and 1860, was thus a godsend to the slaveowners of the upper South and a key to their survival and returning prosperity.

Although respectable planters did not like to think of themselves as raising slaves for market, few would refuse to sell some of their "people" if they needed money to get out of debt or make expensive improvements. The economic effect was clear: the natural increase of their slaves beyond what the planters needed for their operations provided them with a crucial source of capital and, as a result, encouraged the export of surplus slaves from the upper South to the Deep South.

The fact that slave labor was declining in importance in the upper South meant the peculiar institution had a weaker hold on public loyalty there than in the cotton states. Diversification of agriculture was accompanied by a more rapid rate of urban and industrial development than was occurring elsewhere in the South. As a result, Virginians, Marylanders, and Kentuckians were seriously divided on whether their ultimate future lay with the Deep South's plantation economy or with the industrializing free-labor system that was flourishing just north of their borders.

THE RISE OF THE COTTON KINGDOM

The warmer climate and good soils of the lower South made it possible to raise crops more naturally suited than tobacco or cereals to the plantation form of agriculture and the heavy use of slave labor. Since the colonial or revolutionary periods, rice and a special long-staple variety of fine cotton had been grown profitably on vast estates along the coast of South Carolina and Georgia. In lower Louisiana, between New Orleans and Baton Rouge, sugar was the cash crop, and it too required large, well-financed plantations and small armies of slave laborers. Cultivation of rice, long-staple cotton, and sugar was limited by natural conditions to peripheral, semitropical areas. It was the rise of short-staple cotton as the South's major crop that strengthened the hold of slavery and the plantation on the southern economy.

Short-staple cotton differed from the long-staple variety in two important ways: its bolls contained seeds that were much more difficult to extract by hand, and it could be grown almost anywhere south of Virginia and Kentucky—the main requirement was a guarantee of two hundred frost-free days. The invention of the cotton gin in 1793 solved the seed extraction problem and opened vast areas for cotton cultivation. Unlike rice and sugar, cotton could be grown on small farms as well as on plantations. But large planters enjoyed certain advantages that made them the main producers. Only relatively large operators could afford their own gins or possessed the capital to acquire the fertile bottomlands that brought the highest yields. They also had lower transportation costs because they were

Although cotton cultivation required constant attention, many of the tasks involved were relatively simple. Thus on a plantation the majority of slaves were field hands who performed the same tasks. Here field laborers—men and women alike—line up for their return from the field, carrying on their heads the day's load of cotton for weighing.

able to monopolize land along rivers and streams that were the South's natural arteries of transportation.

Cotton was well suited to a plantation form of production. Required tasks were relatively simple and could be performed by supervised gangs of unfree workers. Furthermore, there was enough work to be done in all seasons to keep the force occupied throughout the year. Cotton required constant weeding or "chopping" during the growing season and then could be picked over an extended period. The relative absence of seasonal variations in work needs made the use of slave laborers advantageous.

The first major cotton-producing regions were inland areas of Georgia and South Carolina , but the center of production shifted rapidly westward during the nineteenth century, first to Alabama and Mississippi and then to Arkansas, northwest Louisiana, and east Texas. The rise in total production that accompanied this geographic expansion was phenomenal. In 1792, the South's output of cotton was about 13,000 bales; by 1840, it was 1.35 million; nine years later, it had risen to 2.85 million; and in 1860, production peaked at the colossal figure of 4.8 million bales. Most of the cotton went to supply the booming textile industry of Great Britain.

"Cotton is king!" proclaimed a southern orator in the 1850s, and he was right. By that time, three-quarters of the world's supply of cotton came from the

American South, and this single commodity accounted for more than half the total dollar value of American exports. Cotton growing and the network of commercial and industrial enterprises that marketed and processed the crop constituted the most important economic interest in the United States on the eve of the Civil War. Since slavery and cotton seemed inextricably linked, it appeared obvious to many Southerners that their peculiar institution was the keystone of national wealth and economic progress.

Despite its overall success, however, the rise of the Cotton Kingdom did not bring a uniform or steady prosperity to the lower South. Many planters worked the land until it was exhausted and then took their slaves westward to richer soils, leaving depressed and ravaged areas in their wake.

Fluctuations in markets and prices also ruined many planters. Widespread depressions, including a wave of bankruptcies, followed the boom periods of 1815–1819, 1832–1837, and 1849–1860. But during the eleven years of rising output and high prices preceding the Civil War, planters gradually forgot their earlier troubles and began to imagine they were immune to future economic disasters.

Despite the insecurities associated with its cultivation, cotton represented the Old South's best chance for profitable investment. Prudent planters who had not borrowed too heavily during flush times could survive periods of depression by cutting costs, making their plantations self-sufficient by shifting acreage away from cotton and planting subsistence crops. Those with worn-out land could sell their land and move west, or they could sell their slaves to raise capital for fertilization, crop rotation, and other improvements that could help them survive where they were. Hence planters had little incentive to seek alternatives to slavery, the plantation, and dependence on a single cash crop. From a purely economic point of view, they had every reason to defend slavery and to insist on their right to expand it.

SLAVERY AND INDUSTRIALIZATION

As the sectional quarrel with the North intensified, Southerners became increasingly alarmed by their region's lack of economic self-sufficiency. Dependence on the North for capital, marketing facilities, and manufactured goods was seen as evidence of a dangerous subservience to "external" economic interests. Southern nationalists such as J. D. B. DeBow, editor of the influential *DeBow's Review,* called during the 1850s for the South to develop its own industries, commerce, and shipping. A fervent defender of slavery, DeBow saw no reason why slaves could not be used as the main workforce in an industrial revolution. But his call for a diversified economy went unanswered. Men with capital were doing too well in plantation agriculture to risk their money in other ventures.

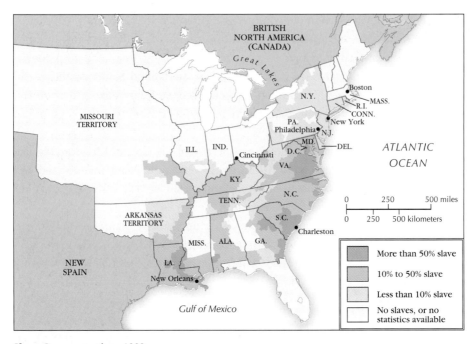

Slave Concentration, 1820

In 1820, most slaves lived in the eastern seaboard states of Virginia and South Carolina and in Louisiana on the Gulf of Mexico.

In the 1840s and 1850s, a debate raged among white capitalists over whether the South should use free whites or enslaved blacks as the labor supply for industry. William Gregg of South Carolina, the foremost promoter of cotton mills in the Old South, defended a white labor policy, arguing that factory work would provide new economic opportunities for a degraded class of poor whites. But other advocates of industrialization feared that the growth of a free working class would lead to social conflict among whites and preferred using slaves for all supervised manual labor. In fact, a minority of slaves—about 5 percent during the 1850s—were employed in industrial tasks. Besides providing most of the labor for mining, lumbering, and constructing roads, canals, and railroads, slaves also worked in cotton mills and tobacco factories. Some factories employed slaves, others white workers, and a few even experimented with integrated workforces.

It is clear, however, that the union of slavery and cotton that was central to the South's prosperity impeded industrialization and left the region dependent on a one-crop agriculture and on the North for capital and marketing. Slaves were the only available workers who could be employed on plantations; rural whites refused to work for low wages when they had the alternative of subsistence farming on marginal lands in the southern backcountry. Industry was con-

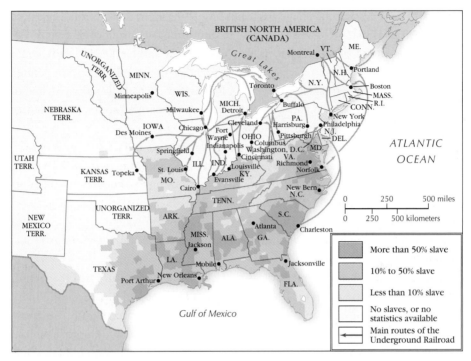

Slave Concentration, 1860

In 1860, slavery had extended throughout the southern states, with the greatest concentrations of slaves in the states of the Deep South. There were also sizable slave populations in the new states of Missouri, Arkansas, Texas, and Florida.

centrated in towns and cities where white labor was more readily available. So long as plantations yielded substantial profits, there could be no major movement of slaves from agriculture to industry. If anything, the trend was in the opposite direction.

THE "PROFITABILITY" ISSUE

Some Southerners were making money, and a great deal of it, using slave labor to raise cotton. But did slavery yield a good return for the great majority of slave-holders who were not large planters? Did it provide the basis for general prosperity and a relatively high standard of living for the southern population in general, or at least for the two-thirds of it who were white and free? These questions have been hotly debated by economic historians. Some knowledge of the main arguments regarding its "profitability" is helpful to an understanding of the South's attachment to slavery.

For many years historians believed that slave-based agriculture was, on the average, not very lucrative. Planters' account books seemed to show at best a modest return on investment. In the 1850s, the price of slaves rose at a faster rate than the price of cotton, allegedly squeezing many operators. Some historians even concluded that slavery was a dying institution by the time of the Civil War. Profitability, they argued, depended on access to new and fertile land suitable for plantation agriculture, and virtually all such land within the limits of the United States had already been taken up by 1860. Hence slavery had allegedly reached its natural limits of expansion and was on the verge of becoming so unprofitable that it would fall of its own weight in the near future.

A more recent interpretation holds that slavery was in fact still an economically sound institution in 1860 and showed no signs of imminent decline. A reexamination of planters' records using modern accounting methods shows that during the 1850s, planters could normally expect an annual return of 8 to 10 percent on capital invested. This yield was roughly equivalent to the best that could then be obtained from the most lucrative sectors of northern industry and commerce.

Furthermore, it is no longer clear that plantation agriculture had reached its natural limits of expansion by 1860. Production in Texas had not yet peaked, and construction of railroads and levees was opening up new areas for cotton growing elsewhere in the South. With the advantage of hindsight, economic historians have pointed out that improvements in transportation and flood control would enable the post–Civil War South to double its cotton acreage. Those who now argue that slavery was profitable and had an expansive future have made a strong and convincing case.

But the larger question remains: What sort of economic development did a slave plantation system foster? The system may have made slaveholders wealthy, but did the benefits trickle down to the rest of the population—to the majority of whites who owned no slaves and to the slaves themselves? Did it promote efficiency and progressive change? Economists Robert Fogel and Stanley Engerman have argued that the plantation's success was due to an internally efficient enterprise with good managers and industrious, well-motivated workers. Other economic historians have attributed the profitability almost exclusively to favorable market conditions.

In any case, only large plantation owners profited substantially. Because of various insecurities—lack of credit, high transportation costs, and a greater vulnerability to market fluctuations—small slaveholders and nonslaveholders had to devote a larger share of their acreage to subsistence crops, especially corn and hogs, than did the planters. They were thus able to survive, but their standard of living was lower than that of most northern farmers. Slaves received sufficient food, clothing, and shelter for their subsistence and to make them capable of working well enough to keep the plantation afloat economically, but their living standard was below that of the poorest free people in the United States. It was proslavery propaganda, rather than documented fact, to maintain that slaves were better off than northern wage laborers.

The South's economic development was skewed in favor of a single route to wealth, open only to the minority possessing both a white skin and access to capital. The concentration of capital and business energies on cotton production foreclosed the kind of diversified industrial and commercial growth that would have provided wider opportunities. Thus, in comparison to the industrializing North, the South was an underdeveloped region in which much of the population had little incentive to work hard. A lack of public education for whites and the denial of even minimal literacy to slaves represented a critical failure to develop human resources. The South's economy was probably condemned to backwardness so long as it was based on slavery.

THE SLAVEHOLDING SOCIETY

If the precise effect of slavery on the South's economic life remains debatable, there is less room for disagreement concerning its impact on social arrangements and attitudes. More than any other factor, the ownership of slaves determined gradations of social prestige and influence among whites. The large planters were the dominant class, and nonslaveholders were of lower social rank. But the fact that all whites were free and most blacks were slaves made it seem that all white Americans enjoyed a basic equality. Inequality in the Old South was determined in two ways: by *class* (differences in status resulting from unequal access to wealth and productive resources) and by *caste* (inherited advantages or disadvantages associated with racial ancestry). Awareness of both systems of social ranking is necessary for an understanding of southern society.

THE PLANTERS' WORLD

Those who know the Old South only from modern novels, films, and television programs are likely to envision a land filled with majestic plantations, where courtly gentlemen and elegant ladies are attended by hordes of uniformed black servants. It is easy to conclude from such images that the typical white Southerner was an aristocrat who belonged to a family that owned large numbers of slaves. Certainly, the great houses existed and some wealthy slaveholders did maintain as aristocratic a lifestyle as was ever seen in the United States. But this was the world of only a small percentage of slaveowners and a minuscule portion of the total white population.

In 1860, only 25 percent of all white Southerners belonged to families owning slaves. Even in the cotton belt of the Deep South, slaveholders were a minority of whites—about 40 percent. Planters, defined as agriculturists owning twenty or more slaves, were the minority of a minority. In 1860, planters and their families constituted about 12 percent of all slaveholders and less than 4 percent of the total white population of the South. Even the master of twenty to fifty slaves could rarely live up to the popular image of aristocratic grandeur. To maintain this lifestyle, a planter had to own at least fifty slaves. In 1860, these substantial planters comprised fewer than 3 percent of all slaveholders and fewer than 1 percent of all whites.

Although few in numbers, the great planters set the tone and values for much of the rest of society. Although many of them were too busy tending to their plantations to become openly involved in politics, wealthy planters held more than their share of high offices and often exerted a decisive influence on public policy. In regions where plantation agriculture predominated, they were a ruling class in every sense of the term.

Contrary to legend, a majority of the great planters of the pre–Civil War period were self-made rather than descendants of the old colonial gentry. Some were ambitious young men who married planters' daughters. Others started as lawyers and used their fees and connections to acquire plantations.

As the Cotton Kingdom spread westward, the men who became the largest slaveholders were less and less likely to have come from old and well-established planter families. A large proportion of them began as hard-driving businessmen who built up capital from commerce, land speculation, banking, and even slave trading. They then used their profits to buy plantations. The highly competitive, boom-or-bust economy of the western Gulf states put a greater premium on sharp dealing and business skills than on genealogy.

To be successful, a planter had to be a shrewd entrepreneur who kept a careful eye on the market, the prices of slaves and land, and the extent of his indebtedness. Reliable "factors"—agents who marketed the crop and provided advances against future sales—could assist him in making decisions, but a planter who failed to spend a good deal of time with his account books could end up in serious trouble. Managing the slaves and plantation production was also difficult and time-consuming, even when overseers were available to supervise day-to-day activities. Hence few planters could be the men of leisure featured in the popular image of the Old South. Likewise, the responsibility of running an extended household that produced much of its own food and clothing kept plantation mistresses from being the idle ladies of legend.

Some of the richest and most secure plantation families did aspire to live in the manner of a traditional landed aristocracy. Big houses, elegant carriages, fancy-dress balls, and excessive numbers of house servants all reflected aristocratic aspirations. The romantic cult of chivalry was in vogue in some circles and even led to the nonviolent reenactment of medieval tournaments. Dueling, despite efforts to repress it, remained the standard way to settle "affairs of honor" among gentlemen. Another sign of gentility was the tendency of planters' sons to avoid "trade" as a primary or secondary career in favor of law or the military. Planters' daughters were trained from girlhood to play the piano, speak French, dress in the latest fashions, and sparkle in the drawing room or on the dance floor. The aristocratic style originated among the older gentry of the seaboard slave states, but by the 1840s and 1850s it had spread southwest as a second generation of wealthy planters began to displace the rough-hewn pioneers of the Cotton Kingdom.

PLANTERS AND SLAVES

No assessment of the planters' outlook or "worldview" can be made without considering their relations with their slaves. Planters owned more than half of all the slaves in the South and set standards for treatment and management. Most planters liked to think of themselves as kindly and paternalistic. Often they referred to their slaves as if they were members of an extended patriarchal family—a favorite phrase was "our people." Blacks in general were described as a

These slave cabins on a prosperous plantation were small and crude but still were better than many that had only a doorway leading into a dirt-floored hovel.

Not all slaves and masters had the benevolent relationship cited in defense of slavery. In fact, masters devised various instruments of torture and punishment to control their slaves. For example, a slave fitted with this belled slave collar could not make a move without alerting the master.

race of perpetual children requiring constant care and supervision by superior whites. Paternalistic rhetoric increased greatly after abolitionists began to charge that most slaveholders were sadistic monsters. To some extent, the planters' response was part of a defensive effort to redeem the South's reputation and self-respect.

There was, nevertheless, a grain of truth in the planters' claim that their slaves were relatively well provided for. Recent comparative studies have suggested that North American slaves of the pre–Civil War period enjoyed a somewhat higher standard of living than those in other New World slave societies. Their food, clothing, and shelter were normally sufficient to sustain life and labor at slightly above a bare subsistence level, and the rapid increase of the slave population in the Old South stands in sharp contrast to the usual failure of slave populations to reproduce themselves.

The concern of many planters for their slaves' health and nutrition does not prove they put ethical considerations ahead of self-interest. The ban on the transatlantic slave trade in 1808 made domestic reproduction of the slave force an economic necessity if slavery was to continue. Rising slave prices inhibited extreme physical abuse and deprivation. Slaves were valuable property and the main tools of production for a booming economy, and it was in the interest of masters to see that their property remained in good enough condition to work hard and produce large numbers of children. Furthermore, a good return on their investment enabled southern planters to spend more on slave maintenance than could masters in less prosperous plantation economies. But some planters failed to control their tempers or tried to work more slaves than they could afford to maintain. Consequently, there were more cases of physical abuse and undernourishment than a purely economic calculation would lead us to expect.

The testimony of slaves themselves and of some independent white observers suggests that masters of large plantations generally did not have close and intimate relationships with the mass of field slaves. The paternalistic relationship appears to have been limited mainly to a few favored house servants or other elite slaves, such as drivers and highly skilled artisans. Field hands on large estates dealt mostly with overseers who were hired or fired on their ability to meet production quotas.

When they were being most realistic, planters conceded that the ultimate basis of their authority was the slaves' fear of force and intimidation. Scattered among their statements are admissions that they relied on the "principle of fear," "more and more on the power of fear," or—most graphically—that it was necessary "to make them stand in fear." Devices for inspiring fear including whipping—a common practice on most plantations—and the threat of sale away from family and friends. Planters and overseers maintained order and productivity by meting out swift punishment for any infraction of the rules or even for a surly attitude.

Slaves had little recourse for protection against abuse from masters. Slaves lacked legal protection because their testimony was not accepted in court. Abolitionists condemned slavery because it gave one human being nearly absolute power over another. Human nature being what it is, such a situation was bound to result in atrocities. Even Harriet Beecher Stowe acknowledged in *Uncle Tom's Cabin*, her celebrated antislavery novel of 1852, that most slaveholders were not as sadistic and brutish as Simon Legree. But—and this was her real point—there was something terribly wrong with an institution that made a Simon Legree possible.

THE WORLD OF THE PLAIN FOLK

As we have seen, 88 percent of all slaveholders in 1860 owned fewer than twenty slaves and thus were not planters in the usual sense of the term. Of these, the great majority had fewer than ten. Some of the small slaveholders were urban merchants or professional men who needed slaves only for domestic service, but more typical were farmers who used one or two slave families to ease the burden of their own labor. Life on these small slaveholding farms was relatively spartan. Masters lived in log cabins or small frame cottages, and slaves lived in lofts or sheds that were not usually up to plantation housing standards.

For better or worse, relations between owners and their slaves were more intimate than on larger estates. Unlike planters, these farmers often worked in the fields alongside their slaves and sometimes ate at the same table or slept under the same roof. But such closeness did not necessarily result in better treatment. Both the best and the worst of slavery could be found on these farms, depending on the character and disposition of the master. Given a choice, most slaves preferred to live on plantations because they offered the sociability, culture, and kinship of the slave quarters, as well as better prospects for adequate food, clothing, and shelter.

Just below the small slaveholders on the social scale was a substantial class of yeoman farmers who owned land they worked themselves. Contrary to another myth about the Old South, most of these people did not fit the image of the degraded, shiftless poor white. The majority of the nonslaveholding rural population were proud, self-reliant farmers whose way of life did not differ markedly from that of family farmers in the Midwest during the early stages of settlement. If they were disadvantaged in comparison with farmers elsewhere in the United States, it was because the lack of economic development and urban growth perpetuated frontier conditions and denied them the opportunity to produce a substantial surplus for market.

The yeomen were mostly concentrated in the backcountry where slaves and plantations were rarely seen. The foothills or interior valleys of the Appalachians and the Ozarks were unsuitable for plantation agriculture but offered reasonably good soils for mixed farming, and long stretches of piney barrens along the Gulf Coast were suitable for raising livestock. In such regions slaveless farmers concentrated, giving rise to the "white counties" that complicated southern politics. A somewhat distinct group were the genuine mountaineers, who lived too high up to succeed at farming and relied heavily on hunting, lumbering, and distilling whiskey.

The lack of transportation facilities limited the prosperity of the yeomen. A large part of their effort was devoted to growing subsistence crops, mainly corn. They raised a small percentage of the South's cotton and tobacco, but the difficulty of marketing severely limited production. Their main source of cash was livestock, especially hogs, which could be walked to market over long distances. But since southern livestock was generally allowed to forage in the woods rather than being fattened on grain, it was of poor quality and did not bring high prices or big profits to raisers.

Although they did not benefit directly from the peculiar institution, most yeomen and other nonslaveholders tolerated slavery and opposed abolitionism in any form. A few antislavery Southerners, most notably Hinton R. Helper of North Carolina, tried to convince the yeomen that slavery and the plantation system created a privileged class and circumscribed the economic opportunities of the nonslaveholding white majority.

Most yeomen were staunch Jacksonians who resented aristocratic preten-sions and feared concentrations of power and wealth in the hands of the few. In state and local politics, they sometimes voted against planter interests on issues involving representation, banking, and internal improvements. Why, then, did they fail to respond to antislavery appeals that called on them to strike at the real source of planter power and privilege?

One reason was that some nonslaveholders hoped to get ahead in the world, and in the South this meant acquiring slaves of their own. Just enough of the more prosperous yeomen broke into the slaveholding classes to make this dream seem believable. Planters, anxious to ensure the loyalty of nonslaveholders, strenuously encouraged the notion that every white man was a potential master.

Even if they did not aspire to own slaves, white farmers often viewed black servitude as a guarantee of their own liberty and independence. A society that gave them the right to vote and the chance to be self-sufficient on land of their own encouraged the feeling they were fundamentally equal to the largest slave-holders. Although they had no natural love of planters and slavery, they be-lieved—or could be induced to believe—that abolition would threaten their lib-erty and independence. In part, their anxieties were economic; freed slaves would compete with them for land or jobs. But an intense racism deepened their fears and made their opposition to black freedom implacable. Emancipation was unthinkable because it would remove the pride and status that automatically went along with a white skin in this acutely race-conscious society. Slavery, despite its drawbacks, served to keep blacks "in their place" and to make all whites, however poor and uneducated they might be, feel they were free and equal members of a master race.

A Closed Mind and a Closed Society

Despite the tacit assent of most nonslaveholders, large planters never lost their fear that lower-class whites would turn against slavery. They felt threatened from two sides: from the slave quarters where a new Nat Turner might be gathering his forces, and from the backcountry where yeomen and poor whites might heed the call of abolitionists and rise up against planter domination. Beginning in the 1830s, the ruling elites used their control of government and communications to create a mood of impending catastrophe designed to ensure that all southern whites were of a single mind on the slavery issue.

Before the 1830s, open discussion of the rights or wrongs of slavery had been possible in many parts of the South. Apologists commonly described the institu-tion as "a necessary evil." In the upper South, as late as the 1820s, there had been significant support for the American Colonization Society program of gradual voluntary emancipation and deportation of the freedmen. In 1831 and 1832, the

Virginia state legislature debated a gradual emancipation plan. But the proposal went down to defeat as the argument that slavery was "a positive good"—rather than an evil slated for gradual elimination—won the day.

The "positive good" defense of slavery was an answer to the abolitionist charge that the institution was inherently sinful. The message was carried in a host of books, pamphlets, and newspaper editorials published between the 1830s and the Civil War. Who, historians have asked, was it meant to persuade? Partly, the argument was aimed at the North, as a way of bolstering the strong current of antiabolitionist sentiment. But Southerners themselves were a prime target; the message was clearly calculated to resolve doubts and misgivings about slavery and to arouse racial anxieties that tended to neutralize antislavery sentiment among the lower classes.

The proslavery argument was based on three main propositions. The first and foremost was that enslavement was the natural and proper status for people of African descent. Blacks, it was alleged, were innately inferior to whites and suited only for slavery. Biased scientific and historical evidence was presented to support this claim. Secondly, slavery was held to be sanctioned by the Bible and Christianity—a position made necessary by the abolitionist appeal to Christian

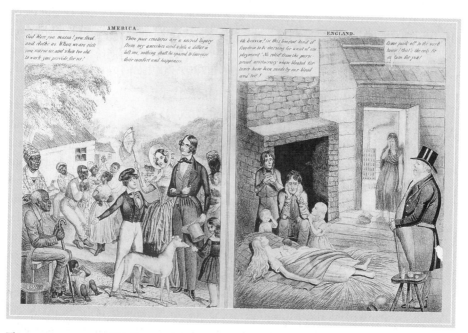

This proslavery cartoon of 1841 contends that the slave in America had a better life than did the working-class white in England. Supposedly, the grateful slaves were clothed, fed, and cared for in their old age by kindly and sympathetic masters, while starving English workers were mercilessly exploited by factory owners.

ethics. Ancient Hebrew slavery was held up as a divinely sanctioned model, and Saint Paul was quoted endlessly on the duty of servants to obey their masters.

Finally, efforts were made to show that slavery was consistent with the humanitarian spirit of the nineteenth century. The premise that blacks were naturally dependent and incapable of caring for themselves led to the notion that they needed some kind of special protective environment. The plantation was viewed as a sort of asylum, where benevolent masters guided and ruled this race of "perpetual children."

By the 1850s, the proslavery argument had gone beyond mere apology for the South and its peculiar institution and featured an ingenious attack on the free-labor system of the North. According to Virginian George Fitzhugh, the master-slave relationship was more humane than the one prevailing between employers and wage laborers in the North. Slaves had security against unemployment and a guarantee of care in old age, whereas free workers might face destitution and even starvation at any time.

In addition to arguing against the abolitionists, proslavery Southerners attempted to seal off their region from antislavery ideas and influences. Whites who criticized slavery publicly were mobbed or persecuted. One of the last and bravest of the southern abolitionists, Cassius M. Clay of Kentucky, armed himself with a brace of pistols when he gave speeches, until the threat of mob violence finally forced him across the Ohio. Clergymen who questioned the morality of slavery were driven from their pulpits, and northern travelers suspected of being abolitionist agents were tarred and feathered. When abolitionists tried to send their literature through the mails during the 1830s, it was seized in southern post offices and publicly burned.

Such flagrant denials of free speech and civil liberties were inspired in part by fears that nonslaveholding whites and slaves would get subversive ideas about slavery. Hinton R. Helper's book *The Impending Crisis of the South,* an 1857 appeal to nonslaveholders to resist the planter regime, was suppressed with particular vigor; those found with copies were beaten up or even lynched. But the deepest fear was that slaves would hear the abolitionist talk or read antislavery literature and be inspired to rebel. Consequently, new laws were passed making it a crime to teach slaves to read and write. Other repressive legislation aimed at slaves banned meetings unless a white man was present, severely restricted the activities of black preachers, and suppressed independent black churches. Free blacks, thought to be possible instigators of slave revolt, were denied basic civil liberties and were the object of growing surveillance and harassment.

All these efforts at thought control and internal security did not allay planters' fears of abolitionist subversion, lower-class white dissent, and, above all, slave revolt. The persistent barrage of proslavery propaganda and the course of national events in the 1850s created a mood of panic and desperation. By this time, an increasing number of Southerners had become convinced that safety from abolitionism and its associated terrors required a formal withdrawal from the Union—secession.

THE BLACK EXPERIENCE UNDER SLAVERY

Most African Americans of the early to mid-nineteenth century experienced slavery on plantations; the majority of slaves lived on units owned by planters who had twenty or more slaves. The masters of these agrarian communities sought to ensure their personal safety and the profitability of their enterprises by using all the means—physical and psychological—at their command to make slaves docile and obedient. By word and deed, they tried to convince the slaves that whites were superior and had a right to rule over blacks. Masters also drew constant attention to their awesome power and ability to deal harshly with rebels and malcontents. As increasing numbers of slaves were converted to Christianity and attended white-supervised services, they were forced to hear, over and over again, that God had commanded slaves to serve and obey their masters.

It is a great tribute to the resourcefulness and spirit of African Americans that most of them resisted these pressures and managed to retain an inner sense of their own worth and dignity. When conditions were right, they openly asserted their desire for freedom and equality and showed their disdain for white claims that slavery was a positive good. But the struggle for freedom involved more than the confrontation between master and slave; free blacks, in both the North and the South, did what they could to speed the day when all African Americans would be free.

FORMS OF SLAVE RESISTANCE

Open rebellion, the bearing of arms against the oppressors by organized groups of slaves, was the most dramatic and clear-cut form of slave resistance. In the period between 1800 and 1831, a number of slaves participated in revolts that showed their willingness to risk their lives in a desperate bid for liberation. In 1800, a Virginia slave named Gabriel Prosser mobilized a large band of his fellows to march on Richmond. But a violent storm dispersed "Gabriel's army" and enabled whites to suppress the uprising without any loss of white life.

In 1811, several hundred Louisiana slaves marched on New Orleans. It took three hundred soldiers of the U.S. Army, aided by armed planters and militiamen, to stop the advance and to end the rebellion. In 1822, whites in Charleston, South Carolina, uncovered an extensive and well-planned conspiracy, organized

Running away was one way to escape slavery, but for most slaves, flight was impossible. Instead, they sought other means by which to improve their condition as slaves.

by a free black man named Denmark Vesey, to seize local armories, arm the slave population, and take possession of the city.

Only a year after the Vesey affair, whites in Norfolk County, Virginia, complained of the activities of a marauding band of runaway slaves that had killed several whites. The militia was sent out and captured the alleged leader—a fugitive of several years' standing named Bob Ferebee. Groups of runaways, who hid for years in places such as the Great Dismal Swamp of Virginia, continued to raid plantations throughout the antebellum period and were inclined to fight to the death rather than be recaptured.

The bloodiest and most terrifying of all slave revolts was the Nat Turner insurrection of 1831. Although it was the last slave rebellion of this kind during the pre–Civil War period, armed resistance had not ended. In Florida, hundreds of black fugitives fought in the Second Seminole War (1835–1842) alongside the

Indians who had given them a haven. The Seminoles were resisting removal to Oklahoma, but for the blacks who took part, the war was a struggle for their own freedom. When it ended, most blacks accompanied their Indian allies to the trans-Mississippi West.

Only a tiny fraction of all slaves ever took part in organized acts of violent resistance against white power. Most realized that the odds against a successful revolt were very high, and bitter experience had shown them that the usual outcome was death to the rebels. As a consequence, they characteristically devised safer or more ingenious ways to resist white dominance.

One way of protesting against slavery was running away, and thousands of slaves showed their discontent and desire for freedom in this fashion. Most fugitives never got beyond the neighborhood of the plantation; after "lying out" for a time, they would return, often after negotiating immunity from punishment. But many escapees remained free for years by hiding in swamps or other remote areas, and a fraction made it to freedom in the North or Mexico. Some fugitives stowed away aboard ships heading to northern ports; others traveled overland for hundreds of miles, avoiding patrols and inquisitive whites by staying off the roads and moving only at night. Light-skinned blacks sometimes made it to freedom by

Henry "Box" Brown emerges from the crate in which he escaped from slavery in Richmond, Virginia, to freedom in Philadelphia.

passing for white, and one resourceful slave even had himself packed in a box and shipped to the North.

For the majority of slaves, however, flight was not a real option. Either they lived too deep in the South to have any chance of reaching free soil, or they were reluctant to leave family and friends behind. Slaves who did not or could not leave the plantation had to register their opposition to the masters' regime while remaining under the yoke of bondage.

The normal way of expressing discontent was engaging in a kind of indirect or passive resistance. Many slaves worked slowly and inefficiently, not because they were naturally lazy (as whites supposed) but as a gesture of protest. Others withheld labor by feigning illness or injury. Stealing provisions—a very common activity on most plantations—was another way to show contempt for authority. According to the code of ethics prevailing in the slave quarters, theft from the master was no sin; it was simply a way for slaves to get a larger share of the fruits of their own labors.

Substantial numbers of slaves committed acts of sabotage. Tools and agricultural implements were deliberately broken, animals were willfully neglected or mistreated, and barns or other outbuildings were set afire. The ultimate act of clandestine resistance was poisoning the master's food. Some slaves, especially the "conjure" men and women who practiced a combination of folk medicine and witchcraft, knew how to mix rare, virtually untraceable poisons; and a suspiciously large number of plantation whites became suddenly and mysteriously ill. Sometimes whole families died from obscure "diseases" that did not infect the slave quarters.

The basic attitude behind such actions was revealed in the folktales that slaves passed down from generation to generation. The famous Brer Rabbit stories showed how a small, apparently defenseless animal could overcome a bigger and stronger one through cunning and deceit. Although these tales often had an African origin, they also served as an allegory for the black view of the master-slave relationship. Other stories—which were not told in front of whites—openly portrayed the slave as a clever trickster outwitting the master.

THE STRUGGLES OF FREE BLACKS

In addition to the 4 million blacks in bondage, there were approximately 500,000 free African Americans in 1860, about half of them living in slave states. Whether they were in the North or in the South, "free Negroes" were treated as social outcasts and denied legal and political equality with whites. Public facilities were strictly segregated, and after the 1830s, blacks in the United States could vote only in four New England states. Nowhere but in Massachusetts could they testify in court cases involving whites.

Free blacks had difficulty finding decent jobs; most employers preferred immigrants or other whites over blacks, and the latter were usually relegated to menial and poorly paid occupations. Many states excluded blacks entirely from public schools, and the federal government barred them from serving in the militia, working for the postal service, and laying claim to public lands. Free blacks were even denied U.S. passports; in effect, they were stateless persons even before the 1857 Supreme Court ruling that no Negro could claim American citizenship.

In the South, free blacks were subject to a set of direct controls that tended to make them semi-slaves. They were often forced to register or have white guardians who were responsible for their behavior. Invariably, they were required to carry papers proving their free status, and in some states, they had to obtain official permission to move from one county to another. Licensing laws excluded blacks from several occupations, and authorities frequently blocked attempts by blacks to hold meetings or form organizations. Sometimes vagrancy and apprenticeship laws were used to force free blacks into a state of economic dependency barely distinguishable from outright slavery. Just before the outbreak of the Civil War, several state legislatures proposed laws giving free Negroes the choice of emigrating from the state or being enslaved.

Although beset by special problems of their own, most free blacks identified with the suffering of the slaves; when circumstances allowed, they protested against the peculiar institution and worked for its abolition. Many of them had once been slaves themselves or were the children of slaves; often they had close relatives who were still in bondage. Furthermore, they knew that the discrimination from which they suffered was rooted in slavery and the racial attitudes that accompanied it. So long as slavery existed, their own rights were likely to be denied, and even their freedom was at risk; former slaves who could not prove they had been legally freed were subject to reenslavement. This threat existed even in the North: Under federal fugitive slave laws, escaped slaves could be returned to bondage. Even blacks who were born free were not perfectly safe. Kidnapping or fraudulent seizure by slave-catchers was always a possibility.

The elaborate system of control and surveillance placed free blacks in the South in a relatively weak position to work against slavery. The wave of repression against the free black population that followed the uncovering of the Denmark Vesey conspiracy revealed the dangers of revolutionary activity and the odds against success. Consequently, most free blacks found that survival depended on creating the impression of loyalty to the planter regime. In some parts of the lower South, groups of relatively privileged free Negroes, mostly of racially mixed origin, were sometimes persuaded that it was to their advantage to preserve the status quo. As skilled artisans and small-business owners dependent on white favors and patronage, they had little incentive to risk everything by taking the side of the slaves. In southern Louisiana, there was even a small group of mulatto planters who lived in luxury, supported by the labor of other African Americans.

Free blacks in the North were in a better position to join the struggle for freedom. Despite all the prejudice and discrimination they faced, they still enjoyed some basic civil liberties denied to southern blacks. They could protest publicly against slavery or white supremacy and could form associations for the advancement and liberation of African Americans. Frederick Douglass, the escaped slave who became an abolitionist orator, was their most eloquent leader. Outspoken women such as Sojourner Truth, Maria Stewart, and Frances Harper also played a significant role in black antislavery activity. The Negro Convention movement, which sponsored national meetings of black leaders beginning in 1830, provided an important forum for independent black expression.

Black newspapers, such as *Freedom's Journal,* first published in 1827, and the *North Star,* founded by Douglass in 1847, gave black writers a chance to preach their gospel of liberation to black readers. African American authors also produced a stream of books and pamphlets attacking slavery, refuting racism, and advocating various forms of resistance. One of the most influential publications was

Harriet Tubman, on the extreme left, is shown here with some of the slaves she helped escape on the Underground Railroad. Born a slave in Maryland, she escaped to Philadelphia in 1849. She is said to have helped as many as three hundred African Americans flee slavery. She led many of them all the way to Canada, where they would be beyond the reach of the Fugitive Slave Law.

David Walker's *Appeal . . . to the Colored Citizens of the World,* which appeared in 1829. Walker denounced slavery in the most vigorous language possible and called for a black revolt against white tyranny.

Free blacks in the North did more than make verbal protests against racial injustice. They were also the main conductors on the fabled Underground Railroad that opened a path for fugitives from slavery. Modern research has shown that the Underground Railroad was largely a black-operated enterprise. Courageous ex-slaves such as Harriet Tubman and Josiah Henson made regular forays into the slave states to lead other blacks to freedom, and many of the "stations" along the way were run by free blacks. In northern towns and cities, free blacks organized "vigilance committees" to protect fugitives and thwart the slave-catchers. Groups of blacks even used force to rescue recaptured fugitives from the authorities. In deeds as well as words, free blacks showed their unyielding hostility to slavery and racism.

AFRICAN AMERICAN RELIGION

African Americans could not have resisted or even endured slavery if they had been utterly demoralized by its oppressiveness. Inner resources and patterns of thought that gave some dignity to their lives and inspired hopes for a brighter fu-

John Antrobus, Plantation Burial, *ca. 1860. The painting depicts slaves gathering in a forest to bury a fellow slave. Many spirituals sung by the slaves on such occasions portrayed death as a welcome release from bondage and created an image of an afterlife in which the trials and cares of this life were unknown.*

ture helped sustain them in their struggle for freedom. From the realm of culture and fundamental beliefs, African Americans drew the strength to hold their heads high and look beyond their immediate condition.

Religion was the cornerstone of this emerging African American culture. Black Christianity may have owed its original existence to the efforts of white missionaries, but it was far from a mere imitation of white religious forms and beliefs. This distinctive variant of evangelical Protestantism incorporated elements of African religion and stressed those portions of the Bible that spoke to the aspirations of an enslaved people thirsting for freedom.

Free blacks formed the first independent black churches by seceding from white congregations that discriminated against them in seating and church governance. Out of these secessions came a variety of autonomous Baptist groups and the highly successful African Methodist Episcopal (AME) Church, organized as a national denomination under the leadership of the Reverend Richard Allen of Philadelphia in 1816. But the mass of blacks did not have access to the independent churches, which mainly served free blacks and urban slaves with indulgent masters. In the Deep South, whites regarded AME churches with suspicion and sometimes suppressed them; a thriving congregation in Charleston was forced to close its doors in 1822 after some of its members had been implicated in the Vesey conspiracy.

Plantation slaves who were exposed to Christianity either attended the neighboring white churches or worshiped at home. On large estates, masters or white missionaries often conducted Sunday services. But white-sanctioned religious activity was only a superficial part of the slaves' spiritual life. The true slave religion was practiced at night, often secretly, and was led by black preachers.

This covert slave religion was a highly emotional affair that featured singing, shouting, and dancing. In some ways, the atmosphere resembled a backwoods revival meeting. But much of what went on was actually an adaptation of African religious beliefs and customs. The chanting mode of preaching—with the congregation responding at regular intervals—and the expression of religious feelings through rhythmic movements, especially the counterclockwise movement known as the ring shout, were clearly African in origin. The black conversion experience was normally a state of ecstasy more akin to possession by spirits—a major form of African religious expression—than to the agony of those "struck down" at white revivals. The emphasis on sinfulness and fear of damnation that were core themes of white evangelicalism played a lesser role among blacks. For them, religion was more an affirmation of the joy of life than a rejection of worldly pleasures and temptations.

Slave sermons and religious songs spoke directly to the plight of a people in bondage and implicitly asserted their right to be free. The most popular of all biblical subjects was the deliverance of the children of Israel from slavery in Egypt. The book of Exodus provided more than its share of texts for sermons and images for songs. In one moving spiritual, God commands Moses to "tell Old Pharaoh" to "let my people Go." Many sermons and songs refer to the crossing of Jordan and the arrival in the Promised Land. Other songs invoke the liberation theme in different ways. One recalls that Jesus had "set poor sinners free," and another prophesies, "We'll soon be free, when the Lord will call us home."

Most of the songs of freedom and deliverance can be interpreted as referring exclusively to religious salvation and the afterlife—and this was undoubtedly how slaves hoped their masters would understand them. But the slaves did not forget that God had once freed a people from slavery in this life and punished their masters. The Bible thus gave African Americans the hope that they, as a people, would repeat the experience of the Israelites and be delivered from bondage. During the Civil War, observers noted that freed slaves seemed to regard their emancipation as something that had been preordained, and some were inclined to view Lincoln as the reincarnation of Moses.

Besides being the basis for a deep-rooted hope for eventual freedom, religion helped the slaves endure bondage without losing their sense of inner worth. Unless their masters were unusually pious, religious slaves could regard themselves as superior to their owners. Some slaves even believed that all whites were damned because of their unjust treatment of blacks, while all slaves would be saved because any sins they committed were the involuntary result of their condition.

More important, slave religion gave African Americans a chance to create and control a world of their own. Preachers, elders, and other leaders of slave congregations could acquire a sense of status within their own community that had not been conferred by whites. Although religion seldom inspired slaves to open rebellion, it helped create a sense of community, solidarity, and self-esteem among slaves by giving them something of their own that they found infinitely precious.

THE SLAVE FAMILY

The African American family was the other institution that prevented slavery from becoming utterly demoralizing. Contrary to what historians and sociologists used to believe, slaves had a strong and abiding sense of family and kinship. But the nature of the families or households that predominated on particular plantations or farms varied according to local circumstances. On large plantations with relatively stable slave populations, a substantial majority of slave children lived in two-parent households, and many marriages lasted for as long as twenty to thirty years. They were more often broken up by the death or sale of

Some slave families managed to stay together, as shown by the footnote to this 1835 bill of sale: "I did intend to leave Nancy['s] child but she made such a damned fuss I had to let her take it. . . ."

one of the partners than by voluntary dissolution of the union. Close bonds united mothers, fathers, and children, and parents shared child-rearing responsibilities (within the limits allowed by the masters). Marital fidelity was encouraged by masters who believed that stable unions produced more offspring and by Christian churches that viewed adultery and divorce as sinful.

But in areas where most slaves lived on farms or small plantations, and especially in areas of the upper South where the trading and hiring out of slaves was frequent, a different pattern seems to have prevailed. Under these circumstances, slaves frequently had spouses who resided on other plantations or farms, often some distance away, and ties between husbands and wives were looser and more fragile. The result was that female-headed families were the norm, and responsibility for child rearing was vested in mothers, assisted in most cases by female relatives and friends. Mother-centered families with weak conjugal ties were a natural response to the infrequent presence of fathers and to the prospect of their being moved or sold beyond visiting distance. Where the breakup of unions by sale or relocation could be expected at any time, it did not pay to invest all of one's emotions in a conjugal relationship. But whether the basic family form was nuclear or matrifocal (female-headed), the ties that it created were infinitely precious to its members. Masters acquired great leverage over the behavior of slaves by invoking the threat of family breakup through sale to enforce discipline.

The terrible anguish that usually accompanied the breakup of families through sale showed the depth of kinship feelings. Masters knew that the first place to look for a fugitive was in the neighborhood of a family member who had been sold away. After emancipation, thousands of freed slaves wandered about looking for spouses, children, or parents from whom they had been forcibly separated years before. The famous spiritual "Sometimes I Feel Like a Motherless Child" was far more than an expression of religious need; it also reflected the family anxieties and personal tragedies of many slaves.

Feelings of kinship and mutual obligation extended beyond the primary family. Grandparents, uncles, aunts, and even cousins were often known to slaves through direct contact or family lore. Nor were kinship ties limited to blood relations. When families were broken up by sale, individual members who found themselves on plantations far from home were likely to be "adopted" into new kinship networks. Orphans or children without responsible parents were quickly absorbed without prejudice into new families.

Studies of slave families suggest that kinship provided a model for personal relationships and the basis for a sense of community. For some purposes, all the slaves on a plantation were in reality members of a single extended family, as their forms of address clearly reveal. Elderly slaves were addressed by everyone else as "uncle" and "aunty," and younger unrelated slaves commonly called each other "brother" or "sister." Slave culture was a family culture, and this was one of its greatest sources of strength and cohesion. Strong kinship ties, whether real or fictive, meant slaves could depend on one another in times of trouble. The kinship network also provided a vehicle for the transmission of African American folk traditions from one generation to the next. Together with slave religion, kinship gave African Americans some sense that they were members of a community, not just a collection of individuals victimized by oppression.

Some historians have argued that a stress on the strength of slave culture obscures the harshness and cruelty of the system and its damaging effects. Slavery was often a demoralizing and even brutalizing experience, and it provided little opportunity for learning about the world outside the plantation, developing mental skills, and exercising individual initiative. Bondspeople on the relatively small southern plantations or farms, with their high turnover of personnel, had limited opportunities to develop communal ties. Nevertheless, their sense of being part of a distinctive group with its own beliefs and ways of doing things, fragile and precarious though it may have been, made *psychic survival* possible and helped engender an African American ethnicity that would be a source of strength in future struggles. Although slave culture did not normally provoke violent resistance to the slaveholders' regime, the inner world that slaves made for themselves gave them the spiritual strength to thwart the masters' efforts to take over their hearts and minds. After emancipation, this resilient cultural heritage would combine with the tradition of open protest created by rebellious slaves and free black abolitionists to inspire and sustain new struggles for equality.

A DIVIDED SOCIETY

If slaves lived to some extent in a separate and distinctive world of their own, so did planters, less affluent whites, and even free blacks. The Old South was thus a deeply divided society. The northern traveler Frederick Law Olmsted, who made three journeys through the slave states in the 1850s, provided a vivid sense of how diverse in outlook and circumstances southern people could be. Visiting a great plantation, he watched the slaves stop working as soon as the overseer turned away; on a small farm, he saw a slave and his owner working in the fields together. Treatment of slaves, he found, ranged from humane paternalism to flagrant cruelty. Olmsted heard nonslaveholding whites damn the planters as "cotton snobs" but also talk about blacks as "niggers" and express fear of interracial marriages if slaves were freed. He received hospitality from poor whites living in crowded one-room cabins as well as from fabulously wealthy planters in pillared mansions, and he found life in the backcountry radically different than in the plantation belts. In short, he showed that the South was a kaleidoscope of groups divided by class, race, culture, and geography. What held it together and provided some measure of unity was a booming plantation economy and a web of customary relationships and loyalties that could obscure the underlying cleavages and antagonisms. The fractured and fragile nature of this society would soon become apparent when it was subjected to the pressures of civil war.

14

THE SECTIONAL CRISIS

On May 22, 1856, Representative Preston Brooks of South Carolina erupted onto the floor of the Senate looking for Charles Sumner, the antislavery senator from Massachusetts who had recently given a fiery oration condemning the South for plotting to extend slavery to the Kansas Territory. When he found Sumner seated at his desk, Brooks proceeded to batter him over the head with a cane. Amazed and stunned, Sumner made a desperate effort to rise and ripped his bolted desk from the floor. He then collapsed under a continued torrent of blows.

Sumner was so badly injured by the assault that he did not return to the Senate for three years. But his home state reelected him in 1857 and kept his seat vacant as testimony against southern brutality and "barbarism." Brooks, denounced in the North as a bully, was lionized by his fellow Southerners. When he resigned from the House after a vote of censure had narrowly failed because of solid southern opposition, his constituents reelected him unanimously.

These contrasting reactions show how bitter sectional antagonism had become by 1856. Sumner spoke for the radical wing of the new Republican party, which was making a bid for national power by mobilizing the North against the alleged aggressions of "the slave power." Southerners viewed the very existence of this party as an insult to their section of the country and a threat to its vital interests. Sumner came closer to being an abolitionist than any other member of Congress, and nothing created greater fear and anxiety among Southerners than their belief that antislavery forces were plotting against their way of life. To many Northerners, "bully Brooks" stood for all the arrogant and violent slaveholders

After his constituents learned of Preston Brooks's caning of Senator Sumner, they sent Brooks a gold-handled cowhide whip to use on other antislavery advocates.

who were allegedly conspiring to extend their barbaric labor system. By 1856, therefore, the sectional cleavage that would lead to the Civil War had already undermined the foundations of national unity.

The crisis of the mid-1850s came only a few years after the elaborate compromise of 1850 had seemingly resolved the dispute over the future of slavery in the territories acquired as a result of the Mexican-American War. The Kansas-Nebraska Act of 1854 renewed agitation over the extension of slavery and revived the sectional conflict that led to the emergence of the Republican party. From that point on, a dramatic series of events increased sectional confrontation and destroyed the prospects for a new compromise. The caning of Charles Sumner was one of these events, and violence on the Senate floor foreshadowed violence on the battlefield.

THE COMPROMISE OF 1850

The conflict over slavery in the territories began in the late 1840s. During the early phase of the sectional controversy, the leaders of two strong national parties, each with substantial followings in both the North and the South, had a vested interest in resolving the crisis. Efforts to create uncompromising sectional parties failed to disrupt what historians call the second party system—the vigorous competition between Whigs and Democrats that had characterized elections since the 1830s. Furthermore, the less tangible features of sectionalism—emotion and ideology—were not as divisive as they would later become. Hence a fragile compromise was achieved through a kind of give-and-take that would not be possible in the changed environment of the mid-1850s.

THE PROBLEM OF SLAVERY IN THE MEXICAN CESSION

As the price of union between states committed to slavery and those in the process of abolishing it, the Founders had attempted to limit the role of the slavery issue in national politics. The Constitution gave the federal government the right to abolish the international slave trade but no definite authority to regulate or destroy the institution where it existed under state law. It was easy to condemn slavery in principle but very difficult to develop a practical program to eliminate it without defying the Constitution.

Radical abolitionists resolved this problem by rejecting the law of the land in favor of a "higher law" prohibiting human bondage. But radical abolitionists constituted only a small minority dedicated to freeing the North, at whatever cost, from the sin of condoning slavery. The majority of Northerners in the 1840s, while they disliked slavery, also detested abolitionism. They were inclined to view slavery as a backward and unwholesome institution, much inferior to their own free-labor system, and could be persuaded that slaveholders were power-hungry aristocrats seeking more than their share of national political influence. But they regarded the Constitution as a binding contract between slave and free states and were likely to be prejudiced against blacks and reluctant to accept large numbers of them as free citizens. Consequently, they saw no legal or desirable way to bring about emancipation within the southern states.

But the Constitution had not predetermined the status of slavery in *future* states. Since Congress had the power to admit new states to the Union under any conditions it wished to impose, a majority could require the abolition of slavery as the price of admission. An effort to use this power had led to the Missouri crisis of 1819–1820 (see Chapter 9). The resulting compromise was designed to decide future cases by drawing a line between slave and free states and extending it westward. When specific territories were settled, organized, and prepared for statehood, slavery would be permitted south of the line and prohibited north of it.

The tradition of providing both the free North and the slave South with opportunities for expansion and the creation of new states broke down when new territories were wrested from Mexico in the 1840s. The acquisition of Texas, New Mexico, and California—all south of the Missouri Compromise line—threatened to upset the parity between slave and free states. Since it was generally assumed in the North that Congress had the power to prohibit slavery in new territories, a movement developed in Congress to do just that.

THE WILMOT PROVISO LAUNCHES THE FREE-SOIL MOVEMENT

The Free-Soil crusade began in August 1846, only three months after the start of the Mexican-American War, when Congressman David Wilmot, a Pennsylvania Democrat, proposed an amendment to the military appropriations bill that would ban slavery in any territory that might be acquired from Mexico.

Wilmot spoke for the large number of northern Democrats who felt neglected and betrayed by the party's choice of Polk in 1844 and by the "prosouthern" policies of Polk's administration. Reductions in tariff duties and Polk's veto of an internal improvement bill upset Democrats in the East and Midwest. Northern expansionists also felt betrayed because Polk had gone back on his pledge to obtain "all of Oregon" up to 54°40' and then had proceeded to wage war to win all of Texas and the Southwest. This twist in the course of Manifest Destiny convinced northern Democrats that the South and its interests were dominating the party and the administration.

The pioneer Free-Soilers had a genuine interest in the issue actually at hand—the question of who would control and settle the new territories. Combining an appeal to racial prejudice with opposition to slavery as an institution, Wilmot proposed prohibiting not only slavery but also settlement by free African Americans in the territory obtained in the Mexican cession. He argued that such bans would protect the common folk of the North form job competition with slaves and free blacks. By linking racism with resistance to the spread of slavery, Wilmot appealed to a broad spectrum of northern opinion.

Northern Whigs backed the Wilmot Proviso because they too were concerned about the outcome of an unregulated competition between slave and free labor in the territories. Many northern Whigs had opposed the annexation of Texas and the Mexican-American War. If expansion was inevitable, however, they endorsed the view that acquisition of Mexican territory should not be used to increase the power of the slave states.

The first House vote on the Wilmot Proviso resulted in a sharp sectional cleavage. Every northern congressman with the exception of two Democrats voted for the amendment, and every Southerner except two Whigs went on record against it. The Proviso passed the House, but a combination of southern influence and Democratic loyalty to the administration blocked it in the Senate. When the appropriations bill went back to the House without the Proviso, the administration's arm-twisting succeeded in changing enough northern Democratic votes to pass the bill and thus send the Proviso down to defeat.

Reactions to the Proviso on the state and local level provided further evidence of the polarizing effect of the territorial issue. The end of the Mexican-American War, the formal acquisition of New Mexico and California, and the approaching election of 1848 gave new urgency to a search for politically feasible solutions to the crisis. The extreme alternatives—the Proviso policy of free soil and the radical southern response that slavery could be extended to any territory—threatened to destroy the national parties because there was no bisectional support for either of them.

SQUATTER SOVEREIGNTY AND THE ELECTION OF 1848

After a futile attempt to extend the Missouri Compromise line to the Pacific—a proposal unacceptable to Northerners because most of the Mexican cession lay south of the line—Senator Lewis Cass of Michigan proposed a new approach, designed to appeal especially to Democrats. Cass, who described his formula as "squatter sovereignty," would leave the determination of the status of slavery in a territory to the actual settlers. From the beginning, this proposal contained an ambiguity that allowed it to be interpreted differently in the North and the South. For northern Democrats, squatter sovereignty—or popular sovereignty as it was later called—meant the settlers could vote slavery up or down at the first meeting of a territorial legislature. For the southern wing of the party, it meant a decision would be made only at the time a convention drew up a constitution and applied for statehood. It was in the interest of national Democratic leaders to leave this ambiguity unresolved for as long as possible.

Congress failed to resolve the future of slavery in the Mexican cession in time for the election of 1848, and the issue entered the arena of presidential politics. The Democrats nominated Cass on a platform of squatter sovereignty. The Whigs evaded the question by running General Zachary Taylor—the hero of the battle of Buena Vista—without a platform. Taylor refused to commit himself on the status of slavery in the territories, but northern Whigs favoring restriction took heart from the general's promise not to veto any territorial legislation passed by Congress. Southern Whigs supported Taylor mainly because he was a southern slaveholder.

A third-party movement attracted northerners who had strongly supported the Wilmot Proviso. In August, a tumultuous convention in Buffalo nominated former president Van Buren to carry the banner of the Free-Soil party. Support for the Free-Soilers came from antislavery Whigs dismayed by their party's nomination of a slaveholder and its evasiveness on the territorial issue, disgruntled Democrats who had backed the Proviso and resented southern influence in their party, and some of the former adherents of the abolitionist Liberty party. Van Buren himself was motivated less by antislavery zeal than by bitterness at being

THE ELECTION OF 1848

CANDIDATE	PARTY	POPULAR VOTE	ELECTORAL VOTE
Taylor	Whig	1,360,967	163
Cass	Democratic	1,222,342	127
Van Buren	Free-Soil	291,263	—

denied the Democratic nomination in 1844. The founding of the Free-Soil party was the first significant effort to create a broadly based sectional party addressing itself to voters' concerns about the extension of slavery.

After a noisy and confusing campaign, Taylor came out on top, winning a majority of the electoral votes in both the North and the South and a total of 1,360,967 popular votes to 1,222,342 for Cass and 291,263 for Van Buren. The Free-Soilers failed to carry a single state but did quite well in the North, coming in second behind Taylor in New York, Massachusetts, and Vermont.

TAYLOR TAKES CHARGE

Once in office, Taylor devised a bold plan to decide the fate of slavery in the Mexican cession. He tried to engineer the immediate admission of California and New Mexico to the Union as states, thus bypassing the territorial stage entirely and avoiding a congressional debate on the status of slavery in the federal domain. Under the administration's urging, California, which was filling up rapidly with settlers drawn by the lust for gold, convened a constitutional convention and applied for admission to the Union as a free state.

Instead of resolving the crisis, President Taylor's initiative only worsened it. Fearing that not only California but also New Mexico—where Mexican law had prohibited slavery— would be admitted as free states, Southerners of both parties accused the president of trying to impose the Wilmot Proviso in a new form. The prospect that only free states would emerge from the entire Mexican cession inspired serious talk of secession.

Senator John C. Calhoun of South Carolina saw in the crisis a chance to achieve his long-standing goal of creating a southern voting bloc that would cut across regular party lines. As state legislatures and conventions throughout the South denounced "northern aggression" against the rights of the slave states, Calhoun rejoiced that the South had never been so "united . . . bold, and decided." In the fall and winter of 1849–1850, several southern states agreed to participate in a convention, to be held in Nashville in June, where grievances could be aired and demands made. For an increasing number of southern political leaders, the survival of the Union would depend on the North's response to the demands of the southern rights movement.

FORGING A COMPROMISE

When it became clear that the president would not abandon or modify his plan in order to appease the South, Congress launched independent efforts to arrange a compromise. Hoping that he could again play the role of "great pacificator" as he had in the Missouri Compromise of 1820, Senator Henry Clay of Kentucky offered a series of resolutions meant to restore sectional harmony. On the critical territorial question, he proposed admitting California as a free state and organizing the rest of the Mexican cession with no explicit prohibition of slavery—in other words, without the Wilmot Proviso. He sought to resolve a major boundary dispute between New Mexico and Texas by granting the disputed region to New Mexico while compensating Texas through federal assumption of its state debt. As a concession to the North on another issue—the existence of slavery in the District of Columbia—he recommended prohibiting the buying and selling

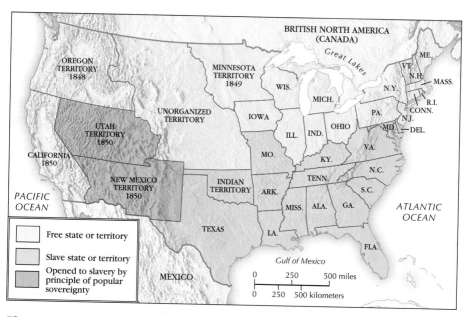

The Compromise of 1850

The "compromise" was actually a series of resolutions granting some concessions to the North—especially admission of California as a free state—and some to the South, such as a stricter Fugitive Slave Law.

In the Senate chamber, its balconies overflowing with spectators, Henry Clay pleads for passage of the Compromise of 1850. John C. Calhoun (standing third from right) was by this time mortally ill; his speech denouncing the compromise was read by Senator James Mason of Virginia. Daniel Webster (seated at left with his head resting on his hand), also in poor health, argued in favor of the compromise plan.

of slaves at auction and permitting the abolition of slavery itself with the consent of the District's white inhabitants. He also called for a more effective Fugitive Slave Law.

Clay's compromise plan, proposed in February 1850, took several months to get through Congress. One obstacle was President Taylor's firm resistance to the proposal; another was the difficulty of getting congressmen to vote for it in the form of a single package or "omnibus bill." Few politicians from either section were willing to go on record as supporting the key concessions to the *other* section. The logjam was broken in July by two crucial developments: President Taylor died and was succeeded by Millard Fillmore, who favored the compromise; and a decision was made to abandon the omnibus strategy in favor of a series of measures that could be voted on separately. After the breakup of the omnibus bill, some of Clay's proposals were modified to make them more acceptable to the South and the Democrats. Senator Stephen A. Douglas, a Democrat from Illinois, was particularly influential in maneuvering the separate provisions of the plan through Congress.

As the price of Democratic support, the popular sovereignty principle was included in the bills organizing New Mexico and Utah. Territorial legislatures in the Mexican cession were explicitly granted power over "all rightful subjects of legislation," which might include slavery. Half of the compensation to Texas for giving up its claims to New Mexico was paid directly to holders of Texas bonds.

Abolition of slave auctions and depots in the District of Columbia and a new Fugitive Slave Law were also enacted. The latter was a particularly outrageous piece of legislation. Suspected fugitives were now denied a jury trial, the right to testify in their own behalf, and other basic constitutional rights. As a result, there were no effective safeguards against false identification by accusers or against the kidnapping of blacks who were legally free.

The compromise passed because its key measures were supported by northern Democrats, southern Whigs, and representatives of both parties from the border states. No single bill was backed by a majority of the congressmen from both sections, and few senators or representatives actually voted for the entire package. Many northern Whigs and southern Democrats thought the end result conceded too much to the other section. Doubts therefore persisted over the value of workability of a "compromise" that was really more like an armistice or a cease-fire.

Yet the Compromise of 1850 did serve for a short

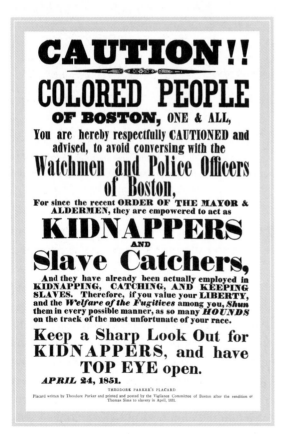

This abolitionist broadside was printed in response to a ruling that fugitive slave Thomas Sims must be returned to his master in Georgia.

time as a basis for sectional peace. In southern state elections during 1850–1851, moderate coalitions won out over radicals, but southern nationalism remained strong. Southerners demanded strict northern adherence to the compromise, especially to the Fugitive Slave Law, as the price for suppressing threats of secession. The compromise received greater support in the North, where it was backed by virtually the entire Democratic party and by one faction of the Whigs.

The Fugitive Slave Law was unpopular in areas where abolitionism was particularly strong because it required Northerners to enforce slavery, and there were a few sensational rescues or attempted rescues of escaped slaves. Despite abolitionist resistance, however, the Fugitive Slave Law was enforced fairly successfully in the early 1850s. Other parts of the compromise were less troublesome. In 1852, when both the Democrats and the Whigs endorsed the compromise in their platforms, it seemed that sharp differences on the slavery issue had once again been banished from national politics.

POLITICAL UPHEAVAL, 1852–1856

The second party system—Democrats versus Whigs—survived the crisis over slavery in the Mexican cession, but in the long run the Compromise of 1850 may have weakened it. Although both national parties had been careful during the 1840s not to take stands on the slavery issue that would alienate their supporters in either section of the country, they had in fact offered voters alternative ways of dealing with the question. Democrats had endorsed headlong territorial expansion with the promise of a fair division of the spoils between slave and free states. Whigs had generally opposed annexations or acquisitions, because they were likely to bring the slavery question to the fore and threaten sectional harmony. With some shifts of emphasis and interpretation, each strategy could be presented to southern voters as a good way to protect slavery and to Northerners as a good way to contain it.

The consensus of 1852 meant the parties had to find other issues on which to base their distinctive appeals. Their failure to do so encouraged voter apathy and disenchantment with the major parties. When the Democrats sought to revive the Manifest Destiny issue in 1854, they reopened the explosive issue of slavery in the territories. By this time, the Whigs were too weak and divided to respond with a policy of their own, and a purely sectional Free-Soil party—the Republicans—gained prominence. The collapse of the second party system released sectional agitation from the earlier constraints imposed by the competition of strong national parties.

THE PARTY SYSTEM IN CRISIS

The presidential campaign of 1852 was singularly devoid of major issues. Some Whigs tried to revive interest in nationalistic economic policies but with business thriving under the Democratic program of limited government involvement, there was little support for Whig proposals for a protective tariff, a national bank, and internal improvements.

Another tempting issue was immigration. Many Whigs were upset by the massive influx from Europe, partly because most of the new arrivals were Catholics, and the Whig following was largely evangelical Protestant. In addition, the immigrants voted overwhelmingly Democratic. The Whig leadership was divided on whether to compete with the Democrats for the immigrant vote or to seek restrictions on immigrant voting rights.

The Whigs nominated war hero General Winfield Scott, who supported the faction that resisted nativism and sought to broaden the appeal of the party. But Scott and his supporters were unable to sway Catholic immigrants from their Democratic allegiance, and some nativist Whigs apparently sat out the election to protest their party's disregard of their cultural prejudices.

But the main cause for Scott's crushing defeat was the support he lost in the South when he allied himself with northern antislavery Whigs, led by Senator William Seward of New York. Democratic candidate Franklin Pierce of New Hampshire, a colorless nonentity compared to his rival, easily swept the Deep South and edged out Scott in most of the free states. In the most one-sided election since 1820, Pierce received 254 electoral votes from 27 states while Scott carried only 4 states with 42 electoral votes. This outcome revealed that the Whig party was in deep trouble because it lacked a program that would distinguish it from the Democrats and would appeal to voters in both sections of the country.

Despite their overwhelming victory in 1852, the Democrats had reasons for anxiety about the loyalty of their supporters. Because the major parties had

THE ELECTION OF 1852

CANDIDATE	PARTY	POPULAR VOTE	ELECTORAL VOTE
Pierce	Democratic	1,601,117	254
Scott	Whig	1,385,453	42
Hale	Free-Soil	155,825	—

ceased to offer clear-cut alternatives to the electorate, voter apathy or alienation was a growing trend in the early 1850s. The Democrats won majorities in both North and South in 1852 primarily because the public viewed them as the most reliable supporters of the Compromise of 1850, not because of firm party allegiance.

THE KANSAS-NEBRASKA ACT RAISES A STORM

In January 1854, Senator Stephen A. Douglas proposed a bill to organize the territory west of Missouri and Iowa. Since this region fell within the area where slavery had been banned by the Missouri Compromise, Douglas hoped to head off Southern opposition and keep the Democratic party united by disregarding the compromise line and setting up the territorial government in Kansas and Nebraska on the basis of popular sovereignty.

Douglas wanted to organize the Kansas-Nebraska area quickly because he was a strong supporter of the expansion of settlement and commerce. He hoped a railroad would soon be built to the Pacific with Chicago (or another midwestern city) as its eastern terminus. A long controversy over the status of slavery in the new territory would slow down the process of organization and settlement and might hinder the building of the railroad. Douglas also hoped his Kansas-Nebraska bill would revive the spirit of Manifest Destiny that had given the party cohesion and electoral success in the mid-1840s. As the main advocate for a new expansionism, he expected to win the Democratic nomination and the presidency.

The price of southern support, Douglas soon discovered, was the addition of an amendment explicitly repealing the Missouri Compromise. He reluctantly agreed, and in this more provocative form, the bill made its way through Congress, passing the Senate by a large margin and the House by a narrow one. Douglas's bill split his party rather than uniting it. A manifesto of "independent Democrats" denounced the bill as "a gross violation of a sacred pledge." For many Northerners, the Kansas-Nebraska Act was an abomination because it permitted the possibility of slavery in an area where it had previously been prohibited. Except for an aggressive minority, Southerners had not pushed for such legislation or even shown much interest in it, but now they felt obligated to support it. Their support provided deadly ammunition to those who were seeking to convince the northern public that there was a conspiracy to extend slavery.

Douglas's bill had a catastrophic effect on sectional harmony. It repudiated a compromise that many in the North regarded as binding. In defiance of the whole compromise tradition, it made a concession to the South on the issue of slavery extension without providing an equivalent concession to the North. It also shattered the fragile sectional accommodation of 1850 and made future compromises less likely. From now on, northern sectionalists would be fighting to regain what they had lost, while Southerners would battle to maintain rights already conceded.

The act also destroyed what was left of the second party system. The already weakened Whig party disintegrated when its congressional representation split cleanly along sectional lines on the Kansas-Nebraska issue. The Democratic party survived, but its ability to act as a unifying national force was seriously impaired. Northern desertions and southern gains (resulting from the recruitment of proslavery Whigs) combined to destroy the sectional balance within the party and place it under firm southern control.

The furor over Kansas-Nebraska also doomed the efforts of the Pierce administration to revive an expansionist foreign policy. Pierce and Secretary of State William Marcy were committed to acquiring Cuba from Spain. In October 1854, the American ministers to England, France, and Spain met in Ostend, Belgium, and drew up a memorandum for the administration urging acquisition of Cuba by any means necessary—including force—if Spain refused to sell the island. The "Ostend Manifesto" became public in the midst of the controversy resulting from the Kansas-Nebraska Act, and those Northerners who were convinced that the administration was trying to extend slavery to the Great Plains were enraged to discover it was also scheming to fulfill the southern expansionist dream of a "Caribbean slave empire." The resulting storm of protest forced Pierce and his cohorts to abandon their scheme.

AN APPEAL TO NATIVISM:
THE KNOW-NOTHING EPISODE

The collapse of the Whigs created the opening for a new political party. The anti-Nebraska coalitions of 1854 suggested that such a party might be organized on the basis of northern opposition to the extension of slavery to the territories. Before such a prospect could be realized, however, an alternative emerged in the form of a major political movement based on hostility to immigrants. For a time, it appeared that the Whigs would be replaced by a nativist party rather than an antislavery one.

Massive immigration of Irish and Germans, most of whom were Catholic, led to increasing tension between ethnic groups during the 1840s and early 1850s. Native-born and even immigrant Protestants viewed the newcomers with suspicion and distrust. They expressed their fears in bloody anti-Catholic riots, in church and convent burnings, and in a barrage of propaganda and lurid literature. Nativist agitators charged that immigrants were agents of a foreign despotism, based in Rome, that was bent on overthrowing the American republic.

An anti–Know-Nothing cartoon portrays the Know-Nothings as gun-wielding ruffians.

Political nativism first emerged during the 1840s in the form of local "American" parties protesting immigrant influence in cities such as New York and Philadelphia. In 1849, a secret fraternal organization, the Order of the Star-Spangled Banner, was founded in New York as a vehicle for anti-immigrant attitudes. Members asked about the organization were instructed to reply, "I know nothing." The order grew rapidly in size, by 1854 reaching a membership of between 800,000 and 1,500,000. The political objective of the Know-Nothings was to extend the period of naturalization in order to undercut immigrant voting strength and to keep aliens in their place.

From 1854 to 1855, the nativist movement surfaced as a major political force, the American party. The party attracted Whigs looking for a new home, some ex-Democrats, and native-born workers who feared competition from low-paid immigrants. Many others supported

Know-Nothings often charged that immigrant voters were stealing American elections. In this cartoon, German and Irish immigrants, represented by German beer and Irish whiskey, steal a ballot box.

the American party simply as an alternative to the Democrats. In the North, Know-Nothing candidates generally opposed the Kansas-Nebraska Act and drew their support from voters more anxious about the expansion of slavery than about the evils of immigration.

The success of the new party was so dramatic that it was compared to a hurricane. In 1854 and 1855, it won control of several state governments from Massachusetts to Maryland to Texas, eventually emerging as the principal opposition to the Democrats everywhere except in the Midwest. By late 1855, the Know-Nothings showed every sign of displacing the Whigs as the nation's second party.

Yet, almost as rapidly as it had risen, the Know-Nothing movement collapsed. Its demise in 1856 is one of the great mysteries of American political history. Although it was a national party, it could not overcome the sectional differences that split its northern and southern delegates on the question of slavery in the territories.

Less clear is why the Know-Nothings failed to become the major opposition party to the Democrats in the North. The most persuasive explanation is that their Free-Soil Republican rivals, who were seeking to build a party committed to the containment of slavery, had an issue with wider appeal. In 1855 and 1856, the rate of immigration declined noticeably, and the conflict in Kansas heightened the concern about slavery. Consequently, voters who opposed both the expansion of slavery and unrestricted immigration were inclined to give priority to the former threat.

But the movement's peculiar "antipolitical" character also contributed to its rapid disintegration. Know-Nothingism was a grass-roots protest against the professional politicians who had led the Whig and Democratic parties. As a result of the Know-Nothing party's distrust of conventional politics, most of its spokesmen and elected officials were neither professional politicians nor established community leaders. With inexperienced leaders and a lack of cohesion, the Know-Nothings were unable to make effective use of power once they had it. When voters discovered that the Know-Nothings also *did* nothing, or at least failed to do anything that a more conventional party could not do better, they looked for more competent and experienced leadership.

Kansas and the Rise of the Republicans

The new Republican party was an outgrowth of the anti-Nebraska coalition of 1854. The Republican name was first used in the Midwest where Know-Nothingism failed to win a mass following. A new political label was required because Free-Soil Democrats—especially strong in the Midwest—refused to march under the Whig banner or even support any candidate for high office who called himself a Whig.

When the Know-Nothing party split over the Kansas-Nebraska issue in 1856, most of the northern nativists went over to the Republicans. Although the Republicans argued persuasively that the "slave-power conspiracy" was a greater threat to American liberty and equality than an alleged "popish plot," nativists did not have to abandon their ethnic and religious prejudices to become Republicans; the party showed a clear commitment to the values of native-born evangelical Protestants. On the local level, Republicans generally supported causes that reflected an anti-immigrant or anti-Catholic bias—such as prohibition of the sale of alcoholic beverages, observance of the Sabbath, defense of Protestant Bible–reading in schools, and opposition to state aid for parochial education.

Unlike the Know-Nothings, the Republican party was led by seasoned professional politicians, men who had earlier been prominent Whigs or Democrats. Adept at organizing the grass roots, building coalitions, and employing all the techniques of popular campaigning, they built up an effective party apparatus in an amazingly short time. By early 1856, the new party was well established throughout the North and was preparing to make a serious bid for the presidency.

Underlying the rapid growth of the Republican party was the strong and growing appeal of its position on slavery in the territories. Republicans viewed the unsettled West as a land of opportunities, a place to which the ambitious and hardworking could migrate in the hope of improving their social and economic position. But if slavery was permitted to expand, the rights of "free labor" would be denied. Slaveholders would monopolize the best land, use their slaves to compete unfairly with free white workers, and block efforts at commercial and industrial development. Some Republicans also pandered to racial prejudice: they presented their policy as a way to keep African Americans out of the territories, thus preserving the new lands for exclusive white occupancy.

Although passage of the Kansas-Nebraska Act raised the territorial issue and gave birth to the Republican party, it was the turmoil associated with attempts to implement popular sovereignty in Kansas that kept the issue alive and enabled the Republicans to increase their following throughout the North. When Kansas was organized in the fall of 1854, a bitter contest began for control of the territorial government between militant Free-soilers from New England and the Midwest and slaveholding settlers from Missouri. In the first territorial elections, thousands of Missouri residents crossed the border to vote illegally. The result was a

Free-Soil settlers in Kansas, outraged by the manner in which the proslavery forces had seized control of the territorial legislature, called for a new state convention to draw up a constitution outlawing slavery.

decisive victory for the slave-state forces. The legislature then proceeded to pass laws that not only legalized slavery but made it a crime to speak or act against it.

Free-Soilers were already a majority of the actual residents of the territory when the fraudulently elected legislature denied them the right to agitate against slavery. To defend themselves and their convictions, they took up arms and established a rival territorial government under a constitution that outlawed slavery.

A small-scale civil war then broke out between the rival regimes, culminating in May 1856 when proslavery adherents raided the free-state capital at Lawrence. Portrayed in Republican propaganda as "the sack of Lawrence," this incursion resulted in substantial property damage but no loss of life. In reprisal, antislavery zealot John Brown and a few followers murdered five proslavery settlers in cold blood. During the next few months—until a truce was arranged by an effective territorial governor in the fall of 1856—a hit-and-run guerrilla war raged between free-state and slave-state factions.

The national Republican press exaggerated the extent of the violence in Kansas but correctly pointed out that the federal government was favoring rule by a proslavery minority over a Free-Soil majority. Since the "sack of Lawrence" occurred at about the same time that Charles Sumner was assaulted on the Senate floor, the Republicans launched their 1856 campaign under the twin slogans "Bleeding Kansas" and "Bleeding Sumner." The image of an evil and aggressive "slave power," using violence to deny constitutional rights to its opponents, was a potent device for arousing northern sympathies and winning votes.

SECTIONAL DIVISION IN THE ELECTION OF 1856

The Republican nominating convention revealed the strictly sectional nature of the new party. Only a handful of the delegates from the slave states attended, and

THE ELECTION OF 1856

CANDIDATE	PARTY	POPULAR VOTE	ELECTORAL VOTE
Buchanan	Democratic	1,832,955	174
Frémont	Republican	1,339,932	114
Fillmore	American (Know-Nothing)	871,731	8

all of these were from the upper South. The platform called for liberation of Kansas from the slave power and for congressional prohibition of slavery in all territories. The nominee was John C. Frémont, explorer of the West and participant in the conquest of California during the Mexican-American War.

The Democrats nominated James Buchanan of Pennsylvania, who had a long career in public service. Their platform endorsed popular sovereignty in the territories. The American party, a Know-Nothing remnant that survived mainly as the rallying point for anti-Democratic conservatives in the border states and parts of the South, chose ex-President Millard Fillmore as its standard-bearer and received the backing of those northern Whigs who hoped to revive the tradition of sectional compromise.

The election was really two separate races—one in the North, where the main contest was between Frémont and Buchanan, and the other in the South, which pitted Fillmore against Buchanan. With strong southern support and narrow victories in four crucial northern states—Pennsylvania, New Jersey, Indiana, and Illinois—Buchanan won the election. But the Republicans did remarkably well for a party that was scarcely more than a year old. Frémont won eleven of the sixteen free states, sweeping the upper North with substantial majorities and winning a larger proportion of the northern popular vote than either of his opponents. Since the free states had a substantial majority in the electoral college, a future Republican candidate could win the presidency simply by overcoming a slim Democratic edge in the lower North.

In the South, the results of the election brought a momentary sense of relief tinged with deep anxiety about the future. The very existence of a sectional party committed to restricting the expansion of slavery constituted an insult to the Southerners' way of life. That such a party was genuinely popular in the North was profoundly alarming and raised grave doubts about the security of slavery within the Union. The continued success of a unified Democratic party under southern control was widely viewed as the last hope for the maintenance of sectional balance and "southern rights."

THE HOUSE DIVIDED, 1857–1860

The sectional quarrel deepened and became virtually "irreconcilable" in the years between Buchanan's election in 1856 and Lincoln's victory in 1860. A series of incidents provoked one side or the other, heightened the tension, and ultimately brought the crisis to a head. Behind the panicky reaction to public events lay a growing sense that the North and South were so different in culture and so opposed in basic interests that they could no longer coexist in the same nation.

CULTURAL SECTIONALISM

Signs of cultural and intellectual cleavage had appeared well before the triumph of sectional politics. In the mid-1840s, differing attitudes toward slaveholding split the Methodist and Baptist churches into northern and southern denominations. Informal northern and southern factions of Presbyterians went their separate ways on the slavery issue. Instead of unifying Americans around a common Protestant faith, the churches became nurseries of sectional discord. Increasingly, northern preachers and congregations denounced slaveholding as a sin, while most southern church leaders rallied to a biblical defense of the peculiar institution and became influential apologists for the southern way of life. In both the North and the South, religious leaders helped turn political questions into moral issues and reduced the prospects for a compromise.

American literature also became sectionalized during the 1840s and 1850s. Southern men of letters, including such notable figures as novelist William Gilmore Simms and Edgar Allan Poe, wrote proslavery polemics. Popular novelists produced a flood of "plantation romances" that seemed to glorify southern civilization and sneer at that of the North. In the North, prominent men of letters—Emerson, Thoreau, James Russell Lowell, and Herman Melville—expressed strong antislavery sentiments in prose and poetry, particularly after the outbreak of the Mexican-American War.

Literary abolitionism reached a climax in 1852 when Harriet Beecher Stowe published *Uncle Tom's Cabin,* an enormously successful novel (it sold more than 300,000 copies in a single year) that fixed in the northern mind the image of the slaveholder as a brutal Simon Legree. Much of its emotional impact came from the book's portrayal of slavery as a threat to the family and the cult of domestic-

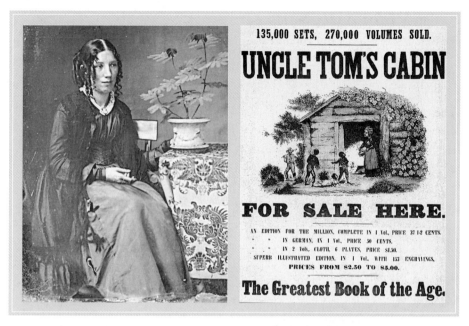

Harriet Beecher Stowe began writing the anti-slavery novel Uncle Tom's Cabin *in 1850, in part to protest passage of the Fugitive Slave Law. Within a year of the novel's publication in 1852, over 300,000 copies had been sold. The poster pictured here advertises a German-language edition, published for German-speaking immigrants.*

ity. When the saintly Uncle Tom was sold away from his adoring wife and children, Northerners shuddered with horror and some Southerners felt a painful twinge of conscience.

Southern defensiveness gradually hardened into cultural and economic nationalism. Northern textbooks were banished from southern schools in favor of those with a prosouthern slant; young men of the planter class were induced to stay in the South for higher education rather than going North (as had been the custom); and a movement developed to encourage southern industry and commerce as a way of reducing dependence on the North. Almost without exception, prominent southern educators and intellectuals of the late 1850s rallied behind southern sectionalism, and many even endorsed the idea of a southern nation.

THE DRED SCOTT CASE

When James Buchanan was inaugurated on March 4, 1857, the dispute over the legal status of slavery in the territories was an open door through which sectional

The case of Dred and Harriet
Scott resulted in a Supreme
Court ruling that has been
called the "most overturned
decision in history."

fears and hatreds could enter the political arena. Buchanan hoped to close that
door by encouraging the Supreme Court to resolve the constitutional issue once
and for all.

The Court was then about to render its decision in the case of *Dred Scott* v.
Sandford. The plaintiff in the case was a Missouri slave who sued for his freedom
on the grounds that he had lived for many years in the Wisconsin Territory, an
area where slavery had been outlawed by the Missouri Compromise. President-
elect Buchanan, in the days just before the inauguration, encouraged the Court to
render a broad decision that would settle the slavery issue.

On March 6, Chief Justice Roger B. Taney announced that the Court had
ruled against Scott, basing its decision on several arguments. The first was that
Scott could not sue because he was not a citizen. Then Taney argued further that
no African American—slave or free—could be a citizen of the United States.
Finally, Taney announced that Scott would not have won his case even if he had

been a legal plaintiff. His residence in the Wisconsin Territory established no right to freedom because Congress had no power to prohibit slavery there. The Missouri Compromise was thus declared unconstitutional and so, implicitly, was the main plank in the Republican platform.

In the North, especially among Republicans, the Court's verdict was viewed as the latest diabolical act of the "slave-power conspiracy." Strong circumstantial evidence supported the charge that the decision was a political maneuver. Five of the six judges who voted in the majority were proslavery Southerners, and their resolution of the territorial issue was close to the extreme southern rights position long advocated by John C. Calhoun.

Republicans denounced the decision as "a wicked and false judgment" and "the greatest crime in the annals of the republic," but they stopped short of openly defying the Court's authority. Instead, they argued on narrow technical grounds that the decision as written was not binding on Congress and that a ban on slavery in the territories could still be enacted. The decision actually helped the Republicans build support; it lent credence to their claim that an aggressive slave power was dominating all branches of the federal government and attempting to use the Constitution to achieve its own ends.

THE LECOMPTON CONTROVERSY

While the Dred Scott case was being decided, leaders of the proslavery faction in Kansas concluded that the time was ripe to draft a constitution and seek admission to the Union as a slave state. Since settlers with free-state views were now an overwhelming majority in the territory, the success of the plan required a rigged, gerrymandered election for convention delegates. When it became clear the election was fixed, the free-staters boycotted it. The resulting constitution, drawn up at Lecompton, was certain to be voted down if submitted to the voters in a fair election and sure to be rejected by Congress if no referendum of any kind was held.

To resolve the dilemma, supporters of the constitution decided to permit a vote on the slavery provision alone, giving the electorate the narrow choice of allowing or forbidding the future importation of slaves. Since there was no way to vote for total abolition, the free-state majority again boycotted, thus allowing ratification of a constitution that protected existing slave property and placed no restriction on importations. Meanwhile, the free-staters, who had finally gained control of the territorial legislature, authorized a second referendum on the constitution as a whole. This time, the proslavery party boycotted the election, and the Lecompton constitution was overwhelmingly rejected.

The Lecompton constitution was such an obvious perversion of popular sovereignty that Stephen A. Douglas spoke out against it. But the Buchanan administration tried to push it through Congress in early 1858, despite overwhelming evidence that the people of Kansas did not wish to enter the Union as a slave state. The bill to admit Kansas as a slave state under the Lecompton constitution passed the Senate but was defeated in the House. A face-saving compromise was then devised. It allowed resubmission of the constitution to the Kansas voters on the pretext that a change in the provisions for a federal land grant was required. Finally, in August 1858, the people of Kansas killed the Lecompton constitution when they voted it down by a margin of 6 to 1.

The Lecompton controversy made the sectional quarrel truly "irreconcilable." Republicans viewed the administration's efforts to admit Kansas as a slave state as evidence of southern dominance of the Democratic party and the lengths to which proslavery conspirators would go to achieve their ends. The affair split the Democratic party between the followers of Douglas and the backers of the Buchanan administration.

For Douglas himself, however, the affair was a disaster; it destroyed his hopes of uniting the Democratic party and defusing the slavery issue through the application of popular sovereignty. What had happened in Kansas suggested that popular sovereignty in practice was an invitation to civil war. Furthermore, the Dred Scott decision implied that the voters of a territory could not legally decide the fate of slavery at any time before the constitution-making stage. Hence, the interpretation of popular sovereignty favored in the North was undermined, and Southerners could insist on full protection of their right to own human property in all federal territories. Although his stand against Lecompton won him some popularity in the North, Douglas was denounced as a traitor in the South, and his hopes of being elected president were seriously diminished.

DEBATING THE MORALITY OF SLAVERY

Douglas's immediate problem winning reelection to the Senate from Illinois in 1858. Here he faced surprisingly tough opposition from the Republican candidate, former Whig Congressman Abraham Lincoln. Lincoln set out to convince the voters that Douglas could not be relied on to oppose the extension of slavery, even though he had opposed the admission of Kansas under a proslavery constitution.

In the speech that opened his campaign, Lincoln tried to distance himself from his opponent by taking a more radical position. "'A house divided against itself cannot stand,'" he argued, paraphrasing a line from the Gospel of Mark. "I believe this government cannot endure, permanently half *slave* and half *free*." He then described the chain of events between the Kansas-Nebraska Act and the Dred Scott decision as evidence of a plot to extend and nationalize slavery and tried to link Douglas to this proslavery conspiracy by pointing to his rival's unwillingness to take a stand on the morality of slavery, to his professed indifference about whether slavery was voted up or down in the territories. For Lincoln, the only security against the triumph of slavery and the slave power was moral opposition to human bondage.

Stephen Douglas, the "Little Giant" from Illinois, won election to Congress when he was just thirty years old. Four years later, he was elected to the Senate.

In the series of debates that focused national attention on the Illinois senatorial contest, Lincoln hammered away at the theme that Douglas was a covert defender of slavery because he was not a principled opponent of it. Douglas responded by accusing Lincoln of endangering the Union by his talk of putting slavery on the path to extinction. Denying that he was an abolitionist, Lincoln made a distinction between tolerating slavery in the South, where it was protected by the Constitution, and allowing it to expand to places where it could legally be prohibited. Restriction of slavery, he argued, had been the policy of the Founders, and it was Douglas and the Democrats who had departed from the great tradition of containing an evil that could not be immediately eliminated.

In the debate at Freeport, Illinois, Lincoln questioned Douglas on how he could reconcile popular sovereignty with the Dred Scott decision. The Little Giant, as Douglas was called by his admirers, responded that slavery could not exist without supportive legislation to sustain it and that territorial legislatures could simply refrain from passing a slave code if they wanted to keep it out.

Abraham Lincoln, shown here in his first full-length portrait. Although Lincoln lost the contest for the Senate seat in 1858, the Lincoln-Douglas debates established his reputation as a rising star of the Republican party.

Coupled with his anti-Lecompton stand, Douglas's "Freeport Doctrine" undoubtedly hardened southern opposition to his presidential ambitions.

Douglas's most effective debating point was charging that Lincoln's moral opposition to slavery implied a belief in racial equality. Lincoln, facing an intensely racist electorate, vigorously denied this charge and affirmed his commitment to white supremacy. He would grant blacks the right to the fruits of their own labor while denying them the "privileges" of citizenship. This was an inherently contradictory position, and Douglas made the most of it.

Although Republican candidates for the state legislature won a majority of the popular votes, the Democrats carried more counties and thus were able to send Douglas back to the Senate. Lincoln lost an office, but he won respect in Republican circles throughout the country. By stressing the moral dimension of the slavery question and undercutting any possibility of fusion between Republicans and Douglas Democrats, he had sharpened his party's ideological focus and had stiffened its backbone against any temptation to compromise its Free-Soil position.

THE SOUTH'S CRISIS OF FEAR

After Kansas became a free territory instead of a slave state in August 1858, the issue of slavery in the territories became a symbolic issue rather than a practical one. The remaining unorganized areas, which were in the Rockies and northern

Great Plains, were unlikely to attract slaveholding settlers. Nevertheless, Southerners continued to demand the "right" to take their slaves into the territories, and Republicans persisted in denying it to them. Although the Republicans repeatedly promised not to interfere with slavery where it already existed, Southerners refused to believe them and interpreted their unyielding stand against the extension of slavery as a threat to southern rights and security.

A chain of events in late 1859 and early 1860 turned southern anxiety about northern attitudes and policies into a "crisis of fear." The first of these incidents was John Brown's raid on Harpers Ferry, Virginia, in October 1859. Brown, who had the appearance and manner of an Old Testament prophet, thought of himself as God's chosen instrument "to purge this land with blood" and eradicate the sin of slaveholding. On October 16, he led a small band of men, including five free blacks, across the Potomac River from his base in Maryland and seized the federal arsenal and armory in Harpers Ferry.

Brown's aim was to launch a guerrilla war from havens in the Appalachians that would eventually extend to the plantation regions of the lower South. But the neighboring slaves did not rise up to join him, and Brown's raiders were driven out of the armory and arsenal by the local militia and forced to take refuge in a fire-engine house. There they held out until a force of U.S. Marines commanded by Colonel Robert E. Lee stormed their bastion. In the course of the fighting, ten of Brown's men were killed or mortally wounded, along with seven of the townspeople and soldiers who opposed them.

The wounded Brown and his remaining followers were put on trial for treason against the state of Virginia. The subsequent investigation produced evidence that several prominent northern abolitionists had approved of Brown's plan and had raised money for his preparations. This seemed to confirm southern fears that abolitionists were actively engaged in fomenting slave insurrection.

After Brown was sentenced to be hanged, Southerners were further stunned by the outpouring of sympathy and admiration that his impending fate aroused in the North. His actual execution on December 2 completed Brown's elevation to the status of a martyred saint of the antislavery cause. The day of his death was marked in parts of the North by the tolling of bells, the firing of cannons, and the holding of memorial services.

Although Republican politicians were quick to denounce John Brown for his violent methods, Southerners interpreted the wave of northern sympathy as an expression of the majority opinion and the Republicans' "real" attitude. Within the South, the raid and its aftermath touched off a frenzy of fear, repression, and mobilization. Witch-hunts searched for the agents of a vast imagined conspiracy to stir up slave rebellion; vigilance committees were organized in many localities to resist subversion and ensure control of slaves; and orators pointed increasingly to secession as the only way to protect southern interests.

Brown was scarcely in his grave when another set of events put southern nerves on edge once more. Next to abolitionist-abetted rebellions, the slaveholding South's greatest fear was that the nonslaveholding majority would turn against the master class and the solidarity of southern whites behind the peculiar institution would crumble. When Congress met to elect a speaker of the House on December 5, Southerners bitterly denounced the Republican candidate— John Sherman of Ohio—because he had endorsed as a campaign document a condensed version of Hinton R. Helper's *Impending Crisis of the South.* Helper's book, which called on lower-class whites to resist planter dominance and abolish slavery in their own interest, was regarded by slaveholders as even more seditious than *Uncle Tom's Cabin.* They feared the spread of "Helperism" among poor whites almost as much as they feared the effect of "John Brownism" on the slaves.

The ensuing contest over the speaker's office lasted almost two months. Southern congressmen threatened secession if Sherman was elected, and feelings became so heated that some representatives began to carry weapons on the floor of the House. When it eventually became clear that Sherman could not be elected, his name was withdrawn in favor of a moderate Republican who had refrained from endorsing Helper's book. The impasse over the speakership was thus resolved, but the contest helped persuade Southerners that the Republicans were committed to stirring up class conflict among southern whites.

Republicans' identification with Helper's ideas may have been decisive in convincing many conservative planters that a Republican victory in the presidential election of 1860 would be intolerable. Anxiety about the future allegiance of nonslaveholding whites had been growing during the 1850s. During the decade, the proportion of white heads of families owning slaves had shrunk from 30 to 25 percent in all the slave states and from 50 to 40 percent in the cotton belt of the lower South. Perceiving in this trend the seeds of class conflict, proslavery extremists had called for the reopening of the Atlantic slave trade as a way to reduce the price of slaves and make them more widely available. Although the interest of large owners in preserving the appreciated value of their human property had helped prevent the "proslavery crusade" from gaining broad support, many slaveholders were concerned about the social and political consequences of their status as a shrinking minority. Even those most strongly committed to the Union were terrified by the prospect that a Republican party in control of the federal government would use its power to foster "Helperism" among the South's nonslaveholding majority.

In this cartoon from the 1860 election, candidates Lincoln and Douglas struggle for control of the country, while Breckinridge tears away the South. John Bell of the Constitutional Union party futilely attempts to repair the damage to the torn nation.

THE ELECTION OF 1860

The Republicans, sniffing victory and generally insensitive to the depth of southern feeling against them, met in Chicago on May 16 to nominate a presidential candidate. The initial front-runner, Senator William H. Seward of New York, proved unacceptable because of his reputation for radicalism and his record of strong opposition to the nativist movement. Most delegates wanted a less controversial nominee who could win two or three of the northern states that had gone Democratic in 1856. Abraham Lincoln met their specifications: he was from Illinois, a state the Republicans needed to win; he had a more moderate image than Seward; and he had kept his personal distaste for Know-Nothingism to himself. In addition, his rise from frontier poverty to legal and political prominence embodied the Republican ideal of equal opportunity for all. Lincoln won the nomination on the third ballot.

The Republican platform, like the nominee, was meant to broaden the party's appeal in the North. Although a commitment to halt the expansion of slavery remained, economic matters received more attention than they had in

THE ELECTION OF 1860

CANDIDATE	PARTY	POPULAR VOTE	ELECTORAL VOTE
Lincoln	Republican	1,865,593	180
Beckinridge	Democratic, Southern	848,356	72
Douglas	Democratic, Northern	1,382,713	12
Bell	Constitutional Union	592,906	39

1856. The platform called for a high protective tariff, endorsed free homesteads, and supported federal aid for internal improvements, especially a transcontinental railroad. The platform was cleverly designed to attract ex-Whigs to the Republican camp and accommodate enough renegade Democrats to give the party a solid majority in the northern states.

The Democrats failed to present a united front against this formidable challenge. When the party first met in Charleston in late April, Douglas commanded a majority of the delegates but was unable to win the two-thirds required for nomination because of unyielding southern opposition. He did succeed in getting the convention to endorse popular sovereignty as its slavery platform, but the price was a walkout by Deep South delegates who favored a federal slave code for the territories.

Unable to agree on a nominee, the convention adjourned to reconvene in Baltimore in June. Then a fight developed over whether to seat newly selected pro-Douglas delegations from some Deep South states in place of the bolters from the first convention. When the Douglas forces won most of the contested seats, another and more massive southern walkout took place. The result was a fracture of the Democratic party. The delegates who remained nominated Douglas and reaffirmed the party's commitment to popular sovereignty, while the bolters convened elsewhere to nominate John Breckinridge of Kentucky on a platform of federal protection for slavery in the territories.

By the time the campaign was under way, four parties were running presidential candidates. In addition to the Republicans, the Douglas Democrats, and the "Southern Rights" Democrats, a remnant of conservative Whigs and Know-Nothings nominated John Bell of Tennessee under the banner of the Constitutional Union party. Taking no explicit stand on the issue of slavery in the territories, the Constitutional Unionists tried to represent the spirit of sectional accommodation that had led to compromise in 1820 and 1850. In effect, the race became a separate two-party contest in each section: in the North, the real choice was between Lincoln and Douglas; in the South, the only candidates with a fighting chance were Breckinridge and Bell. Douglas alone tried to carry on a national campaign, gaining some support in every state, but actually winning only in Missouri.

When the results came in, the Republicans had achieved a stunning victory. Lincoln won a decisive majority—180 to 123 over his combined opponents. In the North, his 54 percent of the popular vote annihilated Douglas. In the South, where Lincoln was not even on the ballot, Breckinridge triumphed everywhere except in Virginia, Kentucky, and Tennessee, which went for Bell and the Constitutional Unionists. The Republican strategy of seeking power by trying to win decisively in the majority section was brilliantly successful. Although fewer than 40 percent of those who went to the polls throughout the nation actually voted for Lincoln, his support in the North was so solid that he would have won in the electoral college even if his opponents had been unified behind a single candidate.

Most Southerners saw the result of the election as a catastrophe. A candidate and a party with no support in their own section had won the presidency on a platform viewed as insulting to southern honor and hostile to vital southern interests. Since the birth of the republic, Southerners had either sat in the White House or exerted considerable influence over those who did. Those days might now be gone forever. Rather than accept permanent minority status in American politics and face the resulting dangers to black slavery and white "liberty," the political leaders of the lower South launched a movement for immediate secession from the Union.

EXPLAINING THE CRISIS

Generations of historians have searched for the underlying causes of the crisis leading to disruption of the Union but have failed to agree on exactly what they were. Some have stressed the clash of economic interests between agrarian and industrializing regions. But this interpretation does not reflect the way people at the time expressed their concerns. The main issues in the sectional debates of the 1850s were whether slavery was right or wrong and whether it should be extended or contained. Disagreements over protective tariffs and other economic measures benefiting one section or the other were clearly secondary.

Another group of historians have blamed the crisis on "irresponsible" politicians and agitators on both sides of the Mason-Dixon line. Public opinion, they argue, was whipped into a frenzy over issues that competent statesmen could have resolved. But this viewpoint has been sharply criticized for failing to acknowledge the depths of feeling that could be aroused by the slavery question and for underestimating the obstacles to a peaceful solution.

The dominant modern view is that the crisis was rooted in profound ideological differences over the morality and utility of slavery as an institution. Most interpreters now agree that the roots of the conflict lay in the fact that the South was a slave society and determined to stay that way, while the North was equally committed to a free-labor system. No other differences divided the regions in this decisive way, and it is hard to imagine that secessionism would have developed if the South abolished slavery in the postrevolutionary period.

Nevertheless, the existence or nonexistence of slavery will not explain why the crisis came when it did and in the way that it did. Why did the conflict become "irreconcilable" in the 1850s and not earlier or later? Why did it take the form of a political struggle over the future of slavery in the territories? Adequate answers to both questions require an understanding of political developments that were not directly caused by tensions over slavery.

By the 1850s, the established Whig and Democratic parties were in trouble partly because they no longer offered the voters clear-cut alternatives on economic issues. This situation created an opening for new parties and issues. After the Know-Nothings failed to make attitudes toward immigrants the basis for a political realignment, the Republicans used the issue of slavery in the territories to build the first successful sectional party in American history. They called for "free soil" rather than freedom for blacks because abolitionism conflicted with the northern majority's commitment to white supremacy and its respect for the original constitutional compromise that established a hands-off policy toward slavery in the southern states. For Southerners, the Republican party now became the main issue, and they fought against it from within the Democratic party.

If politicians seeking new ways to mobilize an apathetic electorate are seen as the main instigators of sectional crisis, the reasons why certain appeals were more effective than others must still be uncovered. Why did the slavery extension issue arouse such strong feelings during the 1850s? The same issue had arisen earlier and had proved adjustable. If the expansion of slavery had been as vital and emotional a question in 1820 as it was in the 1850s, the declining Federalist party presumably would have revived in the form of a northern sectional party adamantly opposed to the admission of slave states to the Union.

Ultimately, therefore, the crisis of the 1850s must be understood as having a deep social and cultural dimension as well as a purely political one. In *Uncle Tom's Cabin,* Harriet Beecher Stowe personified the cultural conflict in her depiction of two brothers with similar personalities, one of whom settled in Vermont "to rule over rocks and stones" and the other in Louisiana "to rule over men and women." The first became a deacon in the church, a member of the local abolition society, and, despite his natural authoritarianism, the adherent of "a democratic theory." The second became indifferent to religion, openly aristocratic, a staunch defender of slavery, and an extreme racist. Stowe's comparison may have been biased, but she showed a good understanding of how the contrasting environments of slavery and freedom could lead very similar men to have sharply conflicting views of the world.

This divergence in basic beliefs and values had widened and become less manageable between the 1820s and the 1850s. Both sections continued to profess allegiance to the traditional "republican" ideals of individual liberty and independence, and both were strongly influenced by evangelical religion. But differences in the economic and social development of each region transformed a common culture into two conflicting cultures. In the North, a rising middle class adapted to the new market economy with the help of an evangelical Christianity that sanctioned self-discipline and social reform. The South, on the other hand, embraced slavery as a foundation for the liberty and independence of whites. Its evangelicalism encouraged personal piety but not social reform. The notion that white liberty and equality depended on resistance to social and economic change and on continuing to have enslaved blacks to do menial labor became more deeply entrenched.

When politicians appealed to sectionalism during the 1850s, therefore, they could evoke conflicting views of what constituted the good society. To most Northerners, the South—with its allegedly idle masters, degraded unfree workers, and shiftless poor whites—seemed to be in flagrant violation of the Protestant work ethic and the ideal of open competition. Southerners tended to view the North as a land of hypocritical money-grubbers who denied the obvious fact that the virtue, independence, and liberty of free citizens was possible only when dependent laboring classes—especially racially inferior ones—were kept under the kind of rigid control that only slavery could provide. According to the ideology of northern Republicans, the freedom of the individual depended on equality of opportunity for everyone; in the minds of southern sectionalists, it required that part of the population be enslaved. Once these contrary views of the world had become the main themes of political discourse, sectional compromise was no longer possible.

15

SECESSION AND THE CIVIL WAR

The man elected to the White House in 1860 was striking in appearance—he was 6 feet 4 inches in height and seemed even taller because of his disproportionately long legs and his habit of wearing a high silk "stovepipe" hat. But Abraham Lincoln's previous career provided no guarantee he would tower over most of the other presidents in more than physical height. When Lincoln sketched the main events of his life for a campaign biographer in June 1860, he was modest almost to the point of self-deprecation. Especially regretting his "want of education," he assured the biographer that "he does what he can to supply the want."

Born to poor and illiterate parents on the Kentucky frontier in 1809, Lincoln received a few months of formal schooling in Indiana after the family moved there in 1816. But mostly he educated himself, reading and rereading a few treasured books by firelight. In 1831, when the family migrated to Illinois, he left home to make a living for himself in the struggling settlement of New Salem. After failing as a merchant, he found a path to success in law and politics. While studying law on his own in New Salem, he won election to the state legislature and in 1837, he moved to Springfield, the state capital. Lincoln combined exceptional political and legal skills with a down-to-earth, humorous way of addressing jurors and voters. Consequently, he became a leader of the Whig party in Illinois and one of the most sought after of the lawyers who rode the central Illinois judicial circuit.

The high point of his political career as a Whig was one term in Congress (1847–1849), but his strong stand against the Mexican-American War alienated

This Matthew Brady photograph of Abraham Lincoln was taken when Lincoln arrived in Washington for his inauguration. In his inaugural address, Lincoln appealed for preservation of the union.

much of his constituency, and he did not seek re-election. He campaigned vigorously for Zachary Taylor in the 1848 presidential contest, but the new president failed to appoint Lincoln to a patronage job he coveted. Having been repudiated by the electorate and ignored by the national leadership of a party he had served loyally and well, Lincoln concentrated on building his law practice.

The Kansas-Nebraska Act of 1854, with its advocacy of popular sovereignty, provided Lincoln with an opportunity to return to politics. For the first time, his driving ambition for political success and his personal convictions about what was best for the country were easy to reconcile. Lincoln had long believed slavery was an unjust institution that should be tolerated only to the extent the Constitution and the tradition of sectional compromise required. Attacking Douglas's plan of popular sovereignty because it broke with precedents for federal containment or control of the growth of slavery, Lincoln threw in his lot with the Republicans and assumed leadership of the new party in Illinois. He attracted national attention in his bid for Douglas's Senate seat in 1858 and turned out to have the right qualifications when the Republicans chose a presidential nominee in 1860. The fact that he had split rails as a young man was used in the campaign to show that he was a man of the people.

After Lincoln's election provoked southern secession and plunged the nation into the greatest crisis in its history, there was understandable skepticism about him in many quarters: was the former rail-splitter from Illinois up to the responsibilities he faced? Lincoln had less experience relevant to a wartime presidency than any previous chief executive; he had never been a governor, senator, cabinet officer, vice president, or high-ranking military officer. But some of his training as a prairie politician would prove extremely useful in the years ahead.

Another reason for Lincoln's effectiveness as a war leader was that he identified wholeheartedly with the northern cause and could inspire others to make sacrifices for it. In his view, the issue in the conflict was nothing less than the survival of the kind of political system that gave men like himself a chance for high office.

The Civil War put on trial the very principle of democracy at a time when most European nations had rejected political liberalism and accepted the conservative view that popular government would inevitably collapse into anarchy. It also showed the shortcomings of a purely white man's democracy and brought the first hesitant steps toward black citizenship. As Lincoln put it in the Gettysburg Address, the only cause great enough to justify the enormous sacrifice of life on the battlefields was the struggle to preserve and extend the democratic ideal, or to ensure that "government of the people, by the people, for the people, shall not perish from the earth."

THE STORM GATHERS

Lincoln's election provoked the secession of seven states of the Deep South but did not lead immediately to armed conflict. Before the sectional quarrel would turn from a cold war into a hot one, two things had to happen: a final effort to defuse the conflict by compromise and conciliation had to fail, and the North needed to develop a firm resolve to maintain the Union by military action. Both of these developments may seem inevitable in retrospect, but for most of those living at the time, it was not clear until the guns blazed at Fort Sumter that the sectional crisis would have to be resolved on the battlefield.

THE DEEP SOUTH SECEDES
South Carolina, which had long been in the forefront of southern rights and proslavery agitation, was the first state to secede, doing so on December 20,

1860, at a convention meeting in Charleston. The constitutional theory behind secession was that the Union was a "compact" among sovereign states, each of which could withdraw from the Union by the vote of a convention similar to the one that had ratified the Constitution in the first place. The South Carolinians justified seceding at that time by charging that "a sectional party" had elected a president "whose opinions and purposes are hostile to slavery."

In other states of the Cotton Kingdom, there was similar outrage at Lincoln's election but less certainty about how to respond to it. Those who advocated immediate secession by each state individually were opposed by the "cooperationists," who believed the slave states should act as a unit. If the cooperationists had triumphed, secession would have been delayed until a southern convention had agreed on it. Some of these moderates hoped a delay would

A South Carolina newspaper announces the dissolution of the Union. South Carolina's secession was celebrated in the South with bonfires, parades, and fireworks.

provide time to extort major concessions from the North and thus remove the need for dissolving the Union. But South Carolina's unilateral action set a precedent that weakened the cooperationists' cause.

When conventions in six other Deep South states met in January 1861, delegates favoring immediate secession were everywhere in the majority. By February 1, seven states had removed themselves from the Union—South Carolina, Alabama, Mississippi, Florida, Georgia, Louisiana, and Texas. In the upper South, however, calls for immediate secession were unsuccessful; majority opinion in Virginia, North Carolina, Tennessee, and Arkansas did not subscribe to the view that Lincoln's election was a sufficient reason for breaking up the

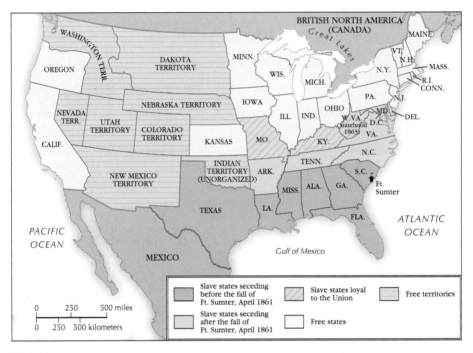

Secession

The fall of Fort Sumter was a watershed for the secessionist movement. With no room left for compromise, slave states of the upper South chose to join the Confederacy.

Union. In these states, with their stronger ties to the northern economy, moderate leaders were more willing than those in the lower South to seek a sectional compromise.

Without waiting for their sister slave states to the north, delegates from the Deep South met in Montgomery, Alabama, on February 4 to establish the Confederate States of America. The convention acted as a provisional government while at the same time drafting a permanent constitution. Relatively moderate leaders, most of whom had not supported secession until *after* Lincoln's election, dominated the proceedings and defeated or modified some of the pet schemes of a radical faction composed of extreme southern nationalists. Voted down were proposals to reopen the Atlantic slave trade, to abolish the three-fifths clause (in favor of counting all slaves in determining congressional representation), and to prohibit the admission of free states to the new Confederacy.

The resulting constitution was surprisingly similar to that of the United States. Most of the differences merely spelled out traditional southern interpretations of the federal charter: The central government was denied the authority to impose protective tariffs, subsidize internal improvements, or interfere with slavery in the states and was required to pass laws protecting slavery in the territories. As provisional president and vice president, the convention chose Jefferson Davis of Mississippi and Alexander Stephens of Georgia, men who had resisted secessionist agitation.

The moderation shown in Montgomery resulted in part from a desire to win support for the cause of secessionism in the reluctant states of the upper South. But it also revealed something important about the nature of the separatist impulse even in the lower South. Proslavery reactionaries had never succeeded in getting a majority behind them. Most Southerners had been opposed to dissolving the Union so long as there had been good reasons to believe slavery was safe from northern interference.

Lincoln's election and the panic that ensued gave Southerners cause to fear that Northerners would no longer keep their "hands off" southern slavery; but the actions of the Montgomery convention made it clear that the goal of the new converts to secessionism was not to establish a slaveholder's reactionary utopia. What they really wanted was to re-create the Union as it had been before the rise of the new Republican party, and they opted for secession only when it seemed clear that separation was the only way to achieve their aim. The decision to allow free states to join the Confederacy reflected a hope that much of the old Union could be reconstituted under southern direction. Some optimists even predicted that all of the North except New England would eventually join the Confederacy.

Secession and the formation of the Confederacy thus amounted to a very conservative and defensive kind of "revolution." The only justification for southern independence on which a majority could agree was the need for greater security for the "peculiar institution." Vice President Stephens spoke for all the founders of the Confederacy when he described the cornerstone of the new government as "the great truth that the negro is not equal to the white man—that slavery—subordination to the superior race—is his natural condition."

THE FAILURE OF COMPROMISE

While the Deep South was opting for independence, moderates in the North and border slave states were trying to devise a compromise that would stem the secessionist tide. In December 1860, Senator John Crittenden of Kentucky presented a plan that advocated extending the Missouri Compromise line to the Pacific to guarantee the protection of slavery in the southwestern territories and in any territories south of the line that might be acquired in the future. Crittenden's proposal also recommended federal compensation to the owners of escaped slaves and a constitutional amendment that would forever prohibit the federal government from abolishing or regulating slavery in the states.

Initially, congressional Republicans showed some willingness to give ground and take the proposals seriously. Somewhat confused about how firmly they should support the party position that slavery must be banned in all territories, Republicans in Congress turned for guidance to the president-elect, who had remained in Springfield. An emissary brought back word that Lincoln was adamantly opposed to the extension of the compromise line. In the words of one of his fellow Republicans, he stood "firm as an oak."

The resounding no to the central provision of the Crittenden plan and other similar compromise proposals stiffened the backbone of congressional Republicans, and they voted against compromise in committee. Also voting against it, and thereby ensuring its defeat, were the remaining senators and congressmen of the seceding states, who had vowed in advance to support no compromise unless the majority of Republicans also endorsed it. Their purpose in taking this stand was to obtain guarantees that the northern sectional party would end its attacks on "southern rights." The Republicans did in the end agree to support Crittenden's "unamendable" amendment guaranteeing that slavery would be immune from future federal action. This action was not really a concession to the South, because Republicans had always acknowledged that the federal government had no constitutional authority to meddle with slavery in the states.

Some historians have blamed Lincoln and the Republicans for causing an unnecessary war by rejecting a compromise that would have appeased southern pride without providing any immediate practical opportunities for the expansion of slavery. But it is questionable whether approval of the compromise would have halted secession of the Deep South. It is quite possible that the secessionists would have been satisfied with nothing less than federal protection of slavery in *all* territories and the active suppression of antislavery agitation in the North.

Furthermore, Lincoln and those who took his advice had what they considered to be very good reasons for not making territorial concessions. First, they mistakenly believed that the secession movement reflected only a minority opinion in the South. Thus, they hoped that a strong stand would win the support of southern Unionists and moderates. It is doubtful, however, that Lincoln and his supporters would have given ground even if they had realized the secession movement was genuinely popular in the Deep South. In their view, extending the Missouri Compromise line of 36°30' to the Pacific would not halt agitation for extending slavery to new areas. The only way to resolve the crisis over the future of slavery and to reunite "the house divided" was to remove any chance that slaveholders could enlarge their domain.

Lincoln was also convinced that backing down in the face of secessionist threats would fatally undermine the democratic principle of majority rule. In his inaugural address of March 4, 1861, he recalled that during the winter, many "patriotic men" had urged him to accept a compromise that would "shift the ground" on which he had been elected. But to do so would have signified that a victorious presidential candidate "cannot be inaugurated till he betrays those who elected him by breaking his pledges, and surrendering to those who tried and failed to defeat him at the polls." Making such a concession would mean that "this government and all popular government is already at an end."

AND THE WAR CAME

By the time of Lincoln's inauguration, seven states had seceded, formed an independent confederacy, and seized most federal forts and other installations in the Deep South without firing a shot. Lincoln's predecessor, James Buchanan, had denied the right of secession but had also refused to use "coercion" to maintain federal authority. Buchanan's doubts about whether a Union held together by force was worth keeping were, for a time, widely shared in the North. The northern business community was reluctant to break commercial links with the cotton-producing South, and some antislavery Republicans and abolitionists opposed coercive action because they thought the nation might be better off if "the erring sisters" of the Deep South were allowed "to depart in peace."

The collapse of compromise efforts narrowed the choices to peaceful separation or war between the sections. By early March, the tide of public opinion was beginning to shift in favor of strong action to preserve the Union. Even the business community came to support coercive measures, reasoning that a temporary disruption of commerce was better than the permanent loss of the South as a market and source of raw materials.

In his inaugural address, Lincoln called for a cautious and limited use of force. He would defend federal forts and installations not yet in Confederate hands but would not attempt to recapture the ones already taken. He thus tried to shift the burden for beginning hostilities to the Confederacy, which would have to attack before it would be attacked.

As Lincoln spoke, only four military installations within the seceded states were still held by U.S. forces. The most important and vulnerable of these was Fort Sumter inside Charleston Harbor. Attention focused on Sumter because the Confederacy was demanding the surrender of a garrison that was within easy reach of shore batteries and running low on supplies. Shortly after taking office, Lincoln was informed that Sumter could not hold out much longer and that he would have to decide whether to reinforce it or let it fall.

Although, the majority of Lincoln's cabinet initially opposed efforts to reinforce or provision Sumter, on April 4, Lincoln ordered that an expedition be prepared to bring food and other provisions to the beleaguered troops in Charleston

Harbor. Two days later, he sent word to the governor of South Carolina that the relief expedition was being sent.

The expedition sailed on April 8 and 9; but before it arrived, Confederate authorities decided the sending of provisions was a hostile act and proceeded to attack the fort. Early on the morning of April 12, shore batteries opened fire; the bombardment continued for forty hours. Finally, on April 13, the Union forces under Major Robert Anderson surrendered, and the Confederate flag was raised over Fort Sumter. The South had won a victory but had also assumed responsibility for firing the first shot.

On April 15, Lincoln proclaimed that an insurrection against federal authority existed in the Deep South and called on the militia of the loyal states to provide 75,000 troops for short-term service to put it down. Two days later, Virginia voted to join the Confederacy. Within the next five weeks, Arkansas, Tennessee, and North Carolina followed suit. These slave states of the upper South had been unwilling to secede just because Lincoln was elected, but when he called on them to provide troops to "coerce" other southern states, they had to choose sides. Believing that secession was a constitutional right, they were quick to cut their ties with a government that opted for the use of force to maintain the Union.

In the North, the firing on Sumter evoked strong feelings of patriotism and dedication to the Union. Stephen A. Douglas, Lincoln's former political rival, pledged his full support for the crusade against secession and literally worked himself to death rallying midwestern Democrats behind the government. By firing on the flag, the Confederacy united the North. Everyone assumed the war would be short and not very bloody. It remained to be seen whether Unionist fervor could be sustained through a long and costly struggle.

The entire Confederacy, which now moved its capital from Montgomery to Richmond, Virginia, contained only eleven of the fifteen states in which slavery was lawful. In the border slave states of Maryland, Delaware, Kentucky, and Missouri, a combination of local Unionism and federal intervention thwarted secession. Kentucky initially proclaimed itself neutral but eventually sided with the Union, mainly because Lincoln provoked the South into violating neutrality first by sending regular troops into the state. Maryland, which surrounded the nation's capital and provided it with access to the free states, was kept in the Union by more ruthless methods, which included the use of martial law to suppress Confederate sympathizers. In Missouri, the presence of regular troops, aided significantly by a staunchly pro-Union German immigrant population, stymied the secession movement. But pro-Union forces failed to maintain order and brutal guerrilla fighting made wartime Missouri an unsafe and bloody place.

Hence the Civil War was not, strictly speaking, a struggle between slave and free states. More than anything else, conflicting views on the right of secession determined the ultimate division of states and the choices of individuals in areas where sentiment was divided. General Robert E. Lee, for example, was neither a defender of slavery nor a southern nationalist. But he followed Virginia out of the Union because he was the loyal son of a "sovereign state." General George Thomas, another Virginian, chose the Union because he believed it was indissoluble. Although concern about the future of slavery had driven the Deep South to secede in the first place, the actual lineup of states and supporters meant the two sides would initially define the war less as a struggle over slavery than as a contest to determine whether the Union was indivisible.

ADJUSTING TO TOTAL WAR

The Civil War was a "total war" involving every aspect of society because the North could achieve its aim of restoring the Union only by defeating the South so thoroughly that its separatist government would be overthrown. It was a long war because the Confederacy put up "a hell of a fight" before it would agree to be put to death. Total war is a test of societies, economies, and political systems, as well as a battle of wits between generals and military strategists—and the Civil War was no exception.

PROSPECTS, PLANS, AND EXPECTATIONS

If the war was to be decided by sheer physical strength, then the North had an enormous edge in population, industrial capacity, and railroad mileage. But the South, too, had some advantages. To achieve its aim of independence, the Confederacy needed only to defend its own territory successfully. The North, on the other hand, had to invade and conquer the South. Consequently, the Confederacy faced a less serious supply problem, had a greater capacity to choose the time and place of combat, and could take advantage of familiar terrain and a friendly civilian population.

The nature of the war meant southern leaders could define their cause as defense of their homeland against Yankee invaders. The northern cause was not nearly as clear-cut as that of the South. It seemed doubtful in 1861 that Northerners would fervently support a war fought for the seemingly abstract principle that the Union was sacred and perpetual.

Confederate optimism on the eve of the war was also fed by more dubious calculations. It was widely assumed that Southerners, who were used to riding and shooting, would make better soldiers than the clerks and factory workers who, it was anticipated, would make up a large part of the Union army. (Actually, a majority of northern soldiers would also be farm boys.) When most of the large proportion of high-ranking officers in the U.S. Army who were of southern ori-

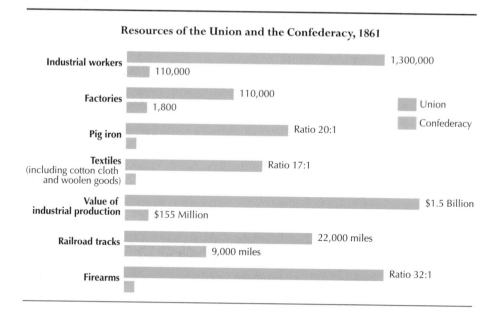

Resources of the Union and the Confederacy, 1861

Industrial workers: 1,300,000 / 110,000

Factories: 110,000 / 1,800

Union

Confederacy

Pig iron: Ratio 20:1

Textiles (including cotton cloth and woolen goods): Ratio 17:1

Value of industrial production: $1.5 Billion / $155 Million

Railroad tracks: 22,000 miles / 9,000 miles

Firearms: Ratio 32:1

gin resigned to accept Confederate commands, Southerners confidently expected that their armies would be better led. If external help was needed, major foreign powers such as England and France might come to the aid of the Confederacy because the industrial economies of those European nations depended on southern cotton.

At the beginning of the war, leaders of both sides tried to find the best way to capitalize on their advantages and compensate for their limitations. The choice before President Davis, who assumed personal direction of the Confederate military effort, was whether to stay on the defensive or seek a sudden and dramatic victory by invading the North. He chose to wage a mainly defensive war in the hope that the northern populace would soon tire of the blood and sacrifice and leave the Confederacy to go its own way. But this plan did not preclude invading the North when good opportunities presented themselves. Although their primary strategic orientation was defensive, it was an "offensive defense" that southern commanders put into effect.

Northern military planners had greater difficulty in working out a basic strategy, and it took a good deal of trial and error (mostly error) before there was a clear sense of what had to be done. Some optimists believed the war could be won quickly and easily by sending an army to capture the Confederate capital of Richmond, scarcely a hundred miles from Washington. The early battles in Virginia ended this optimistic "On to Richmond" strategy. The aged General Winfield Scott, who commanded the Union army during the early months of the war, recommended an "anaconda policy" calling for the North to squeeze the

South into submission by blockading the southern coasts, seizing control of the Mississippi, and cutting off supplies of food and other essential commodities. This plan pointed to the West as the main locus of military operations.

Eventually Lincoln decided on a two-front war, keeping the pressure on Virginia and at the same time authorizing an advance down the Mississippi Valley with the aim of isolating Texas, Arkansas, and Louisiana. Lincoln also attached great importance to the coastal blockade and expected naval operations to seize the ports through which goods entered and left the Confederacy. His basic plan of applying pressure and probing for weaknesses at several points simultaneously took maximum advantage of the North's superiority in manpower and matériel. But it required better military leadership than the North possessed at the beginning of the war and took a painfully long time to put into effect.

MOBILIZING THE HOME FRONTS

The North and South faced similar problems in trying to create the vast support systems needed by armies in the field. At the beginning of the conflict, both sides had more volunteers than could be armed and outfitted. The South was forced to reject about 200,000 men in the first year of the war, and the North could commit only a fraction of its forces to battle. Furthermore, recruiting was done primarily by the states, which were reluctant to surrender control of the forces they had raised. Both Lincoln and Davis had to deal with governors who resisted centralized direction of the military effort.

As hopes for a short and easy war faded, the pool of volunteers began to dry up. Many of the early recruits showed a reluctance to reenlist. To resolve this problem, the Confederacy passed a conscription law in April 1862, and the Union edged toward a draft in July when Congress gave Lincoln the power to assign manpower quotas to each state and resort to conscription if they were not met.

To produce the materials of war, both governments relied mainly on private industry. In the North, especially, the system of contracting with private firms and individuals resulted in much corruption, inefficiency, and shoddy and defective supplies. But the North's economy was strong at the core, and by 1863 its factories and farms were producing more than enough to provision the troops without significantly lowering the living standards of the civilian population.

The southern economy was much less adaptable to the needs of a total war. The South of 1861 depended on the outside world for most of its manufactured goods. As the Union blockade became more effective, the Confederacy had to rely increasingly on a government-sponsored crash program to produce war materials. In addition to encouraging and promoting private initiative, the government built its own munitions plants. Astonishingly, the Confederate Ordnance

Bureau, under the able direction of General Josiah Gorgas, succeeded in producing or procuring sufficient armaments to keep southern armies well supplied throughout the conflict.

Southern agriculture, however, failed to meet the challenge. Planters were reluctant to shift from staples that could no longer be readily exported to foodstuffs that were urgently needed. But more significant was the inadequacy of the South's internal transportation system. Its limited rail network was designed to link plantation regions to port cities rather than to connect food-producing areas with centers of population. New railroad construction during the war did not resolve the problem; most of the new lines were aimed at facilitating the movement of troops rather than the distribution of food.

When northern forces penetrated parts of the South, they created new gaps in the system. Although well armed, Confederate soldiers were increasingly undernourished, and by 1863 civilians in urban areas were rioting to protest shortages of food. To supply the troops, the Confederate commissary resorted to the impressment of available agricultural produce at below the market price, a policy resisted so vigorously by farmers and local politicians that it eventually had to be abandoned.

Both sides faced the challenge of financing an enormously costly struggle. Although both the North and South imposed special war taxes, neither side was willing to resort to the heavy taxation that was needed to maintain fiscal integrity. Besides floating loans and selling bonds, both treasuries deliberately inflated the currency by printing large quantities of paper money that could not be redeemed in gold and silver. Runaway inflation was the inevitable result. The problem was much less severe in the North because of the overall strength of its economy. War taxes on income were more readily collectable than in the South, and bond issues were more successful.

The Confederacy was hampered from the outset by a severe shortage of readily disposable wealth that could be tapped for public purposes. Land and cotton could not easily be turned into rifles and cannons, and the southern treasury had to accept payments "in kind." As a result, Confederate "assets" eventually consisted mainly of bales of cotton that were unexportable because of the blockade. As the Confederate government fell deeper and deeper into debt, its rate of inflation soared out of sight. By August 1863, a Confederate dollar was worth only eight cents in gold.

POLITICAL LEADERSHIP: NORTHERN SUCCESS AND SOUTHERN FAILURE

Total war also forced political adjustments, and both the Union and the Confederacy had to face the question of how much democracy and individual freedom could be permitted when military success required an unprecedented exercise of government authority. Since both constitutions made the president commander in chief of the army and navy, Lincoln and Davis took actions that would have been regarded as arbitrary or even tyrannical in peacetime.

Lincoln was especially bold in assuming new executive powers. He expanded the regular army and advanced public money to private individuals without authorization by Congress. On April 27, 1861, he declared martial law, which enabled the military to arrest civilians suspected of aiding the enemy. He suspended the writ of habeas corpus in the area between Philadelphia and Washington, an action deemed necessary because of mob attacks on Union troops passing through Baltimore. Suspension of the writ enabled the government to arrest Confederate sympathizers and hold them without trial, and in September 1862 Lincoln extended this authority to all parts of the United States where "disloyal" elements were active. He argued that preservation of the Union justified such actions. In fact, however, most of the thousands of civilians arrested by military authorities were suspected deserters and draft dodgers, refugees, smugglers, or people who were simply found wandering in areas under military control.

For the most part, the Lincoln administration showed restraint and tolerated a broad spectrum of political dissent. Although the government closed down a few newspapers for brief periods when they allegedly published false information or military secrets, generally anti-administration journals were allowed to criticize the president and his party at will. A few politicians were arrested for pro-Confederate activity, but a large number of "Peace Democrats"—who called for restoration of the Union by negotiation rather than force—ran successfully for office and thus had ample opportunity to present their views to the public. In fact, the persistence of vigorous two-party competition in the North during the Civil War strengthened Lincoln's hand. Since his war policies were also the platform of his party, he could usually rely on unified partisan backing for the most controversial of his decisions.

Lincoln was singularly adept at the art of party leadership; he was able to accommodate various factions and define party issues and principles in a way that would encourage unity and dedication to the cause. Since the Republican party served during the war as the main vehicle for mobilizing and maintaining devotion to the Union effort, these political skills assumed crucial importance. Lincoln held the party together by persuasion, patronage, and flexible policymaking; this cohesiveness was essential to Lincoln's success in unifying the nation by force.

Jefferson Davis, most historians agree, was a less effective war leader than Lincoln. He defined his powers as commander in chief narrowly and literally,

Jefferson Davis, inaugurated as president of the Confederacy on February 18, 1861, was a West Point graduate and had served as secretary of war under President Franklin Pierce.

which meant he assumed personal direction of the armed forces but left policymaking for the mobilization and control of the civilian population primarily to the Confederate Congress. Unfortunately, he overestimated his capacities as a strategist and lacked the tact to handle field commanders who were as proud and testy as he was. Two of the South's best generals—Joseph E. Johnston and Pierre G. T. Beauregard—were denied the commands they deserved because they could not get along with Davis. One of the worst—Braxton E. Bragg—happened to be a personal favorite of the president and was allowed to keep a major command even after he had clearly demonstrated his incompetence.

Davis's greatest failing, however, was his lack of initiative and leadership in dealing with the problems of the home front. He devoted little attention to a deteriorating economic situation that caused great hardship and sapped Confederate morale. Although the South had a much more serious problem of internal division and disloyalty than the North, he refrained from declaring martial law on his own authority. The Confederate Congress grudgingly voted him such power when he asked for it but allowed it to be applied only in limited areas and for short periods.

As the war dragged on, Davis's political and popular support eroded. He was opposed and obstructed by state governors who resisted conscription and other Confederate policies that violated the tradition of states' rights. Southern newspapers and the Confederate Congress attacked Davis's conduct of the war. Even if he had been a more able and inspiring leader, Davis would have had difficulty maintaining his authority and credibility. He did not have an organized party behind him, for the Confederacy never developed a two-party system. As a result, it was difficult to mobilize the support required for hard decisions and controversial policies.

EARLY CAMPAIGNS AND BATTLES

The war's first major battle was a disaster for the North. Against his better judgment, General Winfield Scott responded to the "On to Richmond" clamor and ordered poorly trained Union troops under General Irvin McDowell to advance against the Confederate forces gathered at Manassas Junction, Virginia. They attacked the enemy position near Bull Run Creek on July 21, 1861. Confederate General Thomas J. Jackson earned the nickname "Stonewall" for holding the line against the northern assault until Confederate reinforcements arrived and routed the invading force. As they retreated toward Washington, the raw Union troops gave in to panic and broke ranks in their stampede to safety.

The humiliating defeat at Bull Run led to a shake-up of the northern high command. George McClellan replaced McDowell as commander of troops in the Washington area and then became general in chief when Scott was eased into re-

Civil War, 1861–1862
Defeats on the battlefield forced a change in the Union's initial military campaign of capturing Richmond, the Confederate capital. The Union's targets in the West were the key cities of Vicksburg and New Orleans.

tirement. A cautious disciplinarian, McClellan spent the fall and winter drilling his troops and whipping them into shape. President Lincoln, who could not understand why McClellan was taking so long to go into the field, became increasingly impatient and finally tried to order the army into action.

Before McClellan made his move, Union forces in the West won some important victories. In February 1862, a joint military-naval operation, commanded by General Ulysses S. Grant, captured Fort Henry on the Tennessee River and Fort Donelson on the Cumberland. The Confederate army was forced to withdraw from Kentucky and middle Tennessee. Southern forces in the West then massed at Corinth, Mississippi, just across the border from Tennessee. When a slow-moving Union army arrived just north of the Mississippi state line, the South launched a surprise attack on April 6. In the battle of Shiloh, one of the bloodiest of the war, only the timely arrival of reinforcements prevented the annihilation of Union troops backed up against the Tennessee River. After a second day of fierce fighting, the Confederates retreated to Corinth, leaving the enemy forces battered and exhausted.

Although the Union's military effort to seize control of the Mississippi Valley was temporarily halted at Shiloh, the Union navy soon contributed dramatically to the pursuit of that objective. On April 26, a fleet under Flag Officer David Farragut, coming up from the Gulf, captured the port of New Orleans. The occupation of New Orleans, besides securing the mouth of the Mississippi, climaxed a series of naval and amphibious operations around the edges of the Confederacy that provided strategically located bases to enforce a blockade of the southern coast. The last serious challenge to the North's naval supremacy ended on March 9, 1862, when the Confederate ironclad vessel *Virginia* (originally the USS *Merrimac*) was repulsed by the *Monitor,* an armored and turreted Union gunship.

Successes around the edges of the Confederacy did not relieve northern frustration at the inactivity or failure of Union forces on the eastern front. Only after Lincoln ordered him to take the offensive did McClellan start toward Richmond. Spurning the treacherous overland route, he moved his forces by water to the peninsula southeast of the Confederate capital. McClellan began moving up the peninsula in early April 1862. For a month he was bogged down before Yorktown, which he chose to besiege rather than assault directly. After Yorktown fell on May 4, he pushed ahead to a point twenty miles from Richmond, where he awaited the additional troops that he expected Lincoln to send.

The reinforcements were not forthcoming. While McClellan was inching his way up the peninsula, a relatively small southern force under Stonewall Jackson had pinned down a much larger Union army in the Shenandoah Valley. When it appeared by late May that Jackson might attack Washington, Lincoln decided to withhold troops from McClellan so they would be available to defend the Union capital.

If McClellan had moved more boldly and decisively, he probably could have captured Richmond with the forces he had. But a combination of faulty intelligence reports and his own natural caution led him to falter in the face of what he wrongly believed to be superior numbers. At the end of May, the Confederates under Joseph E. Johnston took the offensive when they discovered McClellan's army was divided into two segments by the Chickahominy River. In the battle of Seven Pines, McClellan was barely able to hold his ground on the side of the river under attack until a corps from the other side crossed over just in time to save the day. During the battle, General Johnston was severely wounded; succeeding him in command of the Confederate Army of Northern Virginia was native Virginian and West Point graduate Robert E. Lee.

Toward the end of June, Lee began an all-out effort to expel McClellan from the outskirts of Richmond. In a series of battles that lasted for seven days, the two armies clawed at each other indecisively. Nevertheless, McClellan decided to retreat down the peninsula to a more secure base. This backward step convinced Lincoln that the peninsula campaign was an exercise in futility.

On July 11, Lincoln appointed General Henry W. Halleck as general in chief and through Halleck ordered McClellan to withdraw his army from the peninsula

After Antietam, Lincoln visited McClellan's headquarters to urge the general to take action. McClellan is on the left facing the President.

to join a force under General John Pope that was preparing to move on Richmond by the overland route. But the Confederates got to Pope before McClellan did. At the end of August, in the second battle fought near Bull Run, Lee established his reputation for brilliant generalship; he sent Stonewall Jackson to Pope's rear, provoked the rash Union general to attack Jackson with full force, and then threw the main Confederate army against the Union's flank. Badly beaten, Pope retreated to the defenses of Washington, where he was stripped of command. A desperate Lincoln reappointed McClellan to head the Army of the Potomac.

Lee led his exuberant troops on an invasion of Maryland, hoping to isolate Washington from the rest of the North. McClellan caught up with him near Sharpsburg, and the bloodiest one-day battle of the war ensued. When the smoke cleared at Antietam on September 17, almost five thousand men had been killed on the two sides and more than eighteen thousand were wounded. The result was a draw, but Lee was forced to fall back south of the Potomac. McClellan was slow in pursuit, and Lincoln blamed him for letting the enemy escape.

Convinced that McClellan was fatally infected with "the slows," Lincoln put Ambrose E. Burnside in command of the Army of the Potomac. Burnside was aggressive enough, but he was also rather dense. His limitations were disastrously revealed at the battle of Fredericksburg, Virginia, on December 13, 1862, when he launched a direct assault to try to capture an entrenched and elevated position. The debacle at Fredericksburg, where Union forces suffered more than twice as many casualties as their opponents, ended a year of bitter failure for the North on the eastern front.

THE DIPLOMATIC STRUGGLE

The critical period of Civil War diplomacy was 1861 to 1862, when the South tried to induce major foreign powers to recognize its independence and break the Union blockade. The hope that England and France could be persuaded to intervene on the Confederate side stemmed from the fact that these nations depended on the South for three-quarters of their cotton supply.

The Confederate commissioners sent to England and France in May 1861 succeeded in gaining recognition of southern "belligerency," which meant the new government could claim some international rights of a nation at war, such as purchasing and outfitting privateers in neutral ports. The North protested vigorously, but by declaring a blockade of southern ports, it had undermined its official position that the rebellion was merely a domestic insurrection. Confederate raiders built and armed in British shipyards devastated northern shipping to such an extent that insurance costs eventually forced most of the American merchant marine off the high seas for the duration of the war.

In the fall of 1861, the Confederate government dispatched James M. Mason and John Slidell to be its permanent envoys to England and France, respectively, and instructed them to push for full recognition of the Confederacy. They took passage on the British steamer *Trent*, which was stopped and boarded in international waters by a U.S. warship. Mason and Slidell were taken into custody by the Union captain, causing a diplomatic crisis that nearly led to war between England and the United States. After a few weeks of ferocious posturing by both sides, Lincoln and Secretary of State Seward made the prudent decision to allow Mason and Slidell to proceed to their destinations.

These envoys may as well have stayed at home; they failed in their mission to obtain full recognition of the Confederacy from either England or France. The anticipated cotton shortage was slow to develop, for the bumper crop of 1860 had created a large surplus in British and French warehouses. For a brief period in the fall of 1862, Napoleon III, the emperor of France, toyed with the idea of recognition. But he was unwilling to risk war with the United States unless the British would cosponsor his plan to offer European mediation of the American conflict and then recognize the Confederacy if—as expected—the North refused to go along.

British opinion, both official and public, was seriously divided on how to respond to the American conflict. In 1861 and 1862, Lord Palmerston, the prime minister, and Lord Russell, the foreign secretary, played a cautious waiting game. Their government was sympathetic to the South but wary of the danger of war with the United States.

In September 1862, the British cabinet debated mediation and recognition as serious possibilities. Lord Russell pressed for a pro-Confederate policy because he was convinced the South was now strong enough to secure its independence. But Lord Palmerston overruled the foreign secretary and decided to maintain a hands-off policy. Only if the South won decisively on the battlefield would Britian risk the dangers of recognition and intervention.

The cotton famine finally hit in late 1862, causing massive unemployment in the British textile industry. But, contrary to southern hopes, public opinion did not compel the government to abandon its neutrality and use force to break the Union blockade.

Influential interest groups that actually benefited from the famine provided the crucial support for continuing a policy of nonintervention. Among these groups were owners of large cotton mills, who had made bonanza profits on their existing stocks and were happy to see weaker competitors go under while they awaited new sources of supply. By early 1863, cotton from Egypt and India put the industry back on the track toward full production. Other beneficiaries of nonintervention were manufacturers of wool and linen textiles, munitions makers who supplied both sides, and shipping interests that profited from the decline of American competition on the world's sea-lanes. Since the British economy as a whole gained more than it lost from neutrality, it is not surprising that there was little effective pressure for a change in policy.

By early 1863, when it was clear that "King Cotton diplomacy" had failed, the Confederacy broke off formal relations with Great Britain. The European powers, acting out of self-interest, had calculated that the advantages of getting involved were not worth the risk of a long and costly war with the United States. Only a decisive military victory would have gained recognition for southern independence, and if the Confederacy had actually won such a victory, it would not have needed foreign backing.

Fight to the Finish

The last two and a half years of the struggle saw the implementation of more radical war measures. The most dramatic and important of these was the North's effort to follow through on Lincoln's decision to free the slaves and bring the black population into the war on the Union side. The tide of battle turned in the summer of 1863, but the South continued to resist valiantly for two more years, until it was finally overcome by the sheer weight of the North's advantages in manpower and resources.

The Coming of Emancipation

At the beginning of the war, when the North still hoped for a quick and easy victory, only dedicated abolitionists favored turning the struggle for the Union into a crusade against slavery. But as it became clear how hard it was going to be to subdue the "rebels," public and congressional sentiment developed for striking a blow at the South's economic and social system by freeing its slaves. In July 1862 Congress authorized the government to confiscate the slaves of masters who supported the Confederacy. By this time, the actions of the slaves themselves were influencing policymaking. They were deserting their plantations in areas where the Union forces were close enough to offer a haven. In this way, they put pressure on the government to determine their status and, in effect, offered themselves as a source of manpower to the Union on the condition that they be made free.

Although Lincoln favored freedom for blacks as an ultimate goal, he was reluctant to commit his administration to a policy of immediate emancipation. In the fall of 1861 and again in the spring of 1862, he had disallowed the orders of field commanders who sought to free slaves in areas occupied by their forces, thus angering abolitionists and the strongly antislavery Republicans known as

Radicals. Lincoln's caution stemmed from a fear of alienating Unionist elements in the border slave states and from his own preference for a gradual, compensated form of emancipation.

Lincoln was also aware that one of the main obstacles to any program leading to emancipation was the strong racial prejudice of most whites in both the North and the South. Pessimistic about prospects of equality for blacks in the United States, Lincoln coupled moderate proposals with a plea for government subsidies to support the voluntary "colonization" of freed blacks outside of the United States, and he actively sought places that would accept them.

But the slaveholding states that remained loyal to the Union refused to endorse Lincoln's gradual plan, and the failure of Union arms in the spring and summer of 1862 increased the public clamor for striking directly at the South's peculiar institution. The Lincoln administration also realized that emancipation would win sympathy for the Union cause in England and France and thus might counter the growing threat that these nations would come to the aid of the Confederacy. Lincoln drafted an emancipation proclamation in July, but he was persuaded not to issue it until the North had won a victory and could not be accused of acting out of desperation.

The Emancipation Proclamation, here being read to slaves on a Carolina Sea Island plantation, committed the Union to the abolition of slavery as a war aim.

Finally, on September 22, 1862, Lincoln issued his preliminary Emancipation Proclamation. McClellan's success in stopping Lee at Antietam provided the occasion, but the president was also responding to growing political pressures. Most Republican politicians were now firmly committed to an emancipation policy, and many were on the verge of repudiating the administration for its inaction. Had Lincoln failed to act, his party would have been badly split, and he would have been in the minority faction. The proclamation gave the Confederate states one hundred days to give up the struggle without losing their slaves. In December, Lincoln proposed to Congress that it approve a series of constitutional amendments providing for gradual, compensated emancipation and subsidized colonization.

Since there was no response from the South and little enthusiasm in Congress for Lincoln's gradual plan, on January 1, 1863, the president declared that all slaves in those areas under Confederate control "shall be . . . thenceforward, and forever free." He justified the final proclamation as an act of "military necessity" sanctioned by the war powers of the president, and he authorized the enlistment of freed slaves in the Union army. The language and tone of the document—one historian has described it as having "all the moral grandeur of a bill of lading"—made it clear that blacks were being freed for reasons of state and not out of humanitarian conviction.

Despite its uninspiring origin and limited application—it did not extend to slave states loyal to the Union or to occupied areas and thus did not immediately free a single slave—the proclamation did commit the Union to the abolition of slavery as a war aim. It also accelerated the breakdown of slavery as a labor system, a process that was already well under way by early 1863. As word spread among the slaves that emancipation was now official policy, larger numbers of them were inspired to run off and seek the protection of approaching northern armies. Approximately one-quarter of the slave population gained freedom during the war under the terms of the Emancipation Proclamation and thus deprived the South of an important part of its agricultural workforce.

AFRICAN AMERICANS AND THE WAR

Almost 200,000 African Americans, most of them newly freed slaves, eventually served in the Union armed forces and made a vital contribution to the North's victory. Although they were enrolled in segregated units under white officers, were initially paid less than their white counterparts, and were used disproportionately for garrison duty or heavy labor behind the lines, "blacks in blue" fought heroically in several major battles during the last two years of the war.

Those freed during the war who did not serve in the military were often conscripted to serve as contract wage laborers on cotton plantations owned or leased by "loyal" white planters within the occupied areas of the Deep South. Abolitionists protested that the coercion used by military authorities to get blacks back into the cotton fields amounted to slavery in a new form, but those in power argued that the necessities of war and the northern economy required such "temporary" arrangements. To some extent, regimentation of freed slaves within the South was a way of assuring racially prejudiced Northerners, especially in the Midwest, that emancipation would not result in a massive migration of black refugees to their region of the country.

The heroic performance of African American troops and the easing of northern fears of being swamped by black migrants led to a deepening commitment to emancipation as a permanent and comprehensive policy. Realizing that his proclamation had a shaky constitutional foundation and might apply only to slaves actually freed while the war was going on, Lincoln sought to organize and recognize loyal state governments in southern areas under Union control on condition that they abolish slavery in their constitutions.

Finally, Lincoln pressed for an amendment to the federal constitution outlawing involuntary servitude. After supporting its inclusion as a central plank in the Republican platform of 1864, Lincoln used all his influence to win congressional approval for the new Thirteenth Amendment. On January 31, 1865, the House approved the amendment by a narrow margin. The cause of freedom for blacks and the cause of the Union had at last become one and the same. Lincoln, despite his earlier hesitations and misgivings, had earned the right to go down in history as the Great Emancipator.

THE TIDE TURNS

By early 1863, the Confederate economy was in shambles and its diplomacy had collapsed. The social order of the South was also showing signs of severe strain. Masters were losing control of their slaves, and nonslaveholding whites were becoming disillusioned with the hardships of a war that some of them described as "a rich man's war and a poor man's fight."

Yet the North was slow to capitalize on the South's internal weaknesses because it had its own serious morale problems. The long series of defeats on the eastern front had engendered war weariness, and the new policies that "military necessity" forced the government to adopt encountered fierce opposition.

Although popular with Republicans, most Democrats viewed emancipation as a betrayal of northern war aims. Racism was a main ingredient in their opposi-

An 1863 draft call in New York first provoked violence against African Americans, viewed by the rioters as the cause of an unnecessary war, and rage against the rich men who had been able to buy exemptions from the draft.

tion to freeing blacks. Riding a backlash against the preliminary proclamation, Democrats made significant gains in the congressional elections of 1862, especially in the Midwest, where they also captured several state legislatures.

The Enrollment Act of March 1863, which provided for outright conscription of white males but permitted men of wealth to hire substitutes or pay a fee to avoid military service, provoked a violent response from those unable to buy their way out of service and unwilling to fight for blacks. A series of antidraft riots broke out, culminating in one of the bloodiest domestic disorders in American history—the New York Riot of July 1863. The New York mob, composed mainly of Irish-American laborers, burned the draft offices, the homes of leading Republicans, and an orphanage for black children. They also lynched more than a dozen defenseless blacks who fell into their hands. At least 120 people died before federal troops restored order. Besides racial prejudice, the draft riots also reflected working-class anger at the wartime privileges and prosperity of the middle and upper classes; they showed how divided the North really was on the administration's conduct of the war.

To fight dissension and "disloyalty," the government used its martial law authority to arrest a few alleged ringleaders, including one prominent Democratic congressman—Clement Vallandigham of Ohio. Private patriotic organizations also issued a barrage of propaganda aimed at what they believed was a vast secret conspiracy to undermine the northern war effort. Historians disagree about the actual extent of covert and illegal antiwar activity, but militant advocates of "peace at any price"—popularly known as Copperheads—were certainly active in some areas, especially among the immigrant working classes of large cities and in southern Ohio, Indiana, and Illinois. Although many Copperheads presented themselves as believers in limited government who feared a war-induced growth of federal power, it was opposition to emancipation on racial grounds rather than anxiety about big government that gave the movement most of its emotional force.

The only effective way to overcome the disillusionment that fed the peace movement was to start winning battles and thus convince the northern public that victory was assured. Before this could happen, the North suffered one more humiliating defeat on the eastern front. In early May 1863, Union forces under General Joseph Hooker were routed at Chancellorsville, Virginia, by a much smaller Confederate army commanded by Robert E. Lee. Lee sent his forces and Stonewall Jackson to make a devastating surprise attack on the Union right. The Confederacy prevailed, but it did suffer one major loss: Jackson himself died as a result of wounds he received in the battle.

In the West, however, a major Union triumph was taking shape. For more than a year, General Ulysses S. Grant had been trying to put his forces in position to capture Vicksburg, Mississippi, the almost inaccessible Confederate bastion that kept the North from controlling the Mississippi River. Finally, in late March 1863, he crossed to the west bank north of the city and moved his forces to a point south of it, where he joined up with naval forces that had run the Confederate batteries mounted on Vicksburg's high bluffs. In one of the boldest campaigns of the war, Grant crossed the river, deliberately cutting himself off from his sources of supply, and marched into the interior of Mississippi. Living off the land and out of communication with an anxious and perplexed Lincoln, his troops won a series of victories over two separate Confederate armies and advanced on Vicksburg from the east. After unsuccessfully assaulting the city's defenses, Grant settled down for a siege on May 22.

The Confederate government rejected proposals to mount a major offensive into Tennessee and Kentucky to draw Grant away from Vicksburg. Instead, President Davis approved Robert E. Lee's plan for an all-out invasion of the Northeast, an option that might lead to a dramatic victory that would more than compensate for the probable loss of Vicksburg. Lee's army crossed the Potomac

Civil War, 1863–1865

In the western theater of war, Grant's victories at Port Gibson, Jackson, and Champion's Hill cleared the way for his siege of Vicksburg. In the east, after the hard-won Union victory at Gettysburg, the South never again invaded the North. In 1864 and 1865 Union armies gradually closed in on Lee's Confederate forces in Virginia. Leaving Atlanta in flames, Sherman marched to the Georgia coast, took Savannah, then moved his troops north through the Carolinas. Grant's army, though suffering enormous losses, moved on toward Richmond, marching into the Confederate capital on April 3, 1865, and forcing surrender.

in June and kept going until it reached Gettysburg, Pennsylvania. There Lee confronted a Union army that had taken up strong defensive positions on Cemetery Ridge and Culp's Hill. This was one of the few occasions in the war when the North could capitalize on the tactical advantage of choosing its ground and then defending it against an enemy whose supply lines were extended.

A series of Confederate attacks on July 2 failed to dislodge General George Meade's troops from the high ground they occupied. The following day, Lee faced the choice of retreating to protect his lines of communication or launching a final, desperate assault. With more boldness than wisdom, he chose to make a direct attack on the strongest part of the Union line. The resulting charge on Cemetery Ridge was disastrous; advancing Confederate soldiers dropped like flies under the barrage of Union artillery and rifle fire. Only a few made it to the top of the ridge, and they were killed or captured.

Retreat was now inevitable, and Lee withdrew his battered troops to the Potomac, only to find that the river was at flood stage and could not be crossed for several days. But Meade failed to follow up his victory with a vigorous pursuit, and Lee was allowed to escape a predicament that could have resulted in his annihilation. Vicksburg fell to Grant on July 4, the same day Lee began his withdrawal, and Northerners rejoiced at the simultaneous Independence Day victories that turned the tide of the war. The Union had secured control of the Mississippi and had at last won a major battle in the East. But Lincoln's joy turned to frustration when he learned his generals had missed the chance to capture Lee's army and bring a quick end to the war.

LAST STAGES OF THE CONFLICT

Later in 1863, the North finally gained control of the middle South, an area where indecisive fighting had been going on since the beginning of the conflict. The main Union target was Chattanooga, "the gateway to the Southeast." In September, Union troops maneuvered the Confederates out of the city, but were in turn outfought and driven back at Chickamauga. The Union army then retreated into Chattanooga, where it was surrounded and besieged by southern forces. Grant arrived from Vicksburg to take command, breaking the encirclement with daring assaults on the Confederate positions on Lookout Mountain and Missionary Ridge. As a result of its success in the battle of Chattanooga, the North was poised for an invasion of Georgia.

Grant's victories in the West earned him promotion to general in chief of all the Union armies. After assuming that position in March 1864, he ordered a multipronged offensive to finish off the Confederacy. The offensive's main movements were a march on Richmond under Grant's personal command and a thrust by the western armies, now led by General William Tecumseh Sherman, to Atlanta and the heart of Georgia.

In May and early June, Grant and Lee fought a series of bloody battles in northern Virginia that tended to follow a set pattern. Lee would take up an entrenched position in the path of the invading force, and Grant would attack it, sustaining heavy losses but also inflicting casualties the shrinking Confederate army could ill afford. When his direct assault had failed, Grant would move to his left, hoping in vain to maneuver Lee into a less defensible position. In the battles of the Wilderness, Spotsylvania, and Cold Harbor, the Union lost about sixty thousand men—more than twice the number of Confederate casualties—without defeating Lee or opening the road to Richmond. After Cold Harbor, Grant decided to change his tactics and moved his army to the south of Richmond.

Bold and decisive, Confederate General Robert E. Lee (left) often faced an enemy army that greatly outnumbered his own troops. Union General Ulysses S. Grant (right) demonstrated a relentless determination that eventually triumphed.

There he drew up before Petersburg, a rail center that linked Richmond to the rest of the Confederacy; after failing to take it by assault, he settled down for a siege.

The siege of Petersburg was a long, drawn-out affair, and the resulting stalemate in the East caused northern morale to plummet during the summer of 1864. Lincoln was facing reelection, and his failure to end the war dimmed his prospects. Although nominated with ease in June—with Andrew Johnson, a proadministration Democrat from Tennessee, as his running mate—Lincoln confronted growing opposition within his own party, especially from Radicals who disagreed with his apparently lenient approach to the future restoration of seceded states to the Union.

The Democrats seemed to be in a good position to capitalize on Republican divisions and make a strong bid for the White House. Their platform appealed to war weariness by calling for a cease-fire followed by negotiations to reestablish the Union. The party's nominee, General George McClellan, announced he would not be bound by the peace plank and would pursue the war. But he promised to end the conflict sooner than Lincoln could because he would not insist on emancipation as a condition for reconstruction. By late summer, Lincoln confessed privately that he would probably be defeated.

Northern military successes changed the political outlook. Sherman's invasion of Georgia went well. On September 2, Atlanta fell, and northern forces occupied the hub of the Deep South. The news unified the Republican party behind

THE ELECTION OF 1864

CANDIDATE	PARTY	POPULAR VOTE	ELECTORAL VOTE*
Lincoln	Republican	2,218,388	212
McClellan	Democratic	1,812,807	21

*Out of a total of 233 electoral votes. The eleven secessionist states—Alabama, Arkansas, Florida, Georgia, Louisiana, Mississippi, North Carolina, South Carolina, Tennessee, Texas, and Virginia—did not vote.

Lincoln. The election in November was almost an anticlimax: Lincoln won 212 of a possible 233 electoral votes and 55 percent of the popular vote. The Republican cause of "liberty and Union" was secure.

The concluding military operations revealed the futility of further southern resistance. Sherman marched unopposed through Georgia to the sea, destroying almost everything of possible military or economic value in a corridor three hundred miles long and sixty miles wide. The Confederate army that had opposed him at Atlanta moved northward into Tennessee, where it was defeated and almost destroyed by Union forces at Nashville in mid-December. Sherman captured Savannah on December 22. He then turned north and marched through the Carolinas, intending to join up with Grant at Petersburg near Richmond.

While Sherman was bringing the war to the Carolinas, Grant finally ended the stalemate at Petersburg. When Lee's starving and exhausted army tried to break through the Union lines, Grant renewed his attack and forced the Confederates to abandon Petersburg and Richmond on April 2, 1865. He then pursued them westward for a hundred miles, placing his forces in position to cut off their line of retreat to the south. Recognizing the hopelessness of further resistance, Lee surrendered his army at Appomattox Courthouse on April 9.

But the joy of the victorious North turned to sorrow and anger when John Wilkes Booth, a pro-Confederate actor, assassinated Abraham Lincoln as the president watched a play at Ford's Theater in Washington on April 14. Although Booth had a few accomplices, popular theories that the assassination was the result of a vast conspiracy involving Confederate leaders or (according to another version) Radical Republicans have never been substantiated.

The man who had spoken of the need to sacrifice for the Union cause at Gettysburg had himself given "the last full measure of devotion" to the cause of "government of the people, by the people, for the people." Four days after Lincoln's death, the only remaining Confederate force of any significance (the troops under Joseph E. Johnston, who had been opposing Sherman in North Carolina) laid down its arms. The Union was saved.

EFFECTS OF THE WAR

The nation that emerged from four years of total war was not the same America that had split apart in 1861. More than 618,000 young men were in their graves, victims of enemy fire or the diseases that spread rapidly in military encampments in this era before modern medicine and sanitation. The widows and sweethearts they left behind temporarily increased the proportion of unmarried women in the population, and some members of this generation of involuntary "spinsters" sought new opportunities for making a living or serving the community that went beyond the purely domestic roles previously prescribed for women.

During the war, northern women pushed the boundaries of their traditional roles by participating on the home front as fund-raisers and in the rear lines as army nurses and members of the Sanitary Commission. The Sanitary Commission promoted health in the northern army's camps through attention to cleanliness, nutrition, and medical care. Women in the North simultaneously utilized their traditional position as nurturers to participate in the war effort while they advanced new ideas about their role in society. The large number who had served as nurses or volunteer workers during the war were especially responsive to calls for broadening "the woman's sphere." Some of the northern women who were prominent in wartime service organizations became leaders of postwar philanthropic and reform movements. The war did not destroy the barriers to sexual equality that had long existed in American society, but the efforts of women during the Civil War broadened beliefs about what women could accomplish outside of the home.

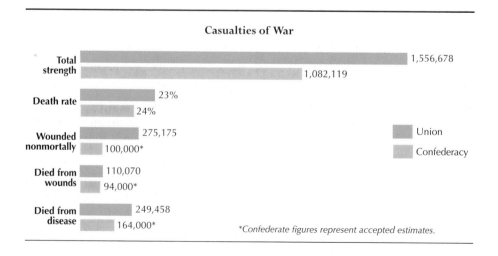

Casualties of War

	Union	Confederacy
Total strength	1,556,678	1,082,119
Death rate	23%	24%
Wounded nonmortally	275,175	100,000*
Died from wounds	110,070	94,000*
Died from disease	249,458	164,000*

Confederate figures represent accepted estimates.

During the war, many women replaced skilled male workers in the manufacturing labor force. These women are filling cartridges in the U.S. Arsenal at Watertown, New York.

The effect on white women in the Confederacy was different from the effect of the war on women in the victorious North. Southern women had always been intimately involved in the administration of the farms and plantations of the South, but the coming of the war forced them to shoulder even greater burdens at home. This was true for wealthy plantation mistresses, who had to take over the administration and maintenance of huge plantations without the benefit of extensive training or the assistance of male relatives. The wives of small farmers found it hard to survive at all, especially at harvest time when they often had to do all the work themselves. The loss of fathers and brothers, the constant advance of Union troops, and the difficulty of controlling a slave labor force destroyed many southern women's allegiance to the Confederate cause. As in the North, the Civil War changed the situation of women in society. The devastation of the southern economy forced many women to play a more conspicuous public and economic role. These women responded by forming associations to assist returning soldiers, entering the workforce as educators, and establishing numerous benevolent and reform societies, or temperance organizations. Although these changes created a more visible presence of southern women in public, the South remained more conservative in its views about women's "proper place" than did the North.

At enormous human and economic cost, the nation had emancipated four million African Americans from slavery, but it had not yet resolved that they would be equal citizens. At the time of Lincoln's assassination, most northern states still denied blacks equality under the law and the right to vote. Whether the North would extend more rights to southern freedmen than it had granted to "free Negroes" was an open question.

The impact of the war on white working people was also unclear. Those in the industrializing parts of the North had suffered and lost ground economically because prices had risen much faster than wages during the conflict. But Republican rhetoric stressing "equal opportunity" and the "dignity of labor" raised hopes that the crusade against slavery could be broadened into a movement to improve the lot of working people in general. Foreign-born workers had additional reason to be optimistic; the fact that so many immigrants had fought and died for the Union cause had—for the moment—weakened nativist sentiment and encouraged ethnic tolerance.

What the war definitely decided was that the federal government was supreme over the states and had a broad grant of constitutional authority to act on matters affecting "the general welfare." The southern principle of state sovereignty and strict construction died at Appomattox, and the United States was on its way to becoming a true nation-state with an effective central government. States still had primary responsibility for most functions of government and the Constitution placed limits on what the national government could do, and questions would continue to arise about where federal authority ended and states' rights began. Still, the war ended all question about where ultimate authority rested.

A broadened definition of federal powers had its greatest impact in the realm of economic policy. During the war, the Republican-dominated Congresses passed a rash of legislation designed to give stimulus and direction to the nation's economic development. Taking advantage of the absence of southern opposition, Republicans rejected the pre–Civil War tradition of virtual laissez-faire and enacted a Whiggish program of active support for business and agriculture. In 1862, Congress passed a high protective tariff, approved a homestead act intended to encourage settlement of the West by providing free land to settlers, granted huge tracts of public land to railroad companies to support the building of a transcontinental railroad, and gave the states land for the establishment of agricultural colleges. The following year, Congress set up a national banking system that required member banks to keep adequate reserves and invest one-third of their capital in government securities. The notes the national banks issued became the country's first standardized and reliable circulating currency.

These wartime achievements added up to a decisive shift in the relationship between the federal government and private enterprise. The Republicans took a limited government that did little more than seek to protect the marketplace from the threat of monopoly and changed it into an activist state that promoted and subsidized the efforts of the economically ambitious and industrious.

The most pervasive effect of the war on northern society was to encourage an "organizational revolution." Aided by government policies, venturesome businessmen took advantage of the new national market created by military procurement to build larger firms that could operate across state lines. Philanthropists also developed more effective national associations. Efforts to care for the wounded influenced the development of the modern hospital and the rise of nursing as a female profession. Both the men who served in the army and those men and women who supported them on the home front or behind the lines became accustomed to working in large, bureaucratic organizations of a kind that had scarcely existed before the war.

Ralph Waldo Emerson, the era's most prominent man of letters, revealed in his wartime writings that the conflict encouraged a dramatic shift in American thought about the relationship between the individual and society. Before the war, Emerson had generally championed "the transcendent individual," who stood apart from institutions and organizations and sought fulfillment in an inner world of imagination and cosmic intuition. During the conflict, he began to exalt the claims of organization, government, and "civilization" over the endeavors of "the private man" to find fulfillment through "self-culture." In purging his thoughts of extreme individualism and hailing the need to accept social discipline and participate in organized, cooperative activity, Emerson epitomized the way the war affected American thought and patterns of behavior.

The North won the war mainly because it had shown a greater capacity than the South to organize, innovate, and modernize. Its victory meant the nation as a whole would now be ready to embrace the concept of progress that the North had affirmed in its war effort—not only its advances in science and technology, but also its success in bringing together and managing large numbers of men and women for economic and social goals. The Civil War was thus a catalyst for the great transformation of American society from an individualistic society of small producers into the more highly organized and "incorporated" America of the late nineteenth century.

16

THE AGONY OF RECONSTRUCTION

During the Reconstruction period immediately following the Civil War, African Americans struggled to become equal citizens of a democratic republic. They produced a number of remarkable leaders who showed that blacks were as capable as other Americans of voting, holding office, and legislating for a complex and rapidly changing society. Among these leaders was Robert Smalls of South Carolina. Although virtually forgotten by the time of his death in 1915, Smalls was perhaps the most famous and widely respected southern black leader of the Civil War and Reconstruction era. His career reveals some of the main features of the African American experience during that crucial period.

Born a slave in 1839, Smalls had a white father whose identity has never been clearly established. But his white ancestry apparently gained him some advantages, and as a young man he was allowed to live and work independently, hiring his own time from a master who may have been his half brother. Smalls worked as a sailor and trained himself to be a pilot in Charleston Harbor. When the Union navy blockaded Charleston in 1862, Smalls, who was then working on a Confederate steamship called the *Planter*, saw a chance to win his freedom. At three o'clock in the morning on May 13, 1862, when the white officers of the *Planter* were ashore, he took command of the vessel and its slave crew, sailed it out of the heavily fortified harbor, and surrendered it to the Union navy. The *Planter* was turned into a Union army transport, and Smalls was made its captain after being commissioned as an officer. During the remainder of the war, he served as captain and pilot of Union vessels off the coast of South Carolina.

Like a number of other African Americans who had fought valiantly for the Union, Smalls went on to a distinguished political career during Reconstruction, serving in the South Carolina constitutional convention, in the state legislature, and for several terms in the U.S. Congress. He was also a shrewd businessman and became the owner of extensive properties in Beaufort, South Carolina, and its vicinity. The electoral organization that he established was so effective that Smalls was able to control local government and get himself elected to Congress even after the election of 1876 had placed the state under the control of white conservatives bent on depriving blacks of political

With the help of several black crewmen, Robert Smalls—then twenty-three years old—commandeered the Planter, a Confederate steamship used to transport guns and ammunition, and surrendered it to the Union vessel, U. S. S. Onward. Smalls provided distinguished service to the Union during the Civil War and after the war went on to become a successful politician and businessman.

power. Organized mob violence defeated him in 1878, but he bounced back to win by decision of Congress a contested congressional election in 1880. He did not leave the House of Representatives for good until 1886, when he lost another contested election that had to be decided by Congress.

In their efforts to defeat him, Smalls's white opponents frequently charged that he had a hand in the corruption that was allegedly rampant in South Carolina during Reconstruction. But careful historical investigation shows that he was, by the standards of the time, an honest and responsible public servant. In the South Carolina convention of 1868 and later in the state legislature, he was a conspicuous champion of free and compulsory public education. In Congress, he fought for the enactment and enforcement of federal civil rights laws. Like other middle-class black political leaders in Reconstruction-era South Carolina, he can perhaps be faulted in hindsight for not doing more to help poor blacks gain access to land of their own. But in 1875, he sponsored congressional legislation that opened for purchase at low prices the land in his own district that had been confiscated by the federal government during the war. As a result, blacks were able to buy most of it, and they soon owned three-fourths of the land in Beaufort and its vicinity.

Smalls spent the later years of his life as U.S. collector of customs for the port of Beaufort, a beneficiary of the patronage that the Republican party continued to provide for a few loyal southern blacks. But the loss of real political clout for Smalls and men like him was one of the tragic consequences of the fall of Reconstruction.

THE PRESIDENT VERSUS CONGRESS

The problem of how to reconstruct the Union in the wake of the South's military defeat was one of the most difficult and perplexing challenges American policy-makers ever faced. The Constitution provided no firm guidelines, for the framers had not anticipated a division of the country into warring sections. Emancipation compounded the problem with a new issue: how far should the federal government go to secure freedom and civil rights for four million former slaves?

The debate that evolved led to a major political crisis. Advocates of a minimal Reconstruction policy favored quick restoration of the Union with no protection for the freed slaves beyond the prohibition of slavery. Proponents of a more radical policy wanted readmission of the southern states to be dependent on guarantees that "loyal" men would displace the Confederate elite in positions of power and that blacks would acquire basic rights of American citizenship. The White House favored the minimal approach, whereas Congress came to endorse the more radical and thoroughgoing form of Reconstruction. The resulting struggle between Congress and the chief executive was the most serious clash between two branches of government in the nation's history.

WARTIME RECONSTRUCTION

Tension between the president and Congress over how to reconstruct the Union began during the war. Occupied mainly with achieving victory, Lincoln never set forth a final and comprehensive plan for bringing rebellious states back into the fold. But he did take initiatives that indicated he favored a lenient and conciliatory policy toward Southerners who would give up the struggle and repudiate slavery. In December 1863, he issued a proclamation offering a full pardon to all Southerners (with the exception of certain classes of Confederate leaders) who would take an oath of allegiance to the Union and acknowledge the legality of emancipation. Once 10 percent or more of the voting population of any occupied state had taken the oath, they were authorized to set up a loyal government.

Efforts to establish such regimes were quickly undertaken in states that were wholly or partially occupied by Union troops; by 1864, Louisiana and Arkansas had fully functioning Unionist governments.

Lincoln's policy was meant to shorten the war. The president hoped that granting pardons and political recognition to oath-taking minorities would weaken the southern cause by making it easy for disillusioned or lukewarm Confederates to switch sides. He also hoped to strengthen his emancipation policy by insisting that the new governments abolish slavery, an action that might prove crucial if the courts or a future Democratic administration were to disallow or revoke the Emancipation Proclamation. When constitutional conventions operating under the 10 percent plan in Louisiana and Arkansas dutifully abolished slavery in 1864, emancipation came closer to being irreversible.

Displeased with the president's Reconstruction experiments, Congress in 1864 refused to seat the Unionists elected to the House and Senate from Louisiana and Arkansas. A minority of congressional Republicans—the strongly antislavery Radicals—favored protection for black rights and provision for black male enfranchisement as preconditions for the readmission of southern states. But a larger moderate group in Congress also opposed Lincoln's plan, not because they favored civil and political equality for blacks, but because they did not trust the repentant Confederates who would play a major role in the new governments.

Congress also believed the president was exceeding his authority by using executive powers to restore the Union. Lincoln operated on the theory that secession, being illegal, did not place the Confederate states outside the Union in a constitutional sense. Since individuals and not states had defied federal authority, the president could use his pardoning power to certify a loyal electorate, which could then function as the legitimate state government. The dominant view in Congress, on the other hand, was that the southern states had forfeited their place in the Union and that it was up to Congress to decide when and how they would be readmitted.

After refusing to recognize Lincoln's 10 percent governments, Congress passed a Reconstruction bill of its own in July 1864. Known as the Wade-Davis Bill, this legislation required that 50 percent of the voters take an oath of future loyalty before the restoration process could begin. Once this had occurred, those who could swear they had never willingly supported the Confederacy could vote in an election for delegates to a constitutional convention. Lincoln exercised a pocket veto by refusing to sign the bill before Congress adjourned. He justified his action by announcing that he did not want to be committed to any single Reconstruction plan. The sponsors of the bill responded with an angry manifesto, and Lincoln's relations with Congress reached their low.

Congress and the president remained stalemated on the Reconstruction issue for the rest of the war. During his last months in office, however, Lincoln showed some willingness to compromise. However, he died without clarifying his intentions, leaving historians to speculate whether his quarrel with Congress would have worsened or been resolved. Given Lincoln's past record of political flexibility, the best bet is that he would have come to terms with the majority of his party.

ANDREW JOHNSON AT THE HELM

Andrew Johnson, the man suddenly made president by an assassin's bullet, attempted to put the Union back together on his own authority in 1865. But his policies eventually set him at odds with Congress and the Republican party and provoked the most serious crisis in the history of relations between the executive and legislative branches of the federal government.

Johnson's background shaped his approach to Reconstruction. Born in dire poverty in North Carolina, he migrated as a young man to eastern Tennessee, where he made his living as a tailor. Lacking formal schooling, he did not learn to read and write until adult life. Entering politics as a Jacksonian Democrat, he became known as an effective stump speaker. His railing against the planter aristocracy made him the spokesman for Tennessee's nonslaveholding whites. He ad-

Nearly insurmountable problems with a Congress determined to enact its own Reconstruction policy plagued Andrew Johnson throughout his presidency. Impeached in 1868, he escaped conviction by a single vote.

vanced from state legislator to congressman to governor and in 1857 was elected to the U.S. Senate.

When Tennessee seceded in 1861, Johnson was the only senator from a Confederate state who remained loyal to the Union and continued to serve in Washington. But his Unionism did not include antislavery sentiments. While campaigning in Tennessee, he had objected only to the fact that slaveholding was the privilege of a wealthy minority. He revealed his attitude when he wished that "every head of family in the United States had one slave to take the drudgery and menial service off his family."

While acting as military governor of Tennessee during the war, Johnson implemented Lincoln's emancipation policy. But he viewed it primarily as a means of destroying the power of the hated planter class rather than as a recognition of black humanity. He was chosen as Lincoln's running mate in 1864 because it was thought that a proadministration Democrat, who was also a southern Unionist, would strengthen the ticket. No one expected that this fervent white supremacist would ever become president

Some Radical Republicans initially welcomed Johnson's ascent to the nation's highest office. Like the Radicals, he was fiercely loyal to the Union and thought that ex-Confederates should be severely treated. More than Lincoln, who had spoken of "malice toward none and charity for all," Johnson seemed likely to punish southern "traitors" and prevent them from regaining political influence. Only gradually did the deep disagreement between the president and the Republican majority in Congress become evident.

The Reconstruction policy that Johnson initiated on May 29, 1865, disturbed some Radicals, but most Republicans were willing to give it a chance. Johnson placed North Carolina and eventually other states under appointed provisional governors chosen mostly from among prominent southern politicians who had opposed the secession movement and had rendered no conspicuous service to the Confederacy. The governors were responsible for calling constitutional conventions and ensuring that only "loyal" whites were permitted to vote for delegates. Confederate leaders and former officeholders who had participated in the rebellion were excluded. To regain their political and property rights, they had to apply for individual presidential pardons. Johnson made one significant addition to the list of the excluded: all those possessing taxable property exceeding $20,000 in value. In this fashion, he sought to prevent his longtime adversaries—the wealthy planters—from participating in the Reconstruction of southern state governments.

Johnson urged the conventions to do three things: declare the ordinances of secession illegal, repudiate the Confederate debt, and ratify the Thirteenth

Amendment abolishing slavery. After governments had been reestablished under constitutions meeting these conditions, the president assumed that the Reconstruction process would be complete and that the ex-Confederate states could regain their full rights under the Constitution.

The conventions accomplished their tasks in a way satisfactory to the president but troubling to many congressional Republicans. Rather than quickly accepting Johnson's recommendations, delegates in several states approved them begrudgingly or with qualifications. Furthermore, all the resulting constitutions limited suffrage to whites, disappointing the large number of Northerners who hoped that at least some African Americans would be given the vote.

Republican uneasiness turned to disillusionment and anger when the state legislatures elected under the new constitutions proceeded to pass "Black Codes" subjecting former slaves to a variety of special regulations and restrictions on their freedom. Vagrancy and apprenticeship laws forced African Americans to work and denied them a free choice of employers. In some states blacks could not testify in court on the same basis as whites and were subject to a separate penal code. To Radicals, the Black Codes looked suspiciously like slavery under a

"Slavery Is Dead?" asks this 1866 cartoon by Thomas Nast. To the cartoonist, the Emancipation Proclamation of 1863 and the North's victory in the Civil War meant little difference to the treatment of the freed slaves in the South. Freed slaves convicted of crimes often endured the same punishments as had slaves—sale, as depicted in the left panel of the cartoon, or beatings, as shown on the right.

new guise. More upsetting to northern public opinion in general, a number of prominent ex-Confederate leaders were elected to Congress in the fall of 1865.

Johnson himself was partly responsible for this turn of events. Despite his lifelong feud with the planter class, he was generous in granting pardons to members of the old elite who came to him, hat in hand, and asked for them. The growing rift between the president and Congress came into the open in December, when the House and Senate refused to seat the recently elected southern delegation. Instead of recognizing the state governments Johnson had called into being, Congress established a joint committee to review Reconstruction policy and set further conditions for readmission of the seceded states.

CONGRESS TAKES THE INITIATIVE

The struggle over how to reconstruct the Union ended with Congress doing the job of setting policy all over again. The clash between Johnson and Congress was a matter of principle and could not be reconciled. Johnson's stubborn and intolerant nature did not help his political cause. But the root of the problem was that he disagreed with the majority of Congress on what Reconstruction was supposed to accomplish. An heir of the Democratic states' rights tradition, he wanted to restore the prewar federal system as quickly as possible and without change except that states would not have the right to legalize slavery or to secede.

Most Republicans wanted firm guarantees that the old southern ruling class would not regain regional power and national influence by devising new ways to subjugate blacks. Since emancipation had nullified the three-fifths clause of the Constitution by which slaves had been counted as three-fifths of a person, all blacks were now to be counted in determining representation. Consequently, Republicans worried about increased southern strength in Congress and the electoral college. The current Congress favored a Reconstruction policy that would give the federal government authority to limit the political role of ex-Confederates and provide some protection for black citizenship.

Except for a few extreme Radicals, Republican leaders did not believe that blacks were inherently equal to whites. They did agree, however, that in a modern democratic state, all citizens must have the same basic rights and opportunities, regardless of natural abilities. Principle coincided easily with political expediency; southern blacks were likely to be loyal to the Republican party that had emancipated them and thus increase that party's political power in the South.

The disagreement between the president and Congress became irreconcilable in early 1866, when Johnson vetoed two bills that had passed with overwhelming Republican support. The first extended the life of the Freedmen's

Bureau—a temporary agency set up to aid the former slaves by providing relief, education, legal help, and assistance in obtaining land or employment. The second was a civil rights bill meant to nullify the Black Codes and guarantee to freedmen "full and equal benefit of all laws and proceedings for the security of person and property as is enjoyed by white citizens."

Johnson's vetoes shocked moderate Republicans who had expected the president to accept the relatively modest measures. Johnson succeeded in blocking the Freedmen's Bureau bill, although a modified version later passed. But Congress overrode his veto of the Civil Rights Act, signifying that the president was now hopelessly at odds with most of the congressmen from what was supposed to be his own party. Never before had Congress overridden a presidential veto.

Johnson soon revealed that he intended to abandon the Republicans and place himself at the head of a new conservative party uniting the small minority of Republicans who supported him with a reviving Democratic party that was rallying behind his Reconstruction policy. He helped found the National Union movement to promote his plan to readmit the southern states to the Union without further qualifications. A National Union convention meeting in Philadelphia

RECONSTRUCTION AMENDMENTS, 1865–1870

AMENDMENT	MAIN PROVISIONS	CONGRESSIONAL PASSAGE (2/3 MAJORITY IN EACH HOUSE REQUIRED)	RATIFICATION PROCESS (3/4 OF ALL STATES REQUIRED, INCLUDING EX-CONFEDERATE STATES)
13	Slavery prohibited in United States	January 1865	December 1865 (27 states, including 8 southern states)
14	1. National citizenship 2. State representation in Congress reduced proportionally to number of voters disfranchised 3. Former Confederates denied right to hold office 4. Confederate debt repudiated	June 1866	Rejected by 12 southern and border states, February 1867; Radicals make readmission of southern states hinge on ratification; ratified July 1868
15	Denial of franchise because of race, color, or past servitude explicitly prohibited	February 1869	Ratification required for readmission of Virginia, Texas, Mississippi, Georgia; ratified March 1870

in August 1866 called for the election to Congress of men who endorsed the presidential plan for Reconstruction.

Meanwhile, the Republican majority on Capitol Hill, fearing that Johnson would not enforce civil rights legislation or that the courts would declare such federal laws unconstitutional, passed the Fourteenth Amendment. This, perhaps the most important of all our constitutional amendments, gave the federal government responsibility for guaranteeing equal rights under the law to all Americans. Section 1 defined national citizenship for the first time as extending to "all persons born or naturalized in the United States." The states were prohibited from abridging the rights of American citizens and could not "deprive any person of life, liberty, or property, without due process of law; nor deny to any person . . . equal protection of the laws."

The other sections of the amendment were important in the context of the time but had fewer long-term implications. The amendment was sent to the states with the understanding that Southerners would not be readmitted to Congress unless their states ratified it.

The congressional elections of 1866 served as a referendum on the Fourteenth Amendment. Johnson opposed the amendment on the grounds that it created a "centralized" government and denied states the right to manage their own affairs. All the southern states except Tennessee rejected the amendment. But the publicity resulting from bloody race riots in New Orleans and Memphis weakened the president's case for state autonomy. Atrocities against blacks made it clear that the existing southern state governments were failing abysmally to protect the "life, liberty, or property" of the ex-slaves.

Johnson further weakened his cause by taking the stump on behalf of candidates who supported his policies. He toured the nation, slandering his opponents in crude language. Johnson's behavior enraged northern voters who repudiated the administration in the 1866 elections. The Republican majority in Congress increased to a solid two-thirds in both houses, and the Radical wing of the party gained strength at the expense of moderates and conservatives.

CONGRESSIONAL RECONSTRUCTION PLAN ENACTED

Congress was now in a position to implement its own plan of Reconstruction. In 1867 and 1868, it passed a series of acts that reorganized the South on a new basis. Generally referred to as Radical Reconstruction, the measures actually represented a compromise between genuine Radicals and more moderate elements within the party.

Consistent Radicals such as Senator Charles Sumner of Massachusetts and Congressmen Thaddeus Stevens of Pennsylvania and George Julian of Indiana

Among the most influential of the Radical Republicans was Congressman Thaddeus Stevens of Pennsylvania. He advocated seizing land from southern planters and distributing it among the freed slaves.

wanted to reshape southern society before readmitting ex-Confederates to the Union. Their plan required an extended period of military rule, confiscation and redistribution of large landholdings among the freedmen, and federal aid for schools to educate blacks and whites for citizenship. But the majority of Republican congressmen found such a program unacceptable because it broke too sharply with American traditions of federalism and regard for property rights.

The First Reconstruction Act, passed over Johnson's veto on March 2, 1867, reorganized the South into five military districts. But military rule would last for only a short time. Acts in 1867 and 1868 opened the way for the quick readmission of any state that framed and ratified a new constitution providing for black suffrage. Since blacks but not ex-Confederates were permitted to vote for delegates to the constitutional conventions or in the elections to ratify the conventions' work, Republicans thought they had found a way to ensure that "loyal" men would dominate the new governments. Republican leaders anticipated they would need votes from the reconstructed South in order to retain control of Congress and the White House in 1868.

Radical Reconstruction was based on the dubious assumption that once blacks had the vote, they would have the power to protect themselves against white supremacists' efforts to deny them their rights. The Reconstruction Acts thus signaled a retreat from the true Radical position that a sustained use of federal authority was needed to complete the transition from slavery to freedom and prevent the resurgence of the South's old ruling class. An extended period of military rule over civilians went beyond the popular northern consensus on necessary and proper Reconstruction measures. Thus, despite strong reservations, Radicals supported the plan of readmitting the southern states on the basis of

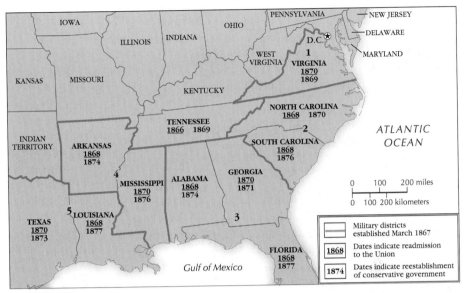

Reconstruction

During the Reconstruction era, the southern state governments passed through three phases: control by white ex-Confederates; domination by Republican legislators, both white and black; and, finally, the regain of control by conservative white Democrats.

black suffrage, recognizing that this was as far as the party and the northern public were willing to go.

Even so, congressional Reconstruction did have a radical aspect. It strongly supported the cause of black male suffrage. The belief that the poor and downtrodden should have access to the ballot box was a bold and innovative application of the principle of government by the consent of the governed. The problem was finding a way to enforce equal suffrage under conditions then existing in the postwar South.

THE IMPEACHMENT CRISIS

The first obstacle to enforcement of congressional Reconstruction was resistance from the White House. Johnson disapproved of the new policy and sought to thwart the will of Congress. He dismissed officeholders who sympathized with Radical Reconstruction, and he countermanded the orders of generals in charge of southern military districts who were zealous in their enforcement of the new legislation. Congress responded by passing laws designed to limit presidential authority over Reconstruction matters. One of the measures was the Tenure of Office Act, requiring Senate approval for the removal of cabinet officers and other officials whose appointment had needed the consent of the

The record of the Senate vote on Andrew Johnson's impeachment trial. Charles Sumner, one of the leaders of the pro-impeachment forces, spoke of the trial as "one of the last great battles with slavery" and urged that "every sentiment, every conviction, every vow against slavery must now be directed against him [Johnson]." James Grimes, who spoke for Johnson's acquittal, argued, "This government can only be preserved and the liberty of the people maintained by preserving intact the coordinate branches of it—legislative, executive, judicial—alike. I am no convert to any doctrine of the omnipotence of Congress."

Senate. Another measure sought to limit Johnson's authority to issue orders to military commanders.

Johnson objected vigorously to the restrictions on the grounds that they violated the constitutional doctrine of the separation of powers. When it became clear that the president would do all in his power to resist the establishment of Radical regimes in the southern states, some congressmen began to call for his impeachment. When Johnson tried to discharge Secretary of War Edwin Stanton, the only Radical in the cabinet, the pro-impeachment forces gained in strength.

In January 1868, Johnson ordered General Grant to replace Stanton as head of the War Department. But Grant had his eye on the Republican presidential nomination and refused to defy Congress. Johnson subsequently appointed General Lorenzo Thomas, who agreed to serve. Faced with this apparent violation of the Tenure of Office Act, the House voted overwhelmingly to impeach the president on February 24, and he was placed on trial before the Senate.

Johnson narrowly avoided conviction and removal from office because seven Republican senators broke with the party leadership and voted for acquittal. The vote thus fell one vote short of the necessary two-thirds. This outcome resulted in part from a skillful defense. Attorneys for the president argued for a narrow interpretation of the constitutional provision that a president could be impeached only for "high crimes and misdemeanors," asserting that this referred only to indictable offenses. Responding to the charge that Johnson had deliberately violated the Tenure of Office Act, the defense contended that the law did not apply to the removal of Stanton because he had been appointed by Lincoln, not Johnson.

The prosecution countered that Johnson had abused the powers of his office in an effort to sabotage the congressional Reconstruction policy. Obstructing the will of the legislative branch, they claimed, was sufficient grounds for conviction even if no crime had been committed. The Republicans who voted for acquittal could not endorse such a broad view of the impeachment power. They feared that removal of a president for essentially political reasons would threaten the constitutional balance of powers and open the way to legislative supremacy over the executive.

Although Johnson's acquittal by the narrowest of margins protected the American presidency from congressional domination, the impeachment episode helped create an impression in the public mind that the Radicals were ready to turn the Constitution to their own use to gain their objectives. But the evidence of congressional ruthlessness and illegality is not as strong as most historians used to think. Modern legal scholars have found merit in the Radicals' claim that their actions did not violate the Constitution.

Failure to remove Johnson from office was an embarrassment to congressional Republicans, but the episode did ensure that Reconstruction in the South would proceed as the majority in Congress intended. During the trial, Johnson helped influence the verdict by pledging to enforce the Reconstruction Acts, and he held to this promise during his remaining months in office. Unable to depose the president, the Radicals had at least succeeded in neutralizing his opposition to their program.

RECONSTRUCTION IN THE SOUTH

The Civil War left the South devastated, demoralized, and destitute. Slavery was dead, but what this meant for future relationships between whites and blacks was still in doubt. Most southern whites wanted to keep blacks adrift between slavery and freedom—without political or civil rights. Blacks sought independence and viewed the acquisition of land, education, and the vote as the best means of achieving this goal. The thousands of Northerners who went south after the war hoped to extend Yankee "civilization" to what they viewed as an unenlightened and barbarous region. For most of them, this reformation required the aid of the freed slaves.

The struggle of these groups to achieve their conflicting goals bred chaos, violence, and instability. The setting was hardly ideal for an experiment in interracial democracy, but one was attempted nonetheless. With massive and sustained support from the federal government, progressive reform could be achieved. When such support faltered, the forces of reaction and white supremacy were unleashed.

SOCIAL AND ECONOMIC ADJUSTMENTS

The Civil War scarred the southern landscape and wrecked its economy. One devastated area—central South Carolina—looked to an 1865 observer "like a broad black streak of ruin and desolation." Several major cities—including Atlanta, Columbia, and Richmond—were gutted by fire. Most factories were dismantled or destroyed, and long stretches of railroad were torn up.

Physical ruin would not have been so disastrous if investment capital had been available for rebuilding. But the substantial wealth represented by Confederate currency and bonds had melted away, and emancipation of the slaves had divested the propertied classes of their most valuable and productive assets. According to some estimates, the South's per capita wealth in 1865 was only about half what it had been in 1860.

Recovery could not even begin until a new labor system replaced slavery. Most Americans assumed that southern prosperity would continue to depend on plantation-grown cotton. Hindering efforts to rebuild the plantation economy were lack of capital, the deep-rooted belief of southern whites that blacks would work only under compulsion, and the freedmen's resistance to labor conditions that recalled slavery.

Blacks strongly preferred to determine their own economic relationships, and they hoped the federal government would support their ambitions. Although they were grateful for the federal aid in ending slavery, freed slaves often had ideas about freedom that contradicted the plans of their northern allies. Many ex-slaves wanted to hold on to the family-based communal work methods that they utilized during slavery rather than adopt the individual piecework system pushed by northern capitalists. Many ex-slaves opposed plans to turn them into

The Civil War brought emancipation to slaves but the sharecropping system kept many of them economically bound to their employers. At the end of a year the sharecropper tenants might owe most—or all—of what they had made to their landlord. Here a sharecropping family poses in front of their cabin. Ex-slaves often built their living quarters near woods in order to have a ready supply of fuel for heating and cooking. The cabin's chimney lists away from the house so that it can be easily pushed away from the living quarters should it catch fire.

wage laborers who produced exclusively for a market. Finally, freed slaves often wanted to stay on the land their families had spent generations farming rather than move elsewhere to assume plots of land as individual farmers.

While not guaranteeing all of the freed slaves' hopes for economic self-determination, the northern military attempted to establish a new economic base for the freed men and women. General Sherman issued an order in January 1865 that set aside the islands and coastal areas of Georgia and South Carolina for exclusive black occupancy on 40-acre plots. The Freedmen's Bureau was given control of hundreds of thousands of acres of abandoned or confiscated land and was authorized to make 40-acre grants to black settlers for three-year periods. By June 1865, forty thousand black farmers were at work on 300,000 acres of what they thought would be their own land.

But for most of them the dream of "forty acres and a mule" was not to be realized. Neither President Johnson nor Congress supported any effective program of land confiscation and redistribution. Consequently, most blacks in physical possession of small farms failed to acquire title, and the mass of freedmen were left with little or no prospect of becoming landowners. Recalling the plight of southern blacks in 1865, an ex-slave later wrote that "they were set free without a dollar, without a foot of land, and without the wherewithal to get the next meal even."

Despite their poverty and landlessness, ex-slaves were reluctant to commit themselves to wage labor for their former masters. Many took to the road, hoping to find something better. Some were still expecting grants of land, but others were simply trying to increase their bargaining power. As the end of 1865 approached, many freedmen had still not signed up for the coming season; anxious planters feared that blacks were plotting to seize land by force. Within a few weeks, however, most holdouts signed for the best terms they could get.

One common form of agricultural employment in 1866 was a contract labor system. Under this system, workers committed themselves for a year in return for fixed wages, a substantial portion of which was withheld until after the harvest. The Freedmen's Bureau assumed responsibility for reviewing the contracts and enforcing them. But bureau officials had differing notions of what it meant to protect African Americans from exploitation. Some stood up strongly for the rights of the freedmen; others served as allies of the planters.

Growing up alongside the contract system and eventually displacing it was an alternative capital-labor relationship—sharecropping. Under this system, blacks worked a piece of land independently for a fixed share of the crop, usually one-half. Credit-starved landlords liked this arrangement because it did not require much expenditure in advance of the harvest and the tenant shared the risks of crop failure or a fall in cotton prices.

African Americans initially viewed sharecropping as a step up from wage labor in the direction of landownership. But during the 1870s, this form of tenancy evolved into a new kind of servitude. Croppers had to live on credit until their cotton was sold, and planters or merchants seized the chance to "provision" them at high prices and exorbitant rates of interest. Creditors were entitled to deduct what was owed to them out of the tenant's share of the crop, and this left most sharecroppers with no net profit at the end of the year—more often than not with a debt that had to be worked off in subsequent years.

African Americans in towns and cities found themselves living in an increasingly segregated society. The Black Codes of 1865 attempted to require separation of the races in public places and facilities; when most of the codes were set aside by federal authorities as violations of the Civil Rights Act of 1866, the same end was often achieved through private initiative and community pressure. Blacks found it almost impossible to gain admittance to most hotels, restaurants, and other privately owned establishments catering to whites. Although separate black, or "Jim Crow," cars were not yet the rule on railroads, African Americans were often denied first-class accommodations. After 1868, black-supported Republican governments passed civil rights acts requiring equal access to public facilities, but little effort was made to enforce the legislation.

A Freedmen's school, one of the more successful endeavors supported by the Freedmen's Bureau. The Bureau, working with teachers from northern abolitionist and missionary societies, founded thousands of schools for freed slaves and poor whites.

Some forms of racial separation were not openly discriminatory, and blacks accepted or even endorsed them. Freedmen who had belonged to white churches as slaves welcomed the chance to join all-black denominations such as the African Methodist Episcopal church. The first schools for ex-slaves were all-black institutions established by the Freedmen's Bureau and various northern missionary societies. Having been denied all education during the antebellum period, most blacks viewed separate schooling as an opportunity rather than as a form of discrimination. When Radical governments set up public school systems, they condoned de facto educational segregation. Only in city schools of New Orleans and at the University of South Carolina were there serious attempts during Reconstruction to bring white and black students together in the same classrooms.

The upshot of all forms of racial separatism was to create a divided society, one in which blacks and whites lived much of the time in separate worlds. There were two exceptions to this pattern: one was at work, where blacks necessarily dealt with white employers; the other was in the political sphere, where blacks sought to exercise their rights as citizens.

POLITICAL RECONSTRUCTION IN THE SOUTH

The state governments that emerged in 1865 had little or no regard for the rights of the freed slaves. Some of their codes made black unemployment a crime, and others limited the rights of African Americans to own property or engage in occupations other than those of servant or laborer. The federal government set aside these codes, but private violence and discrimination against blacks continued on a massive scale unchecked by state authorities. Hundreds, perhaps thousands, of blacks were murdered by whites in 1865–1866, and few of the perpetrators were brought to justice.

The imposition of military rule in 1867 was designed in part to protect former slaves from violence and intimidation, but the task was beyond the capacity of the few thousand troops stationed in the South. When new constitutions were approved and states readmitted to the Union under the congressional plan in 1868, the problem became more severe. White opponents of Radical Reconstruction used systematic terrorism and organized mob violence to keep blacks from voting. The freed slaves tried to protect and defend themselves by organizing their own militia groups. However, these militia groups were not powerful enough to overcome the growing power of the anti-Republican forces. As the military presence was progressively reduced, the new Republican regimes had to fight a losing battle against armed white supremacists.

Hastily organized in 1867, the southern Republican party dominated the constitution making of 1868 and the regimes that came out of it. The party was an attempted coalition of three social groups: newly enfranchised blacks, poor white farmers, and businessmen seeking government aid for private enterprise. Many Republicans in this third group were recent arrivals from the North—the so-called carpetbaggers—but some were "scalawags," former Whig planters or merchants who were born in the South or had immigrated to the region before the war and now saw a chance to realize their dreams for commercial and industrial development.

White owners of small farms expected the Republican party to favor their interests at the expense of the wealthy landowners and to come to their aid with special legislation when they faced the loss of their homesteads to creditors. Blacks formed the vast majority of the Republican rank and file in most states and were concerned mainly with education, civil rights, and landowner-ship.

Under the best of conditions, this coalition would have been difficult to maintain. Each group had its own distinct goals and did not fully support the aims of the other segments. Poor white farmers, for example, had a deeply rooted resistance to black equality. And for how long could one expect essentially conservative businessmen to support costly measures for the elevation or relief of the lower classes of either race? Some Democratic politicians exploited these divisions by appealing to disaffected white Republicans.

But during the relatively brief period when they were in power in the South, the Republicans chalked up some notable achievements. They established (on paper at least) the South's first adequate systems of public education, democratized state and local government, and appropriated funds for an enormous expansion of public services and responsibilities.

Important as these social and political reforms were, they took second place to the Republicans' major effort—to foster economic development and restore southern prosperity by subsidizing the construction of railroads and other internal improvements. But the policy of aiding railroads turned out to be disastrous. Extravagance, corruption, and routes laid out in response to local political pressure rather than on sound economic grounds increased the burden of public debt and taxation. The policy did not produce the promised payoff of efficient, cheap transportation. Subsidized railroads frequently went bankrupt, leaving the taxpayers holding the bag. When the Panic of 1873 brought many southern state governments to the verge of bankruptcy, and railroad building came to an end, it was clear the Republicans' "gospel of prosperity" through state aid to private enterprise had failed miserably. Their political opponents, many of whom had originally favored such policies, now saw an opportunity to take advantage of the situation by charging that Republicans had ruined the southern economy.

In general, the Radical regimes failed to conduct public business honestly and efficiently. Embezzlement of public funds and bribery of state lawmakers or officials were common occurrences. State debts and tax burdens rose enormously, mainly because governments had undertaken heavy new responsibilities, but partly because of waste and graft.

Yet southern corruption was not exceptional, nor was it a special result of the extension of suffrage to uneducated African Americans, as critics of Radical Reconstruction have claimed. It was part of a national pattern during an era when private interests considered buying government favors to be a part of the cost of doing business.

Blacks bore only a limited responsibility for the dishonesty of the Radical governments. Although sixteen African Americans served in Congress—two in the Senate—between 1869 and 1880, only in South Carolina did blacks constitute a majority of even one house of the state legislature. Furthermore, no black governors were elected during Reconstruction (although Pinkney B. S. Pinchback served for a time as acting governor of Louisiana). The biggest grafters were opportunistic whites. Some black legislators went with the tide and accepted "loans" from those railroad lobbyists who would pay most for their votes, but the same men could usually be depended on to vote the will of their constituents on civil rights or educational issues.

If blacks served or supported corrupt and wasteful regimes, it was because they had no alternative. Although the Democrats, or Conservatives as they called themselves in some states, made sporadic efforts to attract African American voters, it was clear that if they won control, they would attempt to strip blacks of their civil and political rights. But opponents of Radical Reconstruction were able to capitalize on racial prejudice and persuade many Americans that "good government" was synonymous with white supremacy.

Contrary to myth, the small number of African Americans elected to state or national office during Reconstruction demonstrated on the average more integrity and competence than their white counterparts. Most were fairly well educated, having been free Negroes or unusually privileged slaves before the war. Among the most capable were Robert Smalls, Senator Blanche K. Bruce of Mississippi, and Congressmen Robert Brown Elliott of South Carolina and James T. Rapier of Alabama.

THE AGE OF GRANT

Ulysses S. Grant was the only president between Jackson and Wilson to serve two full and consecutive terms. But unlike other chief executives so favored by the electorate, Grant is commonly regarded as a failure. His administration was riddled with corruption, and he has also been condemned for the inconsistency and ultimate failure of his southern policy. At times, Grant's highest priority seemed to be loyalty to old friends and to politicians who supported him. But the problems he faced were certainly difficult. A president with a clearer sense of duty might have done little better.

RISE OF THE MONEY QUESTION

The impeachment crisis of 1868 represented the high point of popular interest in Reconstruction issues. Already competing for public attention was the question of how to manage the nation's currency, and more specifically, what to do about greenbacks—paper money issued during the war. Johnson's Sectretary of the Treasury Hugh McCulloch favored a return to "sound" money and in 1866 had initiated a policy of withdrawing greenbacks from circulation. Commercial and financial interests in the East generally endorsed this hard-money policy: they re-

THE ELECTION OF 1868

CANDIDATE	PARTY	POPULAR VOTE	ELECTORAL VOTE
Grant	Republican	3,013,421	214
Seymour	Democratic	2,706,829	80
Not voted*			23

*Unreconstructed states did not participate in the election.

ceived crucial support form intellectuals who regarded government-sponsored inflation as immoral or contrary to the natural laws of classic economics. A number of groups opposed McCulloch's policy; "greenbacks" were the strongest in the West and among expansion-minded manufacturers.

The money question surged to the forefront of national politics in 1868. Faced with a business recession blamed on McCulloch's policy, Congress voted to stop the retirement of greenbacks. The Democratic party, responding to midwestern pressure, included in its platform a plan calling for the redemption of much of the Civil War debt in greenbacks rather than gold. But divisions within the parties prevented the money question from becoming a central issue in the presidential campaign. The Democrats nominated Governor Horatio Seymour of New York, a sound-money supporter, thus nullifying their greenback platform. Republicans based their campaign mainly on a defense of their Reconstruction policy and a celebration of their popular candidate. With the help of votes from the Republican-dominated southern states, Grant won a decisive victory.

In 1869 and 1870, a Republican-controlled Congress passed laws that assured payment in gold to most bondholders but eased the burden of the huge Civil War debt by exchanging bonds soon coming due for those that would not be payable for ten, fifteen, or thirty years. In this way, the public credit was protected.

Still unresolved was the problem of what to do about the $356 million in greenbacks that remained in circulation: retire them quickly as hard-money advocates proposed, or issue more to stimulate the economy, as inflationists argued. The Grant administration decided to allow the greenbacks to float until economic expansion would bring them to a par with gold, thus permitting a painless return to specie payments. But the Panic of 1873, which brought much of the economy to its knees, led to a revival of agitation to inflate the currency. Debt-ridden farmers, who would be the backbone of the greenback movement for years to come, now joined the soft-money clamor for the first time.

Responding to the economic downturn, Congress in 1874 authorized a modest issue of new greenbacks, but Grant, influenced by the opinions of hard-money financiers, vetoed the bill. In 1875 Congress enacted the Specie Resumption Act, which provided for a limited reduction of greenbacks leading to full resumption of specie payments by January 1, 1879. The action was widely interpreted as deflation in the midst of depression, and farmers and workers—who were already suffering acutely from deflation—reacted with dismay and anger.

The Democratic party could not capitalize adequately on these sentiments because of the influence of its own hard-money faction, and in 1876 an independent Greenback party entered the national political arena. The party's nominee for president received an insignificant number of votes, but in 1878 the Greenback Labor party polled more than a million votes and elected fourteen congressmen. The Greenbackers were able to keep the money issue alive into the following decade.

RETREAT FROM RECONSTRUCTION

The Republican effort to make equal rights for blacks the law of the land culminated in the Fifteenth Amendment. Passed by Congress in 1869 and ratified by the states in 1870, the amendment prohibited any state from denying a citizen the right to vote because of race, color, or previous condition of servitude. A more radical version, requiring universal manhood suffrage, was rejected partly because it departed too sharply from traditional views of federal-state relations. States therefore could still limit the suffrage by imposing literacy tests, property qualifications, or poll taxes allegedly applying to all racial groups; such devices would eventually be used to strip southern blacks of the right to vote, though the makers of the amendment did not foresee this result.

Many feminists were bitterly disappointed that the amendment did not extend the vote to women. A militant wing of the women's rights movement, led by Elizabeth Cady Stanton and Susan B. Anthony, was so angered that the Constitution was being amended in a way that, in effect, made gender a qualification for voting that they campaigned against ratification of the Fifteenth Amendment. Another group of feminists led by Lucy Stone supported the amendment on the grounds that this was "the Negro's hour" and that women could afford to wait a few years for the vote. This disagreement divided the women's suffrage movement for a generation to come.

The Grant administration was charged with enforcing the amendment and protecting black men's voting rights in the reconstructed states. Since survival of the Republican regimes depended on African American support, political partisanship dictated federal action, even though the North's emotional and ideological commitment to black citizenship was waning.

Shown seated at the table are feminist leaders Elizabeth Cady Stanton and Susan B. Anthony. They and their adherents split with Lucy Stone (right) and her followers over the Fifteenth Amendment and its failure to extend the vote to women.

Between 1868 and 1872, the main threat to southern Republican regimes came from the Ku Klux Klan and other secret societies bent on restoring white supremacy by intimidating blacks who sought to exercise their political rights. First organized in Tennessee in 1866, the Klan spread rapidly to other states, adopting increasingly lawless and brutal tactics. A grass-roots vigilante movement and not a centralized conspiracy, the Klan thrived on local initiative and gained support from whites of all social classes. Its secrecy, decentralization, popular support, and utter ruthlessness made it very difficult to suppress. As soon as blacks had been granted the right to vote, hooded "night riders" began to visit the cabins of those who were known to be active Republicans; some victims were only threatened, but others were whipped or even murdered.

In the presidential election of 1868, Grant lost in Louisiana and Georgia mainly because the Klan—or the Knights of the White Camelia, as the Louisiana variant was called—launched a reign of terror to prevent prospective black voters from exercising their right. Political violence claimed more than a thousand lives in Louisiana and in Arkansas more than two hundred Republicans, including a congressman, were assassinated.

Thereafter, Klan terrorism was directed mainly at Republican state governments. Virtual insurrections broke out in Arkansas, Tennessee, North Carolina, and parts of South Carolina. Republican governors called out the state militia to

Members of the Ku Klux Klan, a secret white supremacist organization, in typical regalia. Before elections, hooded Klansmen terrorized African Americans to discourage them from voting.

fight the Klan, but only the Arkansas militia succeeded in bringing it to heel. In Tennessee, North Carolina, and Georgia, Klan activities helped undermine Republican control, thus allowing the Democrats to come to power in all of these states by 1870.

In 1870–1871 Congress passed a series of laws designed to enforce the Fifteenth Amendment by providing federal protection for black suffrage and authorizing use of the army against the Klan. The "Ku Klux Klan" or "Force" acts made interference with voting rights a federal crime and established provisions for government supervision of elections. The legislation also empowered the president to call out troops and suspend the writ of habeas corpus to quell insurrection. In 1871–1872, thousands of suspected Klansmen were arrested by the military or U.S. marshals, and the writ was suspended in nine counties of South Carolina that had been virtually taken over by the secret order. Although most of the accused Klansmen were never brought to trial, were acquitted, or received suspended sentences, the enforcement effort was vigorous enough to put a damper on hooded terrorism and ensure relatively fair and peaceful elections in 1872.

A heavy black turnout in these elections enabled the Republicans to hold on to power in most states of the Deep South, despite efforts of the Democratic-Conservative opposition to cut into the Republican vote by taking moderate positions on racial and economic issues. This setback prompted the Democratic-Conservatives to make a significant change in their strategy and ideology. No longer did they try to take votes away from the Republicans by proclaiming support for black suffrage and government aid to business. Instead they began to appeal openly to white supremacy and to the traditional Democratic and agrarian hostility to government promotion of economic development. Consequently, they were able to bring back to the polls a portion of the white electorate, mostly small farmers, who had not been voting because they were alienated by the leadership's apparent concessions to Yankee ideas.

This new and more effective electoral strategy dovetailed with a resurgence of violence meant to reduce Republican, especially black Republican, voting. The new reign of terror differed from the previous Klan episode; its agents no longer wore masks but acted quite openly. They were effective because the northern public was increasingly disenchanted with federal intervention on behalf of what were widely viewed as corrupt and tottering Republican regimes. Grant used force in the South for the last time in 1874 when an overt paramilitary organization in Louisiana tried to overthrow a Republican government accused of stealing an election. When an unofficial militia in Mississippi instigated a series of bloody race riots prior to the state elections of 1875, Grant refused the governor's request for federal troops. Intimidation kept black voters from the polls, and as a result Mississippi fell to the Democratic-Conservatives.

By 1876, Republicans held on to only three southern states: South Carolina, Louisiana, and Florida. Partly because of Grant's hesitant and inconsistent use of presidential power, but mainly because the northern electorate would no longer tolerate military action to sustain Republican governments and black voting rights, Radical Reconstruction was falling into total eclipse.

SPOILSMEN VERSUS REFORMERS

One reason Grant found it increasingly difficult to take strong action to protect southern Republicans was the accusation by reformers that a corrupt national administration was propping up bad governments in the South for personal and partisan advantage. An apparent example was Grant's intervention in Louisiana in 1872 on behalf of an ill-reputed Republican faction headed by his wife's brother-in-law, who controlled federal patronage as collector of customs in New Orleans.

The Republican party in the Grant era was losing the idealism and high purpose associated with the crusade against slavery. By the beginning of the 1870s, the men who had been the conscience of the party were either dead, out of office, or at odds with the administration. New leaders of a different stamp, whom historians have dubbed "spoilsmen" or "politicos," were taking their place. When Grant joined ranks with these new Republicans, such as Senators Roscoe Conkling of New York and James G. Blaine of Maine, he lost credibility with reform-minded members of his party.

During Grant's first administration, an aura of scandal surrounded the White House but did not directly implicate the president. In 1869, the financial buccaneer Jay Gould enlisted the aid of a brother-in-law of Grant to further a fantastic scheme to corner the gold market. Gould failed in the attempt, but he did manage to save himself and come away with a huge profit.

Grant's first-term vice president, Schuyler Colfax of Indiana, was directly involved in the notorious Crédit Mobilier scandal. Crédit Mobilier was a construction company that actually served as a fraudulent device for siphoning off profits that should have gone to the stockholders of the Union Pacific Railroad, which was the beneficiary of massive federal land grants. In order to forestall government inquiry into this arrangement, Crédit Mobilier stock was distributed to influential congressmen, including Colfax (who was speaker of the House before he was elected vice president). The whole business came to light just before the campaign of 1872.

Republicans who could not tolerate such corruption or had other grievances against the administration broke with Grant in 1872 and formed a third party committed to "honest government" and "reconciliation" between the North and the South. These Liberal Republicans endorsed reform of the civil service to curb the corruption-breeding patronage system and advocated a laissez-faire economic policy of low tariffs, an end to government subsidies for railroads, and hard money. Despite their rhetoric of idealism and reform, the Liberal Republicans were extremely conservative in their notions of what government should do to assure justice for blacks and other underprivileged Americans.

The Liberal Republicans' national convention nominated Horace Greeley, editor of the respected New York *Tribune*. This was a curious and divisive choice, since Greeley was at odds with the founders of the movement on the tariff question and was indifferent to civil service reform. The Democrats also nominated

THE ELECTION OF 1872

CANDIDATE	PARTY	POPULAR VOTE	ELECTORAL VOTE*
Grant	Republican	3,598,235	286
Greeley	Democratic and Liberal Republican	2,834,761	Greeley died before the electoral college voted.

*Out of a total of 366 electoral votes. Greeley's votes were divided among the four minor candidates.

Greeley, mainly because he promised to end Radical Reconstruction by restoring "self-government" to the South.

But the journalist turned out to be a poor campaigner who failed to inspire enthusiasm from lifelong supporters of either party. Most Republicans stuck with Grant, and many Democrats, recalling Greeley's previous record as a staunch Republican, simply stayed away from the polls. The result was a decisive victory for Grant.

Grant's second administration seemed to bear out the reformers' worst suspicions about corruption in high places. In 1875, the public learned that federal revenue officials had conspired with distillers to defraud the government of millions of dollars in liquor taxes. Grant's private secretary, Orville E. Babcock, was indicted as a member of the "Whiskey Ring" and was saved from conviction only by the president's personal intercession. The next year, Grant's secretary of war, William E. Belknap, was impeached by the House after an investigation revealed he had taken bribes for the sale of Indian trading posts. He avoided conviction in the Senate only by resigning from office before his trial.

There is no evidence that Grant profited personally from any of the misdeeds of his subordinates. Yet he is not entirely without blame for the corruption in his administration. He failed to take firm action against the malefactors, and, even after their guilt had been clearly established, he sometimes tried to shield them from justice.

REUNION AND THE NEW SOUTH

Congressional Reconstruction prolonged the sense of sectional division and conflict for a dozen years after the guns had fallen silent. Its final liquidation in 1877 opened the way to a reconciliation of North and South. But the costs of reunion were high for less privileged groups in the South. The civil and political rights of African Americans, left unprotected, were progressively and relentlessly stripped away by white supremacist regimes. Lower-class whites saw their interests sacrificed to those of capitalists and landlords. Despite the rhetoric hailing a prosperous "New South," the region remained poor and open to exploitation by northern business interests.

THE COMPROMISE OF 1877

The election of 1876 pitted Republican governor Rutherford B. Hayes of Ohio against Governor Samuel J. Tilden of New York, a Democratic reformer. Honest government was apparently the electorate's highest priority. Tilden won the popular vote and seemed likely to win a narrow victory in the electoral college. But the result was placed in doubt when the returns from the three southern states

THE ELECTION OF 1876

CANDIDATE	PARTY	POPULAR VOTE	UNCONTESTED ELECTORAL VOTE	ELECTORAL TOTAL
Hayes	Republican	4,034,311	165	185
Tilden	Democratic	4,288,546	184	184
Cooper	Greenback	75,973	—	—

still controlled by the Republicans—South Carolina, Florida, and Louisiana—were contested. If Hayes were to be awarded these three states, plus one contested electoral vote in Oregon, Republican strategists realized, he would triumph in the electoral college by a single vote.

The outcome of the election remained undecided for months. To resolve the impasse, Congress appointed a special electoral commission of fifteen members to determine who would receive the votes of the disputed states. Originally composed of seven Democrats, seven Republicans, and an independent, the commission fell under Republican control when the independent member resigned to run for the Senate and a Republican was appointed to take his place. The commission split along party lines and voted 8 to 7 to award Hayes all of the disputed votes. But this decision still had to be ratified by both houses of Congress. The Republican-dominated Senate readily approved it, but the Democrats in the House planned a filibuster to delay the final counting of the electoral votes until after inauguration day. If the filibuster succeeded, neither candidate would have a majority and, as provided in the Constitution, the election would be decided by the House, where the Democrats controlled enough states to elect Tilden.

To ensure Hayes's election, Republican leaders negotiated secretly with conservative southern Democrats, some of whom seemed willing to abandon their opposition if the last troops were withdrawn and "home rule" restored to the South. There were also vague pledges of federal support for southern railroads and internal improvements. Hayes also promised to end federal support for crumbling Radical regimes. Eventually an informal bargain was struck, which historians have dubbed the Compromise of 1877. What precisely was agreed to and by whom remains a matter of dispute; but one thing at least was understood by both sides—Hayes would be president and southern blacks would be abandoned to their fate.

With southern Democratic acquiescence, the filibuster was broken, and Hayes took the oath of office. He immediately ordered the army not to resist a Democratic takeover of state governments in South Carolina and Louisiana. Thus fell the last of the Radical governments, and the entire South was firmly under the control of white Democrats. The trauma of the war and Reconstruction had destroyed the chances for a renewal of two-party competition among white Southerners.

THE NEW SOUTH

The men who came to power after the fall of Radical Reconstruction are usually referred to as the Redeemers. They had differing backgrounds and previous loyalties. Some were members of the Old South's ruling planter class who had warmly supported secession and now sought to reestablish the old order with as few changes as possible. Others, of middle-class origin or outlook, favored commercial and industrial interests over agrarian groups and called for a New South committed to diversified economic development. A third group were professional politicians who shifted positions with the prevailing winds.

The Redeemers subscribed to no single coherent ideology or view of the world but are perhaps best characterized as power brokers mediating among the dominant interest groups of the South in ways that served their own political advantage. In many ways, the "rings" that they established on the state and county level were analogous to the political machines developing at the same time in northern cities.

Redeemers did, however, agree on and endorse two basic principles: laissez-faire and white supremacy. Laissez-faire—the notion that government should be limited and should not intervene openly and directly in the economy—could unite planters, frustrated at seeing direct state support going to businessmen, and capitalist promoters who had come to realize that low taxes and freedom from government regulation were even more advantageous than state subsidies. It soon became clear that the Redeemers responded only to privileged and entrenched interest groups, especially landlords, merchants, and industrialists, and offered little or nothing to tenants, small farmers, and working people. As industrialization began to gather steam in the 1880s, Democratic regimes became increasingly accommodating to manufacturing interests and hospitable to agents of northern capital who were gaining control of the South's transportation system and its extractive industries.

White supremacy was the principal rallying cry that brought the Redeemers to power in the first place. Once in office, they found they could stay there by charging that opponents of ruling Democratic cliques were trying to divide "the white man's party" and open the way for a return to "black domination." Appeals to racism could also deflect attention from the economic grievances of groups without political clout.

The new governments were more economical than those of Reconstruction, mainly because they cut back drastically on appropriations for schools and other needed public services. But they were scarcely more honest—embezzlement of funds and bribery of officials continued to occur to an alarming extent.

The Redeemer regimes of the late 1870s and 1880s badly neglected the interests of small white farmers. Whites, as well as blacks, were suffering from the notorious crop lien system, which gave local merchants who advanced credit at high rates of interest during the growing season the right to take possession of the harvested crop on terms that buried farmers deeper and deeper in debt. As a result, increasing numbers of whites lost title to their homesteads and were reduced to tenancy. When a depression of world cotton prices added to the burden of a ruinous credit system, agrarian protesters began to challenge the ruling elite, first through the Southern Farmers' Alliance of the late 1880s and then by supporting its political descendant—the Populist party of the 1890s.

But African Americans bore the greatest hardships imposed by the new order. The Redeemers had promised, in exchange for the end of federal intervention in 1877, to respect the rights of blacks as set forth in the Fourteenth and Fifteenth Amendments. But when blacks tried to vote Republican in the "redeemed" states, they encountered renewed violence and intimidation. Blacks who withstood the threat of losing their jobs or being evicted from tenant farms if they voted Republican were visited at night and literally whipped into line. The message was clear: vote Democratic, or vote not at all.

Furthermore, white Democrats now controlled the electoral machinery and were able to manipulate the black vote by stuffing ballot boxes, discarding unwanted votes, or reporting fraudulent totals. Some states also imposed complicated new voting requirements to discourage black participation. Full-scale disfranchisement did not occur until literacy tests and other legalized obstacles to voting were imposed in the period from 1890 to 1910, but by that time, less formal and comprehensive methods had already made a mockery of the Fifteenth Amendment.

Nevertheless, blacks continued to vote freely in some localities until the 1890s; a few districts even elected black Republicans to Congress during the immediate post-Reconstruction period. The last of these, Representative George H. White of North Carolina, served until 1901. His farewell address eloquently conveyed the agony of southern blacks in the era of strict segregation:

These parting words are in behalf of an outraged, heart-broken, bruised, and bleeding but God-fearing people, faithful, industrious, loyal people—rising people, full of potential force. . . . The only apology that I have to make for the earnestness with which I have spoken is that I am pleading for the life, the liberty, the future happiness, and manhood suffrage of one-eighth of the entire population of the United States.

The dark night of racism that fell on the South after Reconstruction seemed to unleash all the baser impulses of human nature. Between 1889 and 1899, an average of 187 blacks were lynched every year for alleged offenses against white supremacy. Those convicted of petty crimes against property were often little better off; many were condemned to be leased out to private contractors whose brutality

Perhaps no event better expresses the cruel and barbaric nature of the racism and white supremacy that swept the South after Reconstruction than lynching. Although lynchings were not confined to the South, most occurred there and African American men were the most frequent victims. Here two men lean out of a barn window above a black man who is about to be hanged. Others below prepare to set on fire the pile of hay at the victim's feet. Lynchings were often public events, drawing huge crowds to watch the victim's agonizing death.

SUPREME COURT DECISIONS AFFECTING
BLACK CIVIL RIGHTS, 1875–1900

CASE	EFFECTS OF COURT'S DECISIONS
Hall v. DeCuir (1878)	Struck down Louisiana law prohibiting racial discrimination by "common carriers" (railroads, steamboats, buses). Declared the law a "burden" on interstate commerce, over which states had no authority.
United States v. Harris (1882)	Declared federal laws to punish crimes such as murder and assault unconstitutional. Declared such crimes to be the sole concern of local government. Ignored the frequent racial motivation behind such crimes in the South.
Civil Rights Cases (1883)	Struck down Civil Rights Act of 1875. Declared that Congress may not legislate on civil rights unless a state passes a discriminatory law. Declared the Fourteenth Amendment silent on racial discrimination by private citizens.
Plessy v. Ferguson (1896)	Upheld Louisiana statute requiring "separate but equal" accommodations on railroads. Declared that segregation is *not* necessarily discrimination.
Williams v. Mississippi (1898)	Upheld state law requiring a literacy test to qualify for voting. Refused to find any implication of racial discrimination in the law, although it permitted illiterate whites to vote if they "understood" the Constitution. Using such laws, southern states rapidly disfranchised blacks.

rivaled that of the most sadistic slaveholders. The convict lease system enabled entrepreneurs, such as mine owners and extractors of forest products, to rent prisoners from the state and treat them as they saw fit. Unlike slaveowners, they suffered no loss when a forced laborer died from overwork. (Annual mortality rates in the convict camps ranged as high as 25 percent.) Finally, the dignity of blacks was cruelly affronted by the wave of segregation laws passed around the turn of the century, which served to remind them constantly that they were deemed unfit to associate with whites on any basis that implied equality. To some extent, the segregation laws were a white reaction to the refusal of many blacks to submit to voluntary segregation of railroads, streetcars, and other public facilities.

The North and the federal government did little or nothing to stem the tide of racial oppression in the South. A series of Supreme Court decisions between 1875 and 1896 gutted the Reconstruction amendments and the legislation passed to enforce them, leaving blacks virtually defenseless against political and social discrimination.

The career of Henry McNeal Turner sums up the bitter side of the black experience in the South during and after Reconstruction. Born free in South Carolina in 1834, Turner became a minister of the African Methodist Episcopal (AME) Church just before the outbreak of the Civil War. During the war, he recruited African Americans for the Union army and later served as chaplain for black troops. After the fighting was over, he went to Georgia to work for the Freedmen's Bureau but encountered racial discrimination from white Bureau officers and left government service for church work and Reconstruction politics. Elected to the 1867 Georgia constitutional convention and to the state legis-

Henry McNeal Turner, who was born in freedom, became a bishop of the African Methodist Episcopal Church and was elected to the Georgia legislature.

lature in 1868, he was one of a number of black clergymen who assumed leadership roles among the freedmen. But whites won control of the Georgia legislature and expelled all the black members. As the inhabitant of a state in which blacks never gained the degree of power that they achieved in some other parts of the South, Turner was one of the first black leaders to see the failure of Reconstruction as the betrayal of African American hopes for citizenship.

Becoming a bishop of the AME Church in 1880, Turner emerged as the late nineteenth century's leading proponent of black emigration to Africa. Because he believed that white Americans were so deeply prejudiced against blacks that they would never grant them equal rights, Turner became an early advocate of black nationalism and a total separation of the races. Emigration became a popular movement among southern blacks, but a majority of blacks in the nation as a whole and even in Turner's own church refused to give up on the hope of eventual equality on American soil. But Bishop Turner's anger and despair were the understandable responses of a proud man to the way that he and his fellow African Americans had been treated in the post–Civil War period.

By the late 1880s, the wounds of the Civil War were healing, and white Americans were celebrating the spirit of sectional reconciliation and their common Americanism. But whites could come back together only because Northerners had tacitly agreed to give Southerners a free hand in their efforts to reduce blacks to a new form of servitude. The "outraged, heart-broken, bruised, and bleeding" African Americans of the South paid the heaviest price for sectional reunion.

17

THE WEST
Exploiting an Empire

I n the last three decades of the nineteenth century, a flood of settlers ventured into the vast lands across the Mississippi River. James H. Kyner, a railroad contractor in Oregon, saw in the 1880s "an almost unbroken stream of emigrants from horizon to horizon. . . . Teams and covered wagons, horsemen, little bunches of cows, more wagons, some drawn by cows, men walking, women and children riding—an endless stream of hardy, optimistic folk, going west to seek their fortunes and to settle an empire."

Prospectors poured into unsettled areas in search of "pay dirt," railroads crisscrossed the continent, eastern and foreign capitalists invested in cattle and land bonanzas, and farmers took up the promise of free western lands. In 1867, Horace Greeley, editor of the New York *Tribune,* told New York City's unemployed: "If you strike off into the broad, free West, and make yourself a farm from Uncle Sam's generous domain, you will crowd nobody, starve nobody, and neither you nor your children need evermore beg for something to do."

With the end of the Civil War, white Americans again claimed a special destiny to expand across the continent. In the process, they crushed the culture of the Native Americans and ignored the contributions of people of other races, such as the Chinese miners and laborers and the Mexican herdsmen. As millions moved west, the states of Colorado, Washington, Montana, the Dakotas, Idaho, Wyoming, and Utah were carved out of the lands across the Mississippi. At the turn of the century, only Arizona, New Mexico, and Oklahoma remained as territories.

The West became a great colonial empire, harnessed to eastern capital and tied increasingly to national and international markets. Its raw materials, sent east by wagon, train, and ship, helped fuel eastern factories. Western economies relied heavily on the federal government, which subsidized their railroads, distributed their land, and spent millions of dollars for the upkeep of soldiers and Indians. Regional variations persisted; and Westerners remained proud of their individualistic traditions. Yet they imitated the East's social, cultural, and political patterns.

By the 1890s, the West of the lands beyond the Mississippi had undergone substantial change. In place of buffalo and unfenced vistas, there were cities and towns, health resorts, Paris fashions, homesteads, sheep ranches, and, in the arid regions, the beginnings of the irrigated agriculture that would reshape the West in the twentieth century. Ghost towns, abandoned farms, and the scars in the earth left by miners and farmers spoke to the less favorable side of settlement. As the new century dawned, the West had become a place of conquest and exploitation, as well as a mythic land of cowboys and quick fortunes.

BEYOND THE FRONTIER

The line of white settlement had reached the edge of the Missouri timber country by 1840. Beyond lay an enormous land of rolling prairies, parched deserts, and rugged, majestic mountains. Emerging from the timber country, travelers first encountered the Great Plains—treeless, nearly flat, an endless "sea of grassy hillocks." The Prairie Plains, the eastern part of the region, enjoyed rich soil and good rainfall. To the west were the High Plains, rough, semiarid, rising gently to the foothills of the Rocky Mountains.

Running from Alaska to central New Mexico, the Rockies presented a formidable barrier, and most travelers hurried through the northern passes, emerging in the desolate basin of present-day southern Idaho and Utah. On the west, the lofty Coast Ranges—the Cascades and Sierra Nevada—held back rainfall; beyond were the temperate lands of the Pacific Coast.

Early explorers like Zebulon Pike thought the country beyond the Mississippi was uninhabitable, fit only, Pike said, for "wandering and uncivilized aborigines." Mapmakers agreed; between 1825 and 1860, American maps showed this land as "The Great American Desert." As a result, settlement paused on the edge of the Plains, and most early settlers headed directly for California and Oregon.

Few rivers cut through the Plains; those that did raged in the winter and trickled in the summer. Rainfall usually did not reach 15 inches a year, not enough to support extensive agriculture. There was little lumber for homes and fences, and the tools of eastern settlement—the cast-iron plow, the boat, and the ax—were virtually useless on the tough and treeless Plains soil. "East of the Mississippi," historian Walter Prescott Webb noted, "civilization stood on three legs—land, water, and timber; west of the Mississippi not one but two of these legs were withdrawn—water and timber—and civilization was left on one leg—land."

Hot winds seared the Plains in summer, and northers, blizzards, and hail-storms froze them in winter. Wildlife roamed in profusion. The American bison, better known as the buffalo, grazed in enormous herds from Mexico to Canada. In 1865, perhaps fifteen million buffalo lived on the Plains, so many they seemed like "leaves in a forest" to an early observer. A single herd sighted in 1871 had four million head.

CRUSHING THE NATIVE AMERICANS

When Greeley urged New Yorkers to move West and "crowd nobody," he—like almost all white Americans—ignored the fact that large numbers of people al-ready lived there. At the close of the Civil War, Native Americans inhabited nearly half the United States. By 1880, they had been driven onto smaller and smaller reservations and were no longer an independent people. A decade later, even their culture had crumbled under the impact of white domination.

In 1865, nearly a quarter million Native Americans lived in the western half of the country. Tribes such as the Winnebago, Menominee, Cherokee, and Chippewa were resettled there, forced out of their eastern lands by advancing white settlement. Other tribes were native to the region. In the Southwest there were the Pueblo groups, including the Hopi, Zuni, and Rio Grande Pueblos. Peaceful farmers and herders, they had built up complex traditions around a set-tled way of life.

The Pueblo groups were cultivators of corn. They lived on the subdesert plateau of present-day western New Mexico and eastern Arizona. Harassed by powerful neighboring tribes, they built communal houses of adobe brick on high mesas or in cracks in the cliffs. More nomadic were the Camp Dwellers, the Jicarilla Apache and Navajo who roamed eastern New Mexico and western Texas. Blending elements of the Plains and Plateau environments, they lived in tepees or mud huts, grew some crops to supplement their hunting, and moved readily from place to place. The Navajo herded sheep and produced beautiful ornamental silver, baskets, and blankets. Fierce fighters, Apache horsemen were feared by whites and fellow Indians across the southwestern Plains.

Farther west were the tribes that inhabited present-day California. Divided into many small bands, they eked out a difficult existence living on roots, grubs, berries, acorns, and small game. In the Pacific Northwest, where fish and forest animals made life easier, the Klamath, Chinook, Yurok, and Shasta tribes developed a rich civilization. They built plank houses and canoes, worked extensively in wood, and evolved a complex social and political organization. Settled and determined, they resisted the invasion of the whites.

By the 1870s, most of these tribes had been destroyed or beaten into submission. The powerful Ute, crushed in 1855, ceded most of their Utah lands to the United States and settled on a small reservation near Great Salt Lake. The Navajo and Apache fought back fiercely, but between 1865 and 1873 they too were confined to reservations. The Native Americans of California succumbed to the contagious diseases carried by whites during the Gold Rush of 1849. Miners burned their villages, and by 1880, fewer than twenty thousand Indians lived in California.

LIFE OF THE PLAINS INDIANS

In the mid-nineteenth century, nearly two-thirds of the Native Americans lived on the Great Plains. The Plains tribes included the Sioux of present-day Minnesota and the Dakotas; the Blackfoot of Idaho and Montana; the Cheyenne, Crow, and Arapaho of the central Plains; the Pawnee of western Nebraska; and the Kiowa, Apache, and Comanche of present-day Texas and New Mexico.

Nomadic and warlike, the Plains Indians depended on the buffalo and horse. The modern horse, first brought by Spanish explorers in the 1500s, spread north from Mexico onto the Plains, and by the 1700s the Plains Indians' way of life had changed. The Plains tribes gave up farming almost entirely and hunted the buffalo, ranging widely over the rolling plains. The men became superb warriors and horsemen, among the best light cavalry in the world.

Migratory in culture, the Plains Indians formed tribes of several thousand people but lived in smaller bands of three to five hundred. The Comanche, who numbered perhaps seven thousand, had thirteen bands with such names as Burnt Meat, Making Bags While Moving, and Those Who Move Often. Each band was governed by a chief and a council of elder men, and Indians of the same tribe transferred freely from band to band. Bands acted independently, making it difficult for the U.S. government to deal with the fragmented tribes.

The bands followed and lived off the buffalo. Buffalo provided food, clothing, and shelter; the Indians, unlike later white hunters, used every part of the animal. The meat was dried or "jerked" in the hot Plains air. The skins made tepees, blankets, and robes. Buffalo bones became knives; tendons were made into bowstrings; horns and hooves were boiled into glue. Buffalo "chips"—dried manure—were burned as fuel. All in all, the buffalo was "a galloping department store."

Warfare between tribes usually took the form of brief raids and skirmishes. Plains Indians fought few prolonged wars and rarely coveted territory. Most conflicts involved only a few warriors intent on stealing horses or "counting coup"— touching an enemy's body with the hand or a special stick. Tribes developed a fierce and trained warrior class, recognized for achievements in battle. Speaking different languages, Native Americans of various tribes were nevertheless able to communicate with one another through a highly developed sign language.

The Plains tribes divided labor tasks according to gender. Men hunted, traded, supervised ceremonial activities, and cleared ground for planting. They usually held the positions of authority, such as chief or medicine man. Women were responsible for child rearing and artistic activity. They also performed the camp work, grew vegetables, prepared buffalo meat and hides, and gathered berries and roots. In most tribes, women played an important role in political, economic, and religious activities. Among the Navajo and Zuni, kinship descended from the mother's side, and Navajo women were in charge of most of the family's property. In tribes such as the Sioux, there was little difference in status. Men were respected for hunting and war, women for their artistic skills with quill and paint.

"As Long as Waters Run":
Searching for an Indian Policy

Before the Civil War, Americans used the land west of the Mississippi as "one big reservation." The government named the area "Indian Country," moved eastern tribes there with firm treaty guarantees, and in 1834 passed the Indian Intercourse Act, which prohibited any white person from entering Indian country without a license.

The situation changed in the 1850s. Wagon trains wound their way to California and Oregon, miners pushed into western goldfields, and there was talk of a transcontinental railroad. To clear the way for settlement, the federal government in 1851 abandoned "One Big Reservation" in favor of a new policy of concentration. For the first time, it assigned definite boundaries to each tribe. The Sioux, for example, were given the Dakota country north of the Platte River, the Crows a large area near the Powder River, and the Cheyenne and Arapaho the Colorado foothills between the North Platte and Arkansas rivers for "as long as waters run and the grass shall grow."

The concentration policy lasted only a few years. Accustomed to hunting widely for buffalo, many Native Americans refused to stay within their assigned areas. White settlers poured into Indian lands, then called on the government to protect them. Indians were pushed out of Kansas and Nebraska in the 1850s, even as white reformers fought to hold those territories open for free blacks. In

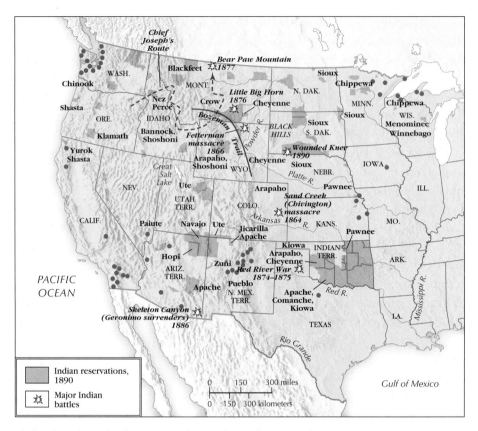

Native Americans in the West: Major Battles and Reservations

"They made us many promises, more than I remember, but they never kept but one; they promised to take our land, and they took it." So said Red Cloud of the Oglala Sioux, summarizing Native American–white relations in the 1870s.

1859, gold miners moved into the Pikes Peak country, touching off warfare with the Cheyenne and Arapaho.

In 1864, tired of the fighting, the two tribes asked for peace. Certain that the war was over, Chief Black Kettle led his seven hundred followers to camp on Sand Creek in southeastern Colorado. Early on the morning of November 29, 1864, a group of Colorado militia led by Colonel John M. Chivington attacked the sleeping group. "Kill and scalp all, big and little," Chivington told his men. "Nits make lice." Black Kettle tried to stop the ambush, raising first an American flag and then a white flag. Neither worked. The Native American men, women, and children were clubbed, stabbed, and scalped.

The Chivington massacre set off angry protests in Colorado and the East. Congress appointed an investigating committee, and the government concluded a treaty with the Cheyenne and Arapaho, condemning "the gross and wanton outrages." Still, the two tribes were forced to surrender their Sand Creek reservation in exchange for lands elsewhere. The Kiowa and Comanche were also ousted from areas they had been granted "forever" only a few years before. As the Sioux chief Spotted Tail said, "Why does not the Great Father put his red children on wheels so that he can move them as he will?"

Before long, the powerful Sioux were on the warpath in the great Sioux War of 1865–1867. Once again, an invasion of gold miners touched off the war, which flared even more intensely when the federal government announced plans to connect the various mining towns by building the Bozeman Trail through the heart of the Sioux hunting grounds in Montana. Red Cloud, the Sioux chief, determined to stop the trail. In December 1866, pursued by an army column under Captain William J. Fetterman, he lured the incautious Fetterman deep into the wilderness, ambushed him, and wiped out all eighty-two soldiers in his command.

The Fetterman massacre, coming so soon after the Chivington massacre, sparked a public debate over the nation's Indian policy. Like the policy itself, the debate reflected differing white views of the Native Americans. In the East, some reform, humanitarian, and church groups wanted a humane peace policy, directed toward educating and "civilizing" the tribes. Many white people, in the East and West, questioned this approach, convinced that Native Americans were savages unfit for civilization. Westerners, of course, had some reason to fear Indian attacks, and the fears often fed on wild rumors of scalped settlers and besieged forts. As a result, Westerners in general favored firm control over the Native Americans, including swift punishment of any who rebelled.

In 1867, the peace advocates won the debate. Halting construction on the Bozeman Trail, Congress created a Peace Commission of four civilians and three generals to end the Sioux War and eliminate permanently the causes of Indian wars. Setting out for the West, the Peace Commissioners agreed that only one policy offered a permanent solution: a policy of "small reservations" to isolate the Native Americans on distant lands, teach them to farm, and gradually "civilize" them.

FINAL BATTLES ON THE PLAINS

Few Native Americans settled peacefully into life on the new reservations. The reservation system not only changed their age-old customs; it chained them in a situation of poverty and isolation. Soon, young warriors and minor chiefs denounced the treaties and drifted back to the open countryside. In late 1868, warfare broke out again, and it took more than a decade of violence to beat the Indians into submission. The Kiowa and Comanche rampaged through the Texas

Panhandle, looting and killing, until the U.S. Army crushed them in the Red River War of 1874–1875 and ended warfare in the Southwest.

On the northern Plains, fighting resulted from the Black Hills Gold Rush of 1875. As prospectors tramped across Native American hunting grounds, the Sioux gathered to stop them. They were led by Rain-in-the-Face, the great war chief Crazy Horse, and the famous medicine man Sitting Bull. The army sent several columns of troops after the Indians, but one, under flamboyant Lieutenant Colonel George Armstrong Custer, pushed recklessly ahead, eager to claim the victory. On the morning of June 25, 1876, thinking he had a small band of Native Americans surrounded in their village on the banks of the Little Bighorn River in Montana, Custer divided his column and took 265 men toward it. Instead of finding a small band, he discovered he had stumbled on the main Sioux camp with 2500 warriors. It was the largest Native American army ever assembled in the United States.

By midafternoon it was over; Custer and his men were dead. Custer was largely responsible for the loss, but "Custer's Last Stand," set in blazing headlines across the country, set off a nationwide demand for revenge. Within a few months, the Sioux were surrounded and beaten, three thousand of them surrendering in October 1876. Sitting Bull and a few followers who had fled to Canada gave up in 1881.

This pictogram by Oglala Sioux Amos Bad Heart Bull is a Native American version of the battle of the Little Bighorn, also known as Custer's Last Stand.

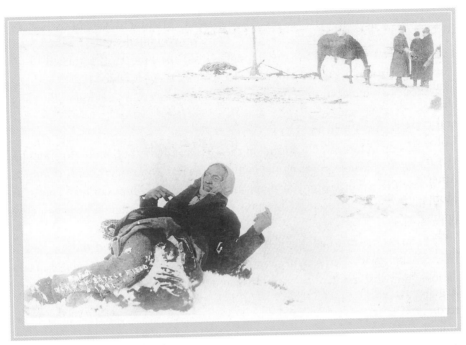

The frozen body of Big Foot, leader of the Sioux band massacred at Wounded Knee, lies covered with snow, awaiting burial by the white burial party shown in the background.

The Sioux War ended the major Indian warfare in the West, but occasional outbreaks occurred for several years thereafter. In 1877, the Nez Percé tribe of Oregon, a people who had warmly welcomed Lewis and Clark in 1805, rebelled against government policy. Hoping to reach Canada, Chief Joseph led the tribe on a courageous flight lasting 75 days and covering 1321 miles. They defeated the pursuing army at every turn but then ran out of food, horses, and ammunition. Surrendering, they were sent to barren lands in the Indian Country of Oklahoma, and there, most of them died from disease.

In 1890, the Teton Sioux of South Dakota, bitter and starving, became restless. Many of them turned to the Ghost Dances, a set of dances and rites that grew from a vision of a Paiute messiah named Wovoka. Performance of the dances, Wovoka said, would bring back Native American lands and would cause the whites to disappear. All Native Americans would reunite, the earth would be covered with dust, and a new earth would come upon the old. The vanished buffalo would return in great herds.

The army intervened to stop the dancing, touching off violence that killed Sitting Bull and a number of other warriors. Frightened Native Americans fled southwest to join other Ghost Dancers under the aging chief Big Foot. Moving quickly, troops of the Seventh Cavalry, Custer's old regiment, caught up with Big Foot's band and took them to the army camp on Wounded Knee Creek in South Dakota. A Native American, it is thought, fired the first shot, returned by the army's new machine guns. Firing a shell a second, they shredded tepees and people. About two hundred men, women, and children were massacred in the snow.

THE END OF TRIBAL LIFE

The final step in Indian policy came in the 1870s and 1880s. Some reformers had long argued against segregating the Native Americans on reservations, urging instead that the nation assimilate them individually into white culture. These "assimilationists" wanted to use education, land policy, and federal law to eradicate tribal society.

Congress began to adopt the policy in 1871 when it ended the practice of treaty making with Native American tribes. Since tribes were no longer separate nations, they lost many of their political and judicial functions, and the power of the chiefs was weakened.

Tom Torlino, a Navajo Indian, photographed before and after his "assimilation." Torlino attended the Carlisle Indian School in Pennsylvania.

While Congress worked to break down the tribes, educators trained young Native Americans to adjust to white culture. In 1879, fifty Pawnee, Kiowa, and Cheyenne youths were brought east to the new Carlisle Indian School in Carlisle, Pennsylvania. Other Native American schools soon opened, including the Haskell Institute in Kansas and numerous day schools on the western reservations. The schools taught students to fix machines and farm; they forced young Indians to trim their long hair and made them speak English, banned the wearing of tribal paint or clothes, and forbade tribal ceremonies and dances. "Kill the Indian and save the man," said Richard H. Pratt, the army officer who founded the Carlisle School.

Land ownership was the final and most important link in the new policy. Native Americans who owned land, it was thought, would become responsible, self-reliant citizens. Deciding to give each Native American a farm, Congress in 1887 passed the Dawes Severalty Act, the most important legal development in Indian-white relations in more than three centuries.

Aiming to end tribal life, the Dawes Act divided tribal lands into small plots for distribution among members of the tribe. Each family head received 160 acres, single adults 80 acres, and children 40 acres.

Through the Dawes Act, 47 million acres of land were distributed to Native Americans and their families. There were another 90 million acres in the reservations, and these lands, often the most fertile, were sold to white settlers. Many Native Americans knew little about farming. Their tools were rudimentary, and in the culture of the Plains Indians, men had not ordinarily participated in farming. In 1934, the government returned to the idea of tribal land ownership, but by then 138 million acres of Indian land had shrunk to 48 million acres, half of which was barren.

The final blow to tribal life came not in the Dawes Act but in the virtual extermination of the buffalo, the Plains Indians' chief resource and the basis for their unique way of life. The killing began in the 1860s as the transcontinental railroads pushed west, and it stepped up as settlers found they could harm the Indians by harming the buffalo. "Kill every buffalo you can," an army officer said. "Every buffalo dead is an Indian gone." Then, in 1871, a Pennsylvania tannery discovered that buffalo hides made valuable leather. Professional hunters such as William F. "Buffalo Bill" Cody swarmed across the Plains, killing millions of the beasts.

Between 1872 and 1874, professional hunters slaughtered three million buffalo a year. In a frontier form of a factory system, riflemen, skinners, and transport wagons pushed through the vast herds, which shrank steadily behind them. A good hunter killed a hundred buffalo a day. Skinners took off the hides, removed the tongue, hump, and tallow, and left the rest.

By 1883, the buffalo were almost gone. When the government set out to produce the famous "buffalo nickel," the designer had to go to the Bronx Zoo in New York City to find a buffalo.

By 1900, there were only 250,000 Native Americans in the country. (There were 600,000 within the limits of the present-day United States in 1800, and more than 5 million in 1492, when Columbus first set foot in the New World.) Most of the Indians lived on reservations. Many lived in poverty. Alcoholism and unemployment were growing problems, and Native Americans, no longer able to live off the buffalo, became wards of the state. They lost their cultural distinctiveness. Once possessors of the entire continent, they had been crowded into smaller and smaller areas, overwhelmed by the demand to become settled, literate, and English-speaking. "Except for the internment of the West Coast Japanese during World War II," said historian Roger L. Nichols, "Indian removal is the only example of large-scale government-enforced migration in American history. For the Japanese, the move was temporary; for the Indians it was not."

Even as the Native Americans lost their identity, they entered the romantic folklore of the West. Dime novels, snapped up by readers young and old, told tales of Indian fighting on the Plains. "Buffalo Bill" Cody turned it all into a profitable business. Beginning in 1883, his Wild West Show ran for more than three decades, playing to millions of viewers in the United States, Canada, and Europe. It featured Plains Indians chasing buffalo, performing a war dance, and attacking a settler's cabin. In 1885, Sitting Bull himself, victor over Custer at the battle of Little Bighorn, performed in the show.

SETTLEMENT OF THE WEST

Between 1870 and 1900, white—and some African, Hispanic, and Asian—Americans settled the enormous total of 430 million acres west of the Mississippi; they took over more land than had been occupied by Americans in all the years before 1870.

People moved West for many reasons. Some sought adventure; others wanted to escape the drab routine of factory or city life. Many moved to California for their health. The Mormons settled Utah to escape religious persecution. Others followed the mining camps, the advancing railroads, and the farming and cattle frontier.

Whatever the specific reason, most people moved West to better their lot. On the whole, their timing was good, for as the nation's population grew, so did demand for the livestock and the agricultural, mineral, and lumber products of the expanding West. Contrary to older historical views, the West did not act as a major "safety valve," an outlet for social and economic tensions. The poor and unemployed did not have the means to move there and establish farms. "Moreover," as Douglass C. North, an economic historian, said, "most people moved West in good times . . . in periods of rising prices, of expanding demand, when the prospects for making money from this new land looked brightest; and this aspect characterized the whole pattern of settlement."

Men and Women on the Overland Trail

The first movement west aimed not for the nearby Plains but for California and Oregon on the continent's far shore. It started in the 1849 Gold Rush to California, and in the next three decades perhaps as many as half a million individuals made the long journey. Some walked; others rode horses alone or in small groups. About half joined great caravans, numbering 150 wagons or more, that inched across the two thousand miles between the Missouri River and the Pacific Coast.

More often than not, men made the decision to make the crossing, but, except for the stampedes to the mines, migration usually turned out to be a family affair. Wives were consulted, though in some cases they had little real choice. They could either go along or live alone at home. While many women regretted leaving family and friends, they agreed to the trip, sometimes as eagerly as the men. The majority of people traveled in family groups, including in-laws, grandchildren, aunts, and uncles. As one historian said, "The quest for something new would take place in the context of the very familiar."

Individuals and wagon trains set out from various points along the Missouri River. Leaving in the spring and traveling through the summer, they hoped to reach their destination before the first snowfall. During April, travelers gradually assembled in spring camp just across the Missouri River, waiting for the new grass to ripen into forage. They packed and repacked the wagons and elected the trains' leaders, who would set the line of march, look for water and campsites, and impose discipline. Some trains adopted detailed rules, fearing a lapse into savagery in the wild lands across the Missouri. "Every man to carry with him a Bible and other religious books, as we hope not to degenerate into a state of barbarism," one agreement said.

Setting out in early May, travelers divided the enormous route into manageable portions. The first leg of the journey followed the Platte River west to Fort Kearney in central Nebraska Territory, a distance of about three hundred miles. The land was even, with good supplies of wood, grass, and water. From a distance, the white-topped wagons seemed driven by a common force, but, in fact, internal discipline broke down almost immediately. Arguments erupted over the pace of the march, the choice of campsites, the number of guards to post, whether to rest or push on. Elected leaders quit; new ones were chosen. Every train was filled with individualists, and as the son of one train captain said, "If you think it's any snap to run a wagon train of 66 wagons with every man in the train having a different idea of what is the best thing to do, all I can say is that some day you ought to try it."

Men, women, and children had different tasks on the trail. Men concerned themselves almost entirely with hunting buffalo and antelope, guard duty, and transportation. They rose at 4 A.M. to hitch the wagons, and after breakfast began the day's march. At noon, they stopped and set the teams to graze. After the midday meal, the march continued until sunset. Then, while the men relaxed, the women fixed dinner and the next day's lunch, and the children kindled the fires, brought water to camp, and searched for wood or other fuel. Walking fifteen miles a day, in searing heat and mountain cold, travelers were exhausted by late afternoon.

For women, the trail was lonely, and they worked to exhaustion. Before long, some adjusted their clothing to the harsh conditions, adopting the new bloomer pants, shortening their skirts, or wearing regular "wash dresses"—so called because they had shorter hemlines that did not drag on the wet ground on washday. Other women continued to wear their long dresses, thinking bloomers "indecent." Both men and women carried firearms in case of Indian attacks, but most emigrants saw few Indians en route.

What they often did see was trash, miles of it, for the wagon trains were an early example of the impact of migration and settlement on the western environment. On the Oregon and other trails, travelers sidestepped mounds of garbage, tin cans, furniture, cooking stoves, kegs, tools, and clothing, all discarded by people who had passed through before. Along a forty-mile trail in the Nevada desert, a migrant tallied two thousand abandoned wagons.

The first stage of the journey was deceptively easy, and travelers usually reached Fort Kearney by late May. The second leg led another 300 miles up the Platte River to Fort Laramie on the eastern edge of Wyoming Territory. The heat of June had dried the grass, and there was no wood. Anxious to beat the early snowfalls, travelers rested a day or two at the fort, then hurried on to South Pass, 280 miles to the west, the best route through the forbidding Rockies. The land was barren. It was now mid-July, but the mountain nights were so cold that ice formed in the water buckets.

Beyond South Pass, some emigrants turned south to the Mormon settlements on the Great Salt Lake, but most headed 340 miles north to Fort Hall on the Snake River in Idaho. It took another three months to cover the remaining 800 miles. California-bound travelers followed the Humboldt River through the summer heat of Nevada. Well into September, they began the final arduous push: first, a 55-mile stretch of desert; then 70 difficult miles up the eastern slopes of

Of the many dangers faced by travelers on the overland trails, among the most severe were prairie blizzards. As temperatures fell to −40 degrees, cattle would inhale particles of snow and sleet and die of suffocation.

the Sierra Nevada, laboriously hoisting wagons over massive outcrops of rock; and finally the last 100 miles down the western slopes to the welcome sight of California's Central Valley in October.

Under the best of conditions the trip took six months, sixteen hours a day, dawn to dusk, of hard, grueling labor. Walking halfway across the continent was no easy task, and it provided a never-to-be-forgotten experience for those who did it. The wagon trains, carrying the dreams of thousands of individuals, reproduced society in small focus: individualistic, hopeful, mobile, divided by age and gender roles, apprehensive, yet willing to strike out for the distant and new.

LAND FOR THE TAKING

As railroads pushed west in the 1870s and 1880s, locomotive trains replaced wagon trains, but the shift was gradual, and until the end of the century, emigrants often combined both modes of travel.

Traffic flowed in all directions, belying the image of a simple "westward" movement. Many people did go west, of course, but others, such as migrants from Mexico, became westerners by moving north, and Asian Americans moved eastward from the Pacific Coast. Whatever their route, they all ended up in the meeting ground of cultures that formed the modern West.

Why did they come? "The motive that induced us to part with the pleasant associations and the dear friends of our childhood days," explained Phoebe Judson, an early emigrant, "was to obtain from the government of the United States a grant of land that 'Uncle Sam' had promised to give to the head of each family who settled in this new country." A popular camp song reflected the same motive:

Come along, come along—don't be alarmed,
Uncle Sam is rich enough to give us all a farm.

Uncle Sam owned about 1 billion acres of land in the 1860s, much of it mountain and desert land unsuited for agriculture. By 1900, the various land laws had distributed half of it. Between 1862 and 1890, the government gave away 48 million acres under the Homestead Act of 1862, sold about 100 million acres to private citizens and corporations, granted 128 million acres to railroad companies to tempt them to build across the unsettled West, and sold huge tracts to the states.

The Homestead Act of 1862, a law of great significance, gave 160 acres of land to anyone who would pay a $10 registration fee and pledge to live on it and cultivate it for five years. The offer set off a mass migration of land-hungry Europeans, dazzled by a country that gave its land away. Americans also seized on the act's provisions, and between 1862 and 1900, nearly 600,000 families claimed free homesteads under it.

Yet the Homestead Act did not work as Congress had hoped. Few farmers and laborers had the cash to move to the frontier, buy farm equipment, and wait out the year or two before the farm became self-supporting. Tailored to the timber and water conditions of the East, the act did not work as well in the semiarid West. In the fertile valleys of the Mississippi, 160 acres provided a generous farm. A farmer on the Great Plains needed either a larger farm for dry farming or a smaller one for irrigation.

The Timber Culture Act of 1873 attempted to adjust the Homestead Act to western conditions. It allowed homesteaders to claim an additional 160 acres if they planted trees on a quarter of it within four years. A successful act, it distributed 10 million acres of land, encouraged needed forestation, and enabled homesteaders to expand their farms to a workable size.

Speculators made ingenious use of the land laws. Sending agents in advance of settlement, they moved along choice river bottoms or irrigable areas, accumulating large holdings to be held for high prices. In the arid West, where control of water meant control of the surrounding land, shrewd ranchers plotted their

LARGE DISCOUNTS FOR CASH.

BETTER TERMS THAN EVER!

PRODUCTS will PAY for LAND and IMPROVEMENTS.

BUY BEFORE JULY 1st, 1875, and Secure these Terms.

VALLEY OF THE BIG BLUE, SOUTH OF SEWARD, NEB.

THE BEST
PRAIRIE LANDS
IN
IOWA AND NEBRASKA
ARE FOR SALE BY THE
Burlington & Missouri River Railroad Co.
10 Years' Credit. | **LOW PRICES** | **6** Per Cent. Interest.
ONLY THE INTEREST PAYMENT DOWN.
PAYMENTS ON PRINCIPAL BEGIN THE FOURTH YEAR.

BUY LAND EXPLORING TICKETS.
And the Cost of Same will be Allowed on First Payment made on Land bought within 90 Days from Date of Ticket-
HALF FARE to Families of Purchasers. LOW FREIGHTS on Household Goods and Farm Stock.
Circulars with full information on every question, will be sent FREE to every applicant.
ADDRESS: LAND COMMISSIONER B. & M. R. R.,
LINCOLN, NEB., for Nebraska Lands.
Large Sectional Maps of Iowa, 30 cents.
BURLINGTON, IOWA, for Iowa Lands.
Nebraska, 30 cents.

PREMIUMS FOR IMPROVEMENTS.

Railroad companies distributed elaborately illustrated brochures and broadsides to lure people to the West, where they could settle on land owned by the railroads.

holdings accordingly. In Colorado, one cattleman, John F. Iliff, owned only 105 small parcels of land, but by placing them around the few water holes, he effectively dominated an empire stretching over 6000 square miles.

Water, in fact, became a dominant western issue, since aside from the Pacific Northwest, northern California, parts of the Rocky Mountain West, and the eastern half of the Great Plains, much of the trans-Mississippi West was arid, receiving less than 20 inches of rainfall annually. People speculated in water as if it were gold and planned great irrigation systems in Utah, eastern Colorado, and California's Central Valley to "make the desert bloom."

Irrigators received a major boost in 1902 when the National Reclamation Act (the Newlands Act) set aside most of the proceeds from the sale of public lands in sixteen western states to finance irrigation projects in the arid states. Over the next decades, dams, canals, and irrigation systems channeled water into dry areas, creating a "hydraulic" society that was rich in crops and cities (such as Los Angeles and Phoenix), but ever thirstier and in danger of outrunning the precious water on which it all depended.

As beneficiaries of the government's policy of land grants for railway construction, the railroad companies were the West's largest landowners. Eager to have immigrants settle on the land they owned near the railroad right-of-way, and eager to boost their freight and passenger business, the companies sent agents to the East and Europe. Attractive brochures touted life in the West. The Union Pacific called the rocky Platte Valley in Nebraska "a flowery meadow of great fertility, clothed in nutritious grasses."

Railroad lines set up land departments and bureaus of immigration. The land departments priced the land, arranged credit terms, and even gave free farming courses to immigrants. The bureaus of immigration employed agents in Europe, met immigrants at eastern seaports, and ran special cars for land seekers heading west.

Half a billion acres of western land were given or sold to speculators and corporations. At the same time, only 600,000 homestead patents were issued, covering 80 million acres. Thus, only one acre in every nine initially went to individual pioneers, the intended beneficiaries of the nation's largesse. Two-thirds of all homestead claimants before 1890 failed in their efforts to farm their new land.

The Spanish-Speaking Southwest

In the nineteenth century, almost all Spanish-speaking people in the United States lived in California, Arizona, New Mexico, Texas, and Colorado. Their numbers were small—California had only 8,086 Mexican residents in 1900—but the influence of their culture and institutions was large. In some respects, the southwestern frontier was more Spanish American than Anglo-American.

Pushing northward from Mexico, the Spanish gradually established the present-day economic structure of the Southwest. They brought with them techniques of mining, stock raising, and irrigated farming. After winning independence in the 1820s, the Mexicans brought new laws and ranching methods as well as chaps and the burro. Both Spanish and Mexicans created the legal framework for distributing land and water, a precious resource in the Southwest.

In Southern California, the Californios, descendants of the original colonizers, began after the 1860s to lose their once vast landholdings to drought and mortgages. But as they died out, Mexican Americans continued the Spanish-Mexican influence. In 1880, one-fourth of the residents of Los Angeles County were Spanish speaking.

In New Mexico, Spanish-speaking citizens remained the majority ethnic group until the 1940s, and the Spanish Mexican culture dominated the territory. Contests over land grants became New Mexico's largest industry; lawyers who dealt in them amassed huge holdings.

Throughout the Southwest, the Spanish Mexican heritage gave a distinctive shape to society. Men headed the families and dominated economic life. Women had substantial economic rights (though few political ones), and they enjoyed a status their English American counterparts did not have. Wives kept full control of property acquired before their marriage; they also held half title to all property in a marriage, which later caused many southwestern states to pass community property laws.

In addition, the Spanish Mexican heritage fostered a modified economic caste system, a strong Roman Catholic influence, and the primary use of the Spanish language. Continuous immigration from Mexico kept language and cultural ties strong. Spanish was the region's first or second language. Confronted by Sheriff Pat Garrett in a darkened room, New Mexico's famous outlaw Billy the Kid died asking, "*Quién es? Quién es?*" ("Who is it? Who is it?").

THE BONANZA WEST

Between 1850 and 1900, wave after wave of newcomers swept across the trans-Mississippi West. There were riches for the taking, hidden in gold-washed streams, spread lushly over grass-covered prairies, or available in the gullible minds of greedy newcomers. The nineteenth-century West took shape in the search for mining, cattle, and land bonanzas that drew eager settlers from the East and around the world.

As with all bonanzas, the consequences in the West were uneven growth, boom-and-bust economic cycles, and wasted resources. Society seemed constantly in the making. People moved here and there, following river bottoms, gold strikes, railroad tracks, and other opportunities. "Instant cities" arose. San Francisco, Salt Lake City, and Denver were the most spectacular examples, but every cow town and mining camp witnessed similar phenomena of growth. Boston needed more than two centuries to attract one-third of a million people; San Francisco did the same in a little more than twenty years.

Many Westerners had left home to get rich quickly, and they adopted institutions that reflected that goal. As a contemporary poem said:

> *Love to see the stir an' bustle*
> *In the busy town,*
> *Everybody on the hustle*
> *Saltin' profits down.*
> *Everybody got a wad a'*
> *Ready cash laid by;*
> *Ain't no flies on Colorado—*
> *Not a cussed fly.*

In their lives, the West was an idea as well as a region, and the idea molded them as much as they molded it.

THE MINING BONANZA

Mining was the first important magnet to attract people to the West. Many hoped to "strike it rich" in gold and silver, but at least half the newcomers had no intention of working in the mines. Instead, they provided food, clothing, and services to the thousands of miners.

The California Gold Rush of 1849 began the mining boom and set the pattern for subsequent strikes in other regions. Individual prospectors made the first strikes, discovering pockets of gold along streams flowing westward from the Sierra Nevada. To get the gold, they used a simple process called placer mining, which required little skill, technology, or capital. A placer miner needed only a shovel, a washing pan, and a good claim. As the placers gave out, a great deal of gold remained, but it was locked in quartz or buried deep in the earth. Mining became an expensive business, far beyond the reach of the average miner.

Large corporations moved in to dig the deep shafts and finance costly equipment. Quartz mining required heavy rock crushers, mercury vats to dissolve the gold, and large retorts to recapture it. Eastern and European financiers assumed

Before the California Gold Rush of 1849, San Francisco was a sleepy little Spanish-Mexican village called Yerba Buena. Gold seekers turned it into a boomtown with an international population. Here, Spanish Mexican rancheros, white prospectors, Chinese laborers, and a top-hatted professional gambler mingle in a San Francisco saloon.

control, labor became unionized, and mining towns took on some of the characteristics of the industrial city. Individual prospectors meanwhile dashed on to the
next find. Unlike other frontiers, the mining frontier moved from west to east, as
the original California miners—the "yonder-siders," they were called—hurried
eastward in search of the big strike.

In 1859, fresh strikes were made near Pikes Peak in Colorado and in the
Carson River Valley of Nevada. News of both discoveries set off wild migrations—100,000 miners were in Pikes Peak country by June 1859. The gold there
quickly played out, but the Nevada find uncovered a thick bluish black ore that
was almost pure silver and gold. A quick-witted drifter named Henry T. P.
Comstock talked his way into partnership in the claim, and word of the
Comstock Lode—with ore worth $3,876 a ton—flashed over the mountains.

Thousands of miners climbed the Sierra Nevada that summer. The biggest
strike was yet to come. In 1873, John W. Mackay and three partners formed a
company to dig deep into the mountain, and at 1,167 feet they hit the Big
Bonanza, a seam of gold and silver more than 54 feet wide. It was the richest discovery in the history of mining. Between 1859 and 1879, the Comstock Lode
produced gold and silver worth $306 million.

In the 1860s and 1870s, important strikes were made in Washington, Idaho,
Nevada, Colorado, Montana, Arizona, and Dakota. Extremely mobile, miners
flocked from strike to strike, and new camps and mining towns sprang up
overnight.

The final fling came in the Black Hills rush of 1874 to 1876. The army had
tried to keep miners out of the area, the heart of the Sioux hunting grounds, and
even sent a scientific party under Colonel George Armstrong Custer to disprove
the rumors of gold and stop the miners' invasion. Instead, Custer found gold all
over the hills, and the rush was on. Miners, gamblers, desperadoes, and prostitutes flocked to Deadwood, the most lawless of all the mining camps. There,
Martha Jane Canary—a crack shot who, as Calamity Jane, won fame as a scout
and teamster—fell in love with "Wild Bill" Hickok. Hickok himself—a western
legend who had tamed Kansas cow towns, killed an unknown number of men,
and toured in Buffalo Bill's Wild West Show—died in Deadwood, shot in the back
of the head. Hickok was 39 years old.

Towns such as Deadwood, in the Dakota Territory; Virginia City, Nevada;
Leadville, Colorado; and Tombstone, Arizona, demonstrated a new development
process in the frontier experience. The farming frontier had developed naturally
in a rural setting. On the mining frontier, the germ of a city—the camp—appeared almost simultaneously with the first "strike." Periodicals, the latest fashions, theaters, schools, literary clubs, and lending libraries came quickly to the
camps, providing civilized refinements not available on other frontiers.

Urbanization also created the need for municipal government, sanitation, and law enforcement.

Mining camps were governed by a simple democracy. Soon after a strike, the miners in the area met to organize a mining "district" and adopted rules governing behavior in it. Rules regulated the size and boundaries of claims, established procedures for settling disputes, and set penalties for crimes. Petty criminals were banished from the district; serious offenders were hanged. In the case of a major dispute, the whole camp gathered, chose legal counsel for both sides, and heard the evidence. If all else failed, miners formed secret vigilance committees to hang a few offenders as a lesson to the rest. Early visitors to the mining country were struck by the way miners, solitary and competitive, joined together, founded a camp, and created a society.

The camps were mostly male, made up of "men who can rough it" and a few "ladies of spirit and energy." In 1870, men outnumbered women in the mining districts by more than two to one; there were few children.

In most camps, between one-quarter and one-half of the population was foreign born. The lure of gold drew large numbers of Chinese, Chileans, Peruvians, Mexicans, French, Germans, and English. Experienced miners, the Latin Americans brought valuable mining techniques. At least six thousand Mexicans joined the California rush of 1849, and by 1852, there were twenty-five thousand

Leadville, Colorado, in the 1870s. Founded as a gold camp in 1860, by the 1880s Leadville, with thirty thousand residents, was the second largest city in the state, trailing only Denver.

Chinese in California. Painstaking, the Chinese profitably worked claims others had abandoned. In the 1860s, almost one-third of the miners in the West were Chinese.

Hostility often surfaced against foreign miners, particularly the French, Latin Americans, and Chinese. In 1850, California passed a Foreign Miners' Tax that charged foreign miners a $20 monthly licensing fee. As intended, it drove out Mexicans and other foreigners. Riots against Chinese laborers occurred in the 1870s and 1880s in Los Angeles, San Francisco, Seattle, Reno, and Denver. Responding to pressure, Congress passed the Chinese Exclusion Act of 1882, which suspended immigration of Chinese laborers for ten years. The number of Chinese in the United States fell drastically.

By the 1890s, the early mining bonanza was over. All told, the western mines contributed billions of dollars to the economy. They had helped finance the Civil War and provided needed capital for industrialization. The vast boost in silver production from the Comstock Lode changed the relative value of gold and silver, the base of American currency. Bitter disputes over the currency affected politics and led to the famous "battle of the standards" in the presidential election of 1896 (see Chapter 20).

The mining frontier populated portions of the West and sped its process of political organization. Nevada, Idaho, and Montana were granted early statehood because of mining. Merchants, editors, lawyers, and ministers moved with the advancing frontier, establishing permanent settlements. Women in the mining camps helped to foster family life and raised the moral tone by campaigning against drinking, gambling, and prostitution. But not all the effects of the mining boom were positive. The industry also left behind painful scars in the form of invaded Indian reservations, pitted hills, and lonely ghost towns.

GOLD FROM THE ROOTS UP: THE CATTLE BONANZA

"There's gold from the grass roots down," said California Joe, a guide in the gold districts of Dakota in the 1870s, "but there's more gold from the grass roots up." Ranchers began to recognize the potential of the vast grasslands of the West. The Plains were covered with buffalo or grama grass, a wiry variety with short, hard stems. Cattle thrived on it.

For twenty years after 1865, cattle ranching dominated the "open range," a vast fenceless area extending from the Texas Panhandle north into Canada. The techniques of the business came from Mexico. Long before American cowboys moved herds north, their Mexican counterparts, the *vaqueros,* developed the essential techniques of branding, roundups, and roping. The cattle themselves, the famous Texas longhorns, also came from Mexico. Spreading over the grasslands of southern Texas, the longhorns multiplied rapidly. Although their meat was coarse and stringy, they fed a nation hungry for beef at the end of the Civil War.

The problem was getting the beef to eastern markets, and Joseph G. McCoy, a livestock shipper from Illinois, solved it. Looking for a way to market Texas beef, McCoy conceived the idea of taking the cattle to railheads in Kansas. He talked first with the president of the Missouri Pacific, who ordered him out of his office, and then with the head of the Kansas Pacific, who laughed at the idea. The persistent McCoy finally signed a contract in 1867 with the Hannibal and St. Joseph Railroad. Searching for an appropriate rail junction, he settled on the sleepy Kansas town of Abilene, "a very small, dead place," he remembered, with about a dozen log huts and one nearly bankrupt saloon.

In September 1867, McCoy shipped the first train of twenty cars of longhorn cattle. By the end of the year, a thousand carloads had followed, all headed for Chicago markets. In 1870, 300,000 head of Texas cattle reached Abilene, followed the next year—the peak year—by 700,000 head. The Alamo Saloon, crowded with tired cowboys at the end of the drive, now employed seventy-five bartenders, working three 8-hour shifts.

The profits were enormous. Drivers bought cheap Texas steers for $4 a head and sold them for $30 or $40 a head at the northern railhead. The most famous trail was the Chisholm, running from southern Texas through Oklahoma Territory to Ellsworth and Abilene, Kansas, on the Kansas Pacific Railroad.

Cowboys pushed steers northward in herds of two to three thousand. Novels and films have portrayed the cowboys as white, but at least a quarter of them were black, and possibly another quarter were Mexicans. A typical crew on the trail north might have eight men, half of them black or Mexican. Most of the trail bosses were white; they earned about $125 a month. James "Jim" Perry, a renowned black cowboy who worked for more than twenty years as a rider, roper, and cook for the XIT ranch, said, "If it weren't for my damned old black face, I'd have been a boss long ago."

Like miners, cattlemen lived beyond the formal reach of the law and so established their own. Ranchers adopted rules for cattle ownership, branding, roundups, and drives, and they formed associations to enforce them. The Wyoming Stock Growers' Association, the largest and most formidable, had four hundred members owning two million cattle; its reach extended well beyond Wyoming into Colorado, Nebraska, Montana, and the Dakotas.

Hollywood images to the contrary, there was little violence in the booming cow towns. The number of homicides in a year never topped five in any town, and in many years no one was killed. Doc Holliday and William B. "Bat"

Masterson never killed anyone. John Wesley Hardin, a legendary teenaged gunman, shot only one man, firing blindly through a hotel room wall to stop him from snoring. Famous western sheriffs had everyday duties. Wild Bill Hickok served as Abilene's street commissioner, and the Wichita city council made its lawmen, including Wyatt Earp, repair streets and sidewalks before each cattle season.

By 1880, more than six million cattle had been driven to northern markets. But the era of the great cattle drive was ending. Farmers were planting wheat on

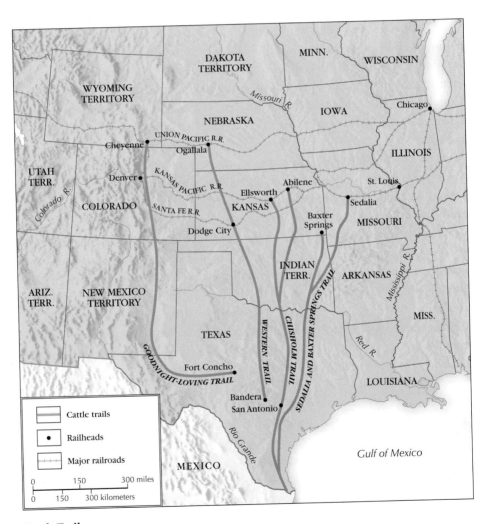

Cattle Trails

Cattle raised in Texas were driven along the cattle trails to the northern railheads, and trains carried them to market.

the old buffalo ranges; barbed wire, a recent invention, cut across the trails and divided up the big ranches. Mechanical improvements in slaughtering, refrigerated transportation, and cold storage modernized the industry. Ranchers bred the Texas longhorns with heavier Hereford and Angus bulls, and as the new breeds proved profitable, more and more ranches opened on the northern ranges.

By the mid-1880s, some 4.5 million cattle grazed the High Plains, reminding people of the once great herds of buffalo. Stories of vast profits circulated, attracting outside capital. Large investments transformed ranching into big business, often controlled by absentee owners and subject to new problems.

The winter of 1886–1887 was one of the worst in western history. Temperatures dropped to 45 degrees below zero, and cattle that once would have saved themselves by drifting ahead of the storms came up against the new barbed wire fences. Herds jammed together, pawing the frozen ground or stripping bark from trees in search of food. Cattle died by the tens of thousands. In the spring of 1887, when the snows thawed, ranchers found stacks of carcasses piled up against the fences.

The melting snows did, however, produce a lush crop of grass for the survivors. The cattle business recovered, but it took different directions. Outside capital, so plentiful in the boom years, dried up. Ranchers began fencing their lands, reducing their herds, and growing hay for winter food.

The last roundup on the northern ranges took place in 1905. Ranches grew smaller, and some ranchers, at first in the scrub country of the Southwest, then on the Plains themselves, switched to raising sheep. By 1900, there were nearly thirty-eight million sheep west of the Missouri River, far more than there were cattle.

Ranchers and sheepherders fought bitterly to control the grazing lands, but they had one problem in common: the troubles ahead. Homesteaders, armed with barbed wire and new strains of wheat, were pushing onto the Plains, and the day of the open range was over.

SODBUSTERS ON THE PLAINS: THE FARMING BONANZA

Like miners and cattle ranchers, millions of farmers moved into the West in the decades after 1870 to seek crop bonanzas and new ways of life. Some realized their dreams; many fought just to survive.

Between 1870 and 1900, farmers cultivated more land than ever before in American history. They peopled the Plains from Dakota to Texas, pushed the Indians out of their last sanctuary in Oklahoma, and poured into the basins and foothills of the Rockies. By 1900, the western half of the nation contained almost 30 percent of the population, compared to less than 1 percent just a half century earlier.

Unlike mining, farm settlement often followed predictable patterns, taking population from states east of the settlement line and moving gradually westward. Crossing the Mississippi, farmers settled first in western Iowa, Minnesota, Nebraska, Kansas, Texas, and South Dakota. The movement slumped during the depression of the 1870s, but then a new wave of optimism carried thousands more west. Several years of above average rainfall convinced farmers that the Dakotas, western Nebraska and Kansas, and eastern Colorado were the "rain belt of the Plains." Between 1870 and 1900, the population on the Plains tripled.

In some areas, the newcomers were blacks who had fled the South, fed up with beatings and murders, crop liens, and the Black Codes that institutionalized their subordinate status. In 1879, about six thousand African Americans known as the Exodusters left their homes in Louisiana, Mississippi, and Texas to establish new and freer lives in Kansas, the home of John Brown and the Free-Soil campaigns of the 1850s. Once there, they farmed or worked as laborers; women worked in the fields alongside the men or cleaned houses and took in washing to make ends meet. All told, the Exodusters homesteaded 20,000 acres of land, and though they met prejudice, it was not as extreme as they had known at home.

Other African Americans moved to Oklahoma, thinking they might establish the first African American state. Whether headed for Oklahoma or Kansas, they picked up and moved in sizable groups that were based on family units; they took with them the customs they had known, and in their new homes they were able, for the first time, to have some measure of self-government.

For blacks and whites alike, farming on the Plains presented new problems. There was little surface water, and wells ranged between 50 and 500 feet deep. Well drillers charged up to $2 a foot. Taking advantage of the steady Plains winds, windmills brought the water to the surface, but they too were expensive, and until 1900, many farmers could not afford them. Lumber for homes and fences was also scarce.

Unable to afford wood, farmers often started out in dreary sod houses. Cut into 3-foot sections, the thick prairie sod was laid like brick, with space left for two windows and a door. Since glass was scarce, cloth hung over the windows; a blanket was hung from the ceiling to make two rooms. Sod houses were small, provided little light and air, and were impossible to keep clean. When it rained, water seeped through the roof. Yet a sod house cost only $2.78 to build.

Disappointed with the failures of Reconstruction and fearful of the violence that surrounded them, many southern blacks migrated to Kansas in the 1870s and 1880s. Comparing their trek to the biblical story of the Israelites' exodus from Egypt, they became known as "Exodusters."

Outside, the Plains environment sorely tested the men and women who moved there. Neighbors were distant; the land stretched on as far as the eye could see. Always the wind blew.

In the winters, savage storms swept the open grasslands. Summertime temperatures stayed near 110 degrees for weeks at a time. Fearsome rainstorms, building in the summer's heat, beat down the young corn and wheat. The summers also brought grasshoppers, arriving without warning, flying in clouds so huge they shut out the sun. The grasshoppers ate everything in sight: crops, clothing, mosquito netting, tree bark, even plow handles. In the summer of 1874, they devastated the whole Plains from Texas to the Dakotas, eating everything "but the mortgage," as one farmer said.

NEW FARMING METHODS

Farmers adopted new techniques to meet conditions on the Plains. For one thing, they needed cheap and effective fencing material, and in 1874, Joseph F. Glidden, a farmer from De Kalb, Illinois, provided it with the invention of barbed wire. By 1883, his factory was turning out 600 miles of barbed wire every day, and farmers were buying it faster than it could be produced.

Dry farming, a new technique, helped compensate for the lack of rainfall. By plowing furrows 12 to 14 inches deep and creating a dust mulch to fill the furrow, farmers loosened the soil and slowed evaporation. Wheat farmers imported European varieties of plants that could withstand the harsh Plains winters.

Farm technology changed long before the Civil War, but later developments improved it. In 1877, James Oliver of Indiana patented a chilled-iron plow with a smooth-surfaced moldboard that did not clog in the thick prairie soils. The spring-tooth harrow (1869) sped soil preparation; the grain drill (1874) opened furrows and scientifically fed seed into the ground. The lister (1880) dug a deep furrow, planted corn at the bottom, and covered the seed—all in one operation.

The first baling press was built in 1866, and the hay loader was patented in 1876. The first successful harvester, the cord binder (1878), cut and tied bundles of grain, enabling two men and a team of horses to harvest 20 acres of wheat a day. Invented earlier, threshers grew larger; employing as many as nine men and ten horses, one machine could thresh 300 bushels of grain a day.

In the late 1870s, huge bonanza farms rose, run by the new machinery and financed with outside capital. Oliver Dalrymple, the most famous of the bonanza farmers, headed an experiment in North Dakota's Red River Valley in 1875, then moved on to manage the Grandin Bonanza of 61,000 acres, five times the size of Manhattan Island. Dalrymple hired armies of workers, bought machinery by the carload, and planted on a scale that dazzled the West.

The bonanza farms—thanks to their size and machinery—captured the country's imagination. Using 200 pairs of harrows, 155 binders, and 16 threshers, Dalrymple produced 600,000 bushels of wheat in 1881. He and other bonanza managers profited from the economies of scale, buying materials at wholesale prices and receiving rebates from the railroads. Then a period of drought began. Rainfall dropped between 1885 and 1890, and the large-scale growers found it hard to compete with smaller farmers who diversified their crops and cultivated more intensively. Many of the large bonanzas slowly disintegrated, and Dalrymple himself went bankrupt in 1896.

DISCONTENT ON THE FARM

Touring the South in the 1860s, Oliver H. Kelley, a clerk in the Department of Agriculture, was struck by the drabness of rural life. In 1867, he founded the National Grange of the Patrons of Husbandry, known simply as the Grange. The Grange provided social, cultural, and educational activities for its members. Its constitution banned involvement in politics, but Grangers often ignored the rules and supported railroad regulation and other measures.

A work crew on the Dalrymple farm in the Red River Valley gathers grain wired into bundles by self-binding harvesters. In 1877, Dalrymple used a hundred workers to harvest his 4000 acres of wheat; by 1884, the number of harvesters employed on the farm had increased to a thousand.

The Grange grew rapidly during the depression of the 1870s, and by 1875, it had more than 800,000 members in 20,000 local Granges. Most were in the Midwest and South. The Granges set up cooperative stores, grain elevators, warehouses, insurance companies, and farm machinery factories. Many failed, but in the meantime the organization made its mark. Picking up where the Grange left off, farm-oriented groups such as the Farmers' Alliance, with branches in both South and West, began to attract followers.

Like the cattle boom, the farming boom ended sharply after 1887. A severe drought that year cut harvests, and other droughts followed in 1889 and 1894. Thousands of new farmers were wiped out on the western Plains. Between 1888 and 1892, more than half the population of western Kansas left. Farmers grew angry and restless. They complained about declining crop prices, rising railroad rates, and heavy mortgages.

Although many farmers were unhappy, the peopling of the West in those years transformed American agriculture. The states beyond the Mississippi became the garden land of the nation. California sent fruit, wine, and wheat to eastern markets. Under the Mormons, Utah flourished with irrigation. Texas beef stocked the country's tables, and vast wheat fields, stretching to the horizon, covered Minnesota, the Dakotas, Montana, and eastern Colorado. All produced more than Americans could consume. By 1890, American farmers were exporting large amounts of wheat and other crops.

Farmers became more commercial and scientific. They needed to know more and work harder. Mail-order houses and rural free delivery diminished their isolation and tied them ever closer to the national future. "This is a new age to the farmer," said a statistician in the Department of Agriculture in 1889. "He is now, more than ever before, a citizen of the world."

THE FINAL FLING

As the West filled in with people, pressure mounted on the president and Congress to open the last Indian territory, Oklahoma, to settlers. In March 1889, Congress acted and forced the Creek and Seminole tribes, who had been moved into Oklahoma in the 1820s, to surrender their rights to the land. With arrangements complete, President Benjamin Harrison announced the opening of the Oklahoma District as of noon, April 22, 1889.

Preparations were feverish all along the frontier. On the morning of April 22, nearly a hundred thousand people lined the Oklahoma borders.

At noon, the starting flag dropped. Bugles and cannon signaled the opening of the "last" territory. Horsemen lunged forward; overloaded wagons collided and overturned.

By sunset that day, settlers claimed twelve thousand homesteads, and the 1.92 million acres of the Oklahoma District were officially settled. Homesteaders threw up shelters for the night. By evening, Oklahoma City, that morning merely a spot on the prairie with cottonwoods and grass, had ten thousand people.

The "Boomers" and "Sooners"—those who had jumped the gun—reflected the speed of western settlement. "Creation!" a character in Edna Ferber's novel *Cimarron* declared. "Hell! That took six days. This was done in one. It was History made in an hour—and I helped make it."

Between the Civil War and 1900, the West witnessed one of the greatest migrations in history. With the Native Americans driven into smaller and smaller areas, farms, ranches, mines, and cities took over the vast lands from the Mississippi to the Pacific. The 1890 census noted that for the first time in the country's history, "there can hardly be said to be a frontier line." Picking up the theme, Frederick Jackson Turner, a young history instructor at the University of Wisconsin, examined its importance in an influential 1893 paper, "The Significance of the Frontier in American History."

"The existence of an area of free land," Turner wrote, "its continuous re-cession, and the advance of American settlement westward, explain American development." It shaped customs and character; gave rise to independence, self-confidence, and individualism; and fostered invention and adaptation. Historians have substantially modified Turner's thesis by pointing to frontier conservatism and imitativeness, the influence of varying racial groups, and the persistence of European ideas and institutions. Most recently, they have shown that family and community loomed as large as individualism on the frontier; men, women, and children played very much the same roles as they had back home.

Rejecting Turner almost completely, a group of "new Western historians" has advanced a different and complex view of the West, and one with few heroes and heroines. Emphasizing the region's racial and ethnic diversity, these historians stress the role of women as well as men, trace struggles between economic inter-ests instead of fights between gunslingers, and question the impact of develop-ment on the environment. White English-speaking Americans, they suggest, could be said to have conquered the West rather than settled it.

The West, in this view, was not settled by a wave of white migrants moving west across the continent (Turner's "frontier") but by a set of waves—Anglo, Mexican American, African American, Asian American, and others—moving in many directions and interacting with each other and with Native American cul-tures to produce the modern West. Nor did western history end in 1890 as Turner would have it. Instead, migration, development, and economic exploita-tion continued into the twentieth century, illustrated in the fact that the number of people who moved to the West after 1900 far exceeded those who had moved there before.

In both the nineteenth and twentieth centuries, there can be no doubt that the image of the frontier and the West influenced American development. Western lands attracted European, Latin American, and Asian immigrants, adding to the society's talent and diversity. The mines, forests, and farms of the West fueled the economy, sent raw materials to eastern factories, and fed the growing cities. Though defeated in warfare, the Native Americans and Mexicans influenced art, architecture, law, and western folklore. The West was the first American empire, and it had a profound impact on the American mind and imagination.

18

THE INDUSTRIAL SOCIETY

In 1876, Americans celebrated their first century of independence. Survivors of a recent civil war, they observed the centenary proudly and rather self-consciously, in song and speech, and above all in a grand Centennial Exposition held in Philadelphia, Pennsylvania.

Spread over 13 acres, the exposition focused more on the present than the past. Fairgoers strolled through exhibits of life in colonial times, then hurried off to see the main attractions: machines, inventions, and products of the new industrial era. They saw linoleum, a new, easy-to-clean floor covering. For the first time, they tasted root beer, supplied by a young druggist named Charles Hires, and the exotic banana, wrapped in foil and selling for a dime. They saw their first bicycle, an awkward high-wheeled contraption with solid tires.

A Japanese pavilion generated widespread interest in the culture of Japan. There was also a women's building, the first ever in a major exposition. Inside were displayed paintings and sculpture by women artists, along with rows of textile machinery staffed by female operators.

In the entire exposition, machinery was the focus, and Machinery Hall was the most popular building. Here were the products of an ever improving civilization. Long lines of the curious waited to see the telephone, Alexander Graham Bell's new device. ("My God, it talks!" the emperor of Brazil exclaimed.) Thomas A. Edison displayed several recent inventions, while nearby, whirring machines turned out bricks, chewing tobacco, and other products. Fairgoers saw the first public display of the typewriter, Elisha Otis's new elevator, and the Westinghouse railroad air brake.

But above all, they crowded around the mighty Corliss engine, the focal point of the exposition. A giant steam engine, it dwarfed everything else in Machinery Hall, its twin vertical cylinders towering almost four stories in the air. Alone, it supplied power for the eight thousand other machines, large and small, on the exposition grounds. Poorly designed, the Corliss was soon obsolete, but for the moment it captured the nation's imagination. It symbolized swift movement toward an industrial and urban society. John Greenleaf Whittier, the aging rural poet, likened it to the snake in the Garden of Eden and refused to see it.

As Whittier feared, the United States was fast becoming an industrial society. Developments earlier in the century laid the basis, but the most spectacular advances in industrialization came during the three decades after the Civil War. At the start of the war, the country lagged well behind industrializing nations such as Great Britain, France, and Germany. By 1900, it had vaulted far into the lead, with a manufacturing output that exceeded the *combined* output of its three European rivals. Over the same years, cities grew, technology advanced, and farm production rose. Developments in manufacturing, mining, agriculture, transportation, and communications changed society.

Many Americans eagerly sought the change. William Dean Howells, a leading novelist, visited the Centennial Exposition and stood in awe before the Corliss. Comparing it to the paintings and sculpture on display, Howells preferred the machine: "It is in these things of iron and steel," he said, "that the national genius most freely speaks."

INDUSTRIAL DEVELOPMENT

American industry owed its remarkable growth to several considerations. It fed on an abundance of natural resources: coal, iron, timber, petroleum, waterpower. An iron manufacturer likened the nation to "a gigantic bowl filled with treasure." Labor was also abundant, drawn from American farm families and the hosts of European immigrants who flocked to American mines, cities, and factories. Nearly eight million immigrants arrived in the 1870s and 1880s; another fifteen million came between 1890 and 1914—large figures for a nation whose total population in 1900 was about seventy-six million people.

The burgeoning population led to expanded markets, which new devices such as the telegraph and telephone helped to exploit. The swiftly growing urban populations devoured goods, and the railroads, spreading pell-mell across the land, linked the cities together and opened a national market. Within its boundaries, the United States had the largest free-trade market in the world, while tariff barriers partially protected its producers from outside competition.

Expansive market and labor conditions buoyed the confidence of investors, European and American, who provided large amounts of capital. Technological progress, so remarkable in these years, doomed some older industries (tallow, for example) but increased productivity in others, such as the kerosene industry, and created entirely new industries as well. Through inventions such as the harvester and the combine, it also helped foster a firm agricultural base, on which industrialization depended.

Eager to promote economic growth, government at all levels—federal, state, and local—gave manufacturers money, land, and other resources. Other benefits, too, flowed from the American system of government: stability, commitment to the concept of private property, and, initially at least, a reluctance to regulate industrial activity. Unlike their European counterparts, American manufacturers faced few legal or social barriers, and their main domestic rivals, the southern planters, had lost political power in the Civil War.

In this atmosphere, entrepreneurs flourished. Taking steps crucial for industrialization, they organized, managed, and assumed the financial risks of the new enterprises. Admirers called them captains of industry; foes labeled them robber barons. To some degree, they were both—creative *and* acquisitive. If sometimes they seemed larger than life, it was because they dealt in concepts, distances, and quantities often unknown to earlier generations.

Industrial growth, it must be remembered, was neither a simple nor steady nor inevitable process. It involved human decisions and brought with it large social benefits and costs. Growth varied from industry to industry and from year to year. It was concentrated in the Northeast, where in 1890, more than 85 percent of America's manufactured goods originated. The more sparsely settled West provided raw materials, while the South, although making major gains in iron, textiles, and tobacco, had to rebuild after wartime devastation.

Still, industrial development proceeded at an extraordinary pace. Between 1865 and 1914, the real gross national product—the total monetary value of all goods and services produced in a year, with prices held stable—grew at a rate of more than 4 percent a year, increasing about eightfold overall. As Robert Higgs, an economic historian, noted, "Never before had such rapid growth continued for so long."

AN EMPIRE ON RAILS

Genuine revolutions happen rarely, but a major one occurred in the nineteenth century: a revolution in transportation and communications. When the nineteenth century began, people traveled and communicated much as they had for centuries before; when it ended, the railroad, the telegraph, the telephone, and the oceangoing steamship had wrought enormous changes.

The steamship sliced in half the time of the Atlantic crossing and, not dependent on wind and tide, introduced new regularity in the movement of goods and passengers. The telegraph, flashing messages almost instantaneously along miles of wire (400,000 miles of it in the early 1880s), transformed communications, as did the telephone a little later. But the railroad worked the largest changes of all. Along with Bessemer steel, it was the most significant technical innovation of the century.

"EMBLEM OF MOTION AND POWER"

The railroad dramatically affected economic and social life. Economic growth would have occurred without it, of course; canals, inland steamboats, and the country's superb system of interior waterways already provided the outlines of an effective transportation network. But the railroad added significantly to the network and contributed advantages all its own.

Those advantages included more direct routes, greater speed, greater safety and comfort than other modes of land travel, more dependable schedules, a larger volume of traffic, and year-round service. A day's land travel on stagecoach or horseback might cover fifty miles. The railroad covered fifty miles in about an hour, seven hundred miles in a day. It went where canals and rivers did not go—directly to the loading platforms of great factories or across the arid West. As construction crews pushed tracks onward, vast areas of the continent opened for settlement.

Consequently, American railroads differed from European ones. In Europe, railroads were usually built between cities and towns that already existed; they carried mostly the same goods that earlier forms of transportation had. In the United States, they did that and more: They often created the very towns they then served, and they ended up carrying cattle from Texas, fruit from Florida, and other goods that had never been carried before.

Linking widely separated cities and villages, the railroad ended the relative isolation and self-sufficiency of the country's "island communities." It tied people together, brought in outside products, fostered greater interdependence, and encouraged economic specialization. Under its stimulus, Chicago supplied meat to the nation, Minneapolis supplied grain, and Saint Louis, beer. For these and other communities, the railroad made possible a national market and in so doing pointed the way toward mass production and mass consumption, two of the hallmarks of twentieth-century society.

It also pointed the way toward later business development. The railroad, as Alfred D. Chandler, a historian of business, has written, was "the nation's first big business"; it worked out "the modern ways of finance, management, labor relations, competition, and government regulation."

A railroad corporation, far-flung and complex, was a new kind of business. It stretched over thousands of miles, employed thousands of people, dealt with countless customers, and required a scale of organization and decision making unknown in earlier business. Railroad managers never met most customers or even many employees; thus arose new problems in marketing and labor relations. Year by year, railroad companies consumed large quantities of iron, steel, coal, lumber, and glass, stimulating growth and employment in numerous industries.

No wonder, then, that the railroad captured so completely the country's imagination. For nearly a hundred years—the railroad era lasted through the 1940s—children gathered at depots, paused in the fields to wave as the fast express flashed by, listened at night to far-off whistles, and wondered what lay down the tracks. They lived in a world grown smaller.

BUILDING THE EMPIRE

When Lee surrendered at Appomattox in 1865, the country already had 35,000 miles of track, and much of the railroad system east of the Mississippi River was in place. Farther west, the rail network stood poised on the edge of settlement. Although southern railroads were in shambles from the war, the United States had nearly as much railroad track as the rest of the world.

After the Civil War, rail construction increased by leaps and bounds. From 35,000 miles in 1865, the network expanded to 93,000 miles in 1880; 166,000 in 1890; and 193,000 in 1900—more than in all Europe, including Russia. Mileage peaked at 254,037 miles in 1916, just before the industry began its long decline into the mid-twentieth century.

To build such an empire took vast amounts of capital. American and European investors provided some of the money; government supplied the rest. In all, local governments gave railroad companies about $300 million, and state governments added $228 million more. The federal government loaned nearly $65 million to a half dozen western railroads and donated millions of acres of the public domain.

Almost 90 percent of the federal land grants lay in twenty states west of the Mississippi River. Federal land grants helped build 18,738 miles of track, less than 8 percent of the system. The land was frequently distant and difficult to market. Railroad companies sometimes sold it to raise cash, but more often they used it as security for bonds or loans.

Beyond doubt, the grants of cash and land promoted waste and corruption. The companies built fast and wastefully, eager to collect the subsidies that went with each mile of track. The grants also enabled railroads to build into territories

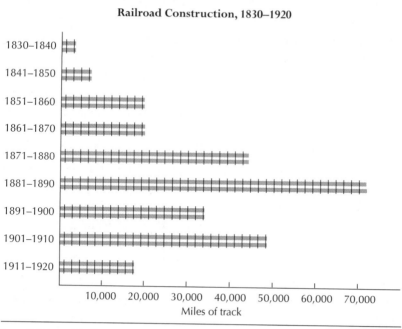

Railroad Construction, 1830–1920

	Miles of track
1830–1840	
1841–1850	
1851–1860	
1861–1870	
1871–1880	
1881–1890	
1891–1900	
1901–1910	
1911–1920	

10,000 20,000 30,000 40,000 50,000 60,000 70,000
Miles of track

Source: U.S. Bureau of the Census, *Historical Statistics of the United States, Colonial Times to 1970*, Bicentennial Edition, Washington, DC, 1975.

that were pledged to the Indians, thus contributing to the wanton destruction of Indian life.

Yet, on balance, the grants probably worked more benefits than evils. As Congress had hoped, the grants were the lure for railroad building across the rugged, unsettled West, where it would be years before the railroads' revenues would repay their construction. Farmers, ranchers, and merchants poured into the newly opened areas, settling the country and boosting the value of government and private land nearby. The grants seemed necessary in a nation which, unlike Europe, expected private enterprise to build the railroads. In return for government aid, Congress required the railroads to carry government freight, troops, and mail at substantially reduced rates—resulting in savings to the government of almost $1 billion between 1850 and 1945. In no other cases of federal subsidies to carriers—canals, highways, and airlines—did Congress exact specific benefits in return.

LINKING THE NATION VIA TRUNK LINES

The early railroads may seem to have linked different regions, but in fact they did not. Built with little regard for through traffic, they were designed more to protect local interests than to tap outside markets. Many extended less than fifty miles. To avoid cooperating with other lines, they adopted conflicting schedules, built separate depots, and above all, used different gauges. Gauges, the distance between the rails, ranged from 4 feet 8½ inches, which became the standard gauge, to 6 feet. Without special equipment, trains of one gauge could not run on tracks of another.

The Civil War showed the value of fast long-distance transportation, and after 1865, railroad managers worked to provide it. In a burst of consolidation, the large companies swallowed the small; integrated rail networks became a reality. Railroads also adopted standard schedules, signals, and equipment and finally, in 1886, the standard gauge. In 1866, in a dramatic innovation to speed traffic, railroad companies introduced fast freight lines that pooled cars for service between cities.

In the Northeast, four great trunk lines took shape, all intended to link eastern seaports with the rich traffic of the Great Lakes and western rivers. Like a massive river system, trunk lines drew traffic from dozens of tributaries (feeder lines) and carried it to major markets. The Baltimore and Ohio (B & O), which reached Chicago in 1874, was one; the Erie Railroad, which ran from New York

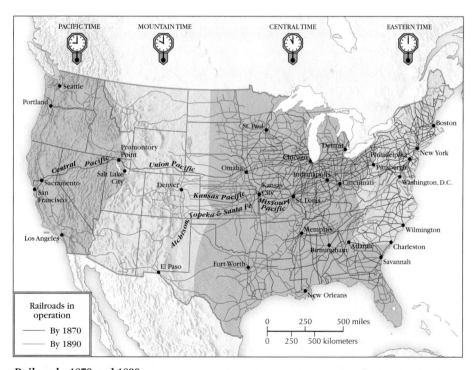

Railroads, 1870 and 1890
In the last quarter of the nineteenth century, railroads expanded into Texas, the far Southwest, and the Northwest, carrying settlers, businesses, and government to the far-flung areas.

to Chicago, was another. The Erie competed bitterly with the New York Central Railroad, the third trunk line, and its owner, Cornelius Vanderbilt—the "Commodore"—a crusty old multimillionaire from the shipping business.

J. Edgar Thomson and Thomas A. Scott built the fourth trunk line, the Pennsylvania Railroad, which initially ran from Philadelphia to Pittsburgh.

In the war-damaged South, consolidation took longer. As Reconstruction waned, northern and European capital rebuilt and integrated the southern lines, especially during the 1880s, when rail construction in the South led the nation. By 1900, the South had five large systems linking its major cities and farming and industrial regions. Four decades after the secession crisis, these systems tied the South into a national transportation network.

Over that rail system, passengers and freight moved in relative speed, comfort, and safety. Automatic couplers (1867), air brakes (1869), refrigerator cars (1867), dining cars, heated cars, electric switches, and stronger locomotives transformed railroad service. George Pullman's lavish sleeping cars became popular. Handsome depots, such as New York's Grand Central and Washington's Union Station, were erected at major terminals.

In November 1883, the railroads even changed time. Ending the crazy quilt jumble of local times that caused scheduling difficulties, the American Railway Association divided the country into four time zones and adopted the modern system of standard time. Congress took thirty-five years longer; it adopted standard time in 1918, in the midst of World War I.

RAILS ACROSS THE CONTINENT

The dream of a transcontinental railroad, linking the Atlantic and Pacific oceans, stretched back many years but had always been lost to sectional quarrels over the route. In 1862 and 1864, with the South out of the picture, Congress moved to build the first transcontinental railroad. It chartered the Union Pacific Railroad Company to build westward from Nebraska and the Central Pacific Railroad Company to build eastward from the Pacific Coast.

Construction began simultaneously at Omaha and Sacramento in 1863, lagged during the war, and moved vigorously ahead after 1865. It became a race, each company vying for land, loans, and potential markets. General Grenville M. Dodge, a tough Union army veteran, served as construction chief for the Union Pacific, while Charles Crocker, a former Sacramento dry goods merchant, led the Central Pacific crews. Dodge organized an army of ten thousand workers, many of them ex-soldiers and Irish immigrants. Pushing rapidly westward, he encountered frequent attacks from Native Americans defending their lands, but he had the advantage of building over flat prairie.

After the last spike was hammered in at Promontory, Utah, the pilots of the two locomotives exchanged champagne toasts. The chief engineers of the two lines are seen shaking hands. Conspicuously absent from the photograph are the Chinese laborers who helped build the railroad.

Crocker faced more trying conditions in the high Sierra Nevada along California's eastern border. After several experiments, he decided that Chinese laborers worked best, and he hired six thousand of them, most brought directly from China. "I built the Central Pacific," Crocker enjoyed boasting, but the Chinese crews in fact did the awesome work. Under the most difficult conditions, they dug, blasted, and pushed their way slowly east.

On May 10, 1869, the two lines met at Promontory, Utah, near the northern tip of the Great Salt Lake. Dodge's crews had built 1086 miles of track, Crocker's 689. The Union Pacific and Central Pacific presidents hammered in a golden spike, and the dreamed-of connection was made. The telegraph flashed the news east and west, setting off wild celebrations. A photograph was taken, but it included none of the Chinese who had worked so hard to build the road; they were all asked to step aside.

The transcontinental railroad symbolized American unity and progress. Along with the Suez Canal, completed the same year, it helped knit the world together. Three more railroads reached the coast in 1883: the Northern Pacific, running from Minnesota to Oregon; the Atchison, Topeka, and Santa Fe, connecting Kansas City and Los Angeles; and the powerful Southern Pacific, running from San Francisco and Los Angeles to New Orleans. Ten years later, James J. Hill's superbly built Great Northern Railway extended from Minneapolis–St. Paul to Seattle, Washington.

By the 1890s, business leaders talked comfortably of railroad systems stretching deep into South America and across the Bering Strait to Asia, Europe, and Africa. In an age of progress, anything seemed possible.

PROBLEMS OF GROWTH

Overbuilding during the 1870s and 1880s caused serious problems for the railroads. Lines paralleled each other, and where they did not, speculators such as Jay Gould often laid one down to force a rival line to buy it at inflated prices. While many managers worked to improve service, Gould and others bought and sold railroads like toys, watered their stock, and milked their assets.

Competition was severe, and managers fought desperately for traffic. They offered special rates and favors: free passes for large shippers; low rates on bulk freight, carload lots, and long hauls; and, above all, rebates—secret, privately negotiated reductions below published rates. Fierce rate wars broke out frequently, convincing managers that ruthless competition helped no one.

Managers such as Albert Fink, the brilliant vice president of the Louisville & Nashville, tried first to arrange pooling agreements, a way to control competition by sharing traffic, but none survived the intense pressures of competition. Legally unenforceable, pools were handshake agreements among individuals who did not always keep their word. Customers grew adept at bargaining for rebates and other privileges, and railroads rarely felt able to refuse them.

Failing to cooperate, railroad owners next tried to consolidate. Through purchase, lease, and merger, they gobbled up competitors and built "self-sustaining systems" that dominated entire regions. But many of the systems, expensive and unwieldy, collapsed in the Panic of 1893. By mid-1894, a quarter of the railroads were bankrupt. The victims of the panic included such legendary names as the Erie, B & O, Santa Fe, Northern Pacific, and Union Pacific.

Needing money, railroads turned naturally to bankers, who finally imposed order on the industry. J. Pierpont Morgan, head of the New York investment house of J. P. Morgan and Company, took the lead. Massively built, with eyes so piercing they seemed like the headlights of an onrushing train, Morgan was the most powerful figure in American finance. He liked efficiency, combination, and order. He disliked "wasteful" competition.

After 1893, Morgan and a few other bankers refinanced ailing railroads, and in the process they took control of the industry. Their methods were direct: fixed costs and debt were ruthlessly cut, new stock was issued to provide capital, rates were stabilized, rebates and competition were eliminated, and control was vested in a "voting trust" of handpicked trustees. Between 1894 and 1898, Morgan reorganized—critics said "Morganized"—the Southern Railway, the Erie, the Northern Pacific, and the B & O. In addition, he took over a half dozen other important railroads. By 1900, he was a dominant figure in American railroading.

As the new century began, the railroads had pioneered the patterns followed by most other industries. Seven giant systems controlled nearly two-thirds of the mileage, and they in turn answered to a few investment banking firms such as the house of Morgan. For good and ill, a national transportation network, centralized and relatively efficient, was now in place.

AN INDUSTRIAL EMPIRE

The new industrial empire was based on steel as well as on railroads. Harder and more durable than other kinds of iron, steel wrought changes in manufacturing, agriculture, transportation, and architecture. It permitted construction of longer bridges, taller buildings, stronger railroad track, deadlier weapons, better plows, heavier machinery, and faster ships. Made in great furnaces by strong men, it symbolized the tough, often brutal nature of industrial society. From the 1870s onward, steel output became the worldwide accepted measure of industrial progress, and nations around the globe vied for leadership.

The Bessemer process, developed in the late 1850s by Henry Bessemer in England and independently by William Kelly in the United States, made increased steel production possible. Both Bessemer and Kelly discovered that a blast of air forced through molten iron burned off carbon and other impurities, resulting in steel of a more uniform and durable quality. The discovery transformed the industry. While earlier methods produced amounts a person could lift, a Bessemer converter handled 5 tons of molten metal at a time. The mass production of steel was now possible.

CARNEGIE AND STEEL

Bessemer plants demanded extensive capital investment, abundant raw materials, and sophisticated production techniques. Using chemical and other processes, the plants required research departments, which became critical components of later American industries. Costly to build, they limited entry into the industry to the handful who could afford them.

Great steel districts arose in Pennsylvania, Ohio, and Alabama—in each case around large coal deposits that fueled the huge furnaces. Pittsburgh became the center of the industry, its giant mills employing thousands of workers. Output

International Steel Production, 1880–1914

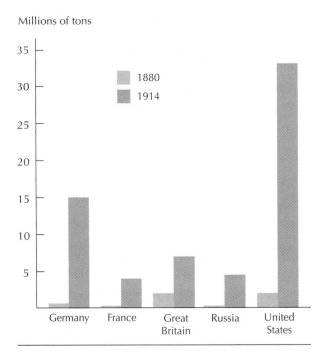

Millions of tons

Legend: 1880, 1914

(Germany, France, Great Britain, Russia, United States)

shot up. In 1874, the United States produced less than half the amount of pig iron produced in Great Britain. By 1890, it took the lead, and in 1900, it produced four times as much as Britain.

Like the railroads, steel companies grew larger and larger. In 1880, only nine companies could produce more than 100,000 tons a year. By the early 1890s, several companies exceeded 250,000 tons, and two—including the great Carnegie Steel Company—produced more than 1 million tons a year. As operations expanded, managers needed more complex skills. Product development, marketing, and consumer preferences became important.

Andrew Carnegie emerged as the undisputed master of the industry. Born in Scotland, he came to the United States in 1848 at the age of 12. Settling near Pittsburgh, he went to work as a bobbin boy in a cotton mill, earning $1.20 a week. He soon took a job in a telegraph office, where in 1852 his hard work and skill caught the eye of Thomas A. Scott of the Pennsylvania Railroad. Starting as Scott's personal telegrapher, Carnegie spent a total of twelve years on the Pennsylvania, a training ground for company managers. By 1859, he had become a divisional superintendent. He was 24 years old.

Soon rich from shrewd investments, Carnegie plunged into the steel industry in 1872. On the Monongahela River south of Pittsburgh, he built the giant

The machinery dwarfs the workers in this engraving of the Bessemer converter in one of Andrew Carnegie's Pittsburgh steel mills. The illustration is from an 1886 issue of Harper's Weekly.

J. Edgar Thomson Steel Works, named after the president of the Pennsylvania Railroad, his biggest customer. With his warmth and salesmanship, he attracted able partners and subordinates such as Henry Clay Frick and Charles M. Schwab, whom he drove hard and paid well. Although he had written magazine articles defending the rights of workers, Carnegie kept the wages of the laborers in his mills low and disliked unions. With the help of Frick, he crushed a violent strike at his Homestead works in 1892 (see p. 600).

In 1878, he won the steel contract for the Brooklyn Bridge. During the next decade, as city building boomed, he converted the huge Homestead works near Pittsburgh to the manufacture of structural beams and angles, which went into the New York City elevated railway, the first skyscrapers, and the Washington Monument. Carnegie profits mounted: from $2 million in 1888 to $40 million in 1900. That year, Carnegie Steel alone produced more steel than Great Britain. Employing twenty thousand people, it was the largest industrial company in the world.

In 1901, Carnegie sold it. Believing that wealth brought social obligations, he wanted to devote his full time to philanthropy. He found a buyer in J. Pierpont Morgan, who in the late 1890s had put together several steel companies, including Federal Steel, Carnegie's chief rival. Carnegie Steel had blocked Morgan's well-known desire for control, and in mid-1900, when a war loomed between the two interests, Morgan decided to buy Carnegie out. In early January 1901, Morgan told Charles M. Schwab: "Go and find his price." Schwab cornered Carnegie on the golf course; Carnegie listened, and the next day he handed Schwab a note, scribbled in blunt pencil, asking almost a half billion dollars. Morgan glanced at it and said, "I accept this price."

Drawing other companies into the combination, Morgan on March 3, 1901, announced the creation of the United States Steel Corporation. The new firm was capitalized at $1.4 billion, the first billion-dollar company. Soon there were other giants, including Bethlehem Steel, Republic Steel, and National Steel. As the nineteenth century ended, steel products—rare just thirty years before—had altered the landscape. Huge firms, investment bankers, and professional managers dominated the industry.

ROCKEFELLER AND OIL

Petroleum worked comparable changes in the economic and social landscape, although mostly after 1900. Distilled into oil, it lubricated the machinery of the industrial age. There seemed little use for gasoline (the internal combustion engine had only just been developed), but kerosene, another major distillate, brought inexpensive illumination into almost every home. Whale oil, cottonseed oil, and even tallow candles were expensive to burn; consequently, many people went to bed at nightfall. Kerosene lamps opened the evenings to activity, altering the patterns of life.

Like other changes in these years, the oil boom happened with surprising speed. In the mid-1850s, petroleum was a bothersome, smelly fluid that occasionally rose to the surface of springs and streams. In 1859, Edwin L. Drake drilled the first oil well near Titusville in northwest Pennsylvania, and the "black gold" fever struck. Chemists soon discovered ways to transform petroleum into lubricating oil, grease, paint, wax, varnish, naphtha, and paraffin. Within a few years, there was a world market in oil.

At first, growth of the oil industry was chaotic. Early drillers and refiners produced for local markets, and since drilling wells and even erecting refineries cost little, competition flourished. Output fluctuated dramatically; prices rose and fell, with devastating effect.

A young merchant from Cleveland named John D. Rockefeller imposed order on the industry. "I had an ambition to build," he later recalled, and beginning in 1863 at the age of 24, he built the Standard Oil Company, soon to become one of the titans of corporate business. Like Morgan, Rockefeller considered competition wasteful, small-scale enterprise inefficient, and consolidation the path of the future.

Methodically, Rockefeller absorbed or destroyed competitors in Cleveland and elsewhere. Like Carnegie, he demanded efficiency, relentless cost cutting, and the latest technology.

Paying careful attention to detail, Rockefeller counted the stoppers in barrels, shortened barrel hoops to save metal, and, in one famous incident, reduced the number of drops of solder on kerosene cans from forty to thirty-nine. In large-scale production, Rockefeller realized, even small reductions meant huge savings. Research uncovered other ways of lowering costs and improving products, and Herman Frasch, a brilliant Standard chemist, solved problem after problem in the refining of oil.

In the end, Rockefeller triumphed over his competitors by marketing products of high quality at the lowest unit cost. But he employed other, less savory methods as well. He threatened rivals and bribed politicians. He employed spies to harass the customers of competing refiners. Above all, he extorted railroad rebates that lowered his transportation costs and undercut competitors. By 1879, he controlled 90 percent of the country's entire oil-refining capacity.

Vertically integrated, Standard Oil owned wells, timberlands, barrel and chemical plants, refineries, warehouses, pipelines, and fleets of tankers and oil cars. Its marketing organization served as the model for the industry. Standard exported oil to Asia, Africa, and South America; its 5-gallon kerosene tin, like Coca-Cola bottles and cans of a later era, was a familiar sight in the most distant parts of the world.

To manage it all, the company developed a new plan of business organization, the trust, which had profound significance for American business. In 1881, Samuel T. C. Dodd, Standard's attorney, set up the Standard Oil Trust, with a board of nine trustees empowered "to hold, control, and manage" all Standard's properties. Stockholders exchanged their stock for trust certificates, on which dividends were paid. On January 2, 1882, the first of the modern trusts was born. As Dodd intended, it immediately centralized control of Standard's far-flung empire.

Competition almost disappeared; profits soared. A trust movement swept the country as industries with similar problems—whiskey, lead, and sugar, among others—followed Standard's example. The word *trust* became synonymous with monopoly, amid vehement protests from the public. *Antitrust* became a watchword for a generation of reformers from the 1880s through the era of

Woodrow Wilson. But Rockefeller's purpose had been *management* of a monopoly, not monopoly itself, which he had already achieved.

Other companies followed suit, including American Sugar Refining, the Northern Securities Company, and the National Biscuit Company. Merger followed merger. By 1900, 1 percent of the nation's companies controlled more than one-third of its industrial production.

In 1897, Rockefeller retired with a fortune of nearly $900 million, but for Standard Oil and petroleum in general, the most expansive period was yet to come. The great oil pools of Texas and Oklahoma had not yet been discovered. Plastics and other oil-based synthetics were several decades in the future. There were only four usable automobiles in the country, and the day of the gasoline engine, automobile, and airplane lay just ahead.

THE BUSINESS OF INVENTION

"America has become known the world around as the home of invention," boasted the commissioner of patents in 1892. It had not always been so; until the last third of the nineteenth century, the country had imported most of its technology. Then an extraordinary group of inventors and tinkerers—"specialists in invention," Thomas A. Edison called them—began to study the world around them. Some of their inventions gave rise to new industries; a few actually changed the quality of life.

The number of patents issued to inventors reflected the trend. During the 1850s, fewer than 2,000 patents were issued each year. By the 1880s and 1890s, the figure reached more than 20,000 a year. Between 1790 and 1860, the U.S. Patent Office issued just 36,000 patents; in the decade of the 1890s alone, it issued more than 200,000.

Some of the inventions transformed communications. In 1866, Cyrus W. Field improved the transatlantic cable linking the telegraph networks of Europe and the United States. By the early 1870s, land and submarine cables ran to Brazil, Japan, and the China coast; in the next two decades, they reached Africa and spread across South America. Diplomats and business leaders could now "talk" to their counterparts in Berlin or Hong Kong. Even before the telephone, the cables quickened the pace of foreign affairs, revolutionized journalism, and allowed businesses to expand and centralize.

The typewriter (1867), stock ticker (1867), cash register (1879), calculating machine (1887), and adding machine (1888) helped business transactions. High-speed spindles, automatic looms, and electric sewing machines transformed the clothing industry, which for the first time in history turned out ready-made clothes for the masses. In 1890, the Census Bureau first used machines to sort

Industrialist George Eastman using his new box camera aboard the S.S. Galia is caught by another photographer using a box camera. The small easy-to-use cameras helped move photography out of the studio and into the realm of every-day activities.

and tabulate data on punched cards, a portent of a new era of information storage and processing.

In 1879, George Eastman patented a process for coating gelatin on photographic dry plates, which led to celluloid film and motion pictures. By 1888, he was marketing the Kodak camera, which weighed 35 ounces, took 100 exposures, and cost $25. Even though early Kodaks had to be returned to the factory, camera and all, for film developing, they revolutionized photography. Now almost anyone could snap a picture.

Other innovations changed the diet. There were new processes for flour, canned meat, vegetables, condensed milk, and even beer (from an offshoot of Louis Pasteur's discoveries about bacteria). Packaged cereals appeared on breakfast tables. Refrigerated railroad cars, ice-cooled, brought fresh fruit from Florida and California to all parts of the country. In the 1870s, Gustavus F. Swift, a Chicago meatpacker, hit on the idea of using the cars to distribute meat nationwide. Setting up "dissembly" factories to butcher meat (Henry Ford later copied them for his famous "assembly" lines), he started an "era of cheap beef," as a newspaper said.

No innovation, however, rivaled the importance of the telephone and the use of electricity for light and power. The telephone was the work of Alexander Graham Bell, a shrewd and genial Scot who settled in Boston in 1871. Interested in the problems of the deaf, Bell experimented with ways to transmit speech electrically, and after several years he had developed electrified metal disks that,

Thomas Edison poses with his favorite invention, the tinfoil phonograph, in Mathew Brady's studio in Washington, DC, in 1878.

much like the human ear, converted sound waves to electrical impulses and back again. On March 10, 1876, he transmitted the first sentence over a telephone: "Mr. Watson, come here; I want you." Later that year, he exhibited the new device to excited crowds at the Centennial Exposition in Philadelphia.

In 1878—the year a telephone was installed in the White House—the first telephone exchange opened in New Haven, Connecticut. Fighting off competitors who challenged the patent, the young Bell Telephone Company dominated the growing industry. By 1895, there were about 310,000 phones; a decade later, there were 10 million—about one for every ten people. American Telephone and Telegraph Company, formed by the Bell interests in 1885, became another of the vast holding companies, consolidating more than a hundred local systems.

If the telephone dissolved communication barriers as old as the human race, Thomas Alva Edison, the "Wizard of Menlo Park," invented processes and products of comparable significance. Born in 1847, Edison had little formal education, although he was an avid reader. Like Carnegie, he went into the new field of telegraphy. Tinkering in his spare time, he made several important improvements, including a telegraph capable of sending four messages over a single wire. Gathering teams of specialists to work on specific problems, Edison built the first modern research laboratory at Menlo Park, New Jersey. It may have been his most important invention.

The laboratory, Edison promised, would turn out "a minor invention every ten days and a big thing every six months or so." In 1877, it turned out a big thing, the phonograph, and in 1879, an even bigger one, the incandescent lamp. Sir Joseph William Swan, an English inventor, had already experimented with the carbon filament, but Edison's task involved more than finding a durable filament. He set out to do nothing less than change light. A trial-and-error inventor, Edison tested sixteen hundred materials before producing, late in 1879, the carbon filament he wanted. Then he had to devise a complex system of conductors, meters, and generators by which electricity could be divided and distributed to homes and businesses.

With the financial backing of J. P. Morgan, he organized the Edison Illuminating Company and built the Pearl Street power station in New York City, the testing ground of the new apparatus. On September 4, 1882, as Morgan and others watched, Edison threw a switch and lit the house of Morgan, the stock exchange, the *New York Times,* and a number of other buildings. Amazed, a *Times* reporter marveled that writing stories in the office at night "seemed almost like writing in daylight." Power stations soon opened in Boston, Philadelphia, and Chicago. By 1900, there were 2774 stations, lighting some 2 million electric lights around the country. In a nation alive with light, the habits of centuries changed. A flick of the switch lit homes and factories at any hour of the day or night.

In a rare blunder, Edison based his system on low-voltage direct current, which could be transmitted only about two miles. George Westinghouse, the inventor of the railroad air brake, demonstrated the advantages of high-voltage alternating current for transmission over great distances. In 1886, he formed the Westinghouse Electric Company and with the inventor Nikola Tesla, a Hungarian immigrant, developed an alternating-current motor that could convert electricity into mechanical power. Electricity could light a lamp or illuminate a skyscraper, pull a streetcar or drive an entire railroad, run a sewing machine or power a mammoth assembly line. Transmitted easily over long distances, it freed factories and cities from location near water or coal. Electricity, in short, brought a revolution.

Taking advantage of the new devices, Frank J. Sprague, a young engineer, electrified the Richmond, Virginia, streetcar system in 1887. Other cities quickly followed. Electric-powered subway systems opened in Boston in 1897 and New York City in 1904. Overhead wires and third rails made urban transportation quieter, faster, and cleaner. Buried under pavement or strung from pole to pole, wires of every description—trolley, telephone, and power—marked the birth of the modern city.

THE SELLERS

The increased output of the industrial age alone was not enough to ensure huge profits. The products still had to be sold, and that gave rise to a new "science" of marketing. Some business leaders—such as Swift in meatpacking, James B. Duke in tobacco, and Rockefeller in oil—built extensive marketing organizations of their own. Others relied on retailers, merchandising techniques, and advertising, developing a host of methods to convince consumers to buy.

In 1867, businesses spent about $50 million on advertising; in 1900, they spent more than $500 million, and the figure was increasing rapidly. The rotary press (1875) churned out newspapers and introduced a new era in newspaper advertising. Brand names became popular, and already Kellogg was promising corn-flake eaters "Genuine Joy, Genuine Appetite, Genuine Health and therefore Genuine Complexion."

Bringing producer and consumer together, nationwide advertising was the final link in the national market. From roadside signs to newspaper ads, it pervaded American life.

R. H. Macy in New York, John Wanamaker in Philadelphia, and Marshall Field in Chicago turned the department store into a national institution. There people could browse (a relatively new concept) and buy. Innovations in pricing, display, and advertising helped customers develop wants they did not know they had. In 1870, Wanamaker took out the first full-page newspaper ad, and Macy, an aggressive advertiser, touted "goods suitable for the millionaire at prices in reach of the millions."

The "chain store"—an American term—spread across the country. The A & P grocery stores, begun in 1859, numbered sixty-seven by 1876, all marked by a familiar red-and-gold facade. By 1915, there were a thousand of them. In 1880, F. W. Woolworth, bored with the family farm, opened the first "Five and Ten Cent Store" in Utica, New York. He had fifty-nine stores in 1900, the year he adopted the bright red storefront and heaping counters to lure customers in and persuade them to buy.

In similar fashion, Sears, Roebuck and Montgomery Ward sold to rural customers through mail-order catalogs—a means of selling that depended on effec-

Macy's first store at 6th Avenue and 14th Street in NewYork City. In addition to the wide variety of house-hold goods and furnishings they offered for sale, the new department stores attempted to attract shoppers with such amenities as tearooms, nurseries, and libraries.

tive transportation and a high level of customer literacy. As a traveler for a dry goods firm, Aaron Montgomery Ward had seen an unfulfilled need of people in the rural West. He started the mail-order trend in 1872, with a one-sheet price list offered from a Chicago loft. By 1884, he offered almost ten thousand items in a catalog of 240 pages.

Richard W. Sears also saw the possibilities in the mail-order business. Starting with watches and jewelry, he gradually expanded his list. In the early 1880s, he moved to Chicago and with Alvah C. Roebuck founded Sears, Roebuck and Company. Sears sold anything and everything, prospering in a business that relied on mutual faith between unseen customers and distant distributors. Sears catalogs, soon more than five hundred pages long, exploited four-color illustration and other new techniques. By the early 1900s, Sears distributed six million catalogs annually.

Advertising, brand names, chain stores, and mail-order houses brought Americans of all varieties into a national market. Even as the country grew, a certain homogeneity of goods bound it together, touching cities and farms, East and West, rich and poor. There was a common language of consumption.

Americans had become a community of consumers, surrounded by goods unavailable just a few decades before, and able to purchase them. They had learned to make, want, and buy. "Because you see the main thing today is—shopping," Arthur Miller, a twentieth-century playwright, said in *The Price:*

> *Years ago a person, he was unhappy, didn't know what to do with himself—he'd go to church, start a revolution—something. Today you're unhappy? Can't figure it out? What is the salvation? Go shopping.*

THE WAGE EARNERS

Although entrepreneurs were important, it was the labor of millions of men and women that built the new industrial society. In their individual stories, nearly all unrecorded, lay much of the achievement, drama, and pain of these years.

In a number of respects, their lot improved during the last quarter of the nineteenth century. Real wages rose, working conditions improved, and the workers' influence in national affairs increased. Between 1880 and 1914, wages of the average worker rose about $7 a year. Like others, workers also benefited from expanding health and educational services.

WORKING MEN, WORKING WOMEN, WORKING CHILDREN

Still, life for workers was not easy. Before 1900, most wage earners worked at least ten hours a day, six days a week. If skilled, they earned about 20 cents an hour; if unskilled, just half that. On average, workers earned between $400 and $500 a year. It took about $600 for a family of four to live decently. Construction workers, machinists, government employees, printers, clerical workers, and western miners made more than the average. Eastern coal miners, agricultural workers, garment workers, and unskilled factory hands made considerably less.

There were few holidays or vacations, and there was little respite from the grueling routine. Skilled workers could turn the system to their own ends—New York City cigar makers, for example, paid someone to read to them while they worked—but the unskilled seldom had such luxury. They were too easily replaced. "A bit of advice to you," said a guidebook for immigrant Jews in the 1890s: "do not take a moment's rest. Run, do, work, and keep your own good in mind."

Work was not only grueling; it was very dangerous. Safety standards were low, and accidents were common, more common in fact than in any other industrial nation in the world at that time. On the railroads, 1 in every 26 workers was

It was not unusual for children in some cities to grow up along with their peers in the factory instead of on the playground, like these girls working in the garment industry.

injured and 1 in every 399 was killed each year. Thousands suffered from chronic illness, unknowing victims of dust, chemicals, and other pollutants. In the early 1900s, physician Alice Hamilton established a link between jobs and disease, but meanwhile, illness weakened or struck down many a breadwinner.

The breadwinner might be a woman or a child; both worked in increasing numbers. In 1870, about 15 percent of women over the age of 16 were employed for wages; in 1900, 20 percent (5.3 million women) were. Of 303 occupations listed in the 1900 census, women were represented in 296. The textile industry was their largest single employer. In 1900, 1 out of every 10 girls and 1 out of every 5 boys between the ages of 10 and 15 held jobs. In Paterson, New Jersey, an important industrial city, about half of all boys and girls aged 11 to 14 had jobs.

There were so many children in the labor force that when people spoke of child labor, they often meant boys and girls under the age of 14. Boys were paid little enough, but girls made even less. Girls, it was argued, were headed for marriage; those who worked were just doing so in order to help out their families. "We try to employ girls who are members of families," a box manufacturer said, "for we don't pay the girls a living wage in this trade."

Most working women were young and single. Many began working at 16 or 17, worked a half dozen years or so, married, and quit. In 1900, only 5 percent of all married women were employed outside the home, although African American women were an important exception. Among them, 25 percent of married women worked in 1900, usually on southern farms or as low-paid laundresses or domestic servants. As clerical work expanded, women learned new skills such as typing and stenography. Moving into formerly male occupations, they became secretaries, bookkeepers, typists, telephone operators, and clerks in the new department stores.

A few women—very few—became ministers, lawyers, and doctors. Arabella Mansfield, admitted to the Iowa bar in 1869, was the first woman lawyer in the country. But change was slow, and in the 1880s, some law schools still were refusing to admit women because they "had not the mentality to study law." Among women entering the professions, the overwhelming majority became nurses, schoolteachers, and librarians. In such professions, a process of "feminization" occurred: women became a majority of the workers, a small number of men took the management roles, and most men left for other jobs, lowering the profession's status.

In most jobs, status and pay were divided unequally between men and women. When employed in factories, women tended to occupy jobs that were viewed as natural extensions of household activity. They made clothes and textiles, processed food, and made cigars, tobacco, and shoes. In the women's garment industry, which employed large numbers of women, they were the sewers and finishers, doing jobs that paid less; men were the higher-paid cutters and pressers.

In general, adults earned more than children, the skilled more than the unskilled, native born more than foreign born, Protestants more than Catholics or Jews, and whites more than blacks and Asians. On average, women made a little more than half as much as men, according to contemporary estimates. In some cases, employers defended the differences—the foreign born, for example, might not speak English—but most simply reflected bias against race, creed, or gender. In the industrial society, white, native-born Protestant men—the bulk of the male population—reaped the greatest rewards.

Blacks labored on the fringes, usually in menial occupations. The last hired and first fired, they earned less than other workers at almost every level of skill. On the Pacific Coast, the Chinese—and later the Japanese—lived in enclaves and suffered periodic attacks of discrimination. In 1879, the Workingmen's party of California got a provision in the state constitution forbidding corporations to employ Chinese, and in 1882, Congress passed the Chinese Exclusion Act, prohibiting the immigration of Chinese workers for ten years.

CULTURE OF WORK

Among almost all groups, industrialization shattered age-old patterns, including work habits and the culture of work, as Herbert G. Gutman, a social historian, noted. It made people adapt "older work routines to new necessities and strained those wedded to premodern patterns of labor." Adaptation was difficult and often demeaning. Virtually everyone went through it, and newcomers repeated the experiences of those who came before.

Men and women fresh from farms were not accustomed to the factory's disciplines. Now they worked indoors rather than out, paced themselves to the clock rather than the movements of the sun, and followed the needs of the market rather than the natural rhythms of the seasons. They had supervisors and hierarchies and strict rules.

As industries grew larger, work became more impersonal. Machines displaced skilled artisans, and the unskilled tended the machines for employers they never saw. Workers picked up and left their jobs with startling frequency, and factories drew on a churning, highly mobile labor supply. Historian Stephan Thernstrom, who carefully studied the census records, found that only about half the people recorded in any census still lived in the same community ten years

A typing pool in the audit division of the Metropolitan Life Insurance Company, 1897. As demand for clerical workers grew, women took over many of the secretarial duties formerly performed by men. Despite their prominence in the workplace, however, the women were usually overseen by male supervisors.

later. "The country had an enormous reservoir of restless and footloose men, who could be lured to new destinations when opportunity beckoned."

Thernstrom and others have also found substantial economic and social mobility. The rags-to-riches stories of Horatio Alger, of course, had always said so, and careers of men such as Andrew Carnegie—the impoverished immigrant boy who made good—seemed to confirm it. The actual record was considerably more limited. Most business leaders in the period came from well-to-do or middle-class families of old American stock. Of 360 iron and steel barons in Pittsburgh, Carnegie's own city, only 5 fit the Carnegie characteristics, and one of those was Carnegie himself. Still, if few workers became steel magnates, many workers made major progress during their lifetimes. Thernstrom discovered that a quarter of the manual laborers rose to middle-class positions, and working-class children were even more likely to move up the ladder.

The chance for advancement played a vital role in American industrial development. It gave workers hope, wedded them to the system, and tempered their response to the appeal of labor unions and working-class agitation. Very few workers rose from rags to riches, but a great many rose to better jobs and higher status.

LABOR UNIONS

Weak throughout the nineteenth century, labor unions never included more than 2 percent of the total labor force or more than 10 percent of industrial workers. To many workers, unions seemed "foreign," radical, and out of step with the American tradition of individual advancement. Craft, ethnic, and other differences fragmented the labor force, and its extraordinary mobility made organization difficult. Employers opposed unions. "I have always had one rule," said an executive of U.S. Steel. "If a worker sticks up his head, hit it."

As the national economy emerged, however, national labor unions gradually took shape. The early unions often represented skilled workers in local areas, but in 1866, William H. Sylvis, a Pennsylvania iron molder, united several unions into a single national organization, the National Labor Union. Like many of the era's labor leaders, Sylvis sought long-range humanitarian reforms, such as the establishment of workers' cooperatives, rather than specific bread-and-butter goals. A talented propagandist, he attracted many members—some 640,000 by 1868—but he died in 1869, and the organization did not long survive him.

The year Sylvis died, Uriah S. Stephens and a group of Philadelphia garment workers founded a far more successful organization, the Noble and Holy Order of the Knights of Labor. A secret fraternal order, it grew slowly through the 1870s, until Terence V. Powderly, the new Grand Master Workman elected in 1879, ended the secrecy and embarked on an aggressive recruitment program.

Women delegates at a national meeting of the Knights of Labor in 1886. Women belonged to separate associations affiliated with local all-male unions.

Wanting to unite all labor, the Knights welcomed everyone who "toiled," regardless of skill, creed, sex, or color. Unlike most unions, it organized women workers, and at its peak, it had 60,000 black members.

Harking back to the Jacksonians, the Knights set the "producers" against monopoly and special privilege. As members they excluded only "nonproducers"—bankers, lawyers, liquor dealers, and gamblers. Since employers were "producers," they could join; and since workers and employers had common interests, the Knights maintained that workers should not strike. The order's platform included the eight-hour day and the abolition of child labor, but more often it focused on uplifting, utopian reform. Powderly, the eloquent and idealistic leader, spun dreams of a new era of harmony and cooperation.

Membership grew steadily—from 42,000 in 1882 to 110,000 in 1885. In March 1885, ignoring Powderly's dislike of strikes, local Knights in St. Louis, Kansas City, and other cities won a victory against Jay Gould's Missouri Pacific Railroad, and membership soared. It soon reached almost 730,000, but neither Powderly nor the union's loose structure could handle the growth. In 1886, the wily Gould struck back, crushing the Knights on the Texas and Pacific Railroad.

The defeat punctured the union's growth and revealed the ineffectiveness of its national leaders. Tens of thousands of unskilled laborers, who had recently rushed to join, deserted the ranks. The Haymarket Riot turned public sympathy against unions like the Knights. By 1890, the order had shrunk to 100,000 members, and a few years later, it was virtually defunct.

Even as the Knights waxed and waned, another organization emerged that was to endure. Founded in 1886, the American Federation of Labor (AFL) was a loose alliance of national craft unions. It organized only skilled workers along craft lines, avoided politics, and worked for specific practical objectives. "I have my own philosophy and my own dreams," said Samuel Gompers, the founder and longtime president, "but first and foremost I want to increase the workingman's welfare year by year."

Born in a London tenement in 1850, Gompers was a child of the union movement. Settling in New York, he worked as a cigar maker, took an active hand in union activities, and experimented for a time with socialism and working-class politics. As leader of the AFL, he adopted a pragmatic approach to labor's needs. Gompers accepted capitalism and did not argue for fundamental changes in it. For labor he wanted simply a recognized place within the system and a greater share of the rewards.

Unlike Powderly, Gompers and the AFL assumed that most workers would remain workers throughout their lives. The task, then, lay in improving lives in "practical" ways: higher wages, shorter hours, and better working conditions. The AFL offered some attractive assurances to employers. As a trade union, the AFL would use the strike and boycott, but only to achieve limited gains; if treated fairly, the organization would provide a stable labor force. The AFL would not oppose monopolies and trusts, as Gompers said, "so long as we obtain fair wages."

By the 1890s, the AFL was the most important labor group in the country, and Gompers, the guiding spirit, was its president, except for one year, until his death in 1924. Membership expanded from 140,000 in 1886, past 250,000 in 1892, to more than 1 million by 1901. The AFL then included almost one-third of the country's skilled workers. By 1914, it had more than 2 million members. The great majority of workers—skilled and unskilled—remained unorganized, but Gompers and the AFL had become a significant force in national life.

The AFL either ignored or opposed women workers. Only two of its national affiliates—the Cigar Makers' Union and the Typographical Union—accepted women as members; others prohibited them outright, and Gompers himself often complained that women workers undercut the pay scales for men. Working conditions improved after 1900, but even then, unions were largely a man's world. In 1910, when there were 6.3 million women at work, only 125,000 of them were in unions.

The AFL did not expressly forbid black workers from joining, but member unions used high initiation fees, technical examinations, and other means to discourage black membership. The AFL's informal exclusion practices were, all in all, a sorry record, but Gompers defended his policy toward blacks, women, and the unskilled by pointing to the dangers that unions faced. Only by restricting membership, he argued, could the union succeed.

LABOR UNREST

Workers used various means to adjust to the factory age. To the dismay of managers and "efficiency" experts, the employees often dictated the pace and quality of their work and set the tone of the workplace. Friends and relatives of newly arrived immigrants found jobs for them, taught them how to deal with factory conditions, and humanized the workplace.

Workers also formed their own institutions to deal with their jobs. Overcoming differences of race or ethnic origin, they often banded together to help each other. They joined social or fraternal organizations, and their unions did more than argue for higher wages. Unions offered companionship, news of job

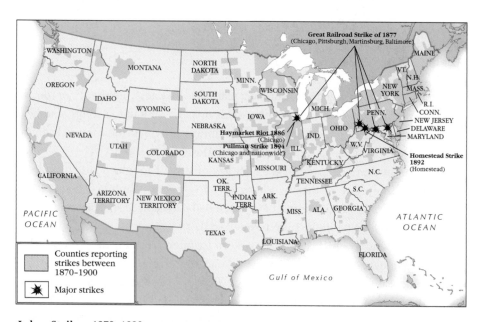

Labor Strikes, 1870–1890
More than 14,000 strikes occurred in the 1880s and early 1890s, involving millions of workers.

Violence and fires associated with the great railroad strike of 1877 destroyed railyards across the country. By the end of the strike, which lasted about two weeks, $10 million of railroad property had been reduced to rubble, and more than a hundred people had died.

openings, and much needed insurance plans for sickness, accident, or death. Workers went to the union hall to play cards or pool, sing union songs, and hear older workers tell of past labor struggles. Unions provided food for sick members, and there were dances, picnics, and parades.

Many employers believed in an "iron law of wages" in which supply and demand, not the welfare of their workers, dictated wages. Wanting a docile labor force, employers fired union members, hired scabs to replace strikers, and used a new weapon, the court injunction, to quell strikes.

The injunction, which forbade workers to interfere with their employers' business, was used to break the great Pullman strike of 1894, and the Supreme Court upheld use of the injunction in *In re Debs* (1895). Court decisions also affected the legal protection offered to workers. In *Holden v. Hardy* (1898), the Court upheld a law limiting working hours for miners because their work was dangerous and long hours might increase injuries. In *Lochner v. New York* (1905), however, it struck down a law limiting bakery workers to a sixty-hour week and ten-hour day. Because baking was safer than mining, the Court saw no need to interfere with the right of bakers to sell their labor freely.

As employers' attitudes hardened, strikes and violence broke out. The United States had the greatest number of violent confrontations between capital and labor in the industrial world. Between 1880 and 1900, there were more than 23,000 strikes involving 6.6 million workers. The great railroad strike of 1877 paralyzed railroads from West Virginia to California, resulted in the deaths of more than a hundred workers, and required federal troops to suppress it. Another outburst of labor unrest occurred during the mid-1880s; in 1886, the peak year, 610,000 workers were off the job because of strikes and lockouts.

The worst incident took place at Haymarket Square in Chicago, where workers had been campaigning for an eight-hour workday. In early May 1886, police, intervening in a strike at the McCormick Harvester works, shot and killed two workers. The next evening, May 4, labor leaders called a protest meeting at

In the rioting that followed the bomb explosion in Haymarket Square in Chicago, seven police officers and four workers died and more than seventy officers were wounded, many of them by fellow police. August Spies, one of the anarchists convicted of murder and sent to the gallows, said at his trial, "Let the world know that in A.D. 1886, in the state of Illinois, eight men were sentenced to death because they believed in a better future; because they had not lost their faith in the ultimate victory of liberty and justice!" (Actually, seven of the agitators were sentenced to death, the eighth to imprisonment.)

Haymarket Square near downtown Chicago. The meeting was peaceful, even a bit dull. About three thousand people were there; police ordered them to disperse, and someone threw a dynamite bomb that instantly killed one policeman and fatally wounded six others. Police fired into the crowd and killed four people.

The authorities never discovered who threw the bomb, but many Americans—not just business leaders—demanded action against labor "radicalism." Cities strengthened their police forces and armories. Uncertain who threw the bomb, Chicago police rounded up eight anarchists, who were convicted of murder. Although there was no evidence of their guilt, four were hanged, one committed suicide, and three remained in jail until pardoned by the governor in 1893. Linking labor and anarchism in the public mind, the Haymarket Riot weakened the national labor movement.

Violence again broke out in the unsettled conditions of the 1890s. In 1892, federal troops crushed a strike of silver miners in the Coeur d'Alene district of Idaho. That same year, Carnegie and Henry Clay Frick, Carnegie's partner and manager, cut wages nearly 20 percent at the Homestead steel plant. The Amalgamated Iron and Steel Workers, an AFL affiliate, struck, and Frick responded by locking the workers out of the plant. The workers surrounded it, and Frick, furious, hired a small private army of Pinkerton detectives to drive them off. But alert workers spotted the detectives, pinned them down with gunfire, and forced them to surrender. Three detectives and ten workers died in the battle.

A few days later, the Pennsylvania governor ordered the state militia to impose peace at Homestead. On July 23, an anarchist named Alexander Berkman, who was not one of the strikers, walked into Frick's office and shot him twice, then stabbed him several times. Incredibly, Frick survived, watched the police take Berkman away, called in a doctor to bandage his wounds, and stayed in the office until closing time. In late July, the Homestead works reopened under military guard, and in November the strikers gave up.

Events like those at Homestead troubled many Americans who wondered whether industrialization, for all its benefits, might carry a heavy price in social upheaval, class tensions, and even outright warfare. Most workers did not share in the immense profits of the industrial age, and as the nineteenth century came to a close, there were some who rebelled against the inequity.

In the half century after the Civil War, the United States became an industrial nation—the leading one, in fact, in the world. On one hand, industrialization meant "progress," growth, world power, and in some sense, fulfillment of the American promise of abundance. National wealth grew from $16 billion in 1860 to $88 billion in 1900; wealth per capita more than doubled. For the bulk of the population, the standard of living—a particularly American concept—rose.

But industrialization also meant rapid change, social instability, exploitation of labor, and growing disparity in income between rich and poor. Industry flourished, but control rested in fewer and fewer hands. Maturing quickly, the young system became a new corporate capitalism: giant businesses, interlocking in ownership, managed by a new professional class, and selling an expanding variety of goods in an increasingly controlled market. As goods spread through the society, so did a sharpened, aggressive materialism. Workers felt the strains of the shift to a new social order.

In 1902, a well-to-do New Yorker named Bessie Van Vorst decided to see what it was like to work for a living in a factory. Disguising herself in coarse woolen clothes, she went to Pittsburgh and got a job in a canning factory. She worked ten hours a day, six days a week, including four hours on Saturday afternoons when she and the other women, on their hands and knees, scrubbed the tables, stands, and entire factory floor. For that she earned $4.20 a week, $3 of which went for food alone.

Van Vorst was lucky—when she tired of the life, she could go back to her home in New York. The working men and women around her were not so fortunate. They stayed on the factory floor and, by dint of their labor, created the new industrial society.

19

TOWARD AN URBAN SOCIETY, 1877–1900

One day around 1900, Harriet Vittum, a settlement house worker in Chicago, went to the aid of a young Polish girl who lived in a nearby slum. The girl, aged 15, had discovered she was pregnant and had taken poison. An ambulance was on the way, and Vittum, told of the poisoning, rushed over to do what she could.

Quickly, she raced up the three flights of stairs to the floor where the girl and her family lived. Pushing open the door, she found the father, several male boarders, and two or three small boys asleep on the kitchen floor. In the next room, the mother was on the floor among several women boarders and one or two small children. Glancing out the window, Vittum saw the wall of another building so close she could reach out and touch it.

There was a third room; in it lay the 15-year-old girl, along with two more small children who were asleep. Looking at the scene, Vittum thought about the girl's life in the crowded tenement. Should she try to save her? Vittum asked herself. Should she even try to bring the girl back "to the misery and hopelessness of the life she was living in that awful place"?

The young girl died, and in later years, Vittum often told her story. It was easy to see why. The girl's life in the slum, the children on the floor, the need to take in boarders to make ends meet, the way the mother and father collapsed at the end of a workday that began long before sunup—all reflected the experiences of millions of people living in the nation's cities.

People poured into cities in the last part of the nineteenth century, lured by glitter and excitement, by friends and relatives who were already there, and, above all, by the greater opportunities for jobs and higher wages. Between 1860 and 1910, the rural population of the United States almost doubled; the number of people living in cities increased sevenfold.

Little of the increase came from natural growth, since urban families had high rates of infant mortality, a declining fertility rate, and a high death rate from injury and disease. Many of the newcomers came from rural America, and many more came from Europe, Latin America, and Asia. In one of the most significant migrations in American history, thousands of African Americans began in the 1880s to move from the rural South to northern cities. By 1900, there were large black communities in New York, Baltimore, Chicago, Washington, DC, and other cities. Yet to come was the even greater black migration during World War I.

Two major forces reshaped American society between 1870 and 1920. One was industrialization; the other was urbanization, the headlong rush of people from their rural roots into the modern urban environment. By 1920, the city had become the center of American economic, social, and cultural life.

THE LURE OF THE CITY

Between 1870 and 1900, the city—like the factory—became a symbol of a new America. Drawn from farms, small towns, and foreign lands, newcomers swelled the population of older cities and created new ones almost overnight. At the beginning of the Civil War, only one-sixth of the American people lived in cities of eight thousand people or more. By 1900, one-third did; by 1920, one-half. "We live in the age of great cities," wrote the Reverend Samuel Lane Loomis in 1887. "Each successive year finds a stronger and more irresistible current sweeping in towards the centers of life."

The current brought growth of an explosive sort. Thousands of years of history had produced only a handful of cities with more than a half million in population. In 1900, the United States had six such cities, including three—New York, Chicago, and Philadelphia—with populations greater than one million.

SKYSCRAPERS AND SUBURBS

Like so many things in these years, the city was transformed by a revolution in technology. Beginning in the 1880s, the age of steel and glass produced the skyscraper; the streetcar produced the suburbs and new residential patterns.

On the eve of the change, American cities were a crowded jumble of small buildings. Church steeples stood out on the skyline, clearly visible above the roofs of factories and office buildings. Buildings were usually made of masonry, and since the massive walls had to support their own weight, they could be no taller than a dozen or so stories. Steel frames and girders ended that limitation and allowed buildings to soar higher and higher. "Curtain walls," which concealed the steel framework, were no longer load bearing; they were pierced by many windows that let in fresh air and light. Completed in 1885, the Home Insurance Building in Chicago was the country's first metal-frame structure.

To a group of talented Chicago architects, the new trends served as a springboard for innovative forms. The leaders of the movement were John Root and Louis H. Sullivan, both of whom were attracted by the chance to rebuild Chicago after the great fire of 1871. Noting that the fire had fed on fancy exterior ornamentation, Root developed a plain, stripped-down style, bold in mass and form—the keynotes of modern architecture. He had another important insight, too. In an age of business, Root thought, the office tower, more than a church or a government building, symbolized the society, and he designed office buildings that carried out, as he said, "the ideas of modern business life: simplicity, stability, breadth, dignity."

Sullivan had studied at the Massachusetts Institute of Technology (MIT) and in Paris before settling in Chicago. In 1886, at the age of 30, he began work on the Chicago Auditorium, one of the last great masonry buildings. "Then came the flash of imagination which saw the single thing," he later said. "The trick was turned; and there swiftly came into being something new under the sun." Sullivan's skyscrapers, that "flash of imagination," changed the urban skyline.

In the Wainwright Building in St. Louis (1890), the Schiller Building (1892) and the Carson, Pirie, and Scott department store (1899) in Chicago, and the Prudential Building in Buffalo (1895), Sullivan developed the new forms. Architects must discard "books, rules, precedents," he announced; responding to the new, they should design for a building's function. "Form follows function," Sullivan believed, and he passed the idea on to a talented disciple, Frank Lloyd Wright. The modern city should stretch to the sky. A skyscraper "must be every inch a proud and soaring thing, rising in sheer exaltation . . . from bottom to top."

Electric elevators, first used in 1871, carried passengers upward in the new skyscrapers. During the same years, streetcars, another innovation, carried the people outward to expanded boundaries that transformed urban life.

Cities were no longer largely "walking cities," confined to a radius of two or three miles, the distance an individual might walk. Streetcar systems extended the radius and changed the urban map. Cable lines, electric surface lines, and elevated rapid transit brought shoppers and workers into central business districts and sped them home again. Offering a modest five-cent fare with a free transfer, the mass transit systems fostered commuting and widely separated business and residential districts sprang up. The middle class moved farther and farther out to the leafy greenness of the suburbs.

As the middle class moved out of the cities, the immigrants and working class poured in. They took over the older brownstones, row houses, and workers' cottages, turning them, under the sheer weight of numbers, into the slums of the central city. In the cities of the past, classes and occupations had been thrown together; without streetcars and subways, there was no other choice. The streetcar city, sprawling and specialized, became a more fragmented and stratified society with middle-class residential rings surrounding a business and working-class core.

TENEMENTS AND PRIVIES

In the shadow of the skyscrapers, grimy rows of tenements filled the central city and crowded people into cramped apartments. In the late 1870s, architect James E. Ware won a competition for tenement design with the "dumbbell tenement." Rising seven or eight stories in height, the dumbbell tenement packed about 30 four-room apartments on a lot only 25 by 100 feet. Between four and sixteen families lived on a floor; two toilets in the hall of each floor served their needs. Narrowed at the middle, the tenement resembled a giant dumbbell in shape. The indented middle created an air shaft between adjoining buildings that provided a little light and ventilation. In case of fire, it also carried flames from one story to the next, making the buildings notorious firetraps. In 1890, nearly half the dwellings in New York City were tenements.

That year, more than 1.4 million people lived on Manhattan Island, one of whose wards had a population density of 334,000 people per square mile.

This 1879 dumbbell floor plan was meant to provide four apartments to a floor. However, a whole family might live in each room. Crowded, unsanitary conditions contributed to the spread of tuberculosis, the chief cause of death in the United States until 1909.

Many people lived in alleys and basements so dark they could not be photographed until flashlight photography was invented in 1887. Exploring the city, William Dean Howells, the prominent author, inhaled "the stenches of the neglected street . . . [and] the yet fouler and dreadfuller poverty smell which breathes from the open doorways."

The kitchen of a tenement apartment was often a multipurpose room. Here the tenement dwellers prepared and ate their meals; the room might also serve as a workroom, and it might be used as sleeping quarters for one or more members of the family.

Howells smelled more than poverty. In the 1870s and 1880s, cities stank. One problem was horse manure, hundreds of tons of it a day in every city. Another was the privy, "a single one of which," said a leading authority on public health, "may render life in a whole neighborhood almost unendurable in the summer."

Baltimore smelled "like a billion polecats," recalled H. L. Mencken, who grew up there. Said one New York City resident, "The stench is something terrible." Another wrote that "the stink is enough to knock you down." In 1880, the Chicago *Times* said that a "solid stink" pervaded the city. "No other word expresses it so well as stink. A stench means something finite. Stink reaches the infinite and becomes sublime in the magnitude of odiousness."

Cities dumped their wastes into the nearest body of water, then drew drinking water from the same site. Many built modern purified waterworks but could not keep pace with spiraling growth. In 1900, fewer than one in ten city dwellers drank filtered water. Factories, the pride of the era, polluted the urban air. At night, Pittsburgh looked and sounded like "Hell with the lid off," according to contemporary observers. Smoke poured from seventy-three glass factories,

The tenement district of New York City's Lower East Side. As millions emigrated to the United States during the last quarter of the nineteenth century, they crammed into already overpopulated ethnic neighborhoods, seeking others who spoke their language, practiced their religion, and followed their customs.

forty-one iron and steel mills, and twenty-nine oil refineries. The choking air helped prevent lung diseases and malaria—or so the city's advertising claimed.

Crime was another growing problem. The nation's homicide rate nearly tripled in the 1880s, much of the increase coming in the cities. After remaining constant for many decades, the suicide rate rose steadily between 1870 and 1900, according to a study of Philadelphia. Alcoholism also rose, especially among men, though recent studies have shown that for working-class men, the urban saloon was as much a gathering spot as it was a place to drink. Nonetheless, a 1905 survey of Chicago counted as many saloons as grocery stores, meat markets, and dry goods stores combined.

STRANGERS IN A NEW LAND

While some of the new city dwellers came from farms and small towns, many more came from abroad. Most came from Europe, where unemployment, food shortages, and increasing threats of war sent millions fleeing across the Atlantic

Immigration to the United States, 1870–1900

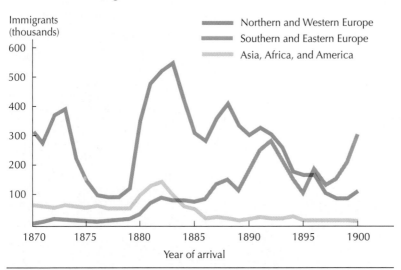

Immigrants (thousands)

— Northern and Western Europe
— Southern and Eastern Europe
— Asia, Africa, and America

Year of arrival

Note: For purposes of classification, "Northern and Western Europe" includes Great Britain, Ireland, Scandinavia, the Netherlands, Belgium, Luxembourg, Switzerland, France, and Germany. "Southern and Eastern Europe" includes Poland, Austria-Hungary, Russia and the Baltic States, Romania, Bulgaria, European Turkey, Italy, Spain, Portugal, and Greece. "Asia, Africa, and America" includes Asian Turkey, China, Japan, India, Canada, the Caribbean, Latin America, and all of Africa.

Source: U.S. Bureau of the Census, *Historical Statistics of the United States, Colonial Times to 1970,* Bicentennial Edition, Washington, DC, 1975.

to make a fresh start. Often they knew someone already in the United States, a friend or relative who had written them about prospects for jobs and freer lives in a new land.

All told, the immigration figures were staggering. Between 1877 and 1890, more than 6.3 million people entered the United States. In one year alone, 1882, almost 789,000 people came. By 1890, about 15 percent of the population, 9 million people, were foreign born.

Most newcomers were job seekers. Nearly two-thirds were males, and the majority were between the ages of 15 and 40. Most were unskilled laborers. Most settled on the eastern seaboard. In 1901, the Industrial Relocation Office was established to relieve overcrowding in the eastern cities; opening Galveston, Texas, as a port of entry, it attracted many Russian Jews to Texas and the Southwest. But most immigrants preferred the shorter, more familiar journey to New York, and they tended to crowd into northern and eastern cities, settling in areas where others of their nationality or religion lived.

They were often dazzled by what they saw. They stared at electric lights, in-door plumbing, soda fountains, streetcars, plush train seats for all classes, ice cream, lemons, and bananas. Relatives whisked them off to buy new "American" clothes and showed them the teeming markets, department stores, and Woolworth's new five-and-ten stores.

Cities had increasingly large foreign-born populations. In 1900, four-fifths of Chicago's population was foreign born or of foreign-born parentage, two-thirds of Boston's, and one-half of Philadelphia's. New York City, where most immigrants arrived and many stayed, had more Italians than lived in Naples, more Germans than lived in Hamburg, and twice as many Irish as lived in Dublin. Four out of five New York City residents in 1890 were of foreign birth or foreign parentage.

Beginning in the 1880s, the sources of immigration shifted dramatically away from northern and western Europe, the chief source of immigration for over two centuries. More and more immigrants came from southern and eastern Europe: Italy, Greece, Austria-Hungary, Poland, and Russia. Between 1880 and 1910, approximately 8.4 million people came from these lands. The "new" immigrants tended to be Catholics or Jews rather than Protestants. Like their predecessors, most were unskilled rather than skilled, and they often spoke "strange" languages. Most were poor and uneducated; sticking together in close-knit communities, they clung to their native customs, languages, and religions.

In a Puck *cartoon titled "Looking Backward," the shadows of their immigrant origins loom over the rich and powerful who wanted to deny the "new" immigrants from central and southern Europe admission to America. The caption on the cartoon reads, "They would close to the newcomer the bridge that carried them and their fathers over."*

More than any previous group, the so-called new immigrants troubled the mainstream society. Could they be assimilated? Did they share "American" values? Such questions preoccupied groups like the American Protective Association, a midwestern anti-Catholic organization that expanded in the 1890s and worked to limit or end immigration.

Anti-Catholicism and anti-Semitism flared up again, as they had in the 1850s. The Immigration Restriction League, founded in 1894, demanded a literacy test for immigrants from southern and eastern Europe. Congress passed such a law in 1896, but President Cleveland vetoed it.

IMMIGRANTS AND THE CITY

Industrial capitalism—the world of factories and foremen and grimy machines—tested the immigrants and placed an enormous strain on their families. Many immigrants came from peasant societies where life proceeded according to outdoor routine and age-old tradition. In their new city homes, they found both new freedoms and new confinements, a different language, and a novel set of customs and expectations. Historians have only recently begun to discover the remarkable ways in which they learned to adjust.

Like native-born families, most immigrant families were nuclear in structure—they consisted of two parents and their children. Though variations occurred from group to group, men and women occupied roles similar to those in native families: men were wage earners, women were housekeepers and mothers. Margaret Byington, who studied steelworkers' homes in Homestead in the early 1900s, learned that the father played a relatively small role in child rearing or managing the family's finances. "His part of the problem is to earn and hers to spend." In Chicago, social reformer Jane Addams discovered that immigrant women made it "a standard of domestic virtue that a man must not touch his pay envelope, but bring it home unopened to his wife."

Although patterns varied among ethnic groups, and between economic classes within ethnic groups, immigrants tended to marry within the group more than did the native born. In one New York community, only 2 percent of French Canadian and 7 percent of Irish workingmen married outside their ethnic group in 1880, compared to almost 40 percent of native-born workingmen. Immigrants also tended to marry at a later age than natives, and they tended to have more children, a fact that worried nativists opposed to immigration.

Immigrants shaped the city as much as it shaped them. Most of them tried to retain their traditional culture for themselves and their children while at the same time adapting to life in their new country. To do this, they spoke their native language, practiced their religious faith, read their own newspapers, and established special parochial or other schools. They observed traditional holidays and formed a myriad of social organizations to maintain ties among members of the group.

Immigrant associations—there were many of them in every city—offered fellowship in a strange land. They helped newcomers find jobs and homes; they provided important services such as unemployment insurance and health insurance. Some groups were no larger than a neighborhood; others spread nationwide. In 1914, the Deutsch-Amerikanischer Nationalbund, the largest of the associations, had more than two million members in dozens of cities and towns. Many women belonged to and participated in the work of the immigrant associations; in addition, there were groups exclusively for women, such as the Polish Women's Alliance, the Jednota Ceskyck Dam (Society of Czech Women), and the National Council of Jewish Women.

Every major city had dozens of foreign language newspapers, with circulations large and small. The first newspaper published in the Lithuanian language appeared in the United States, not in Lithuania. Eagerly read, the papers not only carried news of events in the homeland but also reported on local ethnic leaders, told readers how to vote and become citizens, and gave practical tips on adjusting to life in the United States. The Swedes, Poles, Czechs, and Germans established ethnic theaters that performed national plays and music. The most famous of these, the Yiddish (Jewish) Theater, started in the 1880s in New York City and lasted more than fifty years.

The church and the school were the most important institutions in every immigrant community. Eastern European Jews established synagogues and religious schools wherever they settled; they taught the Hebrew language and raised their children in a heritage they did not want to leave behind. Among such groups as the Irish and the Poles, the Roman Catholic church provided spiritual and educational guidance. In the parish schools, Polish priests and nuns taught Polish American children about Polish as well as American culture in the Polish language.

Church, school, and fraternal societies shaped the way in which immigrants adjusted to life in America. By preserving language, religion, and heritage, they also shaped the country itself.

THE HOUSE THAT TWEED BUILT

Closely connected with explosive urban growth was the emergence of the powerful city political machine. As cities grew, lines of responsibility in city governments became hopelessly confused, increasing the opportunity for corruption and greed. Burgeoning populations required streets, buildings, and public services; immigrants needed even more services. In this situation, political party machines played an important role.

The machines traded services for votes. Loosely knit, they were headed by a strong, influential leader—the "boss"—who tied together a network of ward and precinct captains, each of whom looked after his local constituents. In New York, "Honest" John Kelly, Richard Croker, and Charles F. Murphy led Tammany Hall, the famous Democratic party organization that dominated city politics from the 1850s to the 1930s. Other bosses included "Hinky Dink" Kenna and "Bathhouse John" Coughlin in Chicago, James McManes in Philadelphia, and Christopher A. Buckley—the notorious "Blind Boss," who used an exceptional memory for voices to make up for failing eyesight—in San Francisco.

William M. Tweed, head of the famed Tweed Ring in New York, provided the model for them all. Nearly six feet tall, weighing almost three hundred pounds, Tweed rose through the ranks of Tammany Hall. He served in turn as city alderman, member of Congress, and New York State assemblyman. A man of culture and warmth, he moved easily between the rough back alleys of New York and the parlors and clubs of the city's elite. Behind the scenes, he headed a ring that plundered New York for tens of millions of dollars.

The New York County Courthouse—"the house that Tweed built"—was his masterpiece. Nestled in City Hall Park in downtown Manhattan, the three-story structure was designed to cost $250,000, but the bills ran a bit higher. Furniture, carpets, and window shades alone came to more than $5.5 million. Three tables and forty chairs cost the city $180,000. Tweed's own quarry supplied the marble; the plumber was paid almost $1.5 million for fixtures. Andrew Garvey, the "prince of plasterers," charged $500,000 for plasterwork, and then $1 million to repair the same work. His total bill came to $2,870,464.06. (The *New York Times* suggested that the six cents be donated to charity.) In the end, the building cost more than $13 million—and in 1872, when Tweed fell, it was still not finished.

The role of the political bosses can be overemphasized. Power structures in the turn-of-the-century city were complex, involving a host of people and institutions. Banks, real estate investors, insurance companies, architects, and engineers, among others, played roles in governing the city. Viewed in retrospect, many city governments were remarkably successful. With populations that in some cases doubled every decade, city governments provided water and sewer lines, built parks and playgrounds, and paved streets. When it was over, Boston had the world's largest public library and New York City had the Brooklyn Bridge and Central Park, two of the finest achievements in city planning and architecture of any era. By the 1890s, New York also had 660 miles of water lines, 464 miles of sewers, and 1800 miles of paved streets, far more than comparable cities in Europe.

Bosses, moreover, differed from city to city. Buckley stayed in power in San Francisco by keeping city tax rates low. "Honest" John Kelly earned his nickname serving as a watchdog over the New York City treasury. Tweed was one of the early backers of the Brooklyn Bridge. Some bosses were plainly corrupt; others believed in *honest graft,* a term Tammany's George Washington Plunkitt coined to describe "legitimate" profits made from advance knowledge of city projects.

Why did voters keep the bosses in power? The answers are complex, but two reasons were skillful political organization and the fact that immigrants and others made up the bosses' constituency. Most immigrants had little experience with democratic government and proved easy prey for well-oiled machines. For the most part, however, the bosses stayed in power because they paid attention to the needs of the least privileged city voters. They offered valued services in an era when neither government nor business lent a hand.

If an immigrant, tired and bewildered after the long crossing, came looking for a job, bosses like Tweed, Plunkitt, or Buckley found him one in city offices or local businesses. If a family's breadwinner died or was injured, the bosses donated food and clothing and saw to it that the family made it through the crisis. If the winter was particularly cold, they provided free coal to heat tenement apartments. They ran picnics for slum children on hot summer days and contributed to hospitals, orphanages, and dozens of worthy neighborhood causes.

Most bosses became wealthy; they were not Robin Hoods who took from the rich to give to the poor. They took for themselves as well. Reformers occasionally ousted them. Tweed fell from power in 1872, "Blind Boss" Buckley in 1891, Croker in 1894. But the reformers rarely stayed in power long. Drawn mainly from the middle and upper classes, they had little understanding of the needs of the poor. Before long, they returned to private concerns, and the bosses, who had known that they would all along, cheerily took power again.

"What tells in holdin' your grip on your district," the engaging Plunkitt once said, "is to go right down among the poor families and help them in the different ways they need help. . . . It's philanthropy, but it's politics, too—mighty good politics. . . . The poor are the most grateful people in the world."

SOCIAL AND CULTURAL CHANGE, 1877–1900

The rise of cities and industry between 1877 and the 1890s affected all aspects of American life. Mores changed; family ties loosened. Factories turned out consumer goods, and the newly invented cash register rang up record sales. Public and private educational systems burgeoned, illiteracy declined, life expectancy increased. While many people worked harder and harder just to survive, others found they had a greater amount of leisure time. The roles of women and children changed in a number of ways, and the family took on functions it had not had before. Thanks to advancing technology, news flashed quickly across the oceans, and for the first time in history, people read of the day's events in distant lands when they opened their daily newspapers.

In 1877, the country had 47 million people. In 1900, it had nearly 76 million. Nine-tenths of the population was white; just under one-tenth was black. There were 66,000 Indians, 108,000 Chinese, and 148 Japanese. The bulk of the white population, most of whom were Protestant, came from the so-called Anglo-Saxon countries of northern Europe. WASPs—white Anglo-Saxon Protestants—were the dominant members of American society.

Though the rush to the cities was about to begin, most people of 1877 still lived on farms or in small towns. Their lives revolved around the farm, the church, and the general store. In 1880, nearly 75 percent of the population lived in communities of fewer than 2,500 people. In 1900, in the midst of city growth, 60 percent still did. The average family in 1880 had three children, dramatically fewer than at the beginning of the century, and life expectancy was about 43 years. By 1900, it had risen to 47 years, a result of improved health care. For blacks and other minorities, who often lived in unsanitary rural areas, life expectancy was substantially lower: 33 years in 1900.

Meals tended to be heavy, and so did people. Even breakfast had several courses and could include steak, eggs, fish, potatoes, toast, and coffee. Food prices were low. Families ate fresh homegrown produce in the summer and "put up" their fruits and vegetables for the long winters. Toward the end of the century, eating habits changed. New packaged breakfast cereals became popular; fresh fruit and vegetables came in on fast trains from Florida and California, and commercially canned food became safer and cheaper. The newfangled icebox, cooled by blocks of ice, kept food fresher and added new treats such as ice cream.

Medical science was in the midst of a major revolution. Louis Pasteur's recent discovery that germs cause infection and disease created the new science of microbiology and led the way to the development of vaccines and other preventive measures. But tuberculosis, typhoid, diphtheria, and pneumonia—all now curable—were still the leading causes of death. Infant mortality declined between 1877 and 1900, but the decline was gradual; a great drop did not come until after 1920.

There were few hospitals and no hospital insurance. Most patients stayed at home, although medical practice, especially surgery, expanded rapidly. Once brutal and dangerous, surgery in these years became relatively safe and painless. Anesthetics—ether and chloroform—eliminated pain, and antiseptic practices helped prevent postoperative infections. Antiseptic practices at childbirth also cut down on puerperal fever, an infection that for centuries had killed many women and newborn infants. The new science of psychology began to explore the mind, hitherto uncharted. William James, a leading American psychologist and philosopher, laid the foundations of modern behavioral psychology, which stressed the importance of the environment on human development.

MANNERS AND MORES

The code of Victorian morality, its name derived from the British queen who reigned throughout the period, set the tone for the era. The code prescribed strict standards of dress, manners, and sexual behavior. It was both obeyed and disobeyed, and it reflected the tensions of a generation that was undergoing a change in moral standards.

In 1877, children were to be seen and not heard. They spoke when spoken to, listened rather than chattered—or at least that was the rule. Older boys and girls were often chaperoned, although they could always find moments alone. They played post office and spin the bottle; they puffed cigarettes behind the barn. Journalist William Allen White recalled the high jinks of his boyhood. He and his friends smeared their naked bodies with mud and leaped out in full view of passengers on passing trains. Counterbalancing such youthful exuberance was strong pride in virtue and self-control. "Thank heaven I am absolutely pure," Theodore Roosevelt, the future president, wrote in 1880 after proposing to Alice Lee. "I can tell Alice everything I have ever done."

Gentlemen of the middle class dressed in heavy black suits, derby hats, and white shirts with paper collars. Women wore tight corsets, long dark dresses, and black shoes reaching well above the ankles. As with so many things, styles changed dramatically toward the end of the century, spurred in part by new sporting fads such as golf, tennis, and bicycling, which required looser clothing. By the 1890s, a middle-class woman wore a tailored suit or a dark skirt and a blouse, called a shirtwaist, modeled after men's shirts. Her skirts still draped about the ankles, but more and more she removed or loosened the corset, the dread device that squeezed skin and internal organs into fashionable 18-inch waistlines.

Religious and patriotic values were strong. A center of community life, the church often set the tenor for family and social relationships. In the 1880s, eight out of ten church members were Protestants; most of the rest were Roman Catholics.

With slavery abolished, reformers turned their attention to new moral and political issues. One group, known as the Mugwumps, worked to end corruption in politics. Drawn mostly from the educated and upper class, they included Thomas Nast, the famous political cartoonist, and E. L. Godkin, editor of the influential *Nation*. Other zealous reformers campaigned for prohibition of the sale of intoxicating liquors, hoping to end the social evils that stemmed from drunkenness. In 1874, women who advocated total abstinence from alcoholic beverages formed the Women's Christian Temperance Union (WCTU). Their leader, Frances E. Willard, served as president of the group from 1879 until her death in 1898. By then, the WCTU had 10,000 branches and 500,000 members.

LEISURE AND ENTERTAINMENT

In the 1870s, people tended to rise early. On getting up, they washed from the pitcher and bowl in the bedroom, first breaking the layer of ice if it was winter. After dressing and eating, they went off to work and school. Without large refrigerators, housewives marketed almost daily. In the evening, families gathered in the "second parlor" or living room, where the children did their lessons, played games, sang around the piano, and listened to that day's verse from the Bible.

Popular games included cards, dominoes, backgammon, chess, and checkers. Many homes had a packet of "author cards" that required knowledge of books, authors, and noted quotations. The latest fad was the stereopticon or "magic lantern," which brought three-dimensional life to art, history, and nature. Like author cards and other games, it was instructional as well as entertaining.

The newest outdoor game was croquet, so popular that candles were mounted on the wickets to allow play at night. Croquet was the first outdoor game designed for play by both sexes, and it frequently served as a setting for courtship. Early manuals advised girls how to assume attractive poses while hitting the ball. A popular song of the period told of a pair seated side by side:

Mallets and balls unheeded lay . . .
And I thought to myself, is that Croquet?

Sentimental ballads such as "Silver Threads Among the Gold" (1873) remained the most popular musical form, but the insistent syncopated rhythms of ragtime were being heard, reflecting the influence of the new urban culture. By the time the strains of Scott Joplin's "Maple Leaf Rag" (1899) popularized ragtime, critics complained that "a wave of vulgar, filthy and suggestive music has inundated the land." Classical music flourished. The New England Conservatory (1867), the Cincinnati College of Music (1878), and the Metropolitan Opera (1883) were new sources of civic pride; New York, Boston, and Chicago launched first-rate symphony orchestras between 1878 and 1891.

Fairs, horse races, balloon ascensions, bicycle tournaments, and football and baseball contests attracted avid fans. The years between 1870 and 1900 saw the rise of organized spectator sports, a trend reflecting both the rise of the city and the new uses of leisure. Baseball's first professional team, the Cincinnati Red Stockings, appeared in 1869, and baseball soon became the preeminent national sport. Fans sang songs about it ("Take Me Out to the

Ballgame"), wrote poems about it ("Casey at the Bat"), and made up riddles about it ("What has eighteen feet and catches flies?"). Modern rules were adopted. Umpires were designated to call balls and strikes; catchers wore masks and chest protectors and moved closer to the plate instead of staying back to catch the ball on the bounce. Fielders had to catch the ball on the fly rather than on one bounce in their caps. By 1890, professional baseball teams were drawing crowds of sixty thousand daily. In 1901, the American League was organized, and two years later the Boston Red Sox beat the Pittsburgh Pirates in the first modern World Series.

In 1869, Princeton and Rutgers played the first intercollegiate football game. Soon, other schools picked up the sport, and by the early 1890s, crowds of fifty thousand or more attended the most popular contests. Basketball, invented in 1891, gained a large following. Boxing, a popular topic of conversation in saloons and schoolyards, was outlawed in most states. For a time, championship prize-fights were held in secret, with news of the result spread rapidly by word of mouth. Matches were long and bloody, fought with bare knuckles until the invention in the 1880s of the 5-ounce boxing glove. John L. Sullivan, the "Boston Strong Boy" and the era's most popular champion, won the heavyweight title in 1889 in a brutal 75-round victory over the stubborn Jake Kilrain.

As gas and electric lights brightened the night, and streetcars crisscrossed city streets, leisure habits changed. Delighted with the new technology, people took advantage of an increasing variety of things to do. They stayed home less often. New York City's first electric sign—"Manhattan Beach Swept by Ocean Breezes"—appeared in 1881, and people went out at night, filling the streets on their way to the theater, vaudeville shows, and dance halls or just out for an evening stroll.

CHANGES IN FAMILY LIFE

Under the impact of industrialization and urbanization, family relationships were changing. On the farm, parents and children worked more or less together, and the family was a producing unit. In factories and offices, family members rarely worked together. In working-class families, mothers, fathers, and children separated at dawn and returned, ready for sleep, at dark.

Working-class families of the late nineteenth century, like the family of the young Polish girl that Harriet Vittum saw, often lived in complex household units—taking in relatives and boarders to pay the rent. As many as one-third of all households contained people who were not members of the immediate family. Although driven apart by the daily routine, family ties among the working class tended to remain strong, cemented by the need to join forces in order to survive in the industrial economy.

The middle-class wife and children, however, became increasingly isolated from the world of work. Turning inward, the middle-class family became more self-contained. Older children spent more time in adolescence, and periods of formal schooling were lengthier. Families took in fewer apprentices and boarders. By the end of the century, most middle-class offspring continued to live with their parents into their late teens and their twenties, a larger proportion than today.

Fewer middle-class wives participated directly in their husbands' work. As a result, they and their children occupied what contemporaries called a "separate sphere of domesticity," set apart from the masculine sphere of income-producing work. The family home became a "walled garden," a place to retreat from the crass materialism of the outside world. Middle-class fathers began to move their families out of the city to the suburbs, commuting to work on the new streetcars and leaving wives and children at home and school.

The middle-class family had once functioned in part to transmit a craft or skill, arrange marriages, and offer care for dependent kin. Now, as these functions declined, the family took on new emotional and ideological responsibilities. In a society that worried about the weakening hold of other institutions, the family became more and more important as a means of social control. It also placed new burdens on wives.

"In the old days," said a woman in 1907, "a married woman was supposed to be a frump and a bore and a physical wreck. Now you are supposed to keep up intellectually, to look young and well and be fresh and bright and entertaining." Magazines such as the *Ladies' Home Journal,* which started in 1889, glorified motherhood and the home, but its articles and ads featured women as homebound, child-oriented consumers. While society's leaders spoke fondly of the value of homemaking, the status of housewives declined under the factory system, which emphasized money rewards and devalued household labor.

Underlying all these changes was one of the modern world's most important trends, a major decline in fertility rates that lasted from 1800 to 1939. Though blacks, immigrants, and rural dwellers continued to have more children than white native-born city dwellers, the trend affected all classes and races; among white women, the birthrate fell from 7 in 1800 to just over 4 in 1880 to about 3 in 1900. People everywhere tended to marry later and have fewer children.

Since contraceptive devices were not yet widely used, the decline reflected abstinence and a conscious decision to postpone or limit families. Some women decided to devote greater attention to a smaller number of children, others to pursue their own careers. There was a marked increase in the number of young unmarried women working for wages or attending school, an increase in the number of women delaying marriage or not marrying at all, and a gradual decline in rates of illegitimacy and premarital pregnancy.

In large part, the decline in fertility stemmed from people's responses to the social and economic forces around them, the rise of cities and industry. In a host of individual decisions, they decided to have fewer children, and the result reshaped some of the fundamental attitudes and institutions of American society.

CHANGING VIEWS: A GROWING ASSERTIVENESS AMONG WOMEN

In and out of the family, there was growing recognition of self-sufficient working women, employed in factory, telephone exchange, or business office, who were entering the workforce in increasing numbers. In 1880, 2.6 million women were gainfully employed; in 1890, 4 million. In 1882, the Census Bureau took the first census of working women; most were single and worked out of necessity rather than choice.

Female operators, called "hello girls," were hired to work telephone switchboards after it was discovered that male operators tended to argue too much with subscribers.

Many regarded this "new woman" as a corruption of the ideal vision of the American woman, in which man worshiped "a diviner self than his own," innocent, helpless, and good. Women were to be better than the world around them. They were brought up, said Ida Tarbell, a leading political reformer, "as if wrongdoing were impossible to them."

Views changed, albeit slowly. One important change occurred in the legal codes pertaining to women, particularly in the common law doctrine of *femme couverte*. Under that doctrine, wives were chattel of their husbands; they could not legally control their own earnings, property, or children unless they had drawn up a specific contract before marriage. By 1890, many states had substantially revised the doctrine to allow wives control of their earnings and inherited property. In cases of divorce, the new laws also recognized women's rights to custody or joint custody of their children. Although divorce was still far from being socially acceptable, divorce rates more than doubled during the last third of the century. By 1905, one in twelve marriages was ending in divorce.

In the 1870s and 1880s, a growing number of women were asserting their own humanness. They fought for the vote, lobbied for equal pay, and sought self-fulfillment. The new interest in psychology and medicine strengthened their causes. Charlotte Perkins Gilman, author of *Women and Economics* (1898), joined other women in questioning the ideal of womanly "innocence," which, she argued, actually meant ignorance. In medical and popular literature, menstruation, sexual intercourse, and childbirth were becoming viewed as natural functions instead of taboo topics.

Edward Bliss Foote's *Plain Home Talk of Love, Marriage, and Parentage,* a bestseller that went through many editions between the 1880s and 1900, challenged Victorian notions that sexual intercourse was unhealthy and intended solely to produce children.

Women espoused causes with new fervor. Susan B. Anthony, a veteran of many reform campaigns, tried to vote in the 1872 presidential election and was fined $100, which she refused to pay. In 1890, she helped form the National American Woman Suffrage Association to work for the enfranchisement of women. On New York's Lower East Side, the Ladies Anti–Beef Trust Association, which formed to protest increases in the price of meat, established a boycott of butcher shops. When their demands were ignored, the women invaded the shops, poured kerosene on the meat, and set fire to it. "We don't riot," Rebecca Ablowitz told the judge. "But if all we did was to weep at home, nobody would notice it; so we have to do something to help ourselves."

EDUCATING THE MASSES

Continuing a trend that stretched back a hundred years, childhood was becoming an even more distinct time of life. There was still only a vague concept of adolescence—the special nature of the teenage years—but the role of children was changing. Less and less were children perceived as "little adults," valued for the additional financial gain they might bring into the family. Now children were to grow and learn and be nurtured rather than rushed into adulthood.

As a result, schooling became more important, and American children came closer than ever before to universal education. By 1900, thirty-one states and territories (out of fifty-one) had enacted laws making school attendance compulsory, though most required attendance only until the age of 14. In 1870, there were only 160 public high schools; in 1900, there were 6000. In the same years, illiteracy declined from 20 percent to just over 10 percent of the population. Still, even as late as 1900, the average adult had only five years of schooling.

Educators saw the school as the primary means to train people for life and work in an industrializing society. Hence teachers focused on basic skills—reading and mathematics—and on values—obedience and attentiveness to the clock. Most schools had a highly structured curriculum, built around discipline and rou-

Schools, regarded primarily as training grounds for a life of work, stressed conformity and deportment—feet on the floor, hands folded and resting atop the desk. The teacher was drillmaster and disciplinarian as well as instructor.

tine. In 1892, Joseph Rice, a pediatrician, toured twelve hundred classrooms in thirty-six cities. In a typical classroom, he reported, the atmosphere was "damp and chilly," the teacher strict. "The unkindly spirit of the teacher is strikingly apparent; the pupils being completely subjugated to her will, are silent and motionless." One teacher asked her pupils, "How can you learn anything with your knees and toes out of order?"

School began early; boys attended all day, but girls often stayed home after lunch, since it was thought they needed less in the way of learning. On the teacher's command, students stood and recited from *Webster's Spellers* and *McGuffey's Eclectic Readers,* the period's most popular textbooks. The work of William Holmes McGuffey, a professor of languages at Miami University in Ohio, *McGuffey's Eclectic Readers* had been in use since 1836; 100 million copies were sold in the last half of the nineteenth century. Nearly every child read them; they taught not only reading but also ethics, values, and religion. In the *Readers,* boys grew up to be heroes, girls to be mothers, and hard work always meant success:

> Shall birds, and bees, and ants, be wise,
> > While I my moments waste?
> O let me with the morning rise,
> > And to my duty haste.

The South lagged far behind in education. The average family size there was about twice as large as in the North, and a greater proportion of the population lived in isolated rural areas. State and local authorities mandated fewer weeks in the average school year, and many southern states refused to adopt compulsory education laws. Most important, Southerners insisted on maintaining separate school systems to segregate the races. Supported by the U.S. Supreme Court decision of 1896 in *Plessy v. Ferguson*, segregated schooling added a devastating financial burden to education in the South.

North Carolina and Alabama mandated segregated schools in 1876, South Carolina and Louisiana in 1877, Mississippi in 1878, and Virginia in 1882. A series of Supreme Court decisions in the 1880s and 1890s upheld the concept of segregation. In the *Civil Rights Cases* (1883), the Court ruled that the Fourteenth Amendment barred state governments from discriminating on account of race but did not prevent private individuals or organizations doing so. *Plessy v. Ferguson* (1896) established the doctrine of "separate but equal" and upheld a Louisiana law requiring different railroad cars for whites and blacks. The Court applied the doctrine directly to schools in *Cumming v. County Board of Education* (1899), which approved the creation of separate schools for whites, even if there were no comparable schools for blacks.

Southern school laws often implied that the schools would be "separate but equal," and they were often separate but rarely equal. Black schools were usually dilapidated, and black teachers were paid considerably less than white teachers. In 1890, only 35 percent of black children attended school in the South; 55 percent of white children did. That year nearly two-thirds of the country's black population was illiterate.

Educational techniques changed after the 1870s. Educators paid more attention to early elementary education, a trend that placed young children in school and helped the growing number of mothers who worked outside the home. The kindergarten movement, started in St. Louis in 1873, spread across the country. In kindergartens, 4- to 6-year-old children learned by playing, not by keeping their knees and toes in order. For older children, social reformers advocated "practical" courses in manual training and homemaking.

HIGHER EDUCATION

Nearly 150 new colleges and universities opened in the twenty years between 1880 and 1900. The Morrill Land Grant Act of 1862 gave large grants of land to the states for the establishment of colleges to teach "agriculture and the mechanic arts." The act fostered 69 "land-grant" institutions, including the great state universities of Wisconsin, California, Minnesota, and Illinois.

Private philanthropy, born of the large fortunes of the industrial age, also spurred growth in higher education. Leland Stanford gave $24 million to endow Stanford University on his California ranch, and John D. Rockefeller, founder of the Standard Oil Company, gave $34 million to found the University of Chicago. Other industrialists established Cornell (1865), Vanderbilt (1873), and Tulane (1884).

As colleges expanded, their function changed and their curriculum broadened. No longer did they exist primarily to train young men for the ministry. They moved away from the classical curriculum of rhetoric, mathematics, Latin, and Greek toward "reality and practicality," as President David Starr Jordan of Stanford University said. The Massachusetts Institute of Technology (MIT), founded in 1861, focused on science and engineering.

Charles W. Eliot, who became president of Harvard in 1869 at the age of 35, moved to end, as an admirer said, the "old fogyism" that marked the institution. Revising the curriculum, Eliot set up the elective system, in which students chose their own courses rather than following a rigidly prescribed curriculum. Lectures and discussions replaced rote recitation, and courses in the natural and social sciences, fine arts, and modern languages multiplied. In the 1890s, Eliot's Harvard moved to the forefront of educational innovation.

A physics lecture at the University of Michigan in the late 1880s or early 1890s. The land-grant university admitted women, but seating in the lecture hall was segregated by gender—although not by race. Notice that both whites and African Americans are seated in the back rows of the men's section.

Women still had to fight for educational opportunities. Some formed study clubs, an important movement that spread rapidly between 1870 and 1900. Groups such as the Decatur (Illinois) Art Class, the Boston History Class, and the Barnesville (Georgia) Shakespeare Club aimed "to enlarge the mental horizon as well as the knowledge of our members." Club members read Virgil and Chaucer, studied history and architecture, and discussed women's rights. Although they were usually small, study clubs sparked a greater interest in education among women and their daughters and contributed to a rapid rise in the number of women entering college in the early 1900s.

Before the Civil War, only three private colleges admitted women to study with men. After the war, educational opportunities increased for women. A number of women's colleges opened, including Vassar (1865), Wellesley (1875), Smith (1875), Bryn Mawr (1885), Barnard (1889), and Radcliffe (1893). The land-grant colleges of the Midwest, open to women from the outset, spurred a nationwide trend toward coeducation, although some physicians, such as

Harvard Medical School's Dr. Edward H. Clarke in his popular *Sex in Education* (1873), continued to argue that the strain of learning made women sterile. By 1900, women made up about 40 percent of college students, and four out of five colleges admitted them.

Fewer opportunities existed for African Americans and other minorities. Jane Stanford encouraged the Chinese who had worked on her husband's Central Pacific Railroad to apply to Stanford University, but her policy was unusual. Most colleges did not accept minority students, and only a few applied. W. E. B. Du Bois, the brilliant African American sociologist and civil rights leader, attended Harvard in the late 1880s but found the society of Harvard Yard closed against him. Disdained and disdainful, he "asked no fellowship of my fellow students." Chosen as one of the commencement speakers, Du Bois picked as his topic "Jefferson Davis," treating it, said an onlooker, with "an almost contemptuous fairness."

Black students turned to black colleges such as the Hampton Normal and Industrial Institute in Virginia and the Tuskegee Institute in Alabama. These colleges were often supported by whites who favored manual training for blacks. Booker T. Washington, an ex-slave, put into practice his educational ideas at Tuskegee, which opened in 1881. Washington began Tuskegee with limited funds, four run-down buildings, and only thirty students; by 1900, it was a model industrial and agricultural school. Spread over forty-six buildings, it offered instruction in thirty trades to fourteen hundred students.

Washington stressed patience, manual training, and hard work. "The wisest among my race understand," he said in a widely acclaimed speech at the Atlanta Exposition in 1895, "that the agitation of questions of social equality is the extremest folly." Blacks should focus on economic gains; they should go to school, learn skills, and work their way up the ladder. "No race," he said at Atlanta, "can prosper till it learns that there is as much dignity in tilling a field as in writing a poem. It is at the bottom of life we must begin, and not at the top." Southern whites should help out because they would then have "the most patient, faithful, law-abiding, and unresentful people that the world has seen."

Outlined most forcefully in Washington's speech in Atlanta, the philosophy became known as the Atlanta Compromise, and many whites and some blacks welcomed it. Acknowledging white domination, it called for slow progress through self-improvement, not through lawsuits or agitation. Rather than fighting for equal rights, blacks should acquire property and show they were worthy of their rights. But Washington did believe in black equality. Often secretive in his methods, he worked behind the scenes to organize black voters and lobby against harmful laws. In his own way, he bespoke a racial pride that contributed to the rise of black nationalism in the twentieth century.

Booker T. Washington, who served as the first president of Tuskegee Institute, advocated work efficiency and practical skills as keys to advancement for African Americans. Students like these at Tuskegee studied academic subjects and received training in trades and professions.

Du Bois wanted a more aggressive strategy. Born in Massachusetts in 1868, the son of poor parents, he studied at Fisk University in Tennessee and the University of Berlin before he went to Harvard. Unable to find a teaching job in a white college, he took a low-paying research position at the University of Pennsylvania. He had no office but did not need one. Du Bois used the new discipline of sociology, which emphasized factual observation in the field, to study the condition of blacks.

Notebook in hand, he set out to examine crime in Philadelphia's black seventh ward. He interviewed five thousand people, mapped and classified neighborhoods, and produced *The Philadelphia Negro* (1898). The first study of the effect of urban life on blacks, it cited a wealth of statistics, all suggesting that crime in the ward stemmed not from inborn degeneracy but from the environment in which blacks lived. Change the environment, and people would change, too; education was a good way to go about it.

In *The Souls of Black Folk* (1903), Du Bois openly attacked Booker T. Washington and the philosophy of the Atlanta Compromise. He urged African Americans to aspire to professional careers, to fight for the restoration of their civil rights, and, wherever possible, to get a college education. Calling for integrated schools with equal opportunity for all, Du Bois urged blacks to educate their "talented tenth," a highly trained intellectual elite, to lead them.

Du Bois was not alone in promoting careers in the professions. Throughout higher education there was increased emphasis on professional training, particularly in medicine, dentistry, and law. Enrollments swelled, even as standards of admission tightened. The number of medical schools in the country rose from 75 in 1870 to 160 in 1900, and the number of medical students—including more and more women—almost tripled. Schools of nursing grew from only 15 in 1880 to 432 in 1900. Doctors, lawyers, and others became part of a growing middle class that shaped the concerns of the Progressive Era of the early twentieth century.

Although less than 5 percent of the college-age population attended college during the 1877–1890 period, the new trends had great impact. A generation of men and women encountered new ideas that changed their views of themselves and society. Courses never before offered, like Philosophy II at Harvard, "The Ethics of Social Reform," which students called "drainage, drunkenness, and divorce," heightened interest in social problems and the need for reform. Some graduating students burned with a desire to cure society's ills. "My life began . . . at Johns Hopkins University," Frederic C. Howe, an influential reformer, recalled. "I came alive, I felt a sense of responsibility to the world, I wanted to change things."

THE STIRRINGS OF REFORM

When Henry George, one of the era's leading reformers, asked a friend what could be done about the problem of political corruption in American cities, his friend replied: "Nothing! You and I can do nothing at all. . . . We can only wait for evolution. Perhaps in four or five thousand years evolution may have carried men beyond this state of things."

This stress on the slow pace of change reflected the doctrine of social Darwinism, based on the writings of English social philosopher Herbert Spencer. In several influential books, Spencer took the evolutionary theories of Charles Darwin and applied Darwinian principles of natural selection to society, combining biology and sociology in a theory of "social selection" that tried to explain human progress. Like animals, society evolved, slowly, by adapting to the environment. The "survival of the fittest"—a term that Spencer, not Darwin, invented—preserved the strong and weeded out the weak.

Social Darwinism had a number of influential followers in the United States, including William Graham Sumner, a professor of political and social science at

Yale University. One of the country's best known academic figures, Sumner was forceful and eloquent. In writings such as *What Social Classes Owe to Each Other* (1883) and "The Absurd Effort to Make the World Over" (1894), he argued that government action on behalf of the poor or weak interfered with evolution and sapped the species. Reform tampered with the laws of nature.

The influence of social Darwinism on American thinking has been exaggerated, but in the powerful hands of Sumner and others it did influence some journalists, ministers, and policymakers. Between 1877 and the 1890s, however, it came under increasing attack. In fields like religion, economics, politics, literature, and law, thoughtful people raised questions about established conditions and suggested the need for reform.

PROGRESS AND POVERTY

Read and reread, passed from hand to hand, Henry George's nationwide bestseller *Progress and Poverty* (1879) led the way to a more critical appraisal of American society in the 1880s and beyond. The book jolted traditional thought. "It was responsible," one historian has said, "for starting along new lines of thinking an amazing number of the men and women" who became leaders of reform.

Disturbed by the depression of the 1870s and labor upheavals such as the great railroad strikes of 1877, George saw modern society—rich, complex, with material goods hitherto unknown—as sadly flawed.

"The present century," he wrote, "has been marked by a prodigious increase in wealth-producing power. . . . It was natural to expect, and it was expected, that . . . real poverty [would become] a thing of the past." Instead, he argued:

> it becomes no easier for the masses of our people to make a living. On the contrary, it is becoming harder. The wealthy class is becoming more wealthy; but the poorer class is becoming more dependent. The gulf between the employed and the employer is growing wider; social contrasts are becoming sharper; as liveried carriages appear, so do barefooted children.

George proposed a simple solution. Land, he thought, formed the basis of wealth, and a few people could grow wealthy just because the price of their land rose. Since the rise in price did not result from any effort on their part, it represented an "unearned increment," which, George argued, should be taxed for the good of society. A "single tax" on the increment, replacing all other taxes, would help equalize wealth and raise revenue to aid the poor. "Single-tax" clubs sprang up around the country, but George's solution, simplistic and unappealing, had much less impact than his analysis of the problem itself. He raised questions a generation of readers set out to answer.

New Currents in Social Thought

George's emphasis on deprivation in the environment excited a young country lawyer in Ashtabula, Ohio—Clarence Darrow. Unlike the social Darwinists, Darrow was sure that criminals were made and not born. They grew out of "the unjust condition of human life." In the mid-1880s, he left for Chicago and a forty-year career working to convince people that poverty lay at the root of crime. "There is no such thing as crime as the word is generally understood," he told a group of startled prisoners in the Cook County jail. "If every man, woman and child in the world had a chance to make a decent, fair, honest living there would be no jails and no lawyers and no courts."

As Darrow rejected the implications of social Darwinism, in similar fashion Richard T. Ely and a group of young economists poked holes in traditional economic thought. Fresh from graduate study in Germany, Ely in 1884 attacked classical economics for its dogmatism, simple faith in laissez-faire, and reliance on self-interest as a guide for human conduct. The "younger" economics, he said, must no longer be "a tool in the hands of the greedy and the avaricious for keeping down and oppressing the laboring classes. It does not acknowledge laissez-faire as an excuse for doing nothing while people starve."

Edward Bellamy dreamed of a cooperative society in which poverty, greed, and crime no longer existed. A lawyer from western Massachusetts, Bellamy published *Looking Backward, 2000–1887,* in 1887 and became a national reform figure virtually overnight. The novel's protagonist, Julian West, falls asleep in 1887 and awakes in the year 2000. Wide-eyed, he finds himself in a socialist utopia: the government owns the means of production, and citizens share the material rewards. Cooperation, rather than competition, is the watchword.

The world of *Looking Backward* had limits; it was regimented, paternalistic, and filled with the gadgets and material concerns of Bellamy's own day. But it had a dramatic effect on many readers. The book sold at the rate of ten thousand copies a week, and its followers formed Nationalist Clubs to work for its objectives.

Some Protestant sects stressed individual salvation and a better life in the next world, not in this one. Poverty was evidence of sinfulness; the poor had only themselves to blame. "God has intended the great to be great and the little to be little," said Henry Ward Beecher, the country's best known pastor. Wealth and destitution, suburbs and slums—all formed part of God's plan.

Challenging those traditional doctrines, a number of churches in the 1880s began establishing missions in the city slums. William Dwight Porter Bliss, an Episcopal clergyman, founded the Church of the Carpenter in a working-class district of Boston. Lewis M. Pease worked in the grim Five Points area of New York; Alexander Irvine, a Jewish missionary, lived in a flophouse in the Bowery.

Irvine walked his skid row neighborhood every afternoon to lend a hand to those in need. Living among the poor and homeless, the urban missionaries grew impatient with religious doctrines that endorsed the status quo.

Many of the new trends were reflected in an emerging religious philosophy known as the Social Gospel. As the name suggests, the Social Gospel focused on society as well as individuals, on improving living conditions as well as saving souls. Sermons in Social Gospel churches called on church members to fulfill their social obligations, and adults met before and after the regular service to discuss social and economic problems. Children were excused from sermons, organized into age groups, and encouraged to make the church a center for social as well as religious activity. Soon churches included dining halls, gymnasiums, and even theaters.

The most active Social Gospel leader was Washington Gladden, a Congregational minister and prolific writer. Linking Christianity to the social and economic environment, Gladden spent a lifetime working for "social salvation." He saw Christianity as a fellowship of love and the church as a social agency. In *Applied Christianity* (1886) and other writings, he denounced competition, urged an "industrial partnership" between employers and employees, and called for efforts to help the poor.

THE SETTLEMENT HOUSES

A growing number of social reformers living in the urban slums shared Gladden's concern. Like Tweed and Plunkitt, they appreciated the dependency of the poor; unlike them, they wanted to eradicate the conditions that underlay it. To do so, they formed settlement houses in the slums and went to live in them to experience the problems they were trying to solve.

Youthful, idealistic, and mostly middle class, these social workers took as their model Toynbee Hall, founded in 1884 in the slums of East London to provide community services. Stanton Coit, a moody and poetic graduate of Amherst College, was the first American to borrow the settlement house idea; in 1886, he opened the Neighborhood Guild on the Lower East Side of New York. The idea spread swiftly. By 1900, there were more than a hundred settlements in the country; five years later, there were more than two hundred, and by 1910, more than four hundred.

The settlements included Jane Addams's famous Hull House in Chicago (1889), Robert A. Woods's South End House in Boston (1892), and Lillian Wald's Henry Street Settlement in New York (1893). The reformers wanted to bridge the socioeconomic gap between rich and poor and to bring education, culture, and hope to the slums. They sought to create in the heart of the city the values and sense of community of small-town America.

Many of the settlement workers were women, some of them college graduates, who found that society had little use for their talents and energy. Jane Addams, a graduate of Rockford College in Illinois, opened Hull House on South Halsted Street in the heart of the Chicago slums. Twenty-nine years old, endowed with a forceful and winning personality, she intended "to share the lives of the poor" and humanize the industrial city. "American ideals," she said, "crumbled under the overpowering poverty of the overcrowded city."

Occupying an old, rundown house, Hull House stressed education, offering classes in elementary English and Shakespeare, lectures on ethics and the history of art, and courses in cooking, sewing, and manual skills. A pragmatist, Addams believed in investigating a problem and then doing something to solve it. Noting the lack of medical care in the area, she established an infant welfare clinic and free medical dispensary. Because the tenements lacked bathtubs, she installed showers in the basement of the house and built a bathhouse for the neighbors. Because there was no local library, she opened a reading room. Gradually, Hull House expanded to occupy a dozen buildings sprawling over more than a city block.

Like settlement workers in other cities, Addams and her colleagues studied the immigrants in nearby tenements. Laboriously, they identified the background of every family in a one-third-square-mile area around Hull House. Finding people of eighteen different nationalities, they taught them American history and the English language, yet Addams also encouraged them—through folk festivals and art—to preserve their own heritage.

Florence Kelley, an energetic graduate of Cornell University, taught night school one winter in Chicago. Watching children break under the burden of poverty, she devoted her life to the problem of child labor. Convinced of the need for political activism, she worked with Addams and others to push through the Illinois Factory Act of 1893, which mandated an eight-hour day for women in factories and for children under the age of 14.

The settlement house movement had its limits. Hull House, one of the best, attracted two thousand visitors a week, still just a fraction of the seventy thousand people who lived within six blocks. Immigrants sometimes resented the middle-class "strangers" who told them how to live. Dressed always in a brown suit and dark stockings, Harriet Vittum, the head resident of Chicago's Northwestern University Settlement (who told the story of the suicide victim at the beginning of this chapter), was known in the neighborhood as "the police lady in brown." She once stopped a dance because it was too wild, and then watched

OPENING OF

HULL=HOUSE
PLAY GROUND

Polk Street, Near Halsted

Saturday, May 1st, 1897,
AT 3 O'CLOCK, P. M.

"The air is warm, the skies are clear,
Birds and blossoms all are here,
Come old and young with spirits gay,
To welcome back the charming May."

MUSIC BY THE BRASS BAND

...Kindergarten Games---May Pole Dance...

ALL KINDS OF RACES

Jane Addams founded Chicago's Hull House in 1889. The settlement house provided recreational and day-care facilities; offered extension classes in academic, vocational, and artistic subjects; and, above all, sought to bring hope to poverty-stricken slum dwellers.

in disgust as the boys responded by "making vulgar sounds with their lips." Though her attempts to help were sincere, in private Vittum called the people she was trying to help "ignorant foreigners, who live in an atmosphere of low morals . . . surrounded by anarchy and crime."

Although Addams tried to offer a few programs for blacks, most white reformers did not, and after 1900, a number of black reformers opened their own settlements. Like the whites, they offered employment information, medical care, and recreational facilities, along with concerts, lectures, and other educational events. White and black, the settlement workers made important contributions to urban life.

A CRISIS IN SOCIAL WELFARE

The depression of 1893 jarred the young settlement workers, many of whom had just begun their work. Addams and the Hull House workers helped form the Chicago Bureau of Charities to coordinate emergency relief. Kelley, recently appointed the chief factory inspector of Illinois, worked even harder to end child labor, and in 1899, she moved to New York City to head the National Consumers League, which marshaled the buying power of women to encourage employers to provide better working conditions.

In cities and towns across the country, traditional methods of helping the needy foundered in the crisis. Churches, Charity Organization Societies, and Community Chests did what they could, but their resources were limited, and they functioned on traditional lines. Many of them still tried to change rather than aid individual families, and people were often reluctant to call on them for help.

Gradually, a new class of professional social workers arose to fill the need. Unlike the church and charity volunteers, these social workers wanted not only to feed the poor but to study their condition and alleviate it. Revealingly, they called themselves "case workers" and daily collected data on the income, housing, jobs, health, and habits of the poor. Prowling tenement districts, they gathered information about the number of rooms, number of occupants, ventilation, and sanitation of the buildings, putting together a fund of useful data.

Studies of the poor popped up everywhere. W. E. B. Du Bois did his pioneering study of urban blacks; Lillian Pettengill took a job as a domestic servant to see "the ups and downs of this particular dog-life from the dog's end of the chain." Others became street beggars, miners, lumberjacks, and factory laborers.

William T. Stead, a prominent British editor, visited the Chicago World's Fair in 1893 and stayed to examine the city. He roamed the flophouses and tenements and dropped in at Hull House to drink hot chocolate and talk over conditions with Jane Addams. Later he wrote an influential book, *If Christ Came to Chicago* (1894), and in a series of mass meetings during 1893, he called for a civic revival. In response, Chicagoans formed the Civic Federation, a group of forty leaders who aimed to make Chicago "the best governed, the healthiest city in this country." Setting up task forces for philanthropy, moral improvement, and legislation, the new group helped spawn the National Civic Federation (1900), a nationwide organization devoted to reform of urban life.

"The United States was born in the country and moved to the city," historian Richard Hofstadter said. Much of that movement occurred during the nineteenth century when the United States was the most rapidly urbanizing nation in the Western world. American cities bustled with energy; they absorbed millions of migrants who came from Europe and other distant and not-so-distant parts of the world. That migration, and the urban growth that accompanied it, reshaped American politics and culture.

By 1920, the census showed that, for the first time, most Americans lived in cities. By then, too, almost half the population was descended from people who had arrived after the American Revolution. As European, African, and

Asian cultures met in the American city, a culturally pluralistic society emerged. Dozens of nationalities produced a culture whose members considered themselves Polish Americans, African Americans, and Irish Americans. The melting pot sometimes softened distinctions between the various groups, but it only partially blended them into a unified society.

"Ah, Vera," said a character in Israel Zangwill's popular play *The Melting Pot* (1908), "what is the glory of Rome and Jerusalem where all nations and races come to worship and look back, compared with the glory of America, where all races and nations come to labour and look forward!" Critics scorned the play as "romantic claptrap," and indeed it was. But the metaphor of the melting pot clearly depicted a new national image. In the decades after the 1870s a jumble of ethnic and racial groups struggled for a place in society.

That society, it is clear, experienced a crisis between 1870 and 1900. Together, the growth of cities and the rise of industrial capitalism brought jarring change, the exploitation of labor, ethnic and racial tensions, poverty—and, for a few, wealth beyond the imagination. At Homestead, Pullman, and a host of other places, there was open warfare between capital and labor. As reformers struggled to mediate the situation, they turned more and more to state and federal government to look after human welfare, a tendency the Supreme Court stoutly resisted. In the midst of the crisis, the depression of the 1890s struck, adding to the turmoil and straining American institutions. Tracing the changes wrought by waves of urbanization and industrialization, Henry George described the country as "the House of Have and the House of Want," almost in paraphrase of Lincoln's earlier metaphor of the "house divided." The question was, could this house, unlike that one, stand?

20

POLITICAL REALIGNMENTS IN THE 1890s

I n June 1894, Susan Orcutt, a young farm woman from western Kansas, sat down to write the governor of her state a letter. She was desperate. The nation was in the midst of a devastating economic depression, and, like thousands of other people, she had no money and nothing to eat. "I take my Pen In hand to let you know that we are Starving to death," she wrote. Hail had ruined the Orcutts' crops, and none of the household could find work. "My Husband went away to find work and came home last night and told me that we would have to Starve. [H]e has bin in ten countys and did not Get no work. . . . I havent had nothing to Eat today and It is three oclock[.]"

As bad as conditions were on the farms, they were no better in the cities. "There are thousands of homeless and starving men in the streets," reported a journalist in Chicago in the winter of 1893. "I have seen more misery in this last week than I ever saw in my life before." Charity societies and churches tried to help, but they could not handle the huge numbers of people who were in need. The records of the Massachusetts state medical examiner told a grim story:

K.R., 29   Suicide by drowning
Boston   October 2, 1896
Out of work and despondent for a long while. Body found floating in the
Charles [River].

F.S., 29   Suicide by arsenic
Boston   January 1, 1896
Much depressed for several weeks. Loss of employment. At 7:50 A.M. Jan. 1, she called
her father and told him she had taken poison and wished to die.

L.M., 38   *Hanging suicide*
E. Boston   *October 15, 1895*

Had been out of work for several weeks and was very despondent. Wife went to market at about 11 A.M. and upon returning at about 12 P.M. found him hanging from bedroom door. . . . Slipped noose about his neck and [fell] forward upon it.

R.N., 23   *Suicide by bullet wound of brain*
Boston   *June 22, 1896*

Out of work. Mentally depressed. About 3 P.M. June 21 shot himself in right temple. . . . Left a letter explaining that he killed himself to save others the trouble of caring for him.

Lasting until 1897, the depression was the decisive event of the decade. At its height, three million people were unemployed—fully 20 percent of the workforce. The human costs were enormous, even among the well-to-do. "They were for me years of simple Hell," shattering "my whole scheme of life," said Charles Francis Adams, Jr., the descendant of two American presidents.

Like the Great Depression of the 1930s that gave rise to the New Deal, the depression of the 1890s had profound and lasting effects. Bringing to a head many of the tensions that had been building in the society, it increased rural hostility toward the cities, brought about a bitter fight over the currency, and changed people's thinking about government, unemployment, and reform. There were outbreaks of warfare between capital and labor; farmers demanded a fairer share of economic and social benefits; the "new" immigrants came under fresh attack. The depression of the 1890s changed the course of American history, as did another event of that decade: the war with Spain in 1898.

Under the cruel impact of the depression, ideas changed in many areas, including in politics. A realignment of the American political system, which had been developing since the end of Reconstruction, finally reached its fruition in the 1890s, establishing new patterns that gave rise to the Progressive Era and lasted well into the twentieth century.

POLITICS OF STALEMATE

Politics was a major fascination of the late nineteenth century, its mass entertainment and favorite sport. Political campaigns were events that involved the whole community, even though in most states men were the only ones who could vote. During the weeks leading up to an election, there were rallies, parades, picnics, and torchlight processions. Americans turned out in enormous numbers to vote. In the six presidential elections from 1876 to 1896, an average of almost 79 percent of the electorate voted, a higher percentage than voted before or after.

A delegation of women's rights advocates addressed the judiciary committee of the House of Representatives to present their arguments in favor of woman suffrage. Reading the argument is Victoria Claflin Woodhull, one of the more radical activists in the women's movement.

White males made up the bulk of the electorate; until after the turn of the century, women could vote in national elections only in Wyoming, Utah, Idaho, and Colorado. The National Woman Suffrage Association early sued for the vote, but in 1875, the Supreme Court (*Minor* v. *Happersett*) upheld the power of the states to deny this right to women. On several occasions, Congress refused to pass a constitutional amendment for woman's suffrage, and between 1870 and 1910, nearly a dozen states defeated referenda to grant women the vote.

Black men were another group kept from the polls. In 1877, Georgia adopted the poll tax to make voters pay an annual tax for the right to vote. The technique, aimed at impoverished blacks, was quickly copied across the South.

In 1890, Mississippi required voters to be able to read and interpret the federal Constitution to the satisfaction of registration officials, all of them white. Such literacy tests, which the Supreme Court upheld in the case of *Williams* v. *Mississippi* (1898), excluded poor white voters as well as blacks. In 1898, Louisiana avoided the problem by adopting the famous "grandfather clause," which used a literacy test to disqualify black voters but permitted men who had failed the test to vote anyway if their fathers and grandfathers had voted before 1867—a time, of course, when no blacks could vote. The number of black voters decreased dramatically. In 1896, there were 130,334 registered black voters in Louisiana; in 1904, there were 1,342.

THE PARTY DEADLOCK

The 1870s and 1880s were still dominated by the Civil War generation, the unusual group of people who rose to power in the turbulent 1850s. Five of the six presidents elected between 1865 and 1900 had served in the war, as had many civic, business, and religious leaders. In 1890, well over one million veterans of the Union army were still alive, and Confederate veterans numbered in the hundreds of thousands.

Party loyalties—rooted in Civil War traditions, ethnic and religious differences, and perhaps class distinctions—were remarkably strong. Voters clung to their old parties, shifts were infrequent, and there were relatively few "independent" voters. Although linked to the defeated Confederacy, the Democrats revived quickly after the war. In 1874, they gained control of the House of Representatives, which they maintained for all but four of the succeeding twenty years. The Democrats rested on a less sectional base than the Republicans. Identification with civil rights and military rule cut Republican strength in the South, but the Democratic party's principles of states' rights, decentralization, and limited government won supporters everywhere.

While Democrats wanted to keep government local and small, the Republicans pursued policies for the nation as a whole, in which government was an instrument to promote moral progress and material wealth. The Republicans passed the Homestead Act (1862), granted subsidies to the transcontinental railroads, and pushed other measures to encourage economic growth. They enacted legislation and constitutional amendments to protect civil rights. They advocated a high protective tariff as a tool of economic policy, to keep out foreign products while "infant industries" grew.

In national elections, sixteen states, mostly in New England and the North, consistently voted Republican; fourteen states, mostly in the South, consistently voted Democratic. Elections, therefore, depended on a handful of "doubtful" states, which could swing elections either way. These states—New York, New Jersey, Connecticut, Ohio, Indiana, and Illinois—received special attention at election time. Politicians lavished money and time on them; presidential candidates usually came from them. From 1868 to 1912, eight of the nine Republican presidential candidates and six of the seven Democratic candidates came from the "doubtful" states, especially New York and Ohio.

The two parties were evenly matched, and elections were closely fought. In three of the five presidential elections from 1876 to 1892, the victor won by less than 1 percent of the vote; in 1876 and 1888, the losing candidates actually had more popular votes than the winners but lost in the electoral college. Only twice during these years did one party control both the presidency and the two houses of Congress—the Republicans in 1888 and the Democrats in 1892.

Historians once believed that political leaders accomplished little between 1877 and 1900, but those who saw few achievements were looking in the wrong location. With the impeachment of Andrew Johnson, the authority of the presidency dwindled in relation to congressional strength. For the first time in many years, attention shifted away from Washington itself. North and South, people who were weary of the centralization brought on by war and Reconstruction looked first to state and local governments to deal with the problems of an urban-industrial society.

EXPERIMENTS IN THE STATES

Across the country, state bureaus and commissions were established to regulate the new industrial society. Many of the early commissions were formed to oversee the railroads, at the time the nation's largest businesses. People who shipped goods over the railroads, especially farmers and merchants, wanted to end the policies of rate discrimination and other harmful practices. In 1869, Massachusetts established the first commission to regulate the railroads; by 1900, twenty-eight states had taken such action.

Most of the early commissions were advisory in nature. They collected statistics and published reports on rates and practices—serving, one commissioner said, "as a sort of lens" to focus public attention. Impatient with the results, legislatures in the Midwest and on the Pacific Coast established commissions with greater power to fix rates, outlaw rebates, and investigate rate discrimination. These commissions, experimental in nature, served as models for later policy at the federal level.

Illinois had one of the most thoroughgoing provisions. Responding to local merchants who were upset with existing railroad rate policies, the Illinois state constitution of 1870 declared railroads to be public highways and authorized the legislature to pass laws establishing maximum rates and preventing rate discrimination. In the important case of *Munn* v. *Illinois* (1877), the Supreme Court upheld the Illinois legislation, declaring that private property "affected with the public interest . . . must submit to being controlled by the public for the common good."

But the Court soon weakened that judgment. In the *Wabash* case of 1886 (*Wabash, St. Louis, & Pacific Railway Co.* v. *Illinois*), it narrowed the *Munn* ruling and held that states could not regulate commerce extending beyond their borders. Only Congress could. The *Wabash* decision turned people's attention back to the federal government. It spurred Congress to pass the Interstate Commerce Act

(1887), which created the Interstate Commerce Commission (ICC) to investigate and oversee railroad activities. The act outlawed rebates and pooling agreements, and the ICC became the prototype of the federal commissions that today regulate many parts of the economy.

REESTABLISHING PRESIDENTIAL POWER

Johnson's impeachment, the scandals of the Grant administrations, and the controversy surrounding the 1876 election weakened the presidency. During the last two decades of the nineteenth century, presidents fought to reassert their authority, and by 1900, under William McKinley, they had succeeded to a remarkable degree. The late 1890s, in fact, marked the birth of the modern powerful presidency.

Rutherford B. Hayes entered the White House with his title clouded by the disputed election of 1876. Opponents called him "His Fraudulency" and "Rutherfraud B. Hayes," but soon he began to reassert the authority of the presidency. Hayes worked for reform in the civil service, placed well-known reformers in high offices, and, ordering the last troops out of South Carolina and Louisiana, ended military Reconstruction. Committed to the gold standard—the only basis, Hayes thought, of a sound currency—in 1878 he vetoed the Bland-Allison Silver Purchase Bill, which called for the partial coinage of silver, but Congress passed it over his veto.

James A. Garfield, a Union army hero and longtime member of Congress, succeeded Hayes. Winning by a handful of votes in 1880, he took office energetically, determined to unite the Republican party (which had been split by personality differences and disagreement over policy toward the tariff and the South), lower the tariff to cut taxes, and assert American economic and strategic interests in Latin America. Ambitious and eloquent, Garfield had looked forward to the presidency, yet within a few weeks he said to friends, "My God! What is there in this place that a man should ever want to get into it?"

THE ELECTION OF 1880

CANDIDATE	PARTY	POPULAR VOTE	ELECTORAL VOTE
Garfield	Republican	4,446,158	214
Hancock	Democrat	4,444,260	155
Weaver	Greenback	305,997	0

Office seekers, hordes of them, evoked Garfield's anguish. Each one wanted a government job, and each one thought nothing of cornering the president on every occasion. Garfield planned to leave Washington on July 2, 1881, for a vacation in New England. Walking toward his train, he was shot in the back by Charles J. Guiteau, a deranged lawyer and disappointed office seeker. Suffering through the summer, Garfield died on September 19, 1881, and Vice President Chester A. Arthur—an ally of Senator Conkling—became president.

Arthur was a better president than many had expected. He approved the construction of the modern American navy. Arthur worked to lower the tariff, and in 1883, with his backing, Congress passed the Pendleton Act to reform the civil service. In part a reaction to Garfield's assassination, the act created a bipartisan Civil Service Commission to administer competitive examinations and appoint officeholders on the basis of merit. Initially, the act affected only about 14,000 of some 100,000 government offices, but it laid the basis for the later expansion of the civil service.

In the election of 1884, Grover Cleveland, the Democratic governor of New York, narrowly defeated Republican nominee, James G. Blaine, largely because of the continuing divisions in the Republican party. The first Democratic president since 1861, Cleveland was slow and ponderous, known for his honesty, stubbornness, and hard work. His term in the White House from 1885 to 1889 reflected the Democratic party's desire to curtail federal activities. Cleveland vetoed more than two-thirds of the bills presented to him, more than all his predecessors combined.

Forthright and sincere, he brought a new respectability to a Democratic party still tainted by its link with secession. He continued Arthur's naval construction program. Late in 1887, he devoted his annual message to an attack on the tariff, "the vicious, inequitable, and illogical source of unnecessary taxation," and committed himself and the Democratic party to lowering the tariff.

THE ELECTION OF 1884

CANDIDATE	PARTY	POPULAR VOTE	ELECTORAL VOTE
Cleveland	Democrat	4,874,621	219
Blaine	Republican	4,848,936	182
Butler	Greenback	175,096	0
St. John	Prohibition	147,482	0

THE ELECTION OF 1888

CANDIDATE	PARTY	POPULAR VOTE	ELECTORAL VOTE
Harrison	Republican	5,447,129	233
Cleveland	Democrat	5,537, 857	168
	Minor Parties	396,441	0

The Republicans accused him of undermining American industries, and in 1888, they nominated for the presidency Benjamin Harrison, a defender of the tariff. Cleveland garnered ninety thousand more popular votes than Harrison but won the electoral votes of only two northern states and the South. Harrison won the rest of the North, most of the "doubtful" states, and the election.

REPUBLICANS IN POWER: THE BILLION-DOLLAR CONGRESS

Despite Harrison's narrow margin, the election of 1888 was the most sweeping victory for either party in almost twenty years; it gave the Republicans the presidency and both houses of Congress. The Republicans, it seemed, had broken the party stalemate and become the majority party in the country.

TARIFFS, TRUSTS, AND SILVER

As if a dam had burst, law after law poured out of the Republican Congress during 1890. The Republicans passed the McKinley Tariff Act, which raised tariff duties about 4 percent, higher than ever before; it also included a novel reciprocity provision that allowed the president to lower duties if other countries did the same. In addition, the act used duties to promote new industries, such as tinplate for packaging the new "canned" foods appearing on grocery store shelves. A Dependent Pensions Act granted pensions to Union army veterans and their widows and children. The pensions were modest—$6 to $12 a month—but the number of pensioners doubled by 1893, when nearly 1 million individuals received about $160 million in pensions.

With little debate, the Republicans and Democrats joined in passing the Sherman Antitrust Act, the first federal attempt to regulate big business. As the initial attempt to deal with the problem of trusts and industrial growth, the act shaped all later antitrust policy. It declared illegal "every contract, combination in the form of trust or otherwise, or conspiracy, in restraint of trade or commerce." Penalties for violation were stiff, including fines and imprisonment and the dissolution of guilty trusts. Experimental in nature, the act's terms were often vague and left precise interpretation to later experience and the courts.

One of the most important laws Congress passed, the Sherman Antitrust Act made the United States virtually the only industrial nation to regulate business combinations. It tried to harness big business without harming it. Many members of Congress did not expect the new law to have much effect on businesses, and for a decade, in fact, it did not. The Justice Department rarely filed suit under it, and in the *United States* v. *E. C. Knight Co.* decision (1895), the first judicial interpretation of the law, the Supreme Court severely crippled it. Though the E. C. Knight Co. controlled 98 percent of all sugar refining in the country, the Court drew a sharp distinction between commerce and manufacturing, holding that the company, as a manufacturer, was not subject to the law. But judicial interpretations changed after the turn of the century, and the Sherman Antitrust Act gained fresh power.

Another measure, the Sherman Silver Purchase Act, tried to end the troublesome problem presented by silver. As one of the two most commonly used precious metals, silver had once played a large role in currencies around the world, but by the mid-1800s, it had slipped into disuse. With the discovery of the great bonanza mines in Nevada, American silver production quadrupled between 1870 and 1890, glutting the world market, lowering the price of silver, and persuading many European nations to demonetize silver in favor of the scarcer metal, gold. The United States kept a limited form of silver coinage with congressional passage of the Bland-Allison Act in 1878.

Support for silver coinage was especially strong in the South and West, where people thought it might inflate the currency, raise wages and crop prices, and challenge the power of the gold-oriented Northeast. Eager to avert the free coinage of silver, which would require the coinage of all silver presented at the U.S. mints, President Harrison and other Republican leaders pressed for a compromise that took shape in the Sherman Silver Purchase Act of 1890.

The act directed the Treasury to purchase 4.5 million ounces of silver a month and to issue legal tender in the form of Treasury notes in payment for it. The act was a compromise; it satisfied both sides. Opponents of silver were pleased that it did not include free coinage. Silverites, on the other hand, were delighted that the monthly purchases would buy up most of the country's silver production. The Treasury notes, moreover, could be cashed for either gold or silver at the bank, a gesture toward a true bimetallic system based on silver and gold.

According to the cartoon, a bimetallic system based on both silver and gold would lead to a wobbly economy.

As a final measure, Republicans in the House courageously passed a federal elections bill to protect the voting rights of blacks in the South. Although restrained in language and intent, it set off a storm of denunciation among the Democrats, who called it a "force bill" that would station army troops in the South. Because of the outcry, the bill failed in the Senate; it was the last major effort until the 1950s to enforce the Fifteenth Amendment to the Constitution.

THE 1890 ELECTIONS

The Republican Congress of 1890 was one of the most important Congresses in American history. It passed a record number of significant laws that helped shape later policy and asserted the authority of the federal government to a degree the country would not then accept. Sensing the public reaction, the Democrats labeled it the "Billion-Dollar Congress" for spending that much in appropriations and grants.

"This is a billion-dollar country," Speaker Reed replied, but the voters disagreed. The 1890 elections crushed the Republicans, who lost an extraordinary seventy-eight seats in the House. Political veterans went down to defeat, and new leaders vaulted into sudden prominence. Nebraska elected a Democratic governor for the first time in its history. The state of Iowa, once so staunchly Republican that a local leader had predicted that "Iowa will go Democratic when Hell goes Methodist," went Democratic in 1890.

THE RISE OF THE POPULIST MOVEMENT

The elections of 1890 drew attention to a fast-growing movement among farmers that soon came to be known far and wide as populism. During the summer of 1890, wagonloads of farm families in the South and West converged on campgrounds and picnic areas to socialize and discuss common problems. They came by the thousands, weary of drought, mortgages, and low crop prices. At the campgrounds, they picnicked, talked, and listened to recruiters from an organization called the National Farmers' Alliance and Industrial Union, which promised unified action to solve agricultural problems.

Farmers were joining the Alliance at the rate of 1,000 a week; the Kansas Alliance alone claimed 130,000 members in 1890. The summer of 1890 became "that wonderful picnicking, speech-making Alliance summer," a time of fellowship and spirit long remembered by farmers.

THE FARM PROBLEM

Farm discontent was a worldwide phenomenon between 1870 and 1900. With the new means of transportation and communication, farmers everywhere were caught up in a complex international market they neither controlled nor entirely understood.

American farmers complained bitterly about declining prices for their products, rising railroad rates for shipping them, and burdensome mortgages. Some of their grievances were valid. Farm profits were certainly low; agriculture in general tends to produce low profits because of the ease of entry into the industry. The prices of farm commodities fell between 1865 and 1890, but they did not fall as low as did other commodity prices. Despite the fact that farmers received less for their crops, their purchasing power actually increased.

Neither was the farmers' second grievance—rising railroad rates—entirely justified. Railroad rates actually fell during these years, benefiting shippers of all products. Farm mortgages, the farmers' third grievance, were common because many farmers mortgaged their property to expand their holdings or buy new farm machinery. While certainly burdensome, most mortgages did not bring hardship. They were often short, with a term of four years or less, after which farmers could renegotiate at new rates, and the new machinery the farmers bought enabled them to triple their output and increase their income.

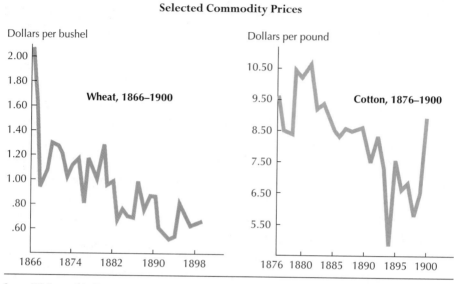

Selected Commodity Prices

Source: U.S. Bureau of the Census, *Historical Statistics of the United States, Colonial Times to 1970,* Bicentennial Edition, Washington, DC, 1975.

The terms of the farm problem varied from area to area and year to year. New England farmers suffered from overworked land; farmers in western Kansas and Nebraska went broke in a severe drought that followed a period of unusual rainfall. Many southern farmers were trapped in the crop lien system that kept them in debt.

Some farmers had valid grievances, though many understandably tended to exaggerate them. More important, many farmers were sure their condition had declined, and this perception—as bitterly real as any actual fact—sparked a growing anger. Equally upsetting, everyone in the 1870s and 1880s seemed excited about factories, not farms. Farmers had become "hayseeds," a word that first appeared in 1889, and they watched their offspring leave for city lights and new careers.

THE FAST-GROWING FARMERS' ALLIANCE

Originally a social organization for farmers, the Grange lost many of its members as it turned more and more toward politics in the late 1870s. In its place, a multitude of farm societies sprang into existence. By the end of the 1880s, they had formed into two major organizations: the National Farmers' Alliance, located on the Plains west of the Mississippi and known as the Northwestern Alliance, and the Farmers' Alliance and Industrial Union, based in the South and known as the Southern Alliance.

The Southern Alliance began in Texas in 1875 but did not assume major proportions until Dr. Charles W. Macune, an energetic and farsighted person, took over the leadership in 1886. Rapidly expanding, the Alliance absorbed other agricultural societies. Its agents spread across the South, where farmers were fed up with crop liens, depleted lands, and sharecropping. In 1890, the Southern Alliance claimed more than a million members. It welcomed to membership the farmers' "natural friends"—country doctors, schoolteachers, preachers, and mechanics. It excluded lawyers, bankers, cotton merchants, and warehouse operators.

An effective organization, the Southern Alliance published a newspaper, and in five years it sent lecturers to forty-three states and territories where they

This advertisement for Farmer's Delight tobacco from the May 21, 1889, issue of the Progressive Farmer *is an example of the type of products sold through Alliance cooperatives. The Alliance organizations formed cooperatives in an effort to guarantee farmers greater profits by negotiating for better prices for farm products sold in bulk. Farmers could also avoid creditors' fees by buying goods through the cooperatives. However, failure to secure the credit necessary to finance the cooperatives and lack of management experience in operating them doomed the cooperative venture to failure.*

spoke to two million farm families. It was "the most massive organizing drive by any citizen institution of nineteenth-century America."

Loosely affiliated with the Southern Alliance, a separate Colored Farmers' National Alliance and Cooperative Union enlisted black farmers in the South. Claiming more than 1 million members, it probably had closer to 250,000, but even that figure was sizable in an era when "uppity" blacks faced not merely defeat, but death. In 1891, black cotton pickers struck for higher wages near Memphis, Tennessee. Led by Ben Patterson, a 30-year-old picker, they walked off several plantations, but a posse hunted them down and, following violence on both sides, lynched fifteen strikers, including Patterson. The abortive strike ended the Colored Farmers' Alliance.

On the Plains, the Northwestern Alliance, a smaller organization, was formed in 1880. Its objectives were similar to those of the Southern Alliance, but it disagreed with the Southerners' emphasis on secrecy, centralized control, and separate organizations for blacks. In 1889, the Southern Alliance changed its name to the National Farmers' Alliance and Industrial Union and persuaded the three strongest state alliances on the Plains—those in North Dakota, South Dakota, and Kansas—to join. Thereafter, the renamed organization dominated the Alliance movement.

The Alliance mainly sponsored social and economic programs, but it turned early to politics. In the West, its leaders rejected both the Republicans and Democrats and organized their own party; in June 1890, Kansas Alliance members formed the first major People's party. The Southern Alliance resisted the idea of a new party for fear it might divide the white vote, thus undercutting white supremacy. The Southerners instead followed leaders such as Benjamin F. Tillman of South Carolina, who wanted to capture control of the dominant Democratic party.

Thomas E. Watson and Leonidas L. Polk, two politically minded Southerners, reflected the high quality of Alliance leadership. Georgia-born, Watson was a talented orator and organizer; he urged Georgia farmers, black and white, to unite against their oppressors. The president of the National Farmers' Alliance, Polk believed in scientific farming and cooperative action. Also from Kansas, Mary E. Lease—Mary Ellen to her friends, "Mary Yellin" to her opponents—helped head a movement remarkably open to female leadership. A captivating speaker, she made 160 speeches during the summer of 1890, calling on farmers to rise against Wall Street and the industrial East.

Meeting in Ocala, Florida, in 1890, the Alliance adopted the Ocala Demands, the platform the organization pushed as long as it existed. First and foremost, the demands called for the creation of a "sub-treasury system," which would allow farmers to store their crops in government warehouses. In return, they could claim Treasury notes for up to 80 percent of the local market value of the crop, a loan to be repaid when the crops were sold. Farmers could thus hold their crops for the best price. The Ocala Demands also urged the free coinage of silver, an end to protective tariffs and national banks, a federal income tax, the direct election of senators by voters instead of state legislatures, and tighter regulation of railroad companies.

The Alliance strategy worked well in the elections of 1890. In Kansas, the Alliance-related People's party, organized just a few months before, elected four congressmen and a U.S. senator. Across the South, the

Populist Mary E. Lease advised farmers to "raise less corn and more hell." She also said, "If one man has not enough to eat three times a day and another man has $25 million, that last man has something that belongs to the first."

Alliance won victories based on the "Alliance yardstick," a demand that Democratic party candidates pledge support for Alliance measures. Alliance leaders claimed thirty-eight Alliance supporters elected to Congress, with at least a dozen more pledged to Alliance principles.

THE PEOPLE'S PARTY

After the 1890 elections, Northern Alliance leaders urged the formation of a national third party to promote reform, although the Southerners remained reluctant, still hopeful of capturing control of the Democratic party. Plans for a new party were discussed at Alliance conventions in 1891 and the following year. In July 1892, a convention in Omaha, Nebraska, formed the new People's (or Populist) party. Southern Alliance leaders joined in, convinced now that there was no reason to cooperate with the Democrats who exploited Alliance popularity but failed to adopt its reforms.

In the South, some Populists had worked to unite black and white farmers. "They are in the ditch just like we are," a white Texas Populist said. Blacks and

whites served on Populist election committees; they spoke from the same platforms, and they ran on the same tickets. Populist sheriffs called blacks for jury
duty, an unheard-of practice in the close-of-the-century South.

Many of the delegates at the Omaha convention had planned to nominate
Leonidas L. Polk for president, but he died suddenly in June, and the convention
turned instead to James B. Weaver of Iowa, a former congressman, Union army
general, and third-party candidate for president in 1880 (on the Greenback-
Labor party ticket). As its platform, the People's party adopted many of the
Ocala Demands.

Weaver waged an active campaign but with mixed results. He won
1,029,000 votes, the first third-party presidential candidate ever to attract more
than a million. He carried Kansas, Idaho, Nevada, and Colorado, along with portions of North Dakota and Oregon, for a total of twenty-two electoral votes. The
Populists elected governors in Kansas and North Dakota, ten congressmen, five
senators, and about fifteen hundred members of state legislatures.

Despite the Populists' victories, the election brought disappointment.
Southern Democrats used intimidation, fraud, and manipulation to hold down
Populist votes. Weaver was held to less than a quarter of the vote in every southern state except Alabama. In most of the country, he lost heavily in urban areas,
with the exception of some mining towns in the Far West. He also failed to win
over most farmers. In no midwestern state except Kansas and North Dakota did
he win as much as 5 percent of the vote.

In the election of 1892, many voters switched parties, but they tended to re-
align with the Democrats rather than the Populists, whose platform on silver and
other issues had relatively little appeal among city dwellers or factory workers.
Although the Populists did run candidates in the next three presidential elec-

THE ELECTION OF 1892

CANDIDATE	PARTY	POPULAR VOTE	ELECTORAL VOTE
Cleveland	Democrat	5,555,426	277
Harrison	Republican	5,182,690	145
Weaver	People's (Populist)	1,029,846	22
	Minor Parties	285,297	0

tions, they had reached their peak in 1892. That year, Farmers' Alliance membership dropped for the second year in a row, and the organization, which was once the breeding ground of the People's party, was broken.

While it lived, the Alliance was one of the most powerful protest movements in American history. Catalyzing the feelings of hundreds of thousands of farmers, it attempted to solve specific economic problems while at the same time advancing a larger vision of harmony and community, in which people who cared about each other were rewarded for what they produced.

THE CRISIS OF THE DEPRESSION

It was economic crisis, however, not harmony and community, that dominated the last decade of the century. Responding to the heady forces of industrialization, the American economy had expanded too rapidly in the 1870s and 1880s. Railroads had overbuilt, gambling on future growth. Companies had grown beyond their markets; farms and businesses had borrowed heavily for expansion.

THE PANIC OF 1893

The mood changed early in 1893. In mid-February, panic suddenly hit the New York stock market. In one day, investors dumped one million shares of a leading company, the Philadelphia and Reading Railroad, and it went bankrupt. Business investment dropped sharply in the railroad and construction industries, touching off the worst economic downturn to that point in the country's history.

Frightened, people hurriedly sold stocks and other assets to buy gold. The overwhelming demand depleted the gold reserve of the U.S. Treasury. Eroding almost daily, in March 1893, the Treasury's reserve slumped toward the $100 million mark, an amount that stood for the government's commitment to maintain the gold standard. On April 22, for the first time since the 1870s, the reserve fell below $100 million.

The news shattered business confidence—the stock market broke. On Wednesday, May 3, railroad and industrial stocks plummeted, and the next day, several major firms went bankrupt. When the market opened on Friday, crowds filled its galleries, anticipating a panic. Within minutes, leading stocks plunged to record lows, and there was pandemonium on the floor and in the streets outside.

Afterward, banks cut back on loans. Unable to get capital, businesses failed at an average rate of two dozen a day during the month of May. On July 26, the Erie Railroad, one of the leading names in railroading history, failed. August 1893 was the worst month. Across the country, factories and mines shut down. On August 15, the Northern Pacific Railroad went bankrupt; the Union Pacific and the Santa

The Panic of 1893 touched off a frenzy of activity on the floor of the New York Stock Exchange as investors attempted to unload their stock. Prices on the Exchange fell to a new low on June 27. By the end of 1893, the gold reserve had dipped to $80 million.

Fe soon followed. Some economists estimated unemployment at 2 million people, or nearly 15 percent of the labor force.

The year 1894 was even worse. The gross national product dropped again, and by midyear the number of unemployed stood at 3 million. One out of every five workers was unemployed. In the summer, a heat wave and drought struck the farm belt west of the Mississippi River, creating conditions unmatched until the devastating Dust Bowl of the 1930s. Corn withered in the fields. In the South, the price of cotton fell below five cents a pound, far under the break-even point.

People became restless and angry. As one newspaper said in 1896: "On every corner stands a man whose fortune in these dull times has made him an ugly critic of everything and everybody." There was even talk of revolution and bloodshed. Some of the unemployed wandered across the country—singly, in small groups, and in small armies. In February 1894, police ejected six hundred unemployed men who stormed the State House in Boston demanding relief. During 1894, there were some fourteen hundred strikes involving more than a half million workers.

THE PULLMAN STRIKE

Discontent mounted. The great Pullman strike—one of the largest strikes in the country's history—began when the employees of the Pullman Palace Car Company, living in a company town just outside Chicago (a town in which everything was owned and meted out by the company), struck to protest wage cuts, continuing high rents, and layoffs. On June 26, 1894, the American Railway Union (ARU) under Eugene V. Debs joined the strike by refusing to handle trains that carried Pullman sleeping cars.

Within hours, the strike paralyzed the western half of the nation. Grain and livestock could not reach markets. Factories shut down for lack of coal. The strike extended into twenty-seven states and territories, tying up the economy and renewing talk of class warfare. In Washington, President Grover Cleveland, who had been reelected to the presidency in 1892, decided to break the strike on the grounds that it obstructed delivery of the mail.

On July 2, he secured a court injunction against the ARU, and he ordered troops to Chicago. When they arrived on the morning of Independence Day, the city was peaceful. Before long, however, violence broke out, and mobs, composed mostly of nonstrikers, overturned freight cars, looted, and burned. Restoring order, the army occupied railroad yards in Illinois, California, and other places. By late July, the strike was over; Debs was jailed for violating the injunction.

The Pullman strike had far-reaching consequences for the development of the labor movement. Working people resented Cleveland's actions in the strike, particularly as it became apparent that he sided with the railroads. Upholding Debs's sentence in *In re Debs* (1895), the Supreme Court endorsed the use of the injunction in labor disputes, thus giving business and government an effective antilabor weapon that hindered union growth in the 1890s. The strike's failure catapulted Debs into prominence. During his time in jail, he turned to socialism, and after his release, he worked to build the Socialist party of America, which experienced some success after 1900.

THE MINERS OF THE MIDWEST

The plight of coal miners in the Midwest illustrated the personal and social impact of the depression. Even in the best of times, mining was a dirty and dangerous business. One miner in twelve died underground; one in three suffered injury. Mines routinely closed for as long as six months a year, and wages fell with the depression.

Midwestern mining was often a family occupation, passed down from father to son. It demanded delicate judgments about when to blast, where to follow a seam, and how to avoid rockfalls. Until 1890, English and Irish immigrants dominated the business. They migrated from mine to mine, and they nearly always lived in flimsy shacks owned by the company.

After 1890, immigration from southern and eastern Europe, hitherto a trickle, became a flood. Italians, Lithuanians, Poles, Slovaks, Magyars, Russians, Bohemians, and Croatians came to the mines to find work. In some mining towns, Italian and Polish miners soon made up almost half the population.

As the depression deepened, tensions grew between miners and their employers and between "old" miners and the "new." Many "new" miners spoke no English, and often they were "birds of passage," transients who had come to the United States to make money to take back home. Lacking the skills handed down by the "old" miners, they were often blamed for accidents, and they worked longer hours for less pay. At many a tavern after work, "old" miners grumbled about the different-looking newcomers and considered ways to get rid of them.

In April 1894, a wave of wage reductions sparked an explosion of labor unrest in the mines. The United Mine Workers, a struggling union formed just four years earlier, called for a strike of bituminous coal miners, and on April 21, virtually all midwestern and Pennsylvania miners—some 170,000 in all—quit working. The flow of crucial coal slackened; cities faced blackouts; factories closed.

The violence that soon broke out followed a significant pattern. Over the years, the English and Irish miners had built up a set of unspoken understandings with their employers. The "new" miners had not, and they were more prone to violent action to win a strike. The depression hit them especially hard, frustrating their plans to earn money and return home. In many areas, anger and frustration turned the 1894 strikes into outright war.

For nearly two weeks in June 1894, fighting rocked the Illinois, Ohio, and Indiana coalfields. Mobs ignited mine shafts, dynamited coal trains, and defied state militias. While miners of all backgrounds participated in the violence, it often divided "old" miners and "new." In Spring Valley, Illinois, exiled Italian anarchists took over the strike leadership and incited rioting despite the opposition of the "old" miners. Elsewhere, a mine fired by arsonists burned because the "new" miners prevented the "old" ones from extinguishing the blaze.

Shocked by the violence, public opinion shifted against the strikers. The strike ended in a matter of weeks, but its effects lingered. English and Irish miners moved out into other jobs or up into supervisory positions. Jokes and songs poked cruel fun at the "new" immigrants, and the Pennsylvania and Illinois legislatures adopted laws to keep them out of the mines. Thousands of "old" miners voted Populist in 1894—the Populist platform called for restrictions on immigration—in one of the Populists' few successes that year.

Occurring at the same time, the Pullman strike pulled attention away from the crisis in the coalfields, yet the miners' strike involved three times as many workers and provided a revealing glimpse of the tensions within American society. The miners of the Midwest were the first large group of skilled workers seriously affected by the flood of immigrants from southern and eastern Europe. Buffeted by depression, they reflected the social and economic discord that permeated every industry.

A BELEAGUERED PRESIDENT

Building on the Democratic party's sweeping triumph in the midterm elections of 1890, Grover Cleveland decisively defeated the Populist candidate, James B. Weaver, and the incumbent president, Benjamin Harrison, in 1892. The Democrats increased their strength in the cities and among working-class voters. For the first time since the 1850s, they controlled the White House and both branches of Congress.

The Democrats, it now seemed, had broken the party stalemate, but unfortunately for Cleveland, the Panic of 1893 struck almost as he took office. He was sure that he knew its cause. The Sherman Silver Purchase Act of 1890, he believed, had damaged business confidence, drained the Treasury's gold reserve, and caused the panic. The solution to the depression was equally simple: repeal the act.

In June 1893, Cleveland summoned Congress into special session. The silverites were on the defensive, although they pleaded for a compromise. Rejecting the pleas, Cleveland pushed the repeal bill through Congress, and on November 1, 1893, he signed it into law. Always sure of himself, he had staked everything on a single measure—a winning strategy if he succeeded, a devastating one if he did not.

Repeal of the Sherman Silver Purchase Act was probably a necessary action. It responded to the realities of international finance, reduced the flight of gold out of the country, and, over the long run, boosted business confidence. Unfortunately, it contracted the currency at a time when inflation might have helped. It did not bring economic revival. The stock market remained listless, businesses continued to close, unemployment spread, and farm prices dropped.

The repeal battle of 1893, discrediting the conservative Cleveland Democrats who had dominated the party since the 1860s, reshaped the politics of the country. It confined the Democratic party largely to the South, helped the Republicans become the majority party in 1894, and strengthened the position of the silver Democrats in their bid for the presidency in 1896. It also focused national attention on the silver issue and thus intensified the silver sentiment Cleveland had intended to dampen. In the end, repeal did not even solve the Treasury's gold problem. By January 1894, the reserve had fallen to $65 million. A year later, it fell to $44.5 million.

Still another blow to the morale of the Democrats came in 1894, when they tried to fulfill their long-standing promise to reduce the tariff. Despite all their efforts, the Wilson-Gorman Tariff Act, passed by Congress in August 1894, contained only modest reductions in duties. It reduced the tariff on coal, iron ore, wool, and sugar, ended the McKinley Tariff Act's popular reciprocity agreements with other countries, and moved some duties higher than ever before. It also imposed a small income tax, a provision the Supreme Court overturned in 1895 (*Pollock* v. *Farmer's Loan and Trust Co.*). Very few Democrats, including Cleveland, were pleased with the measure, and the president let it become law without his signature.

BREAKING THE PARTY DEADLOCK

The Democrats were buried in the elections of 1894. Suffering the greatest defeat in congressional history, they lost 113 House seats, while the Republicans gained 117. In twenty-four states, not a single Democrat was elected to Congress. The Democrats even lost some of the "solid South," and in the Midwest, a crucial battleground of the 1890s, the party was virtually destroyed.

Wooing labor and the unemployed, the Populists made striking inroads in parts of the South and West, yet their progress was far from enough. In a year in which thousands of voters switched parties, the People's party elected only four senators and four congressmen. Southern Democrats again used fraud and violence to keep the Populists' totals down. In the Midwest, the Populists won double the number of votes they had received in 1892, yet still attracted less than 7 percent of the vote. Across the country, the discontented tended to vote for the Republicans, not the Populists, a discouraging sign for the Populist party.

The elections of 1894 marked the end of the party deadlock that had existed since the 1870s. The Democrats lost, the Populists gained somewhat, and the Republicans became the majority party in the country. In the midst of the depression, the Republican doctrines of activism and national authority, which voters had repudiated in the elections of 1890, became more attractive. This was a development of great significance, because as Americans became more accepting of the use of government power to regulate the economy and safeguard individual welfare, the way lay open to the reforms of the Progressive Era, the New Deal, and beyond.

CHANGING ATTITUDES

The depression, brutal and far-reaching, did more than shift political alignments. Across the country, it undermined traditional views and caused people to rethink older ideas about government, the economy, and society. As men and women concluded that established ideas had failed to deal with the depression, they looked for new ones.

In prosperous times, Americans had thought of unemployment as the result of personal failure, affecting primarily the lazy and immoral. In the midst of depression, such views were harder to maintain, since everyone knew people who were both worthy and unemployed. Next door, a respected neighbor might be laid off; down the block, an entire factory might be shut down.

People debated issues they had long taken for granted. New and reinvigorated local institutions—discussion clubs, women's clubs, reform societies, university extension centers, church groups, farmers' societies—gave people a place to discuss alternatives to the existing order. Pressures for reform increased, and demand grew for government intervention to help the poor and unemployed.

"EVERYBODY WORKS BUT FATHER"

Women and children had been entering the labor force for years, and the depression accelerated the trend. As husbands and fathers lost their jobs, more and more women and children went to work. Even as late as 1901, well after the depression had ended, a study of working-class families showed that more than half the principal breadwinners were out of work. So many women and children worked that in 1905 there was a popular song titled "Everybody Works But Father."

During the 1890s, the number of working women rose from 4 million to 5.3 million. Trying to make ends meet, they took in boarders and found jobs as laundresses, cleaners, or domestics. Where possible, they worked in offices and factories. Far more black urban women than white worked to supplement their husbands' meager earnings. In New York City in 1900, nearly 60 percent of all black women worked, compared to 27 percent of the foreign-born and 24 percent of native-born white women. Men still dominated business offices, but during the 1890s, more and more employers noted the relative cheapness of female labor. Women telegraph and telephone operators nearly tripled in number during the decade. Women worked as clerks in the new five-and-tens and department stores, and as nurses; in 1900, a half million were teachers. They increasingly entered office work as stenographers and typists.

Tiny children peddling newspapers and women domestics serving the rich—their meager earnings were desperately needed.

The depression also caused an increasing number of children to work. During the 1890s, the number of children employed in southern textile mills jumped more than 160 percent, and boys and girls under 16 years of age made up nearly one-third of the labor force of the mills. Youngsters of 8 and 9 years worked twelve hours a day for pitiful wages. In most cases, however, children worked not in factories but in farming and city street trades such as peddling and shoe shining.

Concerned about child labor, middle-class women in 1896 formed the League for the Protection of the Family, which called for compulsory education to get children out of factories and into classrooms. The Mothers Congress of 1896 gave rise to the National Congress of Parents and Teachers, the spawning ground of thousands of local Parent-Teacher Associations. The National Council of Women and the General Federation of Women's Clubs took up similar issues. By the end of the 1890s, the Federation had 150,000 members who worked for various civic reforms in the fields of child welfare, education, and sanitation.

CHANGING THEMES IN LITERATURE

The depression also gave point to a growing movement in literature toward realism and naturalism. In the years after the Civil War, literature often reflected the mood of romanticism—sentimental and unrealistic.

The novels of Horatio Alger, which provided simple lessons about how to get ahead in business and life, continued to attract large numbers of readers. They told of poor youngsters who made their way to the top through hard work, thrift, honesty, and luck. Louisa May Alcott's *Little Women* (1868–1869) related the daily lives of four girls in a New England family; Anna Sewell's *Black Beauty* (1877) charmed readers with the story of an abused horse that found a happy home.

After the 1870s, however, a number of talented authors began to reject romanticism and escapism, turning instead to realism. Determined to portray life as it was, they studied local dialects, wrote regional stories, and emphasized the "true" relationships between people. In doing so, they reflected broader trends in the society, such as industrialism; evolutionary theory, which emphasized the effect of the environment on humans; and the new philosophy of pragmatism, which stressed the relativity of values.

Regionalist authors such as Joel Chandler Harris and George Washington Cable depicted life in the South. Hamlin Garland described the grimness of life on the Great Plains, and Sarah Orne Jewett wrote about everyday life in rural New England. Another regionalist, Bret Harte, achieved fame with stories that portrayed the local color of the California mining camps, particularly in his popular tale "The Outcasts of Poker Flat."

Harte was joined by a more talented writer, Mark Twain, who became the country's most outstanding realist author. Growing up along the Mississippi River in Hannibal County, Missouri, the young Samuel Langhorne Clemens observed life around him with a humorous and skeptical eye. Adopting a pen name from the river term "mark twain" (two fathoms), he wrote a number of important works that drew on his own experiences. *Life on the Mississippi* (1883) described his career as a steamboat pilot. *The Adventures of Tom Sawyer* (1876) and *The Adventures of Huckleberry Finn* (1884) gained international prominence. In these books, Twain used dialect and common speech instead of literary language, touching off a major change in American prose style.

William Dean Howells—after Twain, the country's most famous author—came more slowly to the realist approach. At first, he wrote about the happier sides of life, but then he grew worried about the impact of industrialization. *A Traveler from Altruria* (1894), a utopian novel, described an industrial society that consumed lives.

Other writers, the naturalists, became impatient even with realism. Pushing Darwinian theory to its limits, they wrote of a world in which a cruel and merciless environment determined human fate. Often focusing on economic hardship, naturalist writers studied the poor, the lower classes, and the criminal mind; they brought to their writing the social worker's passion for direct and honest experience.

A scene from Stephen Crane's novel Maggie: A Girl of the Streets. *Crane's tale painted a grim picture of life in the tenements of New York City's Bowery as it chronicled the story of slum child Maggie Johnson, victimized and trapped in her squalid, violent world.*

Stephen Crane spent a night in a seven-cent lodging house on the Bowery and in "An Experiment in Misery" captured the smells and sounds of the poor. Crane depicted the carnage of war in *The Red Badge of Courage* (1895) and the impact of poverty in *Maggie: A Girl of the Streets* (1893). His poetry suggested the unimportance of the individual in an uncaring world.

Frank Norris assailed the power of big business in two dramatic novels, *The Octopus* (1901) and *The Pit* (1903), both the story of individual futility in the face of the heartless corporations. Norris's *McTeague* (1899) studied the disintegration of character under economic pressure. Jack London, another naturalist author, traced the power of nature over civilized society in novels such as *The Sea Wolf* (1904) and *The Call of the Wild* (1903), his classic tale of a sled dog that preferred the difficult life of the wilderness to the world of human beings.

Theodore Dreiser, the foremost naturalist writer, grimly portrayed a dark world in which human beings were tossed about by forces beyond their understanding or control. In his great novel *Sister Carrie* (1901), he followed a young farm girl who took a job in a Chicago shoe factory. He described the exhausting nature of factory work: "Her hands began to ache at the wrists and then in the fingers, and towards the last she seemed one mass of dull, complaining muscle, fixed in an eternal position, and performing a single mechanical movement."

Like other naturalists, Dreiser focused on environment and character. He thought writers should tell the truth about human affairs, not fabricate romance, and *Sister Carrie,* he said, was "not intended as a piece of literary craftsmanship, but was a picture of conditions."

THE PRESIDENTIAL ELECTION OF 1896

The election of 1896 was known as the "battle of the standards" because it focused primarily on the gold and silver standards of money. As an election, it was exciting and decisive. New voting patterns replaced old, a new majority party confirmed its control of the country, and national policy shifted to suit new realities.

THE MYSTIQUE OF SILVER

Sentiment for free silver coinage grew swiftly after 1894, dominating the South and West, appearing even in the farming regions of New York and New England. Prosilver literature flooded the country.

People wanted quick solutions to the economic crisis. During 1896, unemployment shot up and farm income and prices fell to the lowest point in the decade. "I can remember back as far as 1858," an Iowa hardware dealer said in February 1896, "and I have never seen such hard times as these are." The silverites offered a solution, simple but compelling: the free and independent coinage of silver at the ratio of 16 ounces of silver to every ounce of gold. Free coinage meant that the U.S. mints would coin all the silver offered to them. Independent coinage meant that the country would coin silver regardless of the policies of other nations, nearly all of which were on the gold standard.

It is difficult now to understand the kind of faith the silverites placed in silver as a cure for the depression. But faith it was, and of a sort that some observers compared to religious fervor. Underlying it all was a belief in a quantity theory of money: the silverites believed the amount of money in circulation determined the level of activity in the economy. If money was short, that meant there was a limit on economic activity and ultimately a depression. If the government coined silver as well as gold, that meant more money in circulation, more business for everyone, and thus prosperity. Farm prices would rise; laborers would go back to work.

By 1896, silver was also a symbol. It had moral and patriotic dimensions—by going to a silver standard, the United States could assert its independence in the world—and it stood for a wide range of popular grievances. For many, it reflected rural values rather than urban ones, suggested a shift of power away from the Northeast, and spoke for the downtrodden instead of the well-to-do. Silver represented the common people.

Silver was more than just a political or economic issue. It was a social movement, one of the largest in American history, but its life span turned out to be brief. As a mass phenomenon, it flourished between 1894 and 1896, then succumbed to electoral defeat, the return of prosperity, and the onset of fresh concerns. But in its time, the silver movement bespoke a national mood and won millions of followers.

THE REPUBLICANS AND GOLD

Scenting victory over the discredited Democrats, numerous Republicans fought for the party's presidential nomination, including a Republican favorite, William McKinley of Ohio.

Able, calm, and affable, McKinley had served in the Union army during the Civil War. In 1876, he won a seat in Congress, where he became the chief sponsor of the tariff act named for him. In the months before the 1896 national convention, Marcus A. Hanna, his campaign manager and trusted friend, built a powerful national organization that featured McKinley as "the advance agent of

The religious symbolism in Bryan's "Cross of Gold" speech is satirized in this cartoon, but his stirring rhetoric captivated his audience and won him the Democratic presidential nomination for the election of 1896.

prosperity," an alluring slogan in a country beset with depression. When the convention met in June, McKinley had the nomination in hand, and he backed a platform that favored the gold standard against the free coinage of silver.

Republicans favoring silver proposed a prosilver platform, but the convention overwhelmingly defeated it. Twenty-three silverite Republicans, far fewer than prosilver forces had hoped, marched out of the convention hall. The remaining delegates waved handkerchiefs and flags and shouted "Good-bye" and "Put them out." Hanna stood on a chair screaming "Go! Go! Go!" William Jennings Bryan, who was there as a special correspondent for a Nebraska newspaper, climbed on a desk to get a better view.

THE DEMOCRATS AND SILVER

Silver, meanwhile, had captured large segments of the Democratic party in the South and West. Despite President Cleveland's opposition, more than twenty Democratic state platforms came out for free silver in 1894. Power in the party shifted to the South, where it remained for decades. The party's base narrowed; its outlook increasingly reflected southern views on silver, race, and other issues. In effect, the Democrats became a sectional—no longer a national—party.

The anti-Cleveland Democrats had their issue, but they lacked a leader. Out in Nebraska, Bryan saw the opportunity to take on that role. He was barely 36 years old and had relatively little political experience. But he had spent months wooing support, and he was a captivating public speaker—tall, slender, and handsome, with a resounding voice that, in an era without microphones, projected easily into every corner of an auditorium.

From the outset of the 1896 Democratic convention, the silver Democrats were in charge, and they put together a platform that stunned the Cleveland wing of the party. It demanded the free coinage of silver and attacked Cleveland's actions in the Pullman strike. On July 9, as delegates debated the platform, Bryan's moment came. Striding to the stage, he stood for an instant, a hand raised for silence, waiting for the applause to die down. He would not contend with the previous speakers, he began, for "this is not a contest between persons. The humblest citizen in all the land, when clad in the armor of a righteous cause, is stronger than all the hosts of error. I come to speak to you in defense of a cause as holy as the cause of liberty—the cause of humanity."

The delegates were captivated. Like a trained choir, they rose, cheered each point, and sat back to listen for more. Easterners, Bryan said, liked to praise businessmen but forgot that plain people—laborers, miners, and farmers—were businessmen, too. Shouts rang through the hall, and delegates pounded on chairs. Savoring each cheer, Bryan defended silver. Then came the famous closing:

"Having behind us the producing masses of this nation and the world . . . we will answer their demand for a gold standard by saying to them: 'You shall not press down upon the brow of labor this crown of thorns, you shall not crucify mankind upon a cross of gold.'"

Bryan moved his fingers down his temples, suggesting blood trickling from his wounds. He ended with his arms outstretched as on a cross. Letting the silence hang, he dropped his arms, stepped back, then started to his seat. Suddenly, there was pandemonium. Delegates shouted and cheered. When the tumult subsided, they adopted the anti-Cleveland platform, and the next day, Bryan won the presidential nomination.

CAMPAIGN AND ELECTION

The Democratic convention presented the Populists with a dilemma. The People's party had staked everything on the assumption that neither major party would endorse silver. Now it faced a painful choice: nominate an independent ticket and risk splitting the silverite forces, or nominate Bryan and give up its separate identity as a party.

The choice was unpleasant, and it shattered the People's party. Meeting late in July, the party's national convention nominated Bryan, but rather than accept the Democratic candidate for vice president, it named Tom Watson instead. The Populists' endorsement probably hurt Bryan as much as it helped. It won him relatively few votes, since many Populists would have voted for him anyway. It also identified him as a Populist, which he was not, allowing the Republicans to accuse him of heading a ragtag army of malcontents. The squabble over Watson seemed to prove that the Democratic-Populist alliance could never stay together long enough to govern.

In August 1896, Bryan set off on a campaign that became an American legend. He took his campaign directly to the voters, the first presidential candidate in history to do so in a systematic way. By his own count, Bryan traveled 18,009 miles, visited 27 states, and spoke 600 times to a total of some 3 million people. He built skillfully on a new "merchandising" style of campaign in which he worked to educate and persuade voters.

Bryan summoned voters to an older America: a land where farms were as important as factories, where the virtues of rural and religious life outweighed the doubtful lure of the city, where common people still ruled and opportunity existed for all. He drew on the Jeffersonian tradition of rural virtue, distrust of central authority, and abiding faith in the powers of human reason.

Urged to take the stump against Bryan, McKinley replied, "I might just as well put up a trapeze on my front lawn and compete with some professional ath-

THE ELECTION OF 1896

CANDIDATE	PARTY	POPULAR VOTE	ELECTORAL VOTE
McKinley	Republican	7,102,246	271
Bryan	Democrat	6,492,559	176
	Minor Parties	315,398	0

lete as go out speaking against Bryan." The Republican candidate let voters come to him. Railroads brought them by the thousands into McKinley's hometown of Canton, Ohio, and he spoke to them from his front porch. Through use of the press, he reached fully as many people as Bryan's more strenuous effort. Appealing to labor, immigrants, well-to-do farmers, businessmen, and the middle class, McKinley defended economic nationalism and the advancing urban-industrial society.

On election day, voter turnout was extraordinarily high, a measure of the intense interest. By nightfall, the outcome was clear: McKinley won 50 percent of the vote to Bryan's 46 percent. He won the Northeast and Midwest and carried four border states. In the cities, McKinley crushed Bryan.

The election struck down the Populists, whose totals sagged nearly everywhere. Many Populist proposals were later adopted under different leadership. The graduated income tax, crop loans to farmers, the secret ballot, and direct election of U.S. senators all were early Populist ideas. But the People's party never could win over a majority of the voters, and failing that, it vanished after 1896.

THE MCKINLEY ADMINISTRATION

The election of 1896 cemented the voter realignment of 1894 and initiated a generation of Republican rule. For more than three decades after 1896, with only a brief Democratic resurgence under Woodrow Wilson, the Republicans remained the country's majority party.

McKinley took office in 1897 under favorable circumstances. To everyone's relief, the economy had begun to revive. The stock market rose, factories once again churned out goods, and farmers prospered. Farm prices climbed sharply during 1897 on bumper crops of wheat, cotton, and corn. Discoveries of gold in Australia and Alaska—together with the development of a new cyanide process for extracting gold from ore—enlarged the world's gold supply, decreased its price, and inflated the currency as the silverites had hoped. For the first time since 1890, the 1897 Treasury statements showed a comfortable gold reserve.

McKinley and the Republicans basked in the glow. They became the party of progress and prosperity, an image that helped them win victories until another depression hit in the 1930s. McKinley's popularity soared. An activist president, he set the policies of the administration. Conscious of the limits of power, he maintained close ties with Congress and worked hard to educate the public on national choices and priorities. McKinley struck new relations with the press and traveled far more than previous presidents. In some ways, he began the modern presidency.

Shortly after taking office, he summoned Congress into special session to revise the tariff. In July 1897, the Dingley Tariff passed the House and Senate. It raised average tariff duties to a record level, and as the final burst of nineteenth-century protectionism, it caused trouble for the Republican party. By the end of the 1890s, consumers, critics, and the Republicans themselves were wondering if the tariff had outlived its usefulness in the maturing American economy.

From the 1860s to the 1890s, the Republicans had built their party on a pledge to *promote* economic growth through the use of state and national power. By 1900, with the industrial system firmly in place, the focus had shifted. The need to *regulate,* to control the effects of industrialism, became a central public concern of the new century. McKinley prodded the Republicans to meet that shift, but he died before his plans matured.

McKinley toyed with the idea of lowering the tariff, but one obstacle always stood in the way: the government needed revenue, and tariff duties were one of the few taxes the public would support. The Spanish-American War of 1898 persuaded people to accept greater federal power and, with it, new forms of taxation. In 1899, McKinley spoke of lowering tariff barriers in a world that technology had made smaller. "God and man have linked the nations together," he said in his last speech at Buffalo, New York, in 1901. "Isolation is no longer possible or desirable."

In 1898 and 1899, the McKinley administration focused on the war with Spain, the peace treaty that followed, and the dawning realization that the war had thrust the United States into a position of world power. In March 1900, Congress passed the Gold Standard Act, which declared gold the standard of currency and ended the silver controversy that had dominated the 1890s.

The presidential campaign of 1900 was a replay of the McKinley-Bryan fight of 1896. McKinley's running mate was Theodore Roosevelt, hero of the Spanish-American War and former governor of New York, who was nominated for vice president to capitalize on his popularity and, his enemies hoped, to sidetrack his

THE ELECTION OF 1900

CANDIDATE	PARTY	POPULAR VOTE	ELECTORAL VOTE
McKinley	Republican	7,218,039	292
Bryan	Democrat	6,358,345	155
Woolley	Prohibition	209,004	0
Debs	Socialist	86,935	0

political career into oblivion. Bryan stressed the issues of imperialism and the trusts; McKinley stressed his record at home and abroad. The result in 1900 was a landslide.

On September 6, 1901, a few months after his second inauguration, McKinley stood in a receiving line at the Pan-American Exposition in Buffalo. Leon Czolgosz, a 28-year-old unemployed laborer and anarchist, moved through the line and, reaching the president, shot him. Surgeons probed the wound but could find nothing. A recent discovery called the X ray was on display at the exposition, but it was not used. On September 14, McKinley died, and Vice President Theodore Roosevelt became president. A new century had begun.

As the funeral train carried McKinley's body back to Ohio, Mark Hanna, McKinley's old friend and ally, sat slumped in his parlor car. "I told William McKinley it was a mistake to nominate that wild man at Philadelphia," he mourned. "I asked him if he realized what would happen if he should die. Now look, that damned cowboy is president of the United States!"

Hanna's world had changed, and so had the nation's—not so much because "that damned cowboy" was suddenly president, but because events of the 1890s had had powerful effects. In the course of that decade, political patterns shifted, the presidency acquired fresh power, and massive unrest prompted social change. The war with Spain brought a new empire and worldwide responsibilities. Economic hardship posed questions of the most difficult sort about industrialization, urbanization, and the quality of American life. Worried, people embraced new ideas and causes. Reform movements begun in the 1890s flowered in the Progressive Era after 1900.

Technology continued to alter the way Americans lived. In 1896, Henry Ford produced a two-cylinder, four-horsepower car, the first of the famous line that bore his name. In 1899, the first automobile salesroom opened in New York, and some innovative thinkers were already imagining a network of service stations to keep the new cars running. At Kitty Hawk, North Carolina, Wilbur and Orville Wright, two bicycle manufacturers, neared the birth of powered flight.

The realignments that reached their peak in the 1890s seem distant, yet they are not. Important decisions in those years shaped nearly everything that came after them. In character and influence, the 1890s were as much a part of the twentieth century as of the nineteenth and continue to have repercussions into the twenty-first century.

21

TOWARD EMPIRE

Many Americans regretted the start of the war with Spain that began in April 1898, but many others welcomed it. War was different then, shorter and more personal than the all-encompassing, lengthy, and mechanistic wars of the twentieth century. Many highly respected people believed that nations must fight every now and then to prove their power and test the national spirit.

Theodore Roosevelt, 39 years old in 1898, was one of them. Nations needed to fight in order to survive, he thought. For months, Roosevelt argued strenuously for war with Spain for three reasons: first, on grounds of freeing Cuba and expelling Spain from the hemisphere; second, because of "the benefit done to our people by giving them something to think of which isn't material gain"; and third, because the army and navy needed the practice.

In April 1898, Roosevelt was serving in the important post of assistant secretary of the navy. When war broke out, he quickly resigned to join the army, rejecting the advice of the secretary of the navy, who warned he would only "ride a horse and brush mosquitoes from his neck in the Florida sands." The secretary was wrong—dead wrong—and later had the grace to admit it. "Roosevelt was right," he said. "His going into the Army led straight to the Presidency."

Joining a friend, Roosevelt chose to enlist his own regiment, and after a few telephone calls to friends, and telegrams to the governors of Arizona, New Mexico, and Oklahoma asking for "good shots and good riders," he had more than enough men. The First United States Volunteer Cavalry, an intriguing mixture of Ivy League athletes and western frontiersmen, was born.

Known as the Rough Riders, it included men from the Harvard, Yale, and Princeton clubs of New York City; the Somerset Club of Boston; and New York's

Colonel Theodore Roosevelt poses in his custom-designed uniform. With surgeon Leonard Wood, Roosevelt organized the First U.S. Volunteer Cavalry—the Rough Riders—for service in the Spanish-American War.

exclusive Knickerbocker Club. Former college athletes—football players, tennis players, and track stars—enlisted. Woodbury Kane, a wealthy yachtsman, signed up and promptly volunteered for kitchen duty.

Other volunteers came from the West—natural soldiers, Roosevelt called them, "tall and sinewy, with resolute, weather-beaten faces, and eyes that looked a man straight in the face without flinching." Among the cowboys, hunters, and prospectors, there were Bucky O'Neill, a legendary Arizona sheriff and Indian fighter; a half dozen other sheriffs and Texas Rangers; a large number of Indians; a famous broncobuster; and an ex-marshal of Dodge City, Kansas.

Eager for war, the men trained hard, played harder, and rarely passed up a chance for an intellectual discussion—if Roosevelt's memoir of the war is to be believed. Once, he overheard Bucky O'Neill and a Princeton graduate "discussing Aryan word-roots together, and then sliding off into a review of the novels of Balzac, and a discussion as to how far Balzac could be said to be the founder of the modern realistic school of fiction." In such a camp, discipline was lax, and enlisted men got on easily with the officers.

The troops howled with joy when orders came to join the invasion army for Cuba. They set sail on June 14, 1898, and Lieutenant Colonel Roosevelt, who had performed a war dance for the troops the night before, caught their mood: "We knew not whither we were bound, nor what we were to do; but we believed that the nearing future held for us many chances of death and hardship, of honor and renown. If we failed, we would share the fate of all who fail; but we were sure that we would win, that we should score the first great triumph in a mighty world-movement."

AMERICA LOOKS OUTWARD

The overseas expansion of the 1890s differed in several important respects from earlier expansionist moves of the United States. From its beginning, the American republic had been expanding. After the first landings in Jamestown and Plymouth, settlers pushed westward: into the trans-Appalachian region, the Louisiana Territory, Florida, Texas, California, Arizona, and New Mexico. Most of these lands were contiguous with existing territories of the United States, and most were intended for settlement, usually agricultural.

The expansion of the 1890s was different. It sought to gain island possessions, the bulk of them already thickly populated. The new territories were intended less for settlement than for use as naval bases, trading outposts, or commercial centers on major trade routes. More often than not, they were viewed as colonies, not as states-in-the-making.

Historian Samuel F. Bemis described the overseas expansion of the 1890s as "the great aberration," a time when the country adopted expansionist policies that did not fit with prior experience. Other historians, pointing to expansionist tendencies in thought and foreign policy that surfaced during the last half of the nineteenth century, have found a developing pattern that led naturally to the overseas adventures of the 1890s. In the view of Walter LaFeber, "the United States did not set out on an expansionist path in the late 1890s in a sudden, spur-of-the-moment fashion. The overseas empire that Americans controlled in 1900 was not a break in their history, but a natural culmination."

CATCHING THE SPIRIT OF EMPIRE

Most people in most times in history tend to look inward, and Americans in the years following the Civil War were no exception. Among other things, they focused on Reconstruction, the movement westward, and simply making a living.

Throughout the nineteenth century, Americans enjoyed "free security" without fully appreciating it. Sheltered by two oceans and the British navy, they could enunciate bold policies such as the Monroe Doctrine, which instructed European nations to stay out of the affairs of the Western Hemisphere, while remaining virtually impregnable to foreign attack.

In the 1870s and after, however, Americans began to take an increasing interest in events abroad. There was a growing sense of internationalism, which stemmed in part from the telegraphs, telephones, and undersea cables that kept people better informed about political and economic developments in distant lands. Many Americans continued to be interested in expansion of the country's borders; relatively few were interested in imperialism. Expansion meant the kind of growth that had brought California and Oregon into the American system. Imperialism meant the imposition of control over other peoples through annexation, military conquest, or economic domination.

Several developments in these years combined to shift attention outward across the seas. The end of the frontier, announced officially in the census report of 1890, sparked fears about diminishing opportunities at home. Further growth, it seemed to some, must take place abroad. Factories and farms multiplied, producing more goods than the domestic market could consume. Both farmers and

Titled "The World Is My Market, My Customers Are All Mankind," this 1877 cartoon reflects America's interest in foreign markets. With its emphasis on agricultural produce and light industry, the cartoon understates America's role in foreign commerce.

industrialists looked for new overseas markets, and the growing volume of exports—including more and more manufactured goods—changed the nature of American trade relations with the world.

Political leaders such as James G. Blaine began to argue for the vital importance of foreign markets to continued economic growth. Blaine, secretary of state under Garfield and again under Harrison, aggressively sought wider markets in Latin America, Asia, and Africa, using tariff reciprocity agreements and other measures. To some extent, he and others were also caught up in a worldwide scramble for empire. In the last third of the century, Great Britain, France, and Germany divided up Africa and looked covetously at Asia. The idea of imperialistic expansion was in the air, and the great powers measured their greatness by the colonies they acquired.

Intellectual currents that supported expansion drew on Charles Darwin's theories of evolution. Adherents pointed, for example, to *The Origin of Species,* which mentioned in its subtitle *The Preservation of Favoured Races in the Struggle for Life.* Applied to human and social development, biological concepts seemed to call for the triumph of the fit and the elimination of the unfit. "In this world," said Theodore Roosevelt, who thought of himself as one of the fit, "the nation that has trained itself to a career of unwarlike and isolated ease is bound, in the end, to go down before other nations which have not lost the manly and adventurous qualities."

John Fiske, a popular writer and lecturer, argued for Anglo-Saxon racial superiority, a result of the process of natural selection. The English and Americans, Fiske said, would occupy every land on the globe that was not already "civilized," bringing the advances of commerce and democratic institutions. Eminent scholars such as John W. Burgess, a professor of political science at Columbia University, argued that people of English origin were destined to impose their political institutions on the world.

The career of Josiah Strong, a Congregational minister and fervent expansionist, suggested the strength of the developing ideas. A champion of overseas missionary work, Strong traveled extensively through the West for the Home Missionary Society, and in 1885, drawing on his experiences, he published a book titled *Our Country: Its Possible Future and Its Present Crisis.* An immediate best-seller, the book called on foreign missions to civilize the world under the Anglo-Saxon races. Strong became a national celebrity.

Our Country argued for expanding American trade and dominion. Trade was important, it said, because the desire for material things was one of the hallmarks of civilized people. So was the Christian religion, and by exporting both trade and religion, Americans could civilize and Christianize "inferior" races around the world. Anglo-Saxons already owned one-third of the earth, Strong said, and in a famous passage he concluded that they would take more. In "the final competition of races," they would win and "move down upon Mexico, down upon Central and South America, out upon the islands of the sea, over upon Africa and beyond."

Taken together, these developments in social, political, and economic thought prepared Americans for a larger role in the world. The change was gradual, and there was never a day when people awoke with a sudden realization of their interests overseas. But change there was, and by the 1890s, Americans were ready to reach out into the world in a more determined and deliberate fashion than ever before. For almost the first time, they felt the need for a foreign "policy."

FOREIGN POLICY APPROACHES, 1867–1900

Rarely consistent, American foreign policy in the last half of the nineteenth century took different approaches to different areas of the world. In relation to Europe, seat of the dominant world powers, policymakers promoted trade and tried to avoid diplomatic entanglements. In North and South America, they based policy on the Monroe Doctrine, a recurrent dream of annexing Canada or Mexico, a hope for extensive trade, and Pan-American unity against the nations of the Old World. In the Pacific, they coveted Hawaii and other outposts on the sea-lanes to China.

Secretary of State William Henry Seward, who served from 1861 to 1869, aggressively pushed an expansive foreign policy. Seward developed a vision of an American empire stretching south into Latin America and west to the shores of Asia. His vision included Canada and Mexico; islands in the Caribbean as strategic bases to protect a canal across the isthmus; and Hawaii and other islands as stepping-stones to Asia, which Seward and many others considered a virtually bottomless outlet for farm and manufactured goods.

Seward tried unsuccessfully to negotiate a commercial treaty with Hawaii in 1867, and the same year he annexed the Midway Islands, a small atoll group twelve hundred miles northwest of Hawaii. In 1867, he concluded a treaty with Russia for the purchase of Alaska (which was promptly labeled "Seward's Folly") partly to sandwich western Canada between American territory and lead to its annexation. As the American empire spread, Seward thought, Mexico City would become its capital.

Secretary of State Hamilton Fish, an urbane New Yorker, followed Seward in 1869, serving under President Ulysses S. Grant. An avid expansionist, Grant wanted to extend American influence in the Caribbean and Pacific, though the more conservative Fish often restrained him. They moved first to repair relations with Great Britain. The first business was settlement of the *Alabama* claims—demands that Britain pay the United States for damages to Union ships caused by

Confederate vessels which, like the *Alabama,* had been built and outfitted in British shipyards. Negotiating patiently, Fish signed the Treaty of Washington in 1871, providing for arbitration of the *Alabama* issue and other nettlesome controversies. The treaty, one of the landmarks in the peaceful settlement of international disputes, marked a significant step in cementing Anglo-American relations.

Grant and Fish looked most eagerly to Latin America. In 1870, Grant became the first president to proclaim the nontransfer principle—"hereafter no territory on this continent shall be regarded as subject to transfer to a European power." Fish also promoted the independence of Cuba, restive under Spanish rule, while holding off the annexation desired by the more eager Grant.

James G. Blaine served briefly as secretary of state under President James Garfield and laid extensive plans to establish closer commercial relations with Latin America. Blaine's successor, Frederick T. Frelinghuysen, changed Blaine's approach but not his strategy. Like Blaine, Frelinghuysen wanted to find Caribbean markets for American goods; he negotiated separate reciprocity treaties with Mexico, Cuba and Puerto Rico, the British West Indies, Santo Domingo, and Colombia. Using these treaties, Frelinghuysen hoped not only to obtain markets for American goods but to bind these countries to American interests.

When Blaine returned to the State Department in 1889 under President Benjamin Harrison, he moved again to expand markets in Latin America. Drawing on earlier ideas, he envisaged a hemispheric system of peaceful intercourse, arbitration of disputes, and expanded trade. He also wanted to annex Hawaii.

Harrison and Blaine toyed with naval acquisitions in the Caribbean and elsewhere, but in general they focused on Pan-Americanism and tariff reciprocity. Blaine presided over the first Inter-American Conference in Washington on October 2, 1889, where delegates from nineteen American nations were present. They negotiated several agreements to promote trade and created the International Bureau of the American Republics, later renamed the Pan-American Union, for the exchange of general information, including political, scientific, and cultural knowledge. The conference, a major step in hemispheric relations, led to later meetings promoting trade and other agreements.

Grover Cleveland, Harrison's successor, also pursued an aggressive policy toward Latin America. In 1895, he brought the United States precariously close to war with Great Britain over a boundary dispute between Venezuela and British Guiana. Cleveland sympathized with Venezuela, and he and Secretary of State Richard Olney urged Britain to arbitrate the dispute. When Britain failed to act, Olney drafted a stiff diplomatic note affirming the Monroe Doctrine and denying European nations the right to meddle in Western Hemisphere affairs.

Four months passed before Lord Salisbury, the British foreign secretary, replied. Rejecting Olney's arguments, he sent two letters, the first bluntly repudiating the Monroe Doctrine as international law. The second letter, carefully reasoned and sometimes sarcastic, rejected Olney's arguments for the Venezuelan boundary. Enraged, Cleveland defended the Monroe Doctrine, and he asked Congress for authority to appoint a commission to decide the boundary and enforce its decision. "I am fully alive to the responsibility incurred and keenly realize all the consequences that may follow," he told Congress, plainly implying war.

Preoccupied with larger diplomatic problems in Africa and Europe, Britain changed its position. In November 1896, the two countries signed a treaty of arbitration, under which Great Britain and Venezuela divided the disputed territory. Though Cleveland's approach was clumsy—throughout the crisis, for example, he rarely consulted Venezuela—the Venezuelan incident demonstrated a growing determination to exert American power in the Western Hemisphere. Cleveland and Olney had persuaded Great Britain to recognize the United States' dominance, and they had increased American influence in Latin America. The Monroe Doctrine assumed new importance. In averting war, an era of Anglo-American friendship was begun.

The Lure of Hawaii and Samoa

The islands of Hawaii offered a tempting way station to Asian markets. In the early 1800s, they were already called the "Crossroads of the Pacific," and trading ships of many nations stopped there. In 1820, the first American missionaries arrived to convert the islanders to Christianity. Like missionaries elsewhere, they advertised Hawaii's economic and other benefits and attracted new settlers.

After the Civil War, the United States tightened its connections with the islands. The reciprocity treaty of 1875 allowed Hawaiian sugar to enter the United States free of duty and bound the Hawaiian monarchy to make no territorial or economic concessions to other powers. The treaty increased Hawaiian economic dependence on the United States; its political clauses effectively made Hawaii an American protectorate. In 1887, a new treaty reaffirmed these arrangements and granted the United States exclusive use of Pearl Harbor, a magnificent harbor that had early caught the eye of naval strategists.

Following the 1875 treaty, white Hawaiians became more and more influential in the islands' political life. The McKinley Tariff Act of 1890 ended the special status given Hawaiian sugar and at the same time awarded American producers a bounty of two cents a pound. Hawaiian sugar production dropped dramatically, unemployment rose, and property values fell. The following year, the weak King Kalakaua died, bringing to power a strong-willed nationalist, Queen Liliuokalani.

Resentful of white minority rule, she decreed a new constitution that gave greater power to native Hawaiians.

Unhappy, the American residents revolted in early 1893 and called on the United States for help. John L. Stevens, the American minister in Honolulu, sent 150 marines ashore from the cruiser *Boston,* and within three days, the bloodless revolution was over. Queen Liliuokalani surrendered "to the superior force of the United States," and the victorious rebels set up a provisional government. On February 14, 1893, Harrison's secretary of state, John W. Foster, and delegates of the new government signed a treaty annexing Hawaii to the United States.

But only two weeks remained in Harrison's term, and the Senate refused to ratify the agreement. Five days after taking office, Cleveland withdrew the treaty; he then sent a representative to investigate the cause of the rebellion. The investigation revealed that the Americans' role in it had been improper, and

The first step toward American annexation of Hawaii came in 1893 when Queen Liliuokalani was removed from the throne. Hawaii was annexed to the United States as a possession in 1898 and became a U.S. territory in 1900.

Cleveland decided to restore the queen to her throne. He made the demand, but the provisional government in Hawaii politely refused and instead established the Republic of Hawaii, which the embarrassed Cleveland, unable to do otherwise, recognized.

The debate over Hawaiian annexation, continuing through the 1890s, foreshadowed the later debate over the treaty to end the Spanish-American War. People in favor of annexation pointed to Hawaii's strategic location, argued that Japan or other powers might seize the islands if the United States did not, and suggested that Americans had a responsibility to civilize and Christianize the native Hawaiians. Opponents warned that annexation might lead to a colonial army and colonial problems, the inclusion of a "mongrel" population in the United States, and rule over an area not destined for statehood.

Annexation came swiftly in July 1898 in the midst of excitement over victories in the Spanish-American War. The year before, President William McKinley had sent a treaty of annexation to the Senate, but opposition quickly arose, and the treaty stalled.

In 1898, annexationists redoubled arguments about Hawaii's commercial and military importance. McKinley and congressional leaders switched strategies to seek a joint resolution, rather than a treaty, for annexation. A joint resolution required only a majority of both houses, while a treaty needed a two-thirds vote in the Senate. Bolstered by the new strategy, the annexation measure moved quickly through Congress, and McKinley signed it on July 7, 1898.

While annexation of Hawaii represented a step toward China, the Samoan Islands, three thousand miles to the south, offered a strategic location astride the sea-lanes of the South Pacific. Americans showed early interest in Samoa, and in 1872, a naval officer negotiated a treaty granting the United States the use of Pago Pago, a splendid harbor on one of its islands. The Senate rejected the treaty, but six years later approved a similar agreement providing for a naval station there. Great Britain and Germany also secured treaty rights in Samoa, and thereafter the three nations jockeyed for position.

The situation grew tense in 1889, when warships from all three countries gathered in a Samoan harbor. But a sudden typhoon damaged the fleets, and tensions eased. A month later, delegates from Britain, Germany, and the United States met in Berlin to negotiate the problem. Britain and Germany wanted to divide up the islands; Secretary of State Blaine held out for some degree of authority by the indigenous population, with American control over Pago Pago.

The agreement, an uneasy one, ended in 1899 when the United States and Germany divided Samoa and compensated Britain with lands elsewhere in the Pacific. Germany claimed the two larger islands in the chain; the United States kept the harbor at Pago Pago.

THE NEW NAVY

Large navies were vital in the scramble for colonies, and in the 1870s the United States had almost no naval power. One of the most powerful fleets in the world during the Civil War, the American navy had fallen into rapid decline. By 1880, there were fewer than two thousand vessels, only forty-eight of which could fire a gun. Ships rotted, and many officers left the service.

Conditions changed during the 1880s. A group of rising young officers, steeped in a new naval philosophy, argued for an expanded navy equipped with fast, aggressive fleets capable of fighting battles across the seas. Big-navy proponents pointed to the growing fleets of Great Britain, France, and Germany, arguing that the United States needed greater fleet strength to protect its economic and other interests in the Caribbean and Pacific.

In 1883, Congress authorized construction of four steel ships, marking the beginning of the new navy. Between 1885 and 1889, Congress budgeted funds for thirty additional ships. The initial building program focused on lightly armored fast cruisers for raiding enemy merchant ships and protecting American shores, but after 1890, the program shifted to the construction of a seagoing offensive battleship navy capable of challenging the strongest fleets of Europe.

Alfred Thayer Mahan and Benjamin F. Tracy were two of the main forces behind the new navy. Austere and scholarly, Mahan was the era's most influential naval strategist. After graduating from the Naval Academy in 1859, he devoted a lifetime to studying the influence of sea power in history; for more than two decades, he headed the Newport Naval War College, where officers imbibed the latest in strategic thinking. A clear, logical writer, Mahan summarized his beliefs in several major books, including *The Influence of Sea Power upon History, 1660–1783* (1890), and *The Interest of America in Sea Power* (1897).

Mahan's reasoning was simple and, to that generation, persuasive. Industrialism, he argued, produced vast surpluses of agricultural and manufactured goods, for which markets must be found. Markets involved distant ports; reaching them required a large merchant marine and a powerful navy to protect it. Navies, in turn, needed coaling stations and repair yards. Coaling stations meant colonies, and colonies became strategic bases, the foundation of a nation's wealth and power. The bases might serve as markets themselves, but they were more important as stepping-stones to other objectives, such as the markets of Latin America and Asia.

Mahan called attention to the worldwide race for power, a race, he warned, the United States could not afford to lose. To compete in the race, Mahan argued, the United States must expand. It needed strategic bases, a powerful oceangoing navy, a canal across the isthmus to link the East Coast with the Pacific, and Hawaii as a way station on the route to Asia.

Mahan influenced a generation of policymakers in the United States and Europe; one of them, Benjamin F. Tracy, became Harrison's secretary of the navy in 1889. Tracy organized the Bureau of Construction and Repair to design and build new ships, established the Naval Reserve in 1891, and ordered construction of the first American submarine in 1893. He also adopted the first heavy rapid-fire guns, smokeless powder, torpedoes, and heavy armor. Above all, Tracy joined with big-navy advocates in Congress to push for a far-ranging battleship fleet capable of attacking distant enemies. He wanted two fleets of battleships, eight ships in the Pacific and twelve in the Atlantic. He got four first-class battleships.

In 1889, when Tracy entered office, the United States ranked twelfth among world navies; in 1893, when he left, it ranked seventh and was climbing rapidly. "The sea," he predicted in 1891, "will be the future seat of empires. And we shall rule it as certainly as the sun doth rise." By the end of the decade, the navy had seventeen steel battleships, six armored cruisers, and many smaller craft. It ranked third in the world.

WAR WITH SPAIN

The war with Spain in 1898 built a mood of national confidence, altered older, more insular patterns of thought, and reshaped the way Americans saw themselves and the world. Its outcome pleased some people but troubled others, who raised questions about war itself, colonies, and subject peoples. The war left a lingering strain of isolationism and antiwar feeling that affected later policy. It also left an American empire, small by European standards, but quite new to the American experience by virtue of its overseas location. When the war ended, American possessions stretched into the Caribbean and deep into the Pacific. American influence went further still, and the United States was recognized as a "world power."

The Spanish-American War established the United States as a dominant force for the twentieth century. It brought America colonies and millions of colonial subjects; it brought the responsibilities of governing an empire and protecting it. For better or worse, it involved the country in other nations' arguments and affairs. The war strengthened the office of the presidency, swept the nation together in a tide of emotion, and confirmed the long-standing belief in the superiority of the New World over the Old. When it was over, Americans looked outward as never before, touched, they were sure, with a special destiny.

A WAR FOR PRINCIPLE

By the 1890s, Cuba and the nearby island of Puerto Rico comprised nearly all that remained of Spain's once vast empire in the New World. Several times,

Cuban insurgents had rebelled against Spanish rule, including a decade-long rebellion from 1868 to 1878 that failed to settle the conflict. The depression of 1893 damaged the Cuban economy, and the Wilson-Gorman Tariff of 1894 prostrated it. Duties on sugar, Cuba's lifeblood, were raised 40 percent. With the island's sugar market in ruins, discontent with Spanish rule heightened, and in late February 1895, revolt again broke out.

Recognizing the importance of the nearby United States, Cuban insurgents established a junta in New York City to raise money, buy weapons, and wage a propaganda war to sway American public opinion. Conditions in Cuba were grim. Spain in January 1896 sent a new commander, General Valeriano Weyler y Nicolau. Relentless and brutal, Weyler gave the rebels ten days to lay down their arms. He then put into effect a "reconcentration" policy designed to move the native population into camps and destroy the rebellion's popular base. Herded into fortified areas, Cubans died by the thousands, victims of unsanitary conditions, overcrowding, and disease.

There was a wave of sympathy for the insurgents, stimulated by the newspapers, but so-called yellow or sensationalist journalism did not cause the war. The conflict stemmed from larger disputes in policies and perceptions between Spain and the United States. Grover Cleveland, under whose administration the rebellion began, preferred Spanish rule to the kind of turmoil that might invite foreign

This illustration appeared in Harper's Weekly. *Titled "Starvation by Proclamation," it shows Cubans being marched into one of General Weyler's "reconcentration" camps.*

intervention. Opposed to the annexation of Cuba, he issued a proclamation of neutrality and tried to restrain public opinion.

Taking office in March 1897, President McKinley also urged neutrality but leaned slightly toward the insurgents. He immediately sent a trusted aide on a fact-finding mission to Cuba; the aide reported in mid-1897 that Weyler's policy had wrapped Cuba "in the stillness of death and the silence of desolation." The report in hand, McKinley offered to mediate the struggle, but, concerned over the suffering, he protested against Spain's "uncivilized and inhuman" conduct. The United States, he made clear, did not contest Spain's right to fight the rebellion but insisted it be done within humane limits.

Late in 1897, a change in government in Madrid brought a temporary lull in the crisis. The new government recalled Weyler and agreed to offer the Cubans some form of autonomy. It also declared an amnesty for political prisoners and released Americans from Cuban jails. The new initiatives pleased McKinley, though he again warned Spain that it must find a humane end to the rebellion. Then, in January 1898, Spanish army officers led riots in Havana against the new autonomy policy, shaking the president's confidence in Madrid's control over conditions in Cuba.

McKinley ordered the battleship *Maine* to Havana to demonstrate strength and protect American citizens if necessary. On February 9, 1898, the *New York Journal,* a leader of the yellow press, published a letter stolen from Enrique Dupuy de Lôme, the Spanish ambassador in Washington. In the letter, which was private correspondence to a friend, de Lôme called McKinley "weak," "a would-be politician," and "a bidder for the admiration of the crowd." Many Americans were angered by the insult; McKinley himself was more worried about other sections of the letter that revealed Spanish insincerity in the negotiations. De Lôme immediately resigned and went home, but the damage was done.

A few days later, at 9:40 in the evening of February 15, an explosion tore through the hull of the *Maine,* riding at anchor in Havana harbor. The ship, a trim symbol of the new steel navy, sank quickly; 266 lives were lost. McKinley cautioned patience and promised an immediate investigation. Crowds gathered quietly on Capitol Hill and outside the White House, mourning the lost men. Soon there was a new slogan: "Remember the *Maine* and to Hell with Spain!"

The most recent study of the *Maine* incident blames the sinking on an accidental internal explosion, caused perhaps by spontaneous combustion in poorly ventilated coal bunkers. In 1898, Americans blamed it on Spain. Roosevelt, William Jennings Bryan, and others urged war, but McKinley delayed, hopeful that Spain might yet agree to an armistice and perhaps Cuban independence.

In early March 1898, wanting to be ready for war if it came, McKinley asked Congress for $50 million in emergency defense appropriations, a request

Headlines like these in William Randolph Hearst's New York Journal *left little doubt among his readers that Spain had sunk the* Maine.

Congress promptly approved. The unanimous vote stunned Spain; allowing the president a latitude that was highly unusual for the era, it appropriated the money "for the National defense and for each and every purpose connected therewith to be expended at the discretion of the President." In late March, the report of the investigating board blamed the sinking of the *Maine* on an external (and thus presumably Spanish) explosion. Pressures for war increased.

On March 27, McKinley cabled Spain his final terms. He asked Spain to declare an armistice, end the reconcentration policy, and—implicitly—move toward Cuban independence. When the Spanish answer came, it conceded some things, but not, in McKinley's judgment, the important ones. Spain offered a suspension of hostilities (but not an armistice) and left the Spanish commander in Cuba to set the length and terms of the suspension. It also revoked the reconcentration policy. But the Spanish response made no mention of a true armistice, McKinley's offer to mediate, or Cuba's independence.

Reluctantly McKinley prepared his war message, and Congress heard it on April 11, 1898. On April 19, Congress passed a joint resolution declaring Cuba independent and authorizing the president to use the army and navy to expel the

Spanish from it. An amendment by Colorado senator Henry M. Teller pledged that the United States had no intention of annexing the island.

On April 21, Spain severed diplomatic relations. The following day, McKinley proclaimed a blockade of Cuba and called for 125,000 volunteers. On Monday, April 25, Congress passed a declaration of war. Late that afternoon, McKinley signed it.

Some historians have suggested that in leading the country toward war, McKinley was weak and indecisive, a victim of war hysteria in the Congress and the country; others have called him a wily manipulator for war and imperial gains. In truth, he was neither. Throughout the Spanish crisis, McKinley pursued a moderate middle course that sought to end the suffering in Cuba, promote Cuba's independence, and allow Spain time to adjust to the loss of the remnant of empire. He also wanted peace, as did Spain, but in the end, the conflicting national interests of the two countries brought them to war.

"A Splendid Little War"

Ten weeks after the declaration of war, the fighting was over. For Americans, they were ten glorious, dizzying weeks, with victories to fill every headline and slogans to suit every taste. No war can be a happy occasion for those who fight it, but the Spanish-American War came closer than most. Declared in April, it ended in August. Relatively few Americans died, and the quick victory seemed to verify burgeoning American power. John Hay, soon to be McKinley's secretary of state, called it "a splendid little war."

At the outset, the United States was militarily unprepared. The regular army consisted of only 28,000 officers and men, most of them more experienced in quelling Indian uprisings than fighting large-scale battles. The Indian wars did produce effective small-scale forces, well trained and tightly disciplined, but the army was unquestionably too small for war against Spain.

When McKinley called for 125,000 volunteers, as many as 1 million young Americans responded. Ohio alone had 100,000 volunteers. Keeping the regular army units intact, War Department officials enlisted the volunteers in National Guard units that were then integrated into the national army. Men clamored to join. William Jennings Bryan, a pacifist by temperament, took command of a regiment of Nebraska volunteers; Roosevelt chafed to get to the front. The secretary of war feared "there is going to be more trouble to satisfy those who are not going than to find those who are willing to go."

In an army inundated with men, problems of equipment and supply quickly appeared. The regulars had the new .30-caliber Krag-Jorgensen rifles, but National Guard units carried Civil War Springfield rifles that used old black-powder cartridges. The cartridges gave off a puff of smoke when fired, neatly marking the troops' position. Spanish troops were better equipped; they had modern Mausers with smokeless powder, which they used to devastating effect. Food was also a problem, as was sickness. Tropical disease felled many soldiers. Scores took ill after landing in Cuba and the Philippines, and it was not uncommon for half a regiment to be unable to answer the bugle call.

Americans then believed that "a foreign war should be fought by the hometown military unit acting as an extension of their community." Soldiers identified with their hometowns, dressed in the local fashion, and thought of themselves as members of a town unit in a national army.

Not surprisingly, then, National Guard units mirrored the social patterns of their communities. Since everyone knew each other, there was an easygoing familiarity, tempered by the deference that went with hometown wealth, occupation, education, and length of residence. Enlisted men resented officers who grabbed too much authority, and they expected officers and men to call each other by their first names. "Officers and men of the Guard mingle on a plane of beautiful equality," said a visitor to one volunteer camp. "Privates invade the tents of their officers at will, and yell at them half the length of the street."

Each community thought of the hometown unit as its own unit, an extension of itself. In later wars, the government censored news and dominated press relations; there was little censorship in the war with Spain, and the freshest news arrived in the latest letter home. Small-town newspapers printed news of the men; towns sent food, clothing, and occasionally even local doctors to the front.

"Smoked Yankees"

When the invasion force sailed for Cuba, nearly one-fourth of it was African American. In 1898, the regular army included four regiments of African American soldiers, the Twenty-fourth and Twenty-fifth Infantry and the Ninth and Tenth Cavalry. Black regiments had served with distinction in campaigns against the Indians in the West. Most African American troops in fact were posted in the West; no eastern community would accept them. A troop of the Ninth Cavalry was stationed in Virginia in 1891, but whites protested and the troop was ordered back to the West.

When the war broke out, the War Department called for five black volunteer regiments. The army needed men, and military authorities were sure that black men had a natural immunity to the climate and diseases of the tropics. But most state governors refused to accept black volunteers. African American leaders protested the discrimination. The McKinley administration intervened, and in the end, the volunteer army included more than ten thousand black troops.

Orders quickly went out to the four black regular army regiments in the West to move to camps in the South to prepare for the invasion of Cuba. Crowds

Charge of the 24th and 25th Colored Infantry and Rescue of the Rough Riders at San Juan Hill, July 2, 1898, *colored lithograph by Kurz and Allison, 1899. The 24th and 25th Colored Infantry regiments served with exceptional gallantry in the Spanish-American War.*

Charles Young, an 1889 graduate of West Point, was the only African American officer in the army during the Spanish-American War except for a few chaplains.

and cheers followed the troop trains across the Plains, but as they crossed into Kentucky and Tennessee, the cheering stopped. Welcoming crowds were kept away from the trains, and the troops were hustled onward. Station restaurants refused to serve them; all waiting rooms were segregated. "It mattered not if we were soldiers of the United States, and going to fight for the honor of our country," Sergeant Frank W. Pullen of the Twenty-fourth Infantry wrote; "we were 'niggers' as they called us and treated us with contempt."

Many soldiers were not prepared to put up with the treatment. Those stationed near Chickamauga Park, Tennessee, shot "at some whites who insulted them" and forcibly desegregated the railroad cars on the line into Chattanooga. Troops training near Macon, Georgia, refused to ride in the segregated "trailers" attached to the trolleys, and fights broke out.

More than four thousand black troops training near Tampa and Lakeland, Florida, found segregated saloons, cafes, and drugstores. "Here the Negro is not allowed to purchase over the same counter in some stores as the white man purchases over," Chaplain George W. Prioleau charged. "Why sir, the Negro of this country is a freeman and yet a slave. Talk about fighting and freeing poor Cuba and of Spain's brutality; of Cuba's murdered thousands, and starving reconcentradoes. Is America any better than Spain?"

When the invasion force sailed a few days later, segregation continued on some of the troopships. Blacks were assigned to the lowest decks, or whites and blacks were placed on different sides of the ship. But the confusion of war often ended the problem, if only temporarily. Blacks took command as white officers died, and Spanish troops soon came to fear the "smoked Yankees," as they called them. Black soldiers played a major role in the Cuban campaign and probably staved off defeat for the Rough Riders at San Juan Hill. In Cuba, they won twenty-six Certificates of Merit and five Congressional Medals of Honor.

THE COURSE OF THE WAR

Mahan's Naval War College had begun studying strategy for a war with Spain in 1895. By 1898, it had a detailed plan for operations in the Caribbean and Pacific. Naval strategy was simple: destroy the Spanish fleet, damage Spain's merchant marine, and harry the colonies or the coast of Spain. Planners were excited; two steam-powered armored fleets had yet to meet in battle anywhere in the world. The army's task was more difficult. It must defend the United States, invade Cuba and probably Puerto Rico, and undertake possible action in far-flung places such as the Philippines or Spain.

Even before war was declared, the secretary of war arranged joint planning between the army and navy. Military intelligence was plentiful, and planners knew the numbers and locations of the Spanish troops. Earlier they had rejected a proposal to send an officer in disguise to map Cuban harbors; such things, they said, were simply not done in peacetime. Still, the War Department's new Military Information Division, a sign of the increasing professionalization of the army, had detailed diagrams of Spanish fortifications in Havana and other points. On the afternoon of April 20, 1898, McKinley summoned the strategists to the White House; to the dismay of those who wanted a more aggressive policy, they decided on the limited strategy of blockading Cuba, sending arms to the insurgents, and annoying the Spanish with small thrusts by the army.

Victories soon changed the strategy. In case of war, long-standing naval plans had called for a holding action against the Spanish base in the Philippines. On May 1, 1898, with the war barely a week old, Commodore George Dewey, commander of the Asiatic Squadron located at Hong Kong, crushed the Spanish fleet in Manila Bay. Suddenly, Manila and the Philippines lay within American grasp. At home, Dewey portraits, songs, and poems blossomed everywhere, and his calm order to the flagship's captain—"You may fire when ready, Gridley"—hung on every tongue. Dewey had two modern cruisers, a gunboat, and a Civil War paddle steamer. He sank eight Spanish warships. Dewey had no troops to attack the Spanish army in Manila, but the War Department, stunned by the speed and size of the victory, quickly raised an expeditionary force. On August 13, 1898, the troops accepted the surrender of Manila, and with it, the Philippines.

McKinley and his aides were worried about Admiral Pascual Cervera's main Spanish fleet, thought to be headed across the Atlantic for an attack on Florida. On May 13, the navy found Cervera's ships near Martinique in the Caribbean but then lost them again. A few days later, Cervera slipped secretly into the harbor of Santiago de Cuba, a city on the island's southern coast. But a spy in the Havana telegraph office alerted the Americans, and on May 28, a superior American force under Admiral William T. Sampson bottled Cervera up.

In early June, a small force of Marines seized Guantánamo Bay, the great harbor on the south of the island. They established depots for the navy to refuel and pinned down Spanish troops in the area. On June 14, an invasion force of about seventeen thousand men set sail from Tampa. Seven days later, they landed at Daiquiri on Cuba's southeastern coast. All was confusion, but the Spanish offered no resistance. Helped by Cuban insurgents, the Americans immediately pushed west toward Santiago, which they hoped to surround and capture. At first, the advance through the lush tropical countryside was peaceful.

The first battle broke out at Las Guasimas, a crossroads on the Santiago road. After a sharp fight, the Spanish fell back. On July 1, the Rough Riders, troops from the four black regiments, and the other regulars reached the strong fortifications at El Caney and San Juan Hill. Black soldiers of the Twenty-fifth Infantry charged the El Caney blockhouses, surprising the Spanish defenders with Comanche yells. For the better part of a day, the defenders fought stubbornly and held back the army's elite corps. In the confusion of battle, Roosevelt rallied an assortment of infantry and cavalry to take Kettle Hill, adjacent to San Juan Hill.

They charged directly into the Spanish guns, Roosevelt at their head, mounted on a horse, a blue polka-dot handkerchief floating from the brim of his sombrero. "I waved my hat and we went up the hill with a rush," he recalled in his autobiography. Actually, it was not quite so easy. Losses were heavy; eighty-nine Rough Riders were killed or wounded in the attack. Dense foliage concealed the enemy; smokeless powder gave no clue to their position. At nightfall, the surviving Spanish defenders withdrew, and the Americans prepared for the counterattack.

American troops now occupied the ridges overlooking Santiago. They were weakened by sickness, a fact unknown to the Spanish, who decided the city was lost. The Spanish command in Havana ordered Cervera to run for the open sea, although he knew the attempt to escape was hopeless. On the morning of July 3, Cervera's squadron steamed down the bay and out through the harbor's narrow channel, but the waiting American fleet closed in, and in a few hours every Spanish vessel was destroyed. Two weeks later, Santiago surrendered.

Soon thereafter, army troops, meeting little resistance, occupied Puerto Rico. Cervera had commanded Spain's only battle fleet, and when it sank, Spain was helpless against attacks on the colonies or even its own shores. The war was over. Lasting 113 days, it took relatively few lives, most of them the result of accident, yellow fever, malaria, and typhoid in Cuba. Of the 5,500 Americans who died in the war, only 379 were killed in battle. The navy lost one man in the battle at Santiago Bay, and only one to heatstroke in the stunning victory in Manila Bay.

DEBATE OVER EMPIRE

Late in the afternoon of August 12, 1898, representatives of Spain and the United States met in McKinley's White House office to sign the preliminary instrument of peace. Secretary of State William R. Day beckoned a presidential aide over to a large globe, remarking, "Let's see what we get by this."

What the United States got was an expansion of its territory and an even larger expansion of its responsibilities. According to the preliminary agreement, Spain granted independence to Cuba, ceded Puerto Rico and the Pacific island of Guam to the United States, and allowed Americans to occupy Manila until the two countries reached final agreement on the Philippines. To McKinley, the Philippines were the problem. Puerto Rico was close to the mainland, and it appealed even to many of the opponents of expansion. Guam was small and unknown; it escaped attention. The Philippines, on the other hand, were huge, sprawling, and thousands of miles from America.

McKinley weighed a number of alternatives for the Philippines, but he liked none of them. He believed he could not give the islands back to Spain; public opinion would not allow it. He might turn them over to another nation, but then they would fall, as he later said, "a golden apple of discord, among the rival powers." Germany, Japan, Great Britain, and Russia had all expressed interest in ac-

A Puck *cartoon titled "School Begins" satirizes Uncle Sam's course in civilization, in which he tells his students that they will soon be glad for all they will learn.*

quiring them. Germany even sent a large fleet to Manila and laid plans to take the Philippines if the United States let them go.

Rejecting those alternatives, McKinley considered independence for the islands but was soon talked out of it. People who had been there, reflecting the era's racism, told him the Filipinos were not ready for independence. He thought of establishing an American protectorate but discarded the idea, convinced it would bring American responsibilities without full American control. Sifting the alternatives, McKinley decided there was only one practical policy: annex the Philippines, with an eye to future independence after a period of tutelage.

At first hesitant, American opinion was swinging to the same conclusion. Religious and missionary organizations appealed to McKinley to hold on to the Philippines in order to "Christianize" them. Some merchants and industrialists saw them as the key to the China market and the wealth of Asia. Many Americans simply regarded them as the legitimate fruits of war. In October 1898, representatives of the United States and Spain met in Paris to discuss a peace treaty. Spain agreed to recognize Cuba's independence, assume the Cuban debt, and cede Puerto Rico and Guam to the United States.

Acting on instructions from McKinley, the American representatives demanded the cession of the Philippines. In return, the United States offered a payment of $20 million. Spain resisted but had little choice, and on December 10, 1898, the American and Spanish representatives signed the Treaty of Paris.

Submitted to the Senate for ratification, the treaty set off a storm of debate throughout the country. Industrialist Andrew Carnegie, reformer Jane Addams, labor leader Samuel Gompers, Mark Twain, and a host of others argued forcefully against annexing the Philippines. Annexation of the Philippines, the anti-imperialists protested over and over again, violated the very principles of independence and self-determination on which the United States was founded.

Some labor leaders feared the importation of cheap labor from new Pacific colonies. Gompers warned about the "half-breeds and semi-barbaric people" who might undercut wages and the union movement. Other anti-imperialists argued against assimilation of different races. Such racial views were also common among those favoring expansion, and the anti-imperialists usually focused on different arguments. If the United States established a tyranny abroad, they were sure, there would soon be tyranny at home. "This nation," declared William Jennings Bryan, "cannot endure half republic and half colony—half free and half vassal."

Charles Francis Adams, Jr., warned that the possession of colonies meant big armies, government, and debts ("an income tax looms up in the largest possible proportions," he said). Bryan scoffed at the argument that colonies were good for trade, pointing out, "It is not necessary to own people to trade with them." Many others thought there was no way to reconcile the country's republican ideals with the practice of keeping people under heel abroad. To Booker T. Washington, the country had more important things to think about at home, including its treatment of Indians and blacks.

In November 1898, opponents of expansion formed the Anti-Imperialist League to fight against the peace treaty. Membership centered in New England; the cause was less popular in the West and South. It enlisted more Democrats than Republicans, though never a majority of either. The anti-imperialists were weakened by the fact that they lacked a coherent program. Some favored keeping naval bases in the conquered areas. Some wanted Hawaii and Puerto Rico but not the Philippines. Others wanted nothing at all to do with any colonies.

The treaty debate in the Senate lasted a month. Pressing hard for ratification, McKinley earlier toured the South to rally support and consulted closely with senators. Though opposed to taking the Philippines, Bryan supported ratification in order to end the war; his support influenced some Democratic votes. Still, on the final weekend before the vote, the treaty was two votes short. That Saturday night, news reached Washington that fighting had broken out between American troops and Filipino insurgents who demanded immediate independence. The news increased pressure to ratify the treaty, which the Senate did on February 6, 1899, with two votes to spare. An amendment promising independence as soon as the Filipinos established a stable government lost by one vote. The United States had a colonial empire.

GUERRILLA WARFARE IN THE PHILIPPINES

Historians rarely write of the Philippine-American War, but it was an important event in American history. The war with Spain was over a few months after it began, but war with the Filipinos lasted more than three years. Four times as many American soldiers fought in the Philippines as in Cuba. For the first time, Americans fought men of a different color in an Asian guerrilla war. The Philippine-American War of 1898–1902 took a heavy toll: 4,300 American lives and untold thousands of Filipino lives (estimates range from 50,000 to 200,000).

Emilio Aguinaldo, the Filipino leader, was 29 years old in 1898. An early organizer of the anti-Spanish resistance, he had gone into exile in Hong Kong, from where he welcomed the outbreak of the Spanish-American War. Certain the United States would grant independence, he worked for an American victory. Filipino insurgents helped guide Dewey into Manila Bay, and Dewey himself sent a ship to Hong Kong to bring back Aguinaldo to lead a native uprising against the Spanish. On June 12, 1898, the insurgents proclaimed their independence.

Cooperating with the Americans, they drove the Spanish out of many areas of the islands. In the liberated regions, Aguinaldo established local governments

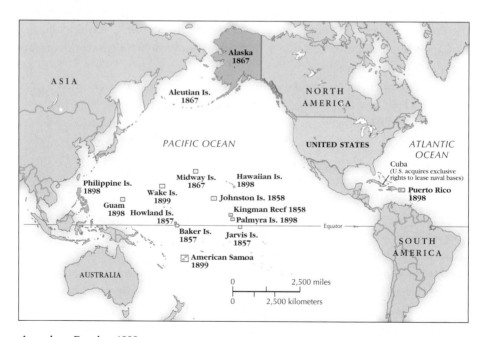

American Empire, 1900
With the Treaty of Paris, the United States gained an expanded colonial empire stretching from the Caribbean to the far Pacific. It embraced Puerto Rico, Alaska, Hawaii, part of Samoa, Guam, the Philippines, and a chain of Pacific islands. The dates on the map refer to the date of U.S. acquisition.

with appointed provincial governors. He waited impatiently for American recognition, but McKinley and others had concluded that the Filipinos were not ready. Soon, warfare broke out between the Filipinos and Americans over the question of Filipino independence.

By late 1899, the American army had defeated and dispersed the organized Filipino army, but claims of victory proved premature. Aguinaldo and his advisers shifted to guerrilla tactics, striking suddenly and then melting into the jungle or friendly native villages. There were terrible atrocities on both sides. The Americans found themselves using brutal, Weyler-like tactics. After any attack on an American patrol, the Americans burned all the houses in the nearest district. They tortured people and executed prisoners. They established protected "zones" and herded Filipinos into them. Seizing or destroying all food outside the zones, they starved many guerrillas into submission.

Emilio Aguinaldo (seated, in vest) and his advisors in the Philippines, 1896. Aguinaldo's forces helped the Americans drive Spain out of the Philippines, expecting that the United States would recognize Filipino independence. When the United States failed to do so, Aguinaldo led his forces in warfare against the Americans.

Bryan tried to turn the election of 1900 into a debate over imperialism, but the attempt failed. For one thing, he himself refused to give up the silver issue, which cost him some support among anti-imperialists in the Northeast who were for gold. McKinley, moreover, was able to take advantage of the surging economy, and he could defend expansion as an accomplished fact. Riding a wave of patriotism and prosperity, McKinley won the election handily—by an even larger margin than he had in 1896.

In 1900, McKinley sent a special Philippine Commission to the islands under William Howard Taft, a prominent Ohio judge. Directed to establish a civil government, the commission organized municipal administrations and, in stages, created a government for the Philippines. In March 1901, five American soldiers tricked their way into Aguinaldo's camp deep in the mountains and took him prisoner. Back in Manila, he signed a proclamation urging his people to end the fighting. Some guerrillas held out for another year, but to no avail. On July 4, 1901, authority was transferred from the army to Taft, who was named civilian governor of the islands, and his civilian commission. McKinley reaffirmed his purpose to grant the Filipinos self-government as soon as they were deemed ready for it.

Given broad powers, the Taft Commission introduced many changes. New schools provided education and vocational training for Filipinos of all social classes. The Americans built roads and bridges, reformed the judiciary, restructured the tax system, and introduced sanitation and vaccination programs. They established local governments built on Filipino traditions and hierarchies. Taft encouraged Filipino participation in government. During the following decades, other measures broadened Filipino rights. Independence finally came on July 4, 1946, nearly fifty years after Aguinaldo proclaimed it.

GOVERNING THE EMPIRE

Ruling the colonies raised new and perplexing questions. How could—and how should—the distant dependencies be governed? Did their inhabitants have the rights of American citizens? Some people contended that acquisition did not automatically incorporate the new possessions into the United States and endow them with constitutional privileges. Others argued that "the Constitution followed the flag," meaning that acquisition made the possessions part of the nation and thus entitled them to all constitutional guarantees. A third group suggested that only "fundamental" constitutional guarantees—citizenship, the right to vote, and the right to trial by jury—not "formal" privileges—the right to use American currency, the right to be taxed, and the right to run for the presidency—were applicable to the new empire.

In a series of cases between 1901 and 1904 (*De Lima* v. *Bidwell, Dooley* v. *U.S.,* and *Downes* v. *Bidwell*), the Supreme Court asserted the principle that the Constitution did not automatically and immediately apply to the people of an annexed territory and did not confer upon them all the privileges of U.S. citizenship. Instead, Congress could specifically extend such constitutional provisions as it saw fit. "Ye-es," the secretary of war said of the Court's ambiguous rulings, "as near as I can make out the Constitution follows the flag—but doesn't quite catch up with it."

Four dependencies—Hawaii, Alaska, Guam, and Puerto Rico—were organized quickly. In 1900, Congress granted territorial status to Hawaii, gave American citizenship to all citizens of the Hawaiian republic, authorized an elective legislature, and provided for a governor appointed from Washington. A similar measure made Alaska a territory in 1912. Guam and American Samoa were simply placed under the control of naval officers.

Unlike the Filipinos, Puerto Ricans readily accepted the war's outcome, and McKinley early withdrew troops from the island. The Foraker Act of 1900 established civil government in Puerto Rico. It organized the island as a territory, made its residents citizens of Puerto Rico (U.S. citizenship was extended to them in 1917), and empowered the president to appoint a governor general and a council to serve as the upper house of the legislature. A lower house of delegates was to be elected.

Cuba proved a trickier matter. McKinley asserted the authority of the United States over conquered territory and promised to govern the island until the Cubans had established a firm and stable government of their own. "I want you to go down there to get the people ready for a republican form of government," he instructed General Leonard Wood, commander of the army in Cuba until 1902. "I leave the details of procedure to you. Give them a good school system, try to straighten out their ports, and put them on their feet as best you can. We want to do all we can for them and to get out of the island as soon as we safely can."

Wood moved quickly to implement the instructions. Early in 1900, he completed a census of the Cuban population, conducted municipal elections, and arranged the election of delegates to a constitutional convention. The convention adopted a constitution modeled on the U.S. Constitution and, at Wood's prodding, included provisions for future relations with the United States. Known as the Platt Amendment to the new Cuban Constitution, the provisions stipulated that Cuba should make no treaties with other powers that might impair its independence, acquire no debts it could not pay, and lease naval bases such as Guantánamo Bay to the United States. Most important, the amendment empowered the United States to intervene in Cuba to maintain orderly government.

Between 1898 and 1902, the American military government worked hard for the economic and political revival of the island, though it often demonstrated a paternalistic attitude toward the Cubans themselves. It repaired the damage of the civil war, built roads and schools, and established order in rural areas. A public health campaign headed by Dr. Walter Reed, an army surgeon, wiped out yellow fever. Most troops withdrew at the end of 1899, but a small American occupation force remained until May 1902. When it sailed for home, the Cubans at last had a form of independence, but they were still under the clear domination of their neighbor to the north.

THE OPEN DOOR

Poised in the Philippines, the United States had become an Asian power on the doorstep of China. Weakened by years of warfare, China in 1898 and 1899 was unable to resist foreign influence. Japan, England, France, Germany, and Russia eyed it covetously, dividing parts of the country into "spheres of influence." They forced China to grant "concessions" that allowed them exclusive rights to develop particular areas and threatened American hopes for extensive trade with the country.

McKinley first outlined a new China policy in September 1898 when he said that Americans sought more trade, "but we seek no advantages in the Orient which are not common to all. Asking only the open door for ourselves, we are ready to accord the open door to others." In September 1899, Secretary of State John Hay addressed identical diplomatic notes to England, Germany, and Russia, and later to France, Japan, and Italy, asking them to join the United States in establishing the "Open Door." The policy urged three agreements: nations possessing a sphere of influence would respect the rights and privileges of other nations in that sphere; the Chinese government would continue to collect tariff duties in all spheres; and nations would not discriminate against other nations in levying port dues and railroad rates within their respective spheres of influence.

Under the Open Door policy, the United States would retain many commercial advantages it might lose if China was partitioned into spheres of influence. McKinley and Hay also attempted to preserve for the Chinese some semblance of national authority. Great Britain most nearly accepted the principle of the Open Door. Russia declined to approve it, and the other powers, sending evasive replies, stated they would agree only if all the other nations did. Hay turned the situation to American advantage by boldly announcing in March 1900 that all the powers had accepted the Open Door policy.

The policy's first test came just three months later with the outbreak of the Boxer Rebellion in Peking (now Beijing). In June 1900, a secret, intensely nationalistic Chinese society called the Boxers tried to oust all foreigners from their

In this 1899 cartoon, "Putting His Foot Down" from Puck, *the nations of Europe are getting ready to cut up China to expand their spheres of influence, but Uncle Sam stands firm on American commitments to preserve China's sovereignty.*

country. Overrunning Peking, they drove foreigners into their legations and penned them up for nearly two months. In the end, the United States joined Britain, Germany, and other powers in sending troops to lift the siege.

Fearing that the rebellion gave some nations, especially Germany and Russia, an excuse to expand their spheres of influence, Hay took quick action to emphasize American policy. In July, he sent off another round of Open Door notes affirming U.S. commitment to equal commercial opportunity and respect for China's independence. While the first Open Door notes had implied recognition of China's continued independence, the second notes explicitly stated the need to preserve it. Together, the two notes comprised the Open Door policy, which became a central element in American policy in the Far East.

To some degree, the policy tried to help China, but it also led to further American meddling in the affairs of another country. Moreover, by committing itself to a policy that Americans were not prepared to defend militarily, the McKinley administration left the opportunity for later controversy with Japan and other expansion-minded powers in the Pacific.

The war with Spain over, Roosevelt and the Rough Riders sailed for home in mid-August 1898. They sauntered through the streets of New York, the heroes of the city. A few weeks later, Roosevelt bade them farewell. Close to tears, he told them, "I am proud of this regiment beyond measure." Soon, Roosevelt was governor of New York and on his way to the White House.

Other soldiers were also glad to be home, although they were sometimes resentful of the reception they found. "The war is over now," said Winslow Hobson, a black trooper from the Ninth Ohio, "and Roosevelt . . . and others (white of course) have all there is to be gotten out of it." Bravery in Cuba and the Philippines won some recognition for black soldiers, but the war itself set back the cause of civil rights. It spurred talk about "inferior" races, at home and abroad, and united whites in the North and South. "The Negro might as well know it now as later," a black editor said, "the closer the North and South get together by this war, the harder he will have to fight to maintain a footing." A fresh outburst of segregation and lynching occurred during the decade after the war.

McKinley and the Republican party soared to new heights of popularity. Firmly established, the Republican majority dominated politics until 1932. Scandals arose about the food and the conduct of the War Department, but there was none of the sharp sense of deception and betrayal that was to mark the years after World War I. In a little more than a century, the United States had grown from thirteen states stretched along a thin Atlantic coastline into a world power that reached from the Caribbean to the Pacific. As Seward and others had hoped, the nation now dominated its own hemisphere, dealt with European powers on more equal terms, and was a major power in Asia.

22

THE PROGRESSIVE ERA

I n 1902, Samuel S. McClure, the shrewd owner of *McClure's Magazine,* sensed something astir in the country that his reporters were not covering. Like *Life, Munsey's,* the *Ladies' Home Journal,* and *Cosmopolitan, McClure's* was reaching more and more people—more than a quarter million readers a month. Americans were snapping up the new popular magazines filled with eye-catching illustrations and up-to-date fiction. Advances in photoengraving during the 1890s dramatically reduced the cost of illustrations; at the same time, income from advertisements rose sharply. By the turn of the century, some magazines earned as much as $60,000 an issue from advertising alone, and publishers could price them as low as 10 cents a copy.

McClure was always chasing new ideas and readers, and in 1902, certain that something was happening in the public mood, he told one of his editors, 36-year-old Lincoln Steffens, a former Wall Street reporter, to find out what it was. "Get out of here, travel, go—somewhere," he said to Steffens. "Buy a railroad ticket, get on a train, and there, where it lands you, there you will learn to edit a magazine."

Steffens traveled west. In St. Louis, he came across a young district attorney named Joseph W. Folk who had found a trail of corruption linking politics and some of the city's respected business leaders. Eager for help, Folk did not mind naming names to the visiting editor from New York. "It is good business men that are corrupting our bad politicians," he stressed again and again. Steffens's story, "Tweed Days in St. Louis," appeared in the October 1902 issue of *McClure's.*

The November *McClure's* carried the first installment of Ida Tarbell's scathing "History of the Standard Oil Company," and in January 1903, Steffens was back

During the Progressive Era, McClure's Magazine *was at the forefront of the journalistic crusade for reform, which took the form of muckraking articles by such writers as Ida Tarbell (left). Her exposé of the Standard Oil Company ran side by side with Lincoln Steffens's article on the alliances between businesses and corrupt political machines in several cities.*

with "The Shame of Minneapolis," another tale of corrupt partnership between business and politics. McClure had what he wanted, and in the January issue he printed an editorial, "Concerning Three Articles in This Number of *McClure's,* and a Coincidence That May Set Us Thinking." Steffens on Minneapolis, Tarbell on Standard Oil, and an article on abuses in labor unions—all, McClure said, on different topics but actually on the same theme: corruption in American life. "Capitalists, workingmen, politicians, citizens—all breaking the law, or letting it be broken."

Readers were enthralled, and articles and books by other muckrakers—Theodore Roosevelt coined the unflattering term in 1906 to describe the practice of exposing the corruption of public and prominent figures—spread swiftly. *Collier's* had articles on questionable stock market practices, patent medicines, and the beef trust. Novelist Upton Sinclair tackled the meatpackers in *The Jungle* (1906). In 1904, Steffens collected his *McClure's* articles in *The Shame of the Cities,* with an introduction expressing confidence that reform was possible, "that our shamelessness is superficial, that beneath it lies a pride which, being real, may save us yet."

Muckraking flourished from 1903 to 1909, and while it did, good writers and bad investigated almost every corner of American life: government, labor unions, big business, Wall Street, health care, the food industry, child labor, women's rights, prostitution, ghetto living, and life insurance.

The muckrakers were a journalistic voice of a larger movement in American society. Called *progressivism,* it lasted from the mid-1890s through World War I. Like muckraking itself, progressivism reflected worry about the state of society, the effects of industrialization and urbanization, social disorder, political corruption, and a host of other issues. With concerns so large, progressivism often had a sense of crisis and urgency, although it was rooted in a spirit of hopefulness and confidence in human progress. For varying reasons, thousands of people became concerned about their society, and, separately and together, they set out to cure some of the ills they saw around them. The efforts of the so-called progressives changed the nation and gave the era its name.

As McClure had hoped, Steffens *had* found something astir in the country, something so important and pervasive that it altered the course of American history in the twentieth century. This chapter examines in detail the economic, social, and intellectual conditions that gave rise to progressivism. Chapter 23 examines progressivism itself, in the cities, states, and nation.

THE CHANGING FACE OF INDUSTRIALISM

As the new century turned, conditions in America were better than just a few years before. Farms and factories were once again prosperous; in 1901, for the first time in years, the economy reached full capacity. Farm prices rose almost 50 percent between 1900 and 1910. Unemployment dropped. Not everyone was progressing. Many of the problems that had angered people in the 1890s continued into the new century, and millions of Americans still suffered from poverty and disease. Racism sat even more heavily on African Americans in both South and North, and there was increasing hostility against immigrants from southern and eastern Europe and from Mexico and Asia. Yet economic conditions were better for many people, and as a result, prosperity became one of the keys to understanding the era and the nature of progressive reform.

The start of the new century was another key as well, for it influenced people to take a fresh look at themselves and their times. Excited about beginning the twentieth century, people believed technology and enterprise would shape a better life. Savoring the word *new,* they talked of the new poetry, new cinema, new history, new democracy, new woman, new art, new immigration, new morality, and new city. Presidents Theodore Roosevelt and Woodrow Wilson called their political programs the New Nationalism and the New Freedom.

The word *mass* also cropped up frequently. Victors in the recent war with Spain, Americans took pride in teeming cities, burgeoning corporations, and other marks of the mass society. They enjoyed the fruits of mass production, read mass circulation newspapers and magazines, and took mass transit from the growing spiral of suburbs into the central cities.

Behind mass production lay significant changes in the nation's industrial system. Businesses grew at a rapid rate. They were large in the three decades after the Civil War, but in the years between 1895 and 1915, industries became mammoth, employing thousands of workers and equipped with assembly lines to turn out huge quantities of the company's product. Inevitably, changes in management attitudes, business organization, and worker roles influenced the entire society. Inevitably, too, the growth of giant businesses gave rise to a widespread fear of "trusts" and a desire among many progressive reformers to break them up or regulate them.

THE INNOVATIVE MODEL T

In the movement toward large-scale business and mass production, the automobile industry was one of those that led the way. In 1895, there were only four cars on the nation's roads; in 1917, there were nearly five million, and the automobile had already helped work a small revolution in industrial methods and social mores.

In 1903, Henry Ford and a small group of associates formed the Ford Motor Company, the firm that transformed the business. Ford was 40 years old. He had tried farming and hated it. During the 1890s, he worked as an engineer, but spent his spare time designing internal combustion engines and automobiles. At first, like many others in the industry, he concentrated on building luxury and racing cars.

In 1903, Ford sold the first Ford car. The price was high, and in 1905, Ford raised prices still higher. Sales plummeted. In 1907, he lowered the price; sales and revenues rose. Ford learned an important lesson of the modern economy: a smaller unit profit on a large number of sales meant enormous revenues. Early in 1908, he introduced the Model T, a four-cylinder, 20-horsepower "Tin Lizzie," costing $850, and available only in black. Eleven thousand were sold the first year.

"I am going to democratize the automobile," Ford proclaimed. "When I'm through everybody will be able to afford one, and about everyone will have one." The key was mass production, and after many experiments, Ford copied the techniques of meatpackers who moved animal carcasses along overhead trolleys from station to station. Adapting the process to automobile assembly, Ford in 1913 set up moving assembly lines in his plant in Highland Park, Michigan, that

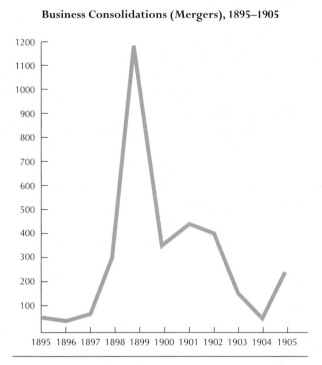

Business Consolidations (Mergers), 1895–1905

dramatically reduced the time and cost of producing cars. Emphasizing continuous movement, he strove for a nonstop flow from raw material to finished product. In 1914, he sold 248,000 Model T cars.

That year, Ford workers assembled a car in 93 minutes, one-tenth the time it had taken just eight months before. By 1925, the Ford plant turned out 9,109 Model T's, a new car for every ten seconds of the workday.

While Ford was putting more and more cars on the road, the 1916 Federal Aid Roads Act, a little noticed measure, set the framework for road building in the twentieth century. Removing control from county governments, it required every state desiring federal funds to establish a highway department to plan routes, oversee construction, and maintain roads. In states that had such departments, the federal government paid half the cost of building the roads. Providing for a planned highway system, the act produced a national network of two-lane all-weather intercity roads.

THE BURGEONING TRUSTS

As businesses like Ford's grew, capital and organization became increasingly important, and the result was the formation of a growing number of trusts. Between 1898 and 1903, a series of mergers and consolidations swept the economy. Many smaller firms disappeared, swallowed up in giant corporations. By 1904, large-scale combinations of one form or another controlled nearly two-fifths of the capital in manufacturing in the country.

The result was not monopoly but oligopoly—control of a commodity or service by a small number of large, powerful companies. Six great financial groups dominated the railroad industry; a handful of holding companies controlled utilities and steel. Rockefeller's Standard Oil owned about 85 percent of the oil business. After 1898, financiers and industrialists formed the Amalgamated Copper Company, Consolidated Tobacco, U.S. Rubber, and a host of others.

By 1909, just 1 percent of the industrial firms were producing nearly half of all manufactured goods. Giant businesses reached abroad for raw materials and new markets. United Fruit, an empire of plantations and steamships in the

As early as 1886, cartoonist Thomas Nast attacked trusts. Here the people's welfare is sinking as the Statue of Liberty is defaced.

THE RISING OF THE USURPERS.

And the sinking of the liberties of the people.

Caribbean, exploited opportunities created by victory in the war with Spain. U.S. Steel worked with overseas companies to fix the price of steel rails, an unattainable dream just a few years before.

Though the trend has been overstated, finance capitalists such as J. P. Morgan tended to replace the industrial capitalists of an earlier era. Able to finance the mergers and reorganizations, investment bankers played a greater and greater role in the economy. A multibillion-dollar financial house, J. P. Morgan and Company operated a network of control that ran from New York City to every industrial and financial center in the nation. Like other investment firms, it held directorships in many corporations, creating "interlocking directorates" that allowed it to control many businesses.

Massive business growth set off a decade-long debate over what government should do about the trusts. Some critics who believed that the giant companies were responsible for stifling individual opportunity and raising prices wanted to break them up into small competitive units. Others argued that large-scale business was a mark of the times, and that it produced more goods and better lives.

The debate over the trusts was one of the issues that shaped the Progressive Era, but it was never a simple contest between high-minded reformers and greedy business titans. Some progressives favored big business; others wanted it broken up. Business leaders themselves were divided in their viewpoints, and some welcomed reform-led assaults on giant competitors. As a rule, both progressives and business leaders drew on similar visions of the country: complex, expansive, hopeful, managerially minded, and oriented toward results and efficiency. They both believed in private property and the importance of economic progress. In fact, in working for reform, the progressives often drew on the managerial methods of a business world they sought to regulate.

MANAGING THE MACHINES

Mass production changed the direction of American industry. Size, system, organization, and marketing became increasingly important. Management focused on speed and product, not on workers. Assembly-line technology changed tasks and, to some extent, values. The goal was no longer to make a unique product that would be better than the one before. "The way to make automobiles," Ford said as early as 1903, "is to make one automobile like another automobile, to make them all alike, to make them come through the factory just alike."

In a development that rivaled assembly lines in importance, businesses established industrial research laboratories where scientists and engineers developed new products. General Electric founded the first one in 1900, housed in a barn. It soon attracted experts who designed improvements in light bulbs, invented the cathode-ray tube, worked on early radio, and even tinkered with atomic theory.

Du Pont opened its labs in 1911, Eastman Kodak in 1912, and Standard Oil in 1919. As the source of new ideas and technology, the labs altered life in the twentieth century.

Through all this, business became large-scale, mechanized, and managed. While many shops still employed fewer than a dozen workers, the proportion of such shops shrank. By 1920, close to one-half of all industrial workers toiled in factories employing more than 250 people. More than one-third worked in factories that were part of multiplant companies.

Industries that processed materials—iron and steel, paper, cement, and chemicals—were increasingly automated and operated continuously. Workers in those industries could not fall behind. Foremen still managed the laborers on the factory floor, but more and more, the rules came down from a central office where trained professional managers supervised production flow. Systematic record keeping, cost accounting, and inventory and production controls became widespread. In the automobile industry, output per worker-hour multiplied an extraordinary four times between 1909 and 1919.

Folkways of the workplace—workers passing job-related knowledge to each other, performing their tasks with little supervision, setting their own pace, and in effect running the shop—began to give way to "scientific" labor management. More than anyone else, Frederick Winslow Taylor, an inventive mechanical engineer, strove to extract maximum efficiency from each worker. "In the past," he believed, "the man has been first; in the future the system must be first."

In his book *The Principles of Scientific Management* (1911), Taylor proposed two major reforms. First, management must take responsibility for job-related knowledge and classify it into "rules, laws, and formulae." Second, management should control the workplace "through *enforced* standardization of methods, *enforced* adoption of the best implements and working conditions, and *enforced* cooperation."

Workers caught up in the changing industrial system experienced the benefits of efficiency and productivity; in some industries, they earned more. But they suffered important losses as well. Performing repetitive tasks, they seemed part of the machinery, moving to the pace and needs of their mechanical pacesetters. Bored, they might easily lose pride of workmanship, though many workers, it is clear, did not. Efficiency engineers experimented with tools and methods, a process many workers found unsettling. Yet the goal was to establish routine—to work out, as someone said of a garment worker, "one single precise motion each second, 3,600 in one hour, and all exactly the same." Praising that worker, the manager said, "She is a sure machine."

Fire nets were of no avail to the workers at the Triangle Shirtwaist Company who jumped from the upper stories to escape the flames. Speaking to a mass meeting after the fire, labor organizer Rose Schneiderman (right) inveighed against a system that treated human beings as expendable commodities.

Jobs became not only monotonous but dangerous. As machines and assembly lines sped up, boredom or miscalculation could bring disaster. In March 1911, a fire at the Triangle Shirtwaist Company in New York focused nationwide attention on unsafe working conditions. When the fire started, five hundred men and women, mostly Italians and Jews from eastern Europe, were just finishing their workday. Firefighters arrived within minutes, but they were already too late. Terrified seamstresses raced to the exits to try to escape the flames, but most exit doors were closed, locked by the company to prevent theft and shut out union organizers. Many died in the stampede down the narrow stairways or the single fire escape. Still others, trapped on the building's top stories far above the reach of the fire department's ladders, jumped to their deaths on the street below. One hundred forty-six people died.

A few days later, eighty thousand people marched silently in the rain in a funeral procession up Fifth Avenue. A quarter million people watched. At a mass meeting held to protest factory working conditions, Rose Schneiderman, a dynamic 29-year-old organizer for the Women's Trade Union League, told New York City's civic and religious leaders that they had not done enough, they had not cared. "Every week I must learn of the untimely death of one of my sister workers. Every year thousands of us are maimed. The life of men and women is so cheap and property is so sacred."

The outcry impelled New York's governor to appoint a State Factory Investigating Commission that recommended laws to shorten the workweek and improve safety in factories and stores.

SOCIETY'S MASSES

Spreading consumer goods through society, mass production not only improved people's lives but sometimes cost lives, too. Tending the machines took hard, painful labor, often under dangerous conditions. As businesses expanded, they required more and more people, and the labor force increased tremendously to keep up with the demand for workers in the factories, mines, and forest. Women, African Americans, Asian Americans, and Mexican Americans played larger and larger roles. Immigration soared. Between 1901 and 1910, nearly 8.8 million immigrants entered the United States; between 1911 and 1920, another 5.7 million came.

For many of these people, life was harsh, spent in crowded slums and long hours on the job. Fortunately, the massive unemployment of the 1890s was over, and in many skilled trades, such as cigar making, there was plenty of work to go around. Though the economic recovery helped nearly everyone, the less skilled continued to be the less fortunate. Migrant workers, lumberjacks, ore shovelers, and others struggled to find jobs that paid decently.

Under such circumstances, many people fought to make a living, and many, too, fought to improve their lot. Their efforts, along with the efforts of the reform-minded people who came to their aid, became another important hallmark of the Progressive Era.

BETTER TIMES ON THE FARM

While people continued to flee the farms—by 1920, fewer than one-third of all Americans lived on farms, and fewer than one-half lived in rural areas—farmers themselves prospered, the beneficiaries of greater production and expanding urban markets. Rural free delivery, begun in 1893, helped diminish the farmers' sense of isolation and changed farm life. The delivery of mail to the farm door opened that door to a wider world; it exposed farmers to urban thinking, national advertising, and political events. In 1911, more than one billion newspapers and magazines were delivered over RFD routes.

Parcel post (1913) permitted the sending of packages through the U.S. mail. Mail-order houses flourished; rural merchants suffered. Within a year, 300 million packages were being mailed annually. While telephones and electricity did not reach most rural areas for decades, better roads, mail-order catalogs, and other innovations knit farmers into the larger society. Early in the new century, Mary E. Lease—who in her Populist days had urged Kansas farmers to raise less corn and more Hell—moved to Brooklyn.

Farmers still had problems. Land prices rose with crop prices, and farm tenancy increased, especially in the South. Tenancy grew from one-quarter of all farms in 1880 to more than one-third in 1910. Many southern tenant farmers were African Americans, and they suffered from farm-bred diseases. In one of the reforms of the Progressive Era, in 1909, the Rockefeller Sanitary Commission, acting on recent scientific discoveries, began a sanitation campaign that eventually wiped out the hookworm disease.

In the arid West, irrigation transformed the land as the federal government and private landholders joined to import water from mountain watersheds. The dry lands bloomed, and so did a rural class structure that sharply separated owners from workers. Under the Newlands Act of 1902, the secretary of the interior formed the U.S. Reclamation Service, which gathered a staff of thousands of engineers and technicians, "the largest bureaucracy ever assembled in irrigation history."

Dams and canals channeled water into places such as California's Imperial Valley, and as the water streamed in, cotton, cantaloupes, oranges, tomatoes, lettuce, and a host of other crops streamed out to national markets. By 1920, Idaho, Montana, Utah, Wyoming, Colorado, and Oregon had extensive irrigation systems, all drawing on scarce water supplies; California, the foremost importer of water, had 4.2 million acres under irrigation, many of them picked by migrant workers from Mexico, China, and Japan.

WOMEN AT WORK

Women worked in larger and larger numbers. In 1900, more than five million worked—one-fifth of all adult women—and among those aged 14 to 24, the employment rate was almost one-third. Of those employed, single women outnumbered married women by seven to one, yet more than one-third of married women worked. Most women held service jobs. Only a small number held higher-paying jobs as professionals or managers.

In the 1890s, women made up more than one-quarter of medical school graduates. Using a variety of techniques, men gradually squeezed them out, and by the 1920s, only about 5 percent of the graduates were women. Few women taught in colleges and universities, and those who did were expected to resign if they married.

More women than men graduated from high school, and with professions like medicine and science largely closed to them, they often turned to the new "business schools" that offered training in stenography, typing, and bookkeeping. In 1920, more than one-quarter of all employed women held clerical jobs. Many others taught school.

Black women had always worked, and in far larger numbers than their white counterparts. The reason was usually economic; an African American man or

LAD FELL TO DEATH IN BIG COAL CHUTE

Dennis McKee Dead and Arthur Allbecker Had Leg Burned In the Lee Mines.

Falling into a chute at the Chauncy colliery of the George S. Lee Coal Company at Avondale, this afternoon, Dennis McKee, aged 13, of West Nanticoke, was smothered to death and Arthur Allbecker, aged 15, had both of his legs burned and injured. Dr. Biel, of Plymouth, was summoned and

He was removed to his home at Avondale.

Both boys were employed as breaker boys, and going too close to the chutes fell in. Fellow workmen rushed to their assistance and soon had them out of the chutes. When taken out, McKee was found to be dead. His remains were removed to his home at West Nanticoke. All-

Breaker boys, who picked out pieces of slate from the coal as it rushed past, often became bent-backed after years of working fourteen hours a day in the coal mines. Accidents—and deaths—were common in the mines.

woman alone could rarely earn enough to support a family. Unlike many white women, black women tended to remain in the labor force after marriage or the start of a family. They also had less opportunity for job advancement, and in 1920, between one-third and one-half of all African American women who were working were restricted to personal and domestic service jobs.

Critics charged that women's employment endangered the home, threatened their reproductive functions, and even, as one man said, stripped them of "that modest demeanor that lends a charm to their kind." Adding to these fears, the birthrate continued to drop between 1900 and 1920, and the divorce rate soared, in part because working-class men took advantage of the newer moral freedom and deserted their families in growing numbers. By 1916, there was one divorce for every nine marriages as compared to one for twenty-one in 1880.

Many children worked. In 1900, about three million children—nearly 20 percent of those between the ages of 5 and 15—held full-time or almost full-time jobs. Twenty-five thousand boys under 16 worked in mining; twenty thousand children under 12, mainly girls, worked in southern cotton mills. Gradually, as public indignation grew, the use of child labor shrank.

Determined to do something about the situation, the Women's Trade Union League lobbied the federal Bureau of Labor to investigate the conditions under which women and children worked. Begun in 1907, the investigation took four years and produced nineteen volumes of data, some of it shocking, all of it factual. In 1911, spurred by the data, the Children's Bureau was formed within the

Margaret Higgins Sanger with her son Stuart in 1904. In 1921, Sanger organized the American Birth Control League, which later became the Planned Parenthood Federation of America.

U.S. Bureau of Labor, with Grace Abbott, a social worker, at its head. It immediately began its own investigations, showing among other things the need for greater protection of maternal and infant health. In 1921, Congress passed the Sheppard-Towner Maternity and Infancy Protection Act, which helped fund maternity and pediatric clinics. Providing a precedent for the Social Security Act of 1935, it demonstrated the increasing effectiveness of women reformers in the Progressive Era.

Numerous middle-class women became involved in the fight for reform, while many others, reflecting the ongoing changes in the family, took increasing pride in homemaking and motherhood. Mother's Day, the national holiday, was formally established in 1913. With families preferring smaller numbers of children, birth control became a more acceptable practice. Margaret Sanger, a nurse and outspoken social reformer, led a campaign to give physicians broad discretion in prescribing contraceptives.

THE NIAGARA MOVEMENT AND THE NAACP

At the turn of the century eight of every ten African Americans still lived in rural areas, mainly in the South. Most were poor sharecroppers. Jim Crow laws segregated many schools, railroad cars, hotels, and hospitals. Poll taxes and other devices disfranchised blacks and many poor whites. Violence was common; from 1900 to 1914, white mobs murdered more than a thousand black people.

Many African Americans labored on the cotton farms and in the railroad camps, sawmills, and mines of the South under conditions of peonage. Peons traded their lives and labor for food and shelter. Often illiterate, they were forced to sign contracts allowing the planter "to use such force as he or his agents may deem necessary to require me to remain on his farm and perform good and satisfactory services." Armed guards patrolled the camps and whipped those trying to escape.

Few blacks belonged to labor unions, and blacks almost always earned less than whites in the same job. Black songs such as "I've Got a White Man Workin' for Me" (1901) voiced more hope than reality. The illiteracy rate among African Americans dropped from 45 percent in 1900 to 30 percent in 1910, but nowhere

The wish to have "our children . . . enjoy fairer conditions than have fallen to our lot" was the impetus behind the NAACP, which sponsored this parade in New York City.

were they given equal school facilities, teachers' salaries, or educational materials. In 1910, scarcely eight thousand African American youths were attending high schools in all the states of the Southeast.

African American leaders grew increasingly impatient with this kind of treatment, and in 1905 a group of them, led by sociologist W. E. B. Du Bois, met near Niagara Falls, New York (they met on the Canadian side of the Falls, since no hotel on the American side would take them). There they pledged action in the matters of voting, equal access to economic opportunity, integration, and equality before the law. Rejecting Booker T. Washington's gradualist approach, the Niagara Movement claimed for African Americans "every single right that belongs to a freeborn American, political, civil and social; and until we get these rights we will never cease to protest."

The Niagara Movement focused on equal rights and the education of African American youth. Keeping alive a program of militant action, it spawned later civil rights movements. Du Bois was its inspiration. In *The Souls of Black Folk* (1903) and other works, he called eloquently for justice and equality.

Still, race riots broke out in Atlanta, Georgia, in 1906 and in Springfield, Illinois, in 1908, the latter the home of Abraham Lincoln. Unlike the riots of the 1960s, white mobs invaded black neighborhoods, burning, looting, and killing. They lynched two blacks—one 84 years old—in Springfield.

Outrage was voiced by William E. Walling, a wealthy southerner and settlement house worker; Mary Ovington, a white anthropology student; and Oswald Garrison Villard, grandson of the famous abolitionist William Lloyd Garrison. Along with other reformers, white and black (among them Jane Addams and John Dewey), they issued a call for the conference that organized the National Association for the Advancement of Colored People, which swiftly became the most important civil rights organization in the country. Created in 1910, within four years the NAACP grew to fifty branches and more than six thousand members. Walling headed it, and Du Bois, the only African American among the top officers, directed publicity and edited *The Crisis,* the voice of the organization.

Joined by the National Urban League, which was created in 1911, the NAACP pressured employers, labor unions, and the government on behalf of African Americans. It had some victories. In 1918, in the midst of World War I, the NAACP and the National Urban League persuaded the federal government to form a special Bureau of Negro Economics within the Labor Department to look after the interests of African American wage earners.

Despite these gains, African Americans continued to experience disfranchisement, poor job opportunities, and segregation. As Booker T. Washington said in 1913, "I have never seen the colored people so discouraged and so bitter as they are at the present time."

"I HEAR THE WHISTLE":
IMMIGRANTS IN THE LABOR FORCE

While women and African Americans worked in growing numbers, much of the huge increase in the labor force in these years came from outside the country, particularly from Europe and Mexico. Between 1901 and 1920, the extraordinarily high total of 14.5 million immigrants entered the country, more than in any previous twenty-year period. Continuing the trend begun in the 1880s, many came from southern and eastern Europe. Still called the "new" immigrants, they met hostility from "older" immigrants of northern European stock who questioned their values, religion (often Catholic or Jewish), traditions, and appearance.

Immigrant patterns often departed from traditional stereotypes. Immigrants, for example, moved both to and from their homelands. Fifty percent or more of the members of some groups returned home, although the proportion varied. Jews and Czechs often brought their families to resettle in America; Serbs and Poles tended to come singly, intent on earning enough money to make a fresh start at home. Many Italian men virtually commuted, "birds of passage" who returned home every slack season.

Older residents lumped the newcomers together, ignoring geographic, religious, and other differences. Preserving important regional distinctions, Italians tended to settle as Cala-

**Immigration to the United States, 1900–1920
(by area of origin)**

Immigrants (thousands)

- Northern and Western Europe
- Southern and Eastern Europe
- Asia, Africa, and America

Note: For purposes of classification, "Northern and Western Europe" includes Great Britain, Ireland, Scandinavia, the Netherlands, Belgium, Luxembourg, Switzerland, France, and Germany. "Southern and Eastern Europe" includes Poland, Austria-Hungary, Russia and the Baltic States, Romania, Bulgaria, European Turkey, Italy, Spain, Portugal, and Greece. "Asia, Africa, and America" includes Asian Turkey, China, Japan, India, Canada, the Caribbean, Latin America, and all of Africa.

Source: U.S. Bureau of the Census, *Historical Statistics of the United States, Colonial Times to 1970*, Bicentennial Edition, Washington, DC, 1975.

breses, Venetians, Abruzzis, and Sicilians. Old-stock Americans viewed them all simply as Italians. Henry Ford and other employers tried to erase the differences through English classes and deliberate "Americanization" programs. The Ford Motor Company ran a school where immigrant employees were first taught to say, "I am a good American." At the graduation ceremony, the pupils acted out a gigantic pantomime in which, clad in their old-country dress, they filed into a large "melting pot." When they emerged, they were wearing identical American-made clothes, and each was waving a little American flag.

In similar fashion, the International Harvester Corporation taught Polish laborers to speak English, but it had other lessons in view as well. According to Lesson One, drilled into the Polish "pupils":

> *I hear the whistle. I must hurry.*
> *I hear the five minute whistle.*
> *It is time to go into the shop.*
> *I take my check from the gate board and hang it on the department board.*
> *I change my clothes and get ready to work.*
> *The starting whistle blows.*
> *I eat my lunch.*
> *It is forbidden to eat until then.*
> *The whistle blows at five minutes of starting time.*
> *I get ready to go to work.*
> *I work until the whistle blows to quit.*
> *I leave my place nice and clean.*
> *I put all my clothes in the locker.*
> *I must go home.*

Labor groups soon learned to counter these techniques. The Women's Trade Union League (WTUL) urged workers to ignore business-sponsored English lessons because they did not "tell the girl worker the things she really wants to know. They do not suggest that $5 a week is not a living wage. They tell her to be respectful to her employer." Designing its own educational program, the WTUL in 1912 published "New World Lessons for Old World Peoples," which provided quite a different kind of English lesson:

> *A Union girl takes me into the Union.*
> *The Union girls are glad to see me.*
> *They call me sister.*
> *I will work hard for our Union.*
> *I will come to all the Union meetings.*

In another significant development at the beginning of the twentieth century, Mexicans for the first time immigrated in large numbers, especially after a revolution in Mexico in 1910 forced many to flee across the northern border into Texas, New Mexico, Arizona, and California. Their exact numbers were unknown. American officials did not count border crossings until 1907, and even then, many migrants avoided the official immigration stations. Almost all came from the Mexican lower class, eager to escape peonage and violence in their native land. Labor agents called *coyotes*—usually in the employ of large corporations or working for ranchers—recruited Mexican workers.

Between 1900 and 1910, the Mexican population of Texas and New Mexico nearly doubled; in Arizona, it more than doubled; in California, it quadrupled. In all four states, it doubled again between 1910 and 1920. After the turn of the century, almost 10 percent of the total population of Mexico moved to the American Southwest.

In time, these Mexican Americans and their children transformed the Southwest. They built most of the early highways in Texas, New Mexico, and Arizona; dug the irrigation ditches that watered crops throughout the area; laid railroad track; and picked the cotton and vegetables that clothed and fed millions of Americans. Many lived in shacks and shanties along the railroad tracks, isolated in a separate Spanish-speaking world. Like other immigrant groups, they also formed enclaves in the cities; these *barrios* became cultural islands of family life, foods, church, and festivals.

Fewer people immigrated from China in these years, deterred in part by anti-Chinese laws and hostility. Like many other immigrants, most Chinese who came did not intend to remain. Wanting to make money and return home, they mined, farmed, and worked as common laborers. In their willingness to work hard for low wages, their desire to preserve clan and family associations from China, and their maintenance of strong ties with their home villages, Chinese Americans resembled other immigrant groups, but they differed in two important respects. As late as 1920, men outnumbered women by ten to one in the Chinese American population, and with a male median age of 42, their communities were generally dominated by the elderly.

The Chinese American population differed in another respect as well. Unlike other immigrant groups, whose numbers tended to grow, the number of Chinese Americans shrank in these years—from about 125,000 in the early 1880s to just over 60,000 in 1920. After 1910, the U.S. government set up a special immigration facility at Angel Island in San Francisco Bay, but unlike European immigrants who landed at Ellis Island in New York and were quickly sent on, Chinese immigrants were kept for weeks and months, examined and reexamined, before being

Immigrants from Asia arrive at the quarantine station at Angel Island, near San Francisco. Quota systems and exclusionary laws severely limited Asian immigration, while other laws placed restrictions on the immigrants, curtailing their right to own or even rent agricultural land. Some Asian immigrants, after months of detention at Angel Island, were refused permission to enter the United States and were forced to return to their homelands.

allowed to cross the narrow band of water to San Francisco. Angel Island remained open until 1940.

Many Japanese also arrived at Angel Island, and though at first fewer in numbers than the Chinese, they developed communities along the Pacific Coast, where they settled mainly on farms. The number of Japanese Americans grew. In 1907, the heaviest year of immigration from Japan, nearly 31,000 Japanese entered the United States; by 1920, there were 111,000 Japanese in the country, nearly three-quarters of them in California.

As the newcomers arrived from Asia, Europe, and Mexico, nativist sentiment, which had criticized earlier waves of immigrants, intensified. Old-stock Americans sneered at their dress and language. Racial theories emphasized the superiority of northern Europeans, and the new "science" of eugenics suggested the need to control the population growth of "inferior" peoples. Hostility toward Catholics and Jews was common but touched other groups as well.

In 1902, Congress enacted a law prohibiting immigration from China. Statutes requiring literacy tests designed to curtail immigration from southern and eastern Europe were vetoed by William Howard Taft in 1913 and by Woodrow Wilson in 1915 and 1917. In 1917, such a measure passed despite Wilson's veto. Other measures tried to limit immigration from Mexico and Japan.

CONFLICT IN THE WORKPLACE

Assembly lines, speedups, long hours, and low pay produced a dramatic increase in American industrial output (and profits) after 1900; they also gave rise to numerous strikes and other kinds of labor unrest. Sometimes strikes took place through the action of unions; sometimes workers just decided they had had enough and walked off the job. Whatever the cause, strikes were frequent. In one industry, in one city—the meatpacking industry in Chicago—there were 251 strikes in 1903 alone.

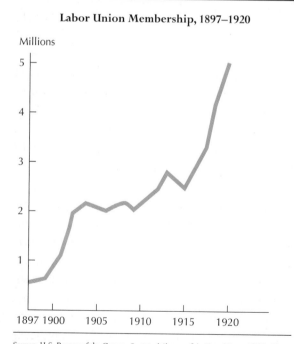

Labor Union Membership, 1897–1920

Millions

Source: U.S. Bureau of the Census, *Statistical Abstract of the United States: 1982–83* (103rd edition). Washington, DC, 1982.

Strikes and absenteeism increased after 1910; labor productivity dropped 10 percent between 1915 and 1918, the first such decline in memory. In many industries, labor turnover became a serious problem; workers changed jobs in droves. Union membership grew. In 1900, only about a million workers—less than 4 percent of the workforce—belonged to unions. By 1920, five million workers belonged, increasing the unionized portion of the workforce to about 13 percent.

As tensions grew between capital and labor, some people in the middle class became fearful that, unless something was done to improve the workers' situation, there might be violence or even revolution. This fear motivated some of the labor-oriented reforms of the Progressive Era. While some reform supporters genuinely wanted to improve labor's lot, others embraced reform because they were afraid of something else.

ORGANIZING LABOR

Samuel Gompers's American Federation of Labor increased from 250,000 members in 1897 to 1.7 million in 1904. By far the largest union organization, it remained devoted to the interests of skilled craftspeople. While it aimed partly at better wages and working conditions, it also sought to limit entry into the crafts and protect worker prerogatives. Within limits, the AFL found acceptance among giant business corporations eager for conservative policies and labor stability.

Of the 8 million female workers in 1910, only 125,000 belonged to unions. Gompers continued to resist organizing them, saying they were too emotional and, as union organizers, "had a way of making serious mistakes." Margaret Dreier Robins, an organizer of proven skill, scoffed at that. "These men died twenty years ago and are just walking around dead!" she protested.

Robins helped found the Women's Trade Union League in 1903. The WTUL led the effort to organize women into trade unions, to lobby for legislation protecting female workers, and to educate the public on the problems and needs of working women. It took in all working women who would join, regardless of skill (although not, at first, African American women), and it won crucial financial support from well-to-do women such as Anne Morgan, daughter of the feared financier J. P. Morgan. Robins's close friend Jane Addams belonged, as did Dr. Alice Hamilton, a pioneer in American research on the causes of industrial disease.

The WTUL never had many members—a few thousand at most—but its influence extended far beyond its membership. In 1909, it supported the "Uprising of the 20,000," a strike of shirtwaist workers in New York City. When female employees of the Triangle Shirtwaist Company tried to form a union, the company fired them, and they walked out; 20,000 men and women in 500 other shops followed. Strike meetings were conducted in three languages—English, Yiddish, and Italian—and before being forced to go back to work, the strikers won a shorter workweek and a few other gains. Sadly, the Triangle women lost out on another important demand—for unlocked shop doors and safe fire escapes. Their loss proved lethal in the famous Triangle Shirtwaist Company fire of 1911.

The WTUL also backed a strike in 1910 against Hart, Schaffner and Marx, Chicago's largest manufacturer of men's clothing. One day, Annie Shapiro, the 18-year-old daughter of Russian immigrants, was told her wages were being cut from $7 a week to $6.20. That was a large cut, and along with sixteen other young women, Shapiro refused to accept it and walked out. "We had to be recognized as people," she said later. Soon other women walked out, and the revolt spread.

In a matter of days, some forty thousand garment workers were on strike, about half of them women. Manufacturers hurried to negotiate, and the result was the important Hart, Schaffner agreement, which created an arbitration committee composed of management and labor to handle grievances and settle disputes. The first successful experiment in collective bargaining, the Hart, Schaffner agreement became the model for the kind of agreements that govern industrial relations today.

Another union, the Industrial Workers of the World (IWW), attracted by far the greatest attention (and the most fears) in these years. Unlike the WTUL, it welcomed everyone regardless of gender or race. Unlike the AFL, it tried to organize the unskilled and foreign-born laborers who worked in the mass production industries. Founded in Chicago in 1905, it aimed to unite the American working class into a mammoth union to promote labor's interests. Its motto—"An injury to one is an injury to all"—stressed labor solidarity, as had the earlier Knights of Labor. But unlike the Knights, the IWW, or Wobblies as they were often known, urged social revolution.

"It is our purpose to overthrow the capitalist system by forcible means if necessary," William D. "Big Bill" Haywood, one of its founders, said; and he went on in his speeches to say he knew of nothing a worker could do that "will bring as much anguish to the boss as a little sabotage in the right place."

IWW leaders included Mary Harris ("Mother") Jones, a famous veteran of battles in the Illinois coalfields; Elizabeth Gurley Flynn, a fiery young radical who joined as a teenager; and Big Bill Haywood himself, the strapping one-eyed founder of the Western Federation of Miners.

The IWW led a number of major strikes. Strikes in Lawrence, Massachusetts (1912), and Paterson, New Jersey (1912), attracted national attention: in Lawrence when the strikers sent their children, ill-clad and hungry, out of the city to stay with sympathetic families; in Paterson when they rented New York's Madison Square Garden for a massive labor pageant. IWW leaders welcomed the revolutionary tumult sweeping Russia and other countries. In the United States, they thought, a series of local strikes would bring about capitalist repression, then a general strike, and eventually a workers' commonwealth.

Elizabeth Gurley Flynn, labor's "Joan of Arc," addresses textile workers on strike at Paterson, New Jersey.

The IWW fell short of these objectives, but during its lifetime—from 1905 to the mid-1920s—it made major gains among immigrant workers in the Northeast, migrant farm laborers on the Plains, and loggers and miners in the South and Far West. In factories like Ford's, it recruited workers resentful of the speedups on the assembly lines. Although IWW membership probably amounted to no more than 100,000 at any one time, workers came and left so often that its total membership may have reached as high as 1 million.

WORKING WITH WORKERS

Concerned about labor unrest, some business leaders used violence and police action to keep workers in line, but others turned to the new fields of applied psychology and personnel management. A school of industrial psychology emerged. As had Taylor, industrial psychologists studied workers' routines, and, further, they showed that output was also affected by job satisfaction. While most businesses pushed ahead with efficiency campaigns, a few did establish industrial relations departments, hire public relations firms to improve their corporate image, and link productivity to job safety and worker happiness.

Ivy L. Lee, a pioneer in the field of corporate public relations, advised clients such as the Pennsylvania Railroad and Standard Oil on how to improve relations with labor and the public. Calling himself a "physician to corporate bodies," Lee urged complete openness on the company's part. To please employees, companies printed newsletters and organized softball teams; they awarded prizes and celebrated retirements. Ford created a "sociology department" staffed by 150 experts who showed workers how to budget their incomes and care for their health. They even taught them how to shop for meat.

On January 5, 1914, Ford took another significant step. He announced the five-dollar day, "the greatest revolution," he said, "in the matter of rewards for workers ever known to the industrial world." With a stroke, he doubled the wage rate for common labor, reduced the working day from nine hours to eight, and established a personnel department to place workers in appropriate jobs. The next day, ten thousand applicants stood outside the gates.

As a result, Ford had the pick of the labor force. Turnover declined; absenteeism, previously as much as one-tenth of all Ford workers every day, fell to 0.3 percent. Output increased; the IWW at Ford collapsed. The plan increased wages, but it also gave the company greater control over a more stable labor force. Workers had to meet a behavior code in order to qualify for the five-dollar day. At first scornful of the "utopian" plan, business leaders across the country soon copied it, and on January 2, 1919, Ford announced the six-dollar day.

AMOSKEAG

In size, system, and worker relations, the record of the Amoskeag Company textile mills was revealing. Located beside the Merrimack River in Manchester, New Hampshire, the mills—an enormous complex of factories, warehouses, canals, and machinery—had been built in the 1830s. By the turn of the century, they were producing nearly 50 miles of cloth an hour, more cloth each day than any other mills in the entire world.

The face of the mills, an almost solid wall of red brick, stretched nearly a mile. Archways and bridges pierced the facade. Amoskeag resembled a walled medieval city within which workers found "a total institution, a closed and almost self-contained world." At first the mills employed young women for labor, but by 1900, more and more immigrant males staffed the machines. French

The playground at Amoskeag, provided for the children of the company's workers. The Amoskeag Textile Club, part of the employer-sponsored employee welfare program, had reading rooms, card tables, billiard and pool tables, a golf course, and a baseball field for the use of the workers. All was demolished when the mill closed in 1935. Many firms between 1910 and 1917 established employee programs similar to those introduced at Amoskeag.

Canadians, Irish, Poles, and Greeks—seventeen thousand in all—worked there, and their experiences revealed a great deal about factory work and life at the turn of the century.

The company hired and fired at will, and it demanded relentless output from the spindles and spinning frames. Yet it also viewed employees as its "children" and looked for total loyalty in return, an expectation often realized. Workers identified with Amoskeag and, decades later, still called themselves Amoskeag men and women. "We were all like a family," one said.

Most Amoskeag workers preferred the industrial world of the mills to the farms they had left behind. They did not feel displaced; they knew the pains of industrial life; and they adapted in ways that fit their own needs and traditions. Families played a large role. They neither disintegrated nor lost their relationships.

French Canadians and others often came in family units. One or two family members left the farm for the mills, maintained close ties with those back home, and then sent for others, creating a form of "chain migration."

Once in Manchester, families often toiled in the same workrooms. Looking after each other, they asked for transfers and promotions for relatives; they taught their children technical skills and how to get along with bosses and fellow workers. Although low paid, Amoskeag employees took pride in their work, and for many of them, a well-turned-out product provided dignity and self-esteem.

As part of its paternal interest in employee welfare, in 1910 the company inaugurated a welfare and efficiency program, which aimed to increase productivity, accustom immigrants to industrial work, instill company loyalty, and curb labor unrest. Playgrounds and visiting nurses, home-buying plans, a cooking school, and dental service were part of the plan. The Amoskeag Textile Club held employee dinners and picnics, organized shooting clubs and a baseball team, sponsored Christmas parties for the children, and put out the *Amoskeag Bulletin,* a monthly magazine of employee news.

From 1885 to 1919, no strike touched the mills. Thereafter, however, labor unrest increased. Overproduction and foreign competition took their toll, and Amoskeag closed in 1935.

A New Urban Culture

For many Americans, the quality of life improved significantly between 1900 and 1920. Jobs were relatively plentiful, and, in a development of great importance, more and more people were entering the professions as doctors, lawyers, teachers, and engineers. With comfortable incomes, a growing middle class could take advantage of new lifestyles, inventions, and forms of entertainment. Mass production could not have worked without mass consumption, and Americans in these years increasingly became a nation of consumers.

Production and Consumption

In 1900, business firms spent about $95 million on advertising; twenty years later, they spent more than $500 million. Ads and billboards touted cigarettes, cars, perfumes, and cosmetics. Advertising agencies boomed. Using new sampling techniques, they developed modern concepts of market testing and research. Sampling customer preferences affected business indirectly as well, making it more responsive to public opinion on social and political issues.

Mass production swept the clothing industry and dressed more Americans better than any people ever before. Using lessons learned in making uniforms during the Civil War, manufacturers for the first time developed standard clothing and shoe sizes that fit most bodies. Clothing prices dropped; the availability of inexpensive "off-the-rack" clothes lessened distinctions between rich and poor. By 1900, nine of every ten men and boys wore the new "ready-to-wear" clothes.

In 1900, people employed in manufacturing earned on average $418 a year. Two decades later, they earned $1342 a year, though inflation took much of the increase. While the middle class expanded, the rich also grew richer. In 1920, the new income tax showed the first accurate tabulation of income, and it confirmed what many had suspected all along. Five percent of the population received almost one-fourth of all income.

LIVING AND DYING IN AN URBAN NATION

In 1920, the median age of the population was only 25. (It is now 30.) Immigration accounted for part of the population's youthfulness, since most immigrants were young. Thanks to medical advances and better living conditions, the death rate dropped in the early years of the century; the average life span increased. Between 1900 and 1920, life expectancy rose from 49 to 56 years for white women and from 47 to 54 years for white men. It rose from 33 to 45 years for blacks and other racial minorities.

Despite the increase in life expectancy, infant mortality remained high; nearly 10 percent of white babies and 20 percent of minority babies died in the first year of life. In comparison to today, fewer babies on average survived to adolescence, and fewer people survived beyond middle age. In 1900, the death rate among people between 45 and 65 was more than twice the modern rate. As a result, there were relatively fewer older people—in 1900, only 4 percent of the population was older than 65 compared to nearly 13 percent today. Fewer children than today knew their grandparents. Still, improvements in health care helped people live longer, and as a result, the incidence of cancer and heart disease increased.

Cities grew, and by any earlier standards, they grew on a colossal scale. Downtowns became a central hive of skyscrapers, department stores, warehouses, and hotels. Strips of factories radiated from the center. As street railways spread, cities took on a systematic pattern of socioeconomic segregation, usually in rings. The innermost ring filled with immigrants, circled by a belt of working-class housing. The remaining rings marked areas of rising affluence outward toward wealthy suburbs, which themselves formed around shopping strips and grid patterns of streets that restricted social interaction.

The giants were New York, Chicago, and Philadelphia, industrial cities that turned out every kind of product from textiles to structural steel. Smaller cities such as Rochester, New York, or Cleveland, Ohio, specialized in manufacturing a specific line of goods or processing regional products for the national market. Railroads instead of highways tied things together; in 1916, the rail network, the largest in the world, reached its peak—254,000 miles of track that carried more than three-fourths of all intercity freight tonnage.

Step by step, cities adopted their twentieth-century forms. Between 1909 and 1915, Los Angeles, a city of 300,000 people, passed a series of ordinances that gave rise to modern urban zoning. For the first time, the ordinances divided a city into three districts of specified use: a residential area, an industrial area, and an area open to residence and a limited list of industries. Other cities followed. Combining several features, the New York zoning law of 1916 became the model for the nation; within a decade, 591 cities copied it.

Zoning ordered city development, keeping skyscrapers out of factory districts, factories out of the suburbs. It also had powerful social repercussions. In the South, zoning became a tool to extend racial segregation; in northern cities, it acted against ethnic minorities. Jews in New York, Italians in Boston, Poles in Detroit, African Americans in Chicago—zoning laws held them all at arm's length. Like other migrants, African Americans often preferred to settle together, but zoning also helped put them there. By 1920, ten districts in Chicago were more than three-quarters black. In Los Angeles, Cleveland, Detroit, and Washington, D.C., most blacks lived in only two or three wards.

POPULAR PASTIMES

Thanks to changing work rules and mechanization, many Americans enjoyed more leisure time. The average workweek for manufacturing laborers fell from 60 hours in 1890 to 51 in 1920. By the early 1900s, white-collar workers might spend only 8 to 10 hours a day at work and a half day on weekends. Greater leisure time gave more people more opportunity for play and people flocked to places of entertainment. Baseball entrenched itself as the national pastime. Automobiles and streetcars carried growing numbers of fans to ballparks; attendance at major league games doubled between 1903 and 1920. Football also drew fans, although critics attacked the sport's violence and the use of "tramp athletes," nonstudents whom colleges paid to play. In 1905, the worst year, 18 players were killed and 150 seriously injured.

Alarmed, President Theodore Roosevelt—who had once said, "I am the father of three boys [and] if I thought any one of them would weigh a possible broken bone against the glory of being chosen to play on Harvard's football team I would disinherit him"—called a White House conference to clean up college sports. The conference founded the Intercollegiate Athletic Association, which in 1910 became the National Collegiate Athletic Association (NCAA).

Movie theaters opened everywhere. By 1910, there were 10,000 of them, drawing a weekly audience of 10 million people. Admission was usually 5 cents, and movies stressing laughter and pathos appealed to a mass market. In 1915, D. W. Griffith, a talented and creative director—as well as a racist—produced the first movie spectacular: *Birth of a Nation*. Griffith adopted new film techniques, including close-ups, fade-outs, and artistic camera angles.

Phonographs brought ready-made entertainment into the home. By 1901, phonograph and record companies included the Victor Talking Machine Company, the Edison Speaking Machine Company, and Columbia Records. Ornate mahogany Victrolas became standard fixtures in middle-class parlors. In 1919, 2.25 million phonographs were produced; two years later, more than 100 million records were sold.

As record sales grew, families sang less and listened more. Music became a business. In 1909, Congress enacted a copyright law that provided a two-cent royalty on each piece of music on phonograph records or piano rolls. The royalty, small as it was, offered welcome income to composers and publishers, and in 1914, composer Victor Herbert and others formed the American Society of Composers, Authors, and Publishers (ASCAP) to protect musical rights and royalties.

The faster rhythms of syncopated ragtime became the rage, especially after 1911, when Irving Berlin, a Russian immigrant, wrote "Alexander's Ragtime Band." Ragtime set off a nationwide dance craze. Secretaries danced on their lunch hour, the first nightclubs opened, and restaurants and hotels introduced dance floors. Waltzes and polkas gave way to a host of new dances, many with animal names: the fox-trot, bunny hop, turkey trot, snake, and kangaroo dip. Partners were not permitted to dance too close; bouncers tapped them on the shoulder if they got closer than 9 inches.

Vaudeville, increasingly popular after 1900, reached maturity around 1915. Drawing on the immigrant experience, it voiced the variety of city life and included skits, songs, comics, acrobats, and magicians. Dances and jokes showed an earthiness new to mass audiences. By 1914, stage runways extended into the crowd; women performers had bared their legs and were beginning to show glimpses of the midriff. Fanny Brice; Ann Pennington, the "shimmy" queen; and

Eva Tanguay, who sang "It's All Been Done Before But Not the Way I Do It," starred in Florenz Ziegfeld's Follies, the peak of vaudeville.

In songs like "St. Louis Blues" (1914), W. C. Handy took the black southern folk music of the blues to northern cities. Gertrude "Ma" Rainey, the daughter of minstrels, sang in black vaudeville for nearly thirty-five years. Performing in Chattanooga, Tennessee, about 1910, she came across a 12-year-old orphan, Bessie Smith, who became the "Empress of the Blues." Smith's voice was huge and sweeping. Recording for the Race division of Columbia Records, she made more than eighty records that together sold nearly ten million copies.

Another musical innovation came north from New Orleans. Charles (Buddy) Bolden, a cornetist; Ferdinand "Jelly Roll" Morton, a pianist; and a youngster named Louis Armstrong played an improvisational music that had no formal name. Reaching Chicago, it became "jas," then "jass," and finally "jazz." Jazz jumped, and jazz musicians relied on feeling and mood.

Popular fiction reflected changing interests. Kate Douglas Wiggins's *Rebecca of Sunnybrook Farm* (1903) and Lucy M. Montgomery's *Anne of Green Gables* (1908) showed the continuing popularity of rural themes. Westerns also sold well, but readers turned more and more to detective thrillers with hard-bitten city detectives and science fiction featuring the latest dream in technology. The Tom Swift series, begun in 1910, looked ahead to spaceships, ray guns, and gravity nullifiers.

Edward L. Stratemeyer, the mind behind Tom Swift, brought the techniques of mass production to book writing. In 1906, he formed the Stratemeyer Literary Syndicate, which employed a stable of writers to turn out hundreds of Tom Swift, Rover Boys, and Bobbsey Twins stories for young readers. Burt Standish, another prolific author, took the pen name Gilbert Patten and created the character of Frank Merriwell, wholesome college athlete. As Patten said, "I took the three qualities I most wanted him to represent—frank and merry in nature, well in body and mind—and made the name Frank Merriwell." The Merriwell books sold twenty-five million copies.

EXPERIMENTATION IN THE ARTS

"There is a state of unrest all over the world in art as in all other things," the director of New York's Metropolitan Museum said in 1908. "It is the same in literature, as in music, in painting, and in sculpture."

Isadora Duncan and Ruth St. Denis transformed the dance. Departing from traditional ballet steps, both women stressed improvisation, emotion, and the human form. "Listen to the music with your soul," Duncan told her students. "Unless your dancing springs from an inner emotion and expresses an idea, it will be meaningless." Draped in flowing robes, she revealed more of her legs than some thought tasteful, and she proclaimed that the "noblest art is the nude." Duncan died tragically in 1927, her neck broken when her long red scarf caught in the wheel of a racing car.

The lofts and apartments of New York's Greenwich Village attracted artists, writers, and poets interested in experimentation and change. To these artists, the city was the focus of national life and the sign of a new culture. Robert Henri and the realist painters—known to their critics as the Ashcan School—relished the city's excitement. They wanted, a friend said, "to paint truth and to paint it with strength and fearlessness and individuality."

To the realists, a painting carried into the future the look of life as it happened. Their paintings depicted street scenes, colorful crowds, and slum children swimming in the river. In paintings such as the *Cliff Dwellers,* George W. Bellows captured the color and excitement of the tenements; John Sloan, one of Henri's most talented students, painted the vitality of ordinary people and familiar scenes.

In 1913, a show at the New York Armory presented sixteen hundred modernist paintings, prints, and sculptures. The work of Picasso, Cézanne, Matisse, Brancusi, Van Gogh, and Gauguin dazed and dazzled American observers. Critics attacked the show as worthless and depraved; a Chicago official wanted it banned from the city because the "idea that people can gaze at this sort of thing without [it] hurting them is all bosh."

The postimpressionists changed the direction of twentieth-century art and influenced adventuresome American painters. John Marin, Max Weber, Georgia O'Keeffe, Arthur Dove, and other modernists experimented in ways foreign to Henri's realists. Defiantly avant-garde, they shook off convention and experimented with new forms. Using bold colors and abstract patterns, they worked to capture the energy of urban life.

There was an extraordinary outburst of poetry. In 1912, Harriet Monroe started the magazine *Poetry* in Chicago, the hotbed of the new poetry; Ezra Pound and Vachel Lindsay, both daring experimenters with ideas and verse, published in the first issue. T. S. Eliot published the classic "Love Song of J. Alfred Prufrock" in *Poetry* in 1915. Attacked bitterly by conservative critics, the poem established Eliot's leadership among a group of poets, many of them living and writing in London, who rejected traditional meter and rhyme as artificial constraints. Eliot, Pound, and Amy Lowell, among others, believed the poet's task was to capture fleeting images in verse.

Others experimenting with new techniques in poetry included Robert Frost (*North of Boston*, 1915), Edgar Lee Masters (*Spoon River Anthology*, 1915), and Carl Sandburg (*Chicago Poems*, 1916). Sandburg's poem "Chicago" celebrated the vitality of the city:

> *Come and show me another city with lifted head*
> > *singing so proud to be*
> > > *alive and coarse and strong and cunning*
>
> ·
>
> *Fierce as a dog with tongue lapping for action,*
> > *cunning as a savage*
> > > *pitted against the wilderness,*
> > > > *Bareheaded,*
> > > > *Shoveling,*
> > > > *Wrecking,*
> > > > *Planning,*
> > > > *Building, breaking, rebuilding,*
>
> ·
>
> *Bragging and laughing that under his wrist is the*
> > *pulse, and under his*
> > > *ribs the heart of the people,*
> > > > *Laughing!*
> *Laughing the stormy, husky, brawling laughter of*
> > *Youth, half-naked,*
> > > *sweating, proud to be Hog Butcher, Tool*
> > > > *Maker, Stacker of Wheat,*
> > > *Player with Railroads and Freight Handler to*
> > > > *the Nation.*

Manners and morals change slowly, and many Americans overlooked the importance of the first two decades of the twentieth century. Yet sweeping change was under way; anyone who doubted it could visit a gallery, see a film, listen to music, or read one of the new literary magazines. Garrets and galleries were filled with a breathtaking sense of change. "There was life in all these new things," Marsden Hartley, a modernist painter, recalled. "There was excitement, there was healthy revolt, investigation, discovery, and an utterly new world out of it all."

The ferment of progressivism in city, state, and nation reshaped the country. In a burst of reform, people built playgrounds, restructured taxes, regulated business, won the vote for women, shortened working hours, altered political systems, opened kindergartens, and improved factory safety. They tried to fulfill the national promise of dignity and liberty.

Marsden Hartley, it turned out, had voiced a mood that went well beyond painters and poets. Across society, people in many walks of life were experiencing a similar sense of excitement and discovery. Racism, repression, and labor conflict were present, to be sure, but there was also talk of hope, progress, and change. In politics, science, journalism, education, and a host of other fields, people believed for a time that they could make a difference, and in trying to do so, they became part of the progressive generation.

23

FROM ROOSEVELT TO WILSON IN THE AGE OF PROGRESSIVISM

O n a sunny spring morning in 1909, Theodore Roosevelt, wearing the greatcoat of a colonel of the Rough Riders, left New York for a safari in Africa. An ex-president at the age of 50, he had turned over the White House to his chosen successor, William Howard Taft, and was now off for "the joy of wandering through lonely lands, the joy of hunting the mighty and terrible lords" of Africa, "where death broods in the dark and silent depths."

Some of Roosevelt's enemies hoped he would not return. "I trust some lion will do its duty," Wall Street magnate J. P. Morgan said. Always prepared, Roosevelt took nine extra pairs of eyeglasses, and, just in case, several expert hunters accompanied him. When the nearsighted Roosevelt took aim, three others aimed at the same moment. "Mr. Roosevelt had a fairly good idea of the general direction," the safari leader said, "but we couldn't take chances with the life of a former president."

It was all good fun, and afterward Roosevelt set off on a tour of Europe. He attended the funeral of the king of England, dined with the king and queen of Italy, and happily spent five hours reviewing troops of the German empire. Less happily, he followed events back home where, in the judgment of many friends, Taft was not working out as president. At almost every stop there were letters waiting for him from disappointed Republicans.

For his part, Taft was puzzled by it all. Honest and warmhearted, he had intended to continue Roosevelt's policies, even writing Roosevelt that he would "see to it that your judgment in selecting me as your successor and bringing about that succession shall be vindicated." But events turned out differently. The conservative and progressive wings of the Republican party split, and Taft often sided with the conservatives. Among progressive Republicans, Taft's troubles stirred talk of a Roosevelt "back from Elba" movement, akin to Napoleon's return from exile.

Thousands gathered to greet Roosevelt on his return from Europe. He sailed into New York harbor on June 18, 1910, to the sound of naval guns and loud cheers. In characteristic fashion, he had helped make the arrangements: "If there is to be a great crowd, do arrange it so that the whole crowd has a chance to see me and that there is as little disappointment as possible."

Roosevelt carried with him a touching letter from Taft, received just before he left Europe. "I have had a hard time—I do not know that I have had harder luck than other Presidents, but I do know that thus far I have succeeded far less than have others. I have been conscientiously trying to carry out your policies but my method of doing so has not worked smoothly." Taft invited Teddy to spend a

Teddy Roosevelt, with his hunting party in Africa, poses with one of the more than 300 animals he and his group took down. As president, Roosevelt had supported measures protecting wildlife in the United States, including designating Pelican Island, Florida, as the nation's first wildlife refuge.

night or two at the White House, but Roosevelt declined, saying that ex-presi-dents should not visit Washington. Relations between the two friends cooled.

A year later, there was a desperate fight between Taft and Roosevelt for the Republican presidential nomination. Taft won the nomination, but, angry and ambitious, Roosevelt bolted and helped form a new party, the Progressive (or "Bull Moose") party, to unseat Taft and capture the White House. With Taft, Roosevelt, Woodrow Wilson (the Democratic party's candidate), and Socialist party candidate Eugene V. Debs all in the race, the election of 1912 became one of the most exciting in American history.

It was also one of the most important. People were worried about the social and economic effects of urban-industrial growth. The election of 1912 provided a forum for those worries, and, to a degree unusual in American politics, it pitted deeply opposed candidates against one another and outlined differing views of the nation's future. In the spirited battle between Roosevelt and Wilson, it also brought to the forefront some of the currents of progressive reform.

THE SPIRIT OF PROGRESSIVISM

In one way or another, progressivism touched all aspects of society. Politically, it fostered a reform movement that sought cures for the problems of city, state, and nation. Intellectually, it drew on the expertise of the new social sciences and re-flected a shift from older absolutes of class and religion to newer schools of thought that emphasized the role of the environment in human development and the relative nature of truth. Culturally, it inspired fresh modes of expression in dance, film, painting, literature, and architecture. Touching individuals in different ways, progressivism became a set of attitudes as well as a definable movement.

Though broad and diverse, progressivism as a whole had a half dozen charac-teristics that gave it definition. First, the progressives acted out of concern about the effects of industrialization and the conditions of industrial life. While their viewpoints varied, they did not, as a rule, set out to harm big business, but in-stead sought to humanize and regulate it.

In pursuing these objectives, the progressives displayed a second characteris-tic: a fundamental optimism about human nature, the possibilities of progress, and the capacity of people to recognize problems and take action to solve them. Progressives believed they could "investigate, educate, and legislate"—learn about a problem, inform people about it, and, with the help of an informed pub-lic, find and enforce a solution.

Third, more than many earlier reformers, the progressives were willing to intervene in people's lives, confident that it was their right to do so. They knew best, some of them thought, and as a result, there was an element of coercion in a number of their ideas. Fourth, while progressives preferred if possible to use voluntary means to achieve reform, they tended to turn more and more to the authority of the state and government at all levels in order to put into effect the reforms they wanted.

As a fifth characteristic, many progressives drew on a combination of evangelical Protestantism (which gave them the desire—and, they thought, the duty—to purge the world of sins such as prostitution and drunkenness) and the natural and social sciences (whose theories made them confident that they could understand and control the environment in which people lived). Progressives tended to view the environment as a key to reform, thinking—in the way some economists, sociologists, and other social scientists were suggesting—that if they could change the environment, they could change the individual.

Finally, progressivism was distinctive because it touched virtually the whole nation. Not everyone, of course, was a progressive, and there were many who opposed or ignored the ideas of the movement. There were also those who were untouched by progressive reforms and those whom the movement overlooked. But in one way or another, a remarkable number of people were caught up in it, giving progressivism a national reach and a mass base.

That was one of the features, in fact, that set it off from populism, which had grown mostly in the rural South and West. Progressivism drew support from across society. "The thing that constantly amazed me," said William Allen White, a leading progressive journalist, "was how many people were with us." Progressivism appealed to the expanding middle class, prosperous farmers, and skilled laborers; it also attracted significant support in the business community.

The progressives believed in progress and disliked waste. No single issue or concern united them all. Some progressives wanted to clean up city governments, others to clean up city streets. Some wanted to purify politics or control corporate abuses, others to eradicate poverty or prostitution. Some demanded social justice in the form of women's rights, child labor laws, temperance, and factory safety. They were Democrats, Republicans, Socialists, and independents.

Progressives believed in a better world and in the ability of people to achieve it. Progress depended on knowledge. The progressives stressed individual morality and collective action, the scientific method, and the value of expert opinion. Like contemporary business leaders, they valued system, planning, management, and predictability. They wanted not only reform but efficiency.

Historians once viewed progressivism as the triumph of one group in society over another. In this view, farmers took on the hated and powerful railroads; upstart reformers challenged the city bosses; business interests fought for favorable legislation; youthful professionals carved out their place in society. Now, historians stress the way progressivism brought people together rather than drove them apart. Disparate groups united in an effort to improve the well-being of many groups in society.

THE RISE OF THE PROFESSIONS

Progressivism fed on an organizational impulse that encouraged people to join forces, share information, and solve problems. Between 1890 and 1920, a host of national societies and associations took shape—nearly four hundred of them in just three decades. Groups such as the National Child Labor Committee, which lobbied for legislation to regulate the employment and working conditions of children, were formed to attack specific issues. Other groups reflected one of the most significant developments in American society at the turn of the century—the rise of the professions.

Growing rapidly in these years, the professions—law, medicine, religion, business, teaching, and social work—were the source of much of the leadership of the progressive movement. The professions attracted young, educated men and women, who in turn were part of a larger trend: a dramatic increase in the number of individuals working in administrative and professional jobs. In businesses, these people were managers, architects, technicians, and accountants. In city governments, they were experts in everything from education to sanitation. They organized and ran the urban-industrial society.

Together these professionals formed part of a new middle class whose members did not derive their status from birth or inherited wealth, as had many members of the older middle class. Instead, they moved ahead through education and personal accomplishment. They had worked to become doctors, lawyers, ministers, and teachers. Proud of their skills, they were ambitious and self-confident, and they thought of themselves as experts who could use their knowledge for the benefit of society.

As a way of asserting their status, they formed professional societies to look after their interests and govern entry into their professions. Just a few years before, for example, a doctor had become a doctor simply by stocking up on patent medicines and hanging out a sign. Now doctors began to insist they were part of a medical profession, and they wanted to set educational requirements and minimum standards for practice. In 1901, they reorganized the American Medical Association (AMA) and made it into a modern national professional society.

Other groups and professions showed the same pattern. Lawyers formed bar associations, created examining boards, and lobbied for regulations restricting entry into the profession. Teachers organized the National Education

Association (1905) and pressed for teacher certification and compulsory education laws. Social workers formed the National Federation of Settlements (1911); business leaders created the National Association of Manufacturers (1895) and the U.S. Chamber of Commerce (1912); and farmers joined the National Farm Bureau Federation to spread information about farming and to try to improve their lot.

Working both as individuals and groups, members of the professions had a major impact on the era, as the career of one of them, Dr. Alice Hamilton, illustrated. Hamilton early decided to devote her life to helping the less fortunate. Choosing medicine, she went to the University of Michigan Medical School, one of a shrinking number of medical schools that admitted women, and then settled in Chicago, where she met Jane Addams and took a room in Hull House. Soon thereafter, she traced a local typhoid epidemic to flies carrying germs from open privies.

Combining field study with meticulous laboratory techniques, she pioneered research into the causes of lead poisoning and other industrial disease. In 1908, the governor of Illinois appointed her to a commission on occupational diseases; two years later, she headed a statewide survey of industrial poisons. Thanks to her work, in 1911, Illinois passed the first state law providing compensation for industrial disease caused by poisonous fumes and dust. By the end of the 1930s, all the major industrial states had such laws.

One of the new professionals, Hamilton had used her education and skill to broaden knowledge of her subject, change industrial practices, and improve the lives of countless workers. "For me," she said later in a comment characteristic of the progressives, "the satisfaction is that things are better now, and I had some part in it."

The Social-Justice Movement

As Alice Hamilton's career exemplified, progressivism began in the cities during the 1890s. It first took form around settlement workers and others interested in freeing individuals from the crushing impact of cities and factories.

Ministers, intellectuals, social workers, and lawyers joined in a social-justice movement that focused national attention on the need for tenement house laws, more stringent child labor legislation, and better working conditions for women. They brought pressure on municipal agencies for more and better parks, playgrounds, day nurseries, schools, and community services. Blending private and public action, settlement leaders turned increasingly to government aid.

Social-justice reformers were more interested in social cures than individual charity. Unlike earlier reformers, they saw problems as endless and interrelated;

individuals became part of a city's larger patterns. With that insight, social-service casework shifted from a focus on an individual's well-being to a scientific analysis of neighborhoods, occupations, and classes.

Social-justice reformers, banding together to work for change, formed the National Conference of Charities and Corrections, which in 1915 became the National Conference of Social Work. Controlled by social workers, the conference reflected the growing professionalization of reform. Through it, social workers discovered each other's efforts, shared methodology, and tried to establish themselves as a separate field within the social sciences. Once content with informal training sessions in a settlement house living room, they now founded complete professional schools at Chicago, Harvard, and other universities. Instead of piecemeal reforms, they aimed at a comprehensive program of minimum wages, maximum hours, workers' compensation, and widows' pensions.

THE PURITY CRUSADE

Working in city neighborhoods, social-justice reformers were often struck by the degree to which alcohol affected the lives of the people they were trying to help. Workers drank away their wages; some men spent more time at the saloon than at home. Drunkenness caused violence, and it angered employers who did not want intoxicated workers on the job. In countless ways, alcohol wasted human resources, the reformers believed, and they launched a crusade to remove the evils of drink from American life.

At the head of the crusade was the Women's Christian Temperance Union (WCTU), which had continued to grow since it was founded in the 1870s. By 1911, the WCTU had nearly a quarter of a million members; it was the largest organization of women in American history to that time. In 1893, it was joined by the Anti-Saloon League, and together the groups pressed to abolish alcohol and the places where it was consumed. By 1916, they had succeeded in nineteen states, but as drinking continued elsewhere, they pushed for a nationwide law. In the midst of the moral fervor of World War I, they succeeded, and the Eighteenth Amendment to the Constitution, prohibiting the manufacture, sale, and transportation of intoxicating liquors, took effect in January 1920.

The amendment encountered troubles later in the 1920s as the social atmosphere changed, but at the time it passed, progressives thought Prohibition was a major step toward eliminating social instability and moral wrong. In a similar fashion, some progressive reformers also worked to get rid of prostitution, convinced that poverty and ignorance drove women to the trade. By 1915, nearly every state had banned brothels, and in 1910, Congress passed the Mann Act, which prohibited the interstate transportation of women for immoral purposes.

WOMAN SUFFRAGE, WOMEN'S RIGHTS

Women played a large role in the social-justice movement. Feminists were particularly active, especially in the political sphere, between 1890 and 1914—feminists were more active then, in fact, than at any other time until the 1960s. Some working-class women pushed for higher wages and better working conditions. College-educated women—five thousand a year graduated after 1900—took up careers in the professions, from which some of them supported reform. From 1890 to 1910, the work of a number of national women's organizations, including the National Council of Jewish Women, the National Congress of Mothers, and the Women's Trade Union League, furthered the aims of the progressive movement.

Excluded from most of these organizations, African American women formed their own groups. The National Association of Colored Women was founded in 1895, fifteen years before the better known male-oriented National Association for the Advancement of Colored People (NAACP). Aimed at social

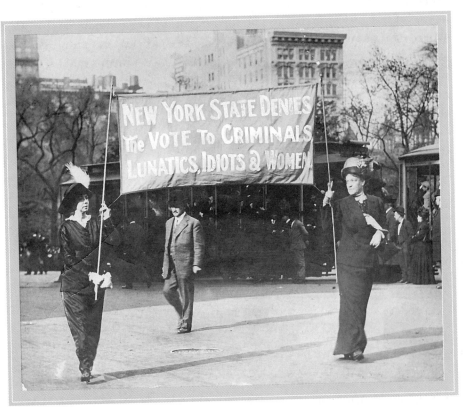

Woman suffrage was a key element in the social-justice movement. Without the right to vote, women working actively for reform had little real power to influence elected officials to support their endeavors.

welfare, the women's organization was the first African American social-service agency in the country.

From 200,000 members in 1900, the General Federation of Women's Clubs grew to more than 1 million by 1912. The clubs met, as they had before, for coffee and literary conversation, but they also began to look closely at conditions around them.

Forming an Industrial Section and a Committee on Legislation for Women and Children, the federation supported reforms to safeguard child and women workers, improve schools, ensure pure food, and beautify the community. Reluctant at first, the federation finally lent support in 1914 to woman suffrage, a cause that dated back to the first women's rights convention in Seneca Falls, New York, in 1848. Divided over tactics since the Civil War, the suffrage movement suffered from disunity, male opposition, indecision over whether to seek action at the state or at the national level, resistance from the Catholic Church, and opposition from liquor interests, who linked the cause to Prohibition.

Because politics was an avenue for reform, growing numbers of women activists became involved in the suffrage movement. After years of disagreement, the two major suffrage organizations, the National Woman Suffrage Association and the American Woman Suffrage Association, merged in 1890 to form the National American Woman Suffrage Association. The merger opened a new phase of the suffrage movement, characterized by unity and a tightly controlled national organization.

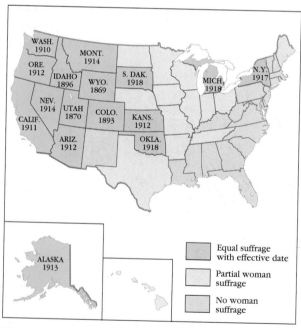

Woman Suffrage Before 1920

State-by-state gains in woman suffrage were limited to the Far West and were agonizingly slow in the early years of the twentieth century.

In 1900, Carrie Chapman Catt, a superb organizer, became

president of the National American Woman Suffrage Association, which by 1920 had nearly two million members. Catt and Anna Howard Shaw, who became the association's head in 1904, believed in organization and peaceful lobbying to win the vote. Alice Paul and Lucy Burns, founders of the Congressional Union, were more militant; they interrupted public meetings, focused on Congress rather than the states, and in 1917 picketed the White House.

Significantly, Catt, Paul, and others made a major change in the argument for woman suffrage. When the campaign began in the nineteenth century, suffragists had claimed the vote as a natural right, owed to women as much as men. Now, they stressed a pragmatic argument: since women were more sensitive to moral issues than men, they would use their votes to help create a better society. They would support temperance, clean government, laws to protect workers, and other reforms. In 1918, the House passed a constitutional amendment stating simply that the right to vote shall not be denied "on account of sex." The Senate and enough states followed, and, after three generations of suffragist efforts, the Nineteenth Amendment took effect in 1920.

The social-justice movement had the most success in passing state laws limiting the working hours of women. By 1913, thirty-nine states set maximum working hours for women or banned the employment of women at night. As early as 1900, thanks to groups such as the National Child Labor Committee, twenty-eight states had laws regulating child labor. But the courts often ruled against such laws, and families—needing extra income—sometimes ignored them. Parents sent children off to jobs with orders to lie about their ages.

A FERMENT OF IDEAS:
CHALLENGING THE STATUS QUO

A dramatic shift in ideas became one of the most important forces behind progressive reform. Most of the ideas focused on the role of the environment in shaping human behavior. Progressive reformers accepted society's growing complexity, called for factual treatment of piecemeal problems, allowed room for new theories, and, above all, rejected age-encrusted divine or natural "laws" in favor of thoughts and actions that worked.

A new doctrine called pragmatism emerged in this ferment of ideas. It came from William James, a brilliant Harvard psychologist who became the key figure in American thought from the 1890s to World War I. A warm, tolerant person, James was impatient with theories that regarded truth as abstract. Truth, he believed, should work for the individual, and it worked best not in abstraction, but in action.

People, James thought, not only were shaped by their environment; they shaped it. In *Pragmatism* (1907), he praised "tough-minded" individuals who could live effectively in a world with no easy answers. The tough-minded accepted change; they knew how to pick manageable problems, gather facts, discard ideas that did not work, and act on those that did. Ideas that worked became truth.

The most influential educator of the Progressive Era, John Dewey, applied pragmatism to educational reform. A friend and disciple of William James, he argued that thought evolves in relation to the environment and that education is directly related to experience. In 1896, Dewey founded a separate School of Pedagogy at the University of Chicago, with a laboratory in which educational theory based on the newer philosophical and psychological studies could be tested and practiced.

Dewey introduced an educational revolution that stressed children's needs and capabilities. He opposed memorization, rote learning, and dogmatic, authoritarian teaching methods; he emphasized personal growth, free inquiry, and creativity.

Rejecting the older view of the law as universal and unchanging, lawyers and legal theorists instead viewed it as a reflection of the environment—an instrument for social change. Law reflected the environment that shaped it. A movement grew among judges for "sociological jurisprudence" that related the law to social reform.

In Denver, Colorado, after Judge Ben Lindsey sentenced a boy to reform school for stealing coal, the boy's mother rushed forward and, grief-stricken, beat her head against the wall. Lindsey investigated the case and found that the father was a smelting worker dying of lead poisoning; the family needed coal for heat. From such experiences, Lindsey concluded that children were not born with a genetic tendency to crime; they were made good or bad by the environment in which they grew. Lindsey "sentenced" youthful offenders to education and good care. He worked for playgrounds, slum clearance, public baths, and technical schools.

Socialism, a reformist political philosophy, grew dramatically before World War I. Eugene V. Debs, president of the American Railway Union, in 1896 formed the Social Democratic party. Gentle and reflective, not at all the popular image of the wild-eyed radical, Debs was thrust into prominence by the Pullman strike. In 1901, he formed the important Socialist party of America. Neither Debs nor the party ever developed a cohesive platform, nor was Debs an effective organizer. But he was eloquent, passionate, and visionary. An excellent speaker, he captivated audiences, attacking the injustices of capitalism and urging a workers' republic.

Some of Eugene Debs's supporters surround the "Red
Special," the train Debs used
in his 1908 presidential
campaign. To attract voters to
his socialist message, Debs
traveled over 9000 miles in
less than four weeks. A
Detroit newspaper, trying to
discredit the socialist candidate, criticized Debs's use of
a "magnificent parlor car."

The Socialist party of America enlisted some intellectuals, factory workers, disillusioned Populists, tenant farmers, miners, and lumberjacks. By 1911, there were Socialist mayors in thirty-two cities. Although its doctrines were aimed at an urban proletariat, the Socialist party drew support in rural Texas, Missouri, Arkansas, Idaho, and Washington. In Oklahoma, it attracted as much as one-third of the vote. Most Socialists who won promised progressive reform rather than threatening to overthrow capitalists.

Although torn by factions, the Socialist party doubled in membership between 1904 and 1908, then tripled in the four years after that. Running for president, Debs garnered 100,000 votes in 1900; 400,000 in 1904; and 900,000 in 1912, the party's peak year.

REFORM IN THE CITIES AND STATES

Progressive reformers realized government could be a crucial agent in accomplishing their goals. They wanted to curb the influence of "special interests" and, through such measures of political reform as the direct primary and the direct election of senators, make government follow the public will. Once it did, they welcomed government action at whatever level was appropriate.

As a result of this thinking, the use of federal power increased, as did the power and prestige of the presidency. Progressives not only lobbied for government-sponsored reform but also worked actively in their home neighborhoods, cities, and states; much of the significant change occurred in local settings, outside the national limelight. Most important, the progressives believed in the ability of experts to solve problems. At every level—local, state, and federal—thousands of commissions and agencies took form. Staffed by trained experts, they oversaw a multitude of matters ranging from railroad rates to public health.

INTEREST GROUPS AND THE DECLINE OF POPULAR POLITICS

Placing government in the hands of experts was one way to get it out of the hands of politicians and political parties. The direct primary was another way. These initiatives and others like them were part of a fundamental change in the way Americans viewed their political system.

As one sign of the change, fewer and fewer people were going to the polls. Voter turnout dropped dramatically after 1900, when the intense partisanship of the decades after the Civil War gave way to media-oriented political campaigns based largely on the personalities of the candidates. From 1876 to 1900, the average turnout in presidential elections was 77 percent. From 1900 to 1916, it was 65 percent, and in the 1920s, it dropped to 52 percent, close to the average today. Turnout was lowest among young people, immigrants, the poor, and, ironically, the newly enfranchised women.

There were numerous causes for the falloff, but among the most important was the fact that people had found another way to achieve some of the objectives they had once assigned to political parties. They had found the "interest group," a means of action that assumed importance in this era and became a major feature of politics ever after. Professional societies, trade associations, labor organizations, farm lobbies, and scores of other interest groups worked outside the party system to pressure government for things their members wanted. Social workers, women's clubs, reform groups, and others learned to apply pressure in similar ways, and the result was much significant legislation of the Progressive Era.

REFORM IN THE CITIES

During the early years of the twentieth century, urban reform movements, many of them born in the depression of the 1890s, spread across the nation. In 1894, the National Municipal League was organized, and it became the forum for debate over civic reform, changes in the tax laws, and municipal ownership of public utilities. Within a few years, nearly every city had a variety of clubs and organizations directed at improving the quality of city life.

In city after city, reformers reordered municipal government. Tightening controls on corporate activities, they broadened the scope of utility regulation and restricted city franchises. They updated tax assessments, often skewed in favor of corporations, and tried to clean up the electoral machinery. Devoted to efficiency, they developed a trained civil service to oversee planning and operations. The generation of the 1880s also had believed in civil service, but the goal then was mostly negative: to get spoilsmen out and "good" people in. Now the goal was efficiency and, above all, results.

In constructing their model governments, urban reformers often turned to recent advances in business management and organization. They stressed continuity and expertise, a system in which professional experts staffed a government overseen by elected officials. At the top, the elected leader surveyed the breadth of city, state, or national affairs and defined directions. Below, a corps of experts—trained in the various disciplines of the new society—funneled the definition into specific scientifically based policies.

Reformers created a growing number of regulatory commissions and municipal departments. They hired engineers to oversee utility and water systems, physicians and nurses to improve municipal health, and city planners to oversee park and highway development.

In the race for reform, a number of city mayors won national reputations—among them Seth Low in New York City and Hazen S. Pingree in Detroit—working to modernize taxes, clean up politics, lower utility rates, and control the awarding of valuable city franchises.

In Cleveland, Ohio, Tom L. Johnson demonstrated an innovative approach to city government. A millionaire who had made his fortune manipulating city franchises, Johnson one day read Henry George's *Progress and Poverty* and turned to reform. Elected mayor of Cleveland, he served from 1901 to 1909. Believing in an informed citizenry, he held outdoor meetings in huge tents. He used colorful charts to give Cleveland residents a course in utilities and taxation. He cut down on corruption, cut off special privilege, updated taxes, and gave Cleveland a reputation as the country's best governed city.

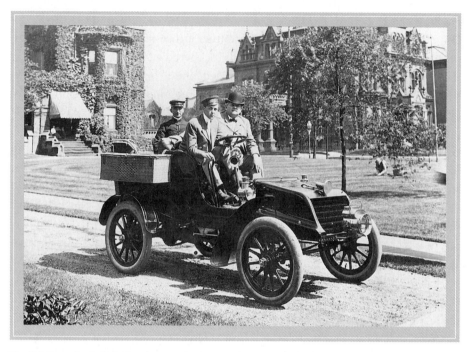

Tom L. Johnson (in derby hat) and companions in a car known as the "Red Devil," the first automobile used in a political campaign. Johnson, who made his fortune in the streetcar business, served as mayor of Cleveland from 1901 to 1909. His administration, noted for its efficiency and many municipal reforms, also waged a long and bitter fight with streetcar business interests opposed to Johnson's efforts to lower streetcar fares to make them affordable for working-class people. Muckraking journalist Lincoln Steffens praised Johnson's Cleveland as "the best-governed city in America."

ACTION IN THE STATES

Reformers soon discovered, however, that many problems lay beyond a city's boundaries, and they turned for action to the state governments. From the 1890s to 1920, reformers worked to stiffen state laws regulating the labor of women and children, to create and strengthen commissions to regulate railroads and utilities, to impose corporate and inheritance taxes, to improve mental and penal institutions, and to allocate more funds for state universities, which were viewed as the training ground for the experts and educated citizenry needed for the new society.

New York was one of the states that led the way in adopting significant reforms. Around 1905, a series of dramatic investigations in the state revealed a systematic and corrupt alliance between politicians and business leaders in the gas, electricity, and insurance industries—all of which directly touched the general public. An angry public responded immediately, supporting greater state regulation and management by independent expert commissions. In 1905 and

1906, the state established regulatory boards to oversee utilities and insurance; it also outlawed corporate contributions to political campaigns and restricted business lobbying in the state legislature.

To regulate business, virtually every state created regulatory commissions empowered to examine corporate books and hold public hearings. Building on earlier experience, state commissions after 1900 were given new power to initiate actions, rather than await complaints, and in some cases to set maximum prices and rates. Dictating company practices, they pioneered regulatory methods later adopted in federal legislation of 1906 and 1910.

Historians have long praised the regulation movement, but the commissions did not always act wisely or even in the public interest. Elective commissions often produced commissioners who had little knowledge of corporate affairs. In addition, to win election, some promised specific rates or reforms, obligations that might bias the commission's investigative functions. Appointive commissions sometimes fared better, but they too had to oversee extraordinarily complex businesses such as the railroads.

To the progressives, commissions offered a way to end the corrupt alliance between business and politics. There was another way, too, and that was to "democratize" government by reducing the power of politicians and increasing the influence of the electorate. To do that, progressives backed three measures to make officeholders responsive to popular will: the initiative, which allowed voters to propose new laws; the referendum, which allowed them to accept or reject a law at the ballot box; and the recall, which gave them a way to remove an elected official from office.

Oregon adopted the initiative and referendum in 1902; by 1912, twelve states had them. That year Congress added the Seventeenth Amendment to the Constitution to provide for the direct election of U.S. senators. By 1916, all but three states had direct primaries, which allowed the people, rather than nominating conventions, to choose candidates for office.

Robert M. La Follette became the most famous reform governor. In 1901, he became governor of Wisconsin, and in the following six years, he put together the "Wisconsin Idea," one of the most important reform programs in the history of state government. He established an industrial commission, the first in the country, to regulate factory safety and sanitation. He improved education, workers' compensation, public utility controls, and resource conservation. He lowered railroad rates and raised railroad taxes. Under La Follette's prodding, Wisconsin became the first state to adopt a direct primary for all political nominations. It also became the first to adopt a state income tax. Theodore Roosevelt called La Follette's Wisconsin "the laboratory of democracy," and the Wisconsin Idea soon spread to many other states.

The most famous of the reform leaders in the states was Wisconsin's Robert M. "Fighting Bob" La Follette, pictured here campaigning in Cumberland, Wisconsin, in 1897.

After 1905, the progressives looked more and more to Washington. For one thing, Teddy Roosevelt was there, with his zest for publicity and his alluring grin. But progressives also had a growing sense that many concerns—corporations and conservation, factory safety and child labor—crossed state lines. Federal action seemed desirable; specific reforms fit into a larger plan perhaps best seen from the nation's center. Within a few years, the focus of progressivism shifted to Washington.

THE REPUBLICAN ROOSEVELT

When President William McKinley died of gunshot wounds in September 1901, Vice President Theodore Roosevelt succeeded him in the White House. The new president initially vowed to carry on McKinley's policies. He continued some, developed others of his own, and in the end brought to them all the particular exuberance of his own personality.

At age 42, Roosevelt was then the youngest president in American history. In contrast to the dignified McKinley, he was open, aggressive, and high-spirited. At his desk by 8:30 every morning, he worked through the day, usually with visitors for breakfast, lunch, and dinner. Politicians, labor leaders, industrialists, poets, artists, and writers paraded through the White House.

If McKinley cut down on presidential isolation, Roosevelt virtually ended it. The presidency, he thought, was the "bully pulpit," a forum of ideas and leadership for the nation. The president was "a steward of the people bound actively and affirmatively to do all he could for the people." Self-confident, Roosevelt enlisted talented associates, including Elihu Root, secretary of war and later secretary of state; William Howard Taft, secretary of war; Gifford Pinchot, the nation's chief forester and leading conservationist; and Oliver Wendell Holmes, Jr., whom he named to the Supreme Court.

In 1901, Roosevelt invited Booker T. Washington, the prominent African American educator, to dinner at the White House. Many Southerners protested—"a crime equal to treason," a newspaper said—and they protested again when Roosevelt appointed several African Americans to important federal offices in South Carolina and Mississippi. At first, Roosevelt considered building a biracial "black-and-tan" southern Republican party, thinking it would foster racial progress and his own renomination in 1904.

But Roosevelt soon retreated. In some areas of the South, he supported "lily-white" Republican organizations, and his policies often reflected his own belief in African American inferiority. He said nothing when a race riot broke out in Atlanta in 1906, although twelve persons died. He joined others in blaming African American soldiers stationed near Brownsville, Texas, after a night of violence there in August 1906. Acting quickly and on little evidence, he discharged "without honor" three companies of African American troops. Six of the soldiers who were discharged held the Congressional Medal of Honor.

BUSTING THE TRUSTS

"There is a widespread conviction in the minds of the American people that the great corporations known as trusts are in certain of their features and tendencies hurtful to the general welfare," Roosevelt reported to Congress in 1901. Like most people, however, the president wavered on the trusts. Large-scale production and industrial growth, he believed, were natural and beneficial; they needed only to be controlled. Still he distrusted the trusts' impact on local enterprise and individual opportunity. Distinguishing between "good" and "bad" trusts, he pledged to protect the former while controlling the latter.

In 1903, Roosevelt asked Congress to create a Department of Commerce and Labor, with a Bureau of Corporations empowered to investigate corporations engaged in interstate commerce. Congress balked; Roosevelt called in reporters and, in an off-the-record interview, charged that John D. Rockefeller had organized the opposition to the measure. The press spread the word, and in the outcry that followed, the proposal passed easily in a matter of weeks. Roosevelt was delighted. With the new Bureau of Corporations publicizing its findings, he thought, the glare of publicity would eliminate most corporate abuses.

Roosevelt also undertook direct legal action. On February 18, 1902, he instructed the Justice Department to bring suit against the Northern Securities Company for violation of the Sherman Antitrust Act. It was a shrewd move. A mammoth holding company, Northern Securities controlled the massive rail networks of the Northern Pacific, Great Northern, and Chicago, Burlington & Quincy railroads.

In 1904, the Supreme Court, in a 5 to 4 decision, upheld the suit against Northern Securities and ordered the company dissolved. Roosevelt was jubilant, and he followed up the victory with several other antitrust suits. In 1902, he had moved against the beef trust, an action applauded by western farmers and urban consumers alike. After a lull, he initiated suits in 1906 and 1907 against the American Tobacco Company, the Du Pont Corporation, the New Haven Railroad, and Standard Oil.

But Roosevelt's policies were not always clear, nor his actions always consistent. He asked for (and received) business support in his bid for reelection in 1904. Large donations came in from industrial leaders, and J. P. Morgan himself later testified that he gave $150,000 to Roosevelt's campaign. In 1907, acting in part to avert a threatened financial panic, the president permitted Morgan's U.S. Steel to absorb the Tennessee Coal and Iron Company, an important competitor.

Roosevelt, in truth, was not a trustbuster, although he was frequently called that. William Howard Taft, his successor in the White House, initiated forty-three antitrust indictments in four years—nearly twice as many as the twenty-five Roosevelt initiated in the seven years of his presidency. Instead, Roosevelt used antitrust threats to keep businesses within bounds. Regulation, he believed, was a better way to control large-scale enterprise.

"SQUARE DEAL" IN THE COALFIELDS

A few months after announcing the Northern Securities suit, Roosevelt intervened in a major labor dispute involving the anthracite coal miners of northeastern Pennsylvania. Led by John Mitchell, a moderate labor leader, the United Mine Workers demanded wage increases, an eight-hour workday, and company recognition of the union. The coal companies refused, and in May 1902, 140,000 miners walked off the job. The mines closed.

As the months passed and the strike continued, coal prices rose. With winter coming on, schools, hospitals, and factories ran short of coal. Public opinion turned against the companies. Morgan and other industrial leaders privately urged them to settle, but George F. Baer, head of one of the largest companies, refused.

Roosevelt was furious. Complaining of the companies' arrogance, he invited both sides in the dispute to an October 1902 conference at the White House. There, Mitchell took a moderate tone and offered to submit the issues to arbitration, but the companies again refused to budge. Roosevelt ordered the army to prepare to seize the mines and then leaked word of his intent to Wall Street leaders.

Alarmed, Morgan and others again urged settlement of the dispute, and at last the companies retreated. They agreed to accept the recommendations of an independent commission the president would appoint. In late October, the strikers returned to work, and in March 1903, the commission awarded them a 10 percent wage increase and a cut in working hours. It recommended, however, against union recognition. The coal companies, in turn, were encouraged to raise prices to offset the wage increase.

More and more, Roosevelt saw the federal government as an honest and impartial "broker" between powerful elements in society. Rather than leaning toward labor, he pursued a middle way to curb corporate and labor abuses, abolish privilege, and enlarge individual opportunity. Conservative by temperament, he sometimes backed reforms in part to head off more radical measures.

During the 1904 campaign, Roosevelt called his actions in the coal miners' strike a "square deal" for both labor and capital, a term that stuck to his administration. Roosevelt was not the first president to take a stand for labor, but he was the first to bring opposing sides in a labor dispute to the White House to settle it.

ROOSEVELT PROGRESSIVISM AT ITS HEIGHT

In the election of 1904, the popular Roosevelt soundly drubbed his Democratic opponent, Alton B. Parker of New York, and the Socialist party candidate, Eugene V. Debs of Indiana. Roosevelt attracted a large campaign chest and won votes everywhere. After a landslide victory, he pledged that "under no circumstances will I be a candidate for or accept another nomination," a statement he later regretted.

THE ELECTION OF 1904

CANDIDATE	PARTY	POPULAR VOTE	ELECTORAL VOTE
T. Roosevelt	Republican	7,626,593	336
Parker	Democrat	5,082,898	140
Debs	Socialist	402,489	0
Swallow	Prohibition	258,596	0

REGULATING THE RAILROADS

Following his election, Roosevelt in late 1904 laid out a reform program that included railroad regulation, employers' liability for federal employees, greater federal control over corporations, and laws regulating child labor, factory inspection, and slum clearance in the District of Columbia. He turned first to railroad regulation. In 1903, he had worked with Congress to pass the Elkins Act to prohibit railroad rebates and increase the powers of the Interstate Commerce Commission (ICC). The Elkins Act, a moderate law, was framed with the consent of railroad leaders. In 1904 and 1905, the president wanted much more, and he urged Congress to empower the ICC to set reasonable and nondiscriminatory rates and prevent inequitable practices.

Widespread demand for railroad regulation strengthened Roosevelt's hand. In the Midwest and Far West, the issue was a popular one, and reform governors La Follette in Wisconsin and Albert B. Cummins in Iowa urged federal action. Roosevelt maneuvered cannily. As the legislative battle opened, he released figures showing that Standard Oil had reaped $750,000 a year from railroad rebates. He also skillfully traded congressional support for a strong railroad measure in return for his promise to postpone a reduction of the tariff, a stratagem that came back to plague President Taft.

Triumph came with passage of the Hepburn Act of 1906. A significant achievement, the act strengthened the rate-making power of the Interstate Commerce Commission. It increased membership on the ICC from five to seven, empowered it to fix reasonable maximum railroad rates, and broadened its jurisdiction to include oil pipeline, express, and sleeping car companies. ICC orders were binding, pending any court appeals, thus placing the burden of proof of injustice on the companies. Delighted, Roosevelt viewed the Hepburn Act as a major step in his plan for continuous expert federal control over industry.

CLEANING UP FOOD AND DRUGS

Soon Roosevelt was dealing with two other important bills, these aimed at regulating the food and drug industries. Muckraking articles had touched frequently on filthy conditions in meatpacking houses, but Upton Sinclair's *The Jungle* (1906) set off a storm of indignation. Ironically, Sinclair had set out to write a novel about the packinghouse workers, the "wage slaves of the Beef Trust," hoping to do for wage slavery what Harriet Beecher Stowe had done for chattel slavery. But readers largely ignored his story of the workers and seized instead on the graphic descriptions of the things that went into their meat.

Sinclair was disappointed at the reaction. "I aimed at the public's heart," he later said, "and by accident I hit it in the stomach." He had, indeed. After reading *The Jungle*, Roosevelt ordered an investigation. The result, he said, was "hideous,"

A poster for the movie version of Upton Sinclair's The Jungle *promises a "wonderful story of the beef packing industry." The conditions that Sinclair described in the book brought to public attention the scandals of the meatpacking industry knowingly selling diseased meat and the filthy, disease-ridden, dangerous conditions in which the workers toiled for their subsistence wages.*

The Pure Food and Drug Act, passed in 1906, did not ban the sale of patent medicines, nor did it curb the exaggerated claims of some of the manufacturers. Reid's Cough and Kidney Remedy, for example, promised relief within 20 minutes from colds, coughs, bronchitis, hoarseness, whooping cough, asthma, and kidney disease. The makers of the drug complied with the Pure Food and Drug Act by noting on the bottle's label that the remedy contained 30 percent grain alcohol.

and he threatened to publish the entire "sickening report" if Congress did not act. Meat sales plummeted in the United States and Europe. Demand for reform grew. Alarmed, the meatpackers themselves supported a reform law, which they hoped would be just strong enough to still the clamor. The Meat Inspection Act of 1906, stronger than the packers wanted, set rules for sanitary meatpacking and government inspection of meat products.

A second measure, the Pure Food and Drug Act, passed more easily. Samuel Hopkins Adams, a muckraker, exposed the dangers of patent medicines in several sensational articles in *Collier's*. Patent medicines, Adams pointed out, contained mostly alcohol, drugs, and "undiluted fraud." Dr. Harvey W. Wiley, the chief chemist in the Department of Agriculture, led a "poison squad" of young assistants who experimented with the medicines. With evidence in hand, Wiley pushed for regulation; Roosevelt and the recently reorganized American Medical Association joined the fight, and the act passed on June 30, 1906. Requiring manufacturers to list certain ingredients on the label, it represented a pioneering effort to ban the manufacture and sale of adulterated, misbranded, or unsanitary food or drugs.

Conserving the Land

An expert on birds, Roosevelt loved nature and the wilderness, and some of his most enduring accomplishments came in the field of conservation. Working closely with Gifford Pinchot, chief of the Forest Service, he established the first comprehensive national conservation policy. To Roosevelt, conservation meant the wise use of natural resources, not locking them away, so those who thought the wilderness should be preserved rather than developed generally opposed his policies.

Using experts in the federal government, Roosevelt undertook a major reclamation program, created the federal Reclamation Service, and strengthened

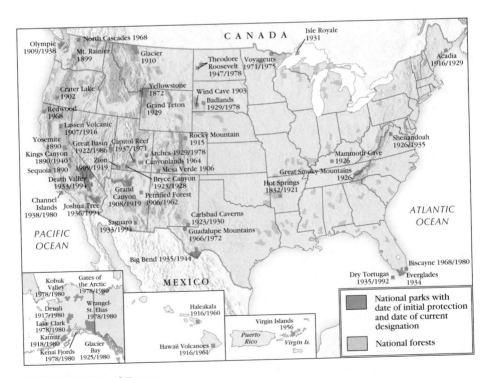

National Parks and Forests

During the presidency of Theodore Roosevelt, who considered conservation his most important domestic achievement, millions of acres of land were set aside for national parks and forests.

the forest preserve program in the Department of Agriculture. Broadening the concept of conservation, he placed power sites, coal lands, and oil reserves as well as national forest in the public domain.

When Roosevelt took office in 1901, there were 45 million acres in government preserves. In 1908, there were almost 195 million.

As 1908 approached, Roosevelt became increasingly strident in his demand for sweeping reforms. He attacked "malefactors of great wealth," urged greater federal regulatory powers, criticized the conservatism of the federal courts, and called for laws protecting factory workers. Many business leaders blamed him for a severe financial panic in the autumn of 1907, and conservatives in Congress stiffened their opposition. Divisions between Republican conservatives and progressives grew.

Immensely popular, Roosevelt prepared in 1908 to turn over the White House to William Howard Taft, his close friend and colleague. As expected, Taft soundly defeated the Democratic standard-bearer William Jennings Bryan, who was making his third try for the presidency. The Republicans retained control of Congress. Taft prepared to move into the White House, ready and willing to carry on the Roosevelt legacy.

THE ORDEAL OF WILLIAM HOWARD TAFT

The Republican national convention that nominated Taft had not satisfied either Roosevelt or Taft. True, Taft won the presidential nomination as planned, but conservative Republicans beat back the attempts of progressive Republicans to influence the convention. They named a conservative, James S. Sherman, for vice president and built a platform that reflected conservative views on labor, the courts, and other issues. Taft wanted a pledge to lower the tariff but got only a promise of revision, which might lower—or raise—it. La Follette, Cummins, Jonathan P. Dolliver of Iowa, Albert J. Beveridge of Indiana, and other progressive Republicans were openly disappointed.

Taking office in 1909, Taft felt "just a bit like a fish out of water." The son of a distinguished Ohio family and a graduate of Yale Law School, he became an Ohio judge, solicitor general of the United States, and a judge of the federal circuit court. In 1900, McKinley asked him to head the Philippine Commission, charged with the difficult and challenging task of forming a civil government in the Philippines. Later Taft was named the first governor general of the Philippines. In 1904, Roosevelt appointed him secretary of war. In all these positions, Taft made his mark as a skillful administrator. He worked quietly behind the scenes, avoided controversy, and shared none of Roosevelt's zest for politics. A good-natured man, Taft had personal charm and infectious humor. He fled from fights rather

THE ELECTION OF 1908

CANDIDATE	PARTY	POPULAR VOTE	ELECTORAL VOTE
Taft	Republican	7,676,258	321
Bryan	Democrat	6,406,801	162
Debs	Socialist	420,380	0
Chafin	Prohibition	252,821	0

than seeking them out, and he disliked political maneuvering, preferring instead quiet solitude. "I don't like politics," he said. "I don't like the limelight."

Weighing close to 300 pounds, Taft enjoyed conversation, golf and bridge, good food, and plenty of rest. Compared to the hardworking Roosevelt and Wilson, he was lazy. He was also honest, kindly, and amiable, and in his own way he knew how to get things done.

Taft's years as president were not happy. As it turned out, he presided over a Republican party torn with tensions that Roosevelt had either brushed aside or concealed. The tariff, business regulation, and other issues split conservatives and progressives, and Taft often wavered or sided with the conservatives. Taft revered the past and distrusted change; although an ardent supporter of Roosevelt, he never had Roosevelt's faith in the ability of government to impose reform and alter individual behavior. He named five corporation attorneys to his cabinet, leaned more to business than to labor, and spoke of a desire to "clean out the unions."

At that time and later, Taft's reputation suffered by comparison to the flair of Roosevelt and the moral majesty of Woodrow Wilson. He deserved better. Taft was an honest and sincere president, who—sometimes firm, sometimes befuddled—faced a series of important and troublesome problems during his term of office.

PARTY INSURGENCY

Taft started his term with an attempt to curb the powerful Republican speaker of the House, Joseph "Uncle Joe" Cannon of Illinois. Using the powers of his position, Cannon had been setting House procedures, appointing committees, and virtually dictating legislation. Straightforward and crusty, he often opposed reform. In March 1909, thirty Republican congressmen joined Taft's effort to curb Cannon's power, and the president sensed success. But Cannon retaliated and, threatening to block all tariff bills, forced a compromise. Taft stopped the anti-Cannon campaign in return for Cannon's pledge to help with tariff cuts.

Republicans were divided over the tariff, and there was a growing party insurgency against high rates. The House quickly passed a bill providing for lower rates, but in the Senate, protectionists raised them. Senate leader Nelson W. Aldrich of Rhode Island introduced a revised bill that added more than eight hundred amendments to the rates approved in the House.

Angry, La Follette and other Republicans attacked the bill as the child of special interests. In speeches on the Senate floor they called themselves "progressives," invoked Roosevelt's name, and urged Taft to defeat the high-tariff proposal. Caught between protectionists and progressives, Taft wavered, then tried to compromise. In the end, he backed Aldrich. The Payne-Aldrich Act, passed in November 1909, called for higher rates than the original House bill, though it lowered them from the Dingley Tariff of 1897. An unpopular law, Payne-Aldrich helped discredit Taft and revealed the tensions in the Republican party.

Republican progressives and conservatives drifted apart. Thin-skinned, Taft resented the persistent pinpricks of the progressives who criticized him for virtually everything he did. He tried to find middle ground but leaned more and more toward the conservatives. During a nationwide speaking tour in the autumn of 1909, he praised Aldrich, scolded the low-tariff insurgents, and called the Payne-Aldrich Act "the best bill that the Republican party ever passed."

By early 1910, progressive Republicans in Congress no longer looked to Taft for leadership. As before, they challenged Cannon's power, and Taft wavered. In an outcome embarrassing to the president, the progressives won, managing to curtail Cannon's authority to dictate committee assignments and schedule debate. In progressive circles there was growing talk of a Roosevelt return to the White House.

THE BALLINGER–PINCHOT AFFAIR

The conservation issue dealt another blow to relations between Roosevelt and President Taft. In 1909, Richard A. Ballinger, Taft's secretary of the interior, offered for sale a million acres of public land that Pinchot, who had stayed on as Taft's chief forester, had withdrawn from sale. Pinchot, fearing that Ballinger would hurt conservation programs, protested and, seizing on a report that Ballinger had helped sell valuable Alaskan coal lands to a syndicate that included J. P. Morgan, asked Taft to intervene. After investigating, Taft supported Ballinger on every count, although he asked Pinchot to remain in office.

Pinchot refused to drop the matter. Behind the scenes, he provided material for two anti-Ballinger magazine articles. Taft had had enough. He fired the insubordinate Pinchot, an action which, though appropriate, again lost support for

Taft. Newspapers followed the controversy for months, and muckrakers assailed the administration's "surrender" to Morgan and other "despoilers of the national heritage."

The Ballinger-Pinchot controversy obscured Taft's important contributions to conservation. He won from Congress the power to remove lands from sale, and he used it to conserve more land than Roosevelt did. Still, the controversy tarred Taft, and it upset his old friend Roosevelt.

TAFT ALIENATES THE PROGRESSIVES

Interested in railroad regulation, Taft backed a bill in 1910 to empower the ICC to fix maximum railroad rates. Progressive Republicans favored that plan but attacked Taft's suggestion of a special Commerce Court to hear appeals from ICC decisions because most judges were traditionally conservative in outlook and usually rejected attempts to regulate railroad rates. They also thought the railroads had been consulted too closely in drawing up the bill. Democratic and Republican progressives tried to amend the bill to strengthen it; Taft made support of it a test of party loyalty.

The Mann-Elkins Act of 1910 gave something to everyone. It gave the ICC power to set rates, stiffened long- and short-haul regulations, and placed telephone and telegraph companies under ICC jurisdiction. These provisions delighted progressives. The act also created a Commerce Court, pleasing conservatives. In a trade-off, conservative Republican Senate leaders pledged their support for a statehood bill for Arizona and New Mexico, which were both predicted to be Democratic. In return, enough Democratic senators promised to vote for the Commerce Court provision to pass the bill. While pleased with the act, Taft and the Republican party lost further ground. In votes on key provisions of the Mann-Elkins Act, Taft raised the issue of party regularity, and progressive Republicans defied him.

Taft attempted to defeat the progressive Republicans in the 1910 elections. He helped form antiprogressive organizations, and he campaigned against progressive Republican candidates for the Senate. Progressive Republicans retaliated by organizing a nationwide network of anti-Taft Progressive Republican Clubs.

The 1910 election results were a major setback for Taft and the Republicans—especially conservative Republicans. A key issue in the election, the high cost of living, gave an edge to the progressive wings in both major parties, lending support to their attack on the tariff and the trusts. In party primaries, progressive Republicans overwhelmed most Taft candidates, and in the general election, they tended to fare better than the conservatives, which increased progressive influence in the Republican party.

For Republicans of all persuasions, however, it was a difficult election. The Democrats swept the urban-industrial states from New York to Illinois. New York, New Jersey, Indiana, and even Taft's Ohio elected Democratic governors. For the first time since 1894, Republicans lost control of both the House and the Senate. Disappointed, Taft called it "not only a landslide, but a tidal wave and holocaust all rolled into one general cataclysm."

Despite the defeat, Taft pushed through several important measures before his term ended. With the help of the new Democratic House, he backed laws to regulate safety in mines and on railroads, create a Children's Bureau in the federal government, establish employers' liability for all work done on government contracts, and mandate an eight-hour workday for government workers.

In 1909, Congress initiated a constitutional amendment authorizing an income tax, which, along with woman suffrage, was one of the most significant legislative measures of the twentieth century. The Sixteenth Amendment took effect early in 1913. A few months later, an important progressive goal was realized when the direct election of senators was ratified as the Seventeenth Amendment to the Constitution.

An ardent supporter of competition, Taft relentlessly pressed a campaign against trusts. The Sherman Antitrust Act, he said in 1911, "is a good law that ought to be enforced, and I propose to enforce it." That year, the Supreme Court in cases against Standard Oil and American Tobacco established the "rule of reason," which allowed the Court to determine whether a business presented "reasonable" restraint on trade. Taft thought the decisions gave the Court too much discretion, and he pushed ahead with the antitrust effort.

In October 1911, he sued U.S. Steel for its acquisition of the Tennessee Coal and Iron Company in 1907. Roosevelt had approved the acquisition, and the suit seemed designed to impugn his action. Enraged, he attacked Taft, and Taft, for once, fought back. He accused Roosevelt of undermining the conservative tradition in the country and began working to undercut the influence of the progressive Republicans. Increasingly now, Roosevelt listened to anti-Taft Republicans who urged him to run for president in 1912. In February 1912, he announced, "My hat is in the ring."

DIFFERING PHILOSOPHIES IN THE ELECTION OF 1912

Delighted Democrats looked on as Taft and Roosevelt fought for the Republican nomination. As the incumbent president, Taft controlled the party machinery, and when the Republican convention met in June 1912, he took the nomination. In early July, the Democrats met in Baltimore and, confident of victory for the first time in two decades, struggled through forty-six ballots before finally nominating Woodrow Wilson, the reform-minded governor of New Jersey.

A month later, some of the anti-Taft and progressive Republicans—now calling themselves the Progressive party—whooped it up in Chicago. Roosevelt was there to give a stirring "Confession of Faith." Naming Roosevelt for president at its convention, the Progressive party—soon known as the Bull Moose party—set the stage for the first important three-cornered presidential contest since 1860.

Taft was out of the running before the campaign even began. "I think I might as well give up so far as being a candidate is concerned," he said in July. "There are so many people in the country who don't like me." Taft stayed at home and made no speeches before the election. Roosevelt campaigned strenuously, even completing one speech after being shot in the chest by an anti-third-term fanatic. "I have a message to deliver," he said, "and will deliver it as long as there is life in my body."

Roosevelt's message involved a program he called the New Nationalism. An important phase in the shaping of twentieth-century American political thought, it demanded a national approach to the country's affairs and a strong president to deal with them. The New Nationalism called for efficiency in government and society. It exalted the executive and the expert; urged social-justice reforms to protect workers, women, and children; and accepted "good" trusts. The New Nationalism encouraged large concentrations of labor and capital, serving the nation's interests under a forceful federal executive.

For the first time in the history of a major political party, the Progressive campaign enlisted women in its organization. Jane Addams, the well-known settlement worker, seconded Roosevelt's nomination at Chicago, and she and other women played a leading role in his campaign. Some labor leaders, who saw potential for union growth, and some business leaders, who saw relief from destructive competition and labor strife, supported the new party.

Wilson, in contrast, set forth a program called the New Freedom that emphasized business competition and small government. A states' rights Democrat, he wanted to rein in federal authority, using it only to sweep away special privilege, release individual energies, and restore competition. Drawing on the thinking of Louis D. Brandeis, the brilliant shaper of reform-minded law, he echoed the Progressive party's social-justice objectives, while continuing to attack Roosevelt's planned state. For Wilson, the vital issue was not a planned economy but a free one. "The history of liberty is the history of the limitation of governmental power," he said in October 1912. "If America is not to have free enterprise, then she can have freedom of no sort whatever."

In the New Nationalism and New Freedom, the election of 1912 offered competing philosophies of government. Both Roosevelt and Wilson saw the central problem of the American nation as economic growth and its effect on individuals and society. Both focused on the government's relation to business, both

The Election of 1912

CANDIDATE	PARTY	POPULAR VOTE	ELECTORAL VOTE
Wison	Democrat	6,296,547	435
Roosevelt	Progressive (Bull Moose)	4,118,571	88
Taft	Republican	3,486,720	8
	Minor Parties	1,135,697	0

believed in bureaucratic reform, and both wanted to use government to protect the ordinary citizen. But Roosevelt welcomed federal power, national planning, and business growth; Wilson distrusted them all.

On election day, Wilson won 6.3 million votes to 4.1 million for Roosevelt (who had recovered quickly from his wound) and 900,000 for Eugene V. Debs, the Socialist party candidate. Taft, the incumbent president, finished third with 3.5 million votes; he carried only Vermont and Utah for 8 electoral votes. The Democrats also won outright control of both houses.

Woodrow Wilson's New Freedom

If under Roosevelt social reform took on the excitement of a circus, "under Wilson it acquired the dedication of a sunrise service." Born in Virginia in 1856 and raised in the South, Wilson was the son of a Presbyterian minister. As a young man, he wanted a career in public service, and he trained himself carefully in history and oratory. A moralist, he reached judgments easily. Once reached, almost nothing shook them. Opponents called him stubborn and smug.

After graduating from Princeton University and the University of Virginia Law School, Wilson found that practicing law bored him. Shifting to history, from 1890 to 1902 he served as professor of jurisprudence and political economy at Princeton. In 1902, he became president of the university. Eight years later, he was governor of New Jersey, where he led a campaign to reform election procedures, abolish corrupt practices, and strengthen railroad regulation.

Wilson's rise was rapid, and he knew relatively little about national issues and personalities. But he learned fast, and in some ways the lack of experience served him well. He had few political debts to repay, and he brought fresh perspectives to older issues. Ideas intrigued Wilson; details bored him. Although he

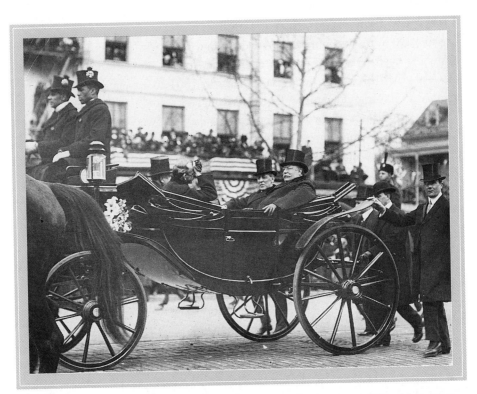

Woodrow Wilson and outgoing President William Taft share a carriage ride en route to Wilson's inauguration following his victory in the election of 1912. The Republican Party split over the election with the Progressives supporting Theodore Roosevelt and his Bull Moose ticket and the party machine supporting Taft. Even though the Republican split encouraged the Democrats to hope for victory, it still took forty-six ballots before they could agree on Wilson as their candidate.

was outgoing at times, he could also be cold and aloof, and aides soon learned that he preferred loyalty and flattery to candid criticism.

Prone to self-righteousness, Wilson often turned differences of opinion into bitter personal quarrels. Like Roosevelt, he believed in strong presidential leadership. A scholar of the party system, he cooperated closely with Democrats in Congress, and his legislative record placed him among the most effective presidents in terms of passing bills that he supported. Forbidding in individual conversation, Wilson could move crowds with graceful oratory. Unlike Taft, and to a greater degree than Roosevelt, he could inspire.

His inaugural address was eloquent. "The Nation," he said, "has been deeply stirred, stirred by a solemn passion, stirred by the knowledge of wrong, of ideals lost, of government too often debauched and made an instrument of evil. The feelings with which we face this new age of right and opportunity sweep across our heartstrings like some air out of God's own presence."

THE NEW FREEDOM IN ACTION

On the day of his inauguration, Wilson called Congress into special session to lower the tariff. When the session opened on April 8, 1913, Wilson himself was there, the first president since John Adams in 1801 to appear personally before Congress. In forceful language, he urged Congress to reduce tariff rates.

As the bill moved through Congress, Wilson showed exceptional skill. He worked closely with congressional leaders, and when lobbyists threatened the bill in the Senate, he appealed for popular support. The result was a triumph for Wilson and the Democratic party. The Underwood Tariff Act passed in 1913. The first tariff cut in nineteen years, it lowered rates about 15 percent and removed duties from sugar, wool, and several other consumer goods.

To make up for lost revenue, the act also levied a modest graduated income tax, authorized under the just ratified Sixteenth Amendment. Marking a significant shift in the American tax structure, it imposed a 1 percent tax on individuals and corporations earning more than $4,000 annually and an additional 1 percent tax on incomes more than $20,000. Above all, the act reflected a new unity within the Democratic party, which had worked together to pass a difficult tariff law.

Wilson himself emerged as an able leader. "At a single stage," a foreign editor said, "[he went] from the man of promise to the man of achievement." Encouraged by his success, Wilson decided to keep Congress in session through the hot Washington summer. Now he focused on banking reform, and the result in December 1913 was the Federal Reserve Act, the most important domestic law of his administration.

Meant to provide the United States with a sound yet flexible currency, the act established the country's first efficient banking system since Andrew Jackson killed the second Bank of the United States in 1832. It created twelve regional banks, each to serve the banks of its district. The regional banks answered to a Federal Reserve Board, appointed by the president, which governed the nation-wide system.

A compromise law, the act blended public and private control of the banking system. Private bankers owned the federal reserve banks but answered to the presidentially appointed Federal Reserve Board. The reserve banks were authorized to issue currency, and through the discount rate—the interest rate at which they loaned money to member banks—they could raise or lower the amount of money in circulation. Monetary affairs no longer depended solely on the price of gold. Within a year, nearly half the nation's banking resources were in the Federal Reserve System.

The Clayton Antitrust Act (1914) completed Wilson's initial legislative program. Like previous antitrust measures, it reflected confusion over how to discipline a growing economy without putting a brake on output. In part it was a response to the revelations of the Pujo Committee of the House, publicized by Brandeis in a disquieting series of articles, "Other People's Money." In its investigation of Wall Street, the committee discovered a pyramid of money and power capped by the Morgan-Rockefeller empire that, through "interlocking directorates," controlled companies worth $22 billion, more than one-tenth of the national wealth.

The Clayton Act outlawed such directorates and prohibited unfair trade practices. It forbade pricing policies that created monopoly, and it made corporate officers personally responsible for antitrust violations. Delighting Samuel Gompers and the labor movement, the act declared that unions were not conspiracies in restraint of trade, outlawed the use of injunctions in labor disputes unless necessary to protect property, and approved lawful strikes and picketing. To Gompers's dismay, the courts continued to rule against union activity.

A related law established a powerful Federal Trade Commission to oversee business methods. Composed of five members, the commission could demand special and annual reports, investigate complaints, and order corporate compliance, subject to court review. At first, Wilson opposed the commission concept, which was an approach more suitable to Roosevelt's New Nationalism, but he changed his mind and, along with Brandeis, called it the cornerstone of his antitrust plan. To reassure business leaders, he appointed a number of conservatives to the new commission and to the Federal Reserve Board.

In November 1914, Wilson proudly announced the completion of his New Freedom program. Tariff, banking, and antitrust laws promised a brighter future, he said, and it was now "a time of healing because a time of just dealing." Many progressives were aghast. That Wilson could think society's ills were so easily cured, the *New Republic* said, "casts suspicion either upon his own sincerity or upon his grasp of the realities of modern social and industrial life."

WILSON MOVES TOWARD THE NEW NATIONALISM

Distracted by the start of war in Europe, Wilson gave less attention to domestic issues for more than a year. When he returned to concern with reform, he adopted more and more of Roosevelt's New Nationalism and blended it with the New Freedom to set it off from his earlier policies.

One of Wilson's problems was the Congress. To his dismay, the Republicans gained substantially in the 1914 elections. Reducing the Democratic majority in the House, they swept key industrial and farm states. At the same time, a recession struck the economy, which had been hurt by the outbreak of the European war in August 1914. Some business leaders blamed the tariff and other New

Freedom laws. On the defensive, Wilson soothed business sentiment and invited bankers and industrialists to the White House. He allowed companies fearful of antitrust actions to seek advice from the Justice Department.

Preoccupied with such problems, Wilson blocked significant action in Congress through most of 1915. He refused to support a bill providing minimum wages for women workers, sidetracked a child labor bill on the ground that it was unconstitutional, and opposed a bill to establish long-term credits for farmers. He also refused to endorse woman suffrage, arguing that the right to vote was a state matter, not a federal one.

Wilson's record on race disappointed African Americans and many progressives. He had appealed to African American voters during the 1912 election, and a number of African American leaders campaigned for him. Soon after the inauguration, Oswald Garrison Villard, a leader of the NAACP, proposed a National Race Commission to study the problem of race relations. Initially sympathetic, Wilson rejected the idea because he feared he might lose southern Democratic votes in Congress. A Virginian himself, he appointed many Southerners to high office, and for the first time since the Civil War, southern views on race dominated the nation's capital.

At one of Wilson's first cabinet meetings, the postmaster general proposed the segregation of all African Americans in the federal service. No one dissented, including Wilson. Several government bureaus promptly began to segregate workers in offices, shops, rest rooms, and restaurants. Employees who objected were fired. African American leaders protested, and they were joined by progressive leaders and clergymen. Surprised at the protest, Wilson backed quietly away from the policy, although he continued to insist that segregation benefited African Americans.

As the year 1916 began, Wilson made a dramatic switch in focus and again pushed for substantial reforms. The result was a virtual river of reform laws, which was significant because it began the second, more national-minded phase of the New Freedom. With scarcely a glance over his shoulder, Wilson embraced important portions of Roosevelt's New Nationalism campaign.

In part, he was motivated by the approaching presidential election. A minority president, Wilson owed his victory in 1912 to the split in the Republican party, now almost healed. Roosevelt was moving back into Republican ranks, and there were issues connected with the war in Europe that he might use against Wilson. Moreover, many progressives were voicing disappointment with Wilson's limited reforms and his failure to support more advanced reform legislation on matters such as farm credits, child labor, and woman suffrage.

Moving quickly to patch up the problem, Wilson named Brandeis to the Supreme Court in January 1916. Popular among progressives, Brandeis was also the first person of Jewish faith to serve on the Court. When conservatives in the Senate tried to defeat the nomination, Wilson stood firm and won, earning further praise from progressives, Jews, and others. In May, he reversed his stand on farm loans and accepted a rural credits bill to establish farm-loan banks backed by federal funds. The Federal Farm Loan Act of 1916 created a Federal Farm Loan Board to give farmers credit similar to the Federal Reserve's benefits for trade and industry.

Wilson was already popular within the labor movement. Going beyond Roosevelt's policies, which had sought a balance between business and labor, he defended union recognition and collective bargaining. In 1913, he appointed William B. Wilson, a respected leader of the United Mine Workers, as the first head of the Labor Department, and he strengthened the department's Division of Conciliation. In 1914, in Ludlow, Colorado, state militia and mine guards fired machine guns into a tent colony of coal strikers, killing twenty-one men,

Miners in Ludlow, Colorado, went on strike in September 1913 for better working conditions and union recognition. Expecting eviction from company housing, they built a tent colony near the company town. The company, John D. Rockefeller's Colorado Fuel and Iron Company, hired guards to break the strike. On April 20, 1914, state troops and guards sprayed the tents with gunfire, then soaked the tents with kerosene and set the colony afire. Twenty-one of the colonists died, including eleven children.

women, and children. Outraged, Wilson stepped in and used federal troops to end the violence while negotiations to end the strike went on.

In August 1916, a threatened railroad strike again revealed Wilson's sympathies with labor. Like Roosevelt, he invited the two sides to the White House, where he urged the railroad companies to grant an eight-hour day and labor leaders to abandon the demand for overtime pay. Labor leaders accepted the proposal; railroad leaders did not. "I pray God to forgive you, I never can," Wilson said as he left the room. Soon he signed the Adamson Act (1916) that imposed the eight-hour day on interstate railways and established a federal commission to study the railroad problem. Ending the threat of a strike, the act marked a milestone in the expansion of the federal government's authority to regulate industry.

With Wilson leading the way, the flow of reform legislation continued until the election. The Federal Workmen's Compensation Act established workers' compensation for government employees. The Keating-Owen Act, the first federal child labor law, prohibited the shipment in interstate commerce of products manufactured by children under the age of 14. It too expanded the authority of the federal government, though it was soon struck down by the Supreme Court. The Warehouse Act authorized licensed warehouses to issue negotiable receipts for farm products deposited with them.

In September, Wilson signed the Tariff Commission Act creating an expert commission to recommend tariff rates. The same month, the Revenue Act of 1916 boosted income taxes and furthered tax reform. Four thousand members of the National American Woman Suffrage Association cheered when Wilson finally came out in support of woman suffrage. Two weeks later he endorsed the eight-hour day for all the nation's workers.

The 1916 presidential election was close, but Wilson won it on the issues of peace and progressivism. By the end of 1916, he and the Democratic party had enacted most of the important parts of Roosevelt's Progressive party platform of 1912. To do it, Wilson abandoned portions of the New Freedom and accepted much of the New Nationalism, including greater federal power and commissions governing trade and tariffs. In mixing the two programs, he blended some of the competing doctrines of the Progressive Era, established the primacy of the federal government, and foreshadowed the pragmatic outlook of Franklin D. Roosevelt's New Deal of the 1930s.

The election of 1916 showed how deeply progressivism had reached into American society. "We have in four years," Wilson said that fall, "come very near to carrying out the platform of the Progressive party as well as our own; for we are also progressives."

In retrospect, however, 1916 also marked the beginning of progressivism's decline. At most, the years of progressive reform lasted from the 1890s to

1921, and in large measure they were compressed into a single decade between 1906 and American entry into World War I in 1917. Many problems the progressives addressed but did not solve; and some important ones, such as race, they did not even tackle. Yet their regulatory commissions, direct primaries, city improvements, and child labor laws marked an era of important and measured reform.

The institution of the presidency expanded. From the White House radiated executive departments that guided a host of activities. Independent commissions, operating within flexible laws, supplemented executive authority.

These developments owed a great deal to both Roosevelt and Wilson. To manage a complex society, TR developed a simple formula: expert advice; growth-minded policies; a balancing of business, labor, and other interests; the use of publicity to gather support; and stern but often permissive oversight of the economy. TR strengthened the executive office, and he called on the newer group of professional, educated, public-minded citizens to help him. "I believe in a strong executive," he said; "I believe in power."

At first, Wilson had different ideas, wanting to dismantle much of Roosevelt's governing apparatus. But driven by outside forces and changes in his own thinking, Wilson soon moved in directions similar to those Roosevelt had championed. Starting out to disperse power, he eventually consolidated it.

Through such movements, government at all levels accepted responsibility for the welfare of various elements in the social order. A reform-minded and bureaucratic society took shape, in which men and women, labor and capital, political parties and social classes competed for shares in the expansive framework of twentieth-century life. But there were limits to reform. As both TR and Wilson found, the new government agencies, understaffed and underfinanced, depended on the responsiveness of those they sought to regulate.

Soon there was a far darker cloud on the horizon. The spirit of progressivism rested on a belief in human potential, peace, and progress. After Napoleon's defeat in 1815, a century of peace began in western Europe, and as the decades passed, war seemed a dying institution. "It looks as though this were going to be the age of treaties rather than the age of wars," an American said in 1912, "the century of reason rather than the century of force." It was not to be. Two years later, the most devastating of wars broke out in Europe, and in 1917, Americans were fighting on the battlefields of France.

24

THE NATION AT WAR

O n the morning of May 1, 1915, the German government took out an advertisement in the *New York World* warning Americans and other voyagers against setting sail for England: "Travellers intending to embark on the Atlantic voyage are reminded that a state of war exists between Germany and her allies and Great Britain and her allies"; anyone sailing "in the war zone on ships of Great Britain or her allies do so at their own risk." At 12:30 that afternoon, the British steamship *Lusitania* set sail from New York to Liverpool. Secretly, it carried a load of ammunition as well as passengers.

The steamer was two hours late in leaving, but it held several speed records and could easily make up the time. Six days later, back on schedule, it reached the coast of Ireland. German U-boats were known to patrol the dangerous waters. When the war began in 1914, Great Britain imposed a naval blockade of Germany. In return, Germany in February 1915 declared the area around the British Isles a war zone; all enemy vessels, armed or unarmed, were at risk. Germany had only a handful of U-boats, but the submarines were a new and frightening weapon. On behalf of the United States, President Woodrow Wilson protested the German action, and on February 10, he warned Germany of its "strict accountability" for any American losses resulting from U-boat attacks.

Off Ireland, the passengers lounged on the deck of the *Lusitania*. As if it were peacetime, the ship sailed straight ahead, with no zigzag maneuvers to throw off pursuit. But the submarine U-20 was there, and its commander, seeing a large ship, fired a single torpedo. Seconds after it hit, a boiler exploded and blew a hole in the *Lusitania*'s side. The ship listed immediately, hindering the launching of lifeboats, and in eighteen minutes it sank. Nearly 1200 people died, including 128 Americans. As the ship's bow lifted and went under, the U-20 commander for the first time read the name: *Lusitania.*

The sinking, the worst since the *Titanic* went down with 1500 people in 1912, horrified Americans. Theodore Roosevelt called it "an act of piracy" and demanded war. Most Americans, however, wanted to stay out of war; like Wilson, they hoped negotiations could solve the problem. "There is such a thing," Wilson said a few days after the sinking, "as a man being too proud to fight. There is such a thing as a nation being so right that it does not need to convince others by force."

In a series of diplomatic notes, Wilson demanded a change in German policy. The first *Lusitania* note (May 13, 1915) called on Germany to abandon unrestricted submarine warfare, disavow the sinking, and compensate for lost American lives. Germany sent an evasive reply, and Wilson drafted a second *Lusitania* note (June 9) insisting on specific pledges. Fearful the demand would

With the sinking of the Lusitania, *the American people learned firsthand of the horrors of total war. President Wilson's decision to protest the incident through diplomacy kept the United States out of the war—but only temporarily.*

lead to war, Secretary of State William Jennings Bryan resigned rather than sign the note. Wilson sent it anyway and followed with a third note (July 21)—almost an ultimatum—warning Germany that the United States would view similar sinkings as "deliberately unfriendly."

Unbeknownst to Wilson, Germany had already ordered U-boat commanders not to sink passenger liners without warning. In August 1915, a U-boat mistakenly torpedoed the British liner *Arabic,* killing two Americans. Wilson protested, and Germany, eager to keep the United States out of the war, backed down. The *Arabic* pledge (September 1) promised that U-boats would stop and warn liners, unless they tried to resist or escape. Germany also apologized for American deaths on the *Arabic,* and for the rest of 1915, U-boats hunted freighters, not passenger liners.

Although Wilson's diplomacy had achieved his immediate goal, the *Lusitania* and *Arabic* crises contained the elements that led to war. Trade and travel tied the world together, and Americans no longer hid behind safe ocean barriers. New weapons, such as the submarine, strained old rules of international law. But while Americans sifted the conflicting claims of Great Britain and Germany, they hoped for peace. A generation of progressives, inspired with confidence in human progress, did not easily accept war.

Wilson also hated war, but he found himself caught up in a worldwide crisis that demanded the best in American will and diplomacy. In the end, diplomacy failed, and in April 1917, the United States entered a war that changed the nation's history.

A NEW WORLD POWER

As they had in the late nineteenth century, Americans after 1900 continued to pay relatively little attention to foreign affairs. Newspapers and magazines ran stories every day about events abroad, but people paid closer attention to what was going on at home.

For Americans at the time, foreign policy was something to be left to the president in office, an attitude the presidents themselves favored. Foreign affairs became an arena in which they could exert a free hand largely unchallenged by Congress or the courts, and Roosevelt, Taft, and Wilson all took advantage of the opportunity to do so.

The foreign policy they pursued from 1901 to 1920 was aggressive and nationalistic. During these years, the United States intervened in Europe, the Far East, and Latin America. It dominated the Caribbean.

In 1898, the United States left the peace table possessing the Philippines, Puerto Rico, and Guam. Holding distant possessions required a colonial policy; it also required a change in foreign policy, reflecting an outward approach. From the Caribbean to the Pacific, policymakers paid attention to issues and countries they had earlier ignored. Like other nations in these years, the United States built a large navy, protected its colonial empire, and became increasingly involved in international affairs.

The nation also became more and more involved in economic ventures abroad. Turning out goods from textiles to steel, mass production industries sold products overseas, and financiers invested in Asia, Africa, Latin America, and Europe. During the years between the Spanish-American War and World War I, investments abroad rose from $445 million to $2.5 billion. While investments and trade never wholly dictated American foreign policy, they fostered greater involvement in foreign lands.

"I TOOK THE CANAL ZONE"

Convinced the United States should take a more active international role, Theodore Roosevelt spent his presidency preparing the nation for world power. Working with Secretary of War Elihu Root, he modernized the army, using lessons learned from the war with Spain. Determined to end dependence on the British fleet, Roosevelt doubled the strength of the navy during his term in office.

Stretching his authority to the limits, Roosevelt took steps to consolidate the country's new position in the Caribbean and Central America. European powers, which had long resisted American initiatives there, now accepted American supremacy. Preoccupied with problems in Europe and Africa, Great Britain agreed to U.S. plans for an Isthmian canal in Central America and withdrew much of its military force from the area.

Roosevelt wanted a canal to link the Atlantic and Pacific oceans across the isthmus connecting North and South America. Secretary of State John Hay negotiated with Britain the Hay-Pauncefote Treaty of 1901 that permitted the United States to construct and control an Isthmian canal, providing it would be free and open to ships of all nations.

Delighted, Roosevelt began selecting the route. One route, fifty miles long, wandered through the rough, swampy terrain of the Panama region of Colombia. A French company had recently tried and failed to dig a canal there. To the northwest, another route ran through mountainous Nicaragua. Although two hundred miles in length, it followed natural waterways, a factor that would make construction easier.

An Isthmian Canal Commission investigated both routes in 1899 and recommended the shorter route through Panama. Roosevelt backed the idea, and he authorized Hay to negotiate an agreement with the Colombian chargé d'affaires, Thomas Herrán. The Hay-Herrán Convention (1903) gave the United States a

99-year lease, with option for renewal, on a canal zone 6 miles in width. In exchange, the United States agreed to pay Colombia a onetime fee of $10 million and an annual rental of $250,000.

To Roosevelt's dismay, the Colombian Senate rejected the treaty, in part because it infringed on Colombian sovereignty. The Colombians also wanted more money. Roosevelt considered seizing Panama, then hinted he would welcome a Panamanian revolt from Colombia. In November 1903, the Panamanians took the hint, and Roosevelt moved quickly to support them. Sending the cruiser *Nashville* to prevent Colombian troops from putting down the revolt, he promptly recognized the new Republic of Panama.

Two weeks later, the Hay-Bunau-Varilla Treaty with Panama granted the United States control of a canal zone 10 miles wide across the Isthmus of Panama. In return, the United States guaranteed the independence of Panama and agreed to pay the same fees offered Colombia. On August 15, 1914, the first ocean steamer sailed through the completed canal, which had cost $375 million to build.

Roosevelt's actions angered many Latin Americans. Trying to soothe feelings, Wilson agreed in 1914 to pay Colombia $25 million in cash, give it preferential treatment in using the canal, and express "sincere regret" over American actions. Roosevelt was furious, and his friends in the Senate blocked the agreement. Colombian-American relations remained strained until 1921, when the two countries signed a treaty that included Wilson's first two provisions but omitted the apology.

For his part, Roosevelt took great pride in the canal, calling it "by far the most important action in foreign affairs." Defending his methods, he said in 1911, "If I had followed traditional conservative methods, I would have submitted a dignified state paper of 200 pages to Congress and the debate on it would have been going on yet; but I took the Canal Zone and let Congress debate; and while the debate goes on the Canal does also."

THE ROOSEVELT COROLLARY

With interests in Puerto Rico, Cuba, and the canal, the United States developed a Caribbean policy to ensure its dominance in the region. It established protectorates over some countries and subsidized others to keep them dependent.

From 1903 to 1920, the United States intervened often in Latin America to protect the canal, promote regional stability, and exclude foreign influence. One problem worrying American policymakers was the scale of Latin American debts to European powers. Many countries in the Western Hemisphere owed money to European governments and banks, and often these nations were poor, prone to revolution, and unable to pay. The situation invited European intervention. In

1902, Venezuela defaulted on debts; England, Germany, and Italy sent Venezuela an ultimatum and blockaded its ports. American pressure forced a settlement of the issue, but the general problem remained.

Roosevelt was concerned about it, and in 1904, when the Dominican Republic defaulted on its debts, he was ready with a major announcement. Known as the Roosevelt Corollary of the Monroe Doctrine, the policy warned Latin American nations to keep their affairs in order or face American intervention.

Applying the new policy immediately, Roosevelt in 1905 took charge of the Dominican Republic's revenue system. American officials collected customs and saw to the payment of debt. Within two years, Roosevelt also established protectorates in Cuba and Panama. Continued by Taft, Wilson, and other presidents, the Roosevelt Corollary guided American policy in Latin America until the 1930s, when Franklin D. Roosevelt's Good Neighbor policy replaced it.

VENTURES IN THE FAR EAST

The Open Door policy toward China and possession of the Philippine Islands shaped American actions in the Far East. Roosevelt wanted to balance Russian and Japanese power, and he was not unhappy at first when war broke out between them in 1904. As Japan won victory after victory, however, Roosevelt grew worried. Acting on a request from Japan, he offered to mediate the conflict, and both Russia and Japan accepted: Russia because it was losing, and Japan because it was financially drained.

In August 1905, Roosevelt convened a peace conference at Portsmouth, New Hampshire. The conference ended the war, but Japan emerged as the dominant force in the Far East. Adjusting policy, Roosevelt sent Secretary of War Taft to Tokyo to negotiate the Taft-Katsura Agreement (1905), which recognized Japan's dominance over Korea in return for its promise not to invade the Philippines. Giving Japan a free hand in Korea violated the Open Door policy, but Roosevelt argued that he had little choice.

Relations between Japan and the United States were again strained in 1907 when the California legislature considered a bill limiting the immigration of Japanese laborers into the state. As resentment mounted in Japan, Roosevelt obtained from Japan the "Gentlemen's Agreement" (1907) promising to stop the flow of Japanese agricultural laborers into the United States.

In case Japan viewed his policy as a sign of weakness, Roosevelt sent sixteen battleships of the new American fleet around the world, including a stop in Tokyo in October 1908. European naval experts felt certain Japan would attack the fleet, but the Japanese welcomed it. For the moment, Japanese-American relations improved, and in 1908 the two nations, in an exchange of diplomatic notes, reached the comprehensive Root-Takahira Agreement in which they promised to maintain the status quo in the Pacific, uphold the Open Door, and support Chinese independence.

TAFT AND DOLLAR DIPLOMACY

In foreign as well as domestic affairs, President Taft tried to continue Roosevelt's policies. For secretary of state he chose Philander C. Knox, Roosevelt's attorney general, and together they pursued a policy of "dollar diplomacy" to promote American financial and business interests abroad. The policy had profit-seeking motives, but it also aimed to substitute economic ties for military alliances with the idea of increasing American influence and bringing lasting peace.

Intent, like Roosevelt, on supremacy in the Caribbean, Taft worked to re-place European loans with American ones, thereby reducing the danger of outside meddling. In 1909, he asked American bankers to assume the Honduran debt in order to fend off English bondholders, and in 1911 he helped Nicaragua secure a large loan in return for American control of Nicaragua's National Bank. When Nicaraguans revolted against the agreement, Taft sent marines to put them down.

In the Far East, Knox worked closely with Willard Straight, an agent of American bankers, who argued that dollar diplomacy was the financial arm of the Open Door. Straight had close ties to Edward H. Harriman, the railroad magnate, who wanted to build railroads in Manchuria in northern China. Roosevelt had tacitly promised Japan he would keep American investors out of the area, and Knox's plan reversed the policy. Trying to organize an international syndicate to loan China money to purchase the Manchurian railroads, Knox approached England, Japan, and Russia. In January 1910, all three turned him down.

The outcome was a blow to American policy and prestige in Asia. Russia and Japan found reasons to cooperate with each other and staked out spheres of influence in violation of the Open Door. Japan resented Taft's initiatives in Manchuria, and China's distrust of the United States deepened. Instead of cultivating friendship, as Roosevelt had envisioned, Taft had started an intense rivalry with Japan for commercial advantage in China.

FOREIGN POLICY UNDER WILSON

When he took office in 1913, Woodrow Wilson knew little about foreign policy. During the 1912 campaign he mentioned foreign policy only when it affected domestic concerns. "It would be the irony of fate if my administration had to deal chiefly with foreign affairs," he said to a friend before becoming president. And so it was. During his two terms, Wilson faced crisis after crisis in foreign affairs, including the outbreak of World War I.

The idealistic Wilson believed in a principled, ethical world in which militarism, colonialism, and war were brought under control. He stressed moral purposes over material interests and said during one crisis, "The force of America is the force of moral principle." Rejecting the policy of dollar diplomacy, Wilson initially chose a course of moral diplomacy, designed to bring right to the world, preserve peace, and extend to other peoples the blessings of democracy.

CONDUCTING MORAL DIPLOMACY

William Jennings Bryan, whom Wilson appointed as secretary of state, was also an amateur in foreign relations. He was a fervent pacifist, and like Wilson, he believed in the American duty to "help" less favored nations.

In 1913 and 1914, he embarked on an idealistic campaign to negotiate treaties of arbitration throughout the world. Known as "cooling-off" treaties, they provided for submitting all international disputes to permanent commissions of investigation. Neither party could declare war or increase armaments until the investigation ended, usually within one year. The idea drew on the era's confidence in commissions and the sense that human reason, given time for emotions to fade, could settle problems without war. Bryan negotiated cooling-off treaties with thirty nations, including Great Britain, France, and Italy. Germany refused to sign one. Based on a generous idea, the treaties were naive, and they did not work.

Wilson and Bryan promised a dramatic new approach in Latin America, concerned not with the "pursuit of material interest" but with "human rights" and "national integrity." Signaling the change, in 1913 they negotiated the treaty with Colombia apologizing for Roosevelt's Panamanian policy. Yet in the end, Wilson, distracted by other problems and impatient with the results of his idealistic approach, continued the Roosevelt-Taft policies. He defended the Monroe Doctrine, gave unspoken support to the Roosevelt Corollary, and intervened in Latin America more than had either Roosevelt or Taft.

In 1914, Wilson negotiated a treaty with Nicaragua to grant the United States exclusive rights to build a canal and lease sites for naval bases. This treaty made Nicaragua an American satellite. In 1915, he sent marines into Haiti to quell a revolution; they stayed until 1934. In 1916, he occupied the Dominican Republic, establishing a protectorate that lasted until 1924. By 1917, American troops "protected" Nicaragua, Haiti, the Dominican Republic, and Cuba—four nations that were U.S. dependencies in all but name.

TROUBLES ACROSS THE BORDER

Wilson's moral diplomacy encountered one of its greatest challenges across the border in Mexico. Porfirio Díaz, president of Mexico for thirty-seven years, was overthrown in 1911, and a liberal reformer, Francisco I. Madero, succeeded him. But Madero could not keep order in the troubled country, and opponents of his reforms undermined him. With support from wealthy landowners, the army, and the Catholic Church, General Victoriano Huerta ousted Madero in 1913, threw him in jail, and arranged his murder. Most European nations immediately recognized Huerta, but Wilson, calling him a "butcher," refused to do so. Instead, he announced a new policy toward revolutionary regimes in Latin America. To win American recognition, they must not only exercise power but reflect "a just government based upon law, not upon arbitrary or irregular force."

On that basis, Wilson withheld recognition from Huerta and maneuvered to oust him. Early in 1914, he stationed naval units off Mexico's ports to cut off arms shipments to the Huerta regime. The action produced trouble. On April 9, 1914, several American sailors, who had gone ashore in Tampico to purchase supplies, were arrested. They were promptly released, but the American admiral demanded an apology and a 21-gun salute to the American flag. Huerta agreed—if the Americans also saluted the Mexican flag.

Wilson asked Congress for authority to use military force if needed; then, just as Congress acted, he learned that a German ship was landing arms at Veracruz on Mexico's eastern coast. With Wilson's approval, American warships shelled the harbor, and marines went ashore. Against heavy resistance, they took the city. Outraged, Mexicans of all factions denounced the invasion, and for a time the two countries hovered on the edge of war.

Retreating hastily, Wilson explained that he desired only to help Mexico. Argentina, Brazil, and Chile came to his aid with an offer to mediate the dispute, and tensions eased. In July 1914, weakened by an armed rebellion, Huerta resigned. Wilson recognized the new government, headed by Venustiano Carranza, an associate of Madero. Early in 1916, Francisco ("Pancho") Villa, one of Carranza's generals, revolted. Hoping to goad the United States into an action that would help him seize power, he raided border towns, injuring American civilians.

Stationing militia along the border, Wilson ordered General John J. Pershing on a punitive expedition to seize Villa in Mexico. Pershing led six thousand troops deep into Mexican territory. At first, Carranza agreed to the drive, but as the Americans pushed farther and farther into his country, he changed his mind. As the wily Villa eluded Pershing, Carranza protested bitterly, and Wilson, worried about events in Europe, ordered Pershing home.

Wilson's policy had laudable goals; he wanted to help the Mexicans achieve political and agrarian reform. But his motives and methods were condescending. Wilson tried to impose gradual progressive reform on a society sharply divided along class and other lines. With little forethought, he interfered in the affairs of another country, and in doing so he revealed the themes—moralism, combined with pragmatic self-interest and a desire for peace—that also shaped his policies in Europe.

TOWARD WAR

In May 1914, Colonel Edward M. House, Wilson's close friend and adviser, sailed to Europe on a fact-finding mission. Tensions there were rising. "The situation is extraordinary," he reported to Wilson. ". . . There is too much hatred, too many jealousies."

In Germany, the ambitious Kaiser Wilhelm II coveted a world empire to match those of Britain and France. Germany had military treaties with Turkey and Austria-Hungary, a sprawling central European country of many nationalities. Linked in another alliance, England, France, and Russia agreed to aid each other in case of attack.

On June 28, 1914, a Bosnian assassin linked to Serbia murdered Archduke Franz Ferdinand, heir to the Austro-Hungarian throne. Within weeks, Germany, Turkey, and Austria-Hungary (the Central Powers) were at war with England, France, and Russia (the Allied Powers). Americans were shocked at the events. Wilson immediately proclaimed neutrality and asked Americans to remain "impartial in thought as well as in action."

The war, he said, was one "with which we have nothing to do, whose causes cannot touch us." In private, Wilson was stunned. A man who loved peace, he had long admired the British parliamentary system, and he respected the leaders of the British Liberal party, who supported social programs akin to his own. "Everything I love most in the world," he said, "is at stake."

THE NEUTRALITY POLICY

In general, Americans accepted neutrality. They saw no need to enter the conflict, especially after the Allies in September 1914 halted the first German drive toward Paris. America resisted involvement in other countries' problems, with the notable exception of Latin America, and had a tradition of freedom from foreign entanglements.

Many of the nation's large number of progressives saw additional reasons to resist. War, they thought, violated the very spirit of progressive reform. Why demand safer factories in which people could work and then kill them by the millions in war? To many progressives, moreover, England represented international finance, an institution they detested. Germany, on the other hand, had pioneered some of their favorite social reforms. Above all, progressives were sure that war would end reform. It consumed money and attention; it inflamed emotions.

As a result, Jane Addams, Florence Kelley, Frederic C. Howe, Lillian Wald, and other progressives fought to keep the United States out of war. In late 1915, they formed the American Union Against Militarism, to throw, they said, "a monkey wrench into the machinery" of war. In 1915, Addams and Wald helped organize the League to Limit Armament, and shortly thereafter, Addams and Carrie Chapman Catt formed the Woman's Peace Party to organize women against the war.

The war's outbreak also tugged at the emotions of millions of immigrant Americans. At the deepest level, a majority in the country, bound by common language and institutions, sympathized with the Allies and blamed Germany for the war. Like Wilson, many Americans admired English literature, customs, and law; they remembered Lafayette and the times when France had helped the United States in its early years. Germany, on the other hand, seemed arrogant and militaristic. When the war began, it invaded Belgium to strike at France and violated a treaty which the German chancellor called "just a scrap of paper."

Both sides sought to sway American opinion, and fierce propaganda campaigns flourished. German propaganda tended to stress strength and will; Allied propaganda called on historical ties and took advantage of German atrocities, both real and alleged. In the end, the propaganda probably made little difference. Ties of heritage and the course of the war, not propaganda, decided the American position. At the outset, no matter which side they cheered for, Americans of all persuasions preferred simply to remain at peace.

FREEDOM OF THE SEAS

The demands of trade tested American neutrality and confronted Wilson with difficult choices. Under international law, neutral countries were permitted to trade in nonmilitary goods with all belligerent countries. But Great Britain controlled the seas, and it intended to cut off shipments of war materials to the Central Powers.

As soon as war broke out, Britain blockaded German ports and limited the goods Americans could sell to Germany. American ships had to carry cargoes to neutral ports from which, after examination, they could be carried to Germany. As time passed, Britain stepped up the economic sanctions by forbidding the shipment to Germany of all foodstuffs and most raw materials, seizing and censoring mail, and "blacklisting" American firms that dealt directly with the Central Powers.

Again and again, Wilson protested against such infringements on neutral rights. Sometimes Britain complied, sometimes not, and Wilson often grew angry. But needing American support and supplies, Britain pursued a careful strategy to disrupt German-American trade without disrupting Anglo-American relations. When necessary, it promised to reimburse American businesses after the war's end.

Other than the German U-boats, there were no constraints on trade with the Allies, and a flood of Allied war orders fueled the American economy. To finance the purchases, the Allies turned to American bankers for loans. By 1917, loans to Allied governments exceeded $2 billion; loans to Germany came to only $27 million.

In a development that influenced Wilson's policy, the war produced the greatest economic boom in the nation's history. Loans and trade drew the United States ever closer to the Allied cause. And even though Wilson often protested English maritime policy, the protests involved American goods and money, whereas Germany's submarine policy threatened American lives.

THE U-BOAT THREAT

A relatively new weapon, the *Unterseeboot,* or submarine, strained the guidelines of international law. Traditional law required a submarine to surface, warn the target to stop, send a boarding party to check papers and cargo, then allow time for passengers and crew to board lifeboats before sinking the vessel. Flimsy and slow, submarines could ill afford to surface while the prey radioed for help. If they did surface, they might be rammed or blown up by deck guns.

When Germany announced the submarine campaign in February 1915, Wilson protested sharply, calling the sinking of merchant ships without checking cargo "a wanton act." The Germans promised not to sink American ships—an agreement that lasted until 1917—and thereafter the issue became the right of Americans to sail on the ships of belligerent nations. In March, an American citizen aboard the British liner *Falaba* perished when the ship was torpedoed off the Irish coast. Bryan urged Wilson to forbid Americans to travel in the war zones, but the president, determined to stand by the principles of international law, refused.

Wilson reacted more harshly in May and August of 1915 when U-boats sank the *Lusitania* and the *Arabic*. He demanded that the Germans protect passenger vessels and pay for American losses. At odds with Wilson's understanding of neutrality, Bryan resigned as secretary of state and was replaced by Robert Lansing, a lawyer and counselor in the State Department. Lansing brought a very different spirit to the job. He favored the Allies and believed that democracy was threat-

A new and terrifying weapon of the war was the German U-boat, which attacked silently and without warning.

ened in a world dominated by Germany. He urged strong stands against German violations of American neutrality.

In February 1916, Germany declared unrestricted submarine warfare against all armed ships. Lansing protested and told Germany it would be held strictly accountable for American losses. A month later, a U-boat torpedoed the unarmed French channel steamer *Sussex* without warning, injuring several Americans. Arguing that the sinking violated the *Arabic* pledge, Lansing urged Wilson to break relations with Germany. Wilson rejected the advice, but on April 18 he sent an ultimatum to Germany, stating that unless the Germans immediately called off attacks on cargo and passenger ships, the United States would sever relations.

The Kaiser, convinced he did not yet have enough submarines to risk war, yielded. In the *Sussex* pledge of May 4, 1916, he agreed to Wilson's demands and promised to shoot on sight only ships of the enemy's navy.

The *Sussex* pledge marked the beginning of a short period of friendly relations between Germany and the United States. The agreement applied not only to passenger liners but to all merchant ships, belligerent or not. There was one problem: Wilson had taken such a strong position that if Germany renewed submarine warfare on merchant shipping, war was likely. Most Americans, however, viewed the agreement as a diplomatic stroke for peace by Wilson, and the issues of peace and preparedness dominated the presidential election of 1916.

"HE KEPT US OUT OF WAR"

The "preparedness" issue pitted antiwar groups against those who wanted to prepare for war. Bellicose as always, Teddy Roosevelt led the preparedness campaign. He called Wilson "yellow" for not pressing Germany harder and scoffed at the popular song "I Didn't Raise My Boy to Be a Soldier," which he compared to singing "I Didn't Raise My Girl to Be a Mother." Defending the military's state of readiness, Wilson refused to be stampeded just because "some amongst us are nervous and excited."

Roosevelt's campaign for preparedness became a personal attack on Wilson, whom TR called a coward and a weakling.

Wilson's position was attacked from both sides as preparedness advocates charged cowardice, while pacifists denounced any attempt at military readiness. The difficulty of his situation, plus the growing U-boat crisis, soon changed Wilson's mind. In mid-1915, he asked the War Department to increase military planning, and he quietly notified congressional leaders of a switch in policy. Later that year, Wilson approved large increases in the army and navy, a move that upset many peace-minded progressives.

For their standard-bearer in the presidential election of 1916, the Republicans nominated Charles Evans Hughes, a moderate justice of the Supreme Court. Hughes seemed to have all the qualifications for victory. A former reform governor of New York, he could lure back the Roosevelt progressives while at the same time appealing to the Republican conservatives. To woo the Roosevelt wing, Hughes called for a tougher line against Germany, thus allowing the Democrats to label him the "war" candidate.

The Democrats renominated Wilson in a convention marked by spontaneous demonstrations for peace. Determined to outdo Republican patriotism, Wilson himself had ordered the convention's theme to be "Americanism." The delegates were to sing "America" and "The Star-Spangled Banner" and to cheer any mention of America and the flag. They did it all dutifully but then broke into spontaneous applause at the mention of Wilson's careful diplomatic moves. As the keynote speaker reviewed them, the delegates shouted, "What did we do? What did we do?" The speaker shouted back, "We didn't go to war! We didn't go to war!"

Picking up the theme, perhaps with reservations, Wilson said in October, "I am not expecting this country to get into war." The campaign slogan "He kept us out of war" was repeated again and again, and just before the election, the Democrats took full-page ads in leading newspapers:

> *You Are Working—Not Fighting!*
> *Alive and Happy—Not Cannon Fodder!*
> *Wilson and Peace with Honor?*
> *or*
> *Hughes with Roosevelt and War?*

On election night, Hughes had swept most of the East, and Wilson retired at 10 P.M. thinking he had lost. During the night, the results came in from California, New Mexico, and North Dakota; all supported Wilson—California by a mere 3773 votes. Wilson won with 9.1 million votes against 8.5 million for Hughes. Holding the Democratic South, he carried key states in the Midwest and West and took large portions of the labor and progressive vote. Women—who

THE ELECTION OF 1916

CANDIDATE	PARTY	POPULAR VOTE	ELECTORAL VOTE
Wilson	Democrat	9,127,695	277
Hughes	Republican	8,533,507	254
	Minor Parties	819,022	0

were then allowed to vote in presidential elections in twelve states—also voted heavily for Wilson.

THE FINAL MONTHS OF PEACE

Just before election day, Great Britain further limited neutral trade, and there were reports from Germany of a renewal of unrestricted submarine warfare. Fresh from his victory, Wilson redoubled his efforts for peace. Aware that time was running out, he hoped to start negotiations to end the bloodshed and create a peaceful postwar world.

In December 1916, he sent messages to both sides asking them to state their war aims. Should they do so, he pledged the "whole force" of the United States to end the war. The Allies refused, although they promised privately to negotiate if the German terms were reasonable. The Germans replied evasively and in January 1917 revealed their real objectives. Close to forcing Russia out of the war, Germany sensed victory and wanted territory in eastern Europe, Africa, Belgium, and France.

On January 22, in an eloquent speech before the Senate, Wilson called for a "peace without victory." Outlining his own ambitious aims, he urged respect for all nations, freedom of the seas, arms limitations, and a League of Nations to keep the peace. The speech made a great impression on many Europeans, but it was too late. The Germans had decided a few weeks before to unleash the submarines and gamble on a quick end to the war. Even as Wilson spoke, U-boats were in the Atlantic west of Ireland, preparing to attack.

On January 31, the German ambassador in Washington informed Lansing that beginning February 1, U-boats would sink on sight all ships—passenger or merchant, neutral or belligerent, armed or unarmed—in the waters around England and France. Staking everything on a last effort, the Germans calculated that if they could sink 600,000 tons of shipping a month, they could defeat

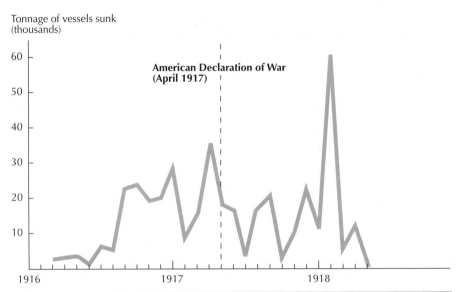

U.S. Losses to the German Submarine Campaign, 1916–1918

Tonnage of vessels sunk
(thousands)

American Declaration of War
(April 1917)

60

50

40

30

20

10

1916   1917   1918

England in six months. As he had pledged in 1916, Wilson broke off relations with Germany, although he still hoped for peace.

On February 25, the British government privately gave Wilson a telegram intercepted from Arthur Zimmermann, the German foreign minister, to the German ambassador in Mexico. A day later, Wilson asked Congress for authority to arm merchant ships to deter U-boat attacks. When La Follette and a handful of others threatened to filibuster, Wilson divulged the contents of the Zimmermann telegram. It proposed an alliance with Mexico in case of war with the United States, offering financial support and recovery of Mexico's "lost territory" in New Mexico, Texas, and Arizona.

Spurred by a wave of public indignation toward the Germans, the House passed Wilson's measure, but La Follette and others still blocked action in the Senate. On March 9, 1917, Wilson ordered merchant ships armed on his own authority. Three days later, he announced the arming, and on March 13, the navy instructed all vessels to fire on submarines. Between March 12 and March 21, U-boats sank five American ships, and Wilson decided to wait no longer.

He called Congress into special session and at 8:30 in the evening on April 2, 1917, asked for a declaration of war. "It is a fearful thing to lead this great peaceful people into war, into the most terrible and disastrous of all wars, civilization itself seeming to be in the balance. But the right is more precious than peace, and we shall fight for the things which we have always carried nearest our hearts,—

for democracy, . . . for the rights and liberties of small nations, for a universal dominion of right by such a concert of free peoples as shall bring peace and safety to all nations and make the world itself at last free."

Congressmen broke into applause and crowded the aisles to congratulate Wilson. "My message today was a message of death for our young men," he said afterward. "How strange it seems to applaud that."

Pacifists in Congress continued to hold out, and for four days they managed to postpone action. Finally, on April 6, the declaration of war passed, with fifty members of the House and six senators voting against it. Even then, the country was divided over entry into the war.

OVER THERE

With a burst of patriotism, the United States entered a war its new allies were in danger of losing. That same month, the Germans sank 881,000 tons of Allied shipping, the highest amount for any one month during the war. There were mutinies in the French army; a costly British drive in Flanders stalled. In November, the Bolsheviks seized power in Russia, and, led by V. I. Lenin, they soon signed a

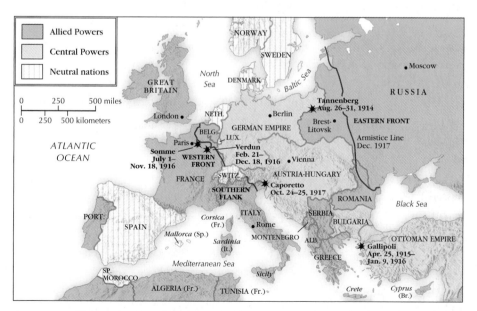

European Alliances and Battlefronts, 1914–1917
Allied forces suffered early defeats on the eastern front (Tannenberg) and in the Dardanelles (Gallipoli). In 1917, the Allies were routed on the southern flank (Caporetto); the western front then became the critical theater of the war.

Administered to soldiers in groups, the IQ test was used in World War I to classify recruits and determine which of them were "officer material." The results of the tests raised questions not only about the mental abilities and backgrounds of the men but also about possible biases in the tests themselves.

separate peace treaty with Germany, freeing German troops to fight in the West. German and Austrian forces routed the Italian army on the southern flank, and the Allies braced for a spring 1918 offensive.

MOBILIZATION

The United States was not prepared for war. Some Americans hoped the declaration of war itself might daunt the Germans; there were those who thought that naval escorts of Allied shipping would be enough. Others hoped money and arms supplied to the Allies would be sufficient to produce victory without sending troops.

Bypassing older generals, Wilson named John J. ("Black Jack") Pershing, leader of the Mexican campaign, to head the American Expeditionary Force (AEF). Pershing inherited an army unready for war. In April 1917, it had 200,000 officers and men, equipped with 300,000 old rifles, 1,500 machine guns, 55 out-of-date airplanes, and 2 field radio sets. Its most recent battle experience had been chasing Pancho Villa around northern Mexico. It had not caught him.

Although some in Congress preferred a voluntary army of the kind that had fought in the Spanish-American War, Wilson turned to conscription, which he believed was both efficient and democratic. In May 1917, Congress passed the Selective Service Act, providing for the registration of all men between the ages of 21 and 30 (later changed to 18 and 45). Early in June, 9.5 million men registered for the draft. By the end of the war, the act had registered 24.2 million men, about 2.8 million of whom were inducted into the army.

The draft included black men as well as white, and four African American regiments were among the first sent into action. Despite their contributions, however, no black soldiers were allowed to march in the victory celebrations that eventually took place in Paris. Nor were they included in a French mural of the different races in the war, even though black servicemen from English and French colonies were represented.

WAR IN THE TRENCHES

World War I may have been the most terrible war of all time, more terrible even than World War II and its vast devastation. After the early offensives, the European armies dug themselves into trenches only hundreds of yards apart in places. Artillery, poison gas, hand grenades, and a new weapon—rapid-fire machine guns—kept them pinned down.

Even in moments of respite, the mud, rats, cold, fear, and disease took a heavy toll. Deafening bombardments shook the earth, and there was a high incidence of shell shock. From time to time, troops went "over the top" of the trenches in an effort to break through the enemy's lines, but the costs were enormous. The German offensive at Verdun in 1916 killed 600,000 men; the British lost 20,000 on the first day of an offensive on the Somme.

The first American soldiers reached France in June 1917. By March of the following year, 300,000 Americans were there, and by war's end, 2 million men had crossed the Atlantic. No troop ships were sunk, a credit to the British and American navies. In the summer of 1917, Admiral William S. Sims, a brilliant American strategist, pushed through a convoy plan that used Allied destroyers to escort merchant vessels across the ocean. At first resisted by English captains who liked to sail alone, the plan soon cut shipping losses in half.

As expected, on March 21, 1918, the Germans launched a massive assault in western Europe. Troops from the Russian front added to the force, and by May they had driven Allied forces back to the Marne River, just 50 miles from Paris.

There, the Americans saw their first action. The American forces blocked the Germans at the town of Château-Thierry and four weeks later forced them out of Belleau Wood, a crucial stronghold. On July 15, the Germans threw everything into a last drive for Paris, but they were halted at the Marne, and in three days of battle they were finished.

With the German drive stalled, the Allies counterattacked along the entire front. On September 12, 1918, a half million Americans and a smaller contingent of French drove the Germans from the St. Mihiel salient, 12 miles south of Verdun. Two weeks later, 896,000 American soldiers attacked between the Meuse River and the Argonne Forest. Focusing their efforts on a main railroad supply line for the German army in the West, American troops broke through in early November, cut the line, and drove the Germans back along the whole front.

The German high command knew that the war was lost. On October 6, 1918, Germany appealed to Wilson for an armistice, and by the end of the month, Turkey, Bulgaria, and Austria-Hungary were out of the war. At 4 A.M. on November 11, Germany signed the armistice. The AEF lost 48,909 dead and 230,000 wounded; losses to disease brought the total of dead to over 112,000.

The American contribution, although small in comparison to the enormous costs to European nations, was vital. Fresh, enthusiastic American troops raised Allied morale; they helped turn the tide at a crucial point in the war.

OVER HERE

Victory at the front depended on economic and emotional mobilization at home. Consolidating federal authority, Wilson moved quickly in 1917 and 1918 to organize war production and distribution. An idealist who knew how to sway public opinion, he also recognized the need to enlist American emotions. To him, the war for people's minds, the "conquest of their convictions," was as vital as events on the battlefield.

THE CONQUEST OF CONVICTIONS

A week after war was declared, Wilson formed the Committee on Public Information (CPI) and asked George Creel, an outspoken progressive journalist, to head it. Creel hired progressives such as Ida Tarbell and Ray Stannard Baker and recruited thousands of people in the arts, advertising, and film industries to publicize the war. He worked out a system of voluntary censorship with the press, plastered walls with colorful posters, and issued more than 75 million pamphlets.

Creel also enlisted 75,000 "four-minute men" to give quick speeches at public gatherings and places of entertainment on "Why We Are Fighting" and "The Meaning of America." At first, they were instructed to stress facts and stay away from emotions, particularly hatred, but by the beginning of 1918, the instructions shifted; the Germans were to be depicted as bloodthirsty Huns bent on world conquest.

Helped along by the propaganda campaign, anti-German sentiment spread rapidly. Many schools stopped offering instruction in the German language—California's state education board called it a language "of autocracy, brutality, and hatred." Sauerkraut became "liberty cabbage"; saloonkeepers removed pretzels from the bar. Orchestral works by Bach, Beethoven, and Brahms vanished from some symphonic programs, and the New York Philharmonic agreed not to perform the music of living German composers.

Rather than curbing the repression, Wilson encouraged it. "Woe be to the man or group of men that seeks to stand in our way," he told peace advocates soon after the war began. At his request, Congress passed the Espionage Act of 1917, which imposed sentences of up to twenty years in prison for persons found guilty of aiding the enemy, obstructing recruitment of soldiers, or encouraging disloyalty. It allowed the postmaster general to remove from the mails materials that incited treason or insurrection. The Trading-with-the-Enemy Act of 1917 authorized the government to censor the foreign language press.

In 1918, Congress passed the Sedition Act, imposing harsh penalties on anyone using "disloyal, profane, scurrilous, or abusive language" about the government, flag, or armed forces uniforms. In all, more than fifteen hundred persons were arrested under the new laws. People indicted or imprisoned included a Californian who laughed at rookies drilling at an army camp, a woman who greeted a Red Cross solicitor in a "hostile" way, and an editor who printed this sentence: "We must make the world safe for democracy even if we have to 'bean' the Goddess of Liberty to do it."

The sedition laws clearly went beyond any clear or present danger. There were, to be sure, German spies in the country, Germans who wanted to encourage strikes in American arms factories. Moreover, the U.S. government and other national leaders were painfully aware of how divided Americans had been about entering the war. They set out to promote unity—by force, if necessary—in order to convince Germany that the nation was united behind the war.

But none of these matters warranted a nationwide program of repression. Conservatives took advantage of wartime feelings to try to stamp out American socialists, who in fact were vulnerable because, unlike their European counterparts, they continued to oppose the war even after their country had entered it.

Eugene V. Debs, serving time in an Atlanta penitentiary for speaking out against the war, is shown here after receiving word of his nomination for the presidency. Debs campaigned in 1920 from behind bars.

Using the sedition laws, conservatives harried the Socialist party and another favorite target, the Industrial Workers of the World.

Wilson's postmaster general banned from the mails more than a dozen socialist publications, including the *Appeal to Reason,* which went to more than half a million people weekly. In 1918, Eugene V. Debs, the Socialist party leader, delivered a speech denouncing capitalism and the war. He was convicted for violation of the Espionage Act and spent the war in a penitentiary in Atlanta. Nominated as the Socialist party candidate in the presidential election of 1920, Debs—prisoner 9653—won nearly a million votes, but the Socialist movement never fully recovered from the repression of the war.

In fostering hostility toward anything that smacked of dissent, the war also gave rise to the great "Red Scare" that began in 1919. Pleased at first with the Russian revolution, Americans in general turned quickly against it, especially after Lenin and the Bolsheviks seized control late in 1917. The Americans feared

Lenin's anticapitalist program, and they denounced his decision in early 1918 to make peace with Germany because it freed German troops to fight in France.

Once again, Wilson himself played a prominent role in the development of anti-Bolshevik sentiment. In the summer of 1918, he sent fifteen thousand American troops into the Soviet Union, where they joined other Allied soldiers. Ostensibly, the troops were there to protect Allied supplies from the Germans and to rescue a large number of Czechs who wanted to return home to fight Germany. But the underlying reason for their presence was that Wilson and others hoped to bring down the fledgling Bolshevik government, fearful it would spread revolution around the world. American troops remained in Russia until April 1920, and on the whole, American willingness to interfere soured Russian-American relations for decades to come.

A BUREAUCRATIC WAR

Quick, effective action was needed to win the war. To meet the need, Wilson and Congress set up an array of new federal agencies, nearly five thousand in all. Staffed largely by businessmen, the agencies drew on funds and powers of a hitherto unknown scope.

By the time the war was over, it had cost $32 billion in direct war expense—in an era when the entire federal budget rarely exceeded $1 billion. To raise the money, the administration sold about $23 billion in "Liberty Bonds," and, using the new Sixteenth Amendment, boosted taxes on corporations and personal incomes. The taxes brought in another $10 billion to help pay for the war.

At first, Wilson tried to organize the wartime economy along decentralized lines, almost in the fashion of his early New Freedom thinking. But that proved unworkable, and he moved instead to a series of highly centralized planning boards, each with broad authority over a specific area of the economy. There were boards to control virtually every aspect of transportation, agriculture, and manufacturing. Though only a few of them were as effective as Wilson had hoped, they did coordinate the war effort to some degree.

The War Industries Board (WIB), one of the most powerful of the new agencies, oversaw the production of all American factories. Headed by millionaire Bernard M. Baruch, a Wall Street broker and speculator, it determined priorities, allocated raw materials, and fixed prices. It told manufacturers what they could and could not make. Working closely with business, Baruch for a time acted as the dictator of the American economy.

Herbert Hoover, the hero of a campaign to feed starving Belgians, headed a new Food Administration, and he set out with customary energy to supply food to the armies overseas. Appealing to the "spirit of self-sacrifice," Hoover convinced people to save food by observing "meatless" and "wheatless" days. He fixed prices to boost production, bought and distributed wheat, and encouraged people to plant "victory gardens" behind homes, churches, and schools. One householder—Wilson—set an example by grazing sheep on the White House lawn.

At another new agency, the Fuel Administration, Harry A. Garfield, the president of Williams College, introduced daylight saving time, rationed coal and oil, and imposed gasless days when motorists could not drive. To save coal, he shut down nonessential factories one day a week, and in January 1918, he closed all factories east of the Mississippi for four days to divert coal to munitions ships stranded in New York harbor. A fourth agency, the Railroad Administration, dictated rail traffic over nearly 400,000 miles of track—standardizing rates, limiting passenger travel, and speeding arms shipments. The War Shipping Board coordinated shipping, the Emergency Fleet Corporation supervised shipbuilding, and the War Trade Board oversaw foreign trade.

As never before, the government intervened in American life. When strikes threatened the telephone and telegraph companies, the government simply seized and ran them. Businessmen, paid a nominal dollar a year, flocked to Washington to run the new agencies, and the partnership between government and business grew closer. As government expanded, business expanded as well, responding to wartime contracts. Industries such as steel, aluminum, and cigarettes boomed, and corporate profits increased threefold between 1914 and 1919.

Labor in the War

The war also brought organized labor into the partnership with government, although the results were more limited than in the business-government alliance. Samuel Gompers, president of the AFL, served on Wilson's Council of National Defense, an advisory group formed to unify business, labor, and government. Gompers hoped to trade labor peace for labor advances, and he formed a War Committee on Labor to enlist workers' support for the war. With the blessing of the Wilson administration, membership in the AFL and other unions grew from about 2.7 million in 1916 to more than 4 million in 1919.

Hoping to encourage production and avoid strikes, Wilson adopted many of the objectives of the social-justice reformers. He supported an eight-hour day in war-related industries and improved wages and working conditions. In May 1918, he named Felix Frankfurter, a brilliant young law professor, to head a new War Labor Board (WLB). The agency standardized wages and hours, and at Wilson's direction, it protected the right of labor to organize and bargain collectively. Although it did not forbid strikes, it used various tactics to discourage them.

Housewives did not leave home for the factory en masse in 1917 as they later did during World War II, but many women already employed outside the home found new, well-paying opportunities in jobs previously held by men.

The WLB also ordered that women be paid equal wages for equal work in war industries. In 1914, the flow of European immigrants suddenly stopped because of the war, and in 1917, the draft began to take large numbers of American men. The result was a labor shortage, filled by women, African Americans, and Mexican Americans. One million women worked in war industries. Some of them took jobs previously held by men, but for the most part, they moved from one set of "women's jobs" into another. From the beginning of the war to the end, the number of women in the workforce held steady at about eight million, and unlike the experience in World War II, large numbers of housewives did not leave the home for machine shops and arms plants.

Still, there were some new opportunities and in some cases higher pay. In food, airplane, and electrical plants, women made up one-fifth or more of the workforce. As their wages increased, so did their expectations; some became more militant, and conflict grew between them and male coworkers. To set standards for female employment, a Women's Bureau was established in the Department of Labor, but the government's influence varied. In the federally run railroad industry, women often made wages equal to those of men; in the federally run telephone industry, they did not.

Looking for more people to fill wartime jobs, corporations found another major source among southern blacks. Beginning in 1916, northern labor agents traveled across the South, promising jobs, high wages, and free transportation. Soon the word spread, and the movement northward became a flood. Between 1916 and 1918, more than 450,000 African Americans left the Old South for the booming industrial cities of Saint Louis, Chicago, Detroit, and Cleveland. In the decade before 1920, Detroit's black population grew by more than 600 percent, Cleveland's by more than 300 percent, and Chicago's by 150 percent.

Most of the newcomers were young, unmarried, and skilled or semiskilled. The men found jobs in factories, railroad yards, steel mills, packinghouses, and coal mines; black women worked in textile factories, department stores, and restaurants. In their new homes, African Americans found greater racial freedom but also different living conditions. If the South was often hostile, the North could be impersonal and lonely. Accustomed to the pace of the farm—ruled by the seasons and the sun—those blacks who were able to enter the industrial sector now worked for hourly wages in mass production industries, where time clocks and line supervisors dictated the daily routine.

Racial tensions increased, resulting in part from growing competition for housing and jobs. In mid-1917, a race war in East St. Louis, Illinois, killed nine whites and about forty blacks. In July 1919, the month President Wilson returned from the peace conference in Paris, a race riot in Washington, DC, killed six people. Riots in Chicago that month killed thirty-eight—fifteen whites and twenty-three blacks—and there were later outbreaks in New York City and Omaha. Lynch mobs killed forty-eight blacks in 1917, sixty-three in 1918, and seventy-eight in 1919. Ten of the victims in 1919 were war veterans, several still in uniform.

Blacks were more and more inclined to fight back. Two hundred thousand blacks served in France—forty-two thousand as combat troops. Returning home, they expected better treatment. "I'm glad I went," a black veteran said. "I done my part and I'm going to fight right here till Uncle Sam does his." Roscoe Jameson, Claude McKay, and other black poets wrote biting poetry, some of it—such as Fenton Johnson's "The New Day"—drawn from the war experience:

> For we have been with thee in No Man's Land,
> Through lake of fire and down to Hell itself;
> And now we ask of thee our liberty,
> Our freedom in the land of Stars and Stripes.

The 369th infantry regiment returning from the war on the Stockholm *in February 1919. They were awarded the Croix de Guerre for bravery in the Meuse-Argonne.*

"Lift Ev'ry Voice and Sing," composed in 1900, became known as the "Negro National Anthem." Parents bought black dolls for their children, and W. E. B. Du Bois spoke of a "New Negro," proud and more militant: "We return. We return from fighting. We return fighting."

Eager for cheap labor, farmers and ranchers in the Southwest persuaded the federal government to relax immigration restrictions, and between 1917 and 1920, more than 100,000 Mexicans migrated into Texas, Arizona, New Mexico, and California. The Mexican American population grew from 385,000 in 1910 to 740,000 in 1920. Tens of thousands of Mexican Americans moved to Chicago, St. Louis, Omaha, and other northern cities to take wartime jobs. Often scorned and insecure, they created urban barrios similar to the Chinatowns and Little Italys around them.

Like most wars, World War I affected patterns at home as much as abroad. Business profits grew, factories expanded, and industries turned out huge amounts of war goods. Government authority swelled, and people came to expect different things of their government. Labor made some gains, as did women and blacks. Society assimilated some of the shifts, but social and economic tensions grew, and when the war ended, they spilled over in the strikes and violence of the Red Scare that followed.

The United States emerged from the war the strongest economic power in the world. In 1914, it was a debtor nation, and American citizens owed foreign investors about $3 billion. Five years later, the United States had become a creditor nation. Foreign governments owed more than $10 billion, and foreign citizens owed American investors nearly $3 billion. The war marked a shift in economic power rarely equaled in history.

THE TREATY OF VERSAILLES

Long before the fighting ended, Wilson began to formulate plans for the peace. Like many others, he was disconcerted when the new Bolshevik government in Russia began revealing the terms of secret agreements among Britain, France, and czarist Russia to divide up Germany's colonies. To try to place the war on a higher plane, he appeared before Congress on January 8, 1918, and outlined terms for a far-reaching, nonpunitive settlement. Wilson's Fourteen Points were

WOODROW WILSON'S FOURTEEN POINTS, 1918: SUCCESS AND FAILURE IN IMPLEMENTATION

1. Open covenants of peace openly arrived at	Not fulfilled
2. Absolute freedom of navigation on the seas in peace and war	Not fulfilled
3. Removal of all economic barriers to the equality of trade among nations	Not fulfilled
4. Reduction of armaments to the level needed only for domestic safety	Not fulfilled
5. Impartial adjustments of colonial claims	Not fulfilled
6. Evacuation of all Russian territory; Russia to be welcomed into the society of free nations	Not fulfilled
7. Evacuation and restoration of Belgium	**Fulfilled**
8. Evacuation and restoration of all French lands; return of Alsace-Lorraine to France	**Fulfilled**
9. Readjustment of Italy's frontiers along lines of Italian nationality	Compromised
10. Self-determination for the former subjects of the Austro-Hungarian Empire	Compromised
11. Evacuation of Rumania, Serbia, and Montenegro; free access to the sea for Serbia	Compromised
12. Self-determination for the former subjects of the Ottoman Empire; secure sovereignty for Turkish portion	Compromised
13. Establishment of an independent Poland, with free and secure access to the sea	**Fulfilled**
14. Establishment of a League of Nations affording mutual guarantees of independence and territorial integrity	Not fulfilled

Sources: Data from G. M. Gathorne-Hardy, *The Fourteen Points and the Treaty of Versailles* (Oxford Pamphlets on World Affairs, no. 6, 1939), pp. 8–34; Thomas G. Paterson et al., *American Foreign Policy: A History Since 1900,* 2nd ed., vol. 2, pp. 282–93.

generous and farsighted, but they failed to satisfy wartime emotions that sought vindication.

England and France distrusted Wilsonian idealism as the basis for peace. They wanted Germany disarmed and crippled; they wanted its colonies; and they were skeptical of the principle of self-determination. As the end of the war neared, the Allies, who had in fact made secret commitments with one another, balked at making the Fourteen Points the basis of peace. When Wilson threatened to negotiate a separate treaty with Germany, however, they accepted.

Wilson had won an important victory, but difficulties lay ahead. As Georges Clemenceau, the 78-year-old French premier, said, "God gave us the Ten Commandments, and we broke them. Wilson gives us the Fourteen Points. We shall see."

A Peace at Paris

Unfortunately, Wilson made a grave error just before the peace conference began. He appealed to voters to elect a Democratic Congress in the November 1918 elections, saying that any other result would be "interpreted on the other side of the water as a repudiation of my leadership." Many Republicans were furious, especially those who had supported the Fourteen Points; Wilson's problems deepened when the Democrats went on to lose both the House and Senate.

Two weeks after the elections, Wilson announced he would attend the peace conference. This was a dramatic break from tradition, and his personal involvement drew attacks from Republicans. They renewed criticism when he named the rest of the delegation: Secretary of State Lansing; Colonel House; General Tasker H. Bliss, a military expert; and Henry White, a career diplomat. Wilson named no member of the Senate, and the only Republican in the group was White.

In selecting the delegation, Wilson passed over Henry Cabot Lodge, the powerful Republican senator from Massachusetts who opposed the Fourteen Points and would soon head the Senate Foreign Relations Committee. He also decided not to appoint Elihu Root or ex-President Taft, both of them enthusiastic internationalists. Never good at accepting criticism or delegating authority, Wilson wanted a delegation he could control—an advantage at the peace table but not in any battle over the treaty at home.

Upon his arrival, Wilson received a tumultuous welcome in England, France, and Italy. Never before had such crowds acclaimed a democratic political figure. In Paris, two million people lined the Champs-Elysées, threw flowers at him, and shouted, "Wilson le Juste [the just]" as his carriage drove by. Overwhelmed, Wilson was sure that the people of Europe shared his goals and would force their leaders to accept his peace. He was wrong. Like their leaders, many people on the Allied side hated Germany and wanted victory unmistakably reflected in the peace.

Opening in January 1919, the Peace Conference at Paris continued until May. Although twenty-seven nations were represented, the "Big Four" dominated it: Wilson; Clemenceau of France, tired and stubborn, determined to end the German threat forever; David Lloyd George, the crafty British prime minister who had pledged to squeeze Germany "until the pips squeak"; and the Italian prime minister, Vittorio Orlando. A clever negotiator, Wilson traded various "small" concessions for his major goals—national self-determination, a reduction in tensions, and a League of Nations to enforce the peace.

Wilson had to surrender some important principles. Departing from the Fourteen Points by violating the principle of self-determination, the treaty created two new independent nations—Poland and Czechoslovakia—with large German-speaking populations. It divided up the German colonies in Asia and Africa.

Instead of a peace without victory, it made Germany accept responsibility for the war and demanded enormous reparations—which eventually totaled $33 billion. It made no mention of disarmament, free trade, or freedom of the seas. Instead of an open covenant openly arrived at, the treaty was drafted behind closed doors.

But Wilson deflected some of the most extreme Allied demands, and he won his coveted Point 14, a League of Nations, designed "to achieve international peace and security." The League

Europe After the Treaty of Versailles, 1919
The treaty changed the map of Europe, creating a number of new and reconstituted nations. (Note the boundary changes from the war map on p. 787.)

included a general assembly; a smaller council composed of the United States, Great Britain, France, Italy, Japan, and four nations to be elected by the assembly; and a court of international justice. League members pledged to submit to arbitration every dispute threatening peace and to enjoin military and economic sanctions against nations resorting to war. Article X, for Wilson the heart of the League, obliged members to look out for one another's independence and territorial integrity.

The draft treaty in hand, Wilson returned home in February 1919 to discuss it with Congress and the people. Most Americans, the polls showed, favored the League. But over dinner with the Senate and House Foreign Relations Committees, Wilson learned of the strength of congressional opposition to it. On March 3, Senator Lodge produced a "round robin" signed by thirty-seven senators declaring they would not vote for the treaty without amendment. Should the numbers hold, Lodge had enough votes to defeat it.

Returning to Paris, Wilson attacked his critics, while he worked privately for changes to improve the chances of Senate approval. In return for major concessions, the Allies amended the League draft treaty, agreeing that domestic affairs remained outside League jurisdiction (exempting the Monroe Doctrine) and allowing nations to withdraw after two years' notice. On June 28, 1919, they signed the treaty in the Hall of Mirrors at Versailles, and Wilson started home for his most difficult fight.

REJECTION IN THE SENATE

There were ninety-six senators in 1919, forty-nine of them Republicans. Fourteen Republicans, led by William E. Borah of Idaho, were the "irreconcilables" who opposed the League on any grounds. Frank B. Kellogg of Minnesota led a group of twelve "mild reservationists" who accepted the treaty but wanted to insert several reservations that would not greatly weaken it. Finally, there were the Lodge-led "strong reservationists," twenty-three of them in all, who wanted major changes that the Allies would have to approve.

With only four Democratic senators opposed to the treaty, the Democrats and Republicans willing to compromise had enough votes to ratify it, once a few reservations were inserted. Democratic leaders urged Wilson to appeal to the Republican "mild reservationists," but he refused: "Anyone who opposes me in that I'll crush!"

Fed up with Lodge's tactics, Wilson set out in early September to take the case directly to the people. Crossing the Midwest, his speeches aroused little emotion, but on the Pacific Coast he won ovations, which heartened him. On his way back to Washington, he stopped in Pueblo, Colorado, where he delivered one of the most eloquent speeches of his career. People wept as he talked of Americans who died in battle and the hope that they would never fight again in foreign lands. That night Wilson felt ill. He returned to Washington, and on October 2, Mrs. Wilson found him lying unconscious on the floor of the White House, the victim of a stroke that paralyzed his left side.

After the stroke, Wilson could not work more than an hour or two at a time. No one was allowed to see him except family members, his secretary, and his physician. For more than seven months, he did not meet with the cabinet. Focusing his remaining energy on the fight over the treaty, Wilson lost touch with other issues, and critics charged that his wife, Edith Bolling Wilson, ran the government.

On November 6, 1919, while Wilson convalesced, Lodge finally reported the treaty out of committee, along with "Fourteen Reservations," one for each of Wilson's points. The most important reservation stipulated that implementation

The skeletal hand signing the Treaty of Versailles in this cartoon reflects the disillusionment many Americans felt with the treaty's emphasis on extracting revenge from Germany. Even though the treaty departed from Wilson's idealistic plan for peace based on his Fourteen Points, he supported it in exchange for endorsement of his plan for a League of Nations. The treaty faced more obstacles in the United States from isolationists who wanted to keep the country out of European affairs and opposed U.S. membership in any League of Nations.

THE ELECTION OF 1920

CANDIDATE	PARTY	POPULAR VOTE	ELECTORAL VOTE
Harding	Republican	16,133,314	404
Cox	Democrat	9,140,884	127
Debs	Socialist	913,664	0

of Article X, Wilson's key article, required the action of Congress before any American intervention abroad.

On November 19, the treaty—with the Lodge reservations—failed, 39 to 55. Following Wilson's instructions, the Democrats voted against it. A motion to approve without the reservations lost 38 to 53, with only one Republican voting in favor. The defeat brought pleas for compromise, but neither Wilson nor Lodge would back down. When the treaty with reservations again came up for vote on March 19, 1920, Wilson ordered the Democrats to hold firm against it. Although twenty-one of them defied him, enough obeyed his orders to defeat it, 49 to 35, seven votes short of the necessary two-thirds majority.

To Wilson, walking now with the help of a cane, one chance remained: the presidential election of 1920. For a time, he thought of running for a third term himself, but his party shunted him aside. The Democrats nominated Governor James M. Cox of Ohio, along with the young and popular Franklin D. Roosevelt, assistant secretary of the navy, for vice president. Wilson called for "a great and solemn referendum" on the treaty. The Democratic platform endorsed the treaty but agreed to accept reservations that clarified the American role in the League.

On the Republican side, Senator Warren G. Harding of Ohio, who had nominated Taft in 1912, won the presidential nomination. Harding waffled on the treaty, but that issue made little difference. Voters wanted a change. Harding won in a landslide, taking 61 percent of the vote and beating Cox by seven million votes. Without a peace treaty, the United States remained technically at war, and it was not until July 1921, almost three years after the last shot was fired, that Congress passed a joint resolution ending the war.

After 1919, there was disillusionment. World War I was feared before it started, popular while it lasted, and hated when it ended. To a whole generation that followed, it appeared futile, killing without cause, sacrificing without benefit.

Books, plays, and movies—Hemingway's *A Farewell to Arms* (1929), John Dos Passos's *Three Soldiers* (1921), Laurence Stallings and Maxwell Anderson's *What Price Glory?* (1924), among others—showed it as waste, horror, and death.

The war and its aftermath damaged the humanitarian, progressive spirit of the early years of the century. It killed "something precious and perhaps irretrievable in the hearts of thinking men and women." Progressivism survived well into the 1920s and the New Deal, but it no longer had the old conviction and broad popular support. Bruising fights over the war and the League drained people's energy and enthusiasm.

Confined to bed, Woodrow Wilson died in Washington in 1924, three years after Harding, the new president, promised "not heroics but healing; not nostrums but normalcy; not revolution but restoration." Nonetheless, the "war to end all wars" and the spirit of Woodrow Wilson left an indelible imprint on the country.

25

TRANSITION TO MODERN AMERICA

The moving assembly line that Henry Ford perfected in 1913 for manufacture of the Model T marked only the first step toward full mass production and the beginning of America's worldwide industrial supremacy. A year later, Ford began buying large plots of land along the Rouge River southeast of Detroit, Michigan. He already had a vision of a vast industrial tract where machines, moving through a sequence of carefully arranged manufacturing operations, would transform raw materials into finished cars, trucks, and tractors. The key would be control over the flow of goods at each step along the way—from lake steamers and railroad cars bringing in the coal and iron ore, to overhead conveyor belts and huge turning tables carrying the moving parts past the stationary workers on the assembly line. "Everything must move," Ford commanded, and by the mid-1920s at River Rouge, as the plant became known, it did.

Ford began fulfilling his industrial dream in 1919 when he built a blast furnace and foundry to make engine blocks for both the Model T and his tractors. By 1924, more than forty thousand workers were turning out nearly all the metal parts used in making Ford vehicles. One tractor factory was so efficient that it took just over twenty-eight hours to convert raw ore into a new farm implement.

Visitors from all over the world came to marvel at River Rouge. Some were disturbed by the jumble of machines (by 1926, there were forty-three thousand in operation) and the apparent congestion on the plant floor, but industrial experts recognized that the arrangement led to incredible productivity because "the work moves and the men stand still."

In May 1927, after producing more than fifteen million Model Ts, Ford closed the assembly line at Highland Park. For the next six months, his engineers worked on designing a more compact and efficient assembly line at River Rouge for the Model A, which went into production in November. By then, River Rouge had more than justified Ford's vision. "Ford had brought together everything at a single site and on a scale no one else had ever attempted," concluded historian Geoffrey Perrett. "The Rouge plant became to a generation of engineers far more than a factory. It was a monument."

Mass production, born in Highland Park in 1913 and perfected at River Rouge in the 1920s, became the hallmark of American industry. Other carmakers copied Ford's methods, and soon his emphasis on the flow of parts moving past stationary workers became the standard in nearly every American factory. The moving assembly line—with its emphasis on uniformity, speed, precision, and coordination—took away the last vestiges of craftsmanship and turned workers into near robots. It led to amazing efficiency that produced both high profits for manufacturers and low prices for buyers. By the mid-1920s, the cost of the Model T had dropped from $950 to $290.

Most important, mass production led to a consumer goods revolution. American factories turned out a flood of automobiles and electrical appliances that made life easier and more pleasant for the vast majority of the American people. The result was the creation of a new America, one in which individualism was sacrificed to conformity as part of the price to be paid for a new era of abundance.

The 1920s, often seen as a time of escape and frivolity before the onset of the Depression, actually marked a beginning, a time when the American people learned to adapt to life in the city, when they decided (wisely or not) to center their existence on the automobile, and when they rejected their rural past while still longing for the old values it had created. It is in the 1920s that we can find the roots of modern America—the America we know today.

THE SECOND INDUSTRIAL REVOLUTION

The first Industrial Revolution in the late nineteenth century had catapulted the United States into the forefront among the world's richest and most highly developed nations. With the advent of the new consumer goods industries, the American people by the 1920s enjoyed the highest standard of living of any nation on earth. After a brief postwar depression, 1922 saw the beginning of a great

On the assembly line at Ford's River Rouge plant, workers performed repetitive tasks on the car chassis that rushed by at a rate of 6 feet per minute.

boom that peaked in 1927 and lasted until 1929. In this brief period, American industrial output nearly doubled, and the gross national product rose by 40 percent. Most of this explosive growth took place in industries producing consumer goods—automobiles, appliances, furniture, and clothing. Equally important, the national per capita income increased by 30 percent to $681 in 1929. American workers became the highest paid in history and thus were able to buy the flood of new goods they were turning out on the assembly lines.

The key to the new affluence lay in technology. The moving assembly line pioneered by Ford became a standard feature in nearly all American plants. Electric motors replaced steam engines as the basic source of energy in factories; by 1929, 70 percent of all industrial power came from electricity. Efficiency experts broke down the industrial process into minute parts, using time and motion studies, and then showed managers and workers how to maximize the output of their labor. Production per worker-hour increased an amazing 75 percent over the decade; in 1929, a workforce no larger than that of 1919 was producing almost twice as many goods.

THE AUTOMOBILE INDUSTRY

The nature of the consumer goods revolution can best be seen in the automobile industry, which became the nation's largest in the 1920s. Rapid growth was its hallmark. In 1920, there were ten million cars in the nation; by the end of the decade, twenty-six million were on the road. Production jumped from fewer than two million units a year to more than five million by 1929.

The automobile boom, at its peak from 1922 to 1927, depended on the apparently insatiable appetite of the American people for cars. But as the decade continued, the market became saturated as more and more of those who could afford the new luxury had become car owners. Marketing became as crucial as production. Automobile makers began to rely heavily on advertising and annual model changes, seeking to make customers dissatisfied with their old vehicles and eager to order new ones. Despite these efforts, sales slumped in 1927 when Ford stopped making the Model T, picked up again the next year with the new Model A, but began to slide again in 1929. The new industry revealed a basic weakness in the consumer goods economy; once people had bought an item with a long life, they would be out of the market for a few years.

In the affluent 1920s, few noticed the emerging economic instability. Instead, contemporary observers focused on the stimulating effect the automobile had on the rest of the economy. The mass production of cars required huge quantities of steel; entire new rolling mills had to be built to supply sheet steel for car bodies. Rubber factories boomed with the demand for tires, and paint and glass suppliers had more business than ever before. The auto changed the pattern of city life, leading to a suburban explosion. Real estate developers, no longer dependent on streetcars and railway lines, could now build houses in ever wider concentric circles around the central cities.

Even in smaller communities, the car ruled. In Muncie, Indiana, site of a famous sociological survey in the 1920s, one elder replied when asked what was taking place, "I can tell you what's happening in just four letters: A-U-T-O!" A nation that had always revered symbols of movement, from the *Mayflower* to the covered wagon, now had a new icon to worship.

PATTERNS OF ECONOMIC GROWTH

Automobiles were the most conspicuous of the consumer products that flourished in the 1920s, but certainly not the only ones. The electrical industry grew almost as quickly. Central power stations, where massive steam generators converted coal into electricity, brought current into the homes of city and town dwellers. Two-thirds of all American families enjoyed electricity by the end of the decade, and they spent vast sums on washing machines, vacuum cleaners, refrigerators, and ranges. The new appliances eased the burdens of housework and ushered in an age of leisure.

Radio broadcasting and motion picture production also boomed in the 1920s. The early success of KDKA in Pittsburgh stimulated the growth of more than eight hundred independent radio stations, and by 1929, NBC had formed the first successful radio network. Five nights a week, *Amos 'n Andy,* a comic serial featuring two "blackface" vaudevillians, held the attention of millions of Americans. The film industry thrived in Hollywood, reaching its maturity in the mid-1920s when in every large city there were huge theaters seating as many as four thousand people. With the advent of the "talkies" by 1929, average weekly movie attendance climbed to nearly 100 million.

The corporation continued to be the dominant economic unit in the 1920s. Growing corporations now had hundreds of thousands of stockholders, and one individual or family rarely held more than 5 percent of the stock. The enormous profits generated by the corporations enabled their managers to finance growth and expansion internally, thus freeing companies from their earlier dependence on investment bankers like J. P. Morgan. Voicing a belief in social responsibility and enlightened capitalism, the new professional class operated independently, free from outside restraint. In the final analysis, the corporate managers were accountable only to other managers.

Another wave of mergers accompanied the growth of corporations during the 1920s. From 1920 to 1928, some eight thousand mergers took place as more and more small firms proved unable to compete effectively with the new giants. By the end of the decade, the two hundred largest nonfinancial corporations owned almost half of the country's corporate wealth.

The most distinctive feature of the new consumer-oriented economy was the emphasis on marketing. Advertising earnings rose from $1.3 billion in 1915 to $3.4 billion in 1926. Skillful practitioners such as Edward Bernays and Bruce Barton sought to control public taste and consumer spending by identifying the good life with the possession of the latest product of American industry, whether it be a car, a refrigerator, or a brand of cigarettes.

Uniformity and standardization, the characteristics of mass production, now prevailed. The farmer in Kansas bought the same kind of car, the same groceries, and the same pills as the factory worker in Pennsylvania. Sectional differences in dress, food, and furniture began to disappear. Even the regional accents that distinguished Americans in different parts of the country were threatened with extinction by the advent of radio and films, which promoted a standard national dialect devoid of any local flavor.

ECONOMIC WEAKNESSES

The New Era, as business leaders labeled the decade, was not as prosperous as it first appeared. The revolution in consumer goods disguised the decline of many traditional industries in the 1920s. Railroads, overcapitalized and poorly managed, suffered from internal woes and from competition with the growing trucking industry. The coal industry was also troubled, with petroleum and natural gas beginning to replace coal as a fuel. The use of cotton textiles declined with the development of rayon and other synthetic fibers. The New England mills moved south in search of cheap labor, leaving behind thousands of unemployed workers and virtual ghost towns in the nation's oldest industrial center.

Hardest hit of all was agriculture. American farmers had expanded production to meet the demands of World War I, when they fed their own nation and most of Europe as well. A sharp cutback of exports in 1919 caused a rapid decline in prices. By 1921, farm exports had fallen by more than $2 billion. Throughout the 1920s, the farmers' share of the national income dropped, until by 1929, the per capita farm income was only $273, compared to the national average of $681.

Workers were better off than farmers in the 1920s, but they did not share fully in the decade's affluence. The industrial labor force remained remarkably steady during this period of economic growth; technical innovations meant the same number of workers could produce far more than before. Most new jobs appeared in the lower-paying service industry. During the decade, factory wage rates rose only a modest 11 percent; by 1929, nearly half of all American families had an income of less than $1500. At the same time, however, conditions of life improved. Prices remained stable, even dropping somewhat in the early 1920s, so workers enjoyed a gain in real wages.

Organized labor proved unable to advance the interests of workers in the 1920s. Conservative leadership in the AFL neglected the task of organizing the vast number of unskilled laborers in the mass production industries. Aggressive management weakened the appeal of unions by portraying them as radical organizations after a series of strikes in 1919. The net result was a decline in union membership from a postwar high of five million to less than three million by 1929.

Black workers remained on the bottom, both economically and socially. Nearly half a million African Americans had migrated northward from the rural South during World War I. Some found jobs in northern industries, but many more worked in menial service areas, collecting garbage, washing dishes, and sweeping floors. Yet even these jobs offered them a better life than they found on the depressed southern farms, where millions of African Americans still lived in poverty, and so the migration continued. The black ghettos in northern cities grew rapidly in the 1920s; Chicago's African American population doubled during the decade, while New York's rose from 152,467 to 327,706, with most African Americans living in Harlem.

Middle- and upper-class Americans were the groups who thrived in the 1920s. The rewards of this second Industrial Revolution went to the managers—the engineers, bankers, and executives—who directed the new industrial economy. Corporate profits nearly doubled in ten years, and income from dividends rose 65 percent, nearly six times the rate of increase in workers' wages. Bank accounts, reflecting the accumulated savings of the upper-middle and wealthy classes, rose from $41.1 billion to $57.9 billion. These were the people who bought the fine new houses in the suburbs and who could afford more than one car.

The economic trends of the decade had both positive and negative implications for the future. On the one hand, there was the solid growth of new consumer-based industries. Automobiles and appliances were not passing fancies; their production and use became a part of the modern American way of life, creating a high standard of living that roused the envy of the rest of the world. The future pattern of American culture—cars and suburbs, shopping centers and skyscrapers—was determined by the end of the 1920s.

But at the same time, there were ominous signs of danger. The unequal distribution of wealth, the saturation of the market for consumer goods, and the growing speculation all created economic instability. The boom of the 1920s would end in a great crash; yet the achievements of the decade would survive even that dire experience to shape the future of American life.

THE NEW URBAN CULTURE

The city replaced the countryside as the focal point of American life in the 1920s. The 1920 census revealed that for the first time, slightly more than half of the population lived in cities (defined broadly to include all places of more than 2,500 people). During the decade, the metropolitan areas grew rapidly as both whites and blacks from rural areas came seeking jobs in the new consumer industries. Between 1920 and 1930, cities with populations of 250,000 or more had added some 8 million people to their ranks. New York City grew by nearly 25 percent, while Detroit more than doubled its population during the decade.

The skyscraper soon became the most visible feature of the city. Faced with inflated land prices, builders turned upward—developing a distinctively American architectural style in the process. New York led the way with the ornate Woolworth Building in 1913. The sleek 102-story Empire State Building, completed in 1930, was for years the tallest building in the world. Other cities

Its 102 stories rising 1,250 feet into the sky (222 feet were added in 1950), the Empire State Building had space for 25,000 workers.

erected their own jagged skylines. By 1929, there were 377 buildings more than 20 stories tall across the nation. Most significantly, the skyscraper came to symbolize the new mass culture. "The New York skyscrapers are the most striking manifestation of the triumph of numbers," wrote one French observer. "One cannot understand or like them without first having tasted and enjoyed the thrill of counting or adding up enormous totals and of living in a gigantic, compact and brilliant world."

In the metropolis, life was different. The old community ties of home, church, and school were absent, but there were important gains to replace them—new ideas, new creativity, new perspectives. Some city dwellers became lost and lonely without the old institutions; others thrived in the urban environment.

WOMEN AND THE FAMILY

The urban culture of the 1920s witnessed important changes in the American family. This vital institution began to break down under the impact of economic and social change. A new freedom for women and children seemed to be emerging in its wake.

Women had already begun to leave the home in the early twentieth century as the second Industrial Revolution opened up new jobs for them. World War I sped up the process, but in the 1920s there was no great permanent gain in the number of working women. Although two million more women were employed in 1930 than in 1920, this represented an increase of only 1 percent. Most women workers, moreover, had low-paying jobs, ranging from stenographers to maids. For the most part, the professions were reserved for men, with women relegated to such fields as teaching and nursing.

Women had won the right to vote in 1920, but the Nineteenth Amendment proved to have less impact than its proponents had hoped. Adoption of the amendment robbed women of a unifying cause, and the exercise of the franchise itself did little to change prevailing sex roles. Men remained the principal breadwinners in the family; women cooked, cleaned, and reared the children. "The creation and fulfillment of a successful home," a

Women finally realized the hard-won right to vote. The cover of Leslie's Illustrated Newspaper *for September 11, 1920, celebrates the fact.*

Ladies Home Journal writer advised women, "is a bit of craftsmanship that compares favorably with building a beautiful cathedral."

The feminist movement, however, still showed signs of vitality in the 1920s. Social feminists pushing for humanitarian reform won enactment of the Sheppard-Towner Act of 1921, which provided for federal aid to establish state programs for maternal and infant health care. Although the failure to enact the child labor amendment in 1925 marked the beginning of a decline in humanitarian reform, for the rest of the decade, women's groups continued to work for good-government measures, for the inclusion of women on juries, and for consumer legislation.

One group of activists, led by Alice Paul's National Woman's Party (NWP), lobbied for full equality for women under the law. In 1923, the NWP succeeded in having an Equal Rights Amendment introduced in Congress. The amendment stated simply, "Men and women shall have equal rights throughout the United States and every place subject to its jurisdiction." Most other women's organizations, notably the League of Women Voters, opposed the amendment because it threatened gender-specific legislation such as the Sheppard-Towner Act that women had fought so hard to enact. The drive for the ERA in the 1920s failed.

Growing assertiveness had a profound impact on feminism in the 1920s. Instead of crusading for social progress, young women concentrated on individual self-expression by rebelling against Victorian restraints. In the larger cities, some quickly adopted what critic H. L. Mencken called the flapper image, portrayed most strikingly by artist John Held, Jr. Cutting their hair short, raising their skirts above the knee, and binding their breasts, "flappers" set out to compete on equal terms with men on the golf course and in the speakeasy. The flappers assaulted the traditional double standard in sex, demanding that equality with men should include sexual fulfillment before and during marriage. New and more liberal laws led to a sharp rise in the divorce rate; by 1928, there were 166 divorces for every 1,000 marriages, compared to only 81 in 1900.

The sense of woman's emancipation was heightened by a continuing drop in the birthrate and by the abundance of consumer goods. With fewer children to care for and with washing machines and vacuum cleaners to ease their household labor, it seemed that women of the 1920s would have more leisure time. Yet appearances were deceptive. Advertisers eagerly sought out women as buyers of laborsaving consumer products, but wives exercised purchasing power only as delegated by their husbands. In addition, many women were not in the position to put the new devices to use—one-fourth of the homes in Cleveland lacked running water in the 1920s, and three-quarters of the nation's families did not have washing machines.

The family, however, did change. It became smaller as new techniques of birth control enabled couples to limit the number of their offspring. More and more married women took jobs outside the home, bringing in an income and gaining a measure of independence (although their rate of pay was always lower than that for men). Young people, who had once joined the labor force when they entered their teens, now discovered adolescence as a stage of life. A high school education was no longer uncommon, and college attendance increased.

Prolonged adolescence led to new strains on the family in the form of youthful revolt. Freed of the traditional burden of earning a living at an early age, youths in the 1920s went on a great spree. Heavy drinking, casual sexual encounters, and a constant search for excitement became the hallmarks of the upperclass youth immortalized by F. Scott Fitzgerald. "I have been kissed by dozens of men," one of his characters commented. "I suppose I'll kiss dozens more." The theme of rebellion against parental authority, which runs through all aspects of the 1920s, was at the heart of the youth movement.

THE ROARING TWENTIES

Frivolity and excitement ran high in the cities as both crime waves and highly publicized sports events flourished. Prohibition ushered in such distinctive features of the decade as speakeasies, bootleggers, and bathtub gin. Crime rose sharply as middle- and upper-class Americans willingly broke the law to gain access to alcoholic beverages. City streets became the scene of violent shoot-outs between rival bootleggers; by 1929, Chicago had witnessed more than five hundred gangland murders.

Sports became a national mania in the 1920s as people found more leisure time. Golf boomed, with some two million men and women playing on nearly five thousand courses across the country. Spectator sports attracted even more attention. Boxing drew huge crowds to see fighters such as Jack Dempsey and Gene Tunney. Baseball attendance soared. More than twenty million fans attended games in 1927, the year Babe Ruth became a national idol by hitting sixty home runs.

In what Frederick Lewis Allen called "the ballyhoo years," the popular yearning for excitement led people to seek vicarious thrills in all kinds of ways—applauding Charles Lindbergh's solo flight across the Atlantic, cheering Gertrude Ederle's swim across the English Channel, and flocking to such bizarre events as six-day bicycle races, dance marathons, and flagpole sittings.

Sex became another popular topic in the 1920s as Victorian standards began to crumble. Sophisticated city dwellers seemed to be intent on exploring a new freedom in sexual expression. Plays and novels focused on adultery, and the new urban tabloids—led by the *New York Daily News*—delighted in telling their readers about love nests and kept women. The popular songs of the decade, such as "Hot Lips" and "Burning Kisses," were less romantic and more explicit than those of years before. Hollywood exploited the obsession with sex by producing movies with such provocative titles as *Up in Mabel's Room, A Shocking Night,* and *Women and Lovers.* Young people embraced the new permissiveness joyfully, with the automobile giving couples an easy way to escape parental supervision.

There is considerable debate, however, over the extent of the sexual revolution in the 1920s. Later studies by Dr. Alfred C. Kinsey showed that premarital intercourse was twice as common among women born after 1900 than for those born before the turn of the century. But a contemporary survey of more than two thousand middle-class women by Katherine B. Davis found that only 7 percent of those who were married had had sexual relations before marriage and that only 14 percent of the single women had engaged in intercourse. Actual changes in sexual behavior are beyond the historian's reach, hidden in the privacy of the bedroom, but the old Victorian prudishness was a clear casualty of the 1920s. Sex was no longer a taboo subject, at least in urban areas; men and women now could discuss it openly, and many of them did.

THE LITERARY FLOWERING

The greatest cultural advance of the 1920s was visible in the outpouring of literature. The city gave rise to a new class of intellectuals—writers who commented on the new industrial society. Many had been uprooted by World War I. They were bewildered by the rapidly changing social patterns of the 1920s and appalled by the materialism of American culture. Some fled to Europe to live as expatriates, congregating in Paris cafés to bemoan the loss of American innocence and purity. Others stayed at home, observing and condemning the excesses of a business civilization. All shared a sense of disillusionment and wrote pessimistically of the flawed promise of American life. Yet, ironically, their body of writing revealed a profound creativity that suggested America was coming of age intellectually.

The exiles included the poets T. S. Eliot and Ezra Pound and the novelist Ernest Hemingway. Pound discarded rhyme and meter in a search for clear, cold images that conveyed reality. Like many of the writers of the 1920s, he reacted against World War I, expressing a deep regret for the tragic waste of a whole generation in defense of a "botched civilization."

Eliot, who was born in Missouri but became a British citizen, displayed even more profound despair. In *The Waste Land,* which appeared in 1922, he evoked images of fragmentation and sterility that had a powerful impact on the other disillusioned writers of the decade. He reached the depths in *The Hollow Men* (1925), a biting description of the emptiness of modern man.

Ernest Hemingway sought redemption from the modern plight in the romantic individualism of his heroes. Preoccupied with violence, he wrote of men alienated from society who found a sense of identity in their own courage and quest for personal honor. His own experiences, ranging from driving an ambulance in the war to stalking lions in Africa, made him a legendary figure; his greatest impact on other writers, however, came from his sparse, direct, and clean prose style.

The writers who stayed home were equally disdainful of contemporary American life. F. Scott Fitzgerald chronicled American youth in *This Side of Paradise* (1920) and *The Great Gatsby* (1925), writing in bittersweet prose about "the beautiful and the damned." Amid the glitter of life among the wealthy on Long Island's North Shore came the haunting realization of emptiness and lack of human concern.

Most savage of all was H. L. Mencken, the Baltimore newspaperman and literary critic who founded *American Mercury* magazine in 1923. Declaring war on "Homo boobiens," Mencken mocked everything he found distasteful in America, from the Rotary Club to the Ku Klux Klan. "From Boy Scouts, and from Home Cooking, from Odd Fellows' funerals, from Socialists, from Christians—Good Lord, deliver us," he pleaded. It was not difficult to discover what Mencken disliked (including Jews, as his published diary makes clear); the hard part was finding out what he affirmed, other than wit and a clever turn of phrase.

The cultural explosion of the 1920s was surprisingly broad. It included novelists such as Sherwood Anderson and John Dos Passos, who described the way the new machine age undermined such traditional American values as craftsmanship and a sense of community, and playwrights such as Eugene O'Neill, Maxwell Anderson, and Elmer Rice, who added greatly to the stature of American theater. Women writers were particularly effective in dealing with regional themes. Edith Wharton continued to write penetratingly about eastern aristocrats in books such as *The House of Mirth* (1905) and *The Age of Innocence* (1921); Willa Cather and Ellen Glasgow focused on the plight of women in the Midwest and the South, respectively, in their short stories and novels. These writers portrayed their heroines in the traditional roles of wives and mothers; playwright Zona Gale, on the other hand (who won the Pulitzer Prize for drama in 1920 for *Miss Lulu Bett*), used her title character to depict the dilemmas facing an unmarried woman in American society.

Art and music lagged behind literature but still made significant advances. Edward Hopper and Charles Burchfield captured the ugliness of city life and the

W. E. B. Du Bois (top left), editor of The Crisis, *was one of the intellectual and political leaders of the Harlem Renaissance, which fostered the rise of literary figures such as Zora Neale Hurston (top right) and Langston Hughes (left). Hurston wrote four novels and two books of black folklore that "helped to remind the Renaissance . . . of the richness in racial heritage." Hughes wrote sensitively and eloquently of the world of common black people.*

loneliness of its inhabitants in their realistic paintings. Aaron Copland and George Gershwin added a new vitality to American music. But African Americans migrating northward brought the most significant contribution: the spread of jazz—first to St. Louis, Kansas City, and Chicago, and finally to New York. The form of jazz known as the blues, so expressive of the suffering of African

Americans, became an authentic national folk music, and performers such as Louis Armstrong enjoyed popularity around the world.

The cultural growth of the 1920s was the work of blacks as well as whites. W. E. B. Du Bois, the editor of the newspaper *Crisis,* became the intellectual voice of the black community developing in New York City's Harlem. In 1917, James Weldon Johnson, who had been a professor of literature at Fisk University, published *Fifty Years and Other Poems,* in which the title poem commented on the half century of suffering that had followed the Emancipation Proclamation. As other African American writers gathered around them, Du Bois and Johnson became the leaders of the Harlem Renaissance. The NAACP moved its headquarters to Harlem, and in 1923, the Urban League began publishing *Opportunity,* a magazine devoted to scholarly studies of racial issues.

Art and music also flourished during Harlem's golden age. Plays and concerts at the 135th Street YMCA; floor shows at Happy Rhone's nightclub (attended by many white celebrities); rent parties where jazz musicians played to raise money to help writers, artists, and neighbors pay their bills—all were part of the ferment that made Harlem "the Negro Capital of the World" in the 1920s. "Almost everything seemed possible above 125th Street in the early twenties for these Americans who were determined to thrive separately to better proclaim the ideals of integration," comments historian David Lewis. "You could be black and proud, politically assertive and economically independent, creative and disciplined—or so it seemed."

Although its most famous writers were identified with New York's Harlem, the new African American cultural awareness spread to other cities in the form of poetry circles and theater groups. The number of African Americans graduating from college rose from 391 in 1920 to 1,903 by 1929. Although blacks were still an oppressed minority in the America of the 1920s, they had taken major strides toward achieving cultural and intellectual fulfillment.

In retrospect, there is a striking paradox about the literary flowering of the 1920s. Nearly all the writers, black as well as white, cried out against the conformity and materialism of the contemporary scene. They were critical of mass production and reliance on the machine; they wrote wistfully of the disappearance of the artisan and of a more relaxed way of life. Few took any interest in politics or in social reform. They retreated instead into individualism, seeking an escape into their art from the prevailing business civilization. Whether they went abroad or stayed home, the writers of the 1920s turned inward to avoid being swept up in the consumer goods revolution. Yet despite their withdrawal, and perhaps because of it, they produced an astonishingly rich and varied body of work. American writing had a greater intensity and depth than in the past; American writers, despite their alienation, had placed their country in the forefront of world literature.

THE RURAL COUNTERATTACK

The shift of population from the countryside to the city led to heightened social tensions in the 1920s. Intent on preserving traditional social values, rural Americans saw in the city all that was evil in contemporary life. Saloons, whorehouses, little Italys and little Polands, communist cells, free love, and atheism—all were identified with the city. Accordingly, the countryside struck back at the newly dominant urban areas, aiming to restore the primacy of the Anglo-Saxon and predominantly Protestant culture they revered. This counterattack won considerable support in the cities from those so recently uprooted from their rural backgrounds.

Other factors contributed to the intensity of the counterattack. The war had unleashed a nationalistic spirit that craved unity and conformity. In a nation where one-third of the people were foreign born, the attack on immigrants and the call for 100 percent Americanism took on a frightening zeal. When the war was over, groups such as the American Legion tried to root out "un-American" behavior and insisted on cultural as well as political conformity. The prewar progressive reform spirit added to the social tension. Stripped of much of its former idealism, progressivism focused on such social problems as drinking and illiteracy to justify repressive measures like Prohibition and immigration restriction. The result was tragic. Amid the emergence of a new urban culture, the movements aimed at preserving the values of an earlier America succeeded only in complicating life in an already difficult period of cultural transition.

THE "RED SCARE"

The first and most intense outbreak of national alarm came in 1919. The heightened nationalism of World War I, aimed at achieving unity at the expense of ethnic diversity, found a new target in bolshevism. The Russian Revolution and the triumph of Marxism frightened many Americans. A growing turn to communism among American radicals (especially the foreign born) accelerated these fears. Although the numbers involved were tiny—at most there were sixty thousand communists in the United States in 1919—they were highly visible. Located in the cities, their influence appeared to be magnified with the outbreak of widespread labor unrest.

A general strike in Seattle, a police strike in Boston, and a violent strike in the iron and steel industry thoroughly alarmed the American people in the spring and summer of 1919. A series of bombings led to panic. First the mayor of strikebound Seattle received a small brown package containing a homemade bomb; then an alert New York postal employee detected sixteen bombs addressed to a variety of famous citizens (including John D. Rockefeller); and finally, on June 2, a bomb shattered the front of Attorney General A. Mitchell Palmer's home. Although the man who delivered it was blown to pieces, authorities quickly identified him as an Italian anarchist from Philadelphia.

In the ensuing public outcry, Attorney General Palmer led the attack on the alien threat. A Quaker and progressive, Palmer abandoned his earlier liberalism to launch a massive roundup of foreign-born radicals. In a series of raids that began on November 7, federal agents seized suspected anarchists and communists and held them for deportation with no regard for due process of law. In December, 249 aliens—including such well-known radical leaders as Emma Goldman and Alexander Berkman—were sent to Russia aboard the *Buford,* dubbed the "Soviet Ark" by the press. Nearly all were innocent of the charges against them.

For a time, it seemed that the Red Scare reflected the prevailing views of the American people. Instead of condemning their government's action, citizens voiced their approval and even urged more drastic steps. One patriot said his solution to the alien problem was simple: "S.O.S.—ship or shoot." General Leonard Wood, the former army chief of staff, favored placing Bolsheviks on "ships of stone with sails of lead," while evangelist Billy Sunday preferred to take "these ornery, wild-eyed Socialists" and "stand them up before a firing squad and save space on our ships."

The very extremism of the Red Scare led to its rapid demise. In early 1920, courageous government officials from the Department of Labor insisted on due process and full hearings before anyone else was deported. Prominent public leaders began to speak out against the acts of terror. Finally, Palmer himself, with evident presidential ambition, went too far. In April 1920, he warned of a vast revolution to occur on May 1; the entire New York City police force, some eleven thousand strong, was placed on duty to prepare for imminent disaster. When no bombings or violence took place on May Day, the public began to react against Palmer's hysteria. Despite a violent explosion on Wall Street in September that killed thirty-three people, the Red Scare died out by the end of 1920. Palmer passed into obscurity, the tiny Communist party became torn with factionalism, and the American people tried hard to forget their loss of balance.

Yet the Red Scare exerted a continuing influence on American society in the 1920s. The foreign born lived in the uneasy realization that they were viewed with hostility and suspicion. Two Italian aliens in Massachusetts, Nicola Sacco and Bartolomeo Vanzetti, were arrested in May 1920 for a payroll robbery and murder. They faced a prosecutor and jury who condemned them more for their ideas

The explosion in Wall Street on September 16, 1920, left thirty-three dead and nearly two hundred wounded. Attorney General Palmer saw the blast as the work of a communist conspiracy, but relatively few Americans subscribed to his view.

than for any evidence of criminal conduct and a judge who referred to them as "those anarchist bastards." Despite a worldwide effort that became the chief liberal cause of the 1920s, the courts rejected all appeals. Sacco, a shoemaker, and Vanzetti, a fish peddler, died in the electric chair on August 23, 1927. Their fate symbolized the bigotry and intolerance that lasted through the 1920s and made that decade one of the least attractive in American history.

PROHIBITION

In December 1917, Congress adopted the Eighteenth Amendment, prohibiting the manufacture and sale of alcoholic beverages. A little over a year later, Nebraska was the necessary thirty-sixth state to ratify, and Prohibition became the law of the land.

As implemented under the Volstead Act, beginning January 16, 1920, it was illegal for anyone to make, sell, or transport any drink that contained more than one-half of 1 percent alcohol by volume. Prohibition was the result of both a rural effort of the Anti-Saloon League, backed by Methodist and Baptist clergymen, and the urban progressive concern over the social disease of drunkenness, especially among industrial workers. The moral issue had already led to the enactment of Prohibition laws in twenty-six states by 1920; the real tragedy would occur in the effort to extend this "noble experiment" to the growing cities, where it was deeply resented by ethnic groups such as the Germans and the Irish and was almost totally disregarded by the well-to-do and the sophisticated.

Prohibition did in fact lead to a decline in drinking. Americans consumed much less alcohol in the 1920s than in the prewar years. Rural areas became totally dry, and in the cities, the consumption of alcoholic beverages dropped sharply among the lower classes, who could not afford the high prices for bootleg liquor. Among the middle class and the wealthy, however, drinking became fashionable; Americans consumed some 150 million quarts of liquor a year in the 1920s. Bootleggers took in nearly $2 billion annually, about 2 percent of the gross national product.

Urban resistance to Prohibition finally led to its repeal in 1933. But in the intervening years, it damaged American society by breeding a profound disrespect for the law. The flamboyant excesses of bootleggers were only the more obvious evils spawned by Prohibition. In city after city, police openly tolerated the traffic in liquor, and judges and prosecutors agreed to let bootleggers pay merely token fines, creating almost a system of licenses. Prohibition satisfied the countryside's desire for vindication, yet rural and urban America alike suffered from this overzealous attempt to legislate morals.

THE KU KLUX KLAN

The most ominous expression of protest against the new urban culture was the rebirth of the Ku Klux Klan. On Thanksgiving night in 1915, on Stone Mountain in Georgia, Colonel William J. Simmons and thirty-four followers founded the modern Klan. Only "native born, white, gentile Americans" were permitted to join "the Invisible Empire, Knights of the Ku Klux Klan." Membership grew slowly during World War I, but after 1920, fueled by postwar fears and shrewd promotional techniques, the Klan mushroomed. In villages, towns, and small cities across the nation, Anglo-Saxon Protestant men flocked into the newly formed chapters, seeking to relieve their anxiety over a changing society by embracing the Klan's unusual rituals and by demonstrating their hatred against blacks, aliens, Jews, and Catholics.

The Klan of the 1920s, unlike the night riders of the post–Civil War era, was not just antiblack; the threat to American culture, as Klansmen perceived it, came from aliens—Italians and Russians, Jews and Catholics. They attributed much of the tension and conflict in society to the prewar flood of immigrants, foreigners who spoke different languages, worshiped in strange churches, and

INITIATION Dec. 8ᵗʰ 1921. HOUSTON TEX.

PHOTO BY

A Ku Klux Klan initiation ceremony in Houston, Texas, December 8, 1921. Only native-born, white Americans "who believe in the tenets of the Christian religion" were admitted into the Klan. The original Ku Klux Klan, formed during the Reconstruction era to terrorize and intimidate former slaves, disbanded in 1869. The Klan that formed in 1915 declined through the 1920s but did not officially disband until 1944. Two years later a third Klan emerged, focusing on the civil rights movement and communism as its enemies.

lived in distant, threatening cities. The Klansmen struck back by coming together and enforcing their own values. They punished blacks who did not know their place, women who practiced the new morality, and aliens who refused to conform. Beating, flogging, burning with acid—even murder—were condoned. They also tried more peaceful methods of coercion, formulating codes of behavior and seeking communitywide support.

The Klan entered politics, at first hesitantly, then with growing confidence. The KKK gained control of the legislatures in Texas, Oklahoma, Oregon, and Indiana; in 1924, it blocked a resolution of censure at the Democratic national convention. With an estimated five million members by the mid-1920s, the Klan seemed to be fully established.

Its appeal lay in the sanctuary it offered to insecure and anxious people. Each Klan had its own Klalendar, held its weekly Klonklave in the local Klavern, and followed the rules set forth in the Kloran. Protestant to the core, the members found in the local Klavern a reassurance missing in their churches. The poor and ignorant became enchanted with the titles, ranging from Imperial Wizard to Grand Dragon. Members found a sense of identity in the group activities, whether they were peaceful picnics, ominous parades in white robes, or fiery cross burnings at night.

The Klan fell even more quickly than it rose. Its more violent activities—which included kidnapping, lynching, setting fire to synagogues and Catholic churches, and, in one case, murdering a priest—began to offend the nation's conscience. Misuse of funds and sexual scandals among Klan leaders, notably in Indiana, repelled many of the rank and file; effective counterattacks by traditional politicians ousted the KKK from control in Texas and Oklahoma. Membership declined sharply after 1925; by the end of the decade, the Klan had virtually disappeared. But its spirit lived on, testimony to the recurring demons of nativism and hatred that have surfaced periodically throughout the American experience.

IMMIGRATION RESTRICTION

The nativism that permeated the Klan found its most successful outlet in the immigration legislation of the 1920s. The sharp increase in immigration in the late nineteenth century had led to a broad-based movement, spearheaded by organized labor and by New England aristocrats such as Henry Cabot Lodge, to restrict the flow of people from Europe. In 1917, over Wilson's veto, Congress enacted a literacy test that reduced the number of immigrants allowed into the country. The war caused a much more drastic decline—from an average of 1 million a year between 1900 and 1914 to only 110,000 in 1918.

After the armistice, however, rumors began to spread of an impending flood of people seeking to escape war-ravaged Europe. Kenneth Roberts, a popular historical novelist, warned that all Europe was on the move, with only the limits of available steamship space likely to stem the flow. Even though the actual number of immigrants, 810,000 in 1920 (fewer than the prewar yearly average), did not match these projections, Congress in 1921 passed an emergency immigration act. The new quota system restricted immigration from Europe to 3 percent of the number of nationals from each country living in the United States in 1910.

The 1921 act failed to satisfy the nativists. The quotas still permitted more than 500,000 Europeans to come to the United States in 1923, nearly half of them from southern and eastern Europe. The declining percentage of Nordic immigrants alarmed writers such as Madison Grant, who warned the American people the Anglo-Saxon stock that had founded the nation was about to be overwhelmed by lesser breeds with inferior genes. "These immigrants adopt the language of the native American, they wear his clothes and are beginning to take his women, but they seldom adopt his religion or understand his ideals," Grant wrote.

In 1924, Congress adopted the National Origins Quota Act, which limited immigration from Europe to 150,000 a year; allocated most of the available slots to immigrants from Great Britain, Ireland, Germany, and Scandinavia; and banned all Asian immigrants. The measure passed Congress with overwhelming rural support.

The new restrictive legislation marked the most enduring achievement of the rural counterattack. Unlike the Red Scare, Prohibition, and the Klan, the quota system would survive until the 1960s, enforcing a racist bias that excluded Asians and limited the immigration of Italians, Greeks, and Poles to a few thousand a year while permitting a steady stream of Irish, English, and Scandinavian immigrants. The large corporations, no longer dependent on armies of unskilled immigrant workers, did not object to the 1924 law; the machine had replaced the immigrant on the assembly line. Yet even here the victory was not complete. A growing tide of Mexican laborers, exempt from the quota act, flowed northward across the Rio Grande to fill the continuing need for unskilled workers on the farms and in the service trades. The Mexican immigrants, as many as 100,000 a year, marked the strengthening of an element in the national ethnic mosaic that would grow in size and influence until it became a major force in modern American society.

THE FUNDAMENTALIST CONTROVERSY

The most famous of all attacks on the new urban culture was the Scopes trial held in Dayton, Tennessee. There, in 1925, William Jennings Bryan, who had unsuccessfully run for president several times in previous decades, engaged in a crusade against the theory of evolution, appearing as a chief witness against John Scopes. Scopes, a high school biology teacher, had initiated the case by deliberately violating a new Tennessee law that forbade the teaching of Darwin's theory.

In the trial, Bryan testified under oath that he believed Jonah had been swallowed by a big fish and declared, "It is better to trust in the Rock of Ages than in the age of rocks." Chicago defense attorney Clarence Darrow succeeded in making Bryan look ridiculous. The court found Scopes guilty but let him off with a token fine; Bryan, exhausted by his efforts, died a few days later. H. L. Mencken, who covered the trial in person, rejoiced in the belief that fundamentalism was dead.

In reality, however, traditional rural religious beliefs were stronger than ever. As middle- and upper-class Americans drifted into a genteel Christianity that stressed good works and respectability, the Baptist and Methodist churches continued to hold on to the old faith. In addition, aggressive fundamentalist sects such as the Churches of Christ, the Pentecostals, and Jehovah's Witnesses grew

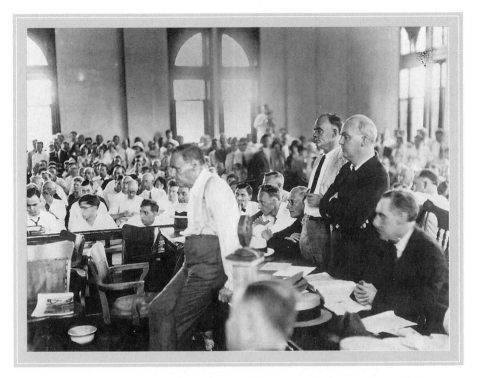

Crowds of spectators throng the courtroom during the Scopes trial as defense attorney Clarence Darrow rests on the table during the proceedings. Scopes is seated to Darrow's right with his arms interlocked, staring straight ahead.

rapidly. While church membership increased from 41.9 million in 1916 to 54.5 million in 1926, the number of churches actually declined during the decade. More and more rural dwellers drove their cars into town instead of going to the local crossroads chapel.

POLITICS OF THE 1920S

The tensions between the city and the countryside also shaped the course of politics in the 1920s. On the surface, it was a Republican decade. The GOP ("Grand Old Party") controlled the White House from 1921 to 1933 and had majorities in both houses of Congress from 1918 to 1930. The Republicans used their return to power after World War I to halt further reform legislation and to establish a friendly relationship between government and business. Important shifts were taking place, however, in the American electorate. The Democrats, although divided into competing urban and rural wings, were laying the groundwork for the future by winning over millions of new voters, especially among the ethnic groups in the cities. The rising tide of urban voters indicated a fundamental shift away from the Republicans toward a new Democratic majority.

HARDING, COOLIDGE, AND HOOVER

The Republicans regained the White House in 1920 with the election of Warren G. Harding of Ohio. A dark-horse contender, Harding won the GOP nomination when the convention deadlocked and he became the compromise choice. Handsome and dignified, Harding reflected both the virtues and blemishes of small-town America. Conventional in outlook, Harding was a genial man who lacked the capacity to govern and who, as president, broadly delegated power.

Attorney General Daugherty struggles to keep the scandals of the Harding administration hidden in the closet.

He made some good cabinet choices, notably Charles Evans Hughes as secretary of state and Herbert C. Hoover as secretary of commerce, but two corrupt officials—Attorney General Harry Daugherty and Secretary of the Interior Albert Fall—sabotaged his administration. Daugherty became involved in a series of questionable deals that led ultimately to his forced resignation; Fall was the chief figure in the Teapot Dome scandal. Two oil promoters gave Fall nearly $400,000 in loans and bribes; in return, he helped them secure leases on naval oil reserves in Elk Hills, California, and Teapot Dome, Wyoming. The scandal came to light after Harding's death from a heart attack in 1923. Fall eventually served a year in jail, and the reputation of the Harding administration never recovered.

Vice President Calvin Coolidge assumed the presidency upon Harding's death, and his honesty and integrity quickly reassured the nation. Coolidge, born in Vermont of old Yankee stock, had first gained national attention in 1919 as governor of Massachusetts when he had dealt firmly with a Boston police strike by declaring, "There is no right to strike against the public safety by anybody, anywhere, any time." A reserved, reticent man, Coolidge became famous for his epigrams, which contemporaries mistook for wisdom. "The business of America is business," he proclaimed. "The man who builds a factory builds a temple; the man who works there worships there." Consistent with this philosophy, he believed his duty was simply to preside benignly, not govern the nation. Satisfied with the prosperity of the mid-1920s, the people responded favorably. Coolidge was elected to a full term by a wide margin in 1924.

When Coolidge announced in 1927 that he did not "choose to run," Herbert Hoover became the Republican choice to succeed him. By far the ablest GOP leader of the decade, Hoover epitomized the American myth of the self-made man. Orphaned as a boy, he had worked his way through Stanford University and had gained both wealth and fame as a mining engineer. During World War I, he had displayed admirable administrative skills in directing Wilson's food program at home and relief activities abroad. Sober, intelligent, and immensely hardworking, Hoover embodied the nation's faith in individualism and free enterprise.

As secretary of commerce under Harding and Coolidge, he had sought cooperation between government and business. Instead of viewing business and government as antagonists, he saw them as partners, working together to achieve efficiency and affluence for all Americans. His optimistic view of the future led him to declare in his speech accepting the Republican presidential nomination in 1928 that "we in America today are nearer to the final triumph over poverty than ever before in the history of any land."

REPUBLICAN POLICIES

During the 1920 campaign, Warren Harding urged a return to "not heroism, but healing, not nostrums, but normalcy." Misreading his speechwriter's "normality," he coined a new word that became the theme for the Republican administrations of the 1920s. Aware that the public was tired of zealous reform-minded presidents such as Teddy Roosevelt and Woodrow Wilson, Harding and his successors sought a return to traditional Republican policies. In some areas they were successful, but in others the Republican leaders were forced to adjust to the new realities of a mass production society. The result was a mixture of traditional and innovative measures that was neither wholly reactionary nor entirely progressive.

The most obvious attempt to go back to the Republicanism of William McKinley came in tariff and tax policy. Fearful of a flood of postwar European imports, Congress passed an emergency tariff act in 1921 and followed it a year later with the protectionist Fordney-McCumber Tariff Act. The net effect was to raise the basic rates substantially over the moderate Underwood Tariff schedules of the Wilson period.

Secretary of the Treasury Andrew Mellon, a wealthy Pittsburgh banker and industrialist, worked hard to achieve a similar return to normalcy in taxation. Using the new budget system adopted by Congress in 1921, he reduced government spending from its World War I peak of $18 billion to just over $3 billion by 1925, thereby creating a slight surplus. Congress responded in 1926 by cutting the highest income tax bracket to a modest 20 percent.

The revenue acts of the 1920s greatly reduced the burden of taxation; by the end of the decade, the government was collecting one-third less than it had in 1921, and the number of people paying income taxes dropped from more than 6.5 million to 4 million. Yet the greatest relief went to the wealthy. The public was shocked to learn in the 1930s that J. P. Morgan and his nineteen partners had paid no income tax at all during the depths of the Depression.

The growing crisis in American farming during the decade forced the Republican administrations to seek new solutions. The end of the European war led to a sharp decline in farm prices and a return to the problem of overproduction. Southern and western lawmakers formed a farm bloc in Congress to press for special legislation for American agriculture. The farm bloc supported the higher tariffs, which included protection for constituents' crops, and helped secure passage of legislation to create federal supervision over stockyards, packinghouses, and grain trading.

Despite Republican rhetoric, the government's role in the economy increased rather than lessened in the 1920s. Herbert Hoover led the way in the Commerce Department, establishing new bureaus to help make American industry more efficient in housing, transportation, and mining. Under his leadership, the government encouraged corporations to develop welfare programs that undercut trade unions, and he tried to minimize labor disturbances by devising new federal machinery to mediate disputes. Instead of going back to the laissez-faire tradition of the nineteenth century, the Republican administrations of the 1920s were pioneering a close relationship between government and private business.

THE DIVIDED DEMOCRATS

While the Republicans ruled in the 1920s, the Democrats seemed bent on self-destruction. The Wilson coalition fell apart in 1920 as pent-up dissatisfaction stemming from the war enabled Harding to win by a landslide. The pace of the second Industrial Revolution and the growing urbanization split the party in two. One faction was centered in the rural South and West. Traditional Democrats who had supported Wilson stood for Prohibition, fundamentalism, the Klan, and other facets of the rural counterattack against the city. In contrast, a new breed of Democrat was emerging in the metropolitan areas of the North and Midwest. Immigrants and their descendants began to become active in the Democratic party. Catholic or Jewish in religion and strongly opposed to Prohibition, they had little in common with their rural counterparts.

The split within the party surfaced dramatically at the national convention in New York in 1924. Held in Madison Square Garden, a hall built in the 1890s and too small and cramped for the more than one thousand delegates, the convention soon degenerated into what one observer described as a "snarling, cursing, tenuous, suicidal, homicidal roughhouse." An urban resolution to condemn the Ku Klux Klan led to a spirited response from the rural faction and its defeat by a single vote. Then for nine days, in the midst of a stifling heat wave, the delegates divided between Alfred E. Smith, the governor of New York, and William G. McAdoo of California, Wilson's secretary of the treasury. When it became clear that neither the city nor the rural candidate could win a majority, both men withdrew; on the 103rd ballot, the weary Democrats finally chose John W. Davis, a former West Virginia congressman and New York corporation lawyer, as their compromise nominee.

In the ensuing election, the conservative Davis had difficulty setting his views apart from those of Republican president Calvin Coolidge. For the discontented, Senator Robert La Follette of Wisconsin offered an alternative by running on an independent Progressive party ticket. Coolidge won easily, receiving 15 million votes to 8 million for Davis and nearly 5 million for La Follette. Davis had made the poorest showing of any Democratic candidate in the twentieth century.

Yet the Democrats were in far better shape than this setback indicated. Beginning in 1922, the party had made heavy inroads into the GOP majority in Congress. The Democrats took seventy-eight seats away from Republicans in that

THE ELECTION OF 1924

CANDIDATE	PARTY	POPULAR VOTE	ELECTORAL VOTE
Coolidge	Republican	15,717,553	382
Davis	Democrat	8,386,169	136
La Follette	Progressive	4,814,050	13

election, many of them in the cities of the East and Midwest. In New York alone, they gained thirteen new congressmen, all but one in districts with heavy immigrant populations. By 1926, the Democrats were within one vote of controlling the Senate and had picked up nine more seats in the House in metropolitan areas. The large cities were swinging clearly into the Democratic column; all the party needed was a charismatic leader who could fuse the older rural elements with the new urban voters.

THE ELECTION OF 1928

The selection of Governor Al Smith of New York as the Democratic candidate in 1928 indicated the growing power of the city. Born on the Lower East Side of Manhattan of mixed Irish-German ancestry, Smith was the prototype of the urban Democrat. He was Catholic; he was associated with a big-city machine; he was a "wet" who wanted to end Prohibition. Rejected by rural Democrats in 1924, he still had to prove he could unite the South and West behind his leadership. His lack of education, poor grammar, and distinctive New York accent all hurt him, as did his eastern provincialism. When reporters asked him about his appeal in the states west of the Mississippi, he replied, "What states are west of the Mississippi?"

The choice facing the American voter in 1928 seemed unusually clear-cut. Herbert Hoover was a Protestant, a dry, and an old-stock American, who stood for efficiency and individualism; Smith was a Catholic, a wet, and a descendant of immigrants, who was closely associated with big-city politics. Just as Smith appealed to new voters in the cities, so Hoover won the support of many old-line Democrats who feared the city, Tammany Hall, and the pope.

Yet beneath the surface, as Allan J. Lichtman points out, there were "striking similarities between Smith and Hoover." Both were self-made men who embodied the American belief in freedom of opportunity and upward mobility. Neither advocated any significant degree of economic change nor any redistri-

THE ELECTION OF 1928

CANDIDATE	PARTY	POPULAR VOTE	ELECTORAL VOTE
Hoover	Republican	21,391,993	444
Smith	Democrat	15,016,169	87
	Minor Parties	330,725	—

bution of national wealth or power. Though religion proved to be the most important issue in the minds of the voters, hurting Smith far more than Prohibition or his identification with the city, the Democratic candidate's failure to spotlight the growing cracks in prosperity or to offer alternative economic policies ensured his defeat.

The 1928 election was a dubious victory for the Republicans. Hoover won easily, defeating Smith by more than six million votes and carrying such traditionally Democratic states as Oklahoma, Texas, and Florida. But Smith succeeded for the first time in winning a majority of votes for the Democrats in the nation's twelve largest cities. A new Democratic electorate was emerging, consisting of Catholics and Jews, Irish and Italians, Poles and Greeks. Now the task was to unite the traditional Democrats of the South and West with the urban voters of the Northeast and Midwest.

The growing influence of the city on politics of the 1920s reflected the sweeping changes taking place throughout the decade in American social and economic development. Al Smith, despite his defeat in 1928, symbolized the emergence of the city as the center of twentieth-century American life. An older nation founded on rural values had given way to a new urban society in which the production and use of consumer goods led to a very different lifestyle. Just as nineteenth-century American culture had revolved around the farm and the railroad, modern America focused on the automobile and the city. Yet despite the genuine economic progress achieved in the 1920s, the decade ended in a severe depression that lasted all through the 1930s. Only after World War II would the American people finally enjoy an abundance and prosperity rooted in the urban transformation that began in the 1920s.

26

FRANKLIN D. ROOSEVELT AND THE NEW DEAL

The prosperity of the 1920s came to an abrupt halt in October 1929. The stock market, which had boomed during the decade, suddenly faltered. Investors who had borrowed heavily to take part in the speculative mania that had swept Wall Street suddenly were forced to sell their securities to cover their loans. The wave of selling triggered an avalanche. On October 24, later known as Black Thursday, nearly thirteen million shares were traded as highfliers such as RCA and Westinghouse lost nearly half their value. The stock market rallied for the next two days, but on Tuesday, October 29, the downslide resumed. Frightened sellers dumped more than sixteen million shares and the industrial average fell by 43 points. The panic ended in November, with stocks at 1927 levels. For the next four years, there was a steady drift downward, until by 1932, prices were 80 percent below their 1929 highs.

The Great Depression that followed the crash of 1929 was the most devastating economic blow ever suffered by the nation. It lasted for more than ten years, dominating every aspect of American life during the 1930s. Unemployment rose to twelve million by 1932, and though it dipped midway through the decade, it still stood at ten million by 1939. Children grew up thinking that economic deprivation was the norm rather than the exception in America. Year after year, people kept looking for a return to prosperity, but the outlook remained dismal. Intractable and all-encompassing, the Depression loosened its grip on the nation only after the outbreak of World War II. Even then, it left enduring psychological scars—never again would the Americans who lived through it be quite so optimistic about their economic future.

The Depression led to a profound shift in American political loyalties. The Republicans, dominant since the 1890s, gave way to a new Democratic majority. The millions of immigrants who had come to the United States before World War I became more active politically, as did their children who were beginning to reach voting age. The result was the election of Franklin D. Roosevelt to the presidency and the development of the New Deal, a broad program of relief, recovery, and reform that greatly increased the role of government in American life.

THE GREAT DEPRESSION

The economic collapse altered American attitudes. In the 1920s, optimism had prevailed as people looked forward to an ever increasing flow of consumer goods and a better way of life. But after 1929, despair set in. Factories closed, machines fell silent, and millions upon millions of people walked the streets, looking for jobs that did not exist.

THE GREAT BULL MARKET

The consumer goods revolution contained the seeds of its own collapse. The steady expansion of the automobile and appliance industries had led gradually to a saturation of the market. Each year after 1924, the rate of increase in the sale of cars and refrigerators and ranges slowed, a natural consequence as more and more people already owned these durable goods. Production began to falter, and in 1927, the nation underwent a mild recession. The sale of durable goods de-

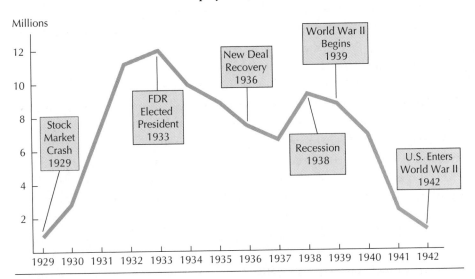

Unemployment, 1929–1942

clined, and construction of houses and buildings fell slightly. If corporate leaders had heeded these warning signs, they might have responded by raising wages or lowering prices, both effective ways to stimulate purchasing power and sustain the consumer goods revolution. Or if government officials had recognized the danger signals and forced a halt in installment buying and slowed bank loans, the nation might have experienced a sharp but brief depression.

Neither government nor business leaders were so farsighted. The Federal Reserve Board lowered the discount rate, charging banks less for loans in an attempt to stimulate the economy. Much of this additional credit, however, went not into solid investment in factories and machinery but instead into the stock market, touching off a new wave of speculation that obscured the growing economic slowdown and ensured a far greater crash to come.

Individuals with excess cash began to invest heavily in the stock market, betting the already impressive rise in security prices would bring them even greater windfall profits. The market had advanced in spurts during the decade; the value of all stocks listed on the New York Stock Exchange rose from $27 billion in 1925 to $67 billion in early 1929. People bet their savings on speculative stocks. Corporations used their large cash reserves to supply money to brokers who in turn loaned it to investors on margin; in 1929, for example, the Standard Oil Company of New Jersey loaned out $69 million a day in this fashion.

Investors could now play the market on credit, buying stock listed at $100 a share with $10 down and $90 on margin, the broker's loan for the balance. If the stock advanced to $150, the investor could sell and reap a gain of 500 percent on the $10 investment. And in the bull market climate of the 1920s, everyone was sure the market would go up.

By 1929, it seemed the whole nation was engaged in speculation. In city after city, brokers opened branch offices, each complete with a stock ticker and a huge board covered with the latest Wall Street quotations. In reality, though, more people were spectators than speculators; fewer than three million Americans owned stocks in 1929, and only about a half million were active buyers and sellers. But the bull market became a national obsession, assuring everyone that the economy was healthy and preventing any serious analysis of its underlying flaws.

The great crash in October 1929 put a sudden and tragic end to the speculative mania. The false confidence that had kept the economy from collapsing in 1927 evaporated overnight. Suddenly, corporations and financial institutions were no longer willing to provide capital for stock market purchases. More important, investors and bankers cut off consumer credit as well, drying up buying power and leading to a sharp decline in the sales of consumer goods. Factories began to cut back production, laying off some workers and reducing hours for others. The layoffs and cutbacks lowered purchasing power even further, so fewer people bought cars and appliances. More factory layoffs resulted, and some plants closed entirely, leading to the availability of even less money for the purchase of consumer goods.

This downward economic spiral continued for four years. By 1932, unemployment had swelled to 25 percent of the workforce, while the gross national product fell to 67 percent of the 1929 level. The bright promise of mass production had ended in a nightmare.

The basic explanation for the Great Depression lies in the fact that U.S. factories produced more goods than the American people could consume. The problem was not that the market for such products was fully saturated. In 1929, there were still millions of Americans who did not own cars or radios or refrigerators, but many of them could not afford the new products. There were other contributing causes—unstable economic conditions in Europe, the agricultural decline since 1919, corporate mismanagement, and excessive speculation—but it all came down to the fact that people did not have enough money to buy the consumer products coming off the assembly lines. Installment sales helped bridge the gap, but by 1929 the burden of debt was just too great.

The new economic system had failed to distribute wealth more broadly. Too much money had gone into profits, dividends, and industrial expansion, and not enough had gone into the hands of the workers, who were also consumers. If the billions that went into stock market speculation had been used instead to increase wages—which would then have increased consumer purchasing power—production and consumption could have been brought into balance. Yet it is too much to expect that the prophets of the new era could have foreseen this flaw and corrected it. They were pioneering a new industrial system, and only out of the bitter experience of the Depression would they discover the full dynamics of the consumer goods economy.

EFFECT OF THE DEPRESSION

It is difficult to measure the human cost of the Great Depression. The material hardships were bad enough. Men and women lived in lean-tos made of scrap wood and metal, and families went without meat and fresh vegetables for months, existing on a diet of soup and beans. The psychological burden was even greater: Americans suffered through year after year of grinding poverty with no letup in sight. The unemployed stood in line for hours waiting for relief checks; veterans sold apples or pencils on street corners, their manhood—once prized so highly by the nation—now in question.

Few escaped the suffering. African Americans who had left the poverty of the rural South for factory jobs in the North were among the first to be laid off. Mexican immigrants, who had flowed in to replace European immigrants, met

Unemployment devastated thousands, who sought any way to earn a few pennies—such as selling apples from a makeshift sidewalk stand.

with competition from angry citizens now willing to do stoop labor in the fields and work as track layers on the railroads. Immigration officials used technicalities to halt the flow across the Rio Grande and even to reverse it; nearly a half million Mexicans were deported in the 1930s, including families with children born in the United States.

The poor—black, brown, and white—survived because they knew better than most Americans how to exist in poverty. They stayed in bed in cold weather, both to keep warm and to avoid unnecessary burning up of calories; they patched their shoes with pieces of rubber from discarded tires, heated only the kitchens of their homes, and ate scraps of food that others would reject.

The suddenly homeless gathered in hobo camps and shantytowns, seeking shelter in flimsy shacks made of corrugated metal or cardboard. The camps were nicknamed "Hoovervilles," for the president who believed that relief for the poor, hungry, and unemployed was the responsibility of local governments and private charities—not the federal government.

The middle class, which had always lived with high expectations, was hit hard. Professionals and white-collar workers refused to ask for charity even while their families went without food; one New York dentist and his wife turned on the gas and left a note saying, "We want to get out of the way before we are forced to accept relief money." People who fell behind in their mortgage payments lost their homes and then faced eviction when they could not pay the rent.

Even the well-to-do were affected, giving up many of their former luxuries and weighed down with guilt as they watched former friends and business associates join the ranks of the impoverished. "My father lost everything in the Depression" became an all-too-familiar refrain among young people who dropped out of college.

Many Americans sought escape in movement. Men, boys, and some women rode the rails in search of jobs, hopping freights to move south in the winter or west in the summer. One town in the Southwest hired special police to keep vagrants from leaving the boxcars. Those who became tramps had to keep on the move, but they did find a sense of community in the hobo jungles that sprang up along the major railroad routes. Here the unfortunate could find a place to eat and sleep, and people with whom to share their misery. Louis Banks, a black veteran, told interviewer Studs Terkel what the informal camps were like:

> Black and white, it didn't make any difference who you were, 'cause everybody was poor. All friendly, sleep in a jungle. We used to take a big pot and cook food, cabbage, meat and beans all together. We all set together, we made a tent. Twenty-five or thirty would be out on the side of the rail, white and colored: They didn't have no mothers or sisters, they didn't have no home, they were dirty, they had overalls on, they didn't have no food, they didn't have anything.

FIGHTING THE DEPRESSION

The Great Depression presented an enormous challenge for American political leadership. The inability of the Republicans to overcome the economic catastrophe provided the Democrats with the chance to regain power. Although they failed to achieve full recovery before the outbreak of World War II, the Democrats did succeed in alleviating some of the suffering and establishing political dominance.

HOOVER AND VOLUNTARISM

Herbert Hoover was the Depression's most prominent victim. When the economic downturn began in late 1929, he tried to rally the nation with bold forecasts of better days ahead. His repeated assertion that prosperity was just around the corner bred cynicism and mistrust. Expressing complete faith in the American economic system, Hoover blamed the Depression on foreign causes, especially unstable European banks. The president rejected proposals for bold government action and relied instead on voluntary cooperation within business to halt the slide.

Hoover also believed in voluntary efforts to relieve the human suffering brought about by the Depression. He called on private charities and local governments to help feed and clothe those in need. But when these sources were exhausted, he rejected all requests for direct federal relief, asserting that such handouts would undermine the character of proud American citizens.

As the Depression deepened, Hoover reluctantly began to move beyond voluntarism to undertake more sweeping government measures. A new Federal Farm Board loaned money to aid cooperatives and bought up surplus crops in the open market in a vain effort to raise farm prices. At Hoover's request, Congress cut taxes in an attempt to restore public confidence and adopted a few federal public works projects, such as Boulder (Hoover) Dam, to provide jobs for idle men.

To help imperiled banks and insurance companies, Hoover proposed the Reconstruction Finance Corporation (RFC), which Congress established in early 1932. The RFC loaned government money to financial institutions to save them from bankruptcy. Hoover's critics, however, pointed out that while he favored aid to business, he still opposed measures such as direct relief and massive public works that would help the millions of unemployed.

By 1932, Hoover's efforts to overcome the Depression had clearly failed. The Democrats had gained control of the House of Representatives in the 1930 elections and were pressing the president to take bolder action, but Hoover stubbornly resisted. His public image suffered its sharpest blow in the summer of 1932 when he ordered General Douglas MacArthur to clear out the "bonus army." This ragged group of some twenty-two thousand World War I veterans had come to Washington in the summer of 1932 to lobby Congress to pay immediately a bonus for military service that was due them in 1945.

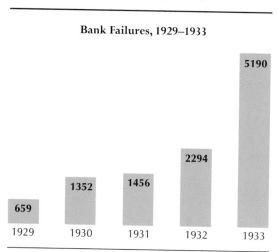

Bank Failures, 1929–1933

1929	1930	1931	1932	1933
659	1352	1456	2294	5190

Source: Data compiled from C. D. Bremer, *American Bank Failures* (New York: Columbia University Press, 1935), p. 42.

Meanwhile, the nation's banking structure approached collapse. Bank failures rose steadily in 1931 and 1932 as customers responded to rumors of bankruptcy by rushing in to withdraw their deposits. The banking crisis completed the nation's disenchantment with Hoover; people were ready for a new leader in the White House.

THE EMERGENCE OF ROOSEVELT

The man who stepped forward to meet this national need was Franklin D. Roosevelt. Born into the old Dutch colonial aristocracy of New York, FDR was a distant cousin of the Republican Teddy. He grew up with all the advantages of wealth—private tutors, his own sailboat and pony, frequent trips to Europe, and education at Groton and Harvard. After graduation from Harvard, he briefly attended law school but left to plunge into politics. He served in the New York legislature and then went to Washington as assistant secretary of the navy under Wilson, a post he filled capably during World War I. Defeated as the Democratic vice presidential candidate in 1920, Roosevelt had just begun a banking career when he suffered an attack of polio in the summer of 1921. Refusing to give in, he fought back bravely, and though he never again walked unaided, he reentered politics in the mid-1920s and was elected governor of New York in 1928.

Roosevelt's dominant trait was his ability to persuade and convince other people. He possessed a marvelous voice, deep and rich; a winning smile; and a buoyant confidence he could easily transmit to others. Some believed he was too vain and superficial as a young man, but his bout with polio gave him both an understanding of human suffering and a broad political appeal as a man who had faced heavy odds and overcome them. He understood the give-and-take of politics, knew how to use flattery to win over doubters, and was especially effective in exploiting the media. Although his mind was quick and agile, he had little patience with philosophical nuances; he dealt with the appearance of issues, not their deeper substance, and he displayed a flexibility toward political principles that often dismayed even his warmest admirers.

Roosevelt took advantage of the opportunity offered by the Depression. With the Republicans discredited, he cultivated the two wings of the divided Democrats, appealing to both the traditionalists from the South and West and the new urban elements in the North. After winning the party's nomination in 1932, he broke with tradition by flying to Chicago and accepting in person, telling the cheering delegates, "I pledge you—I pledge myself to a new deal for the American people."

In the fall, he defeated Herbert Hoover in a near landslide for the Democrats. Roosevelt tallied 472 electoral votes as he swept the South and West and carried nearly all the large industrial states as well. Farmers and workers, Protestants and Catholics, immigrants and native born rallied behind the new

THE ELECTION OF 1932

CANDIDATE	PARTY	POPULAR VOTE	ELECTORAL VOTE
Roosevelt	Democratic	22,809,638	472
Hoover	Republican	15,758,901	59
	Minor Parties	1,153,306	—

leader who promised to restore prosperity. Roosevelt not only met the challenge of the Depression but also solidified the shift to the Democratic party and created an enduring coalition that would dominate American politics for a half century.

THE HUNDRED DAYS

When Franklin Roosevelt took the oath of office on March 4, 1933, the nation's economy was on the brink of collapse. Unemployment stood at nearly thirteen million, one-fourth of the labor force; banks were closed in thirty-eight states. Speaking from the steps of the Capitol, FDR declared boldly, "First of all, let me assert my firm belief that the only thing we have to fear is fear itself—nameless, unreasoning, unjustified terror." Then he announced he would call Congress into special session and request "broad executive power to wage a war against the emergency, as great as the power that would be given to me if we were in fact invaded by a foreign foe."

Within the next ten days, Roosevelt won his first great New Deal victory by saving the nation's banks. On March 5, he issued a decree closing the banks and called Congress back into session. His aides drafted new banking legislation and presented it to Congress on March 9; a few hours later, both houses passed it, and FDR signed the new legislation that evening. The measure provided for government supervision and aid to the banks. Strong ones would be reopened with federal support, weak ones closed, and those in difficulty bolstered by government loans.

On March 12, FDR addressed the nation by radio in the first of his fireside chats. In conversational tones, he told the public what he had done. Some banks would begin to reopen the next day, with the government standing behind them. Other banks, once they became solvent, would open later, and the American people could safely put their money back into these institutions. The next day, March 13, the nation's largest and strongest banks opened their doors; at the end of the day, customers had deposited more cash than they withdrew. The crisis was over; gradually, other banks opened, and the runs and failures ceased.

"Capitalism was saved in eight days," boasted one of Roosevelt's advisers. Most surprising was the conservative nature of FDR's action. Instead of nationalizing the banks, he had simply thrown the government's resources behind them and preserved private ownership. Though some other New Deal measures would be more radical, Roosevelt set a tone in the banking crisis. He was out to reform and restore the American economic system, not change it drastically.

For the next three months, until it adjourned in June, Congress responded to a series of presidential initiatives. During these "Hundred Days," Roosevelt sent fifteen major requests to Congress and received back fifteen pieces of legislation. A few created permanent agencies that have become a part of American life: the Tennessee Valley Authority (TVA) proved to be the most successful and enduring of all Roosevelt's New Deal measures. This innovative effort at regional planning resulted in the building of a series of dams in seven states along the Tennessee River to control floods, ease navigation, and produce electricity.

With his fireside chats, FDR became the first president to use radio to reach and reassure the American people.

Other New Deal agencies were temporary in nature, designed to meet the specific economic problems of the Depression. None were completely successful; the Depression would continue for another six years, immune even to Roosevelt's magic. But psychologically, the nation turned the corner in the spring of 1933. Under FDR, the government seemed to be responding to the economic crisis, enabling people for the first time since 1929 to look to the future with hope.

ROOSEVELT AND RECOVERY

Two major New Deal programs launched during the Hundred Days were aimed at industrial and agricultural recovery. The first was the National Recovery Administration (NRA), FDR's attempt to achieve economic advance through planning and cooperation among government, business, and labor. In the midst of the Depression, businessowners were intent on stabilizing production and raising prices for their goods. Labor leaders were equally determined to spread work through maximum hours and to put a floor under workers' income with minimum wages.

The NRA hoped to achieve both goals by permitting companies in each major industry to cooperate in writing codes of fair competition that would set realistic limits on production, allocate percentages to individual producers, and set firm guidelines for prices. Section 7a of the enabling act mandated protection for labor in all the codes by establishing maximum hours, minimum wage, and the guarantee of collective bargaining by unions. No company could be compelled to join, but the New Deal sought complete participation by appealing to patriotism. Each firm that took part could display a blue eagle and stamp the symbol on its products. By the summer of 1933, more than five hundred industries had adopted codes that covered 2.5 million workers.

The NRA quickly bogged down in a huge bureaucratic morass. The codes proved to be too detailed to enforce easily. Written by the largest companies, the rules favored big business at the expense of smaller competitors. Labor quickly became disenchanted with Section 7a. The minimum wages were often near starvation level, while business avoided the requirement for collective bargaining by creating company unions that did not represent the real needs of workers. After a brief upsurge in the spring of 1933, industrial production began to sag as disillusionment with the NRA grew. When the Supreme Court finally invalidated the NRA in 1935 on constitutional grounds, few mourned its demise. The idea of trying to overcome the Depression by relying on voluntary cooperation between competing businesses and labor leaders had collapsed in the face of individual self-interest and greed.

The New Deal's attempt at farm recovery fared a little better. Henry A. Wallace, FDR's secretary of agriculture, came up with an answer to the farmers' old dilemma of overproduction. The government would act as a clearinghouse for producers of major crops, arranging for them to set production limits for wheat, cotton, corn, and other leading crops. The Agricultural Adjustment Administration (AAA) created by Congress in May 1933 would allocate acreage among individual farmers, encouraging them to take land out of production by paying them subsidies (raised by a tax on food processors). Unfortunately, Wallace preferred not to wait until the 1934 planting season to implement this program, and so farmers were paid in 1933 to plow under crops they had already planted and to kill livestock they were raising. Faced with the problem of hunger in the midst of plenty, the New Deal seemed to respond by destroying the plenty.

The AAA program worked better in 1934 and 1935 as land removed from production led to smaller harvests and rising farm prices. Farm income rose for the first time since World War I, increasing from $2 billion in 1933 to $5 billion by 1935. Severe weather, especially Dust Bowl conditions on the Great Plains, contributed to the crop-limitation program, but most of the gain in farm income came from the subsidy payments themselves rather than from higher market prices.

On the whole, large farmers benefited most from the program. Possessing the capital to buy machinery and fertilizer, they were able to farm more efficiently than before on fewer acres of land. Small farmers, tenants, and sharecroppers did not fare as well, receiving very little of the government payments and often being driven off the land as owners took the acreage previously cultivated by tenants and sharecroppers out of production.

The Supreme Court eventually found the AAA unconstitutional in 1936, but Congress reenacted it in modified form that year and again in 1938. The system of allotments, now financed directly by the government, became a standard feature of the farm economy. The result of the New Deal for American farming was to hasten its transformation into a business in which only the efficient and well capitalized would thrive.

ROOSEVELT AND RELIEF

The New Deal was far more successful in meeting the most immediate problem of the 1930s—relief for the millions of unemployed and destitute citizens. Roosevelt never shared Hoover's distaste for direct federal support; on May 12, 1933, in response to FDR's March request, Congress authorized the RFC to distribute $500 million to the states to help individuals and families in need.

Drought and soil erosion brought on by overfarming turned the agricultural land of the Great Plains into a giant dust bowl during the 1930s. Especially hard hit were western Kansas and Oklahoma, eastern Colorado, and the Texas Panhandle. In May 1934 a dust storm blew across Montana and Wyoming. Picking up as much as 350 million tons of dirt, it blew eastward spreading dust over Chicago, Buffalo, New York, and Boston. Even ships at sea in the Atlantic found dust on their decks.

Roosevelt brought in Harry Hopkins to direct the relief program. A former social worker who seemed to live on black coffee and cigarettes, Hopkins set up a desk in the hallway of the RFC building and proceeded to spend more than $5 million in less than two hours. The relief payments were modest in size, but they enabled millions to avoid starvation and stay out of humiliating breadlines.

Another, more imaginative early effort was the Civilian Conservation Corps (CCC), which was Roosevelt's own idea. The CCC enrolled youth from city families on relief and sent them to the nation's parks and recreational areas to build trails and improve public facilities. Ultimately, more than two million young people served in the CCC, contributing both to their families' incomes and to the nation's welfare.

Hopkins realized the need to do more than just keep people alive, and he soon became an advocate of work relief. Hopkins argued that the government should put the jobless to work, not just to encourage self-respect, but also to enable them to earn enough to purchase consumer goods and thus stimulate the entire economy. In the fall of 1933, Roosevelt created the Civil Works Administration (CWA) and charged Hopkins with getting people off the unemployment lines and relief rolls and back to work. Hopkins had more than four

Federal work relief programs helped millions maintain their self-respect. Workers in the CCC received $30 a month for planting trees and digging drainage ditches.

million men and women at work by January 1934, building roads, schools, playgrounds, and athletic fields. Many of the workers were unskilled, and some of the projects were shoddy, but the CWA at least enabled people to work and earn enough money to survive the winter. Roosevelt, appalled at the huge expenditures involved, shut down the CWA in 1934.

The final commitment to the idea of work relief came in 1935 when Roosevelt established the Works Progress Administration (WPA) to spend nearly $5 billion authorized by Congress for emergency relief. The WPA, under Hopkins, put the unemployed on the federal payroll so they could earn enough to meet their basic needs and help stimulate the stagnant economy. Conservatives complained that the WPA amounted to nothing more than hiring the jobless to do make-work tasks with no real value. But Hopkins cared less about what was accomplished than about helping those who had been unemployed for years to get off the dole and gain self-respect by working again.

In addition to funding the usual construction and conservation projects, the WPA tried to preserve the skills of American artists, actors, and writers. The Federal Theatre Project produced plays, circuses, and puppet shows that enabled

The WPA program employed artists like Jackson Pollock, Willem de Kooning, and Ben Shahn to decorate public buildings with murals that celebrated American culture.

entertainers to practice their crafts and to perform before people who often had never seen a professional production before. Similar projects for writers and artists led to a series of valuable state guidebooks and to murals that adorned public buildings across the land.

The WPA helped ease the burden for the unemployed, but it failed to overcome the Depression. Rather than spending too much, as his critics charged, Roosevelt's greatest failure was not spending enough. The WPA never employed at any one time more than three million of the ten million jobless. The wages, although larger than relief payments, were still pitifully low, averaging only $52 a month. Thus the WPA failed to prime the American economy by increasing consumer purchasing power. Factories remained closed and machinery idle because the American people still did not have the money, either from relief or the WPA, to buy cars, radios, appliances, and the other consumer goods that had been the basis for the prosperity of the 1920s. By responding to basic human needs, Roosevelt had made the Depression bearable. The New Deal's failure, however, to go beyond relief to achieve prosperity led to a growing frustration and the appearance of more radical alternatives that challenged the conservative nature of the New Deal and forced FDR to shift to the left.

ROOSEVELT AND REFORM

In 1935, the focus of the New Deal shifted from relief and recovery to reform. During his first two years in office, FDR had concentrated on fighting the Depression by shoring up the sagging American economy. Roosevelt was developing a "broker-state" concept of government, responding to pressures from organized elements such as corporations, labor unions, and farm groups while ignoring the needs and wants of the dispossessed who had no clear political voice. The early New Deal tried to assist bankers and industrialists, large farmers, and members of the labor unions, but it did little to help unskilled workers and sharecroppers.

As head of the Federal Emergency Relief Administration and later the Works Progress Administration, Harry Hopkins oversaw the distribution of $8.5 billion for unemployment relief. Here he observes a potter working at his wheel at an exhibit entitled "Skills of the Unemployed" held in St. Louis, Missouri, in 1938.

The continuing Depression and high unemployment began to build pressure for more sweeping changes. Roosevelt faced the choice of either providing more radical programs, ones designed to end historical inequities in American life, or deferring to others who put forth solutions to the nation's ills. Bolstered by an impressive Democratic victory in the 1934 congressional elections, Roosevelt responded by embracing a reform program that marked the climax of the New Deal.

ANGRY VOICES

The signs of discontent were visible everywhere by 1935. In the upper Midwest, progressives and agrarian radicals were calling for government action to raise farm and labor income. Upton Sinclair, the muckraking novelist, nearly won the governorship of California in 1934 running on the slogan "End poverty in California," while in the East a violent strike in the textile industry shut down plants in twenty states. The most serious challenge to Roosevelt's leadership, however, came from three demagogues who captured national attention in the mid-1930s.

The first was Father Charles Coughlin, a Roman Catholic priest from Detroit, who had originally supported FDR. Speaking to a rapt nationwide radio audience in his rich, melodious voice, Coughlin appealed to the discontented with a strange mixture of crank monetary schemes and anti-Semitism. He broke with the New Deal in late 1934, denouncing it as the "Pagan Deal," and founded his own National Union for Social Justice.

A more benign but equally threatening figure appeared in California. Francis Townsend, a 67-year-old physician, came forward in 1934 with a scheme to assist the elderly, who were suffering greatly during the Depression. The Townsend Plan proposed giving everyone over the age of 60 a monthly pension of $200 with the proviso that it must be spent within thirty days. Although designed less as an old-age pension plan than as a way to stimulate the economy, the proposal understandably had its greatest appeal among the elderly. Despite the criticism from economists that the plan would transfer more than half the national income to less than 10 percent of the population, more than ten million people signed petitions endorsing the Townsend Plan, and few politicians dared oppose it.

The third new voice of protest was that of Huey Long, the flamboyant senator from Louisiana. Like Coughlin, an original supporter of the New Deal, Long turned against FDR and by 1935 had become a major political threat to the president. A shrewd, ruthless, yet witty man, Long had a remarkable ability to mock those in power. The Kingfish (a nickname he borrowed from *Amos 'n Andy*) announced a nationwide "Share the Wealth" movement in 1934. He spoke grandly of taking from the rich to make "every man a king," guaranteeing each American a home worth $5000 and an annual income of $2500. To finance the plan, Long advocated seizing all fortunes of more than $5 million and levying a tax of 100 percent on incomes greater than $1 million. By 1935, Long claimed to have founded twenty-seven thousand Share the Wealth clubs. Threatening to run as a third-party candidate in 1936, Long generated fear among Democratic leaders that he might attract three to four million votes, possibly enough to swing the election to the Republicans. Although an assassin killed Huey Long in Louisiana in late 1935, his popularity showed the need for the New Deal to do more to help those still in distress.

SOCIAL SECURITY

When the new Congress met in January 1935, Roosevelt was ready to support a series of reform measures designed to take the edge off national dissent. The recent elections had increased Democratic congressional strength significantly, with the Republicans losing thirteen seats in the House and retaining less than one-third of the Senate. Many of the Democrats were to the left of Roosevelt, favoring increased spending and more sweeping federal programs. "Boys—this is our hour," exulted Harry Hopkins. "We've got to get everything we want . . . now or never."

The most significant reform enacted in 1935 was the Social Security Act. The Townsend movement had reminded Americans that the United States, alone among modern industrial nations, had never developed a welfare system to aid the aged, the disabled, and the unemployed. A cabinet committee began studying the problem in 1934, and President Roosevelt sent its recommendations to Congress the following January.

The proposed legislation had three major parts. First, it provided for old-age pensions financed equally by a tax on employers and workers, without government contributions. In addition, it gave states federal matching funds to provide modest pensions for the destitute elderly. Second, it set up a system of unemployment compensation on a federal-state basis, with employers paying a payroll tax and with each state setting benefit levels and administering the program locally. Finally, it provided for direct federal grants to the states, on a matching basis, for welfare payments to the blind, handicapped, needy elderly, and dependent children.

Although there was criticism from conservatives who mourned the passing of traditional American reliance on self-help and individualism, the chief objections came from those who argued that the administration's measure did not go far enough. Democratic leaders, however, defeated efforts to incorporate Townsend's proposal for $200 monthly pensions and increases in unemployment benefits. Congress then passed the Social Security Act by overwhelming margins.

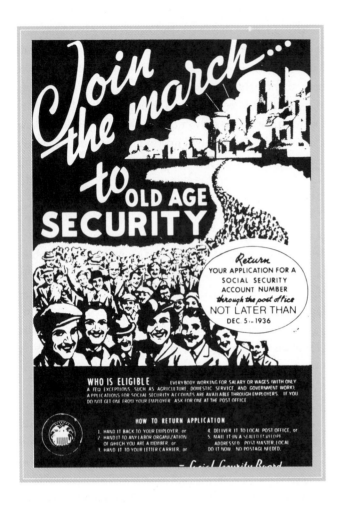

Despite the administration's boosterism, many felt that Social Security could not fulfill its promises.

Critics began to point out its shortcomings, as they have ever since. The old-age pensions were paltry. Designed to begin in 1942, they ranged from $10 to $85 a month. Not everyone was covered; those who most needed protection in their old age, such as farmers and domestic servants, were not included. The regressive feature of the act was even worse. All participants, regardless of income or economic status, paid in at the same rate, with no supplement from the general revenue.

Other portions of the act were equally open to question. The cumbersome unemployment system offered no aid to those currently out of work, only to people who would lose their jobs in the future. The outright grants to the handicapped and dependent children were minute in terms of the need; in New York City, for example, a blind person received only $5 a week in 1937.

The conservative nature of the legislation reflected Roosevelt's own fiscal orthodoxy, but even more it was a product of his political realism. Despite the severity of the Depression, he realized that establishing a system of federal welfare went against deeply rooted American convictions. He insisted on a tax on participants to give those involved in the pension plan a vested interest in Social Security. He wanted them to feel they had earned their pensions and that in the future no one would dare take them away. "With those taxes in there," he explained privately, "no damned politician can ever scrap my social security program." Above all, FDR had succeeded in establishing the principle of government responsibility for the aged, the handicapped, and the unemployed. Whatever the defects of the legislation, Social Security stood as a landmark of the New Deal, creating a system to provide for the welfare of individuals in a complex industrial society.

LABOR LEGISLATION

The other major reform achievement in 1935 was passage of the National Labor Relations Act. Senator Robert Wagner of New York introduced legislation in 1934 to outlaw company unions and other unfair labor practices in order to ensure collective bargaining for unions. FDR, who had little knowledge of labor-management relations and apparently little interest in them, opposed the bill. In 1935, however, Wagner began to gather broad support for his measure, which passed the Senate in May with only twelve opposing votes, and the president, seeing passage as likely, gave it his approval. The bill moved quickly through the House, and Roosevelt signed it into law in July.

The Wagner Act, as it became known, created a National Labor Relations Board to preside over labor-management relations and enable unions to engage in collective bargaining with federal support. The act outlawed a variety of union-busting tactics and in its key provision decreed that whenever the majority of a company's workers voted for a union to represent them, management would be compelled to negotiate with the union on all matters of wages, hours, and working conditions. With this unprecedented government sanction, labor unions could now recruit the large number of unorganized workers throughout the country. The Wagner Act, the most far-reaching of all New Deal measures, led to the revitalization of the American labor movement and a permanent change in labor-management relations.

Three years later, Congress passed a second law that had a lasting impact on American workers—the Fair Labor Standards Act. A long-sought goal of the New Deal, this measure aimed to establish both minimum wages and maximum hours of work per week. Since labor unions usually were able to negotiate adequate levels of pay and work for their members, the act was aimed at unorganized workers and met with only grudging support from unions.

The Fair Labor Standards Act provided for a minimum wage of 40 cents an hour by 1940 and a standard workweek of forty hours, with time and a half for overtime. Despite its loopholes, the legislation did lead to pay raises for the twelve million workers earning less than 40 cents an hour. More important, like Social Security it set up a system—however inadequate—that Congress could build on in the future to reach more generous and humane levels.

All in all, Roosevelt's record in reform was similar to that in relief and recovery—modest success but no sweeping victory. A cautious and pragmatic leader, FDR moved far enough to the left to overcome the challenges of Coughlin, Townsend, and Long without venturing too far from the mainstream. His reforms improved the quality of life in America significantly, but he made no effort to correct all the nation's social and economic wrongs.

IMPACT OF THE NEW DEAL

The New Deal had a broad influence on the quality of life in the United States in the 1930s. Government programs reached into areas hitherto untouched. Many of them brought about long-overdue improvements, but others failed to make any significant dent in historic inequities. The most important advances came with the dramatic growth of labor unions; the conditions for working women and minorities in nonunionized industries showed no comparable advance.

RISE OF ORGANIZED LABOR

Trade unions were weak at the onset of the Depression, with a membership of fewer than three million workers. Most were in the American Federation of Labor (AFL), composed of craft unions that served the needs of skilled workers. The nation's basic industries, such as steel and automobiles, were unorganized; the great mass of unskilled workers thus fared poorly in terms of wages and working conditions.

John L. Lewis, head of the United Mine Workers, took the lead in forming the Committee on Industrial Organization (CIO) in 1935. The son of a Welsh coal miner, Lewis was a dynamic and ruthless man. He had led the mine workers since 1919 and was determined to spread the benefits of unions throughout industry. Lewis first battled with the leadership of the AFL, and then—after being expelled—he renamed his group the Congress of Industrial Organizations and announced in 1936 that he would use the Wagner Act to extend collective bargaining to the nation's auto and steel industries.

Within five years, Lewis had scored a remarkable series of victories. Some came easily. The big steel companies, led by U.S. Steel, surrendered without a fight in 1937; management realized that federal support put the unions in a strong position. There was greater resistance in the automobile industry. When General Motors, the first target, resisted, the newly created United Automobile

Workers (UAW) developed an effective strike technique. In late December 1936, GM workers in Flint, Michigan, simply sat down in the factory, refusing to leave until the company recognized their union, and threatening to destroy the valuable tools and machines if they were removed forcibly. When the Michigan governor refused to call out the national guard to break the strike, General Motors conceded defeat and signed a contract with the UAW. Chrysler quickly followed suit, but Henry Ford refused to give in and fought the UAW, hiring strikebreakers and beating up organizers. In 1941, however, Ford finally recognized the UAW.

By the end of the 1930s, the CIO had some five million members, slightly more than the AFL. The successes were remarkable—in addition to the automaking and steel unions, organizers for the CIO and the AFL had been successful in the textile, rubber, electrical, and metal industries. For the first time, unskilled as well as skilled were unionized. Women and African Americans benefited from the creation of the CIO, not because the union followed enlightened policies, but simply because they made up a substantial proportion of the unskilled workforce that the CIO organized.

Yet despite these impressive gains, only 28 percent of all Americans (excluding farmworkers) belonged to unions by 1940. Millions in the restaurant, retail, and service trades remained unorganized, working long hours for very low wages. Employer resistance and traditional hostility to unions blocked further progress, as did the aloof attitude of President Roosevelt, who commented to labor and management, "A plague on both your houses" during the steel strike. The Wagner Act had helped open the way, but labor leaders such as Lewis, Philip Murray of the Steel Workers Organizing Committee, and Walter Reuther of the United Automobile Workers deserved most of the credit for union achievements.

THE NEW DEAL RECORD ON HELP TO MINORITIES

The Roosevelt administration's attempts to aid the downtrodden were least effective with African Americans and other racial minorities. The Depression had hit blacks with special force. Sharecroppers and tenant farmers had seen the price of cotton drop from 18 to 6 cents a pound, far below the level to sustain a family on the land. In the cities, the saying "Last hired, First fired" proved all too true; by 1933, more than 50 percent of urban blacks were unemployed. Hard times sharpened racial prejudice. "No jobs for niggers until every white man has a job" became a rallying cry for many whites in Atlanta.

The New Deal helped African Americans survive the Depression, but it never tried to confront squarely the racial injustice built into the federal relief programs. Although the programs served blacks as well as whites, in the South the weekly payments blacks received were much smaller. Nor did later reform

African American contralto Marian Anderson sang on the steps of the Lincoln Memorial in a concert given April 9, 1939.

measures help very much. Neither the minimum wage nor Social Security covered those working as farmers or domestic servants, categories that comprised 65 percent of all African American workers. Thus an NAACP official commented that Social Security "looks like a sieve with the holes just large enough for the majority of Negroes to fall through."

Despite this bleak record, African Americans rallied behind Roosevelt's leadership, abandoning their historic ties to the Republican party. In 1936, more than 75 percent of those African Americans who voted supported FDR. In part, this switch came in response to Roosevelt's appointment of a number of prominent African Americans to high-ranking government positions. Eleanor Roosevelt spoke out eloquently throughout the decade against racial discrimination, most notably in 1939 when the Daughters of the American Revolution refused to let African American contralto Marian Anderson sing in Constitution Hall. The First Lady and Interior Secretary Harold Ickes arranged for the singer to perform at the Lincoln Memorial, where 75,000 people gathered to hear her on Easter Sunday.

Perhaps the most influential factor in the African Americans' political switch was the color-blind policy of Harry Hopkins. He had more than one million blacks working for the WPA by 1939, many of them in teaching and artistic positions as well as in construction jobs. Overall, the New Deal provided assistance to 40 percent of the nation's blacks during the Depression. Uneven as his record was, Roosevelt had still done more to aid this oppressed minority than any previous president since Lincoln. One African American newspaper commented that while "relief and WPA are not ideal, they are better than the Hoover bread lines and they'll have to do until the real thing comes along."

The New Deal did far less for Mexican Americans. Engaged primarily in agricultural labor, these people found their wages in California fields dropping from 35 to 14 cents an hour by 1933. The pool of unemployed migrant labor expanded rapidly with Dust Bowl conditions in the Great Plains and the subsequent flight of "Okies" and "Arkies" to the cotton fields of Arizona and the truck farms of California. The Roosevelt administration cut off any further influx from Mexico by barring entry of any immigrant "likely to become a public charge"; local authorities rounded up migrants and shipped them back to Mexico to reduce the welfare rolls.

Native Americans, after decades of neglect, fared slightly better under the New Deal. Roosevelt appointed John Collier, a social worker who championed Indian rights, to serve as commissioner of Indian affairs. In 1934, Congress passed the Indian Reorganization Act, a reform measure designed to stress tribal unity and autonomy instead of attempting (as previous policy had done) to transform Indians into self-sufficient farmers by granting them small plots of land.

Roosevelt appointed John Collier as commissioner of Indian affairs to bring the New Deal to Native Americans. Under the Indian Reorganization Act of 1934, more than 7 million acres of land were restored to Native American control. Still, many Indians continued to distrust the government and its New Deal programs. Collier is shown here with a group of Flathead Indian chiefs standing behind Secretary of the Interior Harold L. Ickes on October 28, 1935, as Ickes signs the first constitution providing for Indian self-rule. Previously, the Bureau of Indian Affairs had directed the government of the Indians.

Despite modest gains, however, the nation's one-third million Indians remained the most impoverished citizens in America.

WOMEN AT WORK

The decade witnessed no significant gain in the status of American women. In the midst of the Depression, there was little concern expressed for protecting or extending their rights. The popular idea that women worked for "pin money" while men were the breadwinners for their families led employers to discriminate in favor of men when cutting the workforce. Working women "are holding jobs that rightfully belong to the God-intended providers of the household," declared a Chicago civic group. More than three-fourths of the nation's school boards refused to hire married women, and more than half of them fired women teachers who married. Federal regulations prohibited more than one member of a family from working in the civil service, and almost always it was the wife who had to defer to her husband.

Many of the working women in the 1930s were either single or the sole supporters of an entire family. Yet their wages remained lower than those for men, and their unemployment rate ran higher than 20 percent throughout the decade. The New Deal offered little encouragement. NRA codes sanctioned lower wages for women, permitting laundries, for example, to pay them as little as 14 cents an hour. The minimum wage did help those women employed in industry, but too many worked as maids and waitresses—jobs not covered by the law—for the new law to have much overall effect on women's income.

The one area of advance in the 1930s came in government. Eleanor Roosevelt set an example that encouraged millions of American women. Instead of presiding sedately over the White House, she traveled continually around the country, always eager to uncover wrongs and bring them to the president's attention. Frances Perkins, the secretary of labor, became the first woman cabinet member, and FDR appointed women as ambassadors and federal judges for the first time.

Women also were elected to office in larger numbers in the 1930s. Hattie W. Caraway of Arkansas succeeded her husband in the Senate, winning a full term in 1934. That same year, voters elected six women to the House of Representatives. Public service, however, was one of the few professions open to women. The nation's leading medical and law schools discouraged women from applying, and the percentage of female faculty members in colleges and universities continued to decline in the 1930s. In sum, a decade that was grim for most Americans was especially hard on American women.

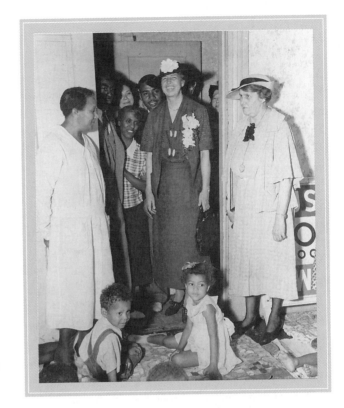

Eleanor Roosevelt visited many sites in her efforts to bring the New Deal to the forgotten and the dispossessed. She is shown here visiting an African American nursery school run by the WPA in Des Moines, Iowa.

END OF THE NEW DEAL

The New Deal reached its high point in 1936, when Roosevelt was overwhelmingly reelected and the Democratic party strengthened its hold on Congress. This political triumph was deceptive. In the next two years, Roosevelt met with a series of defeats in Congress. Yet despite the setbacks, he remained a popular political leader who had restored American self-confidence as he strove to meet the challenges of the Depression.

THE ELECTION OF 1936

Franklin Roosevelt enjoyed his finest political hour in 1936. A man who loved the give-and-take of politics, FDR faced challenges from both the left and the right as he sought reelection. Father Coughlin helped organize a Union party, with North Dakota Progressive Congressman William Lemke heading the ticket. At the other extreme, a group of wealthy industrialists formed the Liberty League to fight what they saw as the New Deal's assault on property rights. The Liberty League

THE ELECTION OF 1936

CANDIDATE	PARTY	POPULAR VOTE	ELECTORAL VOTE
Roosevelt	Democratic	27,752,869	523
Landon	Republican	16,674,665	8

endorsed the Republican presidential candidate, Governor Alfred M. Landon of Kansas. A moderate, colorless figure, Landon disappointed his backers by refusing to campaign for repeal of the popular New Deal reforms.

Roosevelt ignored Lemke and the Union party, focusing attention instead on the assault from the right. In his speeches, FDR condemned the "economic royalists" who were "unanimous in their hatred for me." "I welcome their hatred," he declared, and promised that in his second term, these forces would meet "their master."

This frank appeal to class sympathies proved enormously successful. Roosevelt won easily, receiving five million more votes than he had in 1932 and outscoring Landon in the electoral college by 523 to 8. The Democrats did almost as well in Congress, piling up margins of 331 to 89 in the House and 76 to 16 in the Senate (with 4 not aligned with either major party).

Equally important, the election marked the stunning success of a new political coalition that would dominate American politics for the next three decades. FDR, building on the inroads into the Republican majority that Al Smith had begun in 1928, carried urban areas by impressive margins, winning 3.6 million more votes than his opponents in the nation's twelve largest cities. He held on to the traditional Democratic votes in the South and West and added to them by appealing strongly to the diverse religious and ethnic groups in the northern cities—Catholics and Jews, Italians and Poles, Irish and Slavs. The strong support of labor, together with three-quarters of the black vote, indicated that the nation's new alignment followed economic as well as cultural lines. The poor and the oppressed, who in the Depression years included many middle-class Americans, became attached to the Democratic party, leaving the GOP in a minority position, limited to the well-to-do and to rural and small-town Americans of native stock.

THE SUPREME COURT FIGHT

FDR proved to be far more adept at winning electoral victories than in achieving his goals in Congress. In 1937, he attempted to use his recent success to overcome the one obstacle remaining in his path—the Supreme Court. During his first term, the Court had ruled several New Deal programs unconstitutional, most notably the NRA and the AAA. Only three of the nine justices were sympathetic to the need for emergency measures in the midst of the Depression. Two others were unpredictable, sometimes approving New Deal measures and sometimes opposing them. Four justices were bent on using the Constitution to block Roosevelt's proposals.

When Congress convened in 1937, the president offered a startling proposal to overcome the Court's threat to the New Deal. Instead of seeking a constitutional amendment either to limit the Court's power or to clarify the constitutional issues, FDR chose an oblique attack. Declaring the Court was falling behind schedule because of the age of its members, he asked Congress to appoint a new justice for each member of the Court over the age of 70, up to a maximum of six.

Although this "court-packing" scheme, as critics quickly dubbed it, was perfectly legal, it outraged not only conservatives but liberals as well, who realized it could set a dangerous precedent for the future. Republicans wisely kept silent, letting prominent Democrats lead the fight against Roosevelt's plan. Despite all-out pressure from the White House, resistance in the Senate blocked early action on the proposal.

The Court defended itself well. Chief Justice Charles Evans Hughes testified tellingly to the Senate Judiciary Committee, pointing out that in fact the Court was up to date and not behind schedule as Roosevelt charged. The Court then surprised observers with a series of rulings approving such controversial New Deal measures as the Wagner Act and Social Security. Believing he had proved his point, the president allowed his court-packing plan to die in the Senate.

During the next few years, Roosevelt was able to appoint such distinguished jurists as Hugo Black, William O. Douglas, and Felix Frankfurter to the Supreme Court. Yet the price was high. The court fight had badly weakened the president's relations with Congress, opening deep rifts with members of his own party. Many senators and representatives who had voted reluctantly for Roosevelt's measures during the depths of the Depression now felt free to oppose any further New Deal reforms.

THE NEW DEAL IN DECLINE

The legislative record during Roosevelt's second term was meager. Aside from the minimum wage and maximum-hour law passed in 1938, Congress did not extend the New Deal into any new areas. Disturbed by the growing congressional resistance, Roosevelt set out in the spring of 1938 to defeat a number of conservative Democratic congressmen and senators, primarily in the South. His

MAJOR NEW DEAL LEGISLATION AND AGENCIES

YEAR CREATED	ACT OR AGENCY	PROVISIONS
1933	Agricultural Adjustment Administration (AAA)	Attempted to regulate agricultural production through farm subsidies; reworked after the Supreme Court ruled its key regulatory provisions unconstitutional in 1936; coordinated agricultural production during World War II, after which it was disbanded.
	Banking Act of 1933 (Glass-Steagall Act)	Prohibited commercial banks from selling stock or financing corporations; created FDIC.
	Civilian Conservation Corps (CCC)	Young men between the ages of 18 and 25 volunteered to be placed in camps to work on regional environmental projects, mainly west of the Mississippi; they received $30 a month, of which $25 was sent home; disbanded during World War II.
	Civil Works Administration (CWA)	Emergency work relief program put more than four million people to work during the extremely cold winter of 1933–1934, after which it was disbanded.
	Federal Deposit Insurance Corporation (FDIC)	A federal guarantee of savings bank deposits initially of up to $2,500, raised to $5,000 in 1934, and frequently thereafter; continues today with a limit of $100,000.
	Federal Emergency Relief Administration (FERA)	Combined cash relief to needy families with work relief; superseded in early 1935 by the extensive work relief projects of the WPA and unemployment insurance established by Social Security.
	National Recovery Administration (NRA)	Attempted to combat the Depression through national economic planning by establishing and administering a system of industrial codes to control production, prices, labor relations, and trade practices among leading business interests; ruled unconstitutional by the Supreme Court in 1935.
	Public Works Administration (PWA)	Financed more than 34,000 federal and nonfederal construction projects at a cost of more than $6 billion; initiated the first federal public housing program, made the federal government the nation's leading producer of power, and advanced conservation of the nation's natural resources; discontinued in 1939 due to its effectiveness at reducing unemployment and promoting private investment.
	Tennessee Valley Authority (TVA)	An attempt at regional planning. Included provisions for environment and recreational design; architectural, educational, and health projects; and controversial public power projects; continues today to meet the Tennessee Valley's energy and flood-control needs.
1934	Federal Communications Commission (FCC)	Regulatory agency with wide discretionary powers established to oversee wired and wireless communication; reflected growing importance of radio in everyday lives of Americans during the Depression; continues to regulate television as well as radio.

YEAR CREATED	ACT OR AGENCY	PROVISIONS
	Federal Housing Administration (FHA)	Expanded private home ownership among moderate-income families through federal guarantees of private mortgages, the reduction of down payments from 30 to 10 percent, and the extension of repayment from 20 to 30 years; continues to function today.
	Securities and Exchange Commission (SEC)	Continues today to regulate trading practices in stocks and bonds according to federal laws.
1935	National Labor Relations Board (NLRB); established by Wagner Act	Greatly enhanced power of American labor by overseeing collective bargaining; continues to arbitrate labor-management disputes today.
	National Youth Administration (NYA)	Established by the WPA to reduce competition for jobs by supporting education and training of youth; paid grants to more than 2 million high school and college students in return for work performed in their schools; also trained another 2.6 million out-of-school youths as skilled labor to prepare them for later employment in the private sector; disbanded during World War II.
	Rural Electrification Administration (REA)	Transformed American rural life by making electricity available at low rates to American farm families in areas that private power companies refused to service; closed the cultural gap between rural and urban everyday life by making modern amenities, such as radio, available in rural areas.
	Social Security Act	Guaranteed retirement payments for enrolled workers beginning at age 65; set up federal-state system of unemployment insurance and care for dependent mothers and children, the handicapped, and public health; continues today.
	Works Progress Administration (WPA)	Massive work relief program funded projects ranging from construction to acting; disbanded by FDR during World War II.
1937	Farm Security Administration (FSA)	Granted loans to small farmers and tenants for rehabilitation and purchase of small-sized farms; Congress slashed its appropriations during World War II when many poor farmers entered the armed forces or migrated to urban areas.
1938	Fair Labor Standards Act	Established a minimum wage of 40 cents an hour and a maximum workweek of 40 hours for businesses engaged in interstate commerce.

targets gleefully charged the president with interference in local politics; only one of the men he sought to defeat lost in the primaries. The failure of this attempted purge further undermined Roosevelt's strained relations with Congress.

The worst blow came in the economic sector. The slow but steady improvement in the economy suddenly gave way to a sharp recession in the late summer of 1937. In the following ten months, industrial production fell by one-third, and nearly four million workers lost their jobs. Critics of the New Deal quickly labeled the downturn "the Roosevelt recession," and business executives claimed that it reflected a lack of confidence in FDR's leadership.

Actually, Roosevelt was at fault. In an effort to reduce expanding budget deficits, he had cut back sharply on WPA and other government programs after the election. For several months, Roosevelt refused to heed calls from economists to renew heavy government spending. Finally, in April 1938, Roosevelt asked Congress for a $3.75 billion relief appropriation, and the economy began to revive. But FDR's premature attempt to balance the budget had meant two more years of hard times and had marred his reputation as the energetic foe of the Depression.

The political result of the attempted purge and the recession was a strong Republican upsurge in the elections of 1938. The GOP won an impressive 81 seats in the House and 8 more in the Senate, as well as 13 governorships. The Democrats still held a sizable majority in Congress, but their margin in the House was particularly deceptive. There were 262 Democratic representatives to 169 Republicans, but 93 southern Democrats held the balance of power. More and more often after 1938, anti–New Deal Southerners voted with Republican conservatives to block social and economic reform measures. Thus not only was the New Deal over by the end of 1938, but a new bipartisan conservative coalition that would prevail for a quarter century had formed in Congress.

EVALUATION OF THE NEW DEAL

The New Deal lasted a brief five years, and most of its measures came in two legislative bursts in the spring of 1933 and the summer of 1935. Yet its impact on American life was enduring. Nearly every aspect of economic, social, and political development in the decades that followed bore the imprint of Roosevelt's leadership.

The least impressive achievement of the New Deal came in the economic realm. Whatever credit Roosevelt is given for relieving human suffering in the depths of the Depression must be balanced against his failure to achieve recovery in the 1930s. The moderate nature of his programs, especially the unwieldy NRA, led to slow and halting industrial recovery. Although much of the improvement that was made came as a result of government spending, FDR never embraced the concept of planned deficits, striving instead for a balanced budget. As a result, the nation had barely reached the 1929 level of production a decade later, and there were still nearly ten million men and women unemployed.

Equally important, Roosevelt refused to make any sweeping changes in the American economic system. Aside from the TVA, there were no broad experiments in regional planning and no attempt to alter free enterprise beyond imposing some limited forms of government regulation. The New Deal did nothing to alter the basic distribution of wealth and power in the nation. The outcome was the preservation of the traditional capitalist system with a thin overlay of federal control.

More significant change occurred in American society. With the adoption of Social Security, the government acknowledged for the first time its responsibility to provide for the welfare of those unable to care for themselves in an industrial society. The Wagner Act helped stimulate the growth of labor unions to balance corporate power, and the minimum wage law provided a much needed floor for many workers.

Yet the New Deal tended to help only the more vocal and organized groups, such as union members and commercial farmers. Those without effective voices or political clout—African Americans, Mexican Americans, women, sharecroppers, restaurant and laundry workers—received little help from the New Deal. For all the appealing rhetoric about the "forgotten man," Roosevelt did little more than Hoover in responding to the long-term needs of the dispossessed.

The most lasting impact of the Roosevelt leadership came in politics. Taking advantage of the emerging power of ethnic voters and capitalizing on the frustration growing out of the Depression, FDR proved to be a genius at forging a new coalition. Overcoming the friction between rural and urban Democrats that had prolonged Republican supremacy in the 1920s, he attracted new groups to the Democratic party, principally African Americans and organized labor. His political success led to a major realignment that lasted long after he left the scene.

His political achievement also reveals the true nature of Roosevelt's success. He was a brilliant politician who recognized the essence of leadership in a democracy—appealing directly to the people and giving them a sense of purpose. He succeeded in infusing them with the same indomitable courage and jaunty optimism that had marked his own battle with polio. Thus, despite his limitations as a reformer, Roosevelt proved to be the leader the American people needed in the 1930s—a president who provided the psychological lift that helped them endure and survive the Great Depression.

27

AMERICA AND THE WORLD, 1921–1945

On August 27, 1928, U.S. Secretary of State Frank B. Kellogg, French Foreign Minister Aristide Briand, and representatives of twelve other nations met in Paris to sign a treaty outlawing war. Several hundred spectators crowded into the ornate clock room of the Quai d'Orsay to watch the historic ceremony. Six huge klieg lights illuminated the scene so photographers could record the moment for a world eager for peace. Briand opened the ceremony with a speech in which he declared, "Peace is proclaimed," and then Kellogg signed the document with a foot-long gold pen given to him by the citizens of Le Havre as a token of Franco-American friendship. In the United States, a senator called the Kellogg-Briand Pact "the most telling action ever taken in human history to abolish war."

In reality, the Pact of Paris was the result of a determined American effort to avoid involvement in the European alliance system. In June 1927, Briand had sent a message to the American people inviting the United States to join with France in signing a treaty to outlaw war between the two nations. The invitation struck a sympathetic response, especially among pacifists who had advocated the outlawing of war throughout the 1920s, but the State Department feared correctly that Briand's true intention was to establish a close tie between France and the United States. The French had already created a network of alliances with the smaller countries of eastern Europe; an antiwar treaty with the United States would at least ensure American sympathy, if not involvement, in case of another European war. Kellogg delayed several months and then outmaneuvered Briand by propos-

Secretary of State Frank Kellogg signs the Kellogg-Briand Pact renouncing war. A grand document, the treaty included no method to enforce its provisions. The agreement was formally broken when Japan invaded Manchuria in 1931.

ing the pledge against war not be confined just to France and the United States, but instead be extended to all nations.

Eventually the signers of the Kellogg-Briand Pact included nearly every nation in the world, but the effect was negligible. All promised to renounce war as an instrument of national policy, except of course, as the British made clear in a reservation, in matters of self-defense. Enforcement of the treaty relied solely on the moral force of world opinion. The Pact of Paris was, as one senator shrewdly commented, only "an international kiss."

Unfortunately, the Kellogg-Briand Pact was symbolic of American foreign policy in the years after World War I. Instead of asserting the role of leadership its resources and power commanded, the United States kept aloof from other nations. America went its own way, extending trade and economic dominance but refusing to take the lead in maintaining world order. This retreat from responsibility seemed unimportant in the 1920s when exhaustion from World War I ensured relative peace and tranquility. But in the 1930s, when threats to world order arose in Europe and Asia, the American people retreated even deeper, searching for an isolationist policy that would spare them the agony of another great war.

There was no place to hide in the modern world. The Nazi onslaught in Europe and the Japanese expansion in Asia finally led to American entry into World War II in late 1941, at a time when the chances for an Allied victory seemed most remote. With incredible swiftness, the nation mobilized its military and industrial strength. American armies were soon fighting on three continents, the U.S. Navy controlled the world's oceans, and the nation's factories were sending a vast stream of war supplies to more than twenty Allied countries.

When victory came in 1945, the United States was by far the most powerful nation in the world. But instead of the enduring peace that might have permitted a return to a less active foreign policy, the onset of the Cold War with the Soviet Union brought on a new era of tension and conflict. This time the United States could not retreat from responsibility. World War II was a coming of age for American foreign policy.

RETREAT, REVERSAL, AND RIVALRY

"The day of the armistice America stood on the hilltops of glory, proud in her strength, invincible in her ideals, acclaimed and loved by a world free of an ancient fear at last," wrote journalist George Creel in 1920. "Today we writhe in a pit of our own digging; despising ourselves and despised by the betrayed peoples of earth." The bitter disillusionment Creel described ran through every aspect of American foreign policy in the 1920s. In contrast to diplomatic actions under Wilsonian idealism, American diplomats in the 1920s made loans, negotiated treaties and agreements, and pledged the nation's good faith, but they were careful not to make any binding commitments on behalf of world order. The result was neither isolation nor involvement but rather a cautious middle course that managed to alienate friends and encourage foes.

RETREAT IN EUROPE

The United States emerged from World War I as the richest nation on earth, displacing England from its prewar position of economic primacy. The Allied governments owed the United States a staggering $10 billion in war debts, money they had borrowed during and immediately after the conflict. Each year of the 1920s saw the nation increase its economic lead as the balance of trade tipped heavily in America's favor. By 1929, American exports totaled more than $7 billion a year, three times the prewar level, and American overseas investment had risen to $17.2 billion.

The European nations could no longer compete on equal terms. The high American tariff, first imposed in 1922 and then raised again in 1930, frustrated attempts by England, France, and a defeated Germany to earn the dollars necessary to meet their American financial obligations. The Allied partners in World War I asked Washington to cancel the $10 billion in war debts, particularly after they were forced to scale down their demands for German reparations payments. American leaders from Wilson to Hoover indignantly refused the request, claiming the ungrateful Allies were trying to repudiate their sacred obligations.

Only a continuing flow of private American capital to Germany allowed the payment of reparations to the Allies and the partial repayment of the Allies' war debts in the 1920s. The financial crash of 1929 halted the flow of American dollars across the Atlantic and led to subsequent default on the debt payments, with accompanying bitterness on both sides of the ocean.

Political relations fared little better. The United States never joined the League of Nations, nor did it take part in the attempts by England and France to negotiate European security treaties. The Republican administrations of the 1920s refused to compromise American freedom of action by embracing collective security, the principle on which the League was founded. And FDR, always realistic, made no effort to renew Wilson's futile quest. Thus the United States remained aloof from the European balance of power and refused to stand behind the increasingly shaky Versailles settlement.

The U.S. government ignored the Soviet Union throughout the 1920s. In 1933, Franklin Roosevelt finally ended the long estrangement by signing an agreement opening up diplomatic relations between the two countries. The Soviets soon went back on promises to stop all subversive activity in the United States and to settle prerevolutionary debts, but even if they rarely understood one another, at least the two nations had opened a channel of communication.

COOPERATION IN LATIN AMERICA

U.S. policy was both more active and more enlightened in the Western Hemisphere than in Europe. The State Department sought new ways in the 1920s to pursue traditional goals of political dominance and economic advantage in Latin America. The outcome of World War I lessened any fears of European threats to the area and thus enabled the United States to dismantle the interventions in the Caribbean carried out by Roosevelt, Taft, and Wilson. At the same time, both Republican and Democratic administrations worked hard to extend American trade and investment in the nations to the south.

Under Harding, Coolidge, and Hoover, American marines were withdrawn from Haiti and the Dominican Republic, and in 1924 the last detachment left

Nicaragua, ending a twelve-year occupation. Renewed unrest there the next year, however, led to a second intervention in Nicaragua, which did not end until the early 1930s.

When FDR took office in 1933, relations with Latin America were far better than they had been under Wilson, but American trade in the hemisphere had fallen drastically as the Depression worsened. Roosevelt moved quickly to solidify the improved relations and gain economic benefits. With his usual flair for the dramatic, he proclaimed a policy of the "good neighbor" and then proceeded to win goodwill by renouncing the imperialism of the past.

In 1933, Secretary of State Cordell Hull signed a conditional pledge of nonintervention at a Pan-American conference in Montevideo, Uruguay. A year later, the United States renounced the right to intervene in Cuban affairs it had asserted under the Platt Amendment and loosened its grip on Panama. By 1936, American troops were no longer occupying any Latin American nation.

The United States had not changed its basic goal of political and economic dominance in the hemisphere; rather, the new policy of benevolence reflected Roosevelt's belief that cooperation and friendship were more effective tactics than threats and armed intervention. Mexico tried his patience in 1938 by nationalizing its oil resources; with admirable restraint, the president finally negotiated a settlement in 1941 on terms favorable to Mexico. Yet this economic loss was more than offset by the new trade opportunities opened up by the Good Neighbor policy. American commerce with Latin America increased fourfold in the 1930s, and investment rose substantially from its Depression low. Most important, FDR succeeded in forging a new policy of regional collective security. As the ominous events leading to World War II unfolded in Europe and Asia, the nations of the Western Hemisphere looked to the United States for protection against external danger.

RIVALRY IN ASIA

In the years following World War I, the United States and Japan were on a collision course in the Pacific. The Japanese, lacking the raw materials to sustain their developing industrial economy, were determined to expand onto the Asian mainland. They had taken Korea by 1905 and during World War I had extended their control over the mines, harbors, and railroads of Manchuria, the industrial region of northeast China. The American Open Door policy remained the primary obstacle to complete Japanese dominion over China. The United States thus faced the clear-cut choice of either abandoning China or forcefully opposing Japan's expansion. American efforts to avoid making this painful decision postponed the eventual showdown but not the growing rivalry.

The first attempt at a solution came in 1921 when the United States convened the Washington Conference, which included delegates from the United States, Japan, Great Britain, and six other nations. The major objective was a political settlement of the tense Asian situation, but the most pressing issue was a dangerous naval race between Japan and the United States. Both nations were engaged in extensive shipbuilding programs begun during the war; Great Britain was forced to compete in order to preserve its traditional control of the sea.

In his welcoming address at the Washington Conference, Secretary of State Charles Evans Hughes outlined a specific plan for naval disarmament, calling for the scrapping of sixty-six battleships—thirty American, nineteen British, and seventeen Japanese. Three months later, delegates signed a Five Power Treaty embodying the main elements of Hughes's proposal: limitation of capital ships (battleships and aircraft carriers) in a ratio of 5:5:3 for the United States, Britain, and Japan, respectively, and 1.67:1.67 for France and Italy. England reluctantly accepted equality with the United States, while Japan agreed to the lower ratio only in return for an American pledge not to fortify Pacific bases such as the Philippines and Guam. The treaty cooled off the naval race even though it did not include cruisers, destroyers, or submarines.

The Washington Conference produced two other major agreements: the Nine Power Treaty and the Four Power Treaty. The first simply pledged all the countries involved to uphold the Open Door policy, while the other compact replaced the old Anglo-Japanese alliance with a new Pacific security pact signed by the United States, Great Britain, Japan, and France. Neither document contained any enforcement provision beyond a promise to consult in case of a violation. In essence, the Washington treaties formed a parchment peace, a pious set of pledges that attempted to freeze the status quo in the Pacific.

This compromise lasted less than a decade. In September 1931, Japanese forces violated the Nine Power Treaty and the Kellogg-Briand Pact by overrunning Manchuria in a brutal act of aggression. The United States, paralyzed by the Depression, responded feebly. Secretary of State Henry L. Stimson issued notes in January 1932 vowing the United States would not recognize the legality of the Japanese seizure of Manchuria. Despite concurrence by the League on nonrecognition, the Japanese ignored the American moral sanction and incorporated the former Chinese province, now renamed Manchukuo, into their rapidly expanding empire.

Aside from the Good Neighbor approach in the Western Hemisphere, American foreign policy faithfully reflected the prevailing disillusionment with world power that gripped the country after World War I. The United States avoided taking any constructive steps toward preserving world order, preferring instead the empty symbolism of the Washington treaties and the Kellogg-Briand Pact.

ISOLATIONISM

The retreat from an active world policy in the 1920s turned into a headlong flight back to isolationism in the 1930s. Two factors were responsible. First, the Depression made foreign policy seem remote and unimportant to most Americans. As unemployment increased and the economic crisis intensified after 1929, many people grew apathetic about events abroad. Second, the danger of war abroad, when it did finally penetrate the American consciousness, served only to strengthen the desire to escape involvement.

Three powerful and discontented nations were on the march in the 1930s— Germany, Italy, and Japan. In Germany, Adolf Hitler came to power in 1933 as the head of a National Socialist, or Nazi, movement. A shrewd and charismatic leader, Hitler capitalized on both domestic discontent and bitterness over World War I. Blaming the Jews for all of Germany's ills and asserting the supremacy of the "Aryan" race of blond, blue-eyed Germans, he quickly imposed a totalitarian dictatorship in which the Nazi party ruled and the *Führer* was supreme. Hitler took Germany out of the League of Nations, reoccupied the Rhineland, and formally denounced the Treaty of Versailles. His boasts of uniting all Germans into a Greater Third Reich that would last a thousand years filled his European opponents with terror, blocking any effective challenge to his regime.

In Italy, another dictator, Benito Mussolini, had come to power in 1922. Emboldened by Hitler's success, he embarked on an aggressive foreign policy in 1935. His invasion of the independent African nation of Ethiopia led its emperor, Haile Selassie, to call on the League of Nations for support. With England and France far more concerned about Hitler, the League's halfhearted measures utterly failed to halt Mussolini's conquest. "Fifty-two nations had combined to resist aggression," commented historian A. J. P. Taylor; "all they accomplished was that Haile Selassie lost all his country instead of only half." Collective security had failed its most important test.

Japan formed the third element in the threat to world peace. Militarists began to dominate the government in Tokyo by the mid-1930s, using tactics of fear and even assassination against their liberal opponents. By 1936, Japan had left the League of Nations and had repudiated the Washington treaties. A year later, its armies began an invasion of China that marked the beginning of the Pacific phase of World War II.

The resurgence of militarism in Germany, Italy, and Japan undermined the Versailles settlement and threatened to destroy the existing balance of power. In 1937, the three totalitarian nations signed an anti-Comintern pact completing a Berlin-Rome-Tokyo axis. Their alliance ostensibly was aimed at the Soviet Union, but in fact it threatened the entire world. Only a determined American response could unite the other nations against the Axis threat. Unfortunately, the United States deliberately abstained from assuming the role of leadership until it was nearly too late.

THE LURE OF PACIFISM AND NEUTRALITY

The growing danger of war abroad led to a rising American desire for peace and noninvolvement. Memories of World War I contributed heavily. Erich Maria Remarque's novel *All Quiet on the Western Front,* as well as the movie based on it, reminded people of the brutality of war. Historians began to treat the Great War as a mistake, criticizing Wilson for failing to preserve American neutrality and claiming the clever British had duped the United States into entering the war. Walter Millis advanced this thesis in *America's Road to War, 1914–1917,* published in 1935. It was hailed as a vivid description of the process by which "a peace-loving democracy, muddled but excited, misinformed and whipped to a frenzy, embarked upon its greatest foreign war."

The pacifism that swept college campuses in the 1930s touched students at the University of Chicago. The university undergraduates shown here hold placards bearing antiwar slogans as they wait to join a parade as part of a nationwide demonstration against war.

American youth made clear their determination not to repeat the mistakes of their elders. Pacifism swept across college campuses. A Brown University poll indicated 72 percent of the students opposed military service in wartime. At Princeton, undergraduates formed the Veterans of Future Wars, a parody on veterans' groups, to demand a bonus of $1000 apiece before they marched off to a foreign war.

The pacifist movement found a scapegoat in the munitions industry. The publication of several books exposing the unsavory business tactics of large arms dealers such as Krupp in Germany and Vickers in Britain led to a demand to curb these "merchants of death." Senator Gerald Nye of North Dakota headed a special Senate committee that spent two years investigating American munitions dealers. The committee revealed the enormous profits firms such as Du Pont reaped from World War I, but Nye went further, charging that bankers and munitions makers were responsible for American intervention in 1917. No proof was forthcoming, but the public—prepared to believe the worst of businessmen during the Depression—accepted the "merchants of death" thesis.

The Nye Committee's revelations culminated in neutrality legislation. In 1935, Senator Nye and another Senate colleague introduced measures to ban arms sales and loans to belligerents and to prevent Americans from traveling on belligerent ships. By outlawing the activities that led to World War I, they hoped, the United States could avoid involvement in the new conflict. This "never again" philosophy proved irresistible. In August 1935, Congress passed the first of three neutrality acts. The 1935 law banned the sale of arms to nations at war and warned American citizens not to sail on belligerent ships. In 1936, a second act added a ban on loans, and in 1937, a third neutrality act made these prohibitions permanent and required, on a two-year trial basis, that all trade other than munitions be conducted on a cash-and-carry basis.

President Roosevelt played a passive role in the adoption of the neutrality legislation. At first opposed to the arms embargo, he finally approved it for six months in 1935 in a compromise designed to save important New Deal legislation in Congress. Others in the administration criticized the mandatory nature of the new law, pointing out that it prevented the United States from distinguishing between aggressors and their victims. Privately, Roosevelt expressed some of the same reservations, but publicly he bowed to the prevailing isolationism. He signed the subsequent neutrality acts without protest, and during the 1936 election, he delivered an impassioned denunciation of war.

Yet FDR did take a few steps to try to limit the nation's retreat into isolationism. His failure to invoke the neutrality act after the Japanese invasion of China in 1937 enabled the hard-pressed Chinese to continue buying arms from the United States. FDR's strongest public statement came in Chicago in October 1937, when he denounced "the epidemic of world lawlessness" and called for an international effort to "quarantine" the disease. When reporters asked him if his call for "positive efforts to preserve peace" signaled a repeal of the neutrality acts, however, Roosevelt quickly reaffirmed this isolationist legislation. Whatever his private yearning for cooperation against aggressors, the president had no intention of challenging the prevailing public mood of the 1930s.

WAR IN EUROPE

The neutrality legislation played directly into the hands of Adolf Hitler. Bent on the conquest of Europe, he could now proceed without worrying about American interference. In March 1938, he seized Austria in a bloodless coup. Six months later, he was demanding the Sudetenland, a province of Czechoslovakia with a large German population. When the British and French leaders agreed to meet with Hitler at Munich, FDR voiced his approval. Roosevelt carefully kept the United States aloof from the subsequent surrender of the Sudetenland. At the same time, he gave his tacit approval of the Munich agreement.

Six months after the meeting at Munich, Hitler violated his promises by seizing nearly all of Czechoslovakia. In the United States, Roosevelt permitted the State Department to press for neutrality revision. The administration proposal to repeal the arms embargo and place *all* trade with belligerents, including munitions, on a cash-and-carry basis soon met stubborn resistance from isolationists. They argued that cash-and-carry would favor England and France, who controlled the sea. The House rejected the measure by a narrow margin, and the Senate's Foreign Relations Committee voted 12 to 11 to postpone any action on neutrality revision.

On September 1, 1939, Hitler began World War II by invading Poland. England and France responded two days later by declaring war, although there was no way they could prevent the German conquest of Poland. Russia had played a key role, refusing Western overtures for a common front against Germany and finally signing a nonaggression treaty with Hitler in late August. The Nazi-Soviet Pact enabled Germany to avoid a two-front war; the Russians were rewarded with a generous slice of eastern Poland.

President Roosevelt reacted to the outbreak of war by proclaiming American neutrality, but the successful aggression by Nazi Germany brought into question the isolationist assumption that American well-being did not depend on the European balance of power. Strategic as well as ideological considerations began to undermine the earlier belief that the United States could safely pursue a policy of neutrality and noninvolvement. The long retreat from responsibility was about to end as Americans came to realize that their own democracy and security were at stake in the European war.

Hitler sent his armies into Poland with tremendous force and firepower, devastating the country. When Jews, such as these residents of the Warsaw Ghetto, fell into the hands of the Nazi occupiers, they were deported to slave labor camps that soon became the sites of mass extermination.

THE ROAD TO WAR

For two years, the United States tried to remain at peace while war raged in Europe and Asia. In contrast to the climate of the country while Wilson attempted to be impartial during most of World War I, however, the American people displayed an overwhelming sympathy for the Allies and total distaste for Germany and Japan. Roosevelt made no secret of his preference for an Allied victory, but a fear of isolationist criticism compelled him to move slowly, and often deviously, in adopting a policy of aid for England and France.

FROM NEUTRALITY TO UNDECLARED WAR

Two weeks after the outbreak of war in Europe, Roosevelt called Congress into special session to revise the neutrality legislation. He wanted to repeal the arms embargo in order to supply weapons to England and France, but he refused to state this aim openly. Instead he asked Congress to replace the arms embargo with cash-and-carry regulations. Belligerents would be able to purchase war supplies in the United States, but they would have to pay cash and transport the goods in their own ships. Public opinion strongly supported the president, and

Congress passed the revised neutrality policy by heavy margins in early November 1939.

A series of dramatic German victories had a profound impact on American opinion. Quiet during the winter of 1939–1940, the Germans struck with lightning speed and devastating effect in the spring. In April, they seized Denmark and Norway, and on May 10, 1940, they unleashed the *blitzkrieg* (lightning war) on the western front. Within three weeks, the British were driven off the Continent. In another three weeks, France fell to Hitler's victorious armies.

Americans were stunned. Hitler had taken only six weeks to achieve what Germany had failed to do in four years of fighting in World War I. Suddenly they realized they did have a stake in the outcome; if England fell, Hitler might well gain control of the British navy. The Atlantic would no longer be a barrier; instead, it would be a highway for German penetration of the New World.

Roosevelt responded by invoking a policy of all-out aid to the Allies, short of war. In a speech at Charlottesville, Virginia, in June (just after Italy entered the war by invading France), he denounced Germany and Italy as representing "the gods of force and hate" and vowed, "The whole of our sympathies lies with those nations that are giving their life blood in combat against these forces." It was too late to help France, but in early September, FDR announced the transfer of fifty old destroyers to England in exchange for rights to build air and naval bases on eight British possessions in the Western Hemisphere.

Isolationists cried out against this departure from neutrality. A bold headline in the *St. Louis Post-Dispatch* read, "Dictator Roosevelt Commits Act of War." A group of Roosevelt's opponents in the Midwest formed the America First Committee to protest the drift toward war. Voicing belief in a "Fortress America," they denied that Hitler threatened American security and claimed that the nation had the strength to defend itself regardless of what happened in Europe.

To support the administration's policies, opponents of the isolationists organized the Committee to Defend America by Aiding the Allies. Eastern Anglophiles, moderate New Dealers, and liberal Republicans made up the bulk of the membership, with Kansas newspaper editor William Allen White serving as chairman. The White Committee, as it became known, advocated unlimited assistance to England short of war. Above all, the interventionists challenged the isolationist premise that events in Europe did not affect American security. "The future of western civilization is being decided upon the battlefield of Europe," White declared.

In the ensuing debate, the American people gradually came to agree with the interventionists. The battle of Britain helped. "Every time Hitler bombed London, we got a couple of votes," noted one interventionist. Frightened by the

THE ELECTION OF 1940

CANDIDATE	PARTY	POPULAR VOTE	ELECTORAL VOTE
Roosevelt	Democratic	27,263,448	449
Willkie	Republican	22,336,260	82

events in Europe, Congress approved large sums for preparedness, increasing the defense budget from $2 billion to $10 billion during 1940. Roosevelt courageously asked for a peacetime draft, the first in American history, to build up the army; in September, Congress agreed.

The sense of crisis affected domestic politics. Roosevelt ran for an unprecedented third term in 1940 because of the European war; the Republicans nominated Wendell Willkie, a former Democratic businessman who shared FDR's commitment to aid for England. Both candidates made appeals to peace sentiment during the campaign, but Roosevelt's decisive victory made it clear that the nation supported his increasing departure from neutrality.

After the election, FDR took his boldest step. Responding to British Prime Minister Winston Churchill's warning that England was running out of money, the president asked Congress to approve a new program to lend and lease goods and weapons to countries fighting against aggressors.

Isolationists angrily denounced Lend-Lease as both unnecessary and untruthful. "Lending war equipment is a good deal like lending chewing gum," commented Senator Taft. "You don't want it back." In March 1941, however, Congress voted by substantial margins to authorize the president to "sell, transfer title to, exchange, lease, lend, or otherwise dispose of" war supplies to "any country the President deems vital to the defense of the United States." The accompanying $7 billion appropriation ended the "cash" part of cash-and-carry and ensured Britain full access to American war supplies.

The "carry" problem still remained. German submarines were sinking more than 500,000 tons of shipping a month. England desperately needed the help of the American navy in escorting convoys across the U-boat–infested waters of the North Atlantic. Roosevelt, fearful of isolationist reaction, responded with naval patrols in the western half of the ocean. Hitler placed his submarine commanders under strict restraints to avoid drawing America into the European war.

Nevertheless, incidents were bound to occur. On October 17, 1941, a German submarine damaged the U.S. destroyer *Kearney;* ten days later, another U-boat sank the *Reuben James,* killing more than one hundred American sailors.

FDR issued orders for the destroyers to shoot U-boats on sight. He also asked Congress to repeal the "carry" section of the neutrality laws and permit American ships to deliver supplies to England. In mid-November, Congress approved these moves by slim margins. Now American merchant ships as well as destroyers would become targets for German attacks. By December, it seemed only a matter of weeks—or months at most—until repeated sinkings would lead to a formal declaration of war against Germany.

In leading the nation to the brink of war in Europe, Roosevelt opened himself to criticism from both sides in the domestic debate. Interventionists believed he had been too cautious in dealing with the danger to the nation from Nazi Germany. Isolationists were equally critical of the president, claiming he had misled the American people by professing peace while plotting for war. Roosevelt was certainly less than candid, relying on executive discretion to engage in highly provocative acts in the North Atlantic. He agreed with the interventionists that in the long run a German victory in Europe would threaten American security. But he also was aware that a poll taken in September 1941 showed nearly 80 percent of the American people wanted to stay out of World War II. Realizing that leading a divided nation into war would be disastrous, FDR played for time, inching the country toward war while waiting for the Axis nations to make the ultimate move. Japan finally obliged at Pearl Harbor.

SHOWDOWN IN THE PACIFIC

Japan had taken advantage of the war in Europe to expand farther in Asia. Although successful after 1937 in conquering the populous coastal areas of China, the Japanese had been unable to defeat Chiang Kai-shek, whose forces retreated into the vast interior of the country. The German defeat of France and the Netherlands in 1940, however, left their colonial possessions in the East Indies and Indochina vulnerable and defenseless. Japan now set out to incorporate these territories—rich in oil, tin, and rubber—into a Greater East Asia Co-Prosperity Sphere.

The Roosevelt administration countered with economic pressure. Japan depended heavily on the United States for petroleum and scrap metal. In July 1940, President Roosevelt signed an order setting up a licensing and quota system for the export of these crucial materials to Japan and banned the sale of aviation gasoline altogether.

Tokyo appeared to be unimpressed. In early September, Japanese troops occupied strategic bases in the northern part of French Indochina. Later in the month, Japan signed the Tripartite Pact with Germany and Italy, a defensive treaty that confronted the United States with a possible two-ocean war. The new Axis alignment confirmed American suspicions that Japan was part of a worldwide totalitarian threat. Roosevelt and his advisers, however, saw Germany as the primary danger; thus they pursued a policy of all-out aid to England while hoping that economic measures alone would deter Japan.

The embargo on aviation gasoline, extended to include scrap iron and steel in late September 1940, was a burden Japan could bear, but a possible ban on all oil shipments was a different matter. Japan lacked petroleum reserves of its own and was entirely dependent on imports from the United States and the Dutch East Indies. In an attempt to ease the economic pressure through negotiation, Japan sent a new envoy to Washington in the spring of 1941.

In July 1941, Japan invaded southern Indochina, beginning the chain of events that led to war. Washington knew of this aggression before it occurred. Naval intelligence experts had broken the Japanese diplomatic code and were intercepting and reading all messages between Tokyo and the Japanese embassy in Washington. President Roosevelt responded on July 25, 1941, with an order freezing all Japanese assets in the United States. Trade with Japan, including the vital oil shipments, came to a complete halt. When the Dutch government in exile took similar action, Japan faced a dilemma: in order to have oil shipments resumed, Tokyo would have to end its aggression; the alternative would be to seize the needed petroleum supplies in the Dutch East Indies, an action that would mean war.

After one final diplomatic effort failed, General Hideki Tojo, an army militant, became the new premier of Japan. To mask its war preparations, Tokyo sent yet another envoy to Washington with new peace proposals. Army and navy leaders urged President Roosevelt to seek at least a temporary settlement with Japan to give them time to prepare American defenses in the Pacific. Secretary of State Cordell Hull, however, refused to allow any concession; on November 26, he sent a stiff ten-point reply to Tokyo that included a demand for Japanese withdrawal from China.

The Japanese response came two weeks later. On the evening of December 6, 1941, the first thirteen parts of the reply to Hull's note arrived in Washington, with the fourteenth part to follow the next morning. Naval intelligence actually decoded the message faster than the Japanese embassy clerks. A messenger delivered the text to President Roosevelt late that night; after glancing at it, he commented, "This means war." The next day, December 7, the fourteenth part arrived, revealing that Japan totally rejected the American position.

Officials in Washington immediately sent warning messages to American bases in the Pacific, but they failed to arrive in time. At 7:55 in the morning, just before 1 P.M. in Washington, squadrons of Japanese carrier-based planes caught the American fleet at Pearl Harbor totally by surprise. In little more than an hour,

American ships were destroyed in the surprise attack on Pearl Harbor, December 7, 1941. Caught completely off guard, U.S. forces still managed to shoot down twenty-nine enemy planes.

they crippled the American Pacific fleet and its major base, sinking eight battleships and killing more than twenty-four hundred American sailors.

Speaking before Congress the next day, President Roosevelt termed December 7 "a date which will live in infamy" and asked for a declaration of war on Japan. With only one dissenting vote, both branches passed the measure. On December 11, Germany and Italy declared war against the United States; the nation was now fully involved in World War II.

The whole country united behind Roosevelt's leadership to seek revenge for Pearl Harbor and to defeat the Axis threat to American security. After the war, however, critics charged that FDR had entered the conflict by a back door, claiming the president had deliberately exposed the Pacific fleet to attack. Subsequent investigations uncovered negligence in both Hawaii and Washington but no evidence to support the conspiracy charge. Commanders in Hawaii, like most military experts, believed the Japanese would not launch an attack on a base four thousand miles from Japan. FDR, like too many Americans, had badly underestimated the daring and skill of the Japanese; he and the nation alike paid a heavy price for this cultural and racial prejudice. But there was no plot. Roosevelt could not have known that Hitler, so restrained in the Atlantic, would reverse his policy and foolishly declare war against the United States after Pearl Harbor. Perhaps the most frightening aspect of the whole episode is that it took the shock of the Japanese sneak attack to make the American people aware of the extent of the Axis threat to their well-being and lead them to end the long American retreat from responsibility.

Turning the Tide Against the Axis

In the first few months after the United States entered the war, the outlook for victory was bleak. In Europe, Hitler's armies controlled virtually the entire continent, from Norway in the north to Greece in the south. Despite the nonaggression pact, German armies had penetrated deep into Russia after an initial invasion in June 1941. Although they had failed to capture either Moscow or Leningrad, the Nazi forces had conquered the Ukraine and by the spring of 1942 were threatening to sweep across the Volga River and seize vital oil fields in the Caucasus. In North Africa, General Erwin Rommel's Afrika Korps had pushed the British back into Egypt and threatened the Suez Canal (see the map on p. 896).

The situation was no better in Asia. The Pearl Harbor attack had enabled the Japanese to move unopposed across Southeast Asia. Within three months, they had conquered Malaya and the Dutch East Indies, with its valuable oil fields, and were pressing the British back both in Burma and New Guinea. American forces under General Douglas MacArthur had tried vainly to block the Japanese conquest of the Philippines. MacArthur finally escaped by torpedo boat to Australia; the American garrison at Corregidor surrendered after a long siege, the survivors then enduring the cruel death march across the Bataan peninsula. With the American navy still recovering from the devastation at Pearl Harbor, Japan controlled the western half of the Pacific (see the map on p. 885).

Over the next two years, the United States and its allies would finally halt the German and Japanese offensives in Europe and Asia. But then they faced the difficult process of driving back the enemy, freeing the vast conquered areas, and finally defeating the Axis powers on their home territory. It would be a difficult and costly struggle that would require great sacrifice and heavy losses; World War II would test American will and resourcefulness to the utmost.

WARTIME PARTNERSHIPS

The greatest single advantage that the United States and its partners possessed was their willingness to form a genuine coalition to bring about the defeat of the Axis powers. Although there were many strains within the wartime alliance, it did permit a high degree of coordination. In striking contrast was the behavior of Germany and Japan, each fighting a separate war without any attempt at cooperation.

The United States and Britain achieved a complete wartime partnership. The close cooperation between President Roosevelt and Prime Minister Churchill ensured a common strategy. The leaders decided at the outset that a German victory posed the greater danger and thus gave priority to the European theater in the conduct of the war. In a series of meetings in December 1941, Roosevelt and Churchill signed a Declaration of the United Nations, eventually subscribed to by twenty-six countries, that pledged them to fight together until the Axis powers were defeated.

Relations with the other members of the United Nations coalition in World War II were not quite so harmonious. The decision to defeat Germany first displeased the Chinese, who had been at war with Japan since 1937. France posed a more delicate problem. FDR virtually ignored the Free French government in exile under General Charles de Gaulle; Roosevelt preferred to deal with the Vichy regime.

The greatest strain of all within the wartime coalition was with the Soviet Union. Although Roosevelt had ended the long period of nonrecognition in 1933, close ties had failed to develop. The great Russian purge trials and the temporary Nazi-Soviet alliance from 1939 to 1941, along with deep-seated cultural and ideological differences, made wartime cooperation difficult.

Ever the pragmatist, Roosevelt tried hard to break down the old hostility and establish a more cordial relationship with Russia during the war. Even before Pearl Harbor, he extended Lend-Lease aid to Russia, and after American entry into the war, this economic assistance grew rapidly, limited only by the difficulty of delivering the supplies. Eager to keep Russia in the war, the president promised a visiting Russian diplomat in May 1942 that the United States would create a second front in Europe by the end of that year—a pledge he could not fulfill. In January 1943, Roosevelt and Churchill met in Casablanca, Morocco, where they declared a policy of unconditional surrender, vowing that the Allies would fight until the Axis nations were completely defeated.

Despite these promises, the Soviet Union bore the brunt of battle against Hitler in the early years of the war, fighting alone against more than two hundred German divisions. The United States and England, grateful for the respite to build up their forces, could do little more than offer promises of future help and send Lend-Lease supplies. The result was a rift that never fully healed—one that did not prevent the defeat of Germany but did ensure future tensions and uncertainties between the Soviet Union and the Western nations.

HALTING THE GERMAN BLITZ

From the outset, the United States favored an invasion across the English Channel. Army planners, led by Chief of Staff George C. Marshall and his protégé, Dwight D. Eisenhower, were convinced such a frontal assault would be the quickest way to win the war. Roosevelt concurred, in part because it fulfilled his second-front commitment to the Soviets.

The initial plan, drawn up by Eisenhower, called for a full-scale invasion of Europe in the spring of 1943. Marshall surprised everyone by placing Eisenhower, until then a relatively junior general, in charge of implementing the plan.

But the British, remembering the heavy casualties of trench warfare in World War I, preferred a perimeter approach, with air and naval attacks around the edge of the Continent until Germany was softened up for the final invasion. British strategists assented to the basic plan but strongly urged a preliminary invasion of North Africa in the fall of 1942. Roosevelt agreed and American and British troops landed on the Atlantic and Mediterranean coasts of Morocco and Algeria in November 1942.

The British launched an attack against Rommel at El Alamein in Egypt and soon forced the Afrika Korps to retreat across Libya to Tunisia. Eisenhower, despite initial setbacks, advanced from Algeria, and by May 1943, Germany had been driven from Africa, leaving behind nearly 300,000 troops.

During these same months, the Soviet Union's Red Army had broken the back of German military power in the battle of Stalingrad. Turned back at the critical bend in the Volga, Hitler had poured in division after division in what was ultimately a losing cause; never again would Germany be able to take the offensive in Europe.

At Churchill's insistence, FDR agreed to follow up the North African victory with the invasion first of Sicily and then Italy in the summer of 1943. Italy dropped out of the war when Mussolini fled to Germany, but the Italian campaign proved to be a strategic dead end.

More important, these Mediterranean operations delayed the second front, postponing it eventually to the spring of 1944. Meanwhile, the Soviets began to push the Germans out of Russia and looked forward to the liberation of Poland, Hungary, and Romania, where they could establish "friendly" communist regimes. Having borne the brunt of the fighting against Nazi Germany, Russia was ready to claim its reward—the postwar domination of eastern Europe.

CHECKING JAPAN IN THE PACIFIC

Both the decision to defeat Germany first and the vast expanses of the Pacific dictated the nature of the war against Japan. The United States conducted amphibious island-hopping campaigns rather than attempting to reconquer the Dutch East Indies, Southeast Asia, and China. There would be two separate American operations. One, led by Douglas MacArthur based in Australia, would move from New Guinea back to the Philippines, while the other, commanded by Admiral Chester Nimitz from Hawaii, was directed at key Japanese islands in the Central Pacific.

World War II in the Pacific

The tide of battle turned in the Pacific the same year as in Europe. The balance of sea power shifted back to the United States from Japan after the naval victories of 1942.

Success in the Pacific depended above all else on control of the sea. The devastation at Pearl Harbor gave Japan the initial edge, but fortunately, the United States had not lost any of its four aircraft carriers. The turning point came in June 1942 at Midway. A powerful Japanese task force threatened to seize this remote American outpost more than a thousand miles west of Pearl Harbor; Japan's real objective was the destruction of what remained of the American Pacific fleet. Superior American airpower enabled Nimitz's forces to engage the enemy at long range. The battle of Midway ended with the loss of four Japanese aircraft carriers compared to just one American carrier. It was the first defeat the modern Japanese navy had ever suffered, and it left the United States in control of the Central Pacific.

Encouraged by the victory, American forces launched their first Pacific offensive in the Solomon Islands, east of New Guinea, in August 1942. Both sides suffered heavy losses, but six months later the last Japanese were driven from the key island of Guadalcanal. At the same time, MacArthur began the long, slow, and bloody job of driving the Japanese back along the north coast of New Guinea.

By early 1943, the defensive phase of the war with Japan was over. The enemy surge had been halted in both the central and the southwestern Pacific, and the United States was preparing to penetrate the Gilbert, Marshall, and Caroline Islands and recapture the Philippines. Just as Russia had broken German power in Europe, so the United States, fighting alone except for Australia and New Zealand, had halted the Japanese. And, like the USSR with its plans for eastern Europe, America expected to reap the rewards of victory by dominating the Pacific in the future.

THE HOME FRONT

World War II had a greater impact than the Depression on the future of American life. While American soldiers and sailors fought abroad, the nation underwent sweeping social and economic changes at home.

American industry made the nation's single most important contribution to victory. Even though more than fifteen million Americans served in the armed forces, it was the nearly sixty million who worked on farms and factories who achieved the miracle of production that ensured the defeat of Germany and Japan. The manufacturing plants that had run at half capacity through the 1930s now hummed with activity. In Detroit, automobile assembly lines were converted to produce tanks and airplanes. Henry J. Kaiser, a California industrialist, constructed huge West Coast shipyards to meet the demand for cargo vessels and

American war production was twice that of all the Axis countries. Here, Boeing aircraft workers celebrate the completion of their five thousandth bomber.

landing craft. His plant in Richmond, California, reduced the time to build a merchant ship from 105 to 14 days. In part, America won the battle of the Atlantic by building ships faster than German U-boats could sink them.

This vast industrial expansion, however, created many problems. In 1942, President Roosevelt appointed Donald Nelson, a Sears, Roebuck executive, to head a War Production Board (WPB). A jovial, easygoing man, Nelson soon was outmaneuvered by the army and the navy, which preferred to negotiate directly with large corporations. Shortages of critical materials such as steel, aluminum, and copper led to an allocation system based on military priorities. Rubber, cut off by the Japanese conquest of Southeast Asia, was particularly scarce; the administration finally began gasoline rationing in 1943 to curb pleasure driving and prolong tire life.

Roosevelt revealed the same tendency toward compromise in directing the economic mobilization as he did in shaping the New Deal. When the Office of Price Administration—which tried to curb inflation by controlling prices and rationing scarce goods such as sugar, canned food, and shoes—clashed with the

WPB, FDR appointed James Byrnes to head an Office of Economic Stabilization. Byrnes, a former South Carolina senator and Supreme Court justice, used political judgment to settle disputes between agencies and keep all groups happy.

A result of the wartime economic explosion was a growing affluence. Despite the federal incentives to business, heavy excess-profit taxes and a 94 percent tax rate for the very rich kept the wealthy from benefiting unduly. The huge increase in federal spending, from $9 billion in 1940 to $98 billion in 1944, spread through American society. A government agreement with labor unions in 1943 held wage rates to a 15 percent increase, but the long hours of overtime resulted in doubling and sometimes tripling the weekly paychecks of factory workers. Farmers shared in the new prosperity as their incomes quadrupled between 1940 and 1945. For the first time in the twentieth century, the lowest fifth of wage earners increased their share of the national income in relation to the more affluent; their income rose by 68 percent between 1941 and 1945, compared to a 20 percent increase for the well-to-do. Most important, this rising income ensured postwar prosperity. Workers and farmers saved their money, channeling much of it into government war bonds, waiting for the day when they could buy the cars and home appliances they had done without during the long years of depression and war.

A NATION ON THE MOVE

The war led to a vast migration of the American population. Young men left their homes for training camps and then for service overseas. Defense workers and their families, some nine million people in all, moved to work in the new booming shipyards, munitions factories, and aircraft plants. Rural areas lost population while coastal regions, especially along the Pacific and the Gulf of Mexico, drew millions of people. The location of army camps in the South and West created boom conditions in the future Sunbelt, as did the concentration of aircraft factories and shipyards in this region. California had the greatest gains, adding nearly two million to its population in less than five years.

This movement of people caused severe social problems. Housing was in short supply. Migrating workers crowded into house trailers and boardinghouses, bringing unexpected windfalls to landlords. In one boomtown, a reporter described an old Victorian house that had five bedrooms on the second floor. "Three of them," he wrote, "held two cots apiece, the two others held three cots." But the owner revealed that "the third floor is where we pick up the velvet. . . . We rent to workers in different shifts . . . three shifts a day . . . seven bucks a week apiece."

Family life suffered under these crowded living conditions. An increase in the number of marriages, as young people searched for something to hang on to in the midst of wartime turmoil, was offset by a rising divorce rate. The baby boom

As men left for military service in World War II and U.S. industry expanded to keep up with defense needs, millions of women joined the paid labor force. By 1944, the peak year for female wartime employment, women made up 36 percent of the American workforce. Women took jobs that before the war had been done by men, such as riveting, welding, and operating heavy equipment. "Rosie the Riveter," a popular song of the era, celebrated women's new role in the labor force.

that would peak in the 1950s began during the war and brought its own set of problems. Only a few publicly funded day-care centers were available, and working mothers worried about their "latchkey children."

Despite these problems, women found the war a time of economic opportunity. The demand for workers led to a dramatic rise in women's employment, from fourteen million working women in 1940 to nineteen million by 1945. Most of the new women workers were married and many were middle-aged, thus broadening the composition of the female workforce, which in the past had been composed primarily of young single women. Women entered industries once viewed as exclusively male; by the end of the war, they worked alongside men tending blast furnaces in steel mills and welding hulls in shipyards. Women enjoyed the hefty weekly paychecks, which rose by 50 percent from 1941 to 1943, and they took pride in their contributions to the war effort. "To hell with the life I have had," commented a former fashion designer. "This war is too damn serious, and it is too damn important to win it."

African Americans shared in the wartime migration, but racial prejudice limited their social and economic gains. Nearly one million served in the armed forces, but relatively few saw combat. The army placed black soldiers in segregated units, usually led by white officers, and used them for service and construction tasks. The navy was even worse, relegating them to menial jobs until late in the war. African Americans were denied the chance to become petty officers, Secretary of the Navy Frank Knox explained, because experience had shown that "men of the colored race . . . cannot maintain discipline among men of the white race."

African American civilians fared a little better. In 1941, black labor leader A. Philip Randolph threatened a massive march on Washington to force President Roosevelt to end racial discrimination in defense industries and government employment and to integrate the armed forces. FDR compromised, persuading Randolph to call off the march and drop his integration demand in return for an executive order creating a Fair Employment Practices Committee (FEPC) to ban racial discrimination in war industries. As a result, African American employment by the federal government rose from 60,000 in 1941 to 200,000 by the end of the war. The FEPC proved less successful in the private sector. The nationwide shortage of labor was more influential than the FEPC in accounting for the rise in black employment during wartime. African Americans moved from the rural South to northern and western cities, finding jobs in the automobile, aircraft, and shipbuilding industries.

The movement of an estimated 700,000 people helped transform black-white relations from a regional issue into a national concern that could no longer be ignored. The limited housing and recreational facilities for both black and white war workers created tensions that led to race riots in Detroit and New York City.

These outbursts of racial violence fueled the resentments that would grow into the postwar civil rights movement. For most African Americans, despite economic gains, World War II was a reminder of the inequality of American life. "Just carve on my tombstone," remarked one black soldier in the Pacific, "'Here lies a black man killed fighting a yellow man for the protection of a white man.'"

One-third of a million Mexican Americans served in the armed forces and shared some of the same experiences as African Americans. Although they were not as completely segregated, many served in the 88th Division, made up largely of Mexican American officers and troops, which earned the nickname "Blue Devils" in the Italian campaign. At home, Spanish-speaking people left the rural areas of Texas, New Mexico, and California for jobs in the cities, especially in aircraft plants and petroleum refineries. Despite low wages and union resistance, they improved their economic position substantially. But they still faced discrimination based both on skin color and language. The racial prejudice heightened feelings of ethnic identity and led returning Mexican American veterans to form organizations such as the American G.I. Forum to press for equal rights in the future.

A tragic counterpoint to the voluntary movement of American workers in search of jobs was the forced relocation of 120,000 Japanese Americans from the

A mother and son, interned at a temporary relocation camp, pose with a picture of her older son wearing his U.S. Army uniform. Japanese Americans living on the West Coast were first ordered to large assembly centers such as the racetrack at Santa Anita, California. There whole families were assigned to individual horse stalls while they awaited relocation to one of the internment camps located in isolated areas of California, Arizona, Idaho, Utah, Colorado, Wyoming, and Arkansas. Conditions in the camps were equally dismal. Whole families lived in a single room furnished with little more than a few cots, some blankets, and a single light bulb.

West Coast. Responding to racial fears in California after Pearl Harbor, President Roosevelt approved an army order in February 1942 to move all Japanese Americans on the West Coast to concentration camps in the interior. More than two-thirds of those detained were *Nisei,* native-born Americans whose only crime was their Japanese ancestry. Forced to sell their farms and businesses at distress prices, the Japanese Americans lost not only their liberty but also most of their worldly goods. Herded into ten hastily built detention centers in seven western and southern states, they lived as prisoners in tar-papered barracks behind barbed wire, guarded by armed troops.

Appeals to the Supreme Court proved fruitless; in 1944, six justices upheld relocation on grounds of national security in wartime. Beginning in 1943, individual Nisei could win release by pledging their loyalty and finding a job away from the West Coast. Some thirty-five thousand left the camps during the next two years, including more than thirteen thousand who joined the armed forces. The all-Nisei 442nd Combat Team served gallantly in the European theater, losing more than five hundred men in battle and winning more than a thousand citations for bravery.

For other Nisei, the experience was bitter. More than five thousand re-nounced their American citizenship and chose to live in Japan at the war's end. Japanese Americans never experienced the torture and mass death of the German concentration camps, but their treatment was a disgrace to a nation fighting for freedom and democracy. Finally, in 1988, Congress voted an in-demnity of $1.2 billion for the estimated sixty thousand surviving Japanese Americans detained during World War II. Susumi Emori, who had been moved with his wife and four children from his farm in Stockton, California, to a camp in Arkansas, felt vindicated. "It was terrible," he said, with tears in his eyes, "but it was a time of war. Anything can happen. I didn't blame the United States for that."

WIN-THE-WAR POLITICS

Franklin Roosevelt used World War II to strengthen his leadership and maintain Democratic political dominance. As war brought about prosperity and removed the economic discontent that had sustained the New Deal, FDR announced that "Dr. New Deal" had given way to "Dr. Win-the-War." Congress, already con-trolled by a conservative coalition of southern Democrats and northern Republicans, had almost slipped into GOP hands in 1942. With a very low voter turnout, the Republicans won forty-four new seats in the House and nine in the Senate and elected governors in New York and California as well.

In 1944, Roosevelt responded to the Democratic slippage by dropping Henry Wallace, his liberal and visionary vice president, for Harry Truman, a moderate and down-to-earth Missouri senator who was acceptable to all factions of the Democratic party. Equally important, FDR received increased political support from organized labor, which had grown in membership during the war from ten to fifteen million.

The Republicans nominated Thomas E. Dewey, who had been elected gover-nor of New York after gaining fame as a prosecutor of organized crime. Dewey, moderate in his views, played down opposition to the New Deal and instead tried to make Roosevelt's age and health the primary issues, along with the charge that the Democrats were soft on communism.

Despite his abrasive campaign style, Dewey did not advocate a return to iso-lationism. The Republican party was trying hard to shake the obstructionist im-age it had gained during the League of Nations fight in 1919; it went on record in 1943 as favoring American postwar cooperation for world peace. Indeed, Dewey pioneered a bipartisan approach to foreign policy. He accepted wartime planning for the future United Nations and kept the issue of an international organization out of the campaign.

THE ELECTION OF 1944

CANDIDATE	PARTY	POPULAR VOTE	ELECTORAL VOTE
Roosevelt	Democrat	25,611,936	432
Dewey	Republican	22,013,372	99

Reacting to the issues of his age and health, especially after a long bout with influenza in the spring, FDR took a five-hour drive in an open car through the rain-soaked streets of New York City just before the election. His vitality impressed the voters, and in November 1944 he swept back into office for a fourth term, although the margin of 3.6 million votes was his smallest yet. The campaign, however, had taken its toll. The president, suffering from high blood pressure and congestive heart failure, had only a few months left to lead the nation.

VICTORY

World War II ended with surprising swiftness. By 1943, the Axis tide had been turned in Europe and Asia, and it did not take long for Russia, the United States, and England to mount the offensives that drove Germany and Japan back across the vast areas they had conquered and set the stage for their final defeat.

The long-awaited second front finally came on June 6, 1944. For two years, the United States and England concentrated on building up an invasion force of nearly three million troops and a vast armada of ships and landing craft to carry them across the English Channel. In hopes of catching Hitler by surprise, Eisenhower chose the Normandy peninsula, where the absence of good harbors had led to lighter German fortifications.

D-Day was originally set for June 5, but bad weather forced a delay. Relying on a forecasted break in the storm, Eisenhower gambled on going ahead on June 6. During the night, three divisions parachuted down behind the German defenses; at dawn, the British and American troops fought their way ashore at five points along a sixty-mile stretch of beach, encountering stiff German resistance at several points. By the end of the day, however, Eisenhower had won his beachhead; a week later, more than one-third of a million men were slowly pushing back the German forces through the hedgerows of Normandy. The breakthrough came on July 25 when General Omar Bradley decimated the enemy with a massive artillery and aerial bombardment at Saint-Lô, opening a gap for General George Patton's Third Army. American tanks raced across the French countryside, trapping thousands of Germans and liberating Paris by August 25. Allied troops reached the Rhine River by September, but a shortage of supplies, especially gasoline, forced a three-month halt.

Hitler took advantage of this breathing spell to deliver a daring counterattack. In mid-December, the remaining German armored divisions burst through a weak point in the Allied lines in the Ardennes Forest, planning a breakout to the coast that would have cut off nearly one-third of Eisenhower's forces. But an airborne division dug in at the key crossroads of Bastogne, in Belgium, and held off a much larger German force. Allied reinforcements and clearing weather then combined to end the attack. By committing nearly all his reserves to the Battle of the Bulge, Hitler had delayed Eisenhower's advance into Germany, but he also had fatally weakened German resistance in the west.

The end came quickly. A massive Russian offensive began in mid-January and swept across the Oder River toward Berlin. General Bradley's troops, finding a bridge left virtually intact by the retreating Germans, crossed the Rhine on March 7. The Allied forces advanced on a broad front, capturing the industrial Ruhr basin and meeting the Russians at the Elbe by the last week in April. With the Red Army already in the suburbs of Berlin, Adolf Hitler committed suicide on April 30. A week later, on May 7, 1945, Eisenhower accepted the unconditional surrender of all German forces. Just eleven months and a day after the landings in Normandy, the Allied forces had brought the war in Europe to a successful conclusion.

After they entered Germany, American troops found horrifying evidence of the holocaust—Hitler's eradication of six million European Jews. American soldiers were shocked at the conditions within the German concentration camps—lethal gas chambers, huge ovens for cremation, bodies stacked like cords of wood, and most vivid of all, the emaciated, skeleton-like survivors with their blank stares. One battle-hardened veteran commented on the scene at Nordhausen, where his unit had found 3,000 dead and only 700 survivors:

> The odors, well there is no way to describe the odors . . . . Many of the boys I am talking about now—these were tough soldiers, there were combat men who had been all the way through the invasion—were ill and vomiting, throwing up, just at the sight of this.

These awful discoveries removed any doubt in the minds of the American people about the evil nature of the Nazi regime they had just helped to destroy.

Victims at the Bergen-Belsen concentration camp were buried in a mass grave. The camp was liberated by the Allies on April 14, 1945, less than a month before Germany's surrender.

WAR AIMS AND WARTIME DIPLOMACY

The American contribution to Hitler's defeat was relatively minor compared to the damage inflicted by the Soviet Union. At the height of the German invasion of Russia, more than 300 Soviet divisions had been locked in battle with 250 German ones, a striking contrast to the 58 divisions the United States and Britain used in the Normandy invasion. As his armies overran Poland and the Balkan countries, Joseph Stalin was determined to retain control over this region, which had been the historic pathway for Western invasion into Russia. Delay in opening the second front and an innate distrust of the West convinced the Soviets that they should maximize their territorial gains by imposing communist regimes on eastern Europe.

American postwar goals were quite different. Now believing the failure to join the League of Nations in 1919 had led to the coming of World War II, the American people and their leaders vowed to put their faith in a new attempt at collective security. At Moscow in 1943, Secretary of State Cordell Hull had won Russian agreement to participate in a future world organization at the war's end.

World War II in Europe and North Africa

The tide of battle shifted in this theater during the winter of 1942–1943. The massive German assault on the eastern front was turned back by the Russians at Stalingrad, and the Allied forces recaptured North Africa.

The first wartime Big Three conference brought together Roosevelt, Churchill, and Stalin at Teheran, Iran, in late 1943. Stalin reaffirmed this commitment and also indicated to President Roosevelt that Russia would enter the war against Japan once Germany was defeated.

By the time the Big Three met again at Yalta, in February 1945, the military situation favored the Russians. Stalin drove a series of hard bargains. He refused to give up his plans for communist domination of Poland and the Balkans, although he did agree to Roosevelt's request for a Declaration of Liberated Europe, which called for free elections without providing for any method of enforcement or supervision. More important for the United States, Stalin promised to enter the Pacific war three months after Germany surrendered. In return,

The nation's grief at FDR's death is mirrored in the face of this serviceman as the president's funeral cortege passes.

Roosevelt offered extensive concessions in Asia, including Russian control over Manchuria. While neither a sellout nor a betrayal, as some critics have charged, Yalta was a significant diplomatic victory for the Soviets—one that reflected Russia's major contribution to a victory in Europe.

For the president, the long journey to Yalta proved to be too much. His health continued to fail after his return to Washington. In early April, FDR left the capital for Warm Springs, Georgia, where he had always been able to relax. He was sitting for his portrait at midday on April 12, 1945, when he suddenly complained of a "terrific headache," then slumped forward and died.

The nation mourned a man who had gallantly met the challenge of depression and global war. Unfortunately, FDR had taken no steps to prepare his successor for the difficult problems that lay ahead. The defeat of Nazi Germany dissolved the one strong bond between the United States and the Soviet Union. With very different histories, cultures, and ideologies, the two nations were bound to drift apart. It was now up to the inexperienced Harry Truman to manage the growing rivalry that was destined to develop into the future Cold War.

TRIUMPH AND TRAGEDY IN THE PACIFIC

The total defeat of Germany in May 1945 turned all eyes toward Japan. Although the combined chiefs of staff had originally estimated it would take eighteen months after Germany's surrender to conquer Japan, American forces moved with surprising speed. Admiral Nimitz swept through the Gilbert, Caroline, and Marshall Islands in 1944, while General MacArthur cleared New Guinea of the last Japanese defender and began planning his long-heralded return to the Philippines. American troops landed on the island of Leyte on October 20, 1944, and Manila fell in early February 1945. The Japanese navy launched a daring three-pronged attack on the American invasion fleet in Leyte Gulf. The U.S. Navy rallied to blunt all three Japanese thrusts, sinking four carriers and ending any further Japanese naval threat.

The defeat of Japan was now only a matter of time. The United States had three possible ways to proceed. The military favored a full-scale invasion, beginning on the southernmost island of Kyushu in November 1945 and culminating with an assault on Honshu (the main island of Japan) and a climatic battle for Tokyo in 1946; casualties were expected to run into the hundreds of thousands. Diplomats suggested a negotiated peace, urging the United States to modify the unconditional surrender formula to permit Japan to retain the institution of the emperor.

The third possibility involved the highly secret Manhattan Project. Since 1939, the United States had spent $2 billion to develop an atomic bomb based on the fission of radioactive uranium and plutonium. Scientists, many of them refugees from Europe, worked to perfect this deadly new weapon at the University of Chicago; Oak Ridge, Tennessee; Hanford, Washington; and a remote laboratory in Los Alamos, New Mexico. In the New Mexico desert on July 16, 1945, they successfully tested the first atomic bomb.

Truman had been unaware of the existence of the Manhattan Project before he became president on April 12. Now he simply followed the recommendation of a committee headed by Secretary of War Henry L. Stimson to drop the bomb on a Japanese city. Neither Truman nor Stimson had any qualms about the decision to drop the bomb without warning. They viewed it as a legitimate wartime measure, one designed to save the lives of hundreds of thousands of Americans—and Japanese—that would be lost in a full-scale invasion.

Weather conditions on the morning of August 6 dictated the choice of Hiroshima as the bomb's target. The explosion incinerated 4 square miles of the city, instantly killing more than sixty thousand. Two days later, Russia entered the war against Japan, and the next day, August 9, the United States dropped a second bomb on Nagasaki. The emperor personally broke a deadlock in the Japanese cabinet and persuaded his ministers to surrender unconditionally on August 14, 1945. Three weeks later, Japan signed a formal capitulation agreement on the decks of the battleship *Missouri* in Tokyo Bay to bring World War II to its official close.

The atomic bomb dropped on Nagasaki, a provincial capital and naval base in southern Japan, on August 9, 1945, virtually obliterated the city and killed about 40,000 people. Only buildings made with reinforced concrete remained standing after the blast.

Many years later, scholars charged that Truman had more in mind than defeating Japan when he decided to use the atomic bomb. Citing air force and naval officers who claimed Japan could be defeated by a blockade or by conventional air attacks, these revisionists suggested the real reason for dropping the bomb was to impress the Soviet Union with the fact that the United States had exclusive possession of the ultimate weapon. The available evidence indicates that while Truman and his associates were aware of the possible effect on the Soviet Union, their primary motive was to end World War II as quickly and effortlessly as possible. The saving of American lives, along with a desire for revenge for Pearl Harbor, were uppermost in the decision to bomb Hiroshima and Nagasaki. Yet in using the atomic bomb to defeat Japan, the United States virtually guaranteed a postwar arms race with the Soviet Union.

The second great war of the twentieth century has had a lasting impact on American life. For the first time, the nation's military potential had been reached. In 1945, the United States was unquestionably the strongest country on the earth, with eleven million men and women in uniform; a vast array of shipyards, aircraft plants, and munitions factories in full production; and a monopoly over the atomic bomb. For better or worse, the nation was now launched on a global career. In the future, the United States would be involved in all parts of the world, from western Europe to remote jungles in Asia, from the nearby Caribbean to the distant Persian Gulf. And despite its enormous strength in 1945, the nation's new world role would encompass failure and frustration as well as power and dominion.

The legacy of war was equally strong at home. Four years of fighting brought about industrial recovery and unparalleled prosperity. The old pattern of unregulated free enterprise was as much a victim of the war as of the New Deal; big government and huge deficits had now become the norm as economic control passed from New York and Wall Street to Washington and Pennsylvania Avenue. The war led to far-reaching changes in American society that would become apparent only decades later. Such distinctive patterns of recent American life as the baby boom and the growth of the Sunbelt can be traced back to wartime origins. World War II was a watershed in twentieth-century America, ushering in a new age of global concerns and domestic upheaval.

28

THE ONSET OF THE COLD WAR

"I am getting ready to go see Stalin and Churchill," President Truman wrote to his mother in July 1945, "and it is a chore." On board the cruiser *Augusta,* the new president continued to complain about the upcoming Potsdam conference in his diary. "How I hate this trip!" he confided. "But I have to make it win, lose, or draw and we must win. I am giving nothing away except to save starving people and even then I hope we can only help them to help themselves."

Halfway around the world, Joseph Stalin left Moscow a day late because of a slight heart attack. The Russian leader hated to fly, so he traveled by rail. Moreover, he ordered the heavily guarded train to detour around Poland for fear of an ambush, further delaying his arrival. When he made his entrance into Potsdam, a suburb of Berlin miraculously spared the total destruction that his forces had created in the German capital, he was ready to claim the spoils of war.

These two men, one the veteran revolutionary who had been in power for two decades, the other an untested leader in office for barely three months, symbolized the enormous differences that now separated the wartime allies. Stalin was above all a realist. Brutal in securing total control at home, he was more flexible in his foreign policy, bent on exploiting Russia's victory in World War II rather than aiming at world domination. Cunning and caution were the hallmarks of his diplomatic style. Small in stature, ungainly in build, he radiated a catlike quality as he waited behind his unassuming facade, ready to dazzle an opponent with his "brilliant, terrifying tactical mastery." Truman, in contrast, personified traditional Wilsonian idealism. Lacking Roosevelt's guile, the new president placed his faith in international cooperation. Like many Americans, he believed implicitly in his country's innate goodness. Self-assured to the point of cockiness, he came to Potsdam clothed in the armor of self-righteousness.

Truman and Stalin met for the first time on July 17, 1945. "I told Stalin that I am no diplomat," the president recorded in his diary, "but usually said yes and no to questions after hearing all the argument." The Russian dictator's reaction to Truman remains a mystery, but Truman believed the first encounter went well. "I can deal with Stalin," he wrote. "He is honest—but smart as hell."

Together with Winston Churchill and his replacement, Clement Attlee, whose Labour party had just triumphed in British elections, Truman and Stalin clashed for the next ten days over such difficult issues as reparations, the Polish border, and the fate of eastern Europe. Truman presented the ideas and proposals formulated by his advisers; he saw his task as essentially procedural, and when he presided, he moved the agenda along in brisk fashion. In an indirect, roundabout way, he informed Stalin of the existence of the atomic bomb, tested successfully in the New Mexico desert just before the conference began. Truman offered no details, and the impassive Stalin asked for none, commenting only that he hoped the United States would make "good use of it against the Japanese."

Reparations proved to be the crucial issue at Potsdam. The Russians wanted to rebuild their war-ravaged economy with German industry; the United States feared it would be saddled with the entire cost of caring for the defeated Germans. A compromise was finally reached. Each side would take reparations primarily from its own occupation zone, a solution that foreshadowed the future division of Germany. "Because they could not agree on how to govern Europe," wrote historian Daniel Yergin, "Truman and Stalin began to divide it." The other issues were referred to the newly created Council of Foreign Ministers, which would meet in the fall in London.

The conference thus ended on an apparent note of harmony; beneath the surface, however, the bitter antagonism of the Cold War was festering. America and Russia, each distrustful of the other, were preparing for a long and bitter confrontation. A dozen years later, Truman reminisced to an old associate about Potsdam. "What a show that was!" Describing himself as "an innocent idealist" surrounded by wolves, he claimed that all the agreements reached there were "broken as soon as the unconscionable Russian Dictator returned to Moscow!" He added ruefully, "And I liked the little son of a bitch."

THE COLD WAR BEGINS

The conflict between the United States and the Soviet Union began gradually. For two years, the nations tried to adjust their differences over the division of

Europe, postwar economic aid, and the atomic bomb through discussion and negotiation. The Council of Foreign Ministers provided the forum. Beginning in London during the fall of 1945 and meeting with their Russian counterparts in Paris, New York, and Moscow, American diplomats searched for a way to live in peace with a suspicious Soviet Union.

THE DIVISION OF EUROPE

The fundamental disagreement was over who would control postwar Europe. In the east, the Red Army had swept over Poland and the Balkans, laying the basis for Soviet domination there. American and British forces had liberated western Europe from Scandinavia to Italy. The Russians, mindful of past invasions from the west across the plains of Poland, were intent on imposing communist governments loyal to Moscow in the Soviet sphere. The United States, on the other hand, upheld the principle of national self-determination, insisting the people in each country should freely choose their postwar rulers. The Soviets saw the demand for free elections as subversive, since they knew that popularly chosen regimes would be unfriendly to Russia. Suspecting American duplicity, Stalin brought down an "Iron Curtain" (Churchill's phrase) from the Baltic to the Adriatic as he created a series of satellite governments.

Germany was the key. The temporary zones of occupation gradually hardened into permanent lines of division. Ignoring the Potsdam Conference agreement that the country be treated as an economic unit, the United States and Great Britain were by 1946 refusing to permit the Russians to take reparations from the industrial western zones. The initial harsh occupation policy gave way to more humane treatment of the German people and a slow but steady economic recovery. The United States and England merged their zones and championed the idea of the unification of all Germany. Russia, fearing a resurgence of German military power, responded by intensifying the communization of its zone, which included the jointly occupied city of Berlin.

The Soviet Union consolidated its grip on eastern Europe in 1946 and 1947. One by one, communist regimes replaced coalition governments in Poland, Hungary, Romania, and Bulgaria. Moving cautiously to avoid provoking the West, Stalin used communism as a means to dominate half of Europe, both to protect the security of the Soviet state and to advance its international power. The climax came in March 1948 when a coup in Czechoslovakia overthrew a democratic government and gave the Soviets a strategic foothold in central Europe.

The division of Europe was an inevitable aftereffect of World War II. Both sides were intent on imposing their values in the areas liberated by their troops. A frank recognition of competing spheres of influence might have avoided further escalation of tension. But the Western nations, remembering Hitler's aggression

Europe After World War II

The heavy line splitting Germany shows in graphic form the division of Europe between the Western and Soviet spheres of influence. "From Stettin in the Baltic to Trieste in the Adriatic," said Churchill in a speech at Fulton, Missouri, in 1946, "an iron curtain has descended across the Continent."

in the 1930s, began to see Stalin as an equally dangerous threat to their well-being. Instead of accepting him as a cautious leader bent on protecting Russian security, they perceived him as an aggressive dictator leading a communist drive for world domination.

WITHHOLDING ECONOMIC AID

World War II had inflicted enormous damage on Russia. The brutal fighting had taken between fifteen and twenty million Russian lives, destroyed more than thirty thousand factories, and torn up forty thousand miles of railroad track. The industrialization that Stalin had achieved at such great sacrifice in the 1930s had been badly set back; even agricultural production had fallen by half during the war. Outside aid and assistance were vital for the reconstruction of the Soviet Union.

American leaders knew of Russia's plight and hoped to use it to good advantage. President Truman was convinced that economically "we held all the cards and the Russians had to come to us."

There were two possible forms of postwar assistance: loans and Lend-Lease. In January 1945, the Soviets requested a $6 billion loan to finance postwar reconstruction. Despite initial American encouragement, President Roosevelt deferred action on this request; as relations with Russia cooled, the chances for action dimmed. By the war's end, the loan request, though never formally turned down, was dead.

Lend-Lease proved no more successful. In the spring of 1945, Congress instructed the administration not to use Lend-Lease for postwar reconstruction. President Truman went further, however, by signing an order on May 11, 1945, terminating all shipments to Russia, including those already at sea. Heeding Russian protests, Truman resumed Lend-Lease shipments, but only until the war was over in August. After that, all Lend-Lease ended.

Deprived of American assistance, the Russians were forced to rebuild their economy through reparations. The Soviets systematically removed factories and plants from areas they controlled, including their zone of Germany, eastern Europe, and Manchuria. Slowly, the Russian economy recovered from the war, but the bitterness over the American refusal to extend aid convinced Stalin of Western hostility and thus deepened the growing antagonism between the Soviet Union and the United States.

THE ATOMIC DILEMMA

Overshadowing all else was the atomic bomb. Used by the United States with deadly success at Hiroshima and Nagasaki, the new weapon raised problems that would have been difficult for even friendly nations to resolve. Given the uneasy state of Soviet-American relations, the effect was disastrous.

The wartime policy followed by Roosevelt and Churchill ensured a postwar nuclear arms race. Instead of informing their major ally of the developing atomic bomb, they kept it a closely guarded secret. Stalin learned of the Manhattan Project through espionage and responded by starting a Soviet atomic program in 1943. By the time Truman informed Stalin of the weapon's existence at Potsdam, the Russians, aided by a steady stream of information from spies in the United States, were well on the way to making their own bomb.

After the war, the United States developed a disarmament plan that would turn control of fissionable material, then the processing plants, and ultimately the American stockpile of bombs over to an international agency. When President Truman appointed financier Bernard Baruch to present this proposal to the United Nations, Baruch insisted on changing it in several important ways, adding sanctions against violators and exempting the international agency from the UN veto. Ignoring scientists who pleaded for a more cooperative position, Baruch argued that "we cannot at this time limit our capability to produce or use this weapon." In effect, the Baruch Plan, with its multiple stages and emphasis on inspection, would preserve the American atomic monopoly for the indefinite future.

The Soviets responded predictably. Diplomat Andrei Gromyko presented a simple plan calling for a total ban on the production and use of the new weapon as well as the destruction of all existing bombs. The Russian proposal was founded on the same perception of national self-interest as the Baruch Plan. Russia still had nearly three million men under arms in 1947 and wanted to use its conventional strength to the utmost by outlawing the atomic bomb.

No agreement was possible. Neither the United States nor the Soviet Union could abandon its position without surrendering a vital national interest. Wanting to preserve its monopoly, America stressed inspection and control; hoping to neutralize the U.S. advantage, Russia advocated immediate disarmament. The nuclear dilemma, inherent in the Soviet-American rivalry, blocked any national settlement. Instead, the two superpowers agreed to disagree. Trusting neither each other nor any form of international cooperation, each concentrated on taking maximum advantage of its wartime gains. Thus the Russians exploited the territory they had conquered in Europe while the United States retained its economic and strategic advantages over the Soviet Union. The result was the Cold War.

CONTAINMENT

A major departure in American foreign policy occurred in January 1947, when General George C. Marshall, the wartime army chief of staff, became secretary of state. Calm, mature, and orderly of mind, Marshall had the capability—honed in World War II—to think in broad strategic terms. An extraordinarily good judge of ability, he relied on gifted subordinates to handle the day-to-day implementation of his policies. In the months after taking office, he came to rely on two men in particular: Dean Acheson and George Kennan.

Acheson, an experienced Washington lawyer and bureaucrat, was appointed undersecretary of state and given free rein by Marshall to conduct American diplomacy. A man of keen intelligence, he had a carefully cultivated reputation for arrogance and a low tolerance for mediocrity. As an ardent Anglophile, he wanted to see the United States take over a faltering Britain's role as the supreme arbiter of world affairs. Recalling the lesson of Munich, he opposed appeasement and advocated a policy of negotiating only from strength.

George Kennan, Marshall's other mainstay, headed the newly created Policy Planning Staff. A career foreign service officer, Kennan had become a Soviet expert, mastering Russian history and culture as well as speaking the language fluently. He served in Moscow after U.S. recognition in 1933 and again during World War II, developing there a profound distrust for the Soviet regime. In a crucial telegram in 1946, he advocated a policy of containment, arguing that only strong and sustained resistance could halt the outward flow of Russian power. As self-assured as Acheson, Kennan believed that neither Congress nor public opinion should interfere with the conduct of foreign policy by the experts.

In the spring of 1947, a sense of crisis impelled Marshall, Acheson, and Kennan to set out on a new course in American diplomacy. Dubbed "containment," after an article by Kennan in *Foreign Affairs,* the new policy both consolidated the evolving postwar anticommunism and established guidelines that would shape America's role in the world for more than two decades. What Kennan proposed was "a long-term, patient but firm, and vigilant containment of Russian expansive tendencies." Such a policy of halting Soviet aggression would not lead to any immediate victory, Kennan warned. In the long run, however, he believed that the United States could force the Soviet Union to adopt more reasonable policies and live in peace with the West.

THE TRUMAN DOCTRINE

The initial step toward containment came in response to an urgent British request. Since March 1946, England had been supporting the Greek government in a bitter civil war against communist guerrillas. On February 21, 1947, the British informed the United States that they could no longer afford to aid Greece or Turkey, the latter under heavy pressure from the Soviets for access to the Mediterranean. Believing the Russians responsible for the strife in Greece (in fact, they were not), Marshall, Acheson, and Kennan quickly decided the United States would have to assume Britain's role in the eastern Mediterranean.

Worried about congressional support, especially since the Republicans had gained control of Congress in 1946, Marshall called a meeting with the legislative leadership in late February. He outlined the problem; then Acheson took over to warn that "a highly possible Soviet breakthrough might open three continents to Soviet penetration." Claiming that the Soviets were "playing one of the greatest gambles in history," Acheson concluded that "we and we alone were in a position to break up the play."

The bipartisan group of congressional leaders was deeply impressed. Finally, Republican Senator Arthur M. Vandenberg spoke up, saying he would support the president, but adding that to ensure public backing, Truman would have to "scare hell" out of the American people.

The president followed the senator's advice. On March 12, 1947, he asked Congress for $400 million for military and economic assistance to Greece and Turkey. In stating what would become known as the Truman Doctrine, he made clear that more was involved than just these two countries—the stakes in fact were far higher. "It must be the policy of the United States," Truman told the Congress, "to support free peoples who are resisting attempted subjugation by armed minorities or by outside pressure." After a brief debate, both the House and the Senate approved the program by margins of better than three to one.

The Truman Doctrine marked an informal declaration of cold war against the Soviet Union. Truman used the crisis in Greece to secure congressional approval and build a national consensus for the policy of containment. In less than two years, the civil war in Greece ended, but the American commitment to oppose communist expansion, whether by internal subversion or external aggression, placed the United States on a collision course with the Soviet Union around the globe.

THE MARSHALL PLAN

Despite American interest in controlling Soviet expansion into Greece, western Europe was far more vital to U.S. interests than was the eastern Mediterranean. Yet by 1947, many Americans believed that western Europe was open to Soviet penetration. The problem was economic in nature. Despite $9 billion in piece-meal American loans, England, France, Italy, and the other European countries had great difficulty in recovering from World War II. Food was scarce, with millions existing on less than fifteen hundred calories a day; industrial machinery was broken down and obsolete; and workers were demoralized by years of depression and war. Resentment and discontent led to growing communist voting strength, especially in Italy and France. If the United States could not reverse the process, it seemed as though all Europe might drift into the communist orbit.

In the weeks following proclamation of the Truman Doctrine, American officials dealt with this problem. Secretary of State Marshall, returning from a frustrating Council of Foreign Ministers meeting in Moscow, warned that "the patient is sinking while the doctors deliberate." The experts drew up a plan for the massive infusion of American capital to finance the economic recovery of Europe. Speaking at a Harvard commencement on June 5, 1947, Marshall presented the broad outline. He offered extensive economic aid to all the nations of Europe if they could reach agreement on ways to achieve "the revival of a working economy in the world so as to permit the emergence of political and social conditions in which free institutions can exist."

The fate of the Marshall Plan depended on the reaction of the Soviet Union and the U.S. Congress. Marshall had taken, in the words of one American diplomat, "a hell of a gamble" by including Russia in his offer of aid. At a meeting of the European nations in Paris in July 1947, the Soviet foreign minister ended the suspense by abruptly withdrawing. Neither the Soviet Union nor its satellites would take part. The other European countries then made a formal request for $17 billion in assistance over the next four years.

Congress responded cautiously to the proposal, appointing a special joint committee to investigate. The administration lobbied vigorously, pointing out that the Marshall Plan would help the United States by stimulating trade with Europe as well as checking Soviet expansion. It was the latter argument, however, that proved decisive. When the Czech coup touched off a war scare in March 1948, Congress quickly approved the Marshall Plan by heavy majorities. Over the next four years, the huge American investment paid rich dividends, generating a broad industrial revival in western Europe that became self-sustaining by the 1950s. The threat of communist domination faded, and a prosperous Europe proved to be a bonanza for American farmers, miners, and manufacturers.

THE WESTERN MILITARY ALLIANCE

The third and final phase of containment came in 1949 with the establishment of the North Atlantic Treaty Organization (NATO). NATO grew out of European fears of Russian military aggression. Recalling Hitler's tactics in the 1930s, the people of western Europe wanted assurance that the United States would protect them from attack as they began to achieve economic recovery.

England, France, and the Low Countries (Belgium, the Netherlands, and Luxembourg) began the process in March 1948 when they signed the Brussels Treaty, providing for collective self-defense. In January 1949, President Truman

The Soviet view of the Cold War, as depicted in this Soviet cartoon, shows the United States stretching out long arms to take hold of Korea, Iran, Turkey, Taiwan, and Vietnam.

called for a broader defense pact including the United States; ten European nations, from Norway in the north to Italy in the south, joined the United States and Canada in signing the North Atlantic Treaty in Washington on April 4, 1949. This historic departure from the traditional policy of isolation caused extensive debate, but the Senate ratified it in July by a vote of 82 to 13.

There were two main features of NATO. First, the United States committed itself to the defense of Europe in the key clause, which stated that "an armed attack against one or more shall be considered an attack against them all." In effect, the United States was extending its atomic shield over Europe. The second feature was designed to reassure worried Europeans that the United States would honor this commitment. In late 1950, President Truman authorized the stationing of four American divisions in Europe to serve as the nucleus of the NATO army. It was believed that the threat of American troop involvement in any Russian assault would deter the Soviet Union from making such an attack.

The Western military alliance escalated the developing Cold War. Whatever its advantage in building a sense of security among worried Europeans, it represented an overreaction to the Soviet danger. Americans and Europeans alike were attempting to apply the lesson of Munich to the Cold War. But Stalin was not Hitler, and the Soviets were not the Nazis. There was no evidence of any Russian plan to invade western Europe, and in the face of the American atomic bomb, none was likely. NATO only intensified Russian fears of the West and thus increased the level of international tension.

THE BERLIN BLOCKADE

The main Russian response to containment came in 1948 at the West's most vulnerable point. American, British, French, and Soviet troops each occupied a sector of Berlin, but the city was located more than a hundred miles within the Russian zone of Germany (see the map of postwar Europe on p. 904). Stalin decided to test his opponents' resolve by cutting off all rail and highway traffic to Berlin on June 20, 1948.

The timing was very awkward for Harry Truman. He had his hands full resisting efforts to force him off the Democratic ticket, and he faced a difficult reelection effort against a strong Republican candidate, Governor Thomas E. Dewey of New York. Immersed in election-year politics, Truman was caught unprepared by the Berlin blockade. The alternatives were not very appealing. The United States could withdraw its forces and lose not just a city, but the confidence of all Europe; it could try to send in reinforcements and fight for Berlin; or it could sit tight and attempt to find a diplomatic solution. Truman made the basic decision in characteristic fashion, telling the military that there would be no thought of pulling out. "We were going to stay, period," an aide reported Truman as saying.

In the next few weeks, the president and his advisers adopted a two-phase policy. The first part was a massive airlift of food, fuel, and supplies for the ten thousand troops and the two million civilians in Berlin. A fleet of fifty-two C-54s and eighty C-47s began making two daily round-trip flights to Berlin, carrying 2500 tons every twenty-four hours. Then, to guard against Soviet interruption of the airlift, Truman transferred sixty American B-29s, planes capable of delivering atomic bombs, to bases in England. The president was bluffing; the B-29s were not equipped with atomic bombs, but at the time, the threat was effective.

For a few weeks, the world teetered on the edge of war. Stalin did not attempt to disrupt the flights to Berlin, but he rejected all American diplomatic initiatives. Although at any time the Russians could have halted it by jamming

The Berlin airlift of 1948–1949 broke the Soviet blockade. Called Operation Vittles, it provided food and fuel for West Berliners. Here children wait for the candy that American pilots dropped in tiny handkerchief parachutes.

radar or shooting down the defenseless cargo planes, the airlift gradually increased to more than 4000 tons a day. Governor Dewey patriotically supported the president's policy, thus removing foreign policy from the presidential campaign.

Slowly, the tension eased. The Russians did not shoot down any planes, and the daily airlift climbed to nearly 7000 tons. Truman, a decided underdog, won a surprising second term in November over a complacent Dewey, in part because the Berlin crisis had rallied the nation behind his leadership. In early 1949, the Soviets gave in, ending the blockade in return for another meeting of the Council of Foreign Ministers on Germany—a conclave that proved as unproductive as all the earlier ones.

The Berlin crisis marked the end of the initial phase of the Cold War. The airlift had given the United States a striking political victory, showing the world the triumph of American ingenuity over Russian stubbornness. Yet it could not disguise the fact that the Cold War had cut Europe in two. Behind the Iron Curtain, the Russians had consolidated control over the areas won by their troops in the war, while the United States had used the Marshall Plan to revitalize western Europe. But a divided continent was a far cry from the wartime hopes for a peaceful world. And the rivalry that began in Europe would soon spread into a worldwide contest between the superpowers.

THE COLD WAR EXPANDS

The rivalry between the United States and the Soviet Union grew in the late 1940s and early 1950s. Both sides began to rebuild their military forces with new methods and new weapons. Equally significant, the diplomatic competition spread from Europe to Asia as each of the superpowers sought to enhance its influence in the Far East. By the time Truman left office in early 1953, the Cold War had taken on global proportions.

THE MILITARY DIMENSION

After World War II, American leaders were intent on reforming the nation's military system in light of their wartime experience. Two goals were uppermost. First, nearly everyone agreed in the aftermath of Pearl Harbor that the U.S. armed services should be unified into an integrated military system. The developing Cold War reinforced this decision. Equally important, planners realized, was the need for new institutions to coordinate military and diplomatic strategy so the nation could cope effectively with threats to its security.

In 1947, Congress passed the National Security Act. It established a Department of Defense, headed by a civilian secretary of cabinet rank presiding over three separate services—the army, the navy, and the new air force. In addition, the act created the Central Intelligence Agency (CIA) to coordinate the intelligence-gathering activities of various government agencies. Finally, the act provided for a National Security Council (NSC)—composed of the service secretaries, the secretary of defense, and the secretary of state—to advise the president on all matters regarding the nation's security.

Despite the appearance of equality among the services, the air force quickly emerged as the dominant power in the atomic age, based on its capability both to deter an enemy from attacking and to wage war if deterrence failed. President Truman, intent on cutting back defense expenditures, favored the air force in his 1949 military budget, allotting this branch more than one-half the total sum. After the Czech coup and the resulting war scare, Congress granted an additional $3 billion to the military.

American military planners received even greater support in the fall of 1949 when the Soviet Union exploded its first atomic bomb. President Truman appointed a high-level committee to explore mounting an all-out effort to build a hydrogen bomb to maintain American nuclear supremacy.

Some scientists had technical objections to the H-bomb, which was still far from being perfected, while others opposed the new weapon on moral grounds, claiming that its enormous destructive power (intended to be one thousand times greater than the atomic bomb) made it unthinkable. Dean Acheson—who succeeded Marshall as secretary of state in early 1949—believed it was imperative that the United States develop the hydrogen bomb before the Soviet Union. When Acheson presented the committee's favorable report to the president in January 1950, Truman took only seven minutes to decide to go ahead with the awesome new weapon.

At the same time, Acheson ordered the Policy Planning Staff to draw up a new statement of national defense policy. NSC-68, as the document eventually became known, was based on the premise that the Soviet Union sought "to impose its absolute authority over the rest of the world." Rejecting such options as appeasement or a return to isolation, NSC-68 called for a massive expansion of American military power so the United States could halt and overcome the Soviet threat and proposed an increase in defense spending from $13 to $45 billion annually. Approved in principle by the National Security Council in April 1950, NSC-68 stood as a symbol of the Truman administration's determination to win the Cold War regardless of cost.

THE COLD WAR IN ASIA

The Soviet-American conflict developed more slowly in Asia. At Yalta, the two superpowers had agreed to a Far Eastern balance of power, with the Russians dominating Northeast Asia and the Americans in control of the Pacific, including both Japan and its former island empire.

The United States moved quickly to consolidate its sphere of influence. General Douglas MacArthur, in charge of Japanese occupation, denied the Soviet Union any role in the reconstruction of Japan. Instead, he supervised the transition of the Japanese government into a constitutional democracy, shaped along Western lines, in which communists were barred from all government posts. The Japanese willingly renounced war in their new constitution, relying instead on American forces to protect their security. American policy was equally nationalistic in the Pacific. A trusteeship arrangement with the United Nations merely disguised the fact that the United States held full control over the Marshall, Mariana, and Caroline Islands.

As defined at Yalta, China lay between the Soviet and American spheres. When World War II ended, the country was torn between Chiang Kai-shek's Nationalists in the South and Mao Tse-tung's Communists in the North. Chiang had many advantages, including American political and economic backing and official Soviet recognition. But corruption was widespread among the Nationalist leaders, and a raging inflation that soon reached 100 percent a year devastated the Chinese middle classes and thus eroded Chiang's base of power. Mao used tight discipline and patriotic appeals to strengthen his hold on the peasantry and extend his influence. When the Soviets abruptly vacated Manchuria in 1946, after stripping it of virtually all the industrial machinery Japan had installed, Mao inherited control of this rich northern province. Ignoring American advice, Chiang rushed north to occupy Manchurian cities, overextending his supply lines and exposing his forces to Communist counterattack.

American policy sought to prevent a Chinese civil war. Before he became secretary of state, George Marshall undertook the difficult task of forming a coalition government between Chiang and Mao. There was no basis for compromise. Chiang insisted he "was going to liquidate Communists," while Mao was trying to play the United States against Russia in his bid for power. By 1947, as China plunged into full-scale civil war, the Truman administration had given up any meaningful effort to influence the outcome. Political mediation had failed, military intervention was out of the question so soon after World War II, and a policy of continued American economic aid served only to appease domestic supporters of Chiang Kai-shek; 80 percent of the military supplies ended up in Communist hands.

The Chinese conflict climaxed at the end of the decade. Mao's forces drove the Nationalists out of Manchuria in late 1948 and advanced across the Yangtze by mid-1949. Acheson released a lengthy report justifying American policy in China on the grounds that the civil war there "was beyond the control of the government of the United States." Republican senators, however, disagreed, blaming American diplomats for sabotaging the Nationalists and terming Acheson's report "a 1054-page white-wash of a wishful, do-nothing policy." While the domestic debate raged over responsibility for the loss of China, Chiang's forces fled the mainland for sanctuary on Formosa (Taiwan) in December 1949. Two months later, Mao and Stalin signed a Sino-Soviet treaty of mutual assistance that clearly placed China in the Russian orbit.

The American response to the Communist triumph in China was twofold. First, the State Department refused to recognize the legitimacy of the new regime in Peking, maintaining instead formal diplomatic relations with the Nationalists on Formosa. Citing the Sino-Soviet alliance, Assistant Secretary of State Dean Rusk called the Peking regime "a colonial Russian government." Then, to compensate for the loss of China, the United States focused on Japan as its main ally in Asia. The State Department encouraged the buildup of Japanese industry, and the Pentagon expanded American bases on the Japanese home islands and Okinawa. A Japanese-American security pact led to the end of American occupation by 1952. The Cold War had now split Asia in two.

THE KOREAN WAR

The showdown between the United States and the Soviet Union in Asia came in Korea. Traditionally the cockpit of international rivalry in Northeast Asia, Korea had been divided at the 38th parallel in 1945. The Russians occupied the industrial North, installing a communist government under the leadership of Kim Il-Sung. In the agrarian South, Syngman Rhee, a conservative nationalist, emerged as the American-sponsored ruler. Neither regime heeded a UN call for elections to unify the country. The two superpowers pulled out most of their occupation forces by 1949. The Russians, however, helped train a well-equipped army in the North, while the United States—fearful Rhee would seek unification through armed conquest—gave much more limited military assistance to South Korea.

On June 25, 1950, the North Korean army suddenly crossed the 38th parallel in great strength. We now know that Stalin had approved this act of aggression in advance. In January 1950, the Soviet leader had told Mao Tse-tung that he was ready to overthrow the Yalta settlement in the Far East ("and to hell with it," he exclaimed to Mao). In April, when Kim Il-Sung came to Moscow to gain approval for the assault on South Korea, Stalin gave it willingly, apparently in the belief that the United States was ready to abandon Syngman Rhee. Despite expressing some reservations, Mao also approved the planned North Korean aggression.

Both Stalin and Mao had badly miscalculated the American response. President Truman saw the invasion as a clear-cut case of Soviet aggression reminiscent of the 1930s. "Communism was acting in Korea just as Hitler, Mussolini,

The Korean War, 1950–1953

After a year of rapid movement up and down the Korean peninsula, the fighting stalled just north of the 38th parallel. The resulting truce line has divided North and South Korea since the July 1953 armistice.

Map labels:
CHINA
SOVIET UNION
Farthest UN advance Nov. 1950
Yalu R.
Sea of Japan
NORTH KOREA
Pyongyang
Truce Line 1953
Panmunjom
38th Parallel
Inchon Landing Sept. 15, 1950
Seoul
SOUTH KOREA
Pusan Perimeter Farthest North Korean advance Sept. 1950
Yellow Sea
Pusan

0   75   150 miles
0   75   150 kilometers

International boundaries, 1950
North Korean invasion, June–Sept. 1950
UN offensive, Sept.–Nov. 1950
Communist Chinese offensive, Nov. 1950–Jan. 1951

and the Japanese had acted ten, fifteen, and twenty years earlier," he commented in his memoirs. Following Acheson's advice, the president convened the UN Security Council and, taking advantage of a temporary Soviet boycott, secured a resolution condemning North Korea as an aggressor and calling on the member nations to engage in a collective security action. Within a few days, American troops from Japan were in combat in South Korea. The conflict, which would last for more than three years, was technically a police action fought under UN auspices; in reality, the United States was at war with a Soviet satellite in Asia.

In the beginning, the fighting went badly as the North Koreans continued to drive down the peninsula. But by August, American forces had halted the communist advance near Pusan. In September, General MacArthur changed the whole complexion of the war by carrying out a brilliant amphibious assault at

Douglas MacArthur, supreme commander of UN forces in Korea, launched the invasion at Inchon in September 1950 and within a few days recaptured Seoul, the South Korean capital.

Inchon, on the waist of Korea, cutting off and destroying most of the North Korean army in the South. Encouraged by this victory, Truman began to shift from his original goal of restoring the 38th parallel to a new one: the unification of Korea by military force.

The administration ignored warnings from Peking against an American invasion of North Korea. "I should think it would be sheer madness for the Chinese to intervene," commented Acheson. MacArthur was even more confident. "We are no longer fearful of their intervention," he told Truman at a Wake Island conference in mid-October.

Rarely has an American president received worse advice than Truman did from Acheson and MacArthur. The UN forces crossed the 38th parallel in October, advanced confidently to the Yalu in November, and then were completely routed by a massive Chinese counterattack that drove them out of all North Korea by December. MacArthur finally stabilized the fighting near the

38th parallel, but when Truman decided to give up his attempt to unify Korea, the general protested to Congress, calling for a renewed offensive and proclaiming, "There is no substitute for victory."

Truman courageously relieved the popular hero of the Pacific of his command on April 11, 1951. At first, MacArthur seemed likely to force the president to back down. Huge crowds came forward to welcome him home and hear him call for victory over the communists in Asia. At a special congressional hearing, the administration struck back effectively by warning that MacArthur's strategy would expose all Europe to Soviet attack. General Omar Bradley, Truman's chief military adviser, succinctly pointed out that a "showdown" with communism in Asia would be "the wrong war, at the wrong place, at the wrong time, and with the wrong enemy."

Congress and the American people came to accept MacArthur's recall. The Korean War settled into a stalemate near the 38th parallel as truce talks with the communists bogged down for the rest of Truman's term in office. The president could take heart from the fact that he had achieved his primary goal, defense of South Korea and the principle of collective security. Yet by taking the gamble to unify Korea by force, he had confused the American people and humiliated the United States in the eyes of the world.

In the last analysis, the most significant result of the Korean conflict was the massive American rearmament it brought about. The army expanded to 3.5 million troops, the defense budget increased to $50 billion a year by 1952, and the United States acquired distant military bases from Saudi Arabia to Morocco. America was now committed to waging a global contest against the Soviet Union with arms as well as words.

THE COLD WAR AT HOME

The Cold War cast a long shadow over American life in the late 1940s and early 1950s. Truman tried to carry on the New Deal reform tradition he had inherited from FDR, but the American people were more concerned about events abroad. The Republican party used both growing dissatisfaction with postwar economic adjustment and fears of communist penetration of the United States to revive its sagging fortunes and regain control of the White House in 1952 for the first time in twenty years.

TRUMAN'S TROUBLES

Matching his foreign policy successes with equal achievements at home was not easy for Harry S Truman. As a loyal supporter of Franklin D. Roosevelt's

New Deal programs during his Senate career, Truman had earned a reputation for being a hardworking, reliable, and intensely partisan legislator. But he was relatively unknown to the general public, and his background as a Missouri county official associated with Kansas City machine politics did little to inspire confidence in his ability to lead the nation. Surprisingly well-read—especially in history and biography—Truman possessed sound judgment, the ability to reach decisions quickly, and a fierce and uncompromising sense of right and wrong.

Two weaknesses marred his performance in the White House. One was a fondness for old friends, which resulted in the appointment of many Missouri and Senate cronies to high office. The president's other serious limitation was his lack of political vision. Failing to pursue a coherent legislative program of his own, he tried to perpetuate FDR's New Deal and, as a result, engaged in a running battle with Congress.

The postwar mood was not conducive to an extension of New Deal reforms. Americans were weary of shortages and sacrifices; they wanted the chance to buy the consumer goods denied them under wartime conditions. But in the rush to convert industry from producing planes and tanks to cars and appliances, problems soon emerged. Prices and wages rose quickly as Congress voted to end wartime controls. With prices going up 25 percent in two years, workers demanded higher wages to offset the loss of overtime pay. A wave of labor unrest swept over the country in the spring of 1946.

President Truman was caught in the middle. Sensitive to union demands, he permitted businesses to negotiate large pay increases for their workers and then pass on the cost to consumers in the form of higher prices. He criticized Congress for weakening wartime price controls, but he failed to offer anything else to curb inflation.

In the face of rising discontent, Truman's efforts to extend the New Deal met with little success. The only measure Congress passed was the Employment Act of 1946. This legislation created the Council of Economic Advisers to assist the president and asserted the principle that the government was responsible for the state of the economy, but it failed to address Truman's original goal of mandatory federal planning to achieve full employment.

The Republicans took advantage of increasing public dissatisfaction with postwar economic woes to attack the Democrats. "To err is Truman," the GOP proclaimed and then adopted a very effective two-word slogan for the 1946 congressional elections: "Had enough?" The American people, weary of inflation and labor unrest, responded by electing Republican majorities in both the House and Senate for the first time since 1930.

THE ELECTION OF 1948

CANDIDATE	PARTY	POPULAR VOTE	ELECTORAL VOTE
Truman	Democratic	24,105,182	303
Dewey	Republican	21,970,065	189
Thurmond	States' Rights	1,169,063	39
	Minor Parties	442,667	—

TRUMAN VINDICATED

The president's relations with Congress became even stormier after the 1946 election. Truman successfully vetoed two GOP measures to give large tax cuts to the wealthy, but Congress overrode his veto of the Taft-Hartley Act in 1947. Designed to correct the imbalance in labor-management relations created by the Wagner Act, the Taft-Hartley Act outlawed specific labor union activities—including the closed shop and secondary boycotts. Despite Truman's claim that it was a "slave-labor" bill, unions were able to survive its provisions.

President Truman's political fortunes reached their lowest ebb in early 1948. Former vice president Henry A. Wallace, claiming to represent the New Deal, announced his third-party (Progressive) candidacy in the presidential contest that year. The Democrats reluctantly nominated Truman. His prospects for victory in the fall, however, looked very dim—especially after disgruntled Southerners bolted the Democratic party in protest over a progressive civil rights platform. The Dixiecrats, as they became known, nominated Strom Thurmond, the governor of South Carolina, on a States' Rights party ticket.

The defection of the Dixiecrats in the South and Wallace's liberal followers in the North led political experts to predict an almost certain Republican victory. Governor Thomas E. Dewey of New York, the GOP candidate, was so certain of winning that he waged a cautious and bland campaign designed to give him a free hand once he was in the White House. With nothing to lose, Truman barnstormed around the country denouncing the "do-nothing" Republican Eightieth Congress. To the amazement of the pollsters, Truman won a narrow but decisive victory in November. The old Roosevelt coalition—farmers, organized labor, urban ethnic groups, and blacks—had held together, enabling Truman to remain in the White House and the Democrats to regain control of Congress.

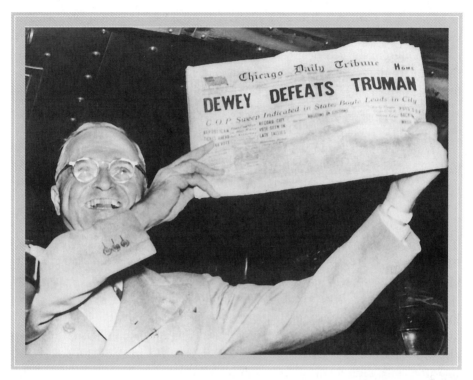

A jubilant Harry Truman, on the morning after his 1948 election win, displays the headline blazoned on the front page of the Chicago Daily Tribune—*a newspaper that believed the pollsters.*

There was one more reason for Truman's win in 1948. During this election, held at the height of the Berlin crisis, the GOP failed to challenge Truman's conduct of the Cold War. Locked in a tense rivalry with the Soviet Union, the American people saw no reason to reject a president who had countered aggression overseas with the Truman Doctrine and the Marshall Plan. The Republicans, committed to support the bipartisan policy of containment, had allowed the Democrats to preempt the foreign policy issue. Until they found a way to challenge Truman's Cold War policies, GOP leaders had little chance to regain the White House.

THE LOYALTY ISSUE

Despite Truman's surprising victory in 1948, there was one area on which the Democrats were vulnerable. The fear of communism abroad that had led to the bipartisan containment policy could be used against them at home by politicians who were more willing to exploit the public's deep-seated anxiety.

Fear of radicalism had been a recurrent feature of American life since the early days of the republic. The Cold War heightened the traditional belief that subversion from abroad endangered the republic. Bold rhetoric from members of the Truman administration, portraying the men in the Kremlin as inspired revolutionaries bent on world conquest, frightened the American people. They viewed the Soviet Union as a successor to Nazi Germany—a totalitarian police state that threatened the basic liberties of a free people.

A series of revelations of communist espionage activities reinforced these fears. Canadian officials uncovered a Soviet spy ring in 1946, and the House Un-American Activities Committee held hearings indicating that communist agents had flourished in the Agriculture and Treasury departments in the 1930s.

Although Truman tried to dismiss the loyalty issue as a "red herring," he felt compelled to take protective measures, thus lending substance to the charges of subversion. In March 1947, he had initiated a loyalty program, ordering security checks of government employees in order to root out communists. Originally intended to remove subversives for whom "reasonable grounds exist for belief that the person involved is disloyal," within four years the Loyalty Review Board was dismissing workers as security risks if there was "reasonable doubt" of their loyalty. Thousands of government workers lost their jobs, charged with guilt by association with radicals or with membership in left-wing organizations. Often those who were charged had no chance to face their accusers.

The most famous disclosure came in August 1948, when Whittaker Chambers, a repentant communist, accused Alger Hiss of having been a Soviet spy in the 1930s. When Hiss, who had been a prominent State Department official, denied the charges, Chambers led investigators to a hollowed-out pumpkin on his Maryland farm. Inside the pumpkin were microfilms of confidential government documents. Chambers claimed that Hiss had passed the State Department materials to him in the late 1930s. Although the statute of limitations prevented a charge of treason against Hiss, he was convicted of perjury in January 1950 and sentenced to a five-year prison term.

Events abroad intensified the sense of danger. The communist triumph in China in the fall of 1949 came as a shock; soon there were charges that "fellow travelers" in the State Department were responsible for "the loss of China." In September 1949, when the Truman administration announced that the Russians had detonated their first atomic bomb, the end of America's nuclear monopoly was blamed on Soviet espionage. In early 1950, Klaus Fuchs—a British scientist who had worked on the wartime Manhattan Project—admitted giving the Russians vital information about the A-bomb.

A few months later, the government charged American communists Ethel and Julius Rosenberg with conspiracy to transmit atomic secrets to the Soviet

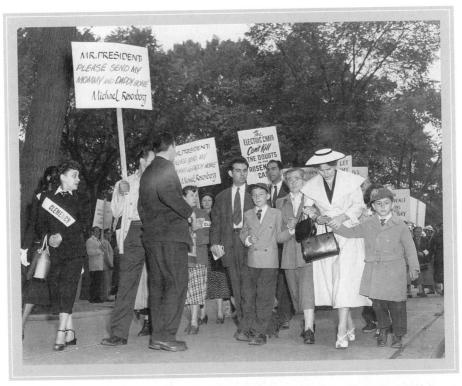

Three days before Julius and Ethel Rosenberg were executed for treason, their two young sons, 10 and 6 years old, marched to the White House to plead executive clemency for their parents.

Union. In 1951, a jury found the Rosenbergs guilty of treason, and Judge Irving Kaufman sentenced them to die for what he termed their "loathsome offense." Despite their insistent claims of innocence and worldwide appeals on their behalf, the Rosenbergs were electrocuted on June 19, 1953. Thus by the early 1950s, nearly all the ingredients were at hand for a new outburst of hysteria— fear of Russia, evidence of espionage, and a belief in a vast unseen conspiracy. The only element missing was a leader to release the new outburst of intolerance.

McCarthyism in Action

On February 12, 1950, Senator Joseph R. McCarthy of Wisconsin delivered a routine Lincoln's Birthday speech in Wheeling, West Virginia. This little known Republican suddenly attracted national attention when he declared, "I have here in my hand a list of 205—a list of names that were made known to the secretary of state as being members of the communist party and who nevertheless are still working and shaping policy in the State Department." The charge that there were communists in the State Department was never substantiated. But McCarthy's Wheeling speech triggered a four-and-a-half-year crusade to hunt down alleged

Senator Joseph McCarthy maintained a steady stream of unsubstantiated charges, always ready to make new accusations of communist infiltration before the preceding ones could be proven untrue. McCarthy's ruthless, vicious attacks cost hundreds of people their jobs and careers.

communists in government. The stridency and sensationalism of the senator's accusations soon won the name "McCarthyism."

McCarthy's basic technique was the multiple untruth. He leveled a bevy of charges of treasonable activities in government. While officials were refuting his initial accusations, he brought forth a steady stream of new ones, so the corrections never caught up with the latest blast. He failed to unearth a single confirmed communist in government, but he kept the Truman administration in turmoil. Drawing on an army of informers, primarily disgruntled federal workers with grievances against their colleagues and superiors, McCarthy charged government agencies with harboring and protecting communist agents and accused the State Department of deliberately losing the Cold War.

The secret of McCarthy's power was the fear he engendered among his Senate colleagues. In 1950, Maryland Senator Millard Tydings, who headed a committee critical of McCarthy's activities, failed to win reelection when

McCarthy opposed him; after that, other senators ran scared. McCarthy delighted in making sweeping, startling charges of communist sympathies against prominent public figures. A favorite target was patrician Secretary of State Dean Acheson; he even went after General George Marshall, claiming that the wartime army chief of staff was an agent of the communist conspiracy. Nor were fellow Republicans immune. One GOP senator was described as "a living miracle in that he is without question the only man who has lived so long with neither brains nor guts."

The attacks on the wealthy, famous, and privileged won McCarthy a devoted national following, though at the height of his influence in early 1954, he gained the approval of only 50 percent of the respondents in a Gallup poll. He offered a simple solution to the complicated Cold War: defeat the enemy at home rather than continue to engage in costly foreign aid programs and entangling alliances abroad. Above all, McCarthy appealed to conservative Republicans in the Midwest who shared his right-wing views and felt cheated by Truman's upset victory in 1948. Even GOP leaders who viewed McCarthy's tactics with distaste, such as Robert A. Taft of Ohio, quietly encouraged him to attack the vulnerable Democrats.

THE REPUBLICANS IN POWER

In 1952, the GOP capitalized on a growing sense of national frustration to capture the presidency. The stalemate in Korea and the fear of communism created a desire for political change; revelations of scandals by several individuals close to Truman intensified the feeling that someone needed to clean up "the mess in Washington." In Dwight D. Eisenhower, the Republican party found the perfect candidate to explore what one senator called K_1C_2—Korea, communism, and corruption.

Immensely popular because of his amiable manner, winning smile, and heroic stature, Eisenhower alone appeared to have the ability to unite a divided nation. In the 1952 campaign, Ike displayed hidden gifts as a politician in running against Adlai Stevenson, the eloquent Illinois governor whose appeal was limited to diehard Democrats and liberal intellectuals. Eisenhower delivered the most telling blow of all on the Korean War. Speaking in Detroit in late October, just after the fighting had intensified again in Korea, Ike promised if elected he would go personally to the battlefield in an attempt "to bring the Korean War to an early and honorable end."

"That does it—Ike is in," several reporters exclaimed after they heard this pledge. The hero of World War II had clinched his election by committing himself to end an unpopular war. Ten days later, he won the presidency handily, carrying thirty-nine states, including four in the formerly solid Democratic South. The

THE ELECTION OF 1952

CANDIDATE	PARTY	POPULAR VOTE	ELECTORAL VOTE
Eisenhower	Republican	33,936,137	442
Stevenson	Democratic	27,314,649	89

Republican party, however, did not fare as well in Congress; it gained just a slight edge in the House and controlled the Senate by only one seat.

Once elected, Eisenhower moved quickly to fulfill his campaign pledge. He spent three days in early December touring the battlefront in Korea, quickly ruling out the new offensive the military favored. "Small attacks on small hills," he later wrote, "would not end the war." Instead he turned to diplomacy, relying on subtle hints to China on the possible use of nuclear weapons to break the stalemated peace talks. These tactics, together with the death of Joseph Stalin in early March, finally led to the signing of an armistice on July 27, 1953, which ended the fighting but left Korea divided—as it had been before the war—near the 38th parallel.

The new president was less effective in dealing with the problem raised by Senator McCarthy's continuing witch-hunt. Instead of toning down his anticommunist crusade after the Republican victory in 1952, McCarthy used his new position as chairman of the Senate Committee on Government Operations as a base for ferreting out communists on the federal payroll. Eisenhower's advisers urged the president to use his own great prestige to stop McCarthy. But Ike refused such a confrontation, saying, "I will not get into a pissing contest with a skunk." Eisenhower preferred to play for time, hoping the American people would eventually come to their senses.

The Wisconsin senator finally overreached himself. In early 1954, he uncovered an army dentist suspected of disloyalty and proceeded to attack the upper echelons of the U.S. Army, telling one much decorated general that he was "not fit to wear the uniform." The controversy culminated in the televised Army-McCarthy hearings. For six weeks, the senator revealed his crude, bullying behavior to the American people. Viewers were repelled by his frequent outbursts that began with the insistent cry, "Point of order, Mr. Chairman, point of order," and by his attempt to slur the reputation of a young lawyer associated with army counsel Joseph Welch.

Courageous Republicans, led by Senators Ralph Flanders of Vermont and Margaret Chase Smith of Maine, joined with Democrats to bring about the Senate's censure of McCarthy in December 1954, by a vote of 67 to 22. Once rebuked, McCarthy fell quickly from prominence. He died three years later virtually unnoticed and unmourned.

Yet his influence was profound. Not only did he paralyze national life with what a Senate subcommittee described as "the most nefarious campaign of half-truth and untruth in the history of the Republic," but he also helped impose a political and cultural conformity that froze dissent for the rest of the 1950s. Long after McCarthy's passing, the nation tolerated loyalty oaths for teachers, the banning of left-wing books in public libraries, and the blacklisting of entertainers in radio, television, and films. Freedom of expression was inhibited, and the opportunity to try out new ideas and approaches was lost as the United States settled into a sterile Cold War consensus.

While Dwight Eisenhower could claim that his policy of giving McCarthy enough rope to hang himself had worked, it is possible that a bolder and more forthright presidential attack on the senator might have spared the nation some of the excesses of the anti-communist crusade.

EISENHOWER WAGES THE COLD WAR

Dwight D. Eisenhower came into the presidency in 1952 unusually well prepared to lead the nation at the height of the Cold War. His long years of military service had exposed him to a wide variety of international issues, both in Asia and in Europe, and to an even broader array of world leaders, such as Winston Churchill and Charles de Gaulle. He was not only an experienced military strategist but a gifted politician and diplomat as well. He was blessed with a sharp, pragmatic mind and organizational genius that enabled him to plan and carry out large enterprises, grasping the precise relationship between the parts and the whole. Above all, he had a serene confidence in his own ability. At the end of his first day in the White House, he confided in his diary: "Plenty of worries and difficult problems. But such has been my portion for a long time—the result is that this just seems like a continuation of all I've been doing since July 1941."

Eisenhower chose John Foster Dulles as his secretary of state. The myth soon developed that Ike had given Dulles free rein to conduct American diplomacy. Appearances were deceptive. Eisenhower preferred to work behind the scenes. He let Dulles make the public speeches and appearances before congressional committees, where the secretary's hard-line views placated GOP extremists. But Dulles carefully consulted with the president before every appearance, meeting

"Don't be afraid—I can always pull you back"

Cartoonist Herblock, a sharp critic of Dulles's hard line, depicts him in a Superman suit pushing Uncle Sam to the brink of nuclear war. (From Herblock's Special for Today *(Simon & Schuster, 1958).)*

frequently with Eisenhower at the White House and telephoning him several times a day. Ike respected his secretary of state's broad knowledge of foreign policy and skill in conducting American diplomacy, but he made all the major decisions himself.

From the outset, Eisenhower was determined to bring the Cold War under control. Ideally, he wanted to end it, but as a realist, he would settle for a relaxation of tensions with the Soviet Union. In part, he was motivated by a deeply held concern about the budget. Defense spending had increased from $13 billion to $50 billion under Truman; Ike was convinced the nation was in danger of going bankrupt unless military spending was reduced. As president, he inaugurated a "new look" for American defense, cutting back on the army and navy and relying even more heavily than Truman had on the air force and its nuclear striking power. As a result, the defense budget dropped below $40 billion annually. In 1954, Dulles announced reliance on massive retaliation—in fact a continuance of Truman's policy of deterrence. Rather than becoming involved in limited wars such as Korea, the United States would consider the possibility of using nuclear weapons to halt any communist aggression that threatened vital U.S. interests anywhere in the world.

While he permitted Dulles to make his veiled nuclear threats, Eisenhower's fondest dream was to end the arms race. Sobered by the development of the hydrogen bomb, successfully tested by the United States in November 1952 and by the Soviet Union in August 1953, the president began a new effort at disarmament with the Russians. Yet before this initiative could take effect, Ike had to weather a series of crises around the world that tested his skill and patience to the utmost.

ENTANGLEMENT IN INDOCHINA

The first crisis facing the new president came in Indochina. Since 1950, the United States had been giving France military and economic aid in a war in Indochina against communist guerrillas led by Ho Chi Minh. The Chinese increased their support to Ho's forces, known as the Vietminh, after the Korean War ended; by the spring of 1954, the French were on the brink of defeat. The Vietminh had surrounded nearly ten thousand French troops at Dien Bien Phu deep in the interior of northern Indochina; in desperation, France turned to the United States for help. Admiral Arthur Radford, chairman of the Joint Chiefs of Staff, proposed an American air strike to lift the siege. Although the other Joint Chiefs had strong objections to involving American forces in another Asian war so soon after Korea, hawkish Republican senators were clamoring for action.

Eisenhower decided against Radford's bold proposal, but he killed it in his typically indirect fashion. Fearful that an air attack would lead inevitably to the use of ground troops, Ike insisted that both Congress and American allies in Europe approve the strike in advance. Congressional leaders, recalling the recent

A French soldier stands guard over a truckload of Vietnamese nationalists captured in the fighting in Indochina. French efforts to quash the rebellion in Vietnam ended on May 7, 1954, when the Vietminh took the French stronghold at Dien Bien Phu.

Korean debacle, were reluctant to agree; the British were appalled and ruled out any joint action. The president used these objections to reject intervention in Indochina in 1954.

Dien Bien Phu fell to the Vietminh in May 1954. At an international conference held in Geneva a few weeks later, Indochina was divided at the 17th parallel. Ho gained control of North Vietnam, while the French continued to rule in the South. The United States gradually took over from the French in South Vietnam, sponsoring a new government in Saigon headed by Ngo Dinh Diem, a Vietnamese nationalist from a northern Catholic family. While Eisenhower can be given credit for refusing to engage American forces on behalf of French colonialism in Indochina, his determination to resist communist expansion had committed the United States to a long and eventually futile struggle to prevent Ho Chi Minh from achieving his long-sought goal of a unified, independent Vietnam.

CONTAINING CHINA

The communist government in Peking posed a serious challenge for the Eisenhower administration. Senate Republicans, led by William Knowland of California, blamed the Democrats for the "loss" of China. They viewed Mao as a puppet of the Soviet Union and insisted the United States recognize the Nationalists on Formosa as the only legitimate government of China. While State Department experts realized there were underlying tensions between China and Russia, Mao's intervention in the Korean War had convinced most Americans that the Chinese communists were an integral part of a larger communist effort at world domination. Thus Truman and Acheson had abandoned any hope of trying to exploit differences between Mao and Stalin by wooing China away from the Soviet Union.

Eisenhower and Dulles chose to accentuate the potential conflict between Russia and China. By taking a strong line against China, the United States could make the Chinese realize that Russia was unable to protect their interests; at the same time, such a hawkish policy would please congressional conservatives such as Knowland. Ultimately, Eisenhower and Dulles hoped that a policy of firmness would not only contain communist Chinese expansion in Asia but also drive a wedge between Moscow and Peking.

A crisis in the Formosa Straits provided the first test of the new policy. In the fall of 1954, communist China threatened to seize coastal islands, notably Quemoy and Matsu, occupied by the Nationalists. Fearful that seizure of these offshore islands would be the first step toward an invasion of Formosa, Eisenhower permitted Dulles to sign a security treaty with Chiang Kai-shek committing the United States to defend Formosa. When the communists began shelling the offshore islands, Eisenhower persuaded Congress to pass a resolution authorizing him to use force to defend Formosa and "closely related localities."

Despite repeated requests, however, the president refused to say whether he would use force to repel a Chinese attack on Quemoy or Matsu. Instead he and Dulles hinted at the use of nuclear weapons. The Chinese leaders, unsure whether Eisenhower was bluffing, decided not to test American resolve. The shelling ended in 1955, and when the communists resumed it again in 1958, another firm but equally ambiguous American response forced them to desist. The apparent refusal of the Soviet Union to come to China's aid in these crises with the United States contributed to a growing rift between the two communist nations by the end of the 1950s. Unfortunately, the Eisenhower administration failed to take full advantage of the opportunity that it had helped to create.

TURMOIL IN THE MIDDLE EAST

The gravest crisis for Eisenhower came in the Middle East when Egyptian leader Gamal Nasser seized the Suez Canal in July 1956. England and France were ready to use force immediately; their citizens owned the canal company, and their economies were dependent on the canal for the flow of oil from the Persian Gulf. President Eisenhower, however, was staunchly opposed to intervention, preferring to seek a diplomatic solution with Nasser, who kept the canal running smoothly. For three months, Dulles did everything possible to restrain the European allies, but finally they decided to take a desperate gamble—they invaded Egypt and seized the canal, relying on the United States to prevent any Russian interference.

Eisenhower was furious when England and France launched their attack in early November. Campaigning for reelection against Adlai Stevenson on the slogan of keeping the peace, Ike had to abandon domestic politics to deal with the threat of war. Unhesitatingly, he instructed Dulles to sponsor a UN resolution calling for British and French withdrawal from Egypt. Yet when the Russians supported the American proposal and went further, threatening rocket attacks on British and French cities and even offering to send "volunteers" to fight in Egypt, Eisenhower made it clear he would not tolerate Soviet interference. He put the Strategic Air Command on alert and said of the Russians, "If those fellows start something, we may have to hit 'em—and, if necessary, with everything in the bucket."

Just after noon on election day, November 6, 1956, British Prime Minister Anthony Eden called the president to inform him that England and France were ending their invasion. Eisenhower breathed a sigh of relief. American voters rallied behind Ike, electing him to a second term by a near landslide. As a result of the Suez crisis, the United States replaced England and France as the main Western influence in the Middle East. With Russia strongly backing Egypt and Syria, the Cold War had found yet another battleground.

Two years later, Eisenhower found it necessary to intervene in the strategic Middle Eastern country of Lebanon. Political power in this neutral nation was divided between Christian and Muslim elements. When the outgoing Christian president, Camille Chamoun, broke with tradition by seeking a second term, Muslim groups (aided by Egypt and Syria) threatened to launch a rebellion. After initial hesitation, Ike decided to act in order to uphold the U.S. commitment to political stability in the Middle East.

American marines from the Sixth Fleet moved swiftly ashore on July 15, 1958, securing the Beirut airport and preparing the way for a force of some fourteen thousand troops airlifted from bases in Germany. The military wanted to occupy the entire country, but Eisenhower insisted on limiting American forces to the area of Beirut. Lebanese political leaders quickly agreed on a successor to Chamoun, and American soldiers left the country before the end of October. The restrained use of force achieved Eisenhower's primary goal of quieting the explosive Middle East. It also served, as Secretary of State Dulles pointed out, "to reassure many small nations that they could call on us in a time of crisis."

COVERT ACTIONS

Amid these dangerous crises, the Eisenhower administration worked behind the scenes in the 1950s to expand the nation's global influence. In 1953, the CIA was instrumental in overthrowing a popularly elected government in Iran and placing the shah in full control of that country. American oil companies were rewarded with lucrative concessions, and Eisenhower believed he had gained a valuable ally on the Russian border. But these short-run gains created a deep-seated animosity among Iranians that would haunt the United States in the future.

Closer to home, in Latin America, Eisenhower once again relied on covert action. In 1954, the CIA masterminded the overthrow of a leftist regime in Guatemala. The immediate advantage was in denying the Soviets a possible foothold in the Western Hemisphere, but Latin Americans resented the thinly disguised interference of the United States in their internal affairs. More important, when Fidel Castro came to power in Cuba in 1959, the Eisenhower administration—after a brief effort at conciliation—adopted a hard line that helped drive Cuba into the Soviet orbit and led to new attempts at covert action.

Eisenhower's record as a cold warrior was thus mixed. His successful ending of the Korean War and his peacekeeping efforts in Indochina and Formosa and in the Suez crisis are all to his credit. Yet his reliance on coups and subversion di-

The first wave of U.S. Marines splashed ashore on the beach near Beirut, Lebanon, in July 1958. Sent to avert a Christian-Muslim civil war, they stayed only one hundred days.

rected by the CIA in Iran and Guatemala reveal Ike's corrupting belief that the ends justified the means.

Nevertheless, Eisenhower did display an admirable ability to stay calm and unruffled in moments of great tension, reassuring the nation and the world. And above all, he could boast, as he did in 1962, of his ability to keep the peace. "In those eight years," he reminded the nation, "we lost no inch of ground to tyranny. One war was ended and incipient wars were blocked."

WAGING PEACE

Eisenhower hoped to ease Cold War tensions by ending the nuclear arms race. The advent of the hydrogen bomb intensified his concern over nuclear warfare; by 1955, both the United States and the Soviet Union had added this dread new weapon to their arsenals. With new long-range ballistic missiles being perfected, it was only a matter of time before Russia and the United States would be capable of destroying each other completely. Peace, as Winston Churchill noted, now depended on a balance of terror.

Throughout the 1950s, Eisenhower sought a way out of the nuclear dilemma. In April 1953, shortly after Stalin's death, he gave a speech in which he called on the Russians to join him in a new effort at disarmament, pointing out that "every warship launched, every rocket fired signifies, in the final sense, a theft from those who hunger and are not fed, those who are cold and are not clothed." When the Soviets ignored this appeal, Eisenhower tried again. At a summit conference in Geneva, Switzerland, in 1955, Ike proposed to Nikita Khrushchev, just emerging as Stalin's successor after a two-year struggle for power, a way to break the disarmament deadlock. "Open skies," as reporters dubbed the plan, would overcome the traditional Russian objection to on-site inspection by having both superpowers open their territory to mutual aerial surveillance. Unfortunately, Khrushchev dismissed open skies as "a very transparent espionage device," and the conference ended without any significant breakthrough in the Cold War.

After his reelection in 1956, the president renewed his efforts toward nuclear arms control. Concern over atmospheric fallout from nuclear testing had led presidential candidate Adlai Stevenson to propose a mutual ban on such experiments. At first, Eisenhower rejected the test ban idea, but in 1958 the president changed his mind after American and Soviet scientists developed a system to detect nuclear testing in the atmosphere. In October 1958, Eisenhower and Khrushchev each voluntarily suspended further weapons tests pending the outcome of a conference held at Geneva to work out a test ban treaty. Although the Geneva Conference failed to make progress, neither the United States nor the Soviet Union resumed testing for the remainder of Ike's term in office.

The suspension of testing halted the pollution of the world's atmosphere, but it did not lead to the improvement in Soviet-American relations that Eisenhower sought. Instead, the Soviet feat in launching *Sputnik,* the first artificial satellite to orbit the earth, intensified the Cold War. Fearful that the Russians were several years ahead of the United States in the development of intercontinental ballistic missiles (ICBMs), Democrats criticized Eisenhower for not spending enough on defense and warned that a dangerous missile gap would open up by the early 1960s—a time when the Russians might have such a commanding lead in ICBMs that they could launch a first strike and destroy America. Despite the president's belief that the American missile program was in good shape, he allowed increased defense spending to speed up the building of American ICBMs and the new Polaris submarine–launched intermediate range missile (IRBM).

The most serious threat came in November 1958, when the Russian leader declared that within six months he would sign a separate peace treaty with East

"Handshake" is the title of this cartoon depicting a British view of relations between Soviet Premier Khrushchev and U.S. President Eisenhower during the Cold War. But the "handshake" between the two superpowers is more a contest of strength than a gesture of cooperation.

Germany, calling for an end to American, British, and French occupation rights in Berlin.

Eisenhower met the second Berlin crisis as firmly as Truman had the first. He refused to abandon the city but also tried to avoid a military showdown. Prudent diplomacy forced Khrushchev to extend his deadline indefinitely. After a trip to the United States, culminating in a personal meeting with Eisenhower at Camp David, the Russian leader agreed to attend a summit conference in Paris in May 1960.

This much heralded meeting never took place. On May 1, two weeks before the leaders were to convene in Paris, the Soviets shot down an American U-2 plane piloted by Francis Gary Powers. The United States had been overflying Russia since 1956 in the high-altitude spy planes, gaining vital information about the Soviet missile program which showed there was little basis for the public's fear that the Russians had opened up a dangerous missile gap. After initially denying any knowledge, Eisenhower took full responsibility for Powers's overflight, and Khrushchev responded with a scathing personal denunciation and a refusal to meet with the American president.

Russians view the wreckage of the U-2 reconnaissance plane piloted by Francis Powers that was shot down over Soviet territory on May 1, 1960. Although Eisenhower originally disavowed any knowledge of Powers's mission, Khrushchev produced photographs of Soviet military and industrial sites, which he said had been taken by the U-2 pilot. Powers was held in a Soviet prison for two years before he was released in exchange for a Russian spy.

Eisenhower deeply regretted the breakup of the Paris summit, telling an aide that "the stupid U-2 mess" had destroyed all his efforts for peace. Khrushchev marked time for the next nine months, waiting for the American people to choose a new president. Eisenhower did make a final effort at peace, however. Three days before leaving office, he delivered a farewell address in which he gave a somber warning about the danger of massive military spending. "In the councils of government," he declared, "we must guard against the acquisition of unwarranted influence, whether sought or unsought, by the military-industrial complex.

Rarely has an American president been more prophetic. In the next few years, the level of defense spending would skyrocket as the Cold War escalated. The military-industrial complex reached its acme of power in the 1960s when the United States realized the full implications of Truman's doctrine of containment. Eisenhower had succeeded in keeping the peace for eight years, but he had failed to halt the momentum of the Cold War he had inherited from Harry Truman. Ike's efforts to ease tension with the Soviet Union were dashed by his own distrust of communism and by Khrushchev's belligerent rhetoric and behavior. Still, he had begun to relax tensions, a process that would survive the troubled 1960s and, after several false starts, would finally begin to erode the Cold War by the end of the 1980s.

29

AFFLUENCE AND ANXIETY

On May 7, 1947, William Levitt announced plans to build two thousand rental houses in a former potato field on Long Island, thirty miles from Midtown Manhattan. Using mass production techniques he had learned while erecting navy housing during the war, Levitt quickly built four thousand homes and rented them to young veterans eager to leave crowded city apartments or their parents' homes to begin raising families. A change in government financing regulations led him to begin offering his houses for sale in 1948 for a small amount down and a low monthly payment. Young couples, many of them the original renters, quickly bought the first four thousand; by the time Levittown—as he called the new community—was completed in 1951, it contained more than seventeen thousand homes. So many babies were born in Levittown that it soon became known as "Fertility Valley" and "the Rabbit Hutch."

Levitt eventually built two more Levittowns, one in Pennsylvania and one in New Jersey; each contained the same curving streets, neighborhood parks and playgrounds, and community swimming pools characteristic of the first development. The secret of Levittown's appeal was the basic house, a 720-square-foot Cape Cod design built on a concrete slab. It had a kitchen, two bedrooms and bath, a living room complete with a fireplace and 16-foot picture window, and an expansion attic with room for two more bedrooms. Levitt built only one interior, but there were four different facades to break the monotony. The original house sold for $6,990 in 1948; even the improved model, a ranch-style house, sold for less than $10,000 in 1951.

A photograph, floor plan, and elevation for a Levittown house. The Levittown builders applied the principles of mass production used in auto manufacturing to house construction. One important difference was the fact that the product stood stationary while workers came to the site to perform their specialized tasks. Construction was broken down into twenty-seven separate tasks, and a house could be assembled in fifteen minutes.

Levitt's houses were ideal for young people just starting out in life. They were cheap, comfortable, and efficient, and each home came with a refrigerator, cooking range, and washing machine. Despite the conformity of the houses, the three Levittowns were surprisingly diverse communities; residents had a wide variety of religious, ethnic, and occupational backgrounds. African Americans, however, were rigidly excluded. In time, as the more successful families moved on to larger homes in more expensive neighborhoods, the Levittowns became enclaves for lower-middle-class families.

Levittown symbolized the most significant social trend of the postwar era in the United States—the flight to the suburbs. The residential areas surrounding cities such as New York and Chicago nearly doubled in the 1950s. While central cities remained relatively stagnant during the decade, suburbs grew by 46 percent; by 1960, some sixty million people, one-third of the nation, lived in suburban rings around the cities. This massive shift in population from the central city was accompanied by a baby boom that started during World War II. Young married couples began to have three, four, or even five children (compared with only one or two children in American families during the 1930s). These larger families led to a 19 percent growth in the nation's population between 1950 and 1960, the highest growth rate since 1910.

The economy boomed as residential construction soared. By 1960, one-fourth of all existing homes were less than ten years old, and factories were turning out large quantities of appliances and television sets for the new households. A multitude of new consumer products—ranging from frozen foods to cars equipped with automatic transmissions and tubeless tires—appeared in stores and showrooms. In the suburbs, the corner grocery gave way to the supermarket carrying a vast array of items that enabled homemakers to provide their families with a more varied diet.

A new affluence replaced the poverty and hunger of the Great Depression for most Americans, but many had haunting memories of the 1930s. The obsession with material goods took on an almost desperate quality, as if a profusion of houses, cars, and home appliances could guarantee that the nightmare of depression would never return. Critics were quick to disparage the quality of life in suburban society. They condemned the conformity, charging the newly affluent with forsaking traditional American individualism to live in identical houses, drive look-alike cars, and accumulate the same material possessions. Folksinger Malvina Reynolds caught the essence of postwar suburbia in a 1963 song:

> *Little boxes on the hillside,*
> *Little boxes made of ticky tacky*
> *Little boxes on the hillside,*
> *Little boxes all the same.*
> *There's a green one and a pink one*
> *And a blue one and a yellow one*
> *And they're all made out of ticky tacky*
> *And they all look just the same.**

Events abroad added to the feeling of anxiety in the postwar years. Nuclear war became a frighteningly real possibility. The rivalry with the Soviet Union had led to the second Red Scare, with charges of treason and disloyalty being leveled at loyal Americans. Many Americans joined Senator Joseph McCarthy in searching for the communist enemy at home rather than abroad. Loyalty oaths and book burning revealed how insecure Americans had become in the era of the Cold War. Thus beneath the bland surface of suburban affluence, a dark current of distrust and insecurity marred the picture of a nation fulfilling its economic destiny.

THE POSTWAR BOOM

For fifteen years following World War II, the nation witnessed a period of unparalleled economic growth. A pent-up demand for consumer goods fueled a steady industrial expansion. Heavy government spending during the Cold War added an extra stimulus to the economy, offsetting brief recessions in 1949 and 1953 and moderating a steeper one in 1957–1958. By the end of the 1950s, the American people had achieved an affluence that finally erased the lingering fears of the Great Depression.

POSTWAR PROSPERITY

The economy began its upward surge as the result of two long-term factors. First, American consumers—after being held in check by depression and then by wartime scarcities—finally had a chance to indulge their suppressed appetites for material goods. At the war's end, personal savings in the United States stood at more than $37 billion, providing a powerful stimulus to consumption. Initially, American factories could not turn out enough automobiles and appliances to satisfy the horde of buyers. By 1950, however, production lines had finally caught up with the demand.

The Cold War provided the additional stimulus the economy needed when postwar expansion slowed. The Marshall Plan and other foreign aid programs financed a heavy export trade. The Korean War helped overturn a brief recession and ensured continued prosperity as the government spent massive amounts on guns, planes, and munitions. In 1952, the nation spent $44 billion, two-thirds of the federal budget, on national defense. Although Eisenhower managed to bring about some modest reductions, defense spending continued at a level of $40 billion throughout the decade.

The nation achieved an affluence in the 1950s that made the persisting fear of another Great Depression seem irrational. The baby boom and the spectacular growth of suburbia served as great stimulants to the consumer goods industries. Manufacturers turned out an ever increasing number of refrigerators, washing machines, and dishwashers to equip the kitchens of Levittown and its many imitators across the country. The automobile industry thrived with suburban expansion as two-car families became more and more common. In 1955, in an era when oil was abundant and gasoline sold for less than 30 cents a gallon, Detroit sold a record eight million cars.

Commercial enterprises snapped up office machines and the first generation of computers; industry installed electronic sensors and processors as it underwent extensive automation; and the military displayed an insatiable appetite for electronic devices for its planes and ships. As a result, American industry averaged more than $10 billion a year in capital investment, and the number of persons employed rose above the long-sought goal of sixty million nationwide.

Yet the economic abundance of the 1950s was not without its problems. While some sections of the nation (notably the emerging Sunbelt areas of the South and West) benefited enormously from the growth of the aircraft and electronics industries, older manufacturing regions, such as New England, did not fare as well. The steel industry increased its capacity during the decade, but it began to fall behind the rate of national growth. Agriculture continued to experience bumper crops and low prices, so rural regions failed to share in the general affluence. Unemployment persisted despite the boom, rising to more than 7 percent in a sharp recession that hit the country in the fall of 1957 and lasted through the summer of 1958.

None of these flaws, however, could disguise the fact that the nation was prospering to an extent no one dreamed possible in the 1930s. The GNP grew to $440 billion by 1960, more than double the 1940 level. By the mid-1950s, the average American family had twice as much real income to spend as its counterpart had possessed in the boom years of the 1920s. From 1945 to 1960, per capita disposable income rose by $500—to $1845—for every man, woman, and child in the country. The American people, in one generation, had moved from poverty and depression to the highest standard of living the world had ever known.

LIFE IN THE SUBURBS

Sociologists had difficulty describing the nature of suburban society in the 1950s. Some saw it as classless, while others noted the absence of both the very rich and the very poor and consequently labeled it "middle class." Rather than forming a homogeneous social group, though, the suburbs contained a surprising variety of people, whether classified as "upper lower," "lower middle," and "upper middle" or simply as blue collar, white collar, and professional. Doctors and lawyers often lived in the same developments as salesclerks and master plumbers. The traditional distinctions of ancestry, education, and size of residence no longer differentiated people as easily as they had in the past.

Yet suburbs could vary widely, from working-class communities clustered near factories built in the countryside to old, elitist areas such as Scarsdale, New York, and Shaker Heights, Ohio. Most were almost exclusively white and Christian, but suburbs such as Great Neck on Long Island and Richmond Heights outside Miami enabled Jews and blacks to take part in the flight from the inner city.

Life in all the suburban communities depended on the automobile. Highways and expressways allowed fathers to commute to jobs in the cities, often an hour or more away. Children might ride buses to and from school, but mothers had to drive them to piano lessons and Little League ballgames. Two cars became a necessity for almost every suburban family, thus helping spur the boom in automobile production.

In the new drive-in culture, people shopped at the stores that grew up first in "miracle miles" along the highways and later at the shopping centers that began to dot the countryside by the mid-1950s. There were only eight shopping centers in the entire country in 1946; hundreds appeared over the next fifteen years, including Poplar Plaza in Memphis, with one large department store, thirty retail shops, and parking for more than five hundred cars.

Despite the increased mobility provided by the car, the home became the focus for activities and aspirations. The postwar shortage of housing that often forced young couples to live with their parents or in-laws created an intense demand for new homes in the suburbs. When questioned, prospective buyers expressed a desire for "more space," for "comfort and roominess," and for "privacy and freedom of action" in their new residences. "Togetherness" became the code word of the 1950s. Families did things together, whether gathering around the TV sets that dominated living rooms, attending community activities, or taking vacations in the huge station wagons of the era.

But there were some less attractive consequences of the new suburban lifestyle. The extended family, in which several generations had lived in close proximity, was a casualty of the boom in small detached homes. As historian Kenneth Jackson has noted, suburban life "ordained that most children would grow up in intimate contact only with their parents and siblings." Grandparents, aunts and uncles, cousins, and more distant relatives would become remote figures, seen only on special occasions.

The nuclear family, typical of the suburb, did nothing to encourage the development of feminism. The end of the war saw many women who had entered the workforce return to the home, where the role of wife and mother continued to be viewed as the ideal for women in the 1950s. Trends toward getting married earlier and having larger families reinforced the pattern of women devoting all their efforts to housework and child raising rather than acquiring professional skills and pursuing careers outside the home. Adlai Stevenson, extolling "the humble role of housewife," told Smith College graduates that there was much they could do "in the living room with a baby in your lap or in the kitchen with a can opener in your hand."

Nonetheless, the number of working wives doubled between 1940 and 1960. By the end of the 1950s, 40 percent of American women, and nearly one-third of all married women, had jobs outside the home. The heavy expenses involved in rearing and educating children led wives and mothers to seek ways to augment the family income, inadvertently preparing the way for a new demand for equality in the 1960s.

THE GOOD LIFE?

Consumerism became the dominant social theme of the 1950s. Yet even with an abundance of creature comforts and added hours of leisure time, the quality of life left many Americans anxious and dissatisfied.

AREAS OF GREATEST GROWTH

Organized religion flourished in the climate of the 1950s. Ministers, priests, and rabbis all commented on the rise in church and synagogue attendance in the new communities. Will Herberg claimed that religious affiliation had become the primary identifying feature of modern American life, dividing the nation into three separate segments—Protestant, Catholic, and Jewish.

Some observers condemned the bland, secular nature of suburban churches, which seemed to be an integral part of the consumer society. "On weekdays one shops for food," wrote one critic, "on Saturdays one shops for recreation, and on Sundays one shops for the Holy Ghost." But the popularity of religious writer Norman Vincent Peale, with his positive gospel that urged people to "start thinking faith, enthusiasm and joy," suggested that the new churches filled a genuine if shallow human need.

Schools provided an immediate problem for the growing new suburban communities. The increase in the number of school-age children, from twenty to thirty million in the first eight grades, overwhelmed the resources of many local districts, leading to demands for federal aid. Congress granted limited help for areas affected by defense plants and military bases, but Eisenhower's reluctance to unbalance the budget blocked further federal assistance prior to 1957, when the government reacted to *Sputnik.*

Equally important, a controversy arose over the nature of education in the 1950s. Critics of "progressive" education called for sweeping educational reforms and a new stress on traditional academic subjects. The one thing all seemed to agree on was the desirability of a college education. The number of young people attending colleges increased from 1.5 million in 1940 to 3.6 million in 1960.

The largest advances were made in the exciting new medium of television. From a shaky start just after the war, TV boomed in the 1950s, pushing radio aside and undermining many of the nation's magazines. By 1957, three networks controlled the airwaves, reaching forty million sets over nearly five hundred stations.

Entertainment for all age levels was the focus of television in the 1950s. Then, as now, shows were targeted for specific age groups, such as these children watching intently the antics of the puppets and live actors on the "Howdy Doody Show." The television became the focal center of rooms where families gathered to spend their leisure time.

At first, the insatiable demand for programs encouraged a burst of creativity. Playwrights such as Reginald Rose, Rod Serling, and Paddy Chayefsky wrote a series of notable dramas for *Playhouse 90, Studio One,* and the *Goodyear Television Playhouse.* Broadcast live from cramped studios, these productions thrived on tight dramatic structures, movable scenery, and frequent close-ups of the actors.

Advertisers, however, quickly became disillusioned with the live anthology programs, which usually dealt with controversial subjects or focused on ordinary people and events. In contrast, sponsors wanted shows that stressed excitement, glamour, and instant success. Aware that audiences were fascinated by contestants with unusual expertise (a shoemaker answering tough questions on operas, a grandmother stumping experts on baseball), producers began giving away huge cash prizes on *The $64,000 Question* and *Twenty-one.* In 1959, the nation was shocked when Charles Van Doren, a Columbia University professor, confessed he had been given the answers in advance to win $129,000 on *Twenty-one.* The three networks quickly dropped all the big-prize quiz programs, replacing them with comedy, action, and adventure shows such as *The Untouchables* and *Bonanza*. Despite its early promise of artistic innovation, television had become a techno-logically sophisticated but safe conveyor of the consumer culture.

CRITICS OF THE CONSUMER SOCIETY

One striking feature of the 1950s was the abundance of self-criticism. A number of widely read books explored the flaws in the new suburbia. John Keats's *The Crack in the Picture Window* described the endless rows of tract houses "vomited up" by developers as "identical boxes spreading like gangrene." Their occupants lost any sense of individuality in their obsession with material goods.

Richard Gordon, Katherine Gordon, and Max Gunther were more con-cerned about the psychological toll of suburban life in their 1960 book *The Split-Level Trap*. They labeled the new lifestyle "Disturbia" and bemoaned the "haggard" men, the "tense and anxious" women, and the "gimme" kids it produced. The most sweeping indictment came in William H. Whyte's *The Organization Man* (1956), based on a study of the Chicago suburb of Park Forest. Whyte perceived a change from the old Protestant ethic, with its emphasis on hard work and per-sonal responsibility, to a new social ethic centered on "the team" with the ulti-mate goal of "belongingness." The result was a stifling conformity and the loss of personal identity.

The most influential social critic of the 1950s was Harvard sociologist David Riesman. His book *The Lonely Crowd* appeared in 1950 and set the tone for intel-lectual commentary about suburbia for the rest of the decade. Riesman described the shift from the "inner-directed" Americans of the past who had relied on such traditional values as self-denial and frugality to the "other-directed" Americans of the consumer society who constantly adapted their behavior to conform to social pressures. The resulting decline in individualism produced a bland and tolerant society of consumers lacking creativity and a sense of adventure.

C. Wright Mills was a far more caustic commentator on American society in the 1950s. Anticipating government statistics that revealed white-collar workers (salesclerks, office workers, bank tellers) now outnumbered blue-collar workers (miners, factory workers, millhands), Mills described the new middle class in ominous terms in his books *White Collar* (1951) and *Power Elite* (1956). The indus-trial assembly line had given way to an even more dehumanizing workplace, the modern office. "At rows of blank-looking counters sat rows of blank-looking girls with blank, white folders in their blank hands, all blankly folding blank papers."

This disenchantment with the consumer culture reached its most eloquent expression with the "beats," literary groups that rebelled against the materialistic society of the 1950s. Jack Kerouac's novel *On the Road*, published in 1957, set the

Novelist Jack Kerouac and his fellow "beat" writers bemoaned the moral bankruptcy of popular culture. They sought not to improve conditions but to find release from the moral and social confines contricting their lives and the literary convention circumscribing their writing.

tone for the new movement. The name came from the quest for beatitude, a state of inner grace sought in Zen Buddhism. Flouting the respectability of suburbia, the "beatniks"—as middle America termed them—were easily identified by their long hair and bizarre clothing; they also had a penchant for sexual promiscuity and drug experimentation. They were conspicuous dropouts from a society they found senseless.

Despite the disapproval they evoked from mainstream Americans, the beat generation had only compassion for their detractors. "We love everything," Kerouac proclaimed, "Billy Graham, the Big Ten, Rock and Roll, Zen, apple pie, Eisenhower—we dig it all." Yet as highly visible nonconformists in an era of stifling conformity, the beats demonstrated a style of social protest that would flower into the counterculture of the 1960s.

THE REACTION TO *SPUTNIK*

The profound insecurity that underlay American life throughout the 1950s burst into view in October 1957, when the Soviets sent the 184-pound satellite *Sputnik* into orbit. People around the world applauded the scientific feat, but in the United States the reaction was one of dismay at being bested by a communist rival.

The Soviet's successful launching of Sputnik shook American confidence and triggered new interest and activity in the "space race." Both houses of Congress established space committees, and President Eisenhower created the National Aeronautics and Space Administration (NASA).

Americans became afraid that their nation had somehow lost its previously unquestioned primacy in the eyes of the world.

The national sense of humiliation only deepened in December, when TV cameras showed the rocket bearing the first American satellite exploding only a few feet after liftoff. Finally, on January 31, 1958, the United States launched its first orbiting satellite. Although the *Explorer,* only 6 inches wide and weighing just over 30 pounds, was tiny compared to *Sputnik,* it carried a much more sophisticated set of scientific instruments to probe the mysteries of space.

In the late 1950s, the president and Congress moved to restore national confidence. Eisenhower appointed James R. Killian, president of the Massachusetts Institute of Technology (MIT), as his special assistant for science and technology and to oversee a crash program in missile development. The House and Senate followed by creating the National Aeronautics and Space Administration (NASA) in 1958. Congress appropriated vast sums to allow the agency to compete with the Russians in the space race. Soon a new group of heroes, the astronauts, began the training that led to suborbital flights and eventually to John Glenn's five-hour flight around the globe in 1962.

Congress also sought to match the Soviet educational advances by passing the National Defense Education Act (NDEA). This legislation authorized federal financing of scientific and foreign language programs in the nation's schools and colleges. Soon American students were hard at work mastering the "new physics" and the "new math."

The belief persisted, however, that the faults lay deeper, that in the midst of affluence and abundance Americans had lost their competitive edge. Economists pointed to the higher rate of Soviet economic growth, and social critics bemoaned a supermarket culture that stressed consumption over production, comfort over hard work.

FAREWELL TO REFORM

It is not surprising that the spirit of reform underlying the New Deal failed to flourish in the postwar years. Growing affluence took away the sense of grievance and the cry for change that was so strong in the 1930s. Eager to enjoy the new prosperity after years of want and sacrifice, the American people turned away from federal regulation and welfare programs.

TRUMAN AND THE FAIR DEAL

Harry Truman tried to capitalize on his upset victory in 1948 to offer a broad program of reform to the nation on January 5, 1949. Venturing beyond earlier proposals by FDR to increase the minimum wage and broaden Social Security coverage, he called for a "Fair Deal," a reform package that comprised a new program of national medical insurance, federal aid to education, enactment of a Fair Employment Practices Commission (FEPC) to prevent economic discrimination against blacks, and an overhaul of the farm subsidy program.

The Fair Deal was never enacted. Except for raising the minimum wage to 75 cents an hour and broadening Social Security to cover ten million more Americans, Congress refused to pass any of Truman's health, education, or civil rights measures. The nation's doctors waged an effective campaign against the president's health insurance plan, and southern senators blocked any action on the FEPC. Aid to education, repeal of Taft-Hartley, and the new farm program all failed to win congressional approval. Despite the Democratic victory in 1948, Congress remained under the control of a bipartisan conservative coalition of northern Republicans and southern Democrats, the same alignment that had halted Roosevelt's reforms after 1938.

Although his legislative failure became certain in 1950, when war once again subordinated domestic issues to foreign policy, President Truman deserves credit for maintaining and consolidating the New Deal. His spirited leadership prevented any Republican effort to repeal the gains of the 1930s. Moreover, even though he failed to get any new measures enacted, he broadened the reform agenda and laid the groundwork for future advances in health care, aid to education, and civil rights.

EISENHOWER'S MODERN REPUBLICANISM

The American people found that moderation was the keynote of the Eisenhower presidency. His major goal from the outset was to restore calm and tranquility to a badly divided nation. Unlike FDR and Truman, Eisenhower had no commitment to social change or economic reform. Ike was a fiscal conservative who was intent on balancing the budget. Yet unlike some Republicans of the extreme right wing, he had no plans to dismantle the social programs of the New Deal. He sought instead to keep military spending in check, to encourage as much private initiative as possible, and to reduce federal activities to the bare minimum. Defining his position as "Modern Republicanism," he claimed that he was "conservative when it comes to money and liberal when it comes to human beings."

On domestic issues, Eisenhower preferred to delegate authority and to play a passive role. He concentrated his own efforts on the Cold War abroad. The men he chose to run the nation reflected his preference for successful corporation executives. Thus George Humphrey, an Ohio industrialist, carried out a policy of fiscal stringency as secretary of the treasury, while Charles E. Wilson (the former head of General Motors) sought to keep the Pentagon budget under control as secretary of defense. Neither man was wholly successful, and both were guilty of tactless public statements. Humphrey warned that unless Congress showed budgetary restraint, "we're gonna have a depression which will curl your hair," and Wilson gained notoriety by proclaiming that "what was good for our country was good for General Motors, and vice versa."

Eisenhower was equally reluctant to play an active role in dealing with Congress. A fervent believer in the separation of powers, Ike did not want to engage in intensive lobbying. He left congressional relations to aides such as Sherman Adams, a former New Hampshire governor who served as White House chief of staff. Adams's skill at resolving problems at lower levels insulated Eisenhower from many of the nation's pressing domestic problems.

Republican losses in the midterm election of 1954 weakened Eisenhower's relations with Congress. The Democrats regained control of both houses and kept it throughout the 1950s. The president had to rely on two Texas Democrats, Senate Majority Leader Lyndon B. Johnson and Speaker of the House Sam Rayburn, for legislative action; at best, it was an awkward and uneasy relationship.

The result was a very modest legislative record. Eisenhower did continue the basic social measures of the New Deal. In 1954, he signed bills extending Social Security benefits to more than seven million Americans, raising the minimum wage to $1 an hour, and adding four million workers to those eligible for unemployment benefits. He consolidated the administration of welfare programs by creating the Department of Health, Education, and Welfare in 1953. But Ike steadfastly opposed Democratic plans for compulsory health insurance—which he condemned as the "socialization of medicine"—and comprehensive federal aid to education, preferring to leave everything except school construction in the hands of local and state authorities. This lack of presidential support and the continuing grip of the conservative coalition in Congress blocked any further reform in the 1950s.

The one significant legislative achievement of the Eisenhower years came with the passage of the Highway Act of 1956. After a twelve-year delay, Congress appropriated funds for a 41,000-mile interstate highway system consisting of multilane divided expressways that would connect the nation's major cities. Justified on grounds of national defense, the 1956 act pleased a variety of highway users: the trucking industry, automobile clubs, organized labor (eager for construction jobs), farmers (needing to speed their crops to market), and state highway officials (anxious for the 90 percent funding contributed by the federal

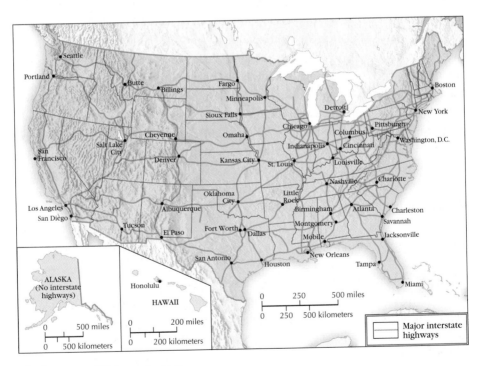

The Interstate Highway System

The 1956 plan to create an interstate highway system drastically changed America's landscape and culture. Today, the system covers about forty-five thousand miles, only a few thousand more miles than called for in the original plan.

THE ELECTION OF 1956

CANDIDATE	PARTY	POPULAR VOTE	ELECTORAL VOTE
Eisenhower	Republican	35,585,245	457
Stevenson	Democratic	26,030,172	73

government). Built over the next twenty years, the interstate highway system had a profound influence on American life. It stimulated the economy and shortened travel time dramatically, while at the same time intensifying the nation's dependence on the automobile and distorting metropolitan growth patterns into long strips paralleling the new expressways.

Overall, the Eisenhower years marked an era of political moderation. The American people, enjoying the abundance of the 1950s, seemed quite content with legislative inaction. The president was sensitive to the nation's economic health; when recessions developed in 1953 and again in 1957 after his landslide reelection victory, he quickly abandoned his goal of a balanced budget in favor of a policy advocating government spending to restore prosperity. These steps, along with modest increases in New Deal welfare programs, led to a steady growth in the federal budget from $29.5 billion in 1950 to $76.5 billion in 1960. Eisenhower was able to balance the budget in only three of his eight years in office, and the $12 billion deficit in 1959 was larger than any ever before recorded in peacetime. In this manner, Eisenhower was able to maintain the New Deal legacy of federal responsibility for social welfare and the state of the economy while at the same time successfully resisting demands for more extensive government involvement in American life.

THE STRUGGLE OVER CIVIL RIGHTS

Despite President Eisenhower's reluctance to champion the cause of reform, powerful pressures for change forced long-overdue action in one area of American life—the denial of basic rights to the nation's black minority. In the midst of the Cold War, the contradiction between the denunciation of the Soviet Union for its human-rights violations and the second-class status of African Americans began to arouse the national conscience. Fighting for freedom against communist tyranny abroad, Americans had to face the reality of the continued denial of freedom to a submerged minority at home.

African Americans had benefited economically from World War II, but they were still a seriously disadvantaged group. Those who had left the South for better opportunities in northern and western cities were concentrated in blighted and segregated neighborhoods, working at low-paying jobs, suffering economic and social discrimination, and failing to share fully in the postwar prosperity.

In the South, conditions were much worse. State laws forced blacks to live almost totally segregated from white society. Not only did African Americans attend separate (and almost always inferior) schools, but they also were rigidly segregated in all public facilities. "Segregation was enforced at all places of public entertainment, including libraries, auditoriums, and circuses," Chief Justice Earl Warren noted. "There was segregation in the hospitals, prisons, mental institutions, and nursing homes. Even ambulance service was segregated."

CIVIL RIGHTS AS A POLITICAL ISSUE

Truman was the first president to attempt to alter the historic pattern of racial discrimination in the United States. In 1946, he appointed a presidential commission on civil rights. A year later, in a sweeping report titled "To Secure These Rights," the commission recommended the reinstatement of the wartime Fair Employment Practices Committee (FEPC), the establishment of a permanent civil rights commission, and the denial of federal aid to any state that condoned segregation in schools and public facilities. But southern resistance blocked any action by Congress, and the inclusion of a strong civil rights plank in the 1948 Democratic platform led to the walkout of some southern delegations and a separate States' Rights (Dixiecrat) ticket in several states of the South that fall.

African American voters in the North overwhelmingly backed Truman over Dewey in the 1948 election. The African American vote in key cities—Los Angeles, Cleveland, and Chicago—ensured the Democratic victory in California, Ohio, and Illinois. Truman responded by including civil rights legislation in his Fair Deal program in 1949. Once again, however, determined southern opposition blocked congressional action.

Even though President Truman was unable to secure any significant legislation, he did succeed in adding civil rights to the liberal agenda. From this time forward, it would be an integral part of the Democratic reform program. Also, Truman used his executive power to assist African Americans, most notably in 1948 when he issued an order calling for the desegregation of the armed forces. The navy and the air force quickly complied, but the army resisted until the personnel needs of the Korean War finally overcame the military's objections. By the end of the 1950s, the armed forces had become far more integrated than American society at large.

DESEGREGATING THE SCHOOLS

The nation's schools soon became the primary target of civil rights advocates. The NAACP concentrated first on universities, successfully waging an intensive legal battle to win admission for qualified African Americans to graduate and professional schools. Led by Thurgood Marshall, NAACP lawyers then took on the broader issue of segregation in the country's public schools. Challenging the 1896 Supreme Court decision (*Plessy* v. *Ferguson*) that upheld the constitutionality of separate but equal public facilities, Marshall argued that even substantially equal but separate schools did profound psychological damage to African American children and thus violated the Fourteenth Amendment.

The Supreme Court was unanimous in its 1954 decision in the case of *Brown* v. *Board of Education of Topeka*. Chief Justice Earl Warren, recently appointed by President Eisenhower, wrote the landmark opinion flatly declaring that "separate educational facilities are inherently unequal." To divide grade school children "solely because of their race," Warren argued, "generates a feeling of inferiority as to their status in the community that may affect their hearts and minds in a way unlikely ever to be undone." Despite this sweeping language, Warren realized it would be difficult to change historic patterns of segregation quickly. Accordingly, in 1955 the Court ruled that desegregation of the schools should proceed "with all deliberate speed" and left the details to the lower federal courts.

Linda Brown (left). Her parents were the plaintiffs in the Brown v. Board of Education of Topeka *landmark Supreme Court case. Thurgood Marshall (right), a leading African American civil rights lawyer, was chief counsel for the Browns.*

"All deliberate speed" proved to be agonizingly slow. Officials in the border states quickly complied with the Court's ruling, but states deeper in the South responded with a policy of massive resistance. Local white citizens' councils organized to fight for retention of racial separation; 101 representatives and senators signed a Southern Manifesto in 1956 that denounced the *Brown* decision as "a clear abuse of judicial power." School boards, encouraged by this show of defiance, found a variety of ways to evade the Court's ruling. These stalling tactics led to long disputes in the federal courts; by the end of the decade, fewer than 1 percent of the black children in the Deep South attended school with whites.

A conspicuous lack of presidential support further weakened the desegregation effort. Dwight Eisenhower was not a racist, but he believed that people's attitudes could not be altered by "cold lawmaking"—only "by appealing to reason, by prayer, and by constantly working at it through our own efforts" could change be enacted. Quietly and unobtrusively, he worked to achieve desegregation in federal facilities, particularly in veterans' hospitals, navy yards, and the District of Columbia school system. Yet he refrained from endorsing the *Brown* decision, which he told an aide he believed had "*set back* progress in the South *at least fifteen years.*"

Southern leaders mistook Ike's silence for tacit support of segregation. In 1957, Governor Orville Faubus of Arkansas called out the national guard to prevent the integration of Little Rock's Central High School on grounds of a threat to public order. After 270 armed troops turned back 9 young African American students, a federal judge ordered the guardsmen removed; but when the black

Angry whites taunt one of the African American students trying to pass through the lines of Arkansas National Guardsmen to enroll in Little Rock's Central High School in 1957.

students entered the school, a mob of 500 jeering whites surrounded the building. Eisenhower, who had told Faubus that "the Federal Constitution will be upheld by me by every legal means at my command," sent in 1000 paratroopers to ensure the rights of the Little Rock Nine to attend Central High. The students finished the school year under armed guard. Then Little Rock authorities closed Central High School for the next two years; when it reopened, there were only three African Americans in attendance.

Despite the snail's pace of school desegregation, the *Brown* decision led to other advances. In 1957, the Eisenhower administration proposed the first general civil rights legislation since Reconstruction. Despite congressional compromises, the final act did create a permanent Commission for Civil Rights, one of Truman's original goals. It also provided for federal efforts aimed at "securing and protecting the right to vote." A second civil rights act in 1960 slightly strengthened the voting rights section.

Like the desegregation effort, the attempt to ensure African American voting rights in the South was still largely symbolic. Southern registrars used a variety of devices, ranging from intimidation to unfair tests, to deny African Americans suffrage. Yet the actions of Congress and the Supreme Court marked a vital turning point in national policy toward racial justice.

THE BEGINNINGS OF BLACK ACTIVISM

The most dynamic force for change came from African Americans themselves. The shift from legal struggles in the courts to protest in the streets began with an incident in Montgomery, Alabama. On December 1, 1955, Rosa Parks—a black seamstress who had been active in the local NAACP chapter—violated a city ordinance by refusing to give up her seat to a white person on a local bus. Her action, often viewed as spontaneous, grew out of a long tradition of black protest against the rigid segregation of the races in the South. Rosa Parks herself had been ejected from a bus a decade earlier for refusing to obey the driver's command, "Niggers move back."

Rosa Parks' arrest sparked a massive protest movement in Montgomery. Black women played a particularly important role in the protest, printing and handing out 50,000 leaflets to rally the African American community behind Parks. The movement also led to the emergence of Martin Luther King, Jr., as an eloquent new spokesman for African Americans.

King agreed to lead the subsequent bus boycott. The son of a famous Atlanta preacher, he had recently taken his first church in Montgomery after years of studying theology while earning a Ph.D. at Boston University. Now he would be able to combine his wide learning with his charismatic appeal in behalf of a prac-

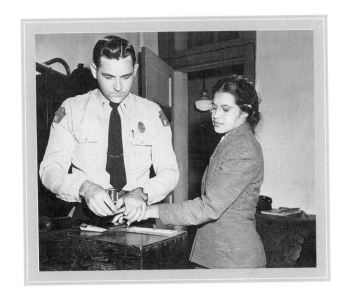

Rosa Parks, whose refusal to give up her seat to a white man ignited the boycott, is fingerprinted in February 1956 after her arrest under an antiboycott law.

tical goal—fair treatment for the African Americans who made up the bulk of the riders on the city's buses.

The Montgomery bus boycott started out with a modest goal. Instead of challenging the legality of segregated seating, King simply asked that seats be taken on a first-come, first-served basis, with African Americans being seated from the back and the whites from the front of each bus. An effective system of car pools enabled the protesters to avoid using the city buses. Soon they were insisting on a complete end to segregated seating as they sang their new song of protest:

> *Ain't gonna ride them buses no more*
> *Ain't gonna ride no more*
> *Why in the hell don't the white folk know*
> *That I ain't gonna ride no more.*

The boycott ended in victory a year later when the Supreme Court ruled the Alabama segregated seating law unconstitutional. King had won far more than this limited dent in the wall of segregation, however. He had emerged as the charismatic leader of a new civil rights movement—a man who won acclaim not only at home but around the world. He led a triumphant Prayer Pilgrimage to Washington in 1957 on the third anniversary of the *Brown* decision, stirring the crowd of thirty thousand with his ringing demand for the right to vote. His cry "Give us the ballot" boomed in salvos that civil rights historian Taylor Branch likened to "cannon bursts in a diplomatic salute." His remarkable voice became familiar to the entire nation. Unlike many African American preachers, he never shouted, yet he captured his audience by presenting his ideas with both passion and a compelling cadence.

Even more important, he had a strategy and message that fitted perfectly with the plight of his followers. King came out of the bus boycott with the concept of passive resistance. "If cursed," he had told protesters in Montgomery, "do not curse back. If struck, do not strike back, but evidence love and goodwill at all times." The essence of his strategy was to use the apparent weakness of southern blacks—their lack of power—and turn it into a conquering weapon.

His ultimate goal was to unite the broken community through bonds of Christian love. He hoped to use nonviolence to appeal to middle-class white America, "to the conscience of the great decent majority who through blindness, fear, pride or irrationality have allowed their consciences to sleep." The result,

At a sit-in demonstration at a Woolworth's lunch counter on May 28, 1963, civil rights activists from Tougaloo College stoically bear the verbal and physical abuse of white hecklers. Sit-ins were one tactic activists used to draw national attention to racial injustice, to demand desegregation of public facilities, and to prompt the federal government to take a more active role to end segregation.

King prophesied, would be to enable future historians to say of the effort, "There lived a great people—a black people—who injected new meaning and dignity into the veins of civilization."

A year after the successful bus boycott, King founded the Southern Christian Leadership Conference (SCLC) to direct the crusade against segregation. Then in February 1960, another spontaneous event sparked a further advance for passive resistance. Four African American students from North Carolina Agricultural and Technical College sat down at a dime-store lunch counter in Greensboro, North Carolina, and refused to move after being denied service. Other students, both whites and blacks, joined in similar "sit-ins" across the South. By the end of the year, some fifty thousand young people had succeeded in desegregating public facilities in more than a hundred southern cities. Several thousand of the demonstrators were arrested and put in jail, but the movement gained strength, leading to the formation of the Student Nonviolent Coordinating Committee (SNCC) in April 1960. From this time on, the SCLC and SNCC, with their tactic of direct, though peaceful, confrontation, would replace the NAACP and its reliance on court action in the forefront of the civil rights movement. The change would eventually lead to dramatic success for the movement, but it also ushered in a period of heightened tension and social turmoil in the 1960s.

The 1950s ended with the national mood less troubled than when the decade began amid the turmoil of the second Red Scare and the Korean War, yet hardly as tranquil or confident as Eisenhower had hoped it would be. The American people felt reassured about the state of the economy, no longer fearing a return to the grim years of the Great Depression. At the same time, however, they were aware that abundance alone did not guarantee the quality of everyday life and realized that there was still a huge gap between American ideals and the reality of race relations, in the North as well as the South.

30

THE TURBULENT SIXTIES

On Monday evening, September 26, 1960, John F. Kennedy and Richard M. Nixon faced each other in the nation's first televised debate between two presidential candidates. Kennedy, the relatively unknown Democratic challenger, had proposed the debates; Nixon, confident of his mastery of television, had accepted even though, as Eisenhower's vice president and the early front-runner in the election, he had more to lose and less to gain.

Richard Nixon arrived an hour early at the CBS studio in Chicago, looking tired and ill at ease. He was still recovering from a knee injury that had slowed his campaign and left him pale and weak as he pursued a hectic catch-up schedule. Makeup experts offered to hide Nixon's heavy beard and soften his prominent jowls, but the GOP candidate declined, preferring to let an aide apply a light coat of Max Factor's "Lazy Shave," a pancake cosmetic. John Kennedy, tanned from open-air campaigning in California and rested by a day spent nearly free of distracting activity, wore very light makeup.

At 8:30 P.M. central time, moderator Howard K. Smith welcomed a viewing audience estimated at seventy-seven million. Kennedy led off, echoing Abraham Lincoln by saying that the nation faced the question of "whether the world will exist half-slave and half-free." Although the ground rules limited the first debate to domestic issues, Kennedy argued that foreign and domestic policy were inseparable. He accused the Republicans of letting the country drift at home and abroad. "I think it's time America started moving again," he concluded. Nixon, caught off guard, seemed to agree with Kennedy's assessment of the nation's problems, but he contended that he had better solutions. "Our disagreement," the vice president pointed out, "is not about the goals for America but only about the means to reach those goals."

For the rest of the hour, the two candidates answered questions from a panel of journalists. Radiating confidence and self-assurance, Kennedy used a flow of statistics and details to create the image of a man deeply knowledgeable about all aspects of government. Nixon fought back with a defense of the Eisenhower record, but he seemed nervous and unsure of himself. The reaction shots of each candidate listening to the other's remarks showed Kennedy calm and serene, Nixon tense and uncomfortable.

Polls taken during the following few weeks revealed a sharp swing to Kennedy. Many Democrats and independents who had thought him too young or too inexperienced were impressed by his performance. Nixon suffered more from his unattractive image than from what he said; those who heard the debate on radio thought the Republican candidate more than held his own. In the three additional debates held during the campaign, Nixon improved his performance notably. But the damage had been done. A postelection poll revealed that of four million voters who were influenced by the debates, three million voted for Kennedy.

The televised debates were only one of many factors influencing the outcome of the 1960 election. In essence, Kennedy won because he took full advantage of all his opportunities. Lightly regarded by Democratic leaders, he won the nomination by appealing to the rank and file in the primaries, but then he astutely chose Lyndon Johnson of Texas as his running mate to blunt Nixon's southern strategy.

During the fall campaign, Kennedy exploited the national mood of frustration that had followed *Sputnik*. At home, he promised to stimulate the lagging economy and carry forward long-overdue reforms in education, health care, and civil rights under the banner of the "New Frontier." Abroad, he pledged a renewed commitment to the Cold War, vowing he would lead the nation to victory over the Soviet Union. He met the issue of his Catholicism head on, telling a group of Protestant ministers in Houston that as president he would always place country above religion. In the shrewdest move of all, he won over African American voters by helping to secure the release of Martin Luther King, Jr., from a Georgia jail where the civil rights leader was being held on a trumped-up charge.

The Democratic victory in 1960 was paper-thin. Kennedy's edge in the popular vote was only two-tenths of 1 percent, and his wide margin in the electoral college (303 to 219) was tainted by voting irregularities in several states—notably Illinois and Texas—which went Democratic by very slender majorities. Yet even though he had no mandate, Kennedy's triumph did mark a sharp political

THE ELECTION OF 1960

CANDIDATE	PARTY	POPULAR VOTE	ELECTORAL VOTE
Kennedy	Democratic	34,227,096	303
Byrd	States' Rights	—	15
Nixon	Republican	34,108,546	219
	Minor Parties	502,363	—

shift. In contrast to the aging Eisenhower, Kennedy symbolized youth, energy, and ambition. His mastery of the new medium of television reflected his sensitivity to the changes taking place in American life in the 1960s. He came to office promising reform at home and advances abroad. Over the next eight years, he and Lyndon Johnson achieved many of their goals. Yet the nation also became engulfed in angry protests, violent demonstrations, and sweeping social change in one of the stormiest decades in American history.

KENNEDY INTENSIFIES THE COLD WAR

John F. Kennedy was determined to succeed where he believed Eisenhower had failed. Critical of his predecessor for holding down defense spending and apparently allowing the Soviet Union to open up a dangerous lead in ICBMs, Kennedy sought to warn the nation of its peril and lead it to victory in the Cold War.

In his inaugural address, the young president sounded the alarm. Ignoring the domestic issues aired during the campaign, he dealt exclusively with the world. "Let every nation know, whether it wishes us well or ill, that we shall pay any price, bear any burden, meet any hardship, support any friend, oppose any foe," Kennedy declared, "to assure the survival and success of liberty. We will do all this and more."

From the day he took office, John F. Kennedy gave foreign policy top priority. In part, the decision reflected the perilous world situation, the immediate dangers ranging from the unresolved Berlin crisis, through a developing civil war in Vietnam, to the emergence of Fidel Castro as a Soviet ally in Cuba. But it also corresponded to Kennedy's personal priorities. As a congressman and senator, he had been an intense cold warrior. Bored by committee work and legislative details, he had focused on foreign policy in the Senate, gaining a seat on the Foreign

Relations Committee and publishing a book of speeches, *The Strategy of Peace*, in early 1960.

His appointments reflected his determination to win the Cold War. His choice of Dean Rusk, an experienced but unassertive diplomat, to head the State Department indicated that Kennedy planned to be his own secretary of state. He surrounded himself with young pragmatic advisers who prided themselves on toughness: McGeorge Bundy, dean of Harvard College, became national security adviser; Walt W. Rostow, an MIT economist, was Bundy's deputy; and Robert McNamara, the youthful president of the Ford Motor Company, took over as secretary of defense.

These New Frontiersmen, later dubbed "the best and the brightest" by journalist David Halberstam, all shared a hard-line view of the Soviet Union and the belief that American security depended on superior force and the willingness to use it.

FLEXIBLE RESPONSE

The first goal of the Kennedy administration was to build up the nation's armed forces. During the 1960 campaign, Kennedy had warned that the Soviets were opening a missile gap. In fact, due largely to Eisenhower's foresight, the United States had a significant lead in nuclear striking power by early 1961. Nevertheless, the new administration, intent on putting the Soviets on the defensive, authorized the construction of an awesome nuclear arsenal that included 1000 Minuteman solid-fuel ICBMs (five times the number Eisenhower had believed necessary) and 32 Polaris submarines carrying 656 missiles. The United States thus opened a missile gap in reverse, creating the possibility of a successful American first strike.

At the same time, the Kennedy administration augmented conventional military strength. Secretary of Defense McNamara developed plans to add five combat-ready army divisions, three tactical air wings, and a ten-division strategic reserve. These vast increases led to a $6 billion jump in the defense budget in 1961 alone. The president took a personal interest in counterinsurgency. He expanded the Special Forces unit at Fort Bragg, North Carolina, and insisted, over army objections, that it adopt a distinctive green beret as a symbol of its elite status.

The purpose of this buildup was to create an alternative to Eisenhower's policy of massive retaliation. Instead of responding to communist moves with nuclear threats, the United States could now call on a wide spectrum of force—ranging from ICBMs to Green Berets. Thus, as Robert McNamara explained, the new strategy of flexible response meant the United States could "choose among several operational plans." The danger was that such a powerful arsenal might tempt the new administration to test its strength against the Soviet Union.

CRISIS OVER BERLIN

The first confrontation came in Germany. Since 1958, Soviet Premier Khrushchev had been threatening to sign a peace treaty that would put access to the isolated western zones of Berlin under the control of East Germany. The steady flight of skilled workers to the West through the Berlin escape route weakened the East German regime dangerously, and the Soviets believed they had to resolve this issue quickly.

At a summit meeting in Vienna in June 1961, Kennedy and Khrushchev focused on Berlin as the key issue. The Russian leader called the current situation "intolerable" and announced the Soviet Union would proceed with an East German peace treaty. Kennedy was equally adamant, defending the American presence in Berlin. "I want peace," Khrushchev declared, "but, if you want war, that is your problem." "It is you, not I," the young president replied, "who wants to force a change." When the Soviet leader said he would sign a German peace treaty by December, Kennedy added, "It will be a cold winter."

The climax came sooner than either man expected. On July 25, Kennedy delivered an impassioned televised address to the American people in which he called the defense of Berlin "essential" to "the entire Free World." Announcing a series of arms increases, including $3 billion more in defense spending, the president took the unprecedented step of calling more than 150,000 reservists and national guardsmen to active duty.

Aware of superior American nuclear striking power, Khrushchev settled for a stalemate. On August 13, the Soviets sealed off their zone of the city. They began the construction of the Berlin Wall to stop the flow of brains and talent to the West. For a brief time, Russian and American tanks maneuvered within sight of each other at Checkpoint Charlie (where the American and Soviet zones met), but by fall, the tension gradually eased. Berlin—like Germany and, indeed, all of Europe—remained divided between the East and the West. Neither side could claim a victory, but Kennedy believed that at least he had proved to the world America's willingness to honor its commitments.

CONTAINMENT IN SOUTHEAST ASIA

Two weeks before Kennedy's inauguration, Khrushchev gave a speech in Moscow in which he declared Soviet support for "wars of national liberation." The Russian leader's words were actually aimed more at China than the United States; the two powerful communist nations were now rivals for influence in the Third World. But the new American president, ignoring the growing Sino-Soviet split, concluded the United States and Russia were locked in a struggle for the hearts and minds of the uncommitted in Asia, Africa, and Latin America.

East German soldiers repair a breach in the Berlin Wall made when an East German mechanic rammed an armored car into the wall while making his escape into West Berlin. On the other side of the wall, West Berliners observe the repair work.

Calling for a new policy of nation building, Kennedy advocated financial and technical assistance designed to help Third World nations achieve economic modernization and stable pro-Western governments. Measures ranging from the formation of the idealistic Peace Corps to the ambitious Alliance for Progress—a massive economic aid program for Latin America—were part of this effort. Unfortunately, Kennedy relied even more on counterinsurgency and the Green Berets to beat back the communist challenge in the Third World.

Southeast Asia offered the gravest test. Ngo Dinh Diem sought to establish a separate government in South Vietnam with large-scale American economic and military assistance. By the time Kennedy entered the White House, however, the communist government in North Vietnam, led by Ho Chi Minh, was directing the efforts of Vietcong rebels in the South. As the guerrilla war intensified in the fall of 1961, the president sent two trusted advisers, Walt Rostow and General Maxwell Taylor, to South Vietnam. They returned favoring the dispatch of eight thousand American combat troops. "As an area for the operation of U.S. troops," reported General Taylor, "SVN [South Vietnam] is not an excessively difficult or unpleasant place to operate."

The president decided against sending in combat troops in 1961, but he authorized substantial increases in economic aid to Diem and in the size of the military mission in Saigon. The number of American advisers in Vietnam grew from fewer than one thousand in 1961 to more than sixteen thousand by late 1963. American helicopters gave government forces mobility against the Vietcong, but by 1963, the situation had again become critical. Diem had failed to win the support of his own people; Buddhist monks set themselves aflame in public protests against him; and even Diem's own generals plotted his overthrow.

President Kennedy was in a quandary. He realized that the fate of South Vietnam would be determined not by America but by the Vietnamese. "In the final analysis," he said in September 1963, "it is their war. They are the ones who have to win it or lose it." But at the same time, Kennedy was not prepared to accept the possible loss of all Southeast Asia. Although aides later claimed he

Flames engulf Buddhist monk, the Reverend Quang Duc, who set himself afire at an intersection in Saigon, Vietnam, to protest persecution of Buddhists by Vietnam president Ngo Dinh Diem and his government. Other monks placed themselves in front of the wheels of nearby fire trucks to prevent them from reaching Duc.

planned to pull out after the 1964 election, Kennedy raised the stakes by tacitly approving a coup that led to Diem's overthrow and death on November 1, 1963. The resulting power vacuum in Saigon made further American involvement in Vietnam almost certain.

CONTAINING FIDEL CASTRO: THE BAY OF PIGS FIASCO

Kennedy's determination to check global communist expansion reached a peak of intensity in Cuba. In the 1960 campaign, pointing to the growing ties between the Soviet Union and Fidel Castro's regime, he had accused the Republicans of permitting a "communist satellite" to arise on "our very doorstep." Kennedy had even issued a statement backing "anti-Castro forces in exile," calling them "fighters for freedom" who held out hope for "overthrowing Castro."

In reality, the Eisenhower administration had been training a group of Cuban exiles in Guatemala since March 1960 as part of a CIA plan to topple the Castro regime. Many of the new president's advisers had doubts about the proposed invasion. The president, however, committed by his own campaign rhetoric and assured of success by the military, decided to proceed.

On April 17, 1961, fourteen hundred Cuban exiles moved ashore at the Bay of Pigs on the southern coast of Cuba. Even though the United States had masterminded the entire operation, Kennedy insisted on covert action, even canceling at the last minute a planned American air strike on the beachhead. With air superiority, Castro's well-trained forces had no difficulty in quashing the invasion. They killed nearly five hundred exiles and forced the rest to surrender within forty-eight hours.

Aghast at the swiftness of the defeat, President Kennedy took personal responsibility for the failure. In his address to the American people, however, he showed no remorse for arranging the violation of a neighboring country's sovereignty, only regret at the outcome. Above all, he expressed renewed defiance, warning the Soviets that "our restraint is not inexhaustible." For the remainder of his presidency, Kennedy continued to harass the Castro regime, imposing an economic blockade on Cuba, supporting a continuing series of raids by exile groups operating out of Florida, and failing to stop the CIA from experimenting with bizarre plots to assassinate Fidel Castro.

CONTAINING CASTRO: THE CUBAN MISSILE CRISIS

The climax of Kennedy's crusade came in October 1962 with the Cuban missile crisis. Throughout the summer and early fall, the Soviets engaged in a massive arms buildup in Cuba, ostensibly to protect Castro from an American invasion. In the United States, Republican candidates in the 1962 congressional elections called for a firm American response; Kennedy contented himself with a stern warning against the introduction of any offensive weapons, believing their presence would directly threaten American security. Khrushchev publicly denied any such intent, but secretly he took a daring gamble, building sites for twenty-four medium-range (1000-mile) and eighteen intermediate-range (2000-mile) missiles in Cuba. Later he claimed his purpose was purely defensive, but most likely he was responding to the pressures from his own military to close the enormous strategic gap in nuclear striking power that Kennedy had opened.

On October 14, 1962, American U-2 planes finally discovered the missile sites that were nearing completion. As soon as he learned of the Russian action, Kennedy decided to seek a showdown with Khrushchev. Insisting on absolute secrecy, he convened a special group of advisers to consider the way to respond.

An initial preference for an immediate air strike gradually gave way to discussion of either a full-scale invasion or a naval blockade. The president and his advisers ruled out diplomacy, rejecting a proposal to offer the withdrawal of ob-

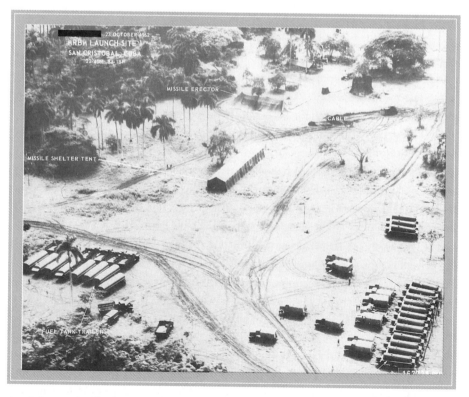

Aerial photographs taken by U-2 reconnaissance planes flying over Cuba revealed the presence of Russian missile sites under construction on the island. Recently released information about the type and number of Soviet nuclear warheads in Cuba reveals just how imminent was the threat of nuclear war had not the Soviets capitulated to U.S. demands for removal of the missiles.

solete American Jupiter missiles from Turkey in return for a similar Russian pull-out in Cuba. Kennedy finally agreed to a two-step procedure. He would proclaim a quarantine of Cuba to prevent the arrival of new missiles and threaten a nuclear confrontation to force the removal of those already there. If the Russians did not cooperate, then the United States would invade Cuba and dismantle the missiles by force.

On the evening of October 22, the president informed the nation of the existence of the Soviet missiles and his plans to remove them. He spared no words in blaming Khrushchev for "this clandestine, reckless, and provocative threat to world peace," and he made it clear that any missile attack from Cuba would lead to "a full retaliatory response upon the Soviet Union."

For the next six days, the world hovered on the brink of nuclear catastrophe. Khrushchev replied defiantly, accusing Kennedy of pushing mankind "to the abyss of a world nuclear-missile war." In the Atlantic, some sixteen Soviet ships continued on course toward Cuba, while the American navy was deployed to intercept them five hundred miles from the island.

The first break came at midweek when the Soviet ships suddenly halted to avert a confrontation at sea. "We're eyeball to eyeball," commented Secretary of State Dean Rusk, "and I think the other fellow just blinked." On Friday, Khrushchev sent Kennedy a long, rambling letter offering a face-saving way out—Russia would remove the missiles in return for an American promise never to invade Cuba. The president was ready to accept when a second Russian message raised the stakes by insisting that American Jupiter missiles be withdrawn from Turkey. Kennedy refused to bargain. Nevertheless, while the military went ahead with plans for the invasion of Cuba, the president, heeding his brother's advice, decided to make one last appeal for peace. Ignoring the second Russian message, he sent a cable to Khrushchev accepting his original offer.

On Saturday night, October 27, Robert Kennedy—the president's brother and most trusted adviser—met with Soviet ambassador Anatoly Dobrynin to make it clear this was the last chance to avert nuclear confrontation. "We had to have a commitment by tomorrow that those bases would be removed," Robert Kennedy recalled telling him. Then the president's brother calmly remarked that if Khrushchev did not back down, "there would be not only dead Americans but dead Russians as well."

In reality, John F. Kennedy was not quite so ready to risk nuclear war. He instructed his brother to assure Dobrynin that the Jupiter missiles would soon be removed from Turkey. The president preferred that the missile swap be done privately, but twenty-five years later, Secretary of State Dean Rusk revealed that JFK had instructed him to arrange a deal through the United Nations involving "the removal of both the Jupiters and the missiles in Cuba." In recently released transcripts of his meetings with his advisers, the president reaffirmed his intention of making a missile trade with Khrushchev publicly as a last resort to avoid nuclear war. "We can't very well invade Cuba with all its toil," he commented, "when we could have gotten them out by making a deal on the same missiles in Turkey."

President Kennedy never had to make this final concession. At nine the next morning, Khrushchev agreed to remove the missiles in return only for Kennedy's promise not to invade Cuba. The crisis was over.

The world, however, had come perilously close to a nuclear conflict. We now know the Soviets had nuclear warheads in Cuba, not only for twenty of the medium-range missiles, but also for short-range tactical launchers designed to be used against an American invading force. If Kennedy had approved the military's recommendations for an invasion of Cuba, the consequences might have been disastrous.

The peaceful resolution of the Cuban missile crisis became a personal and political triumph for John F. Kennedy. His party successfully overcame the Republican challenge in the November elections, and his own popularity reached new heights. The American people, on the defensive since *Sputnik,* suddenly felt that they had proved their superiority over the Russians.

The Cuban missile crisis had more substantial results as well. Shaken by their close call, Kennedy and Khrushchev agreed to install a "hot line" to speed direct communication between Washington and Moscow in an emergency. Long-stalled negotiations over the reduction of nuclear testing suddenly resumed, leading to the limited test ban treaty of 1963, which outlawed tests in the atmosphere while still permitting them underground. Above all, Kennedy displayed a new maturity as a result of the crisis. In a speech at American University in June 1963, he shifted from the rhetoric of confrontation to that of conciliation. Speaking of the Russians, he said, "Our most basic common link is the fact that we all inhabit this planet. We all breathe the same air. We all cherish our children's future. And we are all mortal."

Despite these hopeful words, the missile crisis also had an unfortunate consequence. Those who believed that the Russians understood only the language of force were confirmed in their penchant for a hard line. The Russian leaders drew similar conclusions. Aware the United States had a four-to-one advantage in nuclear striking power during the Cuban crisis, one Soviet official told his American counterpart, "Never will we be caught like this again." After 1962, the Soviets embarked on a crash program to build up their navy and to overtake the American lead in nuclear missiles. Within five years, they had the nucleus of a modern fleet and had surpassed the United States in ICBMs. Kennedy's fleeting moment of triumph thus ensured the escalation of the arms race. His legacy was a bittersweet one of short-term success and long-term anxiety.

THE NEW FRONTIER AT HOME

Kennedy hoped to change the course of history at home as well as abroad. His election marked the arrival of a new generation of leadership. For the first time, people born in the twentieth century who had entered political life after World War II were in charge of national affairs. Kennedy's inaugural call to get the nation moving again was particularly attractive to young people, who had shunned political involvement during the Eisenhower years.

The new administration reflected Kennedy's aura of youth and energy. Major cabinet appointments went to activists—notably Connecticut governor Abraham Ribicoff as secretary of health, education, and welfare; labor lawyer Arthur J. Goldberg as secretary of labor; and Arizona congressman Stuart Udall as secretary of the interior. The most controversial choice was Robert F. Kennedy, the president's brother, as attorney general. Critics scoffed at his lack of legal experience; in fact, the president prized his brother's loyalty and shrewd political advice.

Equally important were the members of the White House staff who handled domestic affairs. Like their counterparts in foreign policy, these New Frontiersmen prided themselves on being tough-minded and pragmatic. In contrast to Eisenhower, Kennedy relied heavily on academics and intellectuals to help him infuse the nation with energy and a new sense of direction.

Kennedy's greatest asset was his own personality. A cool, attractive, and intelligent man, he possessed a sense of style that endeared him to the American public. He invited artists and musicians as well as corporate executives to White House functions, and he sprinkled his speeches with references to Emerson and Shakespeare. He seemed to be a new Lancelot, bent on calling forth the best in national life; admirers likened his inner circle to King Arthur's court at Camelot.

THE CONGRESSIONAL OBSTACLE

Neither Kennedy's wit nor his charm proved strong enough to break the logjam in Congress. Since the late 1940s, a series of reform bills ranging from health care to federal aid to education had been stalled on Capitol Hill. Despite JFK's victory, the election of 1960 clouded the outlook for his New Frontier program. The Democrats had lost twenty seats in the House and two in the Senate; even though they retained majorities in both branches, a conservative coalition of northern Republicans and southern Democrats opposed all efforts at reform.

The situation was especially critical in the House, where 101 southern representatives held the balance of power between 160 northern Democrats and 174 Republicans. Aided by Speaker Sam Rayburn, Kennedy was able to enlarge the Rules Committee and overcome a traditional conservative roadblock, but the narrowness of the vote, 217 to 212, revealed how difficult it would be to enact reform measures. The president gave up the fight for health care in the Senate and settled instead for a modest increase in the minimum wage.

Kennedy had no more success in enacting his program in 1962 and 1963. The conservative coalition stood firmly against education and health-care proposals. Although the composition of Congress was his main obstacle, Kennedy's greater interest in foreign policy and his distaste for legislative infighting contributed to the outcome. JFK did not enjoy "blarneying with pompous congressmen and simply would not take the time to do it," one observer noted. As a result, the New Frontier languished in Congress.

ECONOMIC ADVANCE

Kennedy gave a higher priority to the sluggish American economy. During the last years of Eisenhower's administration, the rate of economic growth had slowed to just over 2 percent annually, while unemployment rose to new heights with each recession. JFK was determined to stimulate the economy to achieve a much higher rate of long-term growth. In part, he wanted to redeem his campaign pledge to get the nation moving again; he also believed the United States had to surpass the Soviet Union in economic vitality.

Kennedy received conflicting advice from the experts. Those who claimed the problem was essentially a technological one urged manpower training and area-redevelopment programs to modernize American industry. Others called for federal spending to rebuild the nation's public facilities. Kennedy sided with the first group, largely because Congress was opposed to massive spending on public works.

The actual stimulation of the economy, however, came not from social programs but from greatly increased appropriations for defense and space. A $6 billion increase in the arms budget in 1961 gave the economy a great lift, and Kennedy's decision to send an astronaut to the moon eventually cost $25 billion. By 1962, more than half the federal budget was devoted to space and defense; aircraft and computer companies in the South and West benefited, but unemployment remained uncomfortably high in the older industrial areas of the Northeast and Midwest.

The administration's desire to keep the inflation rate low led to a serious confrontation with the business community. Kennedy relied on informal wage and price guidelines to hold down the cost of living. But in April 1962, just after the president had persuaded the steelworkers' union to accept a new contract with no wage increases and only a few additional benefits, U.S. Steel head Roger Blough informed Kennedy that his company was raising steel prices by $6 a ton. Outraged, the president publicly called the increase "a wholly unjustifiable and irresponsible defiance of the public interest" and accused Blough of displaying "contempt for the interests of 185 million Americans."

Roger Blough soon gave way. The president's tongue-lashing, along with a cutoff in Pentagon steel orders and the threat of an antitrust suit, forced him to reconsider. When several smaller steel companies refused to raise their prices in hopes of expanding their share of the market, U.S. Steel rolled back its prices. The business community deeply resented the president's action.

Troubled by his strained relations with business and by the continued lag in economic growth, the president decided to adopt a more unorthodox approach in 1963. Walter Heller, chairman of the Council of Economic Advisers, had been arguing since 1961 for a major cut in taxes in the belief it would stimulate consumer spending and give the economy the jolt it needed. The idea of a tax cut and resulting deficits during a period of prosperity went against economic orthodoxy, but Kennedy finally gave his approval. In January 1963, the president proposed a tax reduction of $13.5 billion. When finally enacted by Congress in 1964, the massive tax cut led to sustained economic advance for the rest of the decade.

Kennedy's economic policy was far more successful than his legislative efforts. Although the rate of economic growth doubled to 4.5 percent by the end of 1963 and unemployment was reduced substantially, the cost of living rose only 1.3 percent a year. Personal income went up 13 percent in the early 1960s, but the greatest gains came in corporate profits—up 67 percent in the period. Despite the overall economic growth, the public sector continued to be neglected. "I am not sure what the advantage is," complained economist John Kenneth Galbraith, "in having a few more dollars to spend if the air is too dirty to breathe, the water too polluted to drink, the commuters are losing out in the struggle to get in and out of the cities, the streets are filthy, and the schools so bad that the young, perhaps wisely, stay away."

MOVING SLOWLY ON CIVIL RIGHTS

Kennedy faced a genuine dilemma over the issue of civil rights. Despite his own lack of a strong record while in the Senate, he had portrayed himself during the 1960 campaign as a crusader for African American rights. He had promised to launch an attack on segregation in the Deep South, but his fear of alienating the large bloc of southern Democrats forced him to downplay civil rights legislation.

The president's solution was to defer congressional action in favor of executive leadership in this area. He directed his brother, Attorney General Robert Kennedy, to continue and expand the Eisenhower administration's efforts to achieve voting rights for southern blacks. To register previously disfranchised citizens, the Justice Department worked with the civil rights movement—notably the Student Nonviolent Coordinating Committee (SNCC)—in the Deep South. In two years, the Kennedy administration increased the number of voting rights suits fivefold. Yet the attorney general could not force the FBI to provide protection for the civil rights volunteers who risked their lives by encouraging African Americans to register.

Kennedy did succeed in appointing a number of African Americans to high government positions: Robert Weaver became chief of the federal housing agency, and Thurgood Marshall, who pleaded the *Brown* v. *Topeka* school desegregation case before the Supreme Court, was named to the U.S. Circuit Court. On the other hand, among his judicial appointments, Kennedy included one Mississippi jurist who referred to African Americans in court as "niggers" and once compared them to "a bunch of chimpanzees."

The civil rights movement refused to accept Kennedy's indirect approach. In May 1961, the Congress of Racial Equality (CORE) sponsored a "freedom ride" in which a biracial group attempted to test a 1960 Supreme Court decision outlawing segregation in all bus and train stations used in interstate commerce. When they arrived in Birmingham, Alabama, the freedom riders were attacked by a mob of angry whites. The attorney general quickly dispatched several hundred federal marshals to protect the freedom riders, but the president, deeply involved in the Berlin crisis, was more upset at the distraction the protesters created. Kennedy directed one of his aides to get in touch with the leaders of CORE. "Tell them to call it off," he demanded. "Stop them."

In September, after the attorney general finally convinced the Interstate Commerce Commission to issue an order banning segregation in interstate terminals and buses, the freedom rides ended. The Kennedy administration then sought to prevent further confrontations by involving civil rights activists in its voting drive.

A pattern of belated reaction to southern racism marked the basic approach of the Kennedys. When James Meredith courageously sought admission to the all-white University of Mississippi in 1962, the president and the attorney general worked closely with Mississippi governor Ross Barnett to avoid violence. Despite Barnett's later promise of cooperation, the night before Meredith enrolled at the University of Mississippi, a mob attacked the federal marshals and national guard troops sent to protect him. The violence left 2 dead and 375 injured, including 166 marshals and 12 guardsmen, but Meredith attended the university and eventually graduated.

In 1963, Kennedy sent the deputy attorney general to face down Governor George C. Wallace, an avowed segregationist who had promised "to stand in the schoolhouse door" to prevent the integration of the University of Alabama. After a brief confrontation, Wallace yielded to federal authority, and two African American students peacefully desegregated the state university.

"I HAVE A DREAM"

Martin Luther King, Jr., finally forced Kennedy to abandon his cautious tactics and come out openly in behalf of racial justice. In the spring of 1963, King began a massive protest in Birmingham, one of the South's most segregated cities. Public marches and demonstrations aimed at integrating public facilities and opening up jobs for African Americans quickly led to police harassment and many arrests, including that of King himself. Police Commissioner Eugene "Bull" Connor was determined to crush the civil rights movement; King was equally determined to prevail.

Bull Connor played directly into King's hands. On May 3, as six thousand children marched in place of the jailed protesters, authorities broke up a demonstration with clubs, snarling police dogs, and high-pressure water hoses strong enough to take the bark off a tree. With a horrified nation watching scene after scene of this brutality on television, the Kennedy administration quickly intervened to

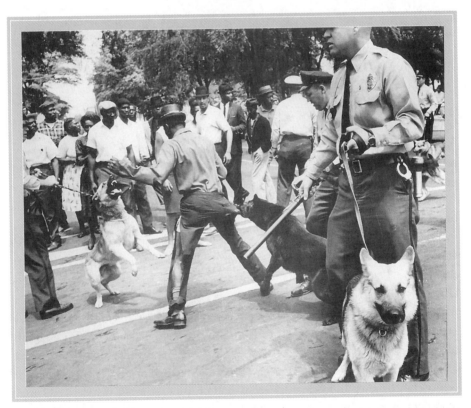

The attempts of African Americans to end discrimination and secure their civil rights met with violent resistance in Birmingham, Alabama, where police used snarling dogs, fire hoses, clubs, and electric cattle prods to turn back the unarmed demonstrators.

Reverend Martin Luther King, Jr., addresses the crowd at the March on Washington in August 1963. The largest single demonstration of the early 1960s, the march reflected the spirit and determination of many devoted to the cause of equality for African Americans. In his speech, King recounted the difficulties of blacks' struggle for freedom, then stirred the crowd with the description of his dream for America: "I have a dream that one day this nation will rise up and live out the true meaning of its creed—we hold these truths to be self-evident, that all men are created equal."

arrange a settlement with the Birmingham civic leaders that ended the violence and granted the protesters most of their demands.

More important, Kennedy finally ended his long hesitation and sounded the call for action. "We are confronted primarily with a moral issue," he told the nation on June 11. "It is as old as the Scriptures and is as clear as the American Constitution." Eight days later, the administration sponsored civil rights legislation providing equal access to all public accommodations as well as an extension of voting rights for African Americans.

Despite pleas from the government for an end to demonstrations and protests, civil rights leaders kept pressure on the administration. They scheduled a massive march on Washington for August 1963. On August 28, more than 200,000 marchers gathered for a daylong rally in front of the Lincoln Memorial where they listened to hymns, speeches, and prayers for racial justice. The climax of the event was Martin Luther King, Jr.'s eloquent description of his dream for America. It concluded:

When we let freedom ring, when we let it ring from every village and every hamlet, from every state and every city, we will be able to speed up that day when all God's children, black men and white men, Jews and Gentiles, Protestants and Catholics, will be able to join hands and sing, in the words of that old Negro spiritual, "Free at last! Free at last! Thank God almighty, we are free at last!"

By the time of Kennedy's death in November 1963, his civil rights legislation was well on its way to passage in Congress. Unlike Eisenhower, he had provided presidential leadership for the civil rights movement. His emphasis on executive action gradually paid off, especially in extending voting rights. By early 1964, 40 percent of southern blacks had the franchise, compared to only 28 percent in 1960. Moreover, Kennedy's sense of caution and restraint, painful and frustrating as it was to African American activists, had proved well founded. Avoiding an early, and possibly fatal, defeat in Congress, he had waited until a national consensus emerged and then had carefully channeled it behind effective legislation. Behaving very much the way Franklin Roosevelt did in guiding the nation into World War II, Kennedy chose to be a fox rather than a lion on civil rights.

THE SUPREME COURT AND REFORM

The most active impulse for social change in the early 1960s came from a surprising source: the usually staid and conservative Supreme Court. Under the leadership of Earl Warren, a pragmatic jurist more noted for his political astuteness than his legal scholarship, the Court ventured into new areas. A group of liberal judges argued for social reform, while advocates of judicial restraint led by Felix Frankfurter fought stubbornly against the new activism.

The resignation of Frankfurter in 1962 enabled President Kennedy to appoint Secretary of Labor Arthur Goldberg, a committed liberal, to the Supreme Court. With a clear majority now favoring judicial intervention, the Warren Court issued a series of landmark decisions designed to extend to state and local jurisdictions the traditional rights afforded the accused in federal courts. Thus in *Gideon* v. *Wainwright* (1963), *Escobedo* v. *Illinois* (1964), and *Miranda* v. *Arizona* (1966), the majority decreed that defendants had to be provided lawyers, had to be informed of their constitutional rights, and could not be interrogated or induced to confess to a crime without defense counsel being present. In effect, the Court extended to the poor and the ignorant those constitutional guarantees that had always been available to the rich and to the legally informed—notably hardened criminals.

The most far-reaching Warren Court decisions came in the area of legislative reapportionment. In 1962, the Court ruled in *Baker* v. *Carr* that Tennessee had to redistribute its legislative seats to give citizens in Memphis equal representation. Subsequent decisions reinforced the ban on rural overrepresentation as the Court proclaimed that places in all legislative bodies, including the House of Representatives, had to be allocated on the basis of "people, not land or trees or pastures." The principle of "one man, one vote" greatly increased the political power of cities at the expense of rural areas.

The activism of the Supreme Court stirred up a storm of criticism. The rulings that extended protection to criminals and those accused of subversive activity led some Americans to charge that the Court was encouraging crime and weakening national security. The 1962 *Engel* v. *Vitale* decision banning school prayer incensed many conservative Americans, who saw the Court as undermining moral values. Legal scholars worried more about the weakening of the Court's prestige as it became more directly involved in the political process. On balance, however, the Warren Court helped achieve greater social justice by protecting the rights of the underprivileged and by permitting dissent and free expression to flourish.

"Let Us Continue"

The New Frontier came to a sudden and violent end on November 22, 1963, when Lee Harvey Oswald assassinated John F. Kennedy as the president rode in a motorcade in downtown Dallas. The shock of losing the young president, who had become a symbol of hope and promise for a whole generation, stunned the entire world. The American people were bewildered by the rapid sequence of events: the brutal killing of their beloved president; the televised slaying of Oswald by Jack Ruby in the basement of the Dallas police station; the composure and dignity of Kennedy's widow, Jacqueline, at the ensuing state funeral; and the hurried Warren Commission report, which identified Oswald as the lone assassin. Afterward, critics would charge that Oswald had been part of a vast conspiracy, but at the time, the prevailing national reaction was a numbing sense of loss.

Vice President Lyndon B. Johnson moved quickly to fill the vacuum left by Kennedy's death. Sworn in on board Air Force One as he returned to Washington, Johnson soon met with a stream of world leaders to reassure them of American political stability. Five days after the tragedy in Dallas, Johnson spoke eloquently to a special joint session of Congress. Recalling JFK's inaugural summons, "Let us begin," the new president declared, "Today in the moment of new resolve, I would say to all my fellow Americans, 'Let us continue.'"

Aboard Air Force One on the return from Dallas to Washington, DC, Judge Sarah Hughes administers the presidential oath of office to a grim Lyndon Johnson.

JOHNSON IN ACTION

Lyndon Johnson suffered from the inevitable comparison with his young and stylish predecessor. LBJ was acutely aware of his own lack of polish; he sought to surround himself with Kennedy advisers and insiders, hoping their sophistication would rub off on him. Johnson's assets were very real—he possessed an intimate knowledge of Congress, an incredible energy and determination to succeed, and a fierce ego. When a young marine officer tried to direct him to the proper helicopter, saying, "This one is yours," Johnson replied, "Son, they are all my helicopters."

LBJ's height and intensity gave him a powerful presence; he dominated any room he entered, and he delighted in using his physical power of persuasion. One Texas politician explained why he had given in to Johnson: "Lyndon got me by the lapels and put his face on top of mine and he talked and talked and talked. I figured it was either getting drowned or joining."

Yet LBJ found it impossible to project his intelligence and vitality to large audiences. Unlike Kennedy, he wilted before the camera, turning his televised speeches into stilted and awkward performances. Trying to belie his reputation as

President Johnson applies the "Johnson treatment" to Senator Theodore Francis Green of Rhode Island. A shrewd politician and master of the legislative process, Johnson always knew which votes he could count on, those he couldn't, and where and how to apply pressure to swing votes his way.

a riverboat gambler, he came across like a foxy grandpa, clever, calculating, and not to be trusted.

Whatever his shortcomings in style, however, Johnson possessed far greater ability than Kennedy in dealing with Congress. He entered the White House with more than thirty years of experience in Washington as a legislative aide, congressman, and senator. His encyclopedic knowledge of the legislative process and his shrewd manipulation of individual senators had enabled him to become the most influential Senate majority leader in history. Famed for "the Johnson treatment," a legendary ability to use personal persuasion to reach his goals, Johnson in fact relied more on his close ties with the Senate's power brokers—or "whales," as he called them—than on his exploitation of the "minnows."

Above all, Johnson sought consensus. Indifferent to ideology, he had moved easily from New Deal liberalism to oil-and-gas conservatism as his career advanced. He had performed a balancing act on civil rights, working with the Eisenhower administration on behalf of the 1957 Voting Rights Act, yet carefully weakening it to avoid alienating southern Democrats. When Kennedy dashed Johnson's own intense presidential ambitions in 1960, LBJ had gracefully agreed to be his running mate and had endured the humiliation of the vice presidency loyally and silently. Suddenly thrust into power, Johnson used his gifts wisely.

Citing his favorite scriptural passage from Isaiah, "Come now, and let us reason together, saith the Lord," he concentrated on securing passage of Kennedy's tax and civil rights bills in 1964.

The tax cut came first. Aware of the power wielded by Senate Finance Committee Chairman Harry Byrd, a Virginia conservative, Johnson astutely lowered Kennedy's projected $101.5 billion budget for 1965 to $97.9 billion. Although Byrd voted against the tax cut, he let the measure out of his committee, telling Johnson, "I'll be working for you behind the scenes." In February, Congress reduced personal income taxes by more than $10 billion, touching off a sustained economic boom.

Johnson was even more influential in passing the Kennedy civil rights measure. Staying in the background, he encouraged liberal amendments that strengthened the bill in the House. Johnson refused all efforts at compromise, counting on growing public pressure to force northern Republicans to abandon their traditional alliance with southern Democrats. Everett M. Dirksen of Illinois, the GOP leader in the Senate, met repeatedly with Johnson at the White House. When LBJ refused to yield, Dirksen finally announced, "The time has come for equality of opportunity in sharing in government, in education, and in employment," and led a Republican vote to end a 57-day filibuster.

The 1964 Civil Rights Act, signed on July 2, made illegal the segregation of African Americans in public facilities, established an Equal Employment Opportunity Commission to lessen racial discrimination in employment, and protected the voting rights of African Americans. An amendment sponsored by segregationists in an effort to weaken the bill added gender to the prohibition of discrimination in Title VII of the act; in the future, women's groups would use the clause to secure government support for greater equality in employment and education.

THE ELECTION OF 1964

Passage of two key Kennedy measures within six months did not satisfy Johnson, who wanted now to win the presidency in his own right. Eager to surpass Kennedy's narrow victory in 1960, he hoped to win by a great landslide.

Searching for a cause of his own, LBJ found one in the issue of poverty. Beginning in the late 1950s, economists had warned that the prevailing affluence disguised a persistent and deep-seated problem of poverty. In 1962 Michael Harrington's book *The Other America* attracted national attention. Writing with passion and eloquence, Harrington claimed that nearly one-fifth of the nation, some thirty-five million Americans, lived in poverty.

Johnson quickly took over poverty proposals that Kennedy had been developing and made them his own. In his January 1964 State of the Union address

LBJ announced, "This administration, today, here and now, declares unconditional war on poverty in America." During the next eight months, Johnson fashioned a comprehensive poverty program under the direction of R. Sargent Shriver, Kennedy's brother-in-law. The president added $500 million to existing programs to come up with a $1 billion effort that Congress passed in August 1964.

The new Office of Economic Opportunity (OEO) set up a wide variety of programs, ranging from Head Start for preschoolers to the Job Corps for high school dropouts in need of vocational training. The level of funding was never high enough to meet the OEO's ambitious goals, and a controversial attempt to include representatives of the poor in the Community Action Program led to bitter political feuding with city and state officials. Nonetheless, the war on poverty, along with the economic growth provided by the tax cut, helped reduce the ranks of the poor by nearly ten million between 1964 and 1967.

The new program established Johnson's reputation as a reformer in an election year, but he still faced two challenges to his authority. The first was Robert F. Kennedy, the late president's brother, who continued as attorney general but who wanted to become vice president and Johnson's eventual successor in the White House. Desperate to prove his ability to succeed without Kennedy help, LBJ commented, "I don't need that little runt to win" and chose Hubert Humphrey as his running mate.

The second challenge was the Republican candidate, Senator Barry Goldwater, an outspoken conservative from Arizona. An attractive and articulate man, Goldwater advocated a rejection of the welfare state and a return to unregulated free enterprise. To Johnson's delight, Goldwater chose to place ideology ahead of political expediency. The senator spoke out boldly against the Tennessee Valley Authority, denounced Social Security, and advocated a hawkish foreign policy. "In Your Heart, You Know He's Right," read the Republican slogan, leading the Democrats to reply, "Yes, Far Right."

Johnson stuck carefully to the middle of the road, embracing the liberal reform program—which he now called the Great Society—while stressing his concern for balanced budgets and fiscal orthodoxy. The more Goldwater sagged in the polls, the harder Johnson campaigned, determined to achieve his treasured landslide. On election day, LBJ received 61.1 percent of the popular vote and an overwhelming majority in the electoral college. Equally important, the Democrats achieved huge gains in Congress, controlling the House by a margin of 295 to 140 and the Senate by 68 to 32. Kennedy's legacy and Goldwater's candor had enabled Johnson to break the conservative grip on Congress for the first time in a quarter century.

THE ELECTION OF 1964

CANDIDATE	PARTY	POPULAR VOTE	ELECTORAL VOTE
Johnson	Democratic	43,126,584	486
Goldwater	Republican	27,177,838	52

THE TRIUMPH OF REFORM

LBJ moved quickly to secure his legislative goals. Despite solid majorities in both Houses, including seventy first-term Democrats who had ridden into office on his coattails, Johnson knew he would have to enact the Great Society as swiftly as possible. "You've got to give it all you can, that first year," he told an aide. "Doesn't matter what kind of majority you come in with. You've got just one year when they treat you right, and before they start worrying about themselves."

Johnson gave two traditional Democratic reforms—health care and education—top priority. Aware of strong opposition to a comprehensive medical program, LBJ settled for Medicare, which mandated health insurance under the Social Security program for Americans over age 65, and a supplementary Medicaid program for the indigent. To symbolize the end of a long struggle, Johnson flew to Independence, Missouri, so Truman could witness the ceremonial signing of the Medicare law, which had its origins in Truman's 1949 health insurance proposal.

LBJ overcame the religious hurdle on education by supporting a child-benefit approach, allocating federal money to advance the education of students in parochial as well as public schools. The Elementary and Secondary Education Act of 1965 provided more than $1 billion in federal aid, the largest share going to school districts with the highest percentage of impoverished pupils.

Civil rights proved to be the most difficult test of Johnson's leadership. Martin Luther King, concerned that three million southern blacks were still denied the right to vote, in early 1965 chose Selma, Alabama, as the site for a test case. The white authorities in Selma, led by Sheriff James Clark, used cattle prods and bullwhips to break up the demonstrations. Johnson intervened in March, after TV cameras showed Sheriff Clark's deputies brutally halting a march from Selma to Montgomery. The president ordered the Alabama National Guard to federal duty to protect the demonstrators, had the Justice Department draw up a new voting rights bill, and personally addressed the Congress on civil rights. LBJ

AFRICAN AMERICAN VOTER REGISTRATION BEFORE AND AFTER THE 1965 VOTING RIGHTS ACT

STATE	1960	1966	INCREASE	PERCENTAGE OF INCREASE OVER 1960
Alabama	66,000	250,000	184,000	278.8
Arkansas	73,000	115,000	42,000	57.5
Florida	183,000	303,000	120,000	65.6
Georgia	180,000	300,000	120,000	66.7
Louisiana	159,000	243,000	84,000	52.8
Mississippi	22,000	175,000	153,000	695.4
North Carolina	210,000	282,000	72,000	34.3
South Carolina	58,000	191,000	133,000	229.3
Tennessee	185,000	225,000	40,000	21.6
Texas	227,000	400,000	173,000	76.2
Virginia	100,000	205,000	105,000	105.0

Compiled from U.S. Bureau of the Census, *Statistical Abstract of the United States.*

issued a compelling call to action. "Their cause must be our cause, too. Because it is not just Negroes, but really it is all of us who must overcome the crippling legacy of bigotry and injustice."

Five months later, Congress passed the Voting Rights Act of 1965. Once again Johnson had worked with Senate Republican leader Dirksen to break a southern filibuster and assure passage of a measure. The act banned literacy tests in states and counties in which less than half the population had voted in 1964 and provided for federal registrars in these areas to assure African Americans the franchise.

The results were dramatic. In less than a year, 166,000 African Americans were added to the voting rolls in Alabama; African American registration went up 400 percent in Mississippi. By the end of the decade, the percentage of eligible African American voters who had registered had risen from 40 to 65 percent. For the first time since Reconstruction, African Americans had become active participants in southern politics.

Before the 89th Congress ended its first session in the fall of 1965, it had passed eighty-nine bills. These included measures to create two new cabinet departments (Transportation, and Housing and Urban Affairs); acts to provide for highway safety and to ensure clean air and water; and large appropriations for higher education, public housing, and the continuing war on poverty. In nine months, Johnson had enacted the entire Democratic reform agenda.

The man responsible for this great leap forward, however, had failed to win the public adulation he so deeply desired. His legislative skills had made the most of the opportunities offered by the 1964 Democratic landslide, but the people did not respond to Johnson's leadership with the warmth and praise they had showered on Kennedy. Reporters continued to portray him as a crude wheeler-dealer; as a maniac who drove around Texas back roads at 90 miles an hour, one hand on the wheel and the other holding a can of beer. No one was more aware of this lack of affection than LBJ himself. His public support, he told an aide, is "like a Western river, broad but not deep."

Johnson's realization of the fleeting nature of his popularity was all too accurate. The dilemmas of the Cold War began to divert his attention from domestic concerns and eventually, in the case of Vietnam, would overwhelm him. Yet his legislative achievements were still remarkable. In one brief outburst of reform, he had accomplished more than any president since FDR.

Difficulties abroad would dim the luster of the Johnson presidency, but they could not diminish the lasting impact of the Great Society on American life. Federal aid to education, the enactment of Medicare and Medicaid, and, above all, the civil rights acts of 1964 and 1965 changed the nation irrevocably. The aged and the poor now were guaranteed access to medical care; communities saw an infusion of federal funds to improve local education; and African Americans could now begin to attend integrated schools, enjoy public facilities, and gain political power by exercising the right to vote. But even at this moment of triumph for liberal reform, new currents of dissent and rebellion were brewing.

JOHNSON ESCALATES THE VIETNAM WAR

Lyndon Johnson stressed continuity in foreign policy just as he had in enacting Kennedy's domestic reforms. He not only inherited the policy of containment from his fallen predecessor, but he shared the same Cold War assumptions and convictions. And, feeling less confident about dealing with international issues, he tended to rely heavily on Kennedy's advisers—notably Secretary of State Rusk, Secretary of Defense McNamara, and McGeorge Bundy, the national security adviser.

Johnson had broad exposure to national security affairs. He had served on the Naval Affairs Committee in the House before and during World War II, and as Senate majority leader he had been briefed and consulted regularly on the crises of the 1950s. A confirmed cold warrior, he had also seen in the 1940s the devastating political impact on the Democratic party of the communist triumph in

China. "I am not going to lose Vietnam," he told the American ambassador to Saigon just after taking office in 1963. "I am not going to be the president who saw Southeast Asia go the way China went."

Aware of the problem Castro had caused John Kennedy, LBJ moved firmly to contain communism in the Western Hemisphere. In 1965, to block the possible emergence of a Castro-type government, LBJ sent twenty thousand American troops to the Dominican Republic. Johnson's flimsy justifications—ranging from the need to protect American tourists to a dubious list of suspected communists among the rebel leaders—served only to alienate liberal critics in the United States, particularly Senate Foreign Relations Committee Chairman J. William Fulbright, a former Johnson favorite. The intervention ended in 1966 with the election of a conservative government. Senator Fulbright, however, continued his criticism of Johnson's foreign policy by publishing *The Arrogance of Power,* a biting analysis of the fallacies of containment. Fulbright's defection symbolized a growing gap between the president and liberal intellectuals; the more LBJ struggled to uphold the Cold War policies he had inherited from Kennedy, the more he found himself under attack from Congress, the media, and the universities.

THE VIETNAM DILEMMA

It was Vietnam rather than Latin America that became Lyndon Johnson's obsession and led ultimately to his political downfall. Inheriting an American commitment that dated back to Eisenhower to support an independent South Vietnam, the new president believed he had little choice but to continue Kennedy's policy in Vietnam. The crisis created by Diem's overthrow only three weeks before Kennedy's assassination led to a vacuum of power in Saigon that prevented Johnson from conducting a thorough review and reassessment of the strategic alternatives in Southeast Asia. In 1964, seven different governments ruled South Vietnam; power changed hands three times within one month.

Resisting pressure from the Joint Chiefs of Staff for direct American military involvement, LBJ continued Kennedy's policy of economic and technical assistance. He sent in seven thousand more military advisers and an additional $50 million in aid. While he insisted it was still up to the Vietnamese themselves to win the war, he expanded American support for covert operations, including amphibious raids on the North.

These undercover activities led directly to the Gulf of Tonkin affair. On August 2, 1964, North Vietnamese torpedo boats attacked the *Maddox,* an American destroyer engaged in electronic intelligence gathering in the Gulf of Tonkin. The attack was prompted by the belief the American ship had been involved in a South Vietnamese raid nearby. The *Maddox* escaped unscathed, but to show American resolve, the navy sent in another destroyer, the *C. Turner Joy.* On the evening of August 4, the two destroyers, responding to sonar and radar contacts, opened fire on North Vietnamese gunboats in the area. Johnson ordered retaliatory air strikes on North Vietnamese naval bases. Later investigation indicated that the North Vietnamese gunboats had not launched a second attack on the American ships.

The next day, the president asked Congress to pass a resolution authorizing him to take "all necessary measures to repel any armed attack against the forces of the United States and to prevent further aggression." Later, critics charged that LBJ wanted a blank check from Congress to carry out the future escalation of the Vietnam War, but such a motive is unlikely. He had already rejected immediate military intervention. In part, he wanted the Gulf of Tonkin Resolution to demonstrate to North Vietnam the American determination to defend South Vietnam at any cost. He also wanted to preempt the Vietnam issue from his Republican opponent, Barry Goldwater, who had been advocating a tougher policy. By taking a firm stand on the Gulf of Tonkin incident, Johnson could both impress the North Vietnamese and outmaneuver a political rival at home.

Congress responded with alacrity. The House acted unanimously, while only two senators voted against the Gulf of Tonkin Resolution. Johnson appeared to have won a spectacular victory. His standing in the Gallup poll shot up from 42 to 72 percent, and he had effectively blocked Goldwater from exploiting Vietnam as a campaign issue.

In the long run, however, this easy victory proved costly. Having used force once against North Vietnam, LBJ was more likely to do so in the future. And although he apparently had no intention of widening the conflict in August 1964, the congressional resolution was phrased broadly enough to enable him to use whatever level of force he wanted—including unlimited military intervention. Above all, when he did wage war in Vietnam, he left himself open to the charge of deliberately misleading Congress. Presidential credibility proved ultimately to be Johnson's Achilles' heel; his political downfall began with the Gulf of Tonkin Resolution.

ESCALATION

Full-scale American involvement in Vietnam began in 1965 in a series of steps designed primarily to prevent a North Vietnamese victory. With the political situation in Saigon growing more hopeless every day, the president's advisers urged the bombing of the North. American air attacks would serve several purposes: they would block North Vietnamese infiltration routes, make Hanoi pay a heavy price for its role, and lift the sagging morale of the South Vietnamese. But most important, as McGeorge Bundy reported after a visit to Pleiku (site of a Vietcong attack on an American base which took nine lives), "Without new U.S. action de-

Southeast Asia and the Vietnam War

American combat forces in South Vietnam rose from sixteen thousand in 1963 to a half million in 1968, but a successful conclusion to the conflict was no closer.

feat appears inevitable—probably not in a matter of weeks or perhaps even months, but within the next year or so." In February 1965 Johnson cited the Pleiku attack in ordering a long-planned aerial bombardment of selected North Vietnamese targets.

The air strikes, aimed at impeding the communist supply line and damaging Hanoi's economy, proved ineffective. In April, Johnson authorized the use of American combat troops in South Vietnam, restricting them to defensive operations intended to protect American air bases. In mid-July, Secretary of Defense McNamara recommended sending a hundred thousand combat troops to Vietnam, more than doubling the American forces there. He believed this escalation would lead to a "favorable outcome," but he also told the president that an additional hundred thousand soldiers might be needed in 1966 and that American battle deaths could rise as high as five hundred a month (by early 1968, they hit a peak of more than five hundred a week).

At the same time, other advisers, most notably Undersecretary of State George Ball, spoke out against military escalation in favor of a political settlement. Warning that the United States was likely to suffer France's fate in Vietnam of "national humiliation," Ball told the president that he had "serious doubt that an army of westerners can successfully fight Orientals in an Asian jungle."

Lyndon Johnson was genuinely torn, asking his advisers at one point, "Are we starting something that in two to three years we simply can't finish?" But he finally decided he had no choice but to persevere in Vietnam. Although he insisted on paring down McNamara's troop request, LBJ settled on a steady military escalation designed to compel Hanoi to accept a diplomatic solution. In late July, the president permitted a gradual increase in the bombing of North Vietnam and allowed American ground commanders to conduct offensive operations in the South. Most ominously, he approved the immediate dispatch of fifty thousand troops to Vietnam and the future commitment of fifty thousand more.

These July decisions formed "an open-ended commitment to employ American military forces as the situation demanded," wrote historian George Herring, and they were "the closest thing to a formal decision for war in Vietnam." Convinced that withdrawal would destroy American credibility before the world and that an invasion of the North would lead to World War III, Johnson opted for large-scale but limited military intervention. Moreover, LBJ feared the domestic consequences of either extreme. A pullout could cause a massive political backlash at home, as conservatives condemned him for betraying South Vietnam to communism. All-out war, however, would mean the end of his social programs. Once Congress focused on the conflict, he explained to biographer Doris Kearns, "that bitch of a war" would destroy "the woman I really loved—the Great Society." So he settled for a limited war, committing a half million American troops to battle in Southeast Asia, all the while pretending it was a minor engagement and refusing to ask the American people for the support and sacrifice required for victory.

Lyndon Johnson was not solely responsible for the Vietnam War. He inherited both a policy that assumed Vietnam was a vital national interest and a deteriorating situation in Saigon that demanded a more active American role. Truman, Eisenhower, and Kennedy had taken the United States deep into the Vietnam maze; it was Johnson's fate to have to find a way out. But LBJ bears full responsibility for the way he tried to resolve his dilemma. The failure to confront the people with the stark choices the nation faced in Vietnam, the insistence on secrecy and deceit, the refusal to acknowledge that he had committed the United States to a dangerous military involvement—these were Johnson's sins in Vietnam. His lack of self-confidence in foreign policy and fear of domestic reaction led directly to his undoing.

STALEMATE

For the next three years, Americans waged an intensive war in Vietnam and succeeded only in preventing a communist victory. American bombing of the North proved ineffective. The rural, undeveloped nature of the North Vietnamese economy meant there were few industrial targets. Nor were the efforts to destroy supply lines any more successful. American planes pounded the Ho Chi Minh trail that ran down through Laos and Cambodia, but the North Vietnamese used the jungle canopy effectively to hide their shipments. In fact, the American air attacks, with their inadvertent civilian casualties, gave North Vietnam a powerful propaganda weapon, which it used to sway world opinion against the United States.

The war in the South went no better. Despite the steady increase in American ground forces, from 184,000 in late 1965 to more than 500,000 by early 1968, the Vietcong still controlled much of the countryside. The search-and-destroy tactics employed by the American commander, General William Westmoreland, proved ill suited to the situation. In a vain effort to destroy the enemy, Westmoreland used superior American firepower wantonly, devastating the countryside, causing many civilian casualties, and driving the peasantry into the arms of the guerrillas. Inevitably, these tactics led to the slaughter of innocent civilians, most notably at the hamlet of My Lai. In March 1968, an American company led by Lieutenant William Calley, Jr., killed more than two hundred unarmed villagers.

The main premise of Westmoreland's strategy was to wage a war of attrition that would finally reach a "crossover point" when communist losses each month would be greater than the number of new troops they could recruit. He hoped to lure the Vietcong and the North Vietnamese regulars into pitched battles in which American firepower would inflict heavy casualties. But soon it was the communists who were deciding where and when the fighting would take place, provoking American attacks in remote areas of South Vietnam that favored the defenders. By the end of 1967, the nearly half million American troops Johnson had sent to Vietnam had failed to defeat the enemy. At best, LBJ had only achieved a bloody stalemate that gradually turned the American people against a war they had once eagerly embraced.

YEARS OF TURMOIL

The Vietnam War became the focal point for a growing movement of youthful protest that made the 1960s the most turbulent decade of the twentieth century. Disenchantment with conventional middle-class values, a rapid increase in college enrollments as a result of the post–World War II baby boom, a reaction against the crass materialism of the affluent society—with its endless suburbs and shopping malls—all led American youth to embrace an alternative lifestyle based on the belief that people are "sensitive, searching, poetic, and capable of love." They were ready to create a counterculture.

The agitation of the 1960s was at its height between 1965 and 1968, the years that marked the escalation of the Vietnam War. Disturbances on college campuses reflected growing discontent in other parts of society, from the urban ghettos to the lettuce fields of the Southwest. All who felt disadvantaged—students, African Americans, Hispanics, Native Americans, women, hippies—took to the streets to give vent to their feelings.

THE STUDENT REVOLT

The first sign of student rebellion came in the fall of 1964 at the prestigious University of California at Berkeley. A small group of radical students resisted university efforts to deny them a place to solicit volunteers and funds for off-campus causes. Forming the Free Speech movement, they struck back by occupying administration buildings and blocking the arrest of a nonstudent protester. For the next two months, the campus was in turmoil until the protesters won the rights of free speech and association that they championed.

The Free Speech movement at Berkeley offered many insights into the causes of campus unrest. It was fueled in part by student suspicion of an older, Depression-born generation that viewed affluence as the answer to all problems. Unable to exert much influence on the power structure that directed the consumer society, the students turned on the university. They viewed higher education as the faithful servant of a corporate culture: the university trained hordes of technicians, harbored research laboratories that perfected dreadful weapons, and used IBM punch cards to regiment students.

Student protest found its full expression in the explosive growth of the Students for a Democratic Society (SDS). Founded in Port Huron, Michigan, in 1962, the radical organization wanted to rid American society of poverty, racism, and violence. Although the SDS embraced many traditional liberal reforms, its founders advocated a new approach called participatory democracy. In contrast to both liberalism and old-style socialism, the SDS sought salvation through the individual rather than the group. Personal control of one's life and destiny, not the creation of new bureaucracies, was the hallmark of the New Left.

In the next few years, the SDS grew phenomenally. Spurred on by the Vietnam War and massive campus unrest, the SDS could count more than a hundred thousand followers and was responsible for disruptions at nearly a thousand colleges in 1968. Yet its very emphasis on the individual and its fear of bureaucracy left it leaderless and subject to division and disunity. By 1970, a split between factions, some of which were given to violence, led to its complete demise.

The meteoric career of the SDS symbolized the turbulence of the 1960s. For a brief time, it seemed as though the nation's youth had gone berserk, indulging in a wave of experimentation with drugs, sex, and rock music. Older Americans believed that all the nation's traditional values, from the Puritan work ethic to the family, were under attack. Not all American youth joined in the cultural insurgency; the rebellion was generally limited to children of the upper middle class. But like the flappers of the 1920s, the protesters set the tone for an entire era and left a lasting impression on American society.

PROTESTING THE VIETNAM WAR

The most dramatic aspect of the youthful rebellion came in opposing the Vietnam War. The first student "teach-ins" began at the University of Michigan in March 1965; soon they spread to campuses across the nation. More than twenty thousand protesters, under SDS auspices, gathered in Washington in April to listen to entertainers Joan Baez and Judy Collins sing antiwar songs. "End the War in Vietnam Now, Stop the Killing" read the signs.

One of the great ironies of the Vietnam War was the system of student draft deferments, which enabled most of those enrolled in college to avoid military service. As a result, the children of the well-to-do, who were more likely to attend college, were able to escape the draft. Consequently, a sense of guilt led many college activists who were safe from Vietnam because of their student status to take the lead in denouncing an unjust war.

As the fighting in Southeast Asia intensified in 1966 and 1967, the protests grew larger and the slogans more extreme. "Hey, Hey, LBJ, how many kids did

Antiwar protesters came face-to-face with military police in the October 1967 March on the Pentagon. Leaders of the march announced that the demonstration marked the end of peaceful protest against the war and the beginning of a new stage of "active resistance." Borrowing techniques from the civil rights movement, some of the demonstrators staged a sit-down in the Pentagon parking lot.

you kill today?" chanted students as they proclaimed, "Hell, no, we won't go!" At the Pentagon in October 1967, more than a hundred thousand demonstrators confronted a cordon of military policemen guarding the heart of the nation's war machine.

The climax came in the spring of 1968. Driven by both opposition to the war and concern for social justice, the SDS and African American radicals at Columbia University joined forces in April. They seized five buildings, effectively paralyzing one of the country's leading colleges. After eight days of tension, the New York City police regained control. The brutal repression quickened the pace of protest elsewhere. Students held sit-ins and marches at more than one hundred colleges, from Cheyney State in Pennsylvania to Northwestern in Illinois.

The students failed to stop the war, but they did succeed in gaining a voice in their education. University administrations allowed undergraduates to sit on faculty curriculum-planning committees and gave up their once rigid control of dormitory and social life. But the students' greatest impact lay outside politics and the campus. They spawned a cultural uprising that transformed the manners and morals of America.

THE CULTURAL REVOLUTION

In contrast to the elitist political revolt of the SDS, the cultural rebellion by youth in the 1960s was pervasive. Led by college students, young people challenged the prevailing adult values in clothing, hairstyles, sexual conduct, work habits, and music. Blue jeans and love beads took the place of business suits and wrist-watches; long hair and unkempt beards for men, bare feet and bralessness for women became the new uniform of protest.

Music became the touchstone of the new departure. Folksingers such as Joan Baez and Bob Dylan, popular for their songs of social protest in the mid-1960s, gave way first to rock groups such as the Beatles, whose lyrics were often sugges-tive of drug use, and then to "acid rock" as symbolized by the Grateful Dead. The climactic event of the decade came at the Woodstock concert at Bethel in upstate New York when 400,000 young people indulged in a three-day festival of rock music, drug experimentation, and public sexual activity.

Former Harvard psychology professor Timothy Leary encouraged youth to join him in trying out the drug scene. Millions accepted his invitation to "tune in, turn on, drop out" literally, as they experimented with marijuana and with LSD, a new and dangerous chemical hallucinogen. The ultimate expression of insurgency was the Yippie movement, led by Jerry Rubin and Abbie Hoffman. Shrewd buf-foons who mocked the consumer culture, they delighted in capitalizing on the mood of social protest to win attention. Once, when testifying before a congres-sional committee investigating internal subversion, Rubin dressed as a Revolutionary War soldier; Hoffman appeared in the gallery of the New York Stock Exchange in 1967, raining money down on the cheering brokers below.

"BLACK POWER"

The civil rights movement, which had spawned the mood of protest in the 1960s, fell on hard times later in the decade. The legislative triumphs of 1964 and 1965 were relatively easy victories over southern bigotry; now the movement faced the far more complex problem of achieving economic equality in the cities of the North, where more than half of the nation's African Americans lived in poverty. The civil rights movement had raised the expectations of urban African Americans for improvement; frustration mounted as they failed to experience any significant economic gain.

The first sign of trouble came in the summer of 1964, when African American teenagers in Harlem and Rochester, New York, rioted. The next sum-mer, a massive outburst of rage and destruction swept over the Watts area of Los Angeles as the inhabitants burned buildings and looted stores. Riots in the sum-mer of 1966 were less destructive, but in 1967 the worst ones yet took place in Newark and in Detroit, where forty-three were killed and thousands were injured. The mobs attacked the shops and stores, expressing a burning grievance against a consumer society from which they were excluded by their poverty.

The civil rights coalition fell apart, a victim of both its legislative success and economic failure. Black militants took over the leadership of the Student Nonviolent Coordinating Committee (SNCC); they disdained white help and even reversed Martin Luther King's insistence on nonviolence. SNCC's new leader, Stokely Carmichael, told blacks they should seize power in those parts of the South where they outnumbered whites. Soon his calls for "black power" became a rallying cry for more militant blacks who advocated the need for African Americans to form "our own institutions, credit unions, co-ops, political parties" and even write "our own history."

King suffered the most from this extremism. His denunciation of the Vietnam War cost him the support of the Johnson administration and alienated him from the more conservative civil rights groups such as the NAACP and the Urban League. He finally seized on poverty as the proper enemy for attack, but before he could lead his Poor People's March on Washington in 1968, he was assassinated in Memphis in early April.

Both blacks and whites realized the nation had lost its most eloquent voice for racial harmony. His tragic death elevated King to the status of a martyr, but it also led to one last outbreak of urban violence. African Americans exploded in angry riots in 125 cities across the nation; the worst rioting took place in Washington, DC, where buildings were set on fire within a few blocks of the White House. "It was as if the city were being abandoned to an invading army," wrote a British journalist. "Clouds of smoke hung over the Potomac, evoking memories of the London blitz."

Yet there was a positive side to the emotions engendered by black nationalism. Leaders urged African Americans to take pride in their ethnic heritage, to embrace their blackness as a positive value. African Americans began to wear Afro hairstyles and dress in dashikis, stressing their African roots. Students began to demand new black studies programs in the colleges; the word *Negro*—identified with white supremacy of the past—virtually disappeared from usage overnight, replaced by the favored *Afro-American* or *black*. Singer James Brown best expressed the sense of racial identity: "Say It Loud—I'm Black and I'm Proud."

ETHNIC NATIONALISM

Other groups quickly emulated the African American phenomenon. Native Americans decried the callous use of their identity as football mascots; in response, universities such as Stanford changed their symbols. Puerto Ricans demanded their history be included in school and college texts. Polish, Italian, and

In March 1966, César Chávez, shown here speaking at the first United Farm Workers convention, led striking grape pickers on a 250-mile march from Delano, California, to the state capital at Sacramento to dramatize the plight of the migrant farmworkers. With the slogan "God is beside you on the picket line," the march took on the character of a religious pilgrimage.

Czech groups insisted on respect for their nationalities. Congress acknowledged these demands with passage of the Ethnic Heritage Studies Act of 1972.

Mexican Americans were in the forefront of the ethnic groups that became active in the 1970s. The primary impulse came from the efforts of César Chávez to organize the poorly paid grape pickers and lettuce workers in California into the National Farm Workers Association (NFWA). Chávez appealed to ethnic nationalism in mobilizing Mexican American field hands to strike against grape growers in the San Joaquin Valley in 1965. A national boycott of grapes by Mexican Americans and their sympathizers among the young people of the counterculture led to a series of hard-fought victories over the growers. The five-year struggle resulted in a union victory in 1970, but at an enormous cost—95 percent of the farmworkers involved had lost their homes and their cars. Nevertheless, Chávez succeeded in raising the hourly wage of farmworkers in California to $3.53 by 1977 (it had been $1.20 in 1965).

Chávez's efforts helped spark an outburst of ethnic consciousness among Mexican Americans that swept through the urban barrios of the Southwest. Mexican American leaders campaigned for bilingual programs and improved educational opportunities. Young activists began to call themselves Chicanos, which had previously been a derogatory term, and to take pride in their cultural heritage; in 1968, they succeeded in establishing the first Mexican American studies program at California State College at Los Angeles.

WOMEN'S LIBERATION

Active as they were in the civil rights and antiwar movements, women soon learned that the male leaders of these causes were little different from corporate executives—they expected women to fix the food and type the communiqués while the men made the decisions. Understandably, women soon realized that they could only achieve respect and equality by mounting their own protest.

In some ways, the position of women in American society was worse in the 1960s than it had been in the 1920s. After forty years, a lower percentage of women were enrolled in the nation's colleges and professional schools. Women were still relegated to stereotyped occupations such as nursing and teaching; there were few female lawyers and even fewer women doctors. And gender roles, as portrayed on television commercials, continued to call for the husband to be the breadwinner and the wife to be the homemaker.

Betty Friedan was one of the first to seize on the sense of grievance and discrimination that developed among white middle-class women in the 1960s. The beginning of the effort to raise women's consciousness was her 1963 book, *The Feminine Mystique.* Calling the American home "a comfortable concentration camp," she attacked the prevailing view that women were completely contented with their housekeeping and child-rearing tasks, claiming that housewives had no self-esteem and no sense of identity.

The 1964 Civil Rights Act helped women attack economic inequality head-on by making it illegal to discriminate in employment on the basis of sex. Women filed suit for equal wages, demanded that companies provide day care for their infants and preschool children, and entered politics to lobby against laws that—in the guise of protection of a weaker sex—were unfair to women. As the women's liberation movement grew, its advocates began to attack laws banning abortion and waged a campaign to toughen the enforcement of rape laws.

The women's movement met with many of the same obstacles as other protest groups in the 1960s. The moderate leadership of the National Organization for Women (NOW), founded by Betty Friedan in 1966, soon was challenged by those with more extreme views. Ti-Grace Atkinson and Susan Brownmiller attacked revered institutions—the family and the home—and denounced sexual intercourse with men, calling it a method of male domination. Many women were repelled by the harsh rhetoric of the extremists and expressed satisfaction with their lives. But despite these disagreements, most women supported the effort to achieve equal status with men, and in 1972, Congress responded by voting to send the Equal Rights Amendment to the state legislatures for ratification.

The Return of Richard Nixon

The turmoil of the 1960s reached a crescendo in 1968 as the American people responded to the two dominant events of the decade—the war in Vietnam and the cultural insurgency at home. In an election marked by a series of bizarre events, including riots and an assassination, Richard Nixon staged a remarkable comeback to win the post denied him in 1960.

Vietnam Undermines Lyndon Johnson

A controversial Vietcong offensive in early 1968 proved to be the decisive event in breaking the stalemate in Vietnam and driving Lyndon Johnson from office. Using deceptive tactics, the North Vietnamese began a prolonged siege of an American marine base at Khe Sanh, deep in the northern interior. Fearing another Dien Bien Phu, Westmoreland rushed in reinforcements, sending more than 40 percent of all American infantry and armor battalions into the two northernmost provinces of South Vietnam.

The Vietcong then used the traditional lull in the fighting at Tet, the lunar New Year, to launch a surprise attack in the heavily populated cities. Beginning on January 30, 1968, the VC struck at thirty-six of the forty-four provincial capitals. The most daring raid came at the American embassy compound in Saigon. Although the guerrillas were unable to penetrate the embassy proper, for six hours television cameras caught the dramatic battle that ensued in the courtyard before military police finally overcame the attackers.

Although caught off guard, American and South Vietnamese forces succeeded in repulsing the Tet offensive quickly everywhere except in Hue, the old imperial capital, which was retaken only after three weeks of heavy fighting that left this beautiful city, in the words of one observer, "a shattered, stinking hulk, its streets choked with rubble and rotting bodies."

Tet proved to be the turning point of the Vietnam War. Although the communists failed to win control of the cities and suffered heavy losses, they still held on to most of the rural areas and had scored an impressive political victory. CBS-TV newscaster Walter Cronkite took a quick trip to Saigon to find out what had hap-

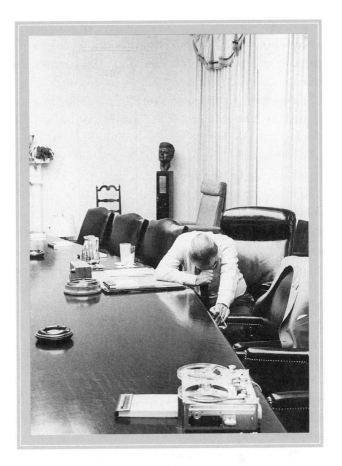

President Johnson, alone in the Cabinet room, rests his head on his hand as he listens to a tape from his son-in-law Marine Captain Charles Robb recounting his combat experiences in Vietnam. Johnson stunned the nation with his announcement on March 31, 1968, that he would not seek reelection. Poor results in the March primaries and public opinion polls indicated that support for LBJ was eroding.

pened. Horrified at what he saw, he exclaimed to his guides, "What the hell is going on? I thought we were winning the war." He returned home to tell the American people, "It seems now more certain than ever that the bloody experience of Vietnam is to end in a stalemate."

President Johnson reluctantly came to the same conclusion after the Joint Chiefs of Staff requested an additional 205,000 troops to achieve victory in Vietnam following the Tet offensive. He began to listen to his new secretary of defense, Clark Clifford, who had replaced Robert McNamara in January 1968. In mid-March, the president decided to limit the bombing of North Vietnam in an effort to open up peace negotiations with Hanoi. In a speech to the nation on Sunday evening, March 31, 1968, Johnson outlined his plans for a new effort at ending the war peacefully and then concluded by saying, as proof of his sincerity, "I shall not seek, and I will not accept, the nomination of my party for another term as your president."

In the fourteen years since the siege of Dien Bien Phu, American policy had gone full cycle in Vietnam. Even though Eisenhower had decided against using force to rescue the French, his commitment to the Diem regime in Saigon had led eventually to American military involvement on a massive scale. Three years of inconclusive fighting and a steadily mounting loss of American lives had disillusioned the American people and finally cost Lyndon Johnson the presidency. And the full price the nation would have to pay for its folly in Southeast Asia was still unknown—the Vietnam experience would continue to cast a shadow over American life for years to come.

THE DEMOCRATS DIVIDE

Lyndon Johnson's withdrawal from the presidential race after the Tet offensive set the tone for the 1968 election. LBJ's decision had come in response to political as well as military realities. By 1966, the antiwar movement had spread from the college campuses to Capitol Hill. Chairman J. William Fulbright gave the protests a new respectability when his Senate Foreign Relations Committee held probing hearings on the war, broadcast on television to the entire country.

The essentially leaderless protest against the war took on a new quality on January 3, 1968, when Senator Eugene McCarthy, a Democrat from Minnesota, announced he was challenging LBJ for the party's presidential nomination. Intellectual, cool, aloof, and almost arrogant, McCarthy raised the banner of idealism, telling audiences, "Whatever is morally necessary must be made politically possible." College students flocked to his campaign, shaving their beards and cutting their hair to be "clean for Gene." In the New Hampshire primary in early March, the nation's earliest political test, McCarthy shocked the political experts by coming within a few thousand votes of defeating President Johnson.

McCarthy's strong showing in New Hampshire led Robert Kennedy, who had been weighing the risks in challenging Johnson, to enter the presidential race. Elected senator from New York in 1964, Bobby Kennedy had become an effective voice for the disadvantaged, as well as an increasingly severe critic of the Vietnam War. He attracted strong support among blue-collar workers, African Americans, Chicanos, and other minorities who formed the nucleus of the continuing New Deal coalition.

Lyndon Johnson's dramatic withdrawal caused an uproar in the Democratic party. With Johnson's tacit backing and strong support from party regulars and organized labor, Vice President Hubert H. Humphrey immediately declared his candidacy. Humphrey, aware that he was totally unacceptable to the antiwar movement, decided to avoid the primaries and work for the nomination within the framework of the party.

Kennedy and McCarthy, the two antiwar candidates, were thus left to compete in the spring primaries, requiring agonizing choices among those who desired change. Kennedy won everywhere except in Oregon, but his narrow victory in California ended in tragedy when a Palestinian immigrant, Sirhan Sirhan, assassinated him in a Los Angeles hotel.

With his strongest opponent struck down, Hubert Humphrey had little difficulty at the Chicago convention. The vice president relied on party leaders to defeat an antiwar resolution and win the nomination on the first ballot by a margin of more than two to one.

Humphrey's triumph was marred by violence outside the heavily guarded convention hall. Radical groups had urged their members to come to Chicago to agitate; the turnout was relatively small but included many who were ready to provoke the authorities in their despair over the convention's outcome. Epithets

While party factions quarreled inside the convention hall at the 1968 Democratic National Convention in Chicago, in the streets outside Chicago police clashed violently with antiwar demonstrators. Here, a Chicago policeman squirts Mace into the crowd of protestors gathered outside the Conrad Hilton hotel where Democratic candidate Hubert H. Humphrey had his convention headquarters.

and cries of "pigs" brought on a savage response from the police. "The cops had one thing on their mind," commented journalist Jimmy Breslin. "Club and then gas, club and then gas, club and then gas."

The bitter fumes of tear gas hung in the streets for days afterward; the battered heads and bodies of demonstrators and innocent bystanders alike flooded the city's hospital emergency rooms. What an official investigation later termed a "police riot" marred Humphrey's nomination and made a sad mockery out of his call for "the politics of joy." The Democratic party itself had become the next victim of the Vietnam War.

THE REPUBLICAN RESURGENCE

The primary beneficiary of the Democratic debacle was Richard Nixon. Written off as politically dead after his unsuccessful race for governor of California in 1962, Nixon had slowly rebuilt his place within the party by working loyally for Barry Goldwater in 1964 and for GOP congressional candidates two years later. At the GOP convention in Miami Beach, Nixon won an easy first-ballot nomination and chose Maryland governor Spiro Agnew as his running mate. Agnew, little known on the national scene, had won the support of conservatives by taking a strong stand against African American rioters.

In the fall campaign, Nixon opened up a wide lead by avoiding controversy and reaping the benefit of discontent with the Vietnam War. He played the peace issue shrewdly, appearing to advocate an end to the conflict without ever taking a definite stand. Above all, he chose the role of reconciler for a nation torn by emotion, a leader who promised to bring a divided country together again.

Humphrey, in contrast, found himself hounded by antiwar demonstrators who heckled him constantly. He walked a tightwire, desperate for the continued support of President Johnson but handicapped by LBJ's stubborn refusal to end all bombing of North Vietnam. Only when he broke with Johnson in late September by announcing that if elected he would "stop the bombing of North Vietnam as an acceptable risk for peace" did his campaign begin to gain momentum.

Unfortunately for Humphrey, a third-party candidate cut deeply into the normal Democratic majority. George Wallace had first gained national attention as the racist governor of Alabama whose motto was "Segregation now . . . segregation tomorrow . . . segregation forever." In 1964, he had shown surprising strength in Democratic primaries in northern states. By attacking both black leaders and their liberal white allies, Wallace appealed to the sense of powerlessness among the urban working classes. "Liberals, intellectuals, and longhairs have

THE ELECTION OF 1968

CANDIDATE	PARTY	POPULAR VOTE	ELECTORAL VOTE
Nixon	Republican	31,770,237	301
Humphrey	Democratic	31,270,533	191
Wallace	American Independent	9,906,141	46
	Minor Parties	239,908	—

run the country for too long," Wallace told his followers. "When I get to Washington," he promised, "I'll throw all these phonies and their briefcases into the Potomac."

Running on the ticket of the American Independent Party, Wallace was a close third in the September polls. But as the election neared, his following declined. Humphrey continued to gain, especially after Johnson agreed in late October to end all bombing of North Vietnam. By the first week in November, the outcome was too close for the experts to call.

Nixon won the election with the smallest share of the popular vote of any winning candidate since 1916. But he swept a broad band of states from Virginia and the Carolinas through the Midwest to the Pacific for a clear-cut victory in the electoral college. Humphrey held on to the urban Northeast; Wallace took just five states in the Deep South, but his heavy inroads into blue-collar districts in the North shattered the New Deal coalition.

The election marked a repudiation of the politics of protest and the cultural insurgency of the mid-1960s. The combined popular vote for Nixon and Wallace, 56.5 percent of the electorate, signified there was a silent majority that was fed up with violence and confrontation. A growing concern over psychedelic drugs, rock music, long hair, and sexual permissiveness had offset the usual Democratic advantage on economic issues and led to the election of a Republican president.

At the election of Richard Nixon, an era came to an end with the passing of two concepts that had guided American life since the 1930s. First, the liberal reform impulse, which reached its zenith with the Great Society legislation in 1965, had clearly run its course. Civil rights, Medicare, and federal aid to education would continue in place, but Nixon's triumph signaled a strong reaction against the growth of federal power. At the same time, the Vietnam fiasco spelled the end of activist foreign policy that had begun with American entry into World War II. Containment, so successful in protecting western Europe against the Soviet threat, had proved a disastrous failure when applied on a global scale. The last three decades of the twentieth century would witness a struggle to replace outmoded liberal internationalism with new policies at home and abroad.

31

A CRISIS IN CONFIDENCE, 1969–1980

On the evening of June 17, 1972, five men broke into the headquarters of the Democratic National Committee in the Watergate complex. They wore surgical gloves and carried cans of Mace, lock-picking tools, camera equipment, and telephone bugging devices. Busy filming documents and checking on electronic bugs planted two weeks before, the burglars were caught by police after an alert security guard discovered they had carelessly left doors taped open.

The leader of the group, Gary McCord, a former CIA employee, was working for CREEP (the Committee to Re-Elect the President), and police quickly found the telephone number of White House aide E. Howard Hunt in his address book. Despite this obvious tie to the Nixon administration, presidential press secretary Ron Ziegler denied any White House involvement in the Watergate break-in, dismissing it as "a third-rate burglary attempt."

In fact, this criminal act was a direct outgrowth of the paranoia that characterized the Nixon presidency. Aware that he had won office by a very narrow margin in 1968, Nixon was determined to do everything possible to ensure his reelection in 1972. Concerned about leaks from the White House, he authorized wiretaps on the telephones of both reporters and key aides. After the *New York Times* and the *Washington Post* began publishing the Pentagon Papers, Nixon took drastic measures to plug any further leaks of secret documents. His aides created

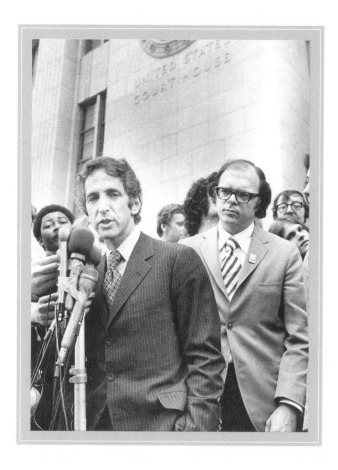

Daniel Ellsberg after the opening session of his trial. Ellsberg was indicted for espionage, theft, and conspiracy, but the case was dismissed on the grounds of government misconduct.

a self-styled "plumbers" unit within the White House directed by G. Gordon Liddy, a former FBI agent, and E. Howard Hunt, a veteran of the CIA. Charged with preserving secrecy and discrediting those who spoke to the press, Hunt and Liddy set out to embarrass Daniel Ellsberg, the Defense Department official who had leaked the Pentagon Papers, going so far as to break into his psychiatrist's office in search of damning information.

Convinced that people throughout society were working for his defeat in 1972, Nixon ordered aides John Dean and Charles Colson to prepare an "enemies list." They eventually compiled a roster of several hundred prominent citizens, ranging from movie stars such as Jane Fonda and Paul Newman to twelve African American congressmen. The plan was to direct the IRS and other government agencies to target these "enemies" for audits and investigations, or, as John Dean put it, to use "the available federal machinery to screw our political enemies." Operating under a siege mentality, the Nixon White House was prepared to do anything necessary to defeat its opponents, who were thought to include the media, the intellectual community, and virtually all minority groups.

The president's greatest concern was guaranteeing his reelection. He appointed Attorney General John Mitchell to head CREEP and gave him access to extensive funds and the use of men similar to Liddy and Hunt. The bungled Watergate break-in, directed by Liddy and Hunt, was thus the culmination of abuses of power that grew directly out of Nixon's personal insecurity.

The president probably did not have any advance knowledge of the break-in, but he committed a criminal act by authorizing a far-reaching cover-up. On June 23, he ordered his aides to instruct the FBI to defer to the CIA in regard to the Watergate burglary, invoking nonexistent national security concerns to block an investigation that might expose White House involvement. Determined to contain the damage, Nixon told John Mitchell, "I want you to stonewall it, let them plead the Fifth Amendment, cover-up, or anything else." Putting John Dean in charge, Nixon successfully covered up the Watergate affair while winning reelection in 1972, only to have the whole matter later unravel and drive him from office.

Watergate was but the first of a series of shocks in the 1970s that shook the confidence of the American people. War in the Middle East led to a sharp increase in the price of oil and waves of inflation that devastated the economy. Revolutions in Nicaragua and Iran added to the dilemmas confronting the nation's leaders. By the end of the decade, the American people were beginning to question the validity of traditional American values and institutions as they tried to cope with difficult challenges at home and abroad.

NIXON IN POWER

Before Watergate cast its long shadow over his presidency, Nixon dealt ably with a wide range of issues at home and abroad. While his domestic policies had only limited success, he proved both skillful and effective in the international arena, achieving a significant, though temporary, reduction in Cold War tensions.

The man who took office as the thirty-sixth president of the United States on January 20, 1969, seemed to be a new Nixon. Gone were the fiery rhetoric and the penchant for making enemies. In their place, observers found an air of moderation and restraint. He appeared to have his emotions under firm control, but beneath the surface he remained bitter, hurt, and sensitive to criticism.

An innately shy man, Nixon hoped to enjoy the power of the presidency in splendid solitude. Described by Barry Goldwater as "the most complete loner I've ever known," Nixon assembled a powerful White House staff whose main task was to isolate him from Congress, the press, and even his own cabinet. Loyal subordinates such as H. R. Haldeman and John Ehrlichman took charge of domestic issues, often making decisions without even consulting Nixon. Foreign policy was Nixon's great passion, and here he relied heavily on Henry Kissinger, his national security adviser, to formulate policy.

The Nixon White House soon could be likened to a fortress under siege. Distrusting everyone, from the media to members of his own party, the president sought to rule the nation without help from either Congress or his cabinet. In his quest for privacy, the president cut himself off from the nation and thus sowed the seeds of his downfall.

RESHAPING THE GREAT SOCIETY

Nixon began his first term on a hopeful note, promising the nation peace and respite from the chaos of the 1960s. Rejecting the divisions that had split Americans apart, he promised in his inaugural address to "bring us together." "We cannot learn from one another until we stop shouting at one another—until we speak quietly enough so that our words can be heard as well as our voices."

Nixon's moderation promised a return to the politics of accommodation that had characterized the Eisenhower era. Faced with a Democratic Congress, Nixon, like Ike, appeared ready to accept the main outlines of the welfare state. Instead of any massive overthrow of the Great Society, he focused on making the federal bureaucracy function more efficiently.

Nixon was successful in shifting responsibility for social problems from Washington to state and local authorities. He developed the concept of revenue sharing, by which federal funds would be dispersed to state, county, and city agencies to meet local needs. In 1972, Congress finally approved a measure to share $30.1 billion with local governments over a five-year period.

In the area of civil rights, Nixon made a shrewd political move. Action by Congress and the outgoing Johnson administration had ensured that massive desegregation of southern schools, delayed for more than a decade by legal action, would finally begin just as Nixon took office. Nixon and his attorney general, John Mitchell, decided to shift the responsibility for this process to the courts. In the summer of 1969, the Justice Department asked a federal judge to delay the integration of thirty-three school districts in Mississippi. The Supreme Court quickly ruled against the Justice Department. Thus, in the minds of southern white voters, it was the hated Supreme Court, not Richard Nixon, who had forced them to integrate their schools.

Nixon used similar tactics in his attempt to reshape the Supreme Court along more conservative lines. His appointment of Warren Burger, an experienced federal judge with moderate views, to replace the retiring Earl Warren as Chief Justice met with little objection. But liberal Democrats succeeded in blocking

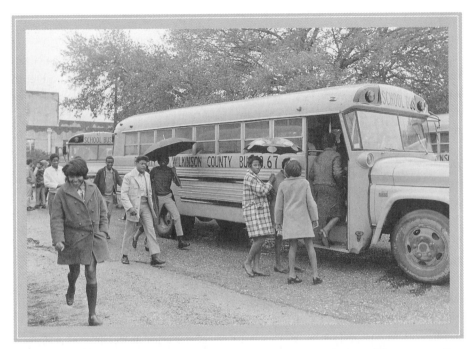

High school students in Woodville, Mississippi, board a school bus after their first day of class in a now all-black school. The school, which was formerly predominantly white, was one of thirty Mississippi schools under court order to speed desegregation.

the nomination first of Clement Haynesworth of South Carolina and then of G. Harrold Carswell of Florida. Nixon denounced his opponents for insulting "millions of Americans who live in the South" by turning down his two southern nominees. Once again, the president had used the Supreme Court to enhance his political appeal to Southerners.

Nixon finally filled the Court position with Harry Blackmun, a respected moderate from Minnesota, who easily won confirmation. Subsequently, the president appointed Lewis Powell, a distinguished Virginia lawyer, and William Rehnquist, a rigidly conservative Justice Department attorney from Arizona, to the Supreme Court. Surprisingly, the Burger Court, despite its more conservative makeup, did not engage in any massive overturn of the Warren Court's decisions.

The moderation of the Supreme Court and the legislative record of the Nixon administration indicated that the nation was not yet ready to abandon the reforms adopted in the 1960s. The pace of change slowed down, but the commitment to social justice was still clear.

Nixonomics

The economy posed a more severe test for Richard Nixon. He inherited growing inflation stemming from the Vietnam War. Although Lyndon Johnson finally secured a tax increase from Congress in 1968 which produced a balanced budget in 1969, the heavy expense of the fighting in Vietnam since 1965 had led to massive deficit spending. As a result, in 1968 the cost of living rose 5 percent. Strongly opposed to the idea of federal controls, Nixon at first opted for a reduction in government spending while encouraging the Federal Reserve Board to raise interest rates, thereby slowing the rate of business expansion.

The result was disastrous. Inflation continued, reaching nearly 6 percent by the end of 1970, the highest rate since the Korean War. At the same time, the economy underwent its first major recession since 1958. Unemployment rose to 6 percent by the end of 1970, and business failures jumped alarmingly. Democrats quickly coined a new word, *Nixonomics,* to describe the disaster.

Conditions seemed to worsen in 1971. Inflation continued unabated, and the nation's balance of trade became negative as imports exceeded exports by a substantial margin, leading to a weakening of the dollar abroad.

In mid-August, Nixon acted boldly to halt the economic decline. Abandoning his earlier resistance to controls, he announced a ninety-day freeze on wages and prices to be followed by federally imposed guidelines in both areas. The new secretary of the treasury, Democrat John Connally, carried out a devaluation of the dollar, which led to a greatly improved balance of trade. The sudden Nixon economic reversal quickly ended the recession, with industrial production increasing more than 5 percent in the first quarter of 1972.

Building a Republican Majority

"The Great Nixon Turnaround," as historian Lloyd Gardner termed it, came too late to help the Republicans in the 1970 congressional elections. From the time he took office in 1969, the president was obsessed with the fact that he had received only 43 percent of the popular vote in 1968. The Republicans were still a minority party, and to be reelected in 1972, Nixon would need to win over southern whites and blue-collar workers who had voted for Wallace in 1968.

Attorney General John Mitchell, who had been Nixon's campaign manager in 1968, had devised a southern strategy to help achieve a Republican majority by 1972. The administration's well-publicized objection to school desegregation in the South and the attempt to put Haynesworth and Carswell on the Court were part of this design. Kevin Phillips, one of Mitchell's aides, urged the Nixon administration to direct its appeal to "middle Americans"—southern whites, Catholic ethnic groups, blue-collar workers, and, above all, the new suburbanites of the South and West, the emerging Sunbelt.

Nixon unleashed Vice President Spiro Agnew in an attempt to exploit the social issue in the 1970 election. Blaming all of society's problems—from drug abuse and sexual permissiveness to crime in the streets—on Democratic liberals and their allies in the media, Agnew delivered a series of scathing speeches. He denounced intellectuals as "an effete corps of impudent snobs" and damned the press as "nattering nabobs of negativism."

The Democrats struck back by changing their tactics. Their candidates were careful to stress economic issues, blaming the Republicans for both inflation and recession. On social issues, they joined in the chorus against crime, pornography, and drugs.

The outcome was a standoff. Agnew's attacks helped the GOP limit the usual off-year losses in the House to nine seats, while the Republicans gained two votes in the Senate. But the Democrats did well in state elections and proved once again that economic issues were crucial in American politics. Nixon and the Republicans still did not command a national majority.

In Search of Détente

Richard Nixon gave foreign policy top priority, and he proved surprisingly adept at it. In Kissinger, he had a White House specialist who had devoted his life to the study of diplomacy. A refugee from Nazi Germany, Kissinger had become a professor of government at Harvard, the author of several influential books, and an acknowledged authority on international affairs. Nixon and Kissinger approached foreign policy from a similar realistic perspective. Instead of viewing the Cold War as an ideological struggle for survival with communism, they saw it as a traditional great-power rivalry, one to be managed and controlled rather than to be won.

Kissinger and Nixon had a grand design. Realizing that recent events, especially the Vietnam War and the rapid Soviet arms buildup of the 1960s, had eroded America's position of primacy in the world, they planned a strategic retreat. Russia had great military strength, but its economy was weak and it had a dangerous rival in China. Kissinger planned to use American trade to induce Soviet cooperation, while at the same time improving U.S. relations with China.

Nixon and Kissinger shrewdly played the China card as their first step toward achieving détente—that is, a relaxation of tension—with the Soviet Union. In February 1972, accompanied by a planeload of reporters and television camera crews, Nixon made a triumphal tour of China, ending more than two decades of Sino-American hostility. Nixon agreed to establish an American liaison mission in Beijing as a first step toward diplomatic recognition.

The Soviets, who viewed China as a dangerous adversary along a 2000-mile frontier in Asia, responded by agreeing to reach an arms control pact with the

United States. The Strategic Arms Limitation Talks (SALT) had been under way since 1969. During a visit to Moscow in May 1972, President Nixon signed two vital documents with Soviet leader Leonid Brezhnev. The first limited the two superpowers to two hundred antiballistic missiles (ABMs) apiece; the second froze the number of offensive ballistic missiles for a five-year period. SALT I recognized the existing Soviet lead in missiles, but the American deployment of multiple independently targeted reentry vehicles (MIRVs) ensured a continuing strategic advantage for the United States.

The SALT I agreements were most important as a symbolic first step toward control of the nuclear arms race. They signified that the United States and Russia were trying to achieve a settlement of their differences by peaceful means.

ENDING THE VIETNAM WAR

Vietnam remained the one foreign policy challenge that Nixon could not overcome. He had a three-part plan to end the conflict—gradual withdrawal of American troops and training of South Vietnamese forces to take over the combat role, renewed bombing, and a hard line in negotiations with Hanoi. The number of American soldiers in Vietnam fell from 543,000 in early 1969 to less than 30,000 by 1972.

Renewed bombing proved the most controversial part of the plan. In April 1970, Nixon ordered both air and ground strikes into neutral Cambodia, causing a massive outburst of antiwar protests at home. Tragedy struck at Kent State University in Ohio in early May. After rioters had firebombed an ROTC building, the governor sent in national guard troops who were taunted and harassed by irate students. The guardsmen then opened fire, killing four students and wounding eleven more. A week later, two African American student demonstrators were killed at Jackson State College in Mississippi; soon riots and protests raged on more than four hundred campuses across the country.

Nixon had little sympathy for the demonstrators, calling the students "bums" who were intent on "blowing up the campuses." The "silent majority" to whom he appealed seemed to agree; one poll showed that most Americans blamed the students, not the national guard, for the deaths at Kent State. Nixon's Cambodian invasion did little to shorten the Vietnam War, but the public reaction reinforced the president's resolve not to surrender.

The third tactic, negotiation with Hanoi, finally proved successful. In the summer and fall of 1972, the two sides were near agreement, but South Vietnamese objections blocked a settlement before the 1972 election. When the North Vietnamese tried to make last-minute changes, Nixon ordered a series of savage B-52 raids on Hanoi that finally led to the signing of a truce on January 27,

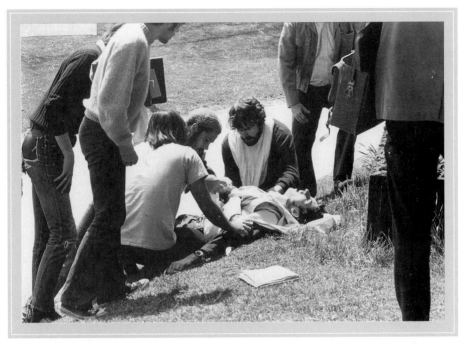

The renewed bombing of North Vietnam and invasion of Cambodia ordered by Nixon in hopes of ending the conflict precipitated student protests at many campuses. At Kent State University in Ohio, demonstrators and bystanders were shot by national guardsmen.

1973. In return for the release of all American prisoners of war, the United States agreed to remove its troops from South Vietnam within sixty days. The political clauses allowed the North Vietnamese to keep their troops in the South, thus virtually guaranteeing future control of all Vietnam by the communists.

The agreement was, in fact, a disguised surrender, but finally the American combat role in the Vietnam War was over. After eight years of fighting, the United States had emerged from the quagmire in Southeast Asia. Yet, known only to a few insiders around the president, the nation was already deeply enmeshed in another dilemma—what Gerald R. Ford termed "the long national nightmare" of Watergate.

THE CRISIS OF DEMOCRACY

The June 1, 1972, break-in at the Democratic National Committee offices came back to haunt Richard Nixon in 1973 and 1974. His determination to stonewall the press on any White House involvement in the burglary—including instructions to his aides to lie under oath—proved successful in the short run, but eventually the cover-up led to his downfall.

THE ELECTION OF 1972

CANDIDATE	PARTY	POPULAR VOTE	ELECTORAL VOTE
Richard Nixon	Republican	46,740,323	520
George McGovern	Democratic	28,901,598	17
John Hospers	Minor Parties	1,983,231	1

THE ELECTION OF 1972

The irony of the Watergate break-in was that by the time it occurred, Nixon's election was assured. Aided by Republican dirty tricks, the Democrats self-destructed. First, Edmund Muskie, the front-runner, replying in the New Hampshire primary to a letter accusing him of prejudice against French Canadians, lost his composure. Then a lone assassin, Arthur Bremer, shot and seriously wounded George Wallace. Paralyzed, Wallace was forced to drop out of the race, leaving Nixon with a complete monopoly over the political right.

Senator George McGovern of South Dakota finally emerged as the Democratic nominee. He ran on a platform that advocated a negotiated settlement in Vietnam, the right to abortion, and tolerance of diverse lifestyles. The South Dakota senator hoped to unite the New Left with traditional Democratic voters, but his strong stand against the Vietnam War greatly strengthened Nixon's appeal.

Instead of focusing on his own record in office, Richard Nixon shrewdly let McGovern's perceived extremism and New Left support become the main issue in the campaign. Nixon let others campaign for him, relying heavily on the recent improvement in the economy and his foreign policy triumphs with China and Russia to sway the nation's voters.

The result was a stunning victory. Nixon won a popular landslide with 60.8 percent of the vote—second only to Lyndon Johnson's record in 1964—and an even more decisive sweep of the electoral college. The very low turnout and Democratic control of both Houses of Congress suggests the election was primarily a repudiation of McGovern, rather than an endorsement of Richard Nixon. The voting patterns did suggest, however, the beginning of a major political realignment, as only blacks, Jews, and low-income voters continued to vote overwhelmingly Democratic, while the GOP made significant gains in the Sunbelt states of the South and West.

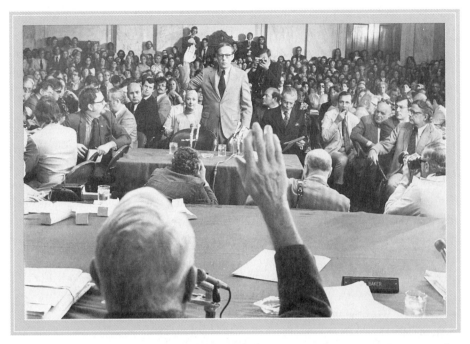

Senator Sam Ervin, chairman of the Senate Watergate Committee, swears in former Nixon White House aide John Dean. Dean's testimony before the Committee implicated Nixon in the Watergate scandal.

THE WATERGATE SCANDAL

Despite the best efforts of John Dean, the Watergate cover-up began to unravel in early 1973. Hunt and Liddy were convicted and went to prison without implicating anyone else in the Nixon administration; James McCord became the first to break the silence. Sentenced to a long jail term by Judge John Sirica, McCord asked for leniency, informing Sirica he had received money from the White House and had been promised a future pardon in return for his silence. By April 1973, Nixon was forced to fire John Dean and to allow Haldeman and Ehrlichman, who were deeply implicated, to resign. The Senate then appointed a special committee to investigate the Watergate episode. In a week of dramatic testimony, John Dean revealed the president's personal involvement in the cover-up. Still, it was basically a matter of whose word was to be believed, that of the president or that of a discredited aide, and Nixon hoped to weather the storm.

The existence of tapes of conversations in the Oval Office, recorded regularly since 1970, finally brought Nixon down. At first, the president tried to invoke executive privilege to withhold the tapes. Then Nixon tried to release only a few of the less damaging ones, but the Supreme Court ruled unanimously in June 1974 that the tapes had to be turned over to Judge Sirica.

By that time, the House Judiciary Committee had voted three articles of impeachment, charging Nixon with obstruction of justice, abuse of power, and contempt of Congress. Faced with the release of tapes that directly implicated him in the cover-up, the president finally chose to resign on August 9, 1974.

Nixon's resignation proved to be the culmination of the Watergate scandal. The entire episode revealed both the weaknesses and strengths of the American political system. Most regrettable was the abuse of presidential authority—a reflection both of the growing power of the modern presidency and of the fatal flaws in Richard Nixon's character. Realizing he had reached the White House almost by accident, Nixon did everything possible to retain his hold on his office. He used the plumbers to maintain executive secrecy, and he directed the Internal

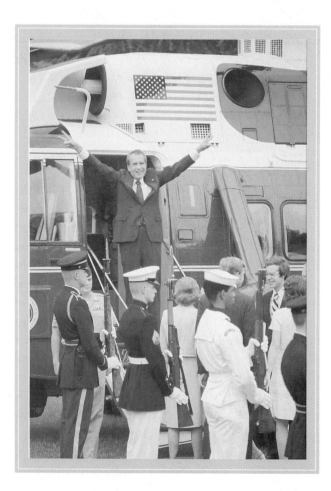

An embattled Richard Nixon waves good-bye after resigning the presidency on August 9, 1974.

Revenue Service and the Justice Department to punish his enemies and reward his friends.

But Watergate also demonstrated the vitality of a democratic society. The press showed how investigative reporting could unlock even the most closely guarded executive secrets. Judge Sirica proved that an independent judiciary was still the best bulwark for individual freedom. And Congress rose to the occasion, both by carrying out a successful investigation of executive misconduct and by following a scrupulous and nonpartisan impeachment process that left Nixon with no chance to escape his fate.

The nation survived the shock of Watergate with its institutions intact. Attorney General John Mitchell and twenty-five presidential aides were sentenced to jail terms. Congress, in decline since Lyndon Johnson's exercise of executive dominance, was rejuvenated, with its members now intent on extending congressional authority into all areas of American life.

Energy and the Economy

In the midst of Watergate, the outbreak of war in the Middle East threatened a vital national interest—the supply and price of the fuel on which the American way of life was based. In the course of the 1970s, the resulting energy crisis helped touch off an inflationary impulse that had a profound impact on the national economy.

The October War

On October 6, 1973, Egypt and Syria launched a surprise attack on Israel. The fighting caught American leaders completely off guard. President Nixon and Henry Kissinger, who had become secretary of state in September, expected Israel to repel the Arab invaders and display the same military dominance it had used to win the Six Day War in 1967. In that conflict, Israel had devastated its Arab neighbors, taking possession of the Golan Heights from Syria, the Sinai peninsula from Egypt, and Jerusalem and the West Bank from Jordan. Instead of increasing Israeli security, however, the conquests had only added to Middle East tensions. They unified the Arab countries, who now called for the return of their lands, and increased their dependence on the Soviet Union for arms and political support.

Henry Kissinger used the October War, which began on the Jewish holy day of Yom Kippur, as an opportunity to shift American policy from its traditional pro-Israeli position to a more neutral stance—as the honest broker between Israel and its Arab neighbors. When the Israelis quickly routed their opponents, the United States intervened diplomatically to prevent a victory for

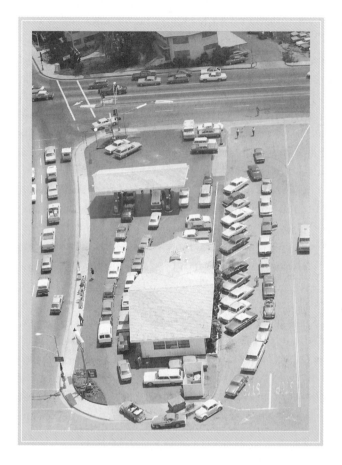

As prices climbed and supplies dwindled, Americans found themselves waiting in long lines to fill their cars' gas tanks. Service stations reduced their operating hours and restricted the amount of gasoline consumers could buy, but many stations still ran out of fuel before they could accommodate all their customers.

Israel that would preclude American mediation. The fighting finally ended in late October; Israel had repulsed the Arab attack but had been stopped short of complete victory.

Kissinger's apparent diplomatic triumph, however, was offset by an unforeseen consequence of the Yom Kippur War. On October 17, the Arab members of the Organization of Petroleum Exporting Countries (OPEC) announced a 5 percent cut in oil production, with additional cuts of 5 percent each month until Israel gave up the lands it had taken in 1967. President Nixon announced a $2.2 billion aid package for Israel on October 19, and the next day Saudi Arabia cut off oil shipments to the United States and to the Netherlands, the European nation that had most strongly supported American policy in the Middle East.

The Arab oil embargo had a disastrous impact on the American economy. Arab countries cut production by 25 percent from the September 1973 level, leading to a 10 percent curtailment in the world supply. For the United States, which imported one-third of its daily consumption, this meant a loss of nearly

2 million barrels a day. Long lines formed at automobile service stations as motorists who feared running out of gas kept filling their tanks.

President Nixon responded with a series of temporary measures, including pleas to turn down thermostats in homes and offices and reduce automobile speed limits to 50 miles an hour. When the Arab oil embargo ended in March, after Kissinger negotiated an Israeli pullback in the Sinai, gasoline once again became plentiful; thermostats were raised, and people resumed their love affair with the automobile.

The energy crisis, however, did not end with the lifting of the embargo. The Arab action marked the beginning of a new era in American history. The United States, with only 6 percent of the world's population, had been responsible for nearly 40 percent of the earth's energy consumption. In 1970, domestic oil production began to decline; the embargo served only to highlight the fact that the nation was now dependent on other countries for its economic well-being. A nation that based its way of life on abundance and expansion suddenly was faced with the reality of limited resources and economic stagnation.

THE OIL SHOCKS

Cheap energy had been the underlying force behind the amazing growth of the American economy after World War II. The world price of oil had actually declined in the 1950s and 1960s as huge new fields in the Middle East and North Africa began to produce. The GNP had more than doubled between 1950 and 1973; the American people had come to base their way of life on gasoline prices that averaged about 35 cents a gallon. The huge gas-guzzling cars, the flight to the suburbs, the detached houses cooled by central air-conditioning represented a dependence on inexpensive energy that everyone took for granted.

The first great oil shock of the 1970s came with the October War and the resulting Arab oil embargo. In the ensuing shortfall, the OPEC nations quickly raised prices, first from $3 to more than $5 a barrel, then to $11.65. The effect on the American economy was devastating. Gasoline prices jumped from 35 to 65 cents a gallon; the cost of manufacturing went up proportionately, while utility rates rose sharply as a result of the higher cost of fuel oil and natural gas. Suddenly, Americans faced drastic and unexpected increases in such everyday expenses as driving to work and heating their homes.

The result was a sharp decline in consumer spending and the worst recession since World War II. The GNP dropped by 6 percent in 1974, and unemployment rose to more than 9 percent, the highest level since the Great Depression of the 1930s. Detroit was hit the hardest. Car sales declined by 20 percent, and by the fall of 1974, America's Big Three automakers had laid off more than 225,000 workers.

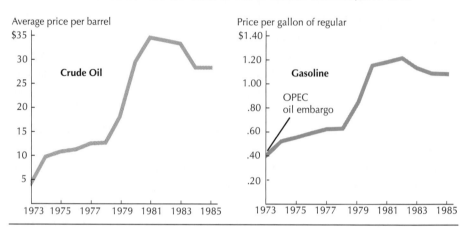

The Oil Shocks: Price Increases of Crude Oil and Gasoline, 1973–1985

President Gerald R. Ford, who followed Richard Nixon into the White House (see p. 1029), responded belatedly to the economic crisis by proposing a tax cut to stimulate consumer spending. Congress passed a $22.8 billion reduction in taxes in early 1975, which led to a gradual recovery by 1976. The resulting budget deficits, however, helped keep inflation above 5 percent and prevented a return to full economic health.

Jimmy Carter of Georgia, who succeeded Ford, had little more success in achieving a rapid rate of economic growth. In 1979, the outbreak of the Iranian Revolution and the overthrow of the shah touched off another oil shock. Although the cutoff of Iranian oil led to a shortfall of only 3 percent of the world's oil supply, the members of the OPEC cartel took advantage of the situation to double prices over the next eighteen months. Gasoline prices climbed to more than $1 a gallon at American service stations, leading to an even greater wave of inflation than in 1973.

The American people panicked. When lines began to form at gas stations in California and Florida in early May 1979, drivers started filling their tanks every day or two. The long lines frustrated American drivers, who took out their fury on the Carter administration. In June, the president's staff warned him of the danger in the "worsening short-term energy crisis." "Nothing else has so frustrated, confused, angered the American people," Carter was told, "or so targeted their distress at you personally."

By the fall of 1979, world supply had caught up with demand, and the oil scare ended. But the price of gasoline remained at more than $1 a gallon, and the inflation rate reached double-digit levels again. The twin oil shocks of the 1970s had left the economy battered and had undermined the average American's faith in the future.

THE SEARCH FOR AN ENERGY POLICY

The oil shocks of 1973 and 1979 were but two symptoms of a much deeper energy crisis. Put simply, the United States was running out of the fossil fuels on which it had relied for its economic growth in the past. Domestic oil production peaked in 1970 and declined every year thereafter; there were more ample reserves of natural gas, but both fuels were nonrenewable sources of energy that eventually would be exhausted. American political leaders had to devise a national policy to meet not only the temporary shortfalls of the 1970s but also the long-term energy problem inherent in past reliance on fossil fuels.

The success of the environmental movement in the late 1960s and early 1970s compounded the problem. Congress created the Environmental Protection Agency in 1970 to monitor industry and passed a Clean Air Act that encouraged public utilities to shift from using coal, which polluted the atmosphere, to clean-burning fuel oil and natural gas to generate electricity.

The energy crunch pitted the environmentalists against advocates of economic growth. Those who put ecology first lost out. By the end of the decade, groups such as the Sierra Club and Friends of the Earth had failed in their efforts to halt the gradual relaxation of environmental regulations that prohibited strip mining of coal and offshore drilling for oil.

The nation's leaders had a difficult time devising a coherent and workable long-term national energy policy. Gerald Ford favored expanding production to overcome the shortage. The Republicans advocated removing price controls on oil and natural gas to bring in new supplies of the fuels as well as greater production of coal and expanded nuclear power plants.

The Democrats, in contrast, were intent on shielding American consumers from the full brunt of the world price increase; Democratic leaders in Congress wanted to continue an elaborate system of price controls instituted by Nixon in 1973. They preferred standby plans for gas rationing to reliance on the marketplace to allocate scarce supplies.

The nation failed to adopt either the Republican or the Democratic energy plans; instead, Congress tried to muddle through with elements of both approaches. Thus, on the production front, it approved construction of the Alaskan pipeline. On the conservation side, Congress continued the price controls on domestic oil and mandated annual increases in automobile gasoline mileage that forced Detroit to produce more fuel-efficient cars.

The overall outcome, however, was a patchwork that fell far short of a coherent national strategy for solving the energy problem. Oil imports actually increased by 50 percent between 1973 and 1979, rising from 6 million to 9 million barrels a day, an amount nearly half of the nation's daily petroleum usage.

THE GREAT INFLATION

The gravest consequence of the oil shocks was inflation. The startling increase in price levels in the 1970s stemmed from many causes. The Vietnam War created budget deficits that grew from $63 billion for the entire decade of the 1960s to a total of $420 billion in the 1970s. A worldwide shortage of food triggered a 20 percent rise in American food prices in 1973 alone. But above all else, the primary source of the great inflation of the 1970s was the sixfold increase in petroleum prices.

The impact on consumers was staggering. The price of an automobile jumped 72 percent between 1973 and 1978. During the decade, the price of a hamburger doubled and the cost of a loaf of bread—the proverbial staff of life— rose from 24 to 89 cents. Corresponding wage increases failed to keep pace with inflation; in 1980, the real income of the average American family fell by 5.5 percent.

Curbing inflation proved to be beyond the power of the federal government. President Ford's early efforts to roll back prices by rhetoric were a casualty of the 1974 recession. President Carter proved equally powerless. Finally, in October 1979, the Federal Reserve Board, led by Carter appointee Paul Volcker, began a sustained effort to halt inflation by curtailing the supply of money in circulation. The new tight-money policy served only to heighten inflation in the short run by driving the prime interest rate to 20 percent in 1980.

THE SHIFTING AMERICAN ECONOMY

Inflation and the oil shocks helped bring about significant changes in American business and industry in the 1970s. The most obvious result was the slowing of the rate of economic growth. More important, American industry began to lose its position of primacy in world markets. In 1959, U.S. firms had been the leaders in eleven of thirteen major industrial sectors. By 1976, American companies led in only seven areas, and in all but one category—aerospace—U.S. corporations had declined in relation to Japanese and western European competitors.

The most serious losses came in the heavy industries in which the United States had once led the world. New steel producers in western Europe, Japan, and the Third World were producing steel far more efficiently than their American counterparts. As a result, by the end of the 1970s, American firms

Explosive charges felled four giant blast furnaces of the U.S. Steel plant in Youngstown, Ohio, in April 1982. The furnaces, which stood 12 stories high and weighed 3000 tons apiece, had been built in the early 1900s. The plant closed in early 1980.

were closing down their obsolete mills in the East and Midwest, idling thousands of workers.

Foreign competition did even more damage in the automobile industry. The oil shocks led to a consumer demand for small, efficient cars. German and Japanese automakers seized the opportunity to expand their once low volume of sales in the United States. By 1977, imported cars had captured 18.3 percent of the American market. In response, Detroit spent $70 billion retooling to produce a new fleet of smaller, lighter front-wheel-drive cars; but American manufacturers barely survived the foreign invasion. Only government-backed loans helped the Chrysler Corporation stave off bankruptcy.

In other areas, American corporations fared much better. The multinationals that had emerged in the boom years of the 1960s continued to thrive. IBM sold computers all over the globe. The growth of high-technology industries proved to be the most profitable new trend of the 1970s. Computer companies and electronics firms grew at a rapid rate, especially after the development of the silicon chip, a small, wafer-thin microprocessor capable of performing complex calculations almost instantly.

The result was a geographic shift of American industry from the East and Midwest to the Sunbelt. Electronics manufacturers flourished in California, Texas, and North Carolina, where they grew up around major universities. At the same time, the decline of the steel and auto industries was leading to massive unemployment and economic stagnation in the northern industrial heartland.

The overall pattern was one of an economy in transition. The oil shocks had caused serious problems of inflation, slower economic growth, and rising unemployment rates. But American business still displayed the enterprise and the ability to develop new technologies that gave promise of renewed economic vitality.

PRIVATE LIVES—PUBLIC ISSUES

Sweeping changes in the private lives of the American people began in the 1970s and continued for the rest of the century. The traditional American family, with the husband the wage earner and the wife the homemaker, gave way to much more diverse living arrangements. The number of working women, including wives and mothers, increased sharply; the wage gap between the sexes narrowed, but women still lagged noticeably behind men in earnings. Finally, the years since 1970 saw the emergence of an active gay rights movement as more and more homosexuals began to disclose their sexual identities and demand an end to discrimination.

THE CHANGING AMERICAN FAMILY

Family life underwent a number of significant shifts after 1970. The most notable was a decline in the number of families with two parents and one or more children under 18. By 1990, in only 21 percent of the two-parent families was the mother solely engaged in child rearing. A few fathers stayed at home with the children, but in the great majority of these families, both parents worked outside the home.

The number of married-couple households without children remained nearly constant at 30 percent, but there was a marked increase in the number of people living alone. The birthrate, however, after a steady fall in the 1970s and early 1980s, climbed again as the baby boom generation began to mature. There was a marked increase in the number of births to women over age 30, as well as a very high proportion of children born to single mothers—27 percent of all births, compared to just 11 percent twenty years earlier.

By the mid-1990s, as the baby boom generation matured, several changes in living patterns were apparent. The divorce rate, which had doubled between the mid-1960s and the late 1970s, leveled off in the 1980s and then dropped slightly between 1990 and 1995. There was a slight drop in the birthrate by the mid-

1990s, as baby boomers moved beyond the childbearing age and younger people postponed marriage until they were in their mid-twenties. Noting that married couples headed 78 percent of all American families, a conservative analyst concluded that "reports of the traditional family's death are greatly exaggerated."

Changes in modern American life have affected traditional family structure. A large number of people either never marry or postpone marriage until late in the childbearing period. The traditional family unit, with the working father and the mother rearing the children at home, is rapidly declining. Women without partners headed more than one-third of all impoverished families, and children made up 40 percent of the nation's poor. Although politicians, especially Republicans, refer to family values during campaigns, the fact remains that the American family underwent great stress due to social changes in the last third of the twentieth century, and children have suffered disproportionately.

GAINS AND SETBACKS FOR WOMEN

American women have experienced significant changes in their way of life and their place in society in the past quarter century. The prevailing theme is the increasing percentage of working women. There was a rapid movement of women into the labor force in the 1970s. The trend continued through the 1980s. Fully 61 percent of the nearly nineteen million new jobs created during the decade were filled by women; many of these new jobs, however, were entry-level or low-paying service positions.

Women scored some impressive breakthroughs. They began to enter corporation boardrooms and became presidents of major universities. Women entered blue-collar, professional, and small-business fields traditionally dominated by men. Reagan's appointment of Sandra Day O'Connor to the Supreme Court in 1981 marked a historic first; Clinton doubled the number of women on the Court with his selection of Ruth Bader Ginsburg.

Yet at the same time, women encountered a great deal of resistance. Most women continued to work in female-dominated fields—as nurses, secretaries, teachers, and waitresses. Those who entered such "male" areas as management and administration soon encountered the "glass ceiling." In 1990, only 4.3 percent of corporate officers were women. Most in business worked at the middle and lower rungs of management with staff jobs in personnel and public relations, not key operational positions in sales and marketing that would lead to the boardroom. The economic boom of the 1990s, however, led to a steady increase in the number of women executives; in 1998, there was an increase of 514,000.

Even with these gains, however, by 1999 women's wages still averaged only 73 percent of men's earnings. Younger women did best; those between 16 and 24 earned almost 90 cents for every dollar paid to a male in the same age group.

Older women, who often had no other source of support, fared poorly; those over the age of 50 earned only 64 percent as much as men their age. Feminists had once hoped to close the gender gap by the year 2000, but experts predicted women would not reach pay equity with men until 2018.

The most encouraging development for women came in business ownership. The number of female business owners increased 40 percent between 1987 and 1992, twice the national rate of business growth. A women's trade group estimated that in 1996, women owned almost eight million businesses, employing more than eighteen million workers—one out of four American workers.

Beyond economic opportunity, the women's movement had two goals in recent years. The first was ratification of the Equal Rights Amendment (ERA). Approved by Congress in 1972, the ERA stated simply, "Equality of rights under the law shall not be denied or abridged by the United States or any state on account of sex." Within a year, twenty-two states had approved the amendment, but the efforts gradually faltered just three states short of ratification. Right-wing activist Phyllis Schlafly led an organized effort to defeat the ERA, claiming the amendment would lead to unisex toilets, homosexual marriages, and the drafting of women. The National Organization for Women (NOW) fought back, persuading Congress to extend the time for ratification by three years and waging intense campaigns for approval in Florida and Illinois. But the deadline for ratification finally passed on June 30, 1982, with the ERA forces still three states short. NOW leader Eleanor Smeal vowed a continuing struggle: "The crusade is not over. We know that we are the wave of the future."

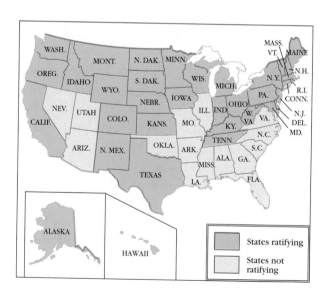

Voting on the Equal Rights Amendment

By the end of 1974, thirty-four states had ratified the ERA; Indiana finally approved the amendment in 1977, but the remaining fifteen states held out, leaving ratification three states short of the required three-fourths majority.

The women's movement focused even more of its energies in protecting a major victory it had won in 1973 in *Roe v. Wade,* affirming that women had the constitutional right to abortion. "Right-to-life" groups, consisting mainly of orthodox Catholics, fundamentalist Protestants, and conservatives, fought back. In 1978, with strong support from President Carter, Congress passed the Hyde amendment, which denied the use of federal funds to pay for abortions for poor women.

As Presidents Reagan and Bush appointed more conservative judges to the Court, prochoice groups began to fear the future overturn of *Roe v. Wade.* The Court avoided a direct challenge, contenting itself with lesser actions that upheld the rights of states to regulate abortion clinics and require the approval of one parent or a judge before a minor could have an abortion. Abortion became an issue in presidential contests, with the Republicans upholding a prolife position and the Democrats taking a prochoice stand. Even the exercise of the right to abortion proved difficult and sometimes dangerous in view of the often violent protests of prolife groups outside abortion clinics. For women, abortion was a hard-won right they still had to struggle to protect.

THE GAY LIBERATION MOVEMENT

On the evening of July 29, 1969, a squad of New York policemen raided the Stonewall Inn, a Greenwich Village bar frequented by "drag queens" and lesbians. As the patrons were being herded into vans, a crowd of gay onlookers began to jeer and taunt the police. A riot quickly broke out. "Beer cans and bottles were heaved at the windows and a rain of coins descended on the cops," reported the *Village Voice.* The next night, more than four hundred police officers battled two thousand gay demonstrators through the streets of Greenwich Village. The two-day Stonewall Riots marked the beginning of the modern gay liberation movement. Refusing to play the role of victims any longer, gays decided to affirm their sexual preference and demand an end to discrimination against homosexuals.

Within a few days, two new organizations were formed in New York, the Gay Liberation Front and the Gay Activist Alliance, with branches and offshoots quickly appearing in cities across the country. The basic theme of gay liberation was to urge all homosexuals to "come out of the closet" and affirm with pride their sexual identity. "Come out for freedom! Come out now!" proclaimed the Gay Liberation Front's newspaper. "Come out of the closet before the door is nailed shut!"

In the course of the 1970s, hundreds of thousands of gays and lesbians responded to this call. They formed more than a thousand local clubs and organizations and won a series of notable victories. In 1974, the American Psychiatric

Association stopped classifying homosexuality as a mental disorder. Gays fought hard in cities and states for laws forbidding discrimination against homosexuals in housing and employment, and in 1980, they finally succeeded in getting a gay rights plank in the Democratic National Platform.

In the 1980s, the onset of the AIDS epidemic forced the gay liberation movement on the defensive. Stung by the accusation that AIDS was a "gay disease," male homosexuals faced new public condemnation at a time when they were trying desperately to care for the growing number of victims of the disease within their ranks. The gay organizations formed in the 1970s to win new rights now were channeling their energies into caring for the ill, promoting safe sex practices, and fighting for more public funding to help conquer AIDS. In 1986, ACT UP (AIDS Coalition to Unleash Power) began a series of violent demonstrations in an effort to shock the nation into doing more about AIDS.

The movement also continued to stimulate gay consciousness in the 1980s. In 1987, an estimated 600,000 gays and lesbians took part in a march on Washington on behalf of gay rights. Every year afterward, gay groups held a National Coming Out Day in October to encourage homosexuals to proclaim proudly their sexual identity. In a more controversial move, some gay leaders encouraged "outing"—releasing the names of prominent homosexuals, primarily politicians and movie stars, in an effort to make the nation aware of how many Americans were gay or lesbian. Gay leaders claimed there were more than twenty million gays and lesbians in the nation. A sociological survey released in the spring of 1993 contradicted those numbers, finding only 1.1 percent of American males exclusively homosexual. Whatever the actual number, it was clear by the 1990s that gays and lesbians formed a significant minority that had succeeded in forcing the nation, however grudgingly, to respect its rights.

There was one battle, however, in which victory eluded the gay liberation movement. In the 1992 election, Democratic candidate Bill Clinton promised to end the ban on homosexuals in the military. In his first days in office, however, President Clinton stirred up great resistance in the Pentagon and Congress when he tried to issue an executive order forbidding such discrimination. The Joint Chiefs of Staff and many Democrats warned that acceptance of gays and lesbians would destroy morale and seriously weaken the armed forces. Clinton finally settled for the Pentagon's compromise "Don't ask, don't tell" policy that would permit homosexuals to continue serving in the military as they had in the past as long as they did not reveal their sexual preference and refrained from homosexual conduct. However disappointed gays and lesbians were in Clinton's retreat, their leaders understood that the real problem was the resistance of mainstream America to full acceptance of homosexuality.

Public attitudes toward gays and lesbians seemed to be changing in the 1990s, but the growing tolerance had definite limits. In a 1996 poll, 85 percent of those questioned believed that gays should be treated equally in the workplace, up from 76 percent in 1992. Violence against gays, however, continued, most notably in the 1998 fatal beating of Matthew Shepard, a 21-year-old gay college student, in Wyoming.

The issue of same-sex marriage came to a head at the end of the century. In 1996, President Clinton signed the Defense of Marriage Act, which decreed that states did not have to recognize same-sex marriages performed elsewhere. But in 2000, following a state supreme court ruling, the Vermont legislature legalized "civil unions" between individuals of the same sex, enabling gays and lesbians to receive all the legal benefits available to married couples. Overall, the American people appeared to be inclined to oppose discrimination against gays and lesbians, while they still refused to sanction the practice of homosexuality.

POLITICS AFTER WATERGATE

The energy crisis and the economic dislocations of the mid-1970s could not have come at a worse time. Watergate had a paralyzing impact on the American political system. An awareness that the Cold War had led to an imperial presidency created a growing demand to weaken the power of the president and strengthen congressional authority. The result was increasing tension between the White House and Capitol Hill, preventing the strong, effective leadership needed to meet the unprecedented problems of the 1970s.

THE FORD ADMINISTRATION

Gerald R. Ford had the distinction of being the first president who had not been elected to national office. Richard Nixon had appointed him to the vice presidency to succeed Spiro Agnew, who had been forced to resign in order to avoid prosecution for accepting bribes while he was governor of Maryland. Ford, an amiable and unpretentious Michigan congressman who had risen to the post of House minority leader, seemed ready to restore public confidence in the presidency when he replaced Nixon in August 1974.

Ford's honeymoon lasted only a month. On September 8, 1974, he shocked the nation by announcing he had granted Richard Nixon a full and unconditional pardon for all federal crimes he may have committed. Some critics charged darkly that Nixon and Ford had made a secret bargain; others pointed out how unfair it was for Nixon's aides to serve their prison terms while the chief criminal went free. Ford apparently acted in an effort to end the bitterness over

Watergate, but his attempt backfired, eroding public confidence in his leadership and linking him indelibly with the scandal.

Ford soon found himself fighting an equally difficult battle on behalf of the beleaguered CIA. The Watergate scandal and the Vietnam fiasco had eroded public confidence in the government and lent credibility to a startling series of disclosures about past covert actions. The president allowed the CIA to confirm some of the charges, and then he made things worse by blurting out to the press the juiciest item of all: the CIA had been involved in plots to assassinate foreign leaders. Senate and House select committees appointed to investigate the CIA now focused on the assassination issue, eventually charging that the agency had been involved in no less than eight separate attempts to kill Fidel Castro.

In late 1975, President Ford finally moved to limit the damage to the CIA. He appointed George Bush, then a respected former Republican congressman, as the agency's new director and gave him the authority both to reform the CIA and to strengthen its role in shaping national security policy. Most notably, Ford issued an executive order outlawing assassination as an instrument of American foreign policy.

Ford proved less successful in his dealings with Congress on other issues. Though he prided himself on his good relations with members of both houses, he opposed Democratic measures such as federal aid to education and control over strip mining. In a little more than a year, he vetoed thirty-nine separate bills. In fact, Ford, who as a congressman had opposed virtually every Great Society measure, proved far more conservative than Nixon in the White House.

THE 1976 CAMPAIGN

Ford's lackluster record and the legacy of Watergate made the Democratic nomination a prize worth fighting for in 1976. A large field of candidates entered the contest, but a virtual unknown, former Georgia governor James Earl Carter, quickly became the front-runner. Aware of the voters' disgust with politicians of both parties, Jimmy Carter ran as an outsider, portraying himself as a Southerner who had no experience in Washington and one who could thus give the nation fresh and untainted leadership.

Carter swept through the primaries and won the Democratic nomination easily, naming Senator Walter Mondale of Minnesota as his running mate. The polls gave Carter a 33-point lead when the campaign began, but he quickly lost ground as he began to hedge on the issues. President Ford counterattacked, but hurt his cause by misspeaking in a televised debate. Responding to a question about Iron Curtain countries, he declared, "There is no Soviet domination of eastern Europe."

THE ELECTION OF 1976

CANDIDATE	PARTY	POPULAR VOTE	ELECTORAL VOTE
Jimmy Carter	Democratic	40,830,763	297
Gerald Ford	Republican	39,147,793	240

Carter won an extremely narrow victory in 1976. Despite Watergate and Ford's weak record, the Democratic candidate took only 49.98 percent of the popular vote. Ford swept nearly the entire West, but Carter carried the South and key northern industrial states. The outcome turned on class and racial factors. "The affluent, the well-educated, the suburbanites largely went for Ford," commented one observer, "the socially and economically disadvantaged for Carter." The black vote clinched the victory for the Democrats. Carter received more than 90 percent of the votes of African Americans, and their ballots provided the margin of victory in Ohio, Pennsylvania, and seven southern states.

DISENCHANTMENT WITH CARTER

The new president, described by an associate as "superficially self-effacing but intensely shrewd," was an ambitious and intelligent politician. He had a rare gift for sensing what people wanted and appearing to give it to them. Liberals thought he clearly stood with them; conservatives were equally convinced he was on their side. He was especially adept at utilizing symbols. He emerged from airplanes carrying his own garment bag; after his inauguration, he walked up Pennsylvania Avenue hand in hand with his wife Rosalynn and daughter Amy. "Look," he seemed to be saying, "I am just an ordinary citizen who happens to be in the White House."

The substance, however, failed to match the style. He had no discernible political philosophy, no clear sense of direction. He sought the White House convinced that he was brighter and better than his competitors, but once there, he had no cause or mission to fulfill.

The makeup of his administration reflected the conflicting tendencies that would eventually prove destructive. In the White House, he surrounded himself with close associates from Georgia, fellow outsiders such as presidential adviser Hamilton Jordan and press secretary Jody Powell. Yet he picked established Democrats for key cabinet positions: Cyrus Vance, a New York lawyer, as secretary of state; and Joseph Califano, a former aide to Lyndon Johnson, to head Health, Education, and Welfare. In the lower ranks, however, he selected liberal activists, people who were intent on regulating business and preserving the environment. The result was bound to be tension and conflict, as the White House staff and the federal bureaucracy worked at cross-purposes, one group seeking change while the other attempted to protect the president.

Lacking both a clear set of priorities and a coherent political philosophy, the Carter administration had little chance to succeed. The president strove hard for a balanced budget but was forced to accept mounting deficits. Federal agencies fought to save the environment and help consumers but served only to anger industry.

In the crucial area of social services, Joseph Califano failed repeatedly in his efforts to carry out long-overdue reforms. His attempts to overhaul the nation's welfare program, which had become a $30 billion annual operation serving some thirty million Americans, won little support from the White House. Carter's unwillingness to take the political risks involved in revamping the overburdened Social Security system by reducing benefits and raising the retirement age blocked Califano's efforts.

Informed by his pollsters in 1979 that he was losing the nation's confidence, Carter sought desperately to redeem himself. He gave a speech in which he seemed to blame his failure on the American people, accusing them of creating "a crisis of confidence . . . that strikes at the very heart and soul and spirit of our national will." Then, a week after what his critics termed the "national malaise" speech, he requested the resignation of Califano and the secretary of the treasury. But neither the attempt to pin responsibility on the American people nor the firing of cabinet members could hide the fact that Carter, despite his good intentions and hard work, had failed to provide the bold leadership the nation needed.

FROM DÉTENTE TO RENEWED COLD WAR

America's political position in the world declined sharply in the 1970s. In part, the fault was internal. The Vietnam War left the American people convinced that the nation should never again intervene abroad, and Watergate discredited strong presidential leadership, shifting power over foreign policy to Congress. The new national consensus was symbolized by the War Powers Act, passed in 1973, which required the president to consult with Congress before sending American troops into action overseas. At the same time, external events and developments, notably the control over oil exercised by OPEC and the threats posed by revolutionary nationalism in the Middle East and Latin America, further weakened

American foreign policy. No longer able to dominate the international scene, the United States began to play the role of spectator, and at times even of victim.

RETREAT IN ASIA

It was Gerald Ford's fate to reap where Nixon had sown. In 1974, Congress cut in half the administration's request for $1.4 billion in military aid to South Vietnam. A year later, when a North Vietnamese offensive proved surprisingly successful, Ford was unable to get Congress to grant any additional aid. Bereft of American assistance, the South Vietnamese government was unable to stop the advance on Saigon in April 1975. American forces concentrated on evacuating 150,000 loyal South Vietnamese, but many more were left behind when the last helicopter left the roof of the embassy in Saigon. After a quarter century of futile effort, the United States finally had to admit defeat in the nation's longest and most humiliating foreign war.

Less than a month later, Ford had a chance to remind the world of American power. The Khmer Rouge government of Cambodia seized an American freighter, the *Mayaguez,* and imprisoned its crew. Ford authorized an armed attack on Cambodia by two thousand marines from bases in Thailand. By the time the

An American official punches a man trying to board a plane already overloaded with refugees during the chaotic evacuation of the city of Nha Trang in South Vietnam in the spring of 1975. Just after this plane left, communist troops took over the city.

American forces landed on a small offshore island, Cambodia had freed the crewmen. The nation took pride in the president's resort to force, but forty Americans paid for his decision with their lives.

ACCOMMODATION IN LATIN AMERICA

President Carter was more successful than Ford in adjusting to the growing nationalism in the world, particularly in Central America, where the United States had imposed order for most of the twentieth century by backing reactionary regimes.

The first test came in Panama. Resentment over American ownership of the Panama Canal had led Lyndon Johnson to enter into negotiations aimed at the eventual return of the waterway to Panama. Carter completed the long diplomatic process in 1977 by signing two treaties. One restored sovereignty in the 500-square-mile Canal Zone to Panama, while the other provided for gradual Panamanian responsibility for operating the canal, with appropriate safeguards for its use and defense by the United States. In negotiating the treaties, Carter was trying both to right an ancient wrong and to create stability in a highly volatile region.

The real struggle over the treaties took place in the Senate. Conservative Republicans expressed outrage over what they termed a "giveaway" of the Panama Canal. Intensive personal lobbying by President Carter, as well as bipartisan support from influential Republicans such as Gerald Ford and Henry Kissinger, finally led to Senate ratification with just one vote to spare, thus paving the way for the return of the canal to Panama by the year 2000.

Carter was less successful, however, in dealing with a growing problem of left-wing uprisings in Central America. In mid-1979, dictator Anastasio Somoza capitulated to the Sandinista forces in Nicaragua. Despite American attempts to moderate the Sandinista revolution, the new regime moved steadily to the left, developing close ties with Castro's Cuba. In neighboring El Salvador, a growing leftist insurgency against a repressive regime put the United States in an awkward position. Carter tried to use American economic aid to encourage the military junta in El Salvador to carry out democratic reforms. But after the guerrillas launched a major offensive in January 1981, he authorized large-scale military assistance to the government for its war against the insurgents, setting a precedent for the future.

THE QUEST FOR PEACE IN THE MIDDLE EAST

The inconclusive results of the 1973 October War gave Henry Kissinger the opportunity to play the role of peacemaker in the troubled Middle East. Shuttling back and forth between Cairo and Jerusalem, and then to Damascus, the secre-

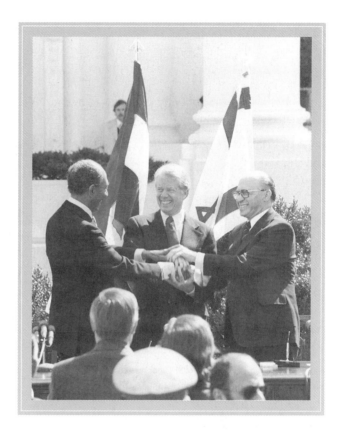

A highlight of Carter's presidency was his role in helping negotiate the Camp David accords between Israeli Prime Minister Menachem Begin (right) and Egyptian President Anwar Sadat (left). The agreements set the stage for a peace treaty between Israel and Egypt.

tary of state finally succeeded in arranging a pullback of Israeli forces in both the Sinai and the Golan Heights. Although he failed to achieve his goal of an Arab-Israeli settlement, Kissinger had succeeded in demonstrating that the United States could play the role of neutral mediator between the Israelis and Arabs.

In November 1977, Egyptian president Anwar Sadat stunned the world by traveling to Jerusalem in an effort to reach agreement directly with Israel. The next year, President Carter invited both Sadat and Israeli prime minister Menachem Begin to negotiate under his guidance at Camp David. For thirteen days, Carter met with Sadat and Begin, finally emerging with the ambiguous Camp David accords. A framework for negotiations rather than an actual peace settlement, the Camp David agreements dealt gingerly with the problem of Palestinian autonomy in the West Bank and Gaza Strip areas. In 1979, Israel and Egypt signed a peace treaty that provided for the gradual return of the entire Sinai to Egypt but left the fate of the Palestine Arabs vague and unsettled.

Any sense of progress in the Middle East as a result of Camp David was quickly offset in 1979 with the outbreak of the Iranian Revolution. Under Nixon

Iranian demonstrators, atop the U.S. embassy in Teheran, burn an American flag. The violent actions and virulent anti-Americanism of the Iranians shocked U.S. citizens.

and Kissinger, the United States had come to depend heavily on the shah and his powerful army for defense of the vital Persian Gulf. Carter continued the close relationship with the shah, despite growing signs of domestic discontent with his leadership. By 1978, Iran was in chaos as the exiled Ayatollah Ruholla Khomeini led a fundamentalist Muslim revolt against the shah.

Unaware of the deep resentment most Iranians felt toward the shah, the Carter administration misjudged the nature of the Iranian Revolution. When the shah decided to leave the country in January 1979, Carter tried to work with a moderate regime rather than encourage an army coup. With Khomeini's return from exile, Muslim militants quickly came to power in Teheran. In October 1979, Carter permitted the exiled shah to enter the United States for medical treatment. Irate mobs in Iran denounced the United States, and on November 4, militants seized the U.S. embassy in Teheran and took fifty-eight Americans prisoner.

The prolonged hostage crisis revealed the extent to which American power had declined in the 1970s. Carter relied first on diplomacy and economic reprisals in a vain attempt to free the hostages. In his State of the Union message in January 1980, the president enunciated a new Carter doctrine, telling the world the United States would fight to protect the vital oil supplies of the Persian Gulf. "Twin threats to the flow of oil—from regional instability and now potentially from the Soviet Union—require that we firmly defend our vital interest when threatened."

Carter was unable to back up his brave words with meaningful action. In April 1980, the president authorized a desperate rescue mission that ended in failure when several helicopters broke down in the Iranian desert. The mission was aborted, an accident cost the lives of eight crewmen, and Secretary of State Cyrus Vance—who had opposed the rescue attempt—resigned in protest. The hostage crisis dragged on through the summer and fall of 1980, a symbol of American weakness that proved to be a powerful political handicap to Carter in the upcoming presidential election.

THE COLD WAR RESUMES

The policy of détente was already in trouble when Carter took office in 1977. Congressional refusal to relax trade restrictions on the Soviet Union had doomed Kissinger's attempts to win political concessions from the Soviets through economic incentives. The Kremlin's repression of the growing dissident movement and its harsh policy restricting the emigration of Soviet Jews had caused many Americans to doubt the wisdom of seeking accommodation with the Soviet Union.

President Carter's emphasis on human rights appeared to the Russians to be a direct repudiation of détente. In his inaugural address, Carter reaffirmed his concern over the mistreatment of human beings anywhere in the world, declaring that "our commitment to human rights must be absolute." It was easier said than done. Carter did withhold aid from authoritarian governments in Chile and Argentina, but equally repressive regimes in South Korea and the Philippines continued to receive generous American support. The Soviets, however, found even an inconsistent human rights policy to be threatening, particularly after Carter received Soviet exiles in the White House.

Zbigniew Brzezinski, Carter's national security adviser, worked from the outset to reverse the policy of détente. Commenting that he was "the first Pole in three hundred years in a position to really stick it to the Russians," he favored confrontation with the Kremlin. Although Carter signed a SALT II treaty with Russia in 1979, lowering the ceiling on nuclear delivery systems to 2250, growing opposition in the Senate played directly into Brzezinski's hands. He prevailed on the president to advocate adoption of a new MX missile to replace the existing Minuteman ICBMs, which some experts thought were now vulnerable to a Soviet first strike. This new weapons system ensured that regardless of SALT, the nuclear arms race would be speeded up in the 1980s.

Brzezinski also was successful in persuading the president to use China to outmaneuver the Soviets. On January 1, 1979, the United States and China exchanged ambassadors, thereby completing the reconciliation that Nixon had begun in 1971. The new relationship between Beijing and Washington presented the Soviet Union with the problem of a link between its two most powerful enemies.

The Cold War, in abeyance for nearly a decade, resumed with full fury in December 1979 when the Soviet Union invaded Afghanistan. Although this move was designed to ensure a regime friendly to the Soviet Union, it appeared to many like the beginning of a Soviet thrust toward the Indian Ocean and the Persian Gulf. Carter responded to this aggression with a series of symbolic acts: the United States banned the sale of high technology to Russia, embargoed the export of grain, and even boycotted the 1980 Moscow Olympics. These American moves did not halt the invasion of Afghanistan; instead, they put the United States and Russia back on a collision course.

The results doomed détente. Aware that he could not get a two-thirds vote in the Senate, Carter withdrew the SALT II treaty. The hopeful phrases of détente gave way to belligerent rhetoric. Jimmy Carter, who had come into office hoping to advance human rights and control the nuclear arms race, now found himself a victim of the renewed Cold War.

National frustration over the hostages in Iran and the Soviet invasion of Afghanistan, coupled with anxiety over the energy crunch and rampant inflation, eroded public confidence in the Carter administration. A leader who had benefited from Vietnam and Watergate had now been betrayed by events. Despite his substantial achievements—the Camp David agreements, the Panama Canal treaties—Carter had to take the blame for developments overseas that were beyond his control. By mid-1980, the president's overall approval rating had fallen to 23 percent in the Gallup poll. The American people, disillusioned by the failures of Nixon, Ford, and Carter, yearned for new political leadership to meet the challenges facing the nation at home and abroad.

32

THE REPUBLICAN RESURGENCE, 1980–1992

I
n October 1964, the Republican National Committee sponsored a televised
address by Hollywood actor Ronald Reagan on behalf of Barry Goldwater's
presidential candidacy. Reagan's speech had originally been aired on a Los
Angeles station; the resulting outpouring of praise and campaign contributions
led to its national rebroadcast.

In contrast to Goldwater's strident rhetoric, Reagan used relaxed, confident,
and persuasive terms to put forth the case for a return to individual freedom.
Instead of the usual choice between increased government activity and less government involvement, often couched in terms of the left and the right, Reagan
presented the options of either going up or down—"up to the maximum of human freedom consistent with law and order, or down to the ant heap of totalitar-
ianism." Then, borrowing a phrase from FDR, he told his audience: "You and I
have a rendezvous with destiny. We can preserve for our children this the last best
hope of man on earth, or we can sentence them to take the first step into a thousand years of darkness."

Although the speech did not rescue Goldwater's unpopular candidacy, it
marked the beginning of Ronald Reagan's remarkable political career. A popular
Hollywood actor whose movie career had begun to fade in the 1950s, Reagan had
become an effective television performer as host of "The General Electric
Theater." His political views, once liberal, moved steadily to the right as he be-

came a spokesperson for a major American corporation. In 1965, a group of wealthy friends persuaded him, largely on the basis of the success of "the speech," to run for the California governorship.

Reagan proved to be an attractive candidate. His friendly, relaxed manner and his mastery of television enabled him to present his strongly conservative message without appearing to be a rigid ideologue of the right. He won handily by appealing effectively to rising middle-class suburban resentment over high taxes, expanding welfare programs, and bureaucratic regulation.

In two terms as governor, Reagan displayed natural ability as a political leader. Instead of insisting on implementing all of his conservative beliefs, he proved surprisingly flexible. Symbolic victories were his specialty; in one example he managed to confront campus radicals and fire Clark Kerr, chancellor of the University of California, while at the same time generously funding higher education.

By the time Reagan left the governor's office in 1974, many signs pointed to a growing conservative mood across the nation. In a popular rebellion against escalating property taxes in 1978, California's voters passed Proposition 13, which called for a 57 percent cut in taxes and resulted in a gradual reduction in social services. Religious leaders were especially outraged over the 1962 Supreme Court

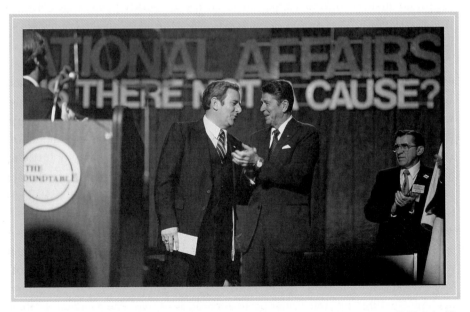

Ronald Reagan appears with Rev. Jerry Falwell at a Moral Majority rally in Dallas, Texas, in 1980. Falwell's Moral Majority and other similar evangelical groups endorsed conservative positions on a variety of issues, including abortion and school prayer. In his two presidential election campaigns, Reagan vigorously sought the support of Falwell's followers.

ruling in *Engel* v. *Vitale* outlawing school prayer. In the South, where daily prayers were the customary way of beginning the school day, the reaction was intense. One Alabama congressman denounced the Supreme Court justices, proclaiming, "They put the Negroes in the schools and now they're driving God out."

Concern over school prayer, along with rising abortion and divorce rates, impelled religious groups to engage in political activity to defend what they viewed as traditional family values. Jerry Falwell, a successful Virginia radio and television evangelist, founded the Moral Majority, a fundamentalist group dedicated to preserving the "American way of life."

The population shift of the 1970s, especially the rapid growth of the Sunbelt region in the South and West, added momentum to the conservative upsurge. Those moving to the Sunbelt tended to be white, middle- and upper-class suburbanites who were attracted both by economic opportunity and by a political climate stressing low taxes, less government regulation, and more reliance on the marketplace. The political impact of population shifts from East to West and North to South during the 1970s was reflected in the congressional gains (seventeen seats) by Sunbelt and Far West states after the 1980 census.

Conservatives also succeeded, for the first time since World War II, in making their cause intellectually respectable. Scholars and academics on the right flourished in new "think tanks." Neoconservatism, led by Norman Podhoretz's magazine *Commentary,* became fashionable among many intellectuals who were former liberal stalwarts. They denounced liberals for being too soft on the communist threat abroad and too willing to compromise high standards at home in the face of demands for equality from African Americans, women, and the disadvantaged.

By the end of the 1970s, Ronald Reagan was recognized as the nation's most effective leader of the conservative resurgence. His personal charm softened the hard edges of his right-wing call to arms, and his conviction that America could regain its traditional self-confidence by reaffirming basic ideals had a broad appeal to a nation shaken by inflation at home and humiliation abroad. In 1976, Reagan had barely lost to Gerald Ford at the Republican convention; four years later, he overcame an early upset by George Bush in Iowa to win the GOP presidential nomination handily.

In his acceptance speech at the Republican convention in Detroit, he set forth the themes that endeared him to conservatives—less government, balanced budget, family values, and peace through increased military spending. Reagan offered reassurance and hope for the future. He spoke of restoring to the federal government "the capacity to do the people's work without dominating their lives." In Ronald Reagan, the Republicans had found the perfect candidate to exploit both the American people's frustration with the failures in domestic and foreign policy of the 1970s and the growing conservative mood of the nation.

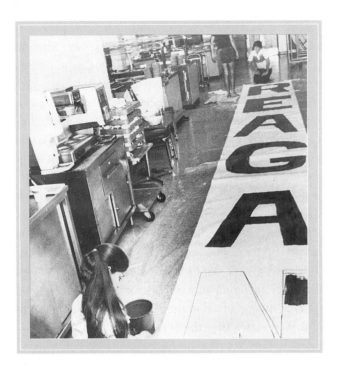

California members of Reagan Youth finish a sign in support of their candidate to be used at the 1980 Republican National Convention in Detroit.

REAGAN IN POWER

The liberal Democratic political coalition, originally created by Franklin D. Roosevelt in the Great Depression, finally split apart by the end of the 1970s. The Watergate scandal gave the Democrats a brief reprieve, but by the end of the decade, the Republicans were using the conservative upsurge to make inroads among such traditionally Democratic groups of voters as Jews, Southerners, and blue-collar workers. Yet the continuing appeal of the New Deal legacy prevented a total political realignment.

THE REAGAN VICTORY

In 1980, Jimmy Carter, who had used the Watergate trauma to win the presidency, found himself in trouble. Inflation, touched off by the second oil shock of the 1970s, reached double-digit figures. The Federal Reserve Board's effort to tighten the money supply had led to a recession. What Ronald Reagan dubbed the "misery index," the combined rate of inflation and unemployment, hit 28 percent early in 1980 and stayed above 20 percent throughout the year.

Foreign policy proved almost as damaging to Carter. The Soviet invasion of Afghanistan eroded hopes for continued détente; the hostage crisis in Iran highlighted the nation's sense of helplessness. In the short run, Carter used that crisis to beat back the challenge to his renomination by Senator Edward Kennedy. The Democrats rallied behind Carter, although the delegates to the party's convention displayed a notable lack of enthusiasm in renominating him.

Ronald Reagan and his running mate, George Bush, hammered away at the state of the economy and the world. Reagan scored heavily among traditionally Democratic blue-collar groups by blaming Carter for inflation. Reagan also accused Carter of allowing the Soviets to outstrip the United States militarily and promised a massive buildup of American forces if he was elected. Although Republican strategists feared Carter might spring an "October surprise"—a negotiated release of the American hostages at the height of the campaign—the Iranian situation actually helped Reagan by accentuating U.S. weakness in the world.

The president struck back by claiming that Reagan was too reckless to conduct American foreign policy in the nuclear age. The attack backfired. In a televised debate arranged late in the campaign, Reagan assured the American people of his devotion to peace, leaving Carter with the onus of trying to land a low blow. At the end of the confrontation, Reagan scored impressively when he summed up the country's dire economic condition by suggesting that voters ask themselves simply, "Are you better off now than you were four years ago?"

On election day, the American people answered with a resounding "no." Reagan carried forty-four states and gained 51 percent of the popular vote. Carter won only six states and 41 percent of the popular vote. Reagan clearly benefited from the growing political power of the Sunbelt; he carried every state west of the Mississippi except Minnesota. In the South, Reagan lost only Georgia, Carter's home state. Even more impressive were Reagan's inroads into the old New Deal coalition. He received 50.5 percent of the blue-collar vote and 46 percent of the Jewish vote, the best showing by a Republican since 1928. Only one group remained loyal to Carter: African American voters gave him 85 percent of their ballots.

THE ELECTION OF 1980

CANDIDATE	PARTY	POPULAR VOTE	ELECTORAL VOTE
Reagan	Republican	43,899,248	489
Carter	Democratic	35,481,435	49
Anderson	Independent	5,719,437	—
	Minor Parties	921,299	—

Republican gains in Congress were even more surprising. For the first time since 1954, the GOP gained control of the Senate, 53 to 46, and the party picked up 33 seats in the House to narrow the Democratic margin from 114 to 50.

The meaning of the election was less clear than its outcome. Nearly all observers agreed that the voters had rendered an adverse judgment on the Carter administration. But most experts did not assess the outcome to be a major realignment in American politics equivalent to the Democratic victory of FDR in 1932. The fact that the Democrats still held a sizable majority in the House was seen as proof of their party's continuing strength. Political scientist Walter Dean Burnham termed the result "a conservative revitalization," but one that stopped short of making the GOP the dominant party.

Journalist Theodore White disagreed, viewing the outcome as a repudiation of the Democratic coalition that had dominated American politics since the days of Franklin D. Roosevelt and the New Deal. White had a strong case. In the eight presidential elections from 1952 to 1980, Republican candidates received 52.3 percent of the popular vote, compared to 47.7 percent for the Democrats; Republicans won four elections (1952, 1956, 1972, and 1980) comfortably, one (1968) narrowly, and lost two close races (1960 and 1976). Only in 1964 did the Republicans lose by a wide margin. Reagan's victory in 1980 thus marked the culmination of a Republican presidential realignment that ended a half-century of Democratic dominance.

CUTTING SPENDING AND TAXES

When Ronald Reagan took office in January 1981, the ravages of inflation had devastated the economy. Interest rates hovered near 20 percent, while the value of the dollar, compared to 1960, had dropped to just 36 cents. The new president blamed what he termed "the worst economic mess since the Great Depression" on high federal spending and excessive taxation. "Government is not the solution to our problems," Reagan announced in his inaugural address, "government is the problem."

The president embraced the concept of supply-side economics as the proper remedy for the nation's economic ills. Supply-side economists believed that the private sector, freed of the ever increasing burden of government spending, would shift its resources from tax shelters to productive investment, leading to an economic boom that would provide enough new income to offset the lost revenue. Although many other economists worried that the 30 percent cut in income taxes that Reagan favored would lead to staggering deficits, the president was confident that his program would both stimulate the economy and reduce the role of government.

In pursuing his economic goals, Reagan relied primarily on the director of the Office of Management and Budget, David Stockman. A former Michigan congressman who had become a convert to supply-side economics, Stockman was charged with carrying out Reagan's policies of cutting government spending and sharply reducing taxes. At the same time, Reagan supported the efforts of Paul Volcker, the banker Carter had appointed to head the Federal Reserve Board, to stem inflation by restricting the money supply, and even appointed him to a second four-year term in 1983.

The president and his budget director made spending the first target. Quickly deciding not to attack such popular middle-class entitlement programs as Social Security and Medicare, and sparing critical social services for the "truly deserving needy," they concentrated on slashing $41.4 billion from the budget by cutting heavily into other social programs. Reagan used his charm and powers of persuasion to woo conservative Democrats from the West and South. Reagan won a commanding 253 to 176 margin of victory for his budget in the House, and an even more lopsided vote of 78 to 20 in the Senate in May. A jubilant Reagan told a Los Angeles audience that he had achieved "the greatest reduction in government spending that has ever been attempted."

The president proved equally successful in reducing taxes. He advocated a cut of 10 percent in personal income taxes for three consecutive years. When the Democrats countered with a two-year plan that would reduce taxes by only 15 percent, Reagan compromised with a proposal to cut taxes by 5 percent the first year but insisted on the full 10 percent reduction for the second and third years. In July, both houses passed the tax cut by impressive margins. In securing reductions in spending and lowering taxes, Reagan had demonstrated beyond any doubt his ability to wield presidential power effectively. As *Time* magazine commented, no president since FDR had "done so much of such magnitude so quickly to change the economic direction of the country."

LIMITING THE ROLE OF GOVERNMENT

Reagan met with only mixed success in his other efforts to restrict government activity and reduce federal regulation of the economy. Cutting back on the scope of federal agencies and limiting their impact on American business was a central tenet of the president's political philosophy. To the outrage of environmentalists, Secretary of the Interior James Watt opened up federal land to coal and timber production and made more than a billion acres of land available for offshore oil drilling. Though Watt was eventually forced to resign, the Reagan administration continued its policy of reducing government intervention in business long after Watt's departure.

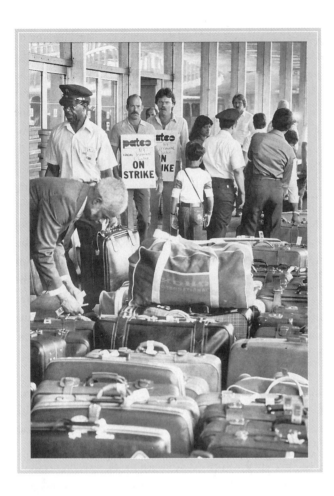

The Professional Air Traffic Controllers' Organization (PATCO) was one of the few unions to support Reagan in the 1980 campaign. But when PATCO struck in August 1981, Reagan unhesitatingly fired the striking air traffic controllers and refused to rehire them when the strike collapsed.

Transportation Secretary Drew Lewis proved to be the most effective cabinet member in the administration's first two years. He helped relieve the troubled American automobile industry of many of the regulations adopted in the 1970s to reduce air pollution and increase passenger safety. At the same time, he played a key role in the behind-the-scenes negotiations that led Japan to agree in the spring of 1981 to restrict its automobile exports to the United States for the next three years.

Lewis gained notoriety in opposing a strike by the air traffic controllers' union (PATCO) in the summer of 1981. The president fired the striking workers, decertified the union, and ordered Lewis to hire and train thousands of new air traffic controllers at a cost of $1.3 billion. For the Reagan administration, the price was worth paying to prove that no group of government employees had the right to defy the public interest.

The Reagan administration was less successful in trying to cut back on the entitlement programs that it viewed as the primary cause of the growing budget deficits. Social Security was the greatest offender. A 500 percent increase in Social Security benefits in the 1970s threatened to bankrupt the system's trust fund by the end of the century. Reagan met a sharp rebuff when he tried to make substantial cuts in future benefits. The president then appointed a bipartisan commission to recommend ways to protect the system's endangered trust fund. In March 1983, Congress approved a series of changes that guaranteed the solvency of Social Security by gradually raising the retirement age, delaying cost-of-living increases for six months, and taxing pensions paid to the well-to-do elderly.

The administration's record in dealing with women's concerns and civil rights proved clumsy and divisive. Although feminist groups were disappointed by the administration's strong rhetorical attacks on legalized abortion, the appointment of Sandra Day O'Connor to the Supreme Court pleased them. His appointments to the lower federal courts were a better indication of his administration's relatively low regard for women and minorities. Of the first seventy-two Reagan nominees to the federal judiciary, only three were women; just one of the sixty-nine men was African American.

Chief Justice Warren Burger swears in Sandra Day O'Connor, the first woman to serve on the U.S. Supreme Court, in September 1981.

The administration's civil rights record proved especially revealing. Aware of how few African Americans had supported the GOP in 1980, Reagan made no effort to reward this group with government jobs or favors. Instead, the Justice Department actively opposed affirmative action measures that resulted in minority hiring quotas. The Republicans also failed to take the lead in renewing the original Voting Rights Act of 1965. After opposing key amendments designed to strengthen the historic legislation that had finally enabled African Americans to participate fully in southern politics, Reagan belatedly endorsed and signed a measure to extend the Voting Rights Act for twenty-five years.

REAGANOMICS

The sweeping reductions in domestic spending and income taxes that Reagan achieved in 1981 gave rise to conflicting economic expectations. Supply-side economists believed that the tax relief granted investors would lead to rapid business growth, which would raise more than enough new revenue to offset the lower rates. The administration's critics, on the other hand, were sure that heavy defense spending coupled with tax reductions would create massive deficits and result in economic stagnation. Neither group proved to be right.

RECESSION AND RECOVERY

The supply-side theory became the first economic casualty of the 1980s. The naive belief that a combination of cuts in social spending and sharply reduced taxes could unleash an economic boom that would avoid huge deficits was the victim of both Reagan's insistence on huge increases in defense spending and the Federal Reserve Board's tight-money policy. It was the latter that touched off a recession that began in the fall of 1981 and grew steadily worse throughout 1982, with unemployment reaching a postwar high of 10.4 percent in October.

Still, Reagan refused to give up his income tax cuts. With the first 10 percent reduction due to come in July 1982, he claimed that his policies had not yet been given a chance. But he did prove flexible in other ways, slightly moderating the defense buildup, accepting fewer cuts in social programs than he proposed, and finally agreeing to a $98 billion increase in miscellaneous federal taxes. He refused, however, to cancel the final 10 percent cut in income taxes due in mid-1983. Instead, he declared that all signs pointed to "a strong recovery."

Whether by design or good luck, the president's optimism proved justified. In the second quarter of 1983, the economy came to life. The final 10 percent tax cut in July stimulated consumer spending. The long-depressed automobile industry began to boom. The American people went on a great buying spree with consumer installment debt increasing as much in the first six months of 1983 as in all of 1982.

Best of all, inflation remained under control as the economy expanded. The cost of living dropped to 3.8 percent in 1983; at the same time, interest rates fell to 10.5 percent, enabling consumers to buy goods and corporations to expand their inventories much more easily. A combination of long-term Federal Reserve policy, the impact of the recession, and a worldwide decline in energy and food prices enabled the Reagan administration to take credit for solving the problem that had proved fatal for Carter and the Democrats.

THE GROWING DEFICIT

A new problem emerged in the mid-1980s to cloud Reagan's claims of economic recovery—the growing federal budget deficit. As the economy weakened and unemployment increased, tax revenues fell below projections while government spending on unemployment insurance and other social programs climbed. The deficit reached $207.8 billion in 1983, nearly triple the pre-Reagan high of $70.5 billion in 1976.

Some economists were predicting that at current spending and tax rates, the deficit would rise to more than $300 billion a year by the end of the decade. The result, many feared, would be soaring interest rates. In fact, a slumping world economy led to a massive infusion of foreign investment, which kept the prime rate from rising above 11 percent.

When the deficit continued to climb during the economic recovery of the mid-1980s, Congress finally came forward with what appeared to be a drastic solution. Republican senators Phil Gramm of Texas and Warren Rudman of New Hampshire joined with Democrat Ernest Hollings of South Carolina to set a series of budgetary ceilings designed to eliminate the deficit entirely by 1991. After considerable revision, the Balanced Budget Act, known as Gramm-Rudman, succeeded in halting the deficit spiral. The president and Congress were able to lower the deficit from a peak of $221 billion in 1986 to a more manageable $155 billion by 1988.

In essence, Gramm-Rudman was a political compromise. The price Reagan had to pay for Democratic help in resolving his budgetary crisis was to stop the increase in defense spending. But at the same time, by agreeing to sizable budget deficits for the next few years, the Democrats who controlled Congress had to give up any hope of expanding existing social programs or enacting new ones, such as a comprehensive national health plan.

Another alarming deficit—in the balance of overseas trade—also became an important issue in the mid-1980s. American exports had been falling steadily since the 1970s as a result of the decline in traditional manufacturing industries—iron and steel, electronics, and automobiles. The Japanese had been the biggest gainers as they dominated the American market in consumer goods such as television sets and VCRs.

A sharp rise in the value of the dollar, beginning in 1983, accentuated the problem by making American goods too expensive in foreign markets. The result was a trade deficit that grew from a modest $31 billion in 1981 to an alarming $171 billion by 1987. The only way the United States could equalize the balance of international payments was to import even more capital from abroad. Led by the Japanese, foreign investors poured large sums into the United States. As a result, in 1985, the United States, a creditor nation since World War I, suddenly became a debtor, owing the rest of the world more each year than it received from previous foreign investments. In late 1985, the Reagan administration joined with the governments of Japan and western Europe to devalue the dollar. The resulting decline in the dollar stimulated American exports and helped reduce the trade deficit to more manageable proportions by 1989.

In the 1980s, the American people had begun living beyond their means. Just as the government incurred large deficits rather than raising taxes to pay for the huge defense buildup, so consumers had cut back on personal saving in order to buy imported cars, television sets, and VCRs, encouraging further foreign investment. By 1988, foreigners held $400 billion in U.S. Treasury securities, had invested another $300 billion in American industry, and owned 21 percent of the nation's banking assets. At the end of the decade, the American people were sending $60 billion a year overseas just to pay the interest on the public and private obligations. Reaganomics had succeeded in continuing America's traditional high standard of living, but at a very high price—massive borrowing that mortgaged the nation's future.

THE RICH GROW RICHER

There were both gains and losses in the Reagan years. Inflation fell from double-digit levels by 1982 and averaged about 4 percent for the rest of the decade. A sharp drop in the world price of oil in late 1985 helped lower the trade deficit and brought inflation down to less than 2 percent.

After the end of the 1982 recession, employment grew steadily; by 1990, there were nearly nineteen million more Americans working than in 1980. There were losers as well, however. Blue-collar jobs declined as American industry, notably steel and autos, streamlined operations by closing obsolete plants and farming out manufacturing to foreign producers with far lower labor costs. Companies that specialized in labor-intensive consumer products, such as Eastman Kodak and General Electric, virtually stopped all manufacturing in the

United States, concentrating instead on marketing and distributing goods made abroad to their specifications.

At the same time, however, the service sector expanded rapidly, especially the financial, transportation, and health-care industries. Accountants, lawyers, and technicians flourished, with women especially benefiting from the change from blue- to white-collar jobs. By 1990, nearly one in three workers was an executive, technician, or professional; only one in five worked in factories. Labor unions were especially hard hit; union membership dropped from 23 percent of the workforce in 1980 to 15.5 percent by 1992.

The most striking change in the decade was the growing inequality of wealth in America. In the five income categories used by the Census Bureau, the poorest 20 percent of Americans fared badly, dropping 6 percent in pretax income in the 1980s. The three middle groups gained about 5 percent. The top fifth did far better, increasing their incomes by 20 percent over the decade. The top 1 percent, the truly rich, did best of all, doubling their after-tax income in ten years.

The income disparity was the product of both economic restructuring and Republican tax policy. The decline in manufacturing meant that many assembly-line workers lost their jobs and were working for little more than the minimum wage in the service sector. At the same time, income tax cuts and adjustments reduced the top tax rate from 70 percent to 31 percent. A parallel increase in Social Security payroll taxes meant that by the end of the decade, the tax burden for a middle-class family was 37.3 cents of every dollar earned, compared to 35 cents for the wealthy.

The economic inequities of the 1980s were most clearly reflected in the transfer of actual wealth—housing, property, stocks, savings, and retirement accounts. Between 1983 and 1989, 55 percent of the gain in family wealth went to the top 0.5 percent of the population. The poor and the lower middle class actually lost $256 billion in assets during this boom period. By the end of the decade, the top fifth of the population owned 80 percent of the nation's entire household wealth.

REAGAN AFFIRMED

"Are you better off now than you were four years ago?" Reagan had asked voters at the end of his 1980 debate with Jimmy Carter. By the mid-1980s, he appeared to have delivered on his implicit promise to stem inflation and revive the stagnant American economy.

Despite the growing gap between the rich and the poor, Reagan could boast of impressive economic gains after weathering the 1982 recession. The recovery led to 16 million new jobs as the unemployment rate dropped back under 6 percent. Inflation remained low and median family income moved steadily upward.

The economic boom that began in 1983 came at just the right time for the Republican party. By early 1984, with personal income rising at an annual rate of 10.3 percent from January to June and unemployment shrinking rapidly, Democratic prospects dimmed for the presidential election. After a long, bruising primary battle, Walter Mondale, former Minnesota senator and Carter's vice president, won the Democratic nomination. In a bold break with tradition, he chose a woman as a running mate, Congresswoman Geraldine Ferraro of New York.

When the Republicans renominated Reagan and Bush, the campaign quickly came down to one issue: leadership. The GOP claimed that Reagan had overcome the problems that overwhelmed Carter, notably inflation at home and disrespect abroad. The president told voters they should reelect him: "You ain't seen nothin' yet."

Mondale and Ferraro, in contrast, accused Reagan of helping the rich at the expense of the poor, saddling future generations with huge deficits. In a surprise move, the Democratic candidate announced he intended to raise taxes to curb the deficit and then accused Reagan of harboring a "secret plan" to increase taxes himself.

These tactics failed to gain support; the outcome was a far greater Reagan victory than in 1980. With a solid base in the South and West, the president cut deeply into the normally Democratic states of the Northeast and the swing states of the Midwest to take the electoral votes of all but Minnesota and the District of Columbia. Exit surveys revealed that economic issues were uppermost in the minds of voters; in the midst of a strong economic recovery, Reagan won a majority among all voters earning more than $12,500 a year. More than two-thirds of the white male voters in the nation stood behind Reagan, who won even a majority of the blue-collar and women's votes. Of all the traditional Democratic groups, only African Americans proved loyal to the party, giving Mondale 90 percent of their votes.

The 1984 election was far more of a triumph for Reagan than for his party. In Congress, the GOP gained only fourteen seats, leaving the Democrats firmly in control of the House; in the Senate, the Republicans lost two places, narrowing

THE ELECTION OF 1984

CANDIDATE	PARTY	POPULAR VOTE	ELECTORAL VOTE
Reagan	Republican	54,451,521	525
Mondale	Democratic	37,565,334	13

their majority to 54 to 46. Republicans were encouraged by a strong showing among the young, with Reagan taking 56 percent of the vote of the baby boomers (those aged 25 to 34) and 60 percent of the postboomers (those aged 18 to 24). The nation seemed to be dividing politically along economic lines, with the wealthy and affluent supporting the president while a growing underclass of African Americans, Hispanics, and the working poor were voting solidly Democratic. Middle-class Americans who held the balance revealed their mixed feelings by backing a Republican for president and Democratic candidates for the House and Senate.

REAGAN AND THE WORLD

Ronald Reagan was even more determined to reverse the course of American policy abroad than at home. He believed that under Carter, American prestige and standing in the world had dropped to an all-time low. Intent on restoring traditional American pride and self-respect, Reagan's mission was to strengthen America's defenses and recapture world supremacy from the Soviet Union.

In reality, the new president was simply continuing the hard line that Carter had begun to take after the invasion of Afghanistan. The Democrats had begun a massive military buildup in 1979 that included plans for cruise missiles in Europe, a rapid deployment force in the Middle East, and a 5 percent increase in the defense budget.

Under Reagan, the Pentagon flourished. Secretary of Defense Caspar Weinberger presented a plan that would more than double defense spending. The emphasis was on new weapons, ranging from the B-1 bomber to the expansion of the navy from 456 to 600 ships. Despite growing opposition in Congress, by 1985 the defense budget grew to more than $300 billion at the very time the administration was cutting back on domestic spending.

After some initial difficulty, Reagan proved more successful than Jimmy Carter in bringing harmony and order to the conduct of American foreign policy. His first secretary of state was Alexander Haig, a former general and White House chief of staff under Nixon. Haig, outspoken and assertive, tried to establish his primacy over the policymaking process, only to alienate the entire White House staff. Finally, in mid-1982, Reagan replaced Haig as secretary of state with George Shultz, a professional economist with extensive government experience, whose low-key and relaxed style brought an air of calm reassurance to the conduct of American foreign policy.

Despite the steady increase in defense spending and the formation of a smoothly functioning foreign policy team, Reagan soon found his diplomatic goals were more difficult to achieve than the budgetary and tax measures he had pushed through Congress so speedily. Yet in the long run, he could claim credit for a goal that had eluded his predecessors in the White House—the end of the Cold War.

CHALLENGING THE "EVIL EMPIRE"

The belief that the Soviet Union was a deadly enemy that threatened the well-being and security of the United States was the central tenet of Reagan's approach to foreign policy. He saw the Russians as bent on world revolution, ready "to commit any crime, to lie, to cheat" to advance their cause. Citing what he called a "record of tyranny," Reagan denounced the Russians before the UN in 1982.

Given this view of Russia as "the focus of evil in the modern world," it is not surprising that the new president continued the hard line that Carter had adopted after the invasion of Afghanistan. Abandoning détente, Reagan proceeded to implement a 1979 decision to place 572 Pershing II and cruise missiles in western Europe within range of Moscow to match Soviet deployment of medium-range missiles aimed at NATO countries. Despite strong protests from the Soviet Union, as well as growing uneasiness in Europe and an increasingly vocal nuclear freeze movement at home, the United States began putting the weapons in bases in Great Britain and Germany in November 1983. The Soviets, claiming the move gave them only ten minutes of warning time in case of an American attack, responded by breaking off disarmament negotiations in Geneva.

The nuclear arms race had now reached a more dangerous level than ever before. The United States stepped up research and development of the Strategic Defense Initiative (SDI), an antimissile system based on the use of lasers and particle beams to destroy incoming missiles in outer space. SDI was quickly dubbed "star wars" by the media. Critics doubted that SDI could be perfected, but they warned that even if it were, the result would be to escalate the arms race by forcing the Russians to build more offensive missiles in order to overcome the American defense system. The Reagan administration, however, defended star wars as a legitimate attempt to free the United States from the deadly trap of deterrence, with its reliance on the threat of nuclear retaliation to keep the peace.

TURMOIL IN THE MIDDLE EAST

Reagan tried to continue Carter's basic policy in the turbulent Middle East. In April 1982, the Israelis honored a Camp David pledge by making their final withdrawal from the Sinai. Reagan hoped to achieve the other Camp David objective of providing a homeland for the Palestinian Arabs on the West Bank, but Israel instead continued to extend Jewish settlements into the disputed area. The threat of the Palestine Liberation Organization (PLO), based in southern Lebanon and frequently raiding across the border into Israel, seemed to be the major obstacle to further progress.

On June 6, 1982, with tacit American encouragement, Israel invaded southern Lebanon in order to secure its northern border and destroy the PLO. The Reagan administration made no effort to halt the offensive but did join with France and Italy in sending a multinational force to permit the PLO to evacuate to Tunisia. Unfortunately, the United States soon became enmeshed in the Lebanese civil war, which had been raging since 1975. American marines, sent to Lebanon as part of the multinational force to restore order, were caught up in the renewed hostilities between Muslim and Christian militia.

In the face of growing congressional demands for the withdrawal of the marines, Reagan declared they were there to protect Lebanon from the designs of Soviet-backed Syria. But finally, after terrorists drove a truck loaded with explosives into the American barracks, killing 239 marines, the president had no choice but to pull out. The last American unit left Beirut in late February 1984. Despite his good intentions, Reagan had experienced a humiliation similar to Carter's in Iran—one that left Lebanon in shambles and the Arab-Israeli situation worse than ever.

CONFRONTATION IN CENTRAL AMERICA

Reagan faced a difficult situation in Central America. In an area marked by great extremes of wealth, with a small landowning elite and a mass of peasants mired in dire poverty, the United States sought moderate middle-class regimes to support. Washington usually ended up backing repressive right-wing dictatorships rather than the more leftist groups who raised the radical issues of land reform and redistribution of wealth. Yet it was often oppression by U.S.-supported regimes that drove those seeking political change to embrace revolutionary tactics.

This is precisely what happened in Nicaragua, where the Sandinista coalition finally succeeded in overthrowing the repressive Somoza regime in 1979. In an effort to strengthen the many middle-class elements in the original Sandinista government and to avoid forcing Nicaragua into the Cuban and Soviet orbit, Carter extended American economic aid.

The Reagan administration quickly reversed this policy. Alexander Haig cut off all aid to Nicaragua in the spring of 1981, accusing the Sandinistas of driving out the moderates and welcoming Cuban advisers and Soviet military assistance. The criticism became a self-fulfilling prophecy as Nicaragua became even more dependent on Cuba and the Soviet Union.

The United States and Nicaragua were soon on a collision course. In April 1983, President Reagan asked Congress for the money and authority to oust the

Sandinistas. When Congress, fearful of repeating the Vietnam fiasco, refused, Reagan opted for covert action. The CIA began supplying the Contras, exiles fighting against the Sandinistas from bases in Honduras and Costa Rica. The U.S.-backed rebels tried to disrupt the Nicaraguan economy, raiding villages, blowing up oil tanks, and even mining harbors. Then, in 1984, Congress passed the Boland Amendment prohibiting any U.S. agency from spending money in Central America. The withdrawal of U.S. financial backing left the Contras in a precarious position.

The situation proved little better in El Salvador where left-wing groups had been waging a guerrilla war against a reactionary regime dominated by wealthy landowners since the 1970s. Reagan stepped up support for a government headed by middle-of-the-roader José Napoleon Duarte. In 1984, Duarte was able to win a decisive election victory over the extreme right and began modest reforms in an effort to undercut the appeal of the guerrillas.

Reagan's only clear-cut triumph in the hemisphere came in the Caribbean. In October 1983, a military coup led to the death of the leftist prime minister of Grenada, who was subsequently replaced by an even more radical regime. The Reagan administration, already upset by Grenada's close ties to Cuba, decided to intervene to prevent the communists from acquiring a strategic military base.

Nearly two thousand U.S. marines invaded Grenada on October 25, 1983. After brief but spirited resistance from eight hundred Cuban workers and troops on the island, the American forces claimed a victory that cost eighteen lives. The administration proudly displayed pictures of captured Soviet arms to justify the resort to force; American medical students, shown on television kissing the ground as they returned to the United States, enabled the administration to label the operation a "rescue mission."

Aside from Grenada, however, the Reagan administration had little to show for its massive military buildup. In the Middle East, its well-intentioned use of marines had ended in disaster; its determined opposition to left-wing groups in Central America had at best achieved a stalemate. Relations with the Soviet Union had fallen into one of the deepest chills of the entire Cold War with the nuclear arms race more intense than ever.

TRADING ARMS FOR HOSTAGES

The Reagan administration's policies in the Middle East and Central America reached a tragic convergence in the Iran-Contra affair. In mid-1985, Robert McFarlane, a retired marine officer who had become national security adviser a year earlier, began a new initiative designed to restore American influence in the troubled Middle East. Concerned over the fate of six Americans held hostage in Lebanon by groups thought to be loyal to Iran's Ayatollah Khomeini, McFarlane

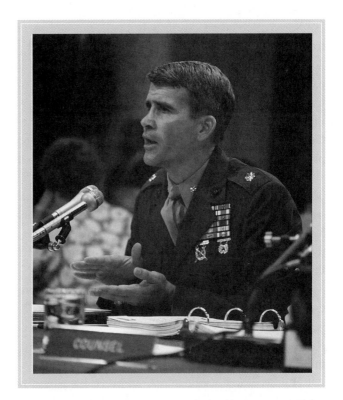

Despite Oliver North's questionable conduct, the public elevated him to near hero status during the televised Iran-Contra hearings. The bemedaled marine testified that he believed his deeds were justified as a defense of democracy.

proposed trading American antitank missiles to Iran in return for the hostages' release. The Iranians, desperate for weapons in the war they had been waging against Iraq since 1980, seemed willing to comply.

McFarlane soon found himself in over his head. He relied heavily on a young marine lieutenant colonel assigned to the National Security Council (NSC), Oliver North, and North in turn sought the assistance of CIA director William Casey. Casey saw the Iran initiative as an opportunity to use the NSC to mount the kind of covert operation denied the CIA under the post-1975 congressional over-sight policy. By early 1986, when John Poindexter, a naval officer with little politi-cal experience, replaced a burned-out McFarlane as national security adviser, Casey was able to persuade the president, over the strenuous objections of both Secretary of State Shultz and Secretary of Defense Weinberger, to go ahead with shipments of TOW antitank missiles and HAWK antiaircraft missiles to Iran.

The concept of trading arms for hostages was fatally flawed. Although one hostage had been released after an initial shipment of antitank missiles to Iran by way of Israel, the shipments of additional TOWs directly from the United States, as well as HAWKs, had led to the release of only two more hostages. Meanwhile, terrorist groups in Iran had seized several more Americans; by

1987, nine Americans were being held hostage in Lebanon. As one observer commented, "As soon as Iran realized how highly we valued getting those hostages back, they apparently kept a good supply of hostages to ensure that we would do their bidding."

The arms deal with Iran was bad policy, but what came next was criminal. Ever since the Boland Amendment in late 1984 had cut off congressional funding, the Reagan administration had been searching for ways to supply the Contras in Nicaragua. In early 1986, Oliver North had what he later described as a "neat idea"—he could use the enormous profits from the sale of weapons to Iran to finance the Contras. North's ploy was clearly not only illegal but unconstitutional, since it meant usurping the congressional power of the purse.

Unlike the policy of trading arms for hostages, the diversion of the profits to the Contras was a closely held secret. Apparently, only North, Casey, and Poindexter were aware of the illegal activity until November 1986, when the press finally learned of the Iranian arms sales. North then hurriedly destroyed most of the incriminating documents, but he overlooked one key memo that revealed the Contra diversion.

The political fallout was very heavy. The administration, having learned from the Watergate cover-up, tried to control the damage by breaking the bad news itself. Every effort was made to protect President Reagan; Attorney General Edwin Meese blamed Poindexter and North, who both were dropped from the NSC. Despite these efforts to spare the president's reputation, a CBS–*New York Times* poll taken in December 1986 revealed that Reagan's popularity had dropped from 67 percent to 46 percent in just a month, the steepest decline ever recorded.

The vital question of whether Ronald Reagan had approved of the Contra diversion was never answered satisfactorily. A protracted congressional hearing in the summer of 1987 did little to clear up the confusion. Oliver North used his televised appearances to win public sympathy if not approval. Poindexter insisted under oath that he had never informed the president he and North had used the profits from arms sales to Iran to fund the Contras in defiance of Congress. The only other man who knew what had actually happened was William Casey; his death from a brain tumor in mid-1987 left the mystery unsolved.

While Reagan escaped the Iran-Contra affair without being held fully responsible for it, his presidency was in serious trouble. In Congress, the Democrats, who gained control of the Senate as well as the House in the 1986 elections, began to override his vetoes, reject his nominees, and bring a total halt to even humanitarian aid to the Contras. Ronald Reagan was still in the White House, but his reliance on others to conduct the affairs of state had robbed him of his power to lead the nation.

REAGAN THE PEACEMAKER

By the end of 1987, the president had made a remarkable recovery. Stepping into the foreign affairs arena, Reagan, with strong pressure from his wife, Nancy, shed his image as a hawk and set out to reverse the course of Soviet-American relations.

A momentous change in leadership in the Soviet Union proved fortunate. The illness and death of Leonid Brezhnev in 1982, followed in rapid succession by the deaths of two aged successors, led finally to the selection of Mikhail Gorbachev, a younger and more dynamic Soviet leader. Gorbachev was intent on improving relations with the United States as part of his new policy of *perestroika* (restructuring the Soviet economy) and *glasnost* (political openness). Soviet economic performance had been deteriorating steadily and the war in Afghanistan had become a major liability. Gorbachev needed a breathing spell in the arms

Reagan and Gorbachev in Red Square. During the summits between the two leaders, the American public grew to admire the Soviet premier for his policies of perestroika ("restructuring") and glasnost ("openness").

race and a reduction in Cold War tensions in order to carry out his sweeping changes at home.

The first meeting between Reagan and Gorbachev, at Geneva in 1985, went well, but it did not lead to any significant agreements. A hurried summit at Reykjavik, Iceland, in October 1986, just before the Iran-Contra affair had become public, nearly led to a historic breakthrough. Only Soviet insistence that Reagan cancel SDI blocked agreement on an ambitious proposal to abolish all nuclear weapons within a decade.

The apparent failure at Reykjavik, however, did not halt the new momentum toward peace; both leaders needed a foreign policy triumph too much not to continue the dialogue. Throughout 1987, experts worked out the details of an Intermediate Nuclear Forces agreement that promised to become the most significant disarmament achievement since SALT I in 1972. Meeting in Washington in December 1987, Reagan and Gorbachev agreed to remove and destroy all intermediate-range missiles and to permit on-site inspection to verify the process.

A fourth Reagan-Gorbachev summit in Moscow in mid-1988 did not achieve any further progress toward the goal of reducing the nuclear arsenals, but the pictures of Reagan and Gorbachev strolling amiably about Red Square in front of Lenin's tomb, saluting tourists, and taking turns kissing babies, gave rise to the hope that an end to the Cold War was finally in sight.

When Reagan returned home, his popularity soared to 70 percent, higher than it had been before the Iran-Contra affair. He had not only succeeded in making a major breakthrough in the nuclear arms race, but he could also claim that his policies had led to a moderation in Soviet behavior when Gorbachev moved to end the war in Afghanistan. The first Soviet units pulled out in April 1988, with the final evacuation due to be completed early the next year. By the time Reagan left office in January 1989, he had scored a series of foreign policy triumphs that offset the Iran-Contra fiasco and thus helped redeem his presidency.

SOCIAL DILEMMAS

Two complex social issues arose in the 1980s that stood in sharp contrast to the prevailing sense of well-being. A massive viral epidemic and a new drug crisis threatened the social fabric of the United States, yet President Reagan failed to respond promptly or effectively to either one; his successors in the White House, George Bush and Bill Clinton, would find the problems equally frustrating.

THE AIDS EPIDEMIC

The outbreak of AIDS (acquired immune deficiency syndrome) in the early 1980s took most Americans by surprise. Even health experts had difficulty grasping the nature and extent of the new public health threat. Doctors first noticed a few cases of a rare form of pneumonia and an unusual type of skin cancer in male patients in New York City and San Francisco in 1981. The Centers for Disease Control noted the phenomenon in a June 1981 bulletin, but it was several years before researchers finally identified it as a hitherto unknown human immunodeficiency virus (HIV). HIV apparently originated in Central Africa and spread to the United States, where it found its first victims primarily among gay men.

Initially, AIDS was perceived as a threat only to gay men. With a growing sense of urgency as the death toll mounted, gay men began to practice safer sex. It soon became clear, however, that AIDS could not be so easily contained. It began to appear among intravenous (IV) drug users who shared the same needles and eventually among hemophiliacs and others receiving frequent blood transfusions. The threat of a contaminated national blood supply terrified middle-class America.

Scientists tried to reassure the public by explaining that the virus could be spread only by the exchange of bodily fluids, primarily blood and semen, and not by casual contact. Controversy soon developed over proposals for mandatory blood tests for suspected HIV carriers and for the quarantine of AIDS victims. The integrity of hospital blood supplies caused the most realistic concern; in 1985, a new test finally gave reassurance that transfusions could be performed safely.

The Reagan administration proved slow and halting in its approach to the AIDS epidemic. The lack of sympathy for gays and a need to reduce the deficit worked against any large increase in health spending; what little money was devoted to AIDS went almost entirely for research rather than for educational measures to slow its spread.

While the administration dallied, the grim toll mounted. Because the average time between the initial HIV infection and the first symptoms of AIDS was five years and the delay could be as long as fourteen years, efforts at prevention had little immediate impact. In November 1983, there were 2803 known cases and 1416 deaths; by mid-1985, more than 12,000 cases and more than 6000 deaths had been reported.

Growing public concern finally led to action. In 1987, Ronald Reagan appointed a special presidential commission headed by Admiral James Watkins to study the AIDS epidemic. The Watkins report in 1988 criticized the administration's AIDS efforts as "inconsistent" and recommended a new effort that included antidiscrimination legislation and explicit prevention education. In the fall, Congress voted to spend $1.3 billion to fight AIDS, with much of the money going for confidential testing and counseling and home care for victims.

Despite the new efforts, the epidemic continued to grow. The U.S. Centers for Disease Control in Atlanta reported more than 200,000 cases at the end of

1991; the total had increased to more than 500,000 by mid-1996. By then, 345,000 AIDS victims had died, making it the leading cause of death for Americans aged 25 to 44.

The number of those infected with HIV appeared to be stabilizing by the mid-1990s at between 650,000 and 900,000. Yet what was once known as the "gay disease" had spread far beyond that one group in society by the end of the century. Minorities and the young were at greatest risk. African American youths made up two-thirds of the new HIV cases among people under 25.

The most encouraging development was a drop in the death rate from AIDS that began in the mid-1990s. Health officials attributed the decline to heavier spending on treatment and prevention and, above all, to powerful new drug combinations. The decline in deaths began to slow by the end of the decade, however, falling from 42 percent in 1997 to just 20 percent in 1998. The so-called AIDS cocktail was very expensive and did not work for everyone. "Too many people are still dying," warned one official, "and too many people are still getting infected." And even the possibility that the most deadly disease in history might be contained in the United States was offset by a growing realization that AIDS was threatening to decimate the population of Third World countries, especially in sub-Sahara Africa.

THE WAR ON DRUGS

The 1980s witnessed the rapid spread of cocaine use in America, leading to a growing sense of social crisis by the end of the decade. Cocaine had long been viewed as a relatively harmless recreational drug used by only a few people— rock musicians, Hollywood producers, and the very wealthy. By the end of the 1970s, the snorting of the pure white powder, distilled from the leaves of coca plants grown in the foothills of the Andes, had spread throughout the upper middle class. Bankers, lawyers, and doctors began to use it occasionally to achieve a moment of ecstasy. The costs, however, were very high—$100 for a few snorts and the danger of dying from an overdose or literally blowing one's mind. "Chronic cocaine use," warned one expert, "is the same as putting one's car in neutral with the brakes on and pressing the accelerator to the floor for hours— eventually, the engine will burn out." Nevertheless, the number of users reached more than four million by 1982.

In the mid-1980s, cocaine suddenly was perceived as a danger to American society. Moat ominous was the emergence of "crack," a cheap cocaine derivative that could be smoked in a pipe to give a very intense high. Dealers sold this new form of cocaine for as little as $10 a dose, opening up a vast new market among the poor in the urban ghettos. By 1986, an estimated 5.8 million people were using cocaine at least once a month, and more than 600,000 were confirmed addicts.

Despite its relatively low cost, crack led to an explosion of urban crime. The brief but intense high lasted only a few minutes, leading users to keep smoking more and forcing them to use ever larger amounts to achieve the by now indispensable euphoria. Needing as much as $1000 worth of crack each day to sustain their habits, users turned to crime to gain the necessary funds.

The Reagan administration tried several approaches to the problem posed by cocaine. In 1982, First Lady Nancy Reagan chose drug education as her special project. Using the slogan "Just say no," she urged schools, churches, and civic groups to inform young people about the dangers of cocaine. Her program helped educate the middle class but had little impact on crack smokers in the ghetto.

In the mid-1980s, the administration began to place greater emphasis on interdiction, using agents of the Drug Enforcement Agency, the Customs Bureau, and the Coast Guard to try to seal off the nation's borders. An international cartel of drug dealers, led by a group of Colombians, overcame this effort by saturating the nation with cocaine. In reality, the Reagan administration was unwilling to devote the personnel and resources that truly effective interdiction would require; with one eye on the deficit, Washington was content with a few highly publicized skirmishes in what it termed the war on drugs.

The very nature of the cocaine industry frustrated a third, and potentially most promising, countermeasure—wiping out the coca fields and processing plants in South America. The administration relied on diplomatic efforts in cooperation with the governments of Colombia, Bolivia, and Peru to curb the trade in cocaine, but with little success. South American farmers could make five times as much money growing coca leaves as food crops; it was estimated that Bolivia received $600 million a year in hard currency from the drug trade, compared to profits of only $400 million from tin and other legal exports.

By the time Ronald Reagan left office, the problem remained as serious as ever. Latin America was producing nearly 400 tons of cocaine a year, five times the amount consumed in the United States; the wholesale price of a kilogram of the white powder in Miami and Los Angeles had dropped from $50,000 to less than $15,000 between 1982 and 1987. A government report in mid-1989 claimed that overall use of drugs, including heroin and marijuana, had declined 25 percent since 1985, while the number of people using cocaine at least once a week had risen from 647,000 to 862,000.

Only one thing had changed dramatically—public awareness. A Gallup poll taken in the summer of 1989 showed that for the first time in recent history, the American people regarded illegal drugs as their greatest concern. Twenty-seven percent of those polled placed drugs highest on the national agenda, a result George Gallup found "virtually unprecedented."

Despite this new awareness, the efforts of the Bush administration proved no more successful than the Reagan program. An ambitious "Andean Strategy," funded at more than $2 billion, pledged American support for antidrug programs in Colombia, Bolivia, and Peru. Yet by 1992, coca leaf production had reached a record level of 336,300 tons, nearly three times as high as in 1984.

The Clinton administration proved equally unsuccessful in its two-part approach to the drug problem. One aspect of the new Democratic strategy was to focus primarily on trying to curtail drug use in the United States. But a reduced budget and the inherent difficulty in attacking the causes of drug addiction blocked any progress. By 1996, the number of Americans engaging in illicit drug use, primarily marijuana, had dropped to twelve million, but the number of heroin and cocaine users remained stable at about three million. More alarming was the dramatic increase in drug use among teenagers, climbing 80 percent between 1992 and 1996.

The other Clinton administration approach to the drug war was to focus its overseas efforts primarily on eradicating the source of cocaine in Colombia, Bolivia, and Peru. A presidential directive issued in November 1993 targeted foreign drug cartels as a "national security threat." The flow of drugs into the United States, however, continued unabated, with Mexico becoming the new pipeline, funneling an estimated 210 tons of cocaine to the United States in 1995. In 2000, the Clinton administration unveiled a plan to spend $1.3 billion on a massive effort to destroy drug cultivation in southern Colombia. The funds were to be used to supply Blackhawk helicopters to three battalions of American-trained Colombian drug-fighting troops and to cover the cost of relocating an estimated 10,000 plantation workers. By the turn of the century, it was clear that there was no end in sight to the war on drugs.

PASSING THE TORCH

Reagan's triumphal reelection in 1984 raised Republican hopes that they had achieved a major political realignment in 1980. The economic boom that had begun after the 1982 recession, along with the promise of the end of the Cold War, reinforced this trend and enabled George Bush to replace Ronald Reagan in the White House.

THE CHANGING PALACE GUARD

Ronald Reagan had always been unusually dependent on aides and assistants. He saw his own role as one above the heat of bureaucratic battle—providing the nation with a set of goals and a vision for the future. As the great communicator, he would build the public consensus and let others manage the more mundane task of turning his dreams into reality.

His initial success depended heavily on the very effective White House team of James Baker, Edwin Meese, and Michael Deaver. Baker, a Texan with extensive Washington experience, became the chief of staff, managing the White House and directing legislative strategy. Shrewd and pragmatic, he outmaneuvered Californian Meese, who accepted the role of counselor to the president, advising Reagan on policy but having little to do with its implementation. Assistant to the President Deaver, the final member of the trio, had the full confidence of Nancy Reagan and devoted himself to the goal of enhancing her husband's public image.

Ronald Reagan's laid-back style was misleading. Although it is true he preferred to be presented with solutions rather than problems, it was Reagan's personal commitment to cutting taxes, reducing domestic spending, and rebuilding America's defenses that gave shape and coherence to his administration's policies. In the Oval Office, he thrived on the interplay among Baker, Meese, and Deaver, letting them present various alternatives and then instinctively suggesting compromises.

An abrupt change in the White House staff in 1985 nearly proved disastrous for Reagan. Tired of the constant infighting, Baker agreed to Secretary of the Treasury Donald Regan's suggestion that the two men swap jobs. A self-made Wall Street operator, Regan possessed a confident, abrasive manner and a determination to assert his authority as White House chief of staff. When Meese became attorney general and Deaver left the government later in 1985, Regan extended his own control and thus ended the give-and-take in the Oval Office that had allowed Reagan to shape the final policy choices during his first term.

At first, Regan and Baker were able to score a major victory. Intent on lowering taxes still more on the wealthy while capitalizing on growing congressional demands for a simpler and fairer revenue system, the two men pressed for a major overhaul of the income tax. Making the necessary compromises with leaders in Congress, they shaped the 1986 Tax Reform Act, which cut the top rate from 50 to 28 percent while sharply reducing unproductive tax shelters. The new rates exempted six million people at the lower end from paying taxes while an alternative minimum tax prevented the rich from escaping their fair share.

The administration had only partial success in another area—appointing conservative federal judges who would simply follow the law and leave policy issues to Congress and state legislatures. In 1986, after a brief skirmish with the Senate, Reagan succeeded in replacing outgoing Chief Justice Warren Burger with the Supreme Court's strongest conservative, William Rehnquist. Equally conservative appeals court judge Antonin Scalia joined the Supreme Court at the same time. But in 1987, when the president nominated Robert Bork, an outspoken opponent of judicial activism, to fill the next vacancy, Democrats drew the line. Opposition from labor and civil rights groups finally led the Senate to reject Bork's nomination by a vote of 58 to 42. It was a bittersweet victory, however, as Reagan responded by appointing the moderately conservative, but far more diplomatic, Anthony Kennedy to the Court.

The Bork defeat was especially hard on Attorney General Meese, who by then had become an embarrassment to Reagan. Charges of loose financial dealings and unethical conduct in office led to the appointment of a special prosecutor. Although he found no evidence that the attorney general had broken the law, the prosecutor admitted that some of Meese's dealings had the "appearance" of impropriety. The Meese affair, along with the conviction of Deaver for lying to Congress, Pentagon procurement scandals, and serious irregularities in the Department of Housing and Urban Development, left the Reagan administration with the appearance of tolerating corruption. Coupled with the far more serious Iran-Contra affair, the scandals indicated that Reagan's habit of delegating authority to his subordinates had greatly weakened his presidency.

THE ELECTION OF 1988

The Democrats approached the 1988 election with growing optimism. They had regained control of the Senate in 1986, Reagan no longer would be on the Republican ticket, and Iran-Contra and the vast increase in the national debt since 1980 all appeared to place the GOP on the defensive. Michael Dukakis, the successful governor of Massachusetts, emerged from the grueling primary contests as the clear-cut winner. With the selection of moderate Texas senator Lloyd Bentsen as his vice presidential running mate, Dukakis left the convention at Atlanta confident of victory, with polls showing him ahead by 17 points.

The Republican nominee, Vice President George Bush, proved to be a much stronger candidate than anyone had expected. Despite the controversial choice of Indiana senator Dan Quayle as his running mate, Bush quickly regained the lead. The Republicans waged a ruthless attack on Dukakis, portraying him as soft on crime and defense. Above all, the GOP candidate repeatedly promised not to raise taxes, reiterating his favorite line: "Read my lips—no new taxes."

The outcome confirmed the pollsters' projections. Bush won overwhelmingly in the South, carried most of the West, and defeated Dukakis in such key industrial states as Michigan and Pennsylvania. His victory reflected the natural advantage of an incumbent at a time when the economy was healthy and the world at relative peace. Yet Dukakis could take some comfort in blocking a Republican landslide. Although the voters elected a Republican president, they also increased the Democratic margins in both the House and Senate. Bush would be the first

THE ELECTION OF 1988

CANDIDATE	PARTY	POPULAR VOTE	ELECTORAL VOTE
Bush	Republican	48,886,097	426
Dukakis	Democratic	41,809,074	112

new president since John F. Kennedy to enter the White House while his party lost ground in Congress.

The election of 1988 indicated that, at least on the presidential level, a significant change had taken place in American politics in 1980. Bush consolidated the GOP's grip on the electoral college, winning in the Sunbelt states of the South and West. At the same time, racial polarization in politics continued, with Dukakis getting 88 percent of the African American vote and 69 percent of the Hispanic ballots. The Democrats, despite their success in Congress, faced the challenge of trying to regain the support of white middle-class voters for their presidential candidates.

DEFAULTS AND DEFICITS

Many people expected the Bush administration to reflect the reputation of the new president—bland and cautious, lacking in vision but safely predictable. At home, he lived up to his reputation, sponsoring few initiatives in education, health care, and environmental protection while continuing the Reagan theme of limiting federal interference in the everyday lives of American citizens. The one exception was the Americans with Disabilities Act (ADA), passed by Congress in 1991, which prohibited discrimination against the disabled in hiring, transportation, and public accommodations. Beginning in July 1992, ADA called for all public buildings, restaurants, and stores to be made accessible to those with physical handicaps and required that businesses with twenty-five or more workers hire new employees without regard to disability.

Most of Bush's time was taken up with two pressing domestic problems. First, the nation's savings and loan industry, based on U.S. government–insured deposits, was in grave trouble as a result of lax regulation and unwise loan policies. After record losses of $13.4 billion in 1988, more than 250 savings and loans had been forced to close. The continuing budget deficit provided an even greater challenge. Despite Gramm-Rudman, the nation continued to spend beyond its means, with deficits still running over $150 billion a year.

The president and Congress finally reached agreement on both issues. In August 1989, Congress passed an administration bill to close or merge more than seven hundred ailing savings and loans at a cost of $157 billion over a ten-year period. A new federal agency, the Resolution Trust Corporation, closed more than five hundred savings and loans, primarily in the Sunbelt states. It took over the properties on which developers had secured loans many times their actual value and gradually sold them off at discount prices. By the time the Resolution Trust Corporation expired in 1992, the initial cost to the government was more than $150 billion, and the eventual bill for the savings and loan cleanup, including interest, was estimated at between $500 and $700 billion.

Action on the budget proved even more difficult. Facing a Gramm-Rudman goal of $110 billion for the 1991 budget, Bush persuaded Congress to accept a deficit of $105 billion in late 1989. In the fall of 1990, Bush finally agreed to break his "no new taxes" pledge and support a budget that included new taxes on the wealthy along with substantial spending cuts. The resulting agreement projected a savings of $500 billion over five years, half from reduced spending and half from new revenue generated by increasing the top tax rate from 28 percent to 31 percent and raising taxes on gasoline, luxury goods, and beer and wine.

Unfortunately for the president, the budget deal coincided with the beginning of a slow but painful recession that ended the Republican prosperity of the 1980s. Not only did Bush face recriminations from voters for breaking his "Read my lips" pledge, but the economic decline led to greatly reduced government revenues. As a result, the deficit continued to soar, rising to just under $300 billion in 1992. Despite the 1990 budget agreement, the national debt increased by more than $1 trillion during Bush's presidency.

THE END OF THE COLD WAR

Abroad, the Bush administration faced an unprecedented year of change that appeared to mark the end of the post–World War II era. In country after country, communism gave way to freedom as the Cold War faded away more quickly than anyone had expected.

The first attempt at internal liberation proved tragically abortive. In May 1989, students in China began a monthlong demonstration for freedom in Beijing's Tiananmen Square that attracted worldwide attention. Americans were fascinated to see the Chinese students call for democracy with a hunger strike and a handcrafted replica of the Statue of Liberty. But on the evening of June 4, the Chinese leaders sent tanks and troops to Tiananmen Square to crush the student demonstration. By the next day, full-scale repression swept over China; several hundred protesters were killed, and thousands were injured. Chinese leaders

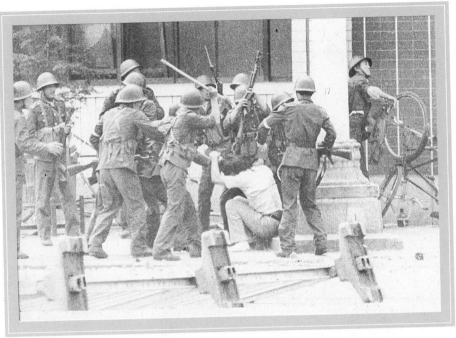

Fed up with government corruption, Chinese students demonstrated for democracy. Their nonviolent protest in Peking's Tiananmen Square was crushed when tanks, armored personnel carriers, and trucks cleared the square after firing randomly on the unarmed students.

imposed martial law to quell the dissent and shatter American hopes for a democratic China.

President Bush responded cautiously. While he did suspend sales of military equipment to China and stopped all government-to-government trade, he neither imposed stiffer sanctions nor engaged in harsh rhetoric. Bush wanted to preserve American influence with the Chinese government.

A far more promising trend toward freedom began in Europe in mid-1989. In June, Lech Walesa and his Solidarity movement came to power in free elections in Poland. Soon the winds of change were sweeping over the former Iron Curtain countries. A new regime in Hungary opened its borders to the West in September, allowing thousands of East German tourists in Hungary to flee to freedom. One by one, the repressive governments of eastern Europe fell. The most heartening scene of all took place in East Germany in early November when the new communist leaders suddenly announced the opening of the Berlin Wall. Workers quickly demolished a 12-foot-high section of this despised physical symbol of the Cold War, joyously singing a German version of "For He's a Jolly Good Fellow."

For three decades the Berlin Wall stood as the most visible symbol of the division between East and West in the Cold War. Dismantling of the Wall in November 1989 marked the beginning of the end of the Cold War.

Most people realized it was Mikhail Gorbachev who was responsible for the liberation of eastern Europe. In late 1988, he signaled the spread of his reforms to the Soviet satellites by renouncing the Brezhnev doctrine, which called for Soviet control of eastern Europe. It was Gorbachev's refusal to use armed force to keep repressive regimes in power that permitted the long-delayed liberation of the captive peoples of eastern Europe.

Yet by the end of 1991, both Gorbachev and the Soviet Union had become victims of the demise of communism. On August 19, 1991, eight right-wing plotters placed Gorbachev under arrest while he was vacationing in the Crimea and attempted to seize control of the government in Moscow. But Boris Yeltsin, the newly elected president of the Russian Republic, broke up the coup by mounting a tank in Moscow and demanding Gorbachev's release. The Red Army rallied to Yeltsin's side. The coup failed and Gorbachev was released, only to resign in December 1991 after the fifteen republics dissolved the Soviet Union. Yeltsin then disbanded the Communist party and continued

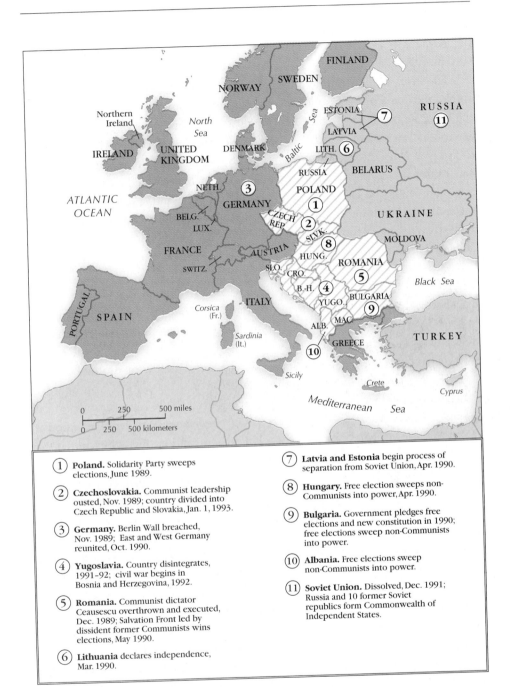

1. **Poland.** Solidarity Party sweeps elections, June 1989.

2. **Czechoslovakia.** Communist leadership ousted, Nov. 1989; country divided into Czech Republic and Slovakia, Jan. 1, 1993.

3. **Germany.** Berlin Wall breached, Nov. 1989; East and West Germany reunited, Oct. 1990.

4. **Yugoslavia.** Country disintegrates, 1991–92; civil war begins in Bosnia and Herzegovina, 1992.

5. **Romania.** Communist dictator Ceausescu overthrown and executed, Dec. 1989; Salvation Front led by dissident former Communists wins elections, May 1990.

6. **Lithuania** declares independence, Mar. 1990.

7. **Latvia and Estonia** begin process of separation from Soviet Union, Apr. 1990.

8. **Hungary.** Free election sweeps non-Communists into power, Apr. 1990.

9. **Bulgaria.** Government pledges free elections and new constitution in 1990; free elections sweep non-Communists into power.

10. **Albania.** Free elections sweep non-Communists into power.

11. **Soviet Union.** Dissolved, Dec. 1991; Russia and 10 former Soviet republics form Commonwealth of Independent States.

The End of the Cold War

Free elections in Poland in June 1989 triggered the domino effect in the fall of communism in eastern Europe and the former Soviet Union. Changes in policy came quickly, but the restructuring of social and economic institutions continues to take time.

the reforms begun by Gorbachev to establish democracy and a free market system in Russia.

The Bush administration, although criticized for its cautious approach, welcomed the demise of communism and offered economic assistance to Russia and the other former Soviet republics. The most important steps came in the critical area of nuclear weapons. In 1991, Bush and Gorbachev signed START I, agreeing to reduce nuclear warheads to less than ten thousand apiece; in late 1992, Bush and Yeltsin agreed on the terms of START II, which would reduce the number of nuclear weapons on each side to just over three thousand, a level not seen since the mid-1960s. Although several of the republics, notably Ukraine, had not yet agreed even to START I, Bush could claim that by the time he left office in January 1993, the Cold War was over.

WAGING PEACE

The end of the Cold War, however, did not bring about a world free of violence. In December 1989, twenty-seven thousand American troops invaded Panama and quickly installed a new government friendly to the United States in the largest American military operation since the Vietnam War. Despite the death of twenty-three Americans and several hundred Panamanians, this action won approval from the people of both countries when it resulted in the capture of drug-trafficking General Manuel Noriega. By taking such bold and decisive action in Panama, Bush was able to shake his reputation for caution. But critics noted that the president had waged war without consulting Congress.

Eight months later, Bush suddenly faced a much graver challenge. On August 2, 1990, Saddam Hussein, the dictatorial ruler of Iraq, stunned the world by invading defenseless Kuwait and threatening Saudi Arabia and the oil-rich Persian Gulf region. The president responded firmly, despite an earlier balance-of-power policy of supporting Iraq against Iran. He accused Saddam of naked aggression and carefully built up a UN coalition to uphold what he termed "a new world order." Equally important, he quickly persuaded Saudi Arabia to accept a huge American troop buildup, dubbed Desert Shield. With the United States once again importing nearly half the oil used each day by the American people, control of the Persian Gulf was clearly a vital national interest.

Debate raged, however, on the best way to meet the Iraqi threat. Many Democrats in Congress supported Bush's efforts to place international economic sanctions on Iraq but opposed the use of force. Bush had clearly opted for a different solution by November, massing far more troops in the Persian Gulf area than were needed to defend Saudi Arabia—Operation Desert Shield was giving way to Desert Storm. After securing UN support, Bush narrowly persuaded Congress to approve the use of force to liberate Kuwait.

Antiaircraft fire lights up the sky over Baghdad, Iraq, during the Persian Gulf War. A month of strikes on Iraqi targets was followed by a ground offensive that lasted only one hundred hours before Iraqi troops began to surrender and President Bush ordered a cease-fire. Critics of Bush's decision argued that stopping the advance allowed an unvanquished Saddam Hussein to remain in power in Iraq.

On January 17, 1991, the president unleashed a devastating aerial assault on Iraq. F-117A stealth fighters and Tomahawk cruise missiles hit key targets in Baghdad. The air attack, virtually unchallenged by the Iraqis, wiped out command and control centers and enabled the coalition bombers to demoralize the beleaguered enemy troops. After five weeks, Bush gave his approval for the long-awaited ground assault. Led by General H. Norman Schwarzkopf, the allied armored units swept across the desert in a great flanking operation while a combined force of U.S. marines and Saudi troops drove directly into Kuwait City. In just one hundred hours, the American-led offensive liberated Kuwait and sent Saddam Hussein's vaunted Republican Guard fleeing back into Iraq.

In a controversial decision, President Bush, acting on the advice of General Colin Powell, chairman of the Joint Chiefs, halted the advance and agreed to an armistice with Iraq. Critics claimed that with just a few more days of fighting American forces could have encircled the Republican Guard and ended Saddam's cruel regime. But the president, fearful of disrupting the allied coalition and of having American troops mired down in a guerrilla war, stopped when he had achieved his announced goal of liberating Kuwait.

Desert Storm brought mixed blessings. It was a great personal victory for George Bush, who saw his approval rating climb to an unprecedented level— nearly 90 percent. American military leaders believed they had finally atoned for Vietnam, a sentiment widely shared by a euphoric public. The United States had deployed more than 500,000 troops, as many as were in Vietnam in 1968, and had lost just 146 lives in inflicting a stinging defeat on a dangerous bully. Best of all, the price of oil, which had climbed to nearly $40 a barrel in October, fell back to less than $20, allowing Americans to fill the gas tanks of their cars for just over $1 a gallon.

At the same time, however, Saddam Hussein continued to rule in Baghdad, persecuting Kurds in northern Iraq and Shi'ite Muslims in the south. He survived several attempts on his life and frustrated U.S. efforts to uncover and destroy his chemical, biological, and nuclear weapons facilities. And over the next few years, American veterans began to complain of debilitating symptoms of what came to be known as Gulf War syndrome.

In the long run, the Persian Gulf War may have damaged George Bush more than it helped him politically. It was his concentration on the Gulf crisis that led him to enter into the budget deal with congressional Democrats in the fall of 1990—a deal that alienated conservative Republicans and left him open to the charge of violating his 1988 campaign pledge not to raise taxes. Most damaging of all for Bush, the Gulf War had halted a slow recovery from the lingering recession and revived fears over America's economic health in the post–Cold War era. For twelve years, the Republicans had relied on a robust economy to enact their programs and consolidate their power—now the Democrats finally had a chance to accuse the GOP of endangering the nation's economic health.

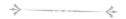

33

AMERICA IN FLUX
The Anxious Nineties

On June 27, 1991, Thurgood Marshall, the first African American to sit on the Supreme Court, informed President Bush he was retiring due to ill health. A month later, Bush announced the nomination of Clarence Thomas, a black judge on the Court of Appeals in Washington, to take Marshall's place.

The contrast between the two justices was startling. Marshall had gained national fame for arguing the case for the *Brown* decision in 1954 that desegregated the nation's schools. A firm believer in affirmative action, he had been the Court's most liberal member. Thomas, on the other hand, was a conservative who believed in black self-help. Born in poverty in Georgia, he took to heart the admonition of the grandfather who raised him: "Anything you got you got by the sweat of your brow." After graduating from Holy Cross College and Yale Law School, Thomas eventually headed the Equal Employment Opportunity Commission (EEOC) during the Reagan years. Dismissing affirmative action as "social engineering" that creates a "narcotic of dependency," Thomas opposed racial quotas.

Despite his color, black organizations such as the NAACP opposed the confirmation of a judge who had once said that civil rights leaders did nothing but "bitch, bitch, bitch, moan, and whine." At the Senate Judiciary Committee hearings on his nomination, Thomas refused to reveal his views on sensitive issues such as abortion, but he did retreat from some of his earlier conservative opinions, even acknowledging that his own career had benefited from affirmative action programs.

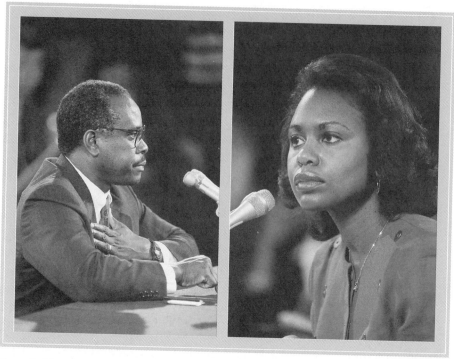

George Bush's controversial nomination of Clarence Thomas to the U.S. Supreme Court culminated in three days of televised hearings when Anita Hill, a law professor at the University of Oklahoma, accused Thomas of sexual harassment. Despite the charges, the Senate confirmed Thomas's appointment by a 52 to 48 margin. Although Hill's charges failed to block Thomas's confirmation, they did help to create a new concern for the treatment of women in the workplace.

Although the Judiciary Committee deadlocked 7 to 7 on his nomination, observers expected the full Senate to confirm his appointment by a wide margin when it voted on October 8. Just before the vote, however, sensational charges of sexual harassment led to three days of new hearings before the Judiciary Committee that were televised to the entire nation. Anita Hill, a black law professor at the University of Oklahoma, testified that while working for Thomas at both the Justice Department and the EEOC, she had turned down his attempts to date her. She then accused Thomas of sexual harassment, recalling in vivid detail the way Thomas described to her scenes of bestiality, rape, and group sex from pornographic movies he had seen and then boasted of his own sexual prowess. Despite his unwelcome advances, Hill admitted, she had followed Thomas from the Justice Department to the EEOC and had called on him on occasion in later years for advice and career assistance.

Thomas categorically denied all the charges. He accused the Judiciary Committee of conducting "a high-tech lynching of an uppity black who in any way deigns to think for himself." His lawyers brought forth four women who had worked with him in the 1980s who all testified his conduct was above reproach, with one suggesting Anita Hill had had a crush on Thomas that he discouraged.

It came down to who people believed was telling the truth. Four witnesses recalled Anita Hill telling them about Thomas's advances; at her own request, she took and passed a lie detector test. But a public opinion poll taken at the close of the televised hearings indicated that 58 percent of the American people believed Thomas while only 24 percent believed Hill. A bare majority of the senators apparently agreed. On October 15, the Senate confirmed Thomas by a vote of 52 to 48, the narrowest margin ever for a Supreme Court appointment.

The Clarence Thomas–Anita Hill confrontation raised issues that did not end with Thomas's confirmation. The extent to which the nation should extend affirmative action to help offset past discrimination continued to be a matter of concern and debate in regard to university admissions and employment opportunities. The issue of sexual harassment, a traditional feminist grievance, took on new importance. American women in particular resented the way the all-male Judiciary Committee had treated the polite and composed Anita Hill. Republican members, notably Senator Arlen Specter of Pennsylvania, had cross-examined her ruthlessly, suggesting she was either a disappointed suitor or mentally unstable.

Most of all, the televised hearings of the Thomas nomination were indicative of the social unrest that characterized American life at the end of the twentieth century. The place of women in society, the continuing racial tension, changes in family structure, and the constantly shifting nature of the American population created a feeling of uneasiness. Despite a sustained economic boom and a welcome federal surplus by the end of the decade, the decline of manufacturing, the drop in defense spending with the end of the Cold War, and the trend toward greater inequality in income all contributed to a sense of disruption. People could rejoice in escaping the fear of nuclear annihilation, but they missed the old certainties of the Cold War era and were unsure of what the future held for them.

THE CHANGING AMERICAN POPULATION

From the *Mayflower* to the covered wagon, movement has always characterized the American people. The 1970s and 1980s witnessed two significant shifts in the American population: movement internally to the Sunbelt region of the South and West and a remarkable influx of immigrants from developing nations. These changes led to increased urbanization, greater ethnic diversity, and growing social unrest.

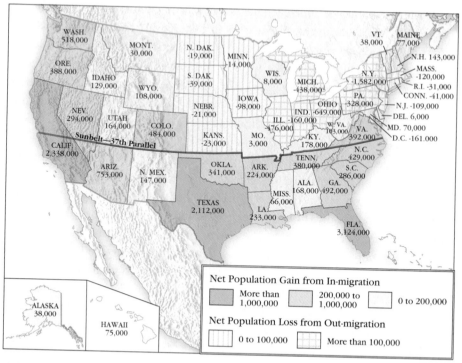

Migration to the Sunbelt, 1970–1981

Florida, California, and Texas gained the most people in the 1970s; New York, Ohio, and Illinois recorded the greatest losses.

A PEOPLE ON THE MOVE

The most striking finding in the 1980 census was that for the first time in American history, more than half the people lived in the South and West; the Sunbelt had boomed. The Sunbelt, best defined as a broad band running across the country below the 37th parallel from the Carolinas to Southern California, had begun to flourish with the buildup of military bases and defense plants during World War II. Rapid population growth continued with the stimulus of heavy Cold War defense spending and accelerated in the 1970s when both new high-technology firms and more established industries were attracted by lower labor costs and the favorable climate of the Sunbelt states. Florida, Texas, and California led the way, each gaining more than two million new residents in the 1970s.

In the next decade and a half, the flow continued, but at a slower rate. The Northeast and Midwest continued to lose population to the South and West. By the late 1980s, however, with the slowing of defense spending, rising real estate prices, and growing congestion, states such as Texas and California no longer attracted as many new residents. With the aging of the baby boom generation and the growth of two-income families, fewer people were pulling up roots by the 1990s. In 1998, 16 percent of the population changed residences, but most stayed in the same county; less than 3 percent moved to another state.

Despite the drop in migration, the South, particularly Florida, continued to boom, and cities throughout the Sunbelt thrived. Eight of the nation's cities now had more than one million residents; four were in the Sunbelt, and of the rest, only New York gained in population in the 1980s.

The increasing urbanization of America had both positive and negative aspects. People living in the large metropolitan areas were both more affluent and better educated than their rural counterparts. Family income among people living in the bigger cities and their suburbs ran $9000 a year more, and three-fourths of the urban population had graduated from high school, compared to two-thirds of other Americans. Yet these advantages were offset by rising urban crime rates, longer commuting time in heavy traffic, and higher living costs. Nevertheless, the big cities and their suburbs continued to thrive, accounting for 75.2 percent of all Americans by 1990.

Another striking population trend was the nationwide rise in the number of the elderly. At the beginning of the century, only 4.1 percent of the population was aged 65 or older; by 1997, those over 65 made up 13 percent of the population, with the nearly four million over 85 the fastest growing group of all. The Census Bureau projected a slower rate of increase to 2010 and then a big jump as the baby boomers reach 65.

Six of every ten older Americans were women, and they tended to have a higher rate of chronic disease and to be worse off economically than men the same age. Many of the oldest old, those over 85, lived in nursing homes and accounted for one-third of all Medicaid payments. Yet only 12.4 percent of the elderly lived below the poverty line; the annual cost-of-living increases in Social Security payments spared them the worst ravages of inflation. Most impressive of all was their political power: two-thirds of those over 65 voted regularly, compared to just under half of the entire population. The American Association of Retired Persons (AARP), with more than thirty million members, proved very effective in Washington in protecting the interests of the elderly, particularly in regard to Medicare.

THE REVIVAL OF IMMIGRATION

The flow of immigrants into the United States reached record proportions in the 1990s as a result of new policies adopted in 1965 replacing the national origins quota system. With an estimated one million newcomers arriving each year, by 2000 nearly one in ten Americans was foreign-born.

The new wave of immigrants came mainly from Latin America and Asia. In the 1980s, Mexico supplied the largest number of immigrants, 1.6 million, followed by the Philippines with more than 500,000. The new immigrants tended to settle in urban areas. In California, the influx of immigrants from Asia and Mexico created growing pressure on public services, especially during the recession of the early 1990s.

The arrival of more than 26 million immigrants in three decades was bound to lead to controversy over whether immigrants were a benefit or a liability to American society. A study by the National Academy of Sciences in 1997 reported that, in the long run, immigrants and their families more than paid their way. In regard to employment, immigrants tended to help consumers and employers by working for relatively low wages in restaurants, the textile industry, and farming, but they hurt low-skilled U.S. workers by keeping wages low. Economist George J. Borjas, himself a refugee from Cuba, claimed that immigrants from developing countries lacked the education and job skills needed to achieve the level of prosperity attained by newcomers in the past; instead of entering the mainstream of American life, they were likely to remain a permanent underclass.

In regard to the often-expressed concern that immigrants are slow to learn English and assimilate, a study covering Southern California in the 1980s offered some reassurance. The number of Hispanic immigrants who spoke English rose from one-third to nearly three-fourths during the decade, while the poverty rate among Asian men fell from one-third to less than one-tenth. "The speed of immigrants' upward mobility is striking," commented demographer Dowell Myers.

Public attitudes began to shift toward the end of the century. A 1997 poll showed that the number of people who believed immigrants were bad for the nation had dropped from 60 percent in 1993 to 42 percent, with 43 percent affirming the benefits of immigration for the country. The booming economy, with resulting low unemployment, made newcomers willing to do the hard jobs shunned by the native-born appear to be a blessing rather than a threat.

ADVANCE AND RETREAT FOR AFRICAN AMERICANS

African Americans formed the largest of the nation's ethnic groups. In 1999, there were 34.8 million blacks in the United States, nearly 13 percent of the population. Although there had been some movement of African Americans back to the South, the great majority lived in the crowded ghettos of cities of the Northeast, Midwest, and Pacific Coast.

Middle-class African Americans had made some gains during the 1970s and 1980s. By 1976, one-third of all black workers held white-collar jobs—double the rate of 1960. Education proved the key to African American advances. Black graduates of the nation's colleges and universities had relatively easy entry into higher-paying jobs in banks, corporations, and government agencies. Black college enrollment increased by 43 percent between 1970 and 2000, giving more African Americans the opportunity for a middle-class lifestyle.

Many well-educated and affluent African Americans tended to behave like whites in similar circumstances. Some joined the flight to the suburbs, leaving the central city in even larger proportions than whites. By the 1980s, many young African Americans, trained as doctors, lawyers, or business executives, returned to cities in the South to pursue their careers. The trend continued in the 1990s. By the end of the century, Atlanta led all metropolitan areas with a gain of 159,830 new black residents in the decade. In fact, the South had become the most thoroughly integrated of all the nation's regions.

Yet despite these gains, there were setbacks as well for African Americans. In the *Bakke* decision, the Supreme Court ruled against racial quotas for blacks at a University of California medical school, although the ruling did permit universities to consider race as "simply one element" in efforts to select diverse student bodies. In subsequent decisions, the Court upheld an affirmative action program designed by Kaiser Aluminum to help advance minority workers and ordered

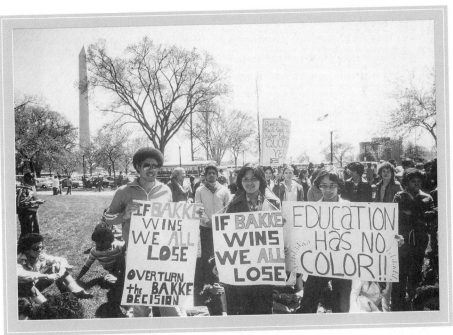

Supporters of affirmative action protested the decision of the U.S. Supreme Court in the Bakke case. The Court ruled against the use of racial quota systems to achieve racial balance. However, the Court did uphold the principle of affirmative action by ruling that race could be one of several factors used in making hiring or admissions decisions.

American Telephone and Telegraph to hire more African Americans and women to make up for past discrimination.

A series of Supreme Court decisions in 1989 sharply narrowed the scope of affirmative action programs. In one case involving setting aside 30 percent of all city contracts in Richmond, Virginia, for minority contractors, the Court ruled against such rigid racial quotas. In 1991, the president and Congress compromised on a new civil rights act that restored in large measure the rights of both blacks and women to sue businesses for acts of racial discrimination and sexual harassment.

Affirmative action yielded only mixed results for blacks. For those able to gain university admission, such programs proved helpful, but even blacks who graduated from college did not do as well economically as their white counterparts. The Census Bureau reported in 1991 that African American college graduates received only 77 percent as much as white graduates employed in executive and administrative positions. For black males with a high school degree, the gap was even larger; they earned only $60 for every $100 paid to white men with a comparable education.

For blacks without education, the situation was much worse. Even in the boom years of the 1980s, unemployment rates for African Americans remained over 10 percent, more than double that for whites, and among black teenagers, the level was a staggering 40 percent. In the recession of 1990–1991, black workers lost 59,579 jobs. Blue-collar African American workers were especially hard hit, losing one-third of the 180,210 blue-collar jobs lost during the recession.

Nor did blacks share equally in the economic recovery of the 1990s. In 1998, the median family income for African Americans was just $25,351, compared to more than $40,000 for white, non-Hispanic households. More than two million black families were living below the poverty line in 1998; the poverty rate for blacks was nearly double that for white Americans.

Rodney King became a symbol of black frustration in the United States. In March 1991, a bystander videotaped four Los Angeles policemen brutally beating King, who had been stopped for a traffic violation. The pictures of the rain of blows on King shocked the nation. Nearly a year later, when an all-white jury acquitted the four officers of charges of police brutality, rioting erupted in South Central Los Angeles that for a time threatened the entire city when the police failed to respond promptly. Looting stores at will and setting businesses on fire, the rioters focused the nation's attention on the plight of urban blacks. In the aftermath of the riot, government and state agencies promised new efforts to help the ghetto dwellers. Urban blacks, however, saw little hope for improvement. A

A bystander recorded on videotape the police beating of motorist Rodney King, whom police had stopped for speeding and drunken driving. The acquittal of four police officers on charges of police brutality touched off the worst incidence of urban violence in the twentieth century. More than fifty people died in the rioting and property damage exceeded $1 billion.

poll taken in April 1992 revealed that 51 percent of African Americans believed life had "gotten worse" during the past ten years, up from 35 percent in mid-1991. For black youths in Los Angeles, surrounded by gang warfare and drive-by shootings, their only aspiration was simply to stay alive.

THE SURGING HISPANICS

People with Spanish surnames, labeled Hispanics by the Census Bureau, formed the nation's second-largest ethnic group. The rapidly growing Hispanic population had climbed to more than 35 million by 2000. Both a high birthrate and heavy immigration from Western Hemisphere countries helped Hispanics account for 12.5 percent of the nation's population, and demographers predicted Hispanics would replace African Americans as the nation's largest minority group by the year 2005.

The Census Bureau identified four major Hispanic categories in 1990. Mexican Americans, the largest group at more than 20 million, were concentrated in the Southwest. There were 3 million Puerto Ricans, mainly living in or near New York City. Cuban Americans, located primarily in South Florida, numbered almost 1.5 million. Finally, there were 6.5 million in the Census Bureau category "other Hispanics."

The Hispanic groups had several features in common. All were relatively youthful, with a median age of 22 and a high fertility rate. They tended to be relatively poor, with one-fourth falling below the poverty line. Although the position of Hispanics had improved considerably in the boom years of the 1980s and 1990s, they still lagged behind mainstream America. The poverty rate among Hispanics was twice the national average, higher even than for blacks; family median income in 1998 was $28,330, only two-thirds of the level for other Americans.

Lack of education was a key factor in preventing economic progress for Hispanics. The American Council on Education released a report in 1991 that found Hispanics "are grossly under-represented at every rung of the educational ladder." Fewer Hispanics graduated from high school than other minorities and their school dropout rate was the nation's highest at more than 50 percent. As a result, in 1999 more than a quarter of Hispanic adults had only a grade-school education, compared to less than 5 percent of non-Hispanic whites.

The entry of several million illegal immigrants from Mexico, once derisively called "wetbacks" and now known as "undocumented aliens," created a substantial social problem for the nation and especially for the Southwest. Critics argued that the aliens took jobs away from U.S. citizens, kept wages artificially low, and received extensive welfare and medical benefits that strained budgets in states such as Texas and California.

Defenders of the undocumented aliens contended that the nation gained from the abundant supply of workers who were willing to work at backbreaking jobs shunned by most Americans. Moreover, defenders stated, illegal entrants usually paid sales and withholding taxes but rarely used government services for fear of being deported. Whichever view was correct, by the mid-1980s, an exploited class of illegal aliens was living on the edge of poverty. The *Wall Street Journal* summed it up best by observing, "The people who benefit the most from this situation are certainly the employers, who have access to an underground market of cheap, productive labor."

Concern about economic competition from an estimated four million Mexican "illegals" led Congress to pass a major immigration reform bill in 1986. The legislation imposed fines and possible prison sentences on those who knowingly employed illegal immigrants. Mexican American leaders feared the sanctions would discourage businesses from hiring anyone of Mexican descent, but they approved of an amnesty provision that enabled aliens who could prove they were living in the United States before January 1, 1982, to become legal residents.

The 1986 law failed to stem the problem of illegal immigration. Authorities noted a decline in the number of illegal entrants a year in the late 1980s, but by the early 1990s there was a new surge from Mexico, Central America, and China. In 1993, Lawrence H. Fuchs, acting chair of the U.S. Commission on

Immigration Reform, estimated the numbers of illegals to be as high as 500,000 a year. In 1997, however, an official study jointly conducted by U.S. and Mexican scholars used census data to arrive at a much lower figure. Whatever the actual yearly addition, the Immigration and Naturalization Service estimated in 1997 that 5 million foreigners, mainly from Mexico and Central America, were living illegally in the United States—2 million in California alone. Thus the projections for the Hispanic population, 24.5 percent of the total by the middle of the next century, may well prove to be too low.

ASIAN AMERICANS ON THE RISE

Asian Americans were the fastest-growing minority group at the end of the century. In 1999, there were nearly 11 million Americans of Asian or Pacific Island descent. Although they represented only 3.9 percent of the total population, they were increasing at seven times the national rate, and future projections indicated that by 2050 one in ten Americans would be of Asian ancestry.

The Chinese formed the largest single group of Asian Americans, followed by Filipinos, Japanese, Indians, Koreans, and Vietnamese. Immigration was the primary reason for the rapid growth of all these groups except the Japanese.

Compared to other minorities, Asian Americans are relatively well educated and affluent. Three out of four Asian youths graduate from high school, compared to less than one out of two for blacks and Hispanics. Asian Americans also have the highest percentage of college graduates and recipients of doctoral degrees of any minority group. Many Asians have entered professional fields, and as a result, the median income for Asian American families is more than $4000 higher than the 1998 national level.

Not all Asian Americans have fared well, however. Refugees from Southeast Asia have experienced both economic hardship and persecution. The median family income for Vietnamese Americans in the mid-1980s was $8000 below that for whites. Vietnamese fishermen who settled on the Gulf Coast experienced repeated attacks on their livelihood in Texas and Louisiana. In the Los Angeles riots in 1992, Korean stores and shops became a main target for looting and firebombing.

But the overall experience of Asian Americans has been a positive one. They came to America seeking economic opportunity, or as many put it, "to climb the mountain of gold." "People are looking for a better life," a Chinese spokeswoman explained. "It's as simple as that, and we will continue to come here."

Jay Kwan, a Korean greengrocer, reflects the economic rewards Asian immigrants were able to achieve by long hours of hard toil. Kwan worked as a janitor on arriving in New York City in the 1970s, saving enough in three years to buy a produce store in Brooklyn. Alongside his wife and brother, he worked 15 hours a day. Despite being robbed several times, he formed good relations with his neighbors and was able to make a modest profit. Yet his goal was always more than simply earning a living. "I am first generation," he told a reporter. "I am not working for myself. I am working for the second generation."

Such dedication has helped Asian Americans to make remarkable progress. Nearly 11 percent of Harvard's entering class in 1985 was of Asian ancestry. Asian Americans, according to sociologist Peter I. Rose, are part of "the most upwardly mobile group in the country. They have caught up to and are even surpassing the Joneses and the Smiths, as well as the Cohens and the Levines."

MELTING POT OR MULTIETHNIC DIVERSITY?

"Cultural diversity probably accelerated more in the 1980s than any other decade," noted demographer Carl Haub. The influx of people from all around the world, not just from Europe, had profound implications for American culture. Traditionally, the favorite American self-image was the melting pot, the title of Israel Zangwill's play written in 1908, at the height of European immigration into the nation. "America is God's crucible, the great Melting-Pot where all the races of Europe are melting and re-forming," one of his characters proclaimed.

The melting pot image carried with it the concept of stripping newcomers of their culture and national traits and casting them into an Anglo-Saxon mold. Dubious for European immigration, this analogy has seemed irrelevant to the Third World migration to America in recent times. Instead of recasting immigrants into an American type, immigration could better be seen as broadening the diversity that always has characterized the United States. Now, instead of the usual division between blacks and whites, America is composed of Asians as well as Europeans, Hispanics as well as African Americans. Sociologist Amitai Etzioni suggests replacing the melting pot image with a "mosaic" portraying a nation in which ethnic groups proudly retain their own identities "while recognizing that they are integral parts of a more encompassing whole."

The new awareness of ethnic diversity manifested itself in many ways. In public education, blacks led a crusade against Eurocentric curriculum and demanded a new emphasis on the influence of African culture; on college campuses, the call for multicultural courses and separate departments for African American, Asian American, and Hispanic studies created controversy. Citing the forecasts of a declining Anglo dominance and the rise of minority groups in the next century, ethnic leaders advocated cultural pluralism. Raul Yzaguirre, president of the National Council of La Raza, an Hispanic advocacy group, argued that

America has never had a real melting pot in which all races contributed to the mix. "What we've had is a pressure cooker, where everybody has had to come in and become Anglophiles."

Many Americans found themselves perplexed and uncertain of their cultural identity by the end of the twentieth century. A Census Bureau survey, asking people to state their ancestry, revealed that fully one-fourth of Americans listed Germany first, with Ireland and England a distant second and third. Some Hispanics found the census racial classifications—black, Asian–Pacific Islander, white, or American Indian—meaningless. "I don't really consider myself Caucasian," objected Jose Arroyo of San Jose, California. "My roots go down into the Indians of Mexico."

In the 1990s, people of mixed racial parentage demanded that the census for 2000 include a box labeled "multiracial" rather than just the meaningless "other." Susan Graham, a white Georgian mother of two multiracial children, founded a group called Project RACE (Reclassify All Children Equally), which argued that the four million children of more than a million interracial marriages deserved their own census category. Civil rights groups, however, objected, fearing cuts in government benefits to minorities based on the census figures. The Census Bureau compromised in 2000 by adding four new dual-race categories— American Indian–white, American Indian–black, Asian-white, and black-white. The government, however, would continue to classify multiracial individuals by the minority portion of their heritage.

Horace Kallen, one of the early critics of Zangwill's melting pot analogy, of-fered the most appealing image of the nation's diverse heritage. He likened the United States to a symphony orchestra, in which each nationality and ethnic group contributed its "own specific timbre and tonality" to create "a multiplicity in a unity, an orchestration of mankind." As Americans wrestle with the continu-ing dilemma embodied in the national motto, E pluribus unum, the image of a great symphony in which all groups blend harmoniously offers a way to balance the pride individuals find in ethnic identity with the need for national unity.

ECONOMIC CROSSCURRENTS

The strains that first hit the American economy in the lean years of the 1970s continued to erode the confidence of the American people. Despite a seven-year boom in the 1980s, recessions in 1982 and 1990 and the abrupt drop in defense spending with the end of the Cold War led to heavy unemployment. At the same time, changes in the economy tended to hurt blue-collar workers and benefit up-per-income groups the most.

RECESSION AND STAGNATION

In July 1990, the American economy, which had been steadily expanding for seven years, suddenly plunged into a recession. Although mild by postwar standards, the 1990 recession proved unusually stubborn. The recovery proved slow and uneven, stalling twice before leading to renewed growth in mid-1992. Unemployment remained flat eighteen months after the recession ended, and the gross domestic product (GDP) rose just 2.9 percent in the same period, only one-third of the average growth following other postwar recessions.

The political impact was devastating for the Bush administration. By June 1992, nearly ten million Americans were unemployed. Unlike the 1982 recession, which had hit hardest in the industrial heartland, the 1990 downturn was experienced most strongly in New England and California, the boom areas of the 1980s. And in contrast to previous recessions, in which blue-collar workers had fared the worst, many white-collar employees and college graduates lost their jobs. The poverty rate, which had remained steady throughout the 1980s, climbed nearly a full point to 14.2 percent.

The sluggish recovery was primarily the result of the massive restructuring of the American economy brought on by the end of the Cold War. The fall of the Berlin Wall had resulted in annual reductions of more than 5 percent in defense spending in the early 1990s. Between 1990 and 1992, defense contractors dismissed 225,000 workers, accounting for more than 15 percent of the almost 1.5 million jobs lost during the recession.

It was George Bush's misfortune that the long-sought end of the Cold War coincided with the 1990 recession. For more than three decades, heavy military spending had kept the nation prosperous while masking a growing lack of U.S. competitiveness in the global economy. The sudden cutback in defense spending, coupled with the surging economic performance of nations such as Japan and Germany, put the United States in a difficult position. The average American worker, whose paycheck dropped from $454 a week in 1988 to $440 by 1992, was ready to look beyond the Republican party for relief.

THE PLIGHT OF THE MIDDLE CLASS

No economic issue had more political impact by 1992 than the widespread belief in the decline of the American middle class. While Democrats blamed Reaganomics for favoring the wealthy at the expense of the average American, the woes of the middle class since the early 1970s transcended partisan explanation.

The actual fate of middle-class Americans since the early 1970s reveals a more complicated pattern. The most frequently cited measure of economic well-being is median family income. Between 1947 and 1973, family income doubled.

The economic inequities of the 1980s, with the growing disparity in income between rich and poor and tax policies that favored the rich over the poor and middle class, came to a head in the recession of the early 1990s. Drawing by Dana Fradon; copyright © 1992. The New Yorker Magazine, Inc.

But after 1973, median family income failed to advance. Inflation caused it to drop in the late 1970s, and the recession of 1982 led to a second decline. Family income rose steadily in the boom years of the 1980s, only to fall back with the 1990 recession. Middle-class Americans suddenly realized that for twenty years their economic position had remained stagnant.

Economists offered conflicting views of the plight of the middle class. A report by the New York City Department of Consumer Affairs claimed that most Americans had to work longer just to keep even. Working wives became a necessity; it took two incomes and many more hours of work in the 1980s for the average family with children to maintain a decent standard of living. As a result, the middle class declined from 71.2 percent of the population in 1969 to 63.3 percent by 1989.

A Congressional Budget Office report in 1993, however, indicated that baby boomers were better off than their parents were. The older half, those between

35 and 44, fared best, but even the young boomers who entered the workforce in the 1980s enjoyed higher incomes than their parents. The rise in disposable personal income reflected the same trend. The amount that individuals had left to save or spend after taxes increased from $11,013 in 1973 to $14,154 in 1990.

More important than the numbers was the growing belief of middle-class Americans that the next generation would not fare as well as their parents had. The feeling of diminished expectations was the product of many factors. The rapid expansion and affluence of the 1950s and 1960s was a happy accident unlikely to occur again. The inflation in real estate by the 1980s added greatly to the net worth of an older generation. The resurgence of Japan and Germany and the relative decline of American industry ensured a much lower rate of national economic growth. Above all, the baby boom generation took the affluence of postwar America for granted and expected to continue to enjoy all the blessings of an abundant society.

The reality of two decades of stagnation in median family income and successive recessions that held back long-term economic growth raised serious questions for a generation that had never known the deprivations of the Great Depression and World War II. Even though they continued to enjoy a standard of living that was the envy of most of the world, they began to wonder if their children would be denied the American dream. It is not surprising, then, that the American people were prepared to listen to new political voices that promised to revitalize not just the economy but the American way of life itself.

DEMOCRATIC REVIVAL

The Democrats, victims of the runaway inflation of the 1970s, became the beneficiaries of the lingering recession of the early 1990s. Moving away from its traditional liberal reliance on big government, the party regained strength by choosing moderate candidates and tailoring its programs to appeal to the hard-pressed middle class. These new tactics enabled the Democrats to regain the White House in 1992 and retain it in 1996, despite a Republican sweep of Congress in 1994. The key figure in this political shift was Bill Clinton, who overcame some early setbacks to reap the rewards of a sustained economic boom.

THE ELECTION OF 1992

The persistence of the recession that had begun two years earlier became the dominant political reality of 1992. As Bush's popularity plummeted, two men sought to capitalize on the dismal state of the U.S. economy. First, Arkansas governor Bill Clinton defeated a field of five other challengers for the Democratic nomination by becoming the champion of economic renewal. Clinton stressed the need for investment in the nation's future—rebuilding roads and bridges, training workers for high-tech jobs, and solving the growing national health care crisis.

Despite his victories in the Democratic primaries, however, Clinton faced a new rival in H. Ross Perot. An eccentric Texas billionaire, Perot singled out the deficit as the nation's gravest problem and agreed to run as an independent candidate in response to a grassroots movement (which he financed) to place his name on the November ballot.

When Clinton and his running mate, Senator Albert Gore, Jr., of Tennessee, succeeded in unifying the Democratic party and gaining agreement on a moderate platform promising economic change, Perot stunned his supporters by suddenly dropping out of the race in July. Clinton immediately became the front-runner, rising from 30 percent to more than 50 percent in the polls, leaving Bush far behind. With unemployment continuing unabated and the economy faltering, the American people turned their backs on George Bush and the Reagan revolution.

A relentless Democratic attack on the administration's lackluster economic performance overcame all the president's efforts to remind the nation of Reagan prosperity and Bush triumphs abroad. Even GOP assaults on Clinton's character, notably his evasion of the draft during the Vietnam War, failed to halt the Democratic momentum. The message that Clinton's political advisers tacked up at the Democratic candidate's headquarters in Little Rock—"The economy, stupid"—provided the key to victory in November. Clinton wound up with 43 percent of the popular vote but with a commanding lead in the electoral college, 370 to 168 for Bush. Perot, who had reentered the race, won 19 percent of the popular vote but failed to carry a single state.

THE ELECTION OF 1992

CANDIDATE	PARTY	POPULAR VOTE	ELECTORAL VOTE
Clinton	Democratic	44,908,232	370
Bush	Republican	39,102,282	168
Perot	Independent	19,725,433	—
	Minor Parties	773,161	—

For political scientists, 1992 was a clear case of a negative referendum. Voters had decisively rejected the Reagan-Bush programs. Clinton maintained the Democratic grip on ethnic minorities, winning 83 percent support from African Americans and 62 percent from Hispanics, and cut deeply into the crucial middle class by doing better than Bush among those earning between $30,000 and $75,000 a year.

Most important, Clinton had broken the GOP's grip on the South and West—only Texas and the interior western states had remained Republican strongholds. Yet while there was no doubt about the rejection of Bush, there remained a question of precisely what change the electorate wanted most—responsible budgetary policies to reduce the deficit or federal spending programs to achieve jobs and economic growth.

ECONOMIC RECOVERY

In the White House, Bill Clinton proved to be the most adept politician since Franklin Roosevelt. Born William Jefferson Clinton in Hope, Arkansas, in 1946, he weathered a difficult childhood by developing skills at dealing with people and using personal charm to achieve his goals. His intelligence and ambition helped him gain a strong education as an undergraduate at Georgetown University and a law student at Yale, with a two-year stint in between as a Rhodes scholar at Oxford. Entering politics, he won election first as Arkansas attorney general and then as governor. Defeated after his first term in 1980, Clinton won the nickname "Comeback Kid" by regaining the governor's office in 1982, using it to earn a reputation as one of the nation's most successful young political leaders during the following ten years.

Bill Clinton's political gifts centered on the easy way in which he was able to reconcile what biographer Martin Walker called "the ambivalence between the bubba and the brains, between the redneck and [the] Rhodes scholar." Raised by women, he had a sensitivity to human suffering and an understanding of the tribulations of daily life that gave him a broad political appeal. Empathy, charm, and understanding, combined with a genuine desire to serve, made him a formidable political leader.

Unfortunately, serious flaws marred his political gifts. His eagerness to please undercut his devotion to principle. Despite his apparently sincere devotion to causes such as civil rights and equality for women, even those who voted for Clinton had doubts about his personal integrity. One writer summed up his contradictory nature by describing him as "a man who loves the fruits of compromise but treasures the idea of his own unbending goodness."

What often saved Clinton from his own worst faults was his loyal wife, Hillary Rodham Clinton. An accomplished attorney, she rescued his candidacy in 1992 by defending him against charges of adultery. But more important, from the outset she was his political partner, sharing in the strategic planning that won him the presidency. They made a formidable political team, with her idealism offsetting his pragmatism.

In his first months in office, Bill Clinton's political skills appeared to evaporate. His inept handling of the "gays in the military" issue, made worse by his own draft evasion during the Vietnam War and several botched cabinet appointments, robbed him of the usual honeymoon period new presidents enjoy. He reacted with bitter indignation to the ensuing media criticism, refusing to hold a White House press conference during his first two months in office.

In appointing his cabinet, Clinton did try to live up to his pledges of ethnic and gender diversity. Hazel O'Leary, a black woman, served as secretary of energy, while Janet Reno, a political unknown, became attorney general. The cabinet included two Hispanics, Henry Cisneros and Federico Peña, and two African Americans, Mike Espy and Ronald Brown.

Diversity ended there, however. Fourteen of the eighteen cabinet members were lawyers, and most were wealthy. Secretary of Labor Robert Reich, a Harvard professor, was one of the few advocates for working-class Americans. Beyond the cabinet, two-thirds of the Clinton administration appointees were white men; minorities made up just 14 percent of the Clinton team, barely higher than the 13 percent under Bush.

Clinton's most important appointments came in the economic realm. In a series of meetings held in Little Rock shortly after the 1992 election, the president-elect learned that the economic dilemmas facing the nation were bleaker than he had realized. During the campaign, he had promised middle-class tax cuts and a spending program to both stimulate the economy and provide a new focus for government activity. But now his advisers warned him that the mounting national budget deficit made such measures impossible. The interest on the debt was running at nearly $300 billion a year; with most of the federal budget tied up in entitlement programs such as Social Security and Medicare, there was no room for additional discretionary spending, much less tax cuts.

Of all the economic advisers who made the pilgrimage to Little Rock, the one whom Clinton found most persuasive was a Republican—Alan Greenspan, the chairman of the Federal Reserve Board. Stressing the need to reduce the deficit, projected to reach nearly $400 billion by 1997, Greenspan argued for a comprehensive deficit reduction plan that would lead to lower interest rates on long-term bonds, thus reducing the government's debt payments and stimulating business growth. In other words, by biting the fiscal bullet now, Clinton could enjoy the best of both worlds—he could gain credit for reducing the deficit while "growing the economy," as he had pledged during the campaign.

The announcement of Clinton's economic team signaled his acceptance of the Greenspan approach. Senator Lloyd Bentsen, a fiscal conservative, became secretary of the treasury, with Robert Rubin, a Wall Street bond trader, serving as special assistant for economic policy. By choosing such a conservative team to guide economic policy, Clinton was risking the fate of his administration on the single issue of deficit reduction.

The president made this crucial decision public in a nationally televised budget speech to both houses of Congress on February 17, 1993. With Alan Greenspan seated next to Hillary Clinton in the gallery, the president boldly outlined a plan to cut the deficit by $500 billion.

The applause for Clinton's economic plan reverberated far beyond the halls of Congress. Polls showed his approval rating rising from 51 to 63 percent in two weeks as the public approved of his willingness to give the deficit his highest priority. More important, in late February, interest rates on 30-year bonds dropped below 7 percent for the first time ever. Greenspan had been right, and Clinton had won his biggest gamble.

The president still had to wage a long and determined fight to complete his economic program. It took all-out arm-twisting from the White House to get Congress to approve the final budget terms—$241 billion in new taxes and $255 billion in spending cuts, for a total reduction of $496 billion over four years. In late August, the House approved the budget by just two votes, and in the Senate, Vice President Gore cast his vote to break a 50 to 50 deadlock.

Despite the narrow margin, it was a major achievement. Clinton stood firm on deficit reduction, compromising on details but insisting on a program that promised to cut the deficit in half within four years. Moreover, he succeeded in increasing income tax rates on the wealthy from 33 to 39.6 percent. At the same time, he secured passage of the earned income tax credit for the working poor, providing as much as $3500 a year to keep a low-income family above the poverty line. And best of all, lower interest rates created by action of the Federal Reserve Board led to a steadily expanding economy that made Clinton's deficit reduction goals realistic. Unlike George Bush in 1990, who sealed his political doom by reneging on his promise not to raise taxes, a healthier economy enabled Clinton both to raise taxes and to win respect by standing on principle. He did, however, risk the same fate as Bush since Republicans were quick to call the budget deal "the biggest tax increase in the history of the world."

PRESIDENT VERSUS CONGRESS

Deficit reduction marked only the beginning of Bill Clinton's struggles with Congress. For the next four years, he engaged in a series of confrontations, winning some and losing some with first Democratic and then Republican majorities in the two houses.

His most important triumph came when Congress approved the North American Free Trade Agreement (NAFTA) in the fall of 1993. NAFTA, initiated and nearly completed by Bush, was a free trade plan that combined 250 million Americans with 90 million Mexicans and 27 million Canadians into a common market without tariff barriers. Clinton saw it as the first step in creating similar free-trade associations with Asia and Europe that would enable the United States to dominate global markets. Calling NAFTA "a defining moment" for the nation, he proclaimed, "This country is now the most productive country in the world."

Critics of NAFTA did not share Clinton's optimism. Representing both ends of the political spectrum, they warned that free trade would undermine small American companies and send millions of American jobs to exploited and underpaid workers in Third World countries. The issue of free trade divided the Democratic party, with many liberals and labor union members strongly opposed. Ross Perot, the defeated 1992 third-party candidate, became the best known critic, especially with his vivid claim about the loud "sucking sound" that would signal the flushing of American jobs down the drain.

As he had done with deficit reduction, Clinton appealed shrewdly to moderates of both parties. He pointed to the increased opportunity for American exports. To allay the objections of environmentalists and organized labor, he negotiated "sidebar" agreements dealing with pollution and workplace standards in Mexico and Canada.

The toughest fight came in the House, but 102 Democrats finally joined with 132 Republicans to approve NAFTA by a 34-vote margin, giving Clinton a solid victory there. The Senate added its consent by a vote of 61 to 38. Thus Clinton triumphed over key elements within his own party to achieve a significant goal.

During the next four years, NAFTA failed to justify either the hopes of its supporters or the fears of its detractors. The true impact of NAFTA will become apparent only in the twenty-first century. If it leads to Clinton's vision of a common market for the entire Western Hemisphere, it may well prove to be his most lasting achievement.

At the height of the debate over NAFTA, President Clinton allowed his wife to make public his administration's massive plan for health reform in an unprecedented appearance before the House Ways and Means Committee. When he first took office, the president had signaled the importance of the health care issue by appointing Hillary Clinton to head a task force to find a comprehensive solution to the nation's health care problem. The Clintons had two primary objectives. The first was an all-embracing health care system that would include the thirty-seven million Americans who lacked health insurance. At the same time, they were committed to reduce the skyrocketing cost of health care—13 percent of the GDP, nearly twice the cost of health care in other industrial nations. The trick would be to devise a system that would reduce costs while extending medical insurance to everyone in the nation, without raising taxes or adding to the deficit. The only possible solution involved rationing health care by having someone in authority place limits on the medical services each American could receive—a strategy that was political dynamite.

The plan that Hillary Clinton presented to the House Ways and Means Committee in October 1993 had two key features. First, it required large companies to offer a generous health care package to all workers, with employers paying 80 percent of the estimated $4200 annual cost per family. The second feature dealt with small businesses, which were required to form large health alliances so that they could purchase equally generous benefit packages from insurance companies. The task force believed that these mandatory health alliances would have enough clout to bargain for competitive rates, thereby sharply reducing health costs.

The initial public reception was favorable. According to a CNN poll, 61 percent of the American people said they were ready to pay higher taxes for a truly comprehensive health care system. When Congress began studying the details, however, attitudes started to change. The complex bill was referred to ten separate committees, inviting legislative chaos. And then opponents, primarily Republicans and representatives of small business, counterattacked. Spending nearly $60 million to fight the Clinton program, its critics claimed that it would deprive Americans of the right to choose their own doctors.

The administration's health care plan was soon in deep trouble. By midsummer, only 39 percent of the American people expressed confidence in the administration's health proposal. When Democrats were unable to round up sixty votes to break a Republican filibuster on procedural issues in late August 1994, the Senate dropped the issue, effectively killing the Clinton health plan.

In retrospect, it seems evident that the incompatible goals of reducing costs while striving for universal coverage had doomed the plan from the outset. Shrewder political maneuvering by the Clintons might have enabled them to salvage a scaled-down health reform.

Clinton's failure to deliver on his health care promise helped fuel a dramatic Republican resurgence. A young maverick congressman from Georgia, Newton

Leroy "Newt" Gingrich, had been leading a Republican attack against the House Democratic leadership. Using a well-funded political action committee, GOPAC, Gingrich supported other young, conservative Republicans who waged constant guerrilla war against the Democratic leadership. Gingrich believed that a vulnerable Clinton made 1994 the right year for an all-out effort to capture control of both houses of Congress.

In an attempt to transform 435 separate races into one national contest, Gingrich asked all GOP candidates to sign a ten-point Contract with America. The Contract consisted of familiar conservative goals, including a balanced budget amendment to the Constitution and term limits for members of Congress. For the first time in recent political history, a party sought to win Congress on ideological issues rather than relying on individual personalities.

A series of embarrassing disclosures involving Bill Clinton's character made this tactic particularly effective in 1994. During the 1992 campaign, the *New York Times* had raised questions about a bankrupt Arkansas land development called Whitewater in which the Clintons had lost a modest investment. In late 1993, the Resolution Trust Corporation began exploring Hillary Clinton's relationship with Madison Guaranty, a failed financial institution that had loaned the Clintons money for their Whitewater investment. Republicans were quick to charge that, in effect, American taxpayers were left holding the bill for a corrupt Arkansas bank that had close ties to the Clintons. Although there was no evidence of illegal acts, at the president's request, Attorney General Janet Reno appointed a special prosecutor to investigate the Whitewater affair.

Additional scandals cropped up over activities that had taken place after Clinton was elected president. Then in early 1994, Paula Jones, a former Arkansas state employee, charged that in 1991, then-Governor Clinton had exposed himself to her in a Little Rock hotel room and asked for oral sex.

While there was no clear-cut evidence to substantiate any of the charges against the president or his wife, Republicans used these episodes to revive earlier questions about Bill Clinton's character. More important, they were able to make more substantial attacks on the president, pointing to his failure to enact health care reform and, above all, reminding voters that in 1993 Clinton had enacted "the biggest tax increase" of all time.

The outcome of the November 1994 vote stunned political observers. The Republicans won both houses, gaining 9 seats in the Senate for a 53 to 47 edge and an astonishing 53 in the House to take control for the first time in forty years, 230 to 204.

There were two ways to view the remarkable about-face. Claiming that voters endorsed their Contract with America, the GOP hailed the outcome as a mandate to dismantle the welfare state in favor of free market economics. Clinton and some of his advisers, however, noted that the 1994 election was hardly representative of the country as a whole. The turnout was low—less than 40 percent, compared to 56 percent when Clinton won the presidency just two years before. Nationally, barely more than half of those voting supported Republicans, so that in effect just 20 percent of the electorate had determined the outcome.

The most striking statistic lay in the gender breakdown. Women voted for Democratic candidates by a margin of 53 to 47, while men went Republican by a much bigger differential, 57 to 43. In effect, an outpouring of "angry white males" who believed that Clinton was unfit to be president determined the outcome. The lesson for Clinton was clear. If he could win back the women and minorities who had voted for him in 1992 but stayed home in 1994, he had a chance to play the part of Comeback Kid once more.

THE CLINTON REBOUND

The Clinton campaign's 1992 slogan—"The economy, stupid"—proved even more apt four years later. The candidate who had accused his opponent of ignoring the economic suffering accompanying the recession of 1990–1991 now became the beneficiary of the recovery that had actually begun before the 1992 election.

The scope of the prosperity that spread throughout America in the 1990s was astonishing. Leaner American corporations, benefiting from downsizing, now found they could compete on favorable terms with Japanese and German rivals. Productivity shot up, keeping labor costs down. By 1996, Clinton could boast that nine million new jobs had been created since he took office and that the United States now led all other nations in the export of manufactured goods.

Clinton not only could claim credit for this remarkable resurgence, but he had the political skill to assuage the heavy human costs involved. He criticized corporations for dismissing so many employees in their quest for competitive advantages in the global marketplace, and he expressed concern over the growing inequality of wealth that benefited the educated and penalized the unskilled. In persuading Congress to pass the Family and Medical Leave Act in 1993 and increasing the minimum wage in 1996, the president was able to present himself as a caring leader concerned about the welfare of all Americans, not just the rich and powerful.

The Republicans, fresh from their sweeping victory in Congress, ironically became the vehicle for Clinton's political rehabilitation. In 1995, despite ma-

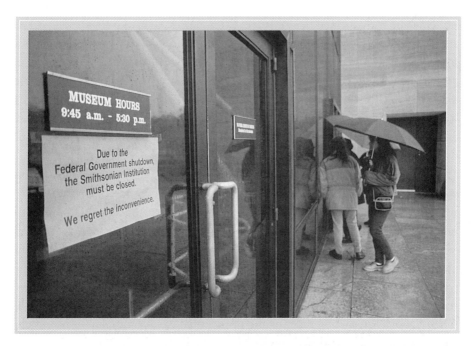

Consumers were the losers in the battle over the balanced budget waged by President Clinton and the Republican Congress when the failure to provide monies for operating expenses forced the shutdown of government services and facilities, like the Smithsonian Institution.

jorities in both houses, the GOP enacted only four minor parts of the Contract with America. Although the House of Representatives passed all but one item, the more cautious Senate refused to go along with such measures as term limits for members of Congress and a constitutional amendment requiring a balanced budget.

The president found Gingrich and his followers a perfect foil. When they demanded a balanced budget by early in the next century, Clinton agreed in principle, but then refused to accept GOP plans to slash programs such as Medicare and Medicaid. Portraying himself as the defender of the downtrodden, Clinton claimed that the Republican cuts in education, college loans, and health care would hurt children, ambitious young people, and the elderly.

The GOP leadership in Congress then made a gross miscalculation by threatening to close down the government to force Clinton to give way. The president stood firm, aware that Gingrich's negative ratings were higher than his own. Twice the Republicans shut down all but the most vital of federal services. The public outcry, however, directed almost entirely against Gingrich and the GOP, finally forced the Republicans to relent. They accepted a compromise in early 1996 that optimistically promised a balanced budget in seven years.

Once he had regained the initiative, Clinton pressed his advantage. The president pursued a policy of "triangulation," in which he distanced himself from both conservative Republicans and liberal Democrats to take the political high ground—the center. He signed a welfare reform bill, slightly more acceptable than the two he had vetoed before, to fulfill his earlier promise "to end welfare as we know it." The new legislation turned the welfare program over to the states, funded by scaled-down federal grants, and required recipients to find work within two years or lose their benefits.

While Republican hopefuls fought each other in a series of grueling and expensive party primaries, Clinton began raising huge sums to conduct a massive television campaign. Throughout the spring and summer, the airwaves were filled with 30-second commercials picturing the Republicans as trying to weaken Medicare and deny social services to those in need. By the time the GOP nominated Bob Dole, the respected but dour Senate majority leader from Kansas, the contest was all but over. Having used up nearly all his federal matching funds in the primaries, Dole was unable to counter Clinton's television blitz. By the traditional Labor Day starting date for the presidential campaign, Clinton had established a double-digit lead in the polls.

The ensuing fall campaign turned out to be anticlimactic. Everything Dole tried proved ineffective. His proposal of a 15 percent across-the-board tax cut found little acceptance. The GOP candidate began raising questions about Clinton's integrity, but an electorate that had grown bored with the unsubstantiated Whitewater charges failed to respond.

On election day, the president won his expected victory. A low turnout (10 million fewer voters than in 1992) and the third-party candidacy of Ross Perot (only a nuisance factor in 1996) prevented Clinton from winning a clear majority of the popular vote. But he carried 31 states with 379 electoral votes, for a deci-

THE ELECTION OF 1996

CANDIDATE	PARTY	POPULAR VOTE	ELECTORAL VOTE
Clinton	Democratic	47,401,185	379
Dole	Republican	39,197,469	159
Perot	Independent	8,085,294	—

sive victory over Dole, who won just 19 states with 159 electoral votes. Clinton's strategy of winning back the vote of women and minorities with his stress on education, health care, and providing opportunities for the young paid off handsomely. The gender gap was evident—men split evenly between Dole and Clinton, but 54 percent of female voters backed the president and only 38 percent voted for his GOP challenger. And, in contrast to 1994, women outnumbered men at the polls by a margin of 52 to 48.

In winning a second term, Clinton was both skillful and lucky. He benefited from the powerful economic growth that surpassed even his own expectations. But Clinton was also fortunate in the men who opposed him. Gingrich and Dole were experienced and able congressional leaders, but neither possessed the charisma or the public sensitivity that enabled Clinton to connect with the voter.

Yet it took both political skill and daring to weather the rejection Clinton experienced in 1994 and to adapt to the changing mood of the American people. Clinton won the gamble that he could turn the Republican shutdown of government into a political victory. And even though the president probably had little to do with the underlying causes of the economic boom, his willingness to adopt Greenspan's fiscal strategy and stake everything on deficit reduction gave him a reasonable claim to some of the credit. Most important, Clinton won in large measure because, unlike his opponents in 1992 and 1996, he seemed to embody, in the words of a British observer, "all the characteristics of his generation, distilled to an intensity that matched his ambition."

AFTER THE COLD WAR

American foreign policy underwent notable changes in the 1990s. Unlike his predecessor, Bill Clinton gave top priority to domestic issues rather than international affairs. And where Bush had viewed the world largely in geopolitical terms, stressing American strategic interests, Clinton gave economics top consideration, seeking markets abroad to stimulate the dormant American economy. Yet there was one similarity—under Clinton, as under Bush, American foreign policy continued to drift, lacking direction in the confusing post–Cold War world.

CLINTON AND THE WORLD

In choosing his foreign policy team, Clinton wisely went with experienced professionals to whom he could delegate foreign policy while he carried out his domestic agenda. Secretary of State Warren M. Christopher, who had served under Jimmy Carter, pursued a cautious, lawyerly approach to world problems. Christopher and his second-term replacement, Madeleine Albright, worked

The lack of any clear principle or philosophy guiding Clinton's foreign policy hampered the effort to define the proper role for and responsibilities of the United States, the only remaining super-power, in the post–Cold War era.

skillfully on the international issues confronting the nation, but they were hampered by the lack of any overarching principle to guide them.

Clinton's greatest challenge was in dealing with America's old Cold War rivals, Russia and China. Inheriting the chaos left by the breakup of the Soviet Union, the president concentrated on two issues. First, he followed Bush's lead in backing Russian President Boris Yeltsin to the hilt. In 1993, Clinton persuaded Congress to provide a $2.5 billion aid package to help Yeltsin carry out his free market reforms of the devastated Russian economy. The Clinton administration strongly supported Yeltsin and his successor, Vladimir V. Putin, despite Russia's continuing brutal war with Chechnya, and succeeded in maintaining good relations with Russia.

Clinton was even more successful on the second issue—preventing the proliferation of nuclear weapons among the former republics of the Soviet Union. With patient diplomacy, Christopher and his aides won agreements from Belarus and Kazakhstan to scrap their deadly ICBMs. Ukraine proved more difficult, but in 1994, Clinton persuaded President Leonid D. Kuchma to surrender his country's entire nuclear stockpile. Clinton's effort on behalf of nuclear nonproliferation in the former Soviet Union was perhaps his most important, if least heralded, achievement.

The president's policy toward China was more questionable. Clinton ignored China's dismal human rights record and continued Bush's policy of extending most favored nation status to Beijing annually. The growing importance of trade with China led Clinton to overlook the memory of the Tiananmen Square massacre and the continued persecution of dissidents in China. As trade with China began to rival that with Japan, the president announced a policy of "constructive engagement." It was better, he and his spokespeople declared, to keep talking and trading with China than to harden Chinese resentment against the West by harping on moral issues. In 2000, Clinton won a notable victory for free trade when the House voted to give China permanent most favored nation status.

The Chinese, however, proved to be less than cooperative. China ignored U.S. protests over its exports of missiles to Iran and continued to stifle dissent at home. The administration did send aircraft carriers to signify its support for Taiwan when China conducted provocative missile tests near the island on the eve of an election.

In the Middle East the administration continued the efforts to broker a peace between Israel and the Palestinian Arabs. Despite a promising beginning at a meeting between Yasir Arafat and Yitzhak Rabin in Washington in 1993, Clinton was unable to overcome the implacable ethnic and religious tensions that blocked the path to peace in the Middle East. Clinton's final attempt, a meeting between Arafat and Israeli Prime Minister Ehud Barak at Camp David in July 2000, proved futile.

In Iraq, Clinton met the continued defiance of Saddam Hussein by twice ordering American cruise missile attacks on Iraqi military targets. U.S. relations with Iran failed to improve, even with the election of a more moderate prime minister in 1997. Saudi Arabia remained a staunch ally, despite strains from a terrorist attack that killed nineteen American air force personnel in 1996. More worrisome was the increasingly heavy U.S. reliance on Persian Gulf oil as a result of Americans' love affair with gas-guzzling vans, pickup trucks, and sport utility vehicles. A sharp increase in the price of oil in early 2000 brought howls of protest from angry motorists and highlighted the risk of continuing American dependence on foreign oil.

INTERVENING IN SOMALIA AND HAITI

The most difficult foreign policy decisions for the Clinton administration came over the question of whether to use American troops to intervene abroad. The end of the Cold War made it much more difficult for the president and his advisers to decide when the national interest required sending American men and women into harm's way. Between 1993 and 1999, Clinton opted for foreign intervention in four areas—Somalia, Haiti, Bosnia, and Kosovo—with decidedly mixed results.

Clinton inherited the Somalian venture. In December 1992, George Bush had sent twenty-five thousand American troops to that starving country on a humanitarian mission. Under Clinton, however, the original aim of using troops to protect the flow of food supplies gradually shifted to supporting a UN effort at nation building. Tragedy struck in October 1993 when eighteen American soldiers died in a botched attempt to capture a local warlord. When television cameras recorded the naked corpse of a U.S. helicopter pilot being dragged through the streets of Somalia's capital, an angry Congress demanded a quick end to the intervention. Secretary of Defense Les Aspin resigned his office, after accepting responsibility for refusing to provide the U.S. commander with the tanks and aerial gunships he had requested. American forces left Somalia by the end of March 1994 in what was unquestionably the low point of Clinton's foreign policy.

The lack of clear criteria governing intervention that had brought on the disaster in Somalia almost led to another fiasco in Haiti. Seeking to halt the flow into Florida of thousands of Haitians fleeing both poverty and tyranny, Clinton worked to compel the military rulers of Haiti to abdicate in favor of the man they had overthrown in 1991, Jean-Bertrand Aristide.

After nearly a year of trade sanctions and increasing diplomatic pressure, the president prepared to use force to remove the generals. At the last minute, a three-member peace mission worked out a compromise that allowed U.S. troops to land unopposed in late September 1994. Aristide returned to Haiti to take power in mid-October, but he could do little either to restore democracy or achieve economic progress in view of his country's bankrupt treasury, devastated economy, and deep political divisions. By the time Aristide turned over the presidency to his elected successor in 1996, Haiti remained mired in hopeless poverty.

HALTING CIVIL WAR IN BOSNIA

Bosnia provided an even sterner test for the president's foreign policy. The breakup of Yugoslavia in 1991 led the Muslim president of Bosnia to ask the European Community to recognize the independence of Bosnia-Herzegovina. Bosnia's ethnic and religious makeup—44 percent Muslim, 31 percent Serb, and 17 percent Croat—quickly led to civil war by the spring of 1992. The Bosnian Serbs used the guns and heavy weaponry of the former Yugoslavian army to seize more than 70 percent of Bosnian territory. The Muslim and Croatian forces, hampered by an international arms embargo, were unable to mount effective resistance as the Serbs began a policy of "ethnic cleansing," driving Muslims and Croats from their ancestral homes and farms and beginning a lethal bombardment of the capital, Sarajevo.

Although Clinton had criticized Bush's failure to stop the fighting in Bosnia, the new president followed an equally cautious policy at first. When the Serbs rejected a proposal to divide Bosnia along ethnic lines in the spring of 1993, the president fell back on using American air power to patrol no-fly zones over Bosnia designed to protect UN peacekeeping efforts. Meanwhile, Serb artillery continued to pour a withering fire on the civilian population of Sarajevo, and journalists reported a series of brutal atrocities in which Serb troops slaughtered thousands of Muslim men.

After two years of passively watching Bosnian suffering, Clinton finally unleashed American air power. In the summer of 1995, American planes under NATO auspices began a series of air strikes on the Serb forces shelling Sarajevo from the surrounding mountains.

The air campaign, which lasted for two weeks, along with a major counteroffensive by Croatian and Muslim forces, finally led to a cease-fire in mid-October 1995. The three warring factions sent delegations to discuss a settlement at Wright-Patterson Air Force Base in Dayton, Ohio. After three weeks of talks, U.S. mediator Richard Holbrooke secured their agreement to create a weak central government for all Bosnia at Sarajevo and to divide the rest of the country into two parts—a Muslim-Croatian federation with 51 percent of the territory and a Serbian enclave with 49 percent. The Dayton plan called for free elections, the return of refugees to their former homes, and a NATO force to oversee the peace process.

Clinton took a calculated risk in sponsoring the Dayton settlement. The division of Bosnia into two competing halves meant only a temporary halt to the fighting rather than an end to the struggle for control of the country. But in halting the fighting at least temporarily, and especially in lifting the siege of Sarajevo, Clinton could take credit for a major humanitarian achievement. He displayed uncharacteristic political courage in agreeing to commit twenty thousand American troops to the International Force (IFOR) that would undertake the dangerous task of supervising the implementation of the Dayton accords.

The American troops, originally scheduled to leave by late 1996, stayed on in reduced numbers when the original departure date was postponed indefinitely. Few refugees were able to return to their original farms and villages. British, French, and U.S. members of IFOR faced tense confrontations with angry Serb mobs. Yet, the net result was an uneasy truce without fighting and without peacekeeping casualties. Clinton had not only been brave; he had been lucky as well.

SAVING KOSOVO

President Clinton faced an even more serious challenge in another Balkan troublespot—Kosovo. Serbian leader Slobodan Milosevic had ended the province's autonomy within Yugoslavia and imposed Serbian rule in 1989, even though 90 percent of the population was ethnic Albanian. When these people, who called themselves Kosovars, resisted by waging guerrilla war against the Serbian police, Milosevic responded with a campaign of repression and ethnic cleansing that outraged world opinion. After diplomatic efforts failed in 1998 and early 1999, the United States and NATO began an aerial assault on Serbia on March 24, 1999, in an effort to end the persecution of the Kosovars.

At first it appeared that Clinton and his outspoken secretary of state, Madeleine Albright, had miscalculated. The initial air attacks, largely directed at remote military bases, failed to persuade Milosevic to seek peace. Instead, he stepped up the ethnic cleansing in Kosovo, forcing hundreds of thousands of Kosovars to flee to neighboring Albania and Macedonia. NATO pilots, restricted to flying above 15,000 feet to avoid antiaircraft fire, were unable to hit the elusive Serbian forces in Kosovo. Other members of NATO ruled out the use of ground forces, the only realistic way to stop the Serbian repression.

Clinton, despite his reputation as an opportunist, stayed the course in Kosovo. He took the high ground, explaining to the American people his devo-

Refugees from Kosovo seeking to escape the physical danger of Serbian leader Slobodan Milosevic's campaign of repression and ethnic cleansing also had to cope with the psychological trauma of terror and fear as they were forced to leave their homes and homeland.

tion to a humanitarian cause. "It is perhaps the first conflict ever fought where no one wanted any land, or money, or geopolitical advantage," he declared. "We just wanted to stop and reverse ethnic cleansing."

His perseverance paid off. Unable to strike effectively at the Serbian army in Kosovo, NATO planes concentrated on the infrastructure of Serbia, targeting bridges, oil refineries, and, most important of all, power stations. By the end of May, Serbia had lost 60 percent of its electrical capacity and the domestic pressure on Milosevic began to mount. Milosevic finally agreed to end his attempts to purge Kosovo of its Albanian inhabitants. An agreement signed on June 10, 1999, called for the withdrawal of all Serb forces and placed Kosovo under UN supervision, with NATO troops acting as peacekeepers.

The conflict over Kosovo revealed both the strengths and weaknesses of the United States in the turbulent post–Cold War world. American military power, while great, was limited by the need to work with allies and by a strong desire to avoid risking American lives. Clinton could boast of an amazing result—NATO had waged a 12-week air campaign without the loss of a single pilot. Yet the United States had been unable to prevent Milosevic from uprooting and terrorizing nearly one million Kosovars.

The Clinton record abroad highlights the dilemma facing the United States in the post–Cold War world. Lacking the central focus of rivalry with another super power, the United States must decide when and where to bring its great power to bear without exhausting itself in endless adventures overseas. Clinton failed in Somalia, achieved only limited success in Haiti, but he could claim credit for ending a bloody civil war in Bosnia and for rescuing the Kosovars from Milosevic's ethnic cleansing. Like his predecessor, however, Clinton was unable to define a clear international mission for post–Cold War America. As a result, instead of setting the global agenda, the United States remained the prisoner of events abroad.

THE END OF THE CENTURY

It was the best of times; it was the worst of times. The nineties witnessed an unparalleled burst of economic growth that clearly established the United States as the world's richest nation. Yet in the same decade, violence in the form of angry protests from both the extreme right and the extreme left, as well as a series of senseless school shootings, shocked the nation. Waco, Oklahoma City, Seattle, Littleton—these sites of violence and devastation revealed deep flaws in American society. Even the man who claimed credit for the prosperity, Bill Clinton, nearly lost the presidency over a sexual affair with a White House intern.

FROM DEFICIT TO SURPLUS

In early 2000, the boom of the 1990s officially became the longest sustained period of economic growth in American history. Since March 1991, the economy had expanded by an incredible 64 percent, creating 20 million new jobs. Unemployment dropped below 5 percent in 1997. Best of all, inflation remained low, averaging just over 2 percent a year and thus enabling family income to surpass the previous all-time high of the early 1970s. The wealthy continued to make the greatest gains, but prosperity reached every level, with those at the bottom making real, if modest, advances.

Economists had difficulty explaining the happy situation. The primary factor appeared to be continued increases in productivity, which allowed the economy to expand without creating inflationary pressures. Businesses invested heavily in new technology—especially computers and sophisticated software—that enabled workers to increase their output steadily. While the growth in exports that Clinton fought for acted as a stimulus, it was the American consumer who was the real hero. Foreign trade accounted for only about 10 percent of the output; the rest came from constantly increasing domestic purchases of cars, computers, household goods, and the myriad items that made up the largest consumer market in the world.

The wise and mysterious policies of Federal Reserve Chairman Alan Greenspan helped sustain the boom by keeping inflation in check. He shrewdly lowered interest rates in late 1997 to stimulate the economy during the Asian turmoil. Then he began to raise them in 1999 and 2000 to the highest level of the decade to slow down the economy and prevent surging world oil prices from leading to a repetition of the great inflation of the 1970s.

The greatest benefit of the remarkable economic boom was the transformation of the federal budget. The worrisome deficits of the early 1990s disappeared, replaced with surpluses, at first modest, but then substantial. By 2000, the surplus was more than $100 billion. The future promised to be even brighter, with the Congressional Budget Office predicting a $2.2 trillion windfall in the first decade of the new century.

The two parties could not agree on how to spend the unexpected bonanza. Republicans called for across-the-board tax reductions, while Democrats wanted to shore up the faltering Social Security and Medicare programs. Clinton's veto of congressional tax cuts led to a deadlock that actually seemed to accomplish what most Americans preferred—paying off the national debt that had grown so large from past deficits.

The optimistic forecasts all depended on sustaining an unprecedented economic expansion. A recession, the normal pattern in the business cycle of the past, would make the debate over whether to reduce taxes or shore up social pro-grams irrelevant. Those who won control of the White House and Congress in 2000, therefore, would face the challenge not only of spending the surplus wisely, but also of ensuring its very existence.

VIOLENCE IN THE 1990s

Amid the unprecedented prosperity, a series of violent episodes disturbed the na-tion in the last decade of the century. Across the political spectrum, those who feared the loss of personal freedom resorted to force to express their discontent.

On the right, the militia movement accelerated after a shoot-out at Ruby Ridge, Idaho, in August 1992. Trying to arrest Christian survivalist Randy Weaver for illegal arms sales, federal agents shot and killed Weaver's wife and son during an eleven-day siege. Ruby Ridge became the rallying cry for right-wing activists who expressed their hatred for blacks, homosexuals, abortionists, and above all, the federal government.

A second tragic incident—the siege and destruction of the Branch Davidian compound in Waco, Texas, in 1993—intensified the militia impulse. What began in January as an attempt to arrest charismatic leader David Koresh on gun-deal-ing charges finally ended in April with the death of 75 Branch Davidians. As a stunned nation tried to understand what had happened at Waco, many dissidents had a ready explanation: An evil government, part of an international conspiracy to create a new world order at the expense of traditional American liberties, was responsible.

On April 19, 1995, the second anniversary of the Waco tragedy, Timothy McVeigh set off a powerful bomb in a rented Ryder truck in the street next to the federal building in Oklahoma City. McVeigh would eventually be sentenced to die for his crime. Yet he showed no remorse, reflecting the views expressed by the bomber in a novel McVeigh sold at gun shows around the country: "There is no way we can destroy the System without hurting many thousands of innocent people—no way."

The hatred of corporate America was as strong on the far left as on the far right. Its most dramatic expression came from the Unabomber—an unknown enemy of the global economy who sent sixteen bombs through the mail to corpo-ration executives and university professors between 1978 and 1995, killing three people and injuring twenty-three others. In 1995, the *Washington Post* published his "manifesto," a 35,000-word polemic in which he blamed modern technology for all of humanity's ills.

Nearly a year later, in April 1996, federal agents arrested Theodore J. Kaczynski at a remote cabin in Montana. Theodore Kaczynski had earned a doc-

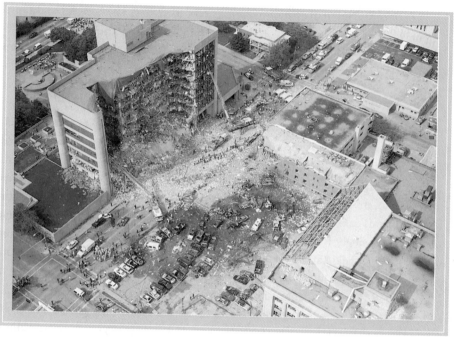

An aerial view of the destroyed Alfred P. Murrah Federal Building in Oklahoma City suggests the extent of the physical damage caused by the bomb blast on April 19, 1995, but cannot come close to expressing the human tragedy of the loss of 169 lives and the hundreds of injuries suffered.

torate in mathematics at Harvard and held a tenure-track teaching position at the University of California in Berkeley, but in 1969 he resigned in order to live in seclusion without modern conveniences. Kaczynski pled guilty to thirteen federal charges and was sentenced to prison for life without the possibility of parole. While few condoned his violent acts, some sympathized with Kaczynski's resentment over the degree to which technology encroached on individual privacy and curtailed personal freedom.

The clearest expression of unhappiness with the global economy of the 1990s came at the World Trade Organization (WTO) meeting in Seattle in late 1999. More than forty thousand protesters gathered to denounce the secret and autocratic way that the WTO encouraged the exploitation of both low-paid workers and natural resources in developing countries. At first, orderly marches led by organized labor and environmental groups drew large crowds and sent an important message of dissent. But then more violent demonstrators, notably black-clad anarchists from Eugene, Oregon, began smashing windows and trashing stores. The police overreacted, using tear gas, nightsticks, and rubber bullets to clear the streets and arrest more than 500 demonstrators. Despite the violence, the protesters succeeded not only in interrupting the WTO meeting, which adjourned without reaching any new trade agreements, but also in gaining worldwide attention for their grievances. Many Americans began to wonder whether the stunning advances in technology and world trade were compromising the traditional values and personal freedom they had always prized.

Even more perplexing were the series of senseless school shootings that occurred in the late 1990s. They began in Pearl, Mississippi, on October 1, 1997, when a 16-year-old boy stabbed his mother to death and then fatally shot two girls and wounded seven other high school students. Similar outbursts at West Paducah, Kentucky; Jonesboro, Arkansas; and Springfield, Oregon, in the 1997–1998 school year saw angry teenagers kill nine of their classmates and three adults. The culmination came at Columbine High School in Littleton, Colorado, in April 1999. Eric Harris and Dylan Klebold used automatic weapons to slaughter twelve fellow students and a teacher in the worst incident of school violence in American history.

The youthful killers had much in common. They all were white, above average in intelligence, attended nonurban schools, came from middle-class families, and were deeply alienated. All appeared to hold grudges against classmates they believed had ostracized them. Harris and Klebold considered themselves outcasts at Columbine and responded by wearing long black coats with swastikas and greeting each other in public with "Heil Hitler" salutes.

Explanations for their violent behavior ranged from easy access to guns to the violence of pop culture. In all five cases it was clear afterward that those who committed the crimes gave ample warning that something was very wrong. At Columbine, the two killers focused their psychology class project on mass murderer Jeffrey Dahmer and prepared a video for another class showing them pretending to shoot their archenemies, the school athletes.

Critics called for tighter gun controls, greater parental supervision of teenagers, and restrictions on the extreme lyrics of popular music and the violent nature of video games. "When you look at the overall pattern," commented one expert, "it's a pretty serious wake-up call." If nothing else, the school shootings revealed that beneath the veneer of prosperity there were deep flaws in both family structure and popular culture at the end of the century.

SHADOW ON THE WHITE HOUSE

"CLINTON ACCUSED OF URGING AIDE TO LIE," read the headline in the *Washington Post* on the morning of January 21, 1998. For the first time, the

American people learned that Kenneth Starr, the special prosecutor appointed in 1994 to probe the Whitewater affair, was now investigating charges that President Clinton had conducted a clandestine affair with a White House intern, Monica Lewinsky. For the next year, the Lewinsky scandal dominated national attention as Bill Clinton fought hard to save his presidency.

Clinton's relationship with Lewinsky began in November 1995 during one of the governmental shutdowns caused by the budget deadlock between the Republican Congress and the White House. With many of the staff temporarily laid off, the 22-year-old intern was able to achieve her goal of meeting privately with the president. For the next few months they had a sexual relationship without engaging in intercourse. Worried aides tried to break off the affair by transferring Lewinsky to a Pentagon job, but Clinton and Lewinsky met twice in early 1997, before the president terminated the relationship in April.

Two developments led to the public disclosure of the relationship. First, lawyers in the Paula Jones case sought to depose Monica Lewinsky in preparation for asking Bill Clinton under oath whether or not he had engaged in a sexual relationship with her. The president telephoned Lewinsky in December 1997 to urge her to file an affidavit denying the affair; in his own deposition on January 17, 1998, the president flatly stated, "I have never had sexual relations with Monica Lewinsky."

Unfortunately for Clinton, Linda Tripp, one of Monica Lewinsky's coworkers at the Pentagon, had recorded twenty hours of telephone conversations in which Lewinsky had described her sexual encounters with the president. On January 12, Tripp informed Starr's office of the tapes, thereby providing evidence, which Starr used to get the authority to investigate the Lewinsky relationship.

Clinton, caught off guard, was slow to respond to the public outcry. At first, he had the White House issue a blanket denial. Five days after the story broke, Bill Clinton finally spoke directly to the nation. At the end of a televised statement on after-school care, he turned to the cameras, wagged his finger, and said, "I want to say one thing to the American people . . . I did not have sexual relations with that woman, Miss Lewinsky."

For the next six months, the president stoutly maintained his innocence, aided greatly by Hillary Clinton who stood by her husband and charged that Starr's investigation was part of a "vast right-wing conspiracy" designed to drive him from the White House. Impressed with her wifely devotion, many Americans withheld judgment. Indeed, with the economy booming, Clinton's approval rate in the polls went from the low 60s to more than 70 percent. Starr's inability to

Members of the House Judiciary Committee listen to Clinton's testimony during the hearings on the president's impeachment in December 1998. The Committee sent four articles of impeachment to the full House, and the House adopted two—one count of perjury and one of obstruction of justice. The Senate could not muster the two-thirds majority required for conviction, and so Clinton was acquitted of both articles.

work out an immunity agreement with Monica Lewinsky allowed the matter to drift for months.

Matters finally came to a head in August when Lewinsky reached agreement with Starr's office. She gave a detailed account of her ten sexual encounters with the president and provided crucial physical evidence implicating Clinton. At the same time, she cast doubt on obstruction of justice charges against Clinton and his associates by denying that they had tried to buy her silence with job offers.

Realizing that he could no longer deny the affair, the president sought to limit the damage. On August 17 he admitted having "inappropriate intimate contact" with Lewinsky to Starr's grand jury, but insisted that he had not engaged in a sexual relationship. That evening Clinton spoke briefly to the nation. The president for the first time admitted to a relationship with Lewinsky that was "not appropriate" and "wrong." He said he regretted misleading the people and especially his wife, but he refused to apologize for his behavior or his false denials.

Clinton's fate hung in the balance. For the first time, some Democrats began to speak out. But just when Clinton was most vulnerable, the special prosecutor rescued him. In early September, Starr sent a 452-page report to Congress outlining eleven possible impeachment charges against Clinton. The key one was perjury, and Starr believed he had to go into excruciating detail on all ten sexual encounters between Clinton and Lewinsky to prove that the president had lied when he denied engaging in sexual relations with the intern.

Many Americans responded by condemning Starr rather than the president. Shocked by the sordid details, they blamed the prosecutor for exposing families to distasteful sexual practices on the evening news. When Hillary Clinton continued to support her husband, a majority of the public seemed to conclude that however bad the president's conduct, it was a private matter, one to be settled between a husband and a wife, not in the public arena.

Republican leaders ignored public sentiment and pressed ahead with impeachment proceedings. The clearest warning sign came in November, when the Democrats surprised the nation by gaining five seats in the House of Representatives and narrowed the GOP margin to six votes. In December, the House voted on four articles of impeachment, rejecting two, but approving two others—perjury and obstruction of justice—by small margins in nearly straight party-line votes.

The final showdown in the Senate was anticlimatic. With a two-thirds vote required to find the president guilty and remove him from office, there was no chance of conviction in the highly charged partisan mood that prevailed. The evidence against Clinton was strongest on the perjury charge, but on February 12, 1999, the GOP was unable to muster even a majority, with 45 in favor and 55 opposed. After a second, closer vote, 50 to 50, on obstruction of justice, the presiding officer, Chief Justice William Rehnquist, declared, "Acquitted of the charges."

Clinton had survived the Monica Lewinsky affair because once again he proved to be a far more skillful politician than his Republican opponents. With his wife's unflagging support, he was able to persuade the American people that his political opponents were waging a vendetta against him.

Yet Bill Clinton emerged from the ordeal with his presidency badly damaged. People forgave him his personal failings during an era of unrivaled prosperity, but they no longer held him in high esteem. His final two years in office would be devoted to a concerted effort to restore his damaged reputation. Desperate for a legacy to mark his White House years, Clinton failed to realize that he had already created an enduring one—he would always be remembered as the president who dishonored his office by his unseemly affair with a young intern.

A NATION DIVIDED

Two dominant trends shaped the election of 2000. The first, which favored the Democrats, was the economic boom that had erased the budget deficit and brought prosperity to nearly all Americans in the 1990s. At the same time, however, many voters felt a sense of disappointment and even betrayal because of Clinton's personal failings. The conflict between material abundance and moral values resulted in the closest election in more than a century.

The two candidates, Governor George W. Bush of Texas and Vice President Al Gore of Tennessee, had little in common. Gore had spent eighteen years in Washington as a congressman, senator, and vice president. Somewhat stiff and aloof in manner, he had mastered the intricacies of all the major policy issues and had the experience and knowledge to lead the nation. Bush, in contrast, had pursued a business career before winning the governorship of Texas in 1994. Personable and outgoing, Bush had the temperament for leadership but lacked not only experience but a full grasp of national issues. Journalists were quick to seize on the weaknesses of both men, accusing Gore of frequent and misleading exaggeration and Bush of mangling words and speaking only in generalities.

Both Bush and Gore were able to win their party's nominations after brief contests. The vice president, the acknowledged heir to Clinton, defeated former New Jersey Senator Bill Bradley with relative ease. The governor had more difficulty in turning back the challenge of Arizona Senator John McCain, who attracted support from independents and Democrats by championing campaign finance reform. But both candidates were hurt by the primaries. Bush was forced to move sharply to the right, jeopardizing his claim to stand for "compassionate conservatism," while Gore's aggressive tactics led Bradley to ask the embarrassing question, "How can we trust what you say as president if you don't tell the truth as a candidate."

The conventional political wisdom pointed to an easy win for Al Gore in the November election, but two factors reduced his chances. In the past, the candidate of a party in power during prosperous times had a clear advantage. A perceived need to separate himself from Clinton's scandals, however, led Gore to run as his own man and fail to capitalize on the president's glowing economic record. The decision of consumer advocate Ralph Nader to run for president on the Green Party ticket further complicated Gore's campaign and forced him to move to the left, enabling Bush to appeal more effectively to moderate independents.

In the fall campaign, the candidates presented American voters with a clear choice. Bush called for limiting the role of government and relying instead on the free market. The centerpiece of his campaign was a proposed across-the-board tax cut that would be of greatest benefit to the wealthy. He also favored partial privatization of Social Security and placed greater weight on the private sector in his prescription drug plan and other reform proposals. Gore became the advocate of government action, calling for an expanded federal role in education and health care. Delivering a fervent populist attack on big business Gore repeatedly charged that Bush's tax cut would not benefit the average American but only help "the wealthiest one percent."

The race for the White House, to the delight of the media, proved to be close and exciting. Bush led in the polls until Gore moved ahead after the Democratic convention in August. His vice presidential choice of Connecticut Senator Joe Lieberman, a moderate and a Jew, proved popular, while Bush's running mate, former defense secretary Dick Cheney, failed to excite the electorate. But the vice president's surprisingly uneven performance in three televised debates allowed Bush to regain a narrow lead in the polls in October until Gore began to draw even in the final week of the campaign.

The early returns on election night proved that the polls were right in stressing the closeness of the presidential race. Gore seemed the likely winner when the networks mistakenly predicted a Democratic victory in Florida. When the TV analysts put Florida back in the undecided column Bush began to forge ahead, sweeping the rest of the south. After midnight, when the networks again mistakenly called Florida, this time for Bush, the vice president telephoned the governor to concede, only to recant an hour later when it became clear that the Bush margin in Florida was paper thin.

For the next five weeks, all eyes were on the outcome in Florida. Gore had a lead of more than 200,000 nationwide in the popular vote and 267 electoral votes, yet Bush, with 246 votes in the Electoral College, could win the presidency with Florida's 25. Both sides sent phalanxes of lawyers to Florida. Bush's team sought to certify the results that showed the governor with a lead of 930 votes out of nearly six million cast. Citing many voting problems disclosed by the

THE ELECTION OF 2000

CANDIDATE	PARTY	POPULAR VOTE	ELECTORAL VOTE
Bush	Republican	50,456,167	271
Gore	Democratic	50,996,064	266*
Nader	Green	2,864,810	—

*One District of Columbia Gore elector abstained.

media, Gore asked for a recount in three heavily Democratic counties in south Florida. All three used antiquated punch card machines that resulted in some ballots not being clearly marked for any presidential candidate. For weeks the results in Florida, and hence of the entire election, appeared to depend on how one divined the intent of a voter based on hanging, dimpled, or pregnant chads.

The decision finally came in the courts. Democrats appealed the initial attempt to certify Bush as the victor to the Florida Supreme Court, where the majority of judges had been appointed by Democratic governors. The Florida court twice ordered recounts, but Bush's lawyers appealed to the United States Supreme Court. On December 12, five weeks after the election, the Court overruled the state court's call for a recount in a 5 to 4 decision that reflected a long-standing ideological divide among the nine justices. The next day, Gore gracefully conceded, and Bush finally became president-elect.

Although the rule of law prevailed, neither the winner nor the loser could take much pride in their party's behavior. The Republicans displayed an unseemly haste to have Bush declared the victor in Florida despite obvious voting irregularities. And the Democrats, while championing the principle of counting every vote, damaged their case from the outset by asking for recounts in just the three counties they believed would help their cause. The courts proved equally susceptible to partisan rather than legal considerations, issuing rulings that mirrored their political makeup.

When the Electoral College finally voted on December 18, there were 271 votes cast for Bush and 266 for Gore (one District of Columbia Gore elector abstained). Nearly complete election totals showed that Gore had received more than 500,000 more popular votes than Bush.

Bush's narrow victory revealed deep divisions in American life at the end of the twentieth century. The rural West and South went for Bush, along with a few key Midwest and border states, while Gore won the urban states along both coasts. There was an equally strong divide along economic lines, with the poor voting for Gore, the rich for Bush, and the middle class dividing evenly between the two candidates. Gore continued to benefit from the gender gap, winning 54 percent of the women's vote, and he won an even larger share of the black vote, 90 percent, than Clinton in 1996. The two candidates split the suburban vote evenly, and Bush succeeded in recapturing the lead among Catholic voters.

Nader proved to be less successful than early polls predicted, winning less than 3 percent of the national vote. Gore carried the states of the Pacific Northwest and the upper Midwest where Nader had the most support, but Nader's 96,837 votes in Florida probably cost Gore that crucial state.

Exit polls confirmed the underlying split in the electorate. More than 60 per-cent of voters surveyed said issues were more important than personality. Yet Bush was the overwhelming choice of those who placed primary emphasis on character and values. It was clear that Bush, who ended every campaign speech with a promise to restore dignity and honor to the White House, had used Clinton's foibles to counter Democratic claims of achieving prosperity. By the narrowest of margins, the American people appeared to have placed values ahead of material well-being in the election of 2000.

APPENDIX

The Declaration of Independence

The Constitution of the United States of America

Amendments to the Constitution

Recommended Reading

Suggested Web Sites

Physical and Political Map of the United States

Political Map of the World

The Declaration of Independence

In Congress, July 4, 1776

The Unanimous Declaration
of the Thirteen United States of America,

When, in the course of human events, it becomes necessary for one people to dissolve the political bonds which have connected them with another, and to assume, among the powers of the earth, the separate and equal station to which the laws of nature and of nature's God entitle them, a decent respect to the opinions of mankind requires that they should declare the causes which impel them to the separation.

We hold these truths to be self-evident: That all men are created equal; that they are endowed by their Creator with certain unalienable rights; that among these are life, liberty, and the pursuit of happiness; that, to secure these rights, governments are instituted among men, deriving their just powers from the consent of the governed; that whenever any form of government becomes destructive of these ends, it is the right of the people to alter or to abolish it, and to institute new government, laying its foundation on such principles, and organizing its powers in such form, as to them shall seem most likely to effect their safety and happiness. Prudence, indeed, will dictate that governments long established should not be changed for light and transient causes; and accordingly all experience hath shown that mankind are more disposed to suffer, while evils are sufferable, than to right themselves by abolishing the forms to which they are accustomed. But when a long train of abuses and usurpations, pursuing invariably the same object, evinces a design to reduce them under absolute despotism, it is their right, it is their duty, to throw off such government, and to provide new guards for their future security. Such has been the patient sufferance of these colonies; and such is now the necessity which constrains them to alter their former systems of government. The history of the present King of Great Britain is a history of repeated injuries and usurpations, all having in direct object the establishment of an absolute tyranny over these states. To prove this, let facts be submitted to a candid world.

He has refused his assent to laws, the most wholesome and necessary for the public good.

He has forbidden his governors to pass laws of immediate and pressing importance, unless suspended in their operation till his assent should be obtained; and, when so suspended, he has utterly neglected to attend to them.

He has refused to pass other laws for the accommodation of large districts of people, unless those people would relinquish the right of representation in the legislature, a right inestimable to them, and formidable to tyrants only.

He has called together legislative bodies at places unusual, uncomfortable, and distant from the depository of their public records, for the sole purpose of fatiguing them into compliance with his measures.

He has dissolved representative houses repeatedly, for opposing, with manly firmness, his invasions on the rights of the people.

He has refused for a long time, after such dissolutions, to cause others to be elected; whereby the legislative powers, incapable of annihilation, have returned to the people at large for their exercise; the state remaining, in the mean time, exposed to all the dangers of invasions from without and convulsions within.

He has endeavored to prevent the population of these states; for that purpose obstructing the laws for naturalization of foreigners; refusing to pass others to encourage their migration hither, and raising the conditions of new appropriations of lands.

He has obstructed the administration of justice, by refusing his assent to laws for establishing judiciary powers.

He has made judges dependent on his will alone, for the tenure of their offices, and the amount and payment of their salaries.

He has erected a multitude of new offices, and sent hither swarms of officers to harass our people and eat out their substance.

He has kept among us, in times of peace, standing armies, without the consent of our legislatures.

He has affected to render the military independent of, and superior to, the civil power.

He has combined with others to subject us to a jurisdiction foreign to our constitution, and unacknowledged by our laws, giving his assent to their acts of pretended legislation:

For quartering large bodies of armed troops among us;

For protecting them, by a mock trial, from punishment for any murder which they should commit on the inhabitants of these states;

For cutting off our trade with all parts of the world;

For imposing taxes on us without our consent;

For depriving us, in many cases, of the benefits of trial by jury;

For transporting us beyond seas, to be tried for pretended offenses;

For abolishing the free system of English laws in a neighboring province, establishing therein an arbitrary government, and enlarging its boundaries, so as to render it at once an example and fit instrument for introducing the same absolute rule into these colonies;

For taking away our charters, abolishing our most valuable laws, and altering fundamentally the forms of our governments;

For suspending our own legislatures, and declaring themselves invested with power to legislate for us in all cases whatsoever.

He has abdicated government here, by declaring us out of his protection and waging war against us.

He has plundered our seas, ravaged our coasts, burned our towns, and destroyed the lives of our people.

He is at this time transporting large armies of foreign mercenaries to complete the works of death, desolation, and tyranny already begun with circumstances of cruelty and perfidy scarcely paralleled in the most barbarous ages, and totally unworthy the head of a civilized nation.

He has constrained our fellow-citizens, taken captive on the high seas, to bear arms against their country, to become the executioners of their friends and brethren, or to fall themselves by their hands.

He has excited domestic insurrection among us, and has endeavored to bring on the inhabitants of our frontiers the merciless Indian savages, whose known rule of warfare is an undistinguished destruction of all ages, sexes, and conditions.

In every stage of these oppressions we have petitioned for redress in the most humble terms; our repeated petitions have been answered only by repeated injury. A prince, whose character is thus marked by every act which may define a tyrant, is unfit to be the ruler of a free people.

Nor have we been wanting in our attentions to our British brethren. We have warned them, from time to time, of attempts by their legislature to extend an unwarrantable jurisdiction over us. We have reminded them of the circumstances of our emigration and settlement here. We have appealed to their native justice and magnanimity; and we have conjured them, by the ties of our common kindred, to disavow these usurpations, which would inevitably interrupt our connections and correspondence. They, too, have been deaf to the voice of justice and of consanguinity. We must, therefore, acquiesce in the necessity which denounces our separation, and hold them, as we hold the rest of mankind, enemies in war, in peace friends.

We, therefore, the representatives of the United States of America, in General Congress assembled, appealing to the Supreme Judge of the world for the rectitude of our intentions, do, in the name and by the authority of the good people of these colonies, solemnly publish and declare, that these United Colonies are, and of right ought to be, FREE AND INDEPENDENT STATES; that they are absolved from all allegiance to the British crown, and that all political connection between them and the state of Great Britain is, and ought to be, totally dissolved; and that, as free and independent states, they have full power to levy war, conclude peace, contract alliances, establish commerce, and do all other acts and things which independent states may of right do. And for the support of this declaration, with a firm reliance on the protection of Divine Providence, we mutually pledge to each other our lives, our fortunes, and our sacred honor.

JOHN HANCOCK

BUTTON GWINNETT
LYMAN HALL
GEO. WALTON
WM. HOOPER
JOSEPH HEWES
JOHN PENN
EDWARD RUTLEDGE
THOS. HEYWARD, JUNR.
THOMAS LYNCH, JUNR.
ARTHUR MIDDLETON
SAMUEL CHASE
WM. PACA
THOS. STONE
CHARLES CARROLL OF
   CARROLLTON
GEORGE WYTHE
RICHARD HENRY LEE
TH. JEFFERSON
BENJ. HARRISON

THOS. NELSON, JR.
FRANCIS LIGHTFOOT LEE
CARTER BRAXTON
ROBT. MORRIS
BENJAMIN RUSH
BENJA. FRANKLIN
JOHN MORTON
GEO. CLYMER
JAS. SMITH
GEO. TAYLOR
JAMES WILSON
GEO. ROSS
CAESAR RODNEY
GEO. READ
THO. M'KEAN
WM. FLOYD
PHIL. LIVINGSTON
FRANS. LEWIS
LEWIS MORRIS

RICHD. STOCKTON
JNO. WITHERSPOON
FRAS. HOPKINSON
JOHN HART
ABRA. CLARK
JOSIAH BARTLETT
WM. WHIPPLE
SAML. ADAMS
JOHN ADAMS
ROBT. TREAT PAINE
ELBRIDGE GERRY
STEP. HOPKINS
WILLIAM ELLERY
ROGER SHERMAN
SAM'EL HUNTINGTON
WM. WILLIAMS
OLIVER WOLCOTT
MATTHEW THORNTON

The Constitution of the United States of America

PREAMBLE

We the People of the United States, in Order to form a more perfect Union, establish Justice, insure domestic Tranquility, provide for the common defence, promote the general Welfare, and secure the Blessings of Liberty to ourselves and our Posterity, do ordain and establish this Constitution for the United States of America.

ARTICLE I

Section 1

All legislative Powers herein granted shall be vested in a Congress of the United States, which shall consist of a Senate and House of Representatives.

Section 2

The House of Representatives shall be composed of Members chosen every second Year by the People of the several States, and the Electors in each State shall have the Qualifications requisite for Electors of the most numerous Branch of the State Legislature.

No Person shall be a Representative who shall not have attained to the Age of twenty five Years, and been seven Years a Citizen of the United States, and who shall not, when elected, be an inhabitant of that State in which he shall be chosen.

Representatives and direct Taxes shall be apportioned among the several States which may be included within this Union, according to their respective Numbers, *which shall be determined by adding to the whole Number of free Persons, including those bound to Service for a Term of Years, and excluding Indians not taxed, three fifths of all other Persons.* * The actual Enumeration shall be made within three Years after the first Meeting of the Congress of the United States, and within every subsequent Term of ten Years, in such Manner as they shall by Law direct. The Number of Representatives shall not exceed one for every thirty Thousand, but each State shall have at Least one Representative; *and until such enumeration shall be made, the State of New Hampshire shall be entitled to chuse three, Massachusetts eight, Rhode-Island and Providence Plantations one, Connecticut five, New York six, New Jersey four, Pennsylvania eight, Delaware one, Maryland six, Virginia ten, North Carolina five, South Carolina five, and Georgia three.*

When vacancies happen in the Representation from any State, the Executive Authority thereof shall issue Writs of Election to fill such Vacancies.

The House of Representatives shall chuse their Speaker and other Officers; and shall have the sole Power of Impeachment.

Section 3

The Senate of the United States shall be composed of two Senators from each State, *chosen by the Legislature thereof,* for six Years; and each Senator shall have one Vote.

---

* *Passages no longer in effect are printed in italic type.*

Immediately after they shall be assembled in Consequence of the first Election, they shall be divided as equally as may be into three Classes. The Seats of the Senators of the first Class shall be vacated at the Expiration of the second Year, of the second Class at the Expiration of the fourth Year, and of the third Class at the Expiration of the sixth Year so that one third may be chosen every second Year; and if Vacancies happen by Resignation, or otherwise, during the Recess of the Legislature of any state, the Executive thereof may make temporary Appointments until the next Meeting of the Legislature, which shall then fill such Vacancies.

No Person shall be a Senator who shall not have attained to the Age of thirty Years, and been nine Years a Citizen of the United States, and who shall not, when elected, be an Inhabitant of that State for which he shall be chosen.

The Vice President of the United States shall be President of the Senate, but shall have no Vote, unless they be equally divided.

The Senate shall chuse their other Officers, and also a President *pro tempore,* in the Absence of the Vice President, or when he shall exercise the Office of President of the United States.

The Senate shall have the sole Power to try all Impeachments. When sitting for that Purpose, they shall be on Oath or Affirmation. When the President of the United States is tried the Chief Justice shall preside: And no Person shall be convicted without the Concurrence of two thirds of the Members present.

Judgment in Cases of Impeachment shall not extend further than to removal from Office, and disqualification to hold and enjoy any Office of honor, Trust or Profit under the United States: but the Party convicted shall nevertheless be liable and subject to Indictment, Trial, Judgment and Punishment, according to Law.

Section 4

The Times, Places and Manner of holding Elections for Senators and Representatives, shall be prescribed in each State by the Legislature thereof; but the Congress may at any time by Law make or alter such Regulations, except as to the Places of chusing Senators.

The Congress shall assemble at least once in every Year, *and such Meeting shall be on the first Monday in December, unless they shall by Law appoint a different Day.*

Section 5

Each House shall be the Judge of the Elections, Returns and Qualifications of its own Members, and a Majority of each shall constitute a Quorum to do Business; but a smaller Number may adjourn from day to day, and may be authorized to compel the Attendance of absent Members, in such Manner, and under such Penalties as each House may provide.

Each House may determine the Rules of its Proceedings, punish its Members for disorderly Behaviour, and, with the Concurrence of two thirds, expel a Member.

Each House shall keep a Journal of its Proceedings, and from time to time publish the same, excepting such Parts as may in their Judgment require Secrecy; and the Yeas and Nays of the Members of either House on any question shall, at the Desire of one fifth of those Present, be entered on the Journal.

Neither House, during the Session of Congress, shall, without the Consent of the other, adjourn for more than three days, nor to any other Place than that in which the two Houses shall be sitting.

Section 6

The Senators and Representatives shall receive a Compensation for their Services, to be ascertained by Law, and paid out of the Treasury of the United States. They shall in all Cases, except

Treason, Felony and Breach of the Peace, be privileged from Arrest during their Attendance at the Session of their respective Houses, and in going to and returning from the same; and for any Speech or Debate in either House, they shall not be questioned in any other Place.

No Senator or Representative shall, during the Time for which he was elected, be appointed to any civil Office under the Authority of the United States, which shall have been created, or the Emoluments whereof shall have been encreased during such time, and no Person holding any Office under the United States, shall be a Member of either House during his Continuance in Office.

Section 7

All Bills for raising Revenue shall originate in the House of Representatives; but the Senate may propose or concur with Amendments as on other Bills.

Every Bill which shall have passed the House of Representatives and the Senate, shall, before it become a Law, be presented to the President of the United States; If he approve he shall sign it, but if not he shall return it, with his Objections to the House in which it shall have originated, who shall enter the Objections at large on their Journal, and proceed to reconsider it. If after such Reconsideration two thirds of that House shall agree to pass the Bill, it shall be sent, together with the Objections, to the other House, by which it shall likewise be reconsidered, and if approved by two thirds of that House, it shall become a Law. But in all such Cases the Votes of both Houses shall be determined by yeas and Nays, and the Names of the Persons voting for and against the Bill shall be entered on the Journal of each House respectively. If any Bill shall not be returned by the President within ten Days (Sundays excepted) after it shall have been presented to him, the Same shall be a Law, in like Manner as if he had signed it, unless the Congress by their Adjournment prevent its Return, in which Case it shall not be a Law.

Every Order, Resolution, or Vote to which the Concurrence of the Senate and House of Representatives may be necessary (except on a question of Adjournment) shall be presented to the President of the United States; and before the Same shall take Effect, shall be approved by him, or being disapproved by him, shall be repassed by two thirds of the Senate and House of Representatives, according to the Rules and Limitations prescribed in the Case of a Bill.

Section 8

The Congress shall have Power To lay and collect Taxes, Duties, Imposts and Excises, to pay the Debts and provide for the common Defence and general Welfare of the United States; but all Duties, Imposts and Excises shall be uniform throughout the United States;

To borrow Money on the credit of the United States;

To regulate Commerce with foreign Nations, and among the several States, and with the Indian Tribes;

To establish an uniform Rule of Naturalization, and uniform Laws on the subject of Bankruptcies throughout the United States;

To coin Money, regulate the Value thereof, and of foreign Coin, and fix the Standard of Weights and Measures;

To provide for the Punishment of counterfeiting the Securities and current Coin of the United States;

To establish Post Offices and post Roads;

To promote the Progress of Science and useful Arts, by securing for limited Times to Authors and Inventors the exclusive Right to their respective Writings and Discoveries;

To constitute Tribunals inferior to the supreme Court;

To define and punish Piracies and Felonies committed on the high Seas, and Offences against the Law of Nations;

To declare War, grant Letters of Marque and Reprisal, and make Rules concerning Captures on Land and Water;

To raise and support Armies, but no Appropriation of Money to that Use shall be for a longer Term than two Years;

To provide and maintain a Navy;

To make Rules for the Government and Regulation of the land and naval Forces;

To provide for calling forth the Militia to execute the Laws of the Union, suppress Insurrections and repel Invasions;

To provide for organizing, arming, and disciplining, the Militia, and for governing such Part of them as may be employed in the Service of the United States, reserving to the States respectively, the Appointment of the Officers, and the Authority of training the Militia according to the discipline prescribed by Congress;

To exercise exclusive Legislation in all Cases whatsoever, over such District (not exceeding ten Miles square) as may, by Cession of particular States, and the Acceptance of Congress, become the Seat of the Government of the United States, and to exercise like Authority over all Places purchased by the Consent of the Legislature of the State in which the Same shall be, for the Erection of Forts, Magazines, Arsenals, dock-Yards, and other needful Buildings;— And

To make all Laws which shall be necessary and proper for carrying into Execution the foregoing Powers, and all other Powers vested by this Constitution in the Government of the United States, or in any Department of Officer thereof.

Section 9

The Migration or Importation of such Persons as any of the States now existing shall think proper to admit, shall not be prohibited by the Congress prior to the Year one thousand eight hundred and eight, but a Tax or duty may be imposed on such Importation, not exceeding ten dollars for each Person.

The Privilege of the Writ of Habeas Corpus shall not be suspended, unless when in Cases of Rebellion or Invasion the public Safety may require it.

No Bill of Attainder or ex post facto Law shall be passed.

No Capitation, or other direct, Tax shall be laid, unless in Proportion to the Census or Enumeration herein before directed to be taken.

No Tax or Duty shall be laid on Articles exported from any State.

No Preference shall be given by any Regulation of Commerce or Revenue to the Ports of one State over those of another: nor shall Vessels bound to, or from, one State, be obliged to enter, clear, or pay Duties in another.

No Money shall be drawn from the Treasury, but in Consequence of Appropriations made by Law; and a regular Statement and Account of the Receipts and Expenditures of all public Money shall be published from time to time.

No Title of Nobility shall be granted by the United States: And no Person holding any Office of Profit or Trust under them, shall, without the Consent of the Congress, accept of any present, Emolument, Office, or Title, of any kind whatever, from any King, Prince, or foreign State.

Section 10

No State shall enter into any Treaty, Alliance, or Confederation; grant Letters of Marque and Reprisal; coin Money; emit Bills of Credit; make any Thing but gold and silver Coin a Tender in Payment of Debts; pass any Bill of Attainder, ex post facto Law, or Law impairing the obligation of Contracts, or grant any Title of Nobility.

No State shall, without the Consent of the Congress, lay any Imposts or Duties on Imports or Exports, except what may be absolutely necessary for executing its inspection Laws: and the net Produce of all Duties and Imposts, laid by any State on Imports or Exports, shall be for the Use of the Treasury of the United States; and all such Laws shall be subject to the Revision and Controul of the Congress.

No State shall, without the Consent of Congress, lay any Duty of Tonnage, keep Troops, or Ships of War in time of Peace, enter into any Agreement or Compact with another State, or with a foreign Power, or engage in War, unless actually invaded, or in such imminent Danger as will not admit of delay.

ARTICLE II

Section 1

The executive Power shall be vested in a President of the United States of America. He shall hold his Office during the Term of four Years, and, together with the Vice President, chosen for the same Term, be elected, as follows:

Each State shall appoint, in such Manner as the Legislature thereof may direct, a Number of Electors, equal to the whole Number of Senators and Representatives to which the State may be entitled in the Congress: but no Senator or Representative, or Person holding an Office of Trust or Profit under the United States, shall be appointed an Elector.

The Electors shall meet in their respective States, and vote by Ballot for two Persons, of whom one at least shall not be an Inhabitant of the same State with themselves. And they shall make a List of all the Persons voted for, and of the Number of Votes for each; which List they shall sign and certify, and transmit sealed to the Seat of the Government of the United States, directed to the President of the Senate. The President of the Senate shall, in the Presence of the Senate and House of Representatives, open all the Certificates, and the Votes shall then be counted. The Person having the greatest Number of Votes shall be the President, if such Number be a Majority of the whole number of Electors appointed; and if there be more than one who have such Majority, and have an equal Number of Votes, then the House of Representatives shall immediately chuse by Ballot one of them for President; and if no Person have a Majority, then from the five highest on the List the said House shall in like Manner chuse the President. But in chusing the President, the Votes shall be taken by States, the Representation from each State having one Vote; A quorum for this Purpose shall consist of a Member or Members from two thirds of the States, and a Majority of all the States shall be necessary to a Choice. In every Case, after the Choice of the President, the Person having the greatest Number of Votes of the Electors shall be the Vice President. But if there should remain two or more who have equal Votes, the Senate shall chuse from them by Ballot the Vice President.

The Congress may determine the time of chusing the Electors, and the Day on which they shall give their Votes; which Day shall be the same throughout the United States.

No person except a natural born Citizen, *or a Citizen of the United States, at the time of the Adoption of this Constitution,* shall be eligible to the Office of President; neither shall any Person be eligible to that Office who shall not have attained to the Age of thirty five Years, and been fourteen Years a Resident within the United States.

In Case of the Removal of the President from Office, or of his Death, Resignation, or Inability to discharge the Powers and Duties of the said Office, the Same shall devolve on the Vice President, and the Congress may by Law provide for the Case of Removal, Death, Resignation or Inability, both of the President and Vice President, declaring what Officer shall then act as President, and such Officer shall act accordingly, until the Disability be removed, or a President shall be elected.

The President shall, at stated Times, receive for his Services, a Compensation, which shall neither be encreased nor diminished during the Period for which he shall have been elected, and he shall not receive within that period any other Emolument from the United States, or any of them.

Before he enter on the Execution of his Office, he shall take the following Oath or Affirmation:—"I do solemnly swear (or affirm) that I will faithfully execute the Office of President of the United States, and will to the best of my Ability, preserve, protect and defend the Constitution of the United States."

Section 2

The President shall be Commander in Chief of the Army and Navy of the United States, and of the Militia of the several States, when called into the actual Service of the United States; he may require the Opinion, in writing, of the principal Officer in each of the executive Departments, upon any Subject relating to the Duties of their respective Offices, and he shall have Power to grant Reprieves and Pardons for Offences against the United States, except in Cases of Impeachment.

He shall have Power, by and with the Advice and Consent of the Senate, to make Treaties, provided two thirds of the Senators present concur; and he shall nominate, and by and with the Advice and Consent of the Senate, shall appoint Ambassadors, other public Ministers and Consuls, Judges of the supreme Court, and all other Officers of the United States, whose Appointments are not herein otherwise provided for, and which shall be established by Law: but the Congress may by Law vest the Appointment of such inferior Officers, as they think proper in the President alone, in the Courts of Law, or in the Heads of Departments.

The President shall have Power to fill up all Vacancies that may happen during the Recess of the Senate, by granting Commissions which shall expire at the End of their next Session.

Section 3

He shall from time to time give to the Congress Information of the State of the Union, and recommend to their Consideration such Measures as he shall judge necessary and expedient; he may, on extraordinary Occasions, convene both Houses, or either of them, and in Case of disagreement between them, with Respect to the Time of Adjournment, he may adjourn them to such Time as he shall think proper; he shall receive Ambassadors and other public Ministers; he shall take Care that the Laws be faithfully executed, and shall Commission all the officers of the United States.

Section 4

The President, Vice President and all civil Officers of the United States, shall be removed from Office on Impeachment for, and Conviction of, Treason, Bribery or other high Crimes and Misdemeanors.

ARTICLE III

Section 1

The judicial Power of the United States, shall be vested in one supreme Court, and in such inferior Courts as the Congress may from time to time ordain and establish. The Judges, both of the supreme and inferior Courts, shall hold their offices during good Behaviour, and shall, at stated Times, receive for their Services, a Compensation, which shall not be diminished during their Continuance in Office.

Section 2

The judicial Power shall extend to all Cases, in Law and Equity, arising under this Constitution, the Laws of the United States, and Treaties made, or which shall be made, under their Authority;—to all Cases affecting Ambassadors, other public Ministers and Consuls;—to all Cases of admiralty and maritime Jurisdiction;—to Controversies to which the United States shall be a Party;—to Controversies between two or more States;—*between a State and Citizens of another State;*—between Citizens of different States;—between Citizens of the same State claiming Lands under Grants of different States, and between a State, or the Citizens thereof, and foreign States, Citizens or Subjects.

In all Cases affecting Ambassadors, other public Ministers and Consuls, and those in which a State shall be Party, the supreme Court shall have original Jurisdiction. In all the other Cases before mentioned, the supreme Court shall have appellate Jurisdiction, both as to Law and Fact, with such Exceptions, and under such Regulations as the Congress shall make.

The Trial of all Crimes, except in Cases of Impeachment, shall be by Jury; and such Trial shall be held in the State where the said Crimes shall have been committed, but when not committed within any State, the Trial shall be at such Place or Places as the Congress may by Law have directed.

Section 3

Treason against the United States, shall consist only in levying War against them, or in adhering to their Enemies, giving them Aid and Comfort. No person shall be convicted of Treason unless on the Testimony of two Witnesses to the same overt Act, or on Confession in open Court.

The Congress shall have Power to declare the Punishment of Treason, but no Attainder of Treason shall work Corruption of Blood, or Forfeiture except during the Life of the Person attainted.

ARTICLE IV

Section 1

Full Faith and Credit shall be given in each State to the public Acts, Records, and judicial Proceedings of every other State. And the Congress may by general Laws prescribe the Manner in which such Acts, Records and Proceedings shall be proved, and the Effect thereof.

Section 2

The Citizens of each State shall be entitled to all Privileges and Immunities of Citizens in the several States.

A Person charged in any State with Treason, Felony, or other Crime, who shall flee from Justice, and be found in another State, shall on Demand of the executive Authority of the State from which he fled, be delivered up, to be removed to the State having Jurisdiction of the Crime.

No Person held to Service or Labour in one State, under the Laws thereof, escaping into another, shall, in Consequence of any Law or Regulation therein, be discharged from such Service or Labour, but shall be delivered up on Claim of the Party to whom such Service or Labour may be due.

Section 3

New States may be admitted by the Congress into this Union; but no new State shall be formed or erected within the Jurisdiction of any other State; nor any State be formed by the Junction of two or more States, or Parts of States, without the Consent of the Legislatures of the States concerned as well as of the Congress.

The Congress shall have Power to dispose of and make all needful Rules and Regulations respecting the Territory or other Property belonging to the United States; and nothing in this Constitution shall be so construed as to Prejudice any Claims of the United States, or of any particular States.

Section 4

The United States shall guarantee to every State in this Union a Republican Form of Government, and shall protect each of them against Invasion; and on Application of the Legislature, or of the Executive (when the Legislature cannot be convened) against domestic violence.

ARTICLE V

The Congress, whenever two thirds of both Houses shall deem it necessary, shall propose Amendments to this Constitution, or, on the Application of the Legislatures of two thirds of the several States, shall call a Convention for proposing Amendments, which, in either Case, shall be valid to all Intents and Purposes, as Part of this Constitution, when ratified by the Legislatures of three fourths of the several States, or by Conventions in three fourths thereof, as the one or the other Mode of Ratification may be proposed by the Congress; Provided *that no Amendment which may be made prior to the Year One thousand eight hundred and eight shall in any Manner affect the first and fourth Clauses in the Ninth Section of the first Article;* and that no State, without its Consent, shall be deprived of its equal Suffrage in the Senate.

ARTICLE VI

All Debts contracted and Engagements entered into, before the Adoption of this Constitution, shall be as valid against the United States under this Constitution, as under the Confederation.

This Constitution, and Laws of the United States which shall be made in Pursuance thereof; and all Treaties made, or which shall be made, under the Authority of the United States, shall be the supreme Law of the Land; and the Judges in every State shall be bound thereby, any Thing in the Constitution or Laws of any State to the Contrary notwithstanding.

The Senators and Representatives before mentioned, and the Members of the several State Legislatures, and all executive and Judicial Officers, both of the United States and of the several States, shall be bound by Oath or Affirmation, to support this Constitution; but no religious Test shall ever be required as a Qualification to any Office of public Trust under the United States.

ARTICLE VII

The Ratification of the Conventions of nine States, shall be sufficient for the Establishment of this Constitution between the States so ratifying the Same.

Done in Convention by the Unanimous Consent of the States present the Seventeenth Day of September in the Year of our Lord one thousand seven hundred and Eighty seven and of the Independence of the United States of America the Twelfth* IN WITNESS whereof We have hereunto subscribed our Names,

GEORGE WASHINGTON
President and Deputy from Virginia

Delaware
GEORGE READ
GUNNING BEDFORD, JR.
JOHN DICKINSON
RICHARD BASSETT
JACOB BROOM

Maryland
JAMES MCHENRY
DANIEL OF ST. THOMAS JENIFER
DANIEL CARROLL

Virginia
JOHN BLAIR
JAMES MADISON, JR.

North Carolina
WILLIAM BLOUNT
RICHARD DOBBS SPRAIGHT
HUGH WILLIAMSON

South Carolina
JOHN RUTLEDGE
CHARLES COTESWORTH PINCKNEY
CHARLES PINCKNEY
PIERCE BUTLER

Georgia
WILLIAM FEW
ABRAHAM BALDWIN

New Hampshire
JOHN LANGDON
NICHOLAS GILMAN

Massachusetts
NATHANIEL GORHAM
RUFUS KING

Connecticut
WILLIAM SAMUEL JOHNSON
ROGER SHERMAN

New York
ALEXANDER HAMILTON

New Jersey
WILLIAM LIVINGSTON
DAVID BREARLEY
WILLIAM PATERSON
JONATHAN DAYTON

Pennsylvania
BENJAMIN FRANKLIN
THOMAS MIFFLIN
ROBERT MORRIS
GEORGE CLYMER
THOMAS FITZSIMONS
JARED INGERSOLL
JAMES WILSON
GOUVERNEUR MORRIS

*The Constitution was submitted on September 17, 1787, by the Constitutional Convention, was ratified by the Convention of several states at various dates up to May 29, 1790, and became effective on March 4, 1789.

Amendments to the Constitution

AMENDMENT I

Congress shall make no law respecting an establishment of religion, or prohibiting the free exercise thereof; or abridging the freedom of speech, or of the press; or the right of the people peaceably to assemble, and to petition the Government for a redress of grievances.

AMENDMENT II

A well regulated Militia being necessary to the security of a free State, the right of the people to keep and bear Arms, shall not be infringed.

AMENDMENT III

No Soldier shall, in time of peace be quartered in any house, without the consent of the Owner, nor in time of war, but in a manner to be prescribed by law.

AMENDMENT IV

The right of the people to be secure in their persons, houses, papers, and effects, against unreasonable searches and seizures, shall not be violated, and no Warrants shall issue, but upon probable cause, supported by Oath or affirmation, and particularly describing the place to be searched, and the persons or things to be seized.

AMENDMENT V

No person shall be held to answer for a capital, or otherwise infamous crime, unless on a presentment or indictment of a Grand Jury, except in cases arising in the land or naval forces, or in the Militia, when in actual service in time of War or public danger; nor shall any person be subject for the same offense to be twice put in jeopardy of life or limb; nor shall be compelled in any criminal case to be a witness against himself, nor be deprived of life, liberty, or property, without due process of law; nor shall private property be taken for public use, without just compensation.

AMENDMENT VI

In all criminal prosecutions, the accused shall enjoy the right to a speedy and public trial, by an impartial jury of the State and district wherein the crime shall have been committed, which district shall have been previously ascertained by law, and to be informed of the nature and cause of the accusation; to be confronted with the witnesses against him; to have compulsory process for obtaining witnesses in his favor, and to have the Assistance of Counsel for his defence.

AMENDMENT VII

In Suits at common law, where the value in controversy shall exceed twenty dollars, the right of trial by jury shall be preserved, and no fact tried by a jury, shall be otherwise re-examined in any Court of the United States, than according to the rules of the common law.

AMENDMENT VIII

Excessive bail shall not be required, nor excessive fines imposed, nor cruel and unusual punishments inflicted.

AMENDMENT IX

The enumeration in the Constitution, of certain rights, shall not be construed to deny or disparage others retained by the people.

AMENDMENT X*

The powers not delegated to the United States by the Constitution, nor prohibited by it to the States, are reserved to the States respectively, or to the people.

AMENDMENT XI
[ADOPTED 1798]

The Judicial power of the United States shall not be construed to extend to any suit in law or equity, commenced or prosecuted against one of the United States by Citizens of another State, or by Citizens or Subjects of any Foreign State.

AMENDMENT XII
[ADOPTED 1804]

The Electors shall meet in their respective states, and vote by ballot for President and Vice President, one of whom, at least, shall not be an inhabitant of the same state with themselves; they shall name in their ballots the person voted for as President, and in distinct ballots the person voted for as Vice President, and they shall make distinct lists of all persons voted for as President, and of all persons voted for as Vice President, and of the number of votes for each, which lists they shall sign and certify, and transmit sealed to the seat of the government of the United States, directed to the President of the Senate;—The President of the Senate shall, in the presence of the Senate and House of Representatives, open all the certificates and the votes shall then be counted;—The person having the greatest number of votes for President, shall be the President, if such number be a majority of the whole number of Electors appointed; and if no person have such majority, then from the persons having the highest numbers not exceeding three on the list of those voted for as President, the House of Representatives shall choose immediately, by ballot, the President. But in choosing the President, the votes shall be taken by states, the representation from each state having one vote; a quorum for this purpose shall consist of a member or members from two-thirds of the states, and a majority of all the states shall be necessary to a choice. And if the House of Representatives shall not choose a President whenever the right of choice shall devolve upon them, before *the fourth day of March* next following, then the Vice President shall act as President, as in the case of the death or other constitutional disability of the President.—The person having the greatest number of votes as Vice President, shall be the Vice President, if such number be a majority of the whole number of Electors appointed, and if no person have a majority, then from the two highest numbers on the list, the Senate shall choose the Vice President; a quorum for the purpose shall consist of two-thirds of the whole number of Senators, and a majority of the whole number shall be necessary to a choice. But no person con-

The first ten amendments (the Bill of Rights) were ratified, and their adoption was certified, on December 15, 1791.

stitutionally ineligible to the office of President shall be eligible to that of Vice President of the United States.

AMENDMENT XIII
[ADOPTED 1865]

Section 1

Neither slavery nor involuntary servitude, except as a punishment for crime whereof the party shall have been duly convicted, shall exist within the United States, or any place subject to their jurisdiction.

Section 2

Congress shall have power to enforce this article by appropriate legislation.

AMENDMENT XIV
[ADOPTED 1868]

Section 1

All persons born or naturalized in the United States, and subject to the jurisdiction thereof, are citizens of the United States and of the State wherein they reside. No State shall make or enforce any law which shall abridge the privileges or immunities of citizens of the United States; nor shall any State deprive any person of life, liberty, or property, without due process of law; nor deny to any person within its jurisdiction the equal protection of the laws.

Section 2

Representatives shall be apportioned among the several States according to their respective numbers, counting the whole number of persons in each State, excluding Indians not taxed. But when the right to vote at any election for the choice of electors for President and Vice President of the United States, Representatives in Congress, the Executive and Judicial officers of a State, or the members of the Legislature thereof, is denied to any of the male inhabitants of such State, being twenty-one years of age, and citizens of the United States, or in any way abridged, except for participation in rebellion, or other crime, the basis of representation therein shall be reduced in the proportion which the number of such male citizens shall bear to the whole number of male citizens twenty-one years of age in such State.

Section 3

No person shall be a Senator or Representative in Congress, or elector of President and Vice President, or hold any office, civil or military, under the United States, or under any State, who, having previously taken an oath, as a member of Congress, or as an officer of the United States, or as a member of any State legislature, or as an executive or judicial officer of any State, to support the Constitution of the United States, shall have engaged in insurrection or rebellion against the same, or given aid or comfort to the enemies thereof. But Congress may by a vote of two-thirds of each House, remove such disability.

Section 4

The validity of the public debt of the United States, authorized by law, including debts incurred for payment of pensions and bounties for services in suppressing insurrection or rebellion, shall not be questioned. But neither the United States nor any State shall assume or pay any debt or obligation incurred in aid of insurrection or rebellion against the United States, or any claim for the loss or emancipation of any slave; but all such debts, obligations and claims shall be held illegal and void.

Section 5

The Congress shall have power to enforce, by appropriate legislation, the provisions of this article.

AMENDMENT XV
[ADOPTED 1870]

Section 1

The right of citizens of the United States to vote shall not be denied or abridged by the United States or by any State on account of race, color, or previous condition of servitude.

Section 2

The Congress shall have power to enforce this article by appropriate legislation.

AMENDMENT XVI
[ADOPTED 1913]

The Congress shall have power to lay and collect taxes on incomes, from whatever source derived, without apportionment among the several States, and without regard to any census or enumeration.

AMENDMENT XVII
[ADOPTED 1913]

The Senate of the United States shall be composed of two Senators from each State, elected by the people thereof, for six years; and each Senator shall have one vote. The electors in each State shall have the qualifications requisite for electors of the most numerous branch of the State legislatures.

When vacancies happen in the representation of any State in the Senate, the executive authority of such State shall issue writs of election to fill such vacancies: *Provided,* That the legislature of any State may empower the executive thereof to make temporary appointments until the people fill the vacancies by election as the legislature may direct.

This amendment shall not be so construed as to affect the election or term of any Senator chosen before it becomes valid as part of the Constitution.

AMENDMENT XVIII
[ADOPTED 1919, REPEALED 1933]

Section 1

After one year from the ratification of this article the manufacture, sale, or transportation of intoxicating liquors within, the importation thereof into, or the exportation thereof from the United States and all territory subject to the jurisdiction thereof for beverage purposes is hereby prohibited.

Section 2

The Congress and the several States shall have concurrent power to enforce this article by appropriate legislation.

Section 3

This article shall be inoperative unless it shall have been ratified as an amendment to the Constitution by the legislatures of the several States, as provided in the Constitution, within seven years from the date of the submission hereof to the States by the Congress.

AMENDMENT XIX
[ADOPTED 1920]

The right of citizens of the United States to vote shall not be denied or abridged by the United States or by any State on account of sex.

Congress shall have power to enforce this article by appropriate legislation.

AMENDMENT XX
[ADOPTED 1933]

Section 1

The terms of the President and Vice President shall end at noon on the 20th day of January, and the terms of Senators and Representatives at noon on the 3d day of January, of the years in which such terms would have ended if this article had not been ratified and the terms of their successors shall then begin.

Section 2

The Congress shall assemble at least once in every year, and such meeting shall begin at noon on the 3d day of January, unless they shall by law appoint a different day.

Section 3

If, at the time fixed for the beginning of the term of the President, the President elect shall have died, the Vice President elect shall become President. If a President shall not have been chosen before the time fixed for the beginning of his term, or if the President elect shall have failed to qualify, then the Vice President elect shall act as President until a President shall have qualified; and the Congress may by law provide for the case wherein neither a President elect nor a Vice President elect shall have qualified, declaring who shall then act as President, or the manner in which one who is to act shall be selected, and such person shall act accordingly until a President or Vice President shall have qualified.

Section 4

The Congress may by law provide for the case of the death of any of the persons from whom the House of Representatives may choose a President whenever the right of choice shall have devolved upon them, and for the case of the death of any of the persons from whom the Senate may choose a Vice President whenever the right of choice shall have devolved upon them.

Section 5

Sections 1 and 2 shall take effect on the 15th day of October following the ratification of this article.

Section 6

This article shall be inoperative unless it shall have been ratified as an amendment to the Constitution by the legislatures of three fourths of the several States within seven years from the date of its submission.

Amendment XXI
[Adopted 1933]

Section 1

The eighteenth article of amendment to the Constitution of the United States is hereby repealed.

Section 2

The transportation or importation into any State, Territory, or possession of the United States for delivery or use therein of intoxicating liquors in violation of the laws thereof, is hereby prohibited.

Section 3

This article shall be inoperative unless it shall have been ratified as an amendment to the Constitution by conventions in the several States, as provided in the Constitution, within seven years from the date of the submission hereof to the States by the Congress.

Amendment XXII
[Adopted 1951]

Section 1

No person shall be elected to the office of the President more than twice, and no person who has held the office of President, or acted as President, for more than two years of a term to which some other person was elected President shall be elected to the office of the President more than once. But this Article shall not apply to any person holding the office of President when this Article was proposed by the Congress, and shall not prevent any person who may be holding the office of President, or acting as President, during the term within which this Article becomes operative from holding the office of President or acting as President during the remainder of such term.

Section 2

This article shall be inoperative unless it shall have been ratified as an amendment to the Constitution by the legislatures of three-fourths of the several States within seven years from the date of its submission to the States by the Congress.

Amendment XXIII
[Adopted 1961]

Section 1

The District constituting the seat of Government of the United States shall appoint in such manner as the Congress shall direct:

A number of electors of President and Vice President equal to the whole number of Senators and Representatives in Congress to which the District would be entitled if it were a State, but in no event more than the least populous State; they shall be in addition to those appointed by the States, but they shall be considered, for the purposes of the election of President and Vice President, to be electors appointed by a State; and they shall meet in the District and perform such duties as provided by the twelfth article of amendment.

Section 2

The Congress shall have power to enforce this article by appropriate legislation.

AMENDMENT XXIV
[ADOPTED 1964]

Section 1

The right of citizens of the United States to vote in any primary or other election for President or Vice President, for electors for President or Vice President, or for Senator or Representative in Congress, shall not be denied or abridged by the United States or any state by reason of failure to pay any poll tax or other tax.

Section 2

The Congress shall have the power to enforce this article by appropriate legislation.

AMENDMENT XXV
[ADOPTED 1967]

Section 1

In case of the removal of the President from office or his death or resignation, the Vice President shall become President.

Section 2

Whenever there is a vacancy in the office of the Vice President, the President shall nominate a Vice President who shall take the office upon confirmation by a majority vote of both houses of Congress.

Section 3

Whenever the President transmits to the President pro tempore of the Senate and the Speaker of the House of Representatives his written declaration that he is unable to discharge the powers and duties of his office, and until he transmits to them a written declaration to the contrary, such powers and duties shall be discharged by the Vice President as Acting President.

Section 4

Whenever the Vice President and a majority of either the principal officers of the executive departments or of such other body as Congress may by law provide, transmit to the President pro tempore of the Senate and the Speaker of the House of Representatives their written declaration that the President is unable to discharge the powers and duties of his office, the Vice President shall immediately assume the powers and duties of the office as Acting President.

Thereafter, when the President transmits to the President pro tempore of the Senate and the Speaker of the House of Representatives his written declaration that no inability exists, he shall resume the powers and duties of his office unless the Vice President and a majority of either the principal officers of the executive department or of such other body as Congress may by law provide, transmit within four days to the President pro tempore of the Senate and the Speaker of the House of Representatives their written declaration that the President is unable to discharge the powers and duties of his office. Thereupon Congress shall decide the issue, assembling within 48 hours for that purpose if not in session. If the Congress, within 21 days after receipt of the latter written declaration, or, if Congress is not in session, within 21 days after Congress is required to assemble, determines by two-thirds vote of both houses that the President is unable to discharge the powers and duties of his office, the Vice President shall continue to discharge the same as Acting President; otherwise, the President shall resume the powers and duties of his office.

AMENDMENT XXVI
[ADOPTED 1971]

Section 1

The right of citizens of the United States, who are 18 years of age or older, to vote shall not be denied or abridged by the United States or any state on account of age.

Section 2

The Congress shall have the power to enforce this article by appropriate legislation.

AMENDMENT XXVII
[ADOPTED 1992]

No law, varying the compensation for the services of the Senators and Representatives shall take effect, until an election of Representatives shall have intervened.

Recommended Reading

CHAPTER 1 | NEW WORLD ENCOUNTERS

The histories of three different peoples coming together for the first time in the New World has generated provocative interdisciplinary scholarship. Two excellent studies of encounters between Native Americans and Europeans—works that attempt to recapture the Indians' side of the story—are Inga Clendinnen, *Aztecs: An Interpretation* (1991), and James Axtell's pioneering ethnography, *The Invasion Within: The Contest of Cultures in Colonial North America* (1986). Other innovative books explore how early European invaders imagined the New World: Stephen Greenblatt, *Marvelous Possessions: The Wonder of the New World* (1991), and Anthony Pagden, *European Encounters with the New World: From Renaissance to Romanticism* (1992). For a readable introduction to the heated controversy over Columbus's proper standing in history, consider Kirkpatrick Sale, *The Conquest of Paradise: Christopher Columbus and the Columbian Legacy* (1990). For a good investigation of Indian culture in New Spain after the conquest, see Stuart B. Schwartz, *Victors and the Vanquished: Spanish and Nahua Views of the Conquest of Mexico* (1999).

CHAPTER 2 | ENGLAND'S COLONIAL EXPERIMENTS: THE SEVENTEENTH CENTURY

For a good survey of the political and economic development of England's thirteen mainland colonies, examine Milton Klein and Jacob Cooke, eds., *A History of the American Colonies in Thirteen Volumes* (1973–1986). Another useful overview of the field is Jack Greene and J. R. Pole, eds., *Colonial British America: Essays in the New History of the Early Modern Era* (1984).

Some of the most readable histories of early colonial settlement were written by actual participants. Two of seventeenth-century New England's celebrated leaders produced splendid accounts. See especially Bradford's *Of Plymouth Plantation,* edited by Samuel E. Morison (1952), and Winthrop's *Journal,* edited by Richard S. Dunn et al. (1996). For a tough-minded account of the ordeal of the first Jamestown colonists, turn to Captain John Smith, *A Selected Edition of His Writings,* edited by Karen O. Kupperman (1988).

CHAPTER 3 | PUTTING DOWN ROOTS: FAMILIES IN AN ATLANTIC EMPIRE

The most innovative research on topics covered in this chapter explores the history of New World slavery during the period before the American Revolution. Much of this literature is boldly interdisciplinary, providing not only a fresh comparative interpretation of the creation and development of African American cultures, but also a splendid insight into how imaginative scholars reconstruct the pasts of peoples who for a very long time have been denied a voice in mainstream histories. Among the most impressive recent works are Ira Berlin, *Many Thousands Gone: The First Two Centuries of Slavery in North America* (2000); Philip Morgan, *Slave Counterpoint: Black Culture in the Eighteenth-Century Chesapeake and Lowcountry* (1998); and Robin Blackburn, *The Making of New*

World Slavery, 1492–1800 (1997). These books owe a lot to several path-breaking studies that deserve careful attention: Winthrop D. Jordan, *White Over Black: American Attitudes Toward the Negro, 1550–1812* (1968), and Edmund S. Morgan, *American Slavery, American Freedom: The Ordeal of Colonial Virginia* (1975).

CHAPTER 4 | FRONTIERS OF EMPIRE: EIGHTEENTH-CENTURY AMERICA

Jon Butler provides a general introduction to the topics addressed in this chapter in *Becoming America: Revolution Before 1776* (2000). But one should not ignore Richard Hofstadter's brilliant, often disturbing discussion of class and race: *America at 1750: A Social Portrait* (1971). An analysis of European migration to British America can be found in Bernard Bailyn, *The Peopling of British North America: An Introduction* (1988). Commercial growth and population expansion are covered thoroughly in John J. McCusker and Russell R. Menard, *The Economy of British America, 1607–1789* (1985). The book that has redefined how we think about eighteenth-century Native American history is Richard White, *The Middle Ground: Indians, Empires, and Republics in the Great Lakes Region* (1991). Fred Anderson offers the most complete treatment of war and empire in *Crucible of War: The Seven Years' War and the Fate of Empire in British North America, 1754–1766* (2000).

CHAPTER 5 | THE AMERICAN REVOLUTION: FROM GENTRY PROTEST TO POPULAR REVOLT, 1763–1783

The American Revolution has generated a rich historiography. No sooner had the fighting ceased than the participants, Loyalists as well as Patriots, began to interpret the events leading to the creating of an independent republic. The most insightful book is David Ramsay's *The History of the American Revolution*, originally published in 1789 and recently reprinted in volumes edited by Lester H. Cohen (1990). A general guide to the period is provided by Jack P. Greene and J. R. Pole, eds., *The Blackwell Encyclopedia of the American Revolution* (1991); and John M. Faragher, ed., *The Encyclopedia of Colonial and Revolutionary America* (1996). Two reliable surveys are Merrill Jensen, *The Founding of a Nation: A History of the American Revolution, 1763–1776* (1968), and Edmund S. Morgan, *Birth of the Republic, 1763–1789*, rev. ed. (1992). Two books that transformed how an entire generation interpreted the Revolution are Edmund S. Morgan and Helen M. Morgan, *The Stamp Act Crisis: Prologue to Revolution* (1953), and Bernard Bailyn, *The Ideological Origins of the American Revolution* (1967).

CHAPTER 6 | THE REPUBLICAN EXPERIMENT

The drafting and ratification of the Constitution has generated many highly partisan interpretations by historians as well as legal scholars. The best way to comprehend the major issues debated at the Philadelphia Convention and then later at the separate state ratifying conventions is to examine the key documents of the period. One could do no better than reading James Madison, *Journal of the Federal Constitution* (reprinted in many modern editions), a detailed account of what actually occurred at the Convention, and Bernard Bailyn, ed., *The Debate on the Constitution: Federalists and Antifederalists Speeches, Articles, and Letters During the Struggle Over Ratification* (1993). Gordon S. Wood analyzed late-eighteenth-century republican political thought in his masterful *The Creation of the American Republic, 1776–1787* (1969), a work now supplemented by his provocative *Radicalism of the American Revolution* (1992). Three recent titles have helped define how we think about the political experience of the 1780s: Jack N. Rakove, *The Beginnings of*

National Politics: An Interpretive History of the Continental Congress (1979); Rakove, *Original Meanings: Politics and Ideas in the Making of the Constitution* (1996); and Peter Onuf, *Statehood and Union: A History of the Northwest Ordinance* (1987).

CHAPTER 7 | DEMOCRACY IN DISTRESS: THE VIOLENCE OF PARTY POLITICS, 1788–1800

Stanley Elkins and Eric McKitrick provides a detailed survey of the major political events of this period in *The Age of Federalism: The Early American Republic* (1993). More than any of the major political figures, Thomas Jefferson has generated interpretive scholarship. Merrill D. Peterson offers an encyclopedic account of Jefferson's day-to-day political activities in *Thomas Jefferson and the New Nation: A Biography* (1970). More recently, Joseph Ellis has attempted to explain the complex character of Jefferson's political thought: *American Sphinx: The Character of Thomas Jefferson* (1997). For thoughtful explorations of the ideological issues that divided Federalists and Republicans, one should look at Gordon Wood, *Radicalism of the American Revolution* (1993); Joyce Appleby, *Liberalism and Republicanism in Historical Imagination* (1992); and Drew McCoy, *The Elusive Republic: The Political Economy in Jeffersonian America* (1980). Still valuable for its imaginative treatment of the development of party politics during the 1790s is Richard Hofstadter, *The Idea of a Party System: The Rise of Legitimate Opposition in the United States, 1780–1840* (1969).

CHAPTER 8 | JEFFERSONIAN ASCENDANCY: THEORY AND PRACTICE OF GOVERNMENT

The best written and in many ways the fullest account of the first two decades of the nineteenth century remains Henry Adams's classic *History of the United States During the Administration of Jefferson and Madison*, 9 vols. (1889–1891). Anyone interested in the problems that Jefferson faced as president should start with Merrill D. Peterson, *Thomas Jefferson and the New Nation: A Biography* (1970), and Peter S. Onuf, *Jeffersonian America* (2001). A fine legal history can be found in Jean Edward Smith, *John Marshall: Definer of a Nation* (1996). A brilliant exploration of the evolution of republican ideas after the retirement of Madison is Drew R. McCoy, *The Last of the Founding Fathers: James Madison and the Republican Legacy* (1989). Nathan O. Hatch provides an excellent account of popular religion in *The Democratization of American Christianity* (1989). Laurel Ulrich has written a splendid study of a remarkable woman in the age of Jefferson: *A Midwife's Tale: The Life of Martha Balland, Based on Her Diary, 1785–1812* (1990). A fine account of the Lewis and Clark Expedition is Stephen Ambrose, *Undaunted Courage: Meriwether Lewis, Thomas Jefferson, and the Opening of the American West* (1996).

CHAPTER 9 | NATION BUILDING AND NATIONALISM

The standard surveys of the period between the War of 1812 and the age of Jackson are two works by George Dangerfield: *The Era of Good Feelings* (1952) and *Awakening of American Nationalism, 1815–1828* (1965); but see also the early chapters of Charles Sellers, *The Market Revolution: Jacksonian America, 1815–1846* (1991). For a positive account of the venturesome, entrepreneurial spirit of the age, see Joyce Appleby, *Inheriting the Revolution: The First Generations of Americans* (2000). Malcolm J. Rohrbough, *The Trans-Appalachian Frontier* (1978), is more comprehensive and authoritative. Outstanding studies of economic transformation and the rise of a market economy are George R. Taylor, *The Transportation Revolution, 1815–1860* (1951); Paul W. Gates, *The Farmer's Age: Agriculture, 1815–1860* (1960); Stuart Bruchey, *Growth of the Modern*

American Economy (1975); and Douglas C. North, *The Economic Growth of the United States, 1790–1860* (1961). The Marshall Court and legal and constitutional developments are covered in Robert K. Faulkner, *The Jurisprudence of John Marshall* (1968), and G. Edward White, *The Marshall Court and Cultural Change, 1815–1835* (1991). Samuel F. Bemis, *John Quincy Adams and the Foundations of American Policy* (1949), provides the classic account of the statesmanship that led to the Monroe Doctrine. But see also Ernest May, *The Making of the Monroe Doctrine* (1976), for a persuasive newer interpretation of how the doctrine originated.

Chapter 10 | The Triumph of White Men's Democracy

Arthur M. Schlesinger, Jr., *The Age of Jackson* (1945), sees Jacksonian democracy as a progressive protest against big business and stresses the participation of urban workers. Marvin Meyers, *The Jacksonian Persuasion: Politics and Belief* (1960), argues that Jacksonians appealed to nostalgia for an older America—"an idealized ancestral way" they believed was threatened by commercialization. Lee Benson, *The Concept of Jacksonian Democracy: New York as a Test Case* (1964), finds an ethnocultural basis for democratic allegiance. A sharply critical view of Jacksonian leadership—one that stresses opportunism, greed, and demagoguery—can be found in Edward Pessen, *Jacksonian America: Society, Personality, and Politics*, rev. ed. (1979). An excellent recent survey of Jacksonian politics is Harry L. Watson, *Liberty and Power* (1990), which stresses the crisis of "republicanism" at a time of "market revolution." Daniel Feller, *Jacksonian Promise: America, 1815–1840* (1995), focuses on the optimism that marked all sides of the political conflict and points to the similarities between the political parties. Development of the view that Jacksonianism was a negative reaction to the rise of market capitalism can be found in Charles Sellers, *The Market Revolution* (1991).

The classic study of the new party system is Richard P. McCormick, *The Second Party System: Party Formation in the Jacksonian Era* (1966). On who the anti-Jacksonians were, what they stood for, and what they accomplished, see Michael Holt's magisterial, *The Rise and Fall of the American Whig Party* (1999). James C. Curtis, *Andrew Jackson and the Search for Vindication* (1976), provides a good introduction to Jackson's career and personality. On Jackson's popular image, see John William Ward, *Andrew Jackson: Symbol for an Age* (1955). On the other towering political figures of the period, see Merrill D. Peterson, *The Great Triumvirate: Webster, Clay, and Calhoun* (1987). The culture of the period is well surveyed in Russel B. Nye, *Society and Culture in America, 1830–1860* (1960). Alexis de Tocqueville, *Democracy in America*, 2 vols. (1945), is a foreign visitor's wise and insightful analysis of American life in the 1830s.

Chapter 11 | The Pursuit of Perfection

Alice Felt Tyler, *Freedom's Ferment: Phases of American Social History from the Colonial Period to the Outbreak of the Civil War* (1944), gives a lively overview of the varieties of pre–Civil War reform activity. Ronald G. Walters, *American Reformers, 1815–1860*, rev. ed. (1997), provides a modern interpretation of these movements. Steven Mintz, *Moralists and Modernizers: America's Pre–Civil War Reformers* (1995), provides another good overview of the reform activities during this period. A particularly useful collection of documents on reform movements and other aspects of antebellum culture is David Brion Davis, *Antebellum American Culture: An Interpretive Anthology* (1979). The best general work on the revivalism of the Second Great Awakening is William G. McLoughlin, *Modern Revivalism* (1959). A general survey of the religious ferment of this period is Nathan O. Hatch, *The Democratization of American Christianity* (1989). Paul E. Johnson,

A Shopkeeper's Millennium: Society and Revivals in Rochester, New York, 1815–1837 (1978), incisively describes the impact of the revival on a single community. The connection between religion and reform is described in Robert H. Abzug, *Cosmos Crumbling: American Reform and the Religious Imagination* (1994). A good introduction to the changing roles of women and the family in nineteenth-century America is Carl N. Degler, *At Odds: Women and the Family in America from the Revolution to the Present* (1980). On the rise of the domestic ideology, see Nancy F. Cott, *The Bonds of Womanhood: "Woman's Sphere" in New England, 1780–1835* (1977). The condition of working-class women is incisively treated in Christine Stansell, *City of Women: Sex and Class in New York, 1789–1860* (1986).

David J. Rothman, *The Discovery of the Asylum: Social Order and Disorder in the New Republic* (1971), provides a penetrating analysis of the movement for institutional reform. On the foremost institutional reformer of the era, see Thomas J. Brown, *Dorothea Dix: New England Reformer* (1998). For good surveys of abolitionism, see James Brewer Stewart, *Holy Warriors: The Abolitionists and American Slavery* (1976), and Julie Roy Jeffrey, *The Great Silent Army of Abolitionism: Ordinary Women in the Antislavery Movement* (1998).

CHAPTER 12 | AN AGE OF EXPANSIONISM

An overview of expansion to the Pacific is Ray A. Billington, *The Far Western Frontier, 1830–1860* (1956). The impulse behind Manifest Destiny has been variously interpreted. Albert K. Weinberg's classic *Manifest Destiny: A Study of National Expansionism in American History* (1935) describes and stresses the ideological rationale. Frederick Merk, *Manifest Destiny and Mission in American History* (1963), analyzes public opinion and shows how divided it was on the question of territorial acquisitions. Norman A. Graebner, *Empire on the Pacific: A Study in American Continental Expansionism* (1956), highlights the desire for Pacific harbors as a motive for adding new territory. The most complete and authoritative account of the diplomatic side of expansionism in this period is David M. Pletcher, *The Diplomacy of Annexation: Texas, Oregon, and the Mexican War* (1973). Charles G. Sellers, *James K. Polk: Continentalist, 1843–1846* (1966), is the definitive work on Polk's election and the expansionist policies of his administration. A very good account of the Mexican-American War is John S. D. Eisenhower, *So Far from God: The U.S. War with Mexico* (1989). On the California gold rush, see Malcolm J. Rohrbough, *Days of Gold: The California Gold Rush and the American Nation* (1997).

Economic developments of the 1840s and 1850s are well covered in George R. Taylor, *The Transportation Revolution, 1815–1960* (1952), and Albert Fishlow, *American Railroads and the Transformation of the Ante-Bellum Economy* (1965). For an overview of immigration in this period, see the early chapters of Roger Daniels, *Coming to America: Immigration and Ethnicity in American Life* (1990). On the Irish, see Kerby A. Miller, *Emigrants and Exiles: Ireland and the Irish Exodus to America* (1985). Oscar Handlin, *Boston Immigrants: A Study in Acculturation,* rev. ed. (1959), is a classic study of immigration to one city. A standard work on the antebellum working class is Sean Wilentz, *Chants Democratic: New York City and the Rise of the American Working Class, 1788–1850* (1984); for the new approach to labor history that emphasizes working-class culture, see Herbert G. Gutman, *Work, Culture, and Society in Industrializing America* (1976). For the rich public life of antebellum cities, see Mary P. Ryan, *Civic Wars: Democracy and Public Life in the American City During the Nineteenth Century* (1997). A pathbreaking and insightful study of workers in the textile industry is Thomas Dublin, *Women at Work: The Transformation of Work and Community in Lowell, Massachusetts, 1826–1860* (1979).

CHAPTER 13 | MASTERS AND SLAVES

Major works that take a broad view of slavery are Kenneth M. Stampp, *The Peculiar Institution: Slavery in the Antebellum South* (1956), which stresses its coercive features; John W. Blassingame, *The Slave Community: Plantation Life in the Antebellum South* (1972), which focuses on slave culture and psychology; and Eugene D. Genovese, *Roll, Jordan, Roll: The World the Slaves Made* (1974), which probes the paternalistic character of the institution and the way in which slaves made a world for themselves within its bounds. For an overview of the history of slavery, see Peter Kolchin, *American Slavery, 1619–1877* (1993).

On the economics of slavery, see Gavin Wright, *The Political Economy of the Cotton South: Households, Markets, and Wealth in the Nineteenth Century* (1978). Clement Eaton, *The Growth of Southern Civilization, 1790–1860* (1961), provides a good introduction to life in the Old South. A more recent and insightful interpretation of antebellum southern society is James Oakes, *Slavery and Freedom: An Interpretation of the Old South* (1990). On the effect of slavery and the plantation on women, see Elizabeth Fox-Genovese, *Within the Plantation Household: Black and White Women of the Old South* (1988), and Deborah Gray White, *Ar'n't I a Woman: Female Slaves in the Plantation South* (1985). On the slave trade, see two excellent studies: Michael Tadman, *Speculators and Slaves: Masters, Traders, and Slaves in the Old South* (1989), and Walter Johnson, *Soul by Soul: Life Inside the Antebellum Slave Market* (1999).

Black resistance to slavery is described in Vincent Harding, *There Is a River: The Black Struggle for Freedom in America* (1981). Slave culture is examined in Albert J. Raboteau, *Slave Religion: The "Invisible Institution" in the Antebellum South* (1978); Herbert G. Gutman, *The Black Family in Slavery and Freedom, 1750–1925* (1976); Lawrence W. Levine, *Black Culture and Consciousness: Afro-American Folk Thought from Slavery to Freedom* (1977); and Sterling Stuckey, *Slave Culture: Nationalist Theory and the Foundations of Black America* (1987). A work that enriches the previously accepted conception of the black family under slavery is Brenda Stevenson, *Life in Black and White: Family and Community in the Slave South* (1996).

CHAPTER 14 | THE SECTIONAL CRISIS

The best general account of the politics of the sectional crisis is David M. Potter, *The Impending Crisis, 1848–1861* (1976). This well-written and authoritative work combines a vivid and detailed narrative of events with a shrewd and detailed interpretation of them. On the demise of the Whigs, see Michael F. Holt, *The Rise and Fall of the American Whig Party* (1999). The most important studies of northern political sectionalism are Eric Foner, *Free Soil, Free Labor, Free Men: The Ideology of the Republican Party Before the Civil War* (1970), and William E. Gienapp, *The Origins of the Republican Party, 1852–1856* (1987), on the Republican party generally; and Don E. Fehrenbacher, *Prelude to Greatness: Lincoln in the 1850s* (1962), on Lincoln's rise to prominence. On the background of southern separatism, see William W. Freehling, *The Road to Disunion: Secessionists at Bay, 1776–1854* (1990), and William L. Barney, *The Road to Secession: A New Perspective on the Old South* (1972).

CHAPTER 15 | SECESSION AND THE CIVIL WAR

The best one-volume history of the Civil War is James M. McPherson, *Battle Cry of Freedom: The Civil War Era* (1988). Other valuable surveys of the war and its aftermath are J. G. Randall and David Herbert Donald, *The Civil War and Reconstruction,* 2nd ed. (1969), and James M. McPherson, *Ordeal by Fire: The Civil War and Reconstruction* (1981). An excellent shorter account is

David Herbert Donald, *Liberty and Union* (1978). The Confederate experience is covered in Clement Eaton, *A History of the Southern Confederacy* (1954), and Emory M. Thomas, *The Confederate Nation, 1861–1865* (1979). Eaton stresses internal problems and weaknesses; Thomas highlights achievements under adversity. Gary W. Gallagher, *The Confederate War* (1997), argues, contrary to a common view, that the South lost the war simply because it was overpowered and not because of low morale or lack of a will to win. On the North's war effort, see Phillip Paludan, *A People's Contest: The Union and the Civil War, 1861–1865* (1988). The best one-volume introduction to the military side of the conflict is still Bruce Catton, *This Hallowed Ground: The Story of the Union Side of the Civil War* (1956).

Lincoln's career and wartime leadership are well treated in David Herbert Donald, *Lincoln* (1995). Another competent biography is Stephen B. Oates, *With Malice Toward None: The Life of Abraham Lincoln* (1977). A penetrating analysis of events immediately preceding the fighting is Kenneth M. Stampp, *And the War Came: The North and the Sectional Crisis* (1950). John Hope Franklin, *The Emancipation Proclamation* (1963), is a good short account of the North's decision to free the slaves. An incisive account of the transition from slavery to freedom is Barbara Jeanne Fields, *Slavery and Freedom on the Middle Ground: Maryland in the Nineteenth Century* (1985). The circumstances and activities of southern women during the war are covered in Drew Faust, *Mothers of Invention: Women of the Slaveholding States in the American Civil War* (1996). The experiences of northern women are described in Elizabeth D. Leonard, *Yankee Women: Gender Battles in the Civil War* (1994). Five leading historians offer conflicting interpretations in their attempts to explain the South's defeat in *Why the North Won the Civil War*, edited by David Donald (1960). A brilliant study of the writings of those who experienced the war is Edmund Wilson, *Patriotic Gore: Studies in the Literature of the American Civil War* (1962). On the intellectual impact of the war, see George M. Fredrickson, *The Inner Civil War: Northern Intellectuals and the Crisis of the Union*, 2nd ed. (1993).

CHAPTER 16 | THE AGONY OF RECONSTRUCTION

The best one-volume account of Reconstruction is Eric Foner, *Reconstruction: America's Unfinished Revolution* (1988). Two excellent short surveys are Kenneth M. Stampp, *The Era of Reconstruction, 1865–1877* (1965), and John Hope Franklin, *Reconstruction: After the Civil War* (1961). Both were early efforts to synthesize modern "revisionist" interpretations. W. E. B. DuBois, *Black Reconstruction in America, 1860–1880* (1935), remains brilliant and provocative. Reconsiderations of Reconstruction issues can be found in J. Morgan Kousser and James M. McPherson, eds., *Region, Race, and Reconstruction: Essays in Honor of C. Vann Woodward* (1982), and Eric Foner, *Nothing But Freedom: Emancipation and Its Legacy* (1983). Morton Keller, *Affairs of State: Public Life in Late Nineteenth Century America* (1977), provides an insightful analysis of American government and politics during Reconstruction and afterward. A perspective on the corruption of the period is provided by Mark Wahlgren Summers in *The Era of Good Stealings* (1993).

Formulation and implementation of northern policies on Reconstruction are covered in Eric L. McKitrick, *Andrew Johnson and Reconstruction, 1865–1867* (1960); William R. Brock, *An American Crisis: Congress and Reconstruction, 1865–1867* (1963); and William Gillette, *Retreat from Reconstruction, 1869–1879* (1979). Leon F. Litwack, *Been in the Storm So Long: The Aftermath of Slavery* (1979), provides a moving portrayal of the black experience of emancipation. On what freedom meant in economic terms, see Gerald David Jaynes, *Branches Without Roots: Genesis of the Black Working Class in the American South, 1862–1882* (1986). A work that focuses on ex-slaves' attempts to create their own economic order is Julie Saville, *The Work of Reconstruction: Free Slave to Wage Laborer in South Carolina, 1860–1870* (1994). The best overview of the postwar southern economy is Gavin Wright, *Old South, New South* (1986). The best introduction to the Grant era is William S. McFeeley, *Grant: A Biography* (1981). On the end of Reconstruction and the character of the post-Reconstruction South, see two classic works by C. Vann Woodward: *Reunion and Reaction,* rev. ed. (1956), and *Origins of the New South, 1877–1913* (1951). A good recent survey of the South after Reconstruction is Edward Ayers, *The Promise of the New South* (1992).

CHAPTER 17 | THE WEST: EXPLOITING AN EMPIRE

The best traditional account of the movement west is Ray Allen Billington, *Westward Expansion* (1967), which also has a first-rate bibliography. Walter Prescott Webb, *The Great Plains* (1931), offers a fascinating analysis of development on the Plains.

For examples of the work of "new Western historians," see Donald Worster, *Rivers of Empire* (1985), a powerful study of the "hydraulic" society, and his *Under Western Skies: Nature and History in the American West* (1992); William Cronon, *Nature's Metropolis: Chicago and the Great West* (1991), a provocative analysis of the relationship of Chicago and the West; Patricia Nelson Limerick, *The Legacy of Conquest* (1987); and Richard White, *"It's Your Misfortune and None of My Own": A History of the American West* (1991).

More recent authors have taken fresh and stimulating looks at older or ignored questions. Robert R. Dykstra, *The Cattle Towns* (1968), examines five Kansas cattle towns, with interesting results. Elliott West discusses childhood in *Growing Up with the Country: Childhood on the Far Western Frontier* (1989), and the Plains, in *The Contested Plains: Indians, Goldseekers, and the Rush to Colorado* (1998). Julie Roy Jeffrey, *Frontier Women: The Trans-Mississippi West* (1979); Joanna L. Stratton, *Pioneer Women: Voices from the Kansas Frontier* (1981); and Deena J. González, *Refusing the Favor: The Spanish-Mexican Women of Santa Fe, 1820–1880* (1999), are perceptive works on a neglected topic. John Mack Faragher, *Women and Men on the Overland Trail* (1979), and John Phillip Reid, *Law for the Elephant* (1980), examine relationships on the trails west.

CHAPTER 18 | THE INDUSTRIAL SOCIETY

Samuel P. Hays, *The Response to Industrialism: 1885–1914* (1957), is an influential interpretation of the period. Douglass C. North, *Growth and Welfare in the American Past: A New Economic History* (1966), is stimulating. David Montgomery, *The Fall of the House of Labor* (1987), is an outstanding study of labor in the period.

Alfred D. Chandler, *The Visible Hand: The Managerial Revolution in American Business* (1978); Olivier Zunz, *Making America Corporate, 1870–1920* (1990); and JoAnne Yates, *Control Through Communication: The Rise of System in American Management* (1989), are perceptive. The railroad empire is treated in John R. Stilgoe, *Metropolitan Corridor: Railroads and the American Scene* (1983); John Hoyt Williams, *A Great and Shining Road: The Epic Story of the Transcontinental Railroad* (1988); and John F. Stover, *American Railroads* (1961). On the steel industry, see Peter Temin, *Iron and Steel in Nineteenth-Century America* (1964).

Two superb books by Sam Bass Warner, Jr., *Streetcar Suburbs: The Process of Growth in Boston, 1870–1900* (1962), and *The Urban Wilderness: A History of the American City* (1973), examine technology and city development. The wage earner is examined in Herbert G. Gutman, *Work, Culture, and Society in Industrializing America* (1976). Two books by Stephan Thernstrom, *Poverty and Progress: Social Mobility in the Nineteenth-Century City* (1964) and *The Other Bostonians: Poverty and Progress in the American Metropolis, 1880–1970* (1973), examine mobility. Philip S. Foner, *Women and the American Labor Movement,* 2 vols. (1979); Susan E. Kennedy, *If All We Did Was to Weep at Home* (1979); Barbara Mayer Wertheimer, *We Were There: The Story of Working Women in America* (1977); and Alice Kessler-Harris, *Out to Work: A History of Wage-Earning Women in the United States* (1982), are excellent on the subject of women in the workplace.

CHAPTER 19 | TOWARD AN URBAN SOCIETY, 1877–1900

On urban America, see Sam Bass Warner, Jr., *Streetcar Suburbs* (1962) and *The Urban Wilderness* (1972). William R. Taylor, *In Pursuit of Gotham: Culture and Commerce in New York* (1992); Eric H. Monkkonen, *America Becomes Urban* (1988); and David Schuyler, *The New Urban Landscape* (1986), are also valuable. See also two books by Jon C. Teaford: *The Unheralded Triumph: City Government in America, 1870–1900* (1984) and *City and Suburb: The Political Fragmentation of Metropolitan America, 1850–1970* (1979).

For family life, see Joseph Kett, *Rites of Passage: Adolescence in America* (1977); Elaine Tyler May, *Great Expectations: Marriage and Divorce in Post-Victorian America* (1980); Steven Mintz, *A Prison of Expectations: The Family in Victorian Culture* (1983); Stephen M. Frank, *Life With Father: Parenthood and Masculinity in the Nineteenth-Century American North* (1998); and Norma Basch, *In the Eyes of the Law: Women, Marriage, and Property in Nineteenth-Century New York* (1982). Karen Lystra, *Searching the Heart: Women, Men, and Romantic Love in Nineteenth-Century America* (1989), is valuable.

Urban reform is examined in Judith Ann Trolander, *Professionalism and Social Change: From the Settlement House Movement to Neighborhood Centers, 1886 to the Present* (1987), and Allen F. Davis, *Spearheads for Reform: The Social Settlements and the Progressive Movement, 1890–1914* (1967), and *American Heroine: The Life and Legend of Jane Addams* (1973).

CHAPTER 20 | POLITICAL REALIGNMENTS IN THE 1890s

The best study of the 1890s depression is Charles Hoffman, *The Depression of the Nineties: An Economic History* (1970). H. Wayne Morgan, *From Hayes to McKinley: National Party Politics, 1877–1896* (1969), and Richard J. Jensen, *The Winning of the Midwest* (1971), are good on politics. David P. Thelen, *The New Citizenship: Origins of Progressivism in Wisconsin, 1885–1900* (1972), stresses the impact of the depression on ideas and attitudes. C. Vann Woodward examines the South in *Origins of the New South, 1877–1913* (1951). Studies of politics in the late nineteenth century include Glenn C. Altschuler and Stuart M. Blumin, *Rude Republic: Americans and Their Politics in the Nineteenth Century* (2000); Steven P. Reti, *Silver and Gold: The Political Economy of International Monetary Conferences, 1867–1892* (1998); Stephen Kantrowitz, *Ben Tillman and the Reconstruction of White Supremacy* (2000).

On Populism, see John D. Hicks, *The Populist Revolt* (1931), and Lawrence Goodwyn, *Democratic Promise: The Populist Moment in America* (1976). See also Victoria Saker Woeste, *The Farmer's Benevolent Trust: Law and Agricultural Cooperation in Industrial America, 1865–1945* (2000); Elizabeth Sanders, *Roots of Reform: Farmers, Workers, and the American State, 1877–1917* (1999); Marion K. Barthelme, (ed.), *Women in the Texas Populist Movement* (1997); and O. Gene Clanton, *Populism: The Humane Preference in America* (1991) and *Congressional Populism and the Crisis of the 1890's* (1999).

Social and labor unrest is covered in Almont Lindsey, *The Pullman Strike* (1942); Stanley Buder, *Pullman* (1967); Nick Salvatore, *Eugene V. Debs* (1982); and Shelton Stromquist, *A Generation of Boomers: The Pattern of Railroad Labor Conflict in Nineteenth-Century America* (1987).

CHAPTER 21 | TOWARD EMPIRE

The best general account of the development of American foreign policy during the last part of the nineteenth century is Walter LaFeber, *The New Empire: An Interpretation of American Expansion, 1860–1898* (1963). William Appleman Williams, *The Tragedy of American Diplomacy* (1959), examines the economic motives for expansion. See also Paul Wolman, *Most Favored Nation: The Republican Revisionists and U.S. Tariff Policy, 1897–1912* (1992). Lewis L. Gould persuasively reassesses McKinley's diplomacy and wartime leadership in *The Presidency of William McKinley* (1980).

Graham A. Cosmas presents a detailed account of military organization and strategy in *An Army for Empire: The United States Army in the Spanish-American War* (1971); Willard B. Gatewood, Jr., offers a fascinating glimpse of the thoughts of some black soldiers in the war in *"Smoked Yankees"and the Struggle for Empire: Letters from Negro Soldiers, 1898–1902* (1971). Gerald F. Linderman relates the war to the home front in *The Mirror of War: American Society and the Spanish-American War* (1974).

CHAPTER 22 | THE PROGRESSIVE ERA

There are several important analyses of the progressive era, including Robert H. Wiebe, *The Search for Order, 1877–1920* (1967); Richard Hofstadter, *The Age of Reform* (1955); Samuel P. Hays, *The Response to Industrialism* (1957); and Gabriel Kolko, *The Triumph of Conservatism* (1963). C. Vann Woodward, *Origins of the New South, 1877–1913* (1951), is a superb account of developments in the South, along with William A. Link, *The Paradox of Southern Progressivism, 1880–1930* (1992).

James T. Kloppenberg, *Uncertain Victory: Social Democracy and Progressivism in European and American Thought, 1870–1920* (1986), examines progressivism at home and abroad. C. Vann Woodward, *The Strange Career of Jim Crow* (1955), traces the civil rights setbacks of the Progressive Era.

Studies of youth, age, and family life include Joseph Kett, *Rites of Passage* (1977); Elizabeth J. Clapp, *Mothers of All Children: Women Reformers and the Rise of Juvenile Courts in Progressive Era America* (1998); Katrina Irving, *Immigrant Mothers: Narratives of Race and Maternity, 1890–1925* (2000); and Tamara K. Hareven, *Transitions: The Family and Life Course in Historical Perspective* (1978). See also Eleanor Flexner, *Century of Struggle: The Women's Rights Movement in the United States* (1959); Nan Enstad, *Ladies of Labor, Girls of Adventure: Working Women, Popular Culture, and Labor Politics at the Turn of the Twentieth Century* (1999); Gayle Gullett, *Becoming Citizens: The Emergence and Development of the California Women's Movement, 1880–1911* (1999); and Rosalyn Terborg-Penn, *African American Women in the Stuggle for the Vote, 1850–1920* (1998).

CHAPTER 23 | FROM ROOSEVELT TO WILSON IN THE AGE OF PROGRESSIVISM

George Mowry, *The Era of Theodore Roosevelt* (1958), and Arthur S. Link, *Woodrow Wilson and the Progressive Era* (1954), trace the social and economic conditions of the period. See also Henry F. Pringle's *Theodore Roosevelt* (1931) and John M. Blum's perceptive and brief *The Republican Roosevelt* (1954). The definitive biography of Wilson is Arthur S. Link, *Wilson,* 5 vols. (1947–1965).

Samuel P. Hays offers an influential interpretation of progressivism in *Conservation and the Gospel of Efficiency* (1959). Albro Martin, *Enterprise Denied: Origins of the Decline of American Railroads, 1897–1917* (1971), argues persuasively that reformers damaged as well as regulated. Samuel Haber, *The Quest for Authority and Honor in the American Professions, 1750–1900* (1991), examines the changing nature of the professions.

CHAPTER 24 | THE NATION AT WAR

American foreign policy between 1901 and 1921 has been the subject of considerable study. Richard W. Leopold, *The Growth of American Foreign Policy* (1962), is balanced and informed. Robert E. Osgood, *Ideals and Self-Interest in America's Foreign Relations* (1953), and William Appleman Williams, *Roots of the Modern American Empire* (1969), explore the forces underlying American foreign policy.

For American policy toward Latin America, see Dana G. Munro's detailed account, *Intervention and Dollar Diplomacy in the Caribbean, 1900–1920* (1964). Arthur S. Link examines Wilson's foreign policy in his exceptional five-volume biography, *Wilson* (1947–1965), and in *Woodrow Wilson: Revolution, War, and Peace* (1979).

Studies of events at home during the war include David M. Kennedy, *Over Here* (1980); Robert D. Cuff, *The War Industries Board* (1973); and Maurine W. Greenwald, *Women, War, and Work* (1980). Arthur Walworth, *America's Moment, 1918: American Diplomacy at the End of World War I* (1977), examines Wilson's attempt to create a peaceful world order.

CHAPTER 25 | TRANSITION TO MODERN AMERICA

William Leuchtenburg provides the best overview of the 1920s in *The Perils of Prosperity, 1914–1932* (1958). He stresses the theme of rural-urban conflict and claims that the achievements of the decade were more significant than its failures. The essays in John Braeman, Robert H. Bremner, and David Brody, eds., *Change and Continuity in Twentieth-Century America: The 1920s* (1968), illuminate important aspects of the period.

A fully detailed account of economic developments in the decade is George Soule, *Prosperity Decade* (1947). Two classic studies, Frederick Lewis Allen, *Only Yesterday* (1931), and Helen Lynd and Robert Lynd, *Middletown* (1929), offer valuable insights into social and cultural trends. The most recent overview of the decade is David J. Goldberg, *Discontented America* (1999).

The spirit of rural discontent with the new urban society is captured best in Lawrence Levine, *Defender of the Faith* (1965), an account of the last ten years of William Jennings Bryan's life. For changing political alignments of the 1920s, see David Burner, *The Politics of Provincialism* (1968).

CHAPTER 26 | FRANKLIN D. ROOSEVELT AND THE NEW DEAL

The best overall account of political developments in the 1930s is William Leuchtenburg, *Franklin D. Roosevelt and the New Deal* (1963). Leuchtenburg offers a balanced treatment but concludes by defending Roosevelt's record. For a more critical view, see James MacGregor Burns, *Roosevelt: The Lion and the Fox* (1956), which portrays FDR as an overly cautious political leader; and Robert A. McElvaine, *The Great Depression: America, 1929–1941* (1984), which laments the New Deal's failure to make more sweeping changes in American life.

David M. Kennedy provides a comprehensive portrait of American life during both the Great Depression and World War II in *Freedom from Fear* (1999). For a sympathetic examination of the New Deal through 1936, see Arthur M. Schlesinger, Jr., *The Age of Roosevelt*, 3 vols. (1957–1960); Paul Conkin offers a brief but provocative critique of Roosevelt's policies in *The New Deal* (1967). George McJimsy, *The Presidency of Franklin Delano Roosevelt* (2000), is the most recent and best-balanced account.

Chapter 27 | America and the World, 1921–1945

The best general account of American attitudes toward the world in the 1920s can be found in Warren I. Cohen, *Empire Without Tears* (1987). Robert Dallek provides a thorough account of FDR's diplomacy in *Franklin D. Roosevelt and American Foreign Policy, 1932–1945* (1979). For a more critical view, see Robert A. Divine, *Roosevelt and World War II* (1969).

Two good books on the continuing controversy over Pearl Harbor are Roberta Wohlstetter, *Pearl Harbor:Warning and Decision* (1962), and Gordon W. Prange, *At Dawn We Slept* (1981). Both authors deny the charge that Roosevelt deliberately exposed the naval base to attack.

In his brief overview of wartime diplomacy, *American Diplomacy During the Second World War,* 2nd ed. (1985), Gaddis Smith stresses the tensions within the victorious coalition. The best accounts of the home front are Richard Polenberg, *War and Society* (1972); John W. Blum, *V Was for Victory* (1976); and Doris Kearns Goodwin, *No Ordinary Time* (1995).

Chapter 28 | The Onset of the Cold War

The Cold War spawned a vast array of books, some enduring in nature and many that are already outdated. The best general guide to American diplomacy since World War II is Walter LaFeber, *America, Russia and the Cold War, 1945–1992,* 8th ed. (1997). On the much debated question of the origins of the Cold War, the most balanced account is Daniel Yergin, *Shattered Peace* (1977). John Lewis Gaddis, *We Now Know* (1997), integrates new disclosures from Soviet and Chinese archives to provide the best rounded account of the Cold War through the early 1960s.

The classic account of containment is still the lucid recollection of its chief architect, George Kennan, *Memoirs, 1925–1950* (1967). John Lewis Gaddis uses Kennan's ideas as a point of departure for his account of the changing nature of American Cold War policy in *Strategies of Containment* (1982). Melvyn P. Leffler offers a full account of the development of containment in *A Preponderance of Power* (1992). For developments in the Far East, consult the perceptive book by Akira Iriye, *The Cold War in Asia* (1974).

The best book on the Truman period is Alonzo L. Hamby, *Man of the People* (1995), which provides a balanced portrait of a controversial leader. Richard M. Fried offers a perceptive overview of the postwar anticommunist crusade in *Nightmare in Red:The McCarthy Era in Perspective* (1990).

Stephen A. Ambrose evaluates Dwight D. Eisenhower positively in the second volume of his biography, *Eisenhower: The President* (1985). For an equally favorable analysis, see Robert A. Divine, *Eisenhower and the Cold War* (1981).

Chapter 29 | Affluence and Anxiety

Two excellent books survey the social, cultural, and political trends in the United States during the postwar period. In *One Nation Divisible* (1980), Richard Polenberg analyzes class, ethnic, and racial changes; James T. Patterson offers a perceptive overview of American life from the end of World War II through the mid-1970s in *Grand Expectations* (1996).

Richard Pells provides a sweeping survey of the American intellectual community's response to the Cold War in *The Liberal Mind in a Conservative Age* (1985). The broadest account of American life during the decade is David Halberstam, *The Fifties* (1993).

Charles Alexander provides a balanced view of the Eisenhower years in *Holding the Line* (1975), portraying the Republican president as an able chief executive who was well suited to the times. Taylor Branch gives a comprehensive account of the genesis of the civil rights movement in

Parting the Waters: America in the King Years, 1954–1963 (1988). Three fine biographies—David L. Lewis's *King* (1970), Stephen B. Oates's *Let the Trumpet Sound* (1982), and David Garrow's *Bearing the Cross* (1986)—present perceptive portraits of Martin Luther King, Jr., the movement's most influential leader.

CHAPTER 30 | THE TURBULENT SIXTIES

The best general account of the 1960s is Jim F. Heath, *Decade of Disillusionment* (1975), which stresses the continuity in policy between the Kennedy and Johnson administrations. Richard Reeves offers a full account of Kennedy's White House years in *President Kennedy* (1993); the best study of Kennedy's foreign policy is Michael R. Beschloss, *The Crisis Years: Kennedy and Khrushchev, 1960–1963* (1991).

Robert Dallek offers a balanced view of Johnson's presidential years in *Flawed Giant* (1998); for LBJ's foreign policy, see H. W. Brands, *The Wages of Globalism* (1995). The best introduction to the Vietnam War is the balanced survey by George Herring, *America's Longest War,* 3rd ed. (1995). For contrasting views of Johnson's responsibility for the Vietnam conflict, see Fredrik Logevall, *Choosing War* (1999), highly critical, and Lloyd Gardner, *Pay Any Price* (1995), more understanding.

The most comprehensive account of the student protests is Terry Anderson, *The Movement and the Sixties* (1995). In *The Sixties* (1987), Todd Gitlin, a sociologist and former SDS leader, offers a sympathetic analysis of the motives and aspirations of the youthful protesters.

Garry Wills provides the most revealing portrait of Richard Nixon's character and prepresidential career in *Nixon Agonistes* (1970). The best account of the 1968 election is Lewis L. Gould, *1968: The Election That Changed America* (1993).

CHAPTER 31 | A CRISIS IN CONFIDENCE, 1969–1980

The most comprehensive account of Nixon's political career and presidency is the three-volume biography by Stephen E. Ambrose, *Nixon* (1987–1992). Melvin Small offers a balanced assessment of Nixon's White House years in *The Presidency of Richard Nixon* (1999).

Stanley Kutler provides a thorough account of the scandal that drove Nixon from office in *The Wars of Watergate* (1990). For foreign policy under Nixon, see William P. Bundy, *A Tangled Web* (1998), and Jeffrey Kimball, *Nixon's Vietnam War* (1998).

In *The Prize* (1991), Daniel Yergin puts the energy crisis of the 1970s in historical perspective. David Frum gives a lively overview of popular culture in *How We Got Here: The 70's* (2000). The best history of the Carter administration is Burton I. Kaufman, *The Presidency of Jimmy Carter* (1993).

CHAPTER 32 | THE REPUBLICAN RESURGENCE, 1980–1992

A British observer, Godfey Hodgson, gives a perceptive and balanced analysis of the conservative movement that led to Reagan's election in *The World Turned Right Side Up* (1996). The most detailed account of the Reagan presidency is the second volume of journalist Lou Cannon's biography, *President Reagan* (1991). Bob Schieffer and Gary Paul Gates offer a critical overview of the Reagan administration in *The Acting President* (1989), which focuses on Reagan's detached style of leadership.

The most revealing accounts by insiders are Martin Anderson, *Revolution* (1988), one of the few to give a positive view of the Reagan presidency, and George Shultz, *Turmoil and Triumph* (1992), the complete treatment of Reagan's foreign policy. John Robert Greene provides a balanced view of the Bush administration in *The Presidency of George Bush* (2000). For foreign policy, see George Bush and Brent Scowcroft, *A World Transformed* (1998).

CHAPTER 33 | AMERICA IN FLUX: THE ANXIOUS NINETIES

The best account of recent immigration into the United States from developing countries is David Reimers, *Still the Golden Door,* 2nd ed. (1992). Steven F. Lawson, *Running for Freedom* (1991), traces the growth of black participation in American politics since World War II, with special emphasis on the South.

British journalist Martin Walker gives a balanced account of Clinton's first term in *The President We Deserve* (1996). For the Lewinsky scandal and the impeachment proceedings, see Michael Isikoff, *Uncovering Clinton* (2000), and Richard A. Posner, *An Affair of State* (1999).

Suggested Web Sites

Vikings in the New World
http://www.anthro.mankato.msus.
edu/prehistory/vikings/vikhome.html
This site explores the history of some of the earliest European visitors to America.

Sir Francis Drake
http://www.mcn.org/2/oseeler/
drake.htm
This comprehensive site covers much of Drake's life and voyages.

Ancient Mesoamerican Civilizations
http://www.angelfire.com/ca/
humanorigins/index.html
Kevin L. Callahan of the University of Minnesota Department of Anthropology maintains this page that supplies information regarding Mesoamerican civilizations with well-organized essays and photos.

National Museum of the American Indian
http://www.si.edu/nmai
The Smithsonian Institution maintains this site, providing information about the museum. The museum is dedicated to everything about Native Americans.

1492: An Ongoing Voyage
http://metalab.unc.edu/expo/1492.
exhibit/Intro.html
An exhibit of the Library of Congress, Washington, D.C. With brief essays and images about early civilizations and contact in the Americas.

The Computerized Information Retrieval System on Columbus and the Age of Discovery
http://muweb.millersv.edu/
~columbus/
The History Department and Academic Computing Services of Millersville University, Pennsylvania, provide this text retrieval system containing more than 1000 text articles from various magazines, journals, newspapers, speeches, official calendars, and other sources relating to various encounter themes

Cahokia Mounds
http://medicine.wustl.edu/
~mckinney/cahokia/cahokia.html
The Cahokia Mounds State Historical Site gives information about a fascinating pre-Columbian culture in North America.

Mexico Pre-Columbian History
http://www.mexonline.com/
precolum.htm
This site "provides information on the Aztecs, Maya, Mexica, Olmecs, Toltec, Zapotecs and other pre-European cultures, as well as information on museums, archeology, language, and education."

White Oak Fur Post
http://www.whiteoak.org/
This site documents an eighteenth-century fur trading post among the Indians in what would become Minnesota.

The Search for La Salle's Ship La Belle
http://www.thc.state.tx.us/Belle/index.html
Texas Historical Commission site about the archaeological dig to recover the ship of one of America's famous early explorers.

The Discoverers' Web
http://www.win.tue.nl/cs/fm/engels/discovery/
Andre Engels maintains this complete collection of information on the various efforts at exploration.

CHAPTER 2 | ENGLAND'S COLONIAL EXPERIMENTS: THE SEVENTEENTH CENTURY

The Plymouth Colony Archive Project at the University of Virginia
http://www.people.virginia.edu/~jfd3a/
This site contains comprehensive and fairly extensive information about late seventeenth-century Plymouth Colony.

Jamestown Rediscovery
http://www.apva.org
This site mounted by the Association for the Preservation of Virginia Antiquity has excellent material on archaeological excavations at Jamestown.

Georgia Before Oglethorpe
http://members.aol.com/jeworth/gboindex.htm
This resources guide informs about Native American Georgia in the seventeenth century.

William Penn, Visionary Proprietor
http://xroads.virginia.edu/~CAP/PENN/pnhome.html
William Penn had an interesting life, and this site is a good introduction to the man and some of his achievements.

LVA Colonial Records Project—Index of digital facsimiles of documents on early Virginia
http://eagle.vsla.edu/colonial/
This site contains numerous early documents, but it is unguided and a little difficult to use.

CHAPTER 3 | PUTTING DOWN ROOTS: FAMILIES IN AN ATLANTIC EMPIRE

DPLS Archive: Slave Movement During the 18th and 19th Centuries (Wisconsin)
http://dpls.dacc.wisc.edu/slavedata/index.html
This site explores the slave ships and the slave trade that carried thousands of Africans to the New World.

Excerpts from Slave Narratives
http://vi.uh.edu/pages/mintz/primary.htm
Accounts of slavery from the seventeenth through nineteenth centuries speak volumes about the many impacts of slavery.

Witchcraft in Salem Village
http://etext.virginia.edu/salem/witchcraft/
Extensive archive of the 1692 trials and life in late seventeenth-century Massachusetts.

Salem Witchcraft Trials (1692)
http://www.law.umkc.edu/faculty/projects/ftrials/salem/salem.htm
Images chronology, court, and official documents by Dr. Doug Linder at University of Missouri–Kansas City Law School.

Colonial Documents
http://www.yale.edu/lawweb/avalon/
18th.htm
The key documents of the Colonial Era are re-produced here, as are some important documents from earlier and later periods in American history.

LVA Colonial Records Project—Index of digital facsimiles of documents on early Virginia
http://eagle.vsla.edu/colonial/
This site contains numerous early documents, but it is unguided and a little difficult to use.

CHAPTER 4 | FRONTIERS OF EMPIRE:
EIGHTEENTH-CENTURY AMERICA

History Buff's Reference Library
http://www.discovery.com/guides/
history/historybuff.html
Brief journalistic essays on newspaper cover-age of sixteenth- to eighteenth-century American history.

Benjamin Franklin Documentary History Web Site
http://www.english.udel.edu/lemay/
franklin/
University of Delaware professor J. A. Leo LeMay tells the story of Franklin's varied life in seven parts on this intriguing site.

Jonathan Edwards
http://www.jonathanedwards.com/
Speeches by this famous preacher of the Great Awakening are on this site.

Religion and the Founding of the American Republic
http://lcweb.loc.gov/exhibits/
religion/religion.html
This Library of Congress site is an on-line ex-hibit about religion and the creation of the United States.

Smithsonian Institution
http://www.americanhistory.si.edu/
hohr/springer
Part of the Smithsonian's on-line museum, this exhibit enables students to examine artifacts from the home of New Castle, Delaware, resi-dents Thomas and Elizabeth Springer and in-terpret the lives of a late eighteenth-century American family.

National Museum of the American Indian
http://www.si.edu/nmai
The Smithsonian Institution maintains this site, providing information about the mu-seum. The museum is dedicated to everything about Native Americans.

The French and Indian War
http://digitalhistory.org
Digital History LTD provides extensive archives in this site not intended for an exclu-sively academic audience.

The French and Indian War
http://web.syr.edu/~laroux/
This site is about French soldiers who came to New France between 1755 and 1760 to fight in the French and Indian War.

DoHistory, Harvard University Film Study Center
http://www.dohistory.org/
Focusing on the life of Martha Ballard, a late eighteenth-century New England woman, this site employs selections from her diary, ex-cerpts from a book and film of her life, and other primary documents to enable students to conduct their own historical investigation.

CHAPTER 5 | THE AMERICAN REVOLUTION: FROM GENTRY PROTEST TO POPULAR REVOLT, 1763–1783

Canada History
http://www.civilization.ca/index1e.html
Canada and the United States shared a colonial past but developed differently in the long run. This site is a part of the virtual museum of the Canadian Museum of Civilization Corporation.

Georgia's Rare Map Collection
http://scarlett.libs.uga.edu/darchive/hargrett/maps/colamer.html
http://scarlett.libs.uga.edu/darchive/hargrett/maps/revamer.html
These two sites contain maps for Colonial and Revolutionary America.

Maryland Loyalists and the American Revolution
http://www.erols.com/candidus/index.htm
This look at Maryland's loyalists promotes the author's book, but the site has good information about an underappreciated phenomenon, including loyalist songs and poems.

The American Revolution
http://revolution.h-net.msu.edu/
This site accompanies the PBS series *Revolution* with essays and resource links.

CHAPTER 6 | THE REPUBLICAN EXPERIMENT

The Leslie Brock Center for the Study of Colonial Currency
http://www.virginia.edu/~econ/brock.html
This site includes both useful primary and secondary documents on early American currency.

Northwest Territory Alliance
http://www.nwta.com/main.html
This Revolutionary Era reenactment organization site contains several links and is an interesting look at historical reenactment.

Independence Hall National Historical Park
http://www.nps.gov/inde/visit.html
This site includes images and historical accounts of Independence Hall and other Philadelphia buildings closely associated with the nation's founding.

Biographies of the Founding Fathers
http://www.colonialhall.com/
This site provides interesting information about the men who signed the Declaration of Independence and includes a trivia section.

The Federalist Papers
http://www.law.emory.edu/FEDERAL/federalist/
This site is a collection of the most important Federalist Papers, a series of documents designed to convince people to support the new Constitution and the Federalist party.

The Constitution and the Amendments
http://www.law.emory.edu/FEDERAL/usconst.html
This is a searchable site to the Constitution, especially useful for its information about the Bill of Rights and other constitutional amendments.

Documents from the Continental Congress and the Constitutional Convention, 1774–1789
http://memory.loc.gov/ammem/
bdsds/bdsdhome.html
The Continental Congress Broadside Collection (253 titles) and the Constitutional Convention Broadside Collection (21 titles) contain 274 documents relating to the work of Congress and the drafting and ratification of the Constitution. Items include extracts of the journals of Congress, resolutions, proclamations, committee reports, treaties, and early printed versions of the United States Constitution and the Declaration of Independence. Most broadsides are one page long; others range from one to twenty-eight pages.

CHAPTER 7 | DEMOCRACY IN DISTRESS: THE VIOLENCE OF PARTY POLITICS, 1788–1800

Temple of Liberty—Building the Capitol for a New Nation
http://www.lcweb.loc.gov/exhibits/
us.capitol/s0.html
Compiled from holdings in the Library of Congress, this site contains detailed information on the design and early construction of the Capitol building in Washington, DC.

The Electoral College
http://www.nara.gov/fedreg/elctcoll/
index.html
This National Archives and Records Administration site explains how the electoral college works.

George Washington Papers
http://www.virginia.edu/gwpapers/
Information on the publishing project, with selected documents, essays, and an index of the published volumes.

George Washington at Home
http://www.mountvernon.org/
Pictures and documents of Mount Vernon, the home of the first president, George Washington.

George Washington Papers at the Library of Congress, 1741–1799
http://memory.loc.gov/ammem/
gwhtml/gwhome.html
This site is "the complete George Washington Papers from the Manuscript Division at the Library of Congress consists of approximately 65,000 documents. This is the largest collection of original Washington documents in the world."

Archiving Early America
http://earlyamerica.com/
Old newspapers are excellent windows into the issues of the past. This site includes the Keigwin and Matthews collection of historic newspapers.

John Adams
http://www.whitehouse.gov/WH/
glimpse/presidents/html/ja2.html
This site contains biographical information about the second president, his inaugural address, and links to his more quotable phrases.

CHAPTER 8 | JEFFERSONIAN ASCENDANCY: THEORY AND PRACTICE OF GOVERNMENT

Thomas Jefferson
http://www.pbs.org/jefferson/
A companion site to the Public Broadcasting Service series on Jefferson, especially important because it contains a fine collection of other people's views of Jefferson.

Some Writings of Thomas Jefferson
http://www.geocities.com/Athens/
Forum/9061/USA/early/jeff.html
This site features many of Jefferson's noted writings as well as some that are less well known.

White House Historical Association
http://www.whitehousehistory.org/whha/default.asp
This site contains a timeline of the history of the White House and several interesting photos and links.

Thomas Jefferson on Politics and Government
http://etext.virginia.edu/jefferson/quotations/
Selected quotations from Jefferson that reveal a strong libertarian bent make up this topical Web site.

Thomas Jefferson On-line Resources at the University of Virginia
http://etext.virginia.edu/jefferson/
Mr. Jefferson's University—the University of Virginia—houses this site with numerous on-line resources about Jefferson and his times.

The Jefferson Bibliography Database
http://etext.virginia.edu/jefferson/bibliog/
This invaluable site compiles and annotates a bibliography of works on Jefferson from 1826 to 1990.

Exploring the West from Monticello: An Exhibition of Maps and Navigational Instruments
http://www.lib.virginia.edu/exhibits/lewis_clark/home.html
Maps and charts reveal knowledge and conceptions about the known and the unknown. This site includes a number of eighteenth-century maps.

Lewis and Clark PBS Web site from PBS
http://www.pbs.org/lewisandclark/
This is a companion site to Ken Burns' containing a timeline of the expedition, a collection of related links, a bibliography, and more than 800 minutes of unedited, full-length RealPlayer interviews with seven experts featured in the film.

The War of 1812
http://members.tripod.com/~war1812/index.html
In-depth and varied information about the War of 1812.

CHAPTER 9 | NATION BUILDING AND NATIONALISM

The Era of the Mountain Men
http://www.xmission.com/~drudy/amm.html
Private letters can speak volumes about the concerns and environment of the writers and recipients. Letters from early settlers west of the Mississippi River are offered on this site.

Prairietown, Indiana
http://www.indianapolis.in.us/cp/stories.html
This fictional model of a town and its inhabitants on the early frontier says much about America's movement westward and the everyday lives of Americans.

The Seminole Indians of Florida
http://www.seminoletribe.com/
Before he was president, Andrew Jackson began a war against the Seminole Indians.

Erie Canal On-line
http://www.syracuse.com/features/eriecanal
This site, built around the diary of a fourteen-year-old girl who traveled from Amsterdam to Syracuse, New York, in the early nineteenth century, explores the construction and importance of the Erie Canal.

Whole Cloth: Discovering Science and Technology Through American Textile History
http://www.si.edu/lemelson/centerpieces/whole_cloth/
The Jerome and Dorothy Lemelson Center for the Study of Invention and Innovation/Society for the History of Technology put together this site, which includes excellent activities and sources concerning early American manufacturing and industry.

The National Road
http://www.connerprairie.org/ntlroad.html
The National Road was a hot political topic in the Early Republic and was part of the beginning of the development of America's infrastructure.

CHAPTER 10 | THE TRIUMPH OF WHITE MEN'S DEMOCRACY

Indian Affairs: Laws and Treaties, compiled and edited by Charles J. Kappler (1904)
http://www.library.okstate.edu/kappler
This digitized text at Oklahoma State University includes preremoval treaties with the Five Civilized Tribes and other tribes.

Jacksonian Era Medicine and Life
http://www.indianapolis.in.us/cp/jmed.html
Survival was far from certain in the Jacksonian Era. This site discusses some of the reasons and some of the possible cures of the times.

The University of Pennsylvania In 1830
http://www.upenn.edu/1830/
This "virtual tour" shows what a fairly typical campus looked like and what student life was like at one of the larger universities in the Antebellum Era.

19th Century Scientific American On-line
http://www.history.rochester.edu/Scientific_American/
Magazines and journals are windows through which we can view society. This site provides on-line editions of one of the more interesting nineteenth-century journals.

National Museum of the American Indian
http://www.si.edu/nmai
The Smithsonian Institution maintains this site, providing information about the museum, which is dedicated to everything about Native Americans.

The Alexis de Tocqueville Tour: Exploring Democracy in America
http://www.tocqueville.org/
Text, images, and teaching suggestions are a part of this companion site to C-SPAN's recent programming on de Tocqueville.

CHAPTER 11 | THE PURSUIT OF PERFECTION

America's First Look into the Camera: Daguerreotype Portraits and Views, 1839–1862
http://memory.loc.gov/ammem/daghtml/daghome.html
The Library of Congress's daguerreotype collection consists of more than 650 photographs dating from 1839 to 1864. Portraits, architectural views, and some street scenes make up most of the collection.

1830s Clothing
http://www.connerprairie.org/clothing.html
See how clothing worn in the Early Republic was quite different from what people wear today.

Votes for Women: Selections from the National American Woman Suffrage Association Collection, 1848–1921
http://memory.loc.gov/ammem/naw/nawshome.html

This Library of Congress site contains 167 books, pamphlets, and other artifacts documenting the suffrage campaign.

History of the Suffrage Movement
http://www.rochester.edu/SBA

This site includes a chronology, important texts relating to women's suffrage, and biographical information about Susan B. Anthony and Elizabeth Cady Stanton.

By Popular Demand: "Votes for Women" Suffrage Pictures, 1850–1920
http://memory.loc.gov/ammem/vfwhtml/vfwhome.html

Portraits, suffrage parades, picketing suffragists, an antisuffrage display, and cartoons commenting on the movement make up this Library of Congress site.

Women in America, 1820 to 1842
http://xroads.virginia.edu/~HYPER/DETOC/FEM/home.htm

This University of Virginia site takes a look at women in antebellum America.

Godey's Lady's Book On-line
http://www.history.rochester.edu/godeys/

Here is on-line text of this interesting nineteenth-century journal.

Important Black Abolitionists
http://www.loc.gov/exhibits/african/influ.html

An exhibit site from the Library of Congress, with pictures and text, which discusses some key African American abolitionists and their efforts to end slavery.

CHAPTER 12 | AN AGE OF EXPANSIONISM

Pioneering the Upper Midwest: Books from Michigan, Minnesota, and Wisconsin, ca. 1820–1910
http://memory.loc.gov/ammem/umhtml/umhome.html

This Library of Congress site looks at first-person accounts, biographies, promotional literature, local histories, ethnographic and antiquarian texts, colonial archival documents, and other works from the seventeenth to the early twentieth century. It covers many topics and issues that affected Americans in the settlement and development of the Upper Midwest.

The Mexican-American War Memorial Homepage
http://sunsite.dcaa.unam.mx/revistas/1847/

Images and text explain the causes, courses, and outcomes of the Mexican-American War.

On the Trail in Kansas
http://www.ukans.edu/carrie/kancoll/galtrl.htm

This Kansas Collection site holds several good primary sources with images concerning the Oregon trail and America's early movement westward.

The Era of the Mountain Men
http://www.xmission.com/~drudy/amm.html

Private letters can speak volumes about the concerns and environment of the writers and recipients. Letters from early settlers west of the Mississippi River are offered on this site.

CHAPTER 13 | MASTERS AND SLAVES

"Been Here So Long": Selections from the WPA American Slave Narratives
http://newdeal.feri.org/asn/index.htm
Slave narratives are some of the more interesting primary sources about slavery.

Exploring Amistad
http://amistad.mysticseaport.org/main/welcome.html
Mystic Seaport runs this site that includes extensive collections of historical resources relating to the revolt and subsequent trial of enslaved Africans.

Africans in America: America's Journey Through Slavery
http://www.pbs.org/wgbh/aia/home.html
This PBS site contains images and documents recounting the slavery in America.

Amistad Trials (1839–1840)
http://www.law.umkc.edu/faculty/projects/ftrials/amistad/AMISTD.HTM
Images, chronology, and court and official documents comprise this site by Dr. Doug Linder at University of Missouri–Kansas City Law School.

Slave Narratives
http://docsouth.unc.edu/neh/neh.html
This site presents the telling narratives of several slaves housed at the Documents of the American South collection and the University of North Carolina.

The Settlement of African Americans in Liberia
http://www.loc.gov/exhibits/african/perstor.html
This site contains images and text relating to the colonization movement to return African Americans to Africa.

Images of African Americans from the Nineteenth Century
http://digital.nypl.org/schomburg/images_aa19/
The New York Public Library–Schomburg Center for Research in Black Culture site contains numerous visuals.

CHAPTER 14 | THE SECTIONAL CRISIS

Secession Era Editorials Project
http://history.furman.edu/~benson/docs/
Furman University is digitizing editorials about the secession crisis and already includes scores of them on this site.

John Brown Trial Links
http://www.law.umkc.edu/faculty/projects/ftrials/Brown.html
For information about the trial of John Brown, this site provides a list of excellent links.

Abraham Lincoln and Slavery
http://odur.let.rug.nl/~usa/H/1990/ch5_p6.htm
This site discusses Lincoln's views and actions concerning slavery, especially the Lincoln-Douglas debate.

Bleeding Kansas
http://www.ukans.edu/carrie/kancoll/galbks.htm
Contemporary and later accounts of America's rehearsal for the Civil War comprise this University of Kansas site.

The Compromise of 1850 and the Fugitive Slave Act

http://www.pbs.org/wgbh/aia/part4

From the series on Africans in America, an analysis of the Compromise of 1850 and of the effects of the Fugitive Slave Act on black Americans.

The 1850s: An Increasingly Divided Union

http://nac.gmu.edu/mmts/50proto.html

A tutorial skills development site focusing on the events in the 1850s leading to the Civil War; from MMTS, the Multi-Media Thinking Skills project.

Words and Deeds in American History

http://lcweb2.loc.gov/ammem/mcchtml/corhome.html

A Library of Congress site containing links to Frederick Douglass; the Compromise of 1850; speeches by John C. Calhoun, Daniel Webster, and Henry Clay; and other topics from the Civil War era.

CHAPTER 15 | SECESSION AND THE CIVIL WAR

The American Civil War Homepage

http://sunsite.utk.edu/civil-war/warweb.html

This site has a great collection of hypertext links to the most useful identified electronic files about the American Civil War.

The Valley of the Shadow: Living the Civil War in Pennsylvania and Virginia

http://jefferson.village.virginia.edu/vshadow/vshadow.html

This project tells the histories of two communities on either side of the Mason-Dixon line during the Civil War. It includes narrative and an electronic archive of sources.

Civil War @ Charleston

http://www.awod.com/gallery/probono/cwchas/cwlayout.html

This site covers the history of the Civil War in and around Charleston, South Carolina.

Abraham Lincoln Association

http://www.alincolnassoc.com/

This site allows the search of digital versions of Lincoln's papers.

Crisis at Fort Sumter

http://www.tulane.edu/~latner/CrisisMain.html

This well-crafted use of hypermedia with assignments or problems explains and explores the events in and around the start of the Civil War.

U.S. Civil War Center

http://www.cwc.lsu.edu/

This is a site whose mission is to "locate, index, and / or make available all appropriate private and public data regarding the Civil War and to promote the study of the Civil War from the perspectives of all professions, occupations, and academic disciplines."

The Papers of Jefferson Davis Home Page

http://www.ruf.rice.edu/~pjdavis/jdp.htm

This site tells about the collection of Jefferson Davis Papers and includes a chronology of his life, a family genealogy, some key Davis documents on-line, and a collection of related links.

History of African Americans in the Civil War
http://www.itd.nps.gov/cwss/history/aa_history.htm

This National Park Service site explores the history of the United States Colored Troops.

Civil War Women
http://scriptorium.lib.duke.edu/collections/civil-war-women.html

This site includes original documents, links, and biographical information about several women and their lives during the Civil War.

Assassination of President Abraham Lincoln
http://memory.loc.gov/ammem/alhtml/alrintr.html

Part of the American Memory series with introduction, timeline, and gallery.

Selected Civil War Photographs
http://lcweb2.loc.gov/ammem/cwphome.html

Library of Congress site with more than 1,000 photographs, many from Matthew Brady.

A Timeline of the Civil War
http://www.historyplace.com/civilwar/index.html

A complete timeline of the Civil War, well illustrated with photographs.

National Civil War Association
http://www.ncwa.org/info.html

One of the many Civil War Reenactment organizations in the United States.

CHAPTER 16 | THE AGONY OF RECONSTRUCTION

Diary and Letters of Rutherford B. Hayes
http://www.ohiohistory.org/onlinedoc/hayes/index.cfm

The Rutherford B. Hayes Presidential Center in Fremont, Ohio, maintains this searchable database of Hayes's writings.

Images of African Americans from the 19th Century
http://digital.nypl.org/schomburg/images_aa19/

The New York Public Library–Schomburg Center for Research in Black Culture site contains numerous visuals.

Freedmen and Southern Society Project (University of Maryland, College Park)
http://www.inform.umd.edu/ARHU/Depts/History/Freedman/home.html

This site contains a chronology and sample documents from several print collections or primary sources about emancipation and freedom in the 1860s.

Andrew Johnson
http://www.whitehouse.gov/WH/glimpse/presidents/html/aj17.html

White House history of Johnson.

Ulysses S. Grant
http://www.whitehouse.gov/WH/glimpse/presidents/html/ug18.html

White House history of Grant.

History of the Suffrage Movement
http://www.rochester.edu/SBA

This site includes a chronology, important texts relating to woman suffrage, and biographical information about Susan B. Anthony and Elizabeth Cady Stanton.

Chapter 17 | The West: Exploiting an Empire

Indian Affairs: Laws and Treaties, compiled and edited by Charles J. Kappler (1904)
http://www.library.okstate.edu/kappler
This digitized text at Oklahoma State University includes preremoval treaties with the Five Civilized Tribes and other tribes.

Native American Documents Project
http://www.csusm.edu/projects/nadp/nadp.htm
California State University at San Marcos has several digital documents relating to Native Americans on this site.

Geronimo
http://odur.let.rug.nl/~usa/B/geronimo/geronixx.htm
This site contains biographical and autobiographical information about the famous Native American who resisted European American domination.

National Museum of the American Indian
http://www.si.edu/nmai
The Smithsonian Institution maintains this site, providing information about the museum. The museum is dedicated to everything about Native Americans.

The Northern Great Plains, 1880–1920: Photographs from the Fred Hultstrand and F. A. Pazandak Photograph Collections
http://memory.loc.gov/ammem/award97/ndfahtml/ngphome.html
This American Memory site from the Library of Congress contains "two collections from the Institute for Regional Studies at North Dakota State University" with "900 photographs of rural and small town life at the turn of the century." Included are "images of sod homes and the people who built them; images of farms and the machinery that made them

prosper; and images of one-room schools and the children that were educated in them."

On the Trail in Kansas
http://www.ukans.edu/carrie/kancoll/galtrl.htm
This Kansas Collection site holds several good primary sources with images concerning the Oregon trail and America's early movement westward.

"California as I Saw It": First-Person Narratives of California's Early Years, 1849–1900
http://memory.loc.gov/ammem/cbhtml/cbhome.html
This site is a part of the American Memory series and contains "full texts and illustrations of 190 works documenting the formative era of California's history through eyewitness accounts." It covers the Gold Rush, the interaction of various groups, and the settling of the region.

Home on the Range/Cowboy Heritage
http://history.cc.ukans.edu/heritage/old_west/cowboy.html
This site tells the history of the cattle trails and towns such as Dodge City, with useful text, links, documents, and maps.

The Evolution of the Conservation Movement, 1850–1920
http://memory.loc.gov/ammem/amrvhtml/conshome.html
This American Memory site brings together scores of primary sources and photographs about "the historical formation and cultural foundations of the movement to conserve and protect America's natural heritage."

Heroes and Villains in Kansas
http://www.ukans.edu/carrie/kancoll/galhero.htm
The Kansas Collection Gallery of both famous and little-known people who made up the history of the state.

CHAPTER 18 | THE INDUSTRIAL SOCIETY

Alexander Graham Bell Family Papers at the Library of Congress
http://memory.loc.gov/ammem/
bellhtml/bellhome.html
This site contains papers from 1862 to 1939, but includes a chronology, images, selected documents, and interpretive essays about Bell.

The Richest Man in the World: Andrew Carnegie
http://www.pbs.org/wgbh/amex/
carnegie/
This American Experience/PBS site provides images and text about Carnegie's life and activities.

Anarchist Archive at Pitzer University
http://dwardmac.pitzer.edu/
Anarchist_Archives/archivehome.html
This archive includes classic anarchist texts, especially information about and graphics of the Haymarket Riot.

John D. Rockefeller and the Standard Oil Company
http://www.micheloud.com/FXM/SO/
This study with accompanying images by François Micheloud tells of the rise of Rockefeller and his mammoth company.

National Refinery Company
http://www.enarco.com/

This positive history of the company reflects the industrial changes of late-nineteenth-century America.

A Short History of American Labor
http://www.unionweb.org/
history.htm
This brief essay is adapted from AFL-CIO *American Federationist,* March 1981.

American Labor History
http://www.geocities.com/CollegePar
k/Quad/6460/AmLabHist/index.html
This site takes a general look at the history of labor in America.

Labor-Management Conflict in American History
http://www.history.ohio-state.edu/
projects/laborconflict/
This Ohio State University site includes primary accounts of some of the major events in the history of labor-management conflict in the late nineteenth and early twentieth centuries.

Samuel Gompers Papers at the University of Maryland
http://www.inform.umd.edu/HIST/
Gompers/web1.html
This site includes information about the papers project but also has a photo gallery, selected documents, and a brief history of the first president of the American Federation of Labor.

CHAPTER 19 | TOWARD AN URBAN SOCIETY, 1877–1900

The American Experience: America 1900
http://www.pbs.org/wgbh/amex/
1900/
Companion to the PBS documentary, this site includes audio clips of respected historians on the economics, politics, and culture of 1900, a primary source database, a timeline of the

year, downloadable software to compile a family tree, and other materials.

Touring Turn-of-the-Century America: Photographs from the Detroit Publishing Company, 1880–1920
http://memory.loc.gov/ammem/
detroit/dethome.html

This Library of Congress collection has thousands of photographs from turn-of-the-century America.

World's Columbian Exposition: Idea, Experience, Aftermath
http://xroads.virginia.edu/~MA96/WCE/title.html
This site has a virtual tour of the fair, along with contemporary reactions and modern analysis.

United States History: The Gilded Age (1890) to World War 1
http://www.emayzine.com/lectures/Gilded~1.htm
This site consists of a good overview essay of the era.

The Gilded Page
http://www.em.edu/~srnels/gilded.html

This site has links to scores of Gilded Age and Progressive Era documents.

Chapter Three: American Socialists and Reformers
http://www.vineyard.net/vineyard/history/pdgech3.htm
This site includes a fine essay about Edward Bellamy and some of the movements and ideas he inspired.

African American Perspectives: Pamphlets from the Daniel A. P. Murray Collection, 1818–1907
http://memory.loc.gov/ammem/aap/aaphome.html
This collection includes writings of famous African Americans, including Frederick Douglass, Booker T. Washington, Ida B. Wells-Barnett, Benjamin W. Arnett, Alexander Crummel, and Emanuel Love.

CHAPTER 20 | POLITICAL REALIGNMENTS IN THE 1890s

World's Columbian Exposition: Idea, Experience, Aftermath
http://xroads.virginia.edu/~MA96/WCE/title.html
This site has a virtual tour of the fair, along with contemporary reactions and modern analysis.

Election of 1896
http://jefferson.village.virginia.edu/seminar
This University of Virginia site contains biographical information, images, cartoons, and related links about the pivotal 1896 election.

The Era of William McKinley
http://www.history.ohio-state.edu/projects/mckinley/default.htm
This site contains numerous images from various stages of William McKinley's career along with a brief biographical essay. This Ohio State University site also has a section with an excellent collection of cartoons from the era.

CHAPTER 21 | TOWARD EMPIRE

William McKinley and the Spanish-American War
http://www.history.ohio-state.edu/projects/mckinley/SpanAmWar.htm
Part of Ohio State University's site about William McKinley, this part highlights the Spanish-American War with an essay and photos.

Sentenaryo/Centennial: The Philippine Revolution and Philippine-American War
http://www.boondocksnet.com/centennial/index.html
Jim Zwick organizes primary documents, images, and essays focusing on the Philippines and American involvement.

Anti-Imperialism in the United States, 1898–1935
http://www.boondocksnet.com/
ail98-35.html
Jim Zwick edits this extensive site, collating a large number of primary documents about anti-imperialism in America.

Photos of the Philippine-American War
http://www.msstate.edu/Archives/
History/USA/filipino/filipino.html
The Philippine-American War is one of the least discussed military engagements in American history. Many tactics employed then were later used in the Vietnam war.

Imperialism Web Page
http://www.smplanet.com/
imperialism/toc.html

Focusing on the period around the turn of the century, this site puts much information about American imperialism in one place.

Images from the Philippine-United States War
http://www.geocities.com/djmabry/
USA/twenty/filipino.html
The Philippine-American War is one of the least discussed military engagements in American history. Many tactics employed then were later used in the Vietnam War. This site is an archive of historical texts.

Theodore Roosevelt Association
http://www.theodoreroosevelt.org/
This site contains much biographical and research information about this famous American.

CHAPTER 22 | THE PROGRESSIVE ERA

NAACP Online
http://www.naacp.org/about/
history.html
The National Association for the Advancement of Colored People official Web site explains its mission and includes a primary document explaining the start of the NAACP.

The Evolution of the Conservation Movement, 1850–1920
http://memory.loc.gov/ammem/
amrvhtml/conshome.html
This American Memory site brings together scores of primary sources and photographs about "the historical formation and cultural foundations of the movement to conserve and protect America's natural heritage."

The Triangle Shirtwaist Factory Fire, March 25, 1911
http://www.ilr.cornell.edu/
trianglefire/
The Kheel Center for Labor-Management Documentation and Archives at Cornell University put together this excellent site

composed of oral histories, cartoons, images, and essays.

Labor-Management Conflict in American History
http://www.history.ohio-
state.edu/projects/laborconflict/
This site at Ohio State University includes primary accounts of some of the major events in the history of labor-management conflict in the late nineteenth and early twentieth centuries.

Inside an American Factory: The Westinghouse Works, 1904
http://lcweb2.loc.gov/ammem/papr/
west/westhome.html
Part of the American Memory Project at the Library of Congress, this site provides a glimpse inside a turn-of-the-century factory.

African American Women Writers of the Nineteenth Century
http://digital.nypl.org/schomburg/
writers_aa19/

The New York Public Library's Schomburg Center for Research in Black Culture maintains this site that contains a large number of digital texts by African American women of the nineteenth century.

Touring Turn-of-the-Century America: Photographs from the Detroit Publishing Company, 1880–1920
http://memory.loc.gov/ammem/detroit/dethome.html
This Library of Congress collection has thousands of photographs from turn-of-the-century America.

Bill Haywood Trial (1907)
http://www.law.umkc.edu/faculty/projects/ftrials/haywood/haywood.htm

This site contains images, chronology, and court and official documents maintained by Dr. Doug Linder at University of Missouri–Kansas City Law School.

Margaret Sanger Papers Project
http://www.nyu.edu/projects/sanger/
This site at New York University contains information about Margaret Sanger and digital versions of several of her works.

National Arts and Crafts Archives
http://arts-crafts.com/index.html
This site serves as a guide to materials on the Arts and Crafts movement, which lasted roughly from 1890 to 1929.

CHAPTER 23 | FROM ROOSEVELT TO WILSON IN THE AGE OF PROGRESSIVISM

Theodore Roosevelt Association
http://www.theodoreroosevelt.org/
This site contains much biographical and research information about Theodore Roosevelt.

Woodrow Wilson
http://www.ipl.org/ref/POTUS/wwilson.html
This page contains basic factual data about

Wilson's election and presidency, speeches, and on-line biographies.

History of the Suffrage Movement
http://www.rochester.edu/SBA
This site includes a chronology, important texts relating to woman suffrage, and biographical information about Susan B. Anthony and Elizabeth Cady Stanton.

CHAPTER 24 | THE NATION AT WAR

Woodrow Wilson
http://www.ipl.org/ref/POTUS/wwilson.html
This page contains basic factual data about Wilson's election and presidency, speeches, and on-line biographies.

World War 1 Document Archive
http://www.lib.byu.edu/~rdh/wwi/
This archive contains sources about World War I in general, not just America's involvement.

World War One: Trenches on the Web
http://www.worldwar1.com/index.html
This site provides a mass of data concerning the prosecution of the world's first global war.

The Great Migration in Chicago
http://lcweb.loc.gov/exhibits/african/afam011.html
This site looks at the black experience in the Great Migration at one prominent destination.

The American Experience: Influenza
http://www.pbs.org/wgbh/pages/
amex/influenza

This PBS site reveals the impact of the great flu epidemic of 1918.

CHAPTER 25 | TRANSITION TO MODERN AMERICA

Automotive History at the Michigan Electronic Library
http://mel.org/business/
autos-history.html
This page has several links to sites about automotive history in America.

Harlem 1900–1940: An African American Community
http://www.si.umich.edu/CHICO/
Harlem/
The New York Public Library's Schomburg Center for Research in Black Culture hosts this site that includes a database, a timeline, and an exhibit.

William P. Gottlieb Photographs of the Golden Age of Jazz
http://memory.loc.gov/ammem/
wghtml/wghome.html
The Music Division of the Library of Congress has numerous images, audio, and scanned articles from the 1940s.

The Scopes Trial
http://xroads.virginia.edu/~UG97/
inherit/1925home.html
This site gives a general description of the trial and the issues surrounding it.

American Temperance and Prohibition
http://www.cohums.ohio-
state.edu/history/projects/
prohibition
This site looks at the temperance movement over time and contains many informative links.

National Arts and Crafts Archives
http://arts-crafts.com/index.html
This site serves as a guide to materials on the Arts and Crafts movement, which lasted roughly from 1890 to 1929.

The Flapper
http://www.pandorasbox.com/
flapper.html
This site contains many links to information about the popular culture of the 1920s with special reference to the flapper.

The Calvin Coolidge Experience
http://www.geocities.com/
CapitolHill/4921/
This site is an unusual look at one of America's less colorful presidents.

CHAPTER 26 | FRANKLIN D. ROOSEVELT AND THE NEW DEAL

Voices from the Dust Bowl: the Charles L. Todd and Robert Sonkin Migrant Worker Collection, 1940–1941
http://memory.loc.gov/ammem/
afctshtml/tshome.html
Farm Security Administration (FSA) studies of migrant work camps in central California in 1940 and 1941 are the bulk of this site. The collection includes audio recordings, photographs, manuscript materials, and publications.

New Deal Network
http://newdeal.feri.org/
This database includes photographs, political cartoons, and texts—including speeches, letters, and other historic documents—from the New Deal period.

Franklin Delano Roosevelt

http://www.ipl.org/ref/POTUS/
fdroosevelt.html

This site provides information about FDR, the only president to serve more than two terms.

Picture Archive: Photographs of the Great Depression, 1935–1942

http://www.corbis.com/fdr/fsa/
map.html

These photographs reveal the real impact of the Great Depression on American life.

Newspaper Events Not Big in History

http://www.ybi.com/brink/author/
1933/index.html

This site lists dozens of events that were front-page news in 1933 but failed to make the history books.

A New Deal for the Arts

http://www.nara.gov/exhall/newdeal/
newdeal.html

Artwork, documents, and photographs recount the federal government's efforts to fund artists in the 1930s in the National Archives site.

America from the Great Depression to World War II: Photographs from the FSA and OWI, ca. 1935–1945

http://memory.loc.gov/ammem/
fsowhome.html

These images in the Farm Security Administration–Office of War Information Collection show Americans from all over the nation experiencing everything from despair to triumph in the 1930s and 1940s.

CHAPTER 27 | AMERICA AND THE WORLD, 1921–1945

A People at War

http://www.nara.gov/exhall/people/
people.html

This National Archives exhibit takes a close look at the contributions millions of Americans made to the war effort.

Powers of Persuasion—Poster Art of World War II

http://www.nara.gov/education/
teaching/posters/poster.html

These powerful posters at the National Archives were part of the battle for the hearts and minds of the American people.

America from the Great Depression to World War II: Photographs from the FSA and OWI, ca. 1935–1945

http://memory.loc.gov/ammem/
fsowhome.html

These images in the Farm Security Administration–Office of War Information Collection show Americans from all over the nation experiencing everything from despair

to triumph in the 1930s and 1940s.

A-Bomb WWW Museum

http://www.csi.ad.jp/ABOMB/

This site offers information about the impact of the first atomic bomb as well as the background and context of weapons of total destruction.

The United States Holocaust Memorial Museum

http://www.ushmm.org/index.html

This is the official Web site of the Holocaust Museum in Washington, DC.

World War II Pictures

http://www.corbis.com/FDR/
ww2.html

This Corbis site houses many pictures about the second world war and American involvement in the conflict.

Tuskegee Airmen

http://www.wpafb.af.mil/museum/
history/prewwii/ta.htm

The Air Force Museum at Wright-Patterson

Air Force Base maintains this site about the African American pilots of World War II.

Abraham Lincoln Brigade Archives
http://www.alba-valb.org
This Brandeis University site has posters and photographs from the Spanish civil war and the unit of American volunteers who fought in it.

World War II Resources: Primary Source Materials on the Web
http://www.ibiblio.org/pha/index.html
This site has a large number of searchable primary texts from all aspects of World War II.

CHAPTER 28 | THE ONSET OF THE COLD WAR

Harry S Truman
http://www.ipl.org/ref/POTUS/hstruman.html
This page contains basic factual data about Truman's election and presidency, speeches, and on-line biographies.

Cold War
http://cnn.com/SPECIALS/cold.war/
This is the companion site to the CNN Perspectives series on the Cold War. It contains information including interactive timelines and a quiz.

Beyond the Playing Field: Jackie Robinson, Civil Rights Advocate
http://www.nara.gov/education/teaching/robinson/robmain.html
This National Archives and Records Administration teaching materials site contains images, essays, and documents about Robinson and Civil Rights.

Negro Leagues Baseball On-line Archive
http://www.negroleaguebaseball.com/
Essays about desegregation, baseball, and Jim Crow as well as images of teams and players comprise much of this site.

Korean War Project
http://www.koreanwar.org
This site has information about the Korean War and is a guide to resources on the struggle.

NATO at 50
http:www.cnn.com/SPECIALS/1999/nato/
This site from CNN has an excellent timeline and images telling the history of the North Atlantic Treaty Organization.

Senator Joe McCarthy—A Multimedia Celebration
http://webcorp.com/mccarthy/
This webcorp site includes audio and visual clips of McCarthy's speeches.

Harry S Truman Library and Museum
http://www.trumanlibrary.org
This presidential library site has numerous photos and various important primary documents relating to Truman.

CHAPTER 29 | AFFLUENCE AND ANXIETY

Fifties Website Home Page
http://www.fiftiesweb.com/
This entertaining site tells about and samples music and television from the 1950s. It also includes a related links page.

1950s America
http://dept.english.upenn.edu/~afilreis/50/home.html
This site by Professor Al Filreis of the University of Pennsylvania contains a large

array of 1950s literature and images in an alphabetical index.

Levittown: Documents of an Ideal American Suburb
http://www.uic.edu/~pbhales/
Levittown/
The postwar boom in housing made suburban living the cultural norm in America and shaped a generation. The story of the classic suburb, Levittown, is told on this site in pictures and text.

Dwight David Eisenhower
http://www.ipl.org/ref/POTUS/
ddeisenhower.html
This site contains basic factual data about Eisenhower's election and presidency, including speeches and other materials.

The Dwight D. Eisenhower Library and Museum
http://www.eisenhower.utexas.edu/
This site contains mainly photos of the presidents.

CHAPTER 30 | THE TURBULENT SIXTIES

Fourteen Days in October: The Cuban Missile Crisis
http://library.advanced.org/11046/
This creative site allows the viewer to explore the Cuban missile crisis.

John Fitzgerald Kennedy
http://www.ipl.org/ref/POTUS/
jfkennedy.html
This site contains basic factual data about Kennedy's election and presidency, speeches, and on-line biographies.

The Kennedy Assassination
http://mcadams.posc.mu.edu/
home.htm
This well-organized site has images, essays, and photos on the assassination.

Lyndon B. Johnson
http://www.ipl.org/ref/POTUS/
lbjohnson.html
This page contains basic factual data about Johnson's election and presidency, speeches, and on-line biographies.

Lyndon B. Johnson Library and Museum
http://www.lbjlib.utexas.edu/
This presidential library contains images and on-line exhibits.

National Aeronautics and Space Administration
http://www.hq.nasa.gov/office/pao/
History/histsub.htm
NASA's Office of Policy and Plans History Office maintains this site about NASA and its history.

Investigating the Vietnam War
http://www.spartacus.schoolnet.co.
uk/vietintro.htm
This site from Spartacus Educational Publishing, U.K., has an excellent list of annotated links to the best Vietnam-related sites.

Vietnam War Bibliography
http://hubcap.clemson.edu/
~eemoise/bibliography.html
Edwin Moise of Clemson University maintains this extensive bibliography of print works about Vietnam and the Vietnam War.

Vietnam On-line
http://www.pbs.org/wgbh/pages/
amex/vietnam/index.html
From PBS and the American Experience, this site contains a detailed, interactive timeline of the war, interpretive essays, and autobiographical reflections.

My Lai Court-Martial (1970)

http://www.law.umkc.edu/faculty/
projects/ftrials/mylai/mylai.htm

This site contains images, chronology, and court and official documents maintained by Dr. Doug Linder at University of Missouri–Kansas City Law School.

JFK Assassination Web Page

http://ourworld.compuserve.com/
homepages/MGriffith_2/jfk.htm

This is a personal but thorough page that is a guide to the best Internet resources for the assassination.

Martin Luther King, Jr. Papers Project

http://www.stanford.edu/group/King/

This site at Stanford University has links and selected digital documents by and concerning Martin Luther King, Jr.

National Civil Rights Museum

http://www.mecca.org/~crights/
nc2.html

This site allows a virtual tour of the museum with its interpretive exhibits.

The Digger Archives

http://www.diggers.org/

This site provides information about The San Francisco Diggers, which became one of the legendary groups in the Haight-Ashbury from 1966 to 1968.

Free Speech Movement: Student Protest—U.C. Berkeley, 1964–65

http://www.lib.berkeley.edu/BANC/
FSM/

The Bancroft Library at U.C. Berkeley houses this exhibit with oral histories, a chronology, and documents.

Voices of the Civil Rights Era

http://www.webcorp.com/
civilrights/index.htm

Webcorp provides audio clips from prominent figures of the Civil Rights era including Martin Luther King, Jr., and Malcolm X.

Martin Luther King, Jr.

http://www.seattletimes.com/mlk/

This site from the *Seattle Times* has several articles about King and the Civil Rights Movement.

The Sixties Project

http://lists.village.virginia.edu/sixties/

This University of Virginia site has extensive exhibits, documents, and personal narratives from the 1960s.

Civil Rights Oral History Bibliography

http://www-dept.usm.edu/~mcrohb/

This University of Southern Mississippi site includes complete transcripts of the selected oral resources.

1969 Woodstock Festival and Concert

http://www.woodstock69.com/index.
htm

This site provides pictures and lists of songs from the famous rock festival.

National Civil Rights Museum in Memphis, Tennessee

http://www.midsouth.rr.com/
civilrights/

This site houses images with annotation from the museum.

United States vs. Cecil Price et al. (The "Mississippi Burning" Trial), 1967

http://www.law.umkc.edu/faculty/
projects/ftrials/price&bowers/
price&bowers.htm

This site contains images, chronology, and court and official documents maintained by Dr. Doug Linder at University of Missouri–Kansas City Law School.

CHAPTER 31 | A CRISIS IN CONFIDENCE, 1969–1980

May 4, 1970: Twenty-five Years of Remembrance
http://www.library.kent.edu/exhibits/4may95/index.html
This site commemorates the twenty-fifth anniversary of the shootings at Kent State University with a detailed chronology and other information.

Documents from the Women's Liberation Movement
http://scriptorium.lib.duke.edu/wlm/
Primary documents on-line from the Special Collections Library at Duke University provide firsthand information about the women's liberation movement.

Constitutional Issues: Watergate and the Constitution
http://www.nara.gov/education/teaching/watergate/watergat.html
From the National Archives' teaching materials, this site has a good chronology of Watergate and a 1974 memorandum from the Watergate Special Prosecution Force weighing the pros and cons of seeking an indictment against former President Richard Nixon.

CNN 1970s Interactive Timeline
http://cnn.com/SPECIALS/1999/century/episodes/08/
CNN has a series of interactive timelines with several interesting sites. This one covers the years from 1970 to 1979.

Richard Milhous Nixon
http://www.ipl.org/ref/POTUS/rmnixon.html
This site contains basic factual data about Nixon's election and presidency, speeches, and on-line biographies.

Watergate 25
http://www.washingtonpost.com/wp-srv/national/longterm/watergate/front.htm
This site features a chronology, images, searchable articles, and a good deal of background information about the burglary and its consequences.

Gerald Rudolph Ford
http://www.ipl.org/ref/POTUS/grford.html
This site contains basic factual data about Ford's election and presidency, speeches, and on-line biographies.

James Earl Carter, Jr.
http://www.ipl.org/ref/POTUS/jecarter.html
This site contains basic factual data about Carter's election and presidency, speeches, and on-line biographies.

Giant Leap
http://cnn.com/TECH/specials/apollo/
This CNN site commemorates the thirtieth anniversary of the 1969 moonwalk and tells the story of NASA and the ongoing space program.

CHAPTER 32 | THE REPUBLICAN RESURGENCE, 1980–1992

The 80s Server
http://www.80s.com/
This site has a variety of sources of information about the 1980s, but the best parts are open to members only.

The Gulf War
http://www.pbs.org/pages/frontline/gulf/index.html
This Frontline and PBS site combines personal accounts with a chronology and general information about the war.

Ronald Wilson Reagan
http://www.ipl.org/ref/POTUS/rwreagan.html
This site contains basic factual data about Reagan's election and presidency, speeches, and on-line biographies.

George Herbert Walker Bush
http://www.ipl.org/ref/POTUS/ghwbush.html
This site contains basic factual data about Bush's election and presidency, speeches, and on-line biographies.

CHAPTER 33 | AMERICA IN FLUX: THE ANXIOUS NINETIES

American Identities
http://xroads.virginia.edu/~YP/ethnic.html
This site suggests resources for studying America's multiple ethnic identities.

William Jefferson Clinton
http://www.ipl.org/ref/POTUS/wjclinton.html
This site contains basic factual data about Clinton's election and presidency, speeches, and on-line biographies.

Investigating the President: The Trial
http://www.cnn.com/ALLPOLITICS/resources/1998/lewinsky
This site from CNN provides information and documents about the scandals surrounding President Clinton and his impeachment.

Special Report: U.S. v. Microsoft
http://www.policy.com/reports/dojvsms/
This site provides background information and documents on the antitrust case.

Virtual Museum of Computing
http://vmoc.i.am/
This site relates the history of computing through a series of on-line exhibits.

A Brief History of the Internet, Version 3.1
http://www.isoc.org/internet-history/
The Internet Society puts out this site that explores the development and impact of the Internet.

Virtual Museum of Computing
http://www.cs.reading.ac.uk/museum/vlmp/computing.html
This University of Reading site says it is "an eclectic collection of World Wide Web hyperlinks connected with the history of computing and on-line computer-based exhibits."

130° W   125° W   120° W   115° W   110° W   105° W   100° W

Cape Flattery
Puget Sound
Tacoma
Seattle
Columbia River
Olympia
WASHINGTON
Spokane
50° N
ROCKY
Mt. St. Helens
8,366 ft.
(2,550 m)
Mt. Rainier
14,410 ft.
(4,300 m)
Columbia River
Portland
CANADA
Great Falls
Missouri River
Grand Forks
Salem
Helena
MONTANA
NORTH DAKOTA
CASCADE
Eugene
COLUMBIA
Billings
Bismarck
Fargo
Cape Blanco
OREGON
PLATEAU
IDAHO
RANGES
Boise
Idaho Falls
WYOMING
SOUTH DAKOTA
Pierre
COAST
Cape
Mendocino
Snake River
Pocatello
BLACK
HILLS
Rapid City
Sioux Fall
40° N
GREAT
Great
Salt
Lake
Ogden
Casper
North Platte River
GREAT
CENTRAL
SIERRA
Reno
NEVADA
Salt Lake City
Laramie
Longs Peak
14,256 ft.
(4,344 m)
Cheyenne
Grand Island
Lincol
NEBRASKA
San Francisco Bay
San Francisco
Sacramento River
Carson City
Lake Tahoe
Sacramento
BASIN
Provo
ROCKY
South Platte River
Platte River
KANSAS
Oakland
San Joaquin
San Jose
VALLEY
UTAH
Green River
Colorado River
Denver
COLORADO
NEVADA
Mt. Whitney
14,500 ft.
(4,400 m)
Fresno
River
Las
Vegas
Mt. Elbert
14,433 ft.
(4,400 m)
Colorado Springs
Pikes Peak
14,110 ft.
(4,300 m)
Pueblo
Arkansas River
35° N
DEATH
VALLEY
CALIFORNIA
COLORADO
PLATEAU
MOUNTAINS
Wichita
COAST
Bakersfield
Santa Fe
OKLAHOMA
Los Angeles
MOJAVE DESERT
ARIZONA
Albuquerque
Oklahoma City
RANGES
Long Beach
Anaheim
Santa Ana
Salton
Sea
Colorado
NEW MEXICO
Lawton
Red River
PACIFIC
OCEAN
San Diego
Phoenix
Mesa
Río Grande
Brazos River
Dallas
Fort Worth
30° N
Tucson
Las Cruces
El Paso
LLANO
ESTACADO
TEXAS

HAWAII inset:
Kauai   Oahu   22° N
Honolulu   Molokai
Lanai   Maui
HAWAII
PACIFIC OCEAN
Hilo
Hawaii
0   50 miles
19° N
0   50 kilometers

ARCTIC OCEAN
70° N
BROOKS   RANGE
RUSSIA
ALASKA
Arctic Circle
Bering Strait
Nome
Yukon River
Fairbanks
CANADA
RANGE
Mt. McKinley
20,320 ft.
(6,194 m)
ALASKA
Anchorage
KENAI
PENINSULA
Gulf of Alaska
Juneau
Kodiak Is.
Bering Sea
60° N
25° N
MEXICO
Austin
San Antonio
Corpus Christi
PACIFIC
OCEAN
50° N
ALEUTIAN   ISLANDS
0   250 miles
0   250 kilometers
Tropic of Cancer

A-60

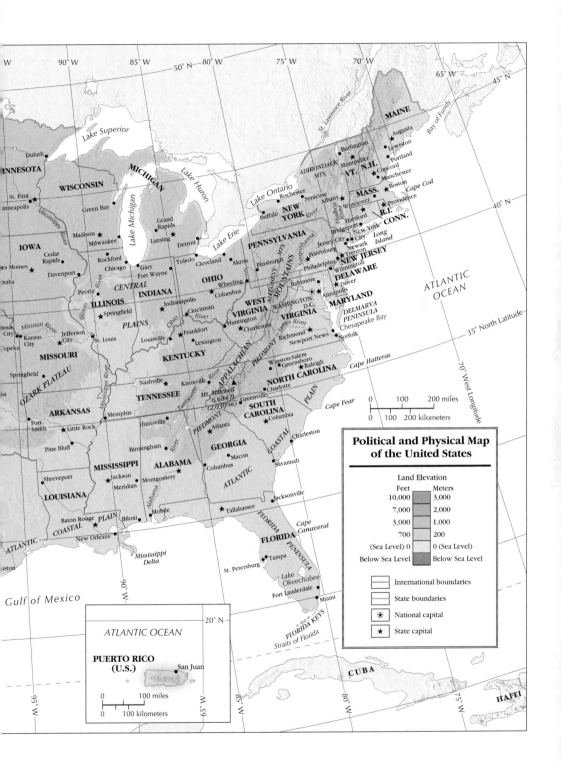

Political and Physical Map of the United States

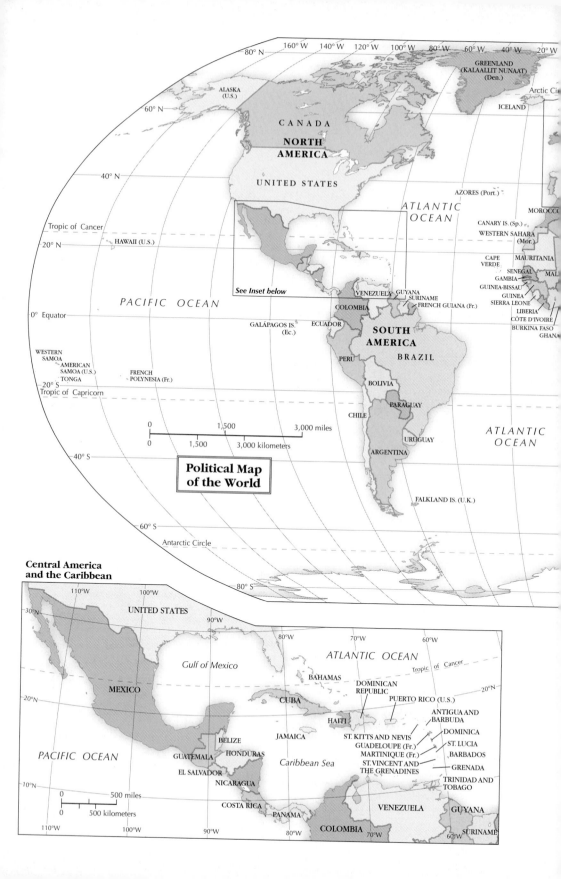

Political Map
of the World

**Central America
and the Caribbean**

CREDITS

Unless otherwise credited, all photographs are the property of Addison Wesley Educational Publishers, Inc. Page abbreviations are as follows: **T** top, **C** center, **B** bottom, **L** left, **R** right.

CHAPTER 1

6 David Muench Photography **13** Biblioteca Medicea Laurenziana, Firenze. Reproduced with permission of Ministero per i beni e le attivita culturali. All rights reserved. Additional reproductions are forbidden. **16** © Frank Fournier/Woodfin Camp and Associates. All Rights Reserved. **17** © Parcs Canada **19** Giraudon/Art Resource, New York **22** Joseph Furtenback, *Architectura Navalis*, Ulm, 1629 **24** The Granger Collection, NY **25** From Theodor de Bry, *America, 1595.* New York Public Library, Astor, Lenox and Tilden Foundations. **27** *La Salle Crossing Lake Michigan on the Ice, December 8, 1681,* by George Catlin. Paul Mellon Collection, © 2001 Board of Trustees, National Gallery of Art, Washington. **34** © The British Museum

CHAPTER 2

42 New York Public Library, Astor, Lenox and Tilden Foundations **43** National Portrait Gallery, Smithsonian Institution/Art Resource, NY **44** Ashmolean Museum, Oxford University **46** Smithsonian Institution **48** Historic St. Mary's City **54** Courtesy, American Antiquarian Society **56** © Paul Skillings/f/Stop Pictures **58** Courtesy of the Massachusetts Historical Society **67** The Library Company of Philadelphia

CHAPTER 3

79L-R New York Public Library, Astor, Lenox and Tilden Foundations **83** David Hiser/Photographers Aspen **91** Courtesy, American Antiquarian Society **92** Abby Aldrich Rockefeller Folk Art Center, Williamsburg, VA **95** New York Public Library, Astor, Lenox and Tilden Foundations **99** Shelburne Museum, Shelburne, Vermont/Photograph by Ken Burris **101** New York Public Library, Astor, Lenox and Tilden Foundations

CHAPTER 4

107 Rare Book Division, New York Public Library, Astor, Lenox and Tilden Collections **108** The Historical Society of Pennsylvania **111** "Pennyslvania German Painted Wooden Box" by Elmer G. Anderson. Index of American Design, © 2001 Board of Trustees, National Gallery of Art, Washington, DC. **113** © Collection of The New-York Historical Society **115** © G. Donald Bain, Bain Digital Graphics **119L** The Historical Society of Pennsylvania **119R** The Library Company of Philadelphia **124** Courtesy of the National Portrait Gallery, London **133** Courtesy of the Trustees of the British Library

CHAPTER 5

143 The Colonial Williamsburg Foundation **153** Bequest of Charles Allen Munn, 1924. The Metropolitan Museum of Art. Photograph © 2001 The Metropolitan Museum of Art. **156** The Library of Congress **159** Massachusetts Historical Society **163** Chicago Historical Society [ICHi-20449] **166L** Courtesy of the National Portrait Gallery, London **166R** The Library of Congress **175** Anne S. K. Brown Military Collection, Brown University Library

CHAPTER 6

182 The Library Company of Philadelphia **184** Maryland Historical Society, Baltimore, Maryland **185** New York Public Library, Astor, Lenox and Tilden Foundations **189** Friends Historical Library of Swarthmore College **197** Chicago Historical Society [(none)-00423] **199T-B** Smithsonian Institution **203** *James Madison* by Charles Willson Peale. From the Collection of Gilcrease Museum, Tulsa, Oklahoma [126.1006]. **205** National Portrait Gallery, Smithsonian Institution/Art Resource, NY

CHAPTER 7

218 American Antiquarian Society **219** *A View of Mount Vernon*, Gift of Edgar William and Bernice Chrysler Garbisch, Photograph © 2001 Board of Trustees, National Gallery of Art, Washington. 1792 or after, oil on canvas, image 23 × 35 ⅛ inches. **220** National Portrait Gallery, Smithsonian Institution/Art Resource, NY **221** National Museum of American History, Smithsonian Institution **223L-R** Independence National Historical Park Collection **231** Bibliotheque Nationale, Paris **233** © Collection of The New-York Historical Society [19] **244** The Library of Congress

CHAPTER 8

251 The Ohio Historical Society **252** The Library of Congress **255** Copyright Yale University Art Gallery, Mabel Brady Garvan Collection **259** Chicago Historical Society [P&S-1932.0018] **264** New York Public Library, Astor, Lenox and Tilden Foundations **266** © Collection of The New-York Historical Society [1931.58] **268** Abby Aldrich Rockefeller Folk Art Museum, Williamsburg, VA **271** © Collection of The New-York Historical Society [7278] **275** Collection of Davenport West, Jr. **278** Anne S. K. Brown Military Collection, Brown University Library

CHAPTER 9

284TL Colorado Historical Society **284TR** Courtesy, National Museum of the American Indian, Smithsonian Institution [15/4658]. Photo by David Heald. **284B** The Walters Art Gallery, Baltimore **288** The Hudson's Bay Company Archives **289** New York Public Library, Astor, Lenox and Tilden Foundations **291** George Tattersall, America 1836–1842, Western Sketches. Gift of Maxim Karolik. Courtesy, Museum of Fine Arts, Boston. Reproduced with permission. © 2001 Museum of Fine Arts, Boston. All Rights Reserved. **292** New York Public Library, Astor, Lenox and Tilden Foundations **297** The Library of Congress **299** Massachusetts Historical Society **306** Washington and Lee University, Lexington, Virginia

CHAPTER 10

317 *Rustic Dance After a Sleigh Ride* by William Sidney Mount, 1830, oil on canvas, 22-⅛ × 27-⅛ inches. Museum of Fine Arts, Boston, Bequest of Martha C. Karolik for the M. and M. Karolik Collection of American Paintings, 1815–1865 [48.458]. Reproduced with permission. © 2001 Museum of Fine Arts, Boston. All Rights Reserved. **318** Thomas Cole, *The Clove, Catskills*, ca. 1827. Charles F. Smith Fund. New Britain Museum of American Art. **325** In the Collection of the Corcoran Gallery of Art, Gift of William Wilson Corcoran, 1869 **326** © Collection of The New-York Historical Society [43440] **327** Courtesy of The Newberry Library, Chicago **330** Corbis **337** Chicago Historical Society [ICHi-12739] **338** © The New-York Historical Society **339** Courtesy Mercantile Library Association, St. Louis

CHAPTER 11

347 New Bedford Whaling Museum **349** Harriet Beecher Stowe Center, Hartford, CT **351** The Historical Society of Pennsylvania **354** © The New-York Historical Society [1941.910] **360** Courtesy of The Newberry Library, Chicago **363** Corbis-Bettmann **364** Massachusetts Historical Society **368** Culver Pictures **369** New York Public Library, Astor, Lenox and Tilden Foundations **372** Shakertown at Pleasant Hill, KY **373L-R** Concord Free Public Library

CHAPTER 12

376 Rare Book Divison/New York Public Library, Astor, Lenox and Tilden Foundations **377** By permission of The Houghton Library/Harvard University, Cambridge, Mass., Gift of the Houghton Library by Mrs. Henry K. Metcalf **383**

Messina Studios/De Golyer Library **384** *Handcart Pioneers* by CCA Christensen. © by Intellectual Reserve, Inc. Courtesy of Museum of Church History and Art. Used by Permission. **391** Corbis-Bettmann **395** Deutches Museum, Munich **397** Chicago Historical Society [ICHi-00013] **401** © Collection of The New-York Historical Society [47825]

CHAPTER 13

408 Culver Pictures **410** © Collection of The New-York Historical Society [47843] **417** From the Penn School Collecton. Permission granted by Penn Center, St. Helena, SC. **418** From the collection of the Louisiana State Museum **422** © Collection of The New-York Historical Society [3087] **425** State Historical Society of Wisconsin **426** The Library of Congress **429** Sophia Smith Collection, Smith College, Northampton, Mass. **430** The Historic New Orleans Collection **433** The Library of Congress

CHAPTER 14

437 New York Public Library, Astor, Lenox and Tilden Foundations **443** The Granger Collection, New York **449B** New York Public Library, Astor, Lenox and Tilden Foundations **449T** Maryland Historical Society, Baltimore, Maryland **455L** Harriet Beecher Stowe Center, Stowe-Day Foundation **455R** From the Bella C. Landauer Collection of Business and Advertising Art. © Collection of The New-York Historical Society [38219] **456** *Frank Leslie's Illustrated Newspaper* **459-463** The Library of Congress

CHAPTER 15

469 Chicago Historical Society [ICHi-11409] **471-485** The Library of Congress **489** Lightfoot Collection **492** © Collection of The New-York Historical Society [71527] **496L-R** The Library of Congress **499** *Harper's Weekly*

CHAPTER 16

503-506 The Library of Congress **508** Chicago Historical Society [(none)-00434] **512** National Archives **514** Stock Montage, Inc. **517** © Collection of The New-York Historical Society [50475] **519** Valentine Museum, Richmond, Virginia **525L** Culver Pictures **525R** Corbis-Bettmann **526** Rutherford B. Hayes Presidential Center, Fremont, Ohio **533** Corbis **535** Yale Joel/LIFE MAGAZINE © Time Inc.

CHAPTER 17

544 From *A Pictographic History of the Oglala Sioux* by Amos Bad Heart Bull, text by Helen Blish, University of Nebraska Press **545** Smithsonian Institution **546L** Arizona Historical Society/Tucson [19831] **546R** Arizona Historical Society/Tucson [19830] **551** Denver Public Library, Western History Collection **553** Baker Library, Harvard Business School **556** © The New-York Historical Society [16212] **558** Denver Public Library, Western History Department **564** From *The Black West* by William Loren Katz **566** Haynes Foundation Collection/Montana Historical Society, Helena

CHAPTER 18

577 Union Pacific Historical Collection **581** © Bettmann/Corbis **585** Courtesy George Eastman House **586** Edison National Historic Site/U.S. Department of the Interior, National Park Service **589** The Museum of the City of New York **591** Brown Brothers **593** Courtesy, Metropolitan Life Insurance Company **595** The Library of Congress **598** The Granger Collection, NY **599** © Bettmann/Corbis

CHAPTER 19

606 Photograph by Byron, The Byron Collection, Museum of the City of New York **607** The Library of Congress **609** New York Public Library, Astor, Lenox and Tilden Foundations **619-621** Brown Brothers **624** Michigan Historical Collections, Bentley Historical Library, University of Michigan **626** The Library of Congress **632L** Brown Brothers **632R** Jane Addams Memorial Collection, Special Collections, University Library, University of Illinois at Chicago

CHAPTER 20

637 The Library of Congress 644 Corbis-Bettmann 647 North Carolina Division of Archives & History 649 The Kansas State Historical Society, Topeka 652 © Minnesota Historical Society/Corbis 658L Valentine Museum 658R © Bettmann/Corbis 660 Corbis-Bettmann 662 Culver Pictures

CHAPTER 21

670 The Library of Congress 672 © The New-York Historical Society 677 Hawaii State Archives 681 *Harper's Weekly* 683 *New York Journal,* February 17, 1898 686T Chicago Historical Society [ICHi-08425] 686B Courtesy of USMA Archives, West Point, NY 690 New York Public Library, Astor, Lenox and Tilden Foundations 693-697 Culver Pictures

CHAPTER 22

700L The Lawrence Lee Pelletier Library, Allegheny College 700R Culver Pictures 704 New York Public Library, Astor, Lenox and Tilden Foundations 707L-R Brown Brothers 710L U.S. Dept. of Labor 710R Courtesy George Eastman House 711 Culver Pictures 712 Corbis-Bettmann 717 National Archives 721 Brown Brothers 723 Manchester, N.H., Historic Association

CHAPTER 23

733-739 Culver Pictures 743 Rare Book, Manuscript, & Special Collections Library, Duke University 746 Cleveland Picture Collection, Cleveland Public Library 748 State Historical Society of Wisconsin Visual Archives [WHi (X3) 13031] 753 Courtesy, The Lilly Library, Indiana University, Bloomington, Indiana 754 Warsaw Collection, Smithsonian Institution 763 Brown Brothers 767T National Archives 767B The Archives of Labor and Urban Affairs, Wayne State University

CHAPTER 24

770 © FPG International Corp. 771 *New York Tribune,* May 8, 1915 782 Dokumentations- und Informationszentrum Munchen GmbH, Bilderdienst 783 *Des Moines Register and Leader,* July 1915 788 National Archives 792 Brown Brothers 795 Corbis-Bettmann 797 National Archives 802 Corbis-Bettmann

CHAPTER 25

807-812 From the collections of the Henry Ford Museum & Greenfield Village 813 *Frank Leslie's Illustrated Newspaper,* September 11, 1920 818TL Brown Brothers 822 Culver Pictures 824 Archive Photos/Getty Images 827 Corbis-Bettmann 828 *Life,* 1922. TimePix

CHAPTER 26

838T AP/Wide World 838B Corbis-Bettmann 843 Brown Brothers 847 AP/Wide World Photos 848 Culver Pictures 849 Archive Photos/Getty Images 852 The Library of Congress 856 UPI/Corbis-Bettmann 857 AP/Wide World Photos 859 The Franklin D. Roosevelt Library, Hyde Park, NY

CHAPTER 27

867 Brown Brothers 873 AP/Wide World Photos 876 UPI/Corbis-Bettmann 881 Official U.S. Navy Photograph 887 Photo by Vernon T. Manion. Courtesy Boeing Aircraft Corporation. 889 The Library of Congress 891 National Archives 895 Courtesy of the World Federation of Bergen-Belsen Associations 897 Ed Clark/LIFE MAGAZINE © Time Inc. 899 Underwood & Underwood/Corbis-Bettmann

CHAPTER 28

910 The Fotomas Index 911 UPI/Corbis-Bettmann 917 Carl Mydens, LIFE MAGAZINE © Time Inc. 921-923 UPI/Corbis-Bettmann 924 Hank Walker, LIFE MAGAZINE © Time Inc. 928 From Herblock's *Special for Today* (Simon

& Schuster, 1958). Originally appeared in *The Washington Post.* **929** AP/Wide World Photos **933** Express Newspapers/Archive Photos/Getty Images **935** From *Cartoons and Lampoons,* © 1982 Samuel A. Tower **936** UPI/Corbis-Bettmann

CHAPTER 29

939L Magnum Photos **945** National Archives **947** © Allen Ginsberg Trust **948** Copyright © 1957 by The New York Times Co. Reprinted by permission. **954L** Carl Iwasaki/TimePix **954R** © Eve Arnold/Magnum **955** UPI/Corbis-Bettmann **957** AP Photo/Gene Herrick **958** AP/Wide World Photos

CHAPTER 30

965 UPI/Corbis-Bettman **966** AP/Wide World Photos **968** Archive Photos/Getty Images **975** Charles Moore/Black Star **976** AP/Wide World Photos **979** UPI/Corbis-Bettmann **980L-R** George Tames/NYT Pictures **993** Paul Conklin/TimePix **996** Bob Fitch/Black Star **999** Lyndon Baines Johnson Library **1001** AP/Wide World Photos

CHAPTER 31

1006-1009 UPI/Corbis-Bettmann **1013** Kent State University Archives **1015** AP/Wide World Photos **1016** Roland Freeman/Magnum Photos **1018** Tony Korody/Corbis-Sygma **1023-1033** UPI/Corbis-Bettmann **1035** Bill Fitz-Patrick/The White House **1036** © Philippe Ledru/Sygma

CHAPTER 32

1040 © John Bryson/Sygma **1042** AP/Wide World Photos **1046** UPI/Corbis-Bettmann **1047** Michael Evans/The White House **1057** Fred Ward/Black Star **1060** Corbis-Bettmann **1069** Black Star **1070** © R. Bossu/Sygma/Corbis **1073** Sygma/Corbis

CHAPTER 33

1076L-R Markel/Gamma-Liaison/Getty Images **1081** Martin Levick/Black Star **1083** © KTLA/Sygma/Corbis **1089** © The New Yorker Collection 1992 Dana Fradon from cartoonbank.com. All Rights Reserved. **1099** © Tom Horan/Sygma/Corbis **1102** King Features Syndicate **1106** Albert Facelly/Sipa Press **1110** © Paul Kregger/Sygma/Corbis **1113** © R. Trippett/Sipa Press

INDEX

ADDITIONAL TITLES
OF INTEREST

Note to Instructors: Any of these Penguin-Putnam, Inc., titles can be packaged with this book at a special discount. Contact your local Longman sales representative for details on how to create a Penguin-Putnam, Inc., Value Package.

Horatio Alger, Jr., *Ragged Dick & Struggling Upward*

Louis Auchincloss, *Woodrow Wilson*

Edward Bellamy, *Looking Backward*

Willa Cather, *O Pioneers!*

Alexis De Tocqueville, *Democracy in America*

Frederick Douglass, *Narrative of the Life of Frederick Douglass*

Gordon Hutner, *Immigrant Voices*

Martin Luther King, Jr., *Why We Can't Wait*

L. Jesse Lemisch (Editor), *Benjamin Franklin: The Autobiography & Other Writings*

Sinclair Lewis, *Babbitt*

Wendy Martin (Editor), *Colonial American Travel Narratives*

Toni Morrison, *Beloved*

Thomas Paine, *Common Sense*

Clinton Rossiter (Editor), *The Federalist Papers*

Upton Sinclair, *The Jungle*

Harriet Beecher Stowe, *Uncle Tom's Cabin*

Mark Twain, *Adventures of Huckleberry Finn*